DOCUMENTA GEIGY

SCIENTIFIC TABLES, SIXTH EDITION

DOCUMENTA
GEIGY

SCIENTIFIC TABLES

SIXTH EDITION

EDITED BY KONRAD DIEM

PUBLISHED BY
GEIGY PHARMACEUTICALS
DIVISION OF GEIGY CHEMICAL CORPORATION
ARDSLEY, NEW YORK

Foreword by the Publishers

This 6th and completely revised edition of the GEIGY *Scientific Tables* has been considerably enlarged not only by the expansion of much of the material contained in the 5th edition but also by the inclusion of a number of entirely new sections. The aim has remained the same, namely to provide medical practitioners and research workers with basic scientific data in a concise form and so spare them much tedious searching in the literature.

Since the appearance of the 5th edition, the publishers have received a great many suggestions for extending the scope of the *Tables*. Although lack of space has made it impossible to adopt all of these, they have repeatedly brought to light the difficulty which doctors and other workers in the medical field often encounter in finding the mathematical, physical or chemical data they require. With this in mind, it has been thought desirable to expand particularly that part of the *Tables* which is not directly concerned with medicine and thereby perhaps also to help toward an appreciation of the debt owed by both medicine and biology to the exact sciences.

Of the new sections, the most important is that on "Metabolism" contributed by a group from the Department of Biochemistry, University of Oxford, England, headed by Professor Sir HANS KREBS, F.R.S., to whom the publishers are very greatly indebted. Their thanks are due also not only to the other contributors whose help has made this new edition possible but also to the many users who have sent suggestions for improving the *Tables* or have drawn attention to errors. It is hoped that this valuable coöperation will continue in the future.

GEIGY PHARMACEUTICALS
Division of Geigy Chemical Corporation
Ardsley, New York

Editorial Foreword

Apart from general revision dictated by advances in the fields covered by the *Scientific Tables*, some major changes distinguish this 6th edition from the previous edition.

The mathematical and statistical sections have been enlarged by the addition of many new numerical tables, consisting in the main of original values obtained by electronic computer. In addition, some numerical tables already available in the literature have been reproduced by kind permission of the authors and organizations named below.

In the physicochemical part of the book the section on units of measurement has been completely rewritten to make it more informative and comprehensive. The internationally recognized definitions and terminology have been strictly adhered to even where these have not yet found their way into everyday use. Many new physical and chemical data have been incorporated, for example decay tables for radioisotopes, conversion tables for gas volumes, vapor pressure tables, etc.

The section on metabolism (not in the original 5th edition but appearing as a supplement in a later reprint) has been augmented in this edition by chapters on porphyrins and lipids.

The rapid advances being made in the biological and medical fields make it inevitable that a publication of this nature is in some respects already out of date by the time it appears from the press. The editors crave the indulgence of users of the *Tables* for any deficiencies in this respect.

Acknowledgements

The publishers and editors are indebted to the following authors for original contributions to this edition:

Dr. A. Brügger	University Neurosurgical Clinic, Zurich
Dr. K. Burton	Department of Biochemistry, University of Oxford
Prof. A. Engeler	Federal Materials Testing and Research Institute, St.Gall
Dr. A. F. Essellier	University Medical Clinic, Zurich
Dr. L. P. Holländer	Municipal Blood Transfusion Service, Basle
Dr. P. Jeanneret	University Medical Clinic, Zurich
Dr. D. B. Keech	(late) Department of Biochemistry, University of Oxford
Dr. H. L. Kornberg	(late) Department of Biochemistry, University of Oxford
Prof. Sir Hans Krebs, F.R.S.	Department of Biochemistry, University of Oxford
Dr. Hilde Levi	Zoophysiological Laboratory A, University of Copenhagen
Dr. J. M. Lowenstein	(late) Department of Biochemistry, University of Oxford
Dr. H. Lüthy	Isotope Laboratory, Municipal Hospital, Basle
Dr. J. R. Quayle	Department of Biochemistry, University of Oxford
Dr. Charlotte Rhonheimer	University Neurosurgical Clinic, Zurich

To the following for very valuable advice:

Prof. E. Batschelet	University of Basle, in mathematical and statistical matters
Dr. N. L. Johnson	Department of Statistics, University College, London, in mathematical and statistical matters
Prof. H. Krayenbühl	University Neurosurgical Clinic, Zurich, in medical matters
Prof. E. Rossi	Jenner Hospital, Berne, in medical matters

To the following authors and organizations for permission to reproduce data from their publications:

(Numerical tables) R. L. Anderson, J. Berkson, A. H. Bowker, L. J. Comrie, W. J. Dixon, D. B. Duncan, R. A. Fisher and F. Yates, A. Hald and S. A. Sinkbaek, B. I. Hart, M. G. Kendall, A. Linder, E. Lord, R. Mavrodineanu and H. Boiteux, J. M. May, K. R. Nair, P. S. Olmstead, E. S. Pearson and H. O. Hartley, F. S. Swed and C. Eisenhart, L. H. C. Tippett, J. W. Tukey, D. Wabeke and C. Van Eeden, B. L. Van der Waerden, J. E. Walsh, C. White; Bell Telephone Laboratories, Inc., New York; Marchant Calculators Division of Smith-Corona Marchant, Inc., Oakland (Cal.); National Bureau of Standards, Washington; International Civil Aviation Organisation (ICAO), Montreal (Canada); Virginia Polytechnic Institute, Blacksburg (Va.); World Health Organization, Geneva.

(Diagrams) W. M. Boothby, J. Berkson and H. L. Dunn, I. Bross, G. A. Harrison, H. M. Lufkin and F. W. Sunderman, F. C. McLean and A. B. Hastings, E. W. Page and F. Houlding, G. Piekarski, D. D. Van Slyke et al., E. C. Vogt and V. S. Vickers.

Notes on the use of the Scientific Tables

As a rule, the meanings of symbols and abbreviations are given where they first occur. For units of measurement it is recommended that use be made of the alphabetical list to be found on page 200.

Zero values are indicated by the figure nought (0) throughout. A dash (–) or question mark means that the value is unknown; this should on no account be confused with a zero value. Plus signs (+, ++) are non-committal indications of relative amount. In the numerical tables, a point over the last figure (or figures) indicates a recurring figure (or figures), thus

$$1.\dot{6} = 1.666\,666\ldots$$

$$1.65\dot{2}7\dot{8} = 1.652\,782\,782\,78\ldots$$

Exact values have been distinguished from rounded-off values by printing the last figure in **bold**-face type. Thus, 1.1257 would be the rounded-off value of, say, 1.125 735 4..., while 1.125**7** is an exact number. This notation is used in particular for the arbitrarily defined values of constants.

In the numerical tables, it should be noted that the number of places given has been dictated by the space available. The user should abstract as many as he needs and round off accordingly.

Normal ranges and *mean values* which have been calculated in accordance with statistical procedures are indicated as follows:

Mean value	**bold**-face type
Range	*italic* type
Standard deviation of the individual values ...	light-face type

When a range is not so calculated, or when the method of calculation is unknown, it is printed in light-face type, as is also the corresponding mean value.

In the literature references the abbreviations used are those recommended by the World Medical Association (Morton, L. T., *World Medical Periodicals*, New York, 1957).

Additional copies of the *Folia medica Geigy* in the inside back cover of these *Tables* may be obtained by application to J. R. Geigy S.A., Department 90, Basle 21, Switzerland.

Contents

Addenda and Errata

Users of the *Scientific Tables* are kindly requested to address any correspondence to J. R. Geigy S.A., Department 90, Basle 16, Switzerland

Addenda

Thermodynamic and atomic constants (page 247): Following on the adoption of the unified scale of atomic weights (see below), the following new (single) values for constants have been calculated (REMY, H., *Angew. Chem.*, **74**, 69 [1962]):

AVOGADRO's constant (see also page 243)
$N_0 = 6.02295 \times 10^{23}$ mol^{-1}

FARADAY constant (see also page 243)
$F = (2.89236 \pm 0.00005) \times 10^{14}$ esu Eq^{-1}
$F' = (9.64786 \pm 0.00015) \times 10^{3}$ emu Eq^{-1}

Normal specific volume of an ideal gas
$v_0 = 2.24135 \times 10^{4}$ cm^{3}mol^{-1}

Universal gas constant
$R_0 = 8.20537 \times 10^{-2}$ l atm mol^{-1} degree^{-1}

Atomic weights of the elements (pages 248 et seq.): The International Atomic Weights 1961 (unified scale based on carbon-12) are given on page 740.

Virus of primary atypical pneumonia (page 696): This organism has recently been shown to be a member of the group of pleuropneumonia-like organisms (see page 685). Cf. Editorial, *Lancet*, **1**, 255 (1962).

Errata

Probabilities (page 147): Under *Example (7)* of (**356**), (*b*), formula for Prob (white, red) should read $\frac{N-x}{N} \times \frac{x}{N-1}$.

Discrete probability distribution (page 149): In left-hand column, line 2, for "Prob ($x > k$)" read "Prob ($x > s$)".

χ^2 Distribution (page 167): In left-hand column, line 14 from bottom, for "section 11F (a)" read "section 11F (b)".

Regressions (page 174): In proposition (**640**), second line, delete root sign.

Conversion factors for units of density (page 212): Under Kilograms per cubic decimeter, in column under **C** headed mg cm^{-3}, etc., for "10^{-3}" read "10^{3}".

Density units (page 213): In line 12 of text, for "$L^{-4}KT^2$" read "$L^{-4}FT^2$".

Entropy units (page 217): Under MKS-system, for "10^{-7} erg °K^{-1}" read "10^{7} erg °K^{-1}"; in last line but one, for "0.2389" read "0.23892", for "4.1854" read "4.1855".

Units of dynamic viscosity (page 217): Under CGS-system, for "(dyn cm^{-2}) ≡ cm^{-1} g s^{1}" read "(dyn s cm^{-2}) ≡ cm^{-1} g s^{-1}".

Electrical conductivity units (page 232): Under Electromagnetic CGS-system, for "c^2 esu" read "$10^{11} c^2$ esu".

Magnetic polarization units (page 233): Under Electromagnetic CGS-system, for "3.3357×10^{-11} esu" read "3.3356×10^{-11} esu".

Magnetic pole strength units (page 234): Under Electrostatic CGS-system, for "$1/c$ esu" read "$1/c$ emu".

Buffer solutions (page 314): Under No. 4, Stock solutions, for "$C_2H_3O_2 \cdot 3H_2O$" read "$NaC_2H_3O_2 \cdot 3H_2O$".

Essential amino acid requirements (page 499): In footnote** to table, for "acids[2]" read "acids[3]"; in bibliographical references, for "*2)* TUTTLE et al." read "*3)* TUTTLE et al.".

Composition of foods (page 501): Under Apples, fresh, *per lb. as purchased*, nicotinic acid content, for "0.08" read "0.8".

Composition of foods (page 503): Under Quinces, excess base, for "0" read "+".

Composition of foods (page 508): Under Chocolate, sweetened, milk, vitamin B_2 content, for "0.04" read "0.28".

Composition of foods (page 513): In footnote, for "cal" read "kcal".

Synopsis of blood (page 570): Under Bromine, whole blood, range, for "0.0007–0.001" read "–", plasma or serum, range, for "–" read "0.0007–0.001".

Mathematical Constants

Constant	Value	$\log_{10}$
π	3.141 593	0.4971
2π	6.283 185	0.7982
3π	9.424 778	0.9743
$\pi/2$	1.570 796	0.1961
$\pi/3$	1.047 198	0.0200
π^2	9.869 604	0.9943
π^3	31.006 277	1.4914
$\sqrt{\pi}$	1.772 454	0.2486
$\sqrt{2\pi}$	2.506 628	0.3991
$\sqrt{\pi/2}$	1.253 314	0.0980
$\sqrt[3]{\pi}$	1.464 592	0.1657
$1/\pi$	0.318 310	$-1+0.5029$
$1/(2\pi)$	0.159 155	$-1+0.2018$
$2/\pi$	0.636 620	$-1+0.8039$
$1/\pi^2$	0.101 321	$-1+0.0057$
$1/\sqrt{\pi}$	0.564 190	$-1+0.7514$
$180°/\pi$	57°.295 780	1.7581
e	2.718 282	0.4343
e^2	7.389 056	0.8686
$1/e$	0.367 879	$-1+0.5657$
$\sqrt{e}$	1.648 721	0.2171
$\log_{10} e = M$*	0.434 294	$-1+0.6378$
$\log_e 10 = 1/M$**	2.302 585	0.3622
C (Euler-Mascheroni Constant)	0.577 216	$-1+0.7613$

* $M \times \log_e x = \log_{10} x$. ** $(1/M) \times \log_{10} x = \log_e x$.

The Greek Alphabet

Greek character	Greek name	English equivalent
Α α	alpha	A a
Β β	beta	B b
Γ γ	gamma	G g
Δ δ	delta	D d
Ε ε	epsilon	Ĕ ĕ
Ζ ζ	zeta	Z z
Η η	eta	Ē ē
Θ θ	theta	Th th
Ι ι	iota	I i
Κ ϰ	kappa	K k
Λ λ	lambda	L l
Μ μ	mu	M m
Ν ν	nu	N n
Ξ ξ	xi	X x
Ο ο	omicron	Ŏ ŏ
Π π	pi	P p
Ρ ρ	rho	R r
Σ σ	sigma	S s
Τ τ	tau	T t
ϒ υ	upsilon	Y y
Φ φ	phi	Ph ph
Χ χ	chi	Ch ch
Ψ ψ	psi	Ps ps
Ω ω	omega	Ō ō

Symbols and Designations of Multiples and Submultiples

Symbol	Designation	Factor	
T	tera-	10^{12}	1 000 000 000 000
G	giga-	10^{9}	1 000 000 000
M	mega-	10^{6}	1 000 000
k	kilo-	10^{3}	1 000
h	hecto-	10^{2}	100
dk*, da**	deka-	10^{1}	10
d	deci-	10^{-1}	0.1
c	centi-	10^{-2}	0.01
m	milli-	10^{-3}	0.001
μ	micro-	10^{-6}	0.000 001
n	nano-	10^{-9}	0.000 000 001
p	pico-	10^{-12}	0.000 000 000 001

* In English-speaking countries. ** In continental European countries.

Four-Place Common Logarithms

x	log x 0	1	2	3	4	5	6	7	8	9	Proportional parts 1	2	3	4	5	6	7	8	9
100	0000	0004	0009	0013	0017	0022	0026	0030	0035	0039	0	1	1	2	2	3	3	3	4
101	0043	0048	0052	0056	0060	0065	0069	0073	0077	0082	0	1	1	2	2	3	3	3	4
102	0086	0090	0095	0099	0103	0107	0111	0116	0120	0124	0	1	1	2	2	3	3	3	4
103	0128	0133	0137	0141	0145	0149	0154	0158	0162	0166	0	1	1	2	2	3	3	3	4
104	0170	0175	0179	0183	0187	0191	0195	0199	0204	0208	0	1	1	2	2	2	3	3	4
105	0212	0216	0220	0224	0228	0233	0237	0241	0245	0249	0	1	1	2	2	2	3	3	4
106	0253	0257	0261	0265	0269	0273	0278	0282	0286	0290	0	1	1	2	2	2	3	3	4
107	0294	0298	0302	0306	0310	0314	0318	0322	0326	0330	0	1	1	2	2	2	3	3	4
108	0334	0338	0342	0346	0350	0354	0358	0362	0366	0370	0	1	1	2	2	2	3	3	4
109	0374	0378	0382	0386	0390	0394	0398	0402	0406	0410	0	1	1	2	2	2	3	3	4
10	0000	0043	0086	0128	0170	0212	0253	0294	0334	0374	4	8	12	17	21	25	29	33	37
11	0414	0453	0492	0531	0569	0607	0645	0682	0719	0755	4	8	11	15	19	23	26	30	34
12	0792	0828	0864	0899	0934	0969	1004	1038	1072	1106	3	7	10	14	17	21	24	28	31
13	1139	1173	1206	1239	1271	1303	1335	1367	1399	1430	3	6	10	13	16	19	23	26	29
14	1461	1492	1523	1553	1584	1614	1644	1673	1703	1732	3	6	9	12	15	18	21	24	27
15	1761	1790	1818	1847	1875	1903	1931	1959	1987	2014	3	6	8	11	14	17	20	22	25
16	2041	2068	2095	2122	2148	2175	2201	2227	2253	2279	3	5	8	11	13	16	18	21	24
17	2304	2330	2355	2380	2405	2430	2455	2480	2504	2529	2	5	7	10	12	15	17	20	22
18	2553	2577	2601	2625	2648	2672	2695	2718	2742	2765	2	5	7	9	12	14	16	19	21
19	2788	2810	2833	2856	2878	2900	2923	2945	2967	2989	2	4	7	9	11	13	16	18	20
20	3010	3032	3054	3075	3096	3118	3139	3160	3181	3201	2	4	6	8	11	13	15	17	19
21	3222	3243	3263	3284	3304	3324	3345	3365	3385	3404	2	4	6	8	10	12	14	16	18
22	3424	3444	3464	3483	3502	3522	3541	3560	3579	3598	2	4	6	8	10	12	14	15	17
23	3617	3636	3655	3674	3692	3711	3729	3747	3766	3784	2	4	6	7	9	11	13	15	17
24	3802	3820	3838	3856	3874	3892	3909	3927	3945	3962	2	4	5	7	9	11	12	14	16
25	3979	3997	4014	4031	4048	4065	4082	4099	4116	4133	2	3	5	7	9	10	12	14	15
26	4150	4166	4183	4200	4216	4232	4249	4265	4281	4298	2	3	5	7	8	10	11	13	15
27	4314	4330	4346	4362	4378	4393	4409	4425	4440	4456	2	3	5	6	8	9	11	13	14
28	4472	4487	4502	4518	4533	4548	4564	4579	4594	4609	2	3	5	6	8	9	11	12	14
29	4624	4639	4654	4669	4683	4698	4713	4728	4742	4757	1	3	4	6	7	9	10	12	13
30	4771	4786	4800	4814	4829	4843	4857	4871	4886	4900	1	3	4	6	7	9	10	11	13
31	4914	4928	4942	4955	4969	4983	4997	5011	5024	5038	1	3	4	6	7	8	10	11	12
32	5051	5065	5079	5092	5105	5119	5132	5145	5159	5172	1	3	4	5	7	8	9	11	12
33	5185	5198	5211	5224	5237	5250	5263	5276	5289	5302	1	3	4	5	6	8	9	10	12
34	5315	5328	5340	5353	5366	5378	5391	5403	5416	5428	1	3	4	5	6	8	9	10	11
35	5441	5453	5465	5478	5490	5502	5514	5527	5539	5551	1	2	4	5	6	7	9	10	11
36	5563	5575	5587	5599	5611	5623	5635	5647	5658	5670	1	2	4	5	6	7	8	10	11
37	5682	5694	5705	5717	5729	5740	5752	5763	5775	5786	1	2	3	5	6	7	8	9	10
38	5798	5809	5821	5832	5843	5855	5866	5877	5888	5899	1	2	3	5	6	7	8	9	10
39	5911	5922	5933	5944	5955	5966	5977	5988	5999	6010	1	2	3	4	5	7	8	9	10
40	6021	6031	6042	6053	6064	6075	6085	6096	6107	6117	1	2	3	4	5	6	8	9	10
41	6128	6138	6149	6160	6170	6180	6191	6201	6212	6222	1	2	3	4	5	6	7	8	9
42	6232	6243	6253	6263	6274	6284	6294	6304	6314	6325	1	2	3	4	5	6	7	8	9
43	6335	6345	6355	6365	6375	6385	6395	6405	6415	6425	1	2	3	4	5	6	7	8	9
44	6435	6444	6454	6464	6474	6484	6493	6503	6513	6522	1	2	3	4	5	6	7	8	9
45	6532	6542	6551	6561	6571	6580	6590	6599	6609	6618	1	2	3	4	5	6	7	8	9
46	6628	6637	6646	6656	6665	6675	6684	6693	6702	6712	1	2	3	4	5	6	7	7	8
47	6721	6730	6739	6749	6758	6767	6776	6785	6794	6803	1	2	3	4	5	5	6	7	8
48	6812	6821	6830	6839	6848	6857	6866	6875	6884	6893	1	2	3	4	4	5	6	7	8
49	6902	6911	6920	6928	6937	6946	6955	6964	6972	6981	1	2	3	4	4	5	6	7	8
50	6990	6998	7007	7016	7024	7033	7042	7050	7059	7067	1	2	3	3	4	5	6	7	8
51	7076	7084	7093	7101	7110	7118	7126	7135	7143	7152	1	2	3	3	4	5	6	7	8
52	7160	7168	7177	7185	7193	7202	7210	7218	7226	7235	1	2	2	3	4	5	6	7	7
53	7243	7251	7259	7267	7275	7284	7292	7300	7308	7316	1	2	2	3	4	5	6	6	7
54	7324	7332	7340	7348	7356	7364	7372	7380	7388	7396	1	2	2	3	4	5	6	6	7
55	7404	7412	7419	7427	7435	7443	7451	7459	7466	7474	1	2	2	3	4	5	5	6	7
56	7482	7490	7497	7505	7513	7520	7528	7536	7543	7551	1	2	2	3	4	5	5	6	7
57	7559	7566	7574	7582	7589	7597	7604	7612	7619	7627	1	2	2	3	4	5	5	6	7
58	7634	7642	7649	7657	7664	7672	7679	7686	7694	7701	1	1	2	3	4	4	5	6	7
59	7709	7716	7723	7731	7738	7745	7752	7760	7767	7774	1	1	2	3	4	4	5	6	7
60	7782	7789	7796	7803	7810	7818	7825	7832	7839	7846	1	1	2	3	4	4	5	6	6
61	7853	7860	7868	7875	7882	7889	7896	7903	7910	7917	1	1	2	3	4	4	5	6	6
62	7924	7931	7938	7945	7952	7959	7966	7973	7980	7987	1	1	2	3	3	4	5	6	6
63	7993	8000	8007	8014	8021	8028	8035	8041	8048	8055	1	1	2	3	3	4	5	5	6
64	8062	8069	8075	8082	8089	8096	8102	8109	8116	8122	1	1	2	3	3	4	5	5	6
65	8129	8136	8142	8149	8156	8162	8169	8176	8182	8189	1	1	2	3	3	4	5	5	6
66	8195	8202	8209	8215	8222	8228	8235	8241	8248	8254	1	1	2	3	3	4	5	5	6
67	8261	8267	8274	8280	8287	8293	8299	8306	8312	8319	1	1	2	3	3	4	5	5	6
68	8325	8331	8338	8344	8351	8357	8363	8370	8376	8382	1	1	2	3	3	4	4	5	6
69	8388	8395	8401	8407	8414	8420	8426	8432	8439	8445	1	1	2	2	3	4	4	5	6
70	8451	8457	8463	8470	8476	8482	8488	8494	8500	8506	1	1	2	2	3	4	4	5	6
71	8513	8519	8525	8531	8537	8543	8549	8555	8561	8567	1	1	2	2	3	4	4	5	5
72	8573	8579	8585	8591	8597	8603	8609	8615	8621	8627	1	1	2	2	3	4	4	5	5
73	8633	8639	8645	8651	8657	8663	8669	8675	8681	8686	1	1	2	2	3	4	4	5	5
74	8692	8698	8704	8710	8716	8722	8727	8733	8739	8745	1	1	2	2	3	4	4	5	5
75	8751	8756	8762	8768	8774	8779	8785	8791	8797	8802	1	1	2	2	3	3	4	5	5
76	8808	8814	8820	8825	8831	8837	8842	8848	8854	8859	1	1	2	2	3	3	4	5	5
77	8865	8871	8876	8882	8887	8893	8899	8904	8910	8915	1	1	2	2	3	3	4	4	5
78	8921	8927	8932	8938	8943	8949	8954	8960	8965	8971	1	1	2	2	3	3	4	4	5
79	8976	8982	8987	8993	8998	9004	9009	9015	9020	9025	1	1	2	2	3	3	4	4	5
80	9031	9036	9042	9047	9053	9058	9063	9069	9074	9079	1	1	2	2	3	3	4	4	5
81	9085	9090	9096	9101	9106	9112	9117	9122	9128	9133	1	1	2	2	3	3	4	4	5
82	9138	9143	9149	9154	9159	9165	9170	9175	9180	9186	1	1	2	2	3	3	4	4	5
83	9191	9196	9201	9206	9212	9217	9222	9227	9232	9238	1	1	2	2	3	3	4	4	5
84	9243	9248	9253	9258	9263	9269	9274	9279	9284	9289	1	1	2	2	3	3	4	4	5
85	9294	9299	9304	9309	9315	9320	9325	9330	9335	9340	1	1	2	2	3	3	4	4	5
86	9345	9350	9355	9360	9365	9370	9375	9380	9385	9390	1	1	2	2	3	3	4	4	5
87	9395	9400	9405	9410	9415	9420	9425	9430	9435	9440	0	1	1	2	2	3	3	4	4
88	9445	9450	9455	9460	9465	9469	9474	9479	9484	9489	0	1	1	2	2	3	3	4	4
89	9494	9499	9504	9509	9513	9518	9523	9528	9533	9538	0	1	1	2	2	3	3	4	4
90	9542	9547	9552	9557	9562	9566	9571	9576	9581	9586	0	1	1	2	2	3	3	4	4
91	9590	9595	9600	9605	9609	9614	9619	9624	9628	9633	0	1	1	2	2	3	3	4	4
92	9638	9643	9647	9652	9657	9661	9666	9671	9675	9680	0	1	1	2	2	3	3	4	4
93	9685	9689	9694	9699	9703	9708	9713	9717	9722	9727	0	1	1	2	2	3	3	4	4
94	9731	9736	9741	9745	9750	9754	9759	9763	9768	9773	0	1	1	2	2	3	3	4	4
95	9777	9782	9786	9791	9795	9800	9805	9809	9814	9818	0	1	1	2	2	3	3	4	4
96	9823	9827	9832	9836	9841	9845	9850	9854	9859	9863	0	1	1	2	2	3	3	4	4
97	9868	9872	9877	9881	9886	9890	9894	9899	9903	9908	0	1	1	2	2	3	3	4	4
98	9912	9917	9921	9926	9930	9934	9939	9943	9948	9952	0	1	1	2	2	3	3	4	4
99	9956	9961	9965	9969	9974	9978	9983	9987	9991	9996	0	1	1	2	2	3	3	3	4

log x ↓	x 0	1	2	3	4	5	6	7	8	9	Proportional parts 1	2	3	4	5	6	7	8	9
.00	1000	1002	1005	1007	1009	1012	1014	1016	1019	1021	0	0	1	1	1	1	2	2	2
.01	1023	1026	1028	1030	1033	1035	1038	1040	1042	1045	0	0	1	1	1	1	2	2	2
.02	1047	1050	1052	1054	1057	1059	1062	1064	1067	1069	0	0	1	1	1	1	2	2	2
.03	1072	1074	1076	1079	1081	1084	1086	1089	1091	1094	0	0	1	1	1	1	2	2	2
.04	1096	1099	1102	1104	1107	1109	1112	1114	1117	1119	0	1	1	1	1	2	2	2	2
.05	1122	1125	1127	1130	1132	1135	1138	1140	1143	1146	0	1	1	1	1	2	2	2	2
.06	1148	1151	1153	1156	1159	1161	1164	1167	1169	1172	0	1	1	1	1	2	2	2	2
.07	1175	1178	1180	1183	1186	1189	1191	1194	1197	1199	0	1	1	1	1	2	2	2	2
.08	1202	1205	1208	1211	1213	1216	1219	1222	1225	1227	0	1	1	1	1	2	2	2	3
.09	1230	1233	1236	1239	1242	1245	1247	1250	1253	1256	0	1	1	1	1	2	2	2	3
.10	1259	1262	1265	1268	1271	1274	1276	1279	1282	1285	0	1	1	1	1	2	2	2	3
.11	1288	1291	1294	1297	1300	1303	1306	1309	1312	1315	0	1	1	1	2	2	2	2	3
.12	1318	1321	1324	1327	1330	1334	1337	1340	1343	1346	0	1	1	1	2	2	2	2	3
.13	1349	1352	1355	1358	1361	1365	1368	1371	1374	1377	0	1	1	1	2	2	2	3	3
.14	1380	1384	1387	1390	1393	1396	1400	1403	1406	1409	0	1	1	1	2	2	2	3	3
.15	1413	1416	1419	1422	1426	1429	1432	1435	1439	1442	0	1	1	1	2	2	2	3	3
.16	1445	1449	1452	1455	1459	1462	1466	1469	1472	1476	0	1	1	1	2	2	2	3	3
.17	1479	1483	1486	1489	1493	1496	1500	1503	1507	1510	0	1	1	1	2	2	2	3	3
.18	1514	1517	1521	1524	1528	1531	1535	1538	1542	1545	0	1	1	1	2	2	2	3	3
.19	1549	1552	1556	1560	1563	1567	1570	1574	1578	1581	0	1	1	1	2	2	3	3	3
.20	1585	1589	1592	1596	1600	1603	1607	1611	1614	1618	0	1	1	1	2	2	3	3	3
.21	1622	1626	1629	1633	1637	1641	1644	1648	1652	1656	0	1	1	2	2	2	3	3	3
.22	1660	1663	1667	1671	1675	1679	1683	1687	1690	1694	0	1	1	2	2	2	3	3	3
.23	1698	1702	1706	1710	1714	1718	1722	1726	1730	1734	0	1	1	2	2	2	3	3	4
.24	1738	1742	1746	1750	1754	1758	1762	1766	1770	1774	0	1	1	2	2	2	3	3	4
.25	1778	1782	1786	1791	1795	1799	1803	1807	1811	1816	0	1	1	2	2	2	3	3	4
.26	1820	1824	1828	1832	1837	1841	1845	1849	1854	1858	0	1	1	2	2	3	3	3	4
.27	1862	1866	1871	1875	1879	1884	1888	1892	1897	1901	0	1	1	2	2	3	3	3	4
.28	1905	1910	1914	1919	1923	1928	1932	1936	1941	1945	0	1	1	2	2	3	3	4	4
.29	1950	1954	1959	1963	1968	1972	1977	1982	1986	1991	0	1	1	2	2	3	3	4	4
.30	1995	2000	2004	2009	2014	2018	2023	2028	2032	2037	0	1	1	2	2	3	3	4	4
.31	2042	2046	2051	2056	2061	2065	2070	2075	2080	2084	0	1	1	2	2	3	3	4	4
.32	2089	2094	2099	2104	2109	2113	2118	2123	2128	2133	0	1	1	2	2	3	3	4	4
.33	2138	2143	2148	2153	2158	2163	2168	2173	2178	2183	0	1	1	2	2	3	3	4	4
.34	2188	2193	2198	2203	2208	2213	2218	2223	2228	2234	1	1	2	2	3	3	4	4	5
.35	2239	2244	2249	2254	2259	2265	2270	2275	2280	2286	1	1	2	2	3	3	4	4	5
.36	2291	2296	2301	2307	2312	2317	2323	2328	2333	2339	1	1	2	2	3	3	4	4	5
.37	2344	2350	2355	2360	2366	2371	2377	2382	2388	2393	1	1	2	2	3	3	4	4	5
.38	2399	2404	2410	2415	2421	2427	2432	2438	2443	2449	1	1	2	2	3	3	4	4	5
.39	2455	2460	2466	2472	2477	2483	2489	2495	2500	2506	1	1	2	2	3	3	4	5	5
.40	2512	2518	2523	2529	2535	2541	2547	2553	2559	2564	1	1	2	2	3	4	4	5	5
.41	2570	2576	2582	2588	2594	2600	2606	2612	2618	2624	1	1	2	2	3	4	4	5	5
.42	2630	2636	2642	2649	2655	2661	2667	2673	2679	2685	1	1	2	2	3	4	4	5	6
.43	2692	2698	2704	2710	2716	2723	2729	2735	2742	2748	1	1	2	3	3	4	4	5	6
.44	2754	2761	2767	2773	2780	2786	2793	2799	2805	2812	1	1	2	3	3	4	4	5	6
.45	2818	2825	2831	2838	2844	2851	2858	2864	2871	2877	1	1	2	3	3	4	5	5	6
.46	2884	2891	2897	2904	2911	2917	2924	2931	2938	2944	1	1	2	3	3	4	5	5	6
.47	2951	2958	2965	2972	2979	2985	2992	2999	3006	3013	1	1	2	3	3	4	5	5	6
.48	3020	3027	3034	3041	3048	3055	3062	3069	3076	3083	1	1	2	3	4	4	5	6	6
.49	3090	3097	3105	3112	3119	3126	3133	3141	3148	3155	1	1	2	3	4	4	5	6	6
.50	3162	3170	3177	3184	3192	3199	3206	3214	3221	3228	1	1	2	3	4	4	5	6	7
.51	3236	3243	3251	3258	3266	3273	3281	3289	3296	3304	1	2	2	3	4	5	5	6	7
.52	3311	3319	3327	3334	3342	3350	3357	3365	3373	3381	1	2	2	3	4	5	5	6	7
.53	3388	3396	3404	3412	3420	3428	3436	3443	3451	3459	1	2	2	3	4	5	6	6	7
.54	3467	3475	3483	3491	3499	3508	3516	3524	3532	3540	1	2	2	3	4	5	6	6	7
.55	3548	3556	3565	3573	3581	3589	3597	3606	3614	3622	1	2	2	3	4	5	6	7	7
.56	3631	3639	3648	3656	3664	3673	3681	3690	3698	3707	1	2	3	3	4	5	6	7	8
.57	3715	3724	3733	3741	3750	3758	3767	3776	3784	3793	1	2	3	3	4	5	6	7	8
.58	3802	3811	3819	3828	3837	3846	3855	3864	3873	3882	1	2	3	4	4	5	6	7	8
.59	3890	3899	3908	3917	3926	3936	3945	3954	3963	3972	1	2	3	4	5	5	6	7	8
.60	3981	3990	3999	4009	4018	4027	4036	4046	4055	4064	1	2	3	4	5	6	6	7	8
.61	4074	4083	4093	4102	4111	4121	4130	4140	4150	4159	1	2	3	4	5	6	7	8	9
.62	4169	4178	4188	4198	4207	4217	4227	4236	4246	4256	1	2	3	4	5	6	7	8	9
.63	4266	4276	4285	4295	4305	4315	4325	4335	4345	4355	1	2	3	4	5	6	7	8	9
.64	4365	4375	4385	4395	4406	4416	4426	4436	4446	4457	1	2	3	4	5	6	7	8	9
.65	4467	4477	4487	4498	4508	4519	4529	4539	4550	4560	1	2	3	4	5	6	7	8	9
.66	4571	4581	4592	4603	4613	4624	4634	4645	4656	4667	1	2	3	4	5	6	7	9	10
.67	4677	4688	4699	4710	4721	4732	4742	4753	4764	4775	1	2	3	4	5	7	8	9	10
.68	4786	4797	4808	4819	4831	4842	4853	4864	4875	4887	1	2	3	4	6	7	8	9	10
.69	4898	4909	4920	4932	4943	4955	4966	4977	4989	5000	1	2	3	5	6	7	8	9	10
.70	5012	5023	5035	5047	5058	5070	5082	5093	5105	5117	1	2	4	5	6	7	8	9	11
.71	5129	5140	5152	5164	5176	5188	5200	5212	5224	5236	1	2	4	5	6	7	8	10	11
.72	5248	5260	5272	5284	5297	5309	5321	5333	5346	5358	1	2	4	5	6	7	9	10	11
.73	5370	5383	5395	5408	5420	5433	5445	5458	5470	5483	1	3	4	5	6	8	9	10	11
.74	5495	5508	5521	5534	5546	5559	5572	5585	5598	5610	1	3	4	5	6	8	9	10	12
.75	5623	5636	5649	5662	5675	5689	5702	5715	5728	5741	1	3	4	5	7	8	9	10	12
.76	5754	5768	5781	5794	5808	5821	5834	5848	5861	5875	1	3	4	5	7	8	9	11	12
.77	5888	5902	5916	5929	5943	5957	5970	5984	5998	6012	1	3	4	5	7	8	10	11	12
.78	6026	6039	6053	6067	6081	6095	6109	6124	6138	6152	1	3	4	6	7	8	10	11	13
.79	6166	6180	6194	6209	6223	6237	6252	6266	6281	6295	1	3	4	6	7	9	10	11	13
.80	6310	6324	6339	6353	6368	6383	6397	6412	6427	6442	1	3	4	6	7	9	10	12	13
.81	6457	6471	6486	6501	6516	6531	6546	6561	6577	6592	2	3	5	6	8	9	11	12	14
.82	6607	6622	6637	6653	6668	6683	6699	6714	6730	6745	2	3	5	6	8	9	11	12	14
.83	6761	6776	6792	6808	6823	6839	6855	6871	6887	6902	2	3	5	6	8	9	11	13	14
.84	6918	6934	6950	6966	6982	6998	7015	7031	7047	7063	2	3	5	6	8	10	11	13	15
.85	7079	7096	7112	7129	7145	7161	7178	7194	7211	7228	2	3	5	7	8	10	12	13	15
.86	7244	7261	7278	7295	7311	7328	7345	7362	7379	7396	2	3	5	7	8	10	12	13	15
.87	7413	7430	7447	7464	7482	7499	7516	7534	7551	7568	2	3	5	7	9	10	12	14	16
.88	7586	7603	7621	7638	7656	7674	7691	7709	7727	7745	2	4	5	7	9	11	12	14	16
.89	7762	7780	7798	7816	7834	7852	7870	7889	7907	7925	2	4	5	7	9	11	13	14	16
.90	7943	7962	7980	7998	8017	8035	8054	8072	8091	8110	2	4	6	7	9	11	13	15	17
.91	8128	8147	8166	8185	8204	8222	8241	8260	8279	8299	2	4	6	8	9	11	13	15	17
.92	8318	8337	8356	8375	8395	8414	8433	8453	8472	8492	2	4	6	8	10	12	14	15	17
.93	8511	8531	8551	8570	8590	8610	8630	8650	8670	8690	2	4	6	8	10	12	14	16	18
.94	8710	8730	8750	8770	8790	8810	8831	8851	8872	8892	2	4	6	8	10	12	14	16	18
.95	8913	8933	8954	8974	8995	9016	9036	9057	9078	9099	2	4	6	8	10	12	15	17	19
.96	9120	9141	9162	9183	9204	9226	9247	9268	9290	9311	2	4	6	8	11	13	15	17	19
.97	9333	9354	9376	9397	9419	9441	9462	9484	9506	9528	2	4	7	9	11	13	15	17	20
.98	9550	9572	9594	9616	9638	9661	9683	9705	9727	9750	2	4	7	9	11	13	16	18	20
.99	9772	9795	9817	9840	9863	9886	9908	9931	9954	9977	2	5	7	9	11	14	16	18	20

x	0.000	0.001	0.002	0.003	0.004	0.005	0.006	0.007	0.008	0.009
0.000	−∞	−6.90776	−6.21461	−5.80914	−5.52146	−5.29832	−5.11600	−4.96185	−4.82831	−4.71053
010	−4.60517	−4.50986	−4.42285	−4.34281	−4.26870	−4.19971	−4.13517	−4.07454	−4.01738	−3.96332
020	−3.91202	−3.86323	−3.81671	−3.77226	−3.72970	−3.68888	−3.64966	−3.61192	−3.57555	54046
030	50656	47377	44202	41125	38139	35241	32424	29684	27017	24419
040	21888	19418	17009	14656	12357	10109	07911	05761	03655	01593
0.050	−2.99573	−2.97593	−2.95651	−2.93746	−2.91877	−2.90042	−2.88240	−2.86470	−2.84731	−2.83022
060	81341	79688	78062	76462	74887	73337	71810	70306	68825	67365
070	65926	64508	63109	61730	60369	59027	57702	56395	55105	53831
080	52573	51331	50104	48891	47694	46510	45341	44185	43042	41912
090	40795	39690	38597	37516	36446	35388	34341	33304	32279	31264
0.100	−2.30259	−2.29263	−2.28278	−2.27303	−2.26336	−2.25379	−2.24432	−2.23493	−2.22562	−2.21641
110	20727	19823	18926	18037	17156	16282	15417	14558	13707	12863
120	12026	11196	10373	09557	08747	07944	07147	06357	05573	04794
130	04022	03256	02495	01741	00992	00248	−1.99510	−1.98777	−1.98050	−1.97328
140	−1.96611	−1.95900	−1.95193	−1.94491	−1.93794	−1.93102	92415	91732	91054	90381
0.150	−1.89712	−1.89048	−1.88387	−1.87732	−1.87080	−1.86433	−1.85790	−1.85151	−1.84516	−1.83885
160	83258	82635	82016	81401	80789	80181	79577	78976	78379	77786
170	77196	76609	76026	75446	74870	74297	73727	73161	72597	72037
180	71480	70926	70375	69827	69282	68740	68201	67665	67131	66601
190	66073	65548	65026	64507	63990	63476	62964	62455	61949	61445
0.200	−1.60944	−1.60445	−1.59949	−1.59455	−1.58964	−1.58475	−1.57988	−1.57504	−1.57022	−1.56542
210	56065	55590	55117	54646	54178	53712	53248	52786	52326	51868
220	51413	50959	50508	50058	49611	49165	48722	48281	47841	47403
230	46968	46534	46102	45672	45243	44817	44392	43970	43548	43129
240	42712	42296	41882	41469	41059	40650	40242	39837	39433	39030
0.250	−1.38629	−1.38230	−1.37833	−1.37437	−1.37042	−1.36649	−1.36258	−1.35868	−1.35480	−1.35093
260	34707	34323	33941	33560	33181	32803	32426	32051	31677	31304
270	30933	30564	30195	29828	29463	29098	28735	28374	28013	27654
280	27297	26940	26585	26231	25878	25527	25176	24827	24479	24133
290	23787	23443	23100	22758	22418	22078	21740	21402	21066	20731
0.300	−1.20397	−1.20065	−1.19733	−1.19402	−1.19073	−1.18744	−1.18417	−1.18091	−1.17766	−1.17441
310	17118	16796	16475	16155	15836	15518	15201	14885	14570	14256
320	13943	13631	13320	13010	12701	12393	12086	11780	11474	11170
330	10866	10564	10262	09961	09661	09362	09064	08767	08471	08176
340	07881	07587	07294	07002	06711	06421	06132	05843	05555	05268
0.350	−1.04982	−1.04697	−1.04412	−1.04129	−1.03846	−1.03564	−1.03282	−1.03002	−1.02722	−1.02443
360	02165	01888	01611	01335	01060	00786	00512	00239	−0.99967	−0.99696
370	−0.99425	−0.99155	−0.98886	−0.98618	−0.98350	−0.98083	−0.97817	−0.97551	97286	97022
380	96758	96496	96233	95972	95711	95451	95192	94933	94675	94418
390	94161	93905	93649	93395	93140	92887	92634	92382	92130	91879
0.400	−0.91629	−0.91379	−0.91130	−0.90882	−0.90634	−0.90387	−0.90140	−0.89894	−0.89649	−0.89404
410	89160	88916	88673	88431	88189	87948	87707	87467	87227	86988
420	86750	86512	86275	86038	85802	85567	85332	85097	84863	84630
430	84397	84165	83933	83702	83471	83241	83011	82782	82554	82326
440	82098	81871	81645	81419	81193	80968	80744	80520	80296	80073
0.450	−0.79851	−0.79629	−0.79407	−0.79186	−0.78966	−0.78746	−0.78526	−0.78307	−0.78089	−0.77871
460	77653	77436	77219	77003	76787	76572	76357	76143	75929	75715
470	75502	75290	75078	74866	74655	74444	74234	74024	73814	73605
480	73397	73189	72981	72774	72567	72361	72155	71949	71744	71539
490	71335	71131	70928	70725	70522	70320	70118	69917	69716	69515
0.500	−0.69315	−0.69115	−0.68916	−0.68717	−0.68518	−0.68320	−0.68122	−0.67924	−0.67727	−0.67531
510	67334	67139	66943	66748	66553	66359	66165	65971	65778	65585
520	65393	65201	65009	64817	64626	64436	64245	64055	63866	63677
530	63488	63299	63111	62923	62736	62549	62362	62176	61990	61804
540	61619	61434	61249	61065	60881	60697	60514	60331	60148	59966
0.550	−0.59784	−0.59602	−0.59421	−0.59240	−0.59059	−0.58879	−0.58699	−0.58519	−0.58340	−0.58161
560	57982	57803	57625	57448	57270	57093	56916	56740	56563	56387
570	56212	56037	55862	55687	55513	55339	55165	54991	54818	54645
580	54473	54300	54128	53957	53785	53614	53444	53273	53103	52933
590	52763	52594	52425	52256	52088	51919	51751	51584	51416	51249
0.600	−0.51083	−0.50916	−0.50750	−0.50584	−0.50418	−0.50253	−0.50088	−0.49923	−0.49758	−0.49594
610	49430	49266	49102	48939	48776	48613	48451	48289	48127	47965
620	47804	47642	47482	47321	47160	47000	46840	46681	46522	46362
630	46204	46045	45887	45728	45571	45413	45256	45099	44942	44785
640	44629	44473	44317	44161	44006	43850	43696	43541	43386	43232
0.650	−0.43078	−0.42925	−0.42771	−0.42618	−0.42465	−0.42312	−0.42159	−0.42007	−0.41855	−0.41703
660	41552	41400	41249	41098	40947	40797	40647	40497	40347	40197
670	40048	39899	39750	39601	39453	39304	39156	39008	38861	38713
680	38566	38419	38273	38126	37980	37834	37688	37542	37397	37251
690	37106	36962	36817	36673	36528	36384	36241	36097	35954	35810
0.700	−0.35667	−0.35525	−0.35382	−0.35240	−0.35098	−0.34956	−0.34814	−0.34672	−0.34531	−0.34390
710	34249	34108	33968	33827	33687	33547	33408	33268	33129	32989
720	32850	32712	32573	32435	32296	32158	32021	31883	31745	31608
730	31471	31334	31197	31061	30925	30788	30653	30517	30381	30246
740	30111	29975	29841	29706	29571	29437	29303	29169	29035	28902
0.750	−0.28768	−0.28635	−0.28502	−0.28369	−0.28236	−0.28104	−0.27971	−0.27839	−0.27707	−0.27575
760	27444	27312	27181	27050	26919	26788	26657	26527	26397	26266
770	26136	26007	25877	25748	25618	25489	25360	25231	25103	24974
780	24846	24718	24590	24462	24335	24207	24080	23953	23826	23699
790	23572	23446	23319	23193	23067	22941	22816	22690	22565	22439
0.800	−0.22314	−0.22189	−0.22065	−0.21940	−0.21816	−0.21691	−0.21567	−0.21443	−0.21319	−0.21196
810	21072	20949	20825	20702	20579	20457	20334	20212	20089	19967
820	19845	19723	19601	19480	19358	19237	19116	18995	18874	18754
830	18633	18513	18392	18272	18152	18032	17913	17793	17674	17554
840	17435	17316	17198	17079	16960	16842	16724	16605	16487	16370
0.850	−0.16252	−0.16134	−0.16017	−0.15900	−0.15782	−0.15665	−0.15548	−0.15432	−0.15315	−0.15199
860	15032	14966	14850	14734	14618	14503	14387	14272	14156	14041
870	13926	13811	13697	13582	13467	13353	13239	13125	13011	12897
880	12783	12670	12556	12443	12330	12217	12104	11991	11878	11766
890	11653	11541	11429	11317	11205	11093	10981	10870	10759	10647
0.900	−0.10536	−0.10425	−0.10314	−0.10203	−0.10093	−0.09982	−0.09872	−0.09761	−0.09651	−0.09541
910	09431	09321	09212	09102	08992	08883	08774	08665	08556	08447
920	08338	08230	08121	08013	07904	07796	07688	07580	07472	07365
930	07257	07150	07042	06935	06828	06721	06614	06507	06401	06294
940	06188	06081	05975	05869	05763	05657	05551	05446	05340	05235
0.950	−0.05129	−0.05024	−0.04919	−0.04814	−0.04709	−0.04604	−0.04500	−0.04395	−0.04291	−0.04186
960	04082	03978	03874	03770	03666	03563	03459	03356	03252	03149
970	03046	02943	02840	02737	02634	02532	02429	02327	02225	02122
980	02020	01918	01816	01715	01613	01511	01410	01309	01207	01106
990	01005	00904	00803	00702	00602	00501	00401	00300	00200	00100

* To find the natural logarithm ($\log_e$) of a number which is a power of ten less or greater than a number given in the table: if the number concerned is *less*, e.g. $^1/_{10}$ (10^{-1}), $^1/_{100}$ (10^{-2}), $^1/_{1000}$ (10^{-3}), etc., *subtract* from the given logarithm $\log_e 10$, $2 \log_e 10$, $3 \log_e 10$, etc.; if the number concerned is *greater*, e.g. 10 times (10^1), 100 times (10^2), 1000 times (10^3), etc., *add* to the given logarithm $\log_e 10$, $2 \log_e 10$, $3 \log_e 10$, etc. Examples: $\log_e 0.02 = \log_e 0.2 - \log_e 10$; $\log_e 2000 = \log_e 200 + \log_e 10$.

Natural Logarithms* 1.00—9.99

x	0.00	0.01	0.02	0.03	0.04	0.05	0.06	0.07	0.08	0.09
1.00	0.00000	0.00995	0.01980	0.02956	0.03922	0.04879	0.05827	0.06766	0.07696	0.08618
10	09531	10436	11333	12222	13103	13976	14842	15700	16551	17395
20	18232	19062	19885	20701	21511	22314	23111	23902	24686	25464
30	26236	27003	27763	28518	29267	30010	30748	31481	32208	32930
40	33647	34359	35066	35767	36464	37156	37844	38526	39204	39878
1.50	0.40547	0.41211	0.41871	0.42527	0.43178	0.43825	0.44469	0.45108	0.45742	0.46373
60	47000	47623	48243	48858	49470	50078	50682	51282	51879	52473
70	53063	53649	54232	54812	55389	55962	56531	57098	57661	58222
80	58779	59333	59884	60432	60977	61519	62058	62594	63127	63658
90	64185	64710	65233	65752	66269	66783	67294	67803	68310	68813
2.00	0.69315	0.69813	0.70310	0.70804	0.71295	0.71784	0.72271	0.72755	0.73237	0.73716
10	74194	74669	75142	75612	76081	76547	77011	77473	77932	78390
20	78846	79299	79751	80200	80648	81093	81536	81978	82418	82855
30	83291	83725	84157	84587	85015	85442	85866	86289	86710	87129
40	87547	87963	88377	88789	89200	89609	90016	90422	90826	91228
2.50	0.91629	0.92028	0.92426	0.92822	0.93216	0.93609	0.94001	0.94391	0.94779	0.95166
60	95551	95935	96317	96698	97078	97456	97833	98208	98582	98954
70	99325	99695	1.00063	1.00430	1.00796	1.01160	1.01523	1.01885	1.02245	1.02604
80	1.02962	1.03318	03674	04028	04380	04732	05082	05431	05779	06126
90	06471	06815	07158	07500	07841	08181	08519	08856	09192	09527
3.00	1.09861	1.10194	1.10526	1.10856	1.11186	1.11514	1.11841	1.12168	1.12493	1.12817
10	13140	13462	13783	14103	14422	14740	15057	15373	15688	16002
20	16315	16627	16938	17248	17557	17865	18173	18479	18784	19089
30	19392	19695	19996	20297	20597	20896	21194	21491	21788	22083
40	22378	22671	22964	23256	23547	23837	24127	24415	24703	24990
3.50	1.25276	1.25562	1.25846	1.26130	1.26413	1.26695	1.26976	1.27257	1.27536	1.27815
60	28093	28371	28647	28923	29198	29473	29746	30019	30291	30563
70	30833	31103	31372	31641	31909	32176	32442	32708	32972	33237
80	33500	33763	34025	34286	34547	34807	35067	35325	35584	35841
90	36098	36354	36609	36864	37118	37372	37624	37877	38128	38379
4.00	1.38629	1.38879	1.39128	1.39377	1.39624	1.39872	1.40118	1.40364	1.40610	1.40854
10	41099	41342	41585	41828	42070	42311	42552	42792	43031	43270
20	43508	43746	43984	44220	44456	44692	44927	45161	45395	45629
30	45862	46094	46326	46557	46787	47018	47247	47476	47705	47933
40	48160	48387	48614	48840	49065	49290	49515	49739	49962	50185
4.50	1.50408	1.50630	1.50851	1.51072	1.51293	1.51513	1.51732	1.51951	1.52170	1.52388
60	52606	52823	53039	53256	53471	53687	53902	54116	54330	54543
70	54756	54969	55181	55393	55604	55814	56025	56235	56444	56653
80	56862	57070	57277	57485	57691	57898	58104	58309	58515	58719
90	58924	59127	59331	59534	59737	59939	60141	60342	60543	60744
5.00	1.60944	1.61144	1.61343	1.61542	1.61741	1.61939	1.62137	1.62334	1.62531	1.62728
10	62924	63120	63315	63511	63705	63900	64094	64287	64481	64673
20	64866	65058	65250	65441	65632	65823	66013	66203	66393	66582
30	66771	66959	67147	67335	67523	67710	67896	68083	68269	68455
40	68640	68825	69010	69194	69378	69562	69745	69928	70111	70293
5.50	1.70475	1.70656	1.70838	1.71019	1.71199	1.71380	1.71560	1.71740	1.71919	1.72098
60	72277	72455	72633	72811	72988	73166	73342	73519	73695	73871
70	74047	74222	74397	74572	74746	74920	75094	75267	75440	75613
80	75786	75958	76130	76302	76473	76644	76815	76985	77156	77326
90	77495	77665	77834	78002	78171	78339	78507	78675	78842	79009
6.00	1.79176	1.79342	1.79509	1.79675	1.79840	1.80006	1.80171	1.80336	1.80500	1.80665
10	80829	80993	81156	81319	81482	81645	81808	81970	82132	82294
20	82455	82616	82777	82938	83098	83258	83418	83578	83737	83896
30	84055	84214	84372	84530	84688	84845	85003	85160	85317	85473
40	85630	85786	85942	86097	86253	86408	86563	86718	86872	87026
6.50	1.87180	1.87334	1.87487	1.87641	1.87794	1.87947	1.88099	1.88251	1.88403	1.88555
60	88707	88858	89010	89160	89311	89462	89612	89762	89912	90061
70	90211	90360	90509	90658	90806	90954	91102	91250	91398	91545
80	91692	91839	91986	92132	92279	92425	92571	92716	92862	93007
90	93152	93297	93442	93586	93730	93874	94018	94162	94305	94448
7.00	1.94591	1.94734	1.94876	1.95019	1.95161	1.95303	1.95445	1.95586	1.95727	1.95869
10	96009	96150	96291	96431	96571	96711	96851	96991	97130	97269
20	97408	97547	97685	97824	97962	98100	98238	98376	98513	98650
30	98787	98924	99061	99198	99334	99470	99606	99742	99877	2.00013
40	2.00148	2.00283	2.00418	2.00553	2.00687	2.00821	2.00956	2.01089	2.01223	01357
7.50	2.01490	2.01624	2.01757	2.01890	2.02022	2.02155	2.02287	2.02419	2.02551	2.02683
60	02815	02946	03078	03209	03340	03471	03601	03732	03862	03992
70	04122	04252	04381	04511	04640	04769	04898	05027	05156	05284
80	05412	05540	05668	05796	05924	06051	06179	06306	06433	06560
90	06686	06813	06939	07065	07191	07317	07443	07568	07694	07819
8.00	2.07944	2.08069	2.08194	2.08318	2.08443	2.08567	2.08691	2.08815	2.08939	2.09063
10	09186	09310	09433	09556	09679	09802	09924	10047	10169	10291
20	10413	10535	10657	10779	10900	11021	11142	11263	11384	11505
30	11626	11746	11866	11986	12106	12226	12346	12465	12585	12704
40	12823	12942	13061	13180	13298	13417	13535	13653	13771	13889
8.50	2.14007	2.14124	2.14242	2.14359	2.14476	2.14593	2.14710	2.14827	2.14943	2.15060
60	15176	15292	15409	15524	15640	15756	15871	15987	16102	16217
70	16332	16447	16562	16677	16791	16905	17020	17134	17248	17361
80	17475	17589	17702	17816	17929	18042	18155	18267	18380	18493
90	18605	18717	18830	18942	19054	19165	19277	19389	19500	19611
9.00	2.19722	2.19834	2.19944	2.20055	2.20166	2.20276	2.20387	2.20497	2.20607	2.20717
10	20827	20937	21047	21157	21266	21375	21485	21594	21703	21812
20	21920	22029	22138	22246	22354	22462	22570	22678	22786	22894
30	23001	23109	23216	23324	23431	23538	23645	23751	23858	23965
40	24071	24177	24284	24390	24496	24601	24707	24813	24918	25024
9.50	2.25129	2.25234	2.25339	2.25444	2.25549	2.25654	2.25759	2.25863	2.25968	2.26072
60	26176	26280	26384	26488	26592	26696	26799	26903	27006	27109
70	27213	27316	27419	27521	27624	27727	27829	27932	28034	28136
80	28238	28340	28442	28544	28646	28747	28849	28950	29051	29152
90	29253	29354	29455	29556	29657	29757	29858	29958	30058	30158

* To find the natural logarithm ($\log_e$) of a number which is a power of ten less or greater than a number given in the table: if the number concerned is *less*, e.g. $^1/_{10}$ (10^{-1}), $^1/_{100}$ (10^{-2}), $^1/_{1000}$ (10^{-3}), etc., *subtract* from the given logarithm $\log_e 10$, $2 \log_e 10$, $3 \log_e 10$, etc.; if the number concerned is *greater*, e.g. 10 times (10^1), 100 times (10^2), 1000 times (10^3), etc., *add* to the given logarithm $\log_e 10$, $2 \log_e 10$, $3 \log_e 10$, etc. Examples: $\log_e 0.02 = \log_e 0.2 - \log_e 10$; $\log_e 2000 = \log_e 200 + \log_e 10$.

Natural Logarithms* 10.0—99.9

x	0.0	0.1	0.2	0.3	0.4	0.5	0.6	0.7	0.8	0.9
10.0	2.30259	2.31254	2.32239	2.33214	2.34181	2.35138	2.36085	2.37024	2.37955	2.38876
11.0	39790	40695	41591	42480	43361	44235	45101	45959	46810	47654
12.0	48491	49321	50144	50960	51770	52573	53370	54160	54945	55723
13.0	56495	57261	58022	58776	59525	60269	61007	61740	62467	63189
14.0	63906	64617	65324	66026	66723	67415	68102	68785	69463	70136
15.0	2.70805	2.71469	2.72130	2.72785	2.73437	2.74084	2.74727	2.75366	2.76001	2.76632
16.0	77259	77882	78501	79117	79728	80336	80940	81541	82138	82731
17.0	83321	83908	84491	85071	85647	86220	86790	87356	87920	88480
18.0	89037	89591	90142	90690	91235	91777	92316	92852	93386	93916
19.0	94444	94969	95491	96011	96527	97041	97553	98062	98568	99072
20.0	2.99573	3.00072	3.00568	3.01062	3.01553	3.02042	3.02529	3.03013	3.03495	3.03975
21.0	3.04452	04927	05400	05871	06339	06805	07269	07731	08191	08649
22.0	09104	09558	10009	10459	10906	11352	11795	12236	12676	13114
23.0	13549	13983	14415	14845	15274	15700	16125	16548	16969	17388
24.0	17805	18221	18635	19048	19458	19867	20275	20680	21084	21487
25.0	3.21888	3.22287	3.22684	3.23080	3.23475	3.23868	3.24259	3.24649	3.25037	3.25424
26.0	25810	26194	26576	26957	27336	27714	28091	28466	28840	29213
27.0	29584	29953	30322	30689	31054	31419	31782	32143	32504	32863
28.0	33220	33577	33932	34286	34639	34990	35341	35690	36038	36384
29.0	36730	37074	37417	37759	38099	38439	38777	39115	39451	39786
30.0	3.40120	3.40453	3.40784	3.41115	3.41444	3.41773	3.42100	3.42426	3.42751	3.43076
31.0	43399	43721	44042	44362	44681	44999	45316	45632	45947	46261
32.0	46574	46886	47197	47507	47816	48124	48431	48738	49043	49347
33.0	49651	49953	50255	50556	50856	51155	51453	51750	52046	52342
34.0	52636	52930	53223	53515	53806	54096	54385	54674	54962	55249
35.0	3.55535	3.55820	3.56105	3.56388	3.56671	3.56953	3.57235	3.57515	3.57795	3.58074
36.0	58352	58629	58906	59182	59457	59731	60005	60278	60550	60821
37.0	61092	61362	61631	61899	62167	62434	62700	62966	63231	63495
38.0	63759	64021	64284	64545	64806	65066	65325	65584	65842	66099
39.0	66356	66612	66868	67122	67377	67630	67883	68135	68387	68638
40.0	3.68888	3.69138	3.69387	3.69635	3.69883	3.70130	3.70377	3.70623	3.70868	3.71113
41.0	71357	71601	71844	72086	72328	72569	72810	73050	73290	73529
42.0	73767	74005	74242	74479	74715	74950	75185	75420	75654	75887
43.0	76120	76352	76584	76815	77046	77276	77506	77735	77963	78191
44.0	78419	78646	78872	79098	79324	79549	79773	79997	80221	80444
45.0	3.80666	3.80888	3.81110	3.81331	3.81551	3.81771	3.81991	3.82210	3.82428	3.82647
46.0	82864	83081	83298	83514	83730	83945	84160	84374	84588	84802
47.0	85015	85227	85439	85651	85862	86073	86283	86493	86703	86912
48.0	87120	87328	87536	87743	87950	88156	88362	88568	88773	88978
49.0	89182	89386	89589	89792	89995	90197	90399	90600	90801	91002
50.0	3.91202	3.91402	3.91602	3.91801	3.91999	3.92197	3.92395	3.92593	3.92790	3.92986
51.0	93183	93378	93574	93769	93964	94158	94352	94546	94739	94932
52.0	95124	95316	95508	95700	95891	96081	96272	96462	96651	96840
53.0	97029	97218	97406	97594	97781	97968	98155	98341	98527	98713
54.0	98898	99083	99268	99452	99636	99820	4.00003	4.00186	4.00369	4.00551
55.0	4.00733	4.00915	4.01096	4.01277	4.01458	4.01638	4.01818	4.01998	4.02177	4.02356
56.0	02535	02714	02892	03069	03247	03424	03601	03777	03954	04130
57.0	04305	04480	04655	04830	05004	05178	05352	05526	05699	05872
58.0	06044	06217	06389	06560	06732	06903	07073	07244	07414	07584
59.0	07754	07923	08092	08261	08429	08598	08766	08933	09101	09268
60.0	4.09434	4.09601	4.09767	4.09933	4.10099	4.10264	4.10429	4.10594	4.10759	4.10923
61.0	11087	11251	11415	11578	11741	11904	12066	12228	12390	12552
62.0	12713	12875	13036	13196	13357	13517	13677	13836	13996	14155
63.0	14313	14472	14630	14789	14946	15104	15261	15418	15575	15732
64.0	15888	16044	16200	16356	16511	16667	16821	16976	17131	17285
65.0	4.17439	4.17592	4.17746	4.17899	4.18052	4.18205	4.18358	4.18510	4.18662	4.18814
66.0	18965	19117	19268	19419	19570	19720	19870	20020	20170	20320
67.0	20469	20618	20767	20916	21065	21213	21361	21509	21656	21804
68.0	21951	22098	22244	22391	22537	22683	22829	22975	23120	23266
69.0	23411	23555	23700	23844	23989	24133	24276	24420	24563	24707
70.0	4.24850	4.24992	4.25135	4.25277	4.25419	4.25561	4.25703	4.25845	4.25986	4.26127
71.0	26268	26409	26549	26690	26830	26970	27110	27249	27388	27528
72.0	27667	27805	27944	28082	28221	28359	28496	28634	28772	28909
73.0	29046	29183	29320	29456	29592	29729	29865	30000	30136	30271
74.0	30407	30542	30676	30811	30946	31080	31214	31348	31482	31615
75.0	4.31749	4.31882	4.32015	4.32149	4.32281	4.32413	4.32546	4.32678	4.32810	4.32942
76.0	33073	33205	33336	33467	33598	33729	33860	33990	34120	34251
77.0	34381	34510	34640	34769	34899	35028	35157	35286	35414	35543
78.0	35671	35800	35927	36055	36182	36310	36437	36564	36691	36818
79.0	36945	37071	37198	37324	37450	37576	37701	37827	37952	38078
80.0	4.38203	4.38328	4.38452	4.38577	4.38701	4.38826	4.38950	4.39074	4.39198	4.39321
81.0	39445	39568	39692	39815	39938	40060	40183	40305	40428	40550
82.0	40672	40794	40916	41037	41159	41280	41401	41522	41643	41764
83.0	41884	42004	42125	42245	42365	42485	42604	42724	42843	42963
84.0	43082	43201	43319	43438	43557	43675	43793	43912	44030	44147
85.0	4.44265	4.44383	4.44500	4.44617	4.44735	4.44852	4.44969	4.45085	4.45202	4.45318
86.0	45435	45551	45667	45783	45899	46014	46130	46245	46361	46476
87.0	46591	46706	46820	46935	47050	47164	47278	47392	47506	47620
88.0	47734	47847	47961	48074	48187	48300	48413	48526	48639	48751
89.0	48864	48976	49088	49200	49312	49424	49536	49647	49758	49870
90.0	4.49981	4.50092	4.50203	4.50314	4.50424	4.50535	4.50645	4.50756	4.50866	4.50976
91.0	51086	51196	51305	51415	51525	51634	51743	51852	51961	52070
92.0	52179	52287	52396	52504	52613	52721	52829	52937	53045	53152
93.0	53260	53367	53475	53582	53689	53796	53903	54010	54116	54223
94.0	54329	54436	54542	54648	54754	54860	54966	55071	55177	55282
95.0	4.55388	4.55493	4.55598	4.55703	4.55808	4.55913	4.56017	4.56122	4.56226	4.56331
96.0	56435	56539	56643	56747	56851	56954	57058	57161	57265	57368
97.0	57471	57574	57677	57780	57883	57985	58088	58190	58292	58395
98.0	58497	58599	58701	58802	58904	59006	59107	59208	59310	59411
99.0	59512	59613	59714	59815	59915	60016	60116	60217	60317	60417

* To find the natural logarithm ($\log_e$) of a number which is a power of ten less or greater than a number given in the table: if the number concerned is *less*, e.g. $^1/_{10}$ (10^{-1}), $^1/_{100}$ (10^{-2}), $^1/_{1000}$ (10^{-3}), etc., *subtract* from the given logarithm $\log_e 10$, $2 \log_e 10$, $3 \log_e 10$, etc.; if the number concerned is *greater*, e.g. 10 times (10^1), 100 times (10^2), 1000 times (10^3), etc., *add* to the given logarithm $\log_e 10$, $2 \log_e 10$, $3 \log_e 10$, etc. Examples: $\log_e 0.02 = \log_e 0.2 - \log_e 10$; $\log_e 2000 = \log_e 200 + \log_e 10$.

x	0	1	2	3	4	5	6	7	8	9
00	∞	0.00000	0.69315	1.09861	1.38629	1.60944	1.79176	1.94591	2.07944	2.19722
10	2.30259	2.39790	2.48491	2.56495	2.63906	2.70805	2.77259	2.83321	89037	94444
20	99573	3.04452	3.09104	3.13549	3.17805	3.21888	3.25810	3.29584	3.33220	3.36730
30	3.40120	43399	46574	49651	52636	55535	58352	61092	63759	66356
40	68888	71357	73767	76120	78419	80666	82864	85015	87120	89182
50	3.91202	3.93183	3.95124	3.97029	3.98898	4.00733	4.02535	4.04305	4.06044	4.07754
60	4.09434	4.11087	4.12713	4.14313	4.15888	17439	18965	20469	21951	23411
70	24850	26268	27667	29046	30407	31749	33073	34381	35671	36945
80	38203	39445	40672	41884	43082	44265	45435	46591	47734	48864
90	49981	51086	52179	53260	54329	55388	56435	57471	58497	59512
100	4.60517	4.61512	4.62497	4.63473	4.64439	4.65396	4.66344	4.67283	4.68213	4.69135
110	70048	70953	71850	72739	73620	74493	75359	76217	77068	77912
120	78749	79579	80402	81218	82028	82831	83628	84419	85203	85981
130	86753	87520	88280	89035	89784	90527	91265	91998	92725	93447
140	94164	94876	95583	96284	96981	97673	98361	99043	99721	5.00395
150	5.01064	5.01728	5.02388	5.03044	5.03695	5.04343	5.04986	5.05625	5.06260	5.06890
160	07517	08140	08760	09375	09987	10595	11199	11799	12396	12990
170	13580	14166	14749	15329	15906	16479	17048	17615	18178	18739
180	19296	19850	20401	20949	21494	22036	22575	23111	23644	24175
190	24702	25227	25750	26269	26786	27300	27811	28320	28827	29330
200	5.29832	5.30330	5.30827	5.31321	5.31812	5.32301	5.32788	5.33272	5.33754	5.34233
210	34711	35186	35659	36129	36598	37064	37528	37990	38450	38907
220	39363	39816	40268	40717	41165	41610	42053	42495	42935	43372
230	43808	44242	44674	45104	45532	45959	46383	46806	47227	47646
240	48064	48480	48894	49306	49717	50126	50533	50939	51343	51745
250	5.52146	5.52545	5.52943	5.53339	5.53733	5.54126	5.54518	5.54908	5.55296	5.55683
260	56068	56452	56834	57215	57595	57973	58350	58725	59099	59471
270	59842	60212	60580	60947	61313	61677	62040	62402	62762	63121
280	63479	63835	64191	64545	64897	65249	65599	65948	66296	66643
290	66988	67332	67675	68017	68358	68698	69036	69373	69709	70044
300	5.70378	5.70711	5.71043	5.71373	5.71703	5.72031	5.72359	5.72685	5.73010	5.73334
310	73657	73979	74300	74620	74939	75257	75574	75890	76205	76519
320	76832	77144	77455	77765	78074	78383	78690	78996	79301	79606
330	79909	80212	80513	80814	81114	81413	81711	82008	82305	82600
340	82895	83188	83481	83773	84064	84354	84644	84932	85220	85507
350	5.85793	5.86079	5.86363	5.86647	5.86930	5.87212	5.87493	5.87774	5.88053	5.88332
360	88610	88888	89164	89440	89715	89990	90263	90536	90808	91080
370	91350	91620	91889	92158	92426	92693	92959	93225	93489	93754
380	94017	94280	94542	94803	95064	95324	95584	95842	96101	96358
390	96615	96871	97126	97381	97635	97889	98141	98394	98645	98896
400	5.99146	5.99396	5.99645	5.99894	6.00141	6.00389	6.00635	6.00881	6.01127	6.01372
410	6.01616	6.01859	6.02102	6.02345	02587	02828	03069	03309	03548	03787
420	04025	04263	04501	04737	04973	05209	05444	05678	05912	06146
430	06379	06611	06843	07074	07304	07535	07764	07993	08222	08450
440	08677	08904	09131	09357	09582	09807	10032	10256	10479	10702
450	6.10925	6.11147	6.11368	6.11589	6.11810	6.12030	6.12249	6.12468	6.12687	6.12905
460	13123	13340	13556	13773	13988	14204	14419	14633	14847	15060
470	15273	15486	15698	15910	16121	16331	16542	16752	16961	17170
480	17379	17587	17794	18002	18208	18415	18621	18826	19032	19236
490	19441	19644	19848	20051	20254	20456	20658	20859	21060	21261
500	6.21461	6.21661	6.21860	6.22059	6.22258	6.22456	6.22654	6.22851	6.23048	6.23245
510	23441	23637	23832	24028	24222	24417	24611	24804	24998	25190
520	25383	25575	25767	25958	26149	26340	26530	26720	26910	27099
530	27288	27476	27664	27852	28040	28227	28413	28600	28786	28972
540	29157	29342	29527	29711	29895	30079	30262	30445	30628	30810
550	6.30992	6.31173	6.31355	6.31536	6.31716	6.31897	6.32077	6.32257	6.32436	6.32615
560	32794	32972	33150	33328	33505	33683	33859	34036	34212	34388
570	34564	34739	34914	35089	35263	35437	35611	35784	35957	36130
580	36303	36475	36647	36819	36990	37161	37332	37502	37673	37843
590	38012	38182	38351	38519	38688	38856	39024	39192	39359	39526
600	6.39693	6.39859	6.40026	6.40192	6.40357	6.40523	6.40688	6.40853	6.41017	6.41182
610	41346	41510	41673	41836	41999	42162	42325	42487	42649	42811
620	42972	43133	43294	43455	43615	43775	43935	44095	44254	44413
630	44572	44731	44889	45047	45205	45362	45520	45677	45834	45990
640	46147	46303	46459	46614	46770	46925	47080	47235	47389	47543
650	6.47697	6.47851	6.48004	6.48158	6.48311	6.48464	6.48616	6.48768	6.48920	6.49072
660	49224	49375	49527	49677	49828	49979	50129	50279	50429	50578
670	50728	50877	51026	51175	51323	51471	51619	51767	51915	52062
680	52209	52356	52503	52649	52796	52942	53088	53233	53379	53524
690	53669	53814	53959	54103	54247	54391	54535	54679	54822	54965
700	6.55108	6.55251	6.55393	6.55536	6.55678	6.55820	6.55962	6.56103	6.56244	6.56386
710	56526	56667	56808	56948	57088	57228	57368	57508	57647	57786
720	57925	58064	58203	58341	58479	58617	58755	58893	59030	59167
730	59304	59441	59578	59715	59851	59987	60123	60259	60394	60530
740	60665	60800	60935	61070	61204	61338	61473	61607	61740	61874
750	6.62007	6.62141	6.62274	6.62407	6.62539	6.62672	6.62804	6.62936	6.63068	6.63200
760	63332	63463	63595	63726	63857	63988	64118	64249	64379	64509
770	64639	64769	64898	65028	65157	65286	65415	65544	65673	65801
780	65929	66058	66185	66313	66441	66568	66696	66823	66950	67077
790	67203	67330	67456	67582	67708	67834	67960	68085	68211	68336
800	6.68461	6.68586	6.68711	6.68835	6.68960	6.69084	6.69208	6.69332	6.69456	6.69580
810	69703	69827	69950	70073	70196	70319	70441	70564	70686	70808
820	70930	71052	71174	71296	71417	71538	71659	71780	71901	72022
830	72143	72263	72383	72503	72623	72743	72863	72982	73102	73221
840	73340	73459	73578	73697	73815	73934	74052	74170	74288	74406
850	6.74524	6.74641	6.74759	6.74876	6.74993	6.75110	6.75227	6.75344	6.75460	6.75577
860	75693	75809	75926	76041	76157	76273	76388	76504	76619	76734
870	76849	76964	77079	77194	77308	77422	77537	77651	77765	77878
880	77992	78106	78219	78333	78446	78559	78672	78784	78897	79010
890	79122	79234	79347	79459	79571	79682	79794	79906	80017	80128
900	6.80239	6.80351	6.80461	6.80572	6.80683	6.80793	6.80904	6.81014	6.81124	6.81235
910	81344	81454	81564	81674	81783	81892	82002	82111	82220	82329
920	82437	82546	82655	82763	82871	82979	83087	83195	83303	83411
930	83518	83626	83733	83841	83948	84055	84162	84268	84375	84482
940	84588	84694	84801	84907	85013	85118	85224	85330	85435	85541
950	6.85646	6.85751	6.85857	6.85961	6.86066	6.86171	6.86276	6.86380	6.86485	6.86589
960	86693	86797	86901	87005	87109	87213	87316	87420	87523	87626
970	87730	87833	87936	88038	88141	88244	88346	88449	88551	88653
980	88755	88857	88959	89061	89163	89264	89366	89467	89568	89669
990	89770	89871	89972	90073	90174	90274	90375	90475	90575	90675

* To find the natural logarithm ($\log_e$) of a number which is a power of ten less or greater than a number given in the table: if the number concerned is *less*, e.g. $^1/_{10}$ (10^{-1}), $^1/_{100}$ (10^{-2}), $^1/_{1000}$ (10^{-3}), etc., *subtract* from the given logarithm $\log_e 10$, $2 \log_e 10$, $3 \log_e 10$, etc.; if the number concerned is *greater*, e.g. 10 times (10^1), 100 times (10^2), 1000 times (10^3), etc., *add* to the given logarithm $\log_e 10$, $2 \log_e 10$, $3 \log_e 10$, etc. Examples: $\log_e 0.02 = \log_e 0.2 - \log_e 10$; $\log_e 2000 = \log_e 200 + \log_e 10$.

Natural Exponential Functions

x	e^x	$\log_{10}(e^x)$	e^{-x}	x	e^x	$\log_{10}(e^x)$	e^{-x}	x	e^x	$\log_{10}(e^x)$	e^{-x}
0.00	1.0000	0.00000	1.000000	**1.00**	2.7183	0.43429	0.367879	**2.00**	7.3891	0.86859	0.135335
0.01	1.0101	00434	0.990050	1.01	2.7456	43864	364219	2.01	7.4633	87293	133989
0.02	1.0202	00869	980199	1.02	2.7732	44298	360595	2.02	7.5383	87727	132655
0.03	1.0305	01303	970446	1.03	2.8011	44732	357007	2.03	7.6141	88162	131336
0.04	1.0408	01737	960789	1.04	2.8292	45167	353455	2.04	7.6906	88596	130029
0.05	1.0513	0.02171	0.951229	**1.05**	2.8577	0.45601	0.349938	**2.05**	7.7679	0.89030	0.128735
0.06	1.0618	02606	941765	1.06	2.8864	46035	346456	2.06	7.8460	89465	127454
0.07	1.0725	03040	932394	1.07	2.9154	46470	343009	2.07	7.9248	89899	126186
0.08	1.0833	03474	923116	1.08	2.9447	46904	339596	2.08	8.0045	90333	124930
0.09	1.0942	03909	913931	1.09	2.9743	47338	336216	2.09	8.0849	90768	123687
0.10	1.1052	0.04343	0.904837	**1.10**	3.0042	0.47772	0.332871	**2.10**	8.1662	0.91202	0.122456
0.11	1.1163	04777	895834	1.11	3.0344	48207	329559	2.11	8.2482	91636	121238
0.12	1.1275	05212	886920	1.12	3.0649	48641	326280	2.12	8.3311	92070	120032
0.13	1.1388	05646	878095	1.13	3.0957	49075	323033	2.13	8.4149	92505	118837
0.14	1.1503	06080	869358	1.14	3.1268	49510	319819	2.14	8.4994	92939	117655
0.15	1.1618	0.06514	0.860708	**1.15**	3.1582	0.49944	0.316637	**2.15**	8.5849	0.93373	0.116484
0.16	1.1735	06949	852144	1.16	3.1899	50378	313486	2.16	8.6711	93808	115325
0.17	1.1853	07383	843665	1.17	3.2220	50812	310367	2.17	8.7583	94242	114178
0.18	1.1972	07817	835270	1.18	3.2544	51247	307279	2.18	8.8463	94676	113042
0.19	1.2092	08252	826959	1.19	3.2871	51681	304221	2.19	8.9352	95110	111917
0.20	1.2214	0.08686	0.818731	**1.20**	3.3201	0.52115	0.301194	**2.20**	9.0250	0.95545	0.110803
0.21	1.2337	09120	810584	1.21	3.3535	52550	298197	2.21	9.1157	95979	109701
0.22	1.2461	09554	802519	1.22	3.3872	52984	295230	2.22	9.2073	96413	108609
0.23	1.2586	09989	794534	1.23	3.4212	53418	292293	2.23	9.2999	96848	107528
0.24	1.2712	10423	786628	1.24	3.4556	53853	289384	2.24	9.3933	97282	106459
0.25	1.2840	0.10857	0.778801	**1.25**	3.4903	0.54287	0.286505	**2.25**	9.4877	0.97716	0.105399
0.26	1.2969	11292	771052	1.26	3.5254	54721	283654	2.26	9.5831	98151	104350
0.27	1.3100	11726	763379	1.27	3.5609	55155	280832	2.27	9.6794	98585	103312
0.28	1.3231	12160	755784	1.28	3.5966	55590	278037	2.28	9.7767	99019	102284
0.29	1.3364	12595	748264	1.29	3.6328	56024	275271	2.29	9.8749	99453	101266
0.30	1.3499	0.13029	0.740818	**1.30**	3.6693	0.56458	0.272532	**2.30**	9.9742	0.99888	0.100259
0.31	1.3634	13463	733447	1.31	3.7062	56893	269820	2.31	10.074	1.00322	099261
0.32	1.3771	13897	726149	1.32	3.7434	57327	267135	2.32	10.176	00756	098274
0.33	1.3910	14332	718924	1.33	3.7810	57761	264477	2.33	10.278	01191	097296
0.34	1.4049	14766	711770	1.34	3.8190	58195	261846	2.34	10.381	01625	096328
0.35	1.4191	0.15200	0.704688	**1.35**	3.8574	0.58630	0.259240	**2.35**	10.486	1.02059	0.095369
0.36	1.4333	15635	697676	1.36	3.8962	59064	256661	2.36	10.591	02493	094420
0.37	1.4477	16069	690734	1.37	3.9354	59498	254107	2.37	10.697	02928	093481
0.38	1.4623	16503	683861	1.38	3.9749	59933	251579	2.38	10.805	03362	092551
0.39	1.4770	16937	677057	1.39	4.0149	60367	249075	2.39	10.913	03796	091630
0.40	1.4918	0.17372	0.670320	**1.40**	4.0552	0.60801	0.246597	**2.40**	11.023	1.04231	0.090718
0.41	1.5068	17806	663650	1.41	4.0960	61236	244143	2.41	11.134	04665	089815
0.42	1.5220	18240	657047	1.42	4.1371	61670	241714	2.42	11.246	05099	088922
0.43	1.5373	18675	650509	1.43	4.1787	62104	239309	2.43	11.359	05534	088037
0.44	1.5527	19109	644036	1.44	4.2207	62538	236928	2.44	11.473	05968	087161
0.45	1.5683	0.19543	0.637628	**1.45**	4.2631	0.62973	0.234570	**2.45**	11.588	1.06402	0.086294
0.46	1.5841	19978	631284	1.46	4.3060	63407	232236	2.46	11.705	06836	085435
0.47	1.6000	20412	625002	1.47	4.3492	63841	229925	2.47	11.822	07271	084585
0.48	1.6161	20846	618783	1.48	4.3929	64276	227638	2.48	11.941	07705	083743
0.49	1.6323	21280	612626	1.49	4.4371	64710	225373	2.49	12.061	08139	082910
0.50	1.6487	0.21715	0.606531	**1.50**	4.4817	0.65144	0.223130	**2.50**	12.182	1.08574	0.082085
0.51	1.6653	22149	600496	1.51	4.5267	65578	220910	2.51	12.305	09008	081268
0.52	1.6820	22583	594521	1.52	4.5722	66013	218712	2.52	12.429	09442	080460
0.53	1.6989	23018	588605	1.53	4.6182	66447	216536	2.53	12.554	09877	079659
0.54	1.7160	23452	582748	1.54	4.6646	66881	214381	2.54	12.680	10311	078866
0.55	1.7333	0.23886	0.576950	**1.55**	4.7115	0.67316	0.212248	**2.55**	12.807	1.10745	0.078082
0.56	1.7507	24320	571209	1.56	4.7588	67750	210136	2.56	12.936	11179	077305
0.57	1.7683	24755	565525	1.57	4.8066	68184	208045	2.57	13.066	11614	076536
0.58	1.7860	25189	559898	1.58	4.8550	68619	205975	2.58	13.197	12048	075774
0.59	1.8040	25623	554327	1.59	4.9037	69053	203926	2.59	13.330	12482	075020
0.60	1.8221	0.26058	0.548812	**1.60**	4.9530	0.69487	0.201897	**2.60**	13.464	1.12917	0.074274
0.61	1.8404	26492	543351	1.61	5.0028	69921	199888	2.61	13.599	13351	073535
0.62	1.8589	26926	537944	1.62	5.0531	70356	197899	2.62	13.736	13785	072803
0.63	1.8776	27361	532592	1.63	5.1039	70790	195930	2.63	13.874	14219	072078
0.64	1.8965	27795	527292	1.64	5.1552	71224	193980	2.64	14.013	14654	071361
0.65	1.9155	0.28229	0.522046	**1.65**	5.2070	0.71659	0.192050	**2.65**	14.154	1.15088	0.070651
0.66	1.9348	28663	516851	1.66	5.2593	72093	190139	2.66	14.296	15522	069948
0.67	1.9542	29098	511709	1.67	5.3122	72527	188247	2.67	14.440	15957	069252
0.68	1.9739	29532	506617	1.68	5.3656	72961	186374	2.68	14.585	16391	068563
0.69	1.9937	29966	501576	1.69	5.4195	73396	184520	2.69	14.732	16825	067881
0.70	2.0138	0.30401	0.496585	**1.70**	5.4739	0.73830	0.182684	**2.70**	14.880	1.17260	0.067206
0.71	2.0340	30835	491644	1.71	5.5290	74264	180866	2.71	15.029	17694	066537
0.72	2.0544	31269	486752	1.72	5.5845	74699	179066	2.72	15.180	18128	065875
0.73	2.0751	31703	481909	1.73	5.6407	75133	177284	2.73	15.333	18562	065219
0.74	2.0959	32138	477114	1.74	5.6973	75567	175520	2.74	15.487	18997	064570
0.75	2.1170	0.32572	0.472367	**1.75**	5.7546	0.76002	0.173774	**2.75**	15.643	1.19431	0.063928
0.76	2.1383	33006	467666	1.76	5.8124	76436	172045	2.76	15.800	19865	063292
0.77	2.1598	33441	463013	1.77	5.8709	76870	170333	2.77	15.959	20300	062662
0.78	2.1815	33875	458406	1.78	5.9299	77304	168638	2.78	16.119	20734	062039
0.79	2.2034	34309	453845	1.79	5.9895	77739	166960	2.79	16.281	21168	061421
0.80	2.2255	0.34744	0.449329	**1.80**	6.0496	0.78173	0.165299	**2.80**	16.445	1.21602	0.060810
0.81	2.2479	35178	444858	1.81	6.1104	78607	163654	2.81	16.610	22037	060205
0.82	2.2705	35612	440432	1.82	6.1719	79042	162026	2.82	16.777	22471	059606
0.83	2.2933	36046	436049	1.83	6.2339	79476	160414	2.83	16.945	22905	059013
0.84	2.3164	36481	431711	1.84	6.2965	79910	158817	2.84	17.116	23340	058426
0.85	2.3396	0.36915	0.427415	**1.85**	6.3598	0.80344	0.157237	**2.85**	17.288	1.23774	0.057844
0.86	2.3632	37349	423162	1.86	6.4237	80779	155673	2.86	17.462	24208	057269
0.87	2.3869	37784	418952	1.87	6.4883	81213	154124	2.87	17.637	24643	056699
0.88	2.4109	38218	414783	1.88	6.5535	81647	152590	2.88	17.814	25077	056135
0.89	2.4351	38652	410656	1.89	6.6194	82082	151072	2.89	17.993	25511	055576
0.90	2.4596	0.39087	0.406570	**1.90**	6.6859	0.82516	0.149569	**2.90**	18.174	1.25945	0.055023
0.91	2.4843	39521	402524	1.91	6.7531	82950	148080	2.91	18.357	26380	054476
0.92	2.5093	39955	398519	1.92	6.8210	83385	146607	2.92	18.541	26814	053934
0.93	2.5345	40389	394554	1.93	6.8895	83819	145148	2.93	18.728	27248	053397
0.94	2.5600	40824	390628	1.94	6.9588	84253	143704	2.94	18.916	27683	052866
0.95	2.5857	0.41258	0.386741	**1.95**	7.0287	0.84687	0.142274	**2.95**	19.106	1.28117	0.052340
0.96	2.6117	41692	382893	1.96	7.0993	85122	140858	2.96	19.298	28551	051819
0.97	2.6379	42127	379083	1.97	7.1707	85556	139457	2.97	19.492	28985	051303
0.98	2.6645	42561	375311	1.98	7.2427	85990	138069	2.98	19.688	29420	050793
0.99	2.6912	42995	371577	1.99	7.3155	86425	136695	2.99	19.886	29854	050287

x	e^x	$\log_{10}(e^x)$	e^{-x}	x	e^x	$\log_{10}(e^x)$	e^{-x}	x	e^x	$\log_{10}(e^x)$	e^{-x}
3.00	20.086	1.30288	0.049787	**4.00**	54.598	1.73718	0.018316	**5.00**	148.41	2.17147	0.006738
3.01	20.287	1.30723	049292	4.01	55.147	1.74152	018133	5.01	149.90	2.17582	006671
3.02	20.491	1.31157	048801	4.02	55.701	1.74586	017953	5.02	151.41	2.18016	006605
3.03	20.697	1.31591	048316	4.03	56.261	1.75021	017774	5.03	152.93	2.18450	006539
3.04	20.905	1.32026	047835	4.04	56.826	1.75455	017597	5.04	154.47	2.18884	006474
3.05	21.115	1.32460	0.047359	**4.05**	57.397	1.75889	0.017422	**5.05**	156.02	2.19319	0.006409
3.06	21.328	1.32894	046888	4.06	57.974	1.76324	017249	5.06	157.59	2.19753	006346
3.07	21.542	1.33328	046421	4.07	58.557	1.76758	017077	5.07	159.17	2.20187	006282
3.08	21.758	1.33763	045959	4.08	59.145	1.77192	016907	5.08	160.77	2.20622	006220
3.09	21.977	1.34197	045502	4.09	59.740	1.77626	016739	5.09	162.39	2.21056	006158
3.10	22.198	1.34631	0.045049	**4.10**	60.340	1.78061	0.016573	**5.10**	164.02	2.21490	0.006097
3.11	22.421	1.35066	044601	4.11	60.947	1.78495	016408	5.11	165.67	2.21924	006036
3.12	22.646	1.35500	044157	4.12	61.559	1.78929	016245	5.12	167.34	2.22359	005976
3.13	22.874	1.35934	043718	4.13	62.178	1.79364	016083	5.13	169.02	2.22793	005917
3.14	23.104	1.36368	043283	4.14	62.803	1.79798	015923	5.14	170.72	2.23227	005858
3.15	23.336	1.36803	0.042852	**4.15**	63.434	1.80232	0.015764	**5.15**	172.43	2.23662	0.005799
3.16	23.571	1.37237	042426	4.16	64.072	1.80667	015608	5.16	174.16	2.24096	005742
3.17	23.807	1.37671	042004	4.17	64.715	1.81101	015452	5.17	175.91	2.24530	005685
3.18	24.047	1.38106	041586	4.18	65.366	1.81535	015299	5.18	177.68	2.24965	005628
3.19	24.288	1.38540	041172	4.19	66.023	1.81969	015146	5.19	179.47	2.25399	005572
3.20	24.533	1.38974	0.040762	**4.20**	66.686	1.82404	0.014996	**5.20**	181.27	2.25833	0.005517
3.21	24.779	1.39409	040357	4.21	67.357	1.82838	014846	5.21	183.09	2.26267	005462
3.22	25.028	1.39843	039955	4.22	68.033	1.83272	014699	5.22	184.93	2.26702	005407
3.23	25.280	1.40277	039557	4.23	68.717	1.83707	014552	5.23	186.79	2.27136	005354
3.24	25.534	1.40711	039164	4.24	69.408	1.84141	014408	5.24	188.67	2.27570	005300
3.25	25.790	1.41146	0.038774	**4.25**	70.105	1.84575	0.014264	**5.25**	190.57	2.28005	0.005248
3.26	26.050	1.41580	038388	4.26	70.810	1.85009	014122	5.26	192.48	2.28439	005195
3.27	26.311	1.42014	038006	4.27	71.522	1.85444	013982	5.27	194.42	2.28873	005144
3.28	26.576	1.42449	037628	4.28	72.240	1.85878	013843	5.28	196.37	2.29307	005092
3.29	26.843	1.42883	037254	4.29	72.966	1.86312	013705	5.29	198.34	2.29742	005042
3.30	27.113	1.43317	0.036883	**4.30**	73.700	1.86747	0.013569	**5.30**	200.34	2.30176	0.004992
3.31	27.385	1.43751	036516	4.31	74.440	1.87181	013434	5.31	202.35	2.30610	004942
3.32	27.660	1.44186	036153	4.32	75.189	1.87615	013300	5.32	204.38	2.31045	004893
3.33	27.938	1.44620	035793	4.33	75.944	1.88050	013168	5.33	206.44	2.31479	004844
3.34	28.219	1.45054	035437	4.34	76.708	1.88484	013037	5.34	208.51	2.31913	004796
3.35	28.503	1.45489	0.035084	**4.35**	77.478	1.88918	0.012907	**5.35**	210.61	2.32348	0.004748
3.36	28.789	1.45923	034735	4.36	78.257	1.89352	012778	5.36	212.72	2.32782	004701
3.37	29.079	1.46357	034390	4.37	79.044	1.89787	012651	5.37	214.86	2.33216	004654
3.38	29.371	1.46792	034047	4.38	79.838	1.90221	012525	5.38	217.02	2.33650	004608
3.39	29.666	1.47226	033709	4.39	80.640	1.90655	012401	5.39	219.20	2.34085	004562
3.40	29.964	1.47660	0.033373	**4.40**	81.451	1.91090	0.012277	**5.40**	221.41	2.34519	0.004517
3.41	30.265	1.48094	033041	4.41	82.269	1.91524	012155	5.41	223.63	2.34953	004472
3.42	30.569	1.48529	032712	4.42	83.096	1.91958	012034	5.42	225.88	2.35388	004427
3.43	30.877	1.48963	032387	4.43	83.931	1.92392	011914	5.43	228.15	2.35822	004383
3.44	31.187	1.49397	032065	4.44	84.775	1.92827	011796	5.44	230.44	2.36256	004339
3.45	31.500	1.49832	0.031746	**4.45**	85.627	1.93261	0.011679	**5.45**	232.76	2.36690	0.004296
3.46	31.817	1.50266	031430	4.46	86.488	1.93695	011562	5.46	235.10	2.37125	004254
3.47	32.137	1.50700	031117	4.47	87.357	1.94130	011447	5.47	237.46	2.37559	004211
3.48	32.460	1.51134	030807	4.48	88.235	1.94564	011333	5.48	239.85	2.37993	004169
3.49	32.786	1.51569	030501	4.49	89.121	1.94998	011221	5.49	242.26	2.38428	004128
3.50	33.115	1.52003	0.030197	**4.50**	90.017	1.95433	0.011109				
3.51	33.448	1.52437	029897	4.51	90.922	1.95867	010998				
3.52	33.784	1.52872	029599	4.52	91.836	1.96301	010889				
3.53	34.124	1.53306	029305	4.53	92.759	1.96735	010781				
3.54	34.467	1.53740	029013	4.54	93.691	1.97170	010673	5.5	244.69	2.38862	0.004087
3.55	34.813	1.54175	0.028725	**4.55**	94.632	1.97604	0.010567	5.6	270.43	2.43205	003698
3.56	35.163	1.54609	028439	4.56	95.583	1.98038	010462	5.7	298.87	2.47548	003346
3.57	35.517	1.55043	028156	4.57	96.544	1.98473	010358	5.8	330.30	2.51891	003028
3.58	35.874	1.55477	027876	4.58	97.514	1.98907	010255	5.9	365.04	2.56234	002739
3.59	36.234	1.55912	027598	4.59	98.494	1.99341	010153	**6.0**	403.43	2.60577	0.002479
3.60	36.598	1.56346	0.027324	**4.60**	99.484	1.99775	0.010052	6.1	445.86	2.64920	002243
3.61	36.966	1.56780	027052	4.61	100.48	2.00210	009952	6.2	492.75	2.69263	002029
3.62	37.338	1.57215	026783	4.62	101.49	2.00644	009853	6.3	544.57	2.73606	001836
3.63	37.713	1.57649	026516	4.63	102.51	2.01078	009755	6.4	601.85	2.77948	001662
3.64	38.092	1.58083	026252	4.64	103.54	2.01513	009658	**6.5**	665.14	2.82291	0.001503
3.65	38.475	1.58517	0.025991	**4.65**	104.58	2.01947	0.009562	6.6	735.10	2.86634	001360
3.66	38.861	1.58952	025733	4.66	105.64	2.02381	009466	6.7	812.41	2.90977	001231
3.67	39.252	1.59386	025476	4.67	106.70	2.02816	009372	6.8	897.85	2.95320	001114
3.68	39.646	1.59820	025223	4.68	107.77	2.03250	009279	6.9	992.27	2.99663	001008
3.69	40.045	1.60255	024972	4.69	108.85	2.03684	009187	**7.0**	1096.6	3.04006	0.000912
3.70	40.447	1.60689	0.024724	**4.70**	109.95	2.04118	0.009095	7.1	1212.0	3.08349	000825
3.71	40.854	1.61123	024478	4.71	111.05	2.04553	009005	7.2	1339.4	3.12692	000747
3.72	41.264	1.61558	024234	4.72	112.17	2.04987	008915	7.3	1480.3	3.17035	000676
3.73	41.679	1.61992	023993	4.73	113.30	2.05421	008826	7.4	1636.0	3.21378	000611
3.74	42.098	1.62426	023754	4.74	114.43	2.05856	008739	**7.5**	1808.0	3.25721	0.000553
3.75	42.521	1.62860	0.023518	**4.75**	115.58	2.06290	0.008652	7.6	1998.2	3.30064	000501
3.76	42.948	1.63295	023284	4.76	116.75	2.06724	008566	7.7	2208.3	3.33407	000453
3.77	43.380	1.63729	023052	4.77	117.92	2.07158	008480	7.8	2440.6	3.38750	000410
3.78	43.816	1.64163	022823	4.78	119.10	2.07593	008396	7.9	2697.3	3.43093	000371
3.79	44.256	1.64598	022596	4.79	120.30	2.08027	008312	**8.0**	2981.0	3.47436	0.000336
3.80	44.701	1.65032	0.022371	**4.80**	121.51	2.08461	0.008230	8.1	3294.5	3.51779	000304
3.81	45.150	1.65466	022148	4.81	122.73	2.08896	008148	8.2	3641.0	3.56121	000275
3.82	45.604	1.65900	021928	4.82	123.97	2.09330	008067	8.3	4023.9	3.60464	000249
3.83	46.063	1.66335	021710	4.83	125.21	2.09764	007987	8.4	4447.1	3.64807	000225
3.84	46.525	1.66769	021494	4.84	126.47	2.10199	007907	**8.5**	4914.8	3.69150	0.000204
3.85	46.993	1.67203	0.021280	**4.85**	127.74	2.10633	0.007828	8.6	5431.7	3.73493	000184
3.86	47.465	1.67638	021068	4.86	129.02	2.11067	007750	8.7	6002.9	3.77836	000167
3.87	47.942	1.68072	020858	4.87	130.32	2.11501	007673	8.8	6634.2	3.82179	000151
3.88	48.424	1.68506	020651	4.88	131.63	2.11936	007597	8.9	7332.0	3.86522	000136
3.89	48.911	1.68941	020445	4.89	132.95	2.12370	007521	**9.0**	8103.1	3.90865	0.000123
3.90	49.402	1.69375	0.020242	**4.90**	134.29	2.12804	0.007447	9.1	8955.3	3.95208	000112
3.91	49.899	1.69809	020041	4.91	135.64	2.13239	007372	9.2	9897.1	3.99551	000101
3.92	50.400	1.70243	019841	4.92	137.00	2.13673	007299	9.3	10 938	4.03894	000091
3.93	50.907	1.70678	019644	4.93	138.38	2.14107	007227	9.4	12 088	4.08237	000083
3.94	51.419	1.71112	019448	4.94	139.77	2.14541	007155	**9.5**	13 360	4.12580	0.000075
3.95	51.935	1.71546	0.019255	**4.95**	141.17	2.14976	0.007083	9.6	14 765	4.16923	000068
3.96	52.457	1.71981	019063	4.96	142.59	2.15410	007013	9.7	16 318	4.21266	000061
3.97	52.985	1.72415	018873	4.97	144.03	2.15844	006943	9.8	18 034	4.25609	000056
3.98	53.517	1.72849	018686	4.98	145.47	2.16279	006874	9.9	19 930	4.29952	000050
3.99	54.055	1.73283	018500	4.99	146.94	2.16713	006806	**10.0**	22 026	4.34294	0.000045

Reciprocals of the Integers 1—999[1]

Reciprocal of $n = 1/n$

n	0	1	2	3	4	5	6	7	8	9
0	–	–	0.5 000 0000	0.3 333 3333	0.2 500 0000	0.2 000 0000	0.1 666 6667	0.1 428 5714	0.1 250 0000	0.1 111 1111
10	0.1 000 0000	0.0 909 0909	0.0 833 3333	0.0 769 2308	0.0 714 2857	0.0 666 6667	0.0 625 0000	0.0 588 2353	0.0 555 5556	0.0 526 3158
20	0.0 500 0000	476 1905	454 5455	434 7826	416 6667	400 0000	384 6154	370 3704	357 1429	344 8276
30	333 3333	322 5806	312 5000	303 0303	294 1176	285 7143	277 7778	270 2703	263 1579	256 4103
40	250 0000	243 9024	238 0952	232 5581	227 2727	222 2222	217 3913	212 7660	208 3333	204 0816
50	0.0 200 0000	0.0 196 0784	0.0 192 3077	0.0 188 6792	0.0 185 1852	0.0 181 8182	0.0 178 5714	0.0 175 4386	0.0 172 4138	0.0 169 4915
60	166 6667	163 9344	161 2903	158 7302	156 2500	153 8462	151 5152	149 2537	147 0588	144 9275
70	142 8571	140 8451	138 8889	136 9863	135 1351	133 3333	131 5789	129 8701	128 2051	126 5823
80	125 0000	123 4568	121 9512	120 4819	119 0476	117 6471	116 2791	114 9425	113 6364	112 3596
90	111 1111	109 8901	108 6957	107 5269	106 3830	105 2632	104 1667	103 0928	102 0408	101 0101
100	0.0 100 0000	0.00 990 0990	0.00 980 3922	0.00 970 8738	0.00 961 5385	0.00 952 3810	0.00 943 3962	0.00 934 5794	0.00 925 9259	0.00 917 4312
110	0.00 909 0909	900 9009	892 8571	884 9558	877 1930	869 5652	862 0690	854 7009	847 4576	840 3361
120	833 3333	826 4463	819 6721	813 0081	806 4516	800 0000	793 6508	787 4016	781 2500	775 1938
130	769 2308	763 3588	757 5758	751 8797	746 2687	740 7407	735 2941	729 9270	724 6377	719 4245
140	714 2857	709 2199	704 2254	699 3007	694 4444	689 6552	684 9315	680 2721	675 6757	671 1409
150	0.00 666 6667	0.00 662 2517	0.00 657 8947	0.00 653 5948	0.00 649 3506	0.00 645 1613	0.00 641 0256	0.00 636 9427	0.00 632 9114	0.00 628 9308
160	625 0000	621 1180	617 2840	613 4969	609 7561	606 0606	602 4096	598 8024	595 2381	591 7160
170	588 2353	584 7953	581 3953	578 0347	574 7126	571 4286	568 1818	564 9718	561 7978	558 6592
180	555 5556	552 4862	549 4505	546 4481	543 4783	540 5405	537 6344	534 7594	531 9149	529 1005
190	526 3158	523 5602	520 8333	518 1347	515 4639	512 8205	510 2041	507 6142	505 0505	502 5126
200	0.00 500 0000	0.00 497 5124	0.00 495 0495	0.00 492 6108	0.00 490 1961	0.00 487 8049	0.00 485 4369	0.00 483 0918	0.00 480 7692	0.00 478 4689
210	476 1905	473 9336	471 6981	469 4836	467 2897	465 1163	462 9630	460 8295	458 7156	456 6210
220	454 5455	452 4887	450 4505	448 4305	446 4286	444 4444	442 4779	440 5286	438 5965	436 6812
230	434 7826	432 9004	431 0345	429 1845	427 3504	425 5319	423 7288	421 9409	420 1681	418 4100
240	416 6667	414 9378	413 2231	411 5226	409 8361	408 1633	406 5041	404 8583	403 2258	401 6064
250	0.00 400 0000	0.00 398 4064	0.00 396 8254	0.00 395 2569	0.00 393 7008	0.00 392 1569	0.00 390 6250	0.00 389 1051	0.00 387 5969	0.00 386 1004
260	384 6154	383 1418	381 6794	380 2281	378 7879	377 3585	375 9398	374 5318	373 1343	371 7472
270	370 3704	369 0037	367 6471	366 3004	364 9635	363 6364	362 3188	361 0108	359 7122	358 4229
280	357 1429	355 8719	354 6099	353 3569	352 1127	350 8772	349 6503	348 4321	347 2222	346 0208
290	344 8276	343 6426	342 4658	341 2969	340 1361	338 9831	337 8378	336 7003	335 5705	334 4482
300	0.00 333 3333	0.00 332 2259	0.00 331 1258	0.00 330 0330	0.00 328 9474	0.00 327 8689	0.00 326 7974	0.00 325 7329	0.00 324 6753	0.00 323 6246
310	322 5806	321 5434	320 5128	319 4888	318 4713	317 4603	316 4557	315 4574	314 4654	313 4796
320	312 5000	311 5265	310 5590	309 5975	308 6420	307 6923	306 7485	305 8104	304 8780	303 9514
330	303 0303	302 1148	301 2048	300 3003	299 4012	298 5075	297 6190	296 7359	295 8580	294 9853
340	294 1176	293 2551	292 3977	291 5452	290 6977	289 8551	289 0173	288 1844	287 3563	286 5330
350	0.00 285 7143	0.00 284 9003	0.00 284 0909	0.00 283 2861	0.00 282 4859	0.00 281 6901	0.00 280 8989	0.00 280 1120	0.00 279 3296	0.00 278 5515
360	277 7778	277 0083	276 2431	275 4821	274 7253	273 9726	273 2240	272 4796	271 7391	271 0027
370	270 2703	269 5418	268 8172	268 0965	267 3797	266 6667	265 9574	265 2520	264 5503	263 8522
380	263 1579	262 4672	261 7801	261 0966	260 4167	259 7403	259 0674	258 3979	257 7320	257 0694
390	256 4103	255 7545	255 1020	254 4529	253 8071	253 1646	252 5253	251 8892	251 2563	250 6266
400	0.00 250 0000	0.00 249 3766	0.00 248 7562	0.00 248 1390	0.00 247 5248	0.00 246 9136	0.00 246 3054	0.00 245 7002	0.00 245 0980	0.00 244 4988
410	243 9024	243 3090	242 7184	242 1308	241 5459	240 9639	240 3846	239 8082	239 2344	238 6635
420	238 0952	237 5297	236 9668	236 4066	235 8491	235 2941	234 7418	234 1920	233 6449	233 1002
430	232 5581	232 0186	231 4815	230 9469	230 4147	229 8851	229 3578	228 8330	228 3105	227 7904
440	227 2727	226 7574	226 2443	225 7336	225 2252	224 7191	224 2152	223 7136	223 2143	222 7171
450	0.00 222 2222	0.00 221 7295	0.00 221 2389	0.00 220 7506	0.00 220 2643	0.00 219 7802	0.00 219 2982	0.00 218 8184	0.00 218 3406	0.00 217 8649
460	217 3913	216 9197	216 4502	215 9827	215 5172	215 0538	214 5923	214 1328	213 6752	213 2196
470	212 7660	212 3142	211 8644	211 4165	210 9705	210 5263	210 0840	209 6436	209 2050	208 7683
480	208 3333	207 9002	207 4689	207 0393	206 6116	206 1856	205 7613	205 3388	204 9180	204 4990
490	204 0816	203 6660	203 2520	202 8398	202 4291	202 0202	201 6129	201 2072	200 8032	200 4008
500	0.00 200 0000	0.00 199 6008	0.00 199 2032	0.00 198 8072	0.00 198 4127	0.00 198 0198	0.00 197 6285	0.00 197 2387	0.00 196 8504	0.00 196 4637
510	196 0784	195 6947	195 3125	194 9318	194 5525	194 1748	193 7984	193 4236	193 0502	192 6782
520	192 3077	191 9386	191 5709	191 2046	190 8397	190 4762	190 1141	189 7533	189 3939	189 0359
530	188 6792	188 3239	187 9699	187 6173	187 2659	186 9159	186 5672	186 2197	185 8736	185 5288
540	185 1852	184 8429	184 5018	184 1621	183 8235	183 4862	183 1502	182 8154	182 4818	182 1494
550	0.00 181 8182	0.00 181 4882	0.00 181 1594	0.00 180 8318	0.00 180 5054	0.00 180 1802	0.00 179 8561	0.00 179 5332	0.00 179 2115	0.00 178 8909
560	178 5714	178 2531	177 9359	177 6199	177 3050	176 9912	176 6784	176 3668	176 0563	175 7469
570	175 4386	175 1313	174 8252	174 5201	174 2160	173 9130	173 6111	173 3102	173 0104	172 7116
580	172 4138	172 1170	171 8213	171 5266	171 2329	170 9402	170 6485	170 3578	170 0680	169 7793
590	169 4915	169 2047	168 9189	168 6341	168 3502	168 0672	167 7852	167 5042	167 2241	166 9449
600	0.00 166 6667	0.00 166 3894	0.00 166 1130	0.00 165 8375	0.00 165 5629	0.00 165 2893	0.00 165 0165	0.00 164 7446	0.00 164 4737	0.00 164 2036
610	163 9344	163 6661	163 3987	163 1321	162 8664	162 6016	162 3377	162 0746	161 8123	161 5509
620	161 2903	161 0306	160 7717	160 5136	160 2564	160 0000	159 7444	159 4896	159 2357	158 9825
630	158 7302	158 4786	158 2278	157 9779	157 7287	157 4803	157 2327	156 9859	156 7398	156 4945
640	156 2500	156 0062	155 7632	155 5210	155 2795	155 0388	154 7988	154 5595	154 3210	154 0832
650	0.00 153 8462	0.00 153 6098	0.00 153 3742	0.00 153 1394	0.00 152 9052	0.00 152 6718	0.00 152 4390	0.00 152 2070	0.00 151 9757	0.00 151 7451
660	151 5152	151 2859	151 0574	150 8296	150 6024	150 3759	150 1502	149 9250	149 7006	149 4768
670	149 2537	149 0313	148 8095	148 5884	148 3680	148 1481	147 9290	147 7105	147 4926	147 2754
680	147 0588	146 8429	146 6276	146 4129	146 1988	145 9854	145 7726	145 5604	145 3488	145 1379
690	144 9275	144 7178	144 5087	144 3001	144 0922	143 8849	143 6782	143 4720	143 2665	143 0615
700	0.00 142 8571	0.00 142 6534	0.00 142 4501	0.00 142 2475	0.00 142 0455	0.00 141 8440	0.00 141 6431	0.00 141 4427	0.00 141 2429	0.00 141 0437
710	140 8451	140 6470	140 4494	140 2525	140 0560	139 8601	139 6648	139 4700	139 2758	139 0821
720	138 8889	138 6963	138 5042	138 3126	138 1215	137 9310	137 7410	137 5516	137 3626	137 1742
730	136 9863	136 7989	136 6120	136 4256	136 2398	136 0544	135 8696	135 6852	135 5014	135 3180
740	135 1351	134 9528	134 7709	134 5895	134 4086	134 2282	134 0483	133 8688	133 6898	133 5113
750	0.00 133 3333	0.00 133 1558	0.00 132 9787	0.00 132 8021	0.00 132 6260	0.00 132 4503	0.00 132 2751	0.00 132 1004	0.00 131 9261	0.00 131 7523
760	131 5789	131 4060	131 2336	131 0616	130 8901	130 7190	130 5483	130 3781	130 2083	130 0390
770	129 8701	129 7017	129 5337	129 3661	129 1990	129 0323	128 8660	128 7001	128 5347	128 3697
780	128 2051	128 0410	127 8772	127 7139	127 5510	127 3885	127 2265	127 0648	126 9036	126 7427
790	126 5823	126 4223	126 2626	126 1034	125 9446	125 7862	125 6281	125 4705	125 3133	125 1564
800	0.00 125 0000	0.00 124 8439	0.00 124 6883	0.00 124 5330	0.00 124 3781	0.00 124 2236	0.00 124 0695	0.00 123 9157	0.00 123 7624	0.00 123 6094
810	123 4568	123 3046	123 1527	123 0012	122 8501	122 6994	122 5490	122 3990	122 2494	122 1001
820	121 9512	121 8027	121 6545	121 5067	121 3592	121 2121	121 0654	120 9190	120 7729	120 6273
830	120 4819	120 3369	120 1923	120 0480	119 9041	119 7605	119 6172	119 4743	119 3317	119 1895
840	119 0476	118 9061	118 7648	118 6240	118 4834	118 3432	118 2033	118 0638	117 9245	117 7856
850	0.00 117 6471	0.00 117 5088	0.00 117 3709	0.00 117 2333	0.00 117 0960	0.00 116 9591	0.00 116 8224	0.00 116 6861	0.00 116 5501	0.00 116 4144
860	116 2791	116 1440	116 0093	115 8749	115 7407	115 6069	115 4734	115 3403	115 2074	115 0748
870	114 9425	114 8106	114 6789	114 5475	114 4165	114 2857	114 1553	114 0251	113 8952	113 7656
880	113 6364	113 5074	113 3787	113 2503	113 1222	112 9944	112 8668	112 7396	112 6126	112 4859
890	112 3596	112 2334	112 1076	111 9821	111 8568	111 7318	111 6071	111 4827	111 3586	111 2347
900	0.00 111 1111	0.00 110 9878	0.00 110 8647	0.00 110 7420	0.00 110 6195	0.00 110 4972	0.00 110 3753	0.00 110 2536	0.00 110 1322	0.00 110 0110
910	109 8901	109 7695	109 6491	109 5290	109 4092	109 2896	109 1703	109 0513	108 9325	108 8139
920	108 6957	108 5776	108 4599	108 3424	108 2251	108 1081	107 9914	107 8749	107 7586	107 6426
930	107 5269	107 4114	107 2961	107 1811	107 0664	106 9519	106 8376	106 7236	106 6098	106 4963
940	106 3830	106 2699	106 1571	106 0445	105 9322	105 8201	105 7082	105 5966	105 4852	105 3741
950	0.00 105 2632	0.00 105 1525	0.00 105 0420	0.00 104 9318	0.00 104 8218	0.00 104 7120	0.00 104 6025	0.00 104 4932	0.00 104 3841	0.00 104 2753
960	104 1667	104 0583	103 9501	103 8422	103 7344	103 6269	103 5197	103 4126	103 3058	103 1992
970	103 0928	102 9866	102 8807	102 7749	102 6694	102 5641	102 4590	102 3541	102 2495	102 1450
980	102 0408	101 9368	101 8330	101 7294	101 6260	101 5228	101 4199	101 3171	101 2146	101 1122
990	101 0101	100 9082	100 8065	100 7049	100 6036	100 5025	100 4016	100 3009	100 2004	100 1001

1) Values from COMRIE, L. J. (Ed.), *Barlow's Tables of Squares, Cubes, Square Roots, Cube Roots and Reciprocals of All Integers up to 12,500*, 4th ed., Spon, London, 1958. Reprinted by kind permission of the editor and publishers.

Cubes of the Integers 1—999[1]

n	0	1	2	3	4	5	6	7	8	9
0	0	1	8	27	64	125	216	343	512	729
10	1 000	1 331	1 728	2 197	2 744	3 375	4 096	4 913	5 832	6 859
20	8 000	9 261	10 648	12 167	13 824	15 625	17 576	19 683	21 952	24 389
30	27 000	29 791	32 768	35 937	39 304	42 875	46 656	50 653	54 872	59 319
40	64 000	68 921	74 088	79 507	85 184	91 125	97 336	103 823	110 592	117 649
50	125 000	132 651	140 608	148 877	157 464	166 375	175 616	185 193	195 112	205 379
60	216 000	226 981	238 328	250 047	262 144	274 625	287 496	300 763	314 432	328 509
70	343 000	357 911	373 248	389 017	405 224	421 875	438 976	456 533	474 552	493 039
80	512 000	531 441	551 368	571 787	592 704	614 125	636 056	658 503	681 472	704 969
90	729 000	753 571	778 688	804 357	830 584	857 375	884 736	912 673	941 192	970 299
100	1 000 000	1 030 301	1 061 208	1 092 727	1 124 864	1 157 625	1 191 016	1 225 043	1 259 712	1 295 029
110	1 331 000	1 367 631	1 404 928	1 442 897	1 481 544	1 520 875	1 560 896	1 601 613	1 643 032	1 685 159
120	1 728 000	1 771 561	1 815 848	1 860 867	1 906 624	1 953 125	2 000 376	2 048 383	2 097 152	2 146 689
130	2 197 000	2 248 091	2 299 968	2 352 637	2 406 104	2 460 375	2 515 456	2 571 353	2 628 072	2 685 619
140	2 744 000	2 803 221	2 863 288	2 924 207	2 985 984	3 048 625	3 112 136	3 176 523	3 241 792	3 307 949
150	3 375 000	3 442 951	3 511 808	3 581 577	3 652 264	3 723 875	3 796 416	3 869 893	3 944 312	4 019 679
160	4 096 000	4 173 281	4 251 528	4 330 747	4 410 944	4 492 125	4 574 296	4 657 463	4 741 632	4 826 809
170	4 913 000	5 000 211	5 088 448	5 177 717	5 268 024	5 359 375	5 451 776	5 545 233	5 639 752	5 735 339
180	5 832 000	5 929 741	6 028 568	6 128 487	6 229 504	6 331 625	6 434 856	6 539 203	6 644 672	6 751 269
190	6 859 000	6 967 871	7 077 888	7 189 057	7 301 384	7 414 875	7 529 536	7 645 373	7 762 392	7 880 599
200	8 000 000	8 120 601	8 242 408	8 365 427	8 489 664	8 615 125	8 741 816	8 869 743	8 998 912	9 129 329
210	9 261 000	9 393 931	9 528 128	9 663 597	9 800 344	9 938 375	10 077 696	10 218 313	10 360 232	10 503 459
220	10 648 000	10 793 861	10 941 048	11 089 567	11 239 424	11 390 625	11 543 176	11 697 083	11 852 352	12 008 989
230	12 167 000	12 326 391	12 487 168	12 649 337	12 812 904	12 977 875	13 144 256	13 312 053	13 481 272	13 651 919
240	13 824 000	13 997 521	14 172 488	14 348 907	14 526 784	14 706 125	14 886 936	15 069 223	15 252 992	15 438 249
250	15 625 000	15 813 251	16 003 008	16 194 277	16 387 064	16 581 375	16 777 216	16 974 593	17 173 512	17 373 979
260	17 576 000	17 779 581	17 984 728	18 191 447	18 399 744	18 609 625	18 821 096	19 034 163	19 248 832	19 465 109
270	19 683 000	19 902 511	20 123 648	20 346 417	20 570 824	20 796 875	21 024 576	21 253 933	21 484 952	21 717 639
280	21 952 000	22 188 041	22 425 768	22 665 187	22 906 304	23 149 125	23 393 656	23 639 903	23 887 872	24 137 569
290	24 389 000	24 642 171	24 897 088	25 153 757	25 412 184	25 672 375	25 934 336	26 198 073	26 463 592	26 730 899
300	27 000 000	27 270 901	27 543 608	27 818 127	28 094 464	28 372 625	28 652 616	28 934 443	29 218 112	29 503 629
310	29 791 000	30 080 231	30 371 328	30 664 297	30 959 144	31 255 875	31 554 496	31 855 013	32 157 432	32 461 759
320	32 768 000	33 076 161	33 386 248	33 698 267	34 012 224	34 328 125	34 645 976	34 965 783	35 287 552	35 611 289
330	35 937 000	36 264 691	36 594 368	36 926 037	37 259 704	37 595 375	37 933 056	38 272 753	38 614 472	38 958 219
340	39 304 000	39 651 821	40 001 688	40 353 607	40 707 584	41 063 625	41 421 736	41 781 923	42 144 192	42 508 549
350	42 875 000	43 243 551	43 614 208	43 986 977	44 361 864	44 738 875	45 118 016	45 499 293	45 882 712	46 268 279
360	46 656 000	47 045 881	47 437 928	47 832 147	48 228 544	48 627 125	49 027 896	49 430 863	49 836 032	50 243 409
370	50 653 000	51 064 811	51 478 848	51 895 117	52 313 624	52 734 375	53 157 376	53 582 633	54 010 152	54 439 939
380	54 872 000	55 306 341	55 742 968	56 181 887	56 623 104	57 066 625	57 512 456	57 960 603	58 411 072	58 863 869
390	59 319 000	59 776 471	60 236 288	60 698 457	61 162 984	61 629 875	62 099 136	62 570 773	63 044 792	63 521 199
400	64 000 000	64 481 201	64 964 808	65 450 827	65 939 264	66 430 125	66 923 416	67 419 143	67 917 312	68 417 929
410	68 921 000	69 426 531	69 934 528	70 444 997	70 957 944	71 473 375	71 991 296	72 511 713	73 034 632	73 560 059
420	74 088 000	74 618 461	75 151 448	75 686 967	76 225 024	76 765 625	77 308 776	77 854 483	78 402 752	78 953 589
430	79 507 000	80 062 991	80 621 568	81 182 737	81 746 504	82 312 875	82 881 856	83 453 453	84 027 672	84 604 519
440	85 184 000	85 766 121	86 350 888	86 938 307	87 528 384	88 121 125	88 716 536	89 314 623	89 915 392	90 518 849
450	91 125 000	91 733 851	92 345 408	92 959 677	93 576 664	94 196 375	94 818 816	95 443 993	96 071 912	96 702 579
460	97 336 000	97 972 181	98 611 128	99 252 847	99 897 344	100 544 625	101 194 696	101 847 563	102 503 232	103 161 709
470	103 823 000	104 487 111	105 154 048	105 823 817	106 496 424	107 171 875	107 850 176	108 531 333	109 215 352	109 902 239
480	110 592 000	111 284 641	111 980 168	112 678 587	113 379 904	114 084 125	114 791 256	115 501 303	116 214 272	116 930 169
490	117 649 000	118 370 771	119 095 488	119 823 157	120 553 784	121 287 375	122 023 936	122 763 473	123 505 992	124 251 499
500	125 000 000	125 751 501	126 506 008	127 263 527	128 024 064	128 787 625	129 554 216	130 323 843	131 096 512	131 872 229
510	132 651 000	133 432 831	134 217 728	135 005 697	135 796 744	136 590 875	137 388 096	138 188 413	138 991 832	139 798 359
520	140 608 000	141 420 761	142 236 648	143 055 667	143 877 824	144 703 125	145 531 576	146 363 183	147 197 952	148 035 889
530	148 877 000	149 721 291	150 568 768	151 419 437	152 273 304	153 130 375	153 990 656	154 854 153	155 720 872	156 590 819
540	157 464 000	158 340 421	159 220 088	160 103 007	160 989 184	161 878 625	162 771 336	163 667 323	164 566 592	165 469 149
550	166 375 000	167 284 151	168 196 608	169 112 377	170 031 464	170 953 875	171 879 616	172 808 693	173 741 112	174 676 879
560	175 616 000	176 558 481	177 504 328	178 453 547	179 406 144	180 362 125	181 321 496	182 284 263	183 250 432	184 220 009
570	185 193 000	186 169 411	187 149 248	188 132 517	189 119 224	190 109 375	191 102 976	192 100 033	193 100 552	194 104 539
580	195 112 000	196 122 941	197 137 368	198 155 287	199 176 704	200 201 625	201 230 056	202 262 003	203 297 472	204 336 469
590	205 379 000	206 425 071	207 474 688	208 527 857	209 584 584	210 644 875	211 708 736	212 776 173	213 847 192	214 921 799
600	216 000 000	217 081 801	218 167 208	219 256 227	220 348 864	221 445 125	222 545 016	223 648 543	224 755 712	225 866 529
610	226 981 000	228 099 131	229 220 928	230 346 397	231 475 544	232 608 375	233 744 896	234 885 113	236 029 032	237 176 659
620	238 328 000	239 483 061	240 641 848	241 804 367	242 970 624	244 140 625	245 314 376	246 491 883	247 673 152	248 858 189
630	250 047 000	251 239 591	252 435 968	253 636 137	254 840 104	256 047 875	257 259 456	258 474 853	259 694 072	260 917 119
640	262 144 000	263 374 721	264 609 288	265 847 707	267 089 984	268 336 125	269 586 136	270 840 023	272 097 792	273 359 449
650	274 625 000	275 894 451	277 167 808	278 445 077	279 726 264	281 011 375	282 300 416	283 593 393	284 890 312	286 191 179
660	287 496 000	288 804 781	290 117 528	291 434 247	292 754 944	294 079 625	295 408 296	296 740 963	298 077 632	299 418 309
670	300 763 000	302 111 711	303 464 448	304 821 217	306 182 024	307 546 875	308 915 776	310 288 733	311 665 752	313 046 839
680	314 432 000	315 821 241	317 214 568	318 611 987	320 013 504	321 419 125	322 828 856	324 242 703	325 660 672	327 082 769
690	328 509 000	329 939 371	331 373 888	332 812 557	334 255 384	335 702 375	337 153 536	338 608 873	340 068 392	341 532 099
700	343 000 000	344 472 101	345 948 408	347 428 927	348 913 664	350 402 625	351 895 816	353 393 243	354 894 912	356 400 829
710	357 911 000	359 425 431	360 944 128	362 467 097	363 994 344	365 525 875	367 061 696	368 601 813	370 146 232	371 694 959
720	373 248 000	374 805 361	376 367 048	377 933 067	379 503 424	381 078 125	382 657 176	384 240 583	385 828 352	387 420 489
730	389 017 000	390 617 891	392 223 168	393 832 837	395 446 904	397 065 375	398 688 256	400 315 553	401 947 272	403 583 419
740	405 224 000	406 869 021	408 518 488	410 172 407	411 830 784	413 493 625	415 160 936	416 832 723	418 508 992	420 189 749
750	421 875 000	423 564 751	425 259 008	426 957 777	428 661 064	430 368 875	432 081 216	433 798 093	435 519 512	437 245 479
760	438 976 000	440 711 081	442 450 728	444 194 947	445 943 744	447 697 125	449 455 096	451 217 663	452 984 832	454 756 609
770	456 533 000	458 314 011	460 099 648	461 889 917	463 684 824	465 484 375	467 288 576	469 097 433	470 910 952	472 729 139
780	474 552 000	476 379 541	478 211 768	480 048 687	481 890 304	483 736 625	485 587 656	487 443 403	489 303 872	491 169 069
790	493 039 000	494 913 671	496 793 088	498 677 257	500 566 184	502 459 875	504 358 336	506 261 573	508 169 592	510 082 399
800	512 000 000	513 922 401	515 849 608	517 781 627	519 718 464	521 660 125	523 606 616	525 557 943	527 514 112	529 475 129
810	531 441 000	533 411 731	535 387 328	537 367 797	539 353 144	541 343 375	543 338 496	545 338 513	547 343 432	549 353 259
820	551 368 000	553 387 661	555 412 248	557 441 767	559 476 224	561 515 625	563 559 976	565 609 283	567 663 552	569 722 789
830	571 787 000	573 856 191	575 930 368	578 009 537	580 093 704	582 182 875	584 277 056	586 376 253	588 480 472	590 589 719
840	592 704 000	594 823 321	596 947 688	599 077 107	601 211 584	603 351 125	605 495 736	607 645 423	609 800 192	611 960 049
850	614 125 000	616 295 051	618 470 208	620 650 477	622 835 864	625 026 375	627 222 016	629 422 793	631 628 712	633 839 779
860	636 056 000	638 277 381	640 503 928	642 735 647	644 972 544	647 214 625	649 461 896	651 714 363	653 972 032	656 234 909
870	658 503 000	660 776 311	663 054 848	665 338 617	667 627 624	669 921 875	672 221 376	674 526 133	676 836 152	679 151 439
880	681 472 000	683 797 841	686 128 968	688 465 387	690 807 104	693 154 125	695 506 456	697 864 103	700 227 072	702 595 369
890	704 969 000	707 347 971	709 732 288	712 121 957	714 516 984	716 917 375	719 323 136	721 734 273	724 150 792	726 572 699
900	729 000 000	731 432 701	733 870 808	736 314 327	738 763 264	741 217 625	743 677 416	746 142 643	748 613 312	751 089 429
910	753 571 000	756 058 031	758 550 528	761 048 497	763 551 944	766 060 875	768 575 296	771 095 213	773 620 632	776 151 559
920	778 688 000	781 229 961	783 777 448	786 330 467	788 889 024	791 453 125	794 022 776	796 597 983	799 178 752	801 765 089
930	804 357 000	806 954 491	809 557 568	812 166 237	814 780 504	817 400 375	820 025 856	822 656 953	825 293 672	827 936 019
940	830 584 000	833 237 621	835 896 888	838 561 807	841 232 384	843 908 625	846 590 536	849 278 123	851 971 392	854 670 349
950	857 375 000	860 085 351	862 801 408	865 523 177	868 250 664	870 983 875	873 722 816	876 467 493	879 217 912	881 974 079
960	884 736 000	887 503 681	890 277 128	893 056 347	895 841 344	898 632 125	901 428 696	904 231 063	907 039 232	909 853 209
970	912 673 000	915 498 611	918 330 048	921 167 317	924 010 424	926 859 375	929 714 176	932 574 833	935 441 352	938 313 739
980	941 192 000	944 076 141	946 966 168	949 862 087	952 763 904	955 671 625	958 585 256	961 504 803	964 430 272	967 361 669
990	970 299 000	973 242 271	976 191 488	979 146 657	982 107 784	985 074 875	988 047 936	991 026 973	994 011 992	997 002 999

1) Values from Comrie, L. J. (Ed.), *Barlow's Tables of Squares, Cubes, Square Roots, Cube Roots and Reciprocals of All Integers up to 12,500*, 4th ed., Spon, London, 1958. Reprinted by kind permission of the editor and publishers.

Squares and Square Roots of the Integers 1—399[1]

$\sqrt{100n} = 10\sqrt{n}$ $\sqrt{1000n} = 10\sqrt{10n}$ $\sqrt{0.1n} = 0.1\sqrt{10n}$ $\sqrt{0.01n} = 0.1\sqrt{n}$ $\sqrt{0.001n} = 0.01\sqrt{10n}$

n	n^2	$\sqrt{n}$	$\sqrt{10n}$	n	n^2	$\sqrt{n}$	$\sqrt{10n}$	n	n^2	$\sqrt{n}$	$\sqrt{10n}$	n	n^2	$\sqrt{n}$	$\sqrt{10n}$
				100	1 00 00	10.000 0000	31.622 777	**200**	4 00 00	14.142 1356	44.721 360	**300**	9 00 00	17.320 5081	54.772 256
1	1	1.000 0000	3.162 2777	101	1 02 01	10.049 8756	31.780 497	201	4 04 01	14.177 4469	44.833 024	301	9 06 01	17.349 3516	54.863 467
2	4	1.414 2136	4.472 1360	102	1 04 04	10.099 5049	31.937 439	202	4 08 04	14.212 6704	44.944 410	302	9 12 04	17.378 1472	54.954 527
3	9	1.732 0508	5.477 2256	103	1 06 09	10.148 8916	32.093 613	203	4 12 09	14.247 8068	45.055 521	303	9 18 09	17.406 8952	55.045 436
4	16	2.000 0000	6.324 5553	104	1 08 16	10.198 0390	32.249 031	204	4 16 16	14.282 8569	45.166 359	304	9 24 16	17.435 5958	55.136 195
5	25	2.236 0680	7.071 0678	**105**	1 10 25	10.246 9508	32.403 703	**205**	4 20 25	14.317 8211	45.276 926	**305**	9 30 25	17.464 2492	55.226 805
6	36	2.449 4897	7.745 9667	106	1 12 36	10.295 6301	32.557 641	206	4 24 36	14.352 7001	45.387 223	306	9 36 36	17.492 8557	55.317 267
7	49	2.645 7513	8.366 6003	107	1 14 49	10.344 0804	32.710 854	207	4 28 49	14.387 4946	45.497 253	307	9 42 49	17.521 4155	55.407 581
8	64	2.828 4271	8.944 2719	108	1 16 64	10.392 3048	32.863 353	208	4 32 64	14.422 2051	45.607 017	308	9 48 64	17.549 9288	55.497 748
9	81	3.000 0000	9.486 8330	109	1 18 81	10.440 3065	33.015 148	209	4 36 81	14.456 8323	45.716 518	309	9 54 81	17.578 3958	55.587 768
10	1 00	3.162 2777	10.000 0000	**110**	1 21 00	10.488 0885	33.166 248	**210**	4 41 00	14.491 3767	45.825 757	**310**	9 61 00	17.606 8169	55.677 644
11	1 21	3.316 6248	10.488 0885	111	1 23 21	10.535 6538	33.316 662	211	4 45 21	14.525 8390	45.934 736	311	9 67 21	17.635 1921	55.767 374
12	1 44	3.464 1016	10.954 4512	112	1 25 44	10.583 0052	33.466 401	212	4 49 44	14.560 2198	46.043 458	312	9 73 44	17.663 5217	55.856 960
13	1 69	3.605 5513	11.401 7543	113	1 27 69	10.630 1458	33.615 473	213	4 53 69	14.594 5195	46.151 923	313	9 79 69	17.691 8060	55.946 403
14	1 96	3.741 6574	11.832 1596	114	1 29 96	10.677 0783	33.763 886	214	4 57 96	14.628 7388	46.260 134	314	9 85 96	17.720 0451	56.035 703
15	2 25	3.872 9833	12.247 4487	**115**	1 32 25	10.723 8053	33.911 650	**215**	4 62 25	14.662 8783	46.368 092	**315**	9 92 25	17.748 2393	56.124 861
16	2 56	4.000 0000	12.649 1106	116	1 34 56	10.770 3296	34.058 773	216	4 66 56	14.696 9385	46.475 800	316	9 98 56	17.776 3888	56.213 877
17	2 89	4.123 1056	13.038 4048	117	1 36 89	10.816 6538	34.205 263	217	4 70 89	14.730 9199	46.583 259	317	10 04 89	17.804 4938	56.302 753
18	3 24	4.242 6407	13.416 4079	118	1 39 24	10.862 7805	34.351 128	218	4 75 24	14.764 8231	46.690 470	318	10 11 24	17.832 5545	56.391 489
19	3 61	4.358 8989	13.784 0488	119	1 41 61	10.908 7121	34.496 377	219	4 79 61	14.798 6486	46.797 436	319	10 17 61	17.860 5711	56.480 085
20	4 00	4.472 1360	14.142 1356	**120**	1 44 00	10.954 4512	34.641 016	**220**	4 84 00	14.832 3970	46.904 158	**320**	10 24 00	17.888 5438	56.568 542
21	4 41	4.582 5757	14.491 3767	121	1 46 41	11.000 0000	34.785 054	221	4 88 41	14.866 0687	47.010 637	321	10 30 41	17.916 4729	56.656 862
22	4 84	4.690 4158	14.832 3970	122	1 48 84	11.045 3610	34.928 498	222	4 92 84	14.899 6644	47.116 876	322	10 36 84	17.944 3584	56.745 044
23	5 29	4.795 8315	15.165 7509	123	1 51 29	11.090 5365	35.071 356	223	4 97 29	14.933 1845	47.222 876	323	10 43 29	17.972 2008	56.833 089
24	5 76	4.898 9795	15.491 9334	124	1 53 76	11.135 5287	35.213 634	224	5 01 76	14.966 6295	47.328 638	324	10 49 76	18.000 0000	56.920 998
25	6 25	5.000 0000	15.811 3883	**125**	1 56 25	11.180 3399	35.355 339	**225**	5 06 25	15.000 0000	47.434 165	**325**	10 56 25	18.027 7564	57.008 771
26	6 76	5.099 0195	16.124 5155	126	1 58 76	11.224 9722	35.496 479	226	5 10 76	15.033 2964	47.539 457	326	10 62 76	18.055 4701	57.096 410
27	7 29	5.196 1524	16.431 6767	127	1 61 29	11.269 4277	35.637 059	227	5 15 29	15.066 5192	47.644 517	327	10 69 29	18.083 1413	57.183 914
28	7 84	5.291 5026	16.733 2005	128	1 63 84	11.313 7085	35.777 088	228	5 19 84	15.099 6689	47.749 346	328	10 75 84	18.110 7703	57.271 284
29	8 41	5.385 1648	17.029 3864	129	1 66 41	11.357 8167	35.916 570	229	5 24 41	15.132 7460	47.853 944	329	10 82 41	18.138 3571	57.358 522
30	9 00	5.477 2256	17.320 5081	**130**	1 69 00	11.401 7543	36.055 513	**230**	5 29 00	15.165 7509	47.958 315	**330**	10 89 00	18.165 9021	57.445 626
31	9 61	5.567 7644	17.606 8169	131	1 71 61	11.445 5231	36.193 922	231	5 33 61	15.198 6842	48.062 459	331	10 95 61	18.193 4054	57.532 599
32	10 24	5.656 8542	17.888 5438	132	1 74 24	11.489 1253	36.331 804	232	5 38 24	15.231 5462	48.166 378	332	11 02 24	18.220 8672	57.619 441
33	10 89	5.744 5626	18.165 9021	133	1 76 89	11.532 5626	36.469 165	233	5 42 89	15.264 3375	48.270 074	333	11 08 89	18.248 2876	57.706 152
34	11 56	5.830 9519	18.439 0889	134	1 79 56	11.575 8369	36.606 010	234	5 47 56	15.297 0585	48.373 546	334	11 15 56	18.275 6669	57.792 733
35	12 25	5.916 0798	18.708 2869	**135**	1 82 25	11.618 9500	36.742 346	**235**	5 52 25	15.329 7097	48.476 799	**335**	11 22 25	18.303 0052	57.879 185
36	12 96	6.000 0000	18.973 6660	136	1 84 96	11.661 9038	36.878 178	236	5 56 96	15.362 2915	48.579 831	336	11 28 96	18.330 3028	57.965 507
37	13 69	6.082 7625	19.235 3841	137	1 87 69	11.704 6999	37.013 511	237	5 61 69	15.394 8043	48.682 646	337	11 35 69	18.357 5598	58.051 701
38	14 44	6.164 4140	19.493 5887	138	1 90 44	11.747 3401	37.148 351	238	5 66 44	15.427 2486	48.785 244	338	11 42 44	18.384 7763	58.137 767
39	15 21	6.244 9980	19.748 4177	139	1 93 21	11.789 8261	37.282 704	239	5 71 21	15.459 6248	48.887 626	339	11 49 21	18.411 9526	58.223 707
40	16 00	6.324 5553	20.000 0000	**140**	1 96 00	11.832 1596	37.416 574	**240**	5 76 00	15.491 9334	48.989 795	**340**	11 56 00	18.439 0889	58.309 519
41	16 81	6.403 1242	20.248 4567	141	1 98 81	11.874 3421	37.549 967	241	5 80 81	15.524 1747	49.091 751	341	11 62 81	18.466 1853	58.395 205
42	17 64	6.480 7407	20.493 9015	142	2 01 64	11.916 3753	37.682 887	242	5 85 64	15.556 3492	49.193 496	342	11 69 64	18.493 2420	58.480 766
43	18 49	6.557 4385	20.736 4414	143	2 04 49	11.958 2607	37.815 341	243	5 90 49	15.588 4573	49.295 030	343	11 76 49	18.520 2592	58.566 202
44	19 36	6.633 2496	20.976 1770	144	2 07 36	12.000 0000	37.947 332	244	5 95 36	15.620 4994	49.396 356	344	11 83 36	18.547 2370	58.651 513
45	20 25	6.708 2039	21.213 2034	**145**	2 10 25	12.041 5946	38.078 866	**245**	6 00 25	15.652 4758	49.497 475	**345**	11 90 25	18.574 1756	58.736 701
46	21 16	6.782 3300	21.447 6106	146	2 13 16	12.083 0460	38.209 946	246	6 05 16	15.684 3871	49.598 387	346	11 97 16	18.601 0752	58.821 765
47	22 09	6.855 6546	21.679 4834	147	2 16 09	12.124 3557	38.340 579	247	6 10 09	15.716 2336	49.699 095	347	12 04 09	18.627 9360	58.906 706
48	23 04	6.928 2032	21.908 9023	148	2 19 04	12.165 5251	38.470 768	248	6 15 04	15.748 0157	49.799 598	348	12 11 04	18.654 7581	58.991 525
49	24 01	7.000 0000	22.135 9436	149	2 22 01	12.206 5556	38.600 518	249	6 20 01	15.779 7338	49.899 900	349	12 18 01	18.681 5417	59.076 222
50	25 00	7.071 0678	22.360 6798	**150**	2 25 00	12.247 4487	38.729 833	**250**	6 25 00	15.811 3883	50.000 000	**350**	12 25 00	18.708 2869	59.160 798
51	26 01	7.141 4284	22.583 1796	151	2 28 01	12.288 2057	38.858 718	251	6 30 01	15.842 9795	50.099 900	351	12 32 01	18.734 9940	59.245 253
52	27 04	7.211 1026	22.803 5085	152	2 31 04	12.328 8280	38.987 177	252	6 35 04	15.874 5079	50.199 602	352	12 39 04	18.761 6630	59.329 588
53	28 09	7.280 1099	23.021 7289	153	2 34 09	12.369 3169	39.115 214	253	6 40 09	15.905 9737	50.299 105	353	12 46 09	18.788 2942	59.413 803
54	29 16	7.348 4692	23.237 9001	154	2 37 16	12.409 6736	39.242 834	254	6 45 16	15.937 3775	50.398 413	354	12 53 16	18.814 8877	59.497 899
55	30 25	7.416 1985	23.452 0788	**155**	2 40 25	12.449 8996	39.370 039	**255**	6 50 25	15.968 7194	50.497 525	**355**	12 60 25	18.841 4437	59.581 876
56	31 36	7.483 3148	23.664 3191	156	2 43 36	12.489 9960	39.496 835	256	6 55 36	16.000 0000	50.596 443	356	12 67 36	18.867 9623	59.665 736
57	32 49	7.549 8344	23.874 6728	157	2 46 49	12.529 9641	39.623 226	257	6 60 49	16.031 2195	50.695 167	357	12 74 49	18.894 4436	59.749 477
58	33 64	7.615 7731	24.083 1892	158	2 49 64	12.569 8051	39.749 214	258	6 65 64	16.062 3784	50.793 700	358	12 81 64	18.920 8879	59.833 101
59	34 81	7.681 1457	24.289 9156	159	2 52 81	12.609 5202	39.874 804	259	6 70 81	16.093 4769	50.892 043	359	12 88 81	18.947 2953	59.916 609
60	36 00	7.745 9667	24.494 8974	**160**	2 56 00	12.649 1106	40.000 000	**260**	6 76 00	16.124 5155	50.990 195	**360**	12 96 00	18.973 6660	60.000 000
61	37 21	7.810 2497	24.698 1781	161	2 59 21	12.688 5775	40.124 805	261	6 81 21	16.155 4944	51.088 159	361	13 03 21	19.000 0000	60.083 276
62	38 44	7.874 0079	24.899 7992	162	2 62 44	12.727 9221	40.249 224	262	6 86 44	16.186 4141	51.185 936	362	13 10 44	19.026 2976	60.166 436
63	39 69	7.937 2539	25.099 8008	163	2 65 69	12.767 1453	40.373 258	263	6 91 69	16.217 2747	51.283 526	363	13 17 69	19.052 5589	60.249 481
64	40 96	8.000 0000	25.298 2213	164	2 68 96	12.806 2485	40.496 913	264	6 96 96	16.248 0768	51.380 930	364	13 24 96	19.078 7840	60.332 413
65	42 25	8.062 2577	25.495 0976	**165**	2 72 25	12.845 2326	40.620 192	**265**	7 02 25	16.278 8206	51.478 151	**365**	13 32 25	19.104 9732	60.415 230
66	43 56	8.124 0384	25.690 4652	166	2 75 56	12.884 0987	40.743 098	266	7 07 56	16.309 5064	51.575 188	366	13 39 56	19.131 1265	60.497 934
67	44 89	8.185 3528	25.884 3582	167	2 78 89	12.922 8480	40.865 633	267	7 12 89	16.340 1346	51.672 043	367	13 46 89	19.157 2441	60.580 525
68	46 24	8.246 2113	26.076 8096	168	2 82 24	12.961 4814	40.987 803	268	7 18 24	16.370 7055	51.768 716	368	13 54 24	19.183 3261	60.663 004
69	47 61	8.306 6239	26.267 8511	169	2 85 61	13.000 0000	41.109 610	269	7 23 61	16.401 2195	51.865 210	369	13 61 61	19.209 3727	60.745 370
70	49 00	8.366 6003	26.457 5131	**170**	2 89 00	13.038 4048	41.231 056	**270**	7 29 00	16.431 6767	51.961 524	**370**	13 69 00	19.235 3841	60.827 625
71	50 41	8.426 1498	26.645 8252	171	2 92 41	13.076 6968	41.352 146	271	7 34 41	16.462 0776	52.057 660	371	13 76 41	19.261 3603	60.909 769
72	51 84	8.485 2814	26.832 8157	172	2 95 84	13.114 8770	41.472 883	272	7 39 84	16.492 4225	52.153 619	372	13 83 84	19.287 3015	60.991 803
73	53 29	8.544 0037	27.018 5122	173	2 99 29	13.152 9464	41.593 269	273	7 45 29	16.522 7116	52.249 402	373	13 91 29	19.313 2079	61.073 726
74	54 76	8.602 3253	27.202 9410	174	3 02 76	13.190 9060	41.713 307	274	7 50 76	16.552 9454	52.345 009	374	13 98 76	19.339 0796	61.155 539
75	56 25	8.660 2540	27.386 1279	**175**	3 06 25	13.228 7566	41.833 001	**275**	7 56 25	16.583 1240	52.440 442	**375**	14 06 25	19.364 9167	61.237 244
76	57 76	8.717 7979	27.568 0975	176	3 09 76	13.266 4992	41.952 354	276	7 61 76	16.613 2477	52.535 702	376	14 13 76	19.390 7194	61.318 839
77	59 29	8.774 9644	27.748 8739	177	3 13 29	13.304 1347	42.071 368	277	7 67 29	16.643 3170	52.630 789	377	14 21 29	19.416 4878	61.400 326
78	60 84	8.831 7609	27.928 4801	178	3 16 84	13.341 6641	42.190 046	278	7 72 84	16.673 3320	52.725 705	378	14 28 84	19.442 2221	61.481 705
79	62 41	8.888 1944	28.106 9386	179	3 20 41	13.379 0882	42.308 392	279	7 78 41	16.703 2931	52.820 451	379	14 36 41	19.467 9223	61.562 976
80	64 00	8.944 2719	28.284 2712	**180**	3 24 00	13.416 4079	42.426 407	**280**	7 84 00	16.733 2005	52.915 026	**380**	14 44 00	19.493 5887	61.644 140
81	65 61	9.000 0000	28.460 4989	181	3 27 61	13.453 6240	42.544 095	281	7 89 61	16.763 0546	53.009 433	381	14 51 61	19.519 2213	61.725 197
82	67 24	9.055 3851	28.635 6421	182	3 31 24	13.490 7376	42.661 458	282	7 95 24	16.792 8556	53.103 672	382	14 59 24	19.544 8203	61.806 149
83	68 89	9.110 4336	28.809 7206	183	3 34 89	13.527 7493	42.778 499	283	8 00 89	16.822 6038	53.197 744	383	14 66 89	19.570 3858	61.886 994
84	70 56	9.165 1514	28.982 7535	184	3 38 56	13.564 6600	42.895 221	284	8 06 56	16.852 2995	53.291 650	384	14 74 56	19.595 9179	61.967 734
85	72 25	9.219 5445	29.154 7595	**185**	3 42 25	13.601 4705	43.011 626	**285**	8 12 25	16.881 9430	53.385 391	**385**	14 82 25	19.621 4169	62.048 368
86	73 96	9.273 6185	29.325 7566	186	3 45 96	13.638 1817	43.127 717	286	8 17 96	16.911 5345	53.478 968	386	14 89 96	19.646 8827	62.128 898
87	75 69	9.327 3791	29.495 7624	187	3 49 69	13.674 7943	43.243 497	287	8 23 69	16.941 0743	53.572 381	387	14 97 69	19.672 3156	62.209 324
88	77 44	9.380 8315	29.664 7939	188	3 53 44	13.711 3092	43.358 967	288	8 29 44	16.970 5627	53.665 631	388	15 05 44	19.697 7156	62.289 646
89	79 21	9.433 9811	29.832 8678	189	3 57 21	13.747 7271	43.474 130	289	8 35 21	17.000 0000	53.758 720	389	15 13 21	19.723 0829	62.369 865
90	81 00	9.486 8330	30.000 0000	**190**	3 61 00	13.784 0488	43.588 989	**290**	8 41 00	17.029 3864	53.851 648	**390**	15 21 00	19.748 4177	62.449 980
91	82 81	9.539 3920	30.166 2063	191	3 64 81	13.820 2750	43.703 547	291	8 46 81	17.058 7221	53.944 416	391	15 28 81	19.773 7199	62.529 993
92	84 64	9.591 6630	30.331 5018	192	3 68 64	13.856 4065	43.817 805	292	8 52 64	17.088 0075	54.037 024	392	15 36 64	19.798 9899	62.609 903
93	86 49	9.643 6508	30.495 9014	193	3 72 49	13.892 4440	43.931 765	293	8 58 49	17.117 2428	54.129 474	393	15 44 49	19.824 2276	62.689 712
94	88 36	9.695 3597	30.659 4194	194	3 76 36	13.928 3883	44.045 431	294	8 64 36	17.146 4282	54.221 767	394	15 52 36	19.849 4332	62.769 419
95	90 25	9.746 7943	30.822 0700	**195**	3 80 25	13.964 2400	44.158 804	**295**	8 70 25	17.175 5640	54.313 902	**395**	15 60 25	19.874 6069	62.849 025
96	92 16	9.797 9590	30.983 8668	196	3 84 16	14.000 0000	44.271 887	296	8 76 16	17.204 6505	54.405 882	396	15 68 16	19.899 7487	62.928 531
97	94 09	9.848 8578	31.144 8230	197	3 88 09	14.035 6688	44.384 682	297	8 82 09	17.233 6879	54.497 706	397	15 76 09	19.924 8588	63.007 936
98	96 04	9.899 4949	31.304 9517	198	3 92 04	14.071 2473	44.497 191	298	8 88 04	17.262 6765	54.589 376	398	15 84 04	19.949 9373	63.087 241
99	98 01	9.949 8744	31.464 2654	199	3 96 01	14.106 7360	44.609 416	299	8 94 01	17.291 6165	54.680 892	399	15 92 01	19.974 9844	63.166 447

1) Values from Comrie, L. J. (Ed.), *Barlow's Tables of Squares, Cubes, Square Roots, Cube Roots and Reciprocals of All Integers up to 12,500*, 4th ed., Spon, London, 1958. Reprinted by kind permission of the editor and publishers.

Squares and Square Roots of the Integers 400—799

$\sqrt{100n} = 10\sqrt{n}$ $\sqrt{1000n} = 10\sqrt{10n}$ $\sqrt{0.1n} = 0.1\sqrt{10n}$ $\sqrt{0.01n} = 0.1\sqrt{n}$ $\sqrt{0.001n} = 0.01\sqrt{10n}$

n	n^2	$\sqrt{n}$	$\sqrt{10n}$
400	16 00 00	20.000 0000	63.245 553
401	16 08 01	20.024 9844	63.324 561
402	16 16 04	20.049 9377	63.403 470
403	16 24 09	20.074 8599	63.482 281
404	16 32 16	20.099 7512	63.560 994
405	16 40 25	20.124 6118	63.639 610
406	16 48 36	20.149 4417	63.718 129
407	16 56 49	20.174 2410	63.796 552
408	16 64 64	20.199 0099	63.874 878
409	16 72 81	20.223 7484	63.953 108
410	16 81 00	20.248 4567	64.031 242
411	16 89 21	20.273 1349	64.109 282
412	16 97 44	20.297 7831	64.187 226
413	17 05 69	20.322 4014	64.265 076
414	17 13 96	20.346 9899	64.342 832
415	17 22 25	20.371 5488	64.420 494
416	17 30 56	20.396 0781	64.498 062
417	17 38 89	20.420 5779	64.575 537
418	17 47 24	20.445 0483	64.652 920
419	17 55 61	20.469 4895	64.730 209
420	17 64 00	20.493 9015	64.807 407
421	17 72 41	20.518 2845	64.884 513
422	17 80 84	20.542 6386	64.961 527
423	17 89 29	20.566 9638	65.038 450
424	17 97 76	20.591 2603	65.115 282
425	18 06 25	20.615 5281	65.192 024
426	18 14 76	20.639 7674	65.268 675
427	18 23 29	20.663 9783	65.345 237
428	18 31 84	20.688 1609	65.421 709
429	18 40 41	20.712 3152	65.498 092
430	18 49 00	20.736 4414	65.574 385
431	18 57 61	20.760 5395	65.650 590
432	18 66 24	20.784 6097	65.726 707
433	18 74 89	20.808 6520	65.802 736
434	18 83 56	20.832 6667	65.878 676
435	18 92 25	20.856 6536	65.954 530
436	19 00 96	20.880 6130	66.030 296
437	19 09 69	20.904 5450	66.105 976
438	19 18 44	20.928 4495	66.181 568
439	19 27 21	20.952 3268	66.257 075
440	19 36 00	20.976 1770	66.332 496
441	19 44 81	21.000 0000	66.407 831
442	19 53 64	21.023 7960	66.483 081
443	19 62 49	21.047 5652	66.558 245
444	19 71 36	21.071 3075	66.633 325
445	19 80 25	21.095 0231	66.708 320
446	19 89 16	21.118 7121	66.783 231
447	19 98 09	21.142 3745	66.858 059
448	20 07 04	21.166 0105	66.932 802
449	20 16 01	21.189 6201	67.007 462
450	20 25 00	21.213 2034	67.082 039
451	20 34 01	21.236 7606	67.156 534
452	20 43 04	21.260 2916	67.230 945
453	20 52 09	21.283 7967	67.305 275
454	20 61 16	21.307 2758	67.379 522
455	20 70 25	21.330 7290	67.453 688
456	20 79 36	21.354 1565	67.527 772
457	20 88 49	21.377 5583	67.601 775
458	20 97 64	21.400 9346	67.675 697
459	21 06 81	21.424 2853	67.749 539
460	21 16 00	21.447 6106	67.823 300
461	21 25 21	21.470 9106	67.896 981
462	21 34 44	21.494 1853	67.970 582
463	21 43 69	21.517 4348	68.044 103
464	21 52 96	21.540 6592	68.117 545
465	21 62 25	21.563 8587	68.190 908
466	21 71 56	21.587 0331	68.264 193
467	21 80 89	21.610 1828	68.337 398
468	21 90 24	21.633 3077	68.410 526
469	21 99 61	21.656 4078	68.483 575
470	22 09 00	21.679 4834	68.556 546
471	22 18 41	21.702 5344	68.629 440
472	22 27 84	21.725 5610	68.702 256
473	22 37 29	21.748 5632	68.774 995
474	22 46 76	21.771 5411	68.847 658
475	22 56 25	21.794 4947	68.920 244
476	22 65 76	21.817 4242	68.992 753
477	22 75 29	21.840 3297	69.065 187
478	22 84 84	21.863 2111	69.137 544
479	22 94 41	21.886 0686	69.209 826
480	23 04 00	21.908 9023	69.282 032
481	23 13 61	21.931 7122	69.354 164
482	23 23 24	21.954 4984	69.426 220
483	23 32 89	21.977 2610	69.498 201
484	23 42 56	22.000 0000	69.570 109
485	23 52 25	22.022 7155	69.641 941
486	23 61 96	22.045 4077	69.713 700
487	23 71 69	22.068 0765	69.785 385
488	23 81 44	22.090 7220	69.856 997
489	23 91 21	22.113 3444	69.928 535
490	24 01 00	22.135 9436	70.000 000
491	24 10 81	22.158 5198	70.071 392
492	24 20 64	22.181 0730	70.142 712
493	24 30 49	22.203 6033	70.213 959
494	24 40 36	22.226 1108	70.285 134
495	24 50 25	22.248 5955	70.356 236
496	24 60 16	22.271 0575	70.427 267
497	24 70 09	22.293 4968	70.498 227
498	24 80 04	22.315 9136	70.569 115
499	24 90 01	22.338 3079	70.639 932

n	n^2	$\sqrt{n}$	$\sqrt{10n}$
500	25 00 00	22.360 6798	70.710 678
501	25 10 01	22.383 0293	70.781 353
502	25 20 04	22.405 3565	70.851 958
503	25 30 09	22.427 6615	70.922 493
504	25 40 16	22.449 9443	70.992 957
505	25 50 25	22.472 2051	71.063 352
506	25 60 36	22.494 4438	71.133 677
507	25 70 49	22.516 6605	71.203 932
508	25 80 64	22.538 8553	71.274 119
509	25 90 81	22.561 0283	71.344 236
510	26 01 00	22.583 1796	71.414 284
511	26 11 21	22.605 3091	71.484 264
512	26 21 44	22.627 4170	71.554 175
513	26 31 69	22.649 5033	71.624 018
514	26 41 96	22.671 5681	71.693 793
515	26 52 25	22.693 6114	71.763 500
516	26 62 56	22.715 6334	71.833 140
517	26 72 89	22.737 6340	71.902 712
518	26 83 24	22.759 6134	71.972 217
519	26 93 61	22.781 5715	72.041 655
520	27 04 00	22.803 5085	72.111 026
521	27 14 41	22.825 4244	72.180 330
522	27 24 84	22.847 3193	72.249 567
523	27 35 29	22.869 1933	72.318 739
524	27 45 76	22.891 0463	72.387 844
525	27 56 25	22.912 8785	72.456 884
526	27 66 76	22.934 6899	72.525 857
527	27 77 29	22.956 4806	72.594 766
528	27 87 84	22.978 2506	72.663 608
529	27 98 41	23.000 0000	72.732 386
530	28 09 00	23.021 7289	72.801 099
531	28 19 61	23.043 4372	72.869 747
532	28 30 24	23.065 1252	72.938 330
533	28 40 89	23.086 7928	73.006 849
534	28 51 56	23.108 4400	73.075 304
535	28 62 25	23.130 0670	73.143 694
536	28 72 96	23.151 6738	73.212 021
537	28 83 69	23.173 2605	73.280 284
538	28 94 44	23.194 8270	73.348 483
539	29 05 21	23.216 3735	73.416 619
540	29 16 00	23.237 9001	73.484 692
541	29 26 81	23.259 4067	73.552 702
542	29 37 64	23.280 8935	73.620 649
543	29 48 49	23.302 3604	73.688 534
544	29 59 36	23.323 8076	73.756 356
545	29 70 25	23.345 2351	73.824 115
546	29 81 16	23.366 6429	73.891 813
547	29 92 09	23.388 0311	73.959 448
548	30 03 04	23.409 3998	74.027 022
549	30 14 01	23.430 7490	74.094 534
550	30 25 00	23.452 0788	74.161 985
551	30 36 01	23.473 3892	74.229 374
552	30 47 04	23.494 6802	74.296 702
553	30 58 09	23.515 9520	74.363 970
554	30 69 16	23.537 2046	74.431 176
555	30 80 25	23.558 4380	74.498 322
556	30 91 36	23.579 6522	74.565 408
557	31 02 49	23.600 8474	74.632 433
558	31 13 64	23.622 0236	74.699 398
559	31 24 81	23.643 1808	74.766 303
560	31 36 00	23.664 3191	74.833 148
561	31 47 21	23.685 4386	74.899 933
562	31 58 44	23.706 5392	74.966 659
563	31 69 69	23.727 6210	75.033 326
564	31 80 96	23.748 6842	75.099 933
565	31 92 25	23.769 7286	75.166 482
566	32 03 56	23.790 7545	75.232 971
567	32 14 89	23.811 7618	75.299 402
568	32 26 24	23.832 7506	75.365 775
569	32 37 61	23.853 7209	75.432 089
570	32 49 00	23.874 6728	75.498 344
571	32 60 41	23.895 6063	75.564 542
572	32 71 84	23.916 5215	75.630 682
573	32 83 29	23.937 4184	75.696 763
574	32 94 76	23.958 2971	75.762 788
575	33 06 25	23.979 1576	75.828 754
576	33 17 76	24.000 0000	75.894 664
577	33 29 29	24.020 8243	75.960 516
578	33 40 84	24.041 6306	76.026 311
579	33 52 41	24.062 4188	76.092 050
580	33 64 00	24.083 1892	76.157 731
581	33 75 61	24.103 9416	76.223 356
582	33 87 24	24.124 6762	76.288 924
583	33 98 89	24.145 3929	76.354 437
584	34 10 56	24.166 0919	76.419 893
585	34 22 25	24.186 7732	76.485 293
586	34 33 96	24.207 4369	76.550 637
587	34 45 69	24.228 0829	76.615 925
588	34 57 44	24.248 7113	76.681 158
589	34 69 21	24.269 3222	76.746 335
590	34 81 00	24.289 9156	76.811 457
591	34 92 81	24.310 4916	76.876 524
592	35 04 64	24.331 0501	76.941 536
593	35 16 49	24.351 5913	77.006 493
594	35 28 36	24.372 1152	77.071 395
595	35 40 25	24.392 6218	77.136 243
596	35 52 16	24.413 1112	77.201 036
597	35 64 09	24.433 5834	77.265 775
598	35 76 04	24.454 0385	77.330 460
599	35 88 01	24.474 4765	77.395 090

n	n^2	$\sqrt{n}$	$\sqrt{10n}$
600	36 00 00	24.494 8974	77.459 667
601	36 12 01	24.515 3013	77.524 190
602	36 24 04	24.535 6883	77.588 659
603	36 36 09	24.556 0583	77.653 075
604	36 48 16	24.576 4115	77.717 437
605	36 60 25	24.596 7478	77.781 746
606	36 72 36	24.617 0673	77.846 002
607	36 84 49	24.637 3700	77.910 205
608	36 96 64	24.657 6560	77.974 355
609	37 08 81	24.677 9254	78.038 452
610	37 21 00	24.698 1781	78.102 497
611	37 33 21	24.718 4142	78.166 489
612	37 45 44	24.738 6338	78.230 429
613	37 57 69	24.758 8368	78.294 317
614	37 69 96	24.779 0234	78.358 152
615	37 82 25	24.799 1935	78.421 936
616	37 94 56	24.819 3473	78.485 667
617	38 06 89	24.839 4847	78.549 348
618	38 19 24	24.859 6058	78.612 976
619	38 31 61	24.879 7106	78.676 553
620	38 44 00	24.899 7992	78.740 079
621	38 56 41	24.919 8716	78.803 553
622	38 68 84	24.939 9278	78.866 977
623	38 81 29	24.959 9679	78.930 349
624	38 93 76	24.979 9920	78.993 671
625	39 06 25	25.000 0000	79.056 942
626	39 18 76	25.019 9920	79.120 162
627	39 31 29	25.039 9681	79.183 332
628	39 43 84	25.059 9282	79.246 451
629	39 56 41	25.079 8724	79.309 520
630	39 69 00	25.099 8008	79.372 539
631	39 81 61	25.119 7134	79.435 508
632	39 94 24	25.139 6102	79.498 428
633	40 06 89	25.159 4913	79.561 297
634	40 19 56	25.179 3566	79.624 117
635	40 32 25	25.199 2063	79.686 887
636	40 44 96	25.219 0404	79.749 608
637	40 57 69	25.238 8589	79.812 280
638	40 70 44	25.258 6619	79.874 902
639	40 83 21	25.278 4493	79.937 476
640	40 96 00	25.298 2213	80.000 000
641	41 08 81	25.317 9778	80.062 476
642	41 21 64	25.337 7189	80.124 902
643	41 34 49	25.357 4447	80.187 281
644	41 47 36	25.377 1551	80.249 611
645	41 60 25	25.396 8502	80.311 892
646	41 73 16	25.416 5301	80.374 125
647	41 86 09	25.436 1947	80.436 310
648	41 99 04	25.455 8441	80.498 447
649	42 12 01	25.475 4784	80.560 536
650	42 25 00	25.495 0976	80.622 577
651	42 38 01	25.514 7016	80.684 571
652	42 51 04	25.534 2907	80.746 517
653	42 64 09	25.553 8647	80.808 415
654	42 77 16	25.573 4237	80.870 266
655	42 90 25	25.592 9678	80.932 070
656	43 03 36	25.612 4969	80.993 827
657	43 16 49	25.632 0112	81.055 537
658	43 29 64	25.651 5107	81.117 199
659	43 42 81	25.670 9953	81.178 815
660	43 56 00	25.690 4652	81.240 384
661	43 69 21	25.709 9203	81.301 906
662	43 82 44	25.729 3607	81.363 382
663	43 95 69	25.748 7864	81.424 812
664	44 08 96	25.768 1975	81.486 195
665	44 22 25	25.787 5939	81.547 532
666	44 35 56	25.806 9758	81.608 823
667	44 48 89	25.826 3431	81.670 068
668	44 62 24	25.845 6960	81.731 267
669	44 75 61	25.865 0343	81.792 420
670	44 89 00	25.884 3582	81.853 528
671	45 02 41	25.903 6677	81.914 590
672	45 15 84	25.922 9628	81.975 606
673	45 29 29	25.942 2435	82.036 577
674	45 42 76	25.961 5100	82.097 503
675	45 56 25	25.980 7621	82.158 384
676	45 69 76	26.000 0000	82.219 219
677	45 83 29	26.019 2237	82.280 010
678	45 96 84	26.038 4331	82.340 755
679	46 10 41	26.057 6284	82.401 456
680	46 24 00	26.076 8096	82.462 113
681	46 37 61	26.095 9767	82.522 724
682	46 51 24	26.115 1297	82.583 291
683	46 64 89	26.134 2687	82.643 814
684	46 78 56	26.153 3937	82.704 293
685	46 92 25	26.172 5047	82.764 727
686	47 05 96	26.191 6017	82.825 117
687	47 19 69	26.210 6848	82.885 463
688	47 33 44	26.229 7541	82.945 765
689	47 47 21	26.248 8095	83.006 024
690	47 61 00	26.267 8511	83.066 239
691	47 74 81	26.286 8789	83.126 410
692	47 88 64	26.305 8929	83.186 537
693	48 02 49	26.324 8932	83.246 622
694	48 16 36	26.343 8797	83.306 662
695	48 30 25	26.362 8527	83.366 660
696	48 44 16	26.381 8119	83.426 614
697	48 58 09	26.400 7576	83.486 526
698	48 72 04	26.419 6896	83.546 394
699	48 86 01	26.438 6081	83.606 220

n	n^2	$\sqrt{n}$	$\sqrt{10n}$
700	49 00 00	26.457 5131	83.666 003
701	49 14 01	26.476 4046	83.725 743
702	49 28 04	26.495 2826	83.785 440
703	49 42 09	26.514 1472	83.845 095
704	49 56 16	26.532 9983	83.904 708
705	49 70 25	26.551 8361	83.964 278
706	49 84 36	26.570 6605	84.023 806
707	49 98 49	26.589 4716	84.083 292
708	50 12 64	26.608 2694	84.142 736
709	50 26 81	26.627 0539	84.202 138
710	50 41 00	26.645 8252	84.261 498
711	50 55 21	26.664 5833	84.320 816
712	50 69 44	26.683 3281	84.380 092
713	50 83 69	26.702 0598	84.439 327
714	50 97 96	26.720 7784	84.498 521
715	51 12 25	26.739 4839	84.557 673
716	51 26 56	26.758 1763	84.616 783
717	51 40 89	26.776 8557	84.675 853
718	51 55 24	26.795 5220	84.734 881
719	51 69 61	26.814 1754	84.793 868
720	51 84 00	26.832 8157	84.852 814
721	51 98 41	26.851 4432	84.911 719
722	52 12 84	26.870 0577	84.970 583
723	52 27 29	26.888 6593	85.029 407
724	52 41 76	26.907 2481	85.088 190
725	52 56 25	26.925 8240	85.146 932
726	52 70 76	26.944 3872	85.205 634
727	52 85 29	26.962 9375	85.264 295
728	52 99 84	26.981 4751	85.322 916
729	53 14 41	27.000 0000	85.381 497
730	53 29 00	27.018 5122	85.440 037
731	53 43 61	27.037 0117	85.498 538
732	53 58 24	27.055 4985	85.556 999
733	53 72 89	27.073 9727	85.615 419
734	53 87 56	27.092 4344	85.673 800
735	54 02 25	27.110 8834	85.732 141
736	54 16 96	27.129 3199	85.790 442
737	54 31 69	27.147 7439	85.848 704
738	54 46 44	27.166 1554	85.906 926
739	54 61 21	27.184 5544	85.965 109
740	54 76 00	27.202 9410	86.023 253
741	54 90 81	27.221 3152	86.081 357
742	55 05 64	27.239 6769	86.139 422
743	55 20 49	27.258 0263	86.197 448
744	55 35 36	27.276 3634	86.255 435
745	55 50 25	27.294 6881	86.313 383
746	55 65 16	27.313 0006	86.371 292
747	55 80 09	27.331 3007	86.429 162
748	55 95 04	27.349 5887	86.486 993
749	56 10 01	27.367 8644	86.544 786
750	56 25 00	27.386 1279	86.602 540
751	56 40 01	27.404 3792	86.660 256
752	56 55 04	27.422 6184	86.717 934
753	56 70 09	27.440 8455	86.775 573
754	56 85 16	27.459 0604	86.833 173
755	57 00 25	27.477 2633	86.890 736
756	57 15 36	27.495 4542	86.948 260
757	57 30 49	27.513 6330	87.005 747
758	57 45 64	27.531 7998	87.063 195
759	57 60 81	27.549 9546	87.120 606
760	57 76 00	27.568 0975	87.177 979
761	57 91 21	27.586 2284	87.235 314
762	58 06 44	27.604 3475	87.292 611
763	58 21 69	27.622 4546	87.349 871
764	58 36 96	27.640 5499	87.407 094
765	58 52 25	27.658 6334	87.464 278
766	58 67 56	27.676 7050	87.521 426
767	58 82 89	27.694 7648	87.578 536
768	58 98 24	27.712 8129	87.635 609
769	59 13 61	27.730 8492	87.692 645
770	59 29 00	27.748 8739	87.749 644
771	59 44 41	27.766 8868	87.806 606
772	59 59 84	27.784 8880	87.863 531
773	59 75 29	27.802 8775	87.920 419
774	59 90 76	27.820 8555	87.977 270
775	60 06 25	27.838 8218	88.034 084
776	60 21 76	27.856 7766	88.090 862
777	60 37 29	27.874 7197	88.147 603
778	60 52 84	27.892 6514	88.204 308
779	60 68 41	27.910 5715	88.260 977
780	60 84 00	27.928 4801	88.317 609
781	60 99 61	27.946 3772	88.374 204
782	61 15 24	27.964 2629	88.430 764
783	61 30 89	27.982 1372	88.487 287
784	61 46 56	28.000 0000	88.543 774
785	61 62 25	28.017 8515	88.600 226
786	61 77 96	28.035 6915	88.656 641
787	61 93 69	28.053 5203	88.713 020
788	62 09 44	28.071 3377	88.769 364
789	62 25 21	28.089 1438	88.825 672
790	62 41 00	28.106 9386	88.881 944
791	62 56 81	28.124 7222	88.938 181
792	62 72 64	28.142 4946	88.994 382
793	62 88 49	28.160 2557	89.050 547
794	63 04 36	28.178 0056	89.106 678
795	63 20 25	28.195 7444	89.162 773
796	63 36 16	28.213 4720	89.218 832
797	63 52 09	28.231 1884	89.274 856
798	63 68 04	28.248 8938	89.330 846
799	63 84 01	28.266 5881	89.386 800

Squares and Square Roots of the Integers 800—1199

$\sqrt{100n} = 10\sqrt{n}$ $\sqrt{1000n} = 10\sqrt{10n}$ $\sqrt{0.1n} = 0.1\sqrt{10n}$ $\sqrt{0.01n} = 0.1\sqrt{n}$ $\sqrt{0.001n} = 0.01\sqrt{10n}$

n	n^2	$\sqrt{n}$	$\sqrt{10n}$	n	n^2	$\sqrt{n}$	$\sqrt{10n}$	n	n^2	$\sqrt{n}$	$\sqrt{10n}$	n	n^2	$\sqrt{n}$	$\sqrt{10n}$
800	64 00 00	28.284 2712	89.442 719	900	81 00 00	30.000 0000	94.868 330	1000	1 00 00 00	31.622 777	100.000 000	1100	1 21 00 00	33.166 248	104.880 885
801	64 16 01	28.301 9434	89.498 603	901	81 18 01	30.016 6620	94.921 020	1001	1 00 20 01	31.638 584	100.049 988	1101	1 21 22 01	33.181 320	104.928 547
802	64 32 04	28.319 6045	89.554 453	902	81 36 04	30.033 3148	94.973 681	1002	1 00 40 04	31.654 384	100.099 950	1102	1 21 44 04	33.196 385	104.976 188
803	64 48 09	28.337 2546	89.610 267	903	81 54 09	30.049 9584	95.026 312	1003	1 00 60 09	31.670 175	100.149 888	1103	1 21 66 09	33.211 444	105.023 807
804	64 64 16	28.354 8938	89.666 047	904	81 72 16	30.066 5928	95.078 915	1004	1 00 80 16	31.685 959	100.199 800	1104	1 21 88 16	33.226 495	105.071 404
805	64 80 25	28.372 5219	89.721 792	905	81 90 25	30.083 2179	95.131 488	1005	1 01 00 25	31.701 735	100.249 688	1105	1 22 10 25	33.241 540	105.118 980
806	64 96 36	28.390 1391	89.777 503	906	82 08 36	30.099 8339	95.184 032	1006	1 01 20 36	31.717 503	100.299 551	1106	1 22 32 36	33.256 578	105.166 535
807	65 12 49	28.407 7454	89.833 179	907	82 26 49	30.116 4407	95.236 548	1007	1 01 40 49	31.733 263	100.349 390	1107	1 22 54 49	33.271 610	105.214 068
808	65 28 64	28.425 3408	89.888 820	908	82 44 64	30.133 0383	95.289 034	1008	1 01 60 64	31.749 016	100.399 203	1108	1 22 76 64	33.286 634	105.261 579
809	65 44 81	28.442 9253	89.944 427	909	82 62 81	30.149 6269	95.341 491	1009	1 01 80 81	31.764 760	100.448 992	1109	1 22 98 81	33.301 652	105.309 069
810	65 61 00	28.460 4989	90.000 000	910	82 81 00	30.166 2063	95.393 920	1010	1 02 01 00	31.780 497	100.498 756	1110	1 23 21 00	33.316 662	105.356 538
811	65 77 21	28.478 0617	90.055 538	911	82 99 21	30.182 7765	95.446 320	1011	1 02 21 21	31.796 226	100.548 496	1111	1 23 43 21	33.331 667	105.403 985
812	65 93 44	28.495 6137	90.111 043	912	83 17 44	30.199 3377	95.498 691	1012	1 02 41 44	31.811 947	100.598 211	1112	1 23 65 44	33.346 664	105.451 411
813	66 09 69	28.513 1549	90.166 513	913	83 35 69	30.215 8899	95.551 033	1013	1 02 61 69	31.827 661	100.647 901	1113	1 23 87 69	33.361 655	105.498 815
814	66 25 96	28.530 6852	90.221 949	914	83 53 96	30.232 4329	95.603 347	1014	1 02 81 96	31.843 367	100.697 567	1114	1 24 09 96	33.376 639	105.546 198
815	66 42 25	28.548 2048	90.277 350	915	83 72 25	30.248 9669	95.655 632	1015	1 03 02 25	31.859 065	100.747 208	1115	1 24 32 25	33.391 616	105.593 560
816	66 58 56	28.565 7137	90.332 718	916	83 90 56	30.265 4919	95.707 889	1016	1 03 22 56	31.874 755	100.796 825	1116	1 24 54 56	33.406 586	105.640 901
817	66 74 89	28.583 2119	90.388 052	917	84 08 89	30.282 0079	95.760 117	1017	1 03 42 89	31.890 437	100.846 418	1117	1 24 76 89	33.421 550	105.688 221
818	66 91 24	28.600 6993	90.443 352	918	84 27 24	30.298 5148	95.812 317	1018	1 03 63 24	31.906 112	100.895 986	1118	1 24 99 24	33.436 507	105.735 519
819	67 07 61	28.618 1760	90.498 619	919	84 45 61	30.315 0128	95.864 488	1019	1 03 83 61	31.921 779	100.945 530	1119	1 25 21 61	33.451 457	105.782 796
820	67 24 00	28.635 6421	90.553 851	920	84 64 00	30.331 5018	95.916 630	1020	1 04 04 00	31.937 439	100.995 049	1120	1 25 44 00	33.466 401	105.830 052
821	67 40 41	28.653 0976	90.609 050	921	84 82 41	30.347 9818	95.968 745	1021	1 04 24 41	31.953 091	101.044 545	1121	1 25 66 41	33.481 338	105.877 287
822	67 56 84	28.670 5424	90.664 216	922	85 00 84	30.364 4529	96.020 831	1022	1 04 44 84	31.968 735	101.094 016	1122	1 25 88 84	33.496 268	105.924 501
823	67 73 29	28.687 9765	90.719 347	923	85 19 29	30.380 9151	96.072 889	1023	1 04 65 29	31.984 371	101.143 462	1123	1 26 11 29	33.511 192	105.971 694
824	67 89 76	28.705 4002	90.774 446	924	85 37 76	30.397 3683	96.124 919	1024	1 04 85 76	32.000 000	101.192 885	1124	1 26 33 76	33.526 109	106.018 866
825	68 06 25	28.722 8132	90.829 511	925	85 56 25	30.413 8127	96.176 920	1025	1 05 06 25	32.015 621	101.242 284	1125	1 26 56 25	33.541 020	106.066 017
826	68 22 76	28.740 2157	90.884 542	926	85 74 76	30.430 2481	96.228 894	1026	1 05 26 76	32.031 235	101.291 658	1126	1 26 78 76	33.555 923	106.113 147
827	68 39 29	28.757 6077	90.939 540	927	85 93 29	30.446 6747	96.280 839	1027	1 05 47 29	32.046 841	101.341 008	1127	1 27 01 29	33.570 821	106.160 256
828	68 55 84	28.774 9891	90.994 505	928	86 11 84	30.463 0924	96.332 757	1028	1 05 67 84	32.062 439	101.390 335	1128	1 27 23 84	33.585 711	106.207 344
829	68 72 41	28.792 3601	91.049 437	929	86 30 41	30.479 5013	96.384 646	1029	1 05 88 41	32.078 030	101.439 637	1129	1 27 46 41	33.600 595	106.254 412
830	68 89 00	28.809 7206	91.104 336	930	86 49 00	30.495 9014	96.436 508	1030	1 06 09 00	32.093 613	101.488 916	1130	1 27 69 00	33.615 473	106.301 458
831	69 05 61	28.827 0706	91.159 201	931	86 67 61	30.512 2926	96.488 341	1031	1 06 29 61	32.109 189	101.538 170	1131	1 27 91 61	33.630 343	106.348 484
832	69 22 24	28.844 4102	91.214 034	932	86 86 24	30.528 6750	96.540 147	1032	1 06 50 24	32.124 757	101.587 401	1132	1 28 14 24	33.645 208	106.395 489
833	69 38 89	28.861 7394	91.268 834	933	87 04 89	30.545 0487	96.591 925	1033	1 06 70 89	32.140 317	101.636 608	1133	1 28 36 89	33.660 065	106.442 473
834	69 55 56	28.879 0582	91.323 600	934	87 23 56	30.561 4136	96.643 675	1034	1 06 91 56	32.155 870	101.685 791	1134	1 28 59 56	33.674 916	106.489 436
835	69 72 25	28.896 3666	91.378 334	935	87 42 25	30.577 7697	96.695 398	1035	1 07 12 25	32.171 416	101.734 950	1135	1 28 82 25	33.689 761	106.536 379
836	69 88 96	28.913 6646	91.433 036	936	87 60 96	30.594 1171	96.747 093	1036	1 07 32 96	32.186 954	101.784 085	1136	1 29 04 96	33.704 599	106.583 301
837	70 05 69	28.930 9523	91.487 704	937	87 79 69	30.610 4557	96.798 760	1037	1 07 53 69	32.202 484	101.833 197	1137	1 29 27 69	33.719 431	106.630 202
838	70 22 44	28.948 2297	91.542 340	938	87 98 44	30.626 7857	96.850 400	1038	1 07 74 44	32.218 007	101.882 285	1138	1 29 50 44	33.734 256	106.677 083
839	70 39 21	28.965 4967	91.596 943	939	88 17 21	30.643 1069	96.902 012	1039	1 07 95 21	32.233 523	101.931 349	1139	1 29 73 21	33.749 074	106.723 943
840	70 56 00	28.982 7535	91.651 514	940	88 36 00	30.659 4194	96.953 597	1040	1 08 16 00	32.249 031	101.980 390	1140	1 29 96 00	33.763 886	106.770 783
841	70 72 81	29.000 0000	91.706 052	941	88 54 81	30.675 7233	97.005 155	1041	1 08 36 81	32.264 532	102.029 408	1141	1 30 18 81	33.778 692	106.817 602
842	70 89 64	29.017 2363	91.760 558	942	88 73 64	30.692 0185	97.056 684	1042	1 08 57 64	32.280 025	102.078 401	1142	1 30 41 64	33.793 490	106.864 400
843	71 06 49	29.034 4623	91.815 031	943	88 92 49	30.708 3051	97.108 187	1043	1 08 78 49	32.295 511	102.127 371	1143	1 30 64 49	33.808 283	106.911 178
844	71 23 36	29.051 6781	91.869 473	944	89 11 36	30.724 5830	97.159 662	1044	1 08 99 36	32.310 989	102.176 318	1144	1 30 87 36	33.823 069	106.957 936
845	71 40 25	29.068 8837	91.923 882	945	89 30 25	30.740 8523	97.211 110	1045	1 09 20 25	32.326 460	102.225 242	1145	1 31 10 25	33.837 849	107.004 673
846	71 57 16	29.086 0791	91.978 258	946	89 49 16	30.757 1130	97.262 531	1046	1 09 41 16	32.341 923	102.274 141	1146	1 31 33 16	33.852 622	107.051 390
847	71 74 09	29.103 2644	92.032 603	947	89 68 09	30.773 3651	97.313 925	1047	1 09 62 09	32.357 379	102.323 018	1147	1 31 56 09	33.867 388	107.098 086
848	71 91 04	29.120 4396	92.086 915	948	89 87 04	30.789 6086	97.365 292	1048	1 09 83 04	32.372 828	102.371 871	1148	1 31 79 04	33.882 149	107.144 762
849	72 08 01	29.137 6046	92.141 196	949	90 06 01	30.805 8436	97.416 631	1049	1 10 04 01	32.388 269	102.420 701	1149	1 32 02 01	33.896 903	107.191 418
850	72 25 00	29.154 7595	92.195 445	950	90 25 00	30.822 0700	97.467 943	1050	1 10 25 00	32.403 703	102.469 508	1150	1 32 25 00	33.911 650	107.238 053
851	72 42 01	29.171 9043	92.249 661	951	90 44 01	30.838 2879	97.519 229	1051	1 10 46 01	32.419 130	102.518 291	1151	1 32 48 01	33.926 391	107.284 668
852	72 59 04	29.189 0390	92.303 846	952	90 63 04	30.854 4972	97.570 487	1052	1 10 67 04	32.434 549	102.567 051	1152	1 32 71 04	33.941 125	107.331 263
853	72 76 09	29.206 1637	92.357 999	953	90 82 09	30.870 6981	97.621 719	1053	1 10 88 09	32.449 961	102.615 788	1153	1 32 94 09	33.955 854	107.377 838
854	72 93 16	29.223 2784	92.412 120	954	91 01 16	30.886 8904	97.672 924	1054	1 11 09 16	32.465 366	102.664 502	1154	1 33 17 16	33.970 576	107.424 392
855	73 10 25	29.240 3830	92.466 210	955	91 20 25	30.903 0743	97.724 101	1055	1 11 30 25	32.480 764	102.713 193	1155	1 33 40 25	33.985 291	107.470 926
856	73 27 36	29.257 4777	92.520 268	956	91 39 36	30.919 2497	97.775 252	1056	1 11 51 36	32.496 154	102.761 861	1156	1 33 63 36	34.000 000	107.517 440
857	73 44 49	29.274 5623	92.574 294	957	91 58 49	30.935 4166	97.826 377	1057	1 11 72 49	32.511 536	102.810 505	1157	1 33 86 49	34.014 703	107.563 934
858	73 61 64	29.291 6370	92.628 289	958	91 77 64	30.951 5751	97.877 474	1058	1 11 93 64	32.526 912	102.859 127	1158	1 34 09 64	34.029 399	107.610 408
859	73 78 81	29.308 7018	92.682 253	959	91 96 81	30.967 7251	97.928 545	1059	1 12 14 81	32.542 280	102.907 726	1159	1 34 32 81	34.044 089	107.656 862
860	73 96 00	29.325 7566	92.736 185	960	92 16 00	30.983 8668	97.979 590	1060	1 12 36 00	32.557 641	102.956 301	1160	1 34 56 00	34.058 773	107.703 296
861	74 13 21	29.342 8015	92.790 086	961	92 35 21	31.000 0000	98.030 607	1061	1 12 57 21	32.572 995	103.004 854	1161	1 34 79 21	34.073 450	107.749 710
862	74 30 44	29.359 8365	92.843 955	962	92 54 44	31.016 1248	98.081 599	1062	1 12 78 44	32.588 341	103.053 384	1162	1 35 02 44	34.088 121	107.796 104
863	74 47 69	29.376 8616	92.897 793	963	92 73 69	31.032 2413	98.132 563	1063	1 12 99 69	32.603 681	103.101 891	1163	1 35 25 69	34.102 786	107.842 478
864	74 64 96	29.393 8769	92.951 600	964	92 92 96	31.048 3494	98.183 502	1064	1 13 20 96	32.619 013	103.150 376	1164	1 35 48 96	34.117 444	107.888 832
865	74 82 25	29.410 8823	93.005 376	965	93 12 25	31.064 4491	98.234 414	1065	1 13 42 25	32.634 338	103.198 837	1165	1 35 72 25	34.132 096	107.935 166
866	74 99 56	29.427 8779	93.059 121	966	93 31 56	31.080 5405	98.285 299	1066	1 13 63 56	32.649 655	103.247 276	1166	1 35 95 56	34.146 742	107.981 480
867	75 16 89	29.444 8637	93.112 835	967	93 50 89	31.096 6236	98.336 158	1067	1 13 84 89	32.664 966	103.295 692	1167	1 36 18 89	34.161 382	108.027 774
868	75 34 24	29.461 8397	93.166 518	968	93 70 24	31.112 6984	98.386 991	1068	1 14 06 24	32.680 269	103.344 085	1168	1 36 42 24	34.176 015	108.074 049
869	75 51 61	29.478 8059	93.220 169	969	93 89 61	31.128 7648	98.437 798	1069	1 14 27 61	32.695 565	103.392 456	1169	1 36 65 61	34.190 642	108.120 303
870	75 69 00	29.495 7624	93.273 791	970	94 09 00	31.144 8230	98.488 578	1070	1 14 49 00	32.710 854	103.440 804	1170	1 36 89 00	34.205 263	108.166 538
871	75 86 41	29.512 7091	93.327 381	971	94 28 41	31.160 8729	98.539 332	1071	1 14 70 41	32.726 136	103.489 130	1171	1 37 12 41	34.219 877	108.212 753
872	76 03 84	29.529 6461	93.380 940	972	94 47 84	31.176 9145	98.590 060	1072	1 14 91 84	32.741 411	103.537 433	1172	1 37 35 84	34.234 486	108.258 949
873	76 21 29	29.546 5734	93.434 469	973	94 67 29	31.192 9479	98.640 762	1073	1 15 13 29	32.756 679	103.585 713	1173	1 37 59 29	34.249 088	108.305 125
874	76 38 76	29.563 4910	93.487 967	974	94 86 76	31.208 9731	98.691 438	1074	1 15 34 76	32.771 939	103.633 971	1174	1 37 82 76	34.263 683	108.351 281
875	76 56 25	29.580 3989	93.541 435	975	95 06 25	31.224 9900	98.742 088	1075	1 15 56 25	32.787 193	103.682 207	1175	1 38 06 25	34.278 273	108.397 417
876	76 73 76	29.597 2972	93.594 872	976	95 25 76	31.240 9987	98.792 712	1076	1 15 77 76	32.802 439	103.730 420	1176	1 38 29 76	34.292 856	108.443 534
877	76 91 29	29.614 1858	93.648 278	977	95 45 29	31.256 9992	98.843 310	1077	1 15 99 29	32.817 678	103.778 611	1177	1 38 53 29	34.307 434	108.489 631
878	77 08 84	29.631 0648	93.701 654	978	95 64 84	31.272 9915	98.893 883	1078	1 16 20 84	32.832 910	103.826 779	1178	1 38 76 84	34.322 005	108.535 708
879	77 26 41	29.647 9342	93.755 000	979	95 84 41	31.288 9757	98.944 429	1079	1 16 42 41	32.848 135	103.874 925	1179	1 39 00 41	34.336 569	108.581 766
880	77 44 00	29.664 7939	93.808 315	980	96 04 00	31.304 9517	98.994 949	1080	1 16 64 00	32.863 353	103.923 048	1180	1 39 24 00	34.351 128	108.627 805
881	77 61 61	29.681 6442	93.861 600	981	96 23 61	31.320 9195	99.045 444	1081	1 16 85 61	32.878 564	103.971 150	1181	1 39 47 61	34.365 681	108.673 824
882	77 79 24	29.698 4848	93.914 855	982	96 43 24	31.336 8792	99.095 913	1082	1 17 07 24	32.893 768	104.019 229	1182	1 39 71 24	34.380 227	108.719 823
883	77 96 89	29.715 3159	93.968 080	983	96 62 89	31.352 8308	99.146 356	1083	1 17 28 89	32.908 965	104.067 286	1183	1 39 94 89	34.394 767	108.765 803
884	78 14 56	29.732 1375	94.021 274	984	96 82 56	31.368 7743	99.196 774	1084	1 17 50 56	32.924 155	104.115 321	1184	1 40 18 56	34.409 301	108.811 764
885	78 32 25	29.748 9496	94.074 439	985	97 02 25	31.384 7097	99.247 166	1085	1 17 72 25	32.939 338	104.163 333	1185	1 40 42 25	34.423 829	108.857 705
886	78 49 96	29.765 7521	94.127 573	986	97 21 96	31.400 6369	99.297 533	1086	1 17 93 96	32.954 514	104.211 324	1186	1 40 65 96	34.438 351	108.903 627
887	78 67 69	29.782 5452	94.180 677	987	97 41 69	31.416 5561	99.347 874	1087	1 18 15 69	32.969 683	104.259 292	1187	1 40 89 69	34.452 866	108.949 530
888	78 85 44	29.799 3289	94.233 752	988	97 61 44	31.432 4673	99.398 189	1088	1 18 37 44	32.984 845	104.307 238	1188	1 41 13 44	34.467 376	108.995 413
889	79 03 21	29.816 1030	94.286 797	989	97 81 21	31.448 3704	99.448 479	1089	1 18 59 21	33.000 000	104.355 163	1189	1 41 37 21	34.481 879	109.041 277
890	79 21 00	29.832 8678	94.339 811	990	98 01 00	31.464 2654	99.498 744	1090	1 18 81 00	33.015 148	104.403 065	1190	1 41 61 00	34.496 377	109.087 121
891	79 38 81	29.849 6231	94.392 796	991	98 20 81	31.480 1525	99.548 983	1091	1 19 02 81	33.030 289	104.450 945	1191	1 41 84 81	34.510 868	109.132 946
892	79 56 64	29.866 3690	94.445 752	992	98 40 64	31.496 0315	99.599 197	1092	1 19 24 64	33.045 423	104.498 804	1192	1 42 08 64	34.525 353	109.178 753
893	79 74 49	29.883 1056	94.498 677	993	98 60 49	31.511 9025	99.649 385	1093	1 19 46 49	33.060 551	104.546 640	1193	1 42 32 49	34.539 832	109.224 539
894	79 92 36	29.899 8328	94.551 573	994	98 80 36	31.527 7655	99.699 549	1094	1 19 68 36	33.075 671	104.594 455	1194	1 42 56 36	34.554 305	109.270 307
895	80 10 25	29.916 5506	94.604 440	995	99 00 25	31.543 6206	99.749 687	1095	1 19 90 25	33.090 784	104.642 248	1195	1 42 80 25	34.568 772	109.316 056
896	80 28 16	29.933 2591	94.657 277	996	99 20 16	31.559 4677	99.799 800	1096	1 20 12 16	33.105 891	104.690 019	1196	1 43 04 16	34.583 233	109.361 785
897	80 46 09	29.949 9583	94.710 084	997	99 40 09	31.575 3068	99.849 887	1097	1 20 34 09	33.120 990	104.737 768	1197	1 43 28 09	34.597 688	109.407 495
898	80 64 04	29.966 6481	94.762 862	998	99 60 04	31.591 1380	99.899 950	1098	1 20 56 04	33.136 083	104.785 495	1198	1 43 52 04	34.612 137	109.453 186
899	80 82 01	29.983 3287	94.815 611	999	99 80 01	31.606 9613	99.949 987	1099	1 20 78 01	33.151 169	104.833 201	1199	1 43 76 01	34.626 579	109.498 858

Reciprocals of Square Roots of the Integers 1—999[1]

Reciprocal of $\sqrt{n} = 1/\sqrt{n}$

n	0	1	2	3	4	5	6	7	8	9
0	0.0000000	0.0000000	0.7071068	0.5773503	0.5000000	0.4472136	0.4082483	0.3779645	0.3535534	0.3333333
10	3162278	3015113	2886751	2773501	2672612	2581989	2500000	2425356	2357023	2294157
20	2236068	2182179	2132007	2085144	2041241	2000000	1961161	1924501	1889822	1856953
30	1825742	1796053	1767767	1740777	1714986	1690309	1666667	1643990	1622214	1601282
40	1581139	1561738	1543034	1524986	1507557	1490712	1474420	1458650	1443376	1428571
50	0.1414214	0.1400280	0.1386750	0.1373606	0.1360828	0.1348400	0.1336306	0.1324532	0.1313064	0.1301889
60	1290994	1280369	1270001	1259882	1250000	1240347	1230915	1221694	1212678	1203859
70	1195229	1186782	1178511	1170411	1162476	1154701	1147079	1139606	1132277	1125088
80	1118034	1111111	1104315	1097643	1091089	1084652	1078328	1072113	1066004	1059998
90	1054093	1048285	1042572	1036952	1031421	1025978	1020621	1015346	1010153	1005038
100	0.1000000	0.0995037	0.0990148	0.0985329	0.0980581	0.0975900	0.0971286	0.0966736	0.0962250	0.0957826
110	0953463	0949158	0944911	0940721	0936586	0932505	0928477	0924500	0920575	0916698
120	0912871	0909091	0905357	0901670	0898027	0894427	0890871	0887357	0883883	0880451
130	0877058	0873704	0870388	0867110	0863868	0860663	0857493	0854358	0851257	0848189
140	0845154	0842152	0839181	0836242	0833333	0830455	0827606	0824786	0821995	0819232
150	0.0816497	0.0813788	0.0811107	0.0808452	0.0805823	0.0803219	0.0800641	0.0798087	0.0795557	0.0793052
160	0790569	0788110	0785674	0783260	0780869	0778499	0776151	0773823	0771517	0769231
170	0766965	0764719	0762493	0760286	0758098	0755929	0753778	0751646	0749532	0747435
180	0745356	0743294	0741249	0739221	0737210	0735215	0733236	0731272	0729325	0727393
190	0725476	0723575	0721688	0719816	0717958	0716115	0714286	0712470	0710669	0708881
200	0.0707107	0.0705346	0.0703598	0.0701862	0.0700140	0.0698430	0.0696733	0.0695048	0.0693375	0.0691714
210	0690066	0688428	0686803	0685189	0683586	0681994	0680414	0678844	0677285	0675737
220	0674200	0672673	0671156	0669650	0668153	0666667	0665190	0663723	0662266	0660819
230	0659380	0657952	0656532	0655122	0653720	0652328	0650945	0649570	0648204	0646846
240	0645497	0644157	0642824	0641500	0640184	0638877	0637577	0636285	0635001	0633724
250	0.0632456	0.0631194	0.0629941	0.0628695	0.0627456	0.0626224	0.0625000	0.0623783	0.0622573	0.0621370
260	0620174	0618984	0617802	0616626	0615457	0614295	0613139	0611990	0610847	0609711
270	0608581	0607457	0606339	0605228	0604122	0603023	0601929	0600842	0599760	0598684
280	0597614	0596550	0595491	0594438	0593391	0592349	0591312	0590281	0589256	0588235
290	0587220	0586210	0585206	0584206	0583212	0582223	0581238	0580259	0579284	0578315
300	0.0577350	0.0576390	0.0575435	0.0574485	0.0573539	0.0572598	0.0571662	0.0570730	0.0569803	0.0568880
310	0567962	0567048	0566139	0565233	0564333	0563436	0562544	0561656	0560772	0559893
320	0559017	0558146	0557278	0556415	0555556	0554700	0553849	0553001	0552158	0551318
330	0550482	0549650	0548821	0547997	0547176	0546358	0545545	0544735	0543928	0543125
340	0542326	0541530	0540738	0539949	0539164	0538382	0537603	0536828	0536056	0535288
350	0.0534522	0.0533761	0.0533002	0.0532246	0.0531494	0.0530745	0.0529999	0.0529256	0.0528516	0.0527780
360	0527046	0526316	0525588	0524864	0524142	0523424	0522708	0521996	0521286	0520579
370	0519875	0519174	0518476	0517780	0517088	0516398	0515711	0515026	0514345	0513665
380	0512989	0512316	0511645	0510976	0510310	0509647	0508987	0508329	0507673	0507020
390	0506370	0505722	0505076	0504433	0503793	0503155	0502519	0501886	0501255	0500626
400	0.0500000	0.0499376	0.0498755	0.0498135	0.0497519	0.0496904	0.0496292	0.0495682	0.0495074	0.0494468
410	0493865	0493264	0492665	0492068	0491473	0490881	0490290	0489702	0489116	0488532
420	0487950	0487370	0486792	0486217	0485643	0485071	0484502	0483934	0483368	0482805
430	0482243	0481683	0481125	0480569	0480015	0479463	0478913	0478365	0477818	0477274
440	0476731	0476190	0475651	0475114	0474579	0474045	0473514	0472984	0472456	0471929
450	0.0471405	0.0470882	0.0470360	0.0469841	0.0469323	0.0468807	0.0468293	0.0467780	0.0467269	0.0466760
460	0466252	0465746	0465242	0464739	0464238	0463739	0463241	0462745	0462250	0461757
470	0461266	0460776	0460287	0459800	0459315	0458831	0458349	0457869	0457389	0456912
480	0456435	0455961	0455488	0455016	0454545	0454077	0453609	0453143	0452679	0452216
490	0451754	0451294	0450835	0450377	0449921	0449467	0449013	0448561	0448111	0447661
500	0.0447214	0.0446767	0.0446322	0.0445878	0.0445435	0.0444994	0.0444554	0.0444116	0.0443678	0.0443242
510	0442807	0442374	0441942	0441511	0441081	0440653	0440225	0439799	0439375	0438951
520	0438529	0438108	0437688	0437269	0436852	0436436	0436021	0435607	0435194	0434783
530	0434372	0433963	0433555	0433148	0432742	0432338	0431934	0431532	0431131	0430730
540	0430331	0429934	0429537	0429141	0428746	0428353	0427960	0427569	0427179	0426790
550	0.0426401	0.0426014	0.0425628	0.0425243	0.0424859	0.0424476	0.0424094	0.0423714	0.0423334	0.0422955
560	0422577	0422200	0421825	0421450	0421076	0420703	0420331	0419961	0419591	0419222
570	0418854	0418487	0418121	0417756	0417392	0417029	0416667	0416305	0415945	0415586
580	0415227	0414870	0414513	0414158	0413803	0413449	0413096	0412744	0412393	0412043
590	0411693	0411345	0410997	0410651	0410305	0409960	0409616	0409273	0408930	0408589
600	0.0408248	0.0407909	0.0407570	0.0407231	0.0406894	0.0406558	0.0406222	0.0405887	0.0405554	0.0405220
610	0404888	0404557	0404226	0403896	0403567	0403239	0402911	0402585	0402259	0401934
620	0401610	0401286	0400963	0400642	0400320	0400000	0399680	0399362	0399043	0398726
630	0398410	0398094	0397779	0397464	0397151	0396838	0396526	0396214	0395904	0395594
640	0395285	0394976	0394669	0394362	0394055	0393750	0393445	0393141	0392837	0392534
650	0.0392232	0.0391931	0.0391630	0.0391330	0.0391031	0.0390732	0.0390434	0.0390137	0.0389841	0.0389545
660	0389249	0388955	0388661	0388368	0388075	0387783	0387492	0387202	0386912	0386622
670	0386334	0386046	0385758	0385472	0385186	0384900	0384615	0384331	0384048	0383765
680	0383482	0383201	0382920	0382639	0382360	0382080	0381802	0381524	0381246	0380970
690	0380693	0380418	0380143	0379869	0379595	0379322	0379049	0378777	0378506	0378235
700	0.0377964	0.0377695	0.0377426	0.0377157	0.0376889	0.0376622	0.0376355	0.0376089	0.0375823	0.0375558
710	0375293	0375029	0374766	0374503	0374241	0373979	0373718	0373457	0373197	0372937
720	0372678	0372419	0372161	0371904	0371647	0371391	0371135	0370879	0370625	0370370
730	0370117	0369863	0369611	0369358	0369107	0368856	0368605	0368355	0368105	0367856
740	0367607	0367359	0367112	0366864	0366618	0366372	0366126	0365881	0365636	0365392
750	0.0365148	0.0364905	0.0364662	0.0364420	0.0364179	0.0363937	0.0363696	0.0363456	0.0363216	0.0362977
760	0362738	0362500	0362262	0362024	0361787	0361551	0361315	0361079	0360844	0360609
770	0360375	0360141	0359908	0359675	0359443	0359211	0358979	0358748	0358517	0358287
780	0358057	0357828	0357599	0357371	0357143	0356915	0356688	0356462	0356235	0356009
790	0355784	0355559	0355335	0355110	0354887	0354663	0354441	0354218	0353996	0353775
800	0.0353553	0.0353333	0.0353112	0.0352892	0.0352673	0.0352454	0.0352235	0.0352017	0.0351799	0.0351581
810	0351364	0351147	0350931	0350715	0350500	0350285	0350070	0349856	0349642	0349428
820	0349215	0349002	0348790	0348578	0348367	0348155	0347945	0347734	0347524	0347314
830	0347105	0346896	0346688	0346479	0346272	0346064	0345857	0345651	0345444	0345238
840	0345033	0344828	0344623	0344418	0344214	0344010	0343807	0343604	0343401	0343199
850	0.0342997	0.0342796	0.0342594	0.0342393	0.0342193	0.0341993	0.0341793	0.0341593	0.0341394	0.0341196
860	0340997	0340799	0340601	0340404	0340207	0340010	0339814	0339618	0339422	0339227
870	0339032	0338837	0338643	0338449	0338255	0338062	0337869	0337676	0337484	0337292
880	0337100	0336909	0336718	0336527	0336336	0336146	0335957	0335767	0335578	0335389
890	0335201	0335013	0334825	0334637	0334450	0334263	0334077	0333890	0333704	0333519
900	0.0333333	0.0333148	0.0332964	0.0332779	0.0332595	0.0332411	0.0332228	0.0332045	0.0331862	0.0331679
910	0331497	0331315	0331133	0330952	0330771	0330590	0330409	0330229	0330049	0329870
920	0329690	0329511	0329332	0329154	0328976	0328798	0328620	0328443	0328266	0328089
930	0327913	0327737	0327561	0327385	0327210	0327035	0326860	0326686	0326512	0326338
940	0326164	0325991	0325818	0325645	0325472	0325300	0325128	0324956	0324785	0324614
950	0.0324443	0.0324272	0.0324102	0.0323932	0.0323762	0.0323592	0.0323423	0.0323254	0.0323085	0.0322917
960	0322749	0322581	0322413	0322245	0322078	0321911	0321745	0321578	0321412	0321246
970	0321081	0320915	0320750	0320585	0320421	0320256	0320092	0319928	0319765	0319601
980	0319438	0319275	0319113	0318950	0318788	0318626	0318465	0318304	0318142	0317982
990	0317821	0317660	0317500	0317340	0317181	0317021	0316862	0316703	0316544	0316386

1) Values from Comrie, L. J. (Ed.), *Barlow's Tables of Squares, Cubes, Square Roots, Cube Roots and Reciprocals of All Integers up to 12,500*, 4th ed., Spon, London, 1958. Reprinted by kind permission of the editor and publishers.

Extraction of Square Roots with Calculators[1]

This table is applicable to any calculating machine with which divisions can be made.

First adjust the number n of which the root is desired by moving its decimal point to the right or left two places at a time until it has a value between 1 and 100. Now look for the two numbers nearest to this in column A of the table and note the values in columns B and C lying between these numbers.

The square root of n is then equal to $\frac{n+B}{C}$

The result is correct to 6 significant places and deviates in the 7th decimal place only by 5 units from the correct value.

The decimal point of the root is located as follows:

(a) Values of n greater than 1:

Count the numbers of pairs of digits lying before the decimal point and add one to this number if an odd digit remains. The result gives the number of digits before the decimal point in the root.

Example: A number with 5 digits before the decimal point yields 2 groups of two plus 1 odd digit. In the root there are therefore 3 digits before the decimal point.

(b) Values of n less than 1:

Count the numbers of pairs of ciphers following the decimal point and ignore an odd cipher which may remain. This number is then the number of ciphers following the decimal point in the root.

Example: A number less than 1 with 5 ciphers following the decimal point yields 2 groups of two. In the root there are therefore 2 ciphers following the decimal point.

Examples:

$\sqrt{0.00\,67\,89\,34\,5}$
$= (67.89\,34\,5 + 68) : 164\,9243$
$= 823\,974\,6962$

Desired square root : 0.082 3974

$\sqrt{129.34\,56}$
$= (1.29\,34\,56 + 1.3) : 228\,036$
$= 113\,730\,1127$

Desired square root: 11.3730

A	B	C
1.00	1	200
1.005	1.01	200 998
1.015	1.02	201 99
1.025	1.03	202 978
1.035	1.04	203 961
1.045	1.05	204 939
1.055	1.06	205 913
1.065	1.07	206 882
1.075	1.08	207 846
1.085	1.09	208 806
1.095	1.1	209 762
1.105	1.11	210 713
1.115	1.12	211 66
1.125	1.13	212 603
1.135	1.14	213 542
1.145	1.15	214 476
1.155	1.16	215 407
1.165	1.17	216 333
1.175	1.18	217 256
1.185	1.19	218 174
1.195	1.2	219 089
1.205	1.21	220
1.215	1.22	220 907
1.225	1.23	221 811
1.235	1.24	222 711
1.245	1.25	223 607
1.255	1.26	224 500 2
1.27	1.28	226 275
1.29	1.3	228 036
1.31	1.32	229 783 3
1.33	1.34	231 517 5
1.35	1.36	233 239
1.37	1.38	234 947 6
1.39	1.4	236 644
1.41	1.42	238 328
1.43	1.44	240 001
1.45	1.46	241 661 6
1.47	1.48	243 311
1.49	1.5	244 949 7
1.51	1.52	246 577
1.53	1.54	248 194
1.55	1.56	249 800 6
1.57	1.58	251 397
1.59	1.6	252 983
1.61	1.62	254 559
1.63	1.64	256 125 6
1.65	1.66	257 682 6
1.67	1.68	259 23
1.69	1.7	260 769
1.71	1.72	262 298
1.73	1.74	263 819
1.75	1.76	265 330 5
1.77	1.78	266 834
1.79	1.8	268 329
1.81	1.82	269 815
1.83	1.84	271 294
1.85	1.86	272 764
1.87	1.88	274 227
1.89	1.9	275 681
1.91	1.92	277 129
1.93	1.94	278 568
1.95	1.96	280
1.97	1.98	281 425
1.99	2	282 843
2.01	2.02	284 254
2.03	2.04	285 658
2.05	2.06	287 054
2.07	2.08	288 445
2.09	2.1	289 828
2.11	2.12	291 205 3

A	B	C
2.135	2.15	293 258 5
2.165	2.18	295 297 4
2.195	2.21	297 322 3
2.225	2.24	299 333 5
2.255	2.27	301 331 2
2.285	2.3	303 316
2.315	2.33	305 287 7
2.345	2.36	307 246 6
2.375	2.39	309 193 3
2.405	2.42	311 127 7
2.435	2.45	313 05
2.465	2.48	314 961
2.495	2.51	316 860 4
2.525	2.54	318 748 4
2.555	2.57	320 625
2.585	2.6	322 491
2.615	2.63	324 346
2.645	2.66	326 191
2.675	2.69	328 025
2.705	2.72	329 849
2.735	2.75	331 663
2.765	2.78	333 467
2.795	2.81	335 262
2.825	2.84	337 046 6
2.855	2.87	338 822
2.885	2.9	340 588
2.915	2.93	342 345
2.945	2.96	344 093 7
2.975	2.99	345 833
3.005	3.02	347 563 6
3.035	3.05	349 285 6
3.065	3.08	350 999
3.095	3.11	352 704
3.125	3.14	354 401 6
3.155	3.17	356 09
3.185	3.2	357 771 7
3.22	3.24	360 001
3.26	3.28	362 216 2
3.30	3.32	364 418 2
3.34	3.36	366 607
3.38	3.4	368 782 6
3.42	3.44	370 945 6
3.46	3.48	373 096
3.50	3.52	375 234
3.54	3.56	377 36
3.58	3.6	379 474
3.62	3.64	381 576 3
3.66	3.68	383 667 3
3.70	3.72	385 747
3.74	3.76	387 815
3.78	3.8	389 872 5
3.82	3.84	391 919
3.86	3.88	393 955
3.90	3.92	395 980 5
3.94	3.96	397 995 6
3.98	4	400 001
4.02	4.04	401 996
4.06	4.08	403 981
4.10	4.12	405 956
4.14	4.16	407 922
4.18	4.2	409 879
4.225	4.25	412 311 5
4.275	4.3	414 729 7
4.325	4.35	417 134
4.375	4.4	419 524 4
4.425	4.45	421 901 3
4.475	4.5	424 265
4.525	4.55	426 615 4
4.575	4.6	428 953
4.625	4.65	431 278

A	B	C
4.675	4.7	433 590 4
4.725	4.75	435 890 6
4.775	4.8	438 179
4.825	4.85	440 455
4.875	4.9	442 719 5
4.925	4.95	444 972 7
4.975	5	447 214
5.025	5.05	449 445
5.075	5.1	451 664
5.125	5.15	453 873
5.175	5.2	456 071
5.225	5.25	458 258
5.275	5.3	460 435
5.325	5.35	462 602
5.375	5.4	464 759
5.425	5.45	466 905
5.475	5.5	469 042
5.525	5.55	471 169
5.575	5.6	473 287
5.625	5.65	475 395
5.675	5.7	477 494
5.725	5.75	479 584
5.775	5.8	481 664
5.825	5.85	483 736
5.875	5.9	485 799
5.925	5.95	487 853
5.975	6	489 898 5
6.025	6.05	491 935 5
6.075	6.1	493 964
6.125	6.15	495 984
6.175	6.2	497 996
6.225	6.25	500 001
6.275	6.3	501 996 5
6.325	6.35	503 985
6.375	6.4	505 965
6.425	6.45	507 937
6.475	6.5	509 902
6.525	6.55	511 86
6.575	6.6	513 81
6.625	6.65	515 752
6.675	6.7	517 688
6.725	6.75	519 616
6.775	6.8	521 537
6.825	6.85	523 45
6.875	6.9	525 357
6.925	6.95	527 257
6.975	7	529 151
7.025	7.05	531 037
7.075	7.1	532 917
7.125	7.15	534 79
7.175	7.2	536 657
7.225	7.25	538 517
7.275	7.3	540 371
7.325	7.35	542 218
7.375	7.4	544 059
7.425	7.45	545 894
7.475	7.5	547 723
7.525	7.55	549 546
7.575	7.6	551 362
7.625	7.65	553 173
7.675	7.7	554 978
7.725	7.75	556 777
7.775	7.8	558 57
7.825	7.85	560 357
7.875	7.9	562 139
7.925	7.95	563 915
7.975	8	565 686
8.025	8.05	567 451
8.075	8.1	569 21
8.125	8.15	570 964

A	B	C
8.175	8.2	572 713
8.225	8.25	574 457
8.275	8.3	576 195
8.325	8.35	577 928
8.375	8.4	579 655
8.425	8.45	581 378
8.475	8.5	583 096
8.525	8.55	584 808
8.575	8.6	586 516
8.625	8.65	588 218
8.675	8.7	589 916
8.725	8.75	591 608
8.775	8.8	593 296
8.825	8.85	594 979
8.875	8.9	596 658
8.925	8.95	598 331
8.975	9	600
9.025	9.05	601 665
9.075	9.1	603 324
9.125	9.15	604 98
9.175	9.2	606 63
9.225	9.25	608 276
9.275	9.3	609 918
9.325	9.35	611 556
9.375	9.4	613 189
9.425	9.45	614 817
9.475	9.5	616 442
9.525	9.55	618 062
9.575	9.6	619 678
9.625	9.65	621 289
9.675	9.7	622 897
9.725	9.75	624 5
9.775	9.8	626 099
9.825	9.85	627 694
9.875	9.9	629 286
9.925	9.95	630 873
9.975	9.99	632 139
10.00*	10	632 456
10.025	10.05	634 035
10.075	10.1	635 61
10.125	10.15	637 181
10.175	10.2	638 749
10.225	10.25	640 313
10.275	10.3	641 872
10.325	10.35	643 429
10.375	10.4	644 981
10.425	10.45	646 529
10.475	10.5	648 074
10.525	10.55	649 615
10.575	10.6	651 153 7
10.65	10.7	654 218
10.75	10.8	657 268
10.85	10.9	660 303 8
10.95	11	663 326
11.05	11.1	666 334
11.15	11.2	669 329
11.25	11.3	672 310 3
11.35	11.4	675 278 6
11.45	11.5	678 233 8
11.55	11.6	681 176 2
11.65	11.7	684 106
11.75	11.8	687 023 3
11.85	11.9	689 928 4
11.95	12	692 821
12.05	12.1	695 702
12.15	12.2	698 570 7
12.25	12.3	701 428
12.35	12.4	704 273 3
12.45	12.5	707 107 5
12.55	12.6	709 93

A	B	C
12.65	12.7	712 742
12.75	12.8	715 542 5
12.85	12.9	718 332
12.95	13	721 111
13.05	13.1	723 879
13.15	13.2	726 637
13.25	13.3	729 384
13.35	13.4	732 121
13.45	13.5	734 848
13.55	13.6	737 564
13.65	13.7	740 271
13.75	13.8	742 968
13.85	13.9	745 655
13.95	14	748 332
14.05	14.1	751
14.15	14.2	753 658
14.25	14.3	756 307
14.35	14.4	758 947
14.45	14.5	761 578
14.55	14.6	764 199 5
14.65	14.7	766 812
14.75	14.8	769 416
14.85	14.9	772 011
14.95	15	774 597
15.05	15.1	777 175
15.15	15.2	779 744
15.25	15.3	782 305
15.35	15.4	784 857
15.45	15.5	787 401
15.55	15.6	789 937
15.65	15.7	792 465
15.75	15.8	794 985
15.85	15.9	797 496 6
15.95	16	800
16.05	16.1	802 497
16.15	16.2	804 985
16.25	16.3	807 466
16.35	16.4	809 939
16.45	16.5	812 404
16.55	16.6	814 862
16.65	16.7	817 313
16.75	16.8	819 756
16.85	16.9	822 193
16.95	17	824 622
17.05	17.1	827 043
17.15	17.2	829 458
17.25	17.3	831 866
17.35	17.4	834 266
17.45	17.5	836 66
17.55	17.6	839 047
17.65	17.7	841 428
17.75	17.8	843 801
17.85	17.9	846 168
17.95	18	848 529
18.05	18.1	850 882
18.15	18.2	853 23
18.25	18.3	855 57
18.35	18.4	857 905
18.45	18.5	860 233
18.55	18.6	862 555
18.65	18.7	864 87
18.75	18.8	867 18
18.85	18.9	869 483
18.95	19	871 78
19.05	19.1	874 071
19.15	19.2	876 356
19.25	19.3	878 636
19.35	19.4	880 909
19.45	19.5	883 176
19.55	19.6	885 438

A	B	C
19.65	19.7	887 694
19.75	19.8	889 944
19.85	19.9	892 189
19.95	20	894 428
20.05	20.1	896 661
20.15	20.2	898 889
20.25	20.3	901 111
20.35	20.4	903 328
20.45	20.5	905 539
20.55	20.6	907 745
20.65	20.7	909 945
20.75	20.8	912 141
20.85	20.9	914 331
20.95	21	916 516
21.05	21.1	918 695
21.15	21.2	920 87
21.25	21.3	923 039
21.35	21.4	925 203
21.45	21.5	927 362
21.55	21.6	929 516
21.65	21.7	931 666
21.75	21.8	933 81
21.85	21.9	935 949
21.95	22	938 084
22.05	22.1	940 213
22.15	22.2	942 338
22.25	22.3	944 458
22.35	22.4	946 573
22.45	22.5	948 683
22.55	22.6	950 789
22.65	22.7	952 891
22.75	22.8	954 987
22.85	22.9	957 079
22.95	23	959 167
23.05	23.1	961 249
23.15	23.2	963 328
23.25	23.3	965 402
23.35	23.4	967 471
23.45	23.5	969 536
23.55	23.6	971 597
23.65	23.7	973 653
23.75	23.8	975 705
23.85	23.9	977 753
23.95	24	979 796
24.05	24.1	981 835
24.15	24.2	983 87
24.25	24.3	985 901
24.35	24.4	987 927
24.45	24.5	989 95
24.55	24.6	991 968
24.65	24.7	993 982
24.75	24.8	995 992
24.85	24.9	997 998
24.95	25	100
25.05	25.1	100 199 8
25.15	25.2	100 399 2
25.25	25.3	100 598 2
25.35	25.4	100 796 8
25.45	25.5	100 995 1
25.55	25.6	101 192 9
25.65	25.7	101 390 4
25.75	25.8	101 587 4
25.85	25.9	101 784 1
25.95	26	101 980 4
26.05	26.1	102 176 3
26.15	26.2	102 371 9
26.25	26.3	102 567 1
26.35	26.4	102 761 9
26.45	26.5	102 956 3
26.55	26.6	103 150 4

* For $\sqrt{10.00}$ use the values in the table between 10.00 and 10.025.

1) Reproduced from Marchant Table 81 by permission of copyright owner, Marchant Calculators Division of Smith-Corona Marchant, Inc., Oakland (Cal.), USA.

A	B	C
26.65	26.7	103 344 1
26.75	26.8	103 537 5
26.85	26.9	103 730 4
26.95	27	103 923 13
27.10	27.2	104 307 33
27.30	27.4	104 690 1
27.50	27.6	105 071 5
27.7	27.8	105 451 5
27.9	28	105 830 15
28.1	28.2	106 207 42
28.3	28.4	106 583 4
28.5	28.6	106 958 02
28.7	28.8	107 331 34
28.9	29	107 703 38
29.1	29.2	108 074 13
29.3	29.4	108 443 6
29.5	29.6	108 811 84
29.7	29.8	109 178 8
29.9	30	109 544 6
30.1	30.2	109 909 14
30.3	30.4	110 272 48
30.5	30.6	110 634 6
30.7	30.8	110 995 57
30.9	31	111 355 35
31.1	31.2	111 714
31.3	31.4	112 071 5
31.5	31.6	112 427 83
31.7	31.8	112 783 05
31.9	32	113 137 15
32.1	32.2	113 490 14
32.3	32.4	113 842 07
32.5	32.6	114 192 9
32.7	32.8	114 542 6
32.9	33	114 891 3
33.1	33.2	115 238 95
33.3	33.4	115 585 5
33.5	33.6	115 931 1
33.7	33.8	116 275 6
33.9	34	116 619 1
34.1	34.2	116 961 6
34.3	34.4	117 303 1
34.5	34.6	117 643 6
34.7		

A	B	C
34.7	34.8	117 983 1
34.9	35	118 321 66
35.1	35.2	118 659 24
35.3	35.4	118 995 86
35.5	35.6	119 331 5
35.7	35.8	119 666 3
35.9	36	120 000 1
36.1	36.2	120 332 9
36.3	36.4	120 664 9
36.5	36.6	120 995 9
36.7	36.8	121 326 1
36.9	37	121 655 3
37.1	37.2	121 983 7
37.3	37.4	122 311 1
37.5	37.6	122 637 7
37.7	37.8	122 963 5
37.9	38	123 288 3
38.1	38.2	123 612 4
38.3	38.4	123 935 5
38.5	38.6	124 257 9
38.7	38.8	124 579 4
38.9	39	124 9
39.1	39.2	125 219 9
39.3	39.4	125 538 9
39.5	39.6	125 857 1
39.7	39.8	126 174 5
39.9	40	126 491 1
40.1	40.2	126 807
40.3	40.4	127 122
40.5	40.6	127 436 3
40.7	40.8	127 749 8
40.9	41	128 062 5
41.1	41.2	128 374 5
41.3	41.4	128 685 7
41.5	41.6	128 996 2
41.7	41.8	129 305 9
41.9	42	129 614 9
42.1	42.2	129 923 1
42.3	42.4	130 230 6
42.5	42.6	130 537 4
42.7	42.8	130 843 5
42.9	43	131 148 8
43.1		

A	B	C
43.1	43.2	131 453 5
43.3	43.4	131 757 4
43.5	43.6	132 060 6
43.7	43.8	132 363 2
43.9	44	132 665 1
44.1	44.2	132 966 2
44.3	44.4	133 266 7
44.5	44.6	133 566 5
44.7	44.8	133 865 6
44.9	45	134 164 1
45.1	45.2	134 461 9
45.3	45.4	134 759 1
45.5	45.6	135 055 6
45.7	45.8	135 351 4
45.9	46	135 646 6
46.1	46.2	135 941 2
46.3	46.4	136 235 1
46.5	46.6	136 528 4
46.70	46.8	136 821 1
46.90	47	137 113 2
47.15	47.3	137 550 1
47.45	47.6	137 985 6
47.75	47.9	138 419 75
48.05	48.2	138 852 53
48.35	48.5	139 283 96
48.65	48.8	139 714 08
48.95	49.1	140 142 86
49.25	49.4	140 570 35
49.55	49.7	140 996 55
49.85	50	141 421 44
50.15	50.3	141 845 07
50.45	50.6	142 267 43
50.75	50.9	142 688 55
51.05	51.2	143 108 44
51.35	51.5	143 527 1
51.65	51.8	143 944 5
51.95	52.1	144 360 74
52.25	52.4	144 775 76
52.55	52.7	145 189 6
52.85	53	145 602 27
53.15	53.3	146 013 77
53.45	53.6	146 424 1
53.75		

A	B	C
53.75	53.9	146 833 3
54.05	54.2	147 241 37
54.35	54.5	147 648 3
54.65	54.8	148 054 1
54.95	55.1	148 458 8
55.25	55.4	148 862 4
55.55	55.7	149 264 9
55.85	56	149 666 4
56.15	56.3	150 066 73
56.45	56.6	150 466
56.75	56.9	150 864 25
57.05	57.2	151 261 4
57.35	57.5	151 657 6
57.65	57.8	152 052 7
57.95	58.1	152 446 8
58.25	58.4	152 839 85
58.55	58.7	153 231 9
58.85	59	153 623
59.15	59.3	154 013 05
59.45	59.6	154 402 14
59.75	59.9	154 790 24
60.05	60.2	155 177 4
60.35	60.5	155 563 6
60.65	60.8	155 948 8
60.95	61.1	156 333
61.25	61.4	156 716 4
61.55	61.7	157 098 8
61.85	62	157 480 2
62.15	62.3	157 860 8
62.45	62.6	158 240 4
62.75	62.9	158 619 1
63.05	63.2	158 996 9
63.35	63.5	159 373 8
63.65	63.8	159 749 9
63.95	64.1	160 125
64.25	64.4	160 499 3
64.55	64.7	160 872 7
64.85	65	161 245 2
65.15	65.3	161 616 9
65.45	65.6	161 987 7
65.75	65.9	162 357 7
66.05	66.2	162 726 8
66.35		

A	B	C
66.35	66.5	163 095 1
66.65	66.8	163 462 6
66.95	67.1	163 829 2
67.25	67.4	164 195 1
67.55	67.7	164 560 1
67.85	68	164 924 3
68.2	68.4	165 408 67
68.6	68.8	165 891 62
69.0	69.2	166 373 17
69.4	69.6	166 853 3
69.8	70	167 332 1
70.2	70.4	167 809 5
70.6	70.8	168 285 56
71.0	71.2	168 760 27
71.4	71.6	169 233 65
71.8	72	169 705 7
72.2	72.4	170 176 46
72.6	72.8	170 645 92
73.0	73.2	171 114 08
73.4	73.6	171 580 96
73.8	74	172 046 6
74.2	74.4	172 510 95
74.6	74.8	172 974 06
75.0	75.2	173 435 95
75.4	75.6	173 896 6
75.8	76	174 356 04
76.2	76.4	174 814 26
76.6	76.8	175 271 3
77.0	77.2	175 727 14
77.4	77.6	176 181 8
77.8	78	176 635 3
78.2	78.4	177 087 6
78.6	78.8	177 538 8
79.0	79.2	177 988 84
79.4	79.6	178 437 74
79.8	80	178 885 5
80.2	80.4	179 332 16
80.6	80.8	179 777 7
81.0	81.2	180 222 15
81.4	81.6	180 665 5
81.8	82	181 107 8
82.2	82.4	181 548 96
82.6		

A	B	C
82.6	82.8	181 989 1
83.0	83.2	182 428 1
83.4	83.6	182 866 14
83.8	84	183 303 1
84.2	84.4	183 739
84.6	84.8	184 173 9
85.0	85.2	184 607 76
85.4	85.6	185 040 6
85.8	86	185 472 4
86.2	86.4	185 903 3
86.6	86.8	186 333 1
87.0	87.2	186 761 94
87.4	87.6	187 189 8
87.8	88	187 616 7
88.2	88.4	188 042 6
88.6	88.8	188 467 6
89.0	89.2	188 891 6
89.4	89.6	189 314 6
89.8	90	189 736 7
90.2	90.4	190 157 9
90.60	90.8	190 578 1
91.00	91.2	190 997 4
91.40	91.6	191 415 8
91.80	92	191 833 35
92.25	92.5	192 353 93
92.75	93	192 873 1
93.25	93.5	193 390 88
93.75	94	193 907 29
94.25	94.5	194 422 3
94.75	95	194 935 96
95.25	95.5	195 448 3
95.75	96.	195 959 26
96.25	96.5	196 468 9
96.75	97	196 977 24
97.25	97.5	197 484 26
97.75	98	197 989 98
98.25	98.5	198 494 4
98.75	99	198 997 57
99.20	99.4	199 399 1
99.60	99.8	199 799 9
100.0		

Binomial Coefficients*

$$\binom{n}{x} = \frac{n!}{x!\,(n-x)!}$$

n	$\binom{n}{0}$	$\binom{n}{1}$	$\binom{n}{2}$	$\binom{n}{3}$	$\binom{n}{4}$	$\binom{n}{5}$	$\binom{n}{6}$	$\binom{n}{7}$	$\binom{n}{8}$	$\binom{n}{9}$	$\binom{n}{10}$	$\binom{n}{11}$	$\binom{n}{12}$	$\binom{n}{13}$	$\binom{n}{14}$	$\binom{n}{15}$
0	1															
1	1	1														
2	1	2	1													
3	1	3	3	1												
4	1	4	6	4	1											
5	1	5	10	10	5	1										
6	1	6	15	20	15	6	1									
7	1	7	21	35	35	21	7	1								
8	1	8	28	56	70	56	28	8	1							
9	1	9	36	84	126	126	84	36	9	1						
10	1	10	45	120	210	252	210	120	45	10	1					
11	1	11	55	165	330	462	462	330	165	55	11	1				
12	1	12	66	220	495	792	924	792	495	220	66	12	1			
13	1	13	78	286	715	1287	1716	1716	1287	715	286	78	13	1		
14	1	14	91	364	1001	2002	3003	3432	3003	2002	1001	364	91	14	1	
15	1	15	105	455	1365	3003	5005	6435	6435	5005	3003	1365	455	105	15	1
16	1	16	120	560	1820	4368	8008	11440	12870	11440	8008	4368	1820	560	120	16
17	1	17	136	680	2380	6188	12376	19448	24310	24310	19448	12376	6188	2380	680	136
18	1	18	153	816	3060	8568	18564	31824	43758	48620	43758	31824	18564	8568	3060	816
19	1	19	171	969	3876	11628	27132	50388	75582	92378	92378	75582	50388	27132	11628	3876
20	1	20	190	1140	4845	15504	38760	77520	125970	167960	184756	167960	125970	77520	38760	15504
21	1	21	210	1330	5985	20349	54264	116280	203490	293930	352716	352716	293930	203490	116280	54264
22	1	22	231	1540	7315	26334	74613	170544	319770	497420	646646	705432	646646	497420	319770	170544
23	1	23	253	1771	8855	33649	100947	245157	490314	817190	1144066	1352078	1352078	1144066	817190	490314
24	1	24	276	2024	10626	42504	134596	346104	735471	1307504	1961256	2496144	2704156	2496144	1961256	1307504
25	1	25	300	2300	12650	53130	177100	480700	1081575	2042975	3268760	4457400	5200300	5200300	4457400	3268760
26	1	26	325	2600	14950	65780	230230	657800	1562275	3124550	5311735	7726160	9657700	10400600	9657700	7726160
27	1	27	351	2925	17550	80730	296010	888030	2220075	4686825	8436285	13037895	17383860	20058300	20058300	17383860
28	1	28	378	3276	20475	98280	376740	1184040	3108105	6906900	13123110	21474180	30421755	37442160	40116600	37442160
29	1	29	406	3654	23751	118755	475020	1560780	4292145	10015005	20030010	34597290	51895935	67863915	77558760	77558760
30	1	30	435	4060	27405	142506	593775	2035800	5852925	14307150	30045015	54627300	86493225	119759850	145422675	155117520
31	1	31	465	4495	31465	169911	736281	2629575	7888725	20160075	44352165	84672315	141120525	206253075	265182525	300540195
32	1	32	496	4960	35960	201376	906192	3365856	10518300	28048800	64512240	129024480	225792840	347373600	471435600	565722720
33	1	33	528	5456	40920	237336	1107568	4272048	13884156	38567100	92561040	193536720	354817320	573166440	818809200	1037158320
34	1	34	561	5984	46376	278256	1344904	5379616	18156204	52451256	131128140	286097760	548354040	927983760	1391975640	1855967520
35	1	35	595	6545	52360	324632	1623160	6724520	23535820	70607460	183579396	417225900	834451800	1476337800	2319959400	3247943160
36	1	36	630	7140	58905	376992	1947792	8347680	30260340	94143280	254186856	600805296	1251677700	2310789600	3796297200	5567902560
37	1	37	666	7770	66045	435897	2324784	10295472	38608020	124403620	348330136	854992152	1852482996	3562467300	6107086800	9364199760
38	1	38	703	8436	73815	501942	2760681	12620256	48903492	163011640	472733756	1203322288	2707475148	5414950296	9669554100	15471286560
39	1	39	741	9139	82251	575757	3262623	15380937	61523748	211915132	635745396	1676056044	3910797436	8122425444	15084504396	25140840660

* For logarithms of binomial coefficients up to $\binom{n}{100}$ see pages 70–77. Reproduction of values from this table only by permission of the publishers of these *Scientific Tables*.

Common Logarithms of Factorials of the Integers 1—999*

Factorial of $n = n! = n \times (n-1) \times \cdots \times 3 \times 2 \times 1$; factorial of $0 = 1$

n → ↓	0	1	2	3	4	5	6	7	8	9
0	0.00000	0.00000	0.30103	0.77815	1.38021	2.07918	2.85733	3.70243	4.60552	5.55976
10	6.55976	7.60116	8.68034	9.79428	10.94041	12.11650	13.32062	14.55107	15.80634	17.08509
20	18.38612	19.70834	21.05077	22.41249	23.79271	25.19065	26.60562	28.03698	29.48414	30.94654
30	32.42366	33.91502	35.42017	36.93869	38.47016	40.01423	41.57054	43.13874	44.71852	46.30959
40	47.91165	49.52443	51.14768	52.78115	54.42460	56.07781	57.74057	59.41267	61.09391	62.78410
50	64.48307	66.19064	67.90665	69.63092	71.36332	73.10368	74.85187	76.60774	78.37117	80.14202
60	81.92017	83.70550	85.49790	87.29724	89.10342	90.91633	92.73587	94.56195	96.39446	98.23331
70	100.07841	101.92966	103.78700	105.65032	107.51955	109.39461	111.27543	113.16192	115.05401	116.95164
80	118.85473	120.76321	122.67703	124.59610	126.52038	128.44980	130.38430	132.32382	134.26830	136.21769
90	138.17194	140.13098	142.09476	144.06325	146.03638	148.01410	149.99637	151.98314	153.97437	155.97000
100	157.97000	159.97433	161.98293	163.99576	166.01280	168.03398	170.05929	172.08867	174.12210	176.15952
110	178.20092	180.24624	182.29546	184.34854	186.40544	188.46614	190.53060	192.59878	194.67067	196.74621
120	198.82539	200.90818	202.99454	205.08444	207.17787	209.27478	211.37515	213.47895	215.58616	217.69675
130	219.81069	221.92797	224.04854	226.17239	228.29950	230.42983	232.56337	234.70009	236.83997	238.98298
140	241.12911	243.27833	245.43062	247.58595	249.74432	251.90568	254.07004	256.23735	258.40762	260.58080
150	262.75689	264.93587	267.11771	269.30240	271.48993	273.68026	275.87338	278.06928	280.26794	282.46933
160	284.67345	286.88028	289.08980	291.30198	293.51683	295.73431	297.95442	300.17713	302.40244	304.63033
170	306.86078	309.09378	311.32930	313.56735	315.80790	318.05094	320.29645	322.54442	324.79484	327.04770
180	329.30297	331.56065	333.82072	336.08317	338.34799	340.61516	342.88467	345.15651	347.43067	349.70713
190	351.98589	354.26692	356.55022	358.83578	361.12358	363.41362	365.70587	368.00034	370.29700	372.59586
200	374.89689	377.20008	379.50544	381.81293	384.12256	386.43432	388.74818	391.06415	393.38222	395.70236
210	398.02458	400.34887	402.67520	405.00358	407.33400	409.66643	412.00089	414.33735	416.67580	419.01625
220	421.35867	423.70306	426.04942	428.39772	430.74797	433.10015	435.45426	437.81029	440.16822	442.52806
230	444.88978	447.25340	449.61888	451.98624	454.35546	456.72652	459.09944	461.47418	463.85076	466.22916
240	468.60937	470.99139	473.37520	475.76081	478.14820	480.53737	482.92830	485.32100	487.71545	490.11165
250	492.50959	494.90926	497.31066	499.71378	502.11862	504.52516	506.93340	509.34333	511.75495	514.16825
260	516.58322	518.99986	521.41816	523.83812	526.25972	528.68297	531.10785	533.53436	535.96250	538.39225
270	540.82361	543.25658	545.69115	548.12731	550.56506	553.00439	555.44530	557.88778	560.33183	562.77743
280	565.22459	567.67330	570.12354	572.57533	575.02865	577.48349	579.93986	582.39774	584.85713	587.31803
290	589.78043	592.24432	594.70971	597.17657	599.64492	602.11474	604.58603	607.05879	609.53301	612.00868
300	614.48580	616.96436	619.44437	621.92581	624.40869	626.89299	629.37871	631.86585	634.35440	636.84436
310	639.33572	641.82848	644.32263	646.81818	649.31511	651.81342	654.31310	656.81416	659.31659	661.82038
320	664.32553	666.83204	669.33989	671.84910	674.35964	676.87152	679.38474	681.89929	684.41516	686.93236
330	689.45087	691.97070	694.49184	697.01428	699.53803	702.06307	704.58941	707.11704	709.64596	712.17616
340	714.70764	717.24039	719.77442	722.30971	724.84627	727.38409	729.92317	732.46350	735.00508	737.54790
350	740.09197	742.63728	745.18382	747.73160	750.28060	752.83083	755.38228	757.93495	760.48883	763.04392
360	765.60023	768.15773	770.71644	773.27635	775.83745	778.39974	780.96323	783.52789	786.09374	788.66077
370	791.22897	793.79834	796.36888	798.94059	801.51347	804.08750	806.66268	809.23903	811.81652	814.39516
380	816.97494	819.55587	822.13793	824.72113	827.30546	829.89092	832.47751	835.06522	837.65405	840.24400
390	842.83507	845.42724	848.02053	850.61492	853.21042	855.80701	858.40471	861.00350	863.60338	866.20436
400	868.80642	871.40956	874.01379	876.61909	879.22547	881.83293	884.44146	887.05105	889.66171	892.27343
410	894.88622	897.50006	900.11496	902.73091	905.34791	907.96595	910.58505	913.20518	915.82636	918.44857
420	921.07182	923.69611	926.32142	928.94776	931.57512	934.20351	936.83292	939.46335	942.09480	944.72725
430	947.36072	949.99520	952.63068	955.26717	957.90466	960.54315	963.18263	965.82312	968.46459	971.10705
440	973.75051	976.39495	979.04037	981.68677	984.33415	986.98251	989.63185	992.28216	994.93344	997.58568
450	1000.23889	1002.89307	1005.54821	1008.20431	1010.86136	1013.51937	1016.17834	1018.83825	1021.49912	1024.16093
460	1026.82369	1029.48739	1032.15203	1034.81761	1037.48413	1040.15158	1042.81997	1045.48929	1048.15953	1050.83071
470	1053.50280	1056.17582	1058.84977	1061.52463	1064.20041	1066.87710	1069.55471	1072.23322	1074.91265	1077.59299
480	1080.27423	1082.95637	1085.63942	1088.32337	1091.00821	1093.69395	1096.38059	1099.06812	1101.75654	1104.44585
490	1107.13604	1109.82712	1112.51909	1115.21194	1117.90566	1120.60027	1123.29575	1125.99211	1128.68934	1131.38744
500	1134.08641	1136.78624	1139.48695	1142.18851	1144.89094	1147.59424	1150.29839	1153.00339	1155.70926	1158.41598
510	1161.12355	1163.83197	1166.54124	1169.25135	1171.96232	1174.67412	1177.38677	1180.10026	1182.81459	1185.52976
520	1188.24576	1190.96260	1193.68027	1196.39877	1199.11810	1201.83826	1204.55925	1207.28106	1210.00369	1212.72715
530	1215.45142	1218.17652	1220.90243	1223.62916	1226.35670	1229.08505	1231.81422	1234.54419	1237.27497	1240.00656
540	1242.73896	1245.47215	1248.20615	1250.94095	1253.67655	1256.41295	1259.15014	1261.88813	1264.62691	1267.36648
550	1270.10684	1272.84799	1275.58993	1278.33266	1281.07617	1283.82046	1286.56554	1289.31139	1292.05803	1294.80544
560	1297.55363	1300.30259	1303.05232	1305.80283	1308.55411	1311.30616	1314.05898	1316.81256	1319.56691	1322.32202
570	1325.07790	1327.83453	1330.59193	1333.35008	1336.10899	1338.86866	1341.62908	1344.39026	1347.15219	1349.91487
580	1352.67829	1355.44247	1358.20739	1360.97306	1363.73948	1366.50663	1369.27453	1372.04317	1374.81254	1377.58266
590	1380.35351	1383.12510	1385.89742	1388.67048	1391.44426	1394.21878	1396.99403	1399.77000	1402.54670	1405.32413
600	1408.10228	1410.88115	1413.66075	1416.44107	1419.22210	1422.00386	1424.78633	1427.56952	1430.35343	1433.13804
610	1435.92337	1438.70941	1441.49617	1444.28363	1447.07179	1449.86067	1452.65025	1455.44054	1458.23152	1461.02322
620	1463.81561	1466.60870	1469.40249	1472.19698	1474.99216	1477.78804	1480.58462	1483.38188	1486.17984	1488.97849
630	1491.77784	1494.57787	1497.37858	1500.17999	1502.98208	1505.78485	1508.58831	1511.39245	1514.19727	1517.00277
640	1519.80895	1522.61581	1525.42334	1528.23155	1531.04044	1533.85000	1536.66023	1539.47114	1542.28271	1545.09496
650	1547.90787	1550.72145	1553.53570	1556.35061	1559.16619	1561.98243	1564.79933	1567.61690	1570.43513	1573.25401
660	1576.07356	1578.89376	1581.71461	1584.53613	1587.35830	1590.18112	1593.00459	1595.82872	1598.65350	1601.47892
670	1604.30500	1607.13172	1609.95909	1612.78710	1615.61576	1618.44507	1621.27501	1624.10560	1626.93683	1629.76870
680	1632.60121	1635.43436	1638.26814	1641.10256	1643.93762	1646.77331	1649.60964	1652.44659	1655.28418	1658.12240
690	1660.96125	1663.80073	1666.64083	1669.48157	1672.32293	1675.16491	1678.00752	1680.85075	1683.69461	1686.53909
700	1689.38418	1692.22990	1695.07624	1697.92320	1700.77077	1703.61896	1706.46776	1709.31718	1712.16721	1715.01786
710	1717.86912	1720.72099	1723.57347	1726.42656	1729.28026	1732.13456	1734.98948	1737.84500	1740.70112	1743.55785
720	1746.41518	1749.27312	1752.13165	1754.99079	1757.85053	1760.71087	1763.57181	1766.43334	1769.29547	1772.15820
730	1775.02152	1777.88544	1780.74995	1783.61505	1786.48075	1789.34704	1792.21391	1795.08138	1797.94944	1800.81808
740	1803.68731	1806.55713	1809.42754	1812.29853	1815.17010	1818.04225	1820.91499	1823.78831	1826.66222	1829.53670
750	1832.41176	1835.28740	1838.16362	1841.04041	1843.91778	1846.79573	1849.67425	1852.55335	1855.43302	1858.31326
760	1861.19407	1864.07546	1866.95741	1869.83994	1872.72303	1875.60669	1878.49092	1881.37571	1884.26108	1887.14700
770	1890.03349	1892.92055	1895.80816	1898.69634	1901.58508	1904.47439	1907.36425	1910.25467	1913.14565	1916.03718
780	1918.92928	1921.82193	1924.71514	1927.60890	1930.50321	1933.39808	1936.29351	1939.18948	1942.08601	1944.98308
790	1947.88071	1950.77889	1953.67761	1956.57689	1959.47671	1962.37707	1965.27799	1968.17944	1971.08145	1973.98399
800	1976.88708	1979.79072	1982.69489	1985.59961	1988.50486	1991.41066	1994.31699	1997.22387	2000.13128	2003.03922
810	2005.94771	2008.85673	2011.76629	2014.67638	2017.58700	2020.49816	2023.40985	2026.32207	2029.23482	2032.14811
820	2035.06192	2037.97626	2040.89114	2043.80654	2046.72246	2049.63892	2052.55590	2055.47340	2058.39143	2061.30999
830	2064.22906	2067.14867	2070.06879	2072.98943	2075.91060	2078.83229	2081.75449	2084.67722	2087.60046	2090.52422
840	2093.44850	2096.37330	2099.29861	2102.22444	2105.15078	2108.07764	2111.00501	2113.93289	2116.86129	2119.79019
850	2122.71961	2125.64954	2128.57998	2131.51093	2134.44239	2137.37435	2140.30683	2143.23981	2146.17330	2149.10729
860	2152.04179	2154.97679	2157.91230	2160.84831	2163.78482	2166.72184	2169.65936	2172.59737	2175.53589	2178.47491
870	2181.41443	2184.35445	2187.29497	2190.23598	2193.17749	2196.11950	2199.06200	2202.00500	2204.94850	2207.89249
880	2210.83697	2213.78195	2216.72741	2219.67338	2222.61983	2225.56677	2228.51420	2231.46213	2234.41054	2237.35944
890	2240.30883	2243.25871	2246.20908	2249.15993	2252.11126	2255.06309	2258.01540	2260.96819	2263.92146	2266.87522
900	2269.82947	2272.78419	2275.73940	2278.69509	2281.65125	2284.60790	2287.56503	2290.52264	2293.48072	2296.43929
910	2299.39833	2302.35785	2305.31784	2308.27831	2311.23926	2314.20068	2317.16258	2320.12495	2323.08779	2326.05111
920	2329.01489	2331.97915	2334.94388	2337.90909	2340.87476	2343.84090	2346.80751	2349.77459	2352.74214	2355.71015
930	2358.67864	2361.64759	2364.61700	2367.58688	2370.55723	2373.52804	2376.49932	2379.47106	2382.44326	2385.41593
940	2388.38906	2391.36265	2394.33670	2397.31121	2400.28618	2403.26161	2406.23750	2409.21385	2412.19066	2415.16793
950	2418.14565	2421.12383	2424.10247	2427.08156	2430.06111	2433.04112	2436.02157	2439.00249	2441.98385	2444.96567
960	2447.94794	2450.93066	2453.91384	2456.89747	2459.88154	2462.86607	2465.85105	2468.83647	2471.82235	2474.80867
970	2477.79545	2480.78266	2483.77033	2486.75844	2489.74700	2492.73601	2495.72546	2498.71535	2501.70569	2504.69647
980	2507.68770	2510.67937	2513.67148	2516.66403	2519.65703	2522.65047	2525.64434	2528.63866	2531.63342	2534.62861
990	2537.62425	2540.62032	2543.61683	2546.61378	2549.61117	2552.60899	2555.60725	2558.60595	2561.60508	2564.60464

Common Logarithms of Reciprocal Factorials of the Integers 1—999*

Reciprocal factorial of $n = 1/n!$. The bold figures are negative characteristics; the mantissas are positive

n	0	1	2	3	4	5	6	7	8	9
0	00000	00000	**1** 69897	**1** 22185	**2** 61979	**3** 92082	**3** 14267	**4** 29757	**5** 39448	**6** 44024
10	**7** 44024	**8** 39884	**9** 31966	**10** 20572	**11** 05959	**13** 88350	**14** 67938	**15** 44893	**16** 19366	**18** 91491
20	**19** 61388	**20** 29166	**22** 94923	**23** 58751	**24** 20729	**26** 80935	**27** 39438	**29** 96302	**30** 51586	**31** 05346
30	**33** 57634	**34** 08498	**36** 57983	**37** 06131	**39** 52984	**41** 98577	**42** 42946	**44** 86126	**45** 28148	**47** 69041
40	**48** 08835	**50** 47557	**52** 85232	**53** 21885	**55** 57540	**57** 92219	**58** 25943	**60** 58733	**62** 90609	**63** 21590
50	**65** 51693	**67** 80936	**68** 09335	**70** 36908	**72** 63668	**74** 89632	**75** 14813	**77** 39226	**79** 62883	**81** 85798
60	**82** 07983	**84** 29450	**86** 50210	**88** 70276	**90** 89658	**91** 08367	**93** 26413	**95** 43805	**97** 60554	**99** 76669
70	**101** 92159	**102** 07034	**104** 21300	**106** 34968	**108** 48045	**110** 60539	**112** 72457	**114** 83808	**116** 94599	**117** 04836
80	**119** 14527	**121** 23679	**123** 32297	**125** 40390	**127** 47962	**129** 55020	**131** 61570	**133** 67618	**135** 73170	**137** 78231
90	**139** 82806	**141** 86902	**143** 90524	**145** 93675	**147** 96362	**149** 98590	**150** 00363	**152** 01686	**154** 02563	**156** 03000
100	**158** 03000	**160** 02567	**162** 01707	**164** 00424	**167** 98720	**169** 96602	**171** 94071	**173** 91133	**175** 87790	**177** 84048
110	**179** 79908	**181** 75376	**183** 70454	**185** 65146	**187** 59456	**189** 53386	**191** 46940	**193** 40122	**195** 32933	**197** 25379
120	**199** 17461	**201** 09182	**203** 00546	**206** 91556	**208** 82213	**210** 72522	**212** 62485	**214** 52105	**216** 41384	**218** 30325
130	**220** 18931	**222** 07203	**225** 95146	**227** 82761	**229** 70050	**231** 57017	**233** 43663	**235** 29991	**237** 16003	**239** 01702
140	**242** 87089	**244** 72167	**246** 56938	**248** 41405	**250** 25568	**252** 09432	**255** 92996	**257** 76265	**259** 59238	**261** 41920
150	**263** 24311	**265** 06413	**268** 88229	**270** 69760	**272** 51007	**274** 31974	**276** 12662	**279** 93072	**281** 73206	**283** 53067
160	**285** 32655	**287** 11972	**290** 91020	**292** 69802	**294** 48317	**296** 26569	**298** 04558	**301** 82287	**303** 59756	**305** 36967
170	**307** 13922	**310** 90622	**312** 67070	**314** 43265	**316** 19210	**319** 94906	**321** 70355	**323** 45558	**325** 20516	**328** 95230
180	**330** 69703	**332** 43935	**334** 17928	**337** 91683	**339** 65201	**341** 38484	**343** 11533	**346** 84349	**348** 56933	**350** 29287
190	**352** 01411	**355** 73308	**357** 44978	**359** 16422	**362** 87642	**364** 58638	**366** 29413	**369** 99966	**371** 70300	**373** 40414
200	**375** 10311	**378** 79992	**380** 49456	**382** 18707	**385** 87744	**387** 56568	**389** 25182	**392** 93585	**394** 61778	**396** 29764
210	**399** 97542	**401** 65113	**403** 32480	**406** 99642	**408** 66600	**410** 33357	**413** 99911	**415** 66265	**417** 32420	**420** 98375
220	**422** 64133	**424** 29694	**427** 95058	**429** 60228	**431** 25203	**434** 89985	**436** 54574	**438** 18971	**441** 83178	**443** 47194
230	**445** 11022	**448** 74660	**450** 38112	**452** 01376	**455** 64454	**457** 27348	**460** 90056	**462** 52582	**464** 14924	**467** 77084
240	**469** 39063	**471** 00861	**474** 62480	**476** 23919	**479** 85180	**481** 46263	**483** 07170	**486** 67900	**488** 28455	**491** 88835
250	**493** 49041	**495** 09074	**498** 68934	**500** 28622	**503** 88138	**505** 47484	**507** 06660	**510** 65667	**512** 24505	**515** 83175
260	**517** 41678	**519** 00014	**522** 58184	**524** 16188	**527** 74028	**529** 31703	**532** 89215	**534** 46564	**536** 03750	**539** 60775
270	**541** 17639	**544** 74342	**546** 30885	**549** 87269	**551** 43494	**554** 99561	**556** 55470	**558** 11222	**561** 66817	**563** 22257
280	**566** 77541	**568** 32670	**571** 87646	**573** 42467	**576** 97135	**578** 51651	**580** 06014	**583** 60226	**585** 14287	**588** 68197
290	**590** 21957	**593** 75568	**595** 29029	**598** 82343	**600** 35508	**603** 88526	**605** 41397	**608** 94121	**610** 46699	**613** 99132
300	**615** 51420	**617** 03564	**620** 55563	**622** 07419	**625** 59131	**627** 10701	**630** 62129	**632** 13415	**635** 64560	**637** 15564
310	**640** 66428	**642** 17152	**645** 67737	**647** 18182	**650** 68489	**652** 18658	**655** 68690	**657** 18584	**660** 68341	**662** 17962
320	**665** 67447	**667** 16796	**670** 66011	**672** 15090	**675** 64036	**677** 12848	**680** 61526	**682** 10071	**685** 58484	**687** 06764
330	**690** 54913	**692** 02930	**695** 50816	**698** 98572	**700** 46197	**703** 93693	**705** 41059	**708** 88296	**710** 35404	**713** 82384
340	**715** 29236	**718** 75961	**720** 22558	**723** 69029	**725** 15373	**728** 61591	**730** 07683	**733** 53650	**736** 99492	**738** 45210
350	**741** 90803	**743** 36272	**746** 81618	**748** 26840	**751** 71940	**753** 16917	**756** 61772	**758** 06505	**761** 51117	**764** 95608
360	**766** 39977	**769** 84227	**771** 28356	**774** 72365	**776** 16255	**779** 60026	**781** 03677	**784** 47211	**787** 90626	**789** 33923
370	**792** 77103	**794** 20166	**797** 63112	**799** 05941	**802** 48653	**805** 91250	**807** 33732	**810** 76097	**812** 18348	**815** 60484
380	**817** 02506	**820** 44413	**823** 86207	**825** 27887	**828** 69454	**830** 10908	**833** 52249	**836** 93478	**838** 34595	**841** 75600
390	**843** 16493	**846** 57276	**849** 97947	**851** 38508	**854** 78958	**856** 19299	**859** 59529	**862** 99650	**864** 39662	**867** 79564
400	**869** 19358	**872** 59044	**875** 98621	**877** 38091	**880** 77453	**882** 16707	**885** 55854	**888** 94895	**890** 33829	**893** 72657
410	**895** 11378	**898** 49994	**901** 88504	**903** 26909	**906** 65209	**908** 03405	**911** 41495	**914** 79482	**916** 17364	**919** 55143
420	**922** 92818	**924** 30389	**927** 67858	**929** 05224	**932** 42488	**935** 79649	**937** 16708	**940** 53665	**943** 90520	**945** 27275
430	**948** 63928	**950** 00480	**953** 36932	**956** 73283	**958** 09534	**961** 45685	**964** 81737	**966** 17688	**969** 53541	**972** 89295
440	**974** 24949	**977** 60505	**980** 95963	**982** 31323	**985** 66585	**987** 01749	**990** 36815	**993** 71784	**995** 06656	**998** 41432
450	**1001** 76111	**1003** 10693	**1006** 45179	**1009** 79569	**1011** 13864	**1014** 48063	**1017** 82166	**1019** 16175	**1022** 50088	**1025** 83907
460	**1027** 17631	**1030** 51261	**1033** 84797	**1035** 18239	**1038** 51587	**1041** 84842	**1043** 18003	**1046** 51071	**1049** 84047	**1051** 16929
470	**1054** 49720	**1057** 82418	**1059** 15023	**1062** 47537	**1065** 79959	**1067** 12290	**1070** 44529	**1073** 76678	**1075** 08735	**1078** 40701
480	**1081** 72577	**1083** 04363	**1086** 36058	**1089** 67663	**1092** 99179	**1094** 30605	**1097** 61941	**1100** 93188	**1102** 24346	**1105** 55415
490	**1108** 86396	**1110** 17288	**1113** 48091	**1116** 78806	**1118** 09434	**1121** 39973	**1124** 70425	**1126** 00789	**1129** 31066	**1132** 61256
500	**1135** 91359	**1137** 21376	**1140** 51305	**1143** 81149	**1145** 10906	**1148** 40576	**1151** 70161	**1154** 99661	**1156** 29074	**1159** 58402
510	**1162** 87645	**1164** 16803	**1167** 45876	**1170** 74865	**1172** 03768	**1175** 32588	**1178** 61323	**1181** 89974	**1183** 18541	**1186** 47024
520	**1189** 75424	**1191** 03740	**1194** 31973	**1197** 60123	**1200** 88190	**1202** 16174	**1205** 44075	**1208** 71894	**1211** 99631	**1213** 27285
530	**1216** 54858	**1219** 82348	**1221** 09757	**1224** 37084	**1227** 64330	**1230** 91495	**1232** 18578	**1235** 45581	**1238** 72503	**1241** 99344
540	**1243** 26104	**1246** 52785	**1249** 79385	**1251** 05905	**1254** 32345	**1257** 58705	**1260** 84986	**1262** 11187	**1265** 37309	**1268** 63352
550	**1271** 89316	**1273** 15201	**1276** 41007	**1279** 66734	**1282** 92383	**1284** 17954	**1287** 43446	**1290** 68861	**1293** 94197	**1295** 19456
560	**1298** 44637	**1301** 69741	**1304** 94768	**1306** 19717	**1309** 44589	**1312** 69384	**1315** 94102	**1317** 18744	**1320** 43309	**1323** 67798
570	**1326** 92210	**1328** 16547	**1331** 40807	**1334** 64992	**1337** 89101	**1339** 13134	**1342** 37092	**1345** 60974	**1348** 84781	**1350** 08513
580	**1353** 32171	**1356** 55753	**1359** 79261	**1361** 02694	**1364** 26052	**1367** 49337	**1370** 72547	**1373** 95683	**1375** 18746	**1378** 41734
590	**1381** 64649	**1384** 87490	**1386** 10258	**1389** 32952	**1392** 55574	**1395** 78122	**1397** 00597	**1400** 23000	**1403** 45330	**1406** 67587
600	**1409** 89772	**1411** 11885	**1414** 33925	**1417** 55893	**1420** 77790	**1423** 99614	**1425** 21367	**1428** 43048	**1431** 64657	**1434** 86196
610	**1436** 07663	**1439** 29059	**1442** 50383	**1445** 71637	**1448** 92821	**1450** 13933	**1453** 34975	**1456** 55946	**1459** 76848	**1462** 97678
620	**1464** 18439	**1467** 39130	**1470** 59751	**1473** 80302	**1475** 00784	**1478** 21196	**1481** 41538	**1484** 61812	**1487** 82016	**1489** 02151
630	**1492** 22216	**1495** 42213	**1498** 62142	**1501** 82001	**1503** 01792	**1506** 21515	**1509** 41169	**1512** 60755	**1515** 80273	**1518** 99723
640	**1520** 19105	**1523** 38419	**1526** 57666	**1529** 76845	**1532** 95956	**1534** 15000	**1537** 33977	**1540** 52886	**1543** 71729	**1546** 90504
650	**1548** 09213	**1551** 27855	**1554** 46430	**1557** 64939	**1560** 83381	**1562** 01757	**1565** 20067	**1568** 38310	**1571** 56487	**1574** 74599
660	**1577** 92644	**1579** 10624	**1582** 28539	**1585** 46387	**1588** 64170	**1591** 81888	**1594** 99541	**1596** 17128	**1599** 34650	**1602** 52108
670	**1605** 69500	**1608** 86828	**1610** 04091	**1613** 21290	**1616** 38424	**1619** 55493	**1622** 72499	**1625** 89440	**1627** 06317	**1630** 23130
680	**1633** 39879	**1636** 56564	**1639** 73186	**1642** 89744	**1644** 06238	**1647** 22669	**1650** 39036	**1653** 55341	**1656** 71582	**1659** 87760
690	**1661** 03875	**1664** 19927	**1667** 35917	**1670** 51843	**1673** 67707	**1676** 83509	**1679** 99248	**1681** 14925	**1684** 30539	**1687** 46091
700	**1690** 61582	**1693** 77010	**1696** 92376	**1698** 07680	**1701** 22923	**1704** 38104	**1707** 53224	**1710** 68282	**1713** 83279	**1716** 98214
710	**1718** 13088	**1721** 27901	**1724** 42653	**1727** 57344	**1730** 71974	**1733** 86544	**1735** 01052	**1738** 15500	**1741** 29888	**1744** 44215
720	**1747** 58482	**1750** 72688	**1753** 86835	**1755** 00921	**1758** 14947	**1761** 28913	**1764** 42819	**1767** 56666	**1770** 70453	**1773** 84180
730	**1776** 97848	**1778** 11456	**1781** 25005	**1784** 38495	**1787** 51925	**1790** 65296	**1793** 78609	**1796** 91862	**1798** 05056	**1801** 18192
740	**1804** 31269	**1807** 44287	**1810** 57246	**1813** 70147	**1816** 82990	**1819** 95775	**1821** 08501	**1824** 21169	**1827** 33778	**1830** 46330
750	**1833** 58824	**1836** 71260	**1839** 83638	**1842** 95959	**1844** 08222	**1847** 20427	**1850** 32575	**1853** 44665	**1856** 56698	**1859** 68674
760	**1862** 80593	**1865** 92454	**1867** 04259	**1870** 16006	**1873** 27697	**1876** 39331	**1879** 50908	**1882** 62429	**1885** 73892	**1888** 85300
770	**1891** 96651	**1893** 07945	**1896** 19184	**1899** 30366	**1902** 41492	**1905** 52561	**1908** 63575	**1911** 74533	**1914** 85435	**1917** 96282
780	**1919** 07072	**1922** 17807	**1925** 28486	**1928** 39110	**1931** 49679	**1934** 60192	**1937** 70649	**1940** 81052	**1943** 91399	**1945** 01692
790	**1948** 11929	**1951** 22111	**1954** 32239	**1957** 42311	**1960** 52329	**1963** 62293	**1966** 72201	**1969** 82056	**1972** 91855	**1974** 01601
800	**1977** 11292	**1980** 20928	**1983** 30511	**1986** 40039	**1989** 49514	**1992** 58934	**1995** 68301	**1998** 77613	**2001** 86872	**2004** 96078
810	**2006** 05229	**2009** 14327	**2012** 23371	**2015** 32362	**2018** 41300	**2021** 50184	**2024** 59015	**2027** 67793	**2030** 76518	**2033** 85189
820	**2036** 93808	**2038** 02374	**2041** 10886	**2044** 19346	**2047** 27754	**2050** 36108	**2053** 44410	**2056** 52660	**2059** 60857	**2062** 69001
830	**2065** 77094	**2068** 85133	**2071** 93121	**2073** 01057	**2076** 08940	**2079** 16771	**2082** 24551	**2085** 32278	**2088** 39954	**2091** 47578
840	**2094** 55150	**2097** 62670	**2100** 70139	**2103** 77556	**2106** 84922	**2109** 92236	**2112** 99499	**2114** 06711	**2117** 13871	**2120** 20981
850	**2123** 28039	**2126** 35046	**2129** 42002	**2132** 48907	**2135** 55761	**2138** 62565	**2141** 69317	**2144** 76019	**2147** 82670	**2150** 89271
860	**2153** 95821	**2155** 02321	**2158** 08770	**2161** 15169	**2164** 21518	**2167** 27816	**2170** 34064	**2173** 40263	**2176** 46411	**2179** 52509
870	**2182** 58557	**2185** 64555	**2188** 70503	**2191** 76402	**2194** 82251	**2197** 88050	**2200** 93800	**2203** 99500	**2205** 05150	**2208** 10751
880	**2211** 16303	**2214** 21805	**2217** 27259	**2220** 32662	**2223** 38017	**2226** 43323	**2229** 48580	**2232** 53787	**2235** 58946	**2238** 64056
890	**2241** 69117	**2244** 74129	**2247** 79092	**2250** 84007	**2253** 88874	**2256** 93691	**2259** 98460	**2261** 03181	**2264** 07854	**2267** 12478
900	**2270** 17053	**2273** 21581	**2276** 26060	**2279** 30491	**2282** 34875	**2285** 39210	**2288** 43497	**2291** 47736	**2294** 51928	**2297** 56071
910	**2300** 60167	**2303** 64215	**2306** 68216	**2309** 72169	**2312** 76074	**2315** 79932	**2318** 83742	**2321** 87505	**2324** 91221	**2327** 94889
920	**2330** 98511	**2332** 02085	**2335** 05612	**2338** 09091	**2341** 12524	**2344** 15910	**2347** 19249	**2350** 22541	**2353** 25786	**2356** 28985
930	**2359** 32136	**2362** 35241	**2365** 38300	**2368** 41312	**2371** 44277	**2374** 47196	**2377** 50068	**2380** 52894	**2383** 55674	**2386** 58407
940	**2389** 61094	**2392** 63735	**2395** 66330	**2398** 68879	**2401** 71382	**2404** 73839	**2407** 76250	**2410** 78615	**2413** 80934	**2416** 83207
950	**2419** 85435	**2422** 87617	**2425** 89753	**2428** 91844	**2431** 93889	**2434** 95888	**2437** 97843	**2440** 99751	**2442** 01615	**2445** 03433
960	**2448** 05206	**2451** 06934	**2454** 08616	**2457** 10253	**2460** 11846	**2463** 13393	**2466** 14895	**2469** 16353	**2472** 17765	**2475** 19133
970	**2478** 20455	**2481** 21734	**2484** 22967	**2487** 24156	**2490** 25300	**2493** 26399	**2496** 27454	**2499** 28465	**2502** 29431	**2505** 30353
980	**2508** 31230	**2511** 32063	**2514** 32852	**2517** 33597	**2520** 34297	**2523** 34953	**2526** 35566	**2529** 36134	**2532** 36658	**2535** 37139
990	**2538** 37575	**2541** 37968	**2544** 38317	**2547** 38622	**2550** 38883	**2553** 39101	**2556** 39275	**2559** 39405	**2562** 39492	**2565** 39536

Integral → Deviation c*

$\int_{-\infty}^{c}$ →	0.000	0.001	0.002	0.003	0.004	0.005	0.006	0.007	0.008	0.009
0.00	∞	*3.0902*	*2.8782*	*2.7478*	*2.6521*	*2.5758*	*2.5121*	*2.4573*	*2.4089*	*2.3656*
0.01	*2.3263*	*2.2904*	*2.2571*	*2.2262*	*2.1973*	*2.1701*	*2.1444*	*2.1201*	*2.0969*	*2.0749*
0.02	*2.0537*	*2.0335*	*2.0141*	*1.9954*	*1.9774*	*1.9600*	*1.9431*	*1.9268*	*1.9110*	*1.8957*
0.03	*1.8808*	*1.8663*	*1.8522*	*1.8384*	*1.8250*	*1.8119*	*1.7991*	*1.7866*	*1.7744*	*1.7624*
0.04	*1.7507*	*1.7392*	*1.7279*	*1.7169*	*1.7060*	*1.6954*	*1.6849*	*1.6747*	*1.6646*	*1.6546*
0.05	*1.6449*	*1.6352*	*1.6258*	*1.6164*	*1.6072*	*1.5982*	*1.5893*	*1.5805*	*1.5718*	*1.5632*
0.06	*1.5548*	*1.5464*	*1.5382*	*1.5301*	*1.5220*	*1.5141*	*1.5063*	*1.4985*	*1.4909*	*1.4833*
0.07	*1.4758*	*1.4684*	*1.4611*	*1.4538*	*1.4466*	*1.4395*	*1.4325*	*1.4255*	*1.4187*	*1.4118*
0.08	*1.4051*	*1.3984*	*1.3917*	*1.3852*	*1.3787*	*1.3722*	*1.3658*	*1.3595*	*1.3532*	*1.3469*
0.09	*1.3408*	*1.3346*	*1.3285*	*1.3225*	*1.3165*	*1.3106*	*1.3047*	*1.2988*	*1.2930*	*1.2873*
0.10	*1.2816*	*1.2759*	*1.2702*	*1.2646*	*1.2591*	*1.2536*	*1.2481*	*1.2426*	*1.2372*	*1.2319*
0.11	*1.2265*	*1.2212*	*1.2160*	*1.2107*	*1.2055*	*1.2004*	*1.1952*	*1.1901*	*1.1850*	*1.1800*
0.12	*1.1750*	*1.1700*	*1.1650*	*1.1601*	*1.1552*	*1.1503*	*1.1455*	*1.1407*	*1.1359*	*1.1311*
0.13	*1.1264*	*1.1217*	*1.1170*	*1.1123*	*1.1077*	*1.1031*	*1.0985*	*1.0939*	*1.0893*	*1.0848*
0.14	*1.0803*	*1.0758*	*1.0714*	*1.0669*	*1.0625*	*1.0581*	*1.0537*	*1.0494*	*1.0450*	*1.0407*
0.15	*1.0364*	*1.0322*	*1.0279*	*1.0237*	*1.0194*	*1.0152*	*1.0110*	*1.0069*	*1.0027*	*0.9986*
0.16	*0.9945*	*0.9904*	*0.9863*	*0.9822*	*0.9782*	*0.9741*	*0.9701*	*0.9661*	*0.9621*	*0.9581*
0.17	*0.9542*	*0.9502*	*0.9463*	*0.9424*	*0.9385*	*0.9346*	*0.9307*	*0.9269*	*0.9230*	*0.9192*
0.18	*0.9154*	*0.9116*	*0.9078*	*0.9040*	*0.9002*	*0.8965*	*0.8927*	*0.8890*	*0.8853*	*0.8816*
0.19	*0.8779*	*0.8742*	*0.8705*	*0.8669*	*0.8633*	*0.8596*	*0.8560*	*0.8524*	*0.8488*	*0.8452*
0.20	*0.8416*	*0.8381*	*0.8345*	*0.8310*	*0.8274*	*0.8239*	*0.8204*	*0.8169*	*0.8134*	*0.8099*
0.21	*0.8064*	*0.8030*	*0.7995*	*0.7961*	*0.7926*	*0.7892*	*0.7858*	*0.7824*	*0.7790*	*0.7756*
0.22	*0.7722*	*0.7688*	*0.7655*	*0.7621*	*0.7588*	*0.7554*	*0.7521*	*0.7488*	*0.7454*	*0.7421*
0.23	*0.7388*	*0.7356*	*0.7323*	*0.7290*	*0.7257*	*0.7225*	*0.7192*	*0.7160*	*0.7128*	*0.7095*
0.24	*0.7063*	*0.7031*	*0.6999*	*0.6967*	*0.6935*	*0.6903*	*0.6871*	*0.6840*	*0.6808*	*0.6776*
0.25	*0.6745*	*0.6713*	*0.6682*	*0.6651*	*0.6620*	*0.6588*	*0.6557*	*0.6526*	*0.6495*	*0.6464*
0.26	*0.6433*	*0.6403*	*0.6372*	*0.6341*	*0.6311*	*0.6280*	*0.6250*	*0.6219*	*0.6189*	*0.6158*
0.27	*0.6128*	*0.6098*	*0.6068*	*0.6038*	*0.6008*	*0.5978*	*0.5948*	*0.5918*	*0.5888*	*0.5858*
0.28	*0.5828*	*0.5799*	*0.5769*	*0.5740*	*0.5710*	*0.5681*	*0.5651*	*0.5622*	*0.5592*	*0.5563*
0.29	*0.5534*	*0.5505*	*0.5476*	*0.5446*	*0.5417*	*0.5388*	*0.5359*	*0.5330*	*0.5302*	*0.5273*
0.30	*0.5244*	*0.5215*	*0.5187*	*0.5158*	*0.5129*	*0.5101*	*0.5072*	*0.5044*	*0.5015*	*0.4987*
0.31	*0.4959*	*0.4930*	*0.4902*	*0.4874*	*0.4845*	*0.4817*	*0.4789*	*0.4761*	*0.4733*	*0.4705*
0.32	*0.4677*	*0.4649*	*0.4621*	*0.4593*	*0.4565*	*0.4538*	*0.4510*	*0.4482*	*0.4454*	*0.4427*
0.33	*0.4399*	*0.4372*	*0.4344*	*0.4316*	*0.4289*	*0.4261*	*0.4234*	*0.4207*	*0.4179*	*0.4152*
0.34	*0.4125*	*0.4097*	*0.4070*	*0.4043*	*0.4016*	*0.3989*	*0.3961*	*0.3934*	*0.3907*	*0.3880*
0.35	*0.3853*	*0.3826*	*0.3799*	*0.3772*	*0.3745*	*0.3719*	*0.3692*	*0.3665*	*0.3638*	*0.3611*
0.36	*0.3585*	*0.3558*	*0.3531*	*0.3505*	*0.3478*	*0.3451*	*0.3425*	*0.3398*	*0.3372*	*0.3345*
0.37	*0.3319*	*0.3292*	*0.3266*	*0.3239*	*0.3213*	*0.3186*	*0.3160*	*0.3134*	*0.3107*	*0.3081*
0.38	*0.3055*	*0.3029*	*0.3002*	*0.2976*	*0.2950*	*0.2924*	*0.2898*	*0.2871*	*0.2845*	*0.2819*
0.39	*0.2793*	*0.2767*	*0.2741*	*0.2715*	*0.2689*	*0.2663*	*0.2637*	*0.2611*	*0.2585*	*0.2559*
0.40	*0.2533*	*0.2508*	*0.2482*	*0.2456*	*0.2430*	*0.2404*	*0.2378*	*0.2353*	*0.2327*	*0.2301*
0.41	*0.2275*	*0.2250*	*0.2224*	*0.2198*	*0.2173*	*0.2147*	*0.2121*	*0.2096*	*0.2070*	*0.2045*
0.42	*0.2019*	*0.1993*	*0.1968*	*0.1942*	*0.1917*	*0.1891*	*0.1866*	*0.1840*	*0.1815*	*0.1789*
0.43	*0.1764*	*0.1738*	*0.1713*	*0.1687*	*0.1662*	*0.1637*	*0.1611*	*0.1586*	*0.1560*	*0.1535*
0.44	*0.1510*	*0.1484*	*0.1459*	*0.1434*	*0.1408*	*0.1383*	*0.1358*	*0.1332*	*0.1307*	*0.1282*
0.45	*0.1257*	*0.1231*	*0.1206*	*0.1181*	*0.1156*	*0.1130*	*0.1105*	*0.1080*	*0.1055*	*0.1030*
0.46	*0.1004*	*0.0979*	*0.0954*	*0.0929*	*0.0904*	*0.0878*	*0.0853*	*0.0828*	*0.0803*	*0.0778*
0.47	*0.0753*	*0.0728*	*0.0702*	*0.0677*	*0.0652*	*0.0627*	*0.0602*	*0.0577*	*0.0552*	*0.0527*
0.48	*0.0502*	*0.0476*	*0.0451*	*0.0426*	*0.0401*	*0.0376*	*0.0351*	*0.0326*	*0.0301*	*0.0276*
0.49	*0.0251*	*0.0226*	*0.0201*	*0.0175*	*0.0150*	*0.0125*	*0.0100*	*0.0075*	*0.0050*	*0.0025*
0.50	0.0000	0.0025	0.0050	0.0075	0.0100	0.0125	0.0150	0.0175	0.0201	0.0226
0.51	0.0251	0.0276	0.0301	0.0326	0.0351	0.0376	0.0401	0.0426	0.0451	0.0476
0.52	0.0502	0.0527	0.0552	0.0577	0.0602	0.0627	0.0652	0.0677	0.0702	0.0728
0.53	0.0753	0.0778	0.0803	0.0828	0.0853	0.0878	0.0904	0.0929	0.0954	0.0979
0.54	0.1004	0.1030	0.1055	0.1080	0.1105	0.1130	0.1156	0.1181	0.1206	0.1231
0.55	0.1257	0.1282	0.1307	0.1332	0.1358	0.1383	0.1408	0.1434	0.1459	0.1484
0.56	0.1510	0.1535	0.1560	0.1586	0.1611	0.1637	0.1662	0.1687	0.1713	0.1738
0.57	0.1764	0.1789	0.1815	0.1840	0.1866	0.1891	0.1917	0.1942	0.1968	0.1993
0.58	0.2019	0.2045	0.2070	0.2096	0.2121	0.2147	0.2173	0.2198	0.2224	0.2250
0.59	0.2275	0.2301	0.2327	0.2353	0.2378	0.2404	0.2430	0.2456	0.2482	0.2508
0.60	0.2533	0.2559	0.2585	0.2611	0.2637	0.2663	0.2689	0.2715	0.2741	0.2767
0.61	0.2793	0.2819	0.2845	0.2871	0.2898	0.2924	0.2950	0.2976	0.3002	0.3029
0.62	0.3055	0.3081	0.3107	0.3134	0.3160	0.3186	0.3213	0.3239	0.3266	0.3292
0.63	0.3319	0.3345	0.3372	0.3398	0.3425	0.3451	0.3478	0.3505	0.3531	0.3558
0.64	0.3585	0.3611	0.3638	0.3665	0.3692	0.3719	0.3745	0.3772	0.3799	0.3826
0.65	0.3853	0.3880	0.3907	0.3934	0.3961	0.3989	0.4016	0.4043	0.4070	0.4097
0.66	0.4125	0.4152	0.4179	0.4207	0.4234	0.4261	0.4289	0.4316	0.4344	0.4372
0.67	0.4399	0.4427	0.4454	0.4482	0.4510	0.4538	0.4565	0.4593	0.4621	0.4649
0.68	0.4677	0.4705	0.4733	0.4761	0.4789	0.4817	0.4845	0.4874	0.4902	0.4930
0.69	0.4959	0.4987	0.5015	0.5044	0.5072	0.5101	0.5129	0.5158	0.5187	0.5215
0.70	0.5244	0.5273	0.5302	0.5330	0.5359	0.5388	0.5417	0.5446	0.5476	0.5505
0.71	0.5534	0.5563	0.5592	0.5622	0.5651	0.5681	0.5710	0.5740	0.5769	0.5799
0.72	0.5828	0.5858	0.5888	0.5918	0.5948	0.5978	0.6008	0.6038	0.6068	0.6098
0.73	0.6128	0.6158	0.6189	0.6219	0.6250	0.6280	0.6311	0.6341	0.6372	0.6403
0.74	0.6433	0.6464	0.6495	0.6526	0.6557	0.6588	0.6620	0.6651	0.6682	0.6713
0.75	0.6745	0.6776	0.6808	0.6840	0.6871	0.6903	0.6935	0.6967	0.6999	0.7031
0.76	0.7063	0.7095	0.7128	0.7160	0.7192	0.7225	0.7257	0.7290	0.7323	0.7356
0.77	0.7388	0.7421	0.7454	0.7488	0.7521	0.7554	0.7588	0.7621	0.7655	0.7688
0.78	0.7722	0.7756	0.7790	0.7824	0.7858	0.7892	0.7926	0.7961	0.7995	0.8030
0.79	0.8064	0.8099	0.8134	0.8169	0.8204	0.8239	0.8274	0.8310	0.8345	0.8381
0.80	0.8416	0.8452	0.8488	0.8524	0.8560	0.8596	0.8633	0.8669	0.8705	0.8742
0.81	0.8779	0.8816	0.8853	0.8890	0.8927	0.8965	0.9002	0.9040	0.9078	0.9116
0.82	0.9154	0.9192	0.9230	0.9269	0.9307	0.9346	0.9385	0.9424	0.9463	0.9502
0.83	0.9542	0.9581	0.9621	0.9661	0.9701	0.9741	0.9782	0.9822	0.9863	0.9904
0.84	0.9945	0.9986	1.0027	1.0069	1.0110	1.0152	1.0194	1.0237	1.0279	1.0322
0.85	1.0364	1.0407	1.0450	1.0494	1.0537	1.0581	1.0625	1.0669	1.0714	1.0758
0.86	1.0803	1.0848	1.0893	1.0939	1.0985	1.1031	1.1077	1.1123	1.1170	1.1217
0.87	1.1264	1.1311	1.1359	1.1407	1.1455	1.1503	1.1552	1.1601	1.1650	1.1700
0.88	1.1750	1.1800	1.1850	1.1901	1.1952	1.2004	1.2055	1.2107	1.2160	1.2212
0.89	1.2265	1.2319	1.2372	1.2426	1.2481	1.2536	1.2591	1.2646	1.2702	1.2759
0.90	1.2816	1.2873	1.2930	1.2988	1.3047	1.3106	1.3165	1.3225	1.3285	1.3346
0.91	1.3408	1.3469	1.3532	1.3595	1.3658	1.3722	1.3787	1.3852	1.3917	1.3984
0.92	1.4051	1.4118	1.4187	1.4255	1.4325	1.4395	1.4466	1.4538	1.4611	1.4684
0.93	1.4758	1.4833	1.4909	1.4985	1.5063	1.5141	1.5220	1.5301	1.5382	1.5464
0.94	1.5548	1.5632	1.5718	1.5805	1.5893	1.5982	1.6072	1.6164	1.6258	1.6352
0.95	1.6449	1.6546	1.6646	1.6747	1.6849	1.6954	1.7060	1.7169	1.7279	1.7392
0.96	1.7507	1.7624	1.7744	1.7866	1.7991	1.8119	1.8250	1.8384	1.8522	1.8663
0.97	1.8808	1.8957	1.9110	1.9268	1.9431	1.9600	1.9774	1.9954	2.0141	2.0335
0.98	2.0537	2.0749	2.0969	2.1201	2.1444	2.1701	2.1973	2.2262	2.2571	2.2904
0.99	2.3263	2.3656	2.4089	2.4573	2.5121	2.5758	2.6521	2.7478	2.8782	3.0902

* Italic figures are negative values.

1) Calculated by the editors of these *Scientific Tables* from N. B. S. tables (see footnote page 29).

Deviation c → Integral

c → ↓	0.00	0.01	0.02	0.03	0.04	0.05	0.06	0.07	0.08	0.09
	0.	0.	0.	0.	0.	0.	0.	0.	0.	0.
−3.2	00069	00066	00064	00062	00060	00058	00056	00054	00052	0005
−3.1	00097	00094	00090	00087	00084	00082	00079	00076	00074	0007
−3.0	00135	00131	00126	00122	00118	00114	00111	00107	00104	0010
−2.9	00187	00181	00175	00169	00164	00159	00154	00149	00144	0013
−2.8	00256	00248	00240	00233	00226	00219	00212	00205	00199	0019
−2.7	00347	00336	00326	00317	00307	00298	00289	00280	00272	0026
−2.6	00466	00453	00440	00427	00415	00402	00391	00379	00368	0035
−2.5	00621	00604	00587	00570	00554	00539	00523	00508	00494	0048
−2.4	00820	00798	00776	00755	00734	00714	00695	00676	00657	0063
−2.3	01072	01044	01017	00990	00964	00939	00914	00889	00866	0084
−2.2	01390	01355	01321	01287	01255	01222	01191	01160	01130	0110
−2.1	01786	01743	01700	01659	01618	01578	01539	01500	01463	0142
−2.0	02275	02222	02169	02118	02068	02018	01970	01923	01876	0183
−1.9	02872	02807	02743	02680	02619	02559	02500	02442	02385	0233
−1.8	03593	03515	03438	03362	03288	03216	03144	03074	03005	0293
−1.7	04457	04363	04272	04182	04093	04006	03920	03836	03754	0367
−1.6	05480	05370	05262	05155	05050	04947	04846	04746	04648	0455
−1.5	06681	06552	06426	06301	06178	06057	05938	05821	05705	0559
−1.4	08076	07927	07780	07636	07493	07353	07215	07078	06944	0681
−1.3	09680	09510	09342	09176	09012	08851	08691	08534	08379	0822
−1.2	11507	11314	11123	10935	10749	10565	10383	10204	10027	0985
−1.1	13567	13350	13136	12924	12714	12507	12302	12100	11900	1170
−1.0	15866	15625	15386	15151	14917	14686	14457	14231	14007	1378
−0.9	18406	18141	17879	17619	17361	17106	16853	16602	16354	1610
−0.8	21186	20897	20611	20327	20045	19766	19489	19215	18943	1867
−0.7	24196	23885	23576	23270	22965	22663	22363	22065	21770	2147
−0.6	27425	27093	26763	26435	26109	25785	25463	25143	24825	2451
−0.5	30854	30503	30153	29806	29460	29116	28774	28434	28096	2776
−0.4	34458	34090	33724	33360	32997	32636	32276	31918	31561	3120
−0.3	38209	37828	37448	37070	36693	36317	35942	35569	35197	3482
−0.2	42074	41683	41294	40905	40517	40129	39743	39358	38974	3859
−0.19	42465	42426	42387	42348	42309	42270	42231	42191	42152	4211
−0.18	42858	42818	42779	42740	42701	42661	42622	42583	42544	4250
−0.17	43251	43211	43172	43133	43093	43054	43015	42975	42936	4289
−0.16	43644	43605	43565	43526	43487	43447	43408	43369	43329	4329
−0.15	44038	43999	43959	43920	43880	43841	43802	43762	43723	4368
−0.14	44433	44393	44354	44315	44275	44236	44196	44157	44117	4407
−0.13	44828	44789	44749	44710	44670	44631	44591	44552	44512	4447
−0.12	45224	45185	45145	45105	45066	45026	44987	44947	44907	4486
−0.11	45620	45581	45541	45502	45462	45422	45383	45343	45303	4526
−0.10	46017	45978	45938	45898	45858	45819	45779	45739	45700	456
−0.09	46414	46375	46335	46295	46255	46216	46176	46136	46097	4605
−0.08	46812	46772	46732	46693	46653	46613	46573	46534	46494	4645
−0.07	47210	47170	47130	47090	47051	47011	46971	46931	46891	4685
−0.06	47608	47568	47528	47488	47449	47409	47369	47329	47289	4724
−0.05	48006	47966	47926	47887	47847	47807	47767	47727	47687	4764
−0.04	48405	48365	48325	48285	48245	48205	48166	48126	48086	4804
−0.03	48803	48763	48724	48684	48644	48604	48564	48524	48484	4844
−0.02	49202	49162	49122	49083	49043	49003	48963	48923	48883	4884
−0.01	49601	49561	49521	49481	49441	49402	49362	49322	49282	4924
−0.00	50000	49960	49920	49880	49840	49801	49761	49721	49681	4964
+0.00	50000	50040	50080	50120	50160	50199	50239	50279	50319	5035
+0.01	50399	50439	50479	50519	50559	50598	50638	50678	50718	5075
+0.02	50798	50838	50878	50917	50957	50997	51037	51077	51117	5115
+0.03	51197	51237	51276	51316	51356	51396	51436	51476	51516	5155
+0.04	51595	51635	51675	51715	51755	51795	51834	51874	51914	5195
+0.05	51994	52034	52074	52113	52153	52193	52233	52273	52313	5235
+0.06	52392	52432	52472	52512	52551	52591	52631	52671	52711	5275
+0.07	52790	52830	52870	52910	52949	52989	53029	53069	53109	5314
+0.08	53188	53228	53268	53307	53347	53387	53427	53466	53506	5354
+0.09	53586	53625	53665	53705	53745	53784	53824	53864	53903	5394
+0.10	53983	54022	54062	54102	54142	54181	54221	54261	54300	5434
+0.11	54380	54419	54459	54498	54538	54578	54617	54657	54697	5473
+0.12	54776	54815	54855	54895	54934	54974	55013	55053	55093	5513
+0.13	55172	55211	55251	55290	55330	55369	55409	55448	55488	5552
+0.14	55567	55607	55646	55685	55725	55764	55804	55843	55883	5592
+0.15	55962	56001	56041	56080	56120	56159	56198	56238	56277	5631
+0.16	56356	56395	56435	56474	56513	56553	56592	56631	56671	567
+0.17	56749	56789	56828	56867	56907	56946	56985	57025	57064	571
+0.18	57142	57182	57221	57260	57299	57339	57378	57417	57456	574
+0.19	57535	57574	57613	57652	57691	57730	57769	57809	57848	578
+0.2	57926	58317	58706	59095	59483	59871	60257	60642	61026	614
+0.3	61791	62172	62552	62930	63307	63683	64058	64431	64803	651
+0.4	65542	65910	66276	66640	67003	67364	67724	68082	68439	687
+0.5	69146	69497	69847	70194	70540	70884	71226	71566	71904	722
+0.6	72575	72907	73237	73565	73891	74215	74537	74857	75175	754
+0.7	75804	76115	76424	76730	77035	77337	77637	77935	78230	785
+0.8	78814	79103	79389	79673	79955	80234	80511	80785	81057	813
+0.9	81594	81859	82121	82381	82639	82894	83147	83398	83646	838
+1.0	84134	84375	84614	84849	85083	85314	85543	85769	85993	862
+1.1	86433	86650	86864	87076	87286	87493	87698	87900	88100	882
+1.2	88493	88686	88877	89065	89251	89435	89617	89796	89973	901
+1.3	90320	90490	90658	90824	90988	91149	91309	91466	91621	917
+1.4	91924	92073	92220	92364	92507	92647	92785	92922	93056	931
+1.5	93319	93448	93574	93699	93822	93943	94062	94179	94295	944
+1.6	94520	94630	94738	94845	94950	95053	95154	95254	95352	954
+1.7	95543	95637	95728	95818	95907	95994	96080	96164	96246	963
+1.8	96407	96485	96562	96638	96712	96784	96856	96926	96995	970
+1.9	97128	97193	97257	97320	97381	97441	97500	97558	97615	976
+2.0	97725	97778	97831	97882	97932	97982	98030	98077	98124	981
+2.1	98214	98257	98300	98341	98382	98422	98461	98500	98537	985
+2.2	98610	98645	98679	98713	98745	98778	98809	98840	98870	988
+2.3	98928	98956	98983	99010	99036	99061	99086	99111	99134	991
+2.4	99180	99202	99224	99245	99266	99286	99305	99324	99343	993
+2.5	99379	99396	99413	99430	99446	99461	99477	99492	99506	995
+2.6	99534	99547	99560	99573	99585	99598	99609	99621	99632	996
+2.7	99653	99664	99674	99683	99693	99702	99711	99720	99728	997
+2.8	99744	99752	99760	99767	99774	99781	99788	99795	99801	998
+2.9	99813	99819	99825	99831	99836	99841	99846	99851	99856	998
+3.0	99865	99869	99874	99878	99882	99886	99889	99893	99896	999
+3.1	99903	99906	99910	99913	99916	99918	99921	99924	99926	999
+3.2	99931	99934	99936	99938	99940	99942	99944	99946	99948	999

Integral → Deviation c

∫ from −c to c ↓ / →	0.000	0.001	0.002	0.003	0.004	0.005	0.006	0.007	0.008	0.009
0.00	0.0000	0.0013	0.0025	0.0038	0.0050	0.0063	0.0075	0.0088	0.0100	0.0113
0.01	0.0125	0.0138	0.0150	0.0163	0.0175	0.0188	0.0201	0.0213	0.0226	0.0238
0.02	0.0251	0.0263	0.0276	0.0288	0.0301	0.0313	0.0326	0.0338	0.0351	0.0364
0.03	0.0376	0.0389	0.0401	0.0414	0.0426	0.0439	0.0451	0.0464	0.0476	0.0489
0.04	0.0502	0.0514	0.0527	0.0539	0.0552	0.0564	0.0577	0.0589	0.0602	0.0615
0.05	0.0627	0.0640	0.0652	0.0665	0.0677	0.0690	0.0702	0.0715	0.0728	0.0740
0.06	0.0753	0.0765	0.0778	0.0790	0.0803	0.0816	0.0828	0.0841	0.0853	0.0866
0.07	0.0878	0.0891	0.0904	0.0916	0.0929	0.0941	0.0954	0.0967	0.0979	0.0992
0.08	0.1004	0.1017	0.1030	0.1042	0.1055	0.1067	0.1080	0.1093	0.1105	0.1118
0.09	0.1130	0.1143	0.1156	0.1168	0.1181	0.1193	0.1206	0.1219	0.1231	0.1244
0.10	0.1257	0.1269	0.1282	0.1295	0.1307	0.1320	0.1332	0.1345	0.1358	0.1370
0.11	0.1383	0.1396	0.1408	0.1421	0.1434	0.1446	0.1459	0.1472	0.1484	0.1497
0.12	0.1510	0.1522	0.1535	0.1548	0.1560	0.1573	0.1586	0.1598	0.1611	0.1624
0.13	0.1637	0.1649	0.1662	0.1675	0.1687	0.1700	0.1713	0.1726	0.1738	0.1751
0.14	0.1764	0.1776	0.1789	0.1802	0.1815	0.1827	0.1840	0.1853	0.1866	0.1878
0.15	0.1891	0.1904	0.1917	0.1929	0.1942	0.1955	0.1968	0.1981	0.1993	0.2006
0.16	0.2019	0.2032	0.2045	0.2057	0.2070	0.2083	0.2096	0.2109	0.2121	0.2134
0.17	0.2147	0.2160	0.2173	0.2186	0.2198	0.2211	0.2224	0.2237	0.2250	0.2263
0.18	0.2275	0.2288	0.2301	0.2314	0.2327	0.2340	0.2353	0.2366	0.2378	0.2391
0.19	0.2404	0.2417	0.2430	0.2443	0.2456	0.2469	0.2482	0.2495	0.2508	0.2521
0.20	0.2533	0.2546	0.2559	0.2572	0.2585	0.2598	0.2611	0.2624	0.2637	0.2650
0.21	0.2663	0.2676	0.2689	0.2702	0.2715	0.2728	0.2741	0.2754	0.2767	0.2780
0.22	0.2793	0.2806	0.2819	0.2832	0.2845	0.2858	0.2871	0.2885	0.2898	0.2911
0.23	0.2924	0.2937	0.2950	0.2963	0.2976	0.2989	0.3002	0.3015	0.3029	0.3042
0.24	0.3055	0.3068	0.3081	0.3094	0.3107	0.3121	0.3134	0.3147	0.3160	0.3173
0.25	0.3186	0.3200	0.3213	0.3226	0.3239	0.3252	0.3266	0.3279	0.3292	0.3305
0.26	0.3319	0.3332	0.3345	0.3358	0.3372	0.3385	0.3398	0.3411	0.3425	0.3438
0.27	0.3451	0.3465	0.3478	0.3491	0.3505	0.3518	0.3531	0.3545	0.3558	0.3571
0.28	0.3585	0.3598	0.3611	0.3625	0.3638	0.3651	0.3665	0.3678	0.3692	0.3705
0.29	0.3719	0.3732	0.3745	0.3759	0.3772	0.3786	0.3799	0.3813	0.3826	0.3840
0.30	0.3853	0.3867	0.3880	0.3894	0.3907	0.3921	0.3934	0.3948	0.3961	0.3975
0.31	0.3989	0.4002	0.4016	0.4029	0.4043	0.4056	0.4070	0.4084	0.4097	0.4111
0.32	0.4125	0.4138	0.4152	0.4166	0.4179	0.4193	0.4207	0.4220	0.4234	0.4248
0.33	0.4261	0.4275	0.4289	0.4303	0.4316	0.4330	0.4344	0.4358	0.4372	0.4385
0.34	0.4399	0.4413	0.4427	0.4441	0.4454	0.4468	0.4482	0.4496	0.4510	0.4524
0.35	0.4538	0.4552	0.4565	0.4579	0.4593	0.4607	0.4621	0.4635	0.4649	0.4663
0.36	0.4677	0.4691	0.4705	0.4719	0.4733	0.4747	0.4761	0.4775	0.4789	0.4803
0.37	0.4817	0.4831	0.4845	0.4860	0.4874	0.4888	0.4902	0.4916	0.4930	0.4944
0.38	0.4959	0.4973	0.4987	0.5001	0.5015	0.5029	0.5044	0.5058	0.5072	0.5086
0.39	0.5101	0.5115	0.5129	0.5144	0.5158	0.5172	0.5187	0.5201	0.5215	0.5230
0.40	0.5244	0.5258	0.5273	0.5287	0.5302	0.5316	0.5330	0.5345	0.5359	0.5374
0.41	0.5388	0.5403	0.5417	0.5432	0.5446	0.5461	0.5476	0.5490	0.5505	0.5519
0.42	0.5534	0.5548	0.5563	0.5578	0.5592	0.5607	0.5622	0.5636	0.5651	0.5666
0.43	0.5681	0.5695	0.5710	0.5725	0.5740	0.5754	0.5769	0.5784	0.5799	0.5814
0.44	0.5828	0.5843	0.5858	0.5873	0.5888	0.5903	0.5918	0.5933	0.5948	0.5963
0.45	0.5978	0.5993	0.6008	0.6023	0.6038	0.6053	0.6068	0.6083	0.6098	0.6113
0.46	0.6128	0.6143	0.6158	0.6174	0.6189	0.6204	0.6219	0.6234	0.6250	0.6265
0.47	0.6280	0.6295	0.6311	0.6326	0.6341	0.6357	0.6372	0.6387	0.6403	0.6418
0.48	0.6433	0.6449	0.6464	0.6480	0.6495	0.6511	0.6526	0.6542	0.6557	0.6573
0.49	0.6588	0.6604	0.6620	0.6635	0.6651	0.6666	0.6682	0.6698	0.6713	0.6729
0.50	0.6745	0.6761	0.6776	0.6792	0.6808	0.6824	0.6840	0.6855	0.6871	0.6887
0.51	0.6903	0.6919	0.6935	0.6951	0.6967	0.6983	0.6999	0.7015	0.7031	0.7047
0.52	0.7063	0.7079	0.7095	0.7111	0.7128	0.7144	0.7160	0.7176	0.7192	0.7209
0.53	0.7225	0.7241	0.7257	0.7274	0.7290	0.7306	0.7323	0.7339	0.7356	0.7372
0.54	0.7388	0.7405	0.7421	0.7438	0.7454	0.7471	0.7488	0.7504	0.7521	0.7537
0.55	0.7554	0.7571	0.7588	0.7604	0.7621	0.7638	0.7655	0.7671	0.7688	0.7705
0.56	0.7722	0.7739	0.7756	0.7773	0.7790	0.7807	0.7824	0.7841	0.7858	0.7875
0.57	0.7892	0.7909	0.7926	0.7943	0.7961	0.7978	0.7995	0.8012	0.8030	0.8047
0.58	0.8064	0.8082	0.8099	0.8116	0.8134	0.8151	0.8169	0.8186	0.8204	0.8221
0.59	0.8239	0.8257	0.8274	0.8292	0.8310	0.8327	0.8345	0.8363	0.8381	0.8398
0.60	0.8416	0.8434	0.8452	0.8470	0.8488	0.8506	0.8524	0.8542	0.8560	0.8578
0.61	0.8596	0.8614	0.8633	0.8651	0.8669	0.8687	0.8705	0.8724	0.8742	0.8761
0.62	0.8779	0.8797	0.8816	0.8834	0.8853	0.8871	0.8890	0.8909	0.8927	0.8946
0.63	0.8965	0.8983	0.9002	0.9021	0.9040	0.9059	0.9078	0.9097	0.9116	0.9135
0.64	0.9154	0.9173	0.9192	0.9211	0.9230	0.9249	0.9269	0.9288	0.9307	0.9327
0.65	0.9346	0.9365	0.9385	0.9404	0.9424	0.9443	0.9463	0.9483	0.9502	0.9522
0.66	0.9542	0.9561	0.9581	0.9601	0.9621	0.9641	0.9661	0.9681	0.9701	0.9721
0.67	0.9741	0.9761	0.9782	0.9802	0.9822	0.9842	0.9863	0.9883	0.9904	0.9924
0.68	0.9945	0.9965	0.9986	1.001	1.003	1.005	1.007	1.009	1.011	1.013
0.69	1.015	1.017	1.019	1.022	1.024	1.026	1.028	1.030	1.032	1.034
0.70	1.036	1.039	1.041	1.043	1.045	1.047	1.049	1.052	1.054	1.056
0.71	1.058	1.060	1.063	1.065	1.067	1.069	1.071	1.074	1.076	1.078
0.72	1.080	1.083	1.085	1.087	1.089	1.092	1.094	1.096	1.098	1.101
0.73	1.103	1.105	1.108	1.110	1.112	1.115	1.117	1.119	1.122	1.124
0.74	1.126	1.129	1.131	1.134	1.136	1.138	1.141	1.143	1.146	1.148
0.75	1.150	1.153	1.155	1.158	1.160	1.163	1.165	1.168	1.170	1.172
0.76	1.175	1.177	1.180	1.183	1.185	1.188	1.190	1.193	1.195	1.198
0.77	1.200	1.203	1.206	1.208	1.211	1.213	1.216	1.219	1.221	1.224
0.78	1.227	1.229	1.232	1.235	1.237	1.240	1.243	1.245	1.248	1.251
0.79	1.254	1.256	1.259	1.262	1.265	1.267	1.270	1.273	1.276	1.279
0.80	1.282	1.284	1.287	1.290	1.293	1.296	1.299	1.302	1.305	1.308
0.81	1.311	1.314	1.317	1.320	1.323	1.326	1.329	1.332	1.335	1.338
0.82	1.341	1.344	1.347	1.350	1.353	1.356	1.359	1.363	1.366	1.369
0.83	1.372	1.375	1.379	1.382	1.385	1.388	1.392	1.395	1.398	1.402
0.84	1.405	1.408	1.412	1.415	1.419	1.422	1.426	1.429	1.433	1.436
0.85	1.440	1.443	1.447	1.450	1.454	1.457	1.461	1.465	1.468	1.472
0.86	1.476	1.480	1.483	1.487	1.491	1.495	1.499	1.502	1.506	1.510
0.87	1.514	1.518	1.522	1.526	1.530	1.534	1.538	1.542	1.546	1.551
0.88	1.555	1.559	1.563	1.567	1.572	1.576	1.580	1.585	1.589	1.594
0.89	1.598	1.603	1.607	1.612	1.616	1.621	1.626	1.630	1.635	1.640
0.90	1.645	1.650	1.655	1.660	1.665	1.670	1.675	1.680	1.685	1.690
0.91	1.695	1.701	1.706	1.711	1.717	1.722	1.728	1.734	1.739	1.745
0.92	1.751	1.757	1.762	1.768	1.774	1.780	1.787	1.793	1.799	1.806
0.93	1.812	1.818	1.825	1.832	1.838	1.845	1.852	1.859	1.866	1.873
0.94	1.881	1.888	1.896	1.903	1.911	1.919	1.927	1.935	1.943	1.951
0.95	1.960	1.969	1.977	1.986	1.995	2.005	2.014	2.024	2.034	2.044
0.96	2.054	2.064	2.075	2.086	2.097	2.108	2.120	2.132	2.144	2.157
0.97	2.170	2.183	2.197	2.212	2.226	2.241	2.257	2.273	2.290	2.308
0.98	2.326	2.346	2.366	2.387	2.409	2.432	2.457	2.484	2.512	2.543
0.99	2.576	2.612	2.652	2.697	2.748	2.807	2.878	2.968	3.090	3.291

Deviation c → Integral

c ↓ / →	0.000	0.001	0.002	0.003	0.004	0.005	0.006	0.007	0.008	0.009
	0.	0.	0.	0.	0.	0.	0.	0.	0.	0.
0.00	00000	00080	00160	00239	00319	00399	00479	00559	00638	00718
0.01	00798	00878	00957	01037	01117	01197	01277	01356	01436	01516
0.02	01596	01675	01755	01835	01915	01995	02074	02154	02234	02314
0.03	02393	02473	02553	02633	02712	02792	02872	02951	03031	03111
0.04	03191	03270	03350	03430	03510	03589	03669	03749	03828	03908
0.05	03988	04067	04147	04227	04306	04386	04466	04545	04625	04705
0.06	04784	04864	04944	05023	05103	05183	05262	05342	05421	05501
0.07	05581	05660	05740	05819	05899	05979	06058	06138	06217	06297
0.08	06376	06456	06535	06615	06694	06774	06853	06933	07012	07092
0.09	07171	07251	07330	07410	07489	07569	07648	07727	07807	07886
0.10	07966	08045	08124	08204	08283	08362	08442	08521	08600	08680
0.11	08759	08838	08918	08997	09076	09155	09235	09314	09393	09472
0.12	09552	09631	09710	09789	09868	09948	10027	10106	10185	10264
0.13	10343	10422	10502	10581	10660	10739	10818	10897	10976	11055
0.14	11134	11213	11292	11371	11450	11529	11608	11687	11766	11845
0.15	11924	12002	12081	12160	12239	12318	12397	12476	12554	12633
0.16	12712	12791	12869	12948	13027	13106	13184	13263	13342	13420
0.17	13499	13578	13656	13735	13813	13892	13971	14049	14128	14206
0.18	14285	14363	14442	14520	14599	14677	14756	14834	14912	14991
0.19	15069	15147	15226	15304	15382	15461	15539	15617	15695	15774
0.20	15852	15930	16008	16086	16165	16243	16321	16399	16477	16555
0.21	16633	16711	16789	16867	16945	17023	17101	17179	17257	17335
0.22	17413	17491	17569	17646	17724	17802	17880	17958	18035	18113
0.23	18191	18269	18346	18424	18502	18579	18657	18734	18812	18889
0.24	18967	19044	19122	19199	19277	19354	19432	19509	19587	19664
0.25	19741	19819	19896	19973	20050	20128	20205	20282	20359	20436
0.26	20514	20591	20668	20745	20822	20899	20976	21053	21130	21207
0.27	21284	21361	21438	21515	21592	21668	21745	21822	21899	21976
0.28	22052	22129	22206	22282	22359	22436	22512	22589	22665	22742
0.29	22818	22895	22971	23048	23124	23201	23277	23353	23430	23506
0.30	23582	23659	23735	23811	23887	23963	24040	24116	24192	24268
0.31	24344	24420	24496	24572	24648	24724	24800	24876	24952	25027
0.32	25103	25179	25255	25330	25406	25482	25558	25633	25709	25784
0.33	25860	25936	26011	26087	26162	26237	26313	26388	26464	26539
0.34	26614	26690	26765	26840	26915	26991	27066	27141	27216	27291
0.35	27366	27441	27516	27591	27666	27741	27816	27891	27966	28040
0.36	28115	28190	28265	28340	28414	28489	28563	28638	28713	28787
0.37	28862	28936	29011	29085	29160	29234	29308	29383	29457	29531
0.38	29605	29680	29754	29828	29902	29976	30050	30124	30198	30272
0.39	30346	30420	30494	30568	30642	30716	30789	30863	30937	31011
0.40	31084	31158	31232	31305	31379	31452	31526	31599	31673	31746
0.41	31819	31893	31966	32039	32113	32186	32259	32332	32405	32478
0.42	32551	32624	32697	32770	32843	32916	32989	33062	33135	33208
0.43	33280	33353	33426	33499	33571	33644	33716	33789	33861	33934
0.44	34006	34079	34151	34223	34296	34368	34440	34512	34585	34657
0.45	34729	34801	34873	34945	35017	35089	35161	35233	35305	35377
0.46	35448	35520	35592	35664	35735	35807	35878	35950	36022	36093
0.47	36164	36236	36307	36379	36450	36521	36593	36664	36735	36806
0.48	36877	36948	37019	37090	37161	37232	37303	37374	37445	37516
0.49	37587	37657	37728	37799	37869	37940	38011	38081	38152	38222
0.50	38292	38363	38433	38504	38574	38644	38714	38785	38855	38925
0.51	38995	39065	39135	39205	39275	39345	39415	39484	39554	39624
0.52	39694	39763	39833	39903	39972	40042	40111	40181	40250	40319
0.53	40389	40458	40527	40597	40666	40735	40804	40873	40942	41011
0.54	41080	41149	41218	41287	41356	41425	41493	41562	41631	41699
0.55	41768	41837	41905	41974	42042	42111	42179	42247	42316	42384
0.56	42452	42520	42588	42657	42725	42793	42861	42929	42997	43064
0.57	43132	43200	43268	43336	43403	43471	43538	43606	43674	43741
0.58	43809	43876	43943	44011	44078	44145	44212	44280	44347	44414
0.59	44481	44548	44615	44682	44749	44816	44882	44949	45016	45083
0.60	45149	45216	45283	45349	45416	45482	45549	45615	45681	45748
0.61	45814	45880	45946	46012	46078	46145	46211	46277	46342	46408
0.62	46474	46540	46606	46672	46737	46803	46869	46934	47000	47065
0.63	47131	47196	47261	47327	47392	47457	47522	47588	47653	47718
0.64	47783	47848	47913	47978	48042	48107	48172	48237	48302	48366
0.65	48431	48495	48560	48624	48689	48753	48818	48882	48946	49010
0.66	49075	49139	49203	49267	49331	49395	49459	49523	49587	49650
0.67	49714	49778	49842	49905	49969	50032	50096	50159	50223	50286
0.68	50350	50413	50476	50539	50602	50666	50729	50792	50855	50918
0.69	50981	51043	51106	51169	51232	51294	51357	51420	51482	51545
0.7	51607	52230	52848	53461	54070	54675	55275	55870	56461	57047
0.8	57629	58206	58778	59346	59909	60467	61021	61570	62114	62653
0.9	63188	63718	64243	64763	65278	65789	66294	66795	67291	67783
1.0	68269	68750	69227	69699	70166	70628	71086	71538	71986	72429
1.1	72867	73300	73729	74152	74571	74986	75395	75800	76200	76595
1.2	76986	77372	77754	78130	78502	78870	79233	79592	79945	80295
1.3	80640	80980	81316	81648	81975	82298	82617	82931	83241	83547
1.4	83849	84146	84439	84728	85013	85294	85571	85844	86113	86378
1.5	86639	86896	87149	87398	87644	87886	88124	88358	88589	88817
1.6	89040	89260	89477	89690	89899	90106	90309	90508	90704	90897
1.7	91087	91273	91457	91637	91814	91988	92159	92327	92492	92655
1.8	92814	92970	93124	93275	93423	93569	93711	93852	93989	94124
1.9	94257	94387	94514	94639	94762	94882	95000	95116	95230	95341
2.0	95450	95557	95662	95764	95865	95964	96060	96155	96247	96338
2.1	96427	96514	96599	96683	96765	96844	96923	96999	97074	97148
2.2	97219	97289	97358	97425	97491	97555	97618	97679	97739	97798
2.3	97855	97911	97966	98019	98072	98123	98173	98221	98269	98315
2.4	98360	98405	98448	98490	98531	98571	98611	98649	98686	98723
2.5	98758	98793	98826	98859	98891	98923	98953	98983	99012	99040
2.6	99068	99095	99121	99146	99171	99195	99219	99241	99264	99285
2.7	99307	99327	99347	99367	99386	99404	99422	99439	99456	99473
2.8	99489	99505	99520	99535	99549	99563	99576	99590	99602	99615
2.9	99627	99639	99650	99661	99672	99682	99692	99702	99712	99721
3.0	99730	99739	99747	99755	99763	99771	99779	99786	99793	99800
3.1	99806	99813	99819	99825	99831	99837	99842	99848	99853	99858
3.2	99863	99867	99872	99876	99880	99885	99889	99892	99896	99900
3.3	99903	99907	99910	99913	99916	99919	99922	99925	99928	99930

3.4: 99933; 3.5: 99953; 3.6: 99968; 3.7: 99978; 3.8: 99986; 3.891: 99990

[1]) Values abridged from National Bureau of Standards *Tables of Normal Probability Functions*, Applied Mathematics Series 23, Washington, 1953. Reproduction of values on this and the preceding page only by permission of the publishers of these *Scientific Tables*, J. R. Geigy S. A., Basle (Switzerland).

2 *P* = twice the integral between *c* and infinity

Integral 2 *P* (outside minus *c* and *c*)

Deviation c → Integral

c	0.000	0.001	0.002	0.003	0.004	0.005	0.006	0.007	0.008	0.009
	0.	0.	0.	0.	0.	0.	0.	0.	0.	0.
0.00	00000*	99920	99840	99761	99681	99601	99521	99441	99362	99282
0.01	99202	99122	99043	98963	98883	98803	98723	98644	98564	98484
0.02	98404	98325	98245	98165	98085	98005	97926	97846	97766	97686
0.03	97607	97527	97447	97367	97288	97208	97128	97049	96969	96889
0.04	96809	96730	96650	96570	96490	96411	96331	96251	96172	96092
0.05	96012	95933	95853	95773	95694	95614	95534	95455	95375	95295
0.06	95216	95136	95056	94977	94897	94817	94738	94658	94579	94499
0.07	94419	94340	94260	94181	94101	94021	93942	93862	93783	93703
0.08	93624	93544	93465	93385	93306	93226	93147	93067	92988	92908
0.09	92829	92749	92670	92590	92511	92431	92352	92273	92193	92114
0.10	92034	91955	91876	91796	91717	91638	91558	91479	91400	91320
0.11	91241	91162	91082	91003	90924	90845	90765	90686	90607	90528
0.12	90448	90369	90290	90211	90132	90052	89974	89894	89815	89736
0.13	89657	89578	89498	89419	89340	89261	89182	89103	89024	88945
0.14	88866	88787	88708	88629	88550	88471	88392	88313	88234	88155
0.15	88076	87998	87919	87840	87761	87682	87603	87524	87446	87367
0.16	87288	87209	87131	87052	86973	86894	86816	86737	86658	86580
0.17	86501	86422	86344	86265	86187	86108	86029	85951	85872	85794
0.18	85715	85637	85558	85480	85401	85323	85244	85166	85088	85009
0.19	84931	84853	84774	84696	84618	84539	84461	84383	84305	84226
0.20	84148	84070	83992	83914	83835	83757	83679	83601	83523	83445
0.21	83367	83289	83211	83133	83055	82977	82899	82821	82743	82665
0.22	82587	82509	82431	82354	82276	82198	82120	82042	81965	81887
0.23	81809	81731	81654	81576	81498	81421	81343	81266	81188	81111
0.24	81033	80956	80878	80801	80723	80646	80568	80491	80413	80336
0.25	80259	80181	80104	80027	79950	79872	79795	79718	79641	79564
0.26	79486	79409	79332	79255	79178	79101	79024	78947	78870	78793
0.27	78716	78639	78562	78485	78408	78332	78255	78178	78101	78024
0.28	77948	77871	77794	77718	77641	77564	77488	77411	77335	77258
0.29	77182	77105	77029	76952	76876	76799	76723	76647	76570	76494
0.30	76418	76341	76265	76189	76113	76037	75960	75884	75808	75732
0.31	75656	75580	75504	75428	75352	75276	75200	75124	75048	74973
0.32	74897	74821	74745	74670	74594	74518	74442	74367	74291	74216
0.33	74140	74064	73989	73913	73838	73763	73687	73612	73536	73461
0.34	73386	73310	73235	73160	73085	73009	72934	72859	72784	72709
0.35	72634	72559	72484	72409	72334	72259	72184	72109	72034	71960
0.36	71885	71810	71735	71660	71586	71511	71437	71362	71287	71213
0.37	71138	71064	70989	70915	70840	70766	70692	70617	70543	70469
0.38	70395	70320	70246	70172	70098	70024	69950	69876	69802	69728
0.39	69654	69580	69506	69432	69358	69284	69211	69137	69063	68989
0.40	68916	68842	68768	68695	68621	68548	68474	68401	68327	68254
0.41	68181	68107	68034	67961	67887	67814	67741	67668	67595	67522
0.42	67449	67376	67303	67230	67157	67084	67011	66938	66865	66792
0.43	66720	66647	66574	66501	66429	66356	66284	66211	66139	66066
0.44	65994	65921	65849	65777	65704	65632	65560	65488	65415	65343
0.45	65271	65199	65127	65055	64983	64911	64839	64767	64695	64623
0.46	64552	64480	64408	64336	64265	64193	64122	64050	63978	63907
0.47	63836	63764	63693	63621	63550	63479	63407	63336	63265	63194
0.48	63123	63052	62981	62910	62839	62768	62697	62626	62555	62484
0.49	62413	62343	62272	62201	62131	62060	61989	61919	61848	61778
0.50	61708	61637	61567	61496	61426	61356	61286	61215	61145	61075
0.51	61005	60935	60865	60795	60725	60655	60585	60516	60446	60376
0.52	60306	60237	60167	60097	60028	59958	59889	59819	59750	59681
0.53	59611	59542	59473	59403	59334	59265	59196	59127	59058	58989
0.54	58920	58851	58782	58713	58644	58575	58507	58438	58369	58301
0.55	58232	58163	58095	58026	57958	57889	57821	57753	57684	57616
0.56	57548	57480	57412	57343	57275	57207	57139	57071	57003	56936
0.57	56868	56800	56732	56664	56597	56529	56462	56394	56326	56259
0.58	56191	56124	56057	55989	55922	55855	55788	55720	55653	55586
0.59	55519	55452	55385	55318	55251	55184	55118	55051	54984	54917
0.60	54851	54784	54717	54651	54584	54518	54451	54385	54319	54252
0.61	54186	54120	54054	53988	53922	53855	53789	53723	53658	53592
0.62	53526	53460	53394	53328	53263	53197	53131	53066	53000	52935
0.63	52869	52804	52739	52673	52608	52543	52478	52412	52347	52282
0.64	52217	52152	52087	52022	51958	51893	51828	51763	51698	51634
0.65	51569	51505	51440	51376	51311	51247	51182	51118	51054	50990
0.66	50925	50861	50797	50733	50669	50605	50541	50477	50413	50350
0.67	50286	50222	50158	50095	50031	49968	49904	49841	49777	49714
0.68	49650	49587	49524	49461	49398	49334	49271	49208	49145	49082
0.69	49019	48957	48894	48831	48768	48706	48643	48580	48518	48455
0.7	48393	47770	47152	46539	45930	45325	44725	44130	43539	42953
0.8	42371	41794	41222	40654	40091	39533	38979	38430	37886	37347
0.9	36812	36282	35757	35237	34722	34211	33706	33205	32709	32217
1.0	31731	31250	30773	30301	29834	29372	28914	28462	28014	27571
1.1	27133	26700	26271	25848	25429	25014	24605	24200	23800	23405
1.2	23014	22628	22246	21870	21498	21130	20767	20408	20055	19705
1.3	19360	19020	18684	18352	18025	17702	17383	17069	16759	16453
1.4	16151	15854	15561	15272	14987	14706	14429	14156	13887	13622
1.5	13361	13104	12851	12602	12356	12114	11876	11642	11411	11183
1.6	10960	10740	10523	10310	10101	09894	09691	09492	09296	09103
1.7	08913	08727	08543	08363	08186	08012	07841	07673	07508	07345
1.8	07186	07030	06876	06725	06577	06431	06289	06148	06011	05876
1.9	05743	05613	05486	05361	05238	05118	05000	04884	04770	04659
2.0	04550	04443	04338	04236	04135	04036	03940	03845	03753	03662
2.1	03573	03486	03401	03317	03235	03156	03077	03001	02926	02852
2.2	02781	02711	02642	02575	02509	02445	02382	02321	02261	02202
2.3	02145	02089	02034	01981	01928	01877	01827	01779	01731	01685
2.4	01640	01595	01552	01510	01469	01429	01389	01351	01314	01277
2.5	01242	01207	01174	01141	01109	01077	01047	01017	00988	00960
2.6	00932	00905	00879	00854	00829	00805	00781	00759	00736	00715
2.7	00693	00673	00653	00633	00614	00596	00578	00561	00544	00527
2.8	00511	00495	00480	00465	00451	00437	00424	00410	00398	00385
2.9	00373	00361	00350	00339	00328	00318	00308	00298	00288	00279
3.0	00270	00261	00253	00245	00237	00229	00221	00214	00207	00200
3.1	00194	00187	00181	00175	00169	00163	00158	00152	00147	00142
3.2	00137	00133	00128	00124	00120	00115	00111	00108	00104	00100
3.3	00097	00093	00090	00087	00084	00081	00078	00075	00072	00070

3.4: 00067; 3.5: 00047; 3.6: 00032; 3.7: 00022; 3.8: 00014; 3.891: 00010

Integral between zero and c

Deviation c → Integral

c	0.000	0.001	0.002	0.003	0.004	0.005	0.006	0.007	0.008	0.009
	0.	0.	0.	0.	0.	0.	0.	0.	0.	0.
0.00	00000	00040	00080	00120	00160	00200	00240	00280	00319	00359
0.01	00399	00439	00479	00519	00559	00599	00639	00678	00718	00758
0.02	00798	00838	00878	00918	00958	00998	01037	01077	01117	01157
0.03	01197	01237	01277	01317	01356	01396	01436	01476	01516	01556
0.04	01596	01635	01675	01715	01755	01795	01835	01875	01914	01954
0.05	01994	02034	02074	02114	02153	02193	02233	02273	02313	02353
0.06	02392	02432	02472	02512	02552	02592	02631	02671	02711	02751
0.07	02791	02830	02870	02910	02950	02990	03029	03069	03109	03149
0.08	03188	03228	03268	03308	03347	03387	03427	03467	03506	03546
0.09	03586	03626	03665	03705	03745	03785	03824	03864	03904	03943
0.10	03983	04023	04062	04102	04142	04181	04221	04261	04300	04340
0.11	04380	04419	04459	04499	04538	04578	04618	04657	04697	04736
0.12	04776	04816	04855	04895	04934	04974	05013	05053	05093	05132
0.13	05172	05211	05251	05291	05330	05370	05409	05449	05488	05528
0.14	05567	05607	05646	05686	05725	05765	05804	05844	05883	05923
0.15	05962	06001	06041	06080	06120	06159	06199	06238	06277	06317
0.16	06356	06396	06435	06474	06514	06553	06592	06632	06671	06710
0.17	06750	06789	06828	06868	06907	06946	06986	07025	07064	07103
0.18	07143	07182	07221	07260	07300	07339	07378	07417	07456	07496
0.19	07535	07574	07613	07652	07691	07731	07770	07809	07848	07887
0.20	07926	07965	08004	08043	08083	08122	08161	08200	08239	08278
0.21	08317	08356	08395	08434	08473	08512	08551	08590	08629	08668
0.22	08707	08746	08785	08823	08862	08901	08940	08979	09018	09057
0.23	09096	09135	09173	09212	09251	09290	09329	09367	09406	09445
0.24	09484	09522	09561	09600	09639	09677	09716	09755	09794	09832
0.25	09871	09910	09948	09987	10025	10064	10103	10141	10180	10218
0.26	10257	10296	10334	10373	10411	10450	10488	10527	10565	10604
0.27	10642	10681	10719	10758	10796	10834	10873	10911	10950	10988
0.28	11026	11065	11103	11141	11180	11218	11256	11295	11333	11371
0.29	11409	11448	11486	11524	11562	11601	11639	11677	11715	11753
0.30	11791	11830	11868	11906	11944	11982	12020	12058	12096	12134
0.31	12172	12210	12248	12286	12324	12362	12400	12438	12476	12514
0.32	12552	12590	12628	12665	12703	12741	12779	12817	12855	12892
0.33	12930	12968	13006	13044	13081	13119	13157	13194	13232	13270
0.34	13307	13345	13383	13420	13458	13496	13533	13571	13608	13646
0.35	13683	13721	13758	13796	13833	13871	13908	13946	13983	14020
0.36	14058	14095	14133	14170	14207	14245	14282	14319	14357	14394
0.37	14431	14468	14506	14543	14580	14617	14654	14692	14729	14766
0.38	14803	14840	14877	14914	14951	14988	15025	15062	15099	15136
0.39	15173	15210	15247	15284	15321	15358	15395	15432	15469	15506
0.40	15542	15579	15616	15653	15690	15726	15763	15800	15837	15873
0.41	15910	15947	15983	16020	16057	16093	16130	16166	16203	16239
0.42	16276	16312	16349	16385	16422	16458	16495	16531	16568	16604
0.43	16640	16677	16713	16750	16786	16822	16858	16895	16931	16967
0.44	17003	17040	17076	17112	17148	17184	17220	17256	17293	17329
0.45	17365	17401	17437	17473	17509	17545	17581	17617	17653	17689
0.46	17724	17760	17796	17832	17868	17904	17939	17975	18011	18047
0.47	18082	18118	18154	18190	18225	18261	18297	18332	18368	18403
0.48	18439	18474	18510	18545	18581	18616	18652	18687	18723	18758
0.49	18794	18829	18864	18900	18935	18970	19006	19041	19076	19111
0.50	19146	19182	19217	19252	19287	19322	19357	19393	19428	19463
0.51	19498	19533	19568	19603	19638	19673	19708	19742	19777	19812
0.52	19847	19882	19917	19952	19986	20021	20056	20091	20125	20160
0.53	20195	20229	20264	20299	20333	20368	20402	20437	20471	20506
0.54	20540	20575	20609	20644	20678	20713	20747	20781	20816	20850
0.55	20884	20919	20953	20987	21021	21056	21090	21124	21158	21192
0.56	21226	21260	21294	21329	21363	21397	21431	21465	21499	21532
0.57	21566	21600	21634	21668	21702	21736	21769	21803	21837	21871
0.58	21905	21938	21972	22006	22039	22073	22106	22140	22174	22207
0.59	22241	22274	22308	22341	22375	22408	22441	22475	22508	22542
0.60	22575	22608	22642	22675	22708	22741	22775	22808	22841	22874
0.61	22907	22940	22973	23006	23039	23073	23106	23139	23171	23204
0.62	23237	23270	23303	23336	23369	23402	23435	23467	23500	23533
0.63	23566	23598	23631	23664	23696	23729	23761	23794	23827	23859
0.64	23892	23924	23957	23989	24021	24054	24086	24119	24151	24183
0.65	24216	24248	24280	24312	24345	24377	24409	24441	24473	24505
0.66	24538	24570	24602	24634	24666	24698	24730	24762	24794	24825
0.67	24857	24889	24921	24953	24985	25016	25048	25080	25112	25143
0.68	25175	25207	25238	25270	25301	25333	25365	25396	25428	25459
0.69	25491	25522	25553	25585	25616	25647	25679	25710	25741	25773
0.7	25804	26115	26424	26731	27035	27338	27638	27935	28231	28524
0.8	28815	29103	29389	29673	29955	30234	30511	30785	31057	31327
0.9	31594	31859	32122	32382	32639	32895	33147	33398	33646	33892
1.0	34135	34375	34614	34850	35083	35314	35543	35769	35993	36215
1.1	36434	36650	36865	37076	37286	37493	37698	37900	38100	38298
1.2	38493	38686	38877	39065	39251	39435	39617	39796	39973	40148
1.3	40320	40490	40658	40824	40988	41149	41309	41466	41621	41774
1.4	41925	42073	42220	42364	42507	42647	42786	42922	43057	43189
1.5	43320	43448	43575	43699	43822	43943	44062	44179	44295	44409
1.6	44520	44630	44739	44845	44950	45053	45155	45254	45352	45449
1.7	45544	45637	45729	45819	45907	45994	46080	46164	46246	46328
1.8	46407	46485	46562	46638	46712	46785	46856	46926	46995	47062
1.9	47129	47194	47257	47320	47381	47441	47500	47558	47615	47671
2.0	47725	47779	47831	47882	47933	47982	48030	48078	48124	48169
2.1	48214	48257	48300	48342	48383	48422	48462	48500	48537	48574
2.2	48610	48645	48679	48713	48746	48778	48809	48840	48870	48899
2.3	48928	48956	48983	49010	49036	49062	49087	49111	49135	49158
2.4	49180	49203	49224	49245	49266	49286	49306	49325	49343	49362
2.5	49379	49397	49413	49430	49446	49462	49477	49492	49506	49520
2.6	49534	49548	49561	49573	49586	49598	49610	49621	49632	49643
2.7	49654	49664	49674	49684	49693	49702	49711	49720	49728	49737
2.8	49745	49753	49760	49768	49775	49782	49788	49795	49801	49808
2.9	49814	49820	49825	49831	49836	49841	49846	49851	49856	49861
3.0	49865	49870	49874	49878	49882	49886	49890	49893	49897	49900
3.1	49903	49907	49910	49913	49916	49919	49921	49924	49927	49929
3.2	49932	49934	49936	49938	49940	49943	49945	49946	49948	49950
3.3	49952	49954	49955	49957	49958	49960	49961	49963	49964	49965

3.4: 49967; 3.5: 49977; 3.6: 49984; 3.7: 49989; 3.8: 49993; 3.891: 49995

* To be read as 1.000 00.

1) Values abridged from National Bureau of Standards *Tables of Normal Probability Functions,* Applied Mathematics Series 23, Washington, 1953. Reproduction only by permission of the publishers of these *Scientific Tables,* J. R. Geigy S. A., Basle (Switzerland).

Deviation |c| → Ordinate f(c)

|c| →	0.000	0.001	0.002	0.003	0.004	0.005	0.006	0.007	0.008	0.009
↓	0.	0.	0.	0.	0.	0.	0.	0.	0.	0.
0.00	39894	39894	39894	39894	39894	39894	39894	39893	39893	39893
0.01	39892	39892	39891	39891	39890	39890	39889	39888	39888	39887
0.02	39886	39885	39885	39884	39883	39882	39881	39880	39879	39877
0.03	39876	39875	39874	39873	39871	39870	39868	39867	39865	39864
0.04	39862	39861	39859	39857	39856	39854	39852	39850	39848	39846
0.05	39844	39842	39840	39838	39836	39834	39832	39829	39827	39825
0.06	39822	39820	39818	39815	39813	39810	39807	39805	39802	39799
0.07	39797	39794	39791	39788	39785	39782	39779	39776	39773	39770
0.08	39767	39764	39760	39757	39754	39750	39747	39744	39740	39737
0.09	39733	39729	39726	39722	39718	39715	39711	39707	39703	39699
0.10	39695	39691	39687	39683	39679	39675	39671	39667	39662	39658
0.11	39654	39649	39645	39640	39636	39631	39627	39622	39617	39613
0.12	39608	39603	39598	39594	39589	39584	39579	39574	39569	39564
0.13	39559	39553	39548	39543	39538	39532	39527	39522	39516	39511
0.14	39505	39500	39494	39488	39483	39477	39471	39466	39460	39454
0.15	39448	39442	39436	39430	39424	39418	39412	39406	39399	39393
0.16	39387	39381	39374	39368	39361	39355	39348	39342	39335	39329
0.17	39322	39315	39308	39302	39295	39288	39281	39274	39267	39260
0.18	39253	39246	39239	39232	39225	39217	39210	39203	39195	39188
0.19	39181	39173	39166	39158	39151	39143	39135	39128	39120	39112
0.20	39104	39096	39089	39081	39073	39065	39057	39049	39041	39032
0.21	39024	39016	39008	38999	38991	38983	38974	38966	38957	38949
0.22	38940	38932	38923	38915	38906	38897	38888	38880	38871	38862
0.23	38853	38844	38835	38826	38817	38808	38799	38789	38780	38771
0.24	38762	38752	38743	38734	38724	38715	38705	38696	38686	38676
0.25	38667	38657	38647	38638	38628	38618	38608	38598	38588	38578
0.26	38568	38558	38548	38538	38528	38518	38508	38497	38487	38477
0.27	38466	38456	38445	38435	38424	38414	38403	38393	38382	38371
0.28	38361	38350	38339	38328	38317	38306	38296	38285	38274	38263
0.29	38251	38240	38229	38218	38207	38196	38184	38173	38162	38150
0.30	38139	38127	38116	38104	38093	38081	38070	38058	38046	38034
0.31	38023	38011	37999	37987	37975	37963	37951	37939	37927	37915
0.32	37903	37891	37879	37867	37854	37842	37830	37817	37805	37793
0.33	37780	37768	37755	37743	37730	37717	37705	37692	37679	37667
0.34	37654	37641	37628	37615	37602	37589	37576	37563	37550	37537
0.35	37524	37511	37498	37484	37471	37458	37445	37431	37418	37405
0.36	37391	37378	37364	37351	37337	37323	37310	37296	37282	37269
0.37	37255	37241	37227	37213	37199	37186	37172	37158	37144	37129
0.38	37115	37101	37087	37073	37059	37044	37030	37016	37002	36987
0.39	36973	36958	36944	36929	36915	36900	36886	36871	36856	36842
0.40	36827	36812	36797	36783	36768	36753	36738	36723	36708	36693
0.41	36678	36663	36648	36633	36618	36603	36587	36572	36557	36542
0.42	36526	36511	36496	36480	36465	36449	36434	36418	36403	36387
0.43	36371	36356	36340	36324	36309	36293	36277	36261	36245	36229
0.44	36213	36198	36182	36166	36150	36133	36117	36101	36085	36069
0.45	36053	36036	36020	36004	35988	35971	35955	35938	35922	35906
0.46	35889	35873	35856	35839	35823	35806	35789	35773	35756	35739
0.47	35723	35706	35689	35672	35655	35638	35621	35604	35587	35570
0.48	35553	35536	35519	35502	35485	35468	35450	35433	35416	35399
0.49	35381	35364	35347	35329	35312	35294	35277	35259	35242	35224
0.50	35207	35189	35171	35154	35136	35118	35100	35083	35065	35047
0.51	35029	35011	34993	34975	34958	34940	34922	34904	34885	34867
0.52	34849	34831	34813	34795	34777	34758	34740	34722	34703	34685
0.53	34667	34648	34630	34612	34593	34575	34556	34538	34519	34500
0.54	34482	34463	34445	34426	34407	34388	34370	34351	34332	34313
0.55	34294	34276	34257	34238	34219	34200	34181	34162	34143	34124
0.56	34105	34085	34066	34047	34028	34009	33990	33970	33951	33932
0.57	33912	33893	33874	33854	33835	33815	33796	33777	33757	33738
0.58	33718	33698	33679	33659	33640	33620	33600	33581	33561	33541
0.59	33521	33502	33482	33462	33442	33422	33402	33382	33362	33342
0.60	33322	33302	33282	33262	33242	33222	33202	33182	33162	33142
0.61	33121	33101	33081	33061	33040	33020	33000	32980	32959	32939
0.62	32918	32898	32878	32857	32837	32816	32796	32775	32754	32734
0.63	32713	32693	32672	32651	32631	32610	32589	32569	32548	32527
0.64	32506	32485	32465	32444	32423	32402	32381	32360	32339	32318
0.65	32297	32276	32255	32234	32213	32192	32171	32150	32129	32108
0.66	32086	32065	32044	32023	32002	31980	31959	31938	31916	31895
0.67	31874	31852	31831	31810	31788	31767	31745	31724	31702	31681
0.68	31659	31638	31616	31595	31573	31551	31530	31508	31487	31465
0.69	31443	31421	31400	31378	31356	31334	31313	31291	31269	31247

|c| →	0.000	0.001	0.002	0.003	0.004	0.005	0.006	0.007	0.008	0.009
↓	0.	0.	0.	0.	0.	0.	0.	0.	0.	0.
0.70	31225	31204	31182	31160	31138	31116	31094	31072	31050	31028
0.71	31006	30984	30962	30940	30918	30896	30874	30852	30829	30807
0.72	30785	30763	30741	30719	30696	30674	30652	30630	30607	30585
0.73	30563	30540	30518	30496	30473	30451	30429	30406	30384	30361
0.74	30339	30316	30294	30272	30249	30227	30204	30181	30159	30136
0.75	30114	30091	30069	30046	30023	30001	29978	29955	29933	29910
0.76	29887	29865	29842	29819	29796	29774	29751	29728	29705	29682
0.77	29659	29637	29614	29591	29568	29545	29522	29499	29476	29453
0.78	29431	29408	29385	29362	29339	29316	29293	29270	29246	29223
0.79	29200	29177	29154	29131	29108	29085	29062	29039	29015	28992
0.80	28969	28946	28923	28900	28876	28853	28830	28807	28783	28760
0.81	28737	28714	28690	28667	28644	28620	28597	28574	28550	28527
0.82	28504	28480	28457	28433	28410	28387	28363	28340	28316	28293
0.83	28269	28246	28223	28199	28176	28152	28129	28105	28081	28058
0.84	28034	28011	27987	27964	27940	27917	27893	27869	27846	27822
0.85	27798	27775	27751	27728	27704	27680	27657	27633	27609	27586
0.86	27562	27538	27514	27491	27467	27443	27419	27396	27372	27348
0.87	27324	27301	27277	27253	27229	27205	27182	27158	27134	27110
0.88	27086	27063	27039	27015	26991	26967	26943	26919	26896	26872
0.89	26848	26824	26800	26776	26752	26728	26704	26680	26656	26632
0.90	26609	26585	26561	26537	26513	26489	26465	26441	26417	26393
0.91	26369	26345	26321	26297	26273	26249	26225	26201	26177	26153
0.92	26129	26105	26081	26056	26032	26008	25984	25960	25936	25912
0.93	25888	25864	25840	25816	25792	25768	25744	25719	25695	25671
0.94	25647	25623	25599	25575	25551	25527	25502	25478	25454	25430
0.95	25406	25382	25358	25333	25309	25285	25261	25237	25213	25189
0.96	25164	25140	25116	25092	25068	25044	25019	24995	24971	24947
0.97	24923	24899	24874	24850	24826	24802	24778	24754	24729	24705
0.98	24681	24657	24633	24608	24584	24560	24536	24512	24487	24463
0.99	24439	24415	24391	24366	24342	24318	24294	24270	24245	24221
1.00	24197	24173	24149	24124	24100	24076	24052	24028	24003	23979
1.01	23955	23931	23907	23883	23858	23834	23810	23786	23762	23737
1.02	23713	23689	23665	23641	23616	23592	23568	23544	23520	23496
1.03	23471	23447	23423	23399	23375	23351	23326	23302	23278	23254
1.04	23230	23206	23181	23157	23133	23109	23085	23061	23036	23012
1.05	22988	22964	22940	22916	22892	22868	22843	22819	22795	22771
1.06	22747	22723	22699	22675	22651	22626	22602	22578	22554	22530
1.07	22506	22482	22458	22434	22410	22386	22362	22338	22313	22289
1.08	22265	22241	22217	22193	22169	22145	22121	22097	22073	22049
1.09	22025	22001	21977	21953	21929	21905	21881	21857	21833	21809
1.1	21785	21546	21307	21069	20831	20594	20357	20121	19886	19652
1.2	19419	19186	18954	18724	18494	18265	18037	17810	17585	17360
1.3	17137	16915	16694	16474	16256	16038	15822	15608	15395	15183
1.4	14973	14764	14556	14350	14146	13943	13742	13542	13344	13147
1.5	12952	12758	12566	12376	12188	12001	11816	11632	11450	11270
1.6	11092	10915	10741	10567	10396	10226	10059	09893	09728	09566
1.7	09405	09246	09089	08933	08780	08628	08478	08329	08183	08038
1.8	07895	07754	07614	07477	07341	07206	07074	06943	06814	06687
1.9	06562	06438	06316	06195	06077	05959	05844	05730	05618	05508
2.0	05399	05292	05186	05082	04980	04879	04780	04682	04586	04491
2.1	04398	04307	04217	04128	04041	03955	03871	03788	03706	03626
2.2	03547	03470	03394	03319	03246	03174	03103	03034	02965	02898
2.3	02833	02768	02705	02643	02582	02522	02463	02406	02349	02294
2.4	02239	02186	02134	02083	02033	01984	01936	01888	01842	01797
2.5	01753	01709	01667	01625	01585	01545	01506	01468	01431	01394
2.6	01358	01323	01289	01256	01223	01191	01160	01130	01100	01071
2.7	01042	01014	00987	00961	00935	00909	00885	00861	00837	00814
2.8	00792	00770	00748	00727	00707	00687	00668	00649	00631	00613
2.9	00595	00578	00562	00545	00530	00514	00499	00485	00470	00457
3.0	00443	00430	00417	00405	00393	00381	00370	00358	00348	00337
3.1	00327	00317	00307	00298	00288	00279	00271	00262	00254	00246
3.2	00238	00231	00224	00216	00210	00203	00196	00190	00184	00178
3.3	00172	00167	00161	00156	00151	00146	00141	00136	00132	00127
3.4	00123	00119	00115	00111	00107	00104	00100	00097	00094	00090
3.5	00087	00084	00081	00079	00076	00073	00071	00068	00066	00063
3.6	00061	00059	00057	00055	00053	00051	00049	00047	00046	00044
3.7	00042	00041	00039	00038	00037	00035	00034	00033	00031	00030
3.8	00029	00028	00027	00026	00025	00024	00023	00022	00021	00021
3.9	00020	00019	00018	00018	00017	00016	00016	00015	00014	00014
4.0	00013	00013	00012	00012	00011	00011	00011	00010	00010	00009

Probability 2 P → Deviation c[2]

2 P = twice the integral between c and infinity

P →	0.00	0.01	0.02	0.03	0.04	0.05	0.06	0.07	0.08	0.09
	Deviation c									
	∞	2.575829	2.326348	2.170090	2.053749	1.959964	1.880794	1.811911	1.750686	1.695398
	1.644854	1.598193	1.554774	1.514102	1.475791	1.439531	1.405072	1.372204	1.340755	1.310579
	1.281552	1.253565	1.226528	1.200359	1.174987	1.150349	1.126391	1.103063	1.080319	1.058122
	1.036433	1.015222	0.994458	0.974114	0.954165	0.934589	0.915365	0.896473	0.877896	0.859617
	0.841621	0.823894	0.806421	0.789192	0.772193	0.755415	0.738847	0.722479	0.706303	0.690309
	0.674490	0.658838	0.643345	0.628006	0.612813	0.597760	0.582842	0.568051	0.553385	0.538836
	0.524401	0.510073	0.495850	0.481727	0.467699	0.453762	0.439913	0.426148	0.412463	0.398855
	0.385320	0.371856	0.358459	0.345126	0.331853	0.318639	0.305481	0.292375	0.279319	0.266311
	0.253347	0.240426	0.227545	0.214702	0.201893	0.189118	0.176374	0.163658	0.150969	0.138304
	0.125661	0.113039	0.100434	0.087845	0.075270	0.062707	0.050154	0.037608	0.025069	0.012533
	Very small values of P									
	. .	. .	. .	0.001 3.29053	0.000 1 3.89059	0.000 01 4.41717	0.000 001 4.89164	0.000 000 1 5.32672	0.000 000 01 5.73073	0.000 000 001 6.10941

Values abridged from National Bureau of Standards *Tables of Normal Probability Functions,* Applied Mathematics Series 23, Washington, 1953. Reproduction y by permission of the publishers of these *Scientific Tables,* J. R. Geigy S. A., Basle (Switzerland). 2) Values from FISHER and YATES, *Statistical Tables for logical, Agricultural and Medical Research,* 4th ed., Oliver and Boyd, Edinburgh, 1953, page 39. Reprinted by kind permission of the authors and publishers.

Significance Limits of the STUDENT Distribution* ν=1—50

$P = P$ (right) = integral between t and infinity. P (left) = P (right)

2 P	0.9995	0.999	0.995	0.99	0.98	0.975	0.95	0.90	0.80	0.70	0.60	0.50	0.40	0.30	0.20	0.10	0.05	0.025	0.02	0.01	0.005	0.001
P	0.49975	0.4995	0.4975	0.495	0.49	0.4875	0.475	0.45	0.40	0.35	0.30	0.25	0.20	0.15	0.10	0.05	0.025	0.0125	0.01	0.005	0.0025	0.0005
ν																						
1	0.0008	0.0015	0.0077	0.0154	0.030	0.0385	0.0770	0.1580	0.3250	0.5100	0.7270	1.0000	1.376	1.963	3.078	6.3138	12.706	25.452	31.821	63.657	127.32	636.619
2	0.0007	0.0014	0.0071	0.0141	0.028	0.0353	0.0707	0.1419	0.2885	0.4448	0.6172	0.8165	1.061	1.386	1.886	2.9200	4.3027	6.2053	6.965	9.9248	14.089	31.598
3	0.0007	0.0014	0.0068	0.0136	0.027	0.0340	0.0681	0.1366	0.2766	0.4243	0.5840	0.7649	0.978	1.250	1.638	2.3534	3.1825	4.1765	4.541	5.8409	7.4533	12.924
4	0.0007	0.0013	0.0067	0.0133	0.026	0.0333	0.0667	0.1338	0.2707	0.4143	0.5692	0.7407	0.941	1.190	1.533	2.1318	2.7764	3.4954	3.747	4.6041	5.5976	8.610
5	0.0007	0.0013	0.0066	0.0132	0.026	0.0329	0.0659	0.1322	0.2672	0.4083	0.5598	0.7267	0.920	1.156	1.476	2.0150	2.5706	3.1634	3.365	4.0321	4.7733	6.869
6	0.0007	0.0013	0.0065	0.0131	0.026	0.0327	0.0654	0.1311	0.2648	0.4044	0.5536	0.7176	0.906	1.134	1.440	1.9432	2.4469	2.9687	3.143	3.7074	4.3168	5.959
7	0.0006	0.0013	0.0065	0.0130	0.025	0.0325	0.0650	0.1303	0.2632	0.4016	0.5493	0.7111	0.896	1.119	1.415	1.8946	2.3646	2.8412	2.998	3.4995	4.0293	5.408
8	0.0006	0.0013	0.0065	0.0129	0.025	0.0323	0.0647	0.1297	0.2619	0.3995	0.5461	0.7064	0.889	1.108	1.397	1.8595	2.3060	2.7515	2.896	3.3554	3.8325	5.041
9	0.0006	0.0013	0.0064	0.0129	0.025	0.0322	0.0645	0.1293	0.2610	0.3979	0.5436	0.7027	0.883	1.100	1.383	1.8331	2.2622	2.6850	2.821	3.2498	3.6897	4.781
10	0.0006	0.0013	0.0064	0.0129	0.025	0.0321	0.0643	0.1289	0.2602	0.3966	0.5416	0.6998	0.879	1.093	1.372	1.8125	2.2281	2.6338	2.764	3.1693	3.5814	4.587
11	0.0006	0.0013	0.0064	0.0128	0.025	0.0321	0.0642	0.1286	0.2596	0.3956	0.5400	0.6975	0.876	1.088	1.363	1.7959	2.2010	2.5931	2.718	3.1058	3.4966	4.437
12	0.0006	0.0013	0.0064	0.0128	0.025	0.0320	0.0640	0.1283	0.2590	0.3947	0.5387	0.6955	0.873	1.083	1.356	1.7823	2.1788	2.5600	2.681	3.0545	3.4284	4.318
13	0.0006	0.0013	0.0064	0.0128	0.025	0.0319	0.0639	0.1281	0.2586	0.3940	0.5375	0.6938	0.870	1.079	1.350	1.7709	2.1604	2.5326	2.650	3.0123	3.3725	4.221
14	0.0006	0.0013	0.0064	0.0128	0.025	0.0319	0.0638	0.1280	0.2582	0.3933	0.5366	0.6924	0.868	1.076	1.345	1.7613	2.1448	2.5096	2.624	2.9768	3.3257	4.140
15	0.0006	0.0013	0.0064	0.0127	0.025	0.0319	0.0638	0.1278	0.2579	0.3928	0.5358	0.6912	0.866	1.074	1.341	1.7530	2.1315	2.4899	2.602	2.9467	3.2860	4.073
16	0.0006	0.0013	0.0064	0.0127	0.025	0.0318	0.0637	0.1277	0.2576	0.3923	0.5350	0.6901	0.865	1.071	1.337	1.7459	2.1199	2.4729	2.583	2.9208	3.2520	4.015
17	0.0006	0.0013	0.0064	0.0127	0.025	0.0318	0.0636	0.1276	0.2574	0.3919	0.5344	0.6892	0.863	1.069	1.333	1.7396	2.1098	2.4581	2.567	2.8982	3.2225	3.965
18	0.0006	0.0013	0.0064	0.0127	0.025	0.0318	0.0636	0.1274	0.2571	0.3915	0.5338	0.6884	0.862	1.067	1.330	1.7341	2.1009	2.4450	2.552	2.8784	3.1966	3.922
19	0.0006	0.0013	0.0063	0.0127	0.025	0.0318	0.0635	0.1274	0.2569	0.3912	0.5333	0.6876	0.861	1.066	1.328	1.7291	2.0930	2.4334	2.539	2.8609	3.1737	3.883
20	0.0006	0.0013	0.0063	0.0127	0.025	0.0317	0.0635	0.1273	0.2567	0.3909	0.5329	0.6870	0.860	1.064	1.325	1.7247	2.0860	2.4231	2.528	2.8453	3.1534	3.850
21	0.0006	0.0013	0.0063	0.0127	0.025	0.0317	0.0635	0.1272	0.2566	0.3906	0.5325	0.6864	0.859	1.063	1.323	1.7207	2.0796	2.4138	2.518	2.8314	3.1352	3.819
22	0.0006	0.0013	0.0063	0.0127	0.025	0.0317	0.0634	0.1271	0.2564	0.3904	0.5321	0.6858	0.858	1.061	1.321	1.7171	2.0739	2.4055	2.508	2.8188	3.1188	3.792
23	0.0006	0.0013	0.0063	0.0127	0.025	0.0317	0.0634	0.1271	0.2563	0.3902	0.5318	0.6853	0.858	1.060	1.319	1.7139	2.0687	2.3979	2.500	2.8073	3.1040	3.767
24	0.0006	0.0013	0.0063	0.0127	0.025	0.0317	0.0634	0.1270	0.2562	0.3900	0.5315	0.6849	0.857	1.059	1.318	1.7109	2.0639	2.3910	2.492	2.7969	3.0905	3.745
25	0.0006	0.0013	0.0063	0.0127	0.025	0.0317	0.0633	0.1269	0.2561	0.3898	0.5312	0.6844	0.856	1.058	1.316	1.7081	2.0595	2.3846	2.485	2.7874	3.0782	3.725
26	0.0006	0.0013	0.0063	0.0127	0.025	0.0316	0.0633	0.1269	0.2560	0.3896	0.5309	0.6841	0.856	1.058	1.315	1.7056	2.0555	2.3788	2.479	2.7787	3.0669	3.707
27	0.0006	0.0013	0.0063	0.0126	0.025	0.0316	0.0633	0.1269	0.2559	0.3895	0.5307	0.6837	0.855	1.057	1.314	1.7033	2.0518	2.3734	2.473	2.7707	3.0565	3.690
28	0.0006	0.0013	0.0063	0.0126	0.025	0.0316	0.0633	0.1268	0.2558	0.3893	0.5304	0.6834	0.855	1.056	1.313	1.7011	2.0484	2.3685	2.467	2.7633	3.0469	3.674
29	0.0006	0.0013	0.0063	0.0126	0.025	0.0316	0.0633	0.1268	0.2557	0.3892	0.5302	0.6830	0.854	1.055	1.311	1.6991	2.0452	2.3638	2.462	2.7564	3.0380	3.659
30	0.0006	0.0013	0.0063	0.0126	0.025	0.0316	0.0632	0.1267	0.2556	0.3890	0.5300	0.6828	0.854	1.055	1.310	1.6973	2.0423	2.3596	2.457	2.7500	3.0298	3.646
31	0.0006	0.0013	0.0063	0.0126	0.025	0.0316	0.0632	0.1267	0.2555	0.3889	0.5298	0.6825	0.8535	1.0541	1.3095	1.6955	2.0395	2.3556	2.453	2.7441	3.0222	3.6338
32	0.0006	0.0013	0.0063	0.0126	0.025	0.0316	0.0632	0.1267	0.2555	0.3888	0.5297	0.6823	0.8531	1.0536	1.3086	1.6939	2.0370	2.3519	2.449	2.7385	3.0150	3.6221
33	0.0006	0.0013	0.0063	0.0126	0.025	0.0316	0.0632	0.1266	0.2554	0.3887	0.5295	0.6820	0.8527	1.0531	1.3078	1.6924	2.0345	2.3484	2.445	2.7333	3.0083	3.6111
34	0.0006	0.0013	0.0063	0.0126	0.025	0.0316	0.0632	0.1266	0.2553	0.3886	0.5294	0.6818	0.8524	1.0526	1.3070	1.6909	2.0323	2.3451	2.441	2.7284	3.0020	3.6011
35	0.0006	0.0013	0.0063	0.0126	0.025	0.0316	0.0632	0.1266	0.2553	0.3885	0.5292	0.6816	0.8521	1.0521	1.3062	1.6896	2.0301	2.3420	2.438	2.7239	2.9962	3.5915
36	0.0006	0.0013	0.0063	0.0126	0.025	0.0316	0.0631	0.1266	0.2552	0.3884	0.5291	0.6814	0.8518	1.0516	1.3055	1.6883	2.0281	2.3391	2.434	2.7195	2.9905	3.5824
37	0.0006	0.0013	0.0063	0.0126	0.025	0.0316	0.0631	0.1265	0.2552	0.3883	0.5290	0.6812	0.8515	1.0512	1.3049	1.6871	2.0262	2.3364	2.431	2.7155	2.9853	3.5741
38	0.0006	0.0013	0.0063	0.0126	0.025	0.0315	0.0631	0.1265	0.2551	0.3883	0.5288	0.6810	0.8512	1.0508	1.3042	1.6860	2.0244	2.3338	2.428	2.7116	2.9804	3.5661
39	0.0006	0.0013	0.0063	0.0126	0.025	0.0315	0.0631	0.1265	0.2551	0.3882	0.5287	0.6808	0.8510	1.0504	1.3037	1.6849	2.0227	2.3313	2.426	2.7079	2.9757	3.5586
40	0.0006	0.0013	0.0063	0.0126	0.025	0.0315	0.0631	0.1265	0.2550	0.3881	0.5286	0.6807	0.8507	1.0501	1.3031	1.6839	2.0211	2.3290	2.423	2.7045	2.9713	3.5511
41	0.0006	0.0013	0.0063	0.0126	0.025	0.0315	0.0631	0.1264	0.2550	0.3880	0.5285	0.6805	0.8505	1.0498	1.3026	1.6829	2.0196	2.3268	2.421	2.7012	2.9671	3.5446
42	0.0006	0.0013	0.0063	0.0126	0.025	0.0315	0.0631	0.1264	0.2550	0.3880	0.5284	0.6804	0.8503	1.0494	1.3020	1.6820	2.0181	2.3247	2.418	2.6981	2.9631	3.5383
43	0.0006	0.0013	0.0063	0.0126	0.025	0.0315	0.0631	0.1264	0.2549	0.3879	0.5283	0.6803	0.8501	1.0491	1.3016	1.6811	2.0167	2.3226	2.416	2.6952	2.9592	3.5323
44	0.0006	0.0013	0.0063	0.0126	0.025	0.0315	0.0631	0.1264	0.2549	0.3879	0.5282	0.6801	0.8499	1.0488	1.3011	1.6802	2.0154	2.3207	2.414	2.6923	2.9556	3.5264
45	0.0006	0.0013	0.0063	0.0126	0.025	0.0315	0.0631	0.1264	0.2549	0.3878	0.5281	0.6800	0.8497	1.0485	1.3007	1.6794	2.0141	2.3189	2.412	2.6896	2.9522	3.5207
46	0.0006	0.0013	0.0063	0.0126	0.025	0.0315	0.0631	0.1264	0.2548	0.3877	0.5281	0.6799	0.8495	1.0483	1.3002	1.6787	2.0129	2.3172	2.410	2.6870	2.9489	3.5153
47	0.0006	0.0013	0.0063	0.0126	0.025	0.0315	0.0630	0.1263	0.2548	0.3877	0.5280	0.6798	0.8494	1.0480	1.2998	1.6779	2.0118	2.3155	2.408	2.6846	2.9457	3.5104
48	0.0006	0.0013	0.0063	0.0126	0.025	0.0315	0.0630	0.1263	0.2548	0.3876	0.5279	0.6796	0.8492	1.0478	1.2994	1.6772	2.0106	2.3139	2.406	2.6822	2.9427	3.5053
49	0.0006	0.0013	0.0063	0.0126	0.025	0.0315	0.0630	0.1263	0.2547	0.3876	0.5278	0.6795	0.8490	1.0476	1.2991	1.6766	2.0096	2.3124	2.405	2.6800	2.9398	3.5010
50	0.0006	0.0013	0.0063	0.0126	0.025	0.0315	0.0630	0.1263	0.2547	0.3875	0.5278	0.6794	0.8489	1.0473	1.2987	1.6759	2.00[illegible]	[illegible]3109	2.403	2.6778	2.9370	3.4965

Significance Limits of the STUDENT Distribution* ν = 51—100

$P = P$ (right) = integral between t and infinity. P (left) = P (right)

2 P	0.9995	0.999	0.995	0.99	0.98	0.975	0.95	0.90	0.80	0.70	0.60	0.50	0.40	0.30	0.20	0.10	0.05	0.025	0.02	0.01	0.005	0.001
P	0.49975	0.4995	0.4975	0.495	0.49	0.4875	0.475	0.45	0.40	0.35	0.30	0.25	0.20	0.15	0.10	0.05	0.025	0.0125	0.01	0.005	0.0025	0.0005
ν																						
51	0.0006	0.0013	0.0063	0.0126	0.025	0.0315	0.0630	0.1263	0.2547	0.3875	0.5277	0.6793	0.8488	1.0471	1.2984	1.6753	2.0077	2.3096	2.402	2.6758	2.9344	3.4924
52	0.0006	0.0013	0.0063	0.0126	0.025	0.0315	0.0630	0.1263-	0.2547	0.3875	0.5276	0.6792	0.8486	1.0469	1.2981	1.6747	2.0067	2.3082	2.400	2.6738	2.9318	3.4883
53	0.0006	0.0013	0.0063	0.0126	0.025	0.0315	0.0630	0.1263	0.2547	0.3875	0.5276	0.6792	0.8485	1.0467	1.2978	1.6742	2.0058	2.3070	2.399	2.6719	2.9295	3.4845
54	0.0006	0.0013	0.0063	0.0126	0.025	0.0315	0.0630	0.1263	0.2546	0.3874	0.5275	0.6791	0.8484	1.0465	1.2975	1.6736	2.0049	2.3057	2.397	2.6700	2.9271	3.4807
55	0.0006	0.0013	0.0063	0.0126	0.025	0.0315	0.0630	0.1263	0.2546	0.3874	0.5275	0.6790	0.8483	1.0463	1.2972	1.6731	2.0041	2.3045	2.396	2.6683	2.9249	3.4770
56	0.0006	0.0013	0.0063	0.0126	0.025	0.0315	0.0630	0.1262	0.2546	0.3873	0.5274	0.6789	0.8481	1.0461	1.2969	1.6725	2.0033	2.3033	2.395	2.6666	2.9226	3.4733
57	0.0006	0.0013	0.0063	0.0126	0.025	0.0315	0.0630	0.1262	0.2546	0.3873	0.5274	0.6789	0.8480	1.0460	1.2967	1.6721	2.0025	2.3022	2.393	2.6650	2.9205	3.4702
58	0.0006	0.0013	0.0063	0.0126	0.025	0.0315	0.0630	0.1262	0.2545	0.3872	0.5273	0.6788	0.8479	1.0458	1.2964	1.6716	2.0017	2.3011	2.392	2.6633	2.9184	3.4670
59	0.0006	0.0013	0.0063	0.0126	0.025	0.0315	0.0630	0.1262	0.2545	0.3872	0.5273	0.6787	0.8478	1.0457	1.2962	1.6712	2.0010	2.3001	2.391	2.6618	2.9165	3.4638
60	0.0006	0.0013	0.0063	0.0126	0.025	0.0315	0.0630	0.1262	0.2545	0.3872	0.5272	0.6786	0.8477	1.0455	1.2959	1.6707	2.0003	2.2991	2.390	2.6603	2.9146	3.4606
61	0.0006	0.0013	0.0063	0.0126	0.025	0.0315	0.0630	0.1262	0.2545	0.3872	0.5272	0.6786	0.8476	1.0454	1.2957	1.6703	1.9997	2.2982	2.389	2.6590	2.9128	3.4577
62	0.0006	0.0013	0.0063	0.0126	0.025	0.0315	0.0630	0.1262	0.2544	0.3871	0.5271	0.6785	0.8475	1.0452	1.2954	1.6698	1.9990	2.2972	2.388	2.6576	2.9110	3.4548
63	0.0006	0.0013	0.0063	0.0126	0.025	0.0315	0.0630	0.1262	0.2544	0.3871	0.5271	0.6785	0.8474	1.0451	1.2952	1.6694	1.9984	2.2963	2.387	2.6563	2.9094	3.4521
64	0.0006	0.0013	0.0063	0.0126	0.025	0.0315	0.0630	0.1262	0.2544	0.3871	0.5270	0.6784	0.8473	1.0449	1.2950	1.6690	1.9977	2.2954	2.386	2.6549	2.9077	3.4494
65	0.0006	0.0013	0.0063	0.0126	0.025	0.0315	0.0630	0.1262	0.2544	0.3871	0.5270	0.6783	0.8472	1.0448	1.2948	1.6687	1.9972	2.2946	2.385	2.6537	2.9061	3.4470
66	0.0006	0.0013	0.0063	0.0126	0.025	0.0315	0.0629	0.1261	0.2544	0.3870	0.5270	0.6782	0.8471	1.0447	1.2945	1.6683	1.9966	2.2937	2.384	2.6525	2.9045	3.4445
67	0.0006	0.0013	0.0063	0.0126	0.025	0.0315	0.0629	0.1261	0.2544	0.3870	0.5270	0.6782	0.8471	1.0446	1.2944	1.6680	1.9961	2.2929	2.383	2.6513	2.9031	3.4423
68	0.0006	0.0013	0.0063	0.0126	0.025	0.0315	0.0629	0.1261	0.2543	0.3870	0.5269	0.6781	0.8470	1.0444	1.2942	1.6676	1.9955	2.2921	2.382	2.6501	2.9016	3.4400
69	0.0006	0.0013	0.0063	0.0126	0.025	0.0315	0.0629	0.1261	0.2543	0.3870	0.5269	0.6781	0.8469	1.0443	1.2940	1.6673	1.9950	2.2914	2.381	2.6491	2.9002	3.4378
70	0.0006	0.0013	0.0063	0.0126	0.025	0.0315	0.0629	0.1261	0.2543	0.3869	0.5268	0.6780	0.8468	1.0442	1.2938	1.6669	1.9945	2.2907	2.381	2.6480	2.8988	3.4355
71	0.0006	0.0013	0.0063	0.0126	0.025	0.0315	0.0629	0.1261	0.2543	0.3869	0.5268	0.6780	0.8468	1.0441	1.2936	1.6666	1.9940	2.2900	2.380	2.6470	2.8976	3.4333
72	0.0006	0.0013	0.0063	0.0126	0.025	0.0314	0.0629	0.1261	0.2543	0.3869	0.5267	0.6779	0.8467	1.0440	1.2934	1.6663	1.9935	2.2893	2.379	2.6459	2.8963	3.4310
73	0.0006	0.0013	0.0063	0.0126	0.025	0.0314	0.0629	0.1261	0.2543	0.3869	0.5267	0.6779	0.8466	1.0439	1.2933	1.6660	1.9931	2.2887	2.378	2.6450	2.8950	3.4291
74	0.0006	0.0013	0.0063	0.0126	0.025	0.0314	0.0629	0.1261	0.2543	0.3868	0.5267	0.6778	0.8465	1.0438	1.2931	1.6657	1.9926	2.2880	2.378	2.6440	2.8937	3.4272
75	0.0006	0.0013	0.0063	0.0126	0.025	0.0314	0.0629	0.1261	0.2543	0.3868	0.5267	0.6778	0.8465	1.0437	1.2930	1.6655	1.9922	2.2874	2.377	2.6431	2.8925	3.4253
76	0.0006	0.0013	0.0063	0.0126	0.025	0.0314	0.0629	0.1261	0.2542	0.3868	0.5266	0.6777	0.8464	1.0436	1.2928	1.6652	1.9917	2.2867	2.376	2.6421	2.8913	3.4234
77	0.0006	0.0013	0.0063	0.0126	0.025	0.0314	0.0629	0.1261	0.2542	0.3868	0.5266	0.6777	0.8464	1.0435	1.2927	1.6649	1.9913	2.2861	2.376	2.6413	2.8903	3.4217
78	0.0006	0.0013	0.0063	0.0126	0.025	0.0314	0.0629	0.1261	0.2542	0.3867	0.5266	0.6777	0.8463	1.0434	1.2925	1.6646	1.9909	2.2855	2.375	2.6404	2.8892	3.4200
79	0.0006	0.0013	0.0063	0.0126	0.025	0.0314	0.0629	0.1261	0.2542	0.3867	0.5266	0.6777	0.8463	1.0433	1.2924	1.6644	1.9905	2.2850	2.374	2.6396	2.8882	3.4185
80	0.0006	0.0013	0.0063	0.0126	0.025	0.0314	0.0629	0.1261	0.2542	0.3867	0.5265	0.6776	0.8462	1.0432	1.2922	1.6641	1.9901	2.2844	2.374	2.6388	2.8871	3.4169
81	0.0006	0.0013	0.0063	0.0126	0.025	0.0314	0.0629	0.1261	0.2542	0.3867	0.5265	0.6776	0.8461	1.0431	1.2921	1.6639	1.9897	2.2839	2.373	2.6380	2.8861	3.4152
82	0.0006	0.0013	0.0063	0.0126	0.025	0.0314	0.0629	0.1261	0.2542	0.3867	0.5265	0.6775	0.8460	1.0430	1.2920	1.6637	1.9893	2.2833	2.372	2.6372	2.8851	3.4135
83	0.0006	0.0013	0.0063	0.0126	0.025	0.0314	0.0629	0.1261	0.2542	0.3867	0.5265	0.6775	0.8460	1.0430	1.2919	1.6635	1.9890	2.2828	2.372	2.6365	2.8842	3.4121
84	0.0006	0.0013	0.0063	0.0126	0.025	0.0314	0.0629	0.1260	0.2542	0.3866	0.5264	0.6774	0.8459	1.0429	1.2917	1.6632	1.9886	2.2823	2.371	2.6357	2.8832	3.4106
85	0.0006	0.0013	0.0063	0.0126	0.025	0.0314	0.0629	0.1260	0.2542	0.3866	0.5264	0.6774	0.8459	1.0428	1.2916	1.6630	1.9883	2.2818	2.371	2.6350	2.8823	3.4091
86	0.0006	0.0013	0.0063	0.0126	0.025	0.0314	0.0629	0.1260	0.2541	0.3866	0.5264	0.6774	0.8458	1.0427	1.2915	1.6628	1.9880	2.2813	2.370	2.6343	2.8814	3.4076
87	0.0006	0.0013	0.0063	0.0126	0.025	0.0314	0.0629	0.1260	0.2541	0.3866	0.5264	0.6774	0.8458	1.0427	1.2914	1.6626	1.9877	2.2809	2.370	2.6336	2.8805	3.4063
88	0.0006	0.0013	0.0063	0.0126	0.025	0.0314	0.0629	0.1260	0.2541	0.3866	0.5263	0.6773	0.8457	1.0426	1.2913	1.6624	1.9873	2.2804	2.369	2.6329	2.8796	3.4050
89	0.0006	0.0013	0.0063	0.0126	0.025	0.0314	0.0629	0.1260	0.2541	0.3866	0.5263	0.6773	0.8457	1.0426	1.2912	1.6622	1.9870	2.2800	2.369	2.6323	2.8788	3.4036
90	0.0006	0.0013	0.0063	0.0126	0.025	0.0314	0.0629	0.1260	0.2541	0.3866	0.5263	0.6772	0.8457	1.0425	1.2910	1.6620	1.9867	2.2795	2.368	2.6316	2.8779	3.4022
91	0.0006	0.0013	0.0063	0.0126	0.025	0.0314	0.0629	0.1260	0.2541	0.3866	0.5263	0.6772	0.8457	1.0424	1.2909	1.6618	1.9864	2.2791	2.368	2.6310	2.8772	3.4010
92	0.0006	0.0013	0.0063	0.0126	0.025	0.0314	0.0629	0.1260	0.2541	0.3865	0.5262	0.6772	0.8456	1.0423	1.2908	1.6616	1.9861	2.2787	2.367	2.6303	2.8764	3.3997
93	0.0006	0.0013	0.0063	0.0126	0.025	0.0314	0.0629	0.1260	0.2541	0.3865	0.5262	0.6772	0.8456	1.0423	1.2907	1.6614	1.9859	2.2783	2.367	2.6298	2.8757	3.3986
94	0.0006	0.0013	0.0063	0.0126	0.025	0.0314	0.0629	0.1260	0.2541	0.3865	0.5262	0.6771	0.8455	1.0422	1.2906	1.6612	1.9856	2.2779	2.366	2.6292	2.8749	3.3975
95	0.0006	0.0013	0.0063	0.0126	0.025	0.0314	0.0629	0.1260	0.2541	0.3865	0.5262	0.6771	0.8455	1.0422	1.2905	1.6611	1.9853	2.2775	2.366	2.6286	2.8742	3.3964
96	0.0006	0.0013	0.0063	0.0126	0.025	0.0314	0.0629	0.1260	0.2541	0.3865	0.5262	0.6771	0.8454	1.0421	1.2904	1.6609	1.9850	2.2771	2.366	2.6280	2.8734	3.3952
97	0.0006	0.0013	0.0063	0.0126	0.025	0.0314	0.0629	0.1260	0.2541	0.3865	0.5262	0.6771	0.8454	1.0421	1.2904	1.6608	1.9848	2.2768	2.365	2.6275	2.8728	3.3940
98	0.0006	0.0013	0.0063	0.0126	0.025	0.0314	0.0629	0.1260	0.2540	0.3865	0.5261	0.6770	0.8453	1.0420	1.2903	1.6606	1.9845	2.2764	2.365	2.6270	2.8721	3.3928
99	0.0006	0.0013	0.0063	0.0126	0.025	0.0314	0.0629	0.1260	0.2540	0.3865	0.5261	0.6770	0.8453	1.0419	1.2902	1.6604	1.9843	2.2761	2.364	2.6265	2.8714	3.3919
100	0.0006	0.0013	0.0063	0.0126	0.025	0.0314	0.0629	0.1260	0.2540	0.3864	0.5261	0.6770	0.8452	1.0418	1.2901	1.6602	1.9840	2.2757	2.364	2.6260	2.8707	3.3909

Significance Limits of the STUDENT Distribution* ν = 101—150

$P = P$ (right) = integral between t and infinity. P (left) = P (right)

2 P	0.9995	0.999	0.995	0.99	0.98	0.975	0.95	0.90	0.80	0.70	0.60	0.50	0.40	0.30	0.20	0.10	0.05	0.025	0.02	0.01	0.005	0.001
P	0.49975	0.4995	0.4975	0.495	0.49	0.4875	0.475	0.45	0.40	0.35	0.30	0.25	0.20	0.15	0.10	0.05	0.025	0.0125	0.01	0.005	0.0025	0.0005
ν																						
101	0.0006	0.0013	0.0063	0.0126	0.025	0.0314	0.0629	0.1260	0.2540	0.3864	0.5261	0.6770	0.8452	1.0418	1.2900	1.6601	1.9838	2.2754	2.364	2.6255	2.8701	3.3899
102	0.0006	0.0013	0.0063	0.0126	0.025	0.0314	0.0629	0.1260	0.2540	0.3864	0.5261	0.6769	0.8452	1.0417	1.2899	1.6599	1.9835	2.2750	2.363	2.6249	2.8695	3.3888
103	0.0006	0.0013	0.0063	0.0126	0.025	0.0314	0.0629	0.1260	0.2540	0.3864	0.5261	0.6769	0.8452	1.0417	1.2899	1.6598	1.9833	2.2747	2.363	2.6245	2.8689	3.3879
104	0.0006	0.0013	0.0063	0.0126	0.025	0.0314	0.0629	0.1260	0.2540	0.3864	0.5260	0.6769	0.8451	1.0416	1.2898	1.6596	1.9831	2.2743	2.363	2.6240	2.8682	3.3870
105	0.0006	0.0013	0.0063	0.0126	0.025	0.0314	0.0629	0.1260	0.2540	0.3864	0.5260	0.6769	0.8451	1.0416	1.2897	1.6595	1.9829	2.2740	2.362	2.6236	2.8677	3.3860
106	0.0006	0.0013	0.0063	0.0126	0.025	0.0314	0.0629	0.1260	0.2540	0.3864	0.5260	0.6768	0.8450	1.0415	1.2896	1.6594	1.9826	2.2737	2.362	2.6231	2.8671	3.3850
107	0.0006	0.0013	0.0063	0.0126	0.025	0.0314	0.0629	0.1260	0.2540	0.3864	0.5260	0.6768	0.8450	1.0415	1.2895	1.6593	1.9824	2.2734	2.362	2.6227	2.8665	3.3840
108	0.0006	0.0013	0.0063	0.0126	0.025	0.0314	0.0629	0.1260	0.2540	0.3864	0.5260	0.6768	0.8450	1.0414	1.2894	1.6591	1.9822	2.2731	2.361	2.6222	2.8659	3.3830
109	0.0006	0.0013	0.0063	0.0126	0.025	0.0314	0.0629	0.1260	0.2540	0.3864	0.5260	0.6768	0.8450	1.0414	1.2894	1.6590	1.9820	2.2728	2.361	2.6218	2.8654	3.3823
110	0.0006	0.0013	0.0063	0.0126	0.025	0.0314	0.0629	0.1260	0.2540	0.3863	0.5259	0.6767	0.8449	1.0414	1.2893	1.6588	1.9818	2.2725	2.361	2.6213	2.8648	3.3816
111	0.0006	0.0013	0.0063	0.0126	0.025	0.0314	0.0629	0.1260	0.2540	0.3863	0.5259	0.6767	0.8449	1.0414	1.2893	1.6587	1.9816	2.2723	2.360	2.6209	2.8643	3.3808
112	0.0006	0.0013	0.0063	0.0126	0.025	0.0314	0.0628	0.1259	0.2540	0.3863	0.5259	0.6767	0.8449	1.0413	1.2892	1.6586	1.9814	2.2720	2.360	2.6205	2.8638	3.3800
113	0.0006	0.0013	0.0063	0.0126	0.025	0.0314	0.0628	0.1259	0.2540	0.3863	0.5259	0.6767	0.8449	1.0413	1.2891	1.6585	1.9812	2.2717	2.360	2.6201	2.8633	3.3791
114	0.0006	0.0013	0.0063	0.0126	0.025	0.0314	0.0628	0.1259	0.2539	0.3863	0.5259	0.6767	0.8448	1.0412	1.2890	1.6583	1.9810	2.2714	2.359	2.6197	2.8627	3.3782
115	0.0006	0.0013	0.0063	0.0126	0.025	0.0314	0.0628	0.1259	0.2539	0.3863	0.5259	0.6767	0.8448	1.0412	1.2890	1.6582	1.9808	2.2712	2.359	2.6193	2.8623	3.3775
116	0.0006	0.0013	0.0063	0.0126	0.025	0.0314	0.0628	0.1259	0.2539	0.3863	0.5259	0.6766	0.8447	1.0411	1.2889	1.6581	1.9806	2.2709	2.359	2.6189	2.8618	3.3767
117	0.0006	0.0013	0.0063	0.0126	0.025	0.0314	0.0628	0.1259	0.2539	0.3863	0.5259	0.6766	0.8447	1.0411	1.2889	1.6580	1.9805	2.2707	2.359	2.6186	2.8613	3.3760
118	0.0006	0.0013	0.0063	0.0126	0.025	0.0314	0.0628	0.1259	0.2539	0.3863	0.5258	0.6766	0.8447	1.0410	1.2888	1.6579	1.9803	2.2704	2.358	2.6182	2.8608	3.3752
119	0.0006	0.0013	0.0063	0.0126	0.025	0.0314	0.0628	0.1259	0.2539	0.3863	0.5258	0.6766	0.8447	1.0410	1.2888	1.6578	1.9801	2.2702	2.358	2.6179	2.8604	3.3744
120	0.0006	0.0013	0.0063	0.0126	0.025	0.0314	0.0628	0.1259	0.2539	0.3862	0.5258	0.6765	0.8446	1.0409	1.2887	1.6577	1.9799	2.2699	2.358	2.6175	2.8599	3.3736
121	0.0006	0.0013	0.0063	0.0126	0.025	0.0314	0.0628	0.1259	0.2539	0.3862	0.5258	0.6765	0.8446	1.0409	1.2886	1.6576	1.9798	2.2697	2.357	2.6172	2.8595	3.3729
122	0.0006	0.0013	0.0063	0.0126	0.025	0.0314	0.0628	0.1259	0.2539	0.3862	0.5258	0.6765	0.8446	1.0409	1.2885	1.6575	1.9796	2.2694	2.357	2.6168	2.8591	3.3721
123	0.0006	0.0013	0.0063	0.0126	0.025	0.0314	0.0628	0.1259	0.2539	0.3862	0.5258	0.6765	0.8446	1.0409	1.2885	1.6574	1.9795	2.2692	2.357	2.6165	2.8587	3.3715
124	0.0006	0.0013	0.0063	0.0126	0.025	0.0314	0.0628	0.1259	0.2539	0.3862	0.5258	0.6765	0.8445	1.0408	1.2884	1.6573	1.9793	2.2690	2.357	2.6161	2.8582	3.3709
125	0.0006	0.0013	0.0063	0.0126	0.025	0.0314	0.0628	0.1259	0.2539	0.3862	0.5258	0.6765	0.8445	1.0408	1.2884	1.6572	1.9792	2.2688	2.356	2.6158	2.8578	3.3702
126	0.0006	0.0013	0.0063	0.0126	0.025	0.0314	0.0628	0.1259	0.2539	0.3862	0.5257	0.6765	0.8445	1.0407	1.2883	1.6571	1.9790	2.2685	2.356	2.6155	2.8574	3.3694
127	0.0006	0.0013	0.0063	0.0126	0.025	0.0314	0.0628	0.1259	0.2539	0.3862	0.5257	0.6765	0.8445	1.0407	1.2883	1.6570	1.9789	2.2683	2.356	2.6152	2.8570	3.3690
128	0.0006	0.0013	0.0063	0.0126	0.025	0.0314	0.0628	0.1259	0.2539	0.3862	0.5257	0.6764	0.8445	1.0407	1.2882	1.6569	1.9787	2.2681	2.356	2.6148	2.8566	3.3685
129	0.0006	0.0013	0.0063	0.0126	0.025	0.0314	0.0628	0.1259	0.2539	0.3862	0.5257	0.6764	0.8445	1.0407	1.2882	1.6568	1.9786	2.2679	2.355	2.6145	2.8562	3.3679
130	0.0006	0.0013	0.0063	0.0126	0.025	0.0314	0.0628	0.1259	0.2539	0.3862	0.5257	0.6764	0.8444	1.0406	1.2881	1.6567	1.9784	2.2677	2.355	2.6142	2.8558	3.3673
131	0.0006	0.0013	0.0063	0.0126	0.025	0.0314	0.0628	0.1259	0.2539	0.3862	0.5257	0.6764	0.8444	1.0406	1.2881	1.6566	1.9783	2.2675	2.355	2.6139	2.8555	3.3667
132	0.0006	0.0013	0.0063	0.0126	0.025	0.0314	0.0628	0.1259	0.2539	0.3862	0.5257	0.6764	0.8444	1.0405	1.2880	1.6565	1.9781	2.2673	2.355	2.6136	2.8551	3.3661
133	0.0006	0.0013	0.0063	0.0126	0.025	0.0314	0.0628	0.1259	0.2539	0.3862	0.5257	0.6764	0.8444	1.0405	1.2880	1.6564	1.9780	2.2671	2.355	2.6134	2.8548	3.3655
134	0.0006	0.0013	0.0063	0.0126	0.025	0.0314	0.0628	0.1259	0.2539	0.3862	0.5257	0.6763	0.8443	1.0405	1.2879	1.6563	1.9778	2.2669	2.354	2.6131	2.8544	3.3648
135	0.0006	0.0013	0.0063	0.0126	0.025	0.0314	0.0628	0.1259	0.2539	0.3862	0.5257	0.6763	0.8443	1.0405	1.2879	1.6563	1.9777	2.2667	2.354	2.6128	2.8540	3.3642
136	0.0006	0.0013	0.0063	0.0126	0.025	0.0314	0.0628	0.1259	0.2538	0.3861	0.5256	0.6763	0.8443	1.0404	1.2878	1.6562	1.9776	2.2665	2.354	2.6125	2.8536	3.3636
137	0.0006	0.0013	0.0063	0.0126	0.025	0.0314	0.0628	0.1259	0.2538	0.3861	0.5256	0.6763	0.8443	1.0404	1.2878	1.6561	1.9775	2.2664	2.354	2.6123	2.8533	3.3631
138	0.0006	0.0013	0.0063	0.0126	0.025	0.0314	0.0628	0.1259	0.2538	0.3861	0.5256	0.6763	0.8442	1.0403	1.2877	1.6560	1.9773	2.2662	2.354	2.6120	2.8529	3.3626
139	0.0006	0.0013	0.0063	0.0126	0.025	0.0314	0.0628	0.1259	0.2538	0.3861	0.5256	0.6763	0.8442	1.0403	1.2877	1.6559	1.9772	2.2660	2.353	2.6117	2.8526	3.3621
140	0.0006	0.0013	0.0063	0.0126	0.025	0.0314	0.0628	0.1259	0.2538	0.3861	0.5256	0.6763	0.8442	1.0403	1.2876	1.6558	1.9771	2.2658	2.353	2.6114	2.8523	3.3615
141	0.0006	0.0013	0.0063	0.0126	0.025	0.0314	0.0628	0.1259	0.2538	0.3861	0.5256	0.6763	0.8442	1.0403	1.2876	1.6558	1.9770	2.2657	2.353	2.6112	2.8520	3.3611
142	0.0006	0.0013	0.0063	0.0126	0.025	0.0314	0.0628	0.1259	0.2538	0.3861	0.5256	0.6762	0.8442	1.0402	1.2876	1.6557	1.9768	2.2655	2.353	2.6109	2.8516	3.3606
143	0.0006	0.0013	0.0063	0.0126	0.025	0.0314	0.0628	0.1259	0.2538	0.3861	0.5256	0.6762	0.8442	1.0402	1.2876	1.6556	1.9767	2.2653	2.353	2.6107	2.8513	3.3600
144	0.0006	0.0013	0.0063	0.0126	0.025	0.0314	0.0628	0.1259	0.2538	0.3861	0.5256	0.6762	0.8441	1.0402	1.2875	1.6555	1.9766	2.2651	2.352	2.6104	2.8510	3.3594
145	0.0006	0.0013	0.0063	0.0126	0.025	0.0314	0.0628	0.1259	0.2538	0.3861	0.5256	0.6762	0.8441	1.0402	1.2875	1.6555	1.9765	2.2650	2.352	2.6102	2.8507	3.3590
146	0.0006	0.0013	0.0063	0.0126	0.025	0.0314	0.0628	0.1259	0.2538	0.3861	0.5256	0.6762	0.8441	1.0401	1.2874	1.6554	1.9764	2.2648	2.352	2.6099	2.8504	3.3585
147	0.0006	0.0013	0.0063	0.0126	0.025	0.0314	0.0628	0.1259	0.2538	0.3861	0.5256	0.6762	0.8441	1.0401	1.2874	1.6553	1.9763	2.2647	2.352	2.6097	2.8501	3.3581
148	0.0006	0.0013	0.0063	0.0126	0.025	0.0314	0.0628	0.1259	0.2538	0.3861	0.5255	0.6762	0.8441	1.0401	1.2873	1.6552	1.9762	2.2645	2.352	2.6095	2.8498	3.3576
149	0.0006	0.0013	0.0063	0.0126	0.025	0.0314	0.0628	0.1259	0.2538	0.3861	0.5255	0.6762	0.8441	1.0401	1.2873	1.6552	1.9761	2.2644	2.352	2.6093	2.8495	3.3572
150	0.0006	0.0013	0.0063	0.0126	0.025	0.0314	0.0628	0.1259	0.2538	0.3861	0.5255	0.6761	0.8440	1.0400	1.2872	1.6551	1.9759	2.2642	2.351	2.6090	2.8492	3.3567

$P = P$ (right) = integral between t and infinity. P (left) = P (right)

2 P	0.9995	0.999	0.995	0.99	0.98	0.975	0.95	0.90	0.80	0.70	0.60	0.50	0.40	0.30	0.20	0.10	0.05	0.025	0.02	0.01	0.005	0.001
P	0.49975	0.4995	0.4975	0.495	0.49	0.4875	0.475	0.45	0.40	0.35	0.30	0.25	0.20	0.15	0.10	0.05	0.025	0.0125	0.01	0.005	0.0025	0.0005
ν																						
151	0.0006	0.0013	0.0063	0.0126	0.025	0.0314	0.0628	0.1259	0.2538	0.3861	0.5255	0.6761	0.8440	1.0400	1.2872	1.6551	1.9758	2.2641	2.351	2.6088	2.8490	3.3563
152	0.0006	0.0013	0.0063	0.0126	0.025	0.0314	0.0628	0.1259	0.2538	0.3861	0.5255	0.6761	0.8440	1.0400	1.2872	1.6550	1.9757	2.2639	2.351	2.6086	2.8487	3.3559
153	0.0006	0.0013	0.0063	0.0126	0.025	0.0314	0.0628	0.1259	0.2538	0.3861	0.5255	0.6761	0.8440	1.0400	1.2872	1.6549	1.9756	2.2638	2.351	2.6084	2.8484	3.3554
154	0.0006	0.0013	0.0063	0.0126	0.025	0.0314	0.0628	0.1259	0.2538	0.3860	0.5255	0.6761	0.8440	1.0399	1.2871	1.6548	1.9755	2.2636	2.351	2.6082	2.8481	3.3548
155	0.0006	0.0013	0.0063	0.0126	0.025	0.0314	0.0628	0.1259	0.2538	0.3860	0.5255	0.6761	0.8440	1.0399	1.2871	1.6548	1.9754	2.2635	2.351	2.6080	2.8478	3.3545
156	0.0006	0.0013	0.0063	0.0126	0.025	0.0314	0.0628	0.1259	0.2538	0.3860	0.5255	0.6761	0.8439	1.0399	1.2870	1.6547	1.9753	2.2633	2.350	2.6077	2.8475	3.3541
157	0.0006	0.0013	0.0063	0.0126	0.025	0.0314	0.0628	0.1259	0.2538	0.3860	0.5255	0.6761	0.8439	1.0399	1.2870	1.6547	1.9752	2.2632	2.350	2.6075	2.8473	3.3538
158	0.0006	0.0013	0.0063	0.0126	0.025	0.0314	0.0628	0.1259	0.2538	0.3860	0.5255	0.6761	0.8439	1.0398	1.2869	1.6546	1.9751	2.2630	2.350	2.6073	2.8471	3.3535
159	0.0006	0.0013	0.0063	0.0126	0.025	0.0314	0.0628	0.1259	0.2538	0.3860	0.5255	0.6761	0.8439	1.0398	1.2869	1.6546	1.9750	2.2629	2.350	2.6072	2.8468	3.3531
160	0.0006	0.0013	0.0063	0.0126	0.025	0.0314	0.0628	0.1259	0.2538	0.3860	0.5255	0.6760	0.8439	1.0398	1.2869	1.6545	1.9749	2.2627	2.350	2.6070	2.8465	3.3527
161	0.0006	0.0013	0.0063	0.0126	0.025	0.0314	0.0628	0.1259	0.2538	0.3860	0.5255	0.6760	0.8439	1.0398	1.2869	1.6544	1.9748	2.2626	2.350	2.6068	2.8463	3.3524
162	0.0006	0.0013	0.0063	0.0126	0.025	0.0314	0.0628	0.1259	0.2538	0.3860	0.5254	0.6760	0.8439	1.0398	1.2868	1.6543	1.9747	2.2625	2.349	2.6066	2.8461	3.3521
163	0.0006	0.0013	0.0063	0.0126	0.025	0.0314	0.0628	0.1259	0.2538	0.3860	0.5254	0.6760	0.8439	1.0398	1.2868	1.6543	1.9747	2.2624	2.349	2.6064	2.8459	3.3517
164	0.0006	0.0013	0.0063	0.0126	0.025	0.0314	0.0628	0.1259	0.2538	0.3860	0.5254	0.6760	0.8438	1.0397	1.2868	1.6542	1.9746	2.2622	2.349	2.6062	2.8456	3.3512
165	0.0006	0.0013	0.0063	0.0126	0.025	0.0314	0.0628	0.1259	0.2538	0.3860	0.5254	0.6760	0.8438	1.0397	1.2868	1.6542	1.9745	2.2621	2.349	2.6060	2.8454	3.3509
166	0.0006	0.0013	0.0063	0.0126	0.025	0.0314	0.0628	0.1259	0.2538	0.3860	0.5254	0.6760	0.8438	1.0397	1.2867	1.6541	1.9744	2.2619	2.349	2.6058	2.8451	3.3506
167	0.0006	0.0013	0.0063	0.0126	0.025	0.0314	0.0628	0.1259	0.2538	0.3860	0.5254	0.6760	0.8438	1.0397	1.2867	1.6541	1.9743	2.2618	2.349	2.6057	2.8449	3.3502
168	0.0006	0.0013	0.0063	0.0126	0.025	0.0314	0.0628	0.1259	0.2538	0.3860	0.5254	0.6760	0.8438	1.0396	1.2866	1.6540	1.9742	2.2617	2.349	2.6055	2.8447	3.3497
169	0.0006	0.0013	0.0063	0.0126	0.025	0.0314	0.0628	0.1259	0.2538	0.3860	0.5254	0.6760	0.8438	1.0396	1.2866	1.6540	1.9741	2.2616	2.348	2.6053	2.8445	3.3493
170	0.0006	0.0013	0.0063	0.0126	0.025	0.0314	0.0628	0.1259	0.2537	0.3860	0.5254	0.6759	0.8438	1.0396	1.2866	1.6539	1.9740	2.2615	2.348	2.6051	2.8442	3.3489
171	0.0006	0.0013	0.0063	0.0126	0.025	0.0314	0.0628	0.1259	0.2537	0.3860	0.5254	0.6759	0.8438	1.0396	1.2866	1.6539	1.9740	2.2614	2.348	2.6050	2.8440	3.3486
172	0.0006	0.0013	0.0063	0.0126	0.025	0.0314	0.0628	0.1258	0.2537	0.3860	0.5254	0.6759	0.8437	1.0396	1.2865	1.6538	1.9739	2.2612	2.348	2.6048	2.8438	3.3482
173	0.0006	0.0013	0.0063	0.0126	0.025	0.0314	0.0628	0.1258	0.2537	0.3860	0.5254	0.6759	0.8437	1.0396	1.2865	1.6538	1.9738	2.2611	2.348	2.6046	2.8436	3.3479
174	0.0006	0.0013	0.0063	0.0126	0.025	0.0314	0.0628	0.1258	0.2537	0.3860	0.5254	0.6759	0.8437	1.0395	1.2865	1.6537	1.9737	2.2610	2.348	2.6044	2.8434	3.3476
175	0.0006	0.0013	0.0063	0.0126	0.025	0.0314	0.0628	0.1258	0.2537	0.3860	0.5254	0.6759	0.8437	1.0395	1.2865	1.6537	1.9737	2.2609	2.348	2.6043	2.8432	3.3474
176	0.0006	0.0013	0.0063	0.0126	0.025	0.0314	0.0628	0.1258	0.2537	0.3860	0.5254	0.6759	0.8437	1.0395	1.2864	1.6536	1.9736	2.2608	2.348	2.6041	2.8430	3.3471
177	0.0006	0.0013	0.0063	0.0126	0.025	0.0314	0.0628	0.1258	0.2537	0.3860	0.5254	0.6759	0.8437	1.0395	1.2864	1.6536	1.9735	2.2607	2.347	2.6040	2.8428	3.3467
178	0.0006	0.0013	0.0063	0.0126	0.025	0.0314	0.0628	0.1258	0.2537	0.3859	0.5253	0.6759	0.8437	1.0395	1.2863	1.6535	1.9734	2.2605	2.347	2.6038	2.8426	3.3462
179	0.0006	0.0013	0.0063	0.0126	0.025	0.0314	0.0628	0.1258	0.2537	0.3859	0.5253	0.6759	0.8437	1.0395	1.2863	1.6535	1.9734	2.2604	2.347	2.6037	2.8424	3.3459
180	0.0006	0.0013	0.0063	0.0126	0.025	0.0314	0.0628	0.1258	0.2537	0.3859	0.5253	0.6759	0.8436	1.0394	1.2863	1.6534	1.9733	2.2603	2.347	2.6035	2.8421	3.3456
181	0.0006	0.0013	0.0063	0.0126	0.025	0.0314	0.0628	0.1258	0.2537	0.3859	0.5253	0.6759	0.8436	1.0394	1.2863	1.6534	1.9732	2.2602	2.347	2.6034	2.8419	3.3453
182	0.0006	0.0013	0.0063	0.0126	0.025	0.0314	0.0628	0.1258	0.2537	0.3859	0.5253	0.6758	0.8436	1.0394	1.2862	1.6533	1.9731	2.2601	2.347	2.6032	2.8417	3.3450
183	0.0006	0.0013	0.0063	0.0126	0.025	0.0314	0.0628	0.1258	0.2537	0.3859	0.5253	0.6758	0.8436	1.0394	1.2862	1.6533	1.9731	2.2600	2.347	2.6031	2.8416	3.3447
184	0.0006	0.0013	0.0063	0.0126	0.025	0.0314	0.0628	0.1258	0.2537	0.3859	0.5253	0.6758	0.8436	1.0394	1.2862	1.6532	1.9730	2.2599	2.347	2.6029	2.8414	3.3444
185	0.0006	0.0013	0.0063	0.0126	0.025	0.0314	0.0628	0.1258	0.2537	0.3859	0.5253	0.6758	0.8436	1.0394	1.2862	1.6532	1.9729	2.2598	2.346	2.6028	2.8412	3.3441
186	0.0006	0.0013	0.0063	0.0126	0.025	0.0314	0.0628	0.1258	0.2537	0.3859	0.5253	0.6758	0.8436	1.0393	1.2861	1.6531	1.9728	2.2597	2.346	2.6026	2.8410	3.3438
187	0.0006	0.0013	0.0063	0.0126	0.025	0.0314	0.0628	0.1258	0.2537	0.3859	0.5253	0.6758	0.8436	1.0393	1.2861	1.6531	1.9728	2.2596	2.346	2.6025	2.8408	3.3435
188	0.0006	0.0013	0.0063	0.0126	0.025	0.0314	0.0628	0.1258	0.2537	0.3859	0.5253	0.6758	0.8435	1.0393	1.2861	1.6530	1.9727	2.2595	2.346	2.6023	2.8406	3.3432
189	0.0006	0.0013	0.0063	0.0126	0.025	0.0314	0.0628	0.1258	0.2537	0.3859	0.5253	0.6758	0.8435	1.0393	1.2861	1.6530	1.9727	2.2594	2.346	2.6022	2.8405	3.3429
190	0.0006	0.0013	0.0063	0.0126	0.025	0.0314	0.0628	0.1258	0.2537	0.3859	0.5253	0.6758	0.8435	1.0393	1.2860	1.6529	1.9726	2.2593	2.346	2.6020	2.8403	3.3426
191	0.0006	0.0013	0.0063	0.0126	0.025	0.0314	0.0628	0.1258	0.2537	0.3859	0.5253	0.6758	0.8435	1.0393	1.2860	1.6529	1.9725	2.2592	2.346	2.6019	2.8401	3.3424
192	0.0006	0.0013	0.0063	0.0126	0.025	0.0314	0.0628	0.1258	0.2537	0.3859	0.5253	0.6758	0.8435	1.0392	1.2860	1.6528	1.9724	2.2591	2.346	2.6017	2.8399	3.3421
193	0.0006	0.0013	0.0063	0.0126	0.025	0.0314	0.0628	0.1258	0.2537	0.3859	0.5253	0.6758	0.8435	1.0392	1.2860	1.6528	1.9724	2.2591	2.346	2.6016	2.8397	3.3418
194	0.0006	0.0013	0.0063	0.0126	0.025	0.0314	0.0628	0.1258	0.2537	0.3859	0.5253	0.6758	0.8435	1.0392	1.2859	1.6528	1.9723	2.2590	2.346	2.6015	2.8395	3.3415
195	0.0006	0.0013	0.0063	0.0126	0.025	0.0314	0.0628	0.1258	0.2537	0.3859	0.5253	0.6758	0.8435	1.0392	1.2859	1.6528	1.9723	2.2589	2.345	2.6014	2.8394	3.3414
196	0.0006	0.0013	0.0063	0.0126	0.025	0.0314	0.0628	0.1258	0.2537	0.3859	0.5253	0.6758	0.8435	1.0392	1.2859	1.6527	1.9722	2.2588	2.345	2.6012	2.8392	3.3412
197	0.0006	0.0013	0.0063	0.0126	0.025	0.0314	0.0628	0.1258	0.2537	0.3859	0.5253	0.6758	0.8435	1.0392	1.2859	1.6527	1.9721	2.2587	2.345	2.6011	2.8391	3.3409
198	0.0006	0.0013	0.0063	0.0126	0.025	0.0314	0.0628	0.1258	0.2537	0.3859	0.5253	0.6757	0.8435	1.0392	1.2859	1.6526	1.9720	2.2586	2.345	2.6009	2.8389	3.3406
199	0.0006	0.0013	0.0063	0.0126	0.025	0.0314	0.0628	0.1258	0.2537	0.3859	0.5253	0.6757	0.8435	1.0392	1.2859	1.6526	1.9720	2.2585	2.345	2.6008	2.8388	3.3403
200	0.0006	0.0013	0.0063	0.0125	0.025	0.0314	0.0628	0.1258	0.2537	0.3859	0.5252	0.6757	0.8434	1.0391	1.2858	1.6525	1.9719	2.2584	2.345	2.6006	2.8386	3.3400

Significance Limits of the χ^2 Distribution[1] $\nu = 1$—50

$\int_r$ = integral between χ^2 and infinity ($1 \int_r = 2\alpha$, $\frac{1}{2}\int_r = \alpha$ in χ^2 tests), $\int_1$ = integral between zero and χ^2

$\int_r$ 1 / ½	0.99950 / 0.49975	0.9990 / 0.4995	0.9950 / 0.4975	0.990 / 0.495	0.9750 / 0.4875	0.950 / 0.475	0.90 / 0.45	0.80 / 0.40	0.70 / 0.35	0.60 / 0.30	0.50 / 0.25	0.40 / 0.20	0.30 / 0.15	0.20 / 0.10	0.10 / 0.05	0.050 / 0.025	0.0250 / 0.0125	0.010 / 0.005	0.0050 / 0.0025	0.0010 / 0.0005	0.00050 / 0.00025
$\int_1$ 1 / ½	0.00050 / 0.00025	0.0010 / 0.0005	0.0050 / 0.0025	0.010 / 0.005	0.0250 / 0.0125	0.050 / 0.025	0.10 / 0.05	0.20 / 0.10	0.30 / 0.15	0.40 / 0.20	0.50 / 0.25	0.60 / 0.30	0.70 / 0.35	0.80 / 0.40	0.90 / 0.45	0.950 / 0.475	0.9750 / 0.4875	0.990 / 0.495	0.9950 / 0.4975	0.9990 / 0.4995	0.99950 / 0.49975
ν																					
1	0.000000393	0.00000157	0.0000393	0.000157	0.000982	0.00393	0.0158	0.0642	0.148	0.275	0.455	0.708	1.074	1.642	2.706	3.841	5.024	6.635	7.879	10.828	12.116
2	0.00100	0.00200	0.0100	0.0201	0.0506	0.103	0.211	0.446	0.713	1.022	1.386	1.833	2.408	3.219	4.605	5.991	7.378	9.210	10.597	13.816	15.202
3	0.0153	0.0243	0.0717	0.115	0.216	0.352	0.584	1.005	1.424	1.869	2.366	2.946	3.665	4.642	6.251	7.815	9.348	11.345	12.838	16.266	17.730
4	0.0639	0.0908	0.207	0.297	0.484	0.711	1.064	1.649	2.195	2.753	3.357	4.045	4.878	5.989	7.779	9.488	11.143	13.277	14.860	18.467	19.998
5	0.158	0.210	0.412	0.554	0.831	1.145	1.610	2.343	3.000	3.655	4.351	5.132	6.064	7.289	9.236	11.070	12.832	15.086	16.750	20.515	22.105
6	0.299	0.381	0.676	0.872	1.237	1.635	2.204	3.070	3.828	4.570	5.348	6.211	7.231	8.558	10.645	12.592	14.449	16.812	18.548	22.458	24.103
7	0.485	0.598	0.989	1.239	1.690	2.167	2.833	3.822	4.671	5.493	6.346	7.283	8.383	9.803	12.017	14.067	16.013	18.475	20.278	24.322	26.018
8	0.710	0.857	1.344	1.646	2.180	2.733	3.490	4.594	5.527	6.423	7.344	8.351	9.524	11.030	13.362	15.507	17.535	20.090	21.955	26.125	27.868
9	0.972	1.153	1.735	2.088	2.700	3.325	4.168	5.380	6.393	7.357	8.343	9.414	10.656	12.242	14.684	16.919	19.023	21.666	23.589	27.877	29.666
10	1.265	1.479	2.156	2.558	3.247	3.940	4.865	6.179	7.267	8.295	9.342	10.473	11.781	13.442	15.987	18.307	20.483	23.209	25.188	29.588	31.419
11	1.587	1.834	2.603	3.053	3.816	4.575	5.578	6.989	8.148	9.237	10.341	11.530	12.899	14.631	17.275	19.675	21.920	24.725	26.757	31.264	33.136
12	1.934	2.214	3.074	3.571	4.404	5.226	6.304	7.807	9.034	10.182	11.340	12.584	14.011	15.812	18.549	21.026	23.336	26.217	28.300	32.909	34.821
13	2.305	2.617	3.565	4.107	5.009	5.892	7.042	8.634	9.926	11.129	12.340	13.636	15.119	16.985	19.812	22.362	24.736	27.688	29.819	34.528	36.478
14	2.697	3.041	4.075	4.660	5.629	6.571	7.790	9.467	10.821	12.079	13.339	14.685	16.222	18.151	21.064	23.685	26.119	29.141	31.319	36.123	38.109
15	3.108	3.483	4.601	5.229	6.262	7.261	8.547	10.307	11.721	13.030	14.339	15.733	17.322	19.311	22.307	24.996	27.488	30.578	32.801	37.697	39.719
16	3.536	3.942	5.142	5.812	6.908	7.962	9.312	11.152	12.624	13.983	15.338	16.780	18.418	20.465	23.542	26.296	28.845	32.000	34.267	39.252	41.308
17	3.980	4.416	5.697	6.408	7.564	8.672	10.085	12.002	13.531	14.937	16.338	17.824	19.511	21.615	24.769	27.587	30.191	33.409	35.718	40.790	42.879
18	4.439	4.905	6.265	7.015	8.231	9.390	10.865	12.857	14.440	15.893	17.338	18.868	20.601	22.760	25.989	28.869	31.526	34.805	37.156	42.312	44.434
19	4.912	5.407	6.844	7.633	8.907	10.117	11.651	13.716	15.352	16.850	18.338	19.910	21.689	23.900	27.204	30.144	32.852	36.191	38.582	43.820	45.973
20	5.398	5.921	7.434	8.260	9.591	10.851	12.443	14.578	16.266	17.809	19.337	20.951	22.775	25.038	28.412	31.410	34.170	37.566	39.997	45.315	47.498
21	5.896	6.447	8.034	8.897	10.283	11.591	13.240	15.445	17.182	18.768	20.337	21.991	23.858	26.171	29.615	32.671	35.479	38.932	41.401	46.797	49.010
22	6.405	6.983	8.643	9.542	10.982	12.338	14.041	16.314	18.101	19.729	21.337	23.031	24.939	27.301	30.813	33.924	36.781	40.289	42.796	48.268	50.511
23	6.924	7.529	9.260	10.196	11.688	13.091	14.848	17.187	19.021	20.690	22.337	24.069	26.018	28.429	32.007	35.172	38.076	41.638	44.181	49.728	52.000
24	7.453	8.085	9.886	10.856	12.401	13.848	15.659	18.062	19.943	21.652	23.337	25.106	27.096	29.553	33.196	36.415	39.364	42.980	45.558	51.179	53.479
25	7.991	8.649	10.520	11.524	13.120	14.611	16.473	18.940	20.867	22.616	24.337	26.143	28.172	30.675	34.382	37.652	40.646	44.314	46.928	52.620	54.947
26	8.538	9.222	11.160	12.198	13.844	15.379	17.292	19.820	21.792	23.579	25.336	27.179	29.246	31.795	35.563	38.885	41.923	45.642	48.290	54.052	56.407
27	9.093	9.803	11.808	12.879	14.573	16.151	18.114	20.703	22.719	24.544	26.336	28.214	30.319	32.912	36.741	40.113	43.194	46.963	49.645	55.476	57.858
28	9.656	10.391	12.461	13.565	15.308	16.928	18.939	21.588	23.647	25.509	27.336	29.249	31.391	34.027	37.916	41.337	44.461	48.278	50.993	56.892	59.300
29	10.227	10.986	13.121	14.256	16.047	17.708	19.768	22.475	24.577	26.475	28.336	30.283	32.461	35.139	39.087	42.557	45.722	49.588	52.336	58.302	60.734
30	10.804	11.588	13.787	14.953	16.791	18.493	20.599	23.364	25.508	27.442	29.336	31.316	33.530	36.250	40.256	43.773	46.979	50.892	53.672	59.703	62.161
31	11.389	12.196	14.458	15.655	17.539	19.281	21.434	24.255	26.440	28.409	30.336	32.349	34.598	37.359	41.422	44.985	48.232	52.191	55.003	61.098	63.582
32	11.979	12.811	15.134	16.362	18.291	20.072	22.271	25.148	27.373	29.376	31.336	33.381	35.665	38.466	42.585	46.194	49.480	53.486	56.328	62.487	64.995
33	12.576	13.431	15.815	17.073	19.047	20.867	23.110	26.042	28.307	30.344	32.336	34.413	36.731	39.572	43.745	47.400	50.725	54.776	57.648	63.870	66.402
34	13.179	14.057	16.501	17.789	19.806	21.664	23.952	26.938	29.242	31.313	33.336	35.444	37.795	40.676	44.903	48.602	51.966	56.061	58.964	65.247	67.803
35	13.788	14.688	17.192	18.509	20.569	22.465	24.797	27.836	30.178	32.282	34.336	36.475	38.859	41.778	46.059	49.802	53.203	57.342	60.275	66.619	69.198
36	14.401	15.324	17.887	19.233	21.336	23.269	25.643	28.735	31.115	33.252	35.336	37.505	39.922	42.879	47.212	50.998	54.437	58.619	61.581	67.985	70.588
37	15.020	15.965	18.586	19.960	22.106	24.075	26.492	29.635	32.053	34.222	36.336	38.535	40.984	43.978	48.363	52.192	55.668	59.892	62.883	69.346	71.972
38	15.644	16.611	19.289	20.691	22.878	24.884	27.343	30.537	32.992	35.192	37.335	39.564	42.045	45.076	49.513	53.384	56.895	61.162	64.181	70.703	73.351
39	16.273	17.261	19.996	21.426	23.654	25.695	28.196	31.441	33.932	36.163	38.335	40.593	43.105	46.173	50.660	54.572	58.120	62.428	65.476	72.055	74.725
40	16.906	17.916	20.707	22.164	24.433	26.509	29.051	32.345	34.872	37.134	39.335	41.622	44.165	47.269	51.805	55.758	59.342	63.691	66.766	73.402	76.095
41	17.544	18.575	21.421	22.906	25.215	27.326	29.907	33.251	35.813	38.105	40.335	42.651	45.224	48.363	52.949	56.942	60.561	64.950	68.053	74.745	77.459
42	18.186	19.238	22.138	23.650	25.999	28.144	30.765	34.157	36.755	39.077	41.335	43.679	46.282	49.456	54.090	58.124	61.777	66.206	69.336	76.084	78.820
43	18.832	19.905	22.859	24.398	26.785	28.965	31.625	35.065	37.698	40.050	42.335	44.706	47.339	50.548	55.230	59.304	62.990	67.459	70.616	77.418	80.176
44	19.482	20.576	23.584	25.148	27.575	29.787	32.487	35.974	38.641	41.022	43.335	45.734	48.396	51.639	56.369	60.481	64.201	68.709	71.893	78.749	81.528
45	20.136	21.251	24.311	25.901	28.366	30.612	33.350	36.884	39.585	41.995	44.335	46.761	49.452	52.729	57.505	61.656	65.410	69.957	73.166	80.077	82.876
46	20.794	21.929	25.041	26.657	29.160	31.439	34.215	37.795	40.529	42.968	45.335	47.787	50.507	53.818	58.641	62.830	66.617	71.201	74.437	81.400	84.220
47	21.456	22.610	25.774	27.416	29.956	32.268	35.081	38.708	41.474	43.942	46.335	48.814	51.562	54.906	59.774	64.001	67.821	72.443	75.704	82.720	85.560
48	22.121	23.295	26.511	28.177	30.755	33.098	35.949	39.621	42.420	44.915	47.335	49.840	52.616	55.993	60.907	65.171	69.023	73.683	76.969	84.037	86.897
49	22.789	23.983	27.249	28.941	31.555	33.930	36.818	40.534	43.366	45.889	48.335	50.866	53.670	57.079	62.038	66.339	70.222	74.919	78.231	85.350	88.231
50	23.461	24.674	27.991	29.707	32.357	34.764	37.689	41.449	44.313	46.864	49.335	51.892	54.723	58.164	63.167	67.505	71.420	76.154	79.490	86.661	89.561

1) Values from HALD and SINKBÆK, *Skand. Aktuar Tidskr.*, **33**, 168 (1950). Reprinted by kind permission of the authors and publishers.

Significance Limits of the χ^2 Distribution[1] $\nu = 51-100$

$\int_r$ = integral between χ^2 and infinity ($1 \int_r = 2\alpha$, $\frac{1}{2} \int_r = \alpha$ in χ^2 tests), $\int_1$ = integral between zero and χ^2

$\int_r$ 1 ½	0.99950 0.49975	0.9990 0.4995	0.9950 0.4975	0.990 0.495	0.9750 0.4875	0.950 0.475	0.90 0.45	0.80 0.40	0.70 0.35	0.60 0.30	0.50 0.25	0.40 0.20	0.30 0.15	0.20 0.10	0.10 0.05	0.050 0.025	0.0250 0.0125	0.010 0.005	0.0050 0.0025	0.0010 0.0005	0.00050 0.00025
$\int_1$ 1 ½	0.00050 0.00025	0.0010 0.0005	0.0050 0.0025	0.010 0.005	0.0250 0.0125	0.050 0.025	0.10 0.05	0.20 0.10	0.30 0.15	0.40 0.20	0.50 0.25	0.60 0.30	0.70 0.35	0.80 0.40	0.90 0.45	0.950 0.475	0.9750 0.4875	0.990 0.495	0.9950 0.4975	0.9990 0.4995	0.99950 0.49975
ν																					
51	24.136	25.368	28.735	30.475	33.162	35.600	38.560	42.365	45.261	47.838	50.335	52.917	55.775	59.248	64.295	68.669	72.616	77.386	80.747	87.968	90.887
52	24.814	26.065	29.481	31.246	33.968	36.437	39.433	43.281	46.209	48.813	51.335	53.942	56.827	60.332	65.422	69.832	73.810	78.616	82.001	89.272	92.211
53	25.495	26.765	30.230	32.018	34.776	37.276	40.308	44.199	47.157	49.788	52.335	54.967	57.879	61.414	66.548	70.993	75.002	79.843	83.253	90.573	93.532
54	26.179	27.468	30.981	32.793	35.586	38.116	41.183	45.117	48.106	50.764	53.335	55.992	58.930	62.496	67.673	72.153	76.192	81.069	84.502	91.872	94.849
55	26.866	28.173	31.735	33.570	36.398	38.958	42.060	46.036	49.056	51.739	54.335	57.016	59.980	63.577	68.796	73.311	77.380	82.292	85.749	93.167	96.163
56	27.556	28.881	32.490	34.350	37.212	39.801	42.937	46.955	50.005	52.715	55.335	58.040	61.031	64.658	69.918	74.468	78.567	83.513	86.994	94.460	97.475
57	28.248	29.592	33.248	35.131	38.027	40.646	43.816	47.876	50.956	53.691	56.335	59.064	62.080	65.737	71.040	75.624	79.752	84.733	88.236	95.751	98.784
58	28.943	30.305	34.008	35.913	38.844	41.492	44.696	48.797	51.906	54.667	57.335	60.088	63.129	66.816	72.160	76.778	80.936	85.950	89.477	97.039	100.090
59	29.640	31.021	34.771	36.698	39.662	42.339	45.577	49.718	52.857	55.643	58.335	61.111	64.178	67.894	73.279	77.931	82.117	87.166	90.715	98.324	101.394
60	30.340	31.739	35.535	37.485	40.482	43.188	46.459	50.641	53.809	56.620	59.335	62.135	65.226	68.972	74.397	79.082	83.298	88.379	91.952	99.607	102.695
61	31.043	32.459	36.301	38.273	41.303	44.038	47.342	51.564	54.761	57.597	60.335	63.158	66.274	70.049	75.514	80.232	84.476	89.591	93.186	100.888	103.993
62	31.748	33.181	37.068	39.063	42.126	44.889	48.226	52.487	55.714	58.574	61.335	64.181	67.322	71.125	76.630	81.381	85.654	90.802	94.419	102.166	105.289
63	32.455	33.906	37.838	39.855	42.950	45.741	49.111	53.411	56.666	59.551	62.335	65.204	68.369	72.201	77.745	82.529	86.830	92.010	95.649	103.442	106.583
64	33.165	34.633	38.610	40.649	43.776	46.595	49.996	54.336	57.619	60.528	63.335	66.226	69.416	73.276	78.860	83.675	88.004	93.217	96.878	104.716	107.874
65	33.877	35.362	39.383	41.444	44.603	47.450	50.883	55.262	58.573	61.506	64.335	67.249	70.462	74.351	79.973	84.821	89.177	94.422	98.105	105.988	109.164
66	34.591	36.093	40.158	42.240	45.431	48.305	51.770	56.188	59.527	62.484	65.335	68.271	71.508	75.425	81.086	85.965	90.349	95.626	99.330	107.258	110.451
67	35.307	36.826	40.935	43.038	46.261	49.162	52.659	57.115	60.481	63.461	66.335	69.293	72.554	76.498	82.197	87.108	91.519	96.828	100.554	108.525	111.735
68	36.025	37.561	41.713	43.838	47.092	50.020	53.548	58.042	61.436	64.440	67.334	70.315	73.600	77.571	83.308	88.250	92.688	98.028	101.776	109.791	113.018
69	36.745	38.298	42.494	44.639	47.924	50.879	54.438	58.970	62.391	65.418	68.334	71.337	74.645	78.643	84.418	89.391	93.856	99.227	102.996	111.055	114.299
70	37.467	39.036	43.275	45.442	48.758	51.739	55.329	59.898	63.346	66.396	69.334	72.358	75.689	79.715	85.527	90.531	95.023	100.425	104.215	112.317	115.577
71	38.192	39.777	44.058	46.246	49.592	52.600	56.221	60.827	64.302	67.375	70.334	73.380	76.734	80.786	86.635	91.670	96.189	101.621	105.432	113.577	116.854
72	38.918	40.520	44.843	47.051	50.428	53.462	57.113	61.756	65.258	68.353	71.334	74.401	77.778	81.857	87.743	92.808	97.353	102.816	106.648	114.835	118.129
73	39.646	41.264	45.629	47.858	51.265	54.325	58.006	62.686	66.214	69.332	72.334	75.422	78.822	82.927	88.850	93.945	98.516	104.010	107.862	116.091	119.402
74	40.376	42.010	46.417	48.666	52.103	55.189	58.900	63.616	67.170	70.311	73.334	76.443	79.865	83.997	89.956	95.081	99.678	105.202	109.074	117.346	120.673
75	41.107	42.757	47.206	49.475	52.942	56.054	59.795	64.547	68.127	71.290	74.334	77.464	80.908	85.066	91.061	96.217	100.839	106.393	110.286	118.599	121.942
76	41.841	43.506	47.998	50.286	53.782	56.920	60.690	65.478	69.084	72.270	75.334	78.485	81.951	86.135	92.166	97.351	101.999	107.583	111.495	119.851	123.209
77	42.576	44.257	48.788	51.097	54.623	57.786	61.586	66.409	70.042	73.249	76.334	79.505	82.994	87.203	93.270	98.484	103.158	108.771	112.704	121.100	124.475
78	43.313	45.010	49.582	51.910	55.466	58.654	62.483	67.341	70.999	74.228	77.334	80.526	84.036	88.271	94.374	99.617	104.316	109.958	113.911	122.348	125.739
79	44.051	45.764	50.376	52.725	56.309	59.522	63.380	68.274	71.957	75.208	78.334	81.546	85.078	89.338	95.476	100.749	105.473	111.144	115.117	123.594	127.001
80	44.791	46.520	51.172	53.540	57.153	60.391	64.278	69.207	72.915	76.188	79.334	82.566	86.120	90.405	96.578	101.879	106.629	112.329	116.321	124.839	128.261
81	45.533	47.277	51.969	54.357	57.998	61.261	65.176	70.140	73.874	77.168	80.334	83.586	87.161	91.472	97.680	103.009	107.783	113.512	117.524	126.083	129.520
82	46.276	48.036	52.767	55.174	58.845	62.132	66.076	71.074	74.833	78.148	81.334	84.606	88.202	92.538	98.780	104.139	108.937	114.695	118.726	127.324	130.777
83	47.021	48.796	53.567	55.993	59.692	63.004	66.976	72.008	75.792	79.128	82.334	85.626	89.243	93.604	99.880	105.267	110.090	115.876	119.927	128.565	132.033
84	47.767	49.557	54.368	56.813	60.540	63.876	67.876	72.943	76.751	80.108	83.334	86.646	90.284	94.669	100.980	106.395	111.242	117.057	121.126	129.804	133.287
85	48.515	50.320	55.170	57.634	61.389	64.749	68.777	73.878	77.710	81.089	84.334	87.665	91.325	95.734	102.079	107.522	112.393	118.236	122.325	131.041	134.540
86	49.264	51.085	55.973	58.456	62.239	65.623	69.679	74.813	78.670	82.069	85.334	88.685	92.365	96.799	103.177	108.648	113.544	119.414	123.522	132.277	135.792
87	50.015	51.850	56.777	59.279	63.089	66.498	70.581	75.749	79.630	83.050	86.334	89.704	93.405	97.863	104.275	109.773	114.693	120.591	124.718	133.512	137.042
88	50.767	52.617	57.582	60.103	63.941	67.373	71.484	76.685	80.590	84.031	87.334	90.723	94.445	98.927	105.372	110.898	115.841	121.767	125.912	134.745	138.290
89	51.521	53.386	58.389	60.928	64.793	68.249	72.387	77.622	81.550	85.012	88.334	91.742	95.484	99.991	106.469	112.022	116.989	122.942	127.106	135.977	139.537
90	52.276	54.155	59.196	61.754	65.647	69.126	73.291	78.558	82.511	85.993	89.334	92.761	96.524	101.054	107.565	113.145	118.136	124.116	128.299	137.208	140.783
91	53.032	54.926	60.005	62.581	66.501	70.003	74.196	79.496	83.472	86.974	90.334	93.780	97.563	102.116	108.661	114.268	119.282	125.289	129.491	138.438	142.027
92	53.790	55.698	60.815	63.409	67.356	70.882	75.101	80.433	84.433	87.955	91.334	94.799	98.602	103.179	109.756	115.390	120.427	126.462	130.681	139.666	143.270
93	54.549	56.471	61.625	64.238	68.211	71.760	76.006	81.371	85.394	88.936	92.334	95.818	99.641	104.242	110.850	116.511	121.571	127.633	131.871	140.893	144.511
94	55.309	57.246	62.437	65.068	69.068	72.640	76.912	82.309	86.356	89.917	93.334	96.836	100.679	105.303	111.944	117.632	122.715	128.803	133.059	142.119	145.751
95	56.070	58.022	63.250	65.898	69.925	73.520	77.818	83.248	87.317	90.899	94.334	97.855	101.717	106.364	113.038	118.752	123.858	129.973	134.247	143.343	146.990
96	56.833	58.799	64.063	66.730	70.783	74.400	78.725	84.187	88.279	91.881	95.334	98.873	102.755	107.425	114.131	119.871	125.000	131.141	135.433	144.567	148.228
97	57.597	59.577	64.878	67.562	71.642	75.282	79.633	85.126	89.241	92.862	96.334	99.892	103.793	108.486	115.223	120.990	126.141	132.309	136.619	145.789	149.464
98	58.362	60.356	65.694	68.396	72.501	76.164	80.541	86.065	90.204	93.844	97.334	100.910	104.831	109.547	116.315	122.108	127.282	133.476	137.803	147.010	150.699
99	59.128	61.136	66.510	69.230	73.361	77.046	81.449	87.005	91.166	94.826	98.334	101.928	105.868	110.607	117.406	123.225	128.422	134.642	138.987	148.230	151.934
100	59.897	61.919	67.328	70.065	74.222	77.930	82.358	87.945	92.129	95.808	99.334	102.946	106.906	111.667	118.498	124.342	129.561	135.806	140.169	149.448	153.165

1) Values from Hald and Sinkbæk, *Skand. Aktuar Tidskr.*, **33**, 168 (1950). Reprinted by kind permission of the authors and publishers.

Significance Limits of the χ^2 Distribution* $\nu = 101$–150

$\int_r$ = integral between χ^2 and infinity ($1\int_r = 2\alpha$, $\frac{1}{2}\int_r = \alpha$ in χ^2 tests), $\int_1$ = integral between zero and χ^2

$\int_r$ 1 / ½	0.99950 / 0.49975	0.9990 / 0.4995	0.9950 / 0.4975	0.990 / 0.495	0.9750 / 0.4875	0.950 / 0.475	0.90 / 0.45	0.80 / 0.40	0.70 / 0.35	0.60 / 0.30	0.50 / 0.25	0.40 / 0.20	0.30 / 0.15	0.20 / 0.10	0.10 / 0.05	0.050 / 0.025	0.0250 / 0.0125	0.010 / 0.005	0.0050 / 0.0025	0.0010 / 0.0005	0.00050 / 0.00025
$\int_1$ 1 / ½	0.00050 / 0.00025	0.0010 / 0.0005	0.0050 / 0.0025	0.010 / 0.005	0.0250 / 0.0125	0.050 / 0.025	0.10 / 0.05	0.20 / 0.10	0.30 / 0.15	0.40 / 0.20	0.50 / 0.25	0.60 / 0.30	0.70 / 0.35	0.80 / 0.40	0.90 / 0.45	0.950 / 0.475	0.9750 / 0.4875	0.990 / 0.495	0.9950 / 0.4975	0.9990 / 0.4995	0.99950 / 0.49975
ν																					
101	60.666	62.702	68.147	70.901	75.084	78.813	83.267	88.886	93.092	96.790	100.334	103.964	107.943	112.726	119.589	125.458	130.700	136.971	141.351	150.666	154.397
102	61.436	63.485	68.966	71.738	75.946	79.698	84.177	89.826	94.055	97.772	101.334	104.982	108.980	113.786	120.679	126.574	131.837	138.134	142.532	151.883	155.628
103	62.207	64.270	69.786	72.575	76.809	80.582	85.088	90.767	95.018	98.754	102.334	105.999	110.017	114.845	121.769	127.689	132.975	139.297	143.712	153.098	156.857
104	62.978	65.056	70.607	73.413	77.672	81.468	85.998	91.709	95.981	99.737	103.334	107.017	111.053	115.903	122.858	128.804	134.111	140.459	144.891	154.313	158.086
105	63.752	65.842	71.429	74.252	78.537	82.354	86.909	92.650	96.945	100.719	104.334	108.035	112.090	116.962	123.947	129.918	135.247	141.620	146.069	155.527	159.313
106	64.526	66.630	72.252	75.092	79.401	83.240	87.821	93.592	97.909	101.701	105.334	109.052	113.126	118.020	125.035	131.031	136.382	142.780	147.246	156.739	160.539
107	65.301	67.419	73.075	75.933	80.267	84.127	88.733	94.534	98.873	102.684	106.334	110.070	114.162	119.078	126.123	132.144	137.517	143.940	148.423	157.951	161.765
108	66.077	68.208	73.899	76.774	81.133	85.015	89.645	95.477	99.837	103.667	107.334	111.087	115.198	120.135	127.211	133.257	138.650	145.099	149.599	159.161	162.989
109	66.854	68.999	74.725	77.616	82.000	85.903	90.558	96.419	100.801	104.649	108.334	112.104	116.233	121.193	128.298	134.369	139.784	146.257	150.774	160.371	164.212
110	67.632	69.791	75.551	78.459	82.867	86.792	91.471	97.362	101.766	105.632	109.334	113.121	117.269	122.250	129.385	135.480	140.916	147.414	151.948	161.580	165.434
111	68.412	70.583	76.377	79.302	83.735	87.681	92.385	98.306	102.730	106.615	110.334	114.138	118.304	123.306	130.472	136.591	142.048	148.571	153.121	162.787	166.655
112	69.192	71.377	77.205	80.146	84.604	88.570	93.299	99.249	103.695	107.598	111.334	115.156	119.340	124.363	131.558	137.701	143.180	149.727	154.294	163.994	167.875
113	69.973	72.171	78.033	80.991	85.473	89.461	94.213	100.193	104.660	108.581	112.334	116.172	120.375	125.419	132.643	138.811	144.311	150.882	155.466	165.200	169.094
114	70.755	72.966	78.862	81.837	86.343	90.351	95.128	101.137	105.625	109.564	113.334	117.189	121.410	126.475	133.729	139.921	145.441	152.036	156.637	166.405	170.312
115	71.538	73.762	79.692	82.683	87.213	91.242	96.043	102.081	106.590	110.547	114.334	118.206	122.444	127.531	134.813	141.030	146.571	153.190	157.807	167.609	171.530
116	72.322	74.559	80.523	83.530	88.084	92.134	96.958	103.025	107.556	111.531	115.334	119.223	123.479	128.587	135.898	142.138	147.700	154.344	158.977	168.812	172.746
117	73.107	75.357	81.354	84.377	88.955	93.026	97.874	103.970	108.521	112.514	116.334	120.239	124.513	129.642	136.982	143.246	148.829	155.496	160.146	170.015	173.961
118	73.893	76.156	82.186	85.225	89.827	93.918	98.790	104.915	109.487	113.497	117.334	121.256	125.548	130.697	138.066	144.354	149.957	156.648	161.314	171.216	175.176
119	74.680	76.956	83.019	86.074	90.700	94.811	99.707	105.860	110.453	114.481	118.334	122.273	126.582	131.752	139.149	145.461	151.084	157.799	162.481	172.417	176.389
120	75.468	77.756	83.852	86.924	91.573	95.705	100.624	106.806	111.419	115.465	119.334	123.289	127.616	132.806	140.233	146.567	152.211	158.950	163.648	173.617	177.602
121	76.256	78.557	84.686	87.774	92.446	96.599	101.541	107.751	112.385	116.448	120.334	124.305	128.650	133.861	141.315	147.673	153.338	160.100	164.814	174.815	178.813
122	77.046	79.360	85.521	88.624	93.320	97.493	102.458	108.697	113.351	117.432	121.334	125.322	129.684	134.915	142.398	148.779	154.464	161.249	165.979	176.014	180.024
123	77.836	80.162	86.356	89.476	94.195	98.388	103.376	109.643	114.317	118.416	122.334	126.338	130.717	135.969	143.480	149.885	155.589	162.398	167.144	177.211	181.234
124	78.627	80.966	87.193	90.328	95.070	99.283	104.295	110.589	115.284	119.399	123.334	127.354	131.751	137.022	144.562	150.989	156.714	163.546	168.308	178.407	182.443
125	79.419	81.771	88.029	91.180	95.946	100.178	105.213	111.536	116.250	120.383	124.334	128.370	132.784	138.076	145.643	152.094	157.838	164.694	169.471	179.603	183.652
126	80.212	82.576	88.867	92.033	96.822	101.074	106.132	112.483	117.217	121.367	125.334	129.386	133.817	139.129	146.724	153.198	158.962	165.841	170.634	180.798	184.859
127	81.006	83.382	89.705	92.887	97.699	101.971	107.051	113.430	118.184	122.351	126.334	130.402	134.850	140.182	147.805	154.301	160.086	166.987	171.796	181.992	186.066
128	81.800	84.189	90.544	93.741	98.576	102.867	107.971	114.377	119.151	123.335	127.334	131.418	135.883	141.235	148.885	155.405	161.209	168.133	172.957	183.186	187.272
129	82.595	84.996	91.383	94.596	99.453	103.765	108.891	115.324	120.118	124.320	128.334	132.434	136.916	142.288	149.965	156.507	162.331	169.278	174.118	184.378	188.477
130	83.391	85.805	92.223	95.451	100.331	104.662	109.811	116.272	121.086	125.304	129.334	133.450	137.949	143.340	151.045	157.610	163.453	170.423	175.278	185.570	189.681
131	84.188	86.614	93.063	96.307	101.210	105.560	110.732	117.219	122.053	126.288	130.334	134.465	138.981	144.392	152.125	158.712	164.575	171.567	176.437	186.761	190.885
132	84.985	87.423	93.905	97.164	102.089	106.459	111.652	118.167	123.021	127.272	131.334	135.481	140.014	145.444	153.204	159.814	165.696	172.711	177.596	187.952	192.087
133	85.784	88.234	94.746	98.021	102.968	107.357	112.573	119.116	123.988	128.257	132.334	136.497	141.046	146.496	154.283	160.915	166.816	173.854	178.755	189.141	193.289
134	86.583	89.045	95.589	98.878	103.848	108.257	113.495	120.064	124.956	129.241	133.334	137.512	142.078	147.548	155.361	162.016	167.936	174.996	179.912	190.330	194.490
135	87.383	89.857	96.432	99.736	104.729	109.156	114.416	121.012	125.924	130.226	134.334	138.528	143.110	148.599	156.440	163.116	169.056	176.138	181.069	191.519	195.691
136	88.183	90.669	97.275	100.595	105.609	110.056	115.338	121.961	126.892	131.210	135.334	139.543	144.142	149.651	157.518	164.216	170.175	177.280	182.226	192.706	196.890
137	88.984	91.483	98.119	101.454	106.491	110.956	116.261	122.910	127.860	132.195	136.334	140.559	145.174	150.702	158.595	165.316	171.294	178.420	183.382	193.893	198.089
138	89.786	92.297	98.964	102.314	107.372	111.857	117.183	123.859	128.829	133.180	137.334	141.574	146.206	151.753	159.673	166.415	172.412	179.561	184.537	195.080	199.288
139	90.589	93.111	99.809	103.174	108.254	112.758	118.106	124.809	129.797	134.164	138.334	142.589	147.237	152.803	160.750	167.514	173.530	180.701	185.692	196.265	200.485
140	91.393	93.926	100.655	104.035	109.137	113.659	119.029	125.758	130.766	135.149	139.334	143.604	148.269	153.854	161.827	168.613	174.648	181.840	186.846	197.450	201.682
141	92.197	94.742	101.502	104.896	110.020	114.561	119.953	126.708	131.734	136.134	140.334	144.619	149.300	154.904	162.904	169.711	175.765	182.979	188.000	198.634	202.878
142	93.001	95.559	102.349	105.757	110.903	115.463	120.876	127.658	132.703	137.119	141.334	145.635	150.331	155.954	163.980	170.809	176.881	184.117	189.153	199.818	204.073
143	93.807	96.376	103.196	106.620	111.787	116.366	121.800	128.608	133.672	138.104	142.334	146.650	151.362	157.004	165.056	171.907	177.998	185.255	190.306	201.001	205.268
144	94.613	97.194	104.044	107.482	112.671	117.268	122.724	129.558	134.641	139.089	143.334	147.665	152.393	158.054	166.132	173.004	179.114	186.393	191.458	202.183	206.462
145	95.420	98.012	104.892	108.345	113.556	118.171	123.649	130.508	135.610	140.074	144.334	148.680	153.424	159.104	167.207	174.101	180.229	187.530	192.610	203.365	207.656
146	96.227	98.832	105.741	109.209	114.441	119.075	124.574	131.459	136.579	141.059	145.334	149.694	154.455	160.153	168.283	175.198	181.344	188.666	193.761	204.546	208.848
147	97.035	99.651	106.591	110.073	115.326	119.979	125.499	132.409	137.548	142.044	146.334	150.709	155.486	161.202	169.358	176.294	182.459	189.802	194.911	205.726	210.040
148	97.844	100.472	107.441	110.937	116.212	120.883	126.424	133.360	138.518	143.029	147.334	151.724	156.516	162.251	170.432	177.390	183.573	190.938	196.061	206.906	211.232
149	98.654	101.293	108.292	111.802	117.098	121.787	127.349	134.311	139.487	144.015	148.334	152.739	157.547	163.300	171.507	178.485	184.687	192.073	197.211	208.085	212.422
150	99.464	102.114	109.143	112.668	117.985	122.692	128.275	135.263	140.457	145.000	149.334	153.753	158.577	164.349	172.581	179.581	185.800	193.207	198.360	209.264	213.613

Significance Limits of the χ^2 Distribution* ν=151—200

$\int_r$ = integral between χ^2 and infinity ($1 \int_r = 2\,\alpha$, $\frac{1}{2}\int_r = \alpha$ in χ^2 tests), $\int_1$ = integral between zero and χ^2

$\int_r$ 1 / ½	0.99950 / 0.49975	0.9990 / 0.4995	0.9950 / 0.4975	0.990 / 0.495	0.9750 / 0.4875	0.950 / 0.475	0.90 / 0.45	0.80 / 0.40	0.70 / 0.35	0.60 / 0.30	0.50 / 0.25	0.40 / 0.20	0.30 / 0.15	0.20 / 0.10	0.10 / 0.05	0.050 / 0.025	0.0250 / 0.0125	0.010 / 0.005	0.0050 / 0.0025	0.0010 / 0.0005	0.00050 / 0.00025
$\int_1$ 1 / ½	0.00050 / 0.00025	0.0010 / 0.0005	0.0050 / 0.0025	0.010 / 0.005	0.0250 / 0.0125	0.050 / 0.025	0.10 / 0.05	0.20 / 0.10	0.30 / 0.15	0.40 / 0.20	0.50 / 0.25	0.60 / 0.30	0.70 / 0.35	0.80 / 0.40	0.90 / 0.45	0.950 / 0.475	0.9750 / 0.4875	0.990 / 0.495	0.9950 / 0.4975	0.9990 / 0.4995	0.99950 / 0.49975
ν																					
151	100.274	102.936	109.994	113.534	118.872	123.597	129.201	136.214	141.427	145.985	150.334	154.768	159.608	165.398	173.655	180.676	186.913	194.342	199.508	210.442	214.802
152	101.086	103.759	110.846	114.400	119.759	124.502	130.127	137.165	142.396	146.971	151.334	155.783	160.638	166.446	174.729	181.770	188.026	195.475	200.656	211.619	215.991
153	101.898	104.582	111.699	115.267	120.646	125.408	131.054	138.117	143.366	147.956	152.334	156.797	161.668	167.495	175.803	182.865	189.139	196.609	201.804	212.796	217.179
154	102.710	105.406	112.552	116.134	121.535	126.314	131.980	139.069	144.336	148.942	153.334	157.812	162.698	168.543	176.876	183.959	190.251	197.742	202.951	213.973	218.367
155	103.523	106.230	113.405	117.001	122.423	127.220	132.907	140.021	145.306	149.927	154.334	158.826	163.728	169.591	177.949	185.052	191.362	198.874	204.098	215.148	219.554
156	104.337	107.055	114.259	117.870	123.312	128.127	133.835	140.973	146.277	150.913	155.334	159.841	164.758	170.639	179.022	186.146	192.473	200.006	205.244	216.323	220.740
157	105.151	107.881	115.114	118.738	124.201	129.034	134.762	141.925	147.247	151.898	156.334	160.855	165.787	171.686	180.094	187.239	193.584	201.138	206.389	217.498	221.926
158	105.966	108.707	115.968	119.607	125.090	129.941	135.690	142.878	148.217	152.884	157.334	161.869	166.817	172.734	181.167	188.332	194.695	202.269	207.535	218.672	223.111
159	106.782	109.534	116.824	120.476	125.980	130.848	136.618	143.831	149.188	153.870	158.334	162.883	167.847	173.781	182.239	189.424	195.805	203.400	208.679	219.845	224.296
160	107.598	110.361	117.680	121.346	126.870	131.756	137.546	144.783	150.158	154.856	159.334	163.898	168.876	174.828	183.311	190.516	196.915	204.530	209.824	221.018	225.480
161	108.415	111.189	118.536	122.216	127.761	132.664	138.474	145.736	151.129	155.841	160.334	164.912	169.905	175.875	184.382	191.608	198.025	205.660	210.967	222.191	226.663
162	109.232	112.017	119.393	123.086	128.651	133.573	139.403	146.689	152.100	156.827	161.334	165.926	170.935	176.922	185.454	192.700	199.134	206.789	212.111	223.363	227.846
163	110.050	112.846	120.250	123.957	129.543	134.481	140.331	147.643	153.070	157.813	162.334	166.940	171.964	177.969	186.525	193.791	200.243	207.919	213.254	224.534	229.029
164	110.868	113.675	121.107	124.829	130.434	135.390	141.260	148.596	154.041	158.799	163.334	167.954	172.993	179.016	187.596	194.883	201.351	209.047	214.396	225.705	230.211
165	111.687	114.505	121.965	125.700	131.326	136.299	142.190	149.549	155.012	159.785	164.334	168.968	174.022	180.062	188.667	195.973	202.459	210.176	215.538	226.875	231.392
166	112.506	115.335	122.824	126.572	132.218	137.209	143.119	150.503	155.984	160.771	165.334	169.982	175.051	181.109	189.737	197.064	203.567	211.304	216.680	228.045	232.573
167	113.326	116.166	123.683	127.445	133.111	138.118	144.049	151.457	156.955	161.757	166.334	170.996	176.079	182.155	190.808	198.154	204.675	212.431	217.821	229.214	233.753
168	114.147	116.998	124.542	128.318	134.003	139.028	144.979	152.411	157.926	162.743	167.334	172.010	177.108	183.201	191.878	199.244	205.782	213.558	218.962	230.383	234.932
169	114.968	117.829	125.401	129.191	134.897	139.939	145.909	153.365	158.897	163.729	168.334	173.024	178.137	184.247	192.948	200.334	206.889	214.685	220.102	231.551	236.111
170	115.790	118.662	126.262	130.065	135.790	140.849	146.839	154.319	159.869	164.716	169.334	174.037	179.165	185.293	194.017	201.423	207.995	215.812	221.242	232.719	237.290
171	116.612	119.495	127.122	130.939	136.684	141.760	147.769	155.273	160.840	165.702	170.334	175.051	180.194	186.338	195.087	202.513	209.102	216.938	222.382	233.886	238.468
172	117.434	120.328	127.983	131.813	137.578	142.671	148.700	156.228	161.812	166.688	171.334	176.065	181.222	187.384	196.156	203.601	210.208	218.063	223.521	235.053	239.646
173	118.257	121.162	128.844	132.688	138.472	143.582	149.631	157.182	162.784	167.675	172.334	177.079	182.250	188.429	197.225	204.690	211.313	219.189	224.660	236.219	240.823
174	119.081	121.996	129.706	133.563	139.367	144.494	150.562	158.137	163.755	168.661	173.334	178.092	183.279	189.475	198.294	205.779	212.419	220.314	225.798	237.385	241.999
175	119.905	122.831	130.568	134.438	140.262	145.406	151.493	159.092	164.727	169.647	174.334	179.106	184.307	190.520	199.363	206.867	213.524	221.438	226.936	238.550	243.175
176	120.730	123.666	131.431	135.314	141.157	146.318	152.425	160.047	165.699	170.634	175.334	180.119	185.335	191.565	200.432	207.955	214.628	222.562	228.073	239.715	244.351
177	121.555	124.502	132.294	136.190	142.053	147.230	153.356	161.002	166.671	171.620	176.334	181.133	186.363	192.610	201.500	209.042	215.733	223.686	229.210	240.880	245.526
178	122.381	125.338	133.157	137.067	142.949	148.143	154.288	161.957	167.643	172.607	177.334	182.146	187.391	193.654	202.568	210.130	216.837	224.810	230.347	242.043	246.700
179	123.207	126.175	134.021	137.943	143.845	149.056	155.220	162.913	168.616	173.593	178.334	183.160	188.418	194.699	203.636	211.217	217.941	225.933	231.484	243.207	247.874
180	124.033	127.012	134.885	138.821	144.741	149.969	156.153	163.868	169.588	174.580	179.334	184.173	189.446	195.743	204.704	212.304	219.044	227.056	232.620	244.370	249.048
181	124.860	127.849	135.749	139.698	145.638	150.882	157.085	164.824	170.560	175.567	180.334	185.187	190.474	196.788	205.771	213.391	220.148	228.178	233.755	245.533	250.221
182	125.688	128.687	136.614	140.576	146.535	151.796	158.018	165.780	171.533	176.553	181.334	186.200	191.501	197.832	206.839	214.477	221.250	229.301	234.890	246.695	251.393
183	126.516	129.526	137.479	141.454	147.432	152.709	158.950	166.735	172.505	177.540	182.334	187.213	192.529	198.876	207.906	215.563	222.353	230.423	236.025	247.856	252.565
184	127.344	130.364	138.345	142.333	148.330	153.624	159.883	167.691	173.478	178.527	183.334	188.226	193.556	199.920	208.973	216.649	223.456	231.544	237.160	249.018	253.737
185	128.173	131.204	139.211	143.211	149.228	154.538	160.817	168.647	174.450	179.513	184.334	189.240	194.584	200.964	210.040	217.735	224.558	232.665	238.294	250.178	254.908
186	129.003	132.043	140.077	144.091	150.126	155.452	161.750	169.604	175.423	180.500	185.334	190.253	195.611	202.008	211.106	218.820	225.660	233.786	239.428	251.339	256.079
187	129.833	132.884	140.944	144.970	151.025	156.367	162.684	170.560	176.396	181.487	186.334	191.266	196.638	203.052	212.173	219.906	226.761	234.907	240.561	252.499	257.249
188	130.663	133.724	141.811	145.850	151.923	157.282	163.617	171.517	177.369	182.474	187.334	192.279	197.665	204.095	213.239	220.991	227.862	236.027	241.694	253.658	258.419
189	131.494	134.565	142.678	146.730	152.822	158.197	164.551	172.473	178.342	183.461	188.334	193.292	198.692	205.139	214.305	222.076	228.964	237.147	242.827	254.817	259.588
190	132.325	135.407	143.546	147.611	153.721	159.113	165.485	173.430	179.315	184.448	189.334	194.305	199.719	206.182	215.371	223.160	230.064	238.266	243.959	255.976	260.757
191	133.157	136.248	144.414	148.491	154.621	160.028	166.419	174.387	180.288	185.435	190.334	195.318	200.746	207.225	216.437	224.245	231.165	239.385	245.091	257.134	261.925
192	133.989	137.091	145.282	149.372	155.521	160.944	167.354	175.343	181.261	186.422	191.334	196.331	201.773	208.268	217.502	225.329	232.265	240.504	246.223	258.292	263.093
193	134.821	137.933	146.151	150.254	156.421	161.860	168.288	176.301	182.234	187.409	192.334	197.344	202.800	209.311	218.568	226.413	233.365	241.623	247.354	259.449	264.261
194	135.654	138.776	147.020	151.136	157.321	162.776	169.223	177.258	183.207	188.396	193.334	198.357	203.827	210.354	219.633	227.496	234.465	242.741	248.485	260.606	265.428
195	136.488	139.620	147.889	152.018	158.222	163.693	170.158	178.215	184.181	189.383	194.334	199.370	204.853	211.397	220.698	228.580	235.564	243.859	249.616	261.763	266.595
196	137.322	140.464	148.759	152.900	159.122	164.610	171.093	179.172	185.154	190.370	195.334	200.383	205.880	212.439	221.763	229.663	236.663	244.977	250.746	262.919	267.761
197	138.156	141.308	149.629	153.783	160.023	165.527	172.029	180.130	186.128	191.358	196.334	201.395	206.906	213.482	222.828	230.746	237.762	246.095	251.876	264.075	268.927
198	138.990	142.153	150.499	154.665	160.925	166.444	172.964	181.087	187.101	192.345	197.334	202.408	207.933	214.524	223.892	231.829	238.861	247.212	253.006	265.230	270.092
199	139.826	142.998	151.370	155.549	161.826	167.361	173.900	182.045	188.075	193.332	198.334	203.421	208.959	215.567	224.957	232.912	239.960	248.328	254.135	266.385	271.257
200	140.661	143.843	152.241	156.432	162.728	168.279	174.835	183.003	189.049	194.319	199.334	204.434	209.985	216.609	226.021	233.994	241.058	249.445	255.264	267.540	272.422

Upper Significance Limits of the *F*-Distribution[1] $P=0.05$

$P = P\text{(right)} =$ integral between F and infinity

ν_2 \ ν_1	1	2	3	4	5	6	7	8	9	10	11	12	13	14	15	16	17	18	19	20	22	24	26	28	30	40	50	60	80	100
1	161.44	200	216	225	230	234	237	239	241	242	243	244	245	245	246	246	247	247	248	248	249	249	249	250	250	251	252	252	252	253
2	18.51	19.0	19.2	19.2	19.3	19.3	19.4	19.4	19.4	19.4	19.4	19.4	19.4	19.4	19.4	19.4	19.4	19.4	19.4	19.4	19.5	19.5	19.5	19.5	19.5	19.5	19.5	19.5	19.5	19.5
3	10.13	9.55	9.28	9.12	9.01	8.94	8.89	8.85	8.81	8.79	8.76	8.74	8.73	8.71	8.70	8.69	8.68	8.67	8.67	8.66	8.65	8.64	8.63	8.62	8.62	8.59	8.58	8.57	8.56	8.55
4	7.71	6.94	6.59	6.39	6.26	6.16	6.09	6.04	6.00	5.96	5.94	5.91	5.89	5.87	5.86	5.84	5.83	5.82	5.81	5.80	5.79	5.77	5.76	5.75	5.75	5.72	5.70	5.69	5.67	5.66
5	6.61	5.79	5.41	5.19	5.05	4.95	4.88	4.82	4.77	4.74	4.70	4.68	4.66	4.64	4.62	4.60	4.59	4.58	4.57	4.56	4.54	4.53	4.52	4.50	4.50	4.46	4.44	4.43	4.41	4.41
6	5.99	5.14	4.76	4.53	4.39	4.28	4.21	4.15	4.10	4.06	4.03	4.00	3.98	3.96	3.94	3.92	3.91	3.90	3.88	3.87	3.86	3.84	3.83	3.82	3.81	3.77	3.75	3.74	3.72	3.71
7	5.59	4.74	4.35	4.12	3.97	3.87	3.79	3.73	3.68	3.64	3.60	3.57	3.55	3.53	3.51	3.49	3.48	3.47	3.46	3.44	3.43	3.41	3.40	3.39	3.38	3.34	3.32	3.30	3.29	3.27
8	5.32	4.46	4.07	3.84	3.69	3.58	3.50	3.44	3.39	3.35	3.31	3.28	3.26	3.24	3.22	3.20	3.19	3.17	3.16	3.15	3.13	3.12	3.10	3.09	3.08	3.04	3.02	3.01	2.99	2.97
9	5.12	4.26	3.86	3.63	3.48	3.37	3.29	3.23	3.18	3.14	3.10	3.07	3.05	3.03	3.01	2.99	2.97	2.96	2.95	2.94	2.92	2.90	2.89	2.87	2.86	2.83	2.80	2.79	2.77	2.76
10	4.96	4.10	3.71	3.48	3.33	3.22	3.14	3.07	3.02	2.98	2.94	2.91	2.89	2.86	2.85	2.83	2.81	2.80	2.78	2.77	2.75	2.74	2.72	2.71	2.70	2.66	2.64	2.62	2.60	2.59
11	4.84	3.98	3.59	3.36	3.20	3.09	3.01	2.95	2.90	2.85	2.82	2.79	2.76	2.74	2.72	2.70	2.69	2.67	2.66	2.65	2.63	2.61	2.59	2.58	2.57	2.53	2.51	2.49	2.47	2.46
12	4.75	3.89	3.49	3.26	3.11	3.00	2.91	2.85	2.80	2.75	2.72	2.69	2.66	2.64	2.62	2.60	2.58	2.57	2.56	2.54	2.52	2.51	2.49	2.48	2.47	2.43	2.40	2.38	2.36	2.35
13	4.67	3.81	3.41	3.18	3.03	2.92	2.83	2.77	2.71	2.67	2.63	2.60	2.58	2.55	2.53	2.51	2.50	2.48	2.47	2.46	2.44	2.42	2.41	2.39	2.38	2.34	2.31	2.30	2.27	2.26
14	4.60	3.74	3.34	3.11	2.96	2.85	2.76	2.70	2.65	2.60	2.57	2.53	2.51	2.48	2.46	2.44	2.43	2.41	2.40	2.39	2.37	2.35	2.33	2.32	2.31	2.27	2.24	2.22	2.20	2.19
15	4.54	3.68	3.29	3.06	2.90	2.79	2.71	2.64	2.59	2.54	2.51	2.48	2.45	2.42	2.40	2.38	2.37	2.35	2.34	2.33	2.31	2.29	2.27	2.26	2.25	2.20	2.18	2.16	2.14	2.12
16	4.49	3.63	3.24	3.01	2.85	2.74	2.66	2.59	2.54	2.49	2.46	2.42	2.40	2.37	2.35	2.33	2.32	2.30	2.29	2.28	2.25	2.24	2.22	2.21	2.19	2.15	2.12	2.11	2.08	2.07
17	4.45	3.59	3.20	2.96	2.81	2.70	2.61	2.55	2.49	2.45	2.41	2.38	2.35	2.33	2.31	2.29	2.27	2.26	2.24	2.23	2.21	2.19	2.17	2.16	2.15	2.10	2.08	2.06	2.03	2.02
18	4.41	3.55	3.16	2.93	2.77	2.66	2.58	2.51	2.46	2.41	2.37	2.34	2.31	2.29	2.27	2.25	2.23	2.22	2.20	2.19	2.17	2.15	2.13	2.12	2.11	2.06	2.04	2.02	1.99	1.98
19	4.38	3.52	3.13	2.90	2.74	2.63	2.54	2.48	2.42	2.38	2.34	2.31	2.28	2.26	2.23	2.21	2.20	2.18	2.17	2.16	2.13	2.11	2.10	2.08	2.07	2.03	2.00	1.98	1.96	1.94
20	4.35	3.49	3.10	2.87	2.71	2.60	2.51	2.45	2.39	2.35	2.31	2.28	2.25	2.22	2.20	2.18	2.17	2.15	2.14	2.12	2.10	2.08	2.07	2.05	2.04	1.99	1.97	1.95	1.92	1.91
21	4.32	3.47	3.07	2.84	2.68	2.57	2.49	2.42	2.37	2.32	2.28	2.25	2.22	2.20	2.18	2.16	2.14	2.12	2.11	2.10	2.07	2.05	2.04	2.02	2.01	1.96	1.94	1.92	1.89	1.88
22	4.30	3.44	3.05	2.82	2.66	2.55	2.46	2.40	2.34	2.30	2.26	2.23	2.20	2.17	2.15	2.13	2.11	2.10	2.08	2.07	2.05	2.03	2.01	2.00	1.98	1.94	1.91	1.89	1.86	1.85
23	4.28	3.42	3.03	2.80	2.64	2.53	2.44	2.37	2.32	2.27	2.23	2.20	2.18	2.15	2.13	2.11	2.09	2.07	2.06	2.05	2.02	2.00	1.99	1.97	1.96	1.91	1.88	1.86	1.84	1.82
24	4.26	3.40	3.01	2.78	2.62	2.51	2.42	2.36	2.30	2.25	2.21	2.18	2.15	2.13	2.11	2.09	2.07	2.05	2.04	2.03	2.00	1.98	1.97	1.95	1.94	1.89	1.86	1.84	1.82	1.80
25	4.24	3.39	2.99	2.76	2.60	2.49	2.40	2.34	2.28	2.24	2.20	2.16	2.14	2.11	2.09	2.07	2.05	2.04	2.02	2.01	1.98	1.96	1.95	1.93	1.92	1.87	1.84	1.82	1.80	1.78
26	4.23	3.37	2.98	2.74	2.59	2.47	2.39	2.32	2.27	2.22	2.18	2.15	2.12	2.09	2.07	2.05	2.03	2.02	2.00	1.99	1.97	1.95	1.93	1.91	1.90	1.85	1.82	1.80	1.78	1.76
27	4.21	3.35	2.96	2.73	2.57	2.46	2.37	2.31	2.25	2.20	2.17	2.13	2.10	2.08	2.06	2.04	2.02	2.00	1.99	1.97	1.95	1.93	1.91	1.90	1.88	1.84	1.81	1.79	1.76	1.74
28	4.20	3.34	2.95	2.71	2.56	2.45	2.36	2.29	2.24	2.19	2.15	2.12	2.09	2.06	2.04	2.02	2.00	1.99	1.97	1.96	1.93	1.91	1.90	1.88	1.87	1.82	1.79	1.77	1.74	1.73
29	4.18	3.33	2.93	2.70	2.55	2.43	2.35	2.28	2.22	2.18	2.14	2.10	2.08	2.05	2.03	2.01	1.99	1.97	1.96	1.94	1.92	1.90	1.88	1.87	1.85	1.81	1.77	1.75	1.73	1.71
30	4.17	3.32	2.92	2.69	2.53	2.42	2.33	2.27	2.21	2.16	2.13	2.09	2.06	2.04	2.01	1.99	1.98	1.96	1.95	1.93	1.91	1.89	1.87	1.85	1.84	1.79	1.76	1.74	1.71	1.70
32	4.15	3.29	2.90	2.67	2.51	2.40	2.31	2.24	2.19	2.14	2.10	2.07	2.04	2.01	1.99	1.97	1.95	1.94	1.92	1.91	1.88	1.86	1.85	1.83	1.82	1.77	1.74	1.71	1.69	1.67
34	4.13	3.28	2.88	2.65	2.49	2.38	2.29	2.23	2.17	2.12	2.08	2.05	2.02	1.99	1.97	1.95	1.93	1.92	1.90	1.89	1.86	1.84	1.82	1.80	1.80	1.75	1.71	1.69	1.66	1.65
36	4.11	3.26	2.87	2.63	2.48	2.36	2.28	2.21	2.15	2.11	2.07	2.03	2.00	1.98	1.95	1.93	1.92	1.90	1.88	1.87	1.85	1.82	1.81	1.79	1.78	1.73	1.69	1.67	1.64	1.62
38	4.10	3.24	2.85	2.62	2.46	2.35	2.26	2.19	2.14	2.09	2.05	2.02	1.99	1.96	1.94	1.92	1.90	1.88	1.87	1.85	1.83	1.81	1.79	1.77	1.76	1.71	1.68	1.65	1.62	1.61
40	4.08	3.23	2.84	2.61	2.45	2.34	2.25	2.18	2.12	2.08	2.04	2.00	1.97	1.95	1.92	1.90	1.89	1.87	1.85	1.84	1.81	1.79	1.77	1.76	1.74	1.69	1.66	1.64	1.61	1.59
42	4.07	3.22	2.83	2.59	2.44	2.32	2.24	2.17	2.11	2.06	2.03	1.99	1.96	1.93	1.91	1.89	1.87	1.86	1.84	1.83	1.80	1.78	1.76	1.74	1.73	1.68	1.65	1.62	1.59	1.57
44	4.06	3.21	2.82	2.58	2.43	2.31	2.23	2.16	2.10	2.05	2.01	1.98	1.95	1.92	1.90	1.88	1.86	1.84	1.83	1.81	1.79	1.77	1.75	1.73	1.72	1.67	1.63	1.61	1.58	1.56
46	4.05	3.20	2.81	2.57	2.42	2.30	2.22	2.15	2.09	2.04	2.00	1.97	1.94	1.91	1.89	1.87	1.85	1.83	1.82	1.80	1.78	1.76	1.74	1.72	1.71	1.65	1.62	1.60	1.57	1.55
48	4.04	3.19	2.80	2.57	2.41	2.29	2.21	2.14	2.08	2.03	1.99	1.96	1.93	1.90	1.88	1.86	1.84	1.82	1.81	1.79	1.77	1.75	1.73	1.71	1.70	1.64	1.61	1.59	1.56	1.54
50	4.03	3.18	2.79	2.56	2.40	2.29	2.20	2.13	2.07	2.03	1.99	1.95	1.92	1.89	1.87	1.85	1.83	1.81	1.80	1.78	1.76	1.74	1.72	1.70	1.69	1.63	1.60	1.58	1.54	1.52
60	4.00	3.15	2.76	2.53	2.37	2.25	2.17	2.10	2.04	1.99	1.95	1.92	1.89	1.86	1.84	1.82	1.80	1.78	1.76	1.75	1.72	1.70	1.68	1.66	1.65	1.59	1.56	1.53	1.50	1.48
70	3.98	3.13	2.74	2.50	2.35	2.23	2.14	2.07	2.02	1.97	1.93	1.89	1.86	1.84	1.81	1.79	1.77	1.75	1.74	1.72	1.70	1.67	1.65	1.64	1.62	1.57	1.53	1.50	1.47	1.45
80	3.96	3.11	2.72	2.49	2.33	2.21	2.13	2.06	2.00	1.95	1.91	1.88	1.84	1.82	1.79	1.77	1.75	1.73	1.72	1.70	1.68	1.65	1.63	1.62	1.60	1.54	1.51	1.48	1.45	1.43
90	3.95	3.10	2.71	2.47	2.32	2.20	2.11	2.04	1.99	1.94	1.90	1.86	1.83	1.80	1.78	1.76	1.74	1.72	1.70	1.69	1.66	1.64	1.62	1.60	1.59	1.53	1.49	1.46	1.43	1.41
100	3.94	3.09	2.70	2.46	2.31	2.19	2.10	2.03	1.97	1.93	1.89	1.85	1.82	1.79	1.77	1.75	1.73	1.71	1.69	1.68	1.65	1.63	1.61	1.59	1.57	1.52	1.48	1.45	1.41	1.39
125	3.92	3.07	2.68	2.44	2.29	2.17	2.08	2.01	1.96	1.91	1.87	1.83	1.80	1.77	1.75	1.72	1.70	1.69	1.67	1.65	1.63	1.60	1.58	1.57	1.55	1.49	1.45	1.42	1.39	1.36
150	3.90	3.06	2.66	2.43	2.27	2.16	2.07	2.00	1.94	1.89	1.85	1.82	1.79	1.76	1.73	1.71	1.69	1.67	1.66	1.64	1.61	1.59	1.57	1.55	1.53	1.48	1.44	1.41	1.37	1.34
200	3.89	3.04	2.65	2.42	2.26	2.14	2.06	1.98	1.93	1.88	1.84	1.80	1.77	1.74	1.72	1.69	1.67	1.66	1.64	1.62	1.60	1.57	1.55	1.53	1.52	1.46	1.41	1.39	1.35	1.32
300	3.87	3.03	2.63	2.40	2.24	2.13	2.04	1.97	1.91	1.86	1.82	1.78	1.75	1.72	1.70	1.68	1.66	1.64	1.62	1.61	1.58	1.55	1.53	1.51	1.50	1.43	1.39	1.36	1.32	1.30
500	3.86	3.01	2.62	2.39	2.23	2.12	2.03	1.96	1.90	1.85	1.81	1.77	1.74	1.71	1.69	1.66	1.64	1.62	1.61	1.59	1.56	1.54	1.52	1.50	1.48	1.42	1.38	1.34	1.30	1.28
1000	3.85	3.00	2.61	2.38	2.22	2.11	2.02	1.95	1.89	1.84	1.80	1.76	1.73	1.70	1.68	1.65	1.63	1.61	1.60	1.58	1.55	1.53	1.51	1.49	1.47	1.41	1.36	1.33	1.29	1.26

1) Values from VAN DER WAERDEN, B. L., *Mathematische Statistik*, Springer, Berlin, 1957, page 340. Reprinted by kind permission of the author and publishers.

Upper Significance Limits of the *F*-Distribution[1] $P = 0.01$

$P = P\,(\text{right}) =$ integral between F and infinity

ν_2 \ ν_1	1	2	3	4	5	6	7	8	9	10	11	12	13	14	15	16	17	18	19	20	22	24	26	28	30	40	50	60	80	100
2	98.50	99.0	99.2	99.2	99.3	99.3	99.4	99.4	99.4	99.4	99.4	99.4	99.4	99.4	99.4	99.4	99.4	99.4	99.4	99.4	99.5	99.5	99.5	99.5	99.5	99.5	99.5	99.5	99.5	99.5
3	34.12	30.8	29.5	28.7	28.2	27.9	27.7	27.5	27.3	27.2	27.1	27.1	27.0	26.9	26.9	26.8	26.8	26.8	26.7	26.7	26.6	26.6	26.6	26.5	26.5	26.4	26.4	26.3	26.3	26.2
4	21.20	18.0	16.7	16.0	15.5	15.2	15.0	14.8	14.7	14.5	14.4	14.4	14.3	14.2	14.2	14.2	14.1	14.1	14.0	14.0	14.0	13.9	13.9	13.9	13.8	13.7	13.7	13.7	13.6	13.6
5	16.26	13.3	12.1	11.4	11.0	10.7	10.5	10.3	10.2	10.1	9.96	9.89	9.82	9.77	9.72	9.68	9.64	9.61	9.58	9.55	9.51	9.47	9.43	9.40	9.38	9.29	9.24	9.20	9.16	9.13
6	13.75	10.9	9.78	9.15	8.75	8.47	8.26	8.10	7.98	7.87	7.79	7.72	7.66	7.60	7.56	7.52	7.48	7.45	7.42	7.40	7.35	7.31	7.28	7.25	7.23	7.14	7.09	7.06	7.01	6.99
7	12.25	9.55	8.45	7.85	7.46	7.19	6.99	6.84	6.72	6.62	6.54	6.47	6.41	6.36	6.31	6.27	6.24	6.21	6.18	6.16	6.11	6.07	6.04	6.02	5.99	5.91	5.86	5.82	5.78	5.75
8	11.26	8.65	7.59	7.01	6.63	6.37	6.18	6.03	5.91	5.81	5.73	5.67	5.61	5.56	5.52	5.48	5.44	5.41	5.38	5.36	5.32	5.28	5.25	5.22	5.20	5.12	5.07	5.03	4.99	4.96
9	10.56	8.02	6.99	6.42	6.06	5.80	5.61	5.47	5.35	5.26	5.18	5.11	5.05	5.00	4.96	4.92	4.89	4.86	4.83	4.81	4.77	4.73	4.70	4.67	4.65	4.57	4.52	4.48	4.44	4.42
10	10.04	7.56	6.55	5.99	5.64	5.39	5.20	5.06	4.94	4.85	4.77	4.71	4.65	4.60	4.56	4.52	4.49	4.46	4.43	4.41	4.36	4.33	4.30	4.27	4.25	4.17	4.12	4.08	4.04	4.01
11	9.65	7.21	6.22	5.67	5.32	5.07	4.89	4.74	4.63	4.54	4.46	4.40	4.34	4.29	4.25	4.21	4.18	4.15	4.12	4.10	4.06	4.02	3.99	3.96	3.94	3.86	3.81	3.78	3.73	3.71
12	9.33	6.93	5.95	5.41	5.06	4.82	4.64	4.50	4.39	4.30	4.22	4.16	4.10	4.05	4.01	3.97	3.94	3.91	3.88	3.86	3.82	3.78	3.75	3.72	3.70	3.62	3.57	3.54	3.49	3.47
13	9.07	6.70	5.74	5.21	4.86	4.62	4.44	4.30	4.19	4.10	4.02	3.96	3.91	3.86	3.82	3.78	3.75	3.72	3.69	3.66	3.62	3.59	3.56	3.53	3.51	3.43	3.38	3.34	3.30	3.27
14	8.86	6.51	5.56	5.04	4.69	4.46	4.28	4.14	4.03	3.94	3.86	3.80	3.75	3.70	3.66	3.62	3.59	3.56	3.53	3.51	3.46	3.43	3.40	3.37	3.35	3.27	3.22	3.18	3.14	3.11
15	8.68	6.36	5.42	4.89	4.56	4.32	4.14	4.00	3.89	3.80	3.73	3.67	3.61	3.56	3.52	3.49	3.45	3.42	3.40	3.37	3.33	3.29	3.26	3.24	3.21	3.13	3.08	3.05	3.00	2.98
16	8.53	6.23	5.29	4.77	4.44	4.20	4.03	3.89	3.78	3.69	3.62	3.55	3.50	3.45	3.41	3.37	3.34	3.31	3.28	3.26	3.22	3.18	3.15	3.12	3.10	3.02	2.97	2.93	2.89	2.86
17	8.40	6.11	5.18	4.67	4.34	4.10	3.93	3.79	3.68	3.59	3.52	3.46	3.40	3.35	3.31	3.27	3.24	3.21	3.18	3.16	3.12	3.08	3.05	3.03	3.00	2.92	2.87	2.83	2.79	2.76
18	8.29	6.01	5.09	4.58	4.25	4.01	3.84	3.71	3.60	3.51	3.43	3.37	3.32	3.27	3.23	3.19	3.16	3.13	3.10	3.08	3.03	3.00	2.97	2.94	2.92	2.84	2.78	2.75	2.70	2.68
19	8.18	5.93	5.01	4.50	4.17	3.94	3.77	3.63	3.52	3.43	3.36	3.30	3.24	3.19	3.15	3.12	3.08	3.05	3.03	3.00	2.96	2.92	2.89	2.87	2.84	2.76	2.71	2.67	2.63	2.60
20	8.10	5.85	4.94	4.43	4.10	3.87	3.70	3.56	3.46	3.37	3.29	3.23	3.18	3.13	3.09	3.05	3.02	2.99	2.96	2.94	2.90	2.86	2.83	2.80	2.78	2.69	2.64	2.61	2.56	2.54
21	8.02	5.78	4.87	4.37	4.04	3.81	3.64	3.51	3.40	3.31	3.24	3.17	3.12	3.07	3.03	2.99	2.96	2.93	2.90	2.88	2.84	2.80	2.77	2.74	2.72	2.64	2.58	2.55	2.50	2.48
22	7.95	5.72	4.82	4.31	3.99	3.76	3.59	3.45	3.35	3.26	3.18	3.12	3.07	3.02	2.98	2.94	2.91	2.88	2.85	2.83	2.78	2.75	2.72	2.69	2.67	2.58	2.53	2.50	2.45	2.42
23	7.88	5.66	4.76	4.26	3.94	3.71	3.54	3.41	3.30	3.21	3.14	3.07	3.02	2.97	2.93	2.89	2.86	2.83	2.80	2.78	2.74	2.70	2.67	2.64	2.62	2.54	2.48	2.45	2.40	2.37
24	7.82	5.61	4.72	4.22	3.90	3.67	3.50	3.36	3.26	3.17	3.09	3.03	2.98	2.93	2.89	2.85	2.82	2.79	2.76	2.74	2.70	2.66	2.63	2.60	2.58	2.49	2.44	2.40	2.36	2.33
25	7.77	5.57	4.68	4.18	3.86	3.63	3.46	3.32	3.22	3.13	3.06	2.99	2.94	2.89	2.85	2.81	2.78	2.75	2.72	2.70	2.66	2.62	2.59	2.56	2.54	2.45	2.40	2.36	2.32	2.29
26	7.72	5.53	4.64	4.14	3.82	3.59	3.42	3.29	3.18	3.09	3.02	2.96	2.90	2.86	2.82	2.78	2.74	2.72	2.69	2.66	2.62	2.58	2.55	2.53	2.50	2.42	2.36	2.33	2.28	2.25
27	7.68	5.49	4.60	4.11	3.78	3.56	3.39	3.26	3.15	3.06	2.99	2.93	2.87	2.82	2.78	2.75	2.71	2.68	2.66	2.63	2.59	2.55	2.52	2.49	2.47	2.38	2.33	2.29	2.25	2.22
28	7.64	5.45	4.57	4.07	3.75	3.53	3.36	3.23	3.12	3.03	2.96	2.90	2.84	2.79	2.75	2.72	2.68	2.65	2.63	2.60	2.56	2.52	2.49	2.46	2.44	2.35	2.30	2.26	2.22	2.19
29	7.60	5.42	4.54	4.04	3.73	3.50	3.33	3.20	3.09	3.00	2.93	2.87	2.81	2.77	2.73	2.69	2.66	2.63	2.60	2.57	2.53	2.49	2.46	2.44	2.41	2.33	2.27	2.23	2.19	2.16
30	7.56	5.39	4.51	4.02	3.70	3.47	3.30	3.17	3.07	2.98	2.91	2.84	2.79	2.74	2.70	2.66	2.63	2.60	2.57	2.55	2.51	2.47	2.44	2.41	2.39	2.30	2.25	2.21	2.16	2.13
32	7.50	5.34	4.46	3.97	3.65	3.43	3.26	3.13	3.02	2.93	2.86	2.80	2.74	2.70	2.66	2.62	2.58	2.55	2.53	2.50	2.46	2.42	2.39	2.36	2.34	2.25	2.20	2.16	2.11	2.08
34	7.44	5.29	4.42	3.93	3.61	3.39	3.22	3.09	2.98	2.89	2.82	2.76	2.70	2.66	2.62	2.58	2.55	2.51	2.49	2.46	2.42	2.38	2.35	2.32	2.30	2.21	2.16	2.12	2.07	2.04
36	7.40	5.25	4.38	3.89	3.57	3.35	3.18	3.05	2.95	2.86	2.79	2.72	2.67	2.62	2.58	2.54	2.51	2.48	2.45	2.43	2.38	2.35	2.32	2.29	2.26	2.17	2.12	2.08	2.03	2.00
38	7.35	5.21	4.34	3.86	3.54	3.32	3.15	3.02	2.92	2.83	2.75	2.69	2.64	2.59	2.55	2.51	2.48	2.45	2.42	2.40	2.35	2.32	2.28	2.26	2.23	2.14	2.09	2.05	2.00	1.97
40	7.31	5.18	4.31	3.83	3.51	3.29	3.12	2.99	2.89	2.80	2.73	2.66	2.61	2.56	2.52	2.48	2.45	2.42	2.39	2.37	2.33	2.29	2.26	2.23	2.20	2.11	2.06	2.02	1.97	1.94
42	7.28	5.15	4.29	3.80	3.49	3.27	3.10	2.97	2.86	2.78	2.70	2.64	2.59	2.54	2.50	2.46	2.43	2.40	2.37	2.34	2.30	2.26	2.23	2.20	2.18	2.09	2.03	1.99	1.94	1.91
44	7.25	5.12	4.26	3.78	3.47	3.24	3.08	2.95	2.84	2.75	2.68	2.62	2.56	2.52	2.47	2.44	2.40	2.37	2.35	2.32	2.28	2.24	2.21	2.18	2.15	2.06	2.01	1.97	1.92	1.89
46	7.22	5.10	4.24	3.76	3.44	3.22	3.06	2.93	2.82	2.73	2.66	2.60	2.54	2.50	2.45	2.42	2.38	2.35	2.33	2.30	2.26	2.22	2.19	2.16	2.13	2.04	1.99	1.95	1.90	1.86
48	7.19	5.08	4.22	3.74	3.43	3.20	3.04	2.91	2.80	2.72	2.64	2.58	2.53	2.48	2.44	2.40	2.37	2.33	2.31	2.28	2.24	2.20	2.17	2.14	2.12	2.02	1.97	1.93	1.88	1.84
50	7.17	5.06	4.20	3.72	3.41	3.19	3.02	2.89	2.79	2.70	2.63	2.56	2.51	2.46	2.42	2.38	2.35	2.32	2.29	2.27	2.22	2.18	2.15	2.12	2.10	2.01	1.95	1.91	1.86	1.82
55	7.12	5.01	4.16	3.68	3.37	3.15	2.98	2.85	2.75	2.66	2.59	2.53	2.47	2.42	2.38	2.34	2.31	2.28	2.25	2.23	2.18	2.15	2.11	2.08	2.06	1.97	1.91	1.87	1.81	1.78
60	7.08	4.98	4.13	3.65	3.34	3.12	2.95	2.82	2.72	2.63	2.56	2.50	2.44	2.39	2.35	2.31	2.28	2.25	2.22	2.20	2.15	2.12	2.08	2.05	2.03	1.94	1.88	1.84	1.78	1.75
70	7.01	4.92	4.08	3.60	3.29	3.07	2.91	2.78	2.67	2.59	2.51	2.45	2.40	2.35	2.31	2.27	2.23	2.20	2.18	2.15	2.11	2.07	2.03	2.01	1.98	1.89	1.83	1.78	1.73	1.70
80	6.96	4.88	4.04	3.56	3.26	3.04	2.87	2.74	2.64	2.55	2.48	2.42	2.36	2.31	2.27	2.23	2.20	2.17	2.14	2.12	2.07	2.03	2.00	1.97	1.94	1.85	1.79	1.75	1.69	1.66
90	6.93	4.85	4.01	3.54	3.23	3.01	2.84	2.72	2.61	2.52	2.45	2.39	2.33	2.29	2.24	2.21	2.17	2.14	2.11	2.09	2.04	2.00	1.97	1.94	1.92	1.82	1.76	1.72	1.66	1.62
100	6.90	4.82	3.98	3.51	3.21	2.99	2.82	2.69	2.59	2.50	2.43	2.37	2.31	2.26	2.22	2.19	2.15	2.12	2.09	2.07	2.02	1.98	1.94	1.92	1.89	1.80	1.73	1.69	1.63	1.60
125	6.84	4.78	3.94	3.47	3.17	2.95	2.79	2.66	2.55	2.47	2.39	2.33	2.28	2.23	2.19	2.15	2.11	2.08	2.05	2.03	1.98	1.94	1.91	1.88	1.85	1.76	1.69	1.65	1.59	1.55
150	6.81	4.75	3.92	3.45	3.14	2.92	2.76	2.63	2.53	2.44	2.37	2.31	2.25	2.20	2.16	2.12	2.09	2.06	2.03	2.00	1.96	1.92	1.88	1.85	1.83	1.73	1.66	1.62	1.56	1.52
200	6.76	4.71	3.88	3.41	3.11	2.89	2.73	2.60	2.50	2.41	2.34	2.27	2.22	2.17	2.13	2.09	2.06	2.02	2.00	1.97	1.93	1.89	1.85	1.82	1.79	1.69	1.63	1.58	1.52	1.48
300	6.72	4.68	3.85	3.38	3.08	2.86	2.70	2.57	2.47	2.38	2.31	2.24	2.19	2.14	2.10	2.06	2.03	1.99	1.97	1.94	1.89	1.85	1.82	1.79	1.76	1.66	1.59	1.55	1.48	1.44
500	6.69	4.65	3.82	3.36	3.05	2.84	2.68	2.55	2.44	2.36	2.28	2.22	2.17	2.12	2.07	2.04	2.00	1.97	1.94	1.92	1.87	1.83	1.79	1.76	1.74	1.63	1.56	1.52	1.45	1.41
1000	6.66	4.63	3.80	3.34	3.04	2.82	2.66	2.53	2.43	2.34	2.27	2.20	2.15	2.10	2.06	2.02	1.98	1.95	1.92	1.90	1.85	1.81	1.77	1.74	1.72	1.61	1.54	1.50	1.43	1.38

[1]) Values from VAN DER WAERDEN, B. L., *Mathematische Statistik*, Springer, Berlin, 1957, page 342. Reprinted by kind permission of the author and publishers.

Squares of STUDENT Deviations*

$P=2\alpha$	0.20	0.10	0.05	0.02	0.01	0.005	0.001	$P=2\alpha$	0.20	0.10	0.05	0.02	0.01	0.005	0.001
½ $P=\alpha$	0.10	0.05	0.025	0.01	0.005	0.0025	0.0005	½ $P=\alpha$	0.10	0.05	0.025	0.01	0.005	0.0025	0.0005
ν								ν							
1	9.474	39.864	161.442	1012.576	4052.214	16210.382	405283.751	101	1.664	2.756	3.935	5.589	6.893	8.237	11.491
2	3.557	8.526	18.513	48.511	98.502	198.500	998.434	102	1.664	2.755	3.934	5.587	6.890	8.234	11.484
3	2.683	5.538	10.128	20.621	34.116	55.552	167.030	103	1.664	2.755	3.933	5.585	6.888	8.231	11.478
4	2.350	4.545	7.708	14.040	21.198	31.333	74.132	104	1.664	2.754	3.933	5.583	6.885	8.227	11.472
5	2.179	4.060	6.608	11.323	16.258	22.784	47.183	105	1.663	2.754	3.932	5.582	6.883	8.224	11.465
6	2.074	3.776	5.987	9.878	13.745	18.635	35.510	106	1.663	2.754	3.931	5.580	6.881	8.220	11.458
7	2.002	3.590	5.591	8.988	12.247	16.235	29.246	107	1.663	2.753	3.930	5.579	6.879	8.217	11.451
8	1.952	3.458	5.318	8.387	11.259	14.688	25.412	108	1.663	2.753	3.929	5.577	6.876	8.213	11.445
9	1.913	3.360	5.118	7.958	10.561	13.614	22.858	109	1.663	2.752	3.928	5.575	6.874	8.211	11.440
10	1.882	3.285	4.964	7.640	10.044	12.826	21.041	110	1.662	2.752	3.928	5.574	6.871	8.207	11.435
11	1.858	3.225	4.844	7.388	9.646	12.226	19.687	111	1.662	2.751	3.927	5.572	6.869	8.204	11.430
12	1.839	3.177	4.747	7.188	9.330	11.754	18.645	112	1.662	2.751	3.926	5.571	6.867	8.201	11.424
13	1.823	3.136	4.667	7.023	9.074	11.374	17.817	113	1.662	2.751	3.925	5.570	6.865	8.198	11.418
14	1.809	3.102	4.600	6.885	8.861	11.060	17.140	114	1.662	2.750	3.924	5.568	6.863	8.195	11.412
15	1.798	3.073	4.543	6.770	8.683	10.798	16.589	115	1.662	2.750	3.924	5.567	6.861	8.193	11.408
16	1.788	3.048	4.494	6.672	8.531	10.576	16.120	116	1.661	2.749	3.923	5.565	6.859	8.190	11.402
17	1.777	3.026	4.451	6.589	8.400	10.385	15.721	117	1.661	2.749	3.922	5.564	6.857	8.187	11.397
18	1.769	3.007	4.414	6.513	8.285	10.218	15.382	118	1.661	2.749	3.922	5.563	6.855	8.184	11.392
19	1.764	2.990	4.381	6.447	8.185	10.072	15.078	119	1.661	2.748	3.921	5.561	6.853	8.182	11.387
20	1.756	2.975	4.351	6.391	8.096	9.944	14.823	120	1.661	2.748	3.920	5.560	6.851	8.179	11.381
21	1.750	2.961	4.325	6.340	8.017	9.829	14.585	121	1.660	2.748	3.920	5.559	6.850	8.177	11.376
22	1.745	2.948	4.301	6.290	7.946	9.727	14.379	122	1.660	2.747	3.919	5.558	6.848	8.174	11.371
23	1.740	2.937	4.280	6.250	7.881	9.635	14.190	123	1.660	2.747	3.918	5.556	6.846	8.172	11.367
24	1.737	2.927	4.260	6.210	7.823	9.551	14.025	124	1.660	2.747	3.918	5.555	6.844	8.169	11.363
25	1.732	2.918	4.242	6.175	7.770	9.475	13.876	125	1.660	2.746	3.917	5.554	6.842	8.167	11.358
26	1.729	2.909	4.225	6.145	7.721	9.406	13.742	126	1.660	2.746	3.916	5.553	6.841	8.165	11.353
27	1.727	2.901	4.210	6.116	7.677	9.342	13.616	127	1.660	2.746	3.916	5.552	6.839	8.162	11.350
28	1.724	2.894	4.196	6.086	7.636	9.284	13.498	128	1.659	2.745	3.915	5.551	6.837	8.160	11.347
29	1.719	2.887	4.183	6.061	7.598	9.229	13.388	129	1.659	2.745	3.915	5.550	6.836	8.158	11.343
30	1.716	2.881	4.171	6.037	7.563	9.180	13.293	130	1.659	2.745	3.914	5.549	6.834	8.156	11.339
31	1.715	2.875	4.160	6.015	7.530	9.134	13.205	131	1.659	2.744	3.914	5.547	6.832	8.154	11.335
32	1.712	2.869	4.149	5.995	7.499	9.090	13.120	132	1.659	2.744	3.913	5.546	6.831	8.152	11.331
33	1.710	2.864	4.139	5.976	7.471	9.050	13.040	133	1.659	2.744	3.912	5.545	6.830	8.150	11.327
34	1.708	2.859	4.130	5.958	7.444	9.012	12.968	134	1.659	2.743	3.912	5.544	6.828	8.148	11.322
35	1.706	2.855	4.121	5.941	7.420	8.977	12.899	135	1.659	2.743	3.911	5.543	6.827	8.145	11.318
36	1.704	2.850	4.113	5.925	7.396	8.943	12.834	136	1.658	2.743	3.911	5.542	6.825	8.143	11.314
37	1.703	2.846	4.105	5.911	7.374	8.912	12.774	137	1.658	2.743	3.911	5.541	6.824	8.141	11.310
38	1.701	2.843	4.098	5.897	7.353	8.883	12.717	138	1.658	2.742	3.910	5.540	6.823	8.139	11.307
39	1.700	2.839	4.091	5.883	7.333	8.855	12.664	139	1.658	2.742	3.909	5.540	6.821	8.137	11.304
40	1.698	2.836	4.085	5.871	7.314	8.829	12.610	140	1.658	2.742	3.909	5.539	6.819	8.136	11.300
41	1.697	2.832	4.079	5.859	7.296	8.804	12.564	141	1.658	2.742	3.909	5.538	6.818	8.134	11.297
42	1.695	2.829	4.073	5.848	7.280	8.780	12.520	142	1.658	2.741	3.908	5.537	6.817	8.132	11.294
43	1.694	2.826	4.067	5.837	7.264	8.757	12.477	143	1.658	2 741	3.907	5.536	6.816	8.130	11.290
44	1.693	2.823	4.062	5.827	7.248	8.736	12.435	144	1.658	2.741	3.907	5.535	6.814	8.128	11.286
45	1.692	2.820	4.057	5.817	7.234	8.715	12.395	145	1.658	2.741	3.907	5.534	6.813	8.126	11.283
46	1.691	2.818	4.052	5.808	7.220	8.696	12.357	146	1.657	2.740	3.906	5.533	6.812	8.125	11.280
47	1.689	2.815	4.047	5.799	7.207	8.677	12.323	147	1.657	2.740	3.906	5.532	6.811	8.123	11.277
48	1.688	2.813	4.043	5.791	7.194	8.659	12.287	148	1.657	2.740	3.905	5.532	6.809	8.121	11.273
49	1.688	2.811	4.038	5.783	7.182	8.642	12.257	149	1.657	2.740	3.905	5.531	6.808	8.120	11.271
50	1.687	2.809	4.034	5.775	7.171	8.626	12.226	150	1.657	2.739	3.904	5.530	6.807	8.118	11.267
51	1.686	2.807	4.031	5.767	7.160	8.611	12.197	151	1.657	2.739	3.904	5.529	6.806	8.117	11.265
52	1.685	2.805	4.027	5.760	7.149	8.595	12.168	152	1.657	2.739	3.903	5.528	6.805	8.115	11.262
53	1.684	2.803	4.023	5.753	7.139	8.582	12.142	153	1.657	2.739	3.903	5.528	6.804	8.113	11.259
54	1.684	2.801	4.020	5.747	7.129	8.568	12.115	154	1.657	2.738	3.903	5.527	6.803	8.112	11.255
55	1.683	2.799	4.016	5.740	7.120	8.555	12.090	155	1.657	2.738	3.902	5.526	6.802	8.110	11.253
56	1.682	2.797	4.013	5.734	7.111	8.542	12.064	156	1.656	2.738	3.902	5.525	6.800	8.108	11.250
57	1.681	2.796	4.010	5.728	7.102	8.529	12.042	157	1.656	2.738	3.901	5.525	6.799	8.107	11.248
58	1.681	2.794	4.007	5.723	7.093	8.517	12.020	158	1.656	2.738	3.901	5.524	6.798	8.106	11.246
59	1.680	2.793	4.004	5.717	7.085	8.506	11.998	159	1.656	2.738	3.901	5.523	6.797	8.104	11.243
60	1.679	2.791	4.001	5.712	7.077	8.495	11.976	160	1.656	2.737	3.900	5.522	6.796	8.103	11.241
61	1.679	2.790	3.999	5.707	7.070	8.484	11.956	161	1.656	2.737	3.900	5.522	6.795	8.101	11.239
62	1.678	2.788	3.996	5.702	7.063	8.474	11.936	162	1.656	2.737	3.899	5.521	6.794	8.100	11.237
63	1.678	2.787	3.994	5.698	7.056	8.465	11.917	163	1.656	2.737	3.899	5.520	6.793	8.099	11.234
64	1.677	2.786	3.991	5.693	7.048	8.455	11.898	164	1.656	2.736	3.899	5.520	6.792	8.097	11.231
65	1.677	2.785	3.989	5.689	7.042	8.445	11.882	165	1.656	2.736	3.899	5.519	6.791	8.096	11.229
66	1.676	2.783	3.986	5.684	7.036	8.436	11.865	166	1.656	2.736	3.898	5.518	6.790	8.095	11.227
67	1.675	2.782	3.984	5.680	7.029	8.428	11.849	167	1.656	2.736	3.898	5.518	6.790	8.093	11.224
68	1.675	2.781	3.982	5.676	7.023	8.419	11.834	168	1.655	2.736	3.897	5.517	6.789	8.092	11.220
69	1.674	2.780	3.980	5.672	7.018	8.411	11.818	169	1.655	2.736	3.897	5.516	6.788	8.091	11.218
70	1.674	2.779	3.978	5.668	7.012	8.403	11.803	170	1.655	2.735	3.897	5.516	6.787	8.089	11.215
71	1.673	2.778	3.976	5.665	7.007	8.396	11.788	171	1.655	2.735	3.897	5.515	6.786	8.088	11.213
72	1.673	2.777	3.974	5.661	7.001	8.389	11.772	172	1.655	2.735	3.896	5.515	6.785	8.087	11.210
73	1.673	2.776	3.972	5.658	6.996	8.381	11.759	173	1.655	2.735	3.896	5.514	6.784	8.086	11.208
74	1.672	2.775	3.970	5.654	6.991	8.373	11.746	174	1.655	2.735	3.895	5.513	6.783	8.085	11.206
75	1.672	2.774	3.969	5.651	6.986	8.367	11.733	175	1.655	2.735	3.895	5.513	6.782	8.084	11.205
76	1.671	2.773	3.967	5.648	6.981	8.360	11.720	176	1.655	2.734	3.895	5.512	6.781	8.083	11.203
77	1.671	2.772	3.965	5.645	6.976	8.354	11.708	177	1.655	2.734	3.895	5.512	6.781	8.082	11.200
78	1.671	2.771	3.964	5.642	6.972	8.347	11.696	178	1.655	2.734	3.894	5.511	6.780	8.080	11.197
79	1.670	2.770	3.962	5.639	6.967	8.342	11.686	179	1.655	2.734	3.894	5.511	6.779	8.079	11.195
80	1.670	2.769	3.960	5.636	6.963	8.335	11.675	180	1.655	2.734	3.894	5.510	6.778	8.078	11.193
81	1.670	2.769	3.959	5.633	6.959	8.330	11.664	181	1.655	2.734	3.894	5.509	6.778	8.076	11.191
82	1.669	2.768	3.957	5.630	6.955	8.324	11.652	182	1.654	2.733	3.893	5.509	6.777	8.075	11.189
83	1.669	2.767	3.956	5.628	6.951	8.319	11.642	183	1.654	2.733	3.893	5.508	6.776	8.075	11.187
84	1.668	2.766	3.955	5.625	6.947	8.313	11.632	184	1.654	2.733	3.893	5.508	6.775	8.074	11.185
85	1.668	2.766	3.953	5.622	6.943	8.308	11.622	185	1.654	2.733	3.892	5.507	6.775	8.072	11.183
86	1.668	2.765	3.952	5.620	6.940	8.302	11.612	186	1.654	2.733	3.892	5.507	6.774	8.071	11.181
87	1.668	2.764	3.951	5.618	6.936	8.297	11.603	187	1.654	2.733	3.892	5.506	6.773	8.070	11.179
88	1.667	2.764	3.949	5.615	6.932	8.292	11.594	188	1.654	2.732	3.892	5.506	6.772	8.069	11.177
89	1.667	2.763	3.948	5.613	6.929	8.287	11.584	189	1.654	2.732	3.892	5.505	6.771	8.068	11.175
90	1.667	2.762	3.947	5.611	6.925	8.282	11.575	190	1.654	2.732	3.891	5.505	6.770	8.067	11.173
91	1.666	2.762	3.946	5.608	6.922	8.278	11.567	191	1.654	2.732	3.891	5.504	6.770	8.066	11.172
92	1.666	2.761	3.945	5.606	6.918	8.274	11.558	192	1.654	2.732	3.890	5.504	6.769	8.065	11.170
93	1.666	2.760	3.944	5.604	6.916	8.270	11.550	193	1.654	2.732	3.890	5.503	6.768	8.064	11.168
94	1.666	2.760	3.943	5.602	6.913	8.265	11.543	194	1.654	2.732	3.890	5.503	6.768	8.063	11.166
95	1.665	2.759	3.941	5.600	6.910	8.261	11.536	195	1.654	2.732	3.890	5.502	6.767	8.062	11.165
96	1.665	2.759	3.940	5.598	6.906	8.256	11.527	196	1.654	2.731	3.890	5.502	6.766	8.061	11.164
97	1.665	2.758	3.939	5.596	6.904	8.253	11.519	197	1.654	2.731	3.889	5.501	6.766	8.060	11.162
98	1.665	2.758	3.938	5.594	6.901	8.249	11.511	198	1.654	2.731	3.889	5.501	6.765	8.059	11.160
99	1.665	2.757	3.937	5.592	6.899	8.245	11.505	199	1.654	2.731	3.889	5.500	6.764	8.059	11.158
100	1.664	2.756	3.936	5.590	6.896	8.241	11.498	200	1.653	2.731	3.888	5.500	6.763	8.058	11.156

Confidence Factors for the Mean μ*

Confidence limits for μ: $\bar{x} \pm k_2 s$; k_2 is given in the table. N = size of the sample from which $\bar{x}$ and s are calculated

100 (1 − 2α) = 95%

N	0	1	2	3	4	5	6	7	8	9
0			8.9845	2.4842	1.5913	1.2416	1.0494	0.9248	0.8360	0.7687
10	0.7154	0.6718	0.6354	0.6043	0.5774	0.5538	0.5329	5142	4973	4820
20	4680	4552	4434	4324	4223	4128	4039	3956	3878	3804
30	3734	3668	3605	3546	3489	3435	3384	3334	3287	3242
40	3198	3156	3116	3078	3040	3004	2970	2936	2904	2872
50	0.2842	0.2813	0.2784	0.2756	0.2730	0.2703	0.2678	0.2653	0.2629	0.2606
60	2583	2561	2540	2519	2498	2478	2458	2439	2421	2402
70	2385	2367	2350	2333	2317	2301	2285	2270	2255	2240
80	2225	2211	2197	2184	2170	2157	2144	2131	2119	2107
90	2095	2083	2071	2060	2048	2037	2026	2016	2005	1995
100	0.1984	0.1974	0.1964	0.1954	0.1945	0.1935	0.1926	0.1917	0.1908	0.1899
110	1890	1881	1872	1864	1856	1847	1839	1831	1823	1815
120	1808	1800	1792	1785	1778	1770	1763	1756	1749	1742
130	1735	1729	1722	1715	1709	1702	1696	1690	1683	1677
140	1671	1665	1659	1653	1647	1642	1636	1630	1625	1619
150	0.1614	0.1608	0.1603	0.1597	0.1592	0.1587	0.1582	0.1577	0.1571	0.1566
160	1561	1556	1552	1547	1542	1537	1533	1528	1523	1519
170	1514	1510	1505	1501	1496	1492	1488	1483	1479	1475
180	1471	1467	1463	1459	1455	1451	1447	1443	1439	1435
190	1431	1427	1424	1420	1416	1412	1409	1405	1402	1398
200	0.1394	0.1391	0.1379	0.1376	0.1372	0.1369	0.1366	0.1362	0.1359	0.1356
210	1353	1349	1346	1343	1340	1337	1334	1331	1328	1324
220	1321	1318	1315	1313	1310	1307	1304	1301	1298	1295
230	1292	1290	1287	1284	1281	1279	1276	1273	1271	1268
240	1265	1263	1260	1257	1255	1252	1250	1247	1245	1242
250	0.1240	0.1237	0.1235	0.1232	0.1230	0.1227	0.1225	0.1223	0.1220	0.1218
260	1216	1213	1211	1209	1206	1204	1202	1200	1197	1195
270	1193	1191	1188	1186	1184	1182	1180	1178	1176	1173
280	1171	1169	1167	1165	1163	1161	1159	1157	1155	1153
290	1151	1149	1147	1145	1143	1141	1139	1137	1135	1134
300	0.1132	0.1130	0.1128	0.1126	0.1124	0.1122	0.1120	0.1119	0.1117	0.1115
310	1113	1111	1110	1108	1106	1104	1103	1101	1099	1097
320	1096	1094	1092	1091	1089	1087	1086	1084	1082	1081
330	1079	1077	1076	1074	1072	1071	1069	1068	1066	1065
340	1063	1061	1060	1058	1057	1055	1054	1052	1051	1049
350	0.1048	0.1046	0.1045	0.1043	0.1042	0.1040	0.1039	0.1037	0.1036	0.1034
360	1033	1032	1030	1029	1027	1026	1025	1023	1022	1020
370	1019	1018	1016	1015	1014	1012	1011	1009	1008	1007
380	1005	1004	1003	1002	1000	0999	0998	0996	0995	0994
390	0993	0991	0990	0989	0987	0986	0985	0984	0982	0981
400	0.0980	0.0979	0.0978	0.0976	0.0975	0.0974	0.0973	0.0972	0.0970	0.0969
410	0968	0967	0966	0964	0963	0962	0961	0960	0959	0958
420	0956	0955	0954	0953	0952	0951	0950	0949	0947	0946
430	0945	0944	0943	0942	0941	0940	0939	0938	0937	0935
440	0934	0933	0932	0931	0930	0929	0928	0927	0926	0925
450	0.0924	0.0923	0.0922	0.0921	0.0920	0.0919	0.0918	0.0917	0.0916	0.0915
460	0914	0913	0912	0911	0910	0909	0908	0907	0906	0905
470	0904	0903	0902	0901	0900	0899	0898	0897	0897	0896
480	0895	0894	0893	0892	0891	0890	0889	0888	0887	0886
490	0885	0885	0884	0883	0882	0881	0880	0879	0878	0877
500	0.0877	0.0876	0.0875	0.0874	0.0873	0.0872	0.0871	0.0871	0.0870	0.0869
510	0868	0867	0866	0865	0865	0864	0863	0862	0861	0860
520	0860	0859	0858	0857	0856	0855	0855	0854	0853	0852
530	0851	0851	0850	0849	0848	0847	0847	0846	0845	0844
540	0843	0843	0842	0841	0840	0840	0839	0838	0837	0837
550	0.0836	0.0835	0.0834	0.0834	0.0833	0.0832	0.0831	0.0831	0.0830	0.0829
560	0828	0828	0827	0826	0825	0825	0824	0823	0822	0822
570	0821	0820	0820	0819	0818	0817	0817	0816	0815	0815
580	0814	0813	0812	0812	0811	0810	0810	0809	0808	0808
590	0807	0806	0806	0805	0804	0804	0803	0802	0802	0801
600	0.0800	0.0800	0.0799	0.0798	0.0798	0.0797	0.0796	0.0796	0.0795	0.0794
610	0794	0793	0792	0792	0791	0790	0790	0789	0788	0788
620	0787	0787	0786	0785	0785	0784	0783	0783	0782	0782
630	0781	0780	0780	0779	0778	0778	0777	0777	0776	0775
640	0775	0774	0774	0773	0772	0772	0771	0771	0770	0769
650	0.0769	0.0768	0.0768	0.0767	0.0766	0.0766	0.0765	0.0765	0.0764	0.0764
660	0763	0762	0762	0761	0761	0760	0760	0759	0758	0758
670	0757	0757	0756	0756	0755	0754	0754	0753	0753	0752
680	0752	0751	0751	0750	0749	0749	0748	0748	0747	0747
690	0746	0746	0745	0745	0744	0744	0743	0742	0742	0741
700	0.0741	0.0740	0.0740	0.0739	0.0739	0.0738	0.0738	0.0737	0.0737	0.0736
710	0736	0735	0735	0734	0734	0733	0733	0732	0732	0731
720	0730	0730	0729	0729	0728	0728	0727	0727	0726	0726
730	0725	0725	0724	0724	0723	0723	0723	0722	0722	0721
740	0721	0720	0720	0719	0719	0718	0718	0717	0717	0716
750	0.0716	0.0715	0.0715	0.0714	0.0714	0.0713	0.0713	0.0712	0.0712	0.0711
760	0711	0711	0710	0710	0709	0709	0708	0708	0707	0707
770	0706	0706	0705	0705	0705	0704	0704	0703	0703	0702
780	0702	0701	0701	0700	0700	0700	0699	0699	0698	0698
790	0697	0697	0696	0696	0696	0695	0695	0694	0694	0693
800	0.0693	0.0693	0.0692	0.0692	0.0691	0.0691	0.0690	0.0690	0.0690	0.0689
810	0689	0688	0688	0687	0687	0687	0686	0686	0685	0685
820	0684	0684	0684	0683	0683	0682	0682	0682	0681	0681
830	0680	0680	0680	0679	0679	0678	0678	0678	0677	0677
840	0676	0676	0675	0675	0675	0674	0674	0674	0673	0673
850	0.0672	0.0672	0.0672	0.0671	0.0671	0.0670	0.0670	0.0670	0.0669	0.0669
860	0668	0668	0668	0667	0667	0666	0666	0666	0665	0665
870	0665	0664	0664	0663	0663	0663	0662	0662	0662	0661
880	0661	0660	0660	0660	0659	0659	0659	0658	0658	0657
890	0657	0657	0656	0656	0656	0655	0655	0654	0654	0654
900	0.0653	0.0653	0.0653	0.0652	0.0652	0.0652	0.0651	0.0651	0.0650	0.0650
910	0650	0649	0649	0649	0648	0648	0648	0647	0647	0647
920	0646	0646	0646	0645	0645	0644	0644	0644	0643	0643
930	0643	0642	0642	0642	0641	0641	0641	0640	0640	0640
940	0639	0639	0639	0638	0638	0638	0637	0637	0637	0636
950	0.0636	0.0636	0.0635	0.0635	0.0635	0.0634	0.0634	0.0634	0.0633	0.0633
960	0633	0632	0632	0632	0631	0631	0631	0630	0630	0630
970	0629	0629	0629	0628	0628	0628	0627	0627	0627	0626
980	0626	0626	0625	0625	0625	0625	0624	0624	0624	0623
990	0623	0623	0622	0622	0622	0621	0621	0621	0620	0620
1000	0.0620									

100 (1 − 2α) = 99%

N	0	1	2	3	4	5	6	7	8	9
0			45.012	5.7301	2.9205	2.0590	1.6461	1.4013	1.2373	1.1185
10	1.0277	0.9556	0.8966	0.8472	0.8051	0.7686	0.7367	0.7084	0.6831	0.6604
20	0.6397	6209	6037	5878	5730	5594	5467	5348	5236	5131
30	5033	4939	4851	4767	4688	4612	4540	4471	4405	4342
40	4282	4224	4168	4115	4063	4013	3966	3919	3875	3832
50	0.3790	0.3750	0.3711	0.3673	0.3636	0.3600	0.3566	0.3532	0.3499	0.3467
60	3436	3406	3377	3348	3320	3293	3267	3241	3215	3190
70	3166	3143	3120	3097	3075	3053	3032	3011	2991	2971
80	2951	2932	2913	2895	2877	2859	2841	2824	2807	2791
90	2775	2759	2743	2728	2712	2698	2683	2668	2654	2640
100	0.2627	0.2613	0.2600	0.2586	0.2574	0.2561	0.2548	0.2536	0.2524	0.2512
110	2500	2488	2477	2465	2454	2443	2432	2421	2411	2400
120	2390	2380	2370	2360	2350	2340	2330	2321	2312	2302
130	2293	2284	2275	2266	2258	2249	2241	2232	2224	2216
140	2207	2199	2191	2183	2176	2168	2160	2153	2145	2138
150	0.2131	0.2123	0.2116	0.2109	0.2102	0.2095	0.2088	0.2081	0.2074	0.2068
160	2061	2055	2048	2042	2035	2029	2023	2016	2010	2004
170	1998	1992	1986	1980	1975	1969	1963	1957	1952	1946
180	1941	1935	1930	1924	1919	1914	1909	1903	1898	1893
190	1888	1883	1878	1873	1868	1863	1858	1853	1849	1844
200	0.1839	0.1834	0.1812	0.1808	0.1803	0.1799	0.1795	0.1790	0.1786	0.1782
210	1778	1773	1769	1765	1761	1757	1753	1749	1745	1741
220	1737	1733	1729	1725	1721	1717	1713	1710	1706	1702
230	1699	1695	1691	1688	1684	1680	1677	1673	1670	1666
240	1663	1659	1656	1652	1649	1646	1642	1639	1636	1632
250	0.1629	0.1626	0.1623	0.1619	0.1616	0.1613	0.1610	0.1607	0.1604	0.1601
260	1598	1594	1591	1588	1585	1582	1579	1576	1573	1571
270	1568	1565	1562	1559	1556	1553	1551	1548	1545	1542
280	1539	1537	1534	1531	1529	1526	1523	1521	1518	1515
290	1513	1510	1507	1505	1502	1500	1497	1495	1492	1490
300	0.1487	0.1485	0.1482	0.1480	0.1477	0.1475	0.1473	0.1470	0.1468	0.1465
310	1463	1461	1458	1456	1454	1451	1449	1447	1445	1442
320	1440	1438	1436	1433	1431	1429	1427	1424	1422	1420
330	1418	1416	1414	1412	1409	1407	1405	1403	1401	1399
340	1397	1395	1393	1391	1389	1387	1385	1383	1381	1379
350	0.1377	0.1375	0.1373	0.1371	0.1369	0.1367	0.1365	0.1363	0.1361	0.1360
360	1358	1356	1354	1352	1350	1348	1346	1345	1343	1341
370	1339	1337	1336	1334	1332	1330	1328	1327	1325	1323
380	1321	1320	1318	1316	1315	1313	1311	1309	1308	1306
390	1304	1303	1301	1299	1298	1296	1294	1293	1291	1290
400	0.1288	0.1286	0.1285	0.1283	0.1282	0.1280	0.1278	0.1277	0.1275	0.1274
410	1272	1271	1269	1268	1266	1264	1263	1261	1260	1258
420	1257	1255	1254	1252	1251	1250	1248	1247	1245	1244
430	1242	1241	1239	1238	1236	1235	1234	1232	1231	1229
440	1228	1227	1225	1224	1222	1221	1220	1218	1217	1216
450	0.1214	0.1213	0.1212	0.1210	0.1209	0.1208	0.1206	0.1205	0.1204	0.1202
460	1201	1200	1198	1197	1196	1195	1193	1192	1191	1189
470	1188	1187	1186	1184	1183	1182	1181	1179	1178	1177
480	1176	1175	1173	1172	1171	1170	1168	1167	1166	1165
490	1164	1163	1161	1160	1159	1158	1157	1155	1154	1153
500	0.1152	0.1151	0.1150	0.1149	0.1147	0.1146	0.1145	0.1144	0.1143	0.1142
510	1141	1140	1138	1137	1136	1135	1134	1133	1132	1131
520	1130	1129	1127	1126	1125	1124	1123	1122	1121	1120
530	1119	1118	1117	1116	1115	1114	1113	1112	1111	1110
540	1109	1107	1106	1105	1104	1103	1102	1101	1100	1099
550	0.1098	0.1097	0.1096	0.1095	0.1094	0.1093	0.1092	0.1091	0.1090	0.1090
560	1089	1088	1087	1086	1085	1084	1083	1082	1081	1080
570	1079	1078	1077	1076	1075	1074	1073	1072	1071	1071
580	1070	1069	1068	1067	1066	1065	1064	1063	1062	1061
590	1061	1060	1059	1058	1057	1056	1055	1054	1053	1053
600	0.1052	0.1051	0.1050	0.1049	0.1048	0.1047	0.1046	0.1046	0.1045	0.1044
610	1043	1042	1041	1040	1040	1039	1038	1037	1036	1035
620	1035	1034	1033	1032	1031	1030	1030	1029	1028	1027
630	1026	1025	1025	1024	1023	1022	1021	1021	1020	1019
640	1018	1017	1017	1016	1015	1014	1013	1013	1012	1011
650	0.1010	0.1010	0.1009	0.1008	0.1007	0.1007	0.1006	0.1005	0.1004	0.1003
660	1003	1002	1001	1000	1000	0999	0998	0997	0997	0996
670	0995	0994	0994	0993	0992	0991	0991	0990	0989	0989
680	0988	0987	0986	0986	0985	0984	0984	0983	0982	0981
690	0981	0980	0979	0979	0978	0977	0976	0976	0975	0974
700	0.0974	0.0973	0.0972	0.0972	0.0971	0.0970	0.0969	0.0969	0.0968	0.0967
710	0967	0966	0965	0965	0964	0963	0963	0962	0961	0961
720	0960	0959	0959	0958	0957	0957	0956	0955	0955	0954
730	0953	0953	0952	0951	0951	0950	0950	0949	0948	0948
740	0947	0946	0946	0945	0944	0944	0943	0942	0942	0941
750	0.0941	0.0940	0.0939	0.0939	0.0938	0.0937	0.0937	0.0936	0.0936	0.0935
760	0934	0934	0933	0933	0932	0931	0931	0930	0930	0929
770	0928	0928	0927	0927	0926	0925	0925	0924	0924	0923
780	0922	0922	0921	0921	0920	0919	0919	0918	0918	0917
790	0916	0916	0915	0915	0914	0914	0913	0912	0912	0911
800	0.0911	0.0910	0.0910	0.0909	0.0908	0.0908	0.0907	0.0907	0.0906	0.0906
810	0905	0905	0904	0903	0903	0902	0902	0901	0901	0900
820	0900	0899	0898	0898	0897	0897	0896	0896	0895	0895
830	0894	0894	0893	0893	0892	0891	0891	0890	0890	0889
840	0889	0888	0888	0887	0887	0886	0886	0885	0885	0884
850	0.0884	0.0883	0.0883	0.0882	0.0881	0.0881	0.0880	0.0880	0.0879	0.0879
860	0878	0878	0877	0877	0876	0876	0875	0875	0874	0874
870	0873	0873	0872	0872	0871	0871	0870	0870	0869	0869
880	0868	0868	0867	0867	0866	0866	0865	0865	0864	0864
890	0863	0863	0863	0862	0862	0861	0861	0860	0860	0859
900	0.0859	0.0858	0.0858	0.0857	0 0857	0.0856	0.0856	0.0855	0.0855	0.0854
910	0854	0853	0853	0853	0852	0852	0851	0851	0850	0850
920	0849	0849	0848	0848	0847	0847	0847	0846	0846	0845
930	0845	0844	0844	0843	0843	0842	0842	0842	0841	0841
940	0840	0840	0839	0839	0838	0838	0838	0837	0837	0836
950	0.0836	0.0835	0.0835	0.0834	0.0834	0.0834	0.0833	0.0833	0.0832	0.0832
960	0831	0831	0831	0830	0830	0829	0829	0828	0828	0828
970	0827	0827	0826	0826	0825	0825	0825	0824	0824	0823
980	0823	0822	0822	0822	0821	0821	0820	0820	0820	0819
990	0819	0818	0818	0817	0817	0817	0816	0816	0815	0815
1000	0.0815									

Tolerance Factors*

$\beta_p = (1-2\alpha_p)$ = tolerance probability; $\beta_t = (1-2\alpha_t)$ = confidence probability; N = size of the sample from which $\bar{x}$ and s are calculated

	A									B										
	k_3 for $(\bar{x} \pm k_3\sigma)$				k_4 for $(\bar{x} \pm k_4 s)$				$\sqrt{\frac{N+1}{N}}$	k_5 for $(\bar{x} \pm k_5\sigma)$				k_6 for $(\mu \pm k_6 s)$						
										$\beta_t = 0.95$		$\beta_t = 0.99$		$\beta_t = 0.95$		$\sqrt{\frac{N-1}{\chi^2(N-1;\,0.95)}}$	$\beta_t = 0.99$		$\sqrt{\frac{N-1}{\chi^2(N-1;\,0.99)}}$
N \ β_p	0.90	0.95	0.98	0.99	0.90	0.95	0.98	0.99		0.90	0.95	0.95	0.99	0.90	0.95		0.95	0.99	
2	2.0145	2.4005	2.8492	3.1547	7.7328	15.562	38.973	77.964	1.224745	2.667	3.031	3.466	4.147	26.231	31.256	15.947	156.38	205.52	79.789
3	1.8993	2.2632	2.6862	2.9743	3.3717	4.9683	8.042	11.460	154701	2.415	2.776	3.132	3.813	7.263	8.654	4.4155	19.550	25.694	9.9749
4	1.8390	2.1913	2.6009	2.8799	2.6312	3.5581	5.077	6.5303	118034	2.265	2.626	2.933	3.614	4.803	5.723	2.9199	10.018	13.166	5.1113
5	1.8018	2.1470	2.5484	2.8217	2.3353	3.0414	4.105	5.0435	1.095445	2.165	2.525	2.797	3.478	3.902	4.650	2.3724	7.191	9.451	3.6692
6	7766	1170	5127	7822	2.1764	2.7766	3.635	4.3552	080123	2.093	450	698	3.370	3.437	4.095	2.0893	5.887	7.736	3.0034
7	7584	0953	4870	7537	2.0774	2.6158	3.360	3.9634	069045	2.038	394	620	3.301	3.151	3.754	1.9154	5.141	6.756	2.6230
8	7446	0789	4675	7321	2.0095	2.5080	3.180	3.7118	060660	1.995	349	558	3.238	2.956	3.522	1.7971	4.659	6.122	2.3769
9	7338	0660	4522	7152	1.9601	2.4307	3.053	3.5369	054092	1.961	313	507	3.186	2.814	3.354	1.7110	4.320	5.678	2.2043
10	1.7251	2.0556	2.4399	2.7016	1.9226	2.3726	2.959	3.4084	1.048809	1.932	2.283	2.465	3.143	2.706	3.225	1.6452	4.069	5.348	2.0762
11	7180	0471	4298	6904	8931	3272	887	3.3102	044466	909	258	428	3.105	620	3.122	5931	3.875	5.093	1.9771
12	7120	0400	4213	6810	8692	2909	829	3.2326	040833	889	236	397	3.073	551	3.039	5506	3.720	4.889	1.8980
13	7069	0340	4142	6731	8496	2610	782	3.1698	037749	872	218	369	3.044	492	2.970	5153	3.593	4.722	1.8332
14	7026	0288	4080	6662	8331	2362	743	3.1180	035098	856	201	345	3.018	443	2.911	4854	3.487	4.583	1.7792
15	1.6988	2.0242	2.4026	2.6603	1.8191	2.2151	2.710	3.0744	1.032796	1.843	2.186	2.324	2.996	2.401	2.861	1.4597	3.397	4.464	1.7332
16	6955	0203	3979	6551	8070	1971	682	3.0374	030776	832	174	309	976	364	817	4373	3.319	4.361	6936
17	6925	0168	3938	6505	7965	1814	658	3.0055	028991	821	162	287	958	332	778	4176	3.252	4.274	6592
18	6899	0137	3901	6464	7873	1676	637	2.9776	027402	812	153	272	941	303	744	4001	3.192	4.196	6288
19	6876	0109	3868	6427	7791	1555	618	2.9532	025978	804	143	258	926	277	714	3845	3.140	4.126	6019
20	1.6855	2.0084	2.3838	2.6394	1.7718	2.1447	2.602	2.9315	1.024695	1.796	2.134	2.245	2.912	2.254	2.686	1.3704	3.092	4.064	1.5777
21	6836	0061	3811	6364	7653	1351	587	9123	023533	789	127	233	899	233	661	3576	3.050	4.008	5560
22	6818	0040	3786	6337	7594	1263	575	8950	022475	783	120	222	887	214	638	3460	3.011	3.957	5363
23	6802	0021	3764	6312	7540	1185	562	8794	021508	777	113	212	876	196	617	3353	2.976	3.911	5184
24	6788	0004	3743	6289	7492	1114	552	8652	020621	772	107	202	866	180	598	3255	2.944	3.869	5020
25	1.6774	1.9988	2.3724	2.6268	1.7448	2.1048	2.541	2.8523	1.019804	1.767	2.101	2.193	2.856	2.165	2.580	1.3165	2.914	3.830	1.4868
26	6762	9973	3707	6249	7406	0987	532	8405	019049	762	096	185	847	152	564	3081	887	794	4729
27	6750	9959	3690	6231	7369	0932	524	8297	018350	758	092	178	839	139	548	3002	861	761	4600
28	6740	9947	3675	6214	7334	0881	517	8197	017700	754	087	171	831	127	534	2929	838	730	4479
29	6730	9935	3661	6199	7302	0834	509	8105	017095	751	083	164	823	115	521	2861	816	701	4367
30	1.6720	1.9924	2.3648	2.6184	1.7272	2.0790	2.503	2.8020	1.016530	1.747	2.079	2.158	2.816	2.105	2.508	1.2797	2.795	3.674	1.4262
31	6712	9913	3636	6170	7245	0750	496	7940	016001	744	075	153	810	095	496	2737	776	648	4164
32	6704	9904	3624	6158	7218	0711	491	7866	015505	741	072	147	803	086	485	2680	758	625	4072
33	6696	9894	3613	6146	7194	0676	486	7797	015039	738	069	142	797	077	475	2626	741	602	3985
34	6689	9886	3603	6134	7171	0642	481	7732	014599	736	066	137	792	069	465	2576	725	581	3903
35	1.6682	1.9878	2.3593	2.6124	1.7149	2.0611	2.476	2.7671	1.014185	1.733	2.063	2.132	2.786	2.061	2.455	1.2528	2.710	3.561	1.3825
36	6675	9870	3584	6114	7129	0581	472	7615	013794	731	060	127	781	053	446	2482	695	542	3751
37	6669	9863	3576	6104	7110	0553	467	7560	013423	728	057	123	776	046	438	2438	682	524	3681
38	6664	9856	3568	6095	7092	0527	463	7510	013072	726	055	119	772	039	430	2397	669	507	3615
39	6658	9849	3560	6086	7075	0502	459	7461	012740	724	053	115	767	033	422	2358	656	491	3552
40	1.6653	1.9843	2.3552	2.6078	1.7058	2.0478	2.456	2.7415	1.012423	1.722	2.051	2.112	2.763	2.026	2.415	1.2320	2.644	3.475	1.3492
41	6648	9837	3545	6071	7043	0456	452	7373	012122	720	048	108	759	020	408	2284	633	460	3434
42	6643	9832	3539	6063	7028	0435	450	7332	011835	718	046	105	755	015	401	2249	622	446	3379
43	6639	9826	3532	6056	7014	0414	446	7293	011561	717	044	102	752	009	394	2216	612	433	3326
44	6634	9821	3526	6049	7001	0395	443	7257	011300	715	042	099	748	004	388	2184	602	420	3276
45	1.6630	1.9816	2.3521	2.6043	1.6988	2.0377	2.441	2.7220	1.011050	1.714	2.040	2.096	2.745	1.999	2.382	1.2154	2.593	3.407	1.3227
46	6626	9812	3515	6037	6976	0359	438	7187	010811	712	039	093	742	994	376	2124	583	395	3181
47	6623	9807	3510	6031	6965	0342	436	7154	010582	711	037	091	738	990	371	2096	575	384	3136
48	6619	9803	3505	6025	6953	0326	433	7124	010363	710	036	088	735	985	365	2069	566	373	3093
49	6616	9799	3500	6020	6942	0310	430	7094	010152	708	034	086	732	981	360	2043	558	361	3052
50	1.6612	1.9795	2.3495	2.6015	1.6933	2.0296	2.429	2.7066	1.009951	1.707	2.033	2.083	2.729	1.977	2.355	1.2017	2.550	3.352	1.3012
51	6609	9791	3490	6010	6923	0282	426	7039	009756	706	031	081	727	973	351	1993	543	342	2974
52	6606	9787	3486	6005	6913	0269	425	7014	009569	705	030	079	724	969	346	1969	536	332	2936
53	6603	9784	3482	6000	6904	0255	423	6989	009390	704	029	077	722	965	341	1946	528	323	2900
54	6600	9780	3478	5996	6896	0243	421	6965	009217	703	028	075	719	961	337	1924	522	314	2866
55	1.6597	1.9777	2.3474	2.5991	1.6887	2.0230	2.419	2.6942	1.009050	1.702	2.026	2.073	2.717	1.958	2.333	1.1903	2.515	3.305	1.2832
56	6595	9774	3470	5987	6879	0219	417	6920	008889	701	025	071	714	954	329	1882	509	297	2800
57	6592	9771	3467	5983	6871	0208	416	6899	008734	700	024	069	712	951	325	1862	503	289	2768
58	6590	9768	3463	5979	6864	0197	414	6878	008584	699	023	067	710	948	321	1842	497	281	2738
59	6587	9765	3460	5976	6857	0186	412	6858	008439	698	022	065	708	945	317	1823	491	273	2708
60	1.6585	1.9762	2.3457	2.5972	1.6850	2.0176	2.411	2.6839	1.008299	1.697	2.021	2.064	2.706	1.942	2.314	1.1805	2.485	3.266	1.2680
61	6583	9760	3453	5969	6843	0166	410	6820	008164	696	020	062	704	939	310	1787	480	259	2652
62	6581	9757	3450	5965	6837	0157	408	6803	008032	695	019	060	702	936	307	1769	474	252	2625
63	6579	9755	3447	5962	6830	0148	407	6785	007906	694	018	059	700	933	303	1752	469	245	2598
64	6577	9752	3445	5959	6824	0139	406	6769	007782	694	017	057	698	930	300	1736	464	239	2573
65	1.6575	1.9750	2.3442	2.5956	1.6818	2.0130	2.404	2.6753	1.007663	1.693	2.016	2.056	2.696	1.928	2.297	1.1720	2.459	3.232	1.2548
66	6573	9748	3439	5953	6813	0122	403	6737	007547	692	016	055	695	925	294	1704	455	226	2524
67	6571	9745	3436	5950	6807	0114	402	6722	007435	691	015	053	693	923	291	1689	450	220	2500
68	6569	9743	3434	5947	6802	0107	400	6707	007326	691	014	052	692	920	288	1674	445	214	2477
69	6567	9741	3431	5944	6796	0099	399	6692	007221	690	013	051	690	918	285	1660	441	208	2455
70	1.6566	1.9739	2.3429	2.5942	1.6791	2.0092	2.398	2.6679	1.007118	1.689	2.012	2.049	2.689	1.916	2.282	1.1645	2.437	3.203	1.2433
71	6564	9737	3427	5939	6786	0085	398	6666	007018	689	012	048	687	913	280	1632	433	197	2411
72	6562	9735	3424	5937	6781	0078	396	6653	006920	688	011	047	686	911	277	1618	429	192	2391
73	6561	9733	3422	5934	6777	0071	395	6640	006826	688	010	046	684	909	275	1605	425	186	2370
74	6559	9732	3420	5932	6772	0065	394	6628	006734	687	010	045	683	907	272	1592	421	181	2350
75	1.6558	1.9730	2.3418	2.5929	1.6768	2.0058	2.394	2.6616	1.006645	1.686	2.009	2.044	2.681	1.905	2.270	1.1579	2.417	3.176	1.2331
76	6556	9728	3416	5927	6764	0052	393	6604	006558	686	009	043	680	903	267	1567	413	171	2312
77	6555	9727	3414	5925	6760	0046	391	6593	006473	685	008	042	679	901	265	1555	410	167	2294
78	6554	9725	3412	5923	6755	0040	391	6582	006390	685	007	041	678	899	263	1543	406	162	2276
79	6552	9723	3410	5921	6751	0035	390	6571	006309	685	007	040	677	897	260	1532	403	158	2258
80	1.6551	1.9722	2.3408	2.5919	1.6747	2.0029	2.389	2.6560	1.006231	1.684	2.006	2.039	2.676	1.895	2.258	1.1521	2.399	3.153	1.2241
81	6550	9720	3407	5917	6743	0023	389	6550	006154	684	006	038	674	893	256	1509	396	149	2224
82	6549	9719	3405	5915	6740	0018	387	6540	006079	683	005	037	673	891	254	1499	393	144	2207
83	6547	9717	3403	5913	6737	0012	386	6530	006006	683	004	036	672	890	252	1488	389	140	2191
84	6546	9716	3402	5911	6734	0007	386	6521	005934	682	004	035	671	888	250	1478	386	136	2175
85	1.6545	1.9715	2.3400	2.5909	1.6730	2.0003	2.385	2.6512	1.005865	1.682	2.004	2.034	2.670	1.886	2.248	1.1468	2.383	3.132	1.2159
86	6544	9713	3398	5908	6726	1.9998	385	6503	005797	681	003	033	669	885	246	1458	380	128	2144
87	6543	9712	3397	5906	6723	9994	384	6494	005731	681	002	032	668	883	244	1448	377	124	2129
88	6542	9711	3395	5904	6720	9989	383	6485	005666	680	002	032	667	881	242	1438	374	121	2115
89	6541	9709	3394	5903	6717	9985	382	6476	005602	680	002	031	666	880	240	1429	372	117	2100
90	1.6540	1.9708	2.3392	2.5901	1.6714	1.9980	2.382	2.6468	1.005541	1.680	2.001	2.030	2.665	1.878	2.238	1.1419	2.369	3.113	1.2086
91	6539	9707	3391	5899	6711	9976	381	6460	005480	679	000	029	664	877	236	1410	366	110	2072
92	6538	9706	3390	5898	6708	9972	381	6452	005420	679	000	029	664	875	235	1401	363	106	2059
93	6537	9705	3388	5896	6705	9968	380	6444	005362	678	000	028	663	874	233	1393	361	103	2045
94	6536	9704	3387	5895	6702	9964	380	6437	005305	678	1.999	027	662	873	231	1384	358	099	2032
95	1.6535	1.9703	2.3386	2.5893	1.6699	1.9960	2.378	2.6430	1.005249	1.678	1.999	2.026	2.661	1.871	2.230	1.1376	2.356	3.096	1.2019
96	6534	9701	3384	5892	6697	9956	378	6423	005195	677	999	026	660	870	228	1367	353	093	2007
97	6533	9700	3383	5891	6694	9952	378	6416	005141	677	998	025	659	868	226	1359	351	090	1994
98	6532	9699	3382	5889	6692	9949	377	6409	005090	677	998	024	658	867	225	1351	348	086	1982
99	6531	9698	3381	5888	6689	9945	377	6402	005038	677	997	024	657	866	223	1343	346	083	1970
100	1.6531	1.9697	2.3380	2.5887	1.6687	1.9942	2.376	2.6396	1.004988	1.676	1.997	2.023	2.657	1.865	2.222	1.1336	2.344	3.080	1.1958
∞	1.6449	1.9600	2.3263	2.5758	1.6449	1.9600	2.326	2.5758	1.000000	1.645	1.960	1.960	2.576	1.645	1.960	1.0000	1.960	2.576	1.0000

Tolerance factors[1] k_τ for determination of the tolerance interval $\bar{x} \pm k_\tau s$. $\beta_p = (1-2\alpha_p)$ = tolerance probability; $\beta_t = (1-2\alpha_t)$ = confidence probability; N = size of the sample from which $\bar{x}$ and s are calculated

	$\beta_t = 0.75$					$\beta_t = 0.90$					$\beta_t = 0.95$					$\beta_t = 0.99$				
β_p / N	0.75	0.90	0.95	0.99	0.999	0.75	0.90	0.95	0.99	0.999	0.75	0.90	0.95	0.99	0.999	0.75	0.90	0.95	0.99	0.999
2	4.498	6.301	7.414	9.531	11.920	11.407	15.978	18.800	24.167	30.227	22.858	32.019	37.674	48.430	60.573	114.363	160.193	188.491	242.300	303.054
3	2.501	3.538	4.187	5.431	6.844	4.132	5.847	6.919	8.974	11.309	5.922	8.380	9.916	12.861	16.208	13.378	18.930	22.401	29.055	36.616
4	2.035	2.892	3.431	4.471	5.657	2.932	4.166	4.943	6.440	8.149	3.779	5.369	6.370	8.299	10.502	6.614	9.398	11.150	14.527	18.383
5	1.825	2.599	3.088	4.033	5.117	2.454	3.494	4.152	5.423	6.879	3.002	4.275	5.079	6.634	8.415	4.643	6.612	7.855	10.260	13.015
6	1.704	2.429	2.889	3.779	4.802	2.196	3.131	3.723	4.870	6.188	2.604	3.712	4.414	5.775	7.337	3.743	5.337	6.345	8.301	10.548
7	1.624	2.318	2.757	3.611	4.593	2.034	2.902	3.452	4.521	5.750	2.361	3.369	4.007	5.248	6.676	3.233	4.613	5.488	7.187	9.142
8	1.568	2.238	2.663	3.491	4.444	1.921	2.743	3.264	4.278	5.446	2.197	3.136	3.732	4.891	6.226	2.905	4.147	4.936	6.468	8.234
9	1.525	2.178	2.593	3.400	4.330	1.839	2.626	3.125	4.098	5.220	2.078	2.967	3.532	4.631	5.899	2.677	3.822	4.550	5.966	7.600
10	1.492	2.131	2.537	3.328	4.241	1.775	2.535	3.018	3.959	5.046	1.987	2.839	3.379	4.433	5.649	2.508	3.582	4.265	5.594	7.129
11	1.465	2.093	2.493	3.271	4.169	1.724	2.463	2.933	3.849	4.906	1.916	2.737	3.259	4.277	5.452	2.378	3.397	4.045	5.308	6.766
12	1.443	2.062	2.456	3.223	4.110	1.683	2.404	2.863	3.758	4.792	1.858	2.655	3.162	4.150	5.291	2.274	3.250	3.870	5.079	6.477
13	1.425	2.036	2.424	3.183	4.059	1.648	2.355	2.805	3.682	4.697	1.810	2.587	3.081	4.044	5.158	2.190	3.130	3.727	4.893	6.240
14	1.409	2.013	2.398	3.148	4.016	1.619	2.314	2.756	3.618	4.615	1.770	2.529	3.012	3.955	5.045	2.120	3.029	3.608	4.737	6.043
15	1.395	1.994	2.375	3.118	3.979	1.594	2.278	2.713	3.562	4.545	1.735	2.480	2.954	3.878	4.949	2.060	2.945	3.507	4.605	5.876
16	1.383	1.977	2.355	3.092	3.946	1.572	2.246	2.676	3.514	4.484	1.705	2.437	2.903	3.812	4.865	2.009	2.872	3.421	4.492	5.732
17	1.372	1.962	2.337	3.069	3.917	1.552	2.219	2.643	3.471	4.430	1.679	2.400	2.858	3.754	4.791	1.965	2.808	3.345	4.393	5.607
18	1.363	1.948	2.321	3.048	3.891	1.535	2.194	2.614	3.433	4.382	1.655	2.366	2.819	3.702	4.725	1.926	2.753	3.279	4.307	5.497
19	1.355	1.936	2.307	3.030	3.867	1.520	2.172	2.588	3.399	4.339	1.635	2.337	2.784	3.656	4.667	1.891	2.703	3.221	4.230	5.399
20	1.347	1.925	2.294	3.013	3.846	1.506	2.152	2.564	3.368	4.300	1.616	2.310	2.752	3.615	4.614	1.860	2.659	3.168	4.161	5.312
21	1.340	1.915	2.282	2.998	3.827	1.493	2.135	2.543	3.340	4.264	1.599	2.286	2.723	3.577	4.567	1.833	2.620	3.121	4.100	5.234
22	1.334	1.906	2.271	2.984	3.809	1.482	2.118	2.524	3.315	4.232	1.584	2.264	2.697	3.543	4.523	1.808	2.584	3.078	4.044	5.163
23	1.328	1.898	2.261	2.971	3.793	1.471	2.103	2.506	3.292	4.203	1.570	2.244	2.673	3.512	4.484	1.785	2.551	3.040	3.993	5.098
24	1.322	1.891	2.252	2.959	3.778	1.462	2.089	2.489	3.270	4.176	1.557	2.225	2.651	3.483	4.447	1.764	2.522	3.004	3.947	5.039
25	1.317	1.883	2.244	2.948	3.764	1.453	2.077	2.474	3.251	4.151	1.545	2.208	2.631	3.457	4.413	1.745	2.494	2.972	3.904	4.985
26	1.313	1.877	2.236	2.938	3.751	1.444	2.065	2.460	3.232	4.127	1.534	2.193	2.612	3.432	4.382	1.727	2.469	2.941	3.865	4.935
27	1.309	1.871	2.229	2.929	3.740	1.437	2.054	2.447	3.215	4.106	1.523	2.178	2.595	3.409	4.353	1.711	2.446	2.914	3.828	4.888
28	1.305	1.865	2.222	2.920	3.728	1.430	2.044	2.435	3.199	4.085	1.514	2.164	2.579	3.388	4.326	1.695	2.424	2.888	3.794	4.845
29	1.301	1.860	2.216	2.911	3.718	1.423	2.034	2.424	3.184	4.066	1.505	2.152	2.564	3.368	4.301	1.681	2.404	2.864	3.763	4.805
30	1.297	1.855	2.210	2.904	3.708	1.417	2.025	2.413	3.170	4.049	1.497	2.140	2.549	3.350	4.278	1.668	2.385	2.841	3.733	4.768
31	1.294	1.850	2.204	2.896	3.699	1.411	2.017	2.403	3.157	4.032	1.489	2.129	2.536	3.332	4.256	1.656	2.367	2.820	3.706	4.732
32	1.291	1.846	2.199	2.890	3.690	1.405	2.009	2.393	3.145	4.016	1.481	2.118	2.524	3.316	4.235	1.644	2.351	2.801	3.680	4.699
33	1.288	1.842	2.194	2.883	3.682	1.400	2.001	2.385	3.133	4.001	1.475	2.108	2.512	3.300	4.215	1.633	2.335	2.782	3.655	4.668
34	1.285	1.838	2.189	2.877	3.674	1.395	1.994	2.376	3.122	3.987	1.468	2.099	2.501	3.286	4.197	1.623	2.320	2.764	3.632	4.639
35	1.283	1.834	2.185	2.871	3.667	1.390	1.988	2.368	3.112	3.974	1.462	2.090	2.490	3.272	4.179	1.613	2.306	2.748	3.611	4.611
36	1.280	1.830	2.181	2.866	3.660	1.386	1.981	2.361	3.102	3.961	1.455	2.081	2.479	3.258	4.161	1.604	2.293	2.732	3.590	4.585
37	1.278	1.827	2.177	2.860	3.653	1.381	1.975	2.353	3.092	3.949	1.450	2.073	2.470	3.246	4.146	1.595	2.281	2.717	3.571	4.560
38	1.275	1.824	2.173	2.855	3.647	1.377	1.969	2.346	3.083	3.938	1.446	2.068	2.464	3.237	4.134	1.587	2.269	2.703	3.552	4.537
39	1.273	1.821	2.169	2.850	3.641	1.374	1.964	2.340	3.075	3.927	1.441	2.060	2.455	3.226	4.120	1.579	2.257	2.690	3.534	4.514
40	1.271	1.818	2.166	2.846	3.635	1.370	1.959	2.334	3.066	3.917	1.435	2.052	2.445	3.213	4.104	1.571	2.247	2.677	3.518	4.493
41	1.269	1.815	2.162	2.841	3.629	1.366	1.954	2.328	3.059	3.907	1.430	2.045	2.437	3.202	4.090	1.564	2.236	2.665	3.502	4.472
42	1.267	1.812	2.159	2.837	3.624	1.363	1.949	2.322	3.051	3.897	1.426	2.039	2.429	3.192	4.077	1.557	2.227	2.653	3.486	4.453
43	1.266	1.810	2.156	2.833	3.619	1.360	1.944	2.316	3.044	3.888	1.422	2.033	2.422	3.183	4.065	1.551	2.217	2.642	3.472	4.434
44	1.264	1.807	2.153	2.829	3.614	1.357	1.940	2.311	3.037	3.879	1.418	2.027	2.415	3.173	4.053	1.545	2.208	2.631	3.458	4.416
45	1.262	1.805	2.150	2.826	3.609	1.354	1.935	2.306	3.030	3.871	1.414	2.021	2.408	3.165	4.042	1.539	2.200	2.621	3.444	4.399
46	1.261	1.802	2.148	2.822	3.605	1.351	1.931	2.301	3.024	3.863	1.410	2.016	2.402	3.156	4.031	1.533	2.192	2.611	3.431	4.383
47	1.259	1.800	2.145	2.819	3.600	1.348	1.927	2.297	3.018	3.855	1.406	2.011	2.396	3.148	4.021	1.527	2 184	2.602	3.419	4.367
48	1.258	1.798	2.143	2.815	3.596	1.345	1.924	2.292	3.012	3.847	1.403	2.006	2.390	3.140	4.011	1.522	2.176	2.593	3.407	4.352
49	1.256	1.796	2.140	2.812	3.592	1.343	1.920	2.288	3.006	3.840	1.399	2.001	2.384	3.133	4.002	1.517	2.169	2.584	3.396	4.337
50	1.255	1.794	2.138	2.809	3.588	1.340	1.916	2.284	3.001	3.833	1.396	1.996	2.379	3.126	3.993	1.512	2.162	2.576	3.385	4.323
51	1.253	1.792	2.135	2.806	3.584	1.338	1.913	2.279	2.995	3.826	1.393	1.992	2.373	3.119	3.984	1.507	2.155	2.568	3.374	4.310
52	1.252	1.790	2.133	2.803	3.581	1.336	1.910	2.276	2.990	3.820	1.390	1.988	2.368	3.112	3.975	1.503	2.148	2.560	3.364	4.297
53	1.251	1.789	2.131	2.801	3.577	1.334	1.907	2.272	2.985	3.813	1.387	1.984	2.363	3.106	3.967	1.498	2.142	2.552	3.354	4.284
54	1.250	1.787	2.129	2.798	3.574	1.331	1.904	2.268	2.981	3.807	1.384	1.980	2.359	3.100	3.959	1.494	2.136	2.545	3.344	4.272
55	1.249	1.785	2.127	2.795	3.571	1.329	1.901	2.265	2.976	3.801	1.382	1.976	2.354	3.094	3.951	1.490	2.130	2.538	3.335	4.260
56	1.247	1.784	2.125	2.793	3.567	1.327	1.898	2.261	2.972	3.796	1.379	1.972	2.350	3.088	3.944	1.486	2.124	2.531	3.326	4.249
57	1.246	1.782	2.123	2.790	3.564	1.325	1.895	2.258	2.967	3.790	1.377	1.968	2.345	3.082	3.937	1.482	2.119	2.524	3.318	4.238
58	1.245	1.781	2.122	2.788	3.561	1.323	1.892	2.255	2.963	3.785	1.374	1.965	2.341	3.076	3.930	1.478	2.113	2.518	3.309	4.227
59	1.244	1.779	2.120	2.786	3.558	1.322	1.890	2.252	2.959	3.779	1.372	1.961	2.337	3.071	3.923	1.474	2.108	2.512	3.301	4.216
60	1.243	1.778	2.118	2.784	3.556	1.320	1.887	2.248	2.955	3.774	1.369	1.958	2.333	3.066	3.916	1.471	2.103	2.506	3.293	4.206
61	1.242	1.776	2.117	2.781	3.553	1.318	1.885	2.245	2.951	3.769	1.367	1.955	2.329	3.061	3.909	1.467	2.098	2.500	3.285	4.196
62	1.241	1.775	2.115	2.779	3.550	1.316	1.882	2.243	2.947	3.765	1.365	1.951	2.325	3.056	3.903	1.464	2.093	2.494	3.278	4.187
63	1.240	1.774	2.113	2.777	3.548	1.315	1.880	2.240	2.944	3.760	1.363	1.948	2.322	3.051	3.897	1.461	2.089	2.489	3.271	4.178
64	1.240	1.772	2.112	2.775	3.545	1.313	1.878	2.237	2.940	3.755	1.361	1.945	2.318	3.046	3.891	1.458	2.084	2.483	3.264	4.169
65	1.239	1.771	2.110	2.773	3.543	1.312	1.875	2.235	2.937	3.751	1.359	1.943	2.315	3.042	3.886	1.455	2.080	2.478	3.257	4.160
66	1.238	1.770	2.109	2.771	3.540	1.310	1.873	2.232	2.933	3.747	1.357	1.940	2.311	3.037	3.880	1.452	2.076	2.473	3.250	4.152
67	1.237	1.769	2.108	2.770	3.538	1.309	1.871	2.229	2.930	3.742	1.355	1.937	2.308	3.033	3.874	1.449	2.071	2.468	3.244	4.143
68	1.236	1.768	2.106	2.768	3.536	1.307	1.869	2.227	2.927	3.738	1.353	1.934	2.305	3.029	3.869	1.446	2.067	2.463	3.237	4.135
69	1.235	1.766	2.105	2.766	3.533	1.306	1.867	2.225	2.923	3.734	1.351	1.932	2.302	3.025	3.864	1.443	2.063	2.459	3.231	4.127
70	1.235	1.765	2.104	2.764	3.531	1.304	1.865	2.222	2.920	3.730	1.349	1.929	2.299	3.021	3.859	1.440	2.060	2.454	3.225	4.120
71	1.234	1.764	2.102	2.763	3.529	1.303	1.863	2.220	2.917	3.727	1.347	1.927	2.296	3.017	3.854	1.438	2.056	2.450	3.219	4.112
72	1.233	1.763	2.101	2.761	3.527	1.302	1.861	2.218	2.915	3.723	1.346	1.924	2.293	3.013	3.849	1.435	2.052	2.445	3.214	4.105
73	1.233	1.762	2.100	2.760	3.525	1.300	1.859	2.216	2.912	3.719	1.344	1.922	2.290	3.009	3.844	1.433	2.049	2.441	3.208	4.098
74	1.232	1.761	2.099	2.758	3.523	1.299	1.858	2.214	2.909	3.716	1.343	1.920	2.287	3.006	3.840	1.430	2.045	2.437	3.203	4.091
75	1.231	1.760	2.098	2.757	3.521	1.298	1.856	2.211	2.906	3.712	1.341	1.917	2.285	3.002	3.835	1.428	2.042	2.433	3.197	4.084
76	1.230	1.759	2.096	2.755	3.519	1.297	1.854	2.209	2.904	3.709	1.339	1.915	2.282	2.999	3.831	1.426	2.039	2.429	3.192	4.078
77	1.230	1.758	2.095	2.754	3.517	1.296	1.853	2.207	2.901	3.706	1.338	1.913	2.279	2.996	3.826	1.423	2.035	2.425	3.187	4.071
78	1.229	1.758	2.094	2.752	3.516	1.295	1.851	2.206	2.898	3.702	1.336	1.911	2.277	2.992	3.822	1.421	2.032	2.421	3.182	4.065
79	1.229	1.757	2.093	2.751	3.514	1.293	1.849	2.204	2.896	3.699	1.335	1.909	2.274	2.989	3.818	1.419	2.029	2.418	3.177	4.059
80	1.228	1.756	2.092	2.749	3.512	1.292	1.848	2.202	2.894	3.696	1.334	1.907	2.272	2.986	3.814	1.417	2.026	2.414	3.173	4.053
81	1.227	1.755	2.091	2.748	3.510	1.291	1.846	2.200	2.891	3.693	1.332	1.905	2.270	2.983	3.810	1.415	2.023	2.411	3.168	4.047
82	1.227	1.754	2.090	2.747	3.509	1.290	1.845	2.198	2.889	3.690	1.331	1.903	2.267	2.980	3.806	1.413	2.020	2.407	3.163	4.041
83	1.226	1.753	2.089	2.746	3.507	1.289	1.843	2.196	2.887	3.687	1.329	1.901	2.265	2.977	3.803	1.411	2.017	2.404	3.159	4.035
84	1.226	1.753	2.088	2.744	3.506	1.288	1.842	2.195	2.884	3.684	1.328	1.899	2.263	2.974	3.799	1.409	2.014	2.400	3.155	4.030
85	1.225	1.752	2.087	2.743	3.504	1.287	1.841	2.193	2.882	3.682	1.327	1.897	2.261	2.971	3.795	1.407	2.012	2.397	3.150	4.024
86	1.225	1.751	2.086	2.742	3.503	1.286	1.839	2.191	2.880	3.679	1.326	1.896	2.259	2.968	3.792	1.405	2.009	2.394	3.146	4.019
87	1.224	1.750	2.086	2.741	3.501	1.285	1.838	2.190	2.878	3.676	1.324	1.894	2.257	2.966	3.788	1.403	2.007	2.391	3.142	4.014
88	1.224	1.749	2.085	2.740	3.500	1.284	1.837	2.188	2.876	3.674	1.323	1.892	2.255	2.963	3.785	1.402	2.004	2.388	3.138	4.009
89	1.223	1.749	2.084	2.738	3.498	1.284	1.835	2.187	2.874	3.671	1.322	1.890	2.253	2.960	3.781	1.400	2.001	2.385	3.134	4.004
90	1.223	1.748	2.083	2.737	3.497	1.283	1.834	2.185	2.872	3.669	1.321	1.889	2.251	2.958	3.778	1.398	1.999	2.382	3.130	3.999
91	1.222	1.747	2.082	2.736	3.495	1.282	1.833	2.184	2.870	3.666	1.320	1.887	2.249	2.955	3.775	1.396	1.997	2.379	3.127	3.994
92	1.222	1.747	2.081	2.735	3.494	1.281	1.832	2.182	2.868	3.664	1.319	1.886	2.247	2.953	3.772	1.395	1.994	2.376	3.123	3.989
93	1.221	1.746	2.081	2.734	3.493	1.280	1.830	2.181	2.866	3.661	1.318	1.884	2.245	2.950	3.769	1.393	1.992	2.373	3.119	3.985
94	1.221	1.745	2.080	2.733	3.491	1.279	1.829	2.180	2.864	3.659	1.317	1.882	2.243	2.948	3.766	1.392	1.990	2.371	3.116	3.980
95	1.220	1.745	2.079	2.732	3.490	1.278	1.828	2.178	2.863	3.657	1.315	1.881	2.241	2.945	3.763	1.390	1.987	2.368	3.112	3.976
96	1.220	1.744	2.078	2.731	3.489	1.278	1.827	2.177	2.861	3.654	1.314	1.880	2.240	2.943	3.760	1.388	1.985	2.366	3.109	3.971
97	1.219	1.743	2.077	2.730	3.488	1.277	1.826	2.175	2.859	3.652	1.313	1.878	2.238	2.941	3.757	1.387	1.983	2.363	3.105	3.967
98	1.219	1.743	2.077	2.729	3.486	1.276	1.825	2.174	2.857	3.650	1.312	1.877	2.236	2.939	3.754	1.385	1.981	2.360	3.102	3.963
99	1.219	1.742	2.076	2.728	3.485	1.275	1.824	2.173	2.856	3.648	1.311	1.875	2.234	2.936	3.751	1.384	1.979	2.358	3.099	3.958

1) Values from BOWKER, A.H., in EISENHART et al. (Eds.), *Selected Techniques of Statistical Analysis for Scientific and Industrial Research and Production and Management Engineering,* McGraw-Hill, New York and London, 1947, page 102. Reprinted by kind permission of the author and publishers.

Tolerance factors[1] k_γ for determination of the tolerance interval $\bar{x} \pm k_\gamma s$. $\beta_p = (1 - 2\alpha_p)$ = tolerance probability; $\beta_t = (1 - 2\alpha_t)$ = confidence probability; N = size of the sample from which $\bar{x}$ and s are calculated

	$\beta_t = 0.75$					$\beta_t = 0.90$					$\beta_t = 0.95$					$\beta_t = 0.99$				
N \ β_p	0.75	0.90	0.95	0.99	0.999	0.75	0.90	0.95	0.99	0.999	0.75	0.90	0.95	0.99	0.999	0.75	0.90	0.95	0.99	0.999
100	1.218	1.742	2.075	2.727	3.484	1.275	1.822	2.172	2.854	3.646	1.311	1.874	2.233	2.934	3.748	1.383	1.977	2.355	3.096	3.954
101	1.218	1.741	2.075	2.726	3.483	1.274	1.821	2.170	2.852	3.644	1.310	1.872	2.231	2.932	3.746	1.381	1.975	2.353	3.092	3.950
102	1.217	1.741	2.074	2.726	3.482	1.273	1.820	2.169	2.851	3.642	1.309	1.871	2.230	2.930	3.743	1.380	1.973	2.351	3.089	3.946
104	1.217	1.739	2.073	2.724	3.480	1.272	1.818	2.167	2.848	3.638	1.307	1.869	2.227	2.926	3.738	1.377	1.969	2.346	3.083	3.939
106	1.216	1.738	2.071	2.722	3.477	1.270	1.816	2.164	2.845	3.634	1.305	1.866	2.224	2.922	3.733	1.374	1.965	2.342	3.077	3.931
108	1.215	1.737	2.070	2.721	3.475	1.269	1.815	2.162	2.842	3.630	1.303	1.864	2.221	2.918	3.728	1.372	1.962	2.337	3.072	3.924
110	1.214	1.736	2.069	2.719	3.473	1.268	1.813	2.160	2.839	3.626	1.302	1.861	2.218	2.915	3.723	1.369	1.958	2.333	3.066	3.917
112	1.214	1.735	2.068	2.717	3.471	1.267	1.811	2.158	2.836	3.623	1.300	1.859	2.215	2.911	3.719	1.367	1.955	2.329	3.061	3.910
114	1.213	1.734	2.067	2.716	3.469	1.265	1.809	2.156	2.833	3.619	1.299	1.857	2.212	2.908	3.714	1.365	1.951	2.325	3.056	3.904
116	1.212	1.733	2.065	2.714	3.468	1.264	1.808	2.154	2.831	3.616	1.297	1.855	2.210	2.904	3.710	1.363	1.948	2.321	3.051	3.897
118	1.212	1.733	2.064	2.713	3.466	1.263	1.806	2.152	2.828	3.613	1.296	1.852	2.207	2.901	3.706	1.360	1.945	2.318	3.046	3.891
120	1.211	1.732	2.063	2.712	3.464	1.262	1.804	2.150	2.826	3.610	1.294	1.850	2.205	2.898	3.702	1.358	1.942	2.314	3.041	3.885
122	1.210	1.731	2.062	2.710	3.462	1.261	1.803	2.148	2.823	3.607	1.293	1.848	2.203	2.895	3.698	1.356	1.939	2.311	3.037	3.879
124	1.210	1.730	2.061	2.709	3.461	1.260	1.801	2.147	2.821	3.604	1.291	1.847	2.200	2.892	3.694	1.354	1.936	2.307	3.032	3.873
126	1.209	1.729	2.060	2.708	3.459	1.259	1.800	2.145	2.819	3.601	1.290	1.845	2.198	2.889	3.690	1.352	1.934	2.304	3.028	3.868
128	1.209	1.728	2.060	2.707	3.458	1.258	1.799	2.143	2.816	3.598	1.289	1.843	2.196	2.886	3.686	1.350	1.931	2.301	3.024	3.862
130	1.208	1.728	2.059	2.705	3.456	1.257	1.797	2.141	2.814	3.595	1.288	1.841	2.194	2.883	3.683	1.349	1.928	2.298	3.019	3.857
132	1.208	1.727	2.058	2.704	3.455	1.256	1.796	2.140	2.812	3.592	1.286	1.839	2.192	2.880	3.679	1.347	1.926	2.295	3.015	3.852
134	1.207	1.726	2.057	2.703	3.453	1.255	1.795	2.138	2.810	3.590	1.285	1.838	2.190	2.878	3.676	1.345	1.923	2.292	3.012	3.84[illegible]
136	1.207	1.725	2.056	2.702	3.452	1.254	1.793	2.137	2.808	3.587	1.284	1.836	2.188	2.875	3.673	1.343	1.921	2.289	3.008	3.842
138	1.206	1.725	2.055	2.701	3.450	1.253	1.792	2.135	2.806	3.585	1.283	1.834	2.186	2.873	3.669	1.342	1.918	2.286	3.004	3.83[illegible]
140	1.206	1.724	2.054	2.700	3.449	1.252	1.791	2.134	2.804	3.582	1.282	1.833	2.184	2.870	3.666	1.340	1.916	2.283	3.000	3.83[illegible]
142	1.205	1.723	2.054	2.699	3.448	1.252	1.790	2.132	2.802	3.580	1.281	1.831	2.182	2.868	3.663	1.338	1.914	2.280	2.997	3.828
144	1.205	1.723	2.053	2.698	3.446	1.251	1.788	2.131	2.801	3.578	1.280	1.830	2.180	2.865	3.660	1.337	1.912	2.278	2.993	3.824
146	1.204	1.722	2.052	2.697	3.445	1.250	1.787	2.130	2.799	3.575	1.279	1.828	2.178	2.863	3.657	1.335	1.909	2.275	2.990	3.820
148	1.204	1.722	2.051	2.696	3.444	1.249	1.786	2.128	2.797	3.573	1.278	1.827	2.177	2.861	3.654	1.334	1.907	2.273	2.987	3.8[illegible]
150	1.204	1.721	2.051	2.695	3.443	1.248	1.785	2.127	2.795	3.571	1.277	1.825	2.175	2.859	3.652	1.332	1.905	2.270	2.983	3.[illegible]
152	1.203	1.720	2.050	2.694	3.441	1.248	1.784	2.126	2.794	3.569	1.276	1.824	2.173	2.856	3.649	1.331	1.903	2.268	2.980	3.[illegible]07
154	1.203	1.720	2.049	2.693	3.440	1.247	1.783	2.125	2.792	3.567	1.275	1.823	2.172	2.854	3.646	1.330	1.901	2.265	2.977	3.803
156	1.202	1.719	2.049	2.692	3.439	1.246	1.782	2.123	2.791	3.565	1.274	1.821	2.170	2.852	3.644	1.328	1.899	2.263	2.974	3.799
158	1.202	1.719	2.048	2.691	3.438	1.246	1.781	2.122	2.789	3.563	1.273	1.820	2.169	2.850	3.641	1.327	1.897	2.261	2.971	3.796
160	1.202	1.718	2.047	2.691	3.437	1.245	1.780	2.121	2.787	3.561	1.272	1.819	2.167	2.848	3.638	1.326	1.896	2.259	2.968	3.792
162	1.201	1.718	2.047	2.690	3.436	1.244	1.779	2.120	2.786	3.559	1.271	1.818	2.166	2.846	3.636	1.324	1.894	2.256	2.965	3.788
164	1.201	1.717	2.046	2.689	3.435	1.244	1.778	2.119	2.785	3.557	1.270	1.816	2.164	2.844	3.634	1.323	1.892	2.254	2.963	3.785
166	1.201	1.717	2.045	2.688	3.434	1.243	1.777	2.118	2.783	3.555	1.269	1.815	2.163	2.843	3.631	1.322	1.890	2.252	2.960	3.781
168	1.200	1.716	2.045	2.687	3.433	1.242	1.776	2.117	2.782	3.553	1.269	1.814	2.162	2.841	3.629	1.321	1.888	2.250	2.957	3.778
170	1.200	1.716	2.044	2.687	3.432	1.242	1.775	2.116	2.780	3.552	1.268	1.813	2.160	2.839	3.627	1.320	1.887	2.248	2.955	3.774
172	1.199	1.715	2.044	2.686	3.431	1.241	1.775	2.115	2.779	3.550	1.267	1.812	2.159	2.837	3.624	1.318	1.885	2.246	2.952	3.771
174	1.199	1.715	2.043	2.685	3.430	1.240	1.774	2.114	2.778	3.548	1.266	1.811	2.158	2.835	3.622	1.317	1.884	2.244	2.950	3.768
176	1.199	1.714	2.043	2.684	3.429	1.240	1.773	2.113	2.776	3.547	1.266	1.810	2.156	2.834	3.620	1.316	1.882	2.243	2.947	3.765
178	1.199	1.714	2.042	2.684	3.428	1.239	1.772	2.112	2.775	3.545	1.265	1.809	2.155	2.832	3.618	1.315	1.880	2.241	2.945	3.762
180	1.198	1.713	2.042	2.683	3.427	1.239	1.771	2.111	2.774	3.543	1.264	1.808	2.154	2.831	3.616	1.314	1.879	2.239	2.942	3.759
185	1.197	1.712	2.040	2.681	3.425	1.237	1.769	2.108	2.771	3.539	1.262	1.805	2.151	2.827	3.611	1.311	1.875	2.234	2.937	3.751
190	1.197	1.711	2.039	2.680	3.423	1.236	1.767	2.106	2.768	3.536	1.261	1.803	2.148	2.823	3.606	1.309	1.872	2.230	2.931	3.744
195	1.196	1.710	2.038	2.678	3.421	1.235	1.766	2.104	2.765	3.532	1.259	1.800	2.145	2.819	3.601	1.307	1.868	2.226	2.926	3.738
200	1.195	1.709	2.037	2.677	3.419	1.234	1.764	2.102	2.762	3.529	1.258	1.798	2.143	2.816	3.597	1.304	1.865	2.222	2.921	3.731
205	1.195	1.708	2.036	2.675	3.418	1.233	1.762	2.100	2.760	3.526	1.256	1.796	2.140	2.812	3.593	1.302	1.862	2.219	2.916	3.725
210	1.194	1.708	2.035	2.674	3.416	1.231	1.761	2.098	2.757	3.522	1.255	1.794	2.138	2.809	3.589	1.300	1.859	2.215	2.911	3.719
215	1.194	1.707	2.034	2.673	3.414	1.230	1.759	2.096	2.755	3.519	1.253	1.792	2.135	2.806	3.585	1.298	1.856	2.212	2.907	3.71[illegible]
220	1.193	1.706	2.033	2.671	3.413	1.229	1.758	2.095	2.753	3.516	1.252	1.790	2.133	2.803	3.581	1.296	1.854	2.209	2.903	3.[illegible]
225	1.192	1.705	2.032	2.670	3.411	1.228	1.756	2.093	2.750	3.514	1.251	1.788	2.131	2.800	3.577	1.294	1.851	2.205	2.898	3.703
230	1.192	1.704	2.031	2.669	3.409	1.227	1.755	2.091	2.748	3.511	1.249	1.787	2.129	2.798	3.574	1.293	1.848	2.202	2.894	3.697
235	1.191	1.704	2.030	2.668	3.408	1.226	1.754	2.090	2.746	3.508	1.248	1.785	2.127	2.795	3.571	1.291	1.846	2.199	2.890	3.692
240	1.191	1.703	2.029	2.667	3.407	1.226	1.752	2.088	2.744	3.506	1.247	1.783	2.125	2.792	3.567	1.289	1.843	2.197	2.887	3.688
245	1.190	1.702	2.028	2.666	3.405	1.225	1.751	2.087	2.742	3.503	1.246	1.782	2.123	2.790	3.564	1.288	1.841	2.194	2.883	3.683
250	1.190	1.702	2.028	2.665	3.404	1.224	1.750	2.085	2.740	3.501	1.245	1.780	2.121	2.788	3.561	1.286	1.839	2.191	2.880	3.678
255	1.190	1.701	2.027	2.664	3.403	1.223	1.749	2.084	2.739	3.499	1.244	1.779	2.119	2.785	3.558	1.284	1.837	2.189	2.876	3.674
260	1.189	1.700	2.026	2.663	3.401	1.222	1.748	2.083	2.737	3.496	1.243	1.777	2.118	2.783	3.555	1.283	1.835	2.186	2.873	3.670
265	1.189	1.700	2.025	2.662	3.400	1.222	1.747	2.081	2.735	3.494	1.242	1.776	2.116	2.781	3.552	1.282	1.833	2.184	2.870	3.666
270	1.188	1.699	2.025	2.661	3.399	1.221	1.746	2.080	2.734	3.492	1.241	1.774	2.114	2.779	3.550	1.280	1.831	2.181	2.867	3.662
275	1.188	1.699	2.024	2.660	3.398	1.220	1.745	2.079	2.732	3.490	1.240	1.773	2.113	2.777	3.547	1.279	1.829	2.179	2.864	3.658
280	1.188	1.698	2.023	2.659	3.397	1.219	1.744	2.078	2.730	3.488	1.239	1.772	2.111	2.775	3.544	1.278	1.827	2.177	2.861	3.655
285	1.187	1.698	2.023	2.658	3.396	1.219	1.743	2.076	2.729	3.486	1.238	1.771	2.110	2.773	3.542	1.276	1.825	2.175	2.858	3.651
290	1.187	1.697	2.022	2.658	3.395	1.218	1.742	2.075	2.727	3.484	1.237	1.769	2.108	2.771	3.540	1.275	1.823	2.173	2.855	3.647
295	1.186	1.697	2.022	2.657	3.394	1.217	1.741	2.074	2.726	3.482	1.237	1.768	2.107	2.769	3.537	1.274	1.822	2.170	2.853	3.644
300	1.186	1.696	2.021	2.656	3.393	1.217	1.740	2.073	2.725	3.481	1.236	1.767	2.106	2.767	3.535	1.273	1.820	2.169	2.850	3.641
310	1.185	1.695	2.020	2.655	3.391	1.216	1.738	2.071	2.722	3.477	1.234	1.765	2.103	2.764	3.531	1.271	1.817	2.165	2.845	3.634
320	1.185	1.694	2.019	2.653	3.389	1.215	1.737	2.069	2.719	3.474	1.233	1.763	2.100	2.760	3.526	1.268	1.814	2.161	2.840	3.628
330	1.184	1.693	2.018	2.652	3.388	1.213	1.735	2.067	2.717	3.471	1.231	1.761	2.098	2.757	3.522	1.266	1.811	2.158	2.836	3.623
340	1.184	1.693	2.017	2.651	3.386	1.212	1.734	2.066	2.715	3.468	1.230	1.759	2.096	2.754	3.519	1.265	1.808	2.154	2.831	3.617
350	1.183	1.692	2.016	2.649	3.384	1.211	1.732	2.064	2.713	3.465	1.229	1.757	2.094	2.752	3.515	1.263	1.805	2.151	2.827	3.612
360	1.183	1.691	2.015	2.648	3.383	1.210	1.731	2.062	2.710	3.463	1.228	1.755	2.092	2.749	3.512	1.261	1.803	2.148	2.823	3.607
370	1.182	1.690	2.014	2.647	3.382	1.210	1.730	2.061	2.708	3.460	1.227	1.754	2.090	2.746	3.508	1.259	1.801	2.146	2.820	3.602
380	1.182	1.690	2.013	2.646	3.380	1.209	1.728	2.059	2.707	3.458	1.225	1.752	2.088	2.744	3.505	1.258	1.798	2.143	2.816	3.598
390	1.181	1.689	2.013	2.645	3.379	1.208	1.727	2.058	2.705	3.455	1.224	1.751	2.086	2.742	3.502	1.256	1.796	2.140	2.813	3.593
400	1.181	1.688	2.012	2.644	3.378	1.207	1.726	2.057	2.703	3.453	1.223	1.749	2.084	2.739	3.499	1.255	1.794	2.138	2.809	3.589
425	1.180	1.687	2.010	2.642	3.375	1.205	1.723	2.054	2.699	3.448	1.221	1.746	2.080	2.734	3.492	1.251	1.789	2.132	2.802	3.579
450	1.179	1.686	2.009	2.640	3.372	1.204	1.721	2.051	2.695	3.443	1.219	1.743	2.077	2.729	3.486	1.248	1.785	2.127	2.795	3.570
475	1.178	1.685	2.007	2.638	3.370	1.202	1.719	2.048	2.692	3.438	1.217	1.740	2.073	2.725	3.481	1.245	1.781	2.122	2.788	3.562
500	1.177	1.683	2.006	2.636	3.368	1.201	1.717	2.046	2.689	3.434	1.215	1.737	2.070	2.721	3.475	1.243	1.777	2.117	2.783	3.555
525	1.177	1.682	2.005	2.635	3.366	1.199	1.715	2.043	2.686	3.431	1.213	1.735	2.067	2.717	3.471	1.240	1.773	2.113	2.777	3.548
550	1.176	1.681	2.004	2.633	3.364	1.198	1.713	2.041	2.683	3.427	1.212	1.733	2.065	2.713	3.466	1.238	1.770	2.109	2.772	3.541
575	1.175	1.681	2.003	2.632	3.362	1.197	1.712	2.039	2.680	3.424	1.210	1.731	2.062	2.710	3.462	1.236	1.767	2.106	2.767	3.535
600	1.175	1.680	2.002	2.631	3.360	1.196	1.710	2.038	2.678	3.421	1.209	1.729	2.060	2.707	3.458	1.234	1.764	2.102	2.763	3.530
625	1.174	1.679	2.001	2.629	3.359	1.195	1.709	2.036	2.676	3.418	1.208	1.727	2.058	2.704	3.455	1.232	1.762	2.099	2.759	3.525
650	1.174	1.678	2.000	2.628	3.357	1.194	1.707	2.034	2.674	3.416	1.207	1.725	2.056	2.702	3.451	1.230	1.759	2.096	2.755	3.520
675	1.173	1.678	1.999	2.627	3.356	1.193	1.706	2.033	2.672	3.413	1.205	1.724	2.054	2.699	3.448	1.229	1.757	2.094	2.752	3.515
700	1.173	1.677	1.998	2.626	3.355	1.192	1.705	2.032	2.670	3.411	1.204	1.722	2.052	2.697	3.445	1.227	1.755	2.091	2.748	3.511
725	1.172	1.676	1.998	2.625	3.354	1.192	1.704	2.030	2.668	3.408	1.203	1.721	2.050	2.694	3.442	1.226	1.753	2.089	2.745	3.507
750	1.172	1.676	1.997	2.624	3.352	1.191	1.703	2.029	2.667	3.406	1.202	1.719	2.049	2.692	3.439	1.225	1.751	2.086	2.742	3.503
800	1.171	1.675	1.996	2.623	3.350	1.189	1.701	2.027	2.663	3.402	1.201	1.717	2.046	2.688	3.434	1.222	1.747	2.082	2.736	3.495
850	1.171	1.674	1.994	2.621	3.348	1.188	1.699	2.025	2.661	3.399	1.199	1.714	2.043	2.685	3.430	1.220	1.744	2.078	2.731	3.489
900	1.170	1.673	1.993	2.620	3.347	1.187	1.697	2.023	2.658	3.396	1.198	1.712	2.040	2.682	3.426	1.218	1.741	2.075	2.726	3.483
950	1.169	1.672	1.992	2.619	3.345	1.186	1.696	2.021	2.656	3.393	1.196	1.710	2.038	2.679	3.422	1.216	1.738	2.071	2.722	3.477
1000	1.169	1.671	1.992	2.617	3.344	1.185	1.695	2.019	2.654	3.390	1.195	1.709	2.036	2.676	3.418	1.214	1.736	2.068	2.718	3.472
∞	1.150	1.645	1.960	2.576	3.291	1.150	1.645	1.960	2.576	3.291	1.150	1.645	1.960	2.576	3.291	1.150	1.645	1.960	2.576	3.291

1) Values from BOWKER, A.H., in EISENHART et al. (Eds.), *Selected Techniques of Statistical Analysis for Scientific and Industrial Research and Production and Management Engineering*, McGraw-Hill, New York and London, 1947, page 102. Reprinted by kind permission of the author and publishers.

Standard Deviation and Extreme Range

For explanation see page 48

Correction[1] and confidence[2] factors for σ

ν	k_s	$1-2\alpha=0.90$	$1-2\alpha=0.95$	$1-2\alpha=0.98$	$1-2\alpha=0.99$
1	1.2533	0.5102–15.947	0.4463–31.910	0.3882–79.789	0.3562–159.58
2	1284	5777– 4.416	5207– 6.285	4660– 9.974	4344– 14.124
3	0854	6196– 2.920	5665– 3.729	5142– 5.111	4834– 6.468
4	0638	6493– 372	5991– 2.874	5489– 3.669	5188– 4.396
5	1.0509	0.6720– 2.089	0.6242– 2.453	0.5757– 3.003	0.5464– 3.485
6	0424	6903– 1.915	6444– 202	5974– 2.623	5688– 2.980
7	0362	7054– 797	6612– 035	6155– 377	5875– 660
8	0317	7183– 711	6755– 1.916	6310– 204	6036– 439
9	0281	7293– 645	6878– 826	6445– 076	6177– 278
10	1.0253	0.7391– 1.593	0.6987– 1.755	0.6564– 1.977	0.6301– 2.154
11	0230	7477– 551	7084– 698	6670– 898	6412– 056
12	0210	7555– 515	7171– 651	6765– 833	6512– 1.976
13	0194	7625– 485	7250– 611	6852– 779	6603– 910
14	0180	7688– 460	7321– 577	6931– 733	6686– 854
15	1.0168	0.7747– 1.437	0.7387– 1.548	0.7004– 1.694	0.6762– 1.806
16	0157	7800– 418	7448– 522	7071– 659	6833– 764
17	0148	7850– 400	7504– 499	7133– 629	6899– 727
18	0140	7896– 384	7556– 479	7191– 602	6960– 695
19	0132	7939– 370	7604– 461	7246– 578	7018– 666
20	1.0126	0.7980– 1.358	0.7651– 1.444	0.7297– 1.556	0.7071– 1.640
21	0120	8017– 346	7694– 429	7344– 536	7122– 617
22	0114	8053– 335	7734– 415	7390– 518	7170– 596
23	0109	8087– 326	7772– 403	7432– 502	7215– 576
24	0105	8118– 316	7808– 391	7473– 487	7258– 558
25	1.0100	0.8148– 1.308	0.7843– 1.380	0.7511– 1.473	0.7299– 1.542
26	0097	8177– 300	7875– 370	7548– 460	7338– 526
27	0093	8204– 293	7906– 361	7582– 448	7375– 512
28	0090	8230– 286	7936– 352	7616– 437	7410– 499
29	0087	8255– 280	7964– 344	7647– 426	7444– 487
30	1.0084	0.8279– 1.274	0.7991– 1.337	0.7678– 1.416	0.7476– 1.475
31	0081	8301– 268	8017– 329	7707– 407	7507– 464
32	0078	8323– 263	8042– 323	7735– 399	7537– 454
33	0076	8344– 258	8066– 316	7762– 390	7566– 445
34	0074	8364– 253	8089– 310	7788– 382	7594– 435
35	1.0072	0.8383– 1.248	0.8111– 1.304	0.7813– 1.375	0.7620– 1.427
36	0070	8402– 244	8132– 299	7837– 368	7646– 419
37	0068	8420– 240	8153– 294	7860– 362	7671– 411
38	0066	8437– 236	8172– 289	7882– 355	7695– 404
39	0064	8454– 232	8192– 284	7904– 349	7718– 397
40	1.0063	0.8470– 1.228	0.8210– 1.279	0.7925– 1.343	0.7740– 1.390
41	0061	8485– 225	8228– 275	7945– 338	7762– 383
42	0060	8501– 222	8245– 271	7965– 333	7783– 377
43	0058	8515– 218	8262– 267	7984– 328	7803– 372
44	0057	8529– 215	8279– 263	8002– 323	7823– 366
45	1.0056	0.8543– 1.212	0.8294– 1.260	0.8020– 1.318	0.7842– 1.361
46	0055	8556– 210	8310– 256	8038– 314	7861– 355
47	0053	8569– 207	8325– 253	8055– 309	7879– 350
48	0052	8582– 204	8339– 249	8071– 305	7897– 346
49	0051	8594– 202	8353– 246	8087– 301	7914– 341
50	1.0050	0.8606– 1.199	0.8367– 1.243	0.8103– 1.297	0.7931– 1.337
51	0049	8618– 197	8380– 240	8118– 294	7947– 332
52	0048	8629– 195	8394– 237	8133– 290	7963– 328
53	0047	8640– 192	8406– 235	8147– 287	7979– 324
54	0046	8651– 190	8419– 232	8161– 283	7994– 320
55	1.0046	0.8662– 1.188	0.8431– 1.229	0.8175– 1.280	0.8009– 1.316
56	0045	8672– 186	8443– 227	8189– 277	8023– 313
57	0044	8682– 184	8454– 224	8202– 274	8037– 309
58	0043	8692– 182	8465– 222	8215– 271	8051– 306
59	0043	8701– 180	8476– 220	8227– 268	8065– 303
60	1.0042	0.8710– 1.179	0.8487– 1.217	0.8239– 1.265	0.8078– 1.299
61	0041	8719– 177	8498– 215	8251– 262	8091– 296
62	0040	8728– 175	8508– 213	8263– 260	8103– 293
63	0040	8737– 174	8518– 211	8275– 257	8116– 290
64	0039	8746– 172	8528– 209	8286– 255	8128– 287
65	1.0039	0.8754– 1.170	0.8537– 1.207	0.8297– 1.252	0.8140– 1.285
66	0038	8762– 169	8547– 205	8308– 250	8151– 282
67	0037	8770– 167	8556– 203	8318– 248	8163– 279
68	0037	8778– 166	8565– 202	8329– 245	8174– 277
69	0036	8786– 165	8574– 200	8339– 243	8185– 274
70	1.0036	0.8793– 1.163	0.8583– 1.198	0.8349– 1.241	0.8196– 1.272
71	0035	8801– 162	8591– 197	8359– 239	8206– 269
72	0035	8808– 160	8600– 195	8368– 237	8217– 267
73	0034	8815– 159	8608– 193	8378– 235	8227– 265
74	0034	8822– 158	8616– 192	8387– 233	8237– 263
75	1.0033	0.8829– 1.157	0.8624– 1.190	0.8396– 1.231	0.8247– 1.260
76	0033	8836– 156	8632– 189	8405– 229	8256– 258
77	0033	8842– 154	8640– 187	8414– 228	8266– 256
78	0032	8849– 153	8647– 186	8422– 226	8275– 254
79	0032	8855– 152	8655– 184	8431– 224	8284– 252
80	1.0031	0.8861– 1.151	0.8662– 1.183	0.8439– 1.222	0.8293– 1.250
81	0031	8868– 150	8669– 182	8447– 221	8302– 248
82	0031	8874– 149	8676– 180	8455– 219	8311– 247
83	0030	8880– 148	8683– 179	8463– 218	8319– 245
84	0030	8885– 147	8690– 178	8471– 216	8328– 243
85	1.0030	0.8891– 1.146	0.8696– 1.177	0.8479– 1.214	0.8336– 1.241
86	0029	8897– 145	8703– 175	8486– 213	8344– 240
87	0029	8902– 144	8709– 174	8494– 211	8352– 238
88	0029	8908– 143	8716– 173	8501– 210	8360– 236
89	0028	8913– 142	8722– 172	8508– 209	8368– 235
90	1.0028	0.8919– 1.141	0.8728– 1.171	0.8515– 1.207	0.8375– 1.233
91	0028	8924– 140	8734– 170	8522– 206	8383– 231
92	0027	8929– 139	8740– 169	8529– 205	8390– 230
93	0027	8934– 138	8746– 168	8536– 203	8398– 228
94	0027	8939– 138	8752– 167	8543– 202	8405– 227
95	1.0026	0.8944– 1.137	0.8758– 1.166	0.8549– 1.201	0.8412– 1.226
96	0026	8949– 136	8764– 165	8556– 199	8419– 224
97	0026	8954– 135	8769– 164	8562– 198	8426– 223
98	0026	8959– 134	8775– 163	8569– 197	8433– 221
99	0025	8963– 134	8780– 162	8575– 196	8440– 220
100	1.0025	0.8968– 1.133	0.8785– 1.161	0.8581– 1.195	0.8446– 1.219
∞	1.0000	1.0000	1.0000	1.0000	1.0000

Mean extreme range[3] as multiple of σ

n	0	1 10	2 20	3 30	4 40	5 50	6 60	7 70	8 80	9 90
0	—	—	1.1284	1.6926	2.0588	2.3259	2.5344	2.7044	2.8472	2.9700
10	3.0775	3.1729	3.2585	3.3360	3.4068	3.4718	3.5320	3.5879	3.6401	3.6890
20	3.7350	3.7783	3.8194	3.8583	3.8954	3.9306	3.9643	3.9965	4.0274	4.0570
30	4.0855	4.1129	4.1393	4.1648	4.1894	4.2132	4.2363	4.2586	4.2802	4.3012
40	4.3216	4.3414	4.3606	4.3794	4.3976	4.4154	4.4328	4.4497	4.4662	4.4824
50	4.4982	4.5136	4.5286	4.5434	4.5578	4.5720	4.5858	4.5994	4.6127	4.6258
60	4.6386	4.6511	4.6635	4.6756	4.6875	4.6992	4.7107	4.7219	4.7331	4.7440
70	4.7547	4.7653	4.7757	4.7860	4.7960	4.8060	4.8158	4.8254	4.8349	4.8443
80	4.8536	4.8627	4.8717	4.8805	4.8893	4.8979	4.9064	4.9148	4.9231	4.9313
90	4.9394	4.9474	4.9553	4.9631	4.9708	4.9784	4.9859	4.9934	5.0007	5.0080
100	5.0152	5.0223	5.0293	5.0363	5.0432	5.0500	5.0567	5.0634	5.0700	5.0765
110	5.0830	5.0893	5.0957	5.1020	5.1082	5.1143	5.1204	5.1264	5.1324	5.1383
120	5.1442	5.1500	5.1557	5.1614	5.1671	5.1727	5.1782	5.1837	5.1892	5.1946
130	5.2000	5.2053	5.2106	5.2158	5.2210	5.2261	5.2312	5.2363	5.2413	5.2462
140	5.2512	5.2561	5.2609	5.2658	5.2705	5.2753	5.2800	5.2847	5.2893	5.2939
150	5.2985	5.3030	5.3075	5.3120	5.3165	5.3209	5.3252	5.3296	5.3339	5.3382
160	5.3424	5.3467	5.3509	5.3550	5.3592	5.3633	5.3674	5.3714	5.3755	5.3795
170	5.3834	5.3874	5.3913	5.3952	5.3991	5.4030	5.4068	5.4106	5.4144	5.4181
180	5.4219	5.4256	5.4293	5.4329	5.4366	5.4402	5.4438	5.4474	5.4509	5.4545
190	5.4580	5.4615	5.4650	5.4684	5.4719	5.4753	5.4787	5.4821	5.4854	5.4888
200	5.4921	5.4954	5.4987	5.5020	5.5052	5.5084	5.5117	5.5149	5.5180	5.5212
210	5.5244	5.5275	5.5306	5.5337	5.5368	5.5399	5.5429	5.5459	5.5490	5.5520
220	5.5550	5.5579	5.5609	5.5639	5.5668	5.5697	5.5726	5.5755	5.5784	5.5812
230	5.5841	5.5869	5.5898	5.5926	5.5954	5.5981	5.6009	5.6037	5.6064	5.6091
240	5.6119	5.6146	5.6173	5.6199	5.6226	5.6253	5.6279	5.6305	5.6332	5.6358
250	5.6384	5.6410	5.6435	5.6461	5.6487	5.6512	5.6537	5.6563	5.6588	5.6613
260	5.6638	5.6662	5.6687	5.6712	5.6736	5.6760	5.6785	5.6809	5.6833	5.6857
270	5.6881	5.6905	5.6928	5.6952	5.6975	5.6999	5.7022	5.7045	5.7068	5.7091
280	5.7114	5.7137	5.7160	5.7183	5.7205	5.7228	5.7250	5.7273	5.7295	5.7317
290	5.7339	5.7361	5.7383	5.7405	5.7427	5.7448	5.7470	5.7491	5.7513	5.7534
300	5.7555	5.7577	5.7598	5.7619	5.7640	5.7661	5.7681	5.7702	5.7723	5.7743
310	5.7764	5.7784	5.7805	5.7825	5.7845	5.7865	5.7886	5.7906	5.7926	5.7945
320	5.7965	5.7985	5.8005	5.8024	5.8044	5.8063	5.8083	5.8102	5.8121	5.8141
330	5.8160	5.8179	5.8198	5.8217	5.8236	5.8255	5.8273	5.8292	5.8311	5.8329
340	5.8348	5.8367	5.8385	5.8403	5.8422	5.8440	5.8458	5.8476	5.8494	5.8512
350	5.8530	5.8548	5.8566	5.8584	5.8602	5.8619	5.8637	5.8655	5.8672	5.8690
360	5.8707	5.8724	5.8742	5.8759	5.8776	5.8793	5.8810	5.8827	5.8844	5.8861
370	5.8878	5.8895	5.8912	5.8929	5.8945	5.8962	5.8979	5.8995	5.9012	5.9028
380	5.9045	5.9061	5.9077	5.9094	5.9110	5.9126	5.9142	5.9158	5.9174	5.9190
390	5.9206	5.9222	5.9238	5.9254	5.9270	5.9286	5.9301	5.9317	5.9333	5.9348
400	5.9364	5.9517	5.9666	5.9811	5.9952	6.0090	6.0225	6.0357	6.0485	6.0611
500	6.0734	6.0854	6.0972	6.1087	6.1200	6.1311	6.1420	6.1526	6.1631	6.1733
600	6.1834	6.1933	6.2030	6.2126	6.2219	6.2312	6.2402	6.2492	6.2579	6.2666
700	6.2751	6.2835	6.2917	6.2999	6.3079	6.3158	6.3235	6.3312	6.3388	6.3462
800	6.3536	6.3608	6.3680	6.3751	6.3820	6.3889	6.3957	6.4025	6.4091	6.4156
900	6.4221	6.4285	6.4348	6.4411	6.4473	6.4534	6.4594	6.4754	6.4713	6.4771

σ as fraction of the mean extreme range[4]

n	0	1 10	2 20	3 30	4 40	5 50	6 60	7 70	8 80	9 90
	0.	0.	0.	0.	0.	0.	0.	0.	0.	0.
0	—	—	88623	59082	48573	42994	39457	36977	35122	33670
10	32494	31517	30689	29976	29353	28803	28313	27872	27472	27108
20	26774	26467	26182	25918	25672	25441	25225	25022	24830	24649
30	24477	24314	24158	24011	23870	23735	23606	23482	23364	23249
40	23140	23034	22932	22834	22739	22648	22559	22473	22390	22310
50	22231	22155	22082	22010	21940	21872	21806	21742	21679	21618
60	21558	21500	21443	21388	21333	21280	21228	21178	21128	21079
70	21032	20985	20939	20894	20851	20807	20765	20724	20683	20643
80	20603	20565	20527	20490	20453	20417	20382	20347	20312	20279
90	20245	20213	20180	20149	20118	20087	20056	20027	19997	19968
100	19939	19911	19883	19856	19829	19802	19776	19750	19724	19699
110	19674	19649	19624	19600	19577	19553	19530	19507	19484	19462
120	19439	19418	19396	19374	19353	19332	19312	19291	19271	19251
130	19231	19211	19192	19173	19154	19135	19116	19098	19079	19061
140	19043	19026	19008	18991	18973	18956	18939	18923	18906	18890
150	18873	18857	18841	18825	18810	18794	18779	18763	18748	18733
160	18718	18703	18689	18674	18660	18645	18631	18617	18603	18589
170	18575	18562	18548	18535	18522	18508	18495	18482	18469	18457
180	18444	18431	18419	18406	18394	18382	18370	18357	18345	18334
190	18322	18310	18298	18287	18275	18264	18253	18241	18230	18219
200	18208	18197	18186	18175	18165	18154	18143	18133	18122	18112
210	18102	18091	18081	18071	18061	18051	18041	18031	18021	18012
220	18002	17992	17983	17973	17964	17954	17945	17936	17926	17917
230	17908	17899	17890	17881	17872	17863	17854	17845	17837	17828
240	17819	17811	17802	17794	17785	17777	17769	17760	17752	17744
250	17736	17727	17719	17711	17703	17695	17687	17680	17672	17664
260	17656	17648	17641	17633	17625	17618	17610	17603	17595	17588
270	17581	17573	17566	17559	17551	17544	17537	17530	17523	17516
280	17509	17502	17495	17488	17481	17474	17467	17460	17454	17447
290	17440	17433	17427	17420	17414	17407	17400	17394	17387	17381
300	17375	17368	17362	17355	17349	17343	17337	17330	17324	17318
310	17312	17306	17300	17294	17287	17281	17275	17270	17264	17258
320	17252	17246	17240	17234	17228	17223	17217	17211	17205	17200
330	17194	17188	17183	17177	17172	17166	17160	17155	17149	17144
340	17139	17133	17128	17122	17117	17112	17106	17101	17096	17090
350	17085	17080	17075	17070	17064	17059	17054	17049	17044	17039
360	17034	17029	17024	17019	17014	17009	17004	16999	16994	16989
370	16984	16979	16974	16970	16965	16960	16955	16951	16946	16941
380	16936	16932	16927	16922	16918	16913	16908	16904	16899	16895
390	16890	16886	16881	16876	16872	16868	16863	16859	16854	16850
400	16845	16802	16760	16719	16680	16642	16604	16568	16533	16499
500	16465	16433	16401	16370	16340	16310	16281	16253	16226	16199
600	16172	16146	16121	16096	16072	16048	16025	16002	15980	15958
700	15936	15915	15894	15873	15853	15833	15814	15795	15776	15757
800	15739	15721	15704	15686	15669	15652	15636	15619	15603	15587
900	15571	15556	15540	15525	15510	15496	15481	15443	15453	15439

For footnotes see page 48.

$\sigma_{\bar{x}}$ as fraction of the mean extreme range[4] (for explanation see below)

m \ n	2	3	4	5	6	7	8	9	10	11	12	13	14	15	16	17	18	19	20
	0. 0.0	*0.* 0.0	*0.* 0.0	*0.* 0.0	*0.* 0.0	*0.* 0.0	*0.* 0.0	*0.* 0.0	*0.* 0.0	0.00	0.00	0.00	0.00	0.00	0.00	0.00 *0.000*	0.00 *0.000*	0.00 *0.000*	0.00 *0.000*
1	*62666*	*34111*	*24287*	*19227*	*16108*	*13976*	*12418*	*11223*	*10275*	95027	88592	83139	78450	74370	70782	67599	64752	62190	59869
2	*44311*	*24120*	*17173*	*13596*	*11390*	98826	87806	79360	72658	67195	62644	58788	55473	52587	50050	47799	45787	43975	42334
3	*36180*	*19694*	*14022*	*11101*	93001	80691	71693	64797	59325	54864	51149	48000	45293	42937	40866	39028	37385	35905	34565
4	*31333*	*17055*	*12143*	96137	80541	69548	62088	56116	51377	47514	44296	41569	39225	37185	35391	33799	32376	31095	29934
5	*28025*	*15255*	*10861*	85987	72038	62503	55533	50192	45953	42498	39620	37181	35084	33259	31655	30231	28958	27812	26774
6	*25583*	*13926*	99150	78495	65762	57057	50695	45819	41949	38795	36168	33941	32027	30361	28897	27597	26435	25389	24441
7	*23685*	*12893*	91795	72672	60883	52825	46934	42420	38838	35917	33485	31424	29651	28109	26753	25550	24474	23506	22628
8	*22156*	*12060*	85866	67979	56951	49413	43903	39680	36329	33597	31322	29394	27736	26294	25025	23900	22893	21987	21167
9	*20889*	*11370*	80955	64091	53694	46587	41392	37411	34251	31676	29531	27713	26150	24790	23594	22533	21584	20730	19956
10	*19817*	*10787*	76801	60802	50939	44196	39268	35491	32494	30050	28015	26291	24808	23518	22383	21377	20476	19666	18932
11	*18894*	*10285*	73227	57973	48568	42140	37440	33839	30982	28652	26712	25067	23654	22423	21342	20382	19524	18751	18051
12	*18090*	98470	70109	55504	46500	40346	35846	32399	29663	27432	25574	24000	22647	21469	20433	19514	18692	17953	17283
13	*17380*	94607	67359	53327	44676	38763	34440	31128	28499	26356	24571	23059	21758	20626	19631	18748	17959	17248	16605
14	*16748*	91165	64909	51387	43051	37353	33187	29995	27462	25397	23677	22220	20967	19876	18917	18066	17306	16621	16001
15	*16180*	88074	62708	49645	41591	36086	32062	28978	26531	24536	22874	21466	20256	19202	18276	17454	16719	16057	15458
16	*15666*	85277	60716	48068	40271	34940	31044	28058	25689	23757	22148	20785	19613	18592	17695	16900	16188	15547	14967
17	*15199*	82731	58904	46633	39068	33897	30117	27220	24922	23048	21487	20164	19027	18037	17167	16395	15705	15083	14520
18	*14770*	80400	57244	45319	37967	32942	29269	26453	24219	22398	20881	19596	18491	17529	16683	15933	15262	14658	14111
19	*14376*	78256	55717	44110	36955	32063	28488	25748	23573	21801	20325	19073	17998	17062	16238	15508	14855	14267	13735
20	*14012*	76274	54306	42994	36019	31252	27767	25096	22977	21249	19810	18590	17542	16630	15827	15115	14479	13906	1338[illegible]
21	*13675*	74436	52998	41957	35151	30498	27097	24491	22423	20737	19332	18142	17119	16229	15446	14751	14130	13571	13064
22	*13360*	72725	51779	40993	34343	29797	26474	23928	21907	20260	18888	17725	16726	15856	15091	14412	13805	13259	12764
23	*13067*	71126	50641	40092	33588	29142	25892	23402	21426	19815	18473	17336	16358	15507	14759	14095	13502	12967	12483
24	*12792*	69628	49575	39248	32881	28529	25347	22909	20975	19397	18084	16971	16014	15181	14448	13799	13218	12694	12220
25	*12533*	68222	48573	38455	32216	27952	24835	22446	20551	19006	17718	16628	15690	14874	14156	13520	12950	12438	11974
26	*12290*	66897	47630	37708	31591	27409	24353	22011	20152	18637	17374	16305	15385	14585	13881	13257	12699	12196	11741
27	*12060*	65646	46740	37003	31000	26897	23898	21599	19775	18288	17050	16000	15098	14312	13622	13009	12462	11968	11522
28	*11843*	64463	45897	36336	30442	26412	23467	21210	19419	17959	16742	15712	14826	14055	13377	12775	12237	11753	11314
29	*11637*	63342	45099	35704	29912	25953	23059	20841	19081	17646	16451	15439	14568	13810	13144	12553	12024	11548	11117
30	*11441*	62278	44341	35104	29409	25517	22671	20491	18760	17350	16175	15179	14323	13578	12923	12342	11822	11354	10930
31	*11255*	61265	43620	34533	28931	25102	22303	20158	18455	17068	15912	14932	14090	13357	12713	12141	11630	11170	10753
32	*11078*	60300	42932	33989	28476	24707	21951	19840	18165	16799	15661	14697	13868	13147	12513	11950	11447	10994	10583
33	*10909*	59379	42277	33470	28041	24329	21616	19537	17887	16542	15422	14473	13656	12946	12322	11767	11272	10826	10422
34	*10747*	58500	41651	32975	27625	23969	21296	19248	17622	16297	15193	14258	13454	12754	12139	11593	11105	10665	10267
35	*10592*	57658	41052	32500	27228	23624	20990	18971	17369	16063	14975	14053	13261	12571	11964	11426	10945	10512	10120
36	*10444*	56851	40478	32046	26847	23294	20696	18705	17126	15838	14765	13856	13075	12395	11797	11266	10792	10365	*99781*
37	*10302*	56078	39927	31610	26482	22977	20414	18451	16893	15623	14565	13668	12897	12226	11636	11113	10645	10224	*98424*
38	*10166*	55335	39398	31191	26131	22672	20144	18206	16669	15416	14372	13487	12726	12064	11482	10966	10504	10089	*97120*
39	*10035*	54621	38890	30788	25794	22380	19884	17972	16454	15217	14186	13313	12562	11909	11334	10824	10369	*99583*	*95867*
40	99083	53934	38400	30401	25469	22098	19634	17745	16247	15025	14008	13145	12404	11759	11192	10688	10238	*98331*	*94661*
41	97867	53272	37929	30028	25157	21827	19393	17528	16048	14841	13836	12984	12252	11615	11054	10557	10113	*97124*	*93499*
42	96695	52634	37475	29668	24856	21566	19161	17318	15855	14663	13670	12829	12105	11476	10922	10431	*99915*	*95961*	*92380*
43	95564	52019	37037	29321	24565	21313	18937	17115	15670	14492	13510	12679	11964	11341	10794	10309	*98746*	*94839*	*91299*
44	94472	51424	36613	28986	24284	21070	18720	16920	15491	14326	13356	12534	11827	11212	10671	10191	*97618*	*93755*	*90256*
45	93416	50849	36204	28662	24013	20834	18511	16731	15318	14166	13207	12394	11695	11086	10552	10077	*96527*	*92707*	*89247*
46	92395	50294	35809	28349	23750	20607	18309	16548	15150	14011	13062	12258	11567	10965	10436	*99668*	*95472*	*91694*	*88272*
47	91407	49756	35426	28046	23496	20386	18113	16371	14988	13861	12923	12127	11443	10848	10325	*98603*	*94451*	*90713*	*87328*
48	90450	49235	35055	27752	23250	20173	17923	16199	14831	13716	12787	12000	11323	10734	10216	*97570*	*93462*	*89763*	*86413*
49	89522	48730	34695	27468	23012	19966	17739	16033	14679	13575	12656	11877	11207	10624	10112	*96569*	*92503*	*88843*	*85527*
50	88623	48240	34346	27192	22780	19765	17561	15872	14532	13439	12529	11758	11095	10517	10010	*95599*	*91574*	*87950*	*84667*

Explanation of the tables on pages 47–49

Correction[1] and confidence[2] factors for σ (page 47)

(a) The estimation of σ^2 from s^2 is unbiassed, but not that of σ from s. This bias is eliminated by multiplying s by the factor k_s.

(b) Confidence limits for σ. Columns 3–6 give the confidence factors by which s must be multiplied in order to obtain the confidence limits which include σ with a probability of $(1-2\alpha)$.

Extreme range

If x_1 is the lowest and x_n the highest value of a sample of size n, then $(x_n - x_1)$ is the extreme range w_n of this sample.

The standardized extreme range of a sample of size n from a population with standard deviation σ is

$$W_n = \frac{w_n}{\sigma} = \frac{x_n - x_1}{\sigma}$$

The mean extreme range of m samples of size n from one and the same population is

$$\overline{w}_{m,n} = \frac{\sum_1^m w_n}{m} = \frac{\sum_1^m (x_n - x_1)}{m}$$

The standardized mean extreme range is

$$\overline{W}_{m,n} = \frac{\overline{w}_{m,n}}{\sigma} = \frac{\sum_1^m w_n}{m\sigma} = \frac{\sum_1^m (x_n - x_1)}{m\sigma}$$

Since the extreme range w_n is merely a special case of the mean extreme range $\overline{w}_{m,n}$ with $m=1$, only the mean extreme range will be referred to in the text which follows.

Mean extreme range[3] as a multiple of σ (page 47)

The expected value $\overline{\boldsymbol{W}}_n$ of the extreme range of random samples of size n from a normally distributed population with unit standard deviation satisfies the relation

$$\overline{W}_{m,n} \underset{(m\to\infty)}{\to} \overline{\boldsymbol{W}}_n$$

The table gives values of $\overline{\boldsymbol{W}}_n$ for the standardized normal distribution as multiples of σ. (Many authors use d_n instead of $\overline{\boldsymbol{W}}_n$.)

σ as a fraction of the mean extreme range[4] (page 47)

The quotient $\dfrac{\overline{w}_{m,n}}{\overline{\boldsymbol{W}}_n} = \overline{w}_{m,n} \times \boldsymbol{A}_n$

gives an unbiassed estimate of σ which improves as m increases, but rapidly worsens as the size n of the individual samples increases. Its variance is also greater than s.

With small samples (n between 5 and 10), however, there is practically no difference between the accuracy of the two estimates, even for $m=1$.

$\sigma_{\bar{x}}$ as a fraction of the mean extreme range[4]

The quotient $\dfrac{\overline{w}_{m,n}}{\overline{\boldsymbol{W}}_n \sqrt{m\,n}} = \overline{w}_{m,n} \times \boldsymbol{A}_{m,n}$

where $m\,n =$ sample size N, gives an unbiassed estimate of the standard deviation $\sigma_{\bar{x}}$ of the estimate $\bar{x}$. See remarks in the previous paragraph. Values of the factor $\boldsymbol{A}_{m,n}$ are given in the table above.

Significance limits for the difference between two means based on the extreme range

The table on page 49 gives the 2α-significance limits for u:

(a) $u = \dfrac{(\bar{x}-\mu)\,m}{\sum (x_n - x_1)\,\boldsymbol{A}_{m,n}}$

(b) $u = \dfrac{(\bar{x}' - \bar{x}'')\sqrt{m'\,m''}}{\left[\sum (x_n' - x_1') + \sum (x_n'' - x_1'')\right]\boldsymbol{A}_{m,n}}$

$(m = m' + m'')$

(a): When $m=1$, the test is much simpler. See page 53.

(b): When $m' = m'' = 1$, the test is much simpler. See page 53.

See also (**618**) and (**619**), page 172.

1) Calculated from values in Pearson and Hartley (Eds.), *Biometrika Tables for Statisticians,* vol. I, Cambridge University Press, 1954. *2)* Confidence factors calculated from χ^2-values in Pearson and Hartley, *loc. cit.*, and from data of Hald and Sinkbæk, *Skand. Aktuar Tidskr.*, **33**, 168 (1950). Reproduction only by permission of the publishers of these *Scientific Tables,* J. R. Geigy S.A., Basle (Switzerland). *3)* Values from Tippett, L. H. C., *Biometrika,* **17**, 364 (1925). Reprinted by kind permission of the author and publishers. *4)* Calculated from values of Tippett, L. H. C., *loc. cit.* Reproduction only by permission of the publishers of these *Scientific Tables.*

Significance Limits for the Difference Between Two Means Based on the Extreme Range[1]

For explanation see page 48

2 α = 0.10

m \ n	2	3	4	5	6	7	8	9	10	11	12	13	14	15	16	17	18	19	20
1	5.04	2.59	2.18	2.02	1.94	1.88	1.85	1.82	1.81	1.79	1.78	1.77	1.76	1.75	1.75	1.74	1.74	1.73	1.73
2	2.62	02	1.88	1.81	78	76	74	73	72	71	71	71	70	70	70	69	69	69	69
3	20	1.88	79	75	73	72	71	70	70	69	69	69	68	68	68	68	68	67	67
4	03	81	75	73	71	70	69	69	68	68	68	68	67	67	67	67	67	67	67
5	1.94	1.77	1.73	1.71	1.70	1.69	1.68	1.68	1.68	1.68	1.67	1.67	1.67	1.67	1.67	1.67	1.66	1.66	1.66
6	89	75	72	70	69	68	68	67	67	67	67	67	66	66	66	66	66	66	66
7	85	73	71	69	68	67	67	67	66	66	66	66	66	66	66	66	66	66	66
8	82	72	70	68	68	67	67	67	66	66	66	66	66	66	66	66	66	66	66
9	80	71	69	68	67	67	67	66	66	66	66	66	66	66	66	66	66	66	66
10	1.78	1.71	1.69	1.68	1.67	1.67	1.66	1.66	1.66	1.66	1.66	1.66	1.66	1.66	1.65	1.65	1.65	1.65	1.65
11	77	71	68	68	67	67	66	66	66	66	66	66	66	66	65	65	65	65	65
12	76	70	68	68	66	66	66	66	65	65	65	65	65	65	65	65	65	65	65
13	75	70	67	67	66	66	66	66	65	65	65	65	65	65	65	65	65	65	65
14	74	69	67	67	66	66	66	66	65	65	65	65	65	65	65	65	65	65	65
15	1.73	1.69	1.67	1.67	1.66	1.66	1.66	1.66	1.65	1.65	1.65	1.65	1.65	1.65	1.65	1.65	1.65	1.65	1.65
16	72	69	67	67	66	66	66	66	65	65	65	65	65	65	65	65	65	65	65
17	72	68	67	67	66	66	66	66	65	65	65	65	65	65	65	65	65	65	65
18	72	68	67	66	66	66	65	65	65	65	65	65	65	65	65	65	65	65	65
19	71	67	67	66	66	66	65	65	65	65	65	65	65	65	65	65	65	65	65
20	1.71	1.67	1.67	1.66	1.66	1.66	1.65	1.65	1.65	1.65	1.65	1.65	1.65	1.65	1.65	1.65	1.65	1.65	1.65
30	69	66	66	66	65	65	65	65	65	65	65	65	65	65	65	65	65	65	65
60	67	66	65	65	65	65	65	65	65	65	65	65	65	65	65	65	65	65	65
120	66	65	65	65	65	65	65	65	65	65	65	65	65	65	65	65	65	65	65

2 α = 0.05

m \ n	2	3	4	5	6	7	8	9	10	11	12	13	14	15	16	17	18	19	20
1	10.14	3.82	2.95	2.63	2.48	2.38	2.32	2.27	2.24	2.21	2.19	2.17	2.16	2.15	2.14	2.13	2.12	2.11	2.11
2	3.87	2.64	37	25	19	15	13	11	09	08	07	06	06	05	05	04	04	03	03
3	2.98	37	22	15	11	09	07	06	05	04	03	02	02	02	02	01	01	01	01
4	66	25	15	10	07	05	04	03	02	01	01	01	01	00	00	00	00	00	00
5	2.49	2.19	2.11	2.07	2.05	2.03	2.02	2.02	2.01	2.01	2.00	2.00	2.00	1.99	1.99	1.99	1.99	1.99	1.99
6	38	14	08	05	03	02	01	01	00	00	00	00	1.99	99	99	99	99	99	99
7	31	11	06	04	02	02	01	00	1.99	1.99	1.99	1.99	99	98	98	98	98	98	98
8	26	09	05	03	01	01	00	00	99	99	99	99	98	98	98	98	98	98	98
9	23	08	04	02	01	00	1.99	1.99	99	99	98	98	98	98	98	98	98	98	98
10	2.20	2.07	2.03	2.01	2.00	2.00	1.99	1.99	1.98	1.98	1.98	1.98	1.98	1.98	1.98	1.98	1.98	1.97	1.97
11	17	06	02	01	00	1.99	99	99	98	98	98	98	98	98	98	98	98	97	97
12	15	05	02	01	00	99	98	99	98	98	97	97	97	97	97	97	97	97	97
13	14	04	02	00	1.99	98	98	98	98	98	97	97	97	97	97	97	97	97	97
14	12	04	01	00	99	98	98	98	98	98	97	97	97	97	97	97	97	97	97
15	2.11	2.03	2.01	2.00	1.99	1.98	1.98	1.98	1.98	1.98	1.97	1.97	1.97	1.97	1.97	1.97	1.97	1.97	1.97
16	10	03	01	00	99	98	98	98	98	98	97	97	97	97	97	97	97	97	97
17	09	02	01	00	99	98	98	98	98	98	97	97	97	97	97	97	97	97	97
18	08	02	00	1.99	98	98	98	97	97	97	97	97	97	97	97	97	97	97	97
19	08	01	00	99	98	98	98	97	97	97	97	97	97	97	97	97	97	97	97
20	2.07	2.01	2.00	1.99	1.98	1.98	1.98	1.97	1.97	1.97	1.97	1.97	1.97	1.97	1.97	1.97	1.97	1.97	1.97
30	03	1.99	1.98	98	97	97	97	97	97	97	97	97	97	97	97	97	97	96	96
60	00	98	97	97	97	97	97	96	96	96	96	96	96	96	96	96	96	96	96
120	1.98	97	97	96	96	96	96	96	96	96	96	96	96	96	96	96	96	96	96

2 α = 0.02

m \ n	2	3	4	5	6	7	8	9	10	11	12	13	14	15	16	17	18	19	20
1	25.39	6.19	4.21	3.56	3.25	3.07	2.95	2.87	2.81	2.76	2.72	2.69	2.67	2.65	2.63	2.61	2.60	2.59	2.58
2	6.27	3.56	3.05	2.84	2.73	2.66	61	58	55	53	51	50	49	48	47	46	46	45	45
3	4.27	05	2.77	65	58	54	51	49	47	46	45	44	43	43	42	42	41	41	41
4	3.60	2.84	65	56	51	48	46	45	44	43	42	42	41	41	40	40	39	39	39
5	3.27	2.72	2.58	2.51	2.47	2.45	2.43	2.42	2.41	2.41	2.40	2.40	2.39	2.39	2.38	2.38	2.38	2.37	2.37
6	08	65	53	48	45	43	42	41	40	39	39	38	38	38	37	37	37	37	37
7	2.95	60	50	46	43	41	40	40	39	38	38	37	37	37	36	36	36	36	36
8	86	56	48	44	42	40	39	39	38	38	37	37	37	37	36	36	36	36	36
9	79	53	46	43	41	39	38	38	37	37	37	36	36	36	35	35	35	35	35
10	2.73	2.51	2.45	2.42	2.40	2.39	2.38	2.37	2.37	2.37	2.36	2.36	2.36	2.36	2.35	2.35	2.35	2.35	2.35
11	69	49	44	41	39	38	37	37	36	36	36	36	36	36	35	35	35	35	35
12	66	48	43	41	38	38	37	37	36	36	36	36	36	36	35	35	35	35	34
13	63	47	42	40	38	38	37	36	36	36	35	35	35	35	35	35	35	35	34
14	61	46	42	40	37	37	36	36	35	35	35	35	35	35	35	34	34	34	34
15	2.59	2.45	2.41	2.39	2.37	2.37	2.36	2.36	2.35	2.35	2.35	2.35	2.35	2.35	2.35	2.34	2.34	2.34	2.34
16	57	44	41	39	37	37	36	36	35	35	35	35	35	35	35	34	34	34	34
17	56	44	40	38	36	37	36	36	35	35	35	35	35	35	35	34	34	34	34
18	54	43	40	38	36	36	35	35	35	34	34	34	34	34	34	34	34	34	34
19	53	42	39	37	36	36	35	35	35	34	34	34	34	34	34	34	34	34	34
20	2.52	2.42	2.39	2.37	2.36	2.36	2.35	2.35	2.35	2.34	2.34	2.34	2.34	2.34	2.34	2.34	2.34	2.34	2.34
30	45	39	37	36	35	35	34	34	34	34	34	34	34	34	34	33	33	33	33
60	39	36	35	34	34	34	34	33	33	33	33	33	33	33	33	33	33	33	33
120	36	34	34	33	33	33	33	33	33	33	33	33	33	33	33	33	33	33	33

2 α = 0.01

m \ n	2	3	4	5	6	7	8	9	10	11	12	13	14	15	16	17	18	19	20
1	50.79	8.82	5.42	4.38	3.90	3.63	3.45	3.33	3.24	3.17	3.12	3.08	3.05	3.02	2.99	2.97	2.95	2.93	2.92
2	8.93	4.34	3.60	3.29	13	03	2.97	2.92	2.88	2.85	2.83	2.81	2.80	2.79	78	77	76	75	74
3	5.49	3.60	20	02	2.93	2.87	83	80	78	76	74	73	72	71	71	70	70	69	69
4	4.43	30	02	2.90	83	79	76	74	72	71	70	69	69	68	67	66	66	66	66
5	3.93	3.14	2.92	2.83	2.78	2.75	2.72	2.71	2.69	2.68	2.68	2.67	2.66	2.66	2.65	2.65	2.65	2.64	2.64
6	64	03	86	79	74	72	70	68	67	66	66	65	65	64	64	64	63	63	63
7	46	2.96	82	75	72	70	68	67	66	65	65	64	64	63	63	63	62	62	62
8	32	91	79	73	70	68	67	66	65	64	64	63	63	62	62	62	62	62	62
9	21	87	77	71	68	67	66	65	64	63	63	63	62	62	62	62	61	61	61
10	3.14	2.84	2.74	2.70	2.67	2.66	2.65	2.64	2.63	2.63	2.62	2.62	2.62	2.62	2.61	2.61	2.61	2.61	2.61
11	08	82	72	69	66	65	64	64	63	62	62	62	62	61	61	61	61	61	61
12	03	80	71	68	66	64	63	63	62	62	62	62	61	61	61	61	61	61	61
13	2.99	78	70	67	65	64	63	63	62	62	61	61	61	60	60	60	60	61	60
14	96	76	69	67	65	63	62	62	61	61	61	61	60	60	60	60	60	60	60
15	2.93	2.75	2.68	2.66	2.64	2.63	2.62	2.62	2.61	2.61	2.61	2.61	2.60	2.60	2.60	2.60	2.60	2.60	2.60
16	91	74	68	66	64	63	62	62	61	61	61	61	60	60	60	60	60	60	60
17	89	73	67	65	63	63	61	62	61	61	61	61	60	60	60	60	60	60	60
18	87	72	67	65	63	62	61	61	60	60	60	60	60	60	60	59	59	59	59
19	85	71	66	64	62	62	61	61	60	60	60	60	60	60	60	59	59	59	59
20	2.84	2.70	2.66	2.64	2.62	2.62	2.61	2.61	2.60	2.60	2.60	2.60	2.60	2.60	2.60	2.59	2.59	2.59	2.59
30	75	66	63	62	61	60	60	60	59	59	59	59	59	59	59	59	59	59	59
60	66	62	60	60	59	59	59	59	59	58	58	58	58	58	58	58	58	58	58
120	62	60	59	59	58	58	58	58	58	58	58	58	58	58	58	58	58	58	58

1) Values from LORD, E., *Biometrika*, **34**, 41 (1947), reprinted by kind permission of the author and publishers. Interpolated values calculated by the editors of these *Scientific Tables.*

Upper Significance Limits for the Extreme Ranges of Several Means[1]

For explanation see page 173

$2\alpha = 0.05$

ν \ n	2	3	4	5	6	7	8	9	10	11	12	13	14	15	16	17	18	19	20
1	18.00	18.00	18.00	18.00	18.00	18.00	18.00	18.00	18.00	18.00	18.00	18.00	18.00	18.00	18.00	18.00	18.00	18.00	18.00
2	6.09	6.09	6.09	6.09	6.09	6.09	6.09	6.09	6.09	6.09	6.09	6.09	6.09	6.09	6.09	6.09	6.09	6.09	6.09
3	4.50	4.50	4.50	4.50	4.50	4.50	4.50	4.50	4.50	4.50	4.50	4.50	4.50	4.50	4.50	4.50	4.50	4.50	4.50
4	3.93	4.01	4.02	4.02	4.02	4.02	4.02	4.02	4.02	4.02	4.02	4.02	4.02	4.02	4.02	4.02	4.02	4.02	4.02
5	3.64	3.74	3.79	3.83	3.83	3.83	3.83	3.83	3.83	3.83	3.83	3.83	3.83	3.83	3.83	3.83	3.83	3.83	3.83
6	3.46	3.58	3.64	3.68	3.68	3.68	3.68	3.68	3.68	3.68	3.68	3.68	3.68	3.68	3.68	3.68	3.68	3.68	3.68
7	3.35	3.47	3.54	3.58	3.60	3.61	3.61	3.61	3.61	3.61	3.61	3.61	3.61	3.61	3.61	3.61	3.61	3.61	3.61
8	3.26	3.39	3.47	3.52	3.55	3.56	3.56	3.56	3.56	3.56	3.56	3.56	3.56	3.56	3.56	3.56	3.56	3.56	3.56
9	3.20	3.34	3.41	3.47	3.50	3.52	3.52	3.52	3.52	3.52	3.52	3.52	3.52	3.52	3.52	3.52	3.52	3.52	3.52
10	3.15	3.30	3.37	3.43	3.46	3.47	3.47	3.47	3.47	3.47	3.47	3.47	3.47	3.47	3.47	3.47	3.47	3.47	3.48
11	3.11	3.27	3.35	3.39	3.43	3.44	3.45	3.46	3.46	3.46	3.46	3.46	3.46	3.46	3.46	3.46	3.47	3.47	3.48
12	3.08	3.23	3.33	3.36	3.40	3.42	3.44	3.44	3.46	3.46	3.46	3.46	3.46	3.46	3.46	3.46	3.47	3.47	3.48
13	3.06	3.21	3.30	3.35	3.38	3.41	3.42	3.44	3.45	3.45	3.45	3.45	3.46	3.46	3.46	3.46	3.47	3.47	3.47
14	3.03	3.18	3.27	3.33	3.37	3.39	3.41	3.42	3.44	3.45	3.45	3.45	3.46	3.46	3.46	3.46	3.47	3.47	3.47
15	3.01	3.16	3.25	3.31	3.36	3.38	3.40	3.42	3.43	3.44	3.44	3.45	3.45	3.45	3.46	3.46	3.47	3.47	3.47
16	3.00	3.15	3.23	3.30	3.34	3.37	3.39	3.41	3.43	3.44	3.44	3.45	3.45	3.45	3.46	3.46	3.47	3.47	3.47
17	2.98	3.13	3.22	3.28	3.33	3.36	3.38	3.40	3.42	3.43	3.44	3.45	3.45	3.45	3.46	3.46	3.47	3.47	3.47
18	2.97	3.12	3.21	3.27	3.32	3.35	3.37	3.39	3.41	3.42	3.43	3.44	3.45	3.45	3.46	3.46	3.47	3.47	3.47
19	2.96	3.11	3.19	3.26	3.31	3.35	3.37	3.39	3.41	3.42	3.43	3.44	3.44	3.45	3.46	3.46	3.47	3.47	3.47
20	2.95	3.10	3.18	3.25	3.30	3.34	3.36	3.38	3.40	3.42	3.43	3.44	3.44	3.45	3.46	3.46	3.46	3.47	3.47
21	2.94	3.09	3.17	3.24	3.29	3.33	3.35	3.38	3.40	3.42	3.42	3.44	3.44	3.45	3.46	3.46	3.46	3.47	3.47
22	2.93	3.08	3.17	3.24	3.29	3.32	3.35	3.37	3.39	3.41	3.42	3.43	3.44	3.45	3.45	3.45	3.46	3.47	3.47
23	2.93	3.08	3.15	3.23	3.28	3.32	3.34	3.37	3.39	3.41	3.42	3.43	3.44	3.45	3.45	3.45	3.46	3.47	3.47
24	2.92	3.07	3.15	3.22	3.28	3.31	3.34	3.37	3.38	3.40	3.41	3.43	3.44	3.45	3.45	3.45	3.46	3.47	3.47
25	2.91	3.06	3.14	3.22	3.27	3.31	3.34	3.36	3.38	3.40	3.41	3.43	3.44	3.45	3.45	3.45	3.46	3.47	3.47
26	2.91	3.06	3.14	3.21	3.27	3.30	3.34	3.36	3.38	3.40	3.41	3.43	3.43	3.44	3.45	3.45	3.46	3.47	3.47
27	2.90	3.05	3.13	3.21	3.26	3.30	3.33	3.36	3.38	3.40	3.40	3.43	3.43	3.44	3.45	3.45	3.46	3.47	3.47
28	2.90	3.04	3.13	3.20	3.26	3.30	3.33	3.35	3.37	3.39	3.40	3.42	3.43	3.44	3.45	3.45	3.46	3.47	3.47
29	2.89	3.04	3.12	3.20	3.25	3.29	3.32	3.35	3.37	3.39	3.40	3.42	3.43	3.44	3.44	3.45	3.46	3.47	3.47
30	2.89	3.04	3.12	3.20	3.25	3.29	3.32	3.35	3.37	3.39	3.40	3.42	3.43	3.44	3.44	3.45	3.46	3.47	3.47
31	2.89	3.04	3.12	3.20	3.25	3.29	3.32	3.35	3.37	3.39	3.40	3.42	3.43	3.44	3.44	3.45	3.46	3.47	3.47
32	2.88	3.03	3.11	3.19	3.24	3.28	3.32	3.35	3.37	3.39	3.40	3.42	3.43	3.44	3.44	3.45	3.46	3.47	3.47
33	2.88	3.03	3.11	3.19	3.24	3.28	3.31	3.34	3.36	3.38	3.40	3.42	3.43	3.44	3.44	3.45	3.46	3.47	3.47
34	2.88	3.03	3.11	3.19	3.24	3.28	3.31	3.34	3.36	3.38	3.39	3.42	3.43	3.44	3.44	3.45	3.46	3.47	3.47
35	2.87	3.02	3.11	3.18	3.23	3.28	3.31	3.34	3.36	3.38	3.39	3.41	3.42	3.44	3.44	3.45	3.46	3.47	3.47
36	2.87	3.02	3.11	3.18	3.23	3.28	3.31	3.34	3.36	3.38	3.39	3.41	3.42	3.43	3.44	3.45	3.46	3.47	3.47
37	2.87	3.02	3.10	3.18	3.23	3.27	3.30	3.34	3.35	3.38	3.39	3.41	3.42	3.43	3.44	3.45	3.46	3.47	3.47
38	2.86	3.02	3.10	3.17	3.22	3.27	3.30	3.33	3.35	3.37	3.39	3.41	3.42	3.43	3.44	3.45	3.46	3.47	3.47
39	2.86	3.01	3.10	3.17	3.22	3.27	3.30	3.33	3.35	3.37	3.39	3.41	3.42	3.43	3.44	3.45	3.46	3.47	3.47
40	2.86	3.01	3.10	3.17	3.22	3.27	3.30	3.33	3.35	3.37	3.39	3.41	3.42	3.43	3.44	3.45	3.46	3.47	3.47
50	2.84	2.99	3.09	3.15	3.21	3.25	3.29	3.32	3.34	3.36	3.38	3.40	3.41	3.42	3.43	3.44	3.45	3.46	3.47
60	2.83	2.98	3.08	3.14	3.20	3.24	3.28	3.31	3.33	3.35	3.37	3.39	3.40	3.42	3.43	3.44	3.45	3.46	3.47
100	2.80	2.95	3.05	3.12	3.18	3.22	3.26	3.29	3.33	3.34	3.36	3.38	3.40	3.41	3.42	3.43	3.45	3.46	3.47
120	2.79	2.94	3.04	3.12	3.17	3.21	3.25	3.29	3.32	3.34	3.36	3.38	3.40	3.41	3.42	3.43	3.45	3.46	3.47
∞	2.77	2.92	3.02	3.09	3.15	3.19	3.23	3.26	3.29	3.32	3.34	3.36	3.38	3.40	3.41	3.43	3.44	3.46	3.47

$2\alpha = 0.01$

ν \ n	2	3	4	5	6	7	8	9	10	11	12	13	14	15	16	17	18	19	20
1	90.00	90.00	90.00	90.00	90.00	90.00	90.00	90.00	90.00	90.00	90.00	90.00	90.00	90.00	90.00	90.00	90.00	90.00	90.00
2	14.00	14.00	14.00	14.00	14.00	14.00	14.00	14.00	14.00	14.00	14.00	14.00	14.00	14.00	14.00	14.00	14.00	14.00	14.00
3	8.26	8.50	8.60	8.70	8.80	8.90	8.90	9.00	9.00	9.00	9.00	9.04	9.10	9.15	9.20	9.25	9.30	9.30	9.30
4	6.51	6.80	6.90	7.00	7.10	7.10	7.20	7.20	7.30	7.30	7.30	7.34	7.40	7.40	7.40	7.44	7.50	7.50	7.50
5	5.70	5.96	6.11	6.18	6.26	6.33	6.40	6.44	6.50	6.55	6.60	6.60	6.60	6.64	6.70	6.70	6.70	6.74	6.80
6	5.24	5.51	5.65	5.73	5.81	5.88	5.95	6.00	6.00	6.04	6.10	6.15	6.20	6.20	6.20	6.24	6.30	6.30	6.30
7	4.95	5.22	5.37	5.45	5.53	5.61	5.69	5.73	5.80	5.80	5.80	5.84	5.90	5.90	5.90	5.94	6.00	6.00	6.00
8	4.74	5.00	5.14	5.23	5.32	5.40	5.47	5.50	5.50	5.54	5.60	5.65	5.70	5.70	5.70	5.74	5.80	5.80	5.80
9	4.60	4.86	4.99	5.08	5.17	5.25	5.32	5.36	5.40	5.45	5.50	5.50	5.50	5.54	5.60	5.65	5.70	5.70	5.70
10	4.48	4.73	4.88	4.96	5.06	5.13	5.20	5.24	5.28	5.32	5.36	5.39	5.42	5.45	5.48	5.51	5.54	5.55	5.55
11	4.39	4.63	4.77	4.86	4.94	5.01	5.06	5.12	5.15	5.20	5.24	5.27	5.28	5.31	5.34	5.36	5.38	5.39	5.39
12	4.32	4.55	4.68	4.76	4.84	4.92	4.96	5.02	5.07	5.11	5.13	5.15	5.17	5.19	5.22	5.23	5.24	5.25	5.26
13	4.26	4.48	4.62	4.69	4.74	4.84	4.88	4.94	4.98	5.02	5.04	5.06	5.08	5.10	5.13	5.14	5.14	5.15	5.15
14	4.21	4.42	4.55	4.63	4.70	4.78	4.83	4.87	4.91	4.94	4.96	4.98	5.00	5.02	5.04	5.05	5.06	5.07	5.07
15	4.17	4.37	4.50	4.58	4.64	4.72	4.77	4.81	4.84	4.87	4.90	4.92	4.94	4.96	4.97	4.98	4.99	5.00	5.00
16	4.13	4.34	4.45	4.54	4.60	4.67	4.72	4.76	4.79	4.82	4.84	4.86	4.88	4.90	4.91	4.92	4.93	4.94	4.94
17	4.10	4.30	4.41	4.50	4.56	4.63	4.68	4.72	4.75	4.78	4.80	4.82	4.83	4.84	4.86	4.87	4.88	4.89	4.89
18	4.07	4.27	4.38	4.46	4.53	4.59	4.64	4.68	4.71	4.74	4.76	4.78	4.79	4.80	4.82	4.83	4.84	4.85	4.85
19	4.05	4.24	4.35	4.43	4.50	4.56	4.61	4.64	4.67	4.70	4.72	4.74	4.76	4.78	4.79	4.80	4.81	4.82	4.82
20	4.02	4.22	4.33	4.40	4.47	4.53	4.58	4.61	4.65	4.67	4.69	4.71	4.73	4.75	4.76	4.77	4.78	4.79	4.79
21	4.00	4.20	4.30	4.37	4.45	4.50	4.55	4.59	4.62	4.65	4.67	4.69	4.71	4.73	4.74	4.75	4.76	4.77	4.77
22	3.99	4.17	4.28	4.36	4.42	4.48	4.53	4.57	4.60	4.63	4.65	4.67	4.68	4.70	4.71	4.72	4.74	4.75	4.75
23	3.97	4.15	4.26	4.34	4.41	4.46	4.51	4.55	4.58	4.60	4.63	4.65	4.67	4.68	4.70	4.71	4.72	4.73	4.73
24	3.96	4.14	4.24	4.33	4.39	4.44	4.49	4.53	4.57	4.60	4.62	4.63	4.64	4.65	4.67	4.68	4.70	4.71	4.72
25	3.94	4.12	4.22	4.32	4.38	4.42	4.47	4.51	4.54	4.57	4.60	4.62	4.64	4.64	4.67	4.67	4.69	4.70	4.70
26	3.93	4.11	4.21	4.30	4.36	4.41	4.46	4.50	4.53	4.56	4.58	4.60	4.62	4.64	4.65	4.66	4.67	4.68	4.69
27	3.92	4.09	4.19	4.29	4.35	4.39	4.44	4.49	4.51	4.54	4.57	4.59	4.61	4.63	4.64	4.65	4.66	4.67	4.68
28	3.91	4.08	4.18	4.27	4.34	4.38	4.43	4.47	4.51	4.54	4.56	4.58	4.60	4.62	4.62	4.63	4.65	4.66	4.67
29	3.90	4.07	4.17	4.23	4.33	4.37	4.42	4.46	4.49	4.52	4.55	4.57	4.59	4.61	4.62	4.63	4.64	4.65	4.66
30	3.89	4.06	4.16	4.22	4.32	4.36	4.41	4.45	4.48	4.51	4.54	4.56	4.58	4.60	4.61	4.62	4.63	4.64	4.65
31	3.88	4.05	4.15	4.21	4.31	4.35	4.40	4.44	4.47	4.50	4.53	4.55	4.57	4.59	4.60	4.61	4.62	4.63	4.64
32	3.87	4.04	4.14	4.20	4.30	4.34	4.39	4.43	4.46	4.49	4.52	4.54	4.56	4.58	4.59	4.60	4.61	4.62	4.63
33	3.86	4.03	4.14	4.20	4.29	4.34	4.38	4.42	4.45	4.48	4.51	4.53	4.55	4.57	4.58	4.60	4.61	4.62	4.63
34	3.86	4.03	4.13	4.19	4.28	4.33	4.38	4.41	4.45	4.48	4.50	4.53	4.55	4.57	4.58	4.59	4.60	4.61	4.62
35	3.85	4.02	4.12	4.19	4.27	4.32	4.37	4.40	4.44	4.47	4.49	4.52	4.54	4.56	4.57	4.58	4.59	4.60	4.62
36	3.84	4.01	4.12	4.18	4.27	4.32	4.36	4.40	4.43	4.46	4.49	4.51	4.53	4.55	4.56	4.58	4.59	4.60	4.61
37	3.84	4.01	4.11	4.18	4.26	4.31	4.36	4.39	4.43	4.46	4.48	4.51	4.53	4.55	4.56	4.57	4.58	4.59	4.60
38	3.83	4.00	4.11	4.18	4.25	4.31	4.35	4.38	4.42	4.45	4.47	4.50	4.51	4.54	4.55	4.57	4.58	4.59	4.60
39	3.83	4.00	4.10	4.17	4.25	4.30	4.34	4.38	4.41	4.45	4.47	4.50	4.51	4.54	4.55	4.56	4.57	4.58	4.59
40	3.82	3.99	4.10	4.17	4.24	4.30	4.34	4.37	4.41	4.44	4.46	4.49	4.51	4.53	4.54	4.56	4.57	4.58	4.59
50	3.78	3.95	4.06	4.14	4.20	4.26	4.30	4.34	4.37	4.40	4.42	4.45	4.47	4.49	4.50	4.51	4.53	4.54	4.55
60	3.76	3.92	4.03	4.12	4.17	4.23	4.27	4.31	4.34	4.37	4.39	4.42	4.44	4.46	4.47	4.48	4.50	4.52	4.53
100	3.71	3.86	3.98	4.06	4.11	4.17	4.21	4.25	4.29	4.32	4.35	4.37	4.38	4.40	4.42	4.44	4.45	4.47	4.48
120	3.70	3.85	3.97	4.05	4.10	4.16	4.20	4.24	4.28	4.31	4.34	4.36	4.37	4.39	4.41	4.43	4.44	4.46	4.47
∞	3.64	3.80	3.90	3.98	4.04	4.09	4.14	4.17	4.20	4.23	4.26	4.29	4.31	4.33	4.34	4.36	4.38	4.40	4.41

1) Values from DUNCAN, D. B., *Biometrics*, **11**, 1 (1955), reprinted by kind permission of the author, publishers and Virginia Polytechnic Institute. Interpolated values calculated by the editors of these *Scientific Tables*.

Upper Significance Limits of the Studentized Extreme Range[1]

Test quotient: $\frac{x_{N_1} - x_1}{s}$ where x_{N_1} is the highest and x_1 the lowest value of the sample of size N_1 to be tested; s = standard deviation with degrees of freedom $\nu = N_2 - 1$ of a sample of size N_2 *independent* of the sample of size N_1

$2\alpha = 0.05$

ν \ N_1	2	3	4	5	6	7	8	9	10	11	12	13	14	15	16	17	18	19	20
1	17.969	26.98	32.82	37.08	40.41	43.12	45.40	47.36	49.07	50.59	51.96	53.20	54.33	55.36	56.32	57.22	58.04	58.83	59.56
2	6.085	8.33	9.80	10.88	11.74	12.44	13.03	13.54	13.99	14.39	14.75	15.08	15.38	15.65	15.91	16.14	16.37	16.57	16.77
3	4.501	5.91	6.82	7.50	8.04	8.48	8.85	9.18	9.46	9.72	9.95	10.15	10.35	10.52	10.69	10.84	10.98	11.11	11.24
4	3.926	5.04	5.76	6.29	6.71	7.05	7.35	7.60	7.83	8.03	8.21	8.37	8.52	8.66	8.79	8.91	9.03	9.13	9.23
5	3.635	4.60	5.22	5.67	6.03	6.33	6.58	6.80	6.99	7.17	7.32	7.47	7.60	7.72	7.83	7.93	8.03	8.12	8.21
6	460	34	4.90	30	5.63	5.90	12	32	49	6.65	6.79	6.92	03	14	24	34	7.43	7.51	7.59
7	344	16	68	06	36	61	5.82	00	16	30	43	55	6.66	6.76	6.85	6.94	02	10	17
8	261	04	53	4.89	17	40	60	5.77	5.92	05	18	29	39	48	57	65	6.73	6.80	6.87
9	199	3.95	41	76	02	24	43	59	74	5.87	5.98	09	19	28	36	44	51	58	64
10	3.151	3.88	4.33	4.65	4.91	5.12	5.30	5.46	5.60	5.72	5.83	5.93	6.03	6.11	6.19	6.27	6.34	6.40	6.47
11	113	82	26	57	82	03	20	35	49	61	71	81	5.90	5.98	06	13	20	27	33
12	081	77	20	51	75	4.95	12	27	39	51	61	71	80	88	5.95	02	09	15	21
13	055	73	15	45	69	88	05	19	32	43	53	63	71	79	86	5.93	5.99	05	11
14	033	70	11	41	64	83	4.99	13	25	36	46	55	64	71	79	85	91	5.97	03
15	3.014	3.67	4.08	4.37	4.59	4.78	4.94	5.08	5.20	5.31	5.40	5.49	5.57	5.65	5.72	5.78	5.85	5.90	5.96
16	2.998	65	05	33	56	74	90	03	15	26	35	44	52	59	66	73	79	84	90
17	984	63	02	30	52	70	86	4.99	11	21	31	39	47	54	61	67	73	79	84
18	971	61	00	28	49	67	82	96	07	17	27	35	43	50	57	63	69	74	79
19	960	59	3.98	25	47	65	79	92	04	14	23	31	39	46	53	59	65	70	75
20	2.950	3.58	3.96	4.23	4.45	4.62	4.77	4.90	5.01	5.11	5.20	5.28	5.36	5.43	5.49	5.55	5.61	5.66	5.71
21	941	56	94	21	43	60	74	87	4.98	08	17	25	33	40	46	52	58	62	67
22	933	55	93	20	41	58	72	85	96	05	15	23	30	37	43	49	55	59	64
23	926	54	91	18	39	56	70	83	94	03	12	20	27	34	40	46	52	57	62
24	919	53	90	17	37	54	68	81	92	01	10	18	25	32	38	44	49	55	59
25	2.913	3.52	3.89	4.16	4.36	4.52	4.66	4.79	4.90	4.99	5.08	5.16	5.23	5.30	5.36	5.42	5.48	5.52	5.57
26	907	51	88	14	34	51	65	78	89	97	06	14	21	28	34	40	46	50	55
27	902	51	87	13	33	50	63	76	87	96	04	12	19	26	32	38	43	48	53
28	897	50	86	12	32	48	62	75	86	94	03	11	18	24	30	36	42	46	51
29	892	49	85	11	31	47	61	73	84	93	01	09	16	23	29	35	40	44	49
30	2.888	3.49	3.85	4.10	4.30	4.46	4.60	4.72	4.82	4.92	5.00	5.08	5.15	5.21	5.27	5.33	5.38	5.43	5.47
31	884	48	83	09	29	45	59	71	82	91	4.99	07	14	20	26	32	37	41	46
32	881	48	83	09	28	44	58	70	81	89	98	06	13	19	24	30	35	40	45
33	877	47	82	08	27	44	57	69	80	88	97	04	11	17	23	29	34	39	44
34	874	47	82	07	27	43	56	68	79	87	96	03	10	16	22	28	33	37	42
35	2.871	3.46	3.81	4.07	4.26	4.42	4.55	4.67	4.78	4.86	4.95	5.02	5.09	5.15	5.21	5.27	5.32	5.36	5.41
36	868	46	81	06	25	41	55	66	77	85	94	01	08	14	20	26	31	35	40
37	865	45	80	05	25	41	54	65	76	84	93	00	08	14	19	25	30	34	39
38	863	45	80	05	24	40	53	64	75	84	92	00	07	13	18	24	29	33	38
39	861	44	79	04	24	40	53	64	75	83	92	4.99	06	12	17	23	28	32	37
40	2.858	3.44	3.79	4.04	4.23	4.39	4.52	4.63	4.73	4.82	4.90	4.98	5.04	5.11	5.16	5.22	5.27	5.31	5.36
50	841	41	76	00	19	34	47	58	69	76	85	92	4.99	05	10	15	20	24	29
60	829	40	74	3.98	16	31	44	55	65	73	81	88	94	00	06	11	15	20	24
120	800	36	68	92	10	24	36	47	56	64	71	78	84	4.90	4.95	00	04	09	13
∞	772	31	63	86	03	17	29	39	47	55	62	68	74	80	85	4.89	4.93	4.97	01

$2\alpha = 0.01$

ν \ N_1	2	3	4	5	6	7	8	9	10	11	12	13	14	15	16	17	18	19	20
1	90.025	135.0	164.3	185.6	202.2	215.8	227.2	237.0	245.6	253.2	260.0	266.2	271.8	277.0	281.8	286.3	290.4	294.3	298.0
2	14.036	19.02	22.29	24.72	26.63	28.20	29.53	30.68	31.69	32.59	33.40	34.13	34.81	35.43	36.00	36.53	37.03	37.50	37.95
3	8.260	10.62	12.17	13.33	14.24	15.00	15.64	16.20	16.69	17.13	17.53	17.89	18.22	18.52	18.81	19.07	19.32	19.55	19.77
4	6.511	8.12	9.17	9.96	10.58	11.10	11.55	11.93	12.27	12.57	12.84	13.09	13.32	13.53	13.73	13.91	14.08	14.24	14.40
5	5.702	6.98	7.80	8.42	8.91	9.32	9.67	9.97	10.24	10.48	10.70	10.89	11.08	11.24	11.40	11.55	11.68	11.81	11.93
6	243	33	03	7.56	7.97	8.32	8.61	8.87	9.10	9.30	9.48	9.65	9.81	9.95	10.08	10.21	10.32	10.43	10.54
7	4.949	5.92	6.54	01	37	7.68	7.94	17	8.37	8.55	8.71	8.86	00	12	9.24	9.35	9.46	9.55	9.65
8	745	64	20	6.62	6.96	24	47	7.68	7.86	03	18	31	8.44	8.55	8.66	8.76	8.85	8.94	03
9	596	43	5.96	35	66	6.91	13	33	49	7.65	7.78	7.91	03	13	23	33	41	49	8.57
10	4.482	5.27	5.77	6.14	6.43	6.67	6.87	7.05	7.21	7.36	7.49	7.60	7.71	7.81	7.91	7.99	8.08	8.15	8.23
11	392	15	62	5.97	25	48	67	6.84	6.99	13	25	36	46	56	65	73	7.81	7.88	7.95
12	320	05	50	84	10	32	51	67	81	6.94	06	17	26	36	44	52	59	66	73
13	260	4.96	40	73	5.98	19	37	53	67	79	6.90	01	10	19	27	35	42	48	55
14	210	89	32	63	88	08	26	41	54	66	77	6.87	6.96	05	13	20	27	33	39
15	4.167	4.84	5.25	5.56	5.80	5.99	6.16	6.31	6.44	6.55	6.66	6.76	6.84	6.93	7.00	7.07	7.14	7.20	7.26
16	131	79	19	49	72	92	08	22	35	46	56	66	74	82	6.90	6.97	03	09	15
17	099	74	14	43	66	85	01	15	27	38	48	57	66	73	81	87	6.94	00	05
18	071	70	09	38	60	79	5.94	08	20	31	41	50	58	65	73	79	85	6.91	6.97
19	045	67	05	33	55	73	89	02	14	25	34	43	51	58	65	72	78	84	89
20	4.024	4.64	5.02	5.29	5.51	5.69	5.84	5.97	6.09	6.19	6.28	6.37	6.45	6.52	6.59	6.65	6.71	6.77	6.82
21	004	61	4.99	26	47	65	80	92	04	14	24	32	39	47	53	59	65	70	76
22	3.986	58	96	22	43	61	76	88	00	10	19	27	35	42	48	54	60	65	70
23	970	56	93	20	40	57	72	84	5.96	06	15	23	30	37	43	49	55	60	65
24	955	55	91	17	37	54	69	81	92	02	11	19	26	33	39	45	51	56	61
25	3.942	4.52	4.89	5.15	5.34	5.51	5.66	5.78	5.89	5.99	6.07	6.15	6.22	6.29	6.35	6.41	6.47	6.52	6.57
26	930	50	87	12	32	49	63	75	86	95	04	12	19	26	32	38	43	48	53
27	918	49	85	10	30	46	61	72	83	93	01	09	16	22	28	34	40	45	50
28	908	47	83	08	28	44	58	70	80	90	5.98	06	13	19	25	31	37	42	47
29	898	46	82	07	26	42	56	67	78	87	95	03	10	17	23	29	34	39	44
30	3.889	4.45	4.80	5.05	5.24	5.40	5.54	5.65	5.76	5.85	5.93	6.01	6.08	6.14	6.20	6.26	6.31	6.36	6.41
31	881	44	79	03	22	38	52	63	74	83	91	5.99	06	12	18	23	29	34	38
32	873	43	78	02	21	37	50	61	72	81	89	97	03	09	16	21	26	31	36
33	865	42	76	01	19	35	48	59	70	79	87	95	01	07	13	19	24	29	34
34	859	41	75	4.99	18	34	47	58	68	77	86	93	5.99	05	12	17	22	27	31
35	3.852	4.41	4.74	4.98	5.16	5.33	5.45	5.56	5.67	5.76	5.84	5.91	5.98	6.04	6.10	6.15	6.20	6.25	6.29
36	846	40	73	97	15	31	44	55	65	74	82	90	96	02	08	13	18	23	28
37	841	39	72	96	14	30	43	54	64	73	81	88	94	00	06	12	17	22	26
38	835	38	72	95	13	29	41	52	62	72	80	87	93	5.99	05	10	15	20	24
39	830	38	71	94	12	28	40	51	61	70	78	85	91	97	03	08	13	18	23
40	3.825	4.37	4.70	4.93	5.11	5.26	5.39	5.50	5.60	5.69	5.76	5.83	5.90	5.96	6.02	6.07	6.12	6.16	6.21
50	787	32	64	86	04	19	30	41	51	59	67	74	80	86	5.91	5.96	01	06	09
60	762	28	59	82	4.99	13	25	36	45	53	60	67	73	78	84	89	5.93	5.97	01
120	702	20	50	71	87	01	12	21	30	37	44	50	56	61	66	71	75	79	5.83
∞	643	12	40	60	76	4.88	4.99	08	16	23	29	35	40	45	49	54	57	61	65

1) Values from MAY, J.M., *Biometrika*, **39**, 192 (1952), with corrections from Table 29 in PEARSON and HARTLEY (Eds.), *Biometrika Tables for Statisticians*, vol. I, Cambridge University Press, 1954, page 176, and from PACHARES, J., *Biometrika*, **46**, 461 (1959). Reprinted by kind permission of the authors and publishers. Values in column 2 and interpolated values calculated by the editors of these *Scientific Tables*.

Upper significance limits of the standardized extreme range*

Test quotient: $\frac{x_N - \mu}{\sigma}$ or $\frac{\mu - x_1}{\sigma}$, where x_N is the highest and x_1 the lowest value of the sample

N \ α	0.10	0.05	0.025	0.01	0.005	0.001	0.0005
1	1.282	1.645	1.960	2.326	2.576	3.090	3.291
2	632	955	2.239	575	807	290	481
3	818	2.121	391	712	935	403	588
4	943	234	494	806	3.023	481	662
5	2.036	2.319	2.572	2.877	3.090	3.540	3.719
6	111	386	635	934	143	588	765
7	172	442	687	981	188	628	803
8	224	490	731	3.022	227	662	836
9	269	531	769	057	260	692	865
10	2.309	2.568	2.803	3.089	3.290	3.719	3.891
11	344	601	834	117	317	743	914
12	376	630	862	143	341	765	935
13	406	657	887	166	363	785	954
14	432	682	910	187	383	803	971
15	2.457	2.705	2.932	3.207	3.402	3.820	3.988
16	480	726	952	226	420	836	4.003
17	502	746	970	243	436	851	017
18	522	765	988	259	452	865	031
19	541	783	3.004	275	466	878	044
20	2.559	2.799	3.020	3.289	3.480	3.890	4.056
21	576	815	034	303	493	902	067
22	592	830	048	316	506	914	078
23	607	844	062	328	517	924	088
24	621	858	075	340	529	934	098
25	2.635	2.870	3.087	3.351	3.539	3.944	4.107
26	648	883	098	362	550	954	116
27	661	895	109	373	560	963	125
28	673	906	120	383	569	971	134
29	685	917	130	392	578	980	142
30	2.696	2.928	3.140	3.402	3.587	3.988	4.149
31	707	938	150	411	596	996	157
32	718	948	159	419	604	4.003	164
33	728	957	168	428	612	010	171
34	738	966	177	436	620	017	178
35	2.747	2.975	3.185	3.444	3.627	4.024	4.185
36	756	984	193	451	635	031	191
37	765	992	201	459	642	037	197
38	774	3.000	209	466	648	044	203
39	782	008	216	473	655	050	209

N \ α	0.10	0.05	0.025	0.01	0.005	0.001	0.0005
40	2.791	3.016	3.224	3.479	3.662	4.056	4.215
41	799	023	231	486	668	061	220
42	806	031	238	493	674	067	226
43	814	038	244	499	680	072	231
44	821	045	251	505	686	078	236
45	2.828	3.051	3.257	3.511	3.692	4.083	4.241
46	835	058	263	517	697	088	246
47	842	064	270	522	703	093	251
48	849	071	276	528	708	098	256
49	856	077	281	533	713	103	260
50	2.862	3.083	3.287	3.539	3.718	4.107	4.265
51	868	089	293	544	723	112	269
52	875	094	298	549	728	116	274
53	880	100	303	554	733	121	278
54	886	106	309	559	738	125	282
55	2.892	3.111	3.314	3.564	3.742	4.129	4.286
56	898	116	319	569	747	134	290
57	903	122	324	573	751	138	294
58	909	127	329	578	756	142	298
59	914	132	333	582	760	146	302
60	2.919	3.137	3.338	3.587	3.764	4.149	4.305
61	924	141	343	591	768	153	309
62	929	146	347	595	772	157	313
63	934	151	352	599	776	160	316
64	939	155	356	603	780	164	320
65	2.944	3.160	3.360	3.607	3.784	4.168	4.323
66	949	164	364	611	788	171	326
67	953	169	369	615	792	175	330
68	958	173	373	619	795	178	333
69	962	177	377	623	799	181	336
70	2.967	3.182	3.381	3.627	3.803	4.184	4.339
71	971	186	384	630	806	188	342
72	976	190	388	634	810	191	346
73	980	194	392	637	813	194	349
74	984	198	396	641	816	197	352
75	2.988	3.201	3.400	3.644	3.820	4.200	4.355
76	992	205	403	648	823	203	357
77	996	209	407	651	826	206	360
78	3.000	213	410	655	829	209	363
79	004	216	414	658	832	212	366

N \ α	0.10	0.05	0.025	0.01	0.005	0.001	0.0005
80	3.008	3.220	3.417	3.661	3.835	4.215	4.369
81	011	224	421	664	839	217	371
82	015	227	424	667	842	220	374
83	019	231	427	670	845	223	377
84	022	234	430	673	847	226	379
85	3.026	3.237	3.434	3.676	3.850	4.228	4.382
86	030	241	437	679	853	231	384
87	033	244	440	682	856	234	387
88	037	247	443	685	859	236	389
89	040	250	446	688	862	239	392
90	3.043	3.254	3.449	3.691	3.864	4.241	4.394
91	047	257	452	694	867	244	397
92	050	260	455	697	870	246	399
93	053	263	458	699	872	249	401
94	056	266	461	702	875	251	404
95	3.060	3.269	3.464	3.705	3.878	4.253	4.406
96	063	272	466	707	880	256	408
97	066	275	469	710	883	258	411
98	069	278	472	713	885	260	413
99	072	281	475	715	888	263	415
100	3.075	3.283	3.477	3.718	3.890	4.265	4.417
200	276	474	659	889	4.055	417	565
300	389	581	762	987	149	504	649
400	467	656	833	4.054	214	565	708
500	3.526	3.713	3.888	4.106	4.264	4.611	4.754
600	574	758	932	148	305	649	790
700	614	797	968	183	339	681	821
800	649	830	4.000	214	368	708	848
900	679	859	028	240	394	732	871
1000	3.706	3.884	4.053	4.264	4.417	4.754	4.892

Upper significance limits of the studentized extreme range[1]

Test quotients: $\frac{x_{N_1} - \bar{x}}{s}$ or $\frac{\bar{x} - x_1}{s}$ $(\nu < \infty)$ and $\frac{x_{N_1} - \bar{x}}{\sigma}$ or $\frac{\bar{x} - x_1}{\sigma}$ $(\nu = \infty)$

where x_{N_1} is the highest value, x_1 the lowest value and $\bar{x}$ the mean of the sample of size N_1 to be tested; s = standard deviation with degrees of freedom $\nu = N_2 - 1$ of a sample of size N_2 *independent* of the sample of size N_1

	α = 0.1							α = 0.05							α = 0.025						
ν \ N_1	3	4	5	6	7	8	9	3	4	5	6	7	8	9	3	4	5	6	7	8	9
10	1.68	1.92	2.09	2.23	2.33	2.42	2.50	2.01	2.27	2.46	2.60	2.72	2.81	2.89	2.34	2.63	2.83	2.98	3.10	3.20	3.29
11	1.66	1.90	2.07	2.20	2.30	2.39	2.46	1.98	2.24	2.42	2.56	2.67	2.76	2.84	2.30	2.58	2.77	2.92	3.03	3.13	3.22
12	1.65	1.88	2.05	2.17	2.28	2.36	2.44	1.96	2.21	2.39	2.52	2.63	2.72	2.80	2.27	2.54	2.73	2.87	2.98	3.08	3.16
13	1.63	1.86	2.03	2.16	2.26	2.34	2.41	1.94	2.19	2.36	2.50	2.60	2.69	2.76	2.24	2.51	2.69	2.83	2.94	3.03	3.11
14	1.62	1.85	2.01	2.14	2.24	2.32	2.39	1.93	2.17	2.34	2.47	2.57	2.66	2.74	2.22	2.48	2.66	2.79	2.90	2.99	3.07
15	1.61	1.84	2.00	2.12	2.22	2.31	2.38	1.91	2.15	2.32	2.45	2.55	2.64	2.71	2.20	2.45	2.63	2.76	2.87	2.96	3.04
16	1.61	1.83	1.99	2.11	2.21	2.29	2.36	1.90	2.14	2.31	2.43	2.53	2.62	2.69	2.18	2.43	2.61	2.74	2.84	2.93	3.01
17	1.60	1.82	1.98	2.10	2.20	2.28	2.35	1.89	2.13	2.29	2.42	2.52	2.60	2.67	2.17	2.42	2.59	2.72	2.82	2.91	2.98
18	1.59	1.82	1.97	2.09	2.19	2.27	2.34	1.88	2.11	2.28	2.40	2.50	2.58	2.65	2.15	2.40	2.57	2.70	2.80	2.89	2.96
19	1.59	1.81	1.96	2.08	2.18	2.26	2.33	1.87	2.11	2.27	2.39	2.49	2.57	2.64	2.14	2.39	2.56	2.68	2.78	2.87	2.94
20	1.58	1.80	1.96	2.08	2.17	2.25	2.32	1.87	2.10	2.26	2.38	2.47	2.56	2.63	2.13	2.37	2.54	2.67	2.77	2.85	2.92
24	1.57	1.78	1.94	2.05	2.15	2.22	2.29	1.84	2.07	2.23	2.34	2.44	2.52	2.58	2.10	2.34	2.50	2.62	2.72	2.80	2.87
30	1.55	1.77	1.92	2.03	2.12	2.20	2.26	1.82	2.04	2.20	2.31	2.40	2.48	2.54	2.07	2.30	2.46	2.58	2.67	2.75	2.81
40	1.54	1.75	1.90	2.01	2.10	2.17	2.23	1.80	2.02	2.17	2.28	2.37	2.44	2.50	2.04	2.27	2.42	2.53	2.62	2.70	2.76
60	1.52	1.73	1.87	1.98	2.07	2.14	2.20	1.78	1.99	2.14	2.25	2.33	2.41	2.47	2.01	2.23	2.38	2.49	2.58	2.65	2.71
120	1.51	1.71	1.85	1.96	2.05	2.12	2.18	1.76	1.96	2.11	2.22	2.30	2.37	2.43	1.98	2.20	2.34	2.45	2.53	2.60	2.66
∞	1.50	1.70	1.83	1.94	2.02	2.09	2.15	1.74	1.94	2.08	2.18	2.27	2.33	2.39	1.95	2.16	2.30	2.41	2.49	2.56	2.61

	α = 0.01							α = 0.005							α = 0.001						
ν \ N_1	3	4	5	6	7	8	9	3	4	5	6	7	8	9	3	4	5	6	7	8	9
10	2.78	3.10	3.32	3.48	3.62	3.73	3.82	3.12	3.46	3.70	3.87	4.02	4.14	4.24	4.0	4.3	4.6	4.8	5.0	5.2	5.3
11	2.72	3.02	3.24	3.39	3.52	3.63	3.72	3.04	3.37	3.59	3.76	3.90	4.01	4.11	3.8	4.2	4.5	4.7	4.8	5.0	5.1
12	2.67	2.96	3.17	3.32	3.45	3.55	3.64	2.98	3.29	3.51	3.67	3.80	3.91	4.00	3.7	4.1	4.3	4.5	4.7	4.8	4.9
13	2.63	2.92	3.12	3.27	3.38	3.48	3.57	2.93	3.23	3.44	3.60	3.72	3.83	3.92	3.6	4.0	4.2	4.4	4.5	4.6	4.7
14	2.60	2.88	3.07	3.22	3.33	3.43	3.51	2.88	3.18	3.38	3.54	3.66	3.76	3.85	3.5	3.9	4.1	4.3	4.4	4.5	4.6
15	2.57	2.84	3.03	3.17	3.29	3.38	3.46	2.84	3.13	3.33	3.48	3.60	3.70	3.78	3.5	3.8	4.0	4.2	4.3	4.4	4.5
16	2.54	2.81	3.00	3.14	3.25	3.34	3.42	2.81	3.10	3.29	3.44	3.56	3.65	3.73	3.4	3.7	4.0	4.1	4.3	4.4	4.5
17	2.52	2.79	2.97	3.11	3.22	3.31	3.38	2.78	3.07	3.26	3.40	3.52	3.61	3.68	3.4	3.7	3.9	4.1	4.2	4.3	4.4
18	2.50	2.77	2.95	3.08	3.19	3.28	3.35	2.76	3.04	3.23	3.37	3.48	3.57	3.64	3.3	3.6	3.9	4.0	4.1	4.2	4.3
19	2.49	2.75	2.93	3.06	3.16	3.25	3.33	2.74	3.01	3.20	3.34	3.45	3.54	3.61	3.3	3.6	3.8	4.0	4.1	4.2	4.3
20	2.47	2.73	2.91	3.04	3.14	3.23	3.30	2.72	2.99	3.17	3.31	3.42	3.51	3.58	3.3	3.6	3.8	3.9	4.0	4.1	4.2
24	2.42	2.68	2.84	2.97	3.07	3.16	3.23	2.66	2.92	3.10	3.23	3.33	3.42	3.49	3.2	3.5	3.7	3.8	3.9	4.0	4.1
30	2.38	2.62	2.79	2.91	3.01	3.08	3.15	2.60	2.86	3.03	3.15	3.25	3.33	3.40	3.1	3.4	3.6	3.7	3.8	3.9	4.0
40	2.34	2.57	2.73	2.85	2.94	3.02	3.08	2.55	2.79	2.96	3.08	3.17	3.25	3.31	3.0	3.3	3.5	3.6	3.7	3.7	3.8
60	2.29	2.52	2.68	2.79	2.88	2.95	3.01	2.50	2.73	2.89	3.01	3.10	3.17	3.23	2.9	3.2	3.4	3.5	3.6	3.6	3.7
120	2.25	2.48	2.62	2.73	2.82	2.89	2.95	2.45	2.67	2.83	2.94	3.02	3.09	3.15	2.9	3.1	3.3	3.4	3.5	3.5	3.6
∞	2.22	2.43	2.57	2.68	2.76	2.83	2.88	2.40	2.62	2.76	2.87	2.95	3.02	3.07	2.8	3.0	3.2	3.3	3.4	3.4	3.5

1) Values from NAIR, K.R., *Biometrika*, **39**, 189 (1952), corrected by DAVID, H.A., *Biometrika*, **43**, 449 (1956). Reprinted by kind permission of the authors and publishers.

Significance limits[1] for testing extreme values of a sample

$x_1 \leqq x_2 \leqq x_3 \ldots \leqq x_N$

N \ α	0.30	0.20	0.10	0.05	0.02	0.01	0.005	Test quotient
3	0.684	0.781	0.886	0.941	0.976	0.988	0.994	$\frac{x_N - x_{N-1}}{x_N - x_1}$
4	471	560	679	765	846	889	926	
5	373	451	557	642	729	780	821	
6	318	386	482	560	644	698	740	
7	281	344	434	507	586	637	680	
8	0.318	0.385	0.479	0.554	0.631	0.683	0.725	$\frac{x_N - x_{N-1}}{x_N - x_2}$
9	288	352	441	512	587	635	677	
10	265	325	409	477	551	597	639	
11	0.391	0.442	0.517	0.576	0.638	0.679	0.713	$\frac{x_N - x_{N-2}}{x_N - x_2}$
12	370	419	490	546	605	642	675	
13	351	399	467	521	578	615	649	
14	0.370	0.421	0.492	0.546	0.602	0.641	0.674	$\frac{x_N - x_{N-2}}{x_N - x_3}$
[illegible]	0.353	0.402	0.472	0.525	0.579	0.616	0.647	
[illegible]	338	386	454	507	559	595	624	
17	325	373	438	490	542	577	605	
18	314	361	424	475	527	561	589	
19	304	350	412	462	514	547	575	
20	0.295	0.340	0.401	0.450	0.502	0.535	0.562	
21	287	331	391	440	491	524	551	
22	280	323	382	430	481	514	541	
23	274	316	374	421	472	505	532	
24	268	310	367	413	464	497	524	
25	0.262	0.304	0.360	0.406	0.457	0.489	0.516	

Significance limits[2] for the difference between the mean of a sample and a hypothetical mean μ

Test quotient: $\frac{\bar{x} - \mu}{x_N - x_1}$; where x_N is the highest and x_1 the lowest value of a sample of size N

N \ 2α	0.10	0.05	0.02	0.01	0.002	0.001
2	3.157	6.353	15.910	31.828	159.16	318.31
3	0.885	1.304	2.111	3.008	6.77	9.58
4	0.529	0.717	1.023	1.316	2.29	2.85
5	0.388	0.507	0.685	0.843	1.32	1.58
6	0.312	0.399	0.523	0.628	0.92	1.07
7	0.263	0.333	0.429	0.507	0.71	0.82
8	0.230	0.288	0.366	0.429	0.59	0.67
9	0.205	0.255	0.322	0.374	0.50	0.57
10	0.186	0.230	0.288	0.333	0.44	0.50
11	0.170	0.210	0.262	0.302	0.40	0.44
12	0.158	0.194	0.241	0.277	0.36	0.40
13	0.147	0.181	0.224	0.256	0.33	0.37
14	0.138	0.170	0.209	0.239	0.31	0.34
15	0.131	0.160	0.197	0.224	0.29	0.32
16	0.124	0.151	0.186	0.212	0.27	0.30
17	0.118	0.144	0.177	0.201	0.26	0.28
18	0.113	0.137	0.168	0.191	0.24	0.26
19	0.108	0.131	0.161	0.182	0.23	0.25
20	0.104	0.126	0.154	0.175	0.22	0.24

Significance limits[2] for the difference between the means of two samples of the same size

Test quotient: $\frac{\bar{x}' - \bar{x}''}{x_N' - x_1' + x_N'' - x_1''}$; where x_N is the highest and x_1 the lowest value of the two samples of size $N' = N'' = N$

N \ 2α	0.10	0.05	0.02	0.01	0.002	0.001
2	1.161	1.714	2.777	3.958	8.91	12.62
3	0.487	0.636	0.857	1.047	1.64	2.09
4	0.322	0.407	0.524	0.619	0.87	1.00
5	0.247	0.307	0.386	0.448	0.61	0.68
6	0.203	0.250	0.311	0.357	0.47	0.52
7	0.174	0.213	0.263	0.300	0.39	0.43
8	0.153	0.187	0.230	0.261	0.34	0.37
9	0.137	0.167	0.205	0.232	0.30	0.32
10	0.125	0.152	0.186	0.210	0.27	0.29
11	0.117	0.140	0.170	0.192	0.24	0.26
12	0.107	0.130	0.158	0.178	0.22	0.24
13	0.101	0.122	0.147	0.166	0.21	0.22
14	0.095	0.114	0.138	0.156	0.20	0.21
15	0.090	0.108	0.131	0.147	0.18	0.20
16	0.085	0.103	0.124	0.139	0.17	0.19
17	0.081	0.098	0.118	0.132	0.17	0.18
18	0.078	0.094	0.113	0.126	0.16	0.17
19	0.075	0.090	0.108	0.121	0.15	0.16
20	0.072	0.086	0.104	0.116	0.15	0.16

Significance limits for the difference between the mean of a sample and a hypothetical mean μ

$\bar{x}$ does not need to be calculated in these tests. The values x are so arranged that $x_1 \leqq x_2 \leqq x_3 \ldots \leqq x_N$. Test B is also suitable for symmetrical distributions which are not normal distributions

A[3] Test quotient: $\frac{x_N + x_1 - 2\mu}{x_N - x_1}$

N \ 2α	0.10	0.05	0.02	0.01
2	6.32	12.70	31.82	63.66
3	1.80	2.60	4.22	6.04
4	1.11	1.48	2.08	2.74
5	0.85	1.04	1.42	1.70
6	0.70	0.86	1.12	1.32
7	0.60	0.75	0.95	1.10
8	0.53	0.66	0.84	0.95
9	0.48	0.60	0.76	0.85
10	0.45	0.55	0.70	0.78

B[4]

N	$\bar{x} \neq \mu\,(2\alpha)$, when — either $\bar{x} < \mu\,(\alpha)$, when	or $\bar{x} > \mu\,(\alpha)$, when	2α
4	$1.055\,x_4 - 0.055\,x_1 < \mu$	$1.055\,x_1 - 0.055\,x_4 > \mu$	0.10
5	$0.63\,x_5 + 0.37\,x_4 < \mu$	$0.63\,x_1 + 0.37\,x_2 > \mu$	0.10
	$1.02\,x_5 - 0.02\,x_1 < \mu$	$1.02\,x_1 - 0.02\,x_5 > \mu$	0.05
6	$0.63\,x_6 + 0.37\,x_5 < \mu$	$0.63\,x_1 + 0.37\,x_2 > \mu$	0.05
	$1.06\,x_6 - 0.06\,x_1 < \mu$	$1.06\,x_1 - 0.06\,x_6 > \mu$	0.02
7	$0.785\,x_7 + 0.215\,x_6 < \mu$	$0.785\,x_1 + 0.215\,x_2 > \mu$	0.02
	$1.05\,x_7 - 0.05\,x_1 < \mu$	$1.05\,x_1 - 0.05\,x_7 > \mu$	0.01
8	the *greater* of the values x_7 or $(0.5\,x_8 + 0.28\,x_6 + 0.22\,x_7) < \mu$	the *smaller* of the values x_2 or $(0.5\,x_1 + 0.28\,x_3 + 0.22\,x_2) > \mu$	≅0.02
	$0.785\,x_8 + 0.215\,x_7 < \mu$	$0.785\,x_1 + 0.215\,x_2 > \mu$	0.01
9	the *greater* of the values x_8 or $0.5\,(x_5 + x_9) < \mu$	the *smaller* of the values x_2 or $0.5\,(x_1 + x_5) > \mu$	0.02
	the *greater* of the values x_8 or $(0.5\,x_9 + 0.28\,x_7 + 0.22\,x_8) < \mu$	the *smaller* of the values x_2 or $(0.5\,x_1 + 0.28\,x_3 + 0.22\,x_2) > \mu$	≅0.01
10	the *greater* of the values x_9 or $0.5\,(x_6 + x_{10}) < \mu$	the *smaller* of the values x_2 or $0.5\,(x_1 + x_5) > \mu$	0.01
11	the *greater* of the values x_7 or $0.5\,(x_4 + x_{11}) < \mu$	the *smaller* of the values x_5 or $0.5\,(x_1 + x_8) > \mu$	≅0.10
	the *greater* of the values x_9 or $0.5\,(x_7 + x_{11}) < \mu$	the *smaller* of the values x_3 or $0.5\,(x_1 + x_5) > \mu$	≅0.01
12	the *greater* of the values x_9 or $0.5\,(x_6 + x_{12}) < \mu$	the *smaller* of the values x_4 or $0.5\,(x_1 + x_7) > \mu$	0.02
13	the *greater* of the values x_{10} or $0.5\,(x_7 + x_{13}) < \mu$	the *smaller* of the values x_4 or $0.5\,(x_1 + x_7) > \mu$	0.01
14	the *greater* of the values x_{10} or $0.5\,(x_6 + x_{14}) < \mu$	the *smaller* of the values x_5 or $0.5\,(x_1 + x_9) > \mu$	0.02
15	the *greater* of the values x_{11} or $0.5\,(x_7 + x_{15}) < \mu$	the *smaller* of the values x_5 or $0.5\,(x_1 + x_9) > \mu$	0.01

1) Values from DIXON, W. J., *Biometrics*, **9**, 74 (1953). *2)* Values from LORD, E., *Biometrika*, **34**, 41 (1947), but recalculated from the simplified test quotient given. *3)* Values from WALSH, J. E., *Ann. math. Statist.*, **20**, 257 (1949). *4)* Values from WALSH, J. E., *loc. cit.*, and from WALSH, J. E., *J. Amer. statist. Ass.*, **44**, 343 (1949). All values reprinted by kind permission of the authors and publishers.

The percentages correspond to 100 times the area under the normal distribution curve between minus infinity and c
The probits are the normal deviates c increased by 5

%→ ↓	0.0	0.1	0.2	0.3	0.4	0.5	0.6	0.7	0.8	0.9	1	2	3	4	5
						Probits									
0	...	1.9098	2.1218	2.2522	2.3479	2.4242	2.4879	2.5427	2.5911	2.6344					
1	2.6737	2.7096	2.7429	2.7738	2.8027	2.8299	2.8556	2.8799	2.9031	2.9251					
2	2.9463	2.9665	2.9859	3.0046	3.0226	3.0400	3.0569	3.0732	3.0890	3.1043					
3	3.1192	3.1337	3.1478	3.1616	3.1750	3.1881	3.2009	3.2134	3.2256	3.2376					
4	3.2493	3.2608	3.2721	3.2831	3.2940	3.3046	3.3151	3.3253	3.3354	3.3454					
5	3.3551	3.3648	3.3742	3.3836	3.3928	3.4018	3.4107	3.4195	3.4282	3.4368	9	18	27	36	45
6	3.4452	3.4536	3.4618	3.4699	3.4780	3.4859	3.4937	3.5015	3.5091	3.5167	8	16	24	32	40
7	3.5242	3.5316	3.5389	3.5462	3.5534	3.5605	3.5675	3.5745	3.5813	3.5882	7	14	21	28	36
8	3.5949	3.6016	3.6083	3.6148	3.6213	3.6278	3.6342	3.6405	3.6468	3.6531	6	13	19	26	32
9	3.6592	3.6654	3.6715	3.6775	3.6835	3.6894	3.6953	3.7012	3.7070	3.7127	6	12	18	24	30
10	3.7184	3.7241	3.7298	3.7354	3.7409	3.7464	3.7519	3.7574	3.7628	3.7681	6	11	17	22	28
11	3.7735	3.7788	3.7840	3.7893	3.7945	3.7996	3.8048	3.8099	3.8150	3.8200	5	10	16	21	26
12	3.8250	3.8300	3.8350	3.8399	3.8448	3.8497	3.8545	3.8593	3.8641	3.8689	5	10	15	20	24
13	3.8736	3.8783	3.8830	3.8877	3.8923	3.8969	3.9015	3.9061	3.9107	3.9152	5	9	14	18	23
14	3.9197	3.9242	3.9286	3.9331	3.9375	3.9419	3.9463	3.9506	3.9550	3.9593	4	9	13	18	22
15	3.9636	3.9678	3.9721	3.9763	3.9806	3.9848	3.9890	3.9931	3.9973	4.0014	4	8	13	17	21
16	4.0055	4.0096	4.0137	4.0178	4.0218	4.0259	4.0299	4.0339	4.0379	4.0419	4	8	12	16	20
17	4.0458	4.0498	4.0537	4.0576	4.0615	4.0654	4.0693	4.0731	4.0770	4.0808	4	8	12	16	19
18	4.0846	4.0884	4.0922	4.0960	4.0998	4.1035	4.1073	4.1110	4.1147	4.1184	4	8	11	15	[illegible]
19	4.1221	4.1258	4.1295	4.1331	4.1367	4.1404	4.1440	4.1476	4.1512	4.1548	4	7	11	15	[illegible]
20	4.1584	4.1619	4.1655	4.1690	4.1726	4.1761	4.1796	4.1831	4.1866	4.1901	4	7	11	14	[illegible]
21	4.1936	4.1970	4.2005	4.2039	4.2074	4.2108	4.2142	4.2176	4.2210	4.2244	3	7	10	14	[illegible]
22	4.2278	4.2312	4.2345	4.2379	4.2412	4.2446	4.2479	4.2512	4.2546	4.2579	3	7	10	13	[illegible]
23	4.2612	4.2644	4.2677	4.2710	4.2743	4.2775	4.2808	4.2840	4.2872	4.2905	3	7	10	13	16
24	4.2937	4.2969	4.3001	4.3033	4.3065	4.3097	4.3129	4.3160	4.3192	4.3224	3	6	10	13	16
25	4.3255	4.3287	4.3318	4.3349	4.3380	4.3412	4.3443	4.3474	4.3505	4.3536	3	6	9	12	16
26	4.3567	4.3597	4.3628	4.3659	4.3689	4.3720	4.3750	4.3781	4.3811	4.3842	3	6	9	12	15
27	4.3872	4.3902	4.3932	4.3962	4.3992	4.4022	4.4052	4.4082	4.4112	4.4142	3	6	9	12	15
28	4.4172	4.4201	4.4231	4.4260	4.4290	4.4319	4.4349	4.4378	4.4408	4.4437	3	6	9	12	15
29	4.4466	4.4495	4.4524	4.4554	4.4583	4.4612	4.4641	4.4670	4.4698	4.4727	3	6	9	12	14
30	4.4756	4.4785	4.4813	4.4842	4.4871	4.4899	4.4928	4.4956	4.4985	4.5013	3	6	9	11	14
31	4.5041	4.5070	4.5098	4.5126	4.5155	4.5183	4.5211	4.5239	4.5267	4.5295	3	6	8	11	14
32	4.5323	4.5351	4.5379	4.5407	4.5435	4.5462	4.5490	4.5518	4.5546	4.5573	3	6	8	11	14
33	4.5601	4.5628	4.5656	4.5684	4.5711	4.5739	4.5766	4.5793	4.5821	4.5848	3	5	8	11	14
34	4.5875	4.5903	4.5930	4.5957	4.5984	4.6011	4.6039	4.6066	4.6093	4.6120	3	5	8	11	14
35	4.6147	4.6174	4.6201	4.6228	4.6255	4.6281	4.6308	4.6335	4.6362	4.6389	3	5	8	11	13
36	4.6415	4.6442	4.6469	4.6495	4.6522	4.6549	4.6575	4.6602	4.6628	4.6655	3	5	8	11	13
37	4.6681	4.6708	4.6734	4.6761	4.6787	4.6814	4.6840	4.6866	4.6893	4.6919	3	5	8	11	13
38	4.6945	4.6971	4.6998	4.7024	4.7050	4.7076	4.7102	4.7129	4.7155	4.7181	3	5	8	10	13
39	4.7207	4.7233	4.7259	4.7285	4.7311	4.7337	4.7363	4.7389	4.7415	4.7441	3	5	8	10	13
40	4.7467	4.7492	4.7518	4.7544	4.7570	4.7596	4.7622	4.7647	4.7673	4.7699	3	5	8	10	13
41	4.7725	4.7750	4.7776	4.7802	4.7827	4.7853	4.7879	4.7904	4.7930	4.7955	3	5	8	10	13
42	4.7981	4.8007	4.8032	4.8058	4.8083	4.8109	4.8134	4.8160	4.8185	4.8211	3	5	8	10	13
43	4.8236	4.8262	4.8287	4.8313	4.8338	4.8363	4.8389	4.8414	4.8440	4.8465	3	5	8	10	13
44	4.8490	4.8516	4.8541	4.8566	4.8592	4.8617	4.8642	4.8668	4.8693	4.8718	3	5	8	10	13
45	4.8743	4.8769	4.8794	4.8819	4.8844	4.8870	4.8895	4.8920	4.8945	4.8970	3	5	8	10	13
46	4.8996	4.9021	4.9046	4.9071	4.9096	4.9122	4.9147	4.9172	4.9197	4.9222	3	5	8	10	13
47	4.9247	4.9272	4.9298	4.9323	4.9348	4.9373	4.9398	4.9423	4.9448	4.9473	3	5	8	10	13
48	4.9498	4.9524	4.9549	4.9574	4.9599	4.9624	4.9649	4.9674	4.9699	4.9724	3	5	8	10	13
49	4.9749	4.9774	4.9799	4.9825	4.9850	4.9875	4.9900	4.9925	4.9950	4.9975	3	5	8	10	13
50	5.0000	5.0025	5.0050	5.0075	5.0100	5.0125	5.0150	5.0175	5.0201	5.0226	3	5	8	10	13
51	5.0251	5.0276	5.0301	5.0326	5.0351	5.0376	5.0401	5.0426	5.0451	5.0476	3	5	8	10	13
52	5.0502	5.0527	5.0552	5.0577	5.0602	5.0627	5.0652	5.0677	5.0702	5.0728	3	5	8	10	[illegible]
53	5.0753	5.0778	5.0803	5.0828	5.0853	5.0878	5.0904	5.0929	5.0954	5.0979	3	5	8	10	[illegible]
54	5.1004	5.1030	5.1055	5.1080	5.1105	5.1130	5.1156	5.1181	5.1206	5.1231	3	5	8	10	13
55	5.1257	5.1282	5.1307	5.1332	5.1358	5.1383	5.1408	5.1434	5.1459	5.1484	3	5	8	10	13
56	5.1510	5.1535	5.1560	5.1586	5.1611	5.1637	5.1662	5.1687	5.1713	5.1738	3	5	8	10	13
57	5.1764	5.1789	5.1815	5.1840	5.1866	5.1891	5.1917	5.1942	5.1968	5.1993	3	5	8	10	13
58	5.2019	5.2045	5.2070	5.2096	5.2121	5.2147	5.2173	5.2198	5.2224	5.2250	3	5	8	10	13
59	5.2275	5.2301	5.2327	5.2353	5.2378	5.2404	5.2430	5.2456	5.2482	5.2508	3	5	8	10	13
60	5.2533	5.2559	5.2585	5.2611	5.2637	5.2663	5.2689	5.2715	5.2741	5.2767	3	5	8	10	13
61	5.2793	5.2819	5.2845	5.2871	5.2898	5.2924	5.2950	5.2976	5.3002	5.3029	3	5	8	10	13
62	5.3055	5.3081	5.3107	5.3134	5.3160	5.3186	5.3213	5.3239	5.3266	5.3292	3	5	8	11	13
63	5.3319	5.3345	5.3372	5.3398	5.3425	5.3451	5.3478	5.3505	5.3531	5.3558	3	5	8	11	13
64	5.3585	5.3611	5.3638	5.3665	5.3692	5.3719	5.3745	5.3772	5.3799	5.3826	3	5	8	11	13
65	5.3853	5.3880	5.3907	5.3934	5.3961	5.3989	5.4016	5.4043	5.4070	5.4097	3	5	8	11	14
66	5.4125	5.4152	5.4179	5.4207	5.4234	5.4261	5.4289	5.4316	5.4344	5.4372	3	5	8	11	14
67	5.4399	5.4427	5.4454	5.4482	5.4510	5.4538	5.4565	5.4593	5.4621	5.4649	3	6	8	11	14
68	5.4677	5.4705	5.4733	5.4761	5.4789	5.4817	5.4845	5.4874	5.4902	5.4930	3	6	8	11	14
69	5.4959	5.4987	5.5015	5.5044	5.5072	5.5101	5.5129	5.5158	5.5187	5.5215	3	6	9	11	14
70	5.5244	5.5273	5.5302	5.5330	5.5359	5.5388	5.5417	5.5446	5.5476	5.5505	3	6	9	12	14
71	5.5534	5.5563	5.5592	5.5622	5.5651	5.5681	5.5710	5.5740	5.5769	5.5799	3	6	9	12	15
72	5.5828	5.5858	5.5888	5.5918	5.5948	5.5978	5.6008	5.6038	5.6068	5.6098	3	6	9	12	15
73	5.6128	5.6158	5.6189	5.6219	5.6250	5.6280	5.6311	5.6341	5.6372	5.6403	3	6	9	12	15
74	5.6433	5.6464	5.6495	5.6526	5.6557	5.6588	5.6620	5.6651	5.6682	5.6713	3	6	9	12	16
75	5.6745	5.6776	5.6808	5.6840	5.6871	5.6903	5.6935	5.6967	5.6999	5.7031	3	6	10	13	16
76	5.7063	5.7095	5.7128	5.7160	5.7192	5.7225	5.7257	5.7290	5.7323	5.7356	3	7	10	13	16
77	5.7388	5.7421	5.7454	5.7488	5.7521	5.7554	5.7588	5.7621	5.7655	5.7688	3	7	10	13	17
78	5.7722	5.7756	5.7790	5.7824	5.7858	5.7892	5.7926	5.7961	5.7995	5.8030	3	7	10	14	17
79	5.8064	5.8099	5.8134	5.8169	5.8204	5.8239	5.8274	5.8310	5.8345	5.8381	4	7	11	14	18
80	5.8416	5.8452	5.8488	5.8524	5.8560	5.8596	5.8633	5.8669	5.8705	5.8742	4	7	11	14	18
81	5.8779	5.8816	5.8853	5.8890	5.8927	5.8965	5.9002	5.9040	5.9078	5.9116	4	7	11	15	19
82	5.9154	5.9192	5.9230	5.9269	5.9307	5.9346	5.9385	5.9424	5.9463	5.9502	4	8	12	15	19
83	5.9542	5.9581	5.9621	5.9661	5.9701	5.9741	5.9782	5.9822	5.9863	5.9904	4	8	12	16	20
84	5.9945	5.9986	6.0027	6.0069	6.0110	6.0152	6.0194	6.0237	6.0279	6.0322	4	8	13	17	21
85	6.0364	6.0407	6.0450	6.0494	6.0537	6.0581	6.0625	6.0669	6.0714	6.0758	4	9	13	18	22
86	6.0803	6.0848	6.0893	6.0939	6.0985	6.1031	6.1077	6.1123	6.1170	6.1217	5	9	14	18	23
87	6.1264	6.1311	6.1359	6.1407	6.1455	6.1503	6.1552	6.1601	6.1650	6.1700	5	10	15	19	24
88	6.1750	6.1800	6.1850	6.1901	6.1952	6.2004	6.2055	6.2107	6.2160	6.2212	5	10	15	21	26
89	6.2265	6.2319	6.2372	6.2426	6.2481	6.2536	6.2591	6.2646	6.2702	6.2759	5	11	16	22	27
90	6.2816	6.2873	6.2930	6.2988	6.3047	6.3106	6.3165	6.3225	6.3285	6.3346	6	12	18	24	29
91	6.3408	6.3469	6.3532	6.3595	6.3658	6.3722	6.3787	6.3852	6.3917	6.3984	6	13	19	26	32
92	6.4051	6.4118	6.4187	6.4255	6.4325	6.4395	6.4466	6.4538	6.4611	6.4684	7	14	21	28	35
93	6.4758	6.4833	6.4909	6.4985	6.5063	6.5141	6.5220	6.5301	6.5382	6.5464	8	16	24	31	39
94	6.5548	6.5632	6.5718	6.5805	6.5893	6.5982	6.6072	6.6164	6.6258	6.6352	9	18	27	36	45

1) Values from FISHER and YATES, *Statistical Tables for Biological, Agricultural and Medical Research,* 4th ed., Oliver and Boyd, Edinburgh, 1953, page 60. Reprinted by kind permission of the authors and publishers.

(continuation of table on page 54)

% → ↓	0.0	0.1	0.2	0.3	0.4	0.5	0.6	0.7	0.8	0.9	1	2	3	4	5
	Probits														
95	6.6449	6.6546	6.6646	6.6747	6.6849	6.6954	6.7060	6.7169	6.7279	6.7392					
	97	100	101	102	105	106	109	110	113	115					
96	6.7507	6.7624	6.7744	6.7866	6.7991	6.8119	6.8250	6.8384	6.8522	6.8663					
	117	120	122	125	128	131	134	138	141	145					
97	6.8808	6.8957	6.9110	6.9268	6.9431	6.9600	6.9774	6.9954	7.0141	7.0335					
	149	153	158	163	169	174	180	187	194	202					
	0.00	0.01	0.02	0.03	0.04	0.05	0.06	0.07	0.08	0.09					
98.0	7.0537	7.0558	7.0579	7.0600	7.0621	7.0642	7.0663	7.0684	7.0706	7.0727	2	4	6	8	11
98.1	7.0749	7.0770	7.0792	7.0814	7.0836	7.0858	7.0880	7.0902	7.0924	7.0947	2	4	7	9	11
98.2	7.0969	7.0992	7.1015	7.1038	7.1061	7.1084	7.1107	7.1130	7.1154	7.1177	2	5	7	9	12
98.3	7.1201	7.1224	7.1248	7.1272	7.1297	7.1321	7.1345	7.1370	7.1394	7.1419	2	5	7	10	12
98.4	7.1444	7.1469	7.1494	7.1520	7.1545	7.1571	7.1596	7.1622	7.1648	7.1675	3	5	8	10	13
98.5	7.1701	7.1727	7.1754	7.1781	7.1808	7.1835	7.1862	7.1890	7.1917	7.1945	3	5	8	11	14
98.6	7.1973	7.2001	7.2029	7.2058	7.2086	7.2115	7.2144	7.2173	7.2203	7.2232	3	6	9	12	14
98.7	7.2262	7.2292	7.2322	7.2353	7.2383	7.2414	7.2445	7.2476	7.2508	7.2539	3	6	9	12	15
98.8	7.2571	7.2603	7.2636	7.2668	7.2701	7.2734	7.2768	7.2801	7.2835	7.2869	3	7	10	13	17
98.9	7.2904	7.2938	7.2973	7.3009	7.3044	7.3080	7.3116	7.3152	7.3189	7.3226	4	7	11	14	18
99.0	7.3263	7.3301	7.3339	7.3378	7.3416	7.3455	7.3495	7.3535	7.3575	7.3615	4	8	12	16	20
99.1	7.3656	7.3698	7.3739	7.3781	7.3824	7.3867	7.3911	7.3954	7.3999	7.4044	4	9	13	17	22
99.2	7.4089	7.4135	7.4181	7.4228	7.4276	7.4324	7.4372	7.4422	7.4471	7.4522	5	10	14	19	24
99.3	7.4573	7.4624	7.4677	7.4730	7.4783	7.4838	7.4893	7.4949	7.5006	7.5063	5	11	16	22	27
99.4	7.5121	7.5181	7.5241	7.5302	7.5364	7.5427	7.5491	7.5556	7.5622	7.5690	6	13	19	25	32
99.5	7.5758	7.5828	7.5899	7.5972	7.6045	7.6121	7.6197	7.6276	7.6356	7.6437					
99.6	7.6521	7.6606	7.6693	7.6783	7.6874	7.6968	7.7065	7.7164	7.7266	7.7370					
99.7	7.7478	7.7589	7.7703	7.7822	7.7944	7.8070	7.8202	7.8338	7.8480	7.8627					
99.8	7.8782	7.8943	7.9112	7.9290	7.9478	7.9677	7.9889	8.0115	8.0357	8.0618					
99.9	8.0902	8.1214	8.1559	8.1947	8.2389	8.2905	8.3528	8.4316	8.5401	8.7190					

Weighting coefficients and probit values to be used for final adjustments

Expected probit Y	Minimum working probit $Y-P/Z$	Range $1/Z$	Maximum working probit $Y+Q/Z$	Weighting coefficient Z^2/PQ	Expected probit Y	Minimum working probit $Y-P/Z$	Range $1/Z$	Maximum working probit $Y+Q/Z$	Weighting coefficient Z^2/PQ
					5.0	3.7467	2.5066	6.2533	0.63662
1.1	0.8579	5034	5035	0.00082	5.1	3.7401	2.5192	6.2593	63431
1.2	0.9522	3425	3426	00118	5.2	3.7186	2.5573	6.2759	62742
1.3	1.0462	2354	2355	00167	5.3	3.6798	2.6220	6.3018	61609
1.4	1.1400	1634	1635	00235	5.4	3.6203	2.7154	6.3357	60052
1.5	1.2335	1146	1147	0.00327	**5.5**	3.5360	2.8404	6.3764	0.58099
1.6	1.3266	811.5	812.8	00451	5.6	3.4220	3.0010	6.4230	55788
1.7	1.4194	580.5	581.9	00614	5.7	3.2724	3.2025	6.4749	53159
1.8	1.5118	419.4	420.9	00828	5.8	3.0794	3.4519	6.5313	50260
1.9	1.6038	306.1	307.7	01104	5.9	2.8335	3.7582	6.5917	47144
2.0	1.6954	225.6	227.3	0.01457	**6.0**	2.5230	4.1327	6.6557	0.43863
2.1	1.7866	168.00	169.79	01903	6.1	2.1324	4.5903	6.7227	40474
2.2	1.8772	126.34	128.22	02459	6.2	1.6429	5.1497	6.7926	37031
2.3	1.9673	95.96	97.93	03143	6.3	1.0295	5.8354	6.8649	33589
2.4	2.0568	73.62	75.68	03977	6.4	0.2606	6.6788	6.9394	30199
2.5	2.1457	57.05	59.20	0.04979	**6.5**	−0.705	7.721	7.0158	0.26907
2.6	2.2340	44.654	46.888	06169	6.6	−1.921	9.015	7.0940	23753
2.7	2.3214	35.302	37.623	07563	6.7	−3.459	10.633	7.1739	20774
2.8	2.4081	28.189	30.597	09179	6.8	−5.411	12.666	7.2551	17994
2.9	2.4938	22.736	25.230	11026	6.9	−7.902	15.240	7.3376	15436
3.0	2.5786	18.522	21.101	0.13112	**7.0**	−11.101	18.522	7.4214	0.13112
3.1	2.6624	15.240	17.902	15436	7.1	−15.230	22.736	7.5062	11026
3.2	2.7449	12.666	15.411	17994	7.2	−20.597	28.189	7.5919	09179
3.3	2.8261	10.633	13.459	20774	7.3	−27.623	35.302	7.6786	07564
3.4	2.9060	9.015	11.921	23753	7.4	−36.888	44.654	7.7661	06168
3.5	2.9842	7.721	10.705	0.26907	**7.5**	−49.20	57.05	7.8543	0.04979
3.6	3.0606	6.6788	9.7394	30199	7.6	−65.68	73.62	7.9432	03977
3.7	3.1351	5.8354	8.9705	33589	7.7	−87.93	95.96	8.0327	03143
3.8	3.2074	5.1497	8.3571	37031	7.8	−118.22	126.34	8.1228	02458
3.9	3.2773	4.5903	7.8676	40474	7.9	−159.79	168.00	8.2134	01903
4.0	3.3443	4.1327	7.4770	0.43863	**8.0**	−217.3	225.6	8.3046	0.01457
4.1	3.4083	3.7582	7.1665	47144	8.1	−297.7	306.1	8.3962	01104
4.2	3.4687	3.4519	6.9206	50260	8.2	−410.9	419.4	8.4882	00828
4.3	3.5251	3.2025	6.7276	53159	8.3	−571.9	580.5	8.5806	00614
4.4	3.5770	3.0010	6.5780	55788	8.4	−802.8	811.5	8.6734	00451
4.5	3.6236	2.8404	6.4640	0.58099	**8.5**	−1137	1146	8.7666	0.00327
4.6	3.6643	2.7154	6.3797	60052	8.6	−1625	1634	8.8600	00235
4.7	3.6982	2.6220	6.3202	61609	8.7	−2345	2354	8.9538	00167
4.8	3.7241	2.5573	6.2814	62741	8.8	−3416	3425	9.0478	00118
4.9	3.7407	2.5192	6.2599	63431	8.9	−5025	5034	9.1421	00082

1) Values from FISHER and YATES, *Statistical Tables for Biological, Agricultural and Medical Research,* 4th ed., Oliver and Boyd, Edinburgh, 1953, pages 60–63. Reprinted by kind permission of the authors and publishers.

Logits and Antilogits[1]

Numbers in *italics* are negative values

p	0.000	0.001	0.002	0.003	0.004	0.005	0.006	0.007	0.008	0.009
0.00	—	*6.90675*	*6.21261*	*5.80614*	*5.51745*	*5.29330*	*5.10998*	*4.95482*	*4.82028*	*4.70149*
0.01	*4.59512*	*4.49880*	*4.41078*	*4.32972*	*4.25460*	*4.18459*	*4.11904*	*4.05740*	*3.99922*	*3.94413*
0.02	*3.89182*	*3.84201*	*3.79447*	*3.74899*	*3.70541*	*3.66356*	*3.62331*	*3.58455*	*3.54715*	*3.51103*
0.03	*3.47610*	*3.44228*	*3.40950*	*3.37769*	*3.34680*	*3.31678*	*3.28757*	*3.25914*	*3.23143*	*3.20441*
0.04	*3.17805*	*3.15232*	*3.12718*	*3.10260*	*3.07857*	*3.05505*	*3.03202*	*3.00947*	*2.98736*	*2.96569*
0.05	*2.94444*	*2.92358*	*2.90311*	*2.88301*	*2.86326*	*2.84385*	*2.82477*	*2.80601*	*2.78756*	*2.76941*
0.06	*2.75154*	*2.73394*	*2.71662*	*2.69955*	*2.68273*	*2.66616*	*2.64982*	*2.63371*	*2.61783*	*2.60215*
0.07	*2.58669*	*2.57143*	*2.55637*	*2.54149*	*2.52681*	*2.51231*	*2.49798*	*2.48382*	*2.46984*	*2.45601*
0.08	*2.44235*	*2.42884*	*2.41548*	*2.40227*	*2.38920*	*2.37627*	*2.36348*	*2.35083*	*2.33830*	*2.32591*
0.09	*2.31363*	*2.30149*	*2.28946*	*2.27754*	*2.26574*	*2.25406*	*2.24248*	*2.23101*	*2.21965*	*2.20839*
0.10	*2.19722*	*2.18616*	*2.17520*	*2.16433*	*2.15355*	*2.14286*	*2.13227*	*2.12176*	*2.11133*	*2.10100*
0.11	*2.09074*	*2.08057*	*2.07047*	*2.06046*	*2.05052*	*2.04066*	*2.03087*	*2.02115*	*2.01151*	*2.00193*
0.12	*1.99243*	*1.98299*	*1.97363*	*1.96432*	*1.95508*	*1.94591*	*1.93680*	*1.92775*	*1.91876*	*1.90983*
0.13	*1.90096*	*1.89215*	*1.88339*	*1.87469*	*1.86605*	*1.85745*	*1.84892*	*1.84043*	*1.83200*	*1.82362*
0.14	*1.81529*	*1.80701*	*1.79878*	*1.79059*	*1.78246*	*1.77437*	*1.76632*	*1.75833*	*1.75037*	*1.74247*
0.15	*1.73460*	*1.72678*	*1.71900*	*1.71126*	*1.70357*	*1.69591*	*1.68830*	*1.68072*	*1.67318*	*1.66569*
0.16	*1.65823*	*1.65081*	*1.64342*	*1.63607*	*1.62876*	*1.62149*	*1.61425*	*1.60704*	*1.59987*	*1.59273*
0.17	*1.58563*	*1.57856*	*1.57152*	*1.56451*	*1.55754*	*1.55060*	*1.54369*	*1.53681*	*1.52996*	*1.52314*
0.18	*1.51635*	*1.50959*	*1.50286*	*1.49615*	*1.48948*	*1.48283*	*1.47621*	*1.46962*	*1.46306*	*1.45652*
0.19	*1.45001*	*1.44353*	*1.43707*	*1.43063*	*1.42423*	*1.41784*	*1.41148*	*1.40515*	*1.39884*	*1.39256*
0.20	*1.38629*	*1.38006*	*1.37384*	*1.36765*	*1.36148*	*1.35533*	*1.34921*	*1.34310*	*1.33702*	*1.33096*
0.21	*1.32493*	*1.31891*	*1.31291*	*1.30694*	*1.30098*	*1.29505*	*1.28913*	*1.28324*	*1.27736*	*1.27150*
0.22	*1.26567*	*1.25985*	*1.25405*	*1.24827*	*1.24251*	*1.23676*	*1.23104*	*1.22533*	*1.21964*	*1.21397*
0.23	*1.20831*	*1.20267*	*1.19705*	*1.19145*	*1.18586*	*1.18029*	*1.17474*	*1.16920*	*1.16368*	*1.15817*
0.24	*1.15268*	*1.14720*	*1.14175*	*1.13630*	*1.13087*	*1.12546*	*1.12006*	*1.11468*	*1.10931*	*1.10395*
0.25	*1.09861*	*1.09329*	*1.08797*	*1.08268*	*1.07739*	*1.07212*	*1.06686*	*1.06162*	*1.05639*	*1.05117*
0.26	*1.04597*	*1.04078*	*1.03560*	*1.03043*	*1.02528*	*1.02014*	*1.01501*	*1.00990*	*1.00479*	*0.99970*
0.27	*0.99462*	*0.98955*	*0.98450*	*0.97945*	*0.97442*	*0.96940*	*0.96439*	*0.95939*	*0.95440*	*0.94943*
0.28	*0.94446*	*0.93951*	*0.93456*	*0.92963*	*0.92471*	*0.91979*	*0.91489*	*0.91000*	*0.90512*	*0.90025*
0.29	*0.89538*	*0.89053*	*0.88569*	*0.88086*	*0.87604*	*0.87122*	*0.86642*	*0.86162*	*0.85684*	*0.85206*
0.30	*0.84730*	*0.84254*	*0.83779*	*0.83305*	*0.82832*	*0.82360*	*0.81889*	*0.81418*	*0.80949*	*0.80480*
0.31	*0.80012*	*0.79545*	*0.79079*	*0.78613*	*0.78148*	*0.77685*	*0.77222*	*0.76759*	*0.76298*	*0.75837*
0.32	*0.75377*	*0.74918*	*0.74460*	*0.74002*	*0.73545*	*0.73089*	*0.72633*	*0.72179*	*0.71724*	*0.71271*
0.33	*0.70819*	*0.70367*	*0.69915*	*0.69465*	*0.69015*	*0.68566*	*0.68117*	*0.67669*	*0.67222*	*0.66775*
0.34	*0.66329*	*0.65884*	*0.65439*	*0.64995*	*0.64552*	*0.64109*	*0.63667*	*0.63225*	*0.62784*	*0.62344*
0.35	*0.61904*	*0.61465*	*0.61026*	*0.60588*	*0.60150*	*0.59713*	*0.59277*	*0.58841*	*0.58406*	*0.57971*
0.36	*0.57536*	*0.57103*	*0.56669*	*0.56237*	*0.55804*	*0.55373*	*0.54942*	*0.54511*	*0.54081*	*0.53651*
0.37	*0.53222*	*0.52793*	*0.52365*	*0.51937*	*0.51509*	*0.51083*	*0.50656*	*0.50230*	*0.49805*	*0.49379*
0.38	*0.48955*	*0.48531*	*0.48107*	*0.47683*	*0.47260*	*0.46838*	*0.46416*	*0.45994*	*0.45573*	*0.45152*
0.39	*0.44731*	*0.44311*	*0.43891*	*0.43472*	*0.43053*	*0.42634*	*0.42216*	*0.41798*	*0.41381*	*0.40963*
0.40	*0.40547*	*0.40130*	*0.39714*	*0.39298*	*0.38883*	*0.38467*	*0.38053*	*0.37638*	*0.37224*	*0.36810*
0.41	*0.36397*	*0.35983*	*0.35570*	*0.35158*	*0.34745*	*0.34333*	*0.33922*	*0.33510*	*0.33099*	*0.32688*
0.42	*0.32277*	*0.31867*	*0.31457*	*0.31047*	*0.30637*	*0.30228*	*0.29819*	*0.29410*	*0.29002*	*0.28593*
0.43	*0.28185*	*0.27777*	*0.27370*	*0.26962*	*0.26555*	*0.26148*	*0.25741*	*0.25335*	*0.24928*	*0.24522*
0.44	*0.24116*	*0.23710*	*0.23305*	*0.22900*	*0.22494*	*0.22089*	*0.21685*	*0.21280*	*0.20875*	*0.20471*
0.45	*0.20067*	*0.19663*	*0.19259*	*0.18856*	*0.18452*	*0.18049*	*0.17646*	*0.17243*	*0.16840*	*0.16437*
0.46	*0.16034*	*0.15632*	*0.15229*	*0.14827*	*0.14425*	*0.14023*	*0.13621*	*0.13219*	*0.12818*	*0.12416*
0.47	*0.12014*	*0.11613*	*0.11212*	*0.10811*	*0.10409*	*0.10008*	*0.09607*	*0.09206*	*0.08806*	*0.08405*
0.48	*0.08004*	*0.07604*	*0.07203*	*0.06803*	*0.06402*	*0.06002*	*0.05601*	*0.05201*	*0.04801*	*0.04401*
0.49	*0.04001*	*0.03600*	*0.03200*	*0.02800*	*0.02400*	*0.02000*	*0.01600*	*0.01200*	*0.00800*	*0.00400*
0.50	0.00000	0.00400	0.00800	0.01200	0.01600	0.02000	0.02400	0.02800	0.03200	0.03600
0.51	0.04001	0.04401	0.04801	0.05201	0.05601	0.06002	0.06402	0.06803	0.07203	0.07604
0.52	0.08004	0.08405	0.08806	0.09206	0.09607	0.10008	0.10409	0.10811	0.11212	0.11613
0.53	0.12014	0.12416	0.12818	0.13219	0.13621	0.14023	0.14425	0.14827	0.15229	0.15632
0.54	0.16034	0.16437	0.16840	0.17243	0.17646	0.18049	0.18452	0.18856	0.19259	0.19663
0.55	0.20067	0.20471	0.20875	0.21280	0.21685	0.22089	0.22494	0.22900	0.23305	0.23710
0.56	0.24116	0.24522	0.24928	0.25335	0.25741	0.26148	0.26555	0.26962	0.27370	0.27777
0.57	0.28185	0.28593	0.29002	0.29410	0.29819	0.30228	0.30637	0.31047	0.31457	0.31867
0.58	0.32277	0.32688	0.33099	0.33510	0.33922	0.34333	0.34745	0.35158	0.35570	0.35983
0.59	0.36397	0.36810	0.37224	0.37638	0.38053	0.38467	0.38883	0.39298	0.39714	0.40130
0.60	0.40547	0.40963	0.41381	0.41798	0.42216	0.42634	0.43053	0.43472	0.43891	0.44311
0.61	0.44731	0.45152	0.45573	0.45994	0.46416	0.46838	0.47260	0.47683	0.48107	0.48531
0.62	0.48955	0.49379	0.49805	0.50230	0.50656	0.51083	0.51509	0.51937	0.52365	0.52793
0.63	0.53222	0.53651	0.54081	0.54511	0.54942	0.55373	0.55804	0.56237	0.56669	0.57103
0.64	0.57536	0.57971	0.58406	0.58841	0.59277	0.59713	0.60150	0.60588	0.61026	0.61465
0.65	0.61904	0.62344	0.62784	0.63225	0.63667	0.64109	0.64552	0.64995	0.65439	0.65884
0.66	0.66329	0.66775	0.67222	0.67669	0.68117	0.68566	0.69015	0.69465	0.69915	0.70367
0.67	0.70819	0.71271	0.71724	0.72179	0.72633	0.73089	0.73545	0.74002	0.74460	0.74918
0.68	0.75377	0.75837	0.76298	0.76759	0.77222	0.77685	0.78148	0.78613	0.79079	0.79545
0.69	0.80012	0.80480	0.80949	0.81418	0.81889	0.82360	0.82832	0.83305	0.83779	0.84254
0.70	0.84730	0.85206	0.85684	0.86162	0.86642	0.87122	0.87604	0.88086	0.88569	0.89053
0.71	0.89538	0.90025	0.90512	0.91000	0.91489	0.91979	0.92471	0.92963	0.93456	0.93951
0.72	0.94446	0.94943	0.95440	0.95939	0.96439	0.96940	0.97442	0.97945	0.98450	0.98955
0.73	0.99462	0.99970	1.00479	1.00990	1.01501	1.02014	1.02528	1.03043	1.03560	1.04078
0.74	1.04597	1.05117	1.05639	1.06162	1.06686	1.07212	1.07739	1.08268	1.08797	1.09329
0.75	1.09861	1.10395	1.10931	1.11468	1.12006	1.12546	1.13087	1.13630	1.14175	1.14720
0.76	1.15268	1.15817	1.16368	1.16920	1.17474	1.18029	1.18586	1.19145	1.19705	1.20267
0.77	1.20831	1.21397	1.21964	1.22533	1.23104	1.23676	1.24251	1.24827	1.25405	1.25985
0.78	1.26567	1.27150	1.27736	1.28324	1.28913	1.29505	1.30098	1.30694	1.31291	1.31891
0.79	1.32493	1.33096	1.33702	1.34310	1.34921	1.35533	1.36148	1.36765	1.37384	1.38006
0.80	1.38269	1.39256	1.39884	1.40515	1.41148	1.41784	1.42423	1.43063	1.43707	1.44353
0.81	1.45001	1.45652	1.46306	1.46962	1.47621	1.48283	1.48948	1.49615	1.50286	1.50959
0.82	1.51635	1.52314	1.52996	1.53681	1.54369	1.55060	1.55754	1.56451	1.57152	1.57856
0.83	1.58563	1.59273	1.59987	1.60704	1.61425	1.62149	1.62876	1.63607	1.64342	1.65081
0.84	1.65823	1.66569	1.67318	1.68072	1.68830	1.69591	1.70357	1.71126	1.71900	1.72678
0.85	1.73460	1.74247	1.75037	1.75833	1.76632	1.77437	1.78246	1.79059	1.79878	1.80701
0.86	1.81529	1.82362	1.83200	1.84043	1.84892	1.85745	1.86605	1.87469	1.88339	1.89215
0.87	1.90096	1.90983	1.91876	1.92775	1.93680	1.94591	1.95508	1.96432	1.97363	1.98299
0.88	1.99243	2.00193	2.01151	2.02115	2.03087	2.04066	2.05052	2.06046	2.07047	2.08057
0.89	2.09074	2.10100	2.11133	2.12176	2.13227	2.14286	2.15355	2.16433	2.17520	2.18616
0.90	2.19722	2.20839	2.21965	2.23101	2.24248	2.25406	2.26574	2.27754	2.28946	2.30149
0.91	2.31363	2.32591	2.33830	2.35083	2.36348	2.37627	2.38920	2.40227	2.41548	2.42884
0.92	2.44235	2.45601	2.46984	2.48382	2.49798	2.51231	2.52681	2.54149	2.55637	2.57143
0.93	2.58669	2.60215	2.61783	2.63371	2.64982	2.66616	2.68273	2.69955	2.71662	2.73394
0.94	2.75154	2.76941	2.78756	2.80601	2.82477	2.84385	2.86326	2.88301	2.90311	2.92358
0.95	2.94444	2.96569	2.98736	3.00947	3.03202	3.05505	3.07857	3.10260	3.12718	3.15232
0.96	3.17805	3.20441	3.23143	3.25914	3.28757	3.31678	3.34680	3.37769	3.40950	3.44228
0.97	3.47610	3.51103	3.54715	3.58455	3.62331	3.66356	3.70541	3.74899	3.79447	3.84201
0.98	3.89182	3.94413	3.99922	4.05740	4.11904	4.18459	4.25460	4.32972	4.41078	4.49880
0.99	4.59512	4.70149	4.82028	4.95482	5.10998	5.29330	5.51745	5.80614	6.21261	6.90675

l	0.00	0.01	0.02	0.03	0.04	0.05	0.06	0.07	0.08	0.09
	0.	0.	0.	0.	0.	0.	0.	0.	0.	0.
− 4.9	00739	00732	00725	00717	00710	00703	00696	00690	00683	00676
− 4.8	00816	00808	00800	00792	00785	00777	00769	00761	00754	00747
− 4.7	00901	00892	00884	00875	00866	00858	00849	00841	00833	00824
− 4.6	00995	00985	00976	00966	00957	00947	00938	00929	00919	00910
− 4.5	01099	01088	01077	01067	01056	01046	01035	01025	01015	01005
− 4.4	01213	01201	01189	01177	01166	01154	01143	01132	01121	01110
− 4.3	01339	01326	01313	01300	01287	01274	01262	01249	01237	01225
− 4.2	01477	01463	01449	01434	01420	01406	01393	01379	01365	01352
− 4.1	01630	01614	01598	01583	01567	01552	01537	01522	01507	01492
− 4.0	01799	01781	01764	01746	01729	01712	01696	01679	01663	01646
− 3.9	01984	01965	01946	01927	01908	01889	01871	01852	01834	01816
− 3.8	02188	02167	02146	02125	02104	02084	02063	02043	02023	02004
− 3.7	02413	02389	02366	02343	02320	02298	02275	02253	02231	02210
− 3.6	02660	02634	02608	02583	02558	02533	02509	02484	02460	02436
− 3.5	02931	02903	02875	02847	02820	02792	02765	02738	02712	02686
− 3.4	03230	03198	03168	03137	03107	03077	03047	03018	02989	02960
− 3.3	03557	03523	03489	03456	03422	03390	03357	03325	03293	03261
− 3.2	03917	03879	03842	03805	03769	03733	03697	03661	03626	03592
− 3.1	04311	04270	04229	04189	04149	04109	04070	04031	03993	03954
− 3.0	04743	04698	04653	04609	04565	04522	04479	04436	04394	04352
− 2.9	05215	05166	05117	05069	05021	04974	04927	04880	04834	04788
− 2.8	05732	05679	05625	05572	05520	05468	05417	05366	05315	05265
− 2.7	06297	06239	06180	06123	06065	06009	05952	05897	05841	05787
− 2.6	06914	06850	06786	06723	06661	06599	06538	06477	06416	06357
− 2.5	07586	07516	07447	07378	07310	07243	07176	07109	07044	06978
− 2.4	08317	08241	08166	08091	08017	07944	07871	07799	07727	07656
− 2.3	09112	09030	08948	08867	08786	08707	08627	08549	08471	08394
− 2.2	09975	09886	09797	09709	09622	09535	09449	09364	09279	09195
− 2.1	10910	10813	10717	10621	10527	10433	10340	10248	10156	10065
− 2.0	11920	11816	11712	11609	11507	11405	11305	11205	11106	11007
− 1.9	13011	12898	12786	12675	12565	12455	12347	12239	12132	12026
− 1.8	14185	14064	13943	13824	13705	13587	13470	13354	13239	13124
− 1.7	15447	15316	15187	15059	14931	14805	14679	14554	14430	14307
− 1.6	16798	16659	16520	16383	16247	16111	15976	15842	15710	15578
− 1.5	18243	18094	17946	17799	17654	17509	17365	17222	17080	16938
− 1.4	19782	19623	19466	19310	19155	19000	18847	18694	18543	18392
− 1.3	21417	21249	21082	20916	20751	20587	20424	20262	20101	19941
− 1.2	23148	22970	22794	22618	22444	22270	22097	21926	21755	21585
− 1.1	24974	24787	24601	24416	24232	24049	23867	23685	23505	23326
− 1.0	26894	26698	26503	26308	26115	25923	25731	25540	25351	25162
− 0.9	28905	28700	28496	28292	28090	27888	27688	27488	27289	27091
− 0.8	31003	30789	30576	30365	30153	29943	29734	29525	29318	29111
− 0.7	33181	32960	32739	32519	32300	32082	31865	31648	31432	31217
− 0.6	35434	35206	34978	34751	34525	34299	34074	33850	33626	33403
− 0.5	37754	37519	37285	37052	36819	36586	36355	36124	35893	35663
− 0.4	40131	39891	39652	39413	39174	38936	38699	38462	38225	37989
− 0.3	42556	42311	42068	41824	41581	41338	41096	40854	40613	40372
− 0.2	45017	44769	44522	44275	44029	43782	43536	43291	43045	42800
− 0.1	47502	47253	47004	46755	46506	46257	46009	45760	45512	45264
− 0.0	50000	49750	49500	49250	49000	48750	48500	48251	48001	47752
+ 0.0	50000	50250	50500	50750	51000	51250	51500	51749	51999	52248
+ 0.1	52498	52747	52996	53245	53494	53743	53991	54240	54488	54736
+ 0.2	54983	55231	55478	55725	55971	56218	56464	56709	56955	57200
+ 0.3	57444	57689	57932	58176	58419	58662	58904	59146	59387	59628
+ 0.4	59869	60109	60348	60587	60826	61064	61301	61538	61775	62011
+ 0.5	62246	62481	62715	62948	63181	63414	63645	63876	64107	64337
+ 0.6	64566	64794	65022	65249	65475	65701	65926	66150	66374	66597
+ 0.7	66819	67040	67261	67481	67700	67918	68135	68352	68568	68783
+ 0.8	68997	69211	69424	69635	69847	70057	70266	70475	70682	70889
+ 0.9	71095	71300	71504	71708	71910	72112	72312	72512	72711	72909
+ 1.0	73106	73302	73497	73692	73885	74077	74269	74460	74649	74838
+ 1.1	75026	75213	75399	75584	75768	75951	76133	76315	76495	76674
+ 1.2	76852	77030	77206	77382	77556	77730	77903	78074	78245	78415
+ 1.3	78583	78751	78918	79084	79249	79413	79576	79738	79899	80059
+ 1.4	80218	80377	80534	80690	80845	81000	81153	81306	81457	81608
+ 1.5	81757	81906	82054	82201	82346	82491	82635	82778	82920	83062
+ 1.6	83202	83341	83480	83617	83753	83889	84024	84158	84290	84422
+ 1.7	84553	84684	84813	84941	85069	85195	85321	85446	85570	85693
+ 1.8	85815	85936	86057	86176	86295	86413	86530	86646	86761	86876
+ 1.9	86989	87102	87214	87325	87435	87545	87653	87761	87868	87974
+ 2.0	88080	88184	88288	88391	88493	88595	88695	88795	88894	88993
+ 2.1	89090	89187	89283	89379	89473	89567	89660	89752	89844	89935
+ 2.2	90025	90114	90203	90291	90378	90465	90551	90636	90721	90805
+ 2.3	90888	90970	91052	91133	91214	91293	91373	91451	91529	91606
+ 2.4	91683	91759	91834	91909	91983	92056	92129	92201	92273	92344
+ 2.5	92414	92484	92553	92622	92690	92757	92824	92891	92956	93022
+ 2.6	93086	93150	93214	93277	93339	93401	93462	93523	93584	93643
+ 2.7	93703	93761	93820	93877	93935	93991	94048	94103	94159	94213
+ 2.8	94268	94321	94375	94428	94480	94532	94583	94634	94685	94735
+ 2.9	94785	94834	94883	94931	94979	95026	95073	95120	95166	95212
+ 3.0	95257	95302	95347	95391	95435	95478	95521	95564	95606	95648
+ 3.1	95689	95730	95771	95811	95851	95891	95930	95969	96007	96046
+ 3.2	96083	96121	96158	96195	96231	96267	96303	96339	96374	96408
+ 3.3	96443	96477	96511	96544	96578	96610	96643	96675	96707	96739
+ 3.4	96770	96802	96832	96863	96893	96923	96953	96982	97011	97040
+ 3.5	97069	97097	97125	97153	97180	97208	97235	97262	97288	97314
+ 3.6	97340	97366	97392	97417	97442	97467	97491	97516	97540	97564
+ 3.7	97587	97611	97634	97657	97680	97702	97725	97747	97769	97790
+ 3.8	97812	97833	97854	97875	97896	97916	97937	97957	97977	97996
+ 3.9	98016	98035	98054	98073	98092	98111	98129	98148	98166	98184
+ 4.0	98201	98219	98236	98254	98271	98288	98304	98321	98337	98354
+ 4.1	98370	98386	98402	98417	98433	98448	98463	98478	98493	98508
+ 4.2	98523	98537	98551	98566	98580	98594	98607	98621	98635	98648
+ 4.3	98661	98674	98687	98700	98713	98726	98738	98751	98763	98775
+ 4.4	98787	98799	98811	98823	98834	98846	98857	98868	98879	98890
+ 4.5	98901	98912	98923	98933	98944	98954	98965	98975	98985	98995
+ 4.6	99005	99015	99024	99034	99043	99053	99062	99071	99081	99090
+ 4.7	99099	99108	99116	99125	99134	99142	99151	99159	99167	99176
+ 4.8	99184	99192	99200	99208	99215	99223	99231	99239	99246	99253
+ 4.9	99261	99268	99275	99283	99290	99297	99304	99310	99317	99324

1) Values of *l* (from + 0.0 to + 4.9) and of *p* from BERKSON, J., *J. Amer. statist. Ass.*, **48**, 565 (1953). Reprinted by kind permission of the author and publishers.

Logistic Weights[1]

In the upper line are values of $w = p\,q$, in the lower line those of $w\,l = p\,q\,l$. Numbers in *italics* are negative values.

p	0.000	0.001	0.002	0.003	0.004	0.005	0.006	0.007	0.008	0.009
	0.	0.	0.	0.	0.	0.	0.	0.	0.	0.
0.00	0000	0010	0020	0030	0040	0050	0060	0070	0079	0089
	—	*0069*	*0124*	*0174*	*0220*	*0263*	*0305*	*0344*	*0383*	*0419*
0.01	0099	0109	0119	0128	0138	0148	0157	0167	0177	0186
	0455	*0489*	*0523*	*0556*	*0587*	*0618*	*0649*	*0678*	*0707*	*0735*
0.02	0196	0206	0215	0225	0234	0244	0253	0263	0272	0282
	0763	*0790*	*0816*	*0842*	*0868*	*0893*	*0918*	*0942*	*0965*	*0989*
0.03	0291	0300	0310	0319	0328	0338	0347	0356	0366	0375
	1012	*1034*	*1056*	*1078*	*1099*	*1120*	*1141*	*1161*	*1181*	*1201*
0.04	0384	0393	0402	0412	0421	0430	0439	0448	0457	0466
	1220	*1239*	*1258*	*1277*	*1295*	*1313*	*1331*	*1348*	*1365*	*1382*
0.05	0475	0484	0493	0502	0511	0520	0529	0538	0546	0555
	1399	*1415*	*1431*	*1447*	*1463*	*1478*	*1493*	*1508*	*1523*	*1538*
0.06	0564	0573	0582	0590	0599	0608	0616	0625	0634	0642
	1552	*1566*	*1580*	*1594*	*1607*	*1620*	*1633*	*1646*	*1659*	*1672*
0.07	0651	0660	0668	0677	0685	0694	0702	0711	0719	0728
	1684	*1696*	*1708*	*1720*	*1731*	*1743*	*1754*	*1765*	*1776*	*1787*
0.08	0736	0744	0753	0761	0769	0778	0786	0794	0803	0811
	1798	*1808*	*1818*	*1828*	*1838*	*1848*	*1858*	*1867*	*1877*	*1886*
0.09	0819	0827	0835	0844	0852	0860	0868	0876	0884	0892
	1895	*1904*	*1913*	*1921*	*1930*	*1938*	*1946*	*1954*	*1962*	*1970*
0.10	0900	0908	0916	0924	0932	0940	0948	0956	0963	0971
	1977	*1985*	*1992*	*2000*	*2007*	*2014*	*2021*	*2027*	*2034*	*2040*
0.11	0979	0987	0995	1002	1010	1018	1025	1033	1041	1048
	2047	*2053*	*2059*	*2065*	*2071*	*2077*	*2083*	*2088*	*2093*	*2099*
0.12	1056	1064	1071	1079	1086	1094	1101	1109	1116	1124
	2104	*2109*	*2114*	*2119*	*2124*	*2128*	*2133*	*2137*	*2142*	*2146*
0.13	1131	1138	1146	1153	1160	1168	1175	1182	1190	1197
	2150	*2154*	*2158*	*2162*	*2165*	*2169*	*2173*	*2176*	*2179*	*2182*
0.14	1204	1211	1218	1226	1233	1240	1247	1254	1261	1268
	2186	*2189*	*2192*	*2194*	*2197*	*2200*	*2202*	*2205*	*2207*	*2209*
0.15	1275	1282	1289	1296	1303	1310	1317	1324	1330	1337
	2212	*2214*	*2216*	*2218*	*2219*	*2221*	*2223*	*2224*	*2226*	*2227*
0.16	1344	1351	1358	1364	1371	1378	1384	1391	1398	1404
	2229	*2230*	*2231*	*2232*	*2233*	*2234*	*2235*	*2236*	*2236*	*2237*
0.17	1411	1418	1424	1431	1437	1444	1450	1457	1463	1470
	2237	*2238*	*2238*	*2238*	*2239*	*2239*	*2239*	*2239*	*2239*	*2238*
0.18	1476	1482	1489	1495	1501	1508	1514	1520	1527	1533
	2238	*2238*	*2237*	*2237*	*2236*	*2236*	*2235*	*2234*	*2233*	*2233*
0.19	1539	1545	1551	1558	1564	1570	1576	1582	1588	1594
	2232	*2231*	*2229*	*2228*	*2227*	*2226*	*2224*	*2223*	*2221*	*2220*
0.20	1600	1606	1612	1618	1624	1630	1636	1642	1647	1653
	2218	*2216*	*2215*	*2213*	*2211*	*2209*	*2207*	*2205*	*2203*	*2200*
0.21	1659	1665	1671	1676	1682	1688	1693	1699	1705	1710
	2198	*2196*	*2193*	*2191*	*2188*	*2186*	*2183*	*2180*	*2178*	*2175*
0.22	1716	1722	1727	1733	1738	1744	1749	1755	1760	1766
	2172	*2169*	*2166*	*2163*	*2160*	*2157*	*2153*	*2150*	*2147*	*2143*
0.23	1771	1776	1782	1787	1792	1798	1803	1808	1814	1819
	2140	*2136*	*2133*	*2129*	*2126*	*2122*	*2118*	*2114*	*2110*	*2106*
0.24	1824	1829	1834	1840	1845	1850	1855	1860	1865	1870
	2102	*2098*	*2094*	*2090*	*2086*	*2082*	*2078*	*2073*	*2069*	*2064*
0.25	1875	1880	1885	1890	1895	1900	1905	1910	1914	1919
	2060	*2055*	*2051*	*2046*	*2041*	*2037*	*2032*	*2027*	*2022*	*2017*
0.26	1924	1929	1934	1938	1943	1948	1952	1957	1962	1966
	2012	*2007*	*2002*	*1997*	*1992*	*1987*	*1982*	*1976*	*1971*	*1966*
0.27	1971	1976	1980	1985	1989	1994	1998	2003	2007	2012
	1960	*1955*	*1949*	*1944*	*1938*	*1933*	*1927*	*1921*	*1916*	*1910*
0.28	2016	2020	2025	2029	2033	2038	2042	2046	2051	2055
	1904	*1898*	*1892*	*1886*	*1880*	*1874*	*1868*	*1862*	*1856*	*1850*
0.29	2059	2063	2067	2072	2076	2080	2084	2088	2092	2096
	1844	*1837*	*1831*	*1825*	*1818*	*1812*	*1805*	*1799*	*1792*	*1786*
0.30	2100	2104	2108	2112	2116	2120	2124	2128	2131	2135
	1779	*1773*	*1766*	*1759*	*1753*	*1746*	*1739*	*1732*	*1725*	*1718*
0.31	2139	2143	2147	2150	2154	2158	2161	2165	2169	2172
	1711	*1704*	*1697*	*1690*	*1683*	*1676*	*1669*	*1662*	*1655*	*1647*
0.32	2176	2180	2183	2187	2190	2194	2197	2201	2204	2208
	1640	*1633*	*1626*	*1618*	*1611*	*1603*	*1596*	*1588*	*1581*	*1573*
0.33	2211	2214	2218	2221	2224	2228	2231	2234	2238	2241
	1566	*1558*	*1551*	*1543*	*1535*	*1527*	*1520*	*1512*	*1504*	*1496*
0.34	2244	2247	2250	2254	2257	2260	2263	2266	2269	2272
	1488	*1481*	*1473*	*1465*	*1457*	*1449*	*1441*	*1433*	*1425*	*1416*
0.35	2275	2278	2281	2284	2287	2290	2293	2296	2298	2301
	1408	*1400*	*1392*	*1384*	*1376*	*1367*	*1359*	*1351*	*1342*	*1334*
0.36	2304	2307	2310	2312	2315	2318	2320	2323	2326	2328
	1326	*1317*	*1309*	*1300*	*1292*	*1283*	*1275*	*1266*	*1258*	*1249*
0.37	2331	2334	2336	2339	2341	2344	2346	2349	2351	2354
	1241	*1232*	*1223*	*1215*	*1206*	*1197*	*1189*	*1180*	*1171*	*1162*
0.38	2356	2358	2361	2363	2365	2368	2370	2372	2375	2377
	1153	*1145*	*1136*	*1127*	*1118*	*1109*	*1100*	*1091*	*1082*	*1073*
0.39	2379	2381	2383	2386	2388	2390	2392	2394	2396	2398
	1064	*1055*	*1046*	*1037*	*1028*	*1019*	*1010*	*1001*	*0991*	*0982*
0.40	2400	2402	2404	2406	2408	2410	2412	2414	2415	2417
	0973	*0964*	*0955*	*0945*	*0936*	*0927*	*0918*	*0908*	*0899*	*0890*
0.41	2419	2421	2423	2424	2426	2428	2429	2431	2433	2434
	0880	*0871*	*0862*	*0852*	*0843*	*0834*	*0824*	*0815*	*0805*	*0796*
0.42	2436	2438	2439	2441	2442	2444	2445	2447	2448	2450
	0786	*0777*	*0767*	*0758*	*0748*	*0739*	*0729*	*0720*	*0710*	*0700*
0.43	2451	2452	2454	2455	2456	2458	2459	2460	2462	2463
	0691	*0681*	*0672*	*0662*	*0652*	*0643*	*0633*	*0623*	*0614*	*0604*
0.44	2464	2465	2466	2468	2469	2470	2471	2472	2473	2474
	0594	*0584*	*0575*	*0565*	*0555*	*0546*	*0536*	*0526*	*0516*	*0506*
0.45	2475	2476	2477	2478	2479	2480	2481	2482	2482	2483
	0497	*0487*	*0477*	*0467*	*0457*	*0448*	*0438*	*0428*	*0418*	*0408*
0.46	2484	2485	2486	2486	2487	2488	2488	2489	2490	2490
	0398	*0388*	*0379*	*0369*	*0359*	*0349*	*0339*	*0329*	*0319*	*0309*
0.47	2491	2492	2492	2493	2493	2494	2494	2495	2495	2496
	0299	*0289*	*0279*	*0269*	*0260*	*0250*	*0240*	*0230*	*0220*	*0210*
0.48	2496	2496	2497	2497	2497	2498	2498	2498	2499	2499
	0200	*0190*	*0180*	*0170*	*0160*	*0150*	*0140*	*0130*	*0120*	*0110*
0.49	2499	2499	2499	2500	2500	2500	2500	2500	2500	2500
	0100	*0090*	*0080*	*0070*	*0060*	*0050*	*0040*	*0030*	*0020*	*0010*

p	0.000	0.001	0.002	0.003	0.004	0.005	0.006	0.007	0.008	0.009
	0.	0.	0.	0.	0.	0.	0.	0.	0.	0.
0.50	2500	2500	2500	2500	2500	2500	2500	2500	2499	2499
	0000	0010	0020	0030	0040	0050	0060	0070	0080	0090
0.51	2499	2499	2499	2498	2498	2498	2497	2497	2497	2496
	0100	0110	0120	0130	0140	0150	0160	0170	0180	0190
0.52	2496	2496	2495	2495	2494	2494	2493	2493	2492	2492
	0200	0210	0220	0230	0240	0250	0260	0269	0279	0289
0.53	2491	2490	2490	2489	2488	2488	2487	2486	2486	2485
	0299	0309	0319	0329	0339	0349	0359	0369	0379	0388
0.54	2484	2483	2482	2482	2481	2480	2479	2478	2477	2476
	0398	0408	0418	0428	0438	0448	0457	0467	0477	0487
0.55	2475	2474	2473	2472	2471	2470	2469	2468	2466	2465
	0497	0506	0516	0526	0536	0546	0555	0565	0575	0584
0.56	2464	2463	2462	2460	2459	2458	2456	2455	2454	2552
	0594	0604	0614	0623	0633	0643	0652	0662	0672	0681
0.57	2451	2450	2448	2447	2445	2444	2442	2441	2439	2438
	0691	0700	0710	0720	0729	0739	0748	0758	0767	0777
0.58	2436	2434	2433	2431	2429	2428	2426	2424	2423	2421
	0786	0796	0805	0815	0824	0834	0843	0852	0862	0871
0.59	2419	2417	2415	2414	2412	2410	2408	2406	2404	2402
	0880	0890	0899	0908	0918	0927	0936	0945	0955	0964
0.60	2400	2398	2396	2394	2392	2390	2388	2386	2383	2381
	0973	0982	0991	1001	1010	1019	1028	1037	1046	1055
0.61	2379	2377	2375	2372	2370	2368	2365	2363	2361	2358
	1064	1073	1082	1091	1100	1109	1118	1127	1136	1145
0.62	2356	2354	2351	2349	2346	2344	2341	2339	2336	2334
	1153	1162	1171	1180	1189	1197	1206	1215	1223	1232
0.63	2331	2328	2326	2323	2320	2318	2315	2312	2310	2307
	1241	1249	1258	1266	1275	1283	1292	1300	1309	1317
0.64	2304	2301	2298	2296	2293	2290	2287	2284	2281	2278
	1326	1334	1342	1351	1359	1367	1376	1384	1392	1400
0.65	2275	2272	2269	2266	2263	2260	2257	2254	2250	2247
	1408	1416	1425	1433	1441	1449	1457	1465	1473	1481
0.66	2244	2241	2238	2234	2231	2228	2224	2221	2218	2214
	1488	1496	1504	1512	1520	1527	1535	1543	1551	1558
0.67	2211	2208	2204	2201	2197	2194	2190	2187	2183	2180
	1566	1573	1581	1588	1596	1603	1611	1618	1626	1633
0.68	2176	2172	2169	2165	2161	2158	2154	2150	2147	2143
	1640	1647	1655	1662	1669	1676	1683	1690	1697	1704
0.69	2139	2135	2131	2128	2124	2120	2116	2112	2108	2104
	1711	1718	1725	1732	1739	1746	1753	1759	1766	1773
0.70	2100	2096	2092	2088	2084	2080	2076	2072	2067	2063
	1779	1786	1792	1799	1805	1812	1818	1825	1831	1837
0.71	2059	2055	2051	2046	2042	2038	2033	2029	2025	2020
	1844	1850	1856	1862	1868	1874	1880	1886	1892	1898
0.72	2016	2012	2007	2003	1998	1994	1989	1985	1980	1976
	1904	1910	1916	1921	1927	1933	1938	1944	1949	1955
0.73	1971	1966	1962	1957	1952	1948	1943	1938	1934	1929
	1960	1966	1971	1976	1982	1987	1992	1997	2002	2007
0.74	1924	1919	1914	1910	1905	1900	1895	1890	1885	1880
	2012	2017	2022	2027	2032	2037	2041	2046	2051	2055
0.75	1875	1870	1865	1860	1855	1850	1845	1840	1834	1829
	2060	2064	2069	2073	2078	2082	2086	2090	2094	2098
0.76	1824	1819	1814	1808	1803	1798	1792	1787	1782	1776
	2102	2106	2110	2114	2118	2122	2126	2129	2133	2136
0.77	1771	1766	1760	1755	1749	1744	1738	1733	1727	1722
	2140	2143	2147	2150	2153	2157	2160	2163	2166	2169
0.78	1716	1710	1705	1699	1693	1688	1682	1676	1671	1665
	2172	2175	2178	2180	2183	2186	2188	2191	2193	2196
0.79	1659	1653	1647	1642	1636	1630	1624	1618	1612	1606
	2198	2200	2203	2205	2207	2209	2211	2213	2215	2216
0.80	1600	1594	1588	1582	1576	1570	1564	1558	1551	1545
	2218	2220	2221	2223	2224	2226	2227	2228	2229	2231
0.81	1539	1533	1527	1520	1514	1508	1501	1495	1489	1482
	2232	2233	2233	2234	2235	2236	2236	2237	2237	2238
0.82	1476	1470	1463	1457	1450	1444	1437	1431	1424	1418
	2238	2238	2239	2239	2239	2239	2239	2238	2238	2238
0.83	1411	1404	1398	1391	1384	1378	1371	1364	1358	1351
	2237	2237	2236	2236	2235	2234	2233	2232	2231	2230
0.84	1344	1337	1330	1324	1317	1310	1303	1296	1289	1282
	2229	2227	2226	2224	2223	2221	2219	2218	2216	2214
0.85	1275	1268	1261	1254	1247	1240	1233	1226	1218	1211
	2212	2209	2207	2205	2202	2200	2197	2194	2192	2189
0.86	1204	1197	1190	1182	1175	1168	1160	1153	1146	1138
	2186	2182	2179	2176	2173	2169	2165	2162	2158	2154
0.87	1131	1124	1116	1109	1101	1094	1086	1079	1071	1064
	2150	2146	2142	2137	2133	2128	2124	2119	2114	2109
0.88	1056	1048	1041	1033	1025	1018	1010	1002	0995	0987
	2104	2099	2093	2088	2083	2077	2071	2065	2059	2053
0.89	0979	0971	0963	0956	0948	0940	0932	0924	0916	0908
	2047	2040	2034	2027	2021	2014	2007	2000	1992	1985
0.90	0900	0892	0884	0876	0868	0860	0852	0844	0835	0827
	1977	1970	1962	1954	1946	1938	1930	1921	1913	1904
0.91	0819	0811	0803	0794	0786	0778	0769	0761	0753	0744
	1895	1886	1877	1867	1858	1848	1838	1828	1818	1808
0.92	0736	0728	0719	0711	0702	0694	0685	0677	0668	0660
	1798	1787	1776	1765	1754	1743	1731	1720	1708	1696
0.93	0651	0642	0634	0625	0616	0608	0599	0590	0582	0573
	1684	1672	1659	1646	1633	1620	1607	1594	1580	1566
0.94	0564	0555	0546	0538	0529	0520	0511	0502	0493	0484
	1552	1538	1523	1508	1493	1478	1463	1447	1431	1415
0.95	0475	0466	0457	0448	0439	0430	0421	0412	0402	0393
	1399	1382	1365	1348	1331	1313	1295	1277	1258	1239
0.96	0384	0375	0366	0356	0347	0338	0328	0319	0310	0300
	1220	1201	1181	1161	1141	1120	1099	1078	1056	1034
0.97	0291	0282	0272	0263	0253	0244	0234	0225	0215	0206
	1012	0989	0965	0942	0918	0893	0868	0842	0816	0790
0.98	0196	0186	0177	0167	0157	0148	0138	0128	0119	0109
	0763	0735	0707	0678	0649	0618	0587	0556	0523	0489
0.99	0099	0089	0079	0070	0060	0050	0040	0030	0020	0010
	0455	0419	0383	0344	0305	0263	0220	0174	0124	0069

1) Values from Berkson, J., *J. Amer. statist. Ass.*, **48**, 565 (1953). Reprinted by kind permission of the author and publishers.

Significance Limits for the Mean Square Successive Difference and for Serial Correlation

Mean square successive difference[1,3]

N = size of sample. Test quotient: $\Sigma\,(x_{i+1} - x_i)^2 \,/\, \Sigma\,(\bar{x} - x_i)^2$

N	$2\alpha = 0.10$	$2\alpha = 0.02$	N	$2\alpha = 0.10$	$2\alpha = 0.02$
			101	1.676–2.324	1.542–2.458
			102	677– 323	544– 456
			103	679– 321	546– 454
4	0.780–3.220	0.626–3.374	104	680– 320	548– 452
5	0.820–3.180	0.538–3.462	**105**	1.682–2.318	1.550–2.450
6	890– 110	561– 439	106	683– 317	552– 448
7	936– 064	614– 386	107	685– 315	554– 446
8	982– 018	663– 337	108	686– 314	556– 444
9	1.024–2.976	709– 291	109	688– 312	558– 442
10	1.062–2.938	0.752–3.248	**110**	1.689–2.311	1.560–2.440
11	096– 904	791– 209	111	691– 309	562– 438
12	128– 872	828– 172	112	692– 308	564– 436
13	156– 844	862– 138	113	693– 307	566– 434
14	182– 818	893– 107	114	695– 305	568– 432
15	1.205–2.795	0.922–3.078	**115**	1.696–2.304	1.570–2.430
16	227– 773	949– 051	116	697– 303	572– 428
17	247– 753	974– 026	117	698– 302	573– 427
18	266– 734	998– 002	118	700– 300	575– 425
19	283– 717	1.020–2.980	119	701– 299	577– 423
20	1.300–2.700	1.041–2.959	**120**	1.702–2.298	1.579–2.421
21	315– 685	060– 940	121	703– 297	580– 420
22	329– 671	078– 922	122	705– 295	582– 418
23	342– 658	096– 904	123	706– 294	584– 416
24	355– 645	112– 888	124	707– 293	585– 415
25	1.367–2.633	1.128–2.872	**125**	1.708–2.292	1.587–2.413
26	378– 622	142– 858	126	709– 291	589– 411
27	389– 611	157– 843	127	710– 290	590– 410
28	399– 601	170– 830	128	711– 289	592– 408
29	409– 591	183– 817	129	713– 287	593– 407
30	1.418–2.582	1.195–2.805	**130**	1.714–2.286	1.595–2.405
31	426– 574	207– 793	131	715– 285	597– 403
32	435– 565	218– 782	132	716– 284	598– 402
33	443– 557	228– 772	133	717– 283	600– 400
34	451– 549	239– 761	134	718– 282	601– 399
35	1.458–2.542	1.248–2.752	**135**	1.719–2.281	1.602–2.398
36	466– 534	258– 742	136	720– 280	604– 396
37	472– 528	267– 733	137	721– 279	605– 395
38	479– 521	276– 724	138	722– 278	607– 393
39	486– 514	285– 715	139	723– 277	608– 392
40	1.492–2.508	1.293–2.707	**140**	1.724–2.276	1.610–2.390
41	498– 502	302– 698	141	725– 275	611– 389
42	504– 496	310– 690	142	726– 274	612– 388
43	510– 490	317–683	143	727– 273	614– 386
44	515– 485	325– 675	144	728– 272	615– 385
45	1.521–2.479	1.332–2.668	**145**	1.729–2.271	1.616–2.384
46	526– 474	339– 661	146	730– 270	618– 382
47	530– 470	345– 655	147	730– 270	619– 381
48	535– 465	351– 649	148	731– 269	620– 380
49	539– 461	357– 643	149	732– 268	621– 379
50	1.544–2.456	1.363–2.637	**150**	1.733–2.267	1.623–2.377
51	548– 452	368– 632	151	734– 266	624– 376
52	552– 448	374– 626	152	735– 265	625– 375
53	556– 444	379– 621	153	736– 264	626– 374
54	559– 441	384– 616	154	737– 263	627– 373
55	1.563–2.437	1.390–2.610	**155**	1.737–2.263	1.629–2.371
56	567– 433	395– 605	156	738– 262	630– 370
57	571– 429	400– 600	157	739– 261	631– 369
58	574– 426	405– 595	158	740– 260	632– 368
59	578– 422	410– 590	159	741– 259	633– 367
60	1.581–2.419	1.414–2.586	**160**	1.742–2.258	1.634–2.366
61	584– 416	419– 581	161	742– 258	636– 364
62	587– 413	423– 577	162	743– 257	637– 363
63	590– 410	427– 573	163	744– 256	638– 362
64	593– 407	431– 569	164	745– 255	639– 361
65	1.596–2.404	1.435–2.565	**165**	1.745–2.255	1.640–2.360
66	599– 401	439– 561	166	746– 254	641– 359
67	602– 398	443– 557	167	747– 253	642– 358
68	605– 395	447– 553	168	748– 252	643– 357
69	608– 392	451– 549	169	748– 252	644– 356
70	1.611–2.389	1.454–2.546	**170**	1.749–2.251	1.645–2.355
71	614– 386	458– 542	171	750– 250	646– 354
72	617– 383	461– 539	172	751– 249	647– 353
73	620– 380	465– 535	173	751– 249	648– 352
74	623– 377	468– 532	174	752– 248	649– 351
75	1.625–2.375	1.471–2.529	**175**	1.753–2.247	1.650–2.350
76	628– 372	474– 526	176	753– 247	651– 349
77	630– 370	477– 523	177	754– 246	652– 348
78	632– 368	480– 520	178	755– 245	653– 347
79	635– 365	483– 517	179	755– 245	654– 346
80	1.637–2.363	1.486–2.514	**180**	1.756–2.244	1.655–2.345
81	639– 361	489– 511	181	757– 243	656– 344
82	641– 359	492– 508	182	757– 243	657– 343
83	643– 357	495– 505	183	758– 242	658– 342
84	645– 355	498– 502	184	759– 241	659– 341
85	1.647–2.353	1.501–2.499	**185**	1.759–2.241	1.660–2.340
86	649– 351	504– 496	186	760– 240	661– 339
87	651– 349	507– 493	187	761– 239	662– 338
88	653– 347	510– 490	188	761– 239	662– 338
89	655– 345	512– 488	189	762– 238	663– 337
90	1.657–2.343	1.515–2.485	**190**	1.763–2.237	1.664–2.336
91	659– 341	518– 482	191	763– 237	665– 335
92	661– 339	520– 480	192	764– 236	666– 334
93	662– 338	523– 477	193	764– 236	667– 333
94	664– 336	525– 475	194	765– 235	668– 332
95	1.666–2.334	1.528–2.472	**195**	1.766–2.234	1.668–2.332
96	668– 332	530– 470	196	766– 234	669– 331
97	669– 331	532– 468	197	767– 233	670– 330
98	671– 329	535– 465	198	767– 233	671– 329
99	673– 327	537– 463	199	768– 232	672– 328
100	1.674–2.326	1.539–2.461	**200**	1.768–2.232	1.673–2.327
			∞	2.000–2.000	2.000–2.000

Serial correlation[2,3] (significance of departure from null hypothesis)

N = size of sample, h = lag. Test quotient: $(\Sigma\, x_i x_{i+h} - \bar{x}\,\Sigma\, x_i) \,/\, \Sigma\,(\bar{x} - x_i)^2$

N	$2\alpha = 0.10$	$2\alpha = 0.02$	N	$2\alpha = 0.10$	$2\alpha = 0.02$
			101	-0.174–+0.154	-0.242–+0.221
			102	173– 153	240– 220
			103	172– 152	239– 219
			104	171– 152	238– 218
5	-0.753–+0.253	-0.798–+0.297	**105**	-0.170–+0.151	-0.237–+0.217
6	708– 345	863– 447	106	169– 150	236– 216
7	674– 370	799– 510	107	168– 150	234– 216
8	625– 371	764– 531	108	167– 149	233– 215
9	593– 366	737– 533	109	167– 148	232– 214
10	-0.564–+0.360	-0.705–+0.525	**110**	-0.166–+0.148	-0.231–+0.213
11	539– 353	679– 515	111	165– 147	230– 212
12	516– 348	655– 505	112	164– 146	229– 211
13	497– 341	634– 495	113	164– 146	228– 210
14	479– 335	615– 485	114	163– 145	227– 209
15	-0.462–+0.328	-0.597–+0.475	**115**	-0.162–+0.145	-0.226–+0.20[illegible]
16	447– 322	580– 465	116	161– 144	225– 207
17	434– 316	564– 456	117	161– 143	224– 20[illegible]
18	421– 310	550– 448	118	160– 143	223– 20[illegible]
19	410– 304	536– 440	119	159– 142	222– 2[illegible]
20	-0.399–+0.299	-0.524–+0.432	**120**	-0.159–+0.142	-0.221–+0.20[illegible]
21	389– 294	512– 424	121	158– 141	220– 2[illegible]
22	380– 289	502– 417	122	157– 141	219– 20[illegible]
23	372– 285	491– 411	123	157– 140	218– 20[illegible]
24	364– 280	482– 404	124	156– 140	217– 201
25	-0.356–+0.276	-0.473–+0.398	**125**	-0.155–+0.139	-0.216–+0.20[illegible]
26	349– 272	464– 392	126	155– 139	215– 19[illegible]
27	343– 268	456– 386	127	154– 138	214– 199
28	336– 264	448– 380	128	153– 138	214– 198
29	331– 260	440– 375	129	153– 137	213– 197
30	-0.325–+0.257	-0.433–+0.370	**130**	-0.152–+0.137	-0.212–+0.196
31	319– 254	426– 365	131	151– 136	211– 196
32	314– 251	420– 361	132	151– 136	210– 195
33	309– 248	413– 356	133	150– 135	209– 194
34	304– 245	408– 352	134	150– 135	209– 193
35	-0.300–+0.242	-0.402–+0.348	**135**	-0.149–+0.134	-0.208–+0.193
36	295– 239	396– 344	136	148– 134	207– 192
37	291– 236	391– 340	137	148– 133	206– 191
38	287– 234	386– 336	138	147– 133	205– 191
39	283– 231	381– 333	139	147– 132	205– 190
40	-0.279–+0.229	-0.377–+0.330	**140**	-0.146–+0.132	-0.204–+0.189
41	275– 227	372– 326	141	146– 131	203– 189
42	272– 224	368– 323	142	145– 131	202– 188
43	268– 222	364– 320	143	145– 131	202– 188
44	265– 220	360– 317	144	144– 130	201– 187
45	-0.262–+0.218	-0.356–+0.314	**145**	-0.144–+0.130	-0.200–+0.186
46	259– 216	352– 311	146	143– 129	199– 186
47	256– 214	348– 308	147	143– 129	199– 185
48	253– 212	345– 305	148	142– 128	198– 184
49	250– 210	341– 302	149	142– 128	197– 184
50	-0.248–+0.208	-0.338–+0.300	**150**	-0.141–+0.128	-0.197–+0.183
51	245– 206	334– 297	151	141– 127	196– 183
52	242– 205	331– 295	152	140– 127	195– 182
53	240– 203	328– 292	153	140– 126	195– 182
54	238– 201	325– 290	154	139– 126	194– 181
55	-0.235–+0.199	-0.322–+0.287	**155**	-0.139–+0.126	-0.193–+0.180
56	233– 198	319– 285	156	138– 125	193– 180
57	231– 196	316– 283	157	138– 125	192– 179
58	229– 195	314– 281	158	137– 125	191– 179
59	227– 193	311– 279	159	137– 124	191– 178
60	-0.225–+0.192	-0.308–+0.276	**160**	-0.136–+0.124	-0.190–+0.178
61	223– 190	306– 274	161	136– 123	190– 177
62	221– 189	303– 272	162	135– 123	189– 177
63	219– 188	301– 270	163	135– 123	188– 176
64	217– 186	299– 269	164	135– 122	188– 176
65	-0.215–+0.185	-0.296–+0.267	**165**	-0.134–+0.122	-0.187–+0.175
66	213– 184	294– 265	166	134– 122	187– 175
67	212– 182	292– 263	167	133– 121	186– 174
68	210– 181	290– 261	168	133– 121	186– 174
69	208– 180	288– 260	169	133– 121	185– 173
70	-0.207–+0.179	-0.286–+0.258	**170**	-0.132–+0.120	-0.184–+0.173
71	205– 177	284– 256	171	132– 120	184– 172
72	203– 176	282– 255	172	131– 120	183– 172
73	202– 175	280– 253	173	131– 119	183– 171
74	200– 174	278– 252	174	131– 119	182– 171
75	-0.199–+0.173	-0.276–+0.250	**175**	-0.130–+0.119	-0.182–+0.170
76	198– 172	275– 249	176	130– 118	181– 170
77	197– 172	273– 248	177	129– 118	181– 169
78	196– 171	272– 247	178	129– 118	180– 169
79	195– 170	271– 246	179	129– 117	180– 168
80	-0.194–+0.169	-0.269–+0.245	**180**	-0.128–+0.117	-0.179–+0.168
81	193– 169	268– 243	181	128– 117	179– 167
82	192– 168	267– 242	182	127– 116	178– 167
83	191– 167	265– 241	183	127– 116	178– 167
84	190– 166	264– 240	184	127– 116	177– 166
85	-0.189–+0.166	-0.263–+0.239	**185**	-0.126–+0.116	-0.177–+0.166
86	188– 165	261– 238	186	126– 115	176– 165
87	187– 164	260– 237	187	126– 115	176– 165
88	186– 163	259– 236	188	125– 115	175– 164
89	185– 163	257– 234	189	125– 114	175– 164
90	-0.184–+0.162	-0.256–+0.233	**190**	-0.125–+0.114	-0.174–+0.164
91	183– 161	255– 232	191	124– 114	174– 163
92	182– 160	254– 231	192	124– 114	173– 163
93	181– 160	252– 230	193	124– 113	173– 162
94	180– 159	251– 229	194	123– 113	172– 162
95	-0.179–+0.158	-0.249–+0.228	**195**	-0.123–+0.113	-0.172–+0.161
96	178– 157	248– 227	196	123– 112	171– 161
97	177– 157	247– 226	197	122– 112	171– 161
98	177– 156	245– 224	198	122– 112	170– 160
99	176– 155	244– 223	199	122– 112	170– 160
100	-0.175–+0.154	-0.243–+0.222	**200**	-0.121–+0.111	-0.170–+0.160
			1000	-0.053–+0.051	-0.075–+0.073

1) Values up to $N = 60$ obtained by converting with the factor $(N-1)/N$ the exact values of HART, B. I., *Ann. math. Statist.*, **13**, 445 (1942). *2)* Values up to $N = 75$ from the exact values of ANDERSON, R.L., *Ann. math. Statist.*, **13**, 1 (1942), with interpolated values from $N = 16$ to 75. *1)* and *2)* reprinted by kind permission of the authors and publishers. *3)* Empirical approximation at transition values, then normal approximation. Reproduction only by permission of the publishers of these *Scientific Tables*.

$\sqrt{1-r^2}$

r	0.000	0.001	0.002	0.003	0.004	0.005	0.006	0.007	0.008	0.009
	0.	0.	0.	0.	0.	0.	0.	0.	0.	0.
0.000	00000*	00000*	00000*	00000*	99999	99999	99998	99998	99997	99996
010	99995	99994	99993	99992	99990	99989	99987	99986	99984	99982
020	99980	99978	99976	99974	99971	99969	99966	99964	99961	99958
030	99955	99952	99949	99946	99942	99939	99935	99932	99928	99924
040	99920	99916	99912	99908	99903	99899	99894	99889	99885	99880
0.050	99875	99870	99865	99859	99854	99849	99843	99837	99832	99826
060	99820	99814	99808	99801	99795	99789	99782	99775	99769	99762
070	99755	99748	99740	99733	99726	99718	99711	99703	99695	99687
080	99679	99671	99663	99655	99647	99638	99630	99621	99612	99603
090	99594	99585	99576	99567	99557	99548	99538	99528	99519	99509
0.100	99499	99489	99478	99468	99458	99447	99437	99426	99415	99404
110	99393	99382	99371	99359	99348	99337	99325	99313	99301	99289
120	99277	99265	99253	99241	99228	99216	99203	99190	99177	99164
130	99151	99138	99125	99112	99098	99085	99071	99057	99043	99029
140	99015	99001	98987	98972	98958	98943	98928	98914	98899	98884
0.150	98869	98853	98838	98823	98807	98791	98776	98760	98744	98728
160	98712	98695	98679	98663	98646	98629	98613	98596	98579	98562
170	98544	98527	98510	98492	98475	98457	98439	98421	98403	98385
180	98367	98348	98330	98311	98293	98274	98255	98236	98217	98198
190	98178	98159	98139	98120	98100	98080	98060	98040	98020	98000
0.200	97980	97959	97939	97918	97897	97876	97855	97834	97813	97792
210	97770	97749	97727	97705	97683	97661	97639	97617	97595	97572
220	97550	97527	97505	97482	97459	97436	97413	97389	97366	97343
230	97319	97295	97272	97248	97224	97200	97175	97151	97127	97102
240	97077	97053	97028	97003	96978	96952	96927	96902	96876	96850
0.250	96825	96799	96773	96747	96720	96694	96668	96641	96614	96588
260	96561	96534	96507	96480	96452	96425	96397	96370	96342	96314
270	96286	96258	96230	96201	96173	96144	96116	96087	96058	96029
280	96000	95971	95941	95912	95882	95853	95823	95793	95763	95733
290	95703	95672	95642	95611	95581	95550	95519	95488	95457	95425
0.300	95394	95362	95331	95299	95267	95235	95203	95171	95139	95106
310	95074	95041	95008	94975	94942	94909	94876	94843	94809	94775
320	94742	94708	94674	94640	94606	94571	94537	94502	94468	94433
330	94398	94363	94328	94293	94257	94222	94186	94150	94115	94079
340	94043	94006	93970	93934	93897	93860	93823	93787	93749	93712
0.350	93675	93638	93600	93562	93525	93487	93449	93410	93372	93334
360	93295	93257	93218	93179	93140	93101	93061	93022	92983	92943
370	92903	92863	92823	92783	92743	92702	92662	92621	92581	92540
380	92499	92458	92416	92375	92333	92292	92250	92208	92166	92124
390	92081	92039	91997	91954	91911	91868	91825	91782	91739	91695
0.400	91652	91608	91564	91520	91476	91432	91387	91343	91298	91253
410	91209	91164	91118	91073	91028	90982	90936	90891	90845	90799
420	90752	90706	90660	90613	90566	90519	90472	90425	90378	90330
430	90283	90235	90187	90139	90091	90043	89995	89946	89897	89849
440	89800	89751	89702	89652	89603	89553	89503	89453	89403	89353
0.450	89303	89252	89202	89151	89100	89049	88998	88947	88895	88844
460	88792	88740	88688	88636	88584	88531	88478	88426	88373	88320
470	88267	88213	88160	88106	88052	87999	87945	87890	87836	87781
480	87727	87672	87617	87562	87507	87451	87396	87340	87284	87228
490	87172	87116	87060	87003	86946	86889	86832	86775	86718	86660
0.500	86603	86545	86487	86429	86370	86312	86253	86195	86136	86077
510	86017	85958	85899	85839	85779	85719	85659	85599	85538	85477
520	85417	85356	85295	85233	85172	85110	85048	84987	84924	84862
530	84800	84737	84674	84612	84548	84485	84422	84358	84294	84231
540	84167	84102	84038	83973	83909	83844	83779	83713	83648	83582
0.550	83516	83451	83384	83318	83252	83185	83118	83051	82984	82917
560	82849	82782	82714	82646	82577	82509	82441	82372	82303	82234
570	82164	82095	82025	81956	81886	81815	81745	81674	81604	81533
580	81462	81390	81319	81247	81175	81103	81031	80959	80886	80813
590	80740	80667	80594	80520	80447	80373	80298	80224	80150	80075
0.600	80000	79925	79850	79774	79698	79623	79546	79470	79394	79317
610	79240	79163	79086	79008	78931	78853	78775	78696	78618	78539
620	78460	78381	78302	78222	78142	78062	77982	77902	77821	77741
630	77660	77578	77497	77415	77333	77251	77169	77086	77004	76921
640	76837	76754	76670	76587	76503	76418	76334	76249	76164	76079
0.650	75993	75908	75822	75736	75649	75563	75476	75389	75302	75214
660	75127	75039	74950	74862	74773	74684	74595	74506	74416	74326
670	74236	74146	74055	73964	73873	73782	73690	73598	73506	73414
680	73321	73228	73135	73042	72948	72854	72760	72666	72571	72476
690	72381	72285	72190	72094	71997	71901	71804	71707	71610	71512
0.700	71414	71316	71218	71119	71020	70921	70821	70721	70621	70521
710	70420	70319	70218	70116	70015	69912	69810	69707	69604	69501
720	69397	69294	69189	69085	68980	68875	68769	68664	68558	68451
730	68345	68238	68130	68023	67915	67807	67698	67589	67480	67371
740	67261	67151	67040	66929	66818	66706	66595	66482	66370	66257
0.750	66144	66030	65916	65802	65687	65572	65457	65341	65225	65109
760	64992	64875	64758	64640	64522	64403	64284	64165	64045	63925
770	63804	63684	63562	63441	63319	63196	63073	62950	62826	62702
780	62578	62453	62328	62202	62076	61950	61823	61695	61568	61439
790	61311	61182	61052	60922	60792	60661	60530	60398	60266	60133
0.800	60000	59866	59732	59598	59463	59327	59192	59055	58918	58781
810	58643	58505	58366	58226	58086	57946	57805	57664	57522	57379
820	57236	57093	56949	56804	56659	56513	56367	56220	56073	55925
830	55776	55627	55478	55327	55176	55025	54873	54720	54567	54413
840	54259	54104	53948	53791	53634	53477	53318	53159	53000	52839
0.850	52678	52517	52354	52191	52027	51863	51698	51532	51365	51198
860	51029	50860	50691	50520	50349	50177	50004	49831	49656	49481
870	49305	49128	48951	48772	48593	48412	48231	48049	47866	47682
880	47497	47312	47125	46937	46749	46559	46369	46177	45984	45791
890	45596	45400	45204	45006	44807	44607	44405	44203	44000	43795
0.900	43589	43382	43174	42964	42753	42541	42328	42113	41897	41680
910	41461	41241	41019	40796	40571	40345	40118	39889	39658	39426
920	39192	38956	38719	38480	38239	37997	37752	37506	37258	37008
930	36756	36502	36246	35988	35727	35465	35200	34933	34664	34392
940	34117	33841	33561	33279	32995	32707	32417	32123	31827	31528
0.950	31225	30919	30610	30297	29981	29661	29337	29009	28677	28341
960	28000	27655	27305	26950	26590	26225	25854	25478	25095	24706
970	24310	23908	23498	23081	22655	22220	21777	21324	20860	20386
980	19900	19401	18888	18361	17817	17255	16675	16072	15445	14792
990	14107	13386	12624	11811	10938	09987	08935	07740	06321	04471

$1-r^2$

r	0.000	0.001	0.002	0.003	0.004	0.005	0.006	0.007	0.008	0.009
	0.	0.	0.	0.	0.	0.	0.	0.	0.	0.
0.000	00000*	00000*	00000*	99999	99998	99998	99996	99995	99994	99992
010	99990	99988	99986	99983	99980	99978	99974	99971	99968	99964
020	99960	99956	99952	99947	99942	99938	99932	99927	99922	99916
030	99910	99904	99898	99891	99884	99878	99870	99863	99856	99848
040	99840	99832	99824	99815	99806	99798	99788	99779	99770	99760
0.050	99750	99740	99730	99719	99708	99698	99686	99675	99664	99652
060	99640	99628	99616	99603	99590	99578	99564	99551	99538	99524
070	99510	99496	99482	99467	99452	99438	99422	99407	99392	99376
080	99360	99344	99328	99311	99294	99278	99260	99243	99226	99208
090	99190	99172	99154	99135	99116	99098	99078	99059	99040	99020
0.100	99000	98980	98960	98939	98918	98898	98876	98855	98834	98812
110	98790	98768	98746	98723	98700	98678	98654	98631	98608	98584
120	98560	98536	98512	98487	98462	98438	98412	98387	98362	98336
130	98310	98284	98258	98231	98204	98178	98150	98123	98096	98068
140	98040	98012	97984	97955	97926	97898	97868	97839	97810	97780
0.150	97750	97720	97690	97659	97628	97598	97566	97535	97504	97472
160	97440	97408	97376	97343	97310	97278	97244	97211	97178	97144
170	97110	97076	97042	97007	96972	96938	96902	96867	96832	96796
180	96760	96724	96688	96651	96614	96578	96540	96503	96466	96428
190	96390	96352	96314	96275	96236	96198	96158	96119	96080	96040
0.200	96000	95960	95920	95879	95838	95798	95756	95715	95674	95632
210	95590	95548	95506	95463	95420	95378	95334	95291	95248	95204
220	95160	95116	95072	95027	94982	94938	94892	94847	94802	94756
230	94710	94664	94618	94571	94524	94478	94430	94383	94336	94288
240	94240	94192	94144	94095	94046	93998	93948	93899	93850	93800
0.250	93750	93700	93650	93599	93548	93498	93446	93395	93344	93292
260	93240	93188	93136	93083	93030	92978	92924	92871	92818	92764
270	92710	92656	92602	92547	92492	92438	92382	92327	92272	92216
280	92160	92104	92048	91991	91934	91878	91820	91763	91706	91648
290	91590	91532	91474	91415	91356	91298	91238	91179	91120	91060
0.300	91000	90940	90880	90819	90758	90698	90636	90575	90514	90452
310	90390	90328	90266	90203	90140	90078	90014	89951	89888	89824
320	89760	89696	89632	89567	89502	89438	89372	89307	89242	89176
330	89110	89044	88978	88911	88844	88778	88710	88643	88576	88508
340	88440	88372	88304	88235	88166	88098	88028	87959	87890	87820
0.350	87750	87680	87610	87539	87468	87398	87326	87255	87184	87112
360	87040	86968	86896	86823	86750	86678	86604	86531	86458	86384
370	86310	86236	86162	86087	86012	85938	85862	85787	85712	85636
380	85560	85484	85408	85331	85254	85178	85100	85023	84946	84868
390	84790	84712	84634	84555	84476	84398	84318	84239	84160	84080
0.400	84000	83920	83840	83759	83678	83598	83516	83435	83354	83272
410	83190	83108	83026	82943	82860	82778	82694	82611	82528	82444
420	82360	82276	82192	82107	82022	81938	81852	81767	81682	81596
430	81510	81424	81338	81251	81164	81078	80990	80903	80816	80728
440	80640	80552	80464	80375	80286	80198	80108	80019	79930	79840
0.450	79750	79660	79570	79479	79388	79298	79206	79115	79024	78932
460	78840	78748	78656	78563	78470	78378	78284	78191	78098	78004
470	77910	77816	77722	77627	77532	77438	77342	77247	77152	77056
480	76960	76864	76768	76671	76574	76478	76380	76283	76186	76088
490	75990	75892	75794	75695	75596	75498	75398	75299	75200	75100
0.500	75000	74900	74800	74699	74598	74498	74396	74295	74194	74092
510	73990	73888	73786	73683	73580	73478	73374	73271	73168	73064
520	72960	72856	72752	72647	72542	72438	72332	72227	72122	72016
530	71910	71804	71698	71591	71484	71378	71270	71163	71056	70948
540	70840	70732	70624	70515	70406	70298	70188	70079	69970	69860
0.550	69750	69640	69530	69419	69308	69198	69086	68975	68864	68752
560	68640	68528	68416	68303	68190	68078	67964	67851	67738	67624
570	67510	67396	67282	67167	67052	66938	66822	66707	66592	66476
580	66360	66244	66128	66011	65894	65778	65660	65543	65426	65308
590	65190	65072	64954	64835	64716	64598	64478	64359	64240	64120
0.600	64000	63880	63760	63639	63518	63398	63276	63155	63034	62912
610	62790	62668	62546	62423	62300	62178	62054	61931	61808	61684
620	61560	61436	61312	61187	61062	60938	60812	60687	60562	60436
630	60310	60184	60058	59931	59804	59678	59550	59423	59296	59168
640	59040	58912	58784	58655	58526	58398	58268	58139	58010	57880
0.650	57750	57620	57490	57359	57228	57098	56966	56835	56704	56572
660	56440	56308	56176	56043	55910	55778	55644	55511	55378	55244
670	55110	54976	54842	54707	54572	54438	54302	54167	54032	53896
680	53760	53624	53488	53351	53214	53078	52940	52803	52666	52528
690	52390	52252	52114	51975	51836	51698	51558	51419	51280	51140
0.700	51000	50860	50720	50579	50438	50298	50156	50015	49874	49732
710	49590	49448	49306	49163	49020	48878	48734	48591	48448	48304
720	48160	48016	47872	47727	47582	47438	47292	47147	47002	46856
730	46710	46564	46418	46271	46124	45978	45830	45683	45536	45388
740	45240	45092	44944	44795	44646	44498	44348	44199	44050	43900
0.750	43750	43600	43450	43299	43148	42998	42846	42695	42544	42392
760	42240	42088	41936	41783	41630	41478	41324	41171	41018	40864
770	40710	40556	40402	40247	40092	39938	39782	39627	39472	39316
780	39160	39004	38848	38691	38534	38378	38220	38063	37906	37748
790	37590	37432	37274	37115	36956	36798	36638	36479	36320	36160
0.800	36000	35840	35680	35519	35358	35198	35036	34875	34714	34552
810	34390	34228	34066	33903	33740	33578	33414	33251	33088	32924
820	32760	32596	32432	32267	32102	31938	31772	31607	31442	31276
830	31110	30944	30778	30611	30444	30278	30110	29943	29776	29608
840	29440	29272	29104	28935	28766	28598	28428	28259	28090	27920
0.850	27750	27580	27410	27239	27068	26898	26726	26555	26384	26212
860	26040	25868	25696	25523	25350	25178	25004	24831	24658	24484
870	24310	24136	23962	23787	23612	23438	23262	23087	22912	22736
880	22560	22384	22208	22031	21854	21678	21500	21323	21146	20968
890	20790	20612	20434	20255	20076	19898	19718	19539	19360	19180
0.900	19000	18820	18640	18459	18278	18098	17916	17735	17554	17372
910	17190	17008	16826	16643	16460	16278	16094	15911	15728	15544
920	15360	15176	14992	14807	14622	14438	14252	14067	13882	13696
930	13510	13324	13138	12951	12764	12578	12390	12203	12016	11828
940	11640	11452	11264	11075	10886	10698	10508	10319	10130	09940
0.950	09750	09560	09370	09179	08988	08798	08606	08415	08224	08032
960	07840	07648	07456	07263	07070	06878	06684	06491	06298	06104
970	05910	05716	05522	05327	05132	04938	04742	04547	04352	04156
980	03960	03764	03568	03371	03174	02978	02780	02583	02386	02188
990	01990	01792	01594	01395	01196	00998	00798	00599	00400	00200

* To be read as 1.00000.

n	$\sqrt{\frac{n-1}{n-2}}$	$\frac{n-1}{n-2}$	n	$\sqrt{\frac{n-1}{n-2}}$	$\frac{n-1}{n-2}$	n	$\sqrt{\frac{n-1}{n-2}}$	$\frac{n-1}{n-2}$	n	$\sqrt{\frac{n-1}{n-2}}$	$\frac{n-1}{n-2}$	n	$\sqrt{\frac{n-1}{n-2}}$	$\frac{n-1}{n-2}$
	1.	1.		1.	1.		1.	1.		1.	1.		1.	1.
0	–	–	**50**	01036	02083	**100**	00509	01020	**150**	00337	00676	**200**	00252	00505
1	–	–	51	01015	02041	101	00504	01010	151	00335	00671	201	00251	00503
2	–	–	52	00995	02000	102	00499	01000	152	00333	00667	202	00250	00500
3	41421	00000**	53	00976	01961	103	00494	00990	153	00331	00662	203	00248	00498
4	22474	50000	54	00957	01923	104	00489	00980	154	00328	00658	204	00247	00495
5	15470	33333	**55**	00939	01887	**105**	00484	00971	**155**	00326	00654	**205**	00246	00493
6	11803	25000	56	00922	01852	106	00480	00962	156	00324	00649	206	00245	00490
7	09545	20000	57	00905	01818	107	00475	00952	157	00322	00645	207	00244	00488
8	08012	16667	58	00889	01786	108	00471	00943	158	00320	00641	208	00242	00485
9	06904	14286	59	00873	01754	109	00466	00935	159	00318	00637	209	00241	00483
10	06066	12500	**60**	00858	01724	**110**	00462	00926	**160**	00316	00633	**210**	00240	00481
11	05409	11111	61	00844	01695	111	00458	00917	161	00314	00629	211	00239	00478
12	04881	10000	62	00830	01667	112	00454	00909	162	00312	00625	212	00238	00476
13	04447	09091	63	00816	01639	113	00449	00901	163	00310	00621	213	00237	00474
14	04083	08333	64	00803	01613	114	00445	00893	164	00308	00617	214	00236	00472
15	03775	07692	**65**	00791	01587	**115**	00442	00885	**165**	00306	00613	**215**	00234	00469
16	03510	07143	66	00778	01563	116	00438	00877	166	00304	00610	216	00233	00467
17	03280	06667	67	00766	01538	117	00434	00870	167	00303	00606	217	00232	00465
18	03078	06250	68	00755	01515	118	00430	00862	168	00301	00602	218	00231	00463
19	02899	05882	69	00744	01493	119	00426	00855	169	00299	00599	219	00230	00461
20	02740	05556	**70**	00733	01471	**120**	00423	00847	**170**	00297	00595	**220**	00229	00459
21	02598	05263	71	00722	01449	121	00419	00840	171	00295	00592	221	00228	00457
22	02470	05000	72	00712	01429	122	00416	00833	172	00294	00588	222	00227	00455
23	02353	04762	73	00702	01408	123	00412	00826	173	00292	00585	223	00226	00452
24	02247	04545	74	00692	01389	124	00409	00820	174	00290	00581	224	00225	00450
25	02151	04348	**75**	00683	01370	**125**	00406	00813	**175**	00289	00578	**225**	00224	00448
26	02062	04167	76	00673	01351	126	00402	00806	176	00287	00575	226	00223	00446
27	01980	04000	77	00664	01333	127	00399	00800	177	00285	00571	227	00222	00444
28	01905	03846	78	00656	01316	128	00396	00794	178	00284	00568	228	00221	00442
29	01835	03704	79	00647	01299	129	00393	00787	179	00282	00565	229	00220	00441
30	01770	03571	**80**	00639	01282	**130**	00390	00781	**180**	00281	00562	**230**	00219	00439
31	01710	03448	81	00631	01266	131	00387	00775	181	00279	00559	231	00218	00437
32	01653	03333	82	00623	01250	132	00384	00769	182	00277	00556	232	00217	00435
33	01600	03226	83	00615	01235	133	00381	00763	183	00276	00552	233	00216	00433
34	01550	03125	84	00608	01220	134	00378	00758	184	00274	00549	234	00215	00431
35	01504	03030	**85**	00601	01205	**135**	00375	00752	**185**	00273	00546	**235**	00214	00429
36	01460	02941	86	00593	01190	136	00372	00746	186	00271	00543	236	00213	00427
37	01419	02857	87	00587	01176	137	00370	00741	187	00270	00541	237	00213	00426
38	01379	02778	88	00580	01163	138	00367	00735	188	00268	00538	238	00212	00424
39	01342	02703	89	00573	01149	139	00364	00730	189	00267	00535	239	00211	00422
40	01307	02632	**90**	00567	01136	**140**	00362	00725	**190**	00266	00532	**240**	00210	00420
41	01274	02564	91	00560	01124	141	00359	00719	191	00264	00529	241	00209	00418
42	01242	02500	92	00554	01111	142	00357	00714	192	00263	00526	242	00208	00417
43	01212	02439	93	00548	01099	143	00354	00709	193	00261	00524	243	00207	00415
44	01183	02381	94	00542	01087	144	00351	00704	194	00260	00521	244	00206	00413
45	01156	02326	**95**	00536	01075	**145**	00349	00699	**195**	00259	00518	**245**	00206	00412
46	01130	02273	96	00531	01064	146	00347	00694	196	00257	00515	246	00205	00410
47	01105	02222	97	00525	01053	147	00344	00690	197	00256	00513	247	00204	00408
48	01081	02174	98	00519	01042	148	00342	00685	198	00255	00510	248	00203	00407
49	01058	02128	99	00514	01031	149	00340	00680	199	00253	00508	249	00202	00405
50	01036	02083	**100**	00509	01020	**150**	00337	00676	**200**	00252	00505	**250**	00202	00403

Example: $s_{y\cdot x} = s_y \sqrt{1-r^2}\sqrt{\frac{n-1}{n-2}}$, $s^2_{y\cdot x} = s^2_y(1-r^2)\frac{n-1}{n-2}$, etc.

Explanation of the table on page 61

The table gives the values of

$$r = \sqrt{\frac{t^2}{t^2+\nu}} \quad \text{(degrees of freedom of } t = \nu)$$

thus enabling it to be decided without calculation whether a correlation coefficient differs significantly from zero. The table also allows the corresponding regression coefficients to be tested automatically in the same way. If, for example, $r_{xy} \neq$ zero, then b_{xy} and b_{yx} are also not equal to zero.

The degrees of freedom are found as follows: from the numbe n of pairs of observations, the number 2 is subtracted and als in the case of partial correlation coefficients, the number of ex cluded variables.

Examples: (variable 1, 2, . . .) r_{12} $\nu = n-2$

$r_{12\cdot 3}$ $\nu = n-2-1$

$r_{12\cdot 34}$ $\nu = n-2-2$

etc.

* Reproduction only by permission of the publishers of these *Scientific Tables.* ** To be read as 2.00000.

Significance Limits for *r* when Population Correlation Coefficient is Zero*

ν \ 2α	0.1	0.05	0.01	0.001	ν \ 2α	0.1	0.05	0.01	0.001
1	0.9877	0.9969	0.9999	1.0000	101	0.1630	0.1937	0.2528	0.3196
2	9000	9500	9900	0.9990	102	1622	1927	2515	3181
3	8054	8783	9587	9911	103	1614	1918	2504	3166
4	7293	8114	9172	9741	104	1606	1909	2492	3152
5	0.6694	0.7545	0.8745	0.9509	**105**	0.1599	0.1900	0.2480	0.3138
6	6215	7067	8343	9249	106	1591	1891	2469	3123
7	5822	6664	7977	8983	107	1584	1882	2458	3109
8	5494	6319	7646	8721	108	1577	1874	2447	3095
9	5214	6021	7348	8471	109	1569	1865	2436	3082
10	0.4973	0.5760	0.7079	0.8233	**110**	0.1562	0.1857	0.2425	0.3069
11	4762	5529	6835	8010	111	1555	1848	2414	3055
12	4575	5324	6614	7800	112	1548	1840	2404	3042
13	4409	5139	6411	7604	113	1542	1832	2393	3029
14	4259	4973	6226	7419	114	1535	1824	2383	3017
15	0.4124	0.4821	0.6055	0.7247	**115**	0.1528	0.1816	0.2373	0.3004
16	4000	4683	5897	7084	116	1522	1809	2363	2992
17	3887	4555	5751	6932	117	1515	1801	2353	2979
18	3783	4438	5614	6788	118	1509	1793	2343	2967
19	3687	4329	5487	6652	119	1502	1786	2334	2955
20	0.3598	0.4227	0.5368	0.6524	**120**	0.1496	0.1779	0.2324	0.2943
21	3515	4132	5256	6402	121	1490	1771	2315	2932
22	3438	4044	5151	6287	122	1484	1764	2305	2920
23	3365	3961	5052	6177	123	1478	1757	2296	2909
24	3297	3882	4958	6073	124	1472	1750	2287	2897
25	0.3233	0.3809	0.4869	0.5974	**125**	0.1466	0.1743	0.2278	0.2886
26	3172	3739	4785	5880	126	1460	1736	2269	2875
27	3115	3673	4705	5790	127	1455	1730	2261	2864
28	3061	3610	4629	5703	128	1449	1723	2252	2854
29	3009	3550	4556	5620	129	1443	1716	2243	2843
30	0.2960	0.3494	0.4487	0.5541	**130**	0.1438	0.1710	0.2235	0.2832
31	2913	3440	4421	5465	131	1432	1703	2226	2822
32	2869	3388	4357	5392	132	1427	1697	2218	2812
33	2826	3338	4297	5322	133	1422	1690	2210	2801
34	2785	3291	4238	5255	134	1416	1684	2202	2791
35	0.2746	0.3246	0.4182	0.5189	**135**	0.1411	0.1678	0.2194	0.2781
36	2709	3202	4128	5126	136	1406	1672	2186	2771
37	2673	3160	4076	5066	137	1401	1666	2178	2762
38	2638	3120	4026	5007	138	1396	1660	2170	2752
39	2605	3081	3978	4951	139	1391	1654	2163	2742
40	0.2573	0.3044	0.3932	0.4896	**140**	0.1386	0.1648	0.2155	0.2733
41	2542	3008	3887	4843	141	1381	1642	2148	2724
42	2512	2973	3843	4792	142	1376	1637	2140	2714
43	2483	2940	3802	4742	143	1371	1631	2133	2705
44	2455	2907	3761	4694	144	1367	1625	2126	2696
45	0.2428	0.2875	0.3721	0.4647	**145**	0.1362	0.1620	0.2118	0.2687
46	2403	2845	3683	4602	146	1357	1614	2111	2678
47	2377	2816	3646	4558	147	1353	1609	2104	2669
48	2353	2787	3610	4515	148	1348	1603	2097	2660
49	2329	2759	3575	4473	149	1344	1598	2090	2652
50	0.2306	0.2732	0.3541	0.4433	**150**	0.1339	0.1593	0.2083	0.2643
51	2284	2706	3509	4393	151	1335	1587	2077	2635
52	2262	2681	3477	4355	152	1330	1582	2070	2626
53	2241	2656	3445	4317	153	1326	1577	2063	2618
54	2221	2632	3415	4281	154	1322	1572	2057	2610
55	0.2201	0.2609	0.3385	0.4245	**155**	0.1318	0.1567	0.2050	0.2602
56	2181	2586	3357	4210	156	1313	1562	2044	2594
57	2162	2564	3329	4176	157	1309	1557	2037	2586
58	2144	2542	3301	4143	158	1305	1552	2031	2578
59	2126	2521	3274	4111	159	1301	1547	2025	2570
60	0.2108	0.2500	0.3248	0.4079	**160**	0.1297	0.1543	0.2019	0.2562
61	2091	2480	3223	4048	161	1293	1538	2012	2554
62	2075	2461	3198	4018	162	1289	1533	2006	2547
63	2058	2442	3174	3988	163	1285	1529	2000	2539
64	2042	2423	3150	3959	164	1281	1524	1994	2532
65	0.2027	0.2405	0.3127	0.3931	**165**	0.1277	0.1519	0.1988	0.2524
66	2012	2387	3104	3904	166	1273	1515	1982	2517
67	1997	2369	3081	3877	167	1270	1510	1977	2510
68	1982	2352	3060	3850	168	1266	1506	1971	2502
69	1968	2335	3038	3824	169	1262	1501	1965	2495
70	0.1954	0.2319	0.3017	0.3798	**170**	0.1258	0.1497	0.1959	0.2488
71	1940	2303	2997	3773	171	1255	1493	1954	2481
72	1927	2287	2977	3749	172	1251	1488	1948	2474
73	1914	2272	2957	3725	173	1248	1484	1943	2467
74	1901	2257	2938	3701	174	1244	1480	1937	2460
75	0.1889	0.2242	0.2919	0.3678	**175**	0.1240	0.1476	0.1932	0.2453
76	1876	2227	2900	3655	176	1237	1471	1926	2446
77	1864	2213	2882	3633	177	1233	1467	1921	2440
78	1852	2199	2864	3611	178	1230	1463	1915	2433
79	1841	2185	2847	3590	179	1227	1459	1910	2426
80	0.1829	0.2172	0.2830	0.3569	**180**	0.1223	0.1455	0.1905	0.2420
81	1818	2159	2813	3548	181	1220	1451	1900	2413
82	1807	2146	2796	3527	182	1216	1447	1895	2407
83	1796	2133	2780	3507	183	1213	1443	1890	2400
84	1786	2120	2764	3488	184	1210	1439	1885	2394
85	0.1775	0.2108	0.2748	0.3468	**185**	0.1207	0.1435	0.1880	0.2388
86	1765	2096	2733	3449	186	1203	1432	1874	2381
87	1755	2084	2717	3430	187	1200	1428	1870	2375
88	1745	2072	2702	3412	188	1197	1424	1865	2369
89	1735	2061	2688	3394	189	1194	1420	1860	2363
90	0.1726	0.2050	0.2673	0.3376	**190**	0.1191	0.1417	0.1855	0.2357
91	1716	2039	2659	3358	191	1188	1413	1850	2351
92	1707	2028	2645	3341	192	1184	1409	1845	2345
93	1698	2017	2631	3324	193	1181	1406	1841	2339
94	1689	2006	2617	3307	194	1178	1402	1836	2333
95	0.1680	0.1996	0.2604	0.3291	**195**	0.1175	0.1399	0.1831	0.2327
96	1671	1986	2591	3274	196	1172	1395	1827	2321
97	1663	1976	2578	3258	197	1169	1391	1822	2316
98	1654	1966	2565	3242	198	1166	1388	1818	2310
99	1646	1956	2552	3227	199	1164	1384	1813	2304
100	0.1638	0.1946	0.2540	0.3211	**200**	0.1161	0.1381	0.1809	0.2299

r	0.000	0.001	0.002	0.003	0.004	0.005	0.006	0.007	0.008	0.009
0.000	0.00000	0.00100	0.00200	0.00300	0.00400	0.00500	0.00600	0.00700	0.00800	0.00900
010	01000	01100	01200	01300	01400	01500	01600	01700	01800	01900
020	02000	02100	02200	02300	02400	02501	02601	02701	02801	02901
030	03001	03101	03201	03301	03401	03501	03602	03702	03802	03902
040	04002	04102	04202	04303	04403	04503	04603	04703	04804	04904
0.050	0.05004	0.05104	0.05205	0.05305	0.05405	0.05506	0.05606	0.05706	0.05806	0.05907
060	06007	06108	06208	06308	06409	06509	06610	06710	06810	06911
070	07011	07112	07212	07313	07414	07514	07615	07715	07816	07916
080	08017	08118	08218	08319	08420	08521	08621	08722	08823	08924
090	09024	09125	09226	09327	09428	09529	09630	09731	09832	09933
0.100	0.10034	0.10135	0.10236	0.10337	0.10438	0.10539	0.10640	0.10741	0.10842	0.10943
110	11045	11146	11247	11348	11450	11551	11652	11754	11855	11957
120	12058	12160	12261	12363	12464	12566	12667	12769	12871	12972
130	13074	13176	13277	13379	13481	13583	13685	13787	13889	13991
140	14093	14195	14297	14399	14501	14603	14705	14807	14910	15012
0.150	0.15114	0.15216	0.15319	0.15421	0.15524	0.15626	0.15728	0.15831	0.15934	0.16036
160	16139	16241	16344	16447	16549	16652	16755	16858	16961	17064
170	17167	17270	17373	17476	17579	17682	17785	17888	17992	18095
180	18198	18302	18405	18509	18612	18716	18819	18923	19026	19130
190	19234	19338	19441	19545	19649	19753	19857	19961	20065	20169
0.200	0.20273	0.20377	0.20482	0.20586	0.20690	0.20795	0.20899	0.21004	0.21108	0.21213
210	21317	21422	21526	21631	21736	21841	21946	22051	22156	22261
220	22366	22471	22576	22681	22786	22892	22997	23102	23208	23313
230	23419	23525	23630	23736	23842	23948	24053	24159	24265	24371
240	24477	24584	24690	24796	24902	25009	25115	25222	25328	25435
0.250	0.25541	0.25648	0.25755	0.25862	0.25968	0.26075	0.26182	0.26289	0.26396	0.26504
260	26611	26718	26825	26933	27040	27148	27255	27363	27471	27579
270	27686	27794	27902	28010	28118	28226	28335	28443	28551	28660
280	28768	28877	28985	29094	29203	29312	29420	29529	29638	29747
290	29857	29966	30075	30184	30294	30403	30513	30623	30732	30842
0.300	0.30952	0.31062	0.31172	0.31282	0.31392	0.31502	0.31613	0.31723	0.31833	0.31944
310	32055	32165	32276	32387	32498	32609	32720	32831	32942	33053
320	33165	33276	33388	33499	33611	33723	33835	33947	34059	34171
330	34283	34395	34507	34620	34732	34845	34958	35070	35183	35296
340	35409	35522	35636	35749	35862	35976	36089	36203	36317	36430
0.350	0.36544	0.36658	0.36772	0.36887	0.37001	0.37115	0.37230	0.37344	0.37459	0.37574
360	37689	37804	37919	38034	38149	38264	38380	38495	38611	38726
370	38842	38958	39074	39190	39307	39423	39539	39656	39772	39889
380	40006	40123	40240	40357	40474	40592	40709	40827	40944	41062
390	41180	41298	41416	41534	41653	41771	41890	42008	42127	42246
0.400	0.42365	0.42484	0.42603	0.42723	0.42842	0.42962	0.43081	0.43201	0.43321	0.43441
410	43561	43681	43802	43922	44043	44164	44284	44405	44527	44648
420	44769	44891	45012	45134	45256	45378	45500	45622	45745	45867
430	45990	46112	46235	46358	46481	46605	46728	46852	46975	47099
440	47223	47347	47471	47596	47720	47845	47970	48094	48220	48345
0.450	0.48470	0.48595	0.48721	0.48847	0.48973	0.49099	0.49225	0.49351	0.49478	0.49604
460	49731	49858	49985	50112	50240	50367	50495	50623	50751	50879
470	51007	51135	51264	51393	51522	51651	51780	51909	52039	52169
480	52298	52428	52559	52689	52819	52950	53081	53212	53343	53475
490	53606	53738	53870	54002	54134	54266	54399	54531	54664	54797
0.500	0.54931	0.55064	0.55198	0.55331	0.55465	0.55600	0.55734	0.55868	0.56003	0.56138
510	56273	56408	56544	56679	56815	56951	57087	57224	57360	57497
520	57634	57771	57908	58046	58184	58322	58460	58598	58737	58876
530	59015	59154	59293	59433	59572	59712	59853	59993	60134	60274
540	60416	60557	60698	60840	60982	61124	61266	61409	61552	61695
0.550	0.61838	0.61982	0.62125	0.62269	0.62413	0.62558	0.62702	0.62847	0.62992	0.63138
560	63283	63429	63575	63721	63868	64015	64162	64309	64457	64604
570	64752	64901	65049	65198	65347	65496	65646	65795	65945	66096
580	66246	66397	66548	66700	66851	67003	67155	67308	67460	67613
590	67767	67920	68074	68228	68382	68537	68692	68847	69003	69159
0.600	0.69315	0.69471	0.69628	0.69785	0.69942	0.70100	0.70258	0.70416	0.70574	0.70733
610	70892	71052	71211	71371	71532	71692	71853	72015	72176	72338
620	72500	72663	72826	72989	73153	73317	73481	73646	73811	73976
630	74142	74308	74474	74641	74808	74975	75143	75311	75479	75648
640	75817	75987	76157	76327	76498	76669	76840	77012	77184	77357
0.650	0.77530	0.77703	0.77877	0.78051	0.78226	0.78401	0.78576	0.78752	0.78928	0.79104
660	79281	79459	79637	79815	79993	80172	80352	80532	80712	80893
670	81074	81256	81438	81621	81804	81987	82171	82355	82540	82726
680	82911	83098	83284	83472	83659	83847	84036	84225	84415	84605
690	84796	84987	85178	85370	85563	85756	85950	86144	86339	86534
0.700	0.86730	0.86926	0.87123	0.87321	0.87519	0.87717	0.87916	0.88116	0.88316	0.88517
710	88718	88920	89123	89326	89530	89734	89939	90144	90350	90557
720	90765	90972	91181	91390	91600	91811	92022	92233	92446	92659
730	92873	93087	93302	93518	93735	93952	94169	94388	94607	94827
740	95048	95269	95491	95714	95938	96162	96387	96613	96840	97067
0.750	0.97296	0.97524	0.97754	0.97985	0.98216	0.98448	0.98681	0.98915	0.99150	0.99385
760	99622	99859	1.00097	1.00336	1.00575	1.00816	1.01058	1.01300	1.01543	1.01788
770	1.02033	1.02279	02526	02774	03023	03273	03524	03775	04028	04282
780	04537	04793	05050	05308	05567	05827	06088	06350	06613	06878
790	07143	07410	07677	07946	08216	08488	08760	09033	09308	09584
0.800	1.09861	1.10140	1.10419	1.10700	1.10982	1.11266	1.11551	1.11837	1.12124	1.12413
810	12703	12994	13287	13581	13877	14174	14473	14773	15074	15377
820	15682	15988	16295	16604	16915	17227	17541	17857	18174	18493
830	18814	19136	19460	19786	20113	20443	20774	21107	21442	21779
840	22117	22458	22801	23145	23492	23840	24191	24544	24899	25256
0.850	1.25615	1.25977	1.26340	1.26706	1.27075	1.27445	1.27818	1.28194	1.28571	1.28952
860	29334	29720	30108	30498	30891	31287	31686	32087	32491	32898
870	33308	33721	34137	34555	34977	35403	35831	36262	36697	37135
880	37577	38022	38470	38922	39378	39838	40301	40768	41239	41714
890	42193	42676	43163	43654	44150	44651	45156	45665	46179	46698
0.900	1.47222	1.47751	1.48285	1.48824	1.49368	1.49918	1.50473	1.51034	1.51601	1.52174
910	52752	53337	53928	54526	55130	55741	56359	56984	57616	58256
920	58903	59558	60221	60892	61571	62260	62957	63663	64379	65104
930	65839	66584	67340	68107	68885	69674	70475	71288	72114	72953
940	73805	74671	75552	76447	77358	78284	79227	80188	81166	82162
0.950	1.83178	1.84214	1.85270	1.86349	1.87450	1.88574	1.89723	1.90898	1.92100	1.93331
960	94591	95882	97207	98566	99961	2.01395	2.02870	2.04388	2.05952	2.07565
970	2.09230	2.10950	2.12730	2.14574	2.16486	18472	20539	22692	24940	27291
980	29756	32346	35075	37958	41014	44266	47741	51472	55499	59875
990	64665	69958	75873	82574	90307	99448	3.10630	3.25039	3.45338	3.80020

z-Transformation

When the population correlation coefficients differ significantly from zero, their distribution deviates from the normal distribution to an extent which is the greater the smaller the number n of pairs of observations and the larger the absolute value of r. The z-transformation can be used to normalize the distribution of the correlation coefficients, as follows:

$$z = {}^1/_2 \log_e \frac{1+r}{1-r} \quad \text{(see table on this page)}$$

and

$$r = \frac{e^{2z}-1}{e^{2z}+1} = \tanh z = \text{hyperbolic tangent of } z$$

(see tables on pages 64 and 65)

The variance of z is

$$\sigma_z^2 \approx \frac{1}{n-p-3} = \frac{1}{n'-3}$$

where n = number of pairs of observations, p = number of excluded variables. In the case of the correlation coefficient r_{xy}, for example, $p = 0$, whence $n' = n$; in the case of the partial correlation coefficient $r_{xy \cdot z}$, $p = 1$, whence $n' = n - 1$.

The approximate expected value of $\boldsymbol{z}$ (see page 179) is

$$\boldsymbol{z} \approx {}^1/_2 \log_e \frac{1+\boldsymbol{r}}{1-\boldsymbol{r}}$$

where $\boldsymbol{r}$ is the population value of r.

$\boldsymbol{z}$ is estimated from z, with k correlation coefficients from $\bar{z}$**:

$$\bar{z} = \frac{\sum_1^k (n_i - 3)\, z_i}{\sum_1^k (n_i - 3)}$$

with the variance

$$\sigma_{\bar{z}}^2 = \frac{1}{\sum_1^k (n_i - 3)}$$

The confidence interval for $\boldsymbol{z}$ is

$$z \pm \frac{|c_\alpha|}{\sqrt{n-3}};$$ (for values of $\frac{|c_\alpha|}{\sqrt{n-3}}$ see the table on the opposite page)

or $\bar{z} \pm |c_\alpha| \sigma_{\bar{z}}$

The confidence interval for $\boldsymbol{r}$ is

$$\tanh\left(z - \frac{|c_\alpha|}{\sqrt{n-3}}\right) \leqq \boldsymbol{r} \leqq \tanh\left(z + \frac{|c_\alpha|}{\sqrt{n-3}}\right)$$

or

$$\tanh(\bar{z} - |c_\alpha| \sigma_{\bar{z}}) \leqq \boldsymbol{r} \leqq \tanh(\bar{z} + |c_\alpha| \sigma_{z})$$

Tests:

Testing for population correlation coefficient $= \boldsymbol{r}$

$$c = \frac{z - \boldsymbol{z}}{\sqrt{n-3}}$$

Testing for $\boldsymbol{r}_1 = \boldsymbol{r}_2$

$$c = \frac{z_1 - z_2}{\sqrt{\frac{1}{n_1-3} + \frac{1}{n_2-3}}}$$

For other tests see page 179.

** $\bar{z}$ can be used for estimating $\boldsymbol{z}$ only when χ^2 is not significant, i.e. when

$$\chi^2 = \sum_1^k (n_i - 3)(z_i - \bar{z})^2$$

does not exceed a chosen upper significance limit with degrees of freedom $\nu = k - 1$.

Confidence Limits for the Correlation Coefficient r*

Confidence limits for $z = \zeta \pm c_g$. The table gives the values for $c_g = |c_\alpha| / \sqrt{n-3}$. See page 179

95% limits $(1 - 2\alpha = 0.95)$

n	0	1	2	3	4	5	6	7	8	9
	0.	0.	0.	0.	0.	0.	0.	0.	0.	0.
10	74080	69295	65332	61980	59095	56579	54360	52382	50606	48999
20	47536	46197	44965	43826	42770	41787	40868	40008	39199	38438
30	37720	37040	36396	35784	35202	34648	34119	33613	33129	32666
40	32222	31795	31385	30990	30609	30243	29889	29548	29217	28898
50	28589	28290	27999	27718	27445	27180	26922	26672	26428	26191
60	25960	25736	25517	25303	25095	24892	24693	24500	24310	24125
70	23945	23768	23595	23426	23260	23098	22940	22784	22632	22482
80	22336	22192	22051	21913	21777	21644	21513	21385	21259	21135
90	21013	20893	20776	20660	20546	20434	20324	20215	20109	20004
100	19900	19799	19698	19600	19502	19407	19312	19219	19127	19037
110	18948	18860	18773	18688	18603	18520	18438	18357	18277	18198
120	18120	18043	17967	17892	17818	17745	17672	17601	17530	17461
130	17392	17324	17257	17190	17124	17059	16995	16932	16869	16807
140	16745	16684	16624	16565	16506	16448	16390	16333	16277	16221
150	16166	16111	16057	16003	15950	15897	15845	15794	15743	15692
160	15642	15593	15544	15495	15447	15399	15352	15305	15258	15212
170	15167	15121	15077	15032	14988	14945	14901	14858	14816	14774
180	14732	14691	14649	14609	14568	14528	14488	14449	14410	14371
190	14333	14295	14257	14219	14182	14145	14108	14072	14036	14000
200	13964	13929	13894	13859	13825	13790	13756	13722	13689	13656
210	13623	13590	13557	13525	13493	13461	13429	13398	13367	13336
220	13305	13275	13244	13214	13184	13154	13125	13096	13066	13037
230	13009	12980	12952	12924	12896	12868	12840	12813	12785	12758
240	12731	12705	12678	12652	12625	12599	12573	12547	12522	12496
250	12471	12446	12421	12396	12371	12347	12322	12298	12274	12250
260	12226	12202	12179	12155	12132	12109	12086	12063	12040	12017
270	11995	11972	11950	11928	11906	11884	11862	11841	11819	11798
280	11776	11755	11734	11713	11692	11671	11651	11630	11610	11590
290	11569	11549	11529	11509	11490	11470	11450	11431	11411	11392
300	11373	11354	11335	11316	11297	11278	11260	11241	11223	11204
310	11186	11168	11150	11132	11114	11096	11078	11061	11043	11026
320	11008	10991	10974	10957	10939	10922	10906	10889	10872	10855
330	10839	10822	10806	10789	10773	10757	10741	10724	10708	10692
340	10677	10661	10645	10629	10614	10598	10583	10567	10552	10537
350	10522	10507	10491	10476	10462	10447	10432	10417	10402	10388
360	10373	10359	10344	10330	10316	10301	10287	10273	10259	10245
370	10231	10217	10203	10189	10176	10162	10148	10135	10121	10108
380	10094	10081	10068	10054	10041	10028	10015	10002	09989	09976
390	09963	09950	09937	09925	09912	09899	09887	09874	09862	09849
400	09837	09824	09812	09800	09788	09775	09763	09751	09739	09727
410	09715	09703	09691	09680	09668	09656	09644	09633	09621	09610
420	09598	09586	09575	09564	09552	09541	09530	09518	09507	09496
430	09485	09474	09463	09452	09441	09430	09419	09408	09397	09387
440	09376	09365	09354	09344	09333	09323	09312	09302	09291	09281
450	09270	09260	09250	09239	09229	09219	09209	09199	09188	09178
460	09168	09158	09148	09138	09128	09119	09109	09099	09089	09079
470	09070	09060	09050	09041	09031	09021	09012	09002	08993	08983
480	08974	08965	08955	08946	08937	08927	08918	08909	08900	08891
490	08881	08872	08863	08854	08845	08836	08827	08818	08809	08800
500	08792	08783	08774	08765	08756	08748	08739	08730	08722	08713
510	08705	08696	08687	08679	08670	08662	08653	08645	08637	08628
520	08620	08612	08603	08595	08587	08579	08570	08562	08554	08546
530	08538	08530	08522	08514	08506	08498	08490	08482	08474	08466
540	08458	08450	08442	08434	08427	08419	08411	08403	08396	08388
550	08380	08373	08365	08357	08350	08342	08335	08327	08320	08312
560	08305	08297	08290	08282	08275	08268	08260	08253	08246	08238
570	08231	08224	08217	08209	08202	08195	08188	08181	08174	08167
580	08159	08152	08145	08138	08131	08124	08117	08110	08103	08097
590	08090	08083	08076	08069	08062	08055	08049	08042	08035	08028
600	08022	08015	08008	08002	07995	07988	07982	07975	07968	07962
610	07955	07949	07942	07936	07929	07923	07916	07910	07903	07897
620	07891	07884	07878	07871	07865	07859	07852	07846	07840	07834
630	07827	07821	07815	07809	07802	07796	07790	07784	07778	07772
640	07766	07760	07753	07747	07741	07735	07729	07723	07717	07711
650	07705	07699	07694	07688	07682	07676	07670	07664	07658	07652
660	07647	07641	07635	07629	07623	07618	07612	07606	07600	07595
670	07589	07583	07578	07572	07566	07561	07555	07549	07544	07538
680	07533	07527	07522	07516	07511	07505	07500	07494	07489	07483
690	07478	07472	07467	07461	07456	07451	07445	07440	07435	07429
700	07424	07419	07413	07408	07403	07397	07392	07387	07382	07376
710	07371	07366	07361	07356	07350	07345	07340	07335	07330	07325
720	07320	07315	07309	07304	07299	07294	07289	07284	07279	07274
730	07269	07264	07259	07254	07249	07244	07239	07234	07229	07225
740	07220	07215	07210	07205	07200	07195	07190	07186	07181	07176
750	07171	07166	07162	07157	07152	07147	07143	07138	07133	07128
760	07124	07119	07114	07110	07105	07100	07096	07091	07086	07082
770	07077	07072	07068	07063	07059	07054	07050	07045	07040	07036
780	07031	07027	07022	07018	07013	07009	07004	07000	06995	06991
790	06987	06982	06978	06973	06969	06964	06960	06956	06951	06947
800	06943	06938	06934	06930	06925	06921	06917	06912	06908	06904
810	06899	06895	06891	06887	06882	06878	06874	06870	06865	06861
820	06857	06853	06849	06844	06840	06836	06832	06828	06824	06820
830	06815	06811	06807	06803	06799	06795	06791	06787	06783	06779
840	06775	06771	06767	06763	06758	06754	06750	06746	06742	06738
850	06735	06731	06727	06723	06719	06715	06711	06707	06703	06699
860	06695	06691	06687	06683	06680	06676	06672	06668	06664	06660
870	06656	06653	06649	06645	06641	06637	06633	06630	06626	06622
880	06618	06615	06611	06607	06603	06600	06596	06592	06588	06585
890	06581	06577	06574	06570	06566	06562	06559	06555	06551	06548
900	06544	06540	06537	06533	06530	06526	06522	06519	06515	06512
910	06508	06504	06501	06497	06494	06490	06487	06483	06479	06476
920	06472	06469	06465	06462	06458	06455	06451	06448	06444	06441
930	06437	06434	06430	06427	06424	06420	06417	06413	06410	06406
940	06403	06400	06396	06393	06389	06386	06383	06379	06376	06372
950	06369	06366	06362	06359	06356	06352	06349	06346	06342	06339
960	06336	06332	06329	06326	06322	06319	06316	06313	06309	06306
970	06303	06300	06296	06293	06290	06287	06283	06280	06277	06274
980	06270	06267	06264	06261	06258	06254	06251	06248	06245	06242
990	06239	06235	06232	06229	06226	06223	06220	06217	06214	06210
1000	06207									

99% limits $(1 - 2\alpha = 0.99)$

n	0	1	2	3	4	5	6	7	8	9
	0.	0.	0.	0.	0.	0.	0.	0.	0.	0.
10	97357	91069	85861	81455	77664	74358	71441	68842	66508	64396
20	62473	60713	59094	57597	56209	54917	53710	52579	51517	50516
30	49572	48679	47832	47028	46263	45535	44839	44175	43539	42930
40	42346	41785	41246	40727	40228	39746	39281	38832	38398	37979
50	37572	37179	36798	36428	36069	35720	35382	35053	34732	34421
60	34118	33822	33534	33254	32980	32713	32452	32198	31949	31706
70	31469	31237	31009	30787	30569	30356	30148	29943	29743	29547
80	29354	29166	28980	28799	28620	28445	28273	28105	27939	27776
90	27616	27458	27304	27152	27002	26855	26710	26568	26427	26289
100	26154	26020	25888	25758	25630	25505	25380	25258	25138	25019
110	24901	24786	24672	24560	24449	24339	24231	24125	24020	23916
120	23814	23712	23613	23514	23417	23320	23225	23132	23039	22947
130	22857	22767	22679	22592	22505	22420	22335	22252	22169	22088
140	22007	21927	21848	21770	21692	21616	21540	21465	21391	21318
150	21245	21173	21102	21032	20962	20893	20824	20757	20690	20623
160	20557	20492	20428	20364	20300	20238	20175	20114	20053	19992
170	19932	19873	19814	19756	19698	19641	19584	19527	19471	19416
180	19361	19307	19253	19199	19146	19093	19041	18989	18938	18887
190	18836	18786	18736	18687	18638	18589	18541	18493	18446	18399
200	18352	18306	18260	18214	18168	18123	18079	18034	17990	17947
210	17903	17860	17817	17775	17733	17691	17649	17608	17567	17526
220	17486	17446	17406	17366	17327	17288	17249	17210	17172	17134
230	17096	17059	17022	16985	16948	16911	16875	16839	16803	16767
240	16732	16697	16662	16627	16592	16558	16524	16490	16456	16423
250	16390	16357	16324	16291	16258	16226	16194	16162	16130	16099
260	16068	16036	16005	15975	15944	15914	15883	15853	15823	15793
270	15764	15734	15705	15676	15647	15618	15590	15561	15533	15505
280	15477	15449	15421	15394	15366	15339	15312	15285	15258	15231
290	15205	15178	15152	15126	15100	15074	15048	15023	14997	14972
300	14946	14921	14896	14872	14847	14822	14798	14773	14749	14725
310	14701	14677	14653	14630	14606	14583	14559	14536	14513	14490
320	14467	14445	14422	14399	14377	14355	14332	14310	14288	14266
330	14244	14223	14201	14179	14158	14137	14115	14094	14073	14052
340	14031	14011	13990	13969	13949	13928	13908	13888	13868	13848
350	13828	13808	13788	13768	13749	13729	13710	13690	13671	13652
360	13633	13614	13595	13576	13557	13538	13520	13501	13483	13464
370	13446	13427	13409	13391	13373	13355	13337	13319	13302	13284
380	13266	13249	13231	13214	13196	13179	13162	13145	13128	13111
390	13094	13077	13060	13043	13027	13010	12993	12977	12960	12944
400	12928	12911	12895	12879	12863	12847	12831	12815	12799	12784
410	12768	12752	12737	12721	12706	12690	12675	12660	12644	12629
420	12614	12599	12584	12569	12554	12539	12524	12509	12495	12480
430	12465	12451	12436	12422	12407	12393	12379	12364	12350	12336
440	12322	12308	12294	12280	12266	12252	12238	12224	12211	12197
450	12183	12170	12156	12143	12129	12116	12102	12089	12076	12062
460	12049	12036	12023	12010	11997	11984	11971	11958	11945	11932
470	11920	11907	11894	11881	11869	11856	11844	11831	11819	11806
480	11794	11782	11769	11757	11745	11733	11720	11708	11696	11684
490	11672	11660	11648	11636	11625	11613	11601	11589	11577	11566
500	11554	11543	11531	11519	11508	11496	11485	11474	11462	11451
510	11440	11428	11417	11406	11395	11384	11373	11361	11350	11339
520	11328	11318	11307	11296	11285	11274	11263	11253	11242	11231
530	11220	11210	11199	11189	11178	11168	11157	11147	11136	11126
540	11116	11105	11095	11085	11074	11064	11054	11044	11034	11024
550	11013	11003	10993	10983	10973	10963	10954	10944	10934	10924
560	10914	10904	10895	10885	10875	10865	10856	10846	10837	10827
570	10817	10808	10798	10789	10780	10770	10761	10751	10742	10733
580	10723	10714	10705	10696	10686	10677	10668	10659	10650	10641
590	10632	10623	10614	10605	10596	10587	10578	10569	10560	10551
600	10542	10533	10525	10516	10507	10498	10490	10481	10472	10464
610	10455	10446	10438	10429	10421	10412	10404	10395	10387	10378
620	10370	10362	10353	10345	10336	10328	10320	10312	10303	10295
630	10287	10279	10271	10262	10254	10246	10238	10230	10222	10214
640	10206	10198	10190	10182	10174	10166	10158	10150	10142	10134
650	10127	10119	10111	10103	10095	10088	10080	10072	10065	10057
660	10049	10042	10034	10026	10019	10011	10004	09996	09989	09981
670	09974	09966	09959	09951	09944	09936	09929	09922	09914	09907
680	09900	09892	09885	09878	09871	09863	09856	09849	09842	09835
690	09827	09820	09813	09806	09799	09792	09785	09778	09771	09764
700	09757	09750	09743	09736	09729	09722	09715	09708	09701	09694
710	09687	09681	09674	09667	09660	09653	09647	09640	09633	09626
720	09620	09613	09606	09600	09593	09586	09580	09573	09566	09560
730	09553	09547	09540	09534	09527	09521	09514	09508	09501	09495
740	09488	09482	09475	09469	09463	09456	09450	09443	09437	09431
750	09424	09418	09412	09406	09399	09393	09387	09381	09374	09368
760	09362	09356	09350	09344	09337	09331	09325	09319	09313	09307
770	09301	09295	09289	09283	09277	09271	09265	09259	09253	09247
780	09241	09235	09229	09223	09217	09211	09205	09199	09194	09188
790	09182	09176	09170	09164	09159	09153	09147	09141	09136	09130
800	09124	09118	09113	09107	09101	09096	09090	09084	09079	09073
810	09067	09062	09056	09051	09045	09039	09034	09028	09023	09017
820	09012	09006	09001	08995	08990	08984	08979	08973	08968	08962
830	08957	08952	08946	08941	08935	08930	08925	08919	08914	08909
840	08903	08898	08893	08887	08882	08877	08872	08866	08861	08856
850	08851	08845	08840	08835	08830	08825	08819	08814	08809	08804
860	08799	08794	08789	08784	08778	08773	08768	08763	08758	08753
870	08748	08743	08738	08733	08728	08723	08718	08713	08708	08703
880	08698	08693	08688	08683	08678	08673	08668	08663	08659	08654
890	08649	08644	08639	08634	08629	08625	08620	08615	08610	08605
900	08600	08596	08591	08586	08581	08577	08572	08567	08562	08558
910	08553	08548	08543	08539	08534	08529	08525	08520	08515	08511
920	08506	08502	08497	08492	08488	08483	08478	08474	08469	08465
930	08460	08456	08451	08446	08442	08437	08433	08428	08424	08419
940	08415	08410	08406	08401	08397	08393	08388	08384	08379	08375
950	08370	08366	08361	08357	08353	08348	08344	08340	08335	08331
960	08326	08322	08318	08313	08309	08305	08300	08296	08292	08288
970	08283	08279	08275	08270	08266	08262	08258	08253	08249	08245
980	08241	08237	08232	08228	08224	08220	08216	08211	08207	08203
990	08199	08195	08191	08187	08182	08178	08174	08170	08166	08162
1000	08158									

$z = \tanh^{-1} r$

z	0.000	0.001	0.002	0.003	0.004	0.005	0.006	0.007	0.008	0.009
0.000	0.00000	0.00100	0.00200	0.00300	0.00400	0.00500	0.00600	0.00700	0.00800	0.00900
010	01000	01100	01200	01300	01400	01500	01600	01700	01800	01900
020	02000	02100	02200	02300	02400	02499	02599	02699	02799	02899
030	02999	03099	03199	03299	03399	03499	03598	03698	03798	03898
040	03998	04098	04198	04297	04397	04497	04597	04697	04796	04896
0.050	0.04996	0.05096	0.05195	0.05295	0.05395	0.05494	0.05594	0.05694	0.05794	0.05893
060	05993	06092	06192	06292	06391	06491	06590	06690	06790	06889
070	06989	07088	07188	07287	07387	07486	07585	07685	07784	07884
080	07983	08082	08182	08281	08380	08480	08579	08678	08777	08877
090	08976	09075	09174	09273	09372	09472	09571	09670	09769	09868
0.100	0.09967	0.10066	0.10165	0.10264	0.10363	0.10462	0.10560	0.10659	0.10758	0.10857
110	10956	11055	11153	11252	11351	11450	11548	11647	11746	11844
120	11943	12041	12140	12238	12337	12435	12534	12632	12731	12829
130	12927	13026	13124	13222	13320	13419	13517	13615	13713	13811
140	13909	14007	14105	14203	14301	14399	14497	14595	14693	14791
0.150	0.14889	0.14986	0.15084	0.15182	0.15279	0.15377	0.15475	0.15572	0.15670	0.15767
160	15865	15962	16060	16157	16255	16352	16449	16546	16644	16741
170	16838	16935	17032	17129	17227	17324	17420	17517	17614	17711
180	17808	17905	18002	18098	18195	18292	18388	18485	18582	18678
190	18775	18871	18967	19064	19160	19257	19353	19449	19545	19641
0.200	0.19738	0.19834	0.19930	0.20026	0.20122	0.20218	0.20313	0.20409	0.20505	0.2060[illegible]
210	20697	20792	20888	20984	21079	21175	21270	21366	21461	2155[illegible]
220	21652	21747	21842	21938	22033	22128	22223	22318	22413	22508
230	22603	22698	22793	22887	22982	23077	23171	23266	23361	2345[illegible]
240	23550	23644	23738	23833	23927	24021	24115	24210	24304	2439[illegible]
0.250	0.24492	0.24586	0.24680	0.24774	0.24868	0.24961	0.25055	0.25149	0.25242	0.2533[illegible]
260	25430	25523	25617	25710	25803	25897	25990	26083	26176	2626[illegible]
270	26362	26456	26548	26641	26734	26827	26920	27013	27105	2719[illegible]
280	27291	27383	27476	27568	27660	27753	27845	27937	28029	2812[illegible]
290	28213	28305	28397	28489	28581	28673	28765	28856	28948	29040
0.300	0.29131	0.29223	0.29314	0.29406	0.29497	0.29588	0.29679	0.29771	0.29862	0.29953
310	30044	30135	30226	30316	30407	30498	30589	30679	30770	30860
320	30951	31041	31131	31222	31312	31402	31492	31582	31672	31762
330	31852	31942	32032	32121	32211	32301	32390	32480	32569	32658
340	32748	32837	32926	33015	33104	33193	33282	33371	33460	33549
0.350	0.33638	0.33726	0.33815	0.33903	0.33992	0.34080	0.34169	0.34257	0.34345	0.34433
360	34521	34609	34697	34785	34873	34961	35049	35136	35224	35312
370	35399	35487	35574	35661	35749	35836	35923	36010	36097	36184
380	36271	36358	36444	36531	36618	36704	36791	36877	36963	37050
390	37136	37222	37308	37394	37480	37566	37652	37738	37824	37909
0.400	0.37995	0.38080	0.38166	0.38251	0.38337	0.38422	0.38507	0.38592	0.38677	0.38762
410	38847	38932	39017	39102	39186	39271	39356	39440	39524	39609
420	39693	39777	39861	39945	40029	40113	40197	40281	40365	40449
430	40532	40616	40699	40783	40866	40949	41032	41115	41199	41282
440	41364	41447	41530	41613	41695	41778	41861	41943	42025	42108
0.450	0.42190	0.42272	0.42354	0.42436	0.42518	0.42600	0.42682	0.42764	0.42845	0.42927
460	43008	43090	43171	43253	43334	43415	43496	43577	43658	43739
470	43820	43901	43981	44062	44143	44223	44303	44384	44464	44544
480	44624	44704	44784	44864	44944	45024	45104	45183	45263	45342
490	45422	45501	45580	45659	45739	45818	45897	45975	46054	46133
0.500	0.46212	0.46290	0.46369	0.46447	0.46526	0.46604	0.46682	0.46760	0.46839	0.46917
510	46995	47072	47150	47228	47306	47383	47461	47538	47615	47693
520	47770	47847	47924	48001	48078	48155	48232	48308	48385	48462
530	48538	48615	48691	48767	48843	48919	48995	49071	49147	49223
540	49299	49374	49450	49526	49601	49676	49752	49827	49902	49977
0.550	0.50052	0.50127	0.50202	0.50277	0.50351	0.50426	0.50500	0.50575	0.50649	0.50724
560	50798	50872	50946	51020	51094	51168	51242	51315	51389	51462
570	51536	51609	51683	51756	51829	51902	51975	52048	52121	52194
580	52267	52339	52412	52484	52557	52629	52701	52773	52846	52918
590	52990	53061	53133	53205	53277	53348	53420	53491	53562	53634
0.600	0.53705	0.53776	0.53847	0.53918	0.53989	0.54060	0.54131	0.54201	0.54272	0.54342
610	54413	54483	54553	54624	54694	54764	54834	54904	54973	55043
620	55113	55182	55252	55321	55391	55460	55529	55598	55667	55736
630	55805	55874	55943	56011	56080	56149	56217	56285	56354	56422
640	56490	56558	56626	56694	56762	56829	56897	56965	57032	57100
0.650	0.57167	0.57234	0.57301	0.57369	0.57436	0.57503	0.57570	0.57636	0.57703	0.57770
660	57836	57903	57969	58036	58102	58168	58234	58300	58366	58432
670	58498	58564	58629	58695	58760	58826	58891	58957	59022	59087
680	59152	59217	59282	59347	59411	59476	59541	59605	59670	59734
690	59798	59862	59927	59991	60055	60118	60182	60246	60310	60373
0.700	0.60437	0.60500	0.60564	0.60627	0.60690	0.60753	0.60816	0.60879	0.60942	0.61005
710	61068	61130	61193	61255	61318	61380	61443	61505	61567	61629
720	61691	61753	61815	61876	61938	62000	62061	62123	62184	62245
730	62307	62368	62429	62490	62551	62611	62672	62733	62794	62854
740	62915	62975	63035	63095	63156	63216	63276	63336	63395	63455
0.750	0.63515	0.63575	0.63634	0.63694	0.63753	0.63812	0.63871	0.63931	0.63990	0.64049
760	64108	64167	64225	64284	64343	64401	64460	64518	64576	64635
770	64693	64751	64809	64867	64925	64983	65040	65098	65156	65213
780	65271	65328	65385	65443	65500	65557	65614	65671	65727	65784
790	65841	65898	65954	66011	66067	66123	66179	66236	66292	66348
0.800	0.66404	0.66460	0.66515	0.66571	0.66627	0.66682	0.66738	0.66793	0.66849	0.66904
810	66959	67014	67069	67124	67179	67234	67289	67343	67398	67453
820	67507	67561	67616	67670	67724	67778	67832	67886	67940	67994
830	68048	68101	68155	68208	68262	68315	68368	68422	68475	68528
840	68581	68634	68687	68739	68792	68845	68897	68950	69002	69055
0.850	0.69107	0.69159	0.69211	0.69263	0.69315	0.69367	0.69419	0.69471	0.69523	0.69574
860	69626	69677	69729	69780	69831	69882	69934	69985	70036	70087
870	70137	70188	70239	70290	70340	70391	70441	70491	70542	70592
880	70642	70692	70742	70792	70842	70892	70941	70991	71040	71090
890	71139	71189	71238	71287	71336	71385	71434	71483	71532	71581
0.900	0.71630	0.71678	0.71727	0.71776	0.71824	0.71872	0.71921	0.71969	0.72017	0.72065
910	72113	72161	72209	72257	72305	72352	72400	72448	72495	72542
920	72590	72637	72684	72731	72778	72825	72872	72919	72966	73013
930	73059	73106	73153	73199	73245	73292	73338	73384	73430	73476
940	73522	73568	73614	73660	73705	73751	73797	73842	73888	73933
0.950	0.73978	0.74024	0.74069	0.74114	0.74159	0.74204	0.74249	0.74294	0.74338	0.74383
960	74428	74472	74517	74561	74606	74650	74694	74738	74782	74826
970	74870	74914	74958	75002	75046	75089	75133	75176	75220	75263
980	75307	75350	75393	75436	75479	75522	75565	75608	75651	75694
990	75736	75779	75821	75864	75906	75949	75991	76033	76075	76117
1.000	0.76159	0.76201	0.76243	0.76285	0.76327	0.76369	0.76410	0.76452	0.76493	0.76535
010	76576	76618	76659	76700	76741	76782	76823	76864	76905	76946
020	76987	77027	77068	77109	77149	77190	77230	77270	77310	77351
030	77391	77431	77471	77511	77551	77591	77630	77670	77710	77749
040	77789	77828	77868	77907	77946	77985	78025	78064	78103	78142

1) Values abridged from National Bureau of Standards *Table of Circular and Hyperbolic Tangents and Cotangents for Radian Arguments,* Columbia University Press, New York, 1947, by kind permission of the authors and publishers.

$z = \tanh^{-1} r$

z	0.000	0.001	0.002	0.003	0.004	0.005	0.006	0.007	0.008	0.009
1.050	0.78181	0.78219	0.78258	0.78297	0.78336	0.78374	0.78413	0.78451	0.78490	0.78528
060	78566	78605	78643	78681	78719	78757	78795	78833	78871	78908
070	78946	78984	79021	79059	79096	79134	79171	79208	79246	79283
080	79320	79357	79394	79431	79468	79505	79541	79578	79615	79651
090	79688	79724	79761	79797	79833	79870	79906	79942	79978	80014
1.100	0.80050	0.80086	0.80122	0.80157	0.80193	0.80229	0.80264	0.80300	0.80335	0.80371
110	80406	80442	80477	80512	80547	80582	80617	80652	80687	80722
120	80757	80792	80826	80861	80896	80930	80965	80999	81033	81068
130	81102	81136	81170	81204	81238	81272	81306	81340	81374	81408
140	81441	81475	81509	81542	81576	81609	81642	81676	81709	81742
1.150	0.81775	0.81809	0.81842	0.81875	0.81907	0.81940	0.81973	0.82006	0.82039	0.82071
160	82104	82137	82169	82202	82234	82266	82299	82331	82363	82395
170	82427	82459	82491	82523	82555	82587	82619	82650	82682	82714
180	82745	82777	82808	82840	82871	82902	82933	82965	82996	83027
190	83058	83089	83120	83151	83182	83212	83243	83274	83304	83335
1.200	0.83365	0.83396	0.83426	0.83457	0.83487	0.83517	0.83548	0.83578	0.83608	0.83638
210	83668	83698	83728	83758	83788	83817	83847	83877	83906	83936
220	83965	83995	84024	84054	84083	84112	84142	84171	84200	84229
230	84258	84287	84316	84345	84374	84402	84431	84460	84488	84517
240	84546	84574	84603	84631	84659	84688	84716	84744	84772	84800
1.250	0.84828	0.84856	0.84884	0.84912	0.84940	0.84968	0.84996	0.85023	0.85051	0.85079
260	85106	85134	85161	85189	85216	85244	85271	85298	85325	85353
270	85380	85407	85434	85461	85488	85515	85542	85568	85595	85622
280	85648	85675	85702	85728	85755	85781	85808	85834	85860	85886
290	85913	85939	85965	85991	86017	86043	86069	86095	86121	86147
1.300	0.86172	0.86198	0.86224	0.86249	0.86275	0.86300	0.86326	0.86351	0.86377	0.86402
310	86428	86453	86478	86503	86528	86554	86579	86604	86629	86654
320	86678	86703	86728	86753	86778	86802	86827	86851	86876	86900
330	86925	86949	86974	86998	87022	87047	87071	87095	87119	87143
340	87167	87191	87215	87239	87263	87287	87311	87334	87358	87382
1.350	0.87405	0.87429	0.87452	0.87476	0.87499	0.87523	0.87546	0.87570	0.87593	0.87616
360	87639	87662	87686	87709	87732	87755	87778	87801	87824	87846
370	87869	87892	87915	87937	87960	87983	88005	88028	88050	88073
380	88095	88118	88140	88162	88184	88207	88229	88251	88273	88295
390	88317	88339	88361	88383	88405	88427	88448	88470	88492	88514
1.400	0.88535	0.88557	0.88578	0.88600	0.88621	0.88643	0.88664	0.88686	0.88707	0.88728
410	88749	88771	88792	88813	88834	88855	88876	88897	88918	88939
420	88960	88981	89002	89022	89043	89064	89084	89105	89126	89146
430	89167	89187	89208	89228	89248	89269	89289	89309	89329	89350
440	89370	89390	89410	89430	89450	89470	89490	89510	89530	89549
1.450	0.89569	0.89589	0.89609	0.89628	0.89648	0.89668	0.89687	0.89707	0.89726	0.89746
460	89765	89785	89804	89823	89843	89862	89881	89900	89920	89939
470	89958	89977	89996	90015	90034	90053	90072	90090	90109	90128
480	90147	90166	90184	90203	90221	90240	90259	90277	90296	90314
490	90332	90351	90369	90388	90406	90424	90442	90460	90479	90497
1.500	0.90515	0.90533	0.90551	0.90569	0.90587	0.90605	0.90623	0.90641	0.90658	0.90676
510	90694	90712	90729	90747	90765	90782	90800	90817	90835	90852
520	90870	90887	90905	90922	90939	90957	90974	90991	91008	91025
530	91042	91060	91077	91094	91111	91128	91145	91161	91178	91195
540	91212	91229	91246	91262	91279	91296	91312	91329	91345	91362
1.550	0.91379	0.91395	0.91411	0.91428	0.91444	0.91461	0.91477	0.91493	0.91510	0.91526
560	91542	91558	91574	91591	91607	91623	91639	91655	91671	91687
570	91703	91718	91734	91750	91766	91782	91797	91813	91829	91845
580	91860	91876	91891	91907	91922	91938	91953	91969	91984	92000
590	92015	92030	92046	92061	92076	92091	92106	92122	92137	92152
1.600	0.92167	0.92182	0.92197	0.92212	0.92227	0.92242	0.92257	0.92272	0.92286	0.92301
610	92316	92331	92346	92360	92375	92390	92404	92419	92433	92448
620	92462	92477	92491	92506	92520	92535	92549	92563	92578	92592
630	92606	92620	92635	92649	92663	92677	92691	92705	92719	92733
640	92747	92761	92775	92789	92803	92817	92831	92844	92858	92872
1.650	0.92886	0.92899	0.92913	0.92927	0.92940	0.92954	0.92968	0.92981	0.92995	0.93008
660	93022	93035	93049	93062	93075	93089	93102	93115	93129	93142
670	93155	93168	93182	93195	93208	93221	93234	93247	93260	93273
680	93286	93299	93312	93325	93338	93351	93364	93376	93389	93402
690	93415	93427	93440	93453	93465	93478	93491	93503	93516	93528
1.700	0.93541	0.93553	0.93566	0.93578	0.93591	0.93603	0.93615	0.93628	0.93640	0.93652
710	93665	93677	93689	93701	93714	93726	93738	93750	93762	93774
720	93786	93798	93810	93822	93834	93846	93858	93870	93882	93894
730	93906	93917	93929	93941	93953	93964	93976	93988	93999	94011
740	94023	94034	94046	94057	94069	94080	94092	94103	94115	94126
1.750	0.94138	0.94149	0.94160	0.94172	0.94183	0.94194	0.94205	0.94217	0.94228	0.94239
760	94250	94261	94273	94284	94295	94306	94317	94328	94339	94350
770	94361	94372	94383	94394	94405	94415	94426	94437	94448	94459
780	94470	94480	94491	94502	94512	94523	94534	94544	94555	94565
790	94576	94587	94597	94608	94618	94629	94639	94649	94660	94670
1.800	0.94681	0.94691	0.94701	0.94712	0.94722	0.94732	0.94742	0.94753	0.94763	0.94773
810	94783	94793	94803	94814	94824	94834	94844	94854	94864	94874
820	94884	94894	94904	94914	94924	94933	94943	94953	94963	94973
830	94983	94992	95002	95012	95022	95031	95041	95051	95060	95070
840	95080	95089	95099	95108	95118	95127	95137	95146	95156	95165
1.850	0.95175	0.95184	0.95193	0.95203	0.95212	0.95221	0.95231	0.95240	0.95249	0.95259
860	95268	95277	95286	95296	95305	95314	95323	95332	95341	95350
870	95359	95368	95378	95387	95396	95405	95413	95422	95431	95440
880	95449	95458	95467	95476	95485	95493	95502	95511	95520	95529
890	95537	95546	95555	95563	95572	95581	95589	95598	95607	95615
1.900	0.95624	0.95632	0.95641	0.95649	0.95658	0.95666	0.95675	0.95683	0.95692	0.95700
910	95709	95717	95725	95734	95742	95750	95759	95767	95775	95783
920	95792	95800	95808	95816	95825	95833	95841	95849	95857	95865
930	95873	95881	95889	95898	95906	95914	95922	95930	95938	95945
940	95953	95961	95969	95977	95985	95993	96001	96009	96016	96024
1.950	0.96032	0.96040	0.96047	0.96055	0.96063	0.96071	0.96078	0.96086	0.96094	0.96101
960	96109	96117	96124	96132	96139	96147	96155	96162	96170	96177
970	96185	96192	96200	96207	96214	96222	96229	96237	96244	96251
980	96259	96266	96273	96281	96288	96295	96303	96310	96317	96324
990	96331	96339	96346	96353	96360	96367	96374	96382	96389	96396

z	0.0	0.1	0.2	0.3	0.4	0.5	0.6	0.7	0.8	0.9
0.0	0.00000 00000	0.09966 79946	0.19737 53202	0.29131 26125	0.37994 89623	0.46211 71573	0.53704 95670	0.60436 77771	0.66403 67703	0.71629 78702
1.0	76159 41560	80049 90218	83365 46070	86172 31593	88535 16482	90514 82536	92166 85544	93540 90706	94680 60128	95623 74581
2.0	96402 75801	97045 19366	97574 31300	98009 63963	98367 48577	98661 42982	98902 74022	99100 74537	99263 15202	99396 31674
3.0	99505 47537	99594 93592	99668 23978	99728 29601	99777 49279	99817 78976	99850 79423	99877 82413	99899 95978	99918 08657
4.0	99932 92997	99945 08437	99955 03665	99963 18562	99969 85793	99975 32108	99979 79416	99983 45656	99986 45517	99988 91030
5.0	0.99990 92043	0.99992 56621	0.99993 91369	0.99995 01692	0.99995 92018	0.99996 65972	0.99997 26520	0.99997 76093	0.99998 16680	0.99998 49910
6.0	99998 77117	99998 99391	99999 17629	99999 32560	99999 44785	99999 54794	99999 62988	99999 69697	99999 75190	99999 79687
7.0	99999 83369	99999 86384	99999 88852	99999 90873	99999 92527	99999 93882	99999 94991	99999 95899	99999 96642	99999 97251
8.0	99999 97749	99999 98157	99999 98491	99999 98765	99999 98989	99999 99172	99999 99322	99999 99445	99999 99546	99999 99628
9.0	99999 99695	99999 99751	99999 99796	99999 99833	99999 99863	99999 99888	99999 99908	99999 99925	99999 99939	99999 99950

1) See footnote on previous page.

Significance Limits when Population Correlation Coefficient is Zero*

$\sum D^2$ = Sum of the squared differences between the two ranks for n pairs of observations. Values for $n = 1$ to 10 are exact[1]. Values in *italics* are values of the tangents through the last exact value ($n = 10$) on the approximation curve $|c_\alpha| / \sqrt{n-1}$ (for $2\alpha = 0.05$, 0.02, 0.01 and 0.001). For $2\alpha = 0.10$ the *italic* values correspond to the extrapolated exponential curve between the two last exact values ($n = 9$ and 10). This ensures being on the safe side with all approximated values.

	$2\alpha = 0.10$		$2\alpha = 0.05$		$2\alpha = 0.02$		$2\alpha = 0.01$		$2\alpha = 0.001$	
n	$\sum D^2$ lower–upper	R (±)	$\sum D^2$ lower–upper	R (±)	$\sum D^2$ lower–upper	R (±)	$\sum D^2$ lower–upper	R (±)	$\sum D^2$ lower–upper	R (±)
5	2–38	0.9000	0–40	1.0000	0–40	1.0000	–	–	–	–
6	6–64	8286	4–66	0.8857	2–68	0.9429	0–70	1.0000	–	–
7	16–96	7143	12–100	7857	6–106	8929	4–108	0.9286	0–112	1.0000
8	30–138	6429	22–146	7381	14–154	8333	10–158	8810	2–166	0.9762
9	48–192	6000	38–202	6833	26–214	7833	20–220	8333	8–232	9333
10	72–258	0.5636	58–272	0.6485	44–286	0.7333	34–296	0.7939	16–314	0.9030
11	*103–337*	*5294*	*83–357*	*6194*	*63–377*	*7110*	*50–390*	*7724*	*24–416*	*8875*
12	*143–429*	*4973*	116–456	5910	*89–483*	*6887*	*71–501*	*7509*	*36–536*	*8720*
13	191–537	4748	158–570	5658	*121–607*	*6634*	*98–630*	*7294*	*52–676*	*8565*
14	247–663	4562	207–703	5436	*161–748*	*6441*	*132–778*	*7080*	*72–838*	*8410*
15	313–807	0.4396	266–854	0.5238	211–909	0.6217	*175–945*	*0.6865*	*97–1023*	*0.8255*
16	391–969	4247	335–1025	5061	271–1089	6007	*227–1133*	*6650*	*129–1231*	*8100*
17	480–1152	4112	416–1216	4900	341–1291	5816	290–1342	6440	*167–1465*	*7945*
18	582–1356	3989	508–1430	4754	422–1516	5642	363–1575	6247	*214–1724*	*779*
19	698–1582	3877	613–1667	4620	514–1766	5483	447–1833	6071	*269–2011*	*763*
20	828–1832	0.3774	731–1929	0.4496	620–2040	0.5337	544–2116	0.5909	*335–2325*	*0.7480*
21	973–2107	3678	865–2215	4383	738–2342	5202	653–2427	5760	*412–2668*	*7325*
22	1135–2407	3589	1013–2529	4277	871–2671	5077	775–2767	5621	*501–3041*	*717*
23	1314–2734	3507	1178–2870	4179	1020–3028	4960	912–3136	5492	*604–3444*	*701*
24	1511–3089	3430	1360–3240	4087	1184–3416	4851	1064–3536	5371	721–3879	686
25	1727–3473	0.3358	1559–3641	0.4001	1365–3835	0.4749	1232–3968	0.5258	853–4347	0.6717
26	1962–3888	3290	1778–4072	3920	1564–4286	4653	1418–4432	5152	1000–4850	658
27	2219–4333	3226	2016–4536	3844	1781–4771	4562	1621–4931	5052	1161–5391	6453
28	2497–4811	3166	2275–5033	3772	2018–5290	4477	1842–5466	4957	1340–5968	6333
29	2797–5323	3108	2556–5564	3704	2275–5845	4396	2083–6037	4868	1535–6585	6219
30	3122–5868	0.3054	2859–6131	0.3640	2553–6437	0.4320	2344–6646	0.4783	1748–7242	0.6110
31	3470–6450	3003	3185–6735	3578	2853–7067	4247	2627–7293	4703	1980–7940	6008
32	3844–7068	2954	3535–7377	3520	3176–7736	4178	2931–7981	4626	2231–8681	5910
33	4244–7724	2908	3910–8058	3465	3523–8445	4112	3259–8709	4553	2503–9465	5817
34	4670–8420	2863	4311–8779	3412	3894–9196	4050	3610–9480	4484	2795–10295	5728
35	5125–9155	0.2821	4740–9540	0.3361	4291–9989	0.3990	3985–10295	0.4418	3110–11170	0.5643
36	5609–9931	2780	5195–10345	3313	4714–10826	3932	4386–11154	4354	3448–12092	5562
37	6123–10749	2741	5680–11192	3267	5165–11707	3877	4814–12058	4293	3809–13063	5484
38	6667–11611	2704	6194–12084	3222	5643–12635	3824	5268–13010	4235	4195–14083	5410
39	7243–12517	2668	6738–13022	3179	6151–13609	3774	5751–14009	4179	4606–15154	5338
40	7852–13468	0.2634	7314–14006	0.3138	6689–14631	0.3725	6263–15057	0.4125	5043–16277	0.5269
41	8494–14466	2601	7922–15038	3099	7257–15703	3678	6804–16156	4073	5507–17453	5203
42	9170–15512	2569	8563–16119	3061	7857–16825	3633	7376–17306	4023	5999–18683	5139
43	9882–16606	2538	9238–17250	3024	8489–17999	3590	7980–18508	3975	6519–19969	5077
44	10630–17750	2508	9948–18432	2989	9155–19225	3548	8616–19764	3928	7069–21311	5018
45	11415–18945	0.2480	10694–19666	0.2955	9856–20504	0.3507	9285–21075	0.3883	7649–22711	0.4961
46	12239–20191	2452	11477–20953	2922	10591–21839	3468	9988–22442	3840	8261–24169	4905
47	13101–21491	2425	12297–22295	2890	11363–23229	3430	10727–23865	3798	8904–25688	4852
48	14003–22845	2399	13156–23692	2859	12172–24676	3393	11501–25347	3757	9580–27268	4800
49	14946–24254	2374	14055–25145	2829	13018–26182	3358	12312–26888	3718	10291–28909	4749
50	15931–25719	0.2350	14994–26656	0.2800	13904–27746	0.3323	13161–28489	0.3680	11035–30615	0.4701
51	16959–27241	2326	15974–28226	2772	14829–29371	3290	14049–30151	3643	11815–32385	4654
52	18030–28822	2303	16996–29856	2744	15794–31058	3258	14976–31876	3607	12632–34220	4608
53	19146–30462	2281	18062–31546	2718	16802–32806	3226	15943–33665	3572	13485–36123	4563
54	20307–32163	2259	19171–33299	2692	17851–34619	3195	16952–35518	3538	14377–38093	4520
55	21515–33925	0.2238	20326–35114	0.2667	18944–36496	0.3166	18003–37437	0.3505	15307–40133	0.4478
56	22770–35750	2218	21527–36993	2643	20081–38439	3137	19097–39423	3473	16277–42243	4437
57	24073–37639	2198	22774–38938	2619	21263–40449	3109	20235–41477	3442	17288–44424	4397
58	25426–39592	2179	24069–40949	2596	22491–42527	3081	21417–43601	3412	18340–46678	4358
59	26829–41611	2160	25413–43027	2574	23767–44673	3055	22646–45794	3382	19434–49006	4321
60	28283–43697	0.2141	26806–45174	0.2552	25089–46891	0.3029	23920–48060	0.3353	20572–51408	0.4284
61	29788–45852	2123	28250–47390	2530	26461–49179	3003	25243–50397	3325	21753–53887	4248
62	31347–48075	2106	29745–49677	2509	27882–51540	2979	26614–52808	3298	22980–56442	4213
63	32960–50368	2089	31293–52035	2489	29354–53974	2954	28034–55294	3271	24252–59076	4179
64	34628–52732	2072	32893–54467	2469	30877–56483	2931	29504–57856	3245	25571–61789	4146
65	36351–55169	0.2056	34549–56971	0.2450	32453–59067	0.2908	31026–60494	0.3220	26938–64582	0.4113
66	38131–57679	2040	36259–59551	2431	34082–61728	2885	32599–63211	3195	28353–67457	4081
67	39969–60263	2025	38025–62207	2413	35765–64467	2864	34226–66006	3171	29817–70415	4050
68	41865–62923	2010	39848–64940	2394	37503–67285	2842	35906–68882	3147	31331–73457	4020
69	43821–65659	1995	41729–67751	2377	39297–70183	2821	37641–71839	3124	32896–76584	3990
70	45837–68473	0.1980	43669–70641	0.2360	41148–73162	0.2801	39431–74879	0.3101	34514–79796	0.3961
71	47914–71366	1966	45668–73612	2343	43056–76224	2781	41278–78002	3079	36183–83097	3933
72	50054–74338	1952	47728–76664	2326	45024–79368	2761	43183–81209	3057	37907–86485	3905
73	52258–77390	1938	49850–79798	2310	47051–82597	2742	45145–84503	3036	39685–89963	3878
74	54525–80525	1925	52035–83015	2294	49139–85911	2723	47167–87883	3015	41519–93531	3851
75	56857–83743	0.1912	54282–86318	0.2278	51288–89312	0.2704	49249–91351	0.2994	43409–97191	0.3825
76	59256–87044	1899	56594–89706	2263	53500–92800	2686	51392–94908	2974	45356–100944	3800
77	61722–90430	1887	58972–93180	2248	55775–96377	2669	53597–98555	2955	47361–104791	3774
78	64255–93903	1874	61416–96742	2234	58114–100044	2651	55865–102293	2935	49425–108733	3750
79	66858–97462	1862	63926–100394	2219	60518–103802	2634	58197–106123	2917	51548–112772	3726
80	69530–101110	0.1851	66505–104135	0.2205	62988–107652	0.2617	60593–110047	0.2898	53733–116907	0.3702
81	72273–104847	1839	69153–107967	2191	65526–111594	2601	63055–114065	2880	55979–121141	3679
82	75088–108674	1828	71871–111891	2178	68131–115631	2585	65584–118178	2862	58287–125475	3656
83	77976–112592	1816	74660–115908	2164	70805–119763	2569	68180–122388	2845	60659–129909	3634
84	80937–116603	1805	77521–120019	2151	73549–123991	2553	70844–126696	2827	63095–134445	3612
85	83973–120707	0.1795	80454–124226	0.2138	76363–128317	0.2538	73577–131103	0.2810	65597–139083	0.3590
86	87084–124906	1784	83461–128529	2126	79249–132741	2523	76381–135609	2794	68164–143826	3569
87	90272–129200	1774	86543–132929	2113	82208–137264	2509	79255–140217	2778	70798–148674	3548
88	93537–133591	1763	89700–137428	2101	85239–141889	2494	82202–144926	2762	73500–153628	3528
89	96880–138080	1753	92934–142026	2089	88346–146614	2480	85221–149739	2746	76271–158689	3508
90	100303–142667	0.1744	96245–146725	0.2078	91527–151443	0.2466	88315–154655	0.2730	79111–163859	0.3488
91	103806–147354	1734	99635–151525	2066	94785–156375	2452	91482–159678	2715	82022–169138	3469
92	107390–152142	1724	103104–156428	2055	98120–161412	2439	94726–164806	2700	85004–174528	3449
93	111057–157031	1715	106653–161435	2043	101533–166555	2425	98046–170042	2685	88058–180030	3431
94	114806–162024	1706	110283–166547	2032	105025–171805	2412	101444–175386	2671	91186–185644	3412
95	118639–167121	0.1697	113996–171764	0.2022	108596–177164	0.2399	104920–180840	0.2657	94387–191373	0.3394
96	122558–172322	1688	117791–177089	2011	112249–182631	2387	108475–186405	2643	97664–197216	3376
97	126562–177630	1679	121671–182521	2000	115983–188209	2374	112110–192082	2629	101016–203176	3358
98	130653–183045	1670	125635–188063	1990	119800–193898	2362	115827–197871	2615	104445–209253	3341
99	134832–188568	1662	129685–193715	1980	123701–199699	2350	119625–203775	2602	107951–215449	3324

1) Values from KENDALL, M. G., *Rank Correlation Methods*, 2nd ed., Charles Griffin, London, 1955, page 172. Reprinted by kind permission of the author and publishers.

Significance Limits when Population Correlation Coefficient is Zero* (continued)

$\sum D^2$ = Sum of the squared differences between the two ranks for n pairs of observations. Approximate values from $R = |c_\alpha| / \sqrt{n-1}$ (c_α = corresponding deviation from the standardized normal distribution).

	$2\alpha = 0.10$		$2\alpha = 0.05$		$2\alpha = 0.02$		$2\alpha = 0.01$		$2\alpha = 0.001$	
n	$\sum D^2$ lower upper	R (±)	$\sum D^2$ lower upper	R (±)	$\sum D^2$ lower upper	R (±)	$\sum D^2$ lower upper	R (±)	$\sum D^2$ lower upper	R (±)
100	139100–194200	0.1653	133822–199478	0.1970	127686–205614	0.2338	123507–209793	0.2589	111537–221763	0.3307
101	143457–199943	1645	138047–205353	1960	131756–211644	2326	127473–215927	2576	115201–228199	3291
102	147905–205797	1637	142360–211342	1950	135913–217789	2315	131523–222179	2563	118946–234756	3274
103	152445–211763	1629	146763–217445	1941	140157–224051	2303	135659–228549	2550	122772–241436	3258
104	157077–217843	1621	151257–223663	1931	144490–230430	2292	139881–235039	2538	126680–248240	3242
105	161803–224037	0.1613	155842–229998	0.1922	148911–236929	0.2281	144192–241648	0.2526	130671–255169	0.3227
106	166623–230347	1605	160520–236450	1913	153423–243547	2270	148590–248380	2514	134746–262224	3211
107	171539–236773	1598	165291–243021	1904	158025–250287	2260	153078–255234	2502	138906–269406	3196
108	176551–243317	1590	170156–249712	1895	162720–257148	2249	157657–262211	2490	143152–276716	3181
109	181660–249980	1583	175116–256524	1886	167508–264132	2239	162327–269313	2479	147484–284156	3166
110	186868–256762	0.1575	180173–263457	0.1877	172389–271241	0.2228	167088–276542	0.2467	151904–291726	0.3152
111	192175–263665	1568	185327–270513	1869	177365–278475	2218	171943–283897	2456	156412–299428	3137
112	197582–270690	1561	190579–277693	1860	182437–285835	2208	176892–291380	2445	161009–307263	3123
113	203090–277838	1554	195930–284998	1852	187605–293323	2198	181936–298992	2434	165697–315231	3109
114	208700–285110	1547	201381–292429	1844	192871–300939	2188	187076–306734	2423	170476–323334	3095
115	214413–292507	0.1541	206932–299988	0.1836	198235–308685	0.2179	192313–314607	0.2412	175347–331573	0.3082
116	220230–300030	1534	212586–307674	1828	203699–316561	2169	197647–322613	2402	180310–339950	3068
117	226152–307680	1527	218343–315489	1820	209263–324569	2160	203080–330752	2392	185368–348464	3055
118	232180–315458	1521	224203–323435	1812	214928–332710	2151	208612–339026	2381	190520–357118	3042
119	238314–323366	1514	230168–331512	1804	220695–340985	2142	214246–347434	2371	195768–365912	3029
120	244557–331403	0.1508	236238–339722	0.1797	226566–349394	0.2133	219980–355980	0.2361	201113–374847	0.3016
121	250908–339572	1502	242415–348065	1789	232541–357939	2124	225817–364663	2351	206554–383926	3004
122	257369–347873	1495	248700–356542	1782	238620–366622	2115	231757–373485	2342	212095–393147	2991
123	263940–356308	1489	255093–365155	1774	244806–375442	2106	237801–382447	2332	217734–402514	2979
124	270624–364876	1483	261595–373905	1767	251098–384402	2098	243951–391549	2323	223474–412026	2967
125	277419–373581	0.1477	268208–382792	0.1760	257499–393501	0.2089	250206–400794	0.2313	229315–421685	0.2955
126	284328–382422	1471	274932–391818	1753	264008–402742	2081	256569–410181	2304	235258–431492	2943
127	291352–391400	1465	281769–400983	1746	270626–412126	2072	263039–419713	2295	241303–441449	2931
128	298491–400517	1460	288718–410290	1739	277355–421653	2064	269618–429390	2286	247453–451555	2920
129	305746–409774	1454	295782–419738	1732	284196–431324	2056	276307–439213	2277	253707–461813	2908
130	313119–419171	0.1448	302961–429329	0.1726	291149–441141	0.2048	283107–449183	0.2268	260067–472223	0.2897
131	320610–428710	1443	310255–439065	1719	298216–451104	2040	290018–459302	2259	266533–482787	2886
132	328220–438392	1437	317667–448945	1712	305397–461215	2033	297042–469570	2251	273107–493505	2875
133	335950–448218	1432	325197–458971	1706	312693–471475	2025	304179–479989	2242	279789–504379	2864
134	343802–458188	1426	332845–469145	1700	320106–481884	2017	311431–490559	2234	286581–515409	2853
135	351775–468305	0.1421	340614–479466	0.1693	327635–492445	0.2010	318798–501282	0.2225	293482–526598	0.2843
136	359872–478568	1416	348503–489937	1687	335283–503157	2002	326282–512158	2217	300495–537945	2832
137	368093–488979	1410	356513–500559	1681	343050–514022	1995	333882–523190	2209	307620–549452	2822
138	376438–499540	1405	364647–511331	1675	350937–525041	1988	341601–534377	2201	314857–561121	2811
139	384910–510250	1400	372904–522256	1668	358944–536216	1980	349439–545721	2193	322209–572951	2801
140	393508–521112	0.1395	381285–533335	0.1662	367074–547546	0.1973	357397–557223	0.2185	329675–584945	0.2791
141	402234–532126	1390	389792–544568	1656	375326–559034	1966	365476–568884	2177	337256–597104	2781
142	411089–543293	1385	398426–555956	1651	383702–570680	1959	373676–580706	2169	344955–609427	2771
143	420074–554614	1380	407187–567501	1645	392203–582485	1952	382000–592688	2162	352771–621917	2761
144	429189–566091	1375	416076–579204	1639	400829–594451	1945	390447–604833	2154	360705–634575	2752
145	438436–577724	0.1371	425095–591065	0.1633	409582–606578	0.1939	399019–617141	0.2147	368758–647402	0.2742
146	447816–589514	1366	434243–603087	1628	418462–618868	1932	407716–629614	2139	376932–660398	2733
147	457329–601463	1361	443523–615269	1622	427471–631321	1925	416540–642252	2132	385227–673565	2723
148	466977–613571	1357	452935–627613	1617	436609–643939	1919	425492–655056	2125	393644–686904	2714
149	476760–625840	1352	462481–640119	1611	445877–656723	1912	434572–668028	2117	402184–700416	2705
150	486680–638270	0.1348	472160–652790	0.1606	455277–669673	0.1906	443781–681169	0.2110	410848–714102	0.2696
151	496737–650863	1343	481974–665626	1600	464809–682791	1899	453120–694480	2103	419636–727964	2687
152	506933–663619	1339	491924–678628	1595	474474–696078	1893	462591–707961	2096	428551–742001	2678
153	517267–676541	1334	502011–691797	1590	484273–709535	1887	472194–721614	2089	437591–756217	2669
154	527742–689628	1330	512236–705134	1585	494207–723163	1881	481930–735440	2082	446760–770610	2660
155	538359–702881	0.1325	522600–718640	0.1579	504277–736963	0.1875	491800–749440	0.2076	456057–785183	0.2652
156	549117–716303	1321	533103–732317	1574	514483–750937	1869	501805–763615	2069	465483–799937	2643
157	560019–729893	1317	543747–746165	1569	524828–765084	1863	511945–777967	2062	475040–814872	2635
158	571065–743653	1313	554533–760185	1564	535311–779407	1857	522223–792495	2056	484728–829990	2626
159	582255–757585	1309	565461–774379	1559	545935–793905	1851	532638–807202	2049	494548–845292	2618
160	593592–771688	0.1304	576533–788747	0.1554	556698–808582	0.1845	543192–822088	0.2043	504500–860780	0.2610
161	605076–785964	1300	587750–803290	1549	567604–823436	1839	553886–837154	2036	514587–876453	2601
162	616708–800414	1296	599111–818011	1545	578652–838470	1833	564720–852402	2030	524809–892313	2593
163	628489–815039	1292	610620–832908	1540	589843–853685	1828	575696–867832	2024	535167–908361	2585
164	640419–829841	1288	622275–847985	1535	601179–869081	1822	586814–883446	2018	545661–924599	2577
165	652500–844820	0.1284	634079–863241	0.1530	612660–884660	0.1817	598075–899245	0.2011	556293–941027	0.2569
166	664734–859976	1281	646032–878678	1526	624287–900423	1811	609481–915229	2005	567064–957646	2562
167	677120–875312	1277	658135–894297	1521	636062–916370	1806	621032–931400	1999	577974–974458	2554
168	689659–890829	1273	670390–910098	1517	647985–932503	1800	632729–947759	1993	589025–991463	2546
169	702353–906527	1269	682797–926083	1512	660057–948823	1795	644574–964306	1987	600216–1008664	2539
170	715203–922407	0.1265	695356–942254	0.1508	672279–965331	0.1789	656566–981044	0.1981	611550–1026060	0.2531
171	728210–938470	1262	708070–958610	1503	684653–982027	1784	668707–997973	1976	623028–1043652	2524
172	741374–954718	1258	720939–975153	1499	697178–998914	1779	680999–1015093	1970	634649–1061443	2516
173	754696–971152	1254	733963–991885	1494	709856–1015992	1774	693441–1032407	1964	646415–1079433	2509
174	768179–987771	1251	747145–1008805	1490	722688–1033262	1769	706035–1049915	1958	658328–1097622	2502
175	781821–1004579	0.1247	760484–1025916	0.1486	735675–1050725	0.1764	718782–1067618	0.1953	670387–1116013	0.2495
176	795625–1021575	1243	773982–1043218	1482	748817–1068383	1759	731682–1085518	1947	682594–1134606	2487
177	809591–1038761	1240	787640–1060712	1477	762117–1086235	1754	744737–1103615	1942	694949–1153403	2480
178	823721–1056137	1236	801458–1078400	1473	775573–1104285	1749	757948–1121910	1936	707455–1172403	2473
179	838014–1073706	1233	815438–1096282	1469	789189–1122531	1744	771315–1140405	1931	720110–1191610	2466
180	852473–1091467	0.1229	829581–1114359	0.1465	802964–1140976	0.1739	784840–1159100	0.1925	732918–1211022	0.2459
181	867099–1109421	1226	843887–1132633	1461	816899–1159621	1734	798523–1177997	1920	745877–1230643	2453
182	881891–1127571	1223	858358–1151104	1457	830996–1178466	1729	812365–1197097	1915	758990–1250472	2446
183	896852–1145916	1219	872995–1169773	1453	845256–1197512	1724	826367–1216401	1909	772257–1270511	2439
184	911981–1164459	1216	887797–1188643	1449	859678–1216762	1720	840531–1235909	1904	785680–1290760	2432
185	927281–1183199	0.1213	902767–1207713	0.1445	874265–1236215	0.1715	854857–1255623	0.1899	799258–1311222	0.2426
186	942752–1202138	1209	917906–1226984	1441	889017–1255873	1710	869346–1275544	1894	812994–1331896	2419
187	958394–1221278	1206	933213–1246459	1437	903936–1275736	1706	883999–1295673	1889	826887–1352785	2413
188	974210–1240618	1203	948691–1266137	1433	919021–1295807	1701	898817–1316011	1884	840939–1373889	2406
189	990199–1260161	1200	964341–1286019	1429	934274–1316086	1697	913801–1336559	1879	855151–1395209	2400
190	1006364–1279906	0.1196	980162–1306108	0.1426	949697–1336573	0.1692	928952–1357318	0.1874	869524–1416746	0.2394
191	1022704–1299856	1193	996156–1326404	1422	965289–1357271	1688	944271–1378289	1869	884059–1438501	2387
192	1039221–1320011	1190	1012325–1346907	1418	981052–1378180	1683	959758–1399474	1864	898756–1460476	2381
193	1055915–1340373	1187	1028668–1367620	1414	996987–1399301	1679	975415–1420873	1859	913616–1482672	2375
194	1072789–1360941	1184	1045188–1388542	1411	1013095–1420635	1675	991243–1442487	1854	928641–1505089	2369
195	1089842–1381718	0.1181	1061884–1409676	0.1407	1029377–1442183	0.1670	1007242–1464318	0.1849	943831–1527729	0.2362
196	1107075–1402705	1178	1078758–1431022	1404	1045833–1463947	1666	1023414–1486366	1845	959188–1550592	2356
197	1124491–1423901	1175	1095811–1452581	1400	1062465–1485927	1662	1039759–1508633	1840	974711–1573681	2350
198	1142089–1445309	1172	1113044–1474354	1396	1079274–1508124	1657	1056279–1531119	1835	990403–1596995	2344
199	1159870–1466930	1169	1130458–1496342	1393	1096260–1530540	1653	1072973–1553827	1831	1006264–1620536	2338

n	0	1	2	3	4	5	6	7	8	9
0			1.00000	$10^{-1}\times 2.50000$	$10^{-1}\times 1.00000$	$10^{-2}\times 5.00000$	$10^{-2}\times 2.85714$	$10^{-2}\times 1.78571$	$10^{-2}\times 1.19048$	$10^{-3}\times 8.33333$
10	$10^{-3}\times 6.06061$	$10^{-3}\times 4.54545$	$10^{-3}\times 3.49650$	$10^{-3}\times 2.74725$	$10^{-3}\times 2.19780$	$10^{-3}\times 1.78571$	$10^{-3}\times 1.47059$	$10^{-3}\times 1.22549$	$10^{-3}\times 1.03199$	$10^{-4}\times 8.77193$
20	$10^{-4}\times 7.51880$	$10^{-4}\times 6.49351$	$10^{-4}\times 5.64653$	$10^{-4}\times 4.94071$	$10^{-4}\times 4.34783$	$10^{-4}\times 3.84615$	$10^{-4}\times 3.41880$	$10^{-4}\times 3.05250$	$10^{-4}\times 2.73673$	2.46305
30	2.22469	2.01613	1.83284	1.67112	1.52788	1.40056	1.28700	1.18540	1.09421	1.01215
40	$10^{-5}\times 9.38086$	$10^{-5}\times 8.71080$	$10^{-5}\times 8.10307$	$10^{-5}\times 7.55059$	$10^{-5}\times 7.04722$	$10^{-5}\times 6.58762$	$10^{-5}\times 6.16713$	$10^{-5}\times 5.78168$	$10^{-5}\times 5.42770$	$10^{-5}\times 5.10204$
50	4.80192	4.52489	4.26876	4.03161	3.81170	3.60750	3.41763	3.24086	3.07607	2.92227
60	2.77855	2.64410	2.51819	2.40015	2.28938	2.18531	2.08746	1.99537	1.90862	1.82682
70	1.74963	1.67673	1.60782	1.54264	1.48093	1.42248	1.36705	1.31447	1.26456	1.21714
80	1.17206	1.12918	1.08836	1.04949	1.01245	$10^{-6}\times 9.77135$	$10^{-6}\times 9.43441$	$10^{-6}\times 9.11278$	$10^{-6}\times 8.80561$	$10^{-6}\times 8.51209$
90	$10^{-6}\times 8.23147$	$10^{-6}\times 7.96305$	$10^{-6}\times 7.70618$	$10^{-6}\times 7.46024$	$10^{-6}\times 7.22465$	6.99888	6.78242	6.57479	6.37556	6.18429
100	$10^{-6}\times 6.00060$	$10^{-6}\times 5.82411$	$10^{-6}\times 5.65448$	$10^{-6}\times 5.49137$	$10^{-6}\times 5.33447$	$10^{-6}\times 5.18350$	$10^{-6}\times 5.03816$	$10^{-6}\times 4.89822$	$10^{-6}\times 4.76340$	$10^{-6}\times 4.63349$
110	4.50826	4.38750	4.27102	4.15863	4.05014	3.94540	3.84423	3.74650	3.65205	3.56075
120	3.47246	3.38707	3.30446	3.22452	3.14713	3.07220	2.99963	2.92932	2.86120	2.79517
130	2.73116	2.66909	2.60888	2.55047	2.49380	2.43879	2.38538	2.33353	2.28316	2.23424
140	2.18670	2.14050	2.09560	2.05194	2.00948	1.96819	1.92803	1.88895	1.85091	1.81389
150	1.77786	1.74277	1.70860	1.67531	1.64289	1.61129	1.58050	1.55049	1.52124	1.49272
160	1.46490	1.43777	1.41131	1.38549	1.36030	1.33572	1.31172	1.28830	1.26543	1.24310
170	1.22129	1.19999	1.17918	1.15885	1.13898	1.11957	1.10059	1.08204	1.06391	1.04618
180	1.02884	1.01188	$10^{-7}\times 9.95291$	$10^{-7}\times 9.79064$	$10^{-7}\times 9.63187$	$10^{-7}\times 9.47652$	$10^{-7}\times 9.32449$	$10^{-7}\times 9.17569$	$10^{-7}\times 9.03005$	$10^{-7}\times 8.88747$
190	$10^{-7}\times 8.74787$	$10^{-7}\times 8.61119$	8.47733	8.34624	8.21784	8.09206	7.96883	7.84809	7.72977	7.61383
200	$10^{-7}\times 7.50019$	$10^{-7}\times 7.38880$	$10^{-7}\times 7.27960$	$10^{-7}\times 7.17255$	$10^{-7}\times 7.06759$	$10^{-7}\times 6.96466$	$10^{-7}\times 6.86372$	$10^{-7}\times 6.76473$	$10^{-7}\times 6.66763$	$10^{-7}\times 6.57237$
210	6.47893	6.38725	6.29728	6.20901	6.12237	6.03733	5.95387	5.87194	5.79150	5.71252
220	5.63498	5.55883	5.48405	5.41060	5.33846	5.26759	5.19798	5.12958	5.06238	4.99635
230	4.93146	4.86770	4.80502	4.74342	4.68286	4.62334	4.56481	4.50727	4.45070	4.39506
240	4.34035	4.28655	4.23363	4.18157	4.13037	4.08000	4.03045	3.98169	3.93372	3.88651
250	3.84006	3.79435	3.74935	3.70507	3.66148	3.61857	3.57633	3.53475	3.49380	3.45349
260	3.41380	3.37471	3.33621	3.29830	3.26096	3.22418	3.18796	3.15227	3.11712	3.08248
270	3.04836	3.01474	2.98161	2.94896	2.91679	2.88509	2.85384	2.82304	2.79269	2.76277
280	2.73327	2.70419	2.67553	2.64726	2.61940	2.59192	2.56483	2.53811	2.51177	2.48578
290	2.46015	2.43488	2.40995	2.38536	2.36110	2.33717	2.31356	2.29027	2.26729	2.24462
300	$10^{-7}\times 2.22225$	$10^{-7}\times 2.20017$	$10^{-7}\times 2.17839$	$10^{-7}\times 2.15689$	$10^{-7}\times 2.13568$	$10^{-7}\times 2.11474$	$10^{-7}\times 2.09407$	$10^{-7}\times 2.07368$	$10^{-7}\times 2.05354$	$10^{-7}\times 2.03367$
310	2.01405	1.99469	1.97557	1.95669	1.93806	1.91966	1.90149	1.88355	1.86584	1.84835
320	1.83107	1.81401	1.79716	1.78052	1.76409	1.74785	1.73182	1.71598	1.70033	1.68487
330	1.66960	1.65452	1.63961	1.62488	1.61033	1.59596	1.58175	1.56771	1.55384	1.54012
340	1.52658	1.51318	1.49995	1.48687	1.47394	1.46116	1.44853	1.43604	1.42370	1.41149
350	1.39943	1.38750	1.37571	1.36405	1.35252	1.34113	1.32986	1.31871	1.30769	1.29679
360	1.28602	1.27536	1.26482	1.25440	1.24409	1.23389	1.22380	1.21383	1.20396	1.19420
370	1.18454	1.17499	1.16554	1.15619	1.14694	1.13779	1.12873	1.11977	1.11091	1.10214
380	1.09346	1.08487	1.07638	1.06797	1.05965	1.05141	1.04326	1.03519	1.02721	1.01931
390	1.01149	1.00375	$10^{-8}\times 9.96084$	$10^{-8}\times 9.88499$	$10^{-8}\times 9.80992$	$10^{-8}\times 9.73560$	$10^{-8}\times 9.66203$	$10^{-8}\times 9.58920$	$10^{-8}\times 9.51710$	$10^{-8}\times 9.44572$
400	$10^{-8}\times 9.37506$	$10^{-8}\times 9.30510$	$10^{-8}\times 9.23583$	$10^{-8}\times 9.16724$	$10^{-8}\times 9.09934$	$10^{-8}\times 9.03210$	$10^{-8}\times 8.96553$	$10^{-8}\times 8.89960$	$10^{-8}\times 8.83432$	$10^{-8}\times 8.76968$
410	8.70567	8.64228	8.57950	8.51733	8.45576	8.39478	8.33439	8.27457	8.21533	8.15665
420	8.09852	8.04095	7.98392	7.92743	7.87147	7.81604	7.76113	7.70673	7.65283	7.59944
430	7.54655	7.49414	7.44222	7.39077	7.33980	7.28930	7.23926	7.18967	7.14054	7.09186
440	7.04361	6.99581	6.94843	6.90148	6.85495	6.80884	6.76315	6.71786	6.67297	6.62849
450	6.58439	6.54069	6.49738	6.45444	6.41189	6.36970	6.32789	6.28644	6.24535	6.20462
460	6.16424	6.12422	6.08453	6.04519	6.00619	5.96753	5.92919	5.89118	5.85350	5.81614
470	5.77909	5.74236	5.70594	5.66983	5.63402	5.59851	5.56330	5.52838	5.49376	5.45942
480	5.42537	5.39160	5.35811	5.32490	5.29197	5.25930	5.22690	5.19477	5.16290	5.13129
490	5.09994	5.06884	5.03800	5.00740	4.97705	4.94695	4.91709	4.88747	4.85808	4.82893

Relationship between R and r*

$$r \cong 2\sin[(\pi/6)\,R]$$

R	0.000	0.001	0.002	0.003	0.004	0.005	0.006	0.007	0.008	0.009
0.00	0.000	0.001	0.002	0.003	0.004	0.005	0.006	0.007	0.008	0.009
01	010	012	013	014	015	016	017	018	019	020
02	021	022	023	024	025	026	027	028	029	030
03	031	032	034	035	036	037	038	039	040	041
04	042	043	044	045	046	047	048	049	050	051
0.05	0.052	0.053	0.054	0.055	0.057	0.058	0.059	0.060	0.061	0.062
06	063	064	065	066	067	068	069	070	071	072
07	073	074	075	076	077	079	080	081	082	083
08	084	085	086	087	088	089	090	091	092	093
09	094	095	096	097	098	099	100	102	103	104
0.10	0.105	0.106	0.107	0.108	0.109	0.110	0.111	0.112	0.113	0.114
11	115	116	117	118	119	120	121	122	123	125
12	126	127	128	129	130	131	132	133	134	135
13	136	137	138	139	140	141	142	143	144	145
14	146	148	149	150	151	152	153	154	155	156
0.15	0.157	0.158	0.159	0.160	0.161	0.162	0.163	0.164	0.165	0.166
16	167	168	169	170	172	173	174	175	176	177
17	178	179	180	181	182	183	184	185	186	187
18	188	189	190	191	192	193	194	196	197	198
19	199	200	201	202	203	204	205	206	207	208
0.20	0.209	0.210	0.211	0.212	0.213	0.214	0.215	0.216	0.217	0.218
21	219	221	222	223	224	225	226	227	228	229
22	230	231	232	233	234	235	236	237	238	239
23	240	241	242	243	244	245	247	248	249	250
24	251	252	253	254	255	256	257	258	259	260
0.25	0.261	0.262	0.263	0.264	0.265	0.266	0.267	0.268	0.269	0.270
26	271	272	274	275	276	277	278	279	280	281
27	282	283	284	285	286	287	288	289	290	291
28	292	293	294	295	296	297	298	299	300	301
29	303	304	305	306	307	308	309	310	311	312
0.30	0.313	0.314	0.315	0.316	0.317	0.318	0.319	0.320	0.321	0.322
31	323	324	325	326	327	328	329	330	331	333
32	334	335	336	337	338	339	340	341	342	343
33	344	345	346	347	348	349	350	351	352	353
34	354	355	356	357	358	359	360	361	362	363
0.35	0.364	0.366	0.367	0.368	0.369	0.370	0.371	0.372	0.373	0.374
36	375	376	377	378	379	380	381	382	383	384
37	385	386	387	388	389	390	391	392	393	394
38	395	396	397	398	399	400	401	402	404	405
39	406	407	408	409	410	411	412	413	414	415
0.40	0.416	0.417	0.418	0.419	0.420	0.421	0.422	0.423	0.424	0.425
41	426	427	428	429	430	431	432	433	434	435
42	436	437	438	439	440	441	442	443	444	445
43	447	448	449	450	451	452	453	454	455	456
44	457	458	459	460	461	462	463	464	465	466
0.45	0.467	0.468	0.469	0.470	0.471	0.472	0.473	0.474	0.475	0.476
46	477	478	479	480	481	482	483	484	485	486
47	487	488	489	490	491	492	493	494	495	496
48	497	498	499	500	501	502	503	504	505	507
49	508	509	510	511	512	513	514	515	516	517

R	0.000	0.001	0.002	0.003	0.004	0.005	0.006	0.007	0.008	0.009
0.50	0.518	0.519	0.520	0.521	0.522	0.523	0.524	0.525	0.526	0.527
51	528	529	530	531	532	533	534	535	536	537
52	538	539	540	541	542	543	544	545	546	547
53	548	549	550	551	552	553	554	555	556	557
54	558	559	560	561	562	563	564	565	566	567
0.55	0.568	0.569	0.570	0.571	0.572	0.573	0.574	0.575	0.576	0.577
56	578	579	580	581	582	583	584	585	586	587
57	588	589	590	591	592	593	594	595	596	597
58	598	599	600	601	602	603	604	605	606	607
59	608	609	610	611	612	613	614	615	616	617
0.60	0.618	0.619	0.620	0.621	0.622	0.623	0.624	0.625	0.626	0.627
61	628	629	630	631	632	633	634	635	636	637
62	638	639	640	641	642	643	644	645	646	647
63	648	649	650	651	652	653	654	655	656	657
64	658	659	660	661	662	663	664	665	666	667
0.65	0.668	0.669	0.670	0.671	0.672	0.673	0.674	0.675	0.676	0.676
66	677	678	679	680	681	682	683	684	685	686
67	687	688	689	690	691	692	693	694	695	696
68	697	698	699	700	701	702	703	704	705	706
69	707	708	709	710	711	712	713	714	715	716
0.70	0.717	0.718	0.719	0.720	0.721	0.722	0.723	0.724	0.725	0.726
71	727	727	728	729	730	731	732	733	734	735
72	736	737	738	739	740	741	742	743	744	745
73	746	747	748	749	750	751	752	753	754	755
74	756	757	758	759	760	761	761	762	763	764
0.75	0.765	0.766	0.767	0.768	0.769	0.770	0.771	0.772	0.773	0.774
76	775	776	777	778	779	780	781	782	783	784
77	785	786	787	788	789	789	790	791	792	793
78	794	795	796	797	798	799	800	801	802	803
79	804	805	806	807	808	809	810	811	812	813
0.80	0.813	0.814	0.815	0.816	0.817	0.818	0.819	0.820	0.821	0.822
81	823	824	825	826	827	828	829	830	831	832
82	833	834	834	835	836	837	838	839	840	841
83	842	843	844	845	846	847	848	849	850	851
84	852	853	853	854	855	856	857	858	859	860
0.85	0.861	0.862	0.863	0.864	0.865	0.866	0.867	0.868	0.869	0.870
86	870	871	872	873	874	875	876	877	878	879
87	880	881	882	883	884	885	886	886	887	888
88	889	890	891	892	893	894	895	896	897	898
89	899	900	901	901	902	903	904	905	906	907
0.90	0.908	0.909	0.910	0.911	0.912	0.913	0.914	0.915	0.915	0.916
91	917	918	919	920	921	922	923	924	925	926
92	927	928	928	929	930	931	932	933	934	935
93	936	937	938	939	940	940	941	942	943	944
94	945	946	947	948	949	950	951	952	952	953
0.95	0.954	0.955	0.956	0.957	0.958	0.959	0.960	0.961	0.962	0.963
96	964	964	965	966	967	968	969	970	971	972
97	973	974	975	975	976	977	978	979	980	981
98	982	983	984	985	985	986	987	988	989	990
99	991	992	993	994	995	995	996	997	998	999

Arc Sin x[1]

(For arc-sine transformations)

x	0.000	0.001	0.002	0.003	0.004	0.005	0.006	0.007	0.008	0.009
0.000	0.00000	0.00100	0.00200	0.00300	0.00400	0.00500	0.00600	0.00700	0.00800	0.00900
0.010	01000	01100	01200	01300	01400	01500	01600	01700	01800	01900
0.020	02000	02100	02200	02300	02400	02500	02600	02700	02800	02900
0.030	03000	03100	03201	03301	03401	03501	03601	03701	03801	03901
0.040	04001	04101	04201	04301	04401	04502	04602	04702	04802	04902
0.050	0.05002	0.05102	0.05202	0.05302	0.05403	0.05503	0.05603	0.05703	0.05803	0.05903
0.060	06004	06104	06204	06304	06404	06505	06605	06705	06805	06905
0.070	07006	07106	07206	07306	07407	07507	07607	07708	07808	07908
0.080	08009	08109	08209	08310	08410	08510	08611	08711	08811	08912
0.090	09012	09113	09213	09313	09414	09514	09615	09715	09816	09916
0.100	0.10017	0.10117	0.10218	0.10318	0.10419	0.10519	0.10620	0.10721	0.10821	0.10922
0.110	11022	11123	11224	11324	11425	11525	11626	11727	11828	11928
0.120	12029	12130	12230	12331	12432	12533	12634	12734	12835	12936
0.130	13037	13138	13239	13340	13440	13541	13642	13743	13844	13945
0.140	14046	14147	14248	14349	14450	14551	14652	14753	14855	14956
0.150	0.15057	0.15158	0.15259	0.15360	0.15462	0.15563	0.15664	0.15765	0.15866	0.15968
0.160	16069	16170	16272	16373	16474	16576	16677	16779	16880	16981
0.170	17083	17184	17286	17387	17489	17591	17692	17794	17895	17997
0.180	18099	18200	18302	18404	18505	18607	18709	18811	18913	19014
0.190	19116	19218	19320	19422	19524	19626	19728	19830	19932	20034
0.200	0.20136	0.20238	0.20340	0.20442	0.20544	0.20646	0.20749	0.20851	0.20953	0.21055
0.210	21157	21260	21362	21464	21567	21669	21772	21874	21976	22079
0.220	22181	22284	22387	22489	22592	22694	22797	22900	23002	23105
0.230	23208	23311	23413	23516	23619	23722	23825	23928	24031	24134
0.240	24237	24340	24443	24546	24649	24752	24855	24958	25062	25165
0.250	0.25268	0.25371	0.25475	0.25578	0.25681	0.25785	0.25888	0.25992	0.26095	0.26199
0.260	26302	26406	26509	26613	26717	26820	26924	27028	27132	27235
0.270	27339	27443	27547	27651	27755	27859	27963	28067	28171	28275
0.280	28379	28484	28588	28692	28796	28901	29005	29109	29214	29318
0.290	29423	29527	29632	29736	29841	29946	30050	30155	30260	30364
0.300	0.30469	0.30574	0.30679	0.30784	0.30889	0.30994	0.31099	0.31204	0.31309	0.31414
0.310	31519	31625	31730	31835	31940	32046	32151	32256	32362	32467
0.320	32573	32679	32784	32890	32995	33101	33207	33313	33419	33524
0.330	33630	33736	33842	33948	34054	34161	34267	34373	34479	34585
0.340	34692	34798	34904	35011	35117	35224	35330	35437	35544	35650
0.350	0.35757	0.35864	0.35971	0.36078	0.36184	0.36291	0.36398	0.36505	0.36613	0.36720
0.360	36827	36934	37041	37149	37256	37363	37471	37578	37686	37793
0.370	37901	38009	38116	38224	38332	38440	38548	38656	38764	38872
0.380	38980	39088	39196	39304	39412	39521	39629	39738	39846	39955
0.390	40063	40172	40280	40389	40498	40607	40716	40825	40934	41043
0.400	0.41152	0.41261	0.41370	0.41479	0.41589	0.41698	0.41807	0.41917	0.42026	0.42136
0.410	42245	42355	42465	42575	42684	42794	42904	43014	43124	43234
0.420	43345	43455	43565	43675	43786	43896	44007	44117	44228	44339
0.430	44449	44560	44671	44782	44893	45004	45115	45226	45337	45449
0.440	45560	45671	45783	45894	46006	46117	46229	46341	46453	46565
0.450	0.46677	0.46789	0.46901	0.47013	0.47125	0.47237	0.47350	0.47462	0.47574	0.47687
0.460	47800	47912	48025	48138	48251	48363	48476	48590	48703	48816
0.470	48929	49042	49156	49269	49383	49496	49610	49724	49838	49952
0.480	50065	50179	50294	50408	50522	50636	50751	50865	50980	51094
0.490	51209	51324	51439	51553	51668	51783	51899	52014	52129	52244
0.500	0.52360	0.52475	0.52591	0.52707	0.52822	0.52938	0.53054	0.53170	0.53286	0.53402
0.510	53518	53635	53751	53868	53984	54101	54217	54334	54451	54568
0.520	54685	54802	54919	55037	55154	55272	55389	55507	55624	55742
0.530	55860	55978	56096	56214	56332	56451	56569	56688	56806	56925
0.540	57044	57163	57282	57401	57520	57639	57758	57878	57997	58117
0.550	0.58236	0.58356	0.58476	0.58596	0.58716	0.58836	0.58957	0.59077	0.59197	0.59318
0.560	59439	59559	59680	59801	59922	60043	60165	60286	60407	60529
0.570	60651	60772	60894	61016	61138	61260	61383	61505	61628	61750
0.580	61873	61996	62119	62242	62365	62488	62611	62735	62858	62982
0.590	63106	63230	63354	63478	63602	63727	63851	63976	64100	64225
0.600	0.64350	0.64475	0.64600	0.64726	0.64851	0.64977	0.65102	0.65228	0.65354	0.65480
0.610	65606	65732	65859	65985	66112	66239	66365	66492	66620	66747
0.620	66874	67002	67129	67257	67385	67513	67641	67770	67898	68027
0.630	68155	68284	68413	68542	68671	68801	68930	69060	69190	69320
0.640	69450	69580	69710	69841	69972	70102	70233	70364	70496	70627
0.650	0.70758	0.70890	0.71022	0.71154	0.71286	0.71418	0.71551	0.71683	0.71816	0.71949
0.660	72082	72215	72348	72482	72616	72749	72883	73017	73152	73286
0.670	73421	73556	73691	73826	73961	74096	74232	74368	74504	74640
0.680	74776	74913	75049	75186	75323	75460	75598	75735	75873	76011
0.690	76149	76287	76426	76564	76703	76842	76981	77121	77260	77400
0.700	0.77540	0.77680	0.77820	0.77961	0.78101	0.78242	0.78383	0.78525	0.78666	0.78808
0.710	78950	79092	79234	79377	79519	79662	79806	79949	80092	80236
0.720	80380	80524	80669	80813	80958	81103	81249	81394	81540	81686
0.730	81832	81979	82125	82272	82419	82567	82714	82862	83010	83158
0.740	83307	83456	83605	83754	83904	84053	84204	84354	84504	84655
0.750	0.84806	0.84958	0.85109	0.85261	0.85413	0.85565	0.85718	0.85871	0.86024	0.86178
0.760	86331	86485	86640	86794	86949	87104	87260	87415	87571	87728
0.770	87884	88041	88198	88356	88513	88672	88830	88989	89148	89307
0.780	89467	89627	89787	89947	90108	90270	90431	90593	90755	90918
0.790	91081	91244	91408	91572	91736	91901	92066	92231	92397	92563
0.800	0.92730	0.92896	0.93064	0.93231	0.93399	0.93568	0.93736	0.93905	0.94075	0.94245
0.810	94415	94586	94757	94929	95101	95273	95446	95619	95793	95967
0.820	96141	96316	96491	96667	96843	97020	97197	97375	97553	97732
0.830	97911	98090	98270	98451	98632	98813	98995	99178	99361	99544
0.840	99728	99913	1.00098	1.00284	1.00470	1.00657	1.00844	1.01032	1.01220	1.01409
0.850	1.01599	1.01789	1.01979	1.02171	1.02363	1.02555	1.02748	1.02942	1.03136	1.03331
0.860	03527	03723	03920	04118	04316	04515	04715	04915	05116	05318
0.870	05520	05723	05927	06132	06337	06544	06751	06958	07167	07376
0.880	07586	07797	08009	08222	08435	08649	08865	09081	09298	09516
0.890	09735	09954	10175	10397	10619	10843	11068	11294	11520	11748
0.900	1.11977	1.12207	1.12438	1.12670	1.12903	1.13138	1.13374	1.13610	1.13849	1.14088
0.910	14328	14570	14813	15058	15304	15551	15799	16049	16301	16554
0.920	16808	17064	17321	17581	17841	18104	18368	18633	18901	19170
0.930	19441	19714	19989	20266	20545	20826	21109	21394	21681	21971
0.940	22263	22557	22854	23153	23455	23759	24067	24376	24689	25005
0.950	1.25324	1.25645	1.25970	1.26299	1.26631	1.26966	1.27305	1.27648	1.27994	1.28345
0.960	28700	29060	29423	29792	30166	30544	30928	31318	31713	32115
0.970	32523	32938	33360	33789	34226	34672	35127	35591	36065	36550
0.980	37046	37555	38077	38614	39167	39737	40327	40938	41572	42234
0.990	42926	43653	44422	45241	46120	47075	48132	49332	50754	52607
1.000	1.57080									

1) Values abridged from National Bureau of Standards *Tables of Arc Sin X*, Columbia University Press, New York, 1945, by kind permission of the authors and publishers.

Common Logarithms of the Binomial Coefficients C and their Reciprocals* $N=2-33$

For explanation see page 77

Exponent of $p(q)$	Exponent of $q(p)$	$\log C$	$\log 1/C$
		$N=2$	
0	2	0.00000	0 00000
1	1	0.30103	1 69897
		$N=3$	
0	3	0.00000	0 00000
1	2	0.47712	1 52288
		$N=4$	
0	4	0.00000	0 00000
1	3	0.60206	1 39794
2	2	0.77815	1 22185
		$N=5$	
0	5	0.00000	0 00000
1	4	0.69897	1 30103
2	3	1.00000	2 00000
		$N=6$	
0	6	0.00000	0 00000
1	5	0.77815	1 22185
2	4	1.17609	2 82391
3	3	1.30103	2 69897
		$N=7$	
0	7	0.00000	0 00000
1	6	0.84510	1 15490
2	5	1.32222	2 67778
3	4	1.54407	2 45593
		$N=8$	
0	8	0.00000	0 00000
1	7	0.90309	1 09691
2	6	1.44716	2 55284
3	5	1.74819	2 25181
4	4	1.84510	2 15490
		$N=9$	
0	9	0.00000	0 00000
1	8	0.95424	1 04576
2	7	1.55630	2 44370
3	6	1.92428	2 07572
4	5	2.10037	3 89963
		$N=10$	
0	10	0.00000	0 00000
1	9	1.00000	2 00000
2	8	1.65321	2 34679
3	7	2.07918	3 92082
4	6	2.32222	3 67778
5	5	2.40140	3 59860
		$N=11$	
0	11	0.00000	0 00000
1	10	1.04139	2 95861
2	9	1.74036	2 25964
3	8	2.21748	3 78252
4	7	2.51851	3 48149
5	6	2.66464	3 33536
		$N=12$	
0	12	0.00000	0 00000
1	11	1.07918	2 92082
2	10	1.81954	2 18046
3	9	2.34242	3 65758
4	8	2.69461	3 30539
5	7	2.89873	3 10127
6	6	2.96567	3 03433
		$N=13$	
0	13	0.00000	0 00000
1	12	1.11394	2 88606
2	11	1.89209	2 10791
3	10	2.45637	3 54363
4	9	2.85431	3 14569
5	8	3.10958	4 89042
6	7	3.23452	4 76548
		$N=14$	
0	14	0.00000	0 00000
1	13	1.14613	2 85387
2	12	1.95904	2 04096
3	11	2.56110	3 43890
4	10	3.00043	4 99957
5	9	3.30146	4 69854
6	8	3.47756	4 52244
7	7	3.53555	4 46445
		$N=15$	
0	15	0.00000	0 00000
1	14	1.17609	2 82391
2	13	2.02119	3 97881
3	12	2.65801	3 34199
4	11	3.13513	4 86487
5	10	3.47756	4 52244
6	9	3.69940	4 30060
7	8	3.80855	4 19145
		$N=16$	
0	16	0.00000	0 00000
1	15	1.20412	2 79588
2	14	2.07918	3 92082
3	13	2.74819	3 25181
4	12	3.26007	4 73993
5	11	3.64028	4 35972
6	10	3.90352	4 09648
7	9	4.05843	5 94157
8	8	4.10958	5 89042
		$N=17$	
0	17	0.00000	0 00000
1	16	1.23045	2 76955
2	15	2.13354	3 86646
3	14	2.83251	3 16749
4	13	3.37658	4 62342
5	12	3.79155	4 20845
6	11	4.09258	5 90742
7	10	4.28887	5 71113
8	9	4.38578	5 61422
		$N=18$	
0	18	0.00000	0 00000
1	17	1.25527	2 74473
2	16	2.18469	3 81531
3	15	2.91169	3 08831
4	14	3.48572	4 51428
5	13	3.93288	4 06712
6	12	4.26867	5 73133
7	11	4.50275	5 49725
8	10	4.64106	5 35894
9	9	4.68681	5 31319
		$N=19$	
0	19	0.00000	0 00000
1	18	1.27875	2 72125
2	17	2.23300	3 76700
3	16	2.98632	3 01368
4	15	3.58838	4 41162
5	14	4.06551	5 93449
6	13	4.43348	5 56652
7	12	4.70233	5 29767
8	11	4.87842	5 12158
9	10	4.96557	5 03443
		$N=20$	
0	20	0.00000	0 00000
1	19	1.30103	2 69897
2	18	2.27875	3 72125
3	17	3.05690	4 94310
4	16	3.68529	4 31471
5	15	4.19044	5 80956
6	14	4.58838	5 41162
7	13	4.88941	5 11059
8	12	5.10027	6 89973
9	11	5.22521	6 77479
10	10	5.26660	6 73340
		$N=21$	
0	21	0.00000	0 00000
1	20	1.32222	2 67778
2	19	2.32222	3 67778
3	18	3.12385	4 87615
4	17	3.77706	4 22294
5	16	4.30854	5 69146
6	15	4.73451	5 26549
7	14	5.06551	6 93449
8	13	5.30854	6 69146
9	12	5.46824	6 53176
10	11	5.54743	6 45257
		$N=22$	
0	22	0.00000	0 00000
1	21	1.34242	2 65758
2	20	2.36361	3 63639
3	19	3.18752	4 81248
4	18	3.86421	4 13579
5	17	4.42052	5 57948
6	16	4.87281	5 12719
7	15	5.23184	6 76816
		$N=22$ (continued)	
8	14	5.50484	6 49516
9	13	5.69672	6 30328
10	12	5.81067	6 18933
11	11	5.84846	6 15154
		$N=23$	
0	23	0.00000	0 00000
1	22	1.36173	2 63827
2	21	2.40312	3 59688
3	20	3.24822	4 75178
4	19	3.94719	4 05281
5	18	4.52697	5 47303
6	17	5.00409	6 99591
7	16	5.38944	6 61056
8	15	5.69047	6 30953
9	14	5.91232	6 08768
10	13	6.05845	7 94155
11	12	6.13100	7 86900
		$N=24$	
0	24	0.00000	0 00000
1	23	1.38021	2 61979
2	22	2.44091	3 55909
3	21	3.30621	4 69379
4	20	4.02637	5 97363
5	19	4.62843	5 37157
6	18	5.12903	6 87097
7	17	5.53921	6 46079
8	16	5.86657	6 13343
9	15	6.11644	7 88356
10	14	6.29253	7 70747
11	13	6.39727	7 60273
12	12	6.43203	7 56797
		$N=25$	
0	25	0.00000	0 00000
1	24	1.39794	2 60206
2	23	2.47712	3 52288
3	22	3.36173	4 63827
4	21	4.10209	5 89791
5	20	4.72534	5 27466
6	19	5.24822	6 75178
7	18	5.68187	6 31813
8	17	6.03406	7 96594
9	16	6.31026	7 68974
10	15	6.51438	7 48562
11	14	6.64908	7 35092
12	13	6.71603	7 28397
		$N=26$	
0	26	0.00000	0 00000
1	25	1.41497	2 58503
2	24	2.51188	3 48812
3	23	3.41497	4 58503
4	22	4.17464	5 82536
5	21	4.81809	5 18191
6	20	5.36216	6 63784
7	19	5.81809	6 18191
8	18	6.19376	7 80624
9	17	6.49479	7 50521
10	16	6.72524	7 27476
11	15	6.88796	7 11204
12	14	6.98487	7 01513
13	13	7.01706	8 98294
		$N=27$	
0	27	0.00000	0 00000
1	26	1.43136	2 56864
2	25	2.54531	3 45469
3	24	3.46613	4 53387
4	23	4.24428	5 75572
5	22	4.90703	5 09297
6	21	5.47131	6 52869
7	20	5.94843	6 05157
8	19	6.34637	7 65363
9	18	6.67088	7 32912
10	17	6.92615	7 07385
11	16	7.11521	8 88479
12	15	7.24015	8 75985
13	14	7.30229	8 69771
		$N=28$	
0	28	0.00000	0 00000
1	27	1.44716	2 55284
2	26	2.57749	3 42251
3	25	3.51534	4 48466
4	24	4.31122	5 68878
5	23	4.99247	5 00753
6	22	5.57604	6 42396
7	21	6.07337	7 92663
		$N=28$ (continued)	
8	20	6.49250	7 50750
9	19	6.83928	7 16072
10	18	7.11804	8 88196
11	17	7.33192	8 66808
12	16	7.48318	8 51682
13	15	7.57336	8 42664
14	14	7.60332	8 39668
		$N=29$	
0	29	0.00000	0 00000
1	28	1.46240	2 53760
2	27	2.60853	3 39147
3	26	3.56277	4 43723
4	25	4.37568	5 62432
5	24	5.07465	6 92535
6	23	5.67671	6 32329
7	22	6.19334	7 80666
8	21	6.63267	7 36733
9	20	7.00065	8 99935
10	19	7.30168	8 69832
11	18	7.53904	8 46096
12	17	7.71513	8 28487
13	16	7.83164	8 16836
14	15	7.88963	8 11037
		$N=30$	
0	30	0.00000	0 00000
1	29	1.47712	2 52288
2	28	2.63849	3 36151
3	27	3.60853	4 39147
4	26	4.43783	5 56217
5	25	5.15383	6 84617
6	24	5.77362	6 22638
7	23	6.30874	7 69126
8	22	6.76737	7 23263
9	21	7.15555	8 84445
10	20	7.47777	8 52223
11	19	7.73741	8 26259
12	18	7.93698	8 06302
13	17	8.07831	9 92169
14	16	8.16263	9 83737
15	15	8.19066	9 80934
		$N=31$	
0	31	0.00000	0 00000
1	30	1.49136	2 50864
2	29	2.66745	3 33255
3	28	3.65273	4 34727
4	27	4.49783	5 50217
5	26	5.23022	6 76978
6	25	5.86704	6 13296
7	24	6.41989	7 58011
8	23	6.89701	7 10299
9	22	7.30449	8 69551
10	21	7.64691	8 35309
11	20	7.92774	8 07226
12	19	8.14959	9 85041
13	18	8.31440	9 68560
14	17	8.42354	9 57646
15	16	8.47790	9 52210
		$N=32$	
0	32	0.00000	0 00000
1	31	1.50515	2 49485
2	30	2.69548	3 30452
3	29	3.69548	4 30452
4	28	4.55582	5 44418
5	27	5.30401	6 69599
6	26	5.95722	6 04278
7	25	6.52710	7 47290
8	24	7.02195	8 97805
9	23	7.44791	8 55209
10	22	7.80964	8 19036
11	21	8.11067	9 88933
12	20	8.35371	9 64629
13	19	8.54080	9 45920
14	18	8.67342	9 32658
15	17	8.75260	9 24740
16	16	8.77893	9 22107
		$N=33$	
0	33	0.00000	0 00000
1	32	1.51851	2 48149
2	31	2.72263	3 27737
3	30	3.73687	4 26313
4	29	4.61194	5 38806
5	28	5.37536	6 62464
6	27	6.04437	7 95563
7	26	6.63064	7 36936
8	25	7.14252	8 85748
9	24	7.58622	8 41378

Exponent of $p(q)$	Exponent of $q(p)$	log C	log $1/C$
$N = 33$ (continued)			
10	23	7.96643	8 03357
11	22	8.28676	9 71324
12	21	8.55000	9 45000
13	20	8.75828	9 24172
14	19	8.91318	9 08682
15	18	9.01585	10 98415
16	17	9.06700	10 93300
$N = 34$			
0	34	0.00000	0 00000
1	33	1.53148	2 46852
2	32	2.74896	3 25104
3	31	3.77699	4 22301
4	30	4.66629	5 33371
5	29	5.44444	6 55556
6	28	6.12869	7 87131
7	27	6.73075	7 26925
8	26	7.25903	8 74097
9	25	7.71976	8 28024
10	24	8.11770	9 88230
11	23	8.45651	9 54349
12	22	8.73906	9 26094
13	21	8.96754	9 03246
14	20	9.14363	10 85637
15	19	9.26857	10 73143
16	18	9.34320	10 65680
17	17	9.36803	10 63197
$N = 35$			
0	35	0.00000	0 00000
1	34	1.54407	2 45593
2	33	2.77452	3 22548
3	32	3.81591	4 18409
4	31	4.71900	5 28100
5	30	5.51139	6 48861
6	29	6.21036	7 78964
7	28	6.82766	7 17234
8	27	7.37173	8 62827
9	26	7.84885	8 15115
10	25	8.26382	9 73618
11	24	8.62037	9 37963
12	23	8.92140	9 07860
13	22	9.16919	10 83081
14	21	9.36548	10 63452
15	20	9.51161	10 48839
16	19	9.60852	10 39148
17	18	9.65682	10 34318
$N = 36$			
0	36	0.00000	0 00000
1	35	1.55630	2 44370
2	34	2.79934	3 20066
3	33	3.85370	4 14630
4	32	4.77015	5 22985
5	31	5.57633	6 42367
6	30	6.28954	7 71046
7	29	6.92157	7 07843
8	28	7.48087	8 51913
9	27	7.97379	8 02621
10	26	8.40515	9 59485
11	25	8.77873	9 22127
12	24	9.09749	10 90251
13	23	9.36376	10 63624
14	22	9.57936	10 42064
15	21	9.74569	10 25431
16	20	9.86379	10 13621
17	19	9.93437	10 06563
18	18	9.95785	10 04215
$N = 37$			
0	37	0.00000	0 00000
1	36	1.56820	2 43180
2	35	2.82347	3 17653
3	34	3.89042	4 10958
4	33	4.81984	5 18016
5	32	5.63938	6 36062
6	31	6.36638	7 63362
7	30	7.01265	8 98735
8	29	7.58668	8 41332
9	28	8.09483	9 90517
10	27	8.54199	9 45801
11	26	8.93196	9 06804
12	25	9.26775	10 73225
13	24	9.55175	10 44825
14	23	9.78583	10 21417
15	22	9.97147	10 02853
16	21	10.10977	11 89023
17	20	10.20154	11 79846
18	19	10.24730	11 75270
$N = 38$			
0	38	0.00000	0 00000
1	37	1.57978	2 42022

Exponent of $p(q)$	Exponent of $q(p)$	log C	log $1/C$
$N = 38$ (continued)			
2	36	2.84696	3 15304
3	35	3.92614	4 07386
4	34	4.86814	5 13186
5	33	5.70065	6 29935
6	32	6.44102	7 55898
7	31	7.10107	8 89893
8	30	7.68934	8 31066
9	29	8.21222	9 78778
10	28	8.67462	9 32538
11	27	9.08038	10 91962
12	26	9.43256	10 56744
13	25	9.73359	10 26641
14	24	9.98541	10 01459
15	23	10.18953	11 81047
16	22	10.34713	11 65287
17	21	10.45911	11 54089
18	20	10.52605	11 47395
19	19	10.54833	11 45167
$N = 39$			
0	39	0.00000	0 00000
1	38	1.59106	2 40894
2	37	2.86982	3 13018
3	36	3.96090	4 03910
4	35	4.91514	5 08486
5	34	5.76024	6 23976
6	33	6.51357	7 48643
7	32	7.18698	8 81302
8	31	7.78904	8 21096
9	30	8.32616	9 67384
10	29	8.80328	9 19672
11	28	9.22429	10 77571
12	27	9.59227	10 40773
13	26	9.90969	10 09031
14	25	10.17853	11 82147
15	24	10.40038	11 59962
16	23	10.57647	11 42353
17	22	10.70775	11 29225
18	21	10.79490	11 20510
19	20	10.83837	11 16163
$N = 40$			
0	40	0.00000	0 00000
1	39	1.60206	2 39794
2	38	2.89209	3 10791
3	37	3.99476	4 00524
4	36	4.96090	5 03910
5	35	5.81823	6 18177
6	34	6.58415	7 41585
7	33	7.27053	8 72947
8	32	7.88595	8 11405
9	31	8.43686	9 56314
10	30	8.92822	9 07178
11	29	9.36395	10 63605
12	28	9.74717	10 25283
13	27	10.08038	11 91962
14	26	10.36562	11 63438
15	25	10.60450	11 39550
16	24	10.79832	11 20168
17	23	10.94808	11 05192
18	22	11.05454	12 94546
19	21	11.11821	12 88179
20	20	11.13940	12 86060
$N = 41$			
0	41	0.00000	0 00000
1	40	1.61278	2 38722
2	39	2.91381	3 08619
3	38	4.02776	5 97224
4	37	5.00548	6 99452
5	36	5.87471	6 12529
6	35	6.65286	7 34714
7	34	7.35183	8 64817
8	33	7.98022	8 01978
9	32	8.54449	9 45551
10	31	9.04964	10 95036
11	30	9.49961	10 50039
12	29	9.89755	10 10245
13	28	10.24601	11 75399
14	27	10.54704	11 45296
15	26	10.80231	11 19769
16	25	11.01316	12 98684
17	24	11.18065	12 81935
18	23	11.30559	12 69441
19	22	11.38857	12 61143
20	21	11.42996	12 57004
$N = 42$			
0	42	0.00000	0 00000
1	41	1.62325	2 37675
2	40	2.93500	3 06500
3	39	4.05994	5 94006

Exponent of $p(q)$	Exponent of $q(p)$	log C	log $1/C$
$N = 42$ (continued)			
4	38	5.04895	6 95105
5	37	5.92976	6 07024
6	36	6.71981	7 28019
7	35	7.43102	8 56898
8	34	8.07199	9 92801
9	33	8.64923	9 35077
10	32	9.16774	10 83226
11	31	9.63150	10 36850
12	30	10.04368	11 95632
13	29	10.40686	11 59314
14	28	10.72313	11 27687
15	27	10.99420	11 00580
16	26	11.22144	12 77856
17	25	11.40596	12 59404
18	24	11.54863	12 45137
19	23	11.65009	12 34991
20	22	11.71079	12 28921
21	21	11.73099	12 26901
$N = 43$			
0	43	0.00000	0 00000
1	42	1.63347	2 36653
2	41	2.95569	3 04431
3	40	4.09135	5 90865
4	39	5.09135	6 90865
5	38	5.98344	6 01656
6	37	6.78508	7 21492
7	36	7.50818	8 49182
8	35	8.16139	9 83861
9	34	8.75122	9 24878
10	33	9.28270	10 71730
11	32	9.75982	10 24018
12	31	10.18579	11 81421
13	30	10.56321	11 43679
14	29	10.89420	11 10580
15	28	11.18051	12 81949
16	27	11.42354	12 57646
17	26	11.62446	12 37554
18	25	11.78416	12 21584
19	24	11.90335	12 09665
20	23	11.98253	12 01747
21	22	12.02204	13 97796
$N = 44$			
0	44	0.00000	0 00000
1	43	1.64345	2 35655
2	42	2.97589	3 02411
3	41	4.12202	5 87798
4	40	5.13274	6 86726
5	39	6.03583	7 96417
6	38	6.84875	7 15125
7	37	7.58343	8 41657
8	36	8.24854	9 75146
9	35	8.85060	9 14940
10	34	9.39467	10 60533
11	33	9.88476	10 11524
12	32	10.32409	11 67591
13	31	10.71530	11 28470
14	30	11.06053	12 93947
15	29	11.36156	12 63844
16	28	11.61984	12 38016
17	27	11.83655	12 16345
18	26	12.01264	13 98736
19	25	12.14886	13 85114
20	24	12.24577	13 75423
21	23	12.30376	13 69624
22	22	12.32307	13 67693
$N = 45$			
0	45	0.00000	0 00000
1	44	1.65321	2 34679
2	43	2.99564	3 00436
3	42	4.15198	5 84802
4	41	5.17317	6 82683
5	40	6.08699	7 91301
6	39	6.91089	7 08911
7	38	7.65686	8 34314
8	37	8.33355	9 66645
9	36	8.94751	9 05249
10	35	9.50382	10 49618
11	34	10.00649	11 99351
12	33	10.45879	11 54121
13	32	10.86336	11 13664
14	31	11.22238	12 77762
15	30	11.53765	12 46235
16	29	11.81065	12 18935
17	28	12.04260	13 95740
18	27	12.23449	13 76551
19	26	12.38710	13 61290
20	25	12.50104	13 49896
21	24	12.57676	13 42324
22	23	12.61455	13 38545

Exponent of $p(q)$	Exponent of $q(p)$	log C	log $1/C$
$N = 46$			
0	46	0.00000	0 00000
1	45	1.66276	2 33724
2	44	3.01494	4 98506
3	43	4.18127	5 81873
4	42	5.21268	6 78732
5	41	6.13696	7 86304
6	40	6.97159	7 02841
7	39	7.72855	8 27145
8	38	8.41653	9 58347
9	37	9.04207	10 95793
10	36	9.61027	10 38973
11	35	10.12518	11 87482
12	34	10.59007	11 40993
13	33	11.00760	12 99240
14	32	11.37999	12 62001
15	31	11.70905	12 29095
16	30	11.99629	12 00371
17	29	12.24296	13 75704
18	28	12.45009	13 54991
19	27	12.61849	13 38151
20	26	12.74883	13 25117
21	25	12.84158	13 15842
22	24	12.89710	13 10290
23	23	12.91558	13 08442
$N = 47$			
0	47	0.00000	0 00000
1	46	1.67210	2 32790
2	45	3.03383	4 96617
3	44	4.20992	5 79008
4	43	5.25131	6 74869
5	42	6.18581	7 81419
6	41	7.03091	8 96909
7	40	7.79859	8 20141
8	39	8.49756	9 50244
9	38	9.13438	10 86562
10	37	9.71417	10 28583
11	36	10.24098	11 75902
12	35	10.71810	11 28190
13	34	11.14822	12 85178
14	33	11.53357	12 46643
15	32	11.87600	12 12400
16	31	12.17703	13 82297
17	30	12.43794	13 56206
18	29	12.65979	13 34021
19	28	12.84343	13 15657
20	27	12.98956	13 01044
21	26	13.09870	14 90130
22	25	13.17126	14 82874
23	24	13.20747	14 79253
$N = 48$			
0	48	0.00000	0 00000
1	47	1.68124	2 31876
2	46	3.05231	4 94769
3	45	4.23795	5 76205
4	44	5.28910	6 71090
5	43	6.23358	7 76642
6	42	7.08890	8 91110
7	41	7.86705	8 13295
8	40	8.57674	9 42326
9	39	9.22456	10 77544
10	38	9.81563	10 18437
11	37	10.35402	11 64598
12	36	10.84304	11 15696
13	35	11.28540	12 71460
14	34	11.68334	12 31666
15	33	12.03872	13 96128
16	32	12.35312	13 64688
17	31	12.62782	13 37218
18	30	12.86391	13 13609
19	29	13.06228	14 93772
20	28	13.22364	14 77636
21	27	13.34858	14 65142
22	26	13.43752	14 56248
23	25	13.49077	14 50923
24	24	13.50850	14 49150
$N = 49$			
0	49	0.00000	0 00000
1	48	1.69020	2 30980
2	47	3.07041	4 92959
3	46	4.26538	5 73462
4	45	5.32608	6 67392
5	44	6.28032	7 71968
6	43	7.14563	8 85437
7	42	7.93400	8 06600
8	41	8.65416	9 34584
9	40	9.31270	10 68730
10	39	9.91476	10 08524
11	38	10.46443	11 53557
12	37	10.96503	11 03497
13	36	11.41929	12 58071
14	35	11.82946	12 17054

Common Logarithms of the Binomial Coefficients C and their Reciprocals* N = 49 − 61

For explanation see page 77

N = 49 (continued)

Exponent of p(q)	Exponent of q(p)	log C	log 1/C
15	34	12.19744	13 80256
16	33	12.52480	13 47520
17	32	12.81286	13 18714
18	31	13.06274	14 93726
19	30	13.27535	14 72465
20	29	13.45144	14 54856
21	28	13.59162	14 40838
22	27	13.69636	14 30364
23	26	13.76599	14 23401
24	25	13.80075	14 19925

N = 50

Exponent of p(q)	Exponent of q(p)	log C	log 1/C
0	50	0.00000	0 00000
1	49	1.69897	2 30103
2	48	3.08814	4 91186
3	47	4.29226	5 70774
4	46	5.36229	6 63771
5	45	6.32608	7 67392
6	44	7.20114	8 79886
7	43	7.99950	8 00050
8	42	8.72988	9 27012
9	41	9.39888	10 60112
10	40	10.01167	11 98833
11	39	10.57233	11 42767
12	38	11.08422	12 91578
13	37	11.55006	12 44994
14	36	11.97213	12 02787
15	35	12.35234	13 64766
16	34	12.69229	13 30771
17	33	12.99332	13 00668
18	32	13.25656	14 74344
19	31	13.48296	14 51704
20	30	13.67329	14 32671
21	29	13.82819	14 17181
22	28	13.94817	14 05183
23	27	14.03360	15 96640
24	26	14.08475	15 91525
25	25	14.10178	15 89822

N = 51

Exponent of p(q)	Exponent of q(p)	log C	log 1/C
0	51	0.00000	0 00000
1	50	1.70757	2 29243
2	49	3.10551	4 89449
3	48	4.31859	5 68141
4	47	5.39777	6 60223
5	46	6.37089	7 62911
6	45	7.25550	8 74450
7	44	8.06362	9 93638
8	43	8.80398	9 19602
9	42	9.48320	10 51680
10	41	10.10645	11 89355
11	40	10.67784	11 32216
12	39	11.20072	12 79928
13	38	11.67784	12 32216
14	37	12.11150	13 88850
15	36	12.50361	13 49639
16	35	12.85579	13 14421
17	34	13.16941	14 83059
18	33	13.44562	14 55438
19	32	13.68538	14 31462
20	31	13.88950	14 11050
21	30	14.05864	15 94136
22	29	14.19334	15 80666
23	28	14.29401	15 70599
24	27	14.36096	15 63904
25	26	14.39438	15 60562

N = 52

Exponent of p(q)	Exponent of q(p)	log C	log 1/C
0	52	0.00000	0 00000
1	51	1.71600	2 28400
2	50	3.12254	4 87746
3	49	4.34439	5 65561
4	48	5.43253	6 56747
5	47	6.41480	7 58520
6	46	7.30875	8 69125
7	45	8.12641	9 87359
8	44	8.87653	9 12347
9	43	9.56574	10 43426
10	42	10.19921	11 80079
11	41	10.78106	11 21894
12	40	11.31467	12 68533
13	39	11.80278	12 19722
14	38	12.24772	13 75228
15	37	12.65141	13 34859
16	36	13.01549	14 98451
17	35	13.34135	14 65865
18	34	13.63014	14 36986
19	33	13.88287	14 11713
20	32	14.10035	15 89965
21	31	14.28328	15 71672
22	30	14.43222	15 56778
23	29	14.54762	15 45238
24	28	14.62980	15 37020

N = 52 (continued)

Exponent of p(q)	Exponent of q(p)	log C	log 1/C
25	27	14.67902	15 32098
26	26	14.69541	15 30459

N = 53

Exponent of p(q)	Exponent of q(p)	log C	log 1/C
0	53	0.00000	0 00000
1	52	1.72428	2 27572
2	51	3.13925	4 86075
3	50	4.36970	5 63030
4	49	5.46661	6 53339
5	48	6.45783	7 54217
6	47	7.36092	8 63908
7	46	8.18792	9 81208
8	45	8.94759	9 05241
9	44	9.64656	10 35344
10	43	10.29001	11 70999
11	42	10.88209	11 11791
12	41	11.42616	12 57384
13	40	11.92500	12 07500
14	39	12.38093	13 61907
15	38	12.79590	13 20410
16	37	13.17157	14 82843
17	36	13.50932	14 49068
18	35	13.81035	14 18965
19	34	14.07567	15 92433
20	33	14.30611	15 69389
21	32	14.50241	15 49759
22	31	14.66514	15 33486
23	30	14.79477	15 20523
24	29	14.89168	15 10832
25	28	14.95614	15 04386
26	27	14.98832	15 01168

N = 54

Exponent of p(q)	Exponent of q(p)	log C	log 1/C
0	54	0.00000	0 00000
1	53	1.73239	2 26761
2	52	3.15564	4 84436
3	51	4.39452	5 60548
4	50	5.50003	6 49997
5	49	6.50003	7 49997
6	48	7.41208	8 58792
7	47	8.24822	9 75178
8	46	9.01723	10 98277
9	45	9.72574	10 27426
10	44	10.37896	11 62104
11	43	10.98102	11 01898
12	42	11.53530	12 46470
13	41	12.04461	13 95539
14	40	12.51126	13 48874
15	39	12.93723	13 06277
16	38	13.32418	14 67582
17	37	13.67351	14 32649
18	36	13.98644	14 01356
19	35	14.26399	15 73601
20	34	14.50703	15 49297
21	33	14.71629	15 28371
22	32	14.89238	15 10762
23	31	15.03580	16 96420
24	30	15.14695	16 85305
25	29	15.22613	16 77387
26	28	15.27356	16 72644
27	27	15.28935	16 71065

N = 55

Exponent of p(q)	Exponent of q(p)	log C	log 1/C
0	55	0.00000	0 00000
1	54	1.74036	2 25964
2	53	3.17173	4 82827
3	52	4.41888	5 58112
4	51	5.53282	6 46718
5	50	6.54142	7 45858
6	49	7.46224	8 53776
7	48	8.30734	9 69266
8	47	9.08549	10 91451
9	46	9.80335	10 19665
10	45	10.46611	11 53389
11	44	11.07793	12 92207
12	43	11.64220	12 35780
13	42	12.16172	13 83828
14	41	12.63884	13 36116
15	40	13.07554	14 92446
16	39	13.47348	14 52652
17	38	13.83409	14 16591
18	37	14.15860	15 84140
19	36	14.44805	15 55195
20	35	14.70332	15 29668
21	34	14.92517	15 07483
22	33	15.11423	16 88577
23	32	15.27101	16 72899
24	31	15.39595	16 60405
25	30	15.48937	16 51063
26	29	15.55152	16 44848
27	28	15.58256	16 41744

N = 56

Exponent of p(q)	Exponent of q(p)	log C	log 1/C
0	56	0.00000	0 00000
1	55	1.74819	2 25181
2	54	3.18752	4 81248
3	53	4.44279	5 55721
4	52	5.56501	6 43499
5	51	6.58204	7 41796
6	50	7.51146	8 48854
7	49	8.36533	9 63467
8	48	9.15244	10 84756
9	47	9.87944	10 12056
10	46	10.55154	11 44846
11	45	11.17290	12 82710
12	44	11.74693	12 25307
13	43	12.27644	13 72356
14	42	12.76378	13 23622
15	41	13.21094	14 78906
16	40	13.61960	14 38040
17	39	13.99122	14 00878
18	38	14.32701	15 67299
19	37	14.62804	15 37196
20	36	14.89521	15 10479
21	35	15.12929	16 87071
22	34	15.33094	16 66906
23	33	15.50069	16 49931
24	32	15.63899	16 36101
25	31	15.74620	16 25380
26	30	15.82259	16 17741
27	29	15.86835	16 13165
28	28	15.88359	16 11641

N = 57

Exponent of p(q)	Exponent of q(p)	log C	log 1/C
0	57	0.00000	0 00000
1	56	1.75587	2 24413
2	55	3.20303	4 79697
3	54	4.46627	5 53373
4	53	5.59661	6 40339
5	52	6.62191	7 37809
6	51	7.55977	8 44023
7	50	8.42224	9 57776
8	49	9.21812	10 78188
9	48	9.95407	10 04593
10	47	10.63531	11 36469
11	46	11.26602	12 73398
12	45	11.84959	12 15041
13	44	12.38886	13 61114
14	43	12.88619	13 11381
15	42	13.34357	14 65643
16	41	13.76270	14 23730
17	40	14.14503	15 85497
18	39	14.49182	15 50818
19	38	14.80413	15 19587
20	37	15.08288	16 91712
21	36	15.32886	16 67114
22	35	15.54274	16 45726
23	34	15.72508	16 27492
24	33	15.87635	16 12365
25	32	15.99693	16 00307
26	31	16.08710	17 91290
27	30	16.14710	17 85290
28	29	16.17706	17 82294

N = 58

Exponent of p(q)	Exponent of q(p)	log C	log 1/C
0	58	0.00000	0 00000
1	57	1.76343	2 23657
2	56	3.21827	4 78173
3	55	4.48934	5 51066
4	54	5.62764	6 37236
5	53	6.66107	7 33893
6	52	7.60719	8 39281
7	51	8.47810	9 52190
8	50	9.28258	10 71742
9	49	10.02730	11 97270
10	48	10.71750	11 28250
11	47	11.35735	12 64265
12	46	11.95026	12 04974
13	45	12.49908	13 50092
14	44	13.00616	14 99384
15	43	13.47353	14 52647
16	42	13.90287	14 09713
17	41	14.29567	15 70433
18	40	14.65319	15 34681
19	39	14.97649	15 02351
20	38	15.26653	16 73347
21	37	15.52409	16 47591
22	36	15.74987	16 25013
23	35	15.94444	16 05556
24	34	16.10830	17 89170
25	33	16.24184	17 75816
26	32	16.34538	17 65462
27	31	16.41917	17 58083
28	30	16.46337	17 53663
29	29	16.47809	17 52191

N = 59

Exponent of p(q)	Exponent of q(p)	log C	log 1/C
0	59	0.00000	0 00000
1	58	1.77085	2 22915
2	57	3.23325	4 76675
3	56	4.51200	5 48800
4	55	5.65813	6 34187
5	54	6.69952	7 30048
6	53	7.65377	8 34623
7	52	8.53294	9 46706
8	51	9.34586	10 65414
9	50	10.09919	11 90081
10	49	10.79816	11 20184
11	48	11.44696	12 55304
12	47	12.04902	13 95098
13	46	12.60717	13 39283
14	45	13.12380	14 87620
15	44	13.60092	14 39908
16	43	14.04026	15 95974
17	42	14.44328	15 55672
18	41	14.81125	15 18875
19	40	15.14528	16 85472
20	39	15.44631	16 55369
21	38	15.71516	16 28484
22	37	15.95252	16 04748
23	36	16.15899	17 84101
24	35	16.33509	17 66491
25	34	16.48121	17 51879
26	33	16.59772	17 40228
27	32	16.68487	17 31513
28	31	16.74286	17 25714
29	30	16.77182	17 22818

N = 60

Exponent of p(q)	Exponent of q(p)	log C	log 1/C
0	60	0.00000	0 00000
1	59	1.77815	2 22185
2	58	3.24797	4 75203
3	57	4.53428	5 46572
4	56	5.68809	6 31191
5	55	6.73731	7 26269
6	54	7.69952	8 30048
7	53	8.58682	9 41318
8	52	9.40801	10 59199
9	51	10.16977	11 83023
10	50	10.87734	11 12266
11	49	11.53491	12 46509
12	48	12.14593	13 85407
13	47	12.71323	13 28677
14	46	13.23920	14 76080
15	45	13.72586	14 27414
16	44	14.17496	15 82504
17	43	14.58796	15 41204
18	42	14.96616	15 03384
19	41	15.31065	16 68935
20	40	15.62241	16 37759
21	39	15.90225	16 09775
22	38	16.15089	17 84911
23	37	16.36894	17 63106
24	36	16.55693	17 44307
25	35	16.71530	17 28470
26	34	16.84439	17 15561
27	33	16.94451	17 05549
28	32	17.01586	18 98414
29	31	17.05861	18 94139
30	30	17.07285	18 92715

N = 61

Exponent of p(q)	Exponent of q(p)	log C	log 1/C
0	61	0.00000	0 00000
1	60	1.78533	2 21467
2	59	3.26245	4 73755
3	58	4.55618	5 44382
4	57	5.71755	6 28245
5	56	6.77445	7 22555
6	55	7.74449	8 25551
7	54	8.63976	9 36024
8	53	9.46906	10 53094
9	52	10.23909	11 76091
10	51	10.95510	11 04490
11	50	11.62127	12 37873
12	49	12.24106	13 75894
13	48	12.81732	13 18268
14	47	13.35243	14 64757
15	46	13.84844	14 15156
16	45	14.30707	15 69293
17	44	14.72984	15 27016
18	43	15.11802	16 88198
19	42	15.47273	16 52727
20	41	15.79495	16 20505
21	40	16.08552	17 91448
22	39	16.34515	17 65485
23	38	16.57449	17 42551
24	37	16.77406	17 22594
25	36	16.94432	17 05568
26	35	17.08565	18 91435
27	34	17.19836	18 80164
28	33	17.28268	18 71732

Common Logarithms of the Binomial Coefficients *C* and their Reciprocals* $N = 61-72$ For explanation see page 77

N = 61 (continued)

Exponent of $p(q)$	$q(p)$	log *C*	log 1/*C*
29	32	17.33879	18 66121
30	31	17.36682	18 63318

N = 62

Exponent of $p(q)$	$q(p)$	log *C*	log 1/*C*
0	62	0.00000	0 00000
1	61	1.79239	2 20761
2	60	3.27669	4 72331
3	59	4.57772	5 42228
4	58	5.74651	6 25349
5	57	6.81097	7 18903
6	56	7.78870	8 21130
7	55	8.69179	9 30821
8	54	9.52906	10 47094
9	53	10.30721	11 69279
10	52	11.03148	12 96852
11	51	11.70610	12 29390
12	50	12.33448	13 66552
13	49	12.91951	13 08049
14	48	13.46358	14 53642
15	47	13.96873	14 03127
16	46	14.43671	15 56329
17	45	14.86902	15 13098
18	44	15.26696	16 73304
19	43	15.63166	16 36834
20	42	15.96409	16 03591
21	41	16.26512	17 73488
22	40	16.53548	17 46452
23	39	16.77582	17 22418
24	38	16.98667	17 01333
25	37	17.16851	18 83149
26	36	17.32174	18 67826
27	35	17.44668	18 55332
28	34	17.54359	18 45641
29	33	17.61267	18 38733
30	32	17.65406	18 34594
31	31	17.66785	18 33215

N = 63

Exponent of $p(q)$	$q(p)$	log *C*	log 1/*C*
0	63	0.00000	0 00000
1	62	1.79934	2 20066
2	61	3.29070	4 70930
3	60	4.59891	5 40109
4	59	5.77500	6 22500
5	58	6.84688	7 15312
6	57	7.83216	8 16784
7	56	8.74294	9 25706
8	55	9.58804	10 41196
9	54	10.37416	11 62584
10	53	11.10655	12 89345
11	52	11.78943	12 21057
12	51	12.42625	13 57375
13	50	13.01988	14 98012
14	49	13.57272	14 42728
15	48	14.08683	15 91317
16	47	14.56395	15 43605
17	46	15.00560	16 99440
18	45	15.41308	16 58692
19	44	15.78754	16 21246
20	43	16.12997	17 87003
21	42	16.44121	17 55879
22	41	16.72204	17 27796
23	40	16.97310	17 02690
24	39	17.19495	18 80505
25	38	17.38807	18 61193
26	37	17.55288	18 44712
27	36	17.68972	18 31028
28	35	17.79886	18 20114
29	34	17.88053	18 11947
30	33	17.93489	18 06511
31	32	17.96204	18 03796

N = 64

Exponent of $p(q)$	$q(p)$	log *C*	log 1/*C*
0	64	0.00000	0 00000
1	63	1.80618	2 19382
2	62	3.30449	4 69551
3	61	4.61976	5 38024
4	60	5.80303	6 19697
5	59	6.88221	7 11779
6	58	7.87491	8 12509
7	57	8.79324	9 20676
8	56	9.64603	10 35397
9	55	10.43997	11 56003
10	54	11.18034	12 81966
11	53	11.87134	12 12866
12	52	12.51643	13 48357
13	51	13.11849	14 88151
14	50	13.67993	14 32007
15	49	14.20281	15 79719
16	48	14.68889	15 31111
17	47	15.13968	16 86032
18	46	15.55651	16 44349
19	45	15.94051	16 05949

N = 64 (continued)

Exponent of $p(q)$	$q(p)$	log *C*	log 1/*C*
20	44	16.29269	17 70731
21	43	16.61393	17 38607
22	42	16.90497	17 09503
23	41	17.16649	18 83351
24	40	17.39907	18 60093
25	39	17.60319	18 39681
26	38	17.77928	18 22072
27	37	17.92770	18 07230
28	36	18.04874	19 95126
29	35	18.14265	19 85735
30	34	18.20959	19 79041
31	33	18.24971	19 75029
32	32	18.26307	19 73693

N = 65

Exponent of $p(q)$	$q(p)$	log *C*	log 1/*C*
0	65	0.00000	0 00000
1	64	1.81291	2 18709
2	63	3.31806	4 68194
3	62	4.64028	5 35972
4	61	5.83061	6 16939
5	60	6.91697	7 08303
6	59	7.91697	8 08303
7	58	8.84273	9 15727
8	57	9.70307	10 29693
9	56	10.50470	11 49530
10	55	11.25289	12 74711
11	54	11.95186	12 04814
12	53	12.60507	13 39493
13	52	13.21540	14 78460
14	51	13.78528	14 21472
15	50	14.31676	15 68324
16	49	14.81161	15 18839
17	48	15.27135	16 72865
18	47	15.69732	16 30268
19	46	16.09067	17 90933
20	45	16.45239	17 54761
21	44	16.78339	17 21661
22	43	17.08442	18 91558
23	42	17.35616	18 64384
24	41	17.59920	18 40080
25	40	17.81404	18 18596
26	39	18.00113	19 99887
27	38	18.16083	19 83917
28	37	18.29345	19 70655
29	36	18.39926	19 60074
30	35	18.47844	19 52156
31	34	18.53114	19 46886
32	33	18.55747	19 44253

N = 66

Exponent of $p(q)$	$q(p)$	log *C*	log 1/*C*
0	66	0.00000	0 00000
1	65	1.81954	2 18046
2	64	3.33143	4 66857
3	63	4.66049	5 33951
4	62	5.85777	6 14223
5	61	6.95119	7 04881
6	60	7.95837	8 04163
7	59	8.89142	9 10858
8	58	9.75918	10 24082
9	57	10.56837	11 43163
10	56	11.32424	12 67576
11	55	12.03104	13 96896
12	54	12.69222	13 30778
13	53	13.31067	14 68933
14	52	13.88882	14 11118
15	51	14.42873	15 57127
16	50	14.93218	15 06782
17	49	15.40070	16 59930
18	48	15.83562	16 16438
19	47	16.23811	17 76189
20	46	16.60918	17 39082
21	45	16.94972	17 05028
22	44	17.26051	18 73949
23	43	17.54223	18 45777
24	42	17.79549	18 20451
25	41	18.02080	19 97920
26	40	18.21861	19 78139
27	39	18.38931	19 61069
28	38	18.53321	19 46679
29	37	18.65060	19 34940
30	36	18.74168	19 25832
31	35	18.80662	19 19338
32	34	18.84554	19 15446
33	33	18.85850	19 14150

N = 67

Exponent of $p(q)$	$q(p)$	log *C*	log 1/*C*
0	67	0.00000	0 00000
1	66	1.82607	2 17393
2	65	3.34459	4 65541
3	64	4.68038	5 31962
4	63	5.88450	6 11550
5	62	6.98487	7 01513
6	61	7.99911	8 00089

N = 67 (continued)

Exponent of $p(q)$	$q(p)$	log *C*	log 1/*C*
7	60	8.93934	9 06066
8	59	9.81440	10 18560
9	58	10.63101	11 36899
10	57	11.39444	12 60556
11	56	12.10892	13 89108
12	55	12.77793	13 22207
13	54	13.40435	14 59565
14	53	13.99062	14 00938
15	52	14.53880	15 46120
16	51	15.05068	16 94932
17	50	15.52781	16 47219
18	49	15.97150	16 02850
19	48	16.38295	17 61705
20	47	16.76316	17 23684
21	46	17.11304	18 88696
22	45	17.43337	18 56663
23	44	17.72486	18 27514
24	43	17.98810	18 01190
25	42	18.22363	19 77637
26	41	18.43190	19 56810
27	40	18.61332	19 38668
28	39	18.76822	19 23178
29	38	18.89689	19 10311
30	37	18.99955	19 00045
31	36	19.07639	20 92361
32	35	19.12754	20 87246
33	34	19.15310	20 84690

N = 68

Exponent of $p(q)$	$q(p)$	log *C*	log 1/*C*
0	68	0.00000	0 00000
1	67	1.83251	2 16749
2	66	3.35755	4 64245
3	65	4.69998	5 30002
4	64	5.91083	6 08917
5	63	7.01804	8 98196
6	62	8.03923	9 96077
7	61	8.98652	9 01348
8	60	9.86876	10 13124
9	59	10.69267	11 30733
10	58	11.46352	12 53648
11	57	12.18556	13 81444
12	56	12.86225	13 13775
13	55	13.49650	14 50350
14	54	14.09073	15 90927
15	53	14.64703	15 35297
16	52	15.16719	16 83281
17	51	15.65274	16 34726
18	50	16.10504	17 89496
19	49	16.52526	17 47474
20	48	16.91442	17 08558
21	47	17.27345	18 72655
22	46	17.60312	18 39688
23	45	17.90415	18 09585
24	44	18.17715	19 82285
25	43	18.42267	19 57733
26	42	18.64116	19 35884
27	41	18.83305	19 16695
28	40	18.99867	19 00133
29	39	19.13833	20 86167
30	38	19.25228	20 74772
31	37	19.34070	20 65930
32	36	19.40375	20 59625
33	35	19.44154	20 55846
34	34	19.45413	20 54587

N = 69

Exponent of $p(q)$	$q(p)$	log *C*	log 1/*C*
0	69	0.00000	0 00000
1	68	1.83885	2 16115
2	67	3.37033	4 62967
3	66	4.71928	5 28072
4	65	5.93677	6 06323
5	64	7.05071	8 94929
6	63	8.07874	9 92126
7	62	9.03298	10 96702
8	61	9.92228	10 07772
9	60	10.75337	11 24663
10	59	11.53152	12 46848
11	58	12.26098	13 73902
12	57	12.94523	13 05477
13	56	13.58716	14 41284
14	55	14.18922	15 81078
15	54	14.75349	15 24651
16	53	15.28176	16 71824
17	52	15.77559	16 22441
18	51	16.23632	17 76368
19	50	16.66514	17 33486
20	49	17.06308	18 93692
21	48	17.43105	18 56895
22	47	17.76987	18 23013
23	46	18.08024	19 91976
24	45	18.36279	19 63721
25	44	18.61806	19 38194
26	43	18.84654	19 15346
27	42	19.04865	20 95135

N = 69 (continued)

Exponent of $p(q)$	$q(p)$	log *C*	log 1/*C*
28	41	19.22474	20 77526
29	40	19.37512	20 62488
30	39	19.50006	20 49994
31	38	19.59976	20 40024
32	37	19.67440	20 32560
33	36	19.72409	20 27591
34	35	19.74891	20 25109

N = 70

Exponent of $p(q)$	$q(p)$	log *C*	log 1/*C*
0	70	0.00000	0 00000
1	69	1.84510	2 15490
2	68	3.38292	4 61708
3	67	4.73830	5 26170
4	66	5.96232	6 03768
5	65	7.08289	8 91711
6	64	8.11766	9 88234
7	63	9.07874	10 92126
8	62	9.97499	10 02501
9	61	10.81314	11 18686
10	60	11.59847	12 40153
11	59	12.33523	13 66477
12	58	13.02690	14 97310
13	57	13.67638	14 32362
14	56	14.28613	15 71387
15	55	14.85822	15 14178
16	54	15.39447	16 60553
17	53	15.89641	16 10359
18	52	16.36542	17 63458
19	51	16.80267	17 19733
20	50	17.20921	18 79079
21	49	17.58596	18 41404
22	48	17.93373	18 06627
23	47	18.25324	19 74676
24	46	18.54513	19 45487
25	45	18.80995	19 19005
26	44	19.04819	20 95181
27	43	19.26028	20 73972
28	42	19.44659	20 55341
29	41	19.60744	20 39256
30	40	19.74310	20 25690
31	39	19.85380	20 14620
32	38	19.93971	20 06029
33	37	20.00098	21 99902
34	36	20.03771	21 96229
35	35	20.04994	21 95006

N = 71

Exponent of $p(q)$	$q(p)$	log *C*	log 1/*C*
0	71	0.00000	0 00000
1	70	1.85126	2 14874
2	69	3.39533	4 60467
3	68	4.75705	5 24295
4	67	5.98750	6 01250
5	66	7.11461	8 88539
6	65	8.15600	9 84400
7	64	9.12382	10 87618
8	63	10.02691	11 97309
9	62	10.87200	11 12800
10	61	11.66440	12 33560
11	60	12.40833	13 59167
12	59	13.10730	14 89270
13	58	13.76421	14 23579
14	57	14.38151	15 61849
15	56	14.96130	15 03870
16	55	15.50536	16 49464
17	54	16.01528	17 98472
18	53	16.49240	17 50760
19	52	16.93792	17 06208
20	51	17.35289	18 64711
21	50	17.73824	18 26176
22	49	18.09479	19 90521
23	48	18.42326	19 57674
24	47	18.72429	19 27571
25	46	18.99845	19 00155
26	45	19.24623	20 75377
27	44	19.46808	20 53192
28	43	19.66438	20 33562
29	42	19.83545	20 16455
30	41	19.98157	20 01843
31	40	20.10300	21 89700
32	39	20.19991	21 80009
33	38	20.27246	21 72754
34	37	20.32076	21 67924
35	36	20.34490	21 65510

N = 72

Exponent of $p(q)$	$q(p)$	log *C*	log 1/*C*
0	72	0.00000	0 00000
1	71	1.85733	2 14267
2	70	3.40756	4 59244
3	69	4.77554	5 22446
4	68	6.01233	7 98767
5	67	7.14587	8 85413
6	66	8.19379	9 80621

Common Logarithms of the Binomial Coefficients C and their Reciprocals* N=72—81

For explanation see page 77

Exponent of $p(q)$	Exponent of $q(p)$	log C	log $1/C$
	$N=72$ (continued)		
7	65	9.16824	**10** 83176
8	64	10.07806	**11** 92194
9	63	10.93000	**11** 07000
10	62	11.72934	**12** 27066
11	61	12.48034	**13** 51966
12	60	13.18648	**14** 81352
13	59	13.85069	**14** 14931
14	58	14.47542	**15** 52458
15	57	15.06275	**16** 93725
16	56	15.61451	**16** 38549
17	55	16.13225	**17** 86775
18	54	16.61734	**17** 38266
19	53	17.07098	**18** 92902
20	52	17.49422	**18** 50578
21	51	17.88801	**18** 11199
22	50	18.25315	**19** 74685
23	49	18.59040	**19** 40960
24	48	18.90038	**19** 09962
25	47	19.18368	**20** 81632
26	46	19.44081	**20** 55919
27	45	19.67220	**20** 32780
28	44	19.87826	**20** 12174
29	43	20.05931	**21** 94069
30	42	20.21566	**21** 78434
31	41	20.34755	**21** 65245
32	40	20.45518	**21** 54482
33	39	20.53873	**21** 46127
34	38	20.59831	**21** 40169
35	37	20.63403	**21** 36597
36	36	20.64593	**21** 35407
	$N=73$		
0	73	0.00000	**0** 00000
1	72	1.86332	**2** 13668
2	71	3.41963	**4** 58037
3	70	4.79376	**5** 20624
4	69	6.03680	**7** 96320
5	68	7.17668	**8** 82332
6	67	8.23104	**9** 76896
7	66	9.21201	**10** 78799
8	65	10.12847	**11** 87153
9	64	10.98714	**11** 01286
10	63	11.79332	**12** 20668
11	62	12.55127	**13** 44873
12	61	13.26448	**14** 73552
13	60	13.93586	**14** 06414
14	59	14.56789	**15** 43211
15	58	15.16265	**16** 83735
16	57	15.72196	**16** 27804
17	56	16.24738	**17** 75262
18	55	16.74030	**17** 25970
19	54	17.20191	**18** 79809
20	53	17.63327	**18** 36673
21	52	18.03533	**19** 96467
22	51	18.40891	**19** 59109
23	50	18.75475	**19** 24525
24	49	19.07351	**20** 92649
25	48	19.36576	**20** 63424
26	47	19.63203	**20** 36797
27	46	19.87277	**20** 12723
28	45	20.08837	**21** 91163
29	44	20.27918	**21** 72082
30	43	20.44551	**21** 55449
31	42	20.58762	**21** 41238
32	41	20.70572	**21** 29428
33	40	20.79999	**21** 20001
34	39	20.87057	**21** 12943
35	38	20.91757	**21** 08243
36	37	20.94105	**21** 05895
	$N=74$		
0	74	0.00000	**0** 00000
1	73	1.86923	**2** 13077
2	72	3.43152	**4** 56848
3	71	4.81174	**5** 18826
4	70	6.06093	**7** 93907
5	69	7.20706	**8** 79294
6	68	8.26776	**9** 73224
7	67	9.25517	**10** 74483
8	66	10.17816	**11** 82184
9	65	11.04346	**12** 95654
10	64	11.85637	**12** 14363
11	63	12.62116	**13** 37884
12	62	13.34132	**14** 65868
13	61	14.01977	**15** 98023
14	60	14.65897	**15** 34103
15	59	15.26103	**16** 73897
16	58	15.82776	**16** 17224
17	57	16.36074	**17** 63926
18	56	16.86134	**17** 13866
19	55	17.33078	**18** 66922
20	54	17.77011	**18** 22989
21	53	18.18028	**19** 81972
22	52	18.56214	**19** 43786
	$N=74$ (continued)		
23	51	18.91641	**19** 08359
24	50	19.24377	**20** 75623
25	49	19.54480	**20** 45520
26	48	19.82002	**20** 17998
27	47	20.06990	**21** 93010
28	46	20.29484	**21** 70516
29	45	20.49520	**21** 50480
30	44	20.67129	**21** 32871
31	43	20.82338	**21** 17662
32	42	20.95170	**21** 04830
33	41	21.05644	**22** 94356
34	40	21.13774	**22** 86226
35	39	21.19573	**22** 80427
36	38	21.23049	**22** 76951
37	37	21.24208	**22** 75792
	$N=75$		
0	75	0.00000	**0** 00000
1	74	1.87506	**2** 12494
2	73	3.44326	**4** 55674
3	72	4.82946	**5** 17054
4	71	6.08474	**7** 91526
5	70	7.23703	**8** 76297
6	69	8.30397	**9** 69603
7	68	9.29772	**10** 70228
8	67	10.22714	**11** 77286
9	66	11.09897	**12** 90103
10	65	11.91852	**12** 08148
11	64	12.69004	**13** 30996
12	63	13.41704	**14** 58296
13	62	14.10244	**15** 89756
14	61	14.74870	**15** 25130
15	60	15.35794	**16** 64206
16	59	15.93197	**16** 06803
17	58	16.47237	**17** 52763
18	57	16.98053	**17** 01947
19	56	17.45765	**18** 54235
20	55	17.90481	**18** 09519
21	54	18.32295	**19** 67705
22	53	18.71292	**19** 28708
23	52	19.07547	**20** 92453
24	51	19.41126	**20** 58874
25	50	19.72089	**20** 27911
26	49	20.00489	**21** 99511
27	48	20.26372	**21** 73628
28	47	20.49780	**21** 50220
29	46	20.70750	**21** 29250
30	45	20.89314	**21** 10686
31	44	21.05499	**22** 94501
32	43	21.19329	**22** 80671
33	42	21.30825	**22** 69175
34	41	21.40002	**22** 59998
35	40	21.46873	**22** 53127
36	39	21.51449	**22** 48551
37	38	21.53735	**22** 46265
	$N=76$		
0	76	0.00000	**0** 00000
1	75	1.88081	**2** 11919
2	74	3.45484	**4** 54516
3	73	4.84696	**5** 15304
4	72	6.10822	**7** 89178
5	71	7.26658	**8** 73342
6	70	8.33969	**9** 66031
7	69	9.33969	**10** 66031
8	68	10.27545	**11** 72455
9	67	11.15371	**12** 84629
10	66	11.97979	**12** 02021
11	65	12.75794	**13** 24206
12	64	13.49167	**14** 50833
13	63	14.18391	**15** 81609
14	62	14.83712	**15** 16288
15	61	15.45342	**16** 54658
16	60	16.03463	**17** 96537
17	59	16.58233	**17** 41767
18	58	17.09791	**18** 90209
19	57	17.58259	**18** 41741
20	56	18.03743	**19** 96257
21	55	18.46340	**19** 53660
22	54	18.86134	**19** 13866
23	53	19.23201	**20** 76799
24	52	19.57607	**20** 42393
25	51	19.89413	**20** 10587
26	50	20.18673	**21** 81327
27	49	20.45434	**21** 54566
28	48	20.69738	**21** 30262
29	47	20.91622	**21** 08378
30	46	21.11120	**22** 88880
31	45	21.28259	**22** 71741
32	44	21.43065	**22** 56935
33	43	21.55559	**22** 44441
34	42	21.65758	**22** 34242
35	41	21.73676	**22** 26324
36	40	21.79325	**22** 20675
	$N=76$ (continued)		
37	39	21.82710	**22** 17290
38	38	21.83838	**22** 16162
	$N=77$		
0	77	0.00000	**0** 00000
1	76	1.88649	**2** 11351
2	75	3.46627	**4** 53373
3	74	4.86421	**5** 13579
4	73	6.13139	**7** 86861
5	72	7.29574	**8** 70426
6	71	8.37492	**9** 62508
7	70	9.38108	**10** 61892
8	69	10.32309	**11** 67691
9	68	11.20770	**12** 79230
10	67	12.04020	**13** 95980
11	66	12.82489	**13** 17511
12	65	13.56525	**14** 43475
13	64	14.26422	**15** 73578
14	63	14.92427	**15** 07573
15	62	15.54752	**16** 45248
16	61	16.13579	**17** 86421
17	60	16.69067	**17** 30933
18	59	17.21355	**18** 78645
19	58	17.70565	**18** 29435
20	57	18.16805	**19** 83195
21	56	18.60170	**19** 39830
22	55	19.00747	**20** 99253
23	54	19.38610	**20** 61390
24	53	19.73829	**20** 26171
25	52	20.06462	**21** 93538
26	51	20.36565	**21** 63435
27	50	20.64186	**21** 35814
28	49	20.89367	**21** 10633
29	48	21.12147	**22** 87853
30	47	21.32559	**22** 67441
31	46	21.50632	**22** 49368
32	45	21.66393	**22** 33607
33	44	21.79863	**22** 20137
34	43	21.91060	**22** 08940
35	42	22.00001	**23** 99999
36	41	22.06695	**23** 93305
37	40	22.11153	**23** 88847
38	39	22.13381	**23** 86619
	$N=78$		
0	78	0.00000	**0** 00000
1	77	1.89209	**2** 10791
2	76	3.47756	**4** 52244
3	75	4.88125	**5** 11875
4	74	6.15425	**7** 84575
5	73	7.32451	**8** 67549
6	72	8.40968	**9** 59032
7	71	9.42192	**10** 57808
8	70	10.37009	**11** 62991
9	69	11.26094	**12** 73906
10	68	12.09979	**13** 90021
11	67	12.89091	**13** 10909
12	66	13.63780	**14** 36220
13	65	14.34340	**15** 65660
14	64	15.01019	**16** 98981
15	63	15.64027	**16** 35973
16	62	16.23549	**17** 76451
17	61	16.79744	**17** 20256
18	60	17.32749	**18** 67251
19	59	17.82689	**18** 17311
20	58	18.29671	**19** 70329
21	57	18.73792	**19** 26208
22	56	19.15138	**20** 84862
23	55	19.53784	**20** 46216
24	54	19.89799	**20** 10201
25	53	20.23244	**21** 76756
26	52	20.54174	**21** 45826
27	51	20.82638	**21** 17362
28	50	21.08679	**22** 91321
29	49	21.32337	**22** 67663
30	48	21.53644	**22** 46356
31	47	21.72632	**22** 27368
32	46	21.89327	**22** 10673
33	45	22.03751	**23** 96249
34	44	22.15925	**23** 84075
35	43	22.25863	**23** 74137
36	42	22.33580	**23** 66420
37	41	22.39084	**23** 60916
38	40	22.42385	**23** 57615
39	39	22.43484	**23** 56516
	$N=79$		
0	79	0.00000	**0** 00000
1	78	1.89763	**2** 10237
2	77	3.48869	**4** 51131
3	76	4.89806	**5** 10194
4	75	6.17681	**7** 82319
5	74	7.35291	**8** 64709
	$N=79$ (continued)		
6	73	8.44399	**9** 55601
7	72	9.46221	**10** 53779
8	71	10.41645	**11** 58355
9	70	11.31347	**12** 68653
10	69	12.15857	**13** 84143
11	68	12.95602	**13** 04398
12	67	13.70935	**14** 29065
13	66	14.42148	**15** 57852
14	65	15.09490	**16** 90510
15	64	15.73172	**16** 26828
16	63	16.33378	**17** 66622
17	62	16.90267	**17** 09733
18	61	17.43979	**18** 56021
19	60	17.94637	**18** 05363
20	59	18.42349	**19** 57651
21	58	18.87212	**19** 12788
22	57	19.29313	**20** 70687
23	56	19.68727	**20** 31273
24	55	20.05525	**21** 94475
25	54	20.39767	**21** 60233
26	53	20.71509	**21** 28491
27	52	21.00801	**22** 99199
28	51	21.27685	**22** 72315
29	50	21.52202	**22** 47798
30	49	21.74387	**22** 25613
31	48	21.94271	**22** 05729
32	47	22.11880	**23** 88120
33	46	22.27238	**23** 72762
34	45	22.40366	**23** 59634
35	44	22.51281	**23** 48719
36	43	22.59996	**23** 40004
37	42	22.66522	**23** 33478
38	41	22.70869	**23** 29131
39	40	22.73041	**23** 26959
	$N=80$		
0	80	0.00000	**0** 00000
1	79	1.90309	**2** 09691
2	78	3.49969	**4** 50031
3	77	4.91466	**5** 08534
4	76	6.19909	**7** 80091
5	75	7.38093	**8** 61907
6	74	8.47784	**9** 52216
7	73	9.50198	**10** 49802
8	72	10.46221	**11** 53779
9	71	11.36530	**12** 63470
10	70	12.21656	**13** 78344
11	69	13.02027	**14** 97973
12	68	13.77993	**14** 22007
13	67	14.49850	**15** 50150
14	66	15.17845	**16** 82155
15	65	15.82190	**16** 17810
16	64	16.43069	**17** 56931
17	63	17.00642	**18** 99358
18	62	17.55049	**18** 44951
19	61	18.06413	**19** 93587
20	60	18.54843	**19** 45157
21	59	19.00436	**20** 99564
22	58	19.43279	**20** 56721
23	57	19.83449	**20** 16551
24	56	20.21015	**21** 78985
25	55	20.56040	**21** 43960
26	54	20.88579	**21** 11421
27	53	21.18682	**22** 81318
28	52	21.46394	**22** 53606
29	51	21.71754	**22** 28246
30	50	21.94799	**22** 05201
31	49	22.15560	**23** 84440
32	48	22.34065	**23** 65935
33	47	22.50337	**23** 49663
34	46	22.64399	**23** 35601
35	45	22.76268	**23** 23732
36	44	22.85959	**23** 14041
37	43	22.93484	**23** 06516
38	42	22.98853	**23** 01147
39	41	23.02071	**24** 97929
40	40	23.03144	**24** 96856
	$N=81$		
0	81	0.00000	**0** 00000
1	80	1.90849	**2** 09151
2	79	3.51055	**4** 48945
3	78	4.93105	**5** 06895
4	77	6.22109	**7** 77891
5	76	7.40861	**8** 59139
6	75	8.51127	**9** 48873
7	74	9.54123	**10** 45877
8	73	10.50737	**11** 49263
9	72	11.41645	**12** 58355
10	71	12.27379	**13** 72621
11	70	13.08365	**14** 91635
12	69	13.84957	**14** 15043
13	68	14.57447	**15** 42553
14	67	15.26086	**16** 73914

Common Logarithms of the Binomial Coefficients C and their Reciprocals* N=81—89

For explanation see page 77

$N = 81$ (continued)

Exponent of p(q)	Exponent of q(p)	log C	log 1/C
15	66	15.91084	16 08916
16	65	16.52626	17 47374
17	64	17.10873	18 89127
18	63	17.65963	18 34037
19	62	18.18022	19 81978
20	61	18.67158	19 32842
21	60	19.13469	20 86531
22	59	19.57042	20 42958
23	58	19.97955	20 02045
24	57	20.36276	21 63724
25	56	20.72070	21 27930
26	55	21.05391	22 94609
27	54	21.36291	22 63709
28	53	21.64815	22 35185
29	52	21.91003	22 08997
30	51	22.14891	23 85109
31	50	22.36512	23 63488
32	49	22.55894	23 44106
33	48	22.73062	23 26938
34	47	22.88038	23 11962
35	46	23.00841	24 99159
36	45	23.11487	24 88513
37	44	23.19988	24 80012
38	43	23.26355	24 73645
39	42	23.30595	24 69405
40	41	23.32714	24 67286

$N = 82$

Exponent of p(q)	Exponent of q(p)	log C	log 1/C
0	82	0.00000	0 00000
1	81	1.91381	2 08619
2	80	3.52127	4 47873
3	79	4.94724	5 05276
4	78	6.24280	7 75720
5	77	7.43593	8 56407
6	76	8.54427	9 45573
7	75	9.57998	10 42002
8	74	10.55196	11 44804
9	73	11.46694	12 53306
10	72	12.33027	13 66973
11	71	13.14621	14 85379
12	70	13.91828	14 08172
13	69	14.64944	15 35056
14	68	15.34216	16 65784
15	67	15.99858	16 00142
16	66	16.62053	17 37947
17	65	17.20963	18 79037
18	64	17.76727	18 23273
19	63	18.29470	19 70530
20	62	18.79301	19 20699
21	61	19.26318	20 73682
22	60	19.70609	20 29391
23	59	20.12251	21 87749
24	58	20.51315	21 48685
25	57	20.87864	21 12136
26	56	21.21954	22 78046
27	55	21.53636	22 46364
28	54	21.82957	22 17043
29	53	22.09956	23 90044
30	52	22.34672	23 65328
31	51	22.57136	23 42864
32	50	22.77378	23 22622
33	49	22.95424	23 04576
34	48	23.11295	24 88705
35	47	23.25013	24 74987
36	46	23.36592	24 63408
37	45	23.46048	24 53952
38	44	23.53391	24 46609
39	43	23.58629	24 41371
40	42	23.61770	24 38230
41	41	23.62817	24 37183

$N = 83$

Exponent of p(q)	Exponent of q(p)	log C	log 1/C
0	83	0.00000	0 00000
1	82	1.91908	2 08092
2	81	3.53186	4 46814
3	80	4.96323	5 03677
4	79	6.26426	7 73574
5	78	7.46291	8 53709
6	77	8.57686	9 42314
7	76	9.61825	10 38175
8	75	10.59597	11 40403
9	74	11.51679	12 48321
10	73	12.38602	13 61398
11	72	13.20795	14 79205
12	71	13.98610	14 01390
13	70	14.72342	15 27658
14	69	15.42239	16 57761
15	68	16.08515	17 91485
16	67	16.71354	17 28646
17	66	17.30916	18 69084
18	65	17.87343	18 12657
19	64	18.40759	19 59241
20	63	18.91274	19 08726
21	62	19.38986	20 61014

$N = 83$ (continued)

Exponent of p(q)	Exponent of q(p)	log C	log 1/C
22	61	19.83983	20 16017
23	60	20.26344	21 73656
24	59	20.66138	21 33862
25	58	21.03429	22 96571
26	57	21.38274	22 61726
27	56	21.70725	22 29275
28	55	22.00828	23 99172
29	54	22.28625	23 71375
30	53	22.54152	23 45848
31	52	22.77443	23 22557
32	51	22.98529	23 01471
33	50	23.17434	24 82566
34	49	23.34184	24 65816
35	48	23.48796	24 51204
36	47	23.61290	24 38710
37	46	23.71680	24 28320
38	45	23.79977	24 20023
39	44	23.86192	24 13808
40	43	23.90331	24 09669
41	42	23.92400	24 07600

$N = 84$

Exponent of p(q)	Exponent of q(p)	log C	log 1/C
0	84	0.00000	0 00000
1	83	1.92428	2 07572
2	82	3.54233	4 45767
3	81	4.97902	5 02098
4	80	6.28545	7 71455
5	79	7.48956	8 51044
6	78	8.60904	9 39096
7	77	9.65604	10 34396
8	76	10.63944	11 36056
9	75	11.56601	12 43399
10	74	12.44107	13 55893
11	73	13.26891	14 73109
12	72	14.05305	15 94695
13	71	14.79644	15 20356
14	70	15.50157	16 49843
15	69	16.17058	17 82942
16	68	16.80531	17 19469
17	67	17.40737	18 59263
18	66	17.97817	18 02183
19	65	18.51896	19 48104
20	64	19.03084	20 96916
21	63	19.51480	20 48520
22	62	19.97172	20 02828
23	61	20.40238	21 59762
24	60	20.80750	21 19250
25	59	21.18771	22 81229
26	58	21.54359	22 45641
27	57	21.87566	22 12434
28	56	22.18437	23 81563
29	55	22.47016	23 52984
30	54	22.73341	23 26659
31	53	22.97444	23 02556
32	52	23.19356	24 80644
33	51	23.39105	24 60895
34	50	23.56714	24 43286
35	49	23.72205	24 27795
36	48	23.85594	24 14406
37	47	23.96898	24 03102
38	46	24.06129	25 93871
39	45	24.13299	25 86701
40	44	24.18414	25 81586
41	43	24.21481	25 78519
42	42	24.22503	25 77497

$N = 85$

Exponent of p(q)	Exponent of q(p)	log C	log 1/C
0	85	0.00000	0 00000
1	84	1.92942	2 07058
2	83	3.55267	4 44733
3	82	4.99463	5 00537
4	81	6.30638	7 69362
5	80	7.51589	8 48411
6	79	8.64083	9 35917
7	78	9.69336	10 30664
8	77	10.68237	11 31763
9	76	11.61461	12 38539
10	75	12.49543	13 50457
11	74	13.32910	14 67090
12	73	14.11915	15 88085
13	72	14.86853	15 13147
14	71	15.57973	16 42027
15	70	16.25490	17 74510
16	69	16.89588	17 10412
17	68	17.50428	18 49572
18	67	18.08151	19 91849
19	66	18.62883	19 37117
20	65	19.14735	20 85265
21	64	19.63804	20 36196
22	63	20.10180	21 89820
23	62	20.53941	21 46059
24	61	20.95159	21 04841
25	60	21.33898	22 66102
26	59	21.70216	22 29784

$N = 85$ (continued)

Exponent of p(q)	Exponent of q(p)	log C	log 1/C
27	58	22.04165	23 95835
28	57	22.35792	23 64208
29	56	22.65140	23 34860
30	55	22.92246	23 07754
31	54	23.17146	24 82854
32	53	23.39871	24 60129
33	52	23.60447	24 39553
34	51	23.78899	24 21101
35	50	23.95250	24 04750
36	49	24.09516	25 90484
37	48	24.21716	25 78284
38	47	24.31861	25 68139
39	46	24.39965	25 60035
40	45	24.46035	25 53965
41	44	24.50077	25 49923
42	43	24.52098	25 47902

$N = 86$

Exponent of p(q)	Exponent of q(p)	log C	log 1/C
0	86	0.00000	0 00000
1	85	1.93450	2 06550
2	84	3.56289	4 43711
3	83	5.01005	6 98995
4	82	6.32706	7 67294
5	81	7.54191	8 45809
6	80	8.67224	9 32776
7	79	9.73023	10 26977
8	78	10.72477	11 27523
9	77	11.66262	12 33738
10	76	12.54911	13 45089
11	75	13.38853	14 61147
12	74	14.18441	15 81559
13	73	14.93970	15 06030
14	72	15.65690	16 34310
15	71	16.33814	17 66186
16	70	16.98528	17 01472
17	69	17.59993	18 40007
18	68	18.18350	19 81650
19	67	18.73726	19 26274
20	66	19.26230	20 73770
21	65	19.75963	20 24037
22	64	20.23012	21 76988
23	63	20.67457	21 32543
24	62	21.09370	22 90630
25	61	21.48815	22 51185
26	60	21.85851	22 14149
27	59	22.20529	23 79471
28	58	22.52899	23 47101
29	57	22.83002	23 16998
30	56	23.10877	24 89123
31	55	23.36560	24 63440
32	54	23.60081	24 39919
33	53	23.81469	24 18531
34	52	24.00749	25 99251
35	51	24.17942	25 82058
36	50	24.33069	25 66931
37	49	24.46146	25 53854
38	48	24.57187	25 42813
39	47	24.66205	25 33795
40	46	24.73209	25 26791
41	45	24.78206	25 21794
42	44	24.81202	25 18798
43	43	24.82201	25 17799

$N = 87$

Exponent of p(q)	Exponent of q(p)	log C	log 1/C
0	87	0.00000	0 00000
1	86	1.93952	2 06048
2	85	3.57299	4 42701
3	84	5.02529	6 97471
4	83	6.34750	7 65250
5	82	7.56761	8 43239
6	81	8.70328	9 29672
7	80	9.76666	10 23334
8	79	10.76666	11 23334
9	78	11.71005	12 28995
10	77	12.60214	13 39786
11	76	13.44724	14 55276
12	75	14.24887	15 75113
13	74	15.00999	16 99001
14	73	15.73309	16 26691
15	72	16.42033	17 57967
16	71	17.07354	18 92646
17	70	17.69435	18 30565
18	69	18.28417	19 71583
19	68	18.84427	19 15573
20	67	19.37575	20 62425
21	66	19.87960	20 12040
22	65	20.35672	21 64328
23	64	20.80791	21 19209
24	63	21.23388	22 76612
25	62	21.63528	22 36472
26	61	22.01270	23 98730
27	60	22.36666	23 63334
28	59	22.69766	23 30234
29	58	23.00611	24 99389

$N = 87$ (continued)

Exponent of p(q)	Exponent of q(p)	log C	log 1/C
30	57	23.29242	24 70758
31	56	23.55693	24 44307
32	55	23.79997	24 20003
33	54	24.02182	25 97818
34	53	24.22273	25 77727
35	52	24.40294	25 59706
36	51	24.56264	25 43736
37	50	24.70201	25 29799
38	49	24.82120	25 17880
39	48	24.92033	25 07967
40	47	24.99951	25 00049
41	46	25.05882	26 94118
42	45	25.09833	26 90167
43	44	25.11807	26 88193

$N = 88$

Exponent of p(q)	Exponent of q(p)	log C	log 1/C
0	88	0.00000	0 00000
1	87	1.94448	2 05552
2	86	3.58297	4 41703
3	85	5.04035	6 95965
4	84	6.36771	7 63229
5	83	7.59302	8 40698
6	82	8.73394	9 26606
7	81	9.80266	10 19734
8	80	10.80806	11 19194
9	79	11.75690	12 24310
10	78	12.65453	13 34547
11	77	13.50523	14 49477
12	76	14.31254	15 68746
13	75	15.07941	16 92059
14	74	15.80834	16 19166
15	73	16.50148	17 49852
16	72	17.16069	18 83931
17	71	17.78757	18 21243
18	70	18.38356	19 61644
19	69	18.94990	19 05010
20	68	19.48772	20 51228
21	67	19.99801	20 00199
22	66	20.48166	21 51834
23	65	20.93948	21 06052
24	64	21.37218	22 62782
25	63	21.78042	22 21958
26	62	22.16479	23 83521
27	61	22.52582	23 47418
28	60	22.86399	23 13601
29	59	23.17974	24 82026
30	58	23.47347	24 52653
31	57	23.74554	24 25446
32	56	23.99626	24 00374
33	55	24.22594	25 77406
34	54	24.43482	25 56518
35	53	24.62315	25 37685
36	52	24.79112	25 20888
37	51	24.93892	25 06108
38	50	25.06671	26 93329
39	49	25.17461	26 82539
40	48	25.26275	26 73725
41	47	25.33121	26 66879
42	46	25.38006	26 61994
43	45	25.40934	26 59066
44	44	25.41910	26 58090

$N = 89$

Exponent of p(q)	Exponent of q(p)	log C	log 1/C
0	89	0.00000	0 00000
1	88	1.94939	2 05061
2	87	3.59284	4 40716
3	86	5.05524	6 94476
4	85	6.38768	7 61232
5	84	7.61813	8 38187
6	83	8.76426	9 23574
7	82	9.83824	10 16176
8	81	10.84896	11 15104
9	80	11.80320	12 19680
10	79	12.70629	13 29371
11	78	13.56253	14 43747
12	77	14.37544	15 62456
13	76	15.14799	16 85201
14	75	15.88267	16 11733
15	74	16.58164	17 41836
16	73	17.24675	18 75325
17	72	17.87963	18 12037
18	71	18.48169	19 51831
19	70	19.05419	20 94581
20	69	19.59826	20 40174
21	68	20.11489	21 88511
22	67	20.60498	21 39502
23	66	21.06932	22 93068
24	65	21.50866	22 49134
25	64	21.92363	22 07637
26	63	22.31484	23 68516
27	62	22.68281	23 31719
28	61	23.02805	24 97195
29	60	23.35098	24 64902
30	59	23.65201	24 34799
31	58	23.93150	24 06850

Common Logarithms of the Binomial Coefficients C and their Reciprocals* N = 89 − 97

For explanation see page 77

N = 89 (continued)

Exponent of $p(q)$	Exponent of $q(p)$	log C	log $1/C$
32	57	24.18978	**25** 81022
33	56	24.42714	**25** 57286
34	55	24.64385	**25** 35615
35	54	24.84014	**25** 15986
36	53	25.01623	**26** 98377
37	52	25.17231	**26** 82769
38	51	25.30853	**26** 69147
39	50	25.42503	**26** 57497
40	49	25.52194	**26** 47806
41	48	25.59936	**26** 40064
42	47	25.65735	**26** 34265
43	46	25.69598	**26** 30402
44	45	25.71528	**26** 28472

N = 90

Exponent of $p(q)$	Exponent of $q(p)$	log C	log $1/C$
0	90	0.00000	**0** 00000
1	89	1.95424	**2** 04576
2	88	3.60260	**4** 39740
3	87	5.06996	**6** 93004
4	86	6.40742	**7** 59258
5	85	7.64295	**8** 35705
6	84	8.79422	**9** 20578
7	83	9.87340	**10** 12660
8	82	10.88939	**11** 11061
9	81	11.84896	**12** 15104
10	80	12.75745	**13** 24255
11	79	13.61914	**14** 38086
12	78	14.43759	**15** 56241
13	77	15.21574	**16** 78426
14	76	15.95610	**16** 04390
15	75	16.66082	**17** 33918
16	74	17.33177	**18** 66823
17	73	17.97055	**18** 02945
18	72	18.57860	**19** 42140
19	71	19.15718	**20** 84282
20	70	19.70741	**20** 29259
21	69	20.23028	**21** 76972
22	68	20.72671	**21** 27329
23	67	21.19749	**22** 80251
24	66	21.64336	**22** 35664
25	65	22.06496	**23** 93504
26	64	22.46290	**23** 53710
27	63	22.83772	**23** 16228
28	62	23.18990	**24** 81010
29	61	23.51989	**24** 48011
30	60	23.82810	**24** 17190
31	59	24.11489	**25** 88511
32	58	24.38059	**25** 61941
33	57	24.62551	**25** 37449
34	56	24.84990	**25** 15010
35	55	25.05402	**26** 94598
36	54	25.23808	**26** 76192
37	53	25.40227	**26** 59773
38	52	25.54677	**26** 45323
39	51	25.67171	**26** 32829
40	50	25.77722	**26** 22278
41	49	25.86340	**26** 13660
42	48	25.93035	**26** 06965
43	47	25.97812	**26** 02188
44	46	26.00677	**27** 99323
45	45	26.01631	**27** 98369

N = 91

Exponent of $p(q)$	Exponent of $q(p)$	log C	log $1/C$
0	91	0.00000	**0** 00000
1	90	1.95904	**2** 04096
2	89	3.61225	**4** 38775
3	88	5.08452	**6** 91548
4	87	6.42695	**7** 57305
5	86	7.66749	**8** 33251
6	85	8.82384	**9** 17616
7	84	9.90816	**10** 09184
8	83	10.92935	**11** 07065
9	82	11.89419	**12** 10581
10	81	12.80800	**13** 19200
11	80	13.67509	**14** 32491
12	79	14.49900	**15** 50100
13	78	15.28269	**16** 71731
14	77	16.02865	**17** 97135
15	76	16.73905	**17** 26095
16	75	17.41575	**18** 58425
17	74	18.06036	**19** 93964
18	73	18.67432	**19** 32568
19	72	19.25889	**20** 74111
20	71	19.81519	**20** 18481
21	70	20.34423	**21** 65577
22	69	20.84690	**21** 15310
23	68	21.32402	**22** 67598
24	67	21.77632	**22** 22368
25	66	22.20446	**23** 79554
26	65	22.60903	**23** 39097
27	64	22.99058	**23** 00942
28	63	23.34960	**24** 65040
29	62	23.68654	**24** 31346
30	61	24.00181	**25** 99819

N = 91 (continued)

Exponent of $p(q)$	Exponent of $q(p)$	log C	log $1/C$
31	60	24.29578	**25** 70422
32	59	24.56878	**25** 43122
33	58	24.82112	**25** 17888
34	57	25.05307	**26** 94693
35	56	25.26488	**26** 73512
36	55	25.45676	**26** 54324
37	54	25.62892	**26** 37108
38	53	25.78153	**26** 21847
39	52	25.91474	**26** 08526
40	51	26.02869	**27** 97131
41	50	26.12347	**27** 87653
42	49	26.19919	**27** 80081
43	48	26.25592	**27** 74408
44	47	26.29371	**27** 70629
45	46	26.31260	**27** 68740

N = 92

Exponent of $p(q)$	Exponent of $q(p)$	log C	log $1/C$
0	92	0.00000	**0** 00000
1	91	1.96379	**2** 03621
2	90	3.62180	**4** 37820
3	89	5.09892	**6** 90108
4	88	6.44625	**7** 55375
5	87	7.69176	**8** 30824
6	86	8.85313	**9** 14687
7	85	9.94253	**10** 05747
8	84	10.96886	**11** 03114
9	83	11.93890	**12** 06110
10	82	12.85798	**13** 14202
11	81	13.73040	**14** 26960
12	80	14.55970	**15** 44030
13	79	15.34885	**16** 65115
14	78	16.10035	**17** 89965
15	77	16.81635	**17** 18365
16	76	17.49872	**18** 50128
17	75	18.14908	**19** 85092
18	74	18.76887	**19** 23113
19	73	19.35935	**20** 64065
20	72	19.92164	**20** 07836
21	71	20.45676	**21** 54324
22	70	20.96559	**21** 03441
23	69	21.44896	**22** 55104
24	68	21.90760	**22** 09240
25	67	22.34217	**23** 65783
26	66	22.75327	**23** 24673
27	65	23.14145	**24** 85855
28	64	23.50721	**24** 49279
29	63	23.85099	**24** 14901
30	62	24.17321	**25** 82679
31	61	24.47424	**25** 52576
32	60	24.75442	**25** 24558
33	59	25.01406	**26** 98594
34	58	25.25343	**26** 74657
35	57	25.47279	**26** 52721
36	56	25.67236	**26** 32764
37	55	25.85235	**26** 14765
38	54	26.01293	**27** 98707
39	53	26.15426	**27** 84574
40	52	26.27647	**27** 72353
41	51	26.37969	**27** 62031
42	50	26.46401	**27** 53599
43	49	26.52951	**27** 47049
44	48	26.57626	**27** 42374
45	47	26.60429	**27** 39571
46	46	26.61363	**27** 38637

N = 93

Exponent of $p(q)$	Exponent of $q(p)$	log C	log $1/C$
0	93	0.00000	**0** 00000
1	92	1.96848	**2** 03152
2	91	3.63124	**4** 36876
3	90	5.11316	**6** 88684
4	89	6.46534	**7** 53466
5	88	7.71576	**8** 28424
6	87	8.88209	**9** 11791
7	86	9.97652	**10** 02348
8	85	11.00792	**12** 99208
9	84	11.98310	**12** 01690
10	83	12.90738	**13** 09262
11	82	13.78507	**14** 21493
12	81	14.61970	**15** 38030
13	80	15.41424	**16** 58576
14	79	16.17120	**17** 82880
15	78	16.89274	**17** 10726
16	77	17.58071	**18** 41929
17	76	18.23675	**19** 76325
18	75	18.86230	**19** 13770
19	74	19.45860	**20** 54140
20	73	20.02680	**21** 97320
21	72	20.56791	**21** 43209
22	71	21.08282	**22** 91718
23	70	21.57235	**22** 42765
24	69	22.03724	**23** 96276
25	68	22.47814	**23** 52186
26	67	22.89568	**23** 10432
27	66	23.29039	**24** 70961

N = 93 (continued)

Exponent of $p(q)$	Exponent of $q(p)$	log C	log $1/C$
28	65	23.66278	**24** 33722
29	64	24.01329	**25** 98671
30	63	24.34235	**25** 65765
31	62	24.65033	**25** 34967
32	61	24.93757	**25** 06243
33	60	25.20439	**26** 79561
34	59	25.45106	**26** 54894
35	58	25.67784	**26** 32216
36	57	25.88497	**26** 11503
37	56	26.07264	**27** 92736
38	55	26.24105	**27** 75895
39	54	26.39034	**27** 60966
40	53	26.52068	**27** 47932
41	52	26.63217	**27** 36783
42	51	26.72492	**27** 27508
43	50	26.79903	**27** 20097
44	49	26.85454	**27** 14546
45	48	26.89153	**27** 10847
46	47	26.91001	**27** 08999

N = 94

Exponent of $p(q)$	Exponent of $q(p)$	log C	log $1/C$
0	94	0.00000	**0** 00000
1	93	1.97313	**2** 02687
2	92	3.64058	**4** 35942
3	91	5.12725	**6** 87275
4	90	6.48423	**7** 51577
5	89	7.73950	**8** 26050
6	88	8.91074	**9** 08926
7	87	10.01012	**11** 98988
8	86	11.04655	**12** 95345
9	85	12.02681	**13** 97319
10	84	12.95623	**13** 04377
11	83	13.83912	**14** 16088
12	82	14.67901	**15** 32099
13	81	15.47888	**16** 52112
14	80	16.24124	**17** 75876
15	79	16.96824	**17** 03176
16	78	17.66175	**18** 33825
17	77	18.32339	**19** 67661
18	76	18.95461	**19** 04539
19	75	19.55667	**20** 44333
20	74	20.13070	**21** 86930
21	73	20.67771	**21** 32229
22	72	21.19861	**22** 80139
23	71	21.69422	**22** 30578
24	70	22.16527	**23** 83473
25	69	22.61242	**23** 38758
26	68	23.03630	**24** 96370
27	67	23.43744	**24** 56256
28	66	23.81636	**24** 18364
29	65	24.17351	**25** 82649
30	64	24.50930	**25** 49070
31	63	24.82412	**25** 17588
32	62	25.11831	**26** 88169
33	61	25.39219	**26** 60781
34	60	25.64604	**26** 35396
35	59	25.88012	**26** 11988
36	58	26.09467	**27** 90533
37	57	26.28990	**27** 71010
38	56	26.46599	**27** 53401
39	55	26.62311	**27** 37689
40	54	26.76141	**27** 23859
41	53	26.88102	**27** 11898
42	52	26.98205	**27** 01795
43	51	27.06458	**28** 93542
44	50	27.12870	**28** 87130
45	49	27.17446	**28** 82554
46	48	27.20190	**28** 79810
47	47	27.21104	**28** 78896

N = 95

Exponent of $p(q)$	Exponent of $q(p)$	log C	log $1/C$
0	95	0.00000	**0** 00000
1	94	1.97772	**2** 02228
2	93	3.64982	**4** 35018
3	92	5.14118	**6** 85882
4	91	6.50291	**7** 49709
5	90	7.76298	**8** 23702
6	89	8.93907	**9** 06093
7	88	10.04337	**11** 95663
8	87	11.08476	**12** 91524
9	86	12.07004	**13** 92996
10	85	13.00453	**14** 99547
11	84	13.89256	**14** 10744
12	83	14.73766	**15** 26234
13	82	15.54279	**16** 45721
14	81	16.31048	**17** 68952
15	80	17.04287	**18** 95713
16	79	17.74184	**18** 25816
17	78	18.40902	**19** 59098
18	77	19.04584	**20** 95416
19	76	19.65358	**20** 34642
20	75	20.23336	**21** 76664
21	74	20.78621	**21** 21379
22	73	21.31301	**22** 68699

N = 95 (continued)

Exponent of $p(q)$	Exponent of $q(p)$	log C	log $1/C$
23	72	21.81461	**22** 18539
24	71	22.29173	**23** 70827
25	70	22.74505	**23** 25495
26	69	23.17517	**24** 82483
27	68	23.58266	**24** 41734
28	67	23.96801	**24** 03199
29	66	24.33169	**25** 66831
30	65	24.67411	**25** 32589
31	64	24.99566	**25** 00434
32	63	25.29669	**26** 70331
33	62	25.57752	**26** 42248
34	61	25.83843	**26** 16157
35	60	26.07969	**27** 92031
36	59	26.30154	**27** 69846
37	58	26.50419	**27** 49581
38	57	26.68784	**27** 31216
39	56	26.85265	**27** 14735
40	55	26.99877	**27** 00123
41	54	27.12635	**28** 87365
42	53	27.23550	**28** 76450
43	52	27.32630	**28** 67370
44	51	27.39886	**28** 60114
45	50	27.45321	**28** 54679
46	49	27.48942	**28** 51058
47	48	27.50752	**28** 49248

N = 96

Exponent of $p(q)$	Exponent of $q(p)$	log C	log $1/C$
0	96	0.00000	**0** 00000
1	95	1.98227	**2** 01773
2	94	3.65896	**4** 34104
3	93	5.15497	**6** 84503
4	92	6.52139	**7** 47861
5	91	7.78621	**8** 21379
6	90	8.96710	**9** 03290
7	89	10.07625	**11** 92375
8	88	11.12255	**12** 87745
9	87	12.11279	**13** 88721
10	86	13.05231	**14** 94769
11	85	13.94541	**14** 05459
12	84	14.79565	**15** 20435
13	83	15.60599	**16** 39401
14	82	16.37894	**17** 62106
15	81	17.11666	**18** 88334
16	80	17.82102	**18** 17898
17	79	18.49366	**19** 50634
18	78	19.13602	**20** 86398
19	77	19.74936	**20** 25064
20	76	20.33482	**21** 66518
21	75	20.89342	**21** 10658
22	74	21.42605	**22** 57395
23	73	21.93356	**22** 06644
24	72	22.41667	**23** 58333
25	71	22.87606	**23** 12394
26	70	23.31235	**24** 68765
27	69	23.72608	**24** 27392
28	68	24.11777	**25** 88223
29	67	24.48788	**25** 51212
30	66	24.83684	**25** 16316
31	65	25.16502	**26** 83498
32	64	25.47278	**26** 52722
33	63	25.76045	**26** 23955
34	62	26.02831	**27** 97169
35	61	26.27663	**27** 72337
36	60	26.50566	**27** 49434
37	59	26.71561	**27** 28439
38	58	26.90668	**27** 09332
39	57	27.07904	**28** 92096
40	56	27.23286	**28** 76714
41	55	27.36826	**28** 63174
42	54	27.48537	**28** 51463
43	53	27.58430	**28** 41570
44	52	27.66512	**28** 33488
45	51	27.72791	**28** 27209
46	50	27.77273	**28** 22727
47	49	27.79960	**28** 20040
48	48	27.80855	**28** 19145

N = 97

Exponent of $p(q)$	Exponent of $q(p)$	log C	log $1/C$
0	97	0.00000	**0** 00000
1	96	1.98677	**2** 01323
2	95	3.66801	**4** 33199
3	94	5.16862	**6** 83138
4	93	6.53968	**7** 46032
5	92	7.80920	**8** 19080
6	91	8.99483	**9** 00517
7	90	10.10878	**11** 89122
8	89	11.15993	**12** 84007
9	88	12.15508	**13** 84492
10	87	13.09956	**14** 90044
11	86	13.99769	**14** 00231
12	85	14.85300	**15** 14700
13	84	15.66848	**16** 33152
14	83	16.44663	**17** 55337
15	82	17.18962	**18** 81038

Common Logarithms of the Binomial Coefficients C and their Reciprocals* N=97—100

Exponent of p(q)	Exponent of q(p)	log C	log 1/C
		N = 97 (continued)	
16	81	17.89931	**18** 10069
17	80	18.57735	**19** 42265
18	79	19.22516	**20** 77484
19	78	19.84404	**20** 15596
20	77	20.43510	**21** 56490
21	76	20.99937	**21** 00063
22	75	21.53776	**22** 46224
23	74	22.05110	**23** 94890
24	73	22.54012	**23** 45988
25	72	23.00550	**24** 99450
26	71	23.44786	**24** 55214
27	70	23.86775	**24** 13225
28	69	24.26569	**25** 73431
29	68	24.64215	**25** 35785
30	67	24.99753	**25** 00247
31	66	25.33225	**26** 66775
32	65	25.64664	**26** 35336
33	64	25.94104	**26** 05896
34	63	26.21574	**27** 78426
35	62	26.47101	**27** 52899
36	61	26.70710	**27** 29290
37	60	26.92423	**27** 07577
38	59	27.12260	**28** 87740
39	58	27.30239	**28** 69761
40	57	27.46375	**28** 53625
41	56	27.60684	**28** 39316
42	55	27.73178	**28** 26822
43	54	27.83868	**28** 16132
44	53	27.92762	**28** 07238
45	52	27.99868	**28** 00132
46	51	28.05193	**29** 94807
47	50	28.08740	**29** 91260
48	49	28.10513	**29** 89487
		N = 98	
0	98	0.00000	**0** 00000
1	97	1.99123	**2** 00877
2	96	3.67697	**4** 32303
3	95	5.18212	**6** 81788
4	94	6.55778	**7** 44222
5	93	7.83194	**8** 16806
6	92	9.02227	**10** 97773
7	91	10.14096	**11** 85904
8	90	11.19691	**12** 80309
9	89	12.19691	**13** 80309
10	88	13.14630	**14** 85370
11	87	14.04939	**15** 95061
12	86	14.90973	**15** 09027
13	85	15.73029	**16** 26971
14	84	16.51358	**17** 48642
15	83	17.26176	**18** 73824
16	82	17.97672	**18** 02328
17	81	18.66009	**19** 33991
18	80	19.31330	**20** 68670
19	79	19.93764	**20** 06236
20	78	20.53423	**21** 46577
21	77	21.10411	**22** 89589
22	76	21.64818	**22** 35182
23	75	22.16726	**23** 83274
24	74	22.66211	**23** 33789
25	73	23.13340	**24** 86660
26	72	23.58175	**24** 41825
27	71	24.00772	**25** 99228
28	70	24.41182	**25** 58818
29	69	24.79452	**25** 20548
30	68	25.15625	**26** 84375
31	67	25.49740	**26** 50260
32	66	25.81832	**26** 18168
33	65	26.11935	**27** 88065
34	64	26.40079	**27** 59921
35	63	26.66290	**27** 33710
36	62	26.90594	**27** 09406
37	61	27.13013	**28** 86987
38	60	27.33567	**28** 66433
39	59	27.52276	**28** 47724
40	58	27.69155	**28** 30845
41	57	27.84220	**28** 15780
42	56	27.97482	**28** 02518
43	55	28.08954	**29** 91046
44	54	28.18645	**29** 81355
45	53	28.26563	**29** 73437
46	52	28.32715	**29** 67285
47	51	28.37106	**29** 62894
48	50	28.39738	**29** 60262
49	49	28.40616	**29** 59384
		N = 99	
0	99	0.00000	**0** 00000
1	98	1.99564	**2** 00436
2	97	3.68583	**4** 31417
3	96	5.19548	**6** 80452
4	95	6.57569	**7** 42431
5	94	7.85445	**8** 14555
6	93	9.04942	**10** 95058

Exponent of p(q)	Exponent of q(p)	log C	log 1/C
		N = 99 (continued)	
7	92	10.17281	**11** 82719
8	91	11.23351	**12** 76649
9	90	12.23830	**13** 76170
10	89	13.19255	**14** 80745
11	88	14.10054	**15** 89946
12	87	14.96585	**15** 03415
13	86	15.79142	**16** 20858
14	85	16.57979	**17** 42021
15	84	17.33312	**18** 66688
16	83	18.05328	**19** 94672
17	82	18.74191	**19** 25809
18	81	19.40045	**20** 59955
19	80	20.03018	**21** 96982
20	79	20.63224	**21** 36776
21	78	21.20765	**22** 79235
22	77	21.75732	**22** 24268
23	76	22.28208	**23** 71792
24	75	22.78269	**23** 21731
25	74	23.25981	**24** 74019
26	73	23.71407	**24** 28593
27	72	24.14602	**25** 85398
28	71	24.55620	**25** 44380
29	70	24.94506	**25** 05494
30	69	25.31304	**26** 68696
31	68	25.66052	**26** 33948
32	67	25.98788	**26** 01212
33	66	26.29544	**27** 70456
34	65	26.58351	**27** 41649
35	64	26.85235	**27** 14765
36	63	27.10223	**28** 89777
37	62	27.33337	**28** 66663
38	61	27.54598	**28** 45402
39	60	27.74024	**28** 25976
40	59	27.91633	**28** 08367
41	58	28.07440	**29** 92560
42	57	28.21458	**29** 78542
43	56	28.33699	**29** 66301
44	55	28.44172	**29** 55828
45	54	28.52887	**29** 47113
46	53	28.59851	**29** 40149
47	52	28.65069	**29** 34931
48	51	28.68545	**29** 31455
49	50	28.70282	**29** 29718
		N = 100	
0	100	0.00000	**0** 00000
1	99	2.00000	**3** 00000
2	98	3.69461	**4** 30539
3	97	5.20871	**6** 79129
4	96	6.59342	**7** 40658
5	95	7.87672	**8** 12328
6	94	9.07630	**10** 92370
7	93	10.20433	**11** 79567
8	92	11.26972	**12** 73028
9	91	12.27926	**13** 72074
10	90	13.23830	**14** 76170
11	89	14.15115	**15** 84885
12	88	15.02136	**16** 97864
13	87	15.85190	**16** 14810
14	86	16.64529	**17** 35471
15	85	17.40370	**18** 59630
16	84	18.12900	**19** 87100
17	83	18.82283	**19** 17717
18	82	19.48664	**20** 51336
19	81	20.12170	**21** 87830
20	80	20.72915	**21** 27085
21	79	21.31002	**22** 68998
22	78	21.86523	**22** 13477
23	77	22.39559	**23** 60441
24	76	22.90187	**23** 09813
25	75	23.38475	**24** 61525
26	74	23.84483	**24** 15517
27	73	24.28270	**25** 71730
28	72	24.69887	**25** 30113
29	71	25.09380	**26** 90620
30	70	25.46794	**26** 53206
31	69	25.82167	**26** 17833
32	68	26.15537	**27** 84463
33	67	26.46937	**27** 53063
34	66	26.76396	**27** 23604
35	65	27.03944	**28** 96056
36	64	27.29605	**28** 70395
37	63	27.53403	**28** 46597
38	62	27.75359	**28** 24641
39	61	27.95491	**28** 04509
40	60	28.13818	**29** 86182
41	59	28.30355	**29** 69645
42	58	28.45115	**29** 54885
43	57	28.58111	**29** 41889
44	56	28.69354	**29** 30646
45	55	28.78851	**29** 21149
46	54	28.86612	**29** 13388
47	53	28.92641	**29** 07359
48	52	28.96945	**29** 03055
49	51	28.99525	**29** 00475
50	50	29.00385	**30** 99615

Explanation of the tables on pages 70–84

The **bold** figures in the tables are negative characteristics. The mantissas are all positive.

Binomial coefficients $C(N,x)=\binom{N}{x}=\dfrac{N!}{x!\,(N-x)!}$

For values of N between 100 and 1000, values of C can be calculated with the help of the tables on pages 26 and 27.

Example:

$\log\binom{54}{6} = 7.41208 \qquad C(54,6)=2.583\times 10^{7}$

$\log 1/\binom{54}{6} = -8+0.58792 \qquad 1/C(54,6)=3.872\times 10^{-8}$

Calculation of individual probabilities Prob $(x_1\,|\,N,N_1,X)$ **in the hypergeometric distribution**

Given are

x_1	N_1-x_1	N_1
x_2	N_2-x_2	N_2
X	$N-X$	N

$$\text{Prob}\,(x_1|N,N_1,X)=\frac{N_1!\,N_2!\,X!\,(N-X)!}{x_1!\,(N_1-x_1)!\,x_2!\,(N_2-x_2)!\,N!}=\dot{P}(x_1)$$

$$=\binom{N_1}{x_1}\times\binom{N_2}{x_2}\times 1/\binom{N}{X}$$

$$\log\dot{P}(x_1)=\underbrace{\log C(N_1,x_1)+\log C(N_2,x_2)+\log 1/C(N,X)}_{\text{from pages 70–77}}$$

Example:

2	5	7
3	2	5
5	7	12

$\log C(7,2)$	$+1$	$+\ 0.32222$
$\log C(5,3)$	$+1$	$+\ 0.00000$
$\log 1/C(12,5)$	-3	$+\ 0.10127$
Sum: $\log\dot{P}(x_1)$	$=-1$	$+\ 0.42349$
$\dot{P}(x_1)$	$=0.2653$	

Calculation of individual probabilities $\dot{P}(x)$ **in the binomial distribution**

Required is $\dot{P}(x)=\binom{N}{x}p^{x}q^{N-x}$

Solution: $\log\dot{P}(x)=\underbrace{\log C(N,x)}_{\text{pages 70–77}}+\underbrace{\log p^{x}+\log q^{N-x}}_{\text{pages 78–84}}$

Example:

$N=32,\ p=0.06,\ x_1=2,\ x_2=30$

$\dot{P}_2$		$\dot{P}_{30}$	
$\log C(32,2)$	$+2+0.69548$	$\log C(32,30)+$	$2+0.69548$
$\log p^{2}$	$-3+0.55630$	$\log p^{30}$	$-37+0.34454$
$\log q^{30}$	$-1+0.19384$	$\log q^{2}$	$-1+0.94626$
$\log\dot{P}_2$	$-2+1.44562$	$\log\dot{P}_{30}$	$-36+1.98628$
	$=-1+0.44562$		$=-35+0.98628$
$\dot{P}_2=$	0.2790	$\dot{P}_{30}=$	9.690×10^{-35}

* Reproduction only by permission of the publishers of these *Scientific Tables.*

For explanation see page 77

n	p(q) 0.01	q(p) 0.99	p(q) 0.02	q(p) 0.98	p(q) 0.03	q(p) 0.97	p(q) 0.04	q(p) 0.96	p(q) 0.05	q(p) 0.95	p(q) 0.06	q(p) 0.94	p(q) 0.07	q(p) 0.93
0	0 00000	0 00000	0 00000	0 00000	0 00000	0 00000	0 00000	0 00000	0 00000	0 00000	0 00000	0 00000	0 00000	0 00000
1	2 00000	1 99564	2 30103	1 99123	2 47712	1 98677	2 60206	1 98227	2 69897	1 97772	2 77815	1 97313	2 84510	1 96848
2	4 00000	1 99127	4 60206	1 98245	4 95424	1 97354	3 20412	1 96454	3 39794	1 95545	3 55630	1 94626	3 69020	1 93697
3	6 00000	1 98691	6 90309	1 97368	5 43136	1 96032	5 80618	1 94681	4 09691	1 93317	4 33445	1 91938	4 53529	1 90545
4	8 00000	1 98254	7 20412	1 96490	7 90849	1 94709	6 40824	1 92908	6 79588	1 91089	5 11261	1 89251	5 38039	1 87393
5	10 00000	1 97818	9 50515	1 95613	8 38561	1 93386	7 01030	1 91136	7 49485	1 88862	7 89076	1 86564	6 22549	1 84241
6	12 00000	1 97381	11 80618	1 94736	10 86273	1 92063	9 61236	1 89363	8 19382	1 86634	8 66891	1 83877	7 07059	1 81090
7	14 00000	1 96945	12 10721	1 93858	11 33985	1 90740	10 21442	1 87590	10 89279	1 84407	9 44706	1 81189	9 91569	1 77938
8	16 00000	1 96508	14 40824	1 92981	13 81697	1 89417	12 81648	1 85817	11 59176	1 82179	10 22521	1 78502	10 76078	1 74786
9	18 00000	1 96072	16 70927	1 92103	14 29409	1 88095	13 41854	1 84044	12 29073	1 79951	11 00336	1 75815	11 60588	1 71635
10	20 00000	1 95635	17 01030	1 91226	16 77121	1 86772	14 02060	1 82271	14 98970	1 77724	13 78151	1 73128	12 45098	1 68483
11	22 00000	1 95199	19 31133	1 90349	17 24833	1 85449	16 62266	1 80498	15 68867	1 75496	14 55966	1 70441	13 29608	1 65331
12	24 00000	1 94762	21 61236	1 89471	19 72546	1 84126	17 22472	1 78725	16 38764	1 73268	15 33782	1 67753	14 14118	1 62180
13	26 00000	1 94326	23 91339	1 88594	20 20258	1 82803	19 82678	1 76953	17 08661	1 71041	16 11597	1 65066	16 98627	1 59028
14	28 00000	1 93889	24 21442	1 87717	22 67970	1 81480	20 42884	1 75180	19 78558	1 68813	18 89412	1 62379	17 83137	1 55876
15	30 00000	1 93453	26 51545	1 86839	23 15682	1 80158	21 03090	1 73407	20 48455	1 66585	19 67227	1 59692	18 67647	1 52724
16	32 00000	1 93016	28 81648	1 85962	25 63394	1 78835	23 63296	1 71634	21 18352	1 64358	20 45042	1 57005	19 52157	1 49573
17	34 00000	1 92580	29 11751	1 85084	26 11106	1 77512	24 23502	1 69861	23 88249	1 62130	21 22857	1 54317	20 36667	1 46421
18	36 00000	1 92143	31 41854	1 84207	28 58818	1 76189	26 83708	1 68088	24 58146	1 59902	22 00672	1 51630	21 21176	1 43269
19	38 00000	1 91707	33 71957	1 83330	29 06530	1 74866	27 43914	1 66315	25 28043	1 57675	24 78487	1 48943	22 05686	1 40118
20	40 00000	1 91270	34 02060	1 82452	31 54243	1 73543	28 04120	1 64542	27 97940	1 55447	25 56303	1 46256	24 90196	1 36966
21	42 00000	1 90834	36 32163	1 81575	32 01955	1 72221	30 64326	1 62770	28 67837	1 53220	26 34118	1 43568	25 74706	1 33814
22	44 00000	1 90397	38 62266	1 80697	34 49667	1 70898	31 24532	1 60997	29 37734	1 50992	27 11933	1 40881	26 59216	1 30662
23	46 00000	1 89961	40 92369	1 79820	36 97379	1 69575	33 84738	1 59224	30 07631	1 48764	29 89748	1 38194	27 43725	1 27511
24	48 00000	1 89524	41 22472	1 78943	37 45091	1 68252	34 44944	1 57451	32 77528	1 46537	30 67563	1 35507	28 28235	1 24359
25	50 00000	1 89088	43 52575	1 78065	39 92803	1 66929	35 05150	1 55678	33 47425	1 44309	31 45378	1 32820	29 12745	1 21207
26	52 00000	1 88652	45 82678	1 77188	40 40515	1 65607	37 65356	1 53905	34 17322	1 42081	32 23193	1 30132	31 97255	1 18056
27	54 00000	1 88215	46 12781	1 76310	42 88227	1 64284	38 25562	1 52132	36 87219	1 39854	33 01008	1 27445	32 81765	1 14904
28	56 00000	1 87779	48 42884	1 75433	43 35940	1 62961	40 85768	1 50359	37 57116	1 37626	35 78824	1 24758	33 66275	1 11752
29	58 00000	1 87342	50 72987	1 74556	45 83652	1 61638	41 45974	1 48587	38 27013	1 35398	36 56639	1 22071	34 50784	1 08601
30	60 00000	1 86906	51 03090	1 73678	46 31364	1 60315	42 06180	1 46814	40 96910	1 33171	37 34454	1 19384	35 35294	1 05449
31	62 00000	1 86469	53 33193	1 72801	48 79076	1 58992	44 66386	1 45041	41 66807	1 30943	38 12269	1 16696	36 19804	1 02297
32	64 00000	1 86033	55 63296	1 71923	49 26788	1 57670	45 26592	1 43268	42 36704	1 28716	40 90084	1 14009	37 04314	2 99145
33	66 00000	1 85596	57 93399	1 71046	51 74500	1 56347	47 86798	1 41495	43 06601	1 26488	41 67899	1 11322	39 88824	2 95994
34	68 00000	1 85160	58 23502	1 70169	52 22212	1 55024	48 47004	1 39722	45 76498	1 24260	42 45714	1 08635	40 73333	2 92842
35	70 00000	1 84723	60 53605	1 69291	54 69924	1 53701	49 07210	1 37949	46 46395	1 22033	43 23529	1 05947	41 57843	2 89690
36	72 00000	1 84287	62 83708	1 68414	55 17637	1 52378	51 67416	1 36176	47 16292	1 19805	44 01345	1 03260	42 42353	2 86539
37	74 00000	1 83850	63 13811	1 67536	57 65349	1 51055	52 27622	1 34404	49 86189	1 17577	46 79160	1 00573	43 26863	2 83387
38	76 00000	1 83414	65 43914	1 66659	58 13061	1 49733	54 87828	1 32631	50 56086	1 15350	47 56975	2 97886	44 11373	2 80235
39	78 00000	1 82977	67 74017	1 65782	60 60773	1 48410	55 48034	1 30858	51 25983	1 13122	48 34790	2 95199	46 95882	2 77083
40	80 00000	1 82541	68 04120	1 64904	61 08485	1 47087	56 08240	1 29085	53 95880	1 10894	49 12605	2 92511	47 80392	2 73932
41	82 00000	1 82104	70 34223	1 64027	63 56197	1 45764	58 68446	1 27312	54 65777	1 08667	51 90420	2 89824	48 64902	2 70780
42	84 00000	1 81668	72 64326	1 63150	64 03909	1 44441	59 28652	1 25539	55 35674	1 06439	52 68235	2 87137	49 49412	2 67628
43	86 00000	1 81231	74 94429	1 62272	66 51621	1 43118	61 88858	1 23766	56 05571	1 04212	53 46050	2 84450	50 33922	2 64477
44	88 00000	1 80795	75 24532	1 61395	68 99334	1 41796	62 49064	1 21993	58 75468	1 01984	54 23866	2 81763	51 18431	2 61325
45	90 00000	1 80358	77 54635	1 60517	69 47046	1 40473	63 09270	1 20221	59 45365	2 99756	55 01681	2 79075	52 02941	2 58173
46	92 00000	1 79922	79 84738	1 59640	71 94758	1 39150	65 69476	1 18448	60 15262	2 97529	57 79496	2 76388	54 87451	2 55022
47	94 00000	1 79485	80 14841	1 58763	72 42470	1 37827	66 29682	1 16675	62 85159	2 95301	58 57311	2 73701	55 71961	2 51870
48	96 00000	1 79049	82 44944	1 57885	74 90182	1 36504	68 89888	1 14902	63 55056	2 93073	59 35126	2 71014	56 56471	2 48718
49	98 00000	1 78612	84 75047	1 57008	75 37894	1 35181	69 50094	1 13129	64 24953	2 90846	60 12941	2 68326	57 40980	2 45566
50	100 00000	1 78176	85 05150	1 56130	77 85606	1 33859	70 10300	1 11356	66 94850	2 88618	62 90756	2 65639	58 25490	2 42415
51	102 00000	1 77739	87 35253	1 55253	78 33318	1 32536	72 70506	1 09583	67 64747	2 86390	63 68571	2 62952	59 10000	2 39263
52	104 00000	1 77303	89 65356	1 54376	80 81031	1 31213	73 30712	1 07810	68 34644	2 84163	64 46387	2 60265	61 94510	2 36111
53	106 00000	1 76867	91 95459	1 53498	81 28743	1 29890	75 90918	1 06038	69 04541	2 81935	65 24202	2 57578	62 79020	2 32960
54	108 00000	1 76430	92 25562	1 52621	83 76455	1 28567	76 51124	1 04265	71 74438	2 79707	66 02017	2 54890	63 63529	2 29808
55	110 00000	1 75994	94 55665	1 51743	84 24167	1 27245	77 11330	1 02492	72 44335	2 77480	68 79832	2 52203	64 48039	2 26656
56	112 00000	1 75557	96 85768	1 50866	86 71879	1 25922	79 71536	1 00719	73 14232	2 75252	69 57647	2 49516	65 32549	2 23505
57	114 00000	1 75121	97 15871	1 49989	87 19591	1 24599	80 31742	2 98946	75 84129	2 73025	70 35462	2 46829	66 17059	2 20353
58	116 00000	1 74684	99 45974	1 49111	89 67303	1 23276	82 91948	2 97173	76 54026	2 70797	71 13277	2 44142	67 01569	2 17201
59	118 00000	1 74248	101 76077	1 48234	90 15015	1 21953	83 52154	2 95400	77 23923	2 68569	73 91092	2 41454	69 86078	2 14049
60	120 00000	1 73811	102 06180	1 47356	92 62728	1 20630	84 12360	2 93627	79 93820	2 66342	74 68908	2 38767	70 70588	2 10898
61	122 00000	1 73375	104 36283	1 46479	93 10440	1 19308	86 72566	2 91855	80 63717	2 64114	75 46723	2 36080	71 55098	2 07746
62	124 00000	1 72938	106 66386	1 45602	95 58152	1 17985	87 32772	2 90082	81 33614	2 61886	76 24538	2 33393	72 39608	2 04594
63	126 00000	1 72502	108 96489	1 44724	96 05864	1 16662	89 92978	2 88309	82 03511	2 59659	77 02353	2 30705	73 24118	2 01443
64	128 00000	1 72065	109 26592	1 43847	98 53576	1 15339	90 53184	2 86536	84 73408	2 57431	79 80168	2 28018	74 08627	3 98291
65	130 00000	1 71629	111 56695	1 42969	99 01288	1 14016	91 13390	2 84763	85 43305	2 55203	80 57983	2 25331	76 93137	3 95139
66	132 00000	1 71192	113 86798	1 42092	101 49000	1 12693	93 73596	2 82990	86 13202	2 52976	81 35798	2 22644	77 77647	3 91987
67	134 00000	1 70756	114 16901	1 41215	103 96712	1 11371	94 33802	2 81217	88 83099	2 50748	82 13613	2 19957	78 62157	3 88836
68	136 00000	1 70319	116 47004	1 40337	104 44425	1 10048	96 94008	2 79444	89 52996	2 48521	84 91429	2 17269	79 46667	3 85684
69	138 00000	1 69883	118 77107	1 39460	106 92137	1 08725	97 54214	2 77672	90 22893	2 46293	85 69244	2 14582	80 31176	3 82532
70	140 00000	1 69446	119 07210	1 38583	107 39849	1 07402	98 14420	2 75899	92 92790	2 44065	86 47059	2 11895	81 15686	3 79381
71	142 00000	1 69010	121 37313	1 37705	109 87561	1 06079	100 74626	2 74126	93 62687	2 41838	87 24874	2 09208	82 00196	3 76229
72	144 00000	1 68573	123 67416	1 36828	110 35273	1 04756	101 34832	2 72353	94 32584	2 39610	88 02689	2 06521	84 84706	3 73077
73	146 00000	1 68137	125 97519	1 35950	112 82985	1 03434	103 95038	2 70580	95 02481	2 37382	90 80504	2 03833	85 69216	3 69926
74	148 00000	1 67700	126 27622	1 35073	113 30697	1 02111	104 55244	2 68807	97 72378	2 35155	91 58319	2 01146	86 53725	3 66774
75	150 00000	1 67264	128 57725	1 34196	115 78409	1 00788	105 15450	2 67034	98 42275	2 32927	92 36134	3 98459	87 38235	3 63622
76	152 00000	1 66827	130 87828	1 33318	116 26122	2 99465	107 75656	2 65261	99 12172	2 30699	93 13950	3 95772	88 22745	3 60470
77	154 00000	1 66391	131 17931	1 32441	118 73834	2 98142	108 35862	2 63488	101 82069	2 28472	95 91765	3 93084	89 07255	3 57319
78	156 00000	1 65955	133 48034	1 31563	119 21546	2 96820	110 96068	2 61716	102 51966	2 26244	96 69580	3 90397	91 91765	3 54167
79	158 00000	1 65518	135 78137	1 30686	121 69258	2 95497	111 56274	2 59943	103 21863	2 24016	97 47395	3 87710	92 76275	3 51015
80	160 00000	1 65082	136 08240	1 29809	122 16970	2 94174	112 16480	2 58170	105 91760	2 21789	98 25210	3 85023	93 60784	3 47864
81	162 00000	1 64645	138 38343	1 28931	124 64682	2 92851	114 76686	2 56397	106 61657	2 19561	99 03025	3 82336	94 45294	3 44712
82	164 00000	1 64209	140 68446	1 28054	125 12394	2 91528	115 36892	2 54624	107 31554	2 17334	101 80840	3 79648	95 29804	3 41560
83	166 00000	1 63772	142 98549	1 27176	127 60106	2 90205	117 97098	2 52851	108 01451	2 15106	102 58655	3 76961	96 14314	3 38408
84	168 00000	1 63336	143 28652	1 26299	128 07819	2 88883	118 57304	2 51078	110 71348	2 12878	103 36471	3 74274	98 98824	3 35257
85	170 00000	1 62899	145 58755	1 25422	130 55531	2 87560	119 17510	2 49305	111 41245	2 10651	104 14286	3 71587	99 83333	3 32105
86	172 00000	1 62463	147 88858	1 24544	131 03243	2 86237	121 77716	2 47533	112 11142	2 08423	106 92101	3 68900	100 67843	3 28953
87	174 00000	1 62026	148 18961	1 23667	133 50955	2 84914	122 37922	2 45760	114 81039	2 06195	107 69916	3 66212	101 52353	3 25802
88	176 00000	1 61590	150 49064	1 22789	135 98667	2 83591	124 98128	2 43987	115 50936	2 03968	108 47731	3 63525	102 36863	3 22650
89	178 00000	1 61153	152 79167	1 21912	136 46379	2 82268	125 58334	2 42214	116 20833	2 01740	109 25546	3 60838	103 21373	3 19498
90	180 00000	1 60717	153 09270	1 21035	138 94091	2 80946	126 18540	2 40441	118 90730	3 99512	110 03361	3 58151	104 05882	3 16347
91	182 00000	1 60280	155 39373	1 20157	139 41803	2 79623	128 78746	2 38668	119 60627	3 97285	112 81176	3 55463	106 90392	3 13195
92	184 00000	1 59844	157 69476	1 19280	141 89516	2 78300	129 38952	2 36895	120 30524	3 95057	113 58992	3 52776	107 74902	3 10043
93	186 00000	1 59407	159 99579	1 18403	142 37228	2 76977	131 99158	2 35122	121 00421	3 92830	114 36807	3 50089	108 59412	3 06891
94	188 00000	1 58971	160 29682	1 17525	144 84940	2 75654	132 59364	2 33350	123 70318	3 90602	115 14622	3 47402	109 43922	3 03740
95	190 00000	1 58534	162 59785	1 16648	145 32652	2 74331	133 19570	2 31577	124 40215	3 88374	117 92437	3 44715	110 28431	3 00588
96	192 00000	1 58098	164 89888	1 15770	147 80364	2 73009	135 79776	2 29804	125 10112	3 86147	118 70252	3 42027	111 12941	4 97436
97	194 00000	1 57661	165 19991	1 14893	148 28076	2 71686	136 39982	2 28031	127 80009	3 83919	119 48067	3 39340	113 97451	4 94285
98	196 00000	1 57225	167 50094	1 14016	150 75788	2 70363	137 00188	2 26258	128 49906	3 81691	120 25882	3 36653	114 81961	4 91133
99	198 00000	1 56788	169 80197	1 13138	151 23500	2 69040	139 60394	2 24485	129 19803	3 79464	121 03697	3 33966	115 66471	4 87981
100	200 00000	1 56352	170 10300	1 12261	153 71213	2 67717	140 20600	2 22712	131 89700	3 77236	123 81513	3 31279	116 50980	4 84829

Common Logarithms of p^n and q^n ($q=1-p$)*

For explanation see page 77

n	p(q) 0.08	q(p) 0.92	p(q) 0.09	q(p) 0.91	p(q) 0.10	q(p) 0.90	p(q) 0.11	q(p) 0.89	p(q) 0.12	q(p) 0.88	p(q) 0.13	q(p) 0.87	p(q) 0.14	q(p) 0.86
0	0 00000	0 00000	0 00000	0 00000	0 00000	0 00000	0 00000	0 00000	0 00000	0 00000	0 00000	0 00000	0 00000	0 00000
1	2 90309	1 96379	2 95424	1 95904	1 00000	1 95424	1 04139	1 94939	1 07918	1 94448	1 11394	1 93952	1 14613	1 93450
2	3 80618	1 92758	3 90849	1 91808	2 00000	1 90849	2 08279	1 89878	2 15836	1 88897	2 22789	1 87904	2 29226	1 86900
3	4 70927	1 89136	4 86273	1 87712	3 00000	1 86273	3 12418	1 84817	3 23754	1 83345	3 34183	1 81856	3 43838	1 80350
4	5 61236	1 85515	5 81697	1 83617	4 00000	1 81697	4 16557	1 79756	4 31672	1 77793	4 45577	1 75808	4 58451	1 73799
5	6 51545	1 81894	6 77121	1 79521	5 00000	1 77121	5 20696	1 74695	5 39591	1 72241	5 56972	1 69760	5 73064	1 67249
6	7 41854	1 78273	7 72546	1 75425	6 00000	1 72546	6 24836	1 69634	6 47509	1 66690	6 68366	1 63712	6 87677	1 60699
7	8 32163	1 74651	8 67970	1 71329	7 00000	1 67970	7 28975	1 64573	7 55427	1 61138	7 79760	1 57663	6 02290	1 54149
8	9 22472	1 71030	9 63394	1 67233	8 00000	1 63394	8 33114	1 59512	8 63345	1 55586	8 91155	1 51615	7 16902	1 47599
9	10 12781	1 67409	10 58818	1 63137	9 00000	1 58818	9 37253	1 54451	9 71263	1 50034	8 02549	1 45567	8 31515	1 41049
10	11 03090	1 63788	11 54243	1 59041	10 00000	1 54243	10 41393	1 49390	10 79181	1 44483	9 13943	1 39519	9 46128	1 34498
11	13 93399	1 60167	12 49667	1 54946	11 00000	1 49667	11 45532	1 44329	11 87099	1 38931	10 25338	1 33471	10 60741	1 27948
12	14 83708	1 56545	13 45091	1 50850	12 00000	1 45091	12 49671	1 39268	12 95017	1 33379	11 36732	1 27423	11 75354	1 21398
13	15 74017	1 52924	14 40515	1 46754	13 00000	1 40515	13 53810	1 34207	12 02936	1 27827	12 48126	1 21375	12 89966	1 14848
14	16 64326	1 49303	15 35940	1 42658	14 00000	1 35940	14 57950	1 29146	13 10854	1 22276	13 59521	1 15327	12 04579	1 08298
15	17 54635	1 45682	16 31364	1 38562	15 00000	1 31364	15 62089	1 24085	14 18772	1 16724	14 70915	1 09279	13 19192	1 01748
16	18 44944	1 42061	17 26788	1 34466	16 00000	1 26788	16 66228	1 19024	15 26690	1 11172	15 82309	1 03231	14 33805	2 95198
17	19 35253	1 38439	18 22212	1 30370	17 00000	1 22212	17 70368	1 13963	16 34608	1 05621	16 93704	2 97183	15 48418	2 88647
18	20 25562	1 34818	19 17637	1 26275	18 00000	1 17637	18 74507	1 08902	17 42526	1 00069	16 05098	2 91135	16 63030	2 82097
19	21 15871	1 31197	20 13061	1 22179	19 00000	1 13061	19 78646	1 03841	18 50444	2 94517	17 16492	2 85087	17 77643	2 75547
20	22 06180	1 27576	21 08485	1 18083	20 00000	1 08485	20 82785	2 98780	19 58362	2 88965	18 27887	2 79039	18 92256	2 68997
21	24 96489	1 23954	22 03909	1 13987	21 00000	1 03909	21 86925	2 93719	20 66281	2 83414	19 39281	2 72990	18 06869	2 62447
22	25 86798	1 20333	24 99334	1 09891	22 00000	2 99334	22 91064	2 88658	21 74199	2 77862	20 50675	2 66942	19 21482	2 55897
23	26 77107	1 16712	25 94758	1 05795	23 00000	2 94758	23 95203	2 83597	22 82117	2 72310	21 62070	2 60894	20 36094	2 49346
24	27 67416	1 13091	26 90182	1 01699	24 00000	2 90182	24 99342	2 78536	23 90035	2 66758	22 73464	2 54846	21 50707	2 42796
25	28 57725	1 09470	27 85606	2 97603	25 00000	2 85606	24 03482	2 73475	24 97953	2 61207	23 84858	2 48798	22 65320	2 36246
26	29 48034	1 05848	28 81031	2 93508	26 00000	2 81031	25 07621	2 68414	24 05871	2 55655	24 96253	2 42750	23 79933	2 29696
27	30 38343	1 02227	29 76455	2 89412	27 00000	2 76455	26 11760	2 63353	25 13789	2 50103	24 07647	2 36702	24 94546	2 23146
28	31 28652	2 98606	30 71879	2 85316	28 00000	2 71879	27 15900	2 58292	26 21707	2 44551	25 19041	2 30654	24 09159	2 16596
29	32 18961	2 94985	31 67303	2 81220	29 00000	2 67303	28 20039	2 53231	27 29626	2 39000	26 30436	2 24606	25 23771	2 10046
30	33 09270	2 91363	32 62728	2 77124	30 00000	2 62728	29 24178	2 48170	28 37544	2 33448	27 41830	2 18558	26 38384	2 03495
31	35 99579	2 87742	33 58152	2 73028	31 00000	2 58152	30 28317	2 43109	29 45462	2 27896	28 53224	2 12510	27 52997	3 96945
32	36 89888	2 84121	34 53576	2 68932	32 00000	2 53576	31 32457	2 38048	30 53380	2 22345	29 64619	2 06462	28 67610	3 90395
33	37 80197	2 80500	35 49000	2 64837	33 00000	2 49000	32 36596	2 32987	31 61298	2 16793	30 76013	2 00414	29 82223	3 83845
34	38 70506	2 76879	36 44425	2 60741	34 00000	2 44425	33 40735	2 27926	32 69216	2 11241	31 87407	3 94365	30 96835	3 77295
35	39 60815	2 73257	37 39849	2 56645	35 00000	2 39849	34 44874	2 22865	33 77134	2 05689	32 98802	3 88317	30 11448	3 70745
36	40 51124	2 69636	38 35273	2 52549	36 00000	2 35273	35 49014	2 17804	34 85052	2 00138	32 10196	3 82269	31 26061	3 64194
37	41 41433	2 66015	39 30697	2 48453	37 00000	2 30697	36 53153	2 12743	35 92971	3 94586	33 21590	3 76221	32 40674	3 57644
38	42 31742	2 62394	40 26122	2 44357	38 00000	2 26122	37 57292	2 07682	35 00889	3 89034	34 32985	3 70173	33 55287	3 51094
39	43 22051	2 58773	41 21546	2 40261	39 00000	2 21546	38 61431	2 02621	36 08807	3 83482	35 44379	3 64125	34 69899	3 44544
40	44 12360	2 55151	42 16970	2 36166	40 00000	2 16970	39 65571	3 97560	37 16725	3 77931	36 55773	3 58077	35 84512	3 37994
41	45 02669	2 51530	43 12394	2 32070	41 00000	2 12394	40 69710	3 92499	38 24643	3 72379	37 67168	3 52029	36 99125	3 31444
42	47 92978	2 47909	44 07819	2 27974	42 00000	2 07819	41 73849	3 87438	39 32561	3 66827	38 78562	3 45981	36 13738	3 24893
43	48 83287	2 44288	45 03243	2 23878	43 00000	2 03243	42 77989	3 82377	40 40479	3 61275	39 89956	3 39933	37 28351	3 18343
44	49 73596	2 40666	47 98667	2 19782	44 00000	3 98667	43 82128	3 77316	41 48397	3 55724	39 01351	3 33885	38 42963	3 11793
45	50 63905	2 37045	48 94091	2 15686	45 00000	3 94091	44 86267	3 72255	42 56316	3 50172	40 12745	3 27837	39 57576	3 05243
46	51 54214	2 33424	49 89516	2 11590	46 00000	3 89516	45 90406	3 67194	43 64234	3 44620	41 24139	3 21789	40 72189	4 98693
47	52 44523	2 29803	50 84940	2 07495	47 00000	3 84940	46 94546	3 62133	44 72152	3 39069	42 35534	3 15740	41 86802	4 92143
48	53 34832	2 26182	51 80364	2 03399	48 00000	3 80364	47 98685	3 57072	45 80070	3 33517	43 46928	3 09692	41 01415	4 85593
49	54 25141	2 22560	52 75788	3 99303	49 00000	3 75788	47 02824	3 52011	46 87988	3 27965	44 58322	3 03644	42 16027	4 79042
50	55 15450	2 18939	53 71213	3 95207	50 00000	3 71213	48 06963	3 46950	47 95906	3 22413	45 69717	4 97596	43 30640	4 72492
51	56 05759	2 15318	54 66637	3 91111	51 00000	3 66637	49 11103	3 41889	47 03824	3 16862	46 81111	4 91548	44 45253	4 65942
52	58 96068	2 11697	55 62061	3 87015	52 00000	3 62061	50 15242	3 36828	48 11742	3 11310	47 92505	4 85500	45 59866	4 59392
53	59 86377	2 08075	56 57485	3 82919	53 00000	3 57485	51 19381	3 31767	49 19661	3 05758	47 03900	4 79452	46 74479	4 52842
54	60 76686	2 04454	57 52910	3 78824	54 00000	3 52910	52 23521	3 26706	50 27579	3 00206	48 15294	4 73404	47 89091	4 46292
55	61 66995	2 00833	58 48334	3 74728	55 00000	3 48334	53 27660	3 21645	51 35497	4 94655	49 26688	4 67356	47 03704	4 39741
56	62 57304	3 97212	59 43758	3 70632	56 00000	3 43758	54 31799	3 16584	52 43415	4 89103	50 38083	4 61308	48 18317	4 33191
57	63 47613	3 93591	60 39182	3 66536	57 00000	3 39182	55 35938	3 11523	53 51333	4 83551	51 49477	4 55260	49 32930	4 26641
58	64 37922	3 89969	61 34607	3 62440	58 00000	3 34607	56 40078	3 06462	54 59251	4 77999	52 60871	4 49212	50 47543	4 20091
59	65 28231	3 86348	62 30031	3 58344	59 00000	3 30031	57 44217	3 01401	55 67169	4 72448	53 72266	4 43164	51 62155	4 13541
60	66 18540	3 82727	63 25455	3 54248	60 00000	3 25455	58 48356	4 96340	56 75087	4 66896	54 83660	4 37116	52 76768	4 06991
61	67 08849	3 79106	64 20879	3 50152	61 00000	3 20879	59 52495	4 91279	57 83006	4 61344	55 95054	4 31067	53 91381	4 00441
62	69 99158	3 75485	65 16304	3 46057	62 00000	3 16304	60 56635	4 86218	58 90924	4 55793	55 06449	4 25019	53 05994	5 93890
63	70 89467	3 71863	66 11728	3 41961	63 00000	3 11728	61 60774	4 81157	59 98842	4 50241	56 17843	4 18971	54 20607	5 87340
64	71 79776	3 68242	67 07152	3 37865	64 00000	3 07152	62 64913	4 76096	59 06760	4 44689	57 29237	4 12923	55 35219	5 80790
65	72 70085	3 64621	68 02576	3 33769	65 00000	3 02576	63 69052	4 71035	60 14678	4 39137	58 40632	4 06875	56 49832	5 74240
66	73 60394	3 61000	70 98001	3 29673	66 00000	4 98001	64 73192	4 65974	61 22596	4 33586	59 52026	4 00827	57 64445	5 67690
67	74 50703	3 57378	71 93425	3 25577	67 00000	4 93425	65 77331	4 60913	62 30514	4 28034	60 63420	5 94779	58 79058	5 61140
68	75 41012	3 53757	72 88849	3 21481	68 00000	4 88849	66 81470	4 55852	63 38432	4 22482	61 74815	5 88731	59 93671	5 54589
69	76 31321	3 50136	73 84273	3 17386	69 00000	4 84273	67 85610	4 50791	64 46351	4 16930	62 86209	5 82683	59 08283	5 48039
70	77 21630	3 46515	74 79698	3 13290	70 00000	4 79698	68 89749	4 45730	65 54269	4 11379	63 97603	5 76635	60 22896	5 41489
71	78 11939	3 42894	75 75122	3 09194	71 00000	4 75122	69 93888	4 40669	66 62187	4 05827	63 08998	5 70587	61 37509	5 34939
72	79 02248	3 39272	76 70546	3 05098	72 00000	4 70546	70 98027	4 35608	67 70105	4 00275	64 20392	5 64539	62 52122	5 28389
73	81 92557	3 35651	77 65970	3 01002	73 00000	4 65970	70 02167	4 30547	68 78023	5 94724	65 31786	5 58491	63 66735	5 21839
74	82 82866	3 32030	78 61395	4 96906	74 00000	4 61395	71 06306	4 25486	69 85941	5 89172	66 43181	5 52442	64 81347	5 15289
75	83 73175	3 28409	79 56819	4 92810	75 00000	4 56819	72 10445	4 20425	70 93859	5 83620	67 54575	5 46394	65 95960	5 08738
76	84 63484	3 24787	80 52243	4 88715	76 00000	4 52243	73 14584	4 15364	70 01777	5 78068	68 65969	5 40346	65 10573	5 02188
77	85 53793	3 21166	81 47667	4 84619	77 00000	4 47667	74 18724	4 10303	71 09696	5 72517	69 77364	5 34298	66 25186	6 95638
78	86 44102	3 17545	82 43092	4 80523	78 00000	4 43092	75 22863	4 05242	72 17614	5 66965	70 88758	5 28250	67 39799	6 89088
79	87 34411	3 13924	83 38516	4 76427	79 00000	4 38516	76 27002	4 00181	73 25532	5 61413	70 00152	5 22202	68 54411	6 82538
80	88 24720	3 10303	84 33940	4 72331	80 00000	4 33940	77 31141	5 95120	74 33450	5 55861	71 11547	5 16154	69 69024	6 75988
81	89 15029	3 06681	85 29364	4 68235	81 00000	4 29364	78 35281	5 90059	75 41368	5 50310	72 22941	5 10106	70 83637	6 69437
82	90 05338	3 03060	86 24789	4 64139	82 00000	4 24789	79 39420	5 84998	76 49286	5 44758	73 34335	5 04058	71 98250	6 62887
83	92 95647	4 99439	87 20213	4 60044	83 00000	4 20213	80 43559	5 79937	77 57204	5 39206	74 45730	6 98010	71 12863	6 56337
84	93 85956	4 95818	88 15637	4 55948	84 00000	4 15637	81 47699	5 74876	78 65122	5 33654	75 57124	6 91962	72 27476	6 49787
85	94 76265	4 92197	89 11061	4 51852	85 00000	4 11061	82 51838	5 69815	79 73041	5 28103	76 68518	6 85914	73 42088	6 43237
86	95 66574	4 88575	90 06486	4 47756	86 00000	4 06486	83 55977	5 64754	80 80959	5 22551	77 79913	6 79866	74 56701	6 36687
87	96 56883	4 84954	91 01910	4 43660	87 00000	4 01910	84 60116	5 59693	81 88877	5 16999	78 91307	6 73817	75 71314	6 30137
88	97 47192	4 81333	93 97334	4 39564	88 00000	5 97334	85 64256	5 54632	82 96795	5 11448	78 02702	6 67769	76 85927	6 23586
89	98 37501	4 77712	94 92758	4 35468	89 00000	5 92758	86 68395	5 49571	82 04713	5 05896	79 14096	6 61721	76 00540	6 17036
90	99 27810	4 74090	95 88183	4 31373	90 00000	5 88183	87 72534	5 44510	83 12631	5 00344	80 25490	6 55673	77 15152	6 10486
91	100 18119	4 70469	96 83607	4 27277	91 00000	5 83607	88 76673	5 39449	84 20549	6 94792	81 36885	6 49625	78 29765	6 03936
92	101 08428	4 66848	97 79031	4 23181	92 00000	5 79031	89 80813	5 34388	85 28467	6 89241	82 48279	6 43577	79 44378	7 97386
93	103 98737	4 63227	98 74455	4 19085	93 00000	5 74455	90 84952	5 29327	86 36386	6 83689	83 59673	6 37529	80 58991	7 90836
94	104 89046	4 59606	99 69880	4 14989	94 00000	5 69880	91 89091	5 24266	87 44304	6 78137	84 71068	6 31481	81 73604	7 84285
95	105 79355	4 55984	100 65304	4 10893	95 00000	5 65304	92 93231	5 19205	88 52222	6 72585	85 82462	6 25433	82 88216	7 77735
96	106 69664	4 52363	101 60728	4 06797	96 00000	5 60728	93 97370	5 14144	89 60140	6 67034	86 93856	6 19385	82 02829	7 71185
97	107 59973	4 48742	102 56152	4 02702	97 00000	5 56152	93 01509	5 09083	90 68058	6 61482	86 05251	6 13337	83 17442	7 64635
98	108 50282	4 45121	103 51577	5 98606	98 00000	5 51577	94 05648	5 04022	91 75976	6 55930	87 16645	6 07289	84 32055	7 58085
99	109 40591	4 41499	104 47001	5 94510	99 00000	5 47001	95 09788	6 98961	92 83894	6 50378	88 28039	6 01241	85 46668	7 51535
100	110 30900	4 37878	105 42425	5 90414	100 00000	5 42425	96 13927	6 93900	93 91812	6 44827	89 39434	7 95193	86 61280	7 44985

Common Logarithms of p^n and q^n ($q=1-p$)*

For explanation see page 77

n	$p(q)$ 0.15	$q(p)$ 0.85	$p(q)$ 0.16	$q(p)$ 0.84	$p(q)$ 0.17	$q(p)$ 0.83	$p(q)$ 0.18	$q(p)$ 0.82	$p(q)$ 0.19	$q(p)$ 0.81	$p(q)$ 0.20	$q(p)$ 0.80	$p(q)$ 0.21	$q(p)$ 0.79
0	0 00000	0 00000	0 00000	0 00000	0 00000	0 00000	0 00000	0 00000	0 00000	0 00000	0 00000	0 00000	0 00000	0 00000
1	1 17609	1 92942	1 20412	1 92428	1 23045	1 91908	1 25527	1 91381	1 27875	1 90849	1 30103	1 90309	1 32222	1 89763
2	2 35218	1 85884	2 40824	1 84856	2 46090	1 83816	2 51055	1 82763	2 55751	1 81697	2 60206	1 80618	2 64444	1 79525
3	3 52827	1 78826	3 61236	1 77284	3 69135	1 75723	3 76582	1 74144	3 83626	1 72546	3 90309	1 70927	3 96666	1 69288
4	4 70437	1 71768	4 81648	1 69712	4 92180	1 67631	3 02109	1 65526	3 11501	1 63394	3 20412	1 61236	3 28888	1 59051
5	5 88046	1 64709	4 02060	1 62140	4 15224	1 59539	4 27636	1 56907	4 39377	1 54243	4 50515	1 51545	4 61110	1 48814
6	5 05655	1 57651	5 22472	1 54568	5 38269	1 51447	5 53164	1 48288	5 67252	1 45091	5 80618	1 41854	5 93332	1 38576
7	6 23264	1 50593	6 42884	1 46996	6 61314	1 43355	6 78691	1 39670	6 95128	1 35940	5 10721	1 32163	5 25554	1 28339
8	7 40873	1 43535	7 63296	1 39423	7 84359	1 35262	6 04218	1 31051	6 23003	1 26788	6 40824	1 22472	6 57775	1 18102
9	8 58482	1 36477	8 83708	1 31851	7 07404	1 27170	7 29745	1 22432	7 50878	1 17637	7 70927	1 12781	7 89997	1 07864
10	9 76091	1 29419	8 04120	1 24279	8 30449	1 19078	8 55273	1 13814	8 78754	1 08485	7 01030	1 03090	7 22219	2 97627
11	10 93700	1 22361	9 24532	1 16707	9 53494	1 10986	9 80800	1 05195	8 06629	2 99334	8 31133	2 93399	8 54441	2 87390
12	10 11310	1 15303	10 44944	1 09135	10 76539	1 02894	9 06327	2 96577	9 34504	2 90182	9 61236	2 83708	9 86663	2 77153
13	11 28919	1 08245	11 65356	1 01563	11 99584	2 94802	10 31854	2 87958	10 62380	2 81031	10 91339	2 74017	9 18885	2 66915
14	12 46528	1 01186	12 85768	2 93991	11 22628	2 86709	11 57382	2 79339	11 90255	2 71879	10 21442	2 64326	10 51107	2 56678
15	13 64137	2 94128	12 06180	2 86419	12 45673	2 78617	12 82909	2 70721	11 18130	2 62728	11 51545	2 54635	11 83329	2 46441
16	14 81746	2 87070	13 26592	2 78847	13 68718	2 70525	12 08436	2 62102	12 46006	2 53576	12 81648	2 44944	11 15551	2 36203
17	15 99355	2 80012	14 47004	2 71275	14 91763	2 62433	13 33963	2 53484	13 73881	2 44425	12 11751	2 35253	12 47773	2 25966
18	15 16964	2 72954	15 67416	2 63703	14 14808	2 54341	14 59491	2 44865	13 01756	2 35273	13 41854	2 25562	13 79995	2 15729
19	16 34573	2 65896	16 87828	2 56131	15 37853	2 46248	15 85018	2 36246	14 29632	2 26122	14 71957	2 15871	13 12217	2 05491
20	17 52183	2 58838	16 08240	2 48559	16 60898	2 38156	15 10545	2 27628	15 57507	2 16970	14 02060	2 06180	14 44439	3 95254
21	18 69792	2 51780	17 28652	2 40987	17 83943	2 30064	16 36072	2 19009	16 85383	2 07819	15 32163	3 96489	15 76661	3 85017
22	19 87401	2 44722	18 49064	2 33414	17 06988	2 21972	17 61600	2 10390	16 13258	3 98667	16 62266	3 86798	15 08882	3 74780
23	19 05010	2 37664	19 69476	2 25842	18 30033	2 13880	18 87127	2 01772	17 41133	3 89516	17 92369	3 77107	16 41104	3 64542
24	20 22619	2 30605	20 89888	2 18270	19 53077	2 05787	18 12654	3 93153	18 69009	3 80364	17 22472	3 67416	17 73326	3 54305
25	21 40228	2 23547	20 10300	2 10698	20 76122	3 97695	19 38181	3 84535	19 96884	3 71213	18 52575	3 57725	17 05548	3 44068
26	22 57837	2 16489	21 30712	2 03126	21 99167	3 89603	20 63709	3 75916	19 24759	3 62061	19 82678	3 48034	18 37770	3 33830
27	23 75446	2 09431	22 51124	3 95554	21 22212	3 81511	21 89236	3 67297	20 52635	3 52910	19 12781	3 38343	19 69992	3 23593
28	24 93056	2 02373	23 71536	3 87982	22 45257	3 73419	21 14763	3 58679	21 80510	3 43758	20 42884	3 28652	19 02214	3 13356
29	24 10665	3 95315	24 91948	3 80410	23 68302	3 65326	22 40290	3 50060	21 08385	3 34607	21 72987	3 18961	20 34436	3 03119
30	25 28274	3 88257	24 12360	3 72838	24 91347	3 57234	23 65818	3 41442	22 36261	3 25455	21 03090	3 09270	21 66658	4 92881
31	26 45883	3 81199	25 32772	3 65266	24 14392	3 49142	24 91345	3 32823	23 64136	3 16304	22 33193	4 99579	22 98880	4 82644
32	27 63492	3 74141	26 53184	3 57694	25 37437	3 41050	24 16872	3 24204	24 92012	3 07152	23 63296	4 89888	22 31102	4 72407
33	28 81101	3 67082	27 73596	3 50122	26 60481	3 32958	25 42399	3 15586	24 19887	4 98001	24 93399	4 80197	23 63324	4 62169
34	29 98710	3 60024	28 94008	3 42550	27 83526	3 24866	26 67927	3 06967	25 47762	4 88849	24 23502	4 70506	24 95546	4 51932
35	29 16319	3 52966	28 14420	3 34978	27 06571	3 16773	27 93454	4 98348	26 75638	4 79698	25 53605	4 60815	24 27768	4 41695
36	30 33929	3 45908	29 34832	3 27405	28 29616	3 08681	27 18981	4 89730	26 03513	4 70546	26 83708	4 51124	25 59989	4 31458
37	31 51538	3 38850	30 55244	3 19833	29 52661	3 00589	28 44508	4 81111	27 31388	4 61395	26 13811	4 41433	26 92211	4 21220
38	32 69147	3 31792	31 75656	3 12261	30 75706	4 92497	29 70036	4 72493	28 59264	4 52243	27 43914	4 31742	26 24433	4 10983
39	33 86756	3 24734	32 96068	3 04689	31 98751	4 84405	30 95563	4 63874	29 87139	4 43092	28 74017	4 22051	27 56655	4 00746
40	33 04365	3 17676	32 16480	4 97117	31 21796	4 76312	30 21090	4 55255	29 15014	4 33940	28 04120	4 12360	28 88877	5 90508
41	34 21974	3 10618	33 36892	4 89545	32 44841	4 68220	31 46617	4 46637	30 42890	4 24789	29 34223	4 02669	28 21099	5 80271
42	35 39583	3 03559	34 57304	4 81973	33 67885	4 60128	32 72145	4 38018	31 70765	4 15637	30 64326	5 92978	29 53321	5 70034
43	36 57192	4 96501	35 77716	4 74401	34 90930	4 52036	33 97672	4 29400	32 98640	4 06486	31 94429	5 83287	30 85543	5 59796
44	37 74802	4 89443	36 98128	4 66829	34 13975	4 43944	33 23199	4 20781	32 26516	5 97334	31 24532	5 73596	30 17765	5 49559
45	38 92411	4 82385	36 18540	4 59257	35 37020	4 35851	34 48726	4 12162	33 54391	5 88183	32 54635	5 63905	31 49987	5 39322
46	38 10020	4 75327	37 38952	4 51685	36 60065	4 27759	35 74254	4 03544	34 82267	5 79031	33 84738	5 54214	32 82209	5 29085
47	39 27629	4 68269	38 59364	4 44113	37 83110	4 19667	36 99781	5 94925	34 10142	5 69880	33 14841	5 44523	32 14431	5 18847
48	40 45238	4 61211	39 79776	4 36541	37 06155	4 11575	36 25308	5 86306	35 38017	5 60728	34 44944	5 34832	33 46653	5 08610
49	41 62847	4 54153	39 00188	4 28969	38 29200	4 03483	37 50835	5 77688	36 65893	5 51577	35 75047	5 25141	34 78875	6 98373
50	42 80456	4 47095	40 20600	4 21396	39 52245	5 95390	38 76363	5 69069	37 93768	5 42425	35 05150	5 15450	34 11096	6 88135
51	43 98065	4 40037	41 41012	4 13824	40 75290	5 87298	38 01890	5 60451	37 21643	5 33274	36 35253	5 05759	35 43318	6 77898
52	43 15675	4 32978	42 61424	4 06252	41 98334	5 79206	39 27417	5 51832	38 49519	5 24122	37 65356	6 96068	36 75540	6 67661
53	44 33284	4 25920	43 81836	5 98680	41 21379	5 71114	40 52944	5 43213	39 77394	5 14971	38 95459	6 86377	36 07762	6 57424
54	45 50893	4 18862	43 02248	5 91108	42 44424	5 63022	41 78472	5 34595	39 05269	5 05819	38 25562	6 76686	37 39984	6 47186
55	46 68502	4 11804	44 22660	5 83536	43 67469	5 54930	41 03999	5 25976	40 33145	6 96668	39 55665	6 66995	38 72206	6 36949
56	47 86111	4 04746	45 43072	5 75964	44 90514	5 46837	42 29526	5 17358	41 61020	6 87516	40 85768	6 57304	38 04428	6 26712
57	47 03720	5 97688	46 63484	5 68392	44 13559	5 38745	43 55053	5 08739	42 88896	6 78365	40 15871	6 47613	39 36650	6 16474
58	48 21329	5 90630	47 83896	5 60820	45 36604	5 30653	44 80581	5 00120	42 16771	6 69213	41 45974	6 37922	40 68872	6 06237
59	49 38938	5 83572	47 04308	5 53248	46 59649	5 22561	44 06108	6 91502	43 44646	6 60062	42 76077	6 28231	40 01094	7 96000
60	50 56548	5 76514	48 24720	5 45676	47 82694	5 14469	45 31635	6 82883	44 72522	6 50910	42 06180	6 18540	41 33316	7 85763
61	51 74157	5 69455	49 45132	5 38104	47 05738	5 06376	46 57162	6 74264	44 00397	6 41759	43 36283	6 08849	42 65538	7 75525
62	52 91766	5 62397	50 65544	5 30532	48 28783	6 98284	47 82690	6 65646	45 28272	6 32607	44 66386	7 99158	43 97760	7 65288
63	52 09375	5 55339	51 85956	5 22960	49 51828	6 90192	47 08217	6 57027	46 56148	6 23456	45 96489	7 89467	43 29982	7 55051
64	53 26984	5 48281	51 06368	5 15387	50 74873	6 82100	48 33744	6 48409	47 84023	6 14304	45 26592	7 79776	44 62203	7 44813
65	54 44593	5 41223	52 26780	5 07815	51 97918	6 74008	49 59271	6 39790	47 11898	6 05153	46 56695	7 70085	45 94425	7 34576
66	55 62202	5 34165	53 47192	5 00243	51 20963	6 65915	50 84799	6 31171	48 39774	7 96001	47 86798	7 60394	45 26647	7 24339
67	56 79811	5 27107	54 67604	6 92671	52 44008	6 57823	50 10326	6 22553	49 67649	7 86850	47 16901	7 50703	46 58869	7 14102
68	57 97421	5 20049	55 88016	6 85099	53 67053	6 49731	51 35853	6 13934	50 95524	7 77698	48 47004	7 41012	47 91091	7 03864
69	57 15030	5 12991	55 08428	6 77527	54 90098	6 41639	52 61380	6 05316	50 23400	7 68547	49 77107	7 31321	47 23313	8 93627
70	58 32639	5 05932	56 28840	6 69955	54 13142	6 33547	53 86908	7 96697	51 51275	7 59395	49 07210	7 21630	48 55535	8 83390
71	59 50248	6 98874	57 49252	6 62383	55 36187	6 25454	53 12435	7 88078	52 79151	7 50244	50 37313	7 11939	49 87757	8 73152
72	60 67857	6 91816	58 69664	6 54811	56 59232	6 17362	54 37962	7 79460	52 07026	7 41092	51 67416	7 02248	49 19979	8 62915
73	61 85466	6 84758	59 90076	6 47239	57 82277	6 09270	55 63489	7 70841	53 34901	7 31941	52 97519	8 92557	50 52201	8 52678
74	61 03075	6 77700	59 10488	6 39667	57 05322	6 01178	56 89017	7 62223	54 62777	7 22789	52 27622	8 82866	51 84423	8 42440
75	62 20684	6 70642	60 30900	6 32095	58 28367	7 93086	56 14544	7 53604	55 90652	7 13638	53 57725	8 73175	51 16645	8 32203
76	63 38294	6 63584	61 51312	6 24523	59 51412	7 84994	57 40071	7 44985	55 18527	7 04486	54 87828	8 63484	52 48867	8 21966
77	64 55903	6 56526	62 71724	6 16951	60 74457	7 76901	58 65598	7 36367	56 46403	8 95335	54 17931	8 53793	53 81089	8 11729
78	65 73512	6 49468	63 92136	6 09378	61 97502	7 68809	59 91126	7 27748	57 74278	8 86183	55 48034	8 44102	53 13311	8 01491
79	66 91121	6 42410	63 12548	6 01806	61 20546	7 60717	59 16653	7 19129	57 02153	8 77032	56 78137	8 34411	54 45532	9 91254
80	66 08730	6 35351	64 32960	7 94234	62 43591	7 52625	60 42180	7 10511	58 30029	8 67880	56 08240	8 24720	55 77754	9 81017
81	67 26339	6 28293	65 53372	7 86662	63 66636	7 44533	61 67707	7 01892	59 57904	8 58729	57 38343	8 15029	55 09976	9 70779
82	68 43948	6 21235	66 73784	7 79090	64 89681	7 36440	62 93235	8 93274	60 85780	8 49577	58 68446	8 05338	56 42198	9 60542
83	69 61557	6 14177	67 94196	7 71518	64 12726	7 28348	62 18762	8 84655	60 13655	8 40426	59 98549	9 95647	57 74420	9 50305
84	70 79167	6 07119	67 14608	7 63946	65 35771	7 20256	63 44289	8 76036	61 41530	8 31274	59 28652	9 85956	57 06642	9 40068
85	71 96776	6 00061	68 35020	7 56374	66 58816	7 12164	64 69816	8 67418	62 69406	8 22123	60 58755	9 76265	58 38864	9 29830
86	71 14385	7 93003	69 55432	7 48802	67 81861	7 04072	65 95344	8 58799	63 97281	8 12971	61 88858	9 66574	59 71086	9 19593
87	72 31994	7 85945	70 75844	7 41230	67 04906	8 95979	65 20871	8 50181	63 25156	8 03820	61 18961	9 56883	59 03308	9 09356
88	73 49603	7 78887	71 96256	7 33658	68 27951	8 87887	66 46398	8 41562	64 53032	9 94668	62 49064	9 47192	60 35530	10 99118
89	74 67212	7 71828	71 16668	7 26086	69 50995	8 79795	67 71925	8 32943	65 80907	9 85517	63 79167	9 37501	61 67752	10 88881
90	75 84821	7 64770	72 37080	7 18514	70 74040	8 71703	68 97453	8 24325	65 08782	9 76365	63 09270	9 27810	62 99974	10 78644
91	75 02430	7 57712	73 57492	7 10942	71 97085	8 63611	68 22980	8 15706	66 36658	9 67214	64 39373	9 18119	62 32196	10 68407
92	76 20040	7 50654	74 77904	7 03369	71 20130	8 55518	69 48507	8 07087	67 64533	9 58062	65 69476	9 08428	63 64418	10 58169
93	77 37649	7 43596	75 98316	8 95797	72 43175	8 47426	70 74034	9 98469	68 92408	9 48911	66 99579	10 98737	64 96639	10 47932
94	78 55258	7 36538	75 18728	8 88225	73 66220	8 39334	71 99562	9 89850	68 20284	9 39759	66 29682	10 89046	64 28861	10 37695
95	79 72867	7 29480	76 39140	8 80653	74 89265	8 31242	71 25089	9 81232	69 48159	9 30608	67 59785	10 79355	65 61083	10 27457
96	80 90476	7 22422	77 59552	8 73081	74 12310	8 23150	72 50616	9 72613	70 76035	9 21456	68 89888	10 69664	66 93305	10 17220
97	80 08085	7 15364	78 79964	8 65509	75 35355	8 15057	73 76143	9 63994	70 03910	9 12305	68 19991	10 59973	66 25527	10 06983
98	81 25694	7 08305	78 00376	8 57937	76 58399	8 06965	73 01671	9 55376	71 31785	9 03153	69 50094	10 50282	67 57749	11 96745
99	82 43303	7 01247	79 20788	8 50365	77 81444	9 98873	74 27198	9 46757	72 59661	10 94002	70 80197	10 40591	68 89971	11 86508
100	83 60913	8 94189	80 41200	8 42793	77 04489	9 90781	75 52725	9 38139	73 87536	10 84850	70 10300	10 30900	68 22193	11 76271

For explanation see page 77

n	p(q) 0.22	q(p) 0.78	p(q) 0.23	q(p) 0.77	p(q) 0.24	q(p) 0.76	p(q) 0.25	q(p) 0.75	p(q) 0.26	q(p) 0.74	p(q) 0.27	q(p) 0.73	p(q) 0.28	q(p) 0.72
0	0 00000	0 00000	0 00000	0 00000	0 00000	0 00000	0 00000	0 00000	0 00000	0 00000	0 00000	0 00000	0 00000	0 00000
1	1 34242	1 89209	1 36173	1 88649	1 38021	1 88081	1 39794	1 87506	1 41497	1 86923	1 43136	1 86332	1 44716	1 85733
2	2 68485	1 78419	2 72346	1 77298	2 76042	1 76163	2 79588	1 75012	2 82995	1 73846	2 86273	1 72665	2 89432	1 71466
3	2 02727	1 67628	2 08518	1 65947	2 14063	1 64244	2 19382	1 62518	2 24492	1 60770	2 29409	1 58997	2 34147	1 57200
4	3 36969	1 56838	3 44691	1 54596	3 52084	1 52325	3 59176	1 50025	3 65989	1 47693	3 72546	1 45329	3 78863	1 42933
5	4 71211	1 46047	4 80864	1 43245	4 90106	1 40407	4 98970	1 37531	3 07487	1 34616	3 15682	1 31661	3 23579	1 28666
6	4 05454	1 35257	4 17037	1 31894	4 28127	1 28488	4 38764	1 25037	4 48984	1 21539	4 58818	1 17994	4 68295	1 14399
7	5 39696	1 24466	5 53209	1 20544	5 66148	1 16570	5 78558	1 12543	5 90481	1 08462	4 01955	1 04326	4 13011	1 00133
8	6 73938	1 13676	6 89382	1 09193	5 04169	1 04651	5 18352	1 00049	5 31979	2 95385	5 45091	2 90658	5 57726	2 85866
9	6 08180	1 02885	6 25555	2 97842	6 42190	2 92732	6 58146	2 87555	6 73476	2 82309	6 88227	2 76991	5 02442	2 71599
10	7 42423	2 92095	7 61728	2 86491	7 80211	2 80814	7 97940	2 75061	6 14973	2 69232	6 31364	2 63323	6 47158	2 57332
11	8 76665	2 81304	8 97901	2 75140	7 18232	2 68895	7 37734	2 62567	7 56471	2 56155	7 74500	2 49655	7 91874	2 43066
12	8 10907	2 70514	8 34073	2 63789	8 56253	2 56976	8 77528	2 50074	8 97968	2 43078	7 17637	2 35987	7 36590	2 28799
13	9 45149	2 59723	9 70246	2 52438	9 94275	2 45058	8 17322	2 37580	8 39465	2 30001	8 60773	2 22320	8 81305	2 14532
14	10 79392	2 48932	9 06419	2 41087	9 32296	2 33139	9 57116	2 25086	9 80963	2 16924	8 03909	2 08652	8 26021	2 00265
15	10 13634	2 38142	10 42592	2 29736	10 70317	2 21220	10 96910	2 12592	9 22460	2 03848	9 47046	3 94984	9 70737	3 85999
16	11 47876	2 27351	11 78765	2 18385	10 08338	2 09302	10 36704	2 00098	10 63957	3 90771	10 90182	3 81317	9 15453	3 71732
17	12 82119	2 16561	11 14937	2 07034	11 46359	3 97383	11 76498	3 87604	10 05455	3 77694	10 33318	3 67649	10 60169	3 57465
18	12 16361	2 05770	12 51110	3 95683	12 84380	3 85464	11 16292	3 75110	11 46952	3 64617	11 76455	3 53981	10 04884	3 43198
19	13 50603	3 94980	13 87283	3 84332	12 22401	3 73546	12 56086	3 62616	12 88449	3 51540	11 19591	3 40313	11 49600	3 28932
20	14 84845	3 84189	13 23456	3 72981	13 60422	3 61627	13 95880	3 50123	12 29947	3 38463	12 62728	3 26646	12 94316	3 14665
21	14 19088	3 73399	14 59628	3 61631	14 98444	3 49709	13 35674	3 37629	13 71444	3 25387	12 05864	3 12978	12 39032	3 00398
22	15 53330	3 62608	15 95801	3 50280	14 36465	3 37790	14 75468	3 25135	13 12941	3 12310	13 49000	4 99310	13 83748	4 86131
23	16 87572	3 51818	15 31974	3 38929	15 74486	3 25871	14 15262	3 12641	14 54439	4 99233	14 92137	4 85643	13 28463	4 71865
24	16 21814	3 41027	16 68147	3 27578	15 12507	3 13953	15 55056	3 00147	15 95936	4 86156	14 35273	4 71975	14 73179	4 57598
25	17 56057	3 30237	16 04320	3 16227	16 50528	3 02034	16 94850	4 87653	15 37433	4 73079	15 78409	4 58307	14 17895	4 43331
26	18 90299	3 19446	17 40492	3 04876	17 88549	4 90115	16 34644	4 75159	16 78931	4 60002	15 21546	4 44639	15 62611	4 29064
27	18 24541	3 08655	18 76665	4 93525	17 26570	4 78197	17 74438	4 62665	16 20428	4 46926	16 64682	4 30972	15 07327	4 14798
28	19 58784	4 97865	18 12838	4 82174	18 64591	4 66278	17 14232	4 50172	17 61925	4 33849	16 07819	4 17304	16 52042	4 00531
29	20 93026	4 87074	19 49011	4 70823	18 02613	4 54359	18 54026	4 37678	17 03423	4 20772	17 50955	4 03636	17 96758	5 86264
30	20 27268	4 76284	20 85184	4 59472	19 40634	4 42441	19 93820	4 25184	18 44920	4 07695	18 94091	5 89969	17 41474	5 71997
31	21 61510	4 65493	20 21356	4 48121	20 78655	4 30522	19 33614	4 12690	19 86417	5 94618	18 37228	5 76301	18 86190	5 57731
32	22 95753	4 54703	21 57529	4 36770	20 16676	4 18603	20 73408	4 00196	19 27915	5 81542	19 80364	5 62633	18 30906	5 43464
33	22 29995	4 43912	22 93702	4 25419	21 54697	4 06685	20 13202	5 87702	20 69412	5 68465	19 23500	5 48965	19 75622	5 29197
34	23 64237	4 33122	22 29875	4 14068	22 92718	5 94766	21 52996	5 75208	20 10909	5 55388	20 66637	5 35298	19 20337	5 14930
35	24 98479	4 22331	23 66047	4 02718	22 30739	5 82848	22 92790	5 62714	21 52407	5 42311	20 09773	5 21630	20 65053	5 00664
36	24 32722	4 11541	23 02220	5 91367	23 68760	5 70929	22 32584	5 50221	22 93904	5 29234	21 52910	5 07962	20 09769	6 86397
37	25 66964	4 00750	24 38393	5 80016	23 06782	5 59010	23 72378	5 37727	22 35401	5 16157	22 96046	6 94295	21 54485	6 72130
38	25 01206	5 89959	25 74566	5 68665	24 44803	5 47092	23 12172	5 25233	23 76899	5 03081	22 39182	6 80627	22 99201	6 57863
39	26 35448	5 79169	25 10739	5 57314	25 82824	5 35173	24 51966	5 12739	23 18396	6 90004	23 82319	6 66959	22 43916	6 43597
40	27 69691	5 68378	26 46911	5 45963	25 20845	5 23254	25 91760	5 00245	24 59893	6 76927	23 25455	6 53291	23 88632	6 29330
41	27 03933	5 57588	27 83084	5 34612	26 58866	5 11336	25 31554	6 87751	24 01391	6 63850	24 68591	6 39624	23 33348	6 15063
42	28 38175	5 46797	27 19257	5 23261	27 96887	6 99417	26 71348	6 75257	25 42888	6 50773	24 11728	6 25956	24 78064	6 00796
43	29 72418	5 36007	28 55430	5 11910	27 34908	6 87498	26 11142	6 62763	26 84385	6 37696	25 54864	6 12288	24 22780	7 86530
44	29 06660	5 25216	29 91602	5 00559	28 72929	6 75580	27 50936	6 50270	26 25883	6 24620	26 98001	7 98621	25 67495	7 72263
45	30 40902	5 14426	29 27775	6 89208	28 10951	6 63661	28 90730	6 37776	27 67380	6 11543	26 41137	7 84953	25 12211	7 57996
46	31 75144	5 03635	30 63948	6 77857	29 48972	6 51743	28 30524	6 25282	27 08877	7 98466	27 84273	7 71285	26 56927	7 43729
47	31 09387	6 92845	30 00121	6 66506	30 86993	6 39824	29 70318	6 12788	28 50375	7 85389	27 27410	7 57617	26 01643	7 29463
48	32 43629	6 82054	31 36294	6 55155	30 25014	6 27905	29 10112	6 00294	29 91872	7 72312	28 70546	7 43950	27 46359	7 15196
49	33 77871	6 71264	32 72466	6 43805	31 63035	6 15987	30 49906	7 87800	29 33369	7 59235	28 13682	7 30282	28 91074	7 00929
50	33 12113	6 60473	32 08639	6 32454	31 01056	6 04068	31 89700	7 75306	30 74867	7 46159	29 56819	7 16614	28 35790	8 86662
51	34 46356	6 49682	33 44812	6 21103	32 39077	7 92149	31 29494	7 62812	30 16364	7 33082	30 99955	7 02947	29 80506	8 72396
52	35 80598	6 38892	34 80985	6 09752	33 77098	7 80231	32 69288	7 50319	31 57861	7 20005	30 43092	8 89279	29 25222	8 58129
53	35 14840	6 28101	34 17158	7 98401	33 15120	7 68312	32 09082	7 37825	32 99359	7 06928	31 86228	8 75611	30 69938	8 43862
54	36 49082	6 17311	35 53330	7 87050	34 53141	7 56393	33 48876	7 25331	32 40856	8 93851	31 29364	8 61943	30 14653	8 29595
55	37 83325	6 06520	36 89503	7 75699	35 91162	7 44475	34 88670	7 12837	33 82353	8 80774	32 72501	8 48276	31 59369	8 15329
56	37 17567	7 95730	36 25676	7 64348	35 29183	7 32556	34 28464	7 00343	33 23851	8 67698	32 15637	8 34608	31 04085	8 01062
57	38 51809	7 84939	37 61849	7 52997	36 67204	7 20637	35 68258	8 87849	34 65348	8 54621	33 58773	8 20940	32 48801	9 86795
58	39 86052	7 74149	38 98021	7 41646	36 05225	7 08719	35 08052	8 75355	34 06845	8 41544	33 01910	8 07273	33 93517	9 72528
59	39 20294	7 63358	38 34194	7 30295	37 43246	8 96800	36 47846	8 62861	35 48343	8 28467	34 45046	9 93605	33 38232	9 58262
60	40 54536	7 52568	39 70367	7 18944	38 81267	8 84882	37 87640	8 50368	36 89840	8 15390	35 88183	9 79937	34 82948	9 43995
61	41 88778	7 41777	39 06540	7 07593	38 19289	8 72963	37 27434	8 37874	36 31337	8 02313	35 31319	9 66269	34 27664	9 29728
62	41 23021	7 30987	40 42713	8 96242	39 57310	8 61044	38 67228	8 25380	37 72835	9 89237	36 74455	9 52602	35 72380	9 15461
63	42 57263	7 20196	41 78885	8 84892	40 95331	8 49126	38 07022	8 12886	37 14332	9 76160	36 17592	9 38934	35 17096	9 01195
64	43 91505	7 09405	41 15058	8 73541	40 33352	8 37207	39 46816	8 00392	38 55829	9 63083	37 60728	9 25266	36 61811	10 86928
65	43 25747	8 98615	42 51231	8 62190	41 71373	8 25288	40 86610	9 87898	39 97327	9 50006	37 03864	9 11599	36 06527	10 72661
66	44 59990	8 87824	43 87404	8 50839	41 09394	8 13370	40 26404	9 75404	39 38824	9 36929	38 47001	10 97931	37 51243	10 58394
67	45 94232	8 77034	43 23577	8 39488	42 47415	8 01451	41 66198	9 62910	40 80321	9 23853	39 90137	10 84263	38 95959	10 44128
68	45 28474	8 66243	44 59749	8 28137	43 85436	9 89532	41 05992	9 50417	40 21819	9 10776	39 33274	10 70595	38 40675	10 29861
69	46 62716	8 55453	45 95922	8 16786	43 23458	9 77614	42 45786	9 37923	41 63316	10 97699	40 76410	10 56928	39 85390	10 15594
70	47 96959	8 44662	45 32095	8 05435	44 61479	9 65695	43 85580	9 25429	41 04813	10 84622	40 19546	10 43260	39 30106	10 01327
71	47 31201	8 33872	46 68268	9 94084	45 99500	9 53777	43 25374	9 12935	42 46311	10 71545	41 62683	10 29592	40 74822	11 87061
72	48 65443	8 23081	46 04440	9 82733	45 37521	9 41858	44 65168	9 00441	43 87808	10 58468	41 05819	10 15925	40 19538	11 72794
73	49 99686	8 12291	47 40613	9 71382	46 75542	9 29939	44 04962	10 87947	43 29305	10 45392	42 48955	10 02257	41 64254	11 58527
74	49 33928	8 01500	48 76786	9 60031	46 13563	9 18021	45 44756	10 75453	44 70803	10 32315	43 92092	11 88589	41 08969	11 44260
75	50 68170	9 90710	48 12959	9 48680	47 51584	9 06102	46 84550	10 62959	44 12300	10 19238	43 35228	11 74921	42 53685	11 29994
76	50 02412	9 79919	49 49132	9 37330	48 89605	10 94183	46 24344	10 50466	45 53797	10 06161	44 78365	11 61254	43 98401	11 15727
77	51 36655	9 69128	50 85304	9 25979	48 27627	10 82265	47 64138	10 37972	46 95295	11 93084	44 21501	11 47586	43 43117	11 01460
78	52 70897	9 58338	50 21477	9 14628	49 65648	10 70346	47 03932	10 25478	46 36792	11 80007	45 64637	11 33918	44 87833	12 87193
79	52 05139	9 47547	51 57650	9 03277	49 03669	10 58427	48 43726	10 12984	47 78289	11 66931	45 07774	11 20251	44 32548	12 72927
80	53 39381	9 36757	52 93823	10 91926	50 41690	10 46509	49 83520	10 00490	47 19787	11 53854	46 50910	11 06583	45 77264	12 58660
81	54 73624	9 25966	52 29995	10 80575	51 79711	10 34590	49 23314	11 87996	48 61284	11 40777	47 94046	12 92915	45 21980	12 44393
82	54 07866	9 15176	53 66168	10 69224	51 17732	10 22671	50 63108	11 75502	48 02781	11 27700	47 37183	12 79247	46 66696	12 30126
83	55 42108	9 04385	53 02341	10 57873	52 55753	10 10753	50 02902	11 63008	49 44279	11 14623	48 80319	12 65580	46 11412	12 15860
84	56 76351	10 93595	54 38514	10 46522	53 93774	11 98834	51 42696	11 50515	50 85776	11 01546	48 23456	12 51912	47 56127	12 01593
85	56 10593	10 82804	55 74687	10 35171	53 31796	11 86916	52 82490	11 38021	50 27273	12 88470	49 66592	12 38244	47 00843	13 87326
86	57 44835	10 72014	55 10859	10 23820	54 69817	11 74997	52 22284	11 25527	51 68771	12 75393	49 09728	12 24577	48 45559	13 73059
87	58 79077	10 61223	56 47032	10 12469	54 07838	11 63078	53 62078	11 13033	51 10268	12 62316	50 52865	12 10909	49 90275	13 58793
88	58 13320	10 50433	57 83205	10 01118	55 45859	11 51160	53 01872	11 00539	52 51765	12 49239	51 96001	13 97241	49 34991	13 44526
89	59 47562	10 39642	57 19378	11 89767	56 83880	11 39241	54 41666	12 88045	53 93263	12 36162	51 39138	13 83573	50 79706	13 30259
90	60 81804	10 28851	58 55551	11 78417	56 21901	11 27322	55 81460	12 75551	53 34760	12 23085	52 82274	13 69906	50 24422	13 15992
91	60 16046	10 18061	59 91723	11 67066	57 59922	11 15404	55 21254	12 63057	54 76257	12 10009	52 25410	13 56238	51 69138	13 01726
92	61 50289	10 07270	59 27896	11 55715	58 97943	11 03485	56 61048	12 50564	54 17755	13 96932	53 68547	13 42570	51 13854	14 87459
93	62 84531	11 96480	60 64069	11 44364	58 35965	12 91566	56 00842	12 38070	55 59252	13 83855	53 11683	13 28903	52 58570	14 73192
94	62 18773	11 85689	60 00242	11 33013	59 73986	12 79648	57 40636	12 25576	55 00749	13 70778	54 54819	13 15235	52 03285	14 58925
95	63 53015	11 74899	61 36414	11 21662	59 12007	12 67729	58 80430	12 13082	56 42247	13 57701	55 97956	13 01567	53 48001	14 44659
96	64 87258	11 64108	62 72587	11 10311	60 50028	12 55810	58 20224	12 00588	57 83744	13 44625	55 41092	14 87899	54 92717	14 30392
97	64 21500	11 53318	62 08760	12 98960	61 88049	12 43892	59 60018	13 88094	57 25241	13 31548	56 84229	14 74232	54 37433	14 16125
98	65 55742	11 42527	63 44933	12 87609	61 26070	12 31973	60 99812	13 75600	58 66739	13 18471	56 27365	14 60564	55 82149	14 01858
99	66 89985	11 31737	64 81106	12 76258	62 64091	12 20055	60 39606	13 63107	58 08236	13 05394	57 70501	14 46896	55 26865	15 87592
100	66 24227	11 20946	64 17278	12 64907	62 02112	12 08136	61 79400	13 50613	59 49733	14 92317	57 13638	14 33229	56 71580	15 73325

Common Logarithms of p^n and q^n $(q=1-p)$*

For explanation see page 77

n	$p(q)$ 0.29	$q(p)$ 0.71	$p(q)$ 0.30	$q(p)$ 0.70	$p(q)$ 0.31	$q(p)$ 0.69	$p(q)$ 0.32	$q(p)$ 0.68	$p(q)$ 0.33	$q(p)$ 0.67	$p(q)$ 0.34	$q(p)$ 0.66	$p(q)$ 0.35	$q(p)$ 0.65
0	0 00000	0 00000	0 00000	0 00000	0 00000	0 00000	0 00000	0 00000	0 00000	0 00000	0 00000	0 00000	0 00000	0 00000
1	1 46240	1 85126	1 47712	1 84510	1 49136	1 83885	1 50515	1 83251	1 51851	1 82607	1 53148	1 81954	1 54407	1 81291
2	2 92480	1 70252	2 95424	1 69020	2 98272	1 67770	1 01030	1 66502	1 03703	1 65215	1 06296	1 63909	1 08814	1 62583
3	2 38719	1 55378	2 43136	1 53529	2 47409	1 51655	2 51545	1 49753	2 55554	1 47822	2 59444	1 45863	2 63220	1 43874
4	3 84959	1 40503	3 90849	1 38039	3 96545	1 35540	2 02060	1 33004	2 07406	1 30430	2 12592	1 27818	2 17627	1 25165
5	3 31199	1 25629	3 38561	1 22549	3 45681	1 19425	3 52575	1 16254	3 59257	1 13037	3 65739	1 09772	3 72034	1 06457
6	4 77439	1 10755	4 86273	1 07059	4 94817	1 03309	3 03090	2 99505	3 11108	2 95645	3 18887	2 91726	3 26441	2 87748
7	4 23679	2 95881	4 33985	2 91569	4 43953	2 87194	4 53605	2 82756	4 62960	2 78252	4 72035	2 73681	4 80848	2 69039
8	5 69918	2 81007	5 81697	2 76078	5 93089	2 71079	4 04120	2 66007	4 14811	2 60860	4 25183	2 55635	4 35254	2 50331
9	5 16158	2 66133	5 29409	2 60588	5 42226	2 54964	5 54635	2 49258	5 66663	2 43467	5 78331	2 37590	5 89661	2 31622
10	6 62398	2 51258	6 77121	2 45098	6 91362	2 38849	5 05150	2 32509	5 18514	2 26075	5 31479	2 19544	5 44068	2 12913
11	6 08638	2 36384	6 24833	2 29608	6 40498	2 22734	6 55665	2 15760	6 70365	2 08682	6 84627	2 01498	6 98475	3 94205
12	7 54878	2 21510	7 72546	2 14118	7 89634	2 06619	6 06180	3 99011	6 22217	3 91290	6 37775	3 83453	6 52882	3 75496
13	7 01117	2 06636	7 20258	3 98627	7 38770	3 90504	7 56695	3 82262	7 74068	3 73897	7 90923	3 65407	6 07288	3 56787
14	8 47357	3 91762	8 67970	3 83137	8 87906	3 74389	7 07210	3 65512	7 25920	3 56505	7 44070	3 47362	7 61695	3 38079
15	9 93597	3 76888	8 15682	3 67647	8 37043	3 58274	8 57725	3 48763	8 77771	3 39112	8 97218	3 29316	7 16102	3 19370
16	9 39837	3 62013	9 63394	3 52157	9 86179	3 42159	8 08240	3 32014	8 29622	3 21720	8 50366	3 11270	8 70509	3 00661
17	10 86077	3 47139	9 11106	3 36667	9 35315	3 26043	9 58755	3 15265	9 81474	3 04327	8 03514	4 93225	8 24916	4 81953
18	10 32316	3 32265	10 58818	3 21176	10 84451	3 09928	9 09270	4 98516	9 33325	4 86935	9 56662	4 75179	9 79322	4 63244
19	11 78556	3 17391	10 06530	3 05686	10 33587	4 93813	10 59785	4 81767	10 85176	4 69542	9 09810	4 57133	9 33729	4 44535
20	11 24796	3 02517	11 54243	4 90196	11 82723	4 77698	10 10300	4 65018	10 37028	4 52150	10 62958	4 39088	10 88136	4 25827
21	12 71036	4 87643	11 01955	4 74706	11 31860	4 61583	11 60815	4 48269	11 88879	4 34757	10 16106	4 21042	10 42543	4 07118
22	12 17276	4 72768	12 49667	4 59216	12 80996	4 45468	11 11330	4 31520	11 40731	4 17365	11 69254	4 02997	11 96950	5 88409
23	13 63515	4 57894	13 97379	4 43725	12 30132	4 29353	12 61845	4 14770	12 92582	5 99972	11 22402	5 84951	11 51357	5 69701
24	13 09755	4 43020	13 45091	4 28235	13 79268	4 13238	12 12360	5 98021	12 44433	5 82580	12 75549	5 66905	11 05763	5 50992
25	14 55995	4 28146	14 92803	4 12745	13 28404	5 97123	13 62875	5 81272	13 96285	5 65187	12 28697	5 48860	12 60170	5 32283
26	14 02235	4 13272	14 40515	5 97255	14 77540	5 81008	13 13390	5 64523	13 48136	5 47794	13 81845	5 30814	12 14577	5 13575
27	15 48475	5 98398	15 88227	5 81765	14 26677	5 64893	14 63905	5 47774	14 99988	5 30402	13 34993	5 12769	13 68984	6 94866
28	16 94714	5 83523	15 35940	5 66275	15 75813	5 48777	14 14420	5 31025	14 51839	5 13009	14 88141	6 94723	13 23391	6 76157
29	16 40954	5 68649	16 83652	5 50784	15 24949	5 32662	15 64935	5 14276	14 03690	6 95617	14 41289	6 76677	14 77797	6 57449
30	17 87194	5 53775	16 31364	5 35294	16 74085	5 16547	15 15450	6 97527	15 55542	6 78224	15 94437	6 58632	14 32204	6 38740
31	17 33434	5 38901	17 79076	5 19804	16 23221	5 00432	16 65965	6 80778	15 07393	6 60832	15 47585	6 40586	15 86611	6 20031
32	18 79674	5 24027	17 26788	5 04314	17 72357	6 84317	16 16480	6 64029	16 59245	6 43439	15 00733	6 22541	15 41018	6 01323
33	18 25913	5 09153	18 74500	6 88824	17 21494	6 68202	17 66995	6 47279	16 11096	6 26047	16 53880	6 04495	16 95425	7 82614
34	19 72153	6 94278	18 22212	6 73333	18 70630	6 52087	17 17510	6 30530	17 62947	6 08654	16 07028	7 86449	16 49831	7 63905
35	19 18393	6 79404	19 69924	6 57843	18 19766	6 35972	18 68025	6 13781	17 14799	7 91262	17 60176	7 68404	16 04238	7 45197
36	20 64633	6 64530	19 17637	6 42353	19 68902	6 19857	18 18540	7 97032	18 66650	7 73869	17 13324	7 50358	17 58645	7 26488
37	20 10873	6 49656	20 65349	6 26863	19 18038	6 03742	19 69055	7 80283	18 18502	7 56477	18 66472	7 32313	17 13052	7 07779
38	21 57112	6 34782	20 13061	6 11373	20 67174	7 87627	19 19570	7 63534	19 70353	7 39084	18 19620	7 14267	18 67459	8 89071
39	21 03352	6 19908	21 60773	7 95882	20 16311	7 71511	20 70085	7 46785	19 22204	7 21692	19 72768	8 96221	18 21865	8 70362
40	22 49592	6 05033	21 08485	7 80392	21 65447	7 55396	20 20600	7 30036	20 74056	7 04299	19 25916	8 78176	19 76272	8 51653
41	23 95832	7 90159	22 56197	7 64902	21 14583	7 39281	21 71115	7 13287	20 25907	8 86907	20 79064	8 60130	19 30679	8 32945
42	23 42072	7 75285	22 03909	7 49412	22 63719	7 23166	21 21630	8 96537	21 77759	8 69514	20 32211	8 42085	20 85086	8 14236
43	24 88311	7 60411	23 51621	7 33922	22 12855	7 07051	22 72145	8 79788	21 29610	8 52122	21 85359	8 24039	20 39493	9 95527
44	24 34551	7 45537	24 99334	7 18431	23 61991	8 90936	22 22660	8 63039	22 81461	8 34729	21 38507	8 05993	21 93899	9 76819
45	25 80791	7 30663	24 47046	7 02941	23 11128	8 74821	23 73175	8 46290	22 33313	8 17337	22 91655	9 87948	21 48306	9 58110
46	25 27031	7 15788	25 94758	8 87451	24 60264	8 58706	23 23690	8 29541	23 85164	9 99944	22 44803	9 69902	21 02713	9 39401
47	26 73271	7 00914	25 42470	8 71961	24 09400	8 42591	24 74205	8 12792	23 37016	9 82552	23 97951	9 51856	22 57120	9 20693
48	26 19510	8 86040	26 90182	8 56471	25 58536	8 26476	24 24720	9 96043	24 88867	9 65159	23 51099	9 33811	22 11527	9 01984
49	27 65750	8 71166	26 37894	8 40980	25 07672	8 10361	25 75235	9 79294	24 40718	9 47767	23 04247	9 15765	23 65933	10 83275
50	27 11990	8 56292	27 85606	8 25490	26 56808	9 94245	25 25750	9 62545	25 92570	9 30374	24 57395	10 97720	23 20340	10 64567
51	28 58230	8 41418	27 33318	8 10000	26 05945	9 78130	26 76265	9 45795	25 44421	9 12981	24 10542	10 79674	24 74747	10 45858
52	28 04470	8 26543	28 81031	9 94510	27 55081	9 62015	26 26780	9 29046	26 96272	10 95589	25 63690	10 61628	24 29154	10 27149
53	29 50709	8 11669	28 28743	9 79020	27 04217	9 45900	27 77295	9 12297	26 48124	10 78196	25 16838	10 43583	25 83561	10 08441
54	30 96949	9 96795	29 76455	9 63529	28 53353	9 29785	27 27810	10 95548	27 99975	10 60804	26 69986	10 25537	25 37967	11 89732
55	30 43189	9 81921	29 24167	9 48039	28 02489	9 13670	28 78325	10 78799	27 51827	10 43411	26 23134	10 07492	26 92374	11 71023
56	31 89429	9 67047	30 71879	9 32549	29 51625	10 97555	28 28840	10 62050	27 03678	10 26019	27 76282	11 89446	26 46781	11 52315
57	31 35669	9 52173	30 19591	9 17059	29 00762	10 81440	29 79355	10 45301	28 55529	10 08626	27 29430	11 71400	26 01188	11 33606
58	32 81908	9 37298	31 67303	9 01569	30 49898	10 65325	29 29870	10 28552	28 07381	11 91234	28 82578	11 53355	27 55595	11 14897
59	32 28148	9 22424	31 15015	10 86078	31 99034	10 49210	30 80385	10 11803	29 59232	11 73841	28 35726	11 35309	27 10001	12 96189
60	33 74388	9 07550	32 62728	10 70588	31 48170	10 33095	30 30900	11 95053	29 11084	11 56449	29 88874	11 17264	28 64408	12 77480
61	33 20628	10 92676	32 10440	10 55098	32 97306	10 16979	31 81415	11 78304	30 62935	11 39056	29 42021	12 99218	28 18815	12 58771
62	34 66868	10 77802	33 58152	10 39608	32 46443	10 00864	31 31930	11 61555	30 14786	11 21664	30 95169	12 81172	29 73222	12 40063
63	34 13107	10 62928	33 05864	10 24118	33 95579	11 84749	32 82445	11 44806	31 66638	11 04271	30 48317	12 63127	29 27629	12 21354
64	35 59347	10 48053	34 53576	10 08627	33 44715	11 68634	32 32960	11 28057	31 18489	12 86879	30 01465	12 45081	30 82035	12 02645
65	35 05587	10 33179	34 01288	11 93137	34 93851	11 52519	33 83475	11 11308	32 70341	12 69486	31 54613	12 27036	30 36442	13 83937
66	36 51827	10 18305	35 49000	11 77647	34 42987	11 36404	33 33990	12 94559	32 22192	12 52094	31 07761	12 08990	31 90849	13 65228
67	37 98067	10 03431	36 96712	11 62157	35 92123	11 20289	34 84505	12 77810	33 74043	12 34701	32 60909	13 90944	31 45256	13 46519
68	37 44306	11 88557	36 44425	11 46667	35 41260	11 04174	34 35020	12 61061	33 25895	12 17309	32 14057	13 72899	32 99663	13 27811
69	38 90546	11 73683	37 92137	11 31176	36 90396	12 88059	35 85535	12 44311	34 77746	13 99916	33 67205	13 54853	32 54070	13 09102
70	38 36786	11 58808	37 39849	11 15686	36 39532	12 71944	35 36050	12 27562	34 29598	13 82524	33 20352	13 36808	32 08476	14 90393
71	39 83026	11 43934	38 87561	11 00196	37 88668	12 55829	36 86565	12 10813	35 81449	13 65131	34 73500	13 18762	33 62883	14 71685
72	39 29266	11 29060	38 35273	12 84706	37 37804	12 39713	36 37080	13 94064	35 33300	13 47739	34 26648	13 00716	33 17290	14 52976
73	40 75505	11 14186	39 82985	12 69216	38 86940	12 23598	37 87595	13 77315	36 85152	13 30346	35 79796	14 82671	34 71697	14 34268
74	40 21745	12 99312	39 30697	12 53725	38 36077	12 07483	37 38110	13 60566	36 37003	13 12954	35 32944	14 64625	34 26104	14 15559
75	41 67985	12 84438	40 78409	12 38235	39 85213	13 91368	38 88625	13 43817	37 88855	14 95561	36 86092	14 46580	35 80510	15 96850
76	41 14225	12 69563	40 26122	12 22745	39 34349	13 75253	38 39140	13 27068	37 40706	14 78169	36 39240	14 28534	35 34917	15 78142
77	42 60465	12 54689	41 73834	12 07255	40 83485	13 59138	39 89655	13 10319	38 92557	14 60776	37 92388	14 10488	36 89324	15 59433
78	42 06704	12 39815	41 21546	13 91765	40 32621	13 43023	39 40170	14 93570	38 44409	14 43383	37 45536	15 92443	36 43731	15 40724
79	43 52944	12 24941	42 69258	13 76275	41 81757	13 26908	40 90685	14 76820	39 96260	14 25991	38 98683	15 74397	37 98138	15 22016
80	44 99184	12 10067	42 16970	13 60784	41 30894	13 10793	40 41200	14 60071	39 48112	14 08598	38 51831	15 56351	37 52544	15 03307
81	44 45424	13 95193	43 64682	13 45294	42 80030	14 94678	41 91715	14 43322	40 99963	15 91206	38 04979	15 38306	37 06951	16 84598
82	45 91664	13 80318	43 12394	13 29804	42 29166	14 78563	41 42230	14 26573	40 51814	15 73813	39 58127	15 20260	38 61358	16 65890
83	45 37903	13 65444	44 60106	13 14314	43 78302	14 62447	42 92745	14 09824	40 03666	15 56421	39 11275	15 02215	38 15765	16 47181
84	46 84143	13 50570	44 07819	14 98824	43 27438	14 46332	42 43260	15 93075	41 55517	15 39028	40 64423	16 84169	39 70172	16 28472
85	46 30383	13 35696	45 55531	14 83333	44 76574	14 30217	43 93775	15 76326	41 07368	15 21636	40 17571	16 66123	39 24578	16 09764
86	47 76623	13 20822	45 03243	14 67843	44 25711	14 14102	43 44290	15 59577	42 59220	15 04243	41 70719	16 48078	40 78985	17 91055
87	47 22863	13 05948	46 50955	14 52353	45 74847	15 97987	44 94805	15 42828	42 11071	16 86851	41 23867	16 30032	40 33392	17 72346
88	48 69102	14 91073	47 98667	14 36863	45 23983	15 81872	44 45320	15 26078	43 62923	16 69458	42 77014	16 11987	41 87799	17 53638
89	48 15342	14 76199	47 46379	14 21373	46 73119	15 65757	45 95835	15 09329	43 14774	16 52066	42 30162	17 93941	41 42206	17 34929
90	49 61582	14 61325	48 94091	14 05882	46 22255	15 49642	45 46350	16 92580	44 66625	16 34673	43 83310	17 75895	42 96612	17 16220
91	49 07822	14 46451	48 41803	15 90392	47 71391	15 33527	46 96865	16 75831	44 18477	16 17281	43 36458	17 57850	42 51019	18 97512
92	50 54062	14 31577	49 89516	15 74902	47 20528	15 17412	46 47380	16 59082	45 70328	17 99888	44 89606	17 39804	42 05426	18 78803
93	50 00301	14 16703	49 37228	15 59412	48 69664	15 01297	47 97895	16 42333	45 22180	17 82496	44 42754	17 21759	43 59833	18 60094
94	51 46541	14 01828	50 84940	15 43922	48 18800	16 85181	47 48410	16 25584	46 74031	17 65103	45 95902	17 03713	43 14240	18 41386
95	52 92781	15 86954	50 32652	15 28431	49 67936	16 69066	48 98925	16 08835	46 25882	17 47711	45 49050	18 85667	44 68646	18 22677
96	52 39021	15 72080	51 80364	15 12941	49 17072	16 52951	48 49440	17 92086	47 77734	17 30318	45 02198	18 67622	44 23053	18 03968
97	53 85261	15 57206	51 28076	16 97451	50 66208	16 36836	49 99955	17 75336	47 29585	17 12926	46 55345	18 49576	45 77460	19 85260
98	53 31500	15 42332	52 75788	16 81961	50 15345	16 20721	49 50470	17 58587	48 81437	18 95533	46 08493	18 31531	45 31867	19 66551
99	54 77740	15 27458	52 23500	16 66471	51 64481	16 04606	49 00985	17 41838	48 33288	18 78141	47 61641	18 13485	46 86274	19 47842
100	54 23980	15 12583	53 71213	16 50980	51 13617	17 88491	50 51500	17 25089	49 85139	18 60748	47 14789	19 95439	46 40680	19 29134

Common Logarithms of p^n and q^n $(q=1-p)$*

For explanation see page 77

n	$p(q)$ 0.36	$q(p)$ 0.64	$p(q)$ 0.37	$q(p)$ 0.63	$p(q)$ 0.38	$q(p)$ 0.62	$p(q)$ 0.39	$q(p)$ 0.61	$p(q)$ 0.40	$q(p)$ 0.60	$p(q)$ 0.41	$q(p)$ 0.59	$p(q)$ 0.42	$q(p)$ 0.58
0	0 00000	0 00000	0 00000	0 00000	0 00000	0 00000	0 00000	0 00000	0 00000	0 00000	0 00000	0 00000	0 00000	0 00000
1	1 55630	1 80618	1 56820	1 79934	1 57978	1 79239	1 59106	1 78533	1 60206	1 77815	1 61278	1 77085	1 62325	1 76343
2	1 11261	1 61236	1 13640	1 59868	1 15957	1 58478	1 18213	1 57066	1 20412	1 55630	1 22557	1 54170	1 24650	1 52686
3	2 66891	1 41854	2 70461	1 39802	2 73935	1 37718	2 77319	1 35599	2 80618	1 33445	2 83835	1 31256	2 86975	1 29028
4	2 22521	1 22472	2 27281	1 19736	2 31913	1 16957	2 36426	1 14132	2 40824	1 11261	2 45114	1 08341	2 49300	1 05371
5	3 78151	1 03090	3 84101	2 99670	3 89892	2 96196	3 95532	2 92665	2 01030	2 89076	2 06392	2 85426	2 11625	2 81714
6	3 33782	2 83708	3 40921	2 79604	3 47870	2 75435	3 54639	2 71198	3 61236	2 66891	3 67670	2 62511	3 73950	2 58057
7	4 89412	2 64326	4 97741	2 59538	3 05849	2 54674	3 13745	2 49731	3 21442	2 44706	3 28949	2 39596	3 36275	2 34400
8	4 45042	2 44944	4 54561	2 39472	4 63827	2 33913	4 72852	2 28264	4 81648	2 22521	4 90227	2 16682	4 98599	2 10742
9	4 00672	2 25562	4 11382	2 19406	4 21805	2 13153	4 31958	2 06797	4 41854	2 00336	4 51505	3 93767	4 60924	3 87085
10	5 56303	2 06180	5 68202	3 99341	5 79784	3 92392	5 91065	3 85330	4 02060	3 78151	4 12784	3 70852	4 23249	3 63428
11	5 11933	3 86798	5 25022	3 79275	5 37762	3 71631	5 50171	3 63863	5 62266	3 55966	5 74062	3 47937	5 85574	3 39771
12	6 67563	3 67416	6 81842	3 59209	6 95740	3 50870	5 09278	3 42396	5 22472	3 33782	5 35341	3 25022	5 47899	3 16114
13	6 23193	3 48034	6 38662	3 39143	6 53719	3 30109	6 68384	3 20929	6 82678	3 11597	6 96619	3 02108	5 10224	4 92456
14	7 78824	3 28652	7 95482	3 19077	6 11697	3 09348	6 27490	4 99462	6 42884	4 89412	6 57897	4 79193	6 72549	4 68799
15	7 34454	3 09270	7 52303	4 99011	7 69675	4 88588	7 86597	4 77995	6 03090	4 67227	6 19176	4 56278	6 34874	4 45142
16	8 90084	4 89888	7 09123	4 78945	7 27654	4 67827	7 45703	4 56528	7 63296	4 45042	7 80454	4 33363	7 97199	4 21485
17	8 45714	4 70506	8 65943	4 58879	8 85632	4 47066	7 04810	4 35061	7 23502	4 22857	7 41733	4 10448	7 59524	5 97828
18	8 01345	4 51124	8 22763	4 38813	8 43610	4 26305	8 63916	4 13594	8 83708	4 00672	7 03011	5 87534	7 21849	5 74170
19	9 56975	4 31742	9 79583	4 18747	8 01589	4 05544	8 23023	5 92127	8 43914	5 78487	8 64289	5 64619	8 84174	5 50513
20	9 12605	4 12360	9 36403	5 98681	9 59567	5 84783	9 82129	5 70660	8 04120	5 56303	8 25568	5 41704	8 46499	5 26856
21	10 68235	5 92978	10 93224	5 78615	9 17546	5 64023	9 41236	5 49193	9 64326	5 34118	9 86846	5 18789	8 08824	5 03199
22	10 23866	5 73596	10 50044	5 58549	10 75524	5 43262	9 00342	5 27726	9 24532	5 11933	9 48124	6 95874	9 71148	6 79542
23	11 79496	5 54214	10 06864	5 38483	10 33502	5 22501	10 59449	5 06259	10 84738	6 89748	9 09403	6 72960	9 33473	6 55884
24	11 35126	5 34832	11 63684	5 18417	11 91481	5 01740	10 18555	6 84792	10 44944	6 67563	10 70681	6 50045	10 95798	6 32227
25	12 90756	5 15450	11 20504	6 98351	11 49459	6 80979	11 77662	6 63325	10 05150	6 45378	10 31960	6 27130	10 58123	6 08570
26	12 46387	6 96068	12 77324	6 78285	11 07437	6 60218	11 36768	6 41858	11 65356	6 23193	11 93238	6 04215	10 20448	7 84913
27	12 02017	6 76686	12 34145	6 58219	12 65416	6 39458	12 95874	6 20391	11 25562	6 01008	11 54516	7 81300	11 82773	7 61256
28	13 57647	6 57304	13 90965	6 38154	12 23394	6 18697	12 54981	7 98924	12 85768	7 78824	11 15795	7 58386	11 45098	7 37598
29	13 13277	6 37922	13 47785	6 18088	13 81372	7 97936	12 14087	7 77457	12 45974	7 56639	12 77073	7 35471	11 07423	7 13941
30	14 68908	6 18540	13 04605	7 98022	13 39351	7 77175	13 73194	7 55990	12 06180	7 34454	12 38352	7 12556	12 69748	8 90284
31	14 24538	7 99158	14 61425	7 77956	14 97329	7 56414	13 32300	7 34522	13 66386	7 12269	13 99630	8 89641	12 32073	8 66627
32	15 80168	7 79776	14 18246	7 57890	14 55308	7 35653	14 91407	7 13055	13 26592	8 90084	13 60908	8 66726	13 94398	8 42970
33	15 35798	7 60394	15 75066	7 37824	14 13286	7 14893	14 50513	8 91588	14 86798	8 67899	13 22187	8 43812	13 56723	8 19312
34	16 91429	7 41012	15 31886	7 17758	15 71264	8 94132	14 09620	8 70121	14 47004	8 45714	14 83465	8 20897	13 19048	9 95655
35	16 47059	7 21630	16 88706	8 97692	15 29243	8 73371	15 68726	8 48654	14 07210	8 23529	14 44743	9 97982	14 81373	9 71998
36	16 02689	7 02248	16 45526	8 77626	16 87221	8 52610	15 27833	8 27187	15 67416	8 01345	14 06022	9 75067	14 43697	9 48341
37	17 58319	8 82866	16 02346	8 57560	16 45199	8 31849	16 86939	8 05720	15 27622	9 79160	15 67300	9 52152	14 06022	9 24684
38	17 13950	8 63484	17 59167	8 37494	16 03178	8 11088	16 46046	9 84253	16 87828	9 56975	15 28579	9 29238	15 68347	9 01026
39	18 69580	8 44102	17 15987	8 17428	17 61156	9 90328	16 05152	9 62786	16 48034	9 34790	16 89857	9 06323	15 30672	10 77369
40	18 25210	8 24720	18 72807	9 97362	17 19134	9 69567	17 64258	9 41319	16 08240	9 12605	16 51135	10 83408	16 92997	10 53712
41	19 80840	8 05338	18 29627	9 77296	18 77113	9 48806	17 23365	9 19852	17 68446	10 90420	16 12414	10 60493	16 55322	10 30055
42	19 36471	9 85956	19 86447	9 57230	18 35091	9 28045	18 82471	10 98385	17 28652	10 68235	17 73692	10 37578	16 17647	10 06398
43	20 92101	9 66574	19 43267	9 37164	19 93069	9 07284	18 41578	10 76918	18 88858	10 46050	17 34971	10 14664	17 79972	11 82740
44	20 47731	9 47192	19 00088	9 17098	19 51048	10 86523	18 00684	10 55451	18 49064	10 23866	18 96249	11 91749	17 42297	11 59083
45	20 03361	9 27810	20 56908	10 97032	19 09026	10 65763	19 59791	10 33984	18 09270	10 01681	18 57527	11 68834	17 04622	11 35426
46	21 58992	9 08428	20 13728	10 76967	20 67005	10 45002	19 18897	10 12517	19 69476	11 79496	18 18806	11 45919	18 66947	11 11769
47	21 14622	10 89046	21 70548	10 56901	20 24983	10 24241	20 78004	11 91050	19 29682	11 57311	19 80084	11 23004	18 29272	12 88112
48	22 70252	10 69664	21 27368	10 36835	21 82961	10 03480	20 37110	11 69583	20 89888	11 35126	19 41363	11 00090	19 91597	12 64454
49	22 25882	10 50282	22 84188	10 16769	21 40940	11 82719	21 96217	11 48116	20 50094	11 12941	19 02641	12 77175	19 53922	12 40797
50	23 81513	10 30900	22 41009	11 96703	22 98918	11 61958	21 55323	11 26649	20 10300	12 90756	20 63919	12 54260	19 16246	12 17140
51	23 37143	10 11518	23 97829	11 76637	22 56896	11 41198	21 14429	11 05182	21 70506	12 68571	20 25198	12 31345	20 78571	13 93483
52	24 92773	11 92136	23 54649	11 56571	22 14875	11 20437	22 73536	12 83715	21 30712	12 46387	21 86476	12 08430	20 40896	13 69826
53	24 48403	11 72754	23 11469	11 36505	23 72853	12 99676	22 32642	12 62248	22 90918	12 24202	21 47754	13 85516	20 03221	13 46168
54	24 04034	11 53372	24 68289	11 16439	23 30831	12 78915	23 91749	12 40781	22 51124	12 02017	21 09033	13 62601	21 65546	13 22511
55	25 59664	11 33990	24 25109	12 96373	24 88810	12 58154	23 50855	12 19314	22 11330	13 79832	22 70311	13 39686	21 27871	14 98854
56	25 15294	11 14608	25 81930	12 76307	24 46788	12 37393	23 09962	13 97847	23 71536	13 57647	22 31590	13 16771	22 90196	14 75197
57	26 70924	12 95226	25 38750	12 56241	24 04767	12 16633	24 69068	13 76380	23 31742	13 35462	23 92868	14 93856	22 52521	14 51540
58	26 26555	12 75844	26 95570	12 36175	25 62745	13 95872	24 28175	13 54913	24 91948	13 13277	23 54146	14 70942	22 14846	14 27882
59	27 82185	12 56462	26 52390	12 16109	25 20723	13 75111	25 87281	13 33446	24 52154	14 91092	23 15425	14 48027	23 77171	14 04225
60	27 37815	12 37080	26 09210	13 96043	26 78702	13 54350	25 46388	13 11979	24 12360	14 68908	24 76703	14 25112	23 39496	15 80568
61	28 93445	12 17698	27 66031	13 75977	26 36680	13 33589	25 05494	14 90512	25 72566	14 46723	24 37982	14 02197	23 01821	15 56911
62	28 49076	13 98316	27 22851	13 55911	27 94658	13 12828	26 64601	14 69045	25 32772	14 24538	25 99260	15 79282	24 64146	15 33254
63	28 04706	13 78934	28 79671	13 35845	27 52637	14 92068	26 23707	14 47578	26 92978	14 02353	25 60538	15 56368	24 26471	15 09596
64	29 60336	13 59552	28 36491	13 15780	27 10615	14 71307	27 82813	14 26111	26 53184	15 80168	25 21817	15 33453	25 88795	16 85939
65	29 15966	13 40170	29 93311	14 95714	28 68593	14 50546	27 41920	14 04644	26 13390	15 57983	26 83095	15 10538	25 51120	16 62282
66	30 71597	13 20788	29 50131	14 75648	28 26572	14 29785	27 01026	15 83177	27 73596	15 35798	26 44373	16 87623	25 13445	16 38625
67	30 27227	13 01406	29 06952	14 55582	29 84550	14 09024	28 60133	15 61710	27 33802	15 13613	26 05652	16 64708	26 75770	16 14968
68	31 82857	14 82024	30 63772	14 35516	29 42528	15 88263	28 19239	15 40243	28 94008	16 91429	27 66930	16 41794	26 38095	17 91310
69	31 38487	14 62642	30 20592	14 15450	29 00507	15 67503	29 78346	15 18776	28 54214	16 69244	27 28209	16 18879	26 00420	17 67653
70	32 94118	14 43260	31 77412	15 95384	30 58485	15 46742	29 37452	16 97309	28 14420	16 47059	28 89487	17 95964	27 62745	17 43996
71	32 49748	14 23878	31 34232	15 75318	30 16464	15 25981	30 96559	16 75842	29 74626	16 24874	28 50765	17 73049	27 25070	17 20339
72	32 05378	14 04496	32 91052	15 55252	31 74442	15 05220	30 55665	16 54375	29 34832	16 02689	28 12044	17 50134	28 87395	18 96682
73	33 61008	15 85114	32 47873	15 35186	31 32420	16 84459	30 14772	16 32908	30 95038	17 80504	29 73322	17 27220	28 49720	18 73024
74	33 16639	15 65732	32 04693	15 15120	32 90399	16 63699	31 73878	16 11441	30 55244	17 58319	29 34601	17 04305	28 12045	18 49367
75	34 72269	15 46350	33 61513	16 95054	32 48377	16 42938	31 32985	17 89974	30 15450	17 36134	30 95879	18 81390	29 74370	18 25710
76	34 27899	15 26968	33 18333	16 74988	32 06355	16 22177	32 92091	17 68507	31 75656	17 13950	30 57157	18 58475	29 36695	18 02053
77	35 83529	15 07586	34 75153	16 54922	33 64334	16 01416	32 51197	17 47040	31 35862	18 91765	30 18436	18 35560	30 99020	19 78396
78	35 39160	16 88204	34 31973	16 34856	33 22312	17 80655	32 10304	17 25573	32 96068	18 69580	31 79714	18 12646	30 61344	19 54738
79	36 94790	16 68822	35 88794	16 14790	34 80290	17 59894	33 69410	17 04106	32 56274	18 47395	31 40992	19 89731	30 23669	19 31081
80	36 50420	16 49440	35 45614	17 94724	34 38269	17 39134	33 28517	18 82639	32 16480	18 25210	31 02271	19 66816	31 85994	19 07424
81	36 06050	16 30058	35 02434	17 74658	35 96247	17 18373	34 87623	18 61172	33 76686	18 03025	32 63549	19 43901	31 48319	20 83767
82	37 61681	16 10676	36 59254	17 54593	35 54225	18 97612	34 46730	18 39705	33 36892	19 80840	32 24828	19 20986	31 10644	20 60110
83	37 17311	17 91294	36 16074	17 34527	35 12204	18 76851	34 05836	18 18238	34 97098	19 58655	33 86106	20 98072	32 72969	20 36452
84	38 72941	17 71912	37 72894	17 14461	36 70182	18 56090	35 64943	19 96771	34 57304	19 36471	33 47384	20 75157	32 35294	20 12795
85	38 28571	17 52530	37 29715	18 94395	36 28161	18 35329	35 24049	19 75304	34 17510	19 14286	33 08663	20 52242	33 97619	21 89138
86	39 84202	17 33148	38 86535	18 74329	37 86139	18 14569	36 83156	19 53837	35 77716	20 92101	34 69941	20 29327	33 59944	21 65481
87	39 39832	17 13766	38 43355	18 54263	37 44117	19 93808	36 42262	19 32370	35 37922	20 69916	34 31220	20 06413	33 22269	21 41824
88	40 95462	18 94384	38 00175	18 34197	37 02096	19 73047	36 01369	19 10903	36 98128	20 47731	35 92498	21 83498	34 84594	21 18166
89	40 51092	18 75002	39 56995	18 14131	38 60074	19 52286	37 60475	20 89436	36 58334	20 25546	35 53776	21 60583	34 46919	22 94509
90	40 06723	18 55620	39 13816	19 94065	38 18052	19 31525	37 19581	20 67969	36 18540	20 03361	35 15055	21 37668	34 09244	22 70852
91	41 62353	18 36238	40 70636	19 73999	39 76031	19 10764	38 78688	20 46501	37 78746	21 81176	36 76333	21 14753	35 71569	22 47195
92	41 17983	18 16856	40 27456	19 53933	39 34009	20 90004	38 37794	20 25034	37 38952	21 58992	36 37611	22 91839	35 33893	22 23538
93	42 73613	19 97474	41 84276	19 33867	40 91987	20 69243	39 96901	20 03567	38 99158	21 36807	37 98890	22 68924	36 96218	23 99880
94	42 29244	19 78092	41 41096	19 13801	40 49966	20 48482	39 56007	21 82100	38 59364	21 14622	37 60168	22 46009	36 58543	23 76223
95	43 84874	19 58710	42 97916	20 93735	40 07944	20 27721	39 15114	21 60633	38 19570	22 92437	37 21447	22 23094	36 20868	23 52566
96	43 40504	19 39328	42 54737	20 73669	41 65923	20 06960	40 74220	21 39166	39 79776	22 70252	38 82725	22 00179	37 83193	23 28909
97	44 96134	19 19946	42 11557	20 53603	41 23901	21 86199	40 33327	21 17699	39 39982	22 48067	38 44003	23 77265	37 45518	23 05252
98	44 51765	19 00564	43 68377	20 33537	42 81879	21 65439	41 92433	22 96232	39 00188	22 25882	38 05282	23 54350	37 07843	24 81594
99	44 07395	20 81182	43 25197	20 13471	42 39858	21 44678	41 51540	22 74765	40 60394	22 03697	39 66560	23 31435	38 70168	24 57937
100	45 63025	20 61800	44 82017	21 93405	43 97836	21 23917	41 10646	22 53298	40 20600	23 81513	39 27839	23 08520	38 32493	24 34280

For explanation see page 77

n	p(q) 0.43	q(p) 0.57	p(q) 0.44	q(p) 0.56	p(q) 0.45	q(p) 0.55	p(q) 0.46	q(p) 0.54	p(q) 0.47	q(p) 0.53	p(q) 0.48	q(p) 0.52	p(q) 0.49	q(p) 0.51	p(q) 0.50	q(p) 0.50
0	0 00000	0 00000	0 00000	0 00000	0 00000	0 00000	0 00000	0 00000	0 00000	0 00000	0 00000	0 00000	0 00000	0 00000	0 00000	0 00000
1	1 63347	1 75587	1 64345	1 74819	1 65321	1 74036	1 66276	1 73239	1 67210	1 72428	1 68124	1 71600	1 69020	1 70757	1 69897	1 69897
2	1 26694	1 51175	1 28691	1 49638	1 30643	1 48073	1 32552	1 46479	1 34420	1 44855	1 36248	1 43201	1 38039	1 41514	1 39794	1 39794
3	2 90041	1 26762	2 93036	1 24456	2 95964	1 22109	2 98827	1 19718	1 01629	1 17283	1 04372	1 14801	1 07059	1 12271	1 09691	1 09691
4	2 53387	1 02350	2 57381	2 99275	2 61285	2 96145	2 65103	2 92958	2 68839	2 89710	2 72496	2 86401	2 76078	2 83028	2 79588	2 79588
5	2 16734	2 77937	2 21726	2 74094	2 26606	2 70181	2 31379	2 66197	2 36049	2 62138	2 40621	2 58002	2 45098	2 53785	2 49485	2 49485
6	3 80081	2 53525	3 86072	2 48913	3 91928	2 44218	3 97655	2 39436	2 03259	2 34566	2 08745	2 29602	2 14118	2 24542	2 19382	2 19382
7	3 43428	2 29112	3 50417	2 23732	3 57249	2 18254	3 63930	2 12676	3 70469	2 06993	3 76869	2 01202	3 83137	3 95299	3 89279	3 89279
8	3 06775	2 04700	3 14762	3 98550	3 22570	3 92290	3 30206	3 85915	3 37678	3 79421	3 44993	3 72803	3 52157	3 66056	3 59176	3 59176
9	4 70122	3 80287	4 79107	3 73369	4 87891	3 66326	4 96482	3 59154	3 04888	3 51848	3 13117	3 44403	3 21176	3 36813	3 29073	3 29073
10	4 33468	3 55875	4 43453	3 48188	4 53213	3 40363	4 62758	3 32394	4 72098	3 24276	4 81241	3 16003	4 90196	3 07570	4 98970	4 98970
11	5 96815	3 31462	4 07798	3 23007	4 18534	3 14399	4 29034	3 05633	4 39308	4 96703	4 49365	4 87604	4 59216	4 78327	4 68867	4 68867
12	5 60162	3 07050	5 72143	4 97826	5 83855	4 88435	5 95309	4 78873	4 06517	4 69131	4 17489	4 59204	4 28235	4 49084	4 38764	4 38764
13	5 23509	4 82637	5 36488	4 72644	5 49176	4 62471	5 61585	4 52112	5 73727	4 41559	5 85614	4 30804	5 97255	4 19841	4 08661	4 08661
14	6 86856	4 58225	5 00834	4 47463	5 14498	4 36508	5 27861	4 25351	5 40937	4 13986	5 53738	4 02405	5 66275	5 90598	5 78558	5 78558
15	6 50203	4 33812	6 65179	4 22282	6 79819	4 10544	6 94137	5 98591	5 08147	5 86414	5 21862	5 74005	5 35294	5 61355	5 48455	5 48455
16	6 13550	4 09400	6 29524	5 97101	6 45140	5 84580	6 60413	5 71830	6 75357	5 58841	6 89986	5 45605	5 04314	5 32112	5 18352	5 18352
17	7 76896	5 84987	7 93870	5 71920	6 10461	5 58617	6 26688	5 45069	6 42566	5 31269	6 58110	5 17206	6 73333	5 02869	6 88249	6 88249
18	7 40243	5 60575	7 58215	5 46738	7 75783	5 32653	7 92964	5 18309	6 09776	5 03697	6 26234	6 88806	6 42353	6 73626	6 58146	6 58146
19	7 03590	5 36162	7 22560	5 21557	7 41104	5 06689	7 59240	6 91548	7 76986	6 76124	7 94358	6 60406	6 11373	6 44383	6 28043	6 28043
20	8 66937	5 11750	8 86905	6 96376	7 06425	6 80725	7 25516	6 64788	7 44196	6 48552	7 62482	6 32007	7 80392	6 15140	7 97940	7 97940
21	8 30284	6 87337	8 51251	6 71195	8 71746	6 54762	8 91791	6 38027	7 11406	6 20979	7 30607	6 03607	7 49412	7 85897	7 67837	7 67837
22	9 93631	6 62925	8 15596	6 46014	8 37068	6 28798	8 58067	6 11266	8 78615	7 93407	8 98731	7 75207	7 18431	7 56654	7 37734	7 37734
23	9 56977	6 38512	9 79941	6 20832	8 02389	6 02834	8 24343	7 84506	8 45825	7 65835	8 66855	7 46808	8 87451	7 27411	7 07631	7 07631
24	9 20324	6 14100	9 44286	7 95651	9 67710	7 76870	9 90619	7 57745	8 13035	7 38262	8 34979	7 18408	8 56471	8 98168	8 77528	8 77528
25	10 83671	7 89687	9 08632	7 70470	9 33031	7 50907	9 56895	7 30984	9 80245	7 10690	8 03103	8 90008	8 25490	8 68925	8 47425	8 47425
26	10 47018	7 65275	10 72977	7 45289	10 98353	7 24943	9 23170	7 04224	9 47454	8 83117	9 71227	8 61609	9 94510	8 39682	8 17322	8 17322
27	10 10365	7 40862	10 37322	7 20108	10 63674	8 98979	10 89446	8 77463	9 14664	8 55545	9 39351	8 33209	9 63529	8 10439	9 87219	9 87219
28	11 73712	7 16450	10 01667	8 94926	10 28995	8 73016	10 55722	8 50703	10 81874	8 27972	9 07475	8 04809	9 32549	9 81196	9 57116	9 57116
29	11 37059	8 92037	11 66013	8 69745	11 94316	8 47052	10 21998	8 23942	10 49084	8 00400	10 75600	9 76410	9 01569	9 51954	9 27013	9 27013
30	11 00405	8 67625	11 30358	8 44564	11 59638	8 21088	11 88273	9 97181	10 16294	9 72828	10 43724	9 48010	10 70588	9 22711	10 96910	10 96910
31	12 63752	8 43212	12 94703	8 19383	11 24959	9 95124	11 54549	9 70421	11 83503	9 45255	10 11848	9 19610	10 39608	10 93468	10 66807	10 66807
32	12 27099	8 18800	12 59049	9 94202	12 90280	9 69161	11 20825	9 43660	11 50713	9 17683	11 79972	10 91211	10 08627	10 64225	10 36704	10 36704
33	13 90446	9 94387	12 23394	9 69020	12 55601	9 43197	12 87101	9 16899	11 17923	10 90110	11 48096	10 62811	11 77647	10 34982	10 06601	10 06601
34	13 53793	9 69975	13 87739	9 43839	12 20923	9 17233	12 53377	10 90139	12 85133	10 62538	11 16220	10 34411	11 46667	10 05739	11 76498	11 76498
35	13 17140	9 45562	13 52084	9 18658	13 86244	10 91269	12 19652	10 63378	12 52343	10 34966	12 84344	10 06012	11 15686	11 76496	11 46395	11 46395
36	14 80486	9 21149	13 16430	10 93477	13 51565	10 65306	13 85928	10 36618	12 19552	10 07393	12 52468	11 77612	12 84706	11 47253	11 16292	11 16292
37	14 43833	10 96737	14 80775	10 68296	13 16886	10 39342	13 52204	10 09857	13 86762	11 79821	12 20593	11 49212	12 53725	11 18010	12 86189	12 86189
38	14 07180	10 72324	14 45120	10 43115	14 82208	10 13378	13 18480	11 83096	13 53972	11 52248	13 88717	11 20813	12 22745	12 88767	12 56086	12 56086
39	15 70527	10 47912	14 09465	10 17933	14 47529	11 87414	14 84756	11 56336	13 21182	11 24676	13 56841	12 92413	13 91765	12 59524	12 25983	12 25983
40	15 33874	10 23499	15 73811	11 92752	14 12850	11 61451	14 51031	11 29575	14 88391	12 97103	13 24965	12 64013	13 60784	12 30281	13 95880	13 95880
41	16 97221	11 99087	15 38156	11 67571	15 78171	11 35487	14 17307	11 02814	14 55601	12 69531	14 93089	12 35614	13 29804	12 01038	13 65777	13 65777
42	16 60568	11 74674	15 02501	11 42390	15 43493	11 09523	15 83583	12 76054	14 22811	12 41959	14 61213	12 07214	14 98824	13 71795	13 35674	13 35674
43	16 23914	11 50262	16 66847	11 17209	15 08814	12 83560	15 49859	12 49293	15 90021	12 14386	14 29337	13 78814	14 67843	13 42552	13 05571	13 05571
44	17 87261	11 25849	16 31192	12 92027	16 74135	12 57596	15 16134	12 22533	15 57231	13 86814	15 97461	13 50415	14 36863	13 13309	14 75468	14 75468
45	17 50608	11 01437	17 95537	12 66846	16 39456	12 31632	16 82410	13 95772	15 24440	13 59241	15 65586	13 22015	14 05882	14 84066	14 45365	14 45365
46	17 13955	12 77024	17 59882	12 41665	16 04778	12 05668	16 48686	13 69011	16 91650	13 31669	15 33710	14 93615	15 74902	14 54823	14 15262	14 15262
47	18 77302	12 52612	17 24228	12 16484	17 70099	13 79705	16 14962	13 42251	16 58860	13 04097	15 01834	14 65216	15 43922	14 25580	15 85159	15 85159
48	18 40649	12 28199	18 88573	13 91303	17 35420	13 53741	17 81238	13 15490	16 26070	14 76524	16 69958	14 36816	15 12941	15 96337	15 55056	15 55056
49	18 03995	12 03787	18 52918	13 66121	17 00741	13 27777	17 47513	14 88729	17 93280	14 48952	16 38082	14 08416	16 81961	15 67094	15 24953	15 24953
50	19 67342	13 79374	18 17263	13 40940	18 66063	13 01813	17 13789	14 61969	17 60489	14 21379	16 06206	15 80017	16 50980	15 37851	16 94850	16 94850
51	19 30689	13 54962	19 81609	13 15759	18 31384	14 75850	18 80065	14 35208	17 27699	15 93807	17 74330	15 51617	16 20000	15 08608	16 64747	16 64747
52	20 94036	13 30549	19 45954	14 90578	19 96705	14 49886	18 46341	14 08448	18 94909	15 66235	17 42454	15 23217	17 89020	16 79365	16 34644	16 34644
53	20 57383	13 06137	19 10299	14 65397	19 62026	14 23922	18 12617	15 81687	18 62119	15 38662	17 10579	16 94818	17 58039	16 50122	16 04541	16 04541
54	20 20730	14 81724	20 74644	14 40215	19 27348	15 97959	19 78892	15 54926	18 29328	15 11090	18 78703	16 66418	17 27059	16 20879	17 74438	17 74438
55	21 84077	14 57312	20 38990	14 15034	20 92669	15 71995	19 45168	15 28166	19 96538	16 83517	18 46827	16 38018	18 96078	17 91636	17 44335	17 44335
56	21 47423	14 32899	20 03335	15 89853	20 57990	15 46031	19 11444	15 01405	19 63748	16 55945	18 14951	16 09619	18 65098	17 62393	17 14232	17 14232
57	21 10770	14 08487	21 67680	15 64672	20 23311	15 20067	20 77720	16 74644	19 30958	16 28372	19 83075	17 81219	18 34118	17 33150	18 84129	18 84129
58	22 74117	15 84074	21 32026	15 39491	21 88633	16 94104	20 43995	16 47884	20 98168	16 00800	19 51199	17 52819	18 03137	17 03907	18 54026	18 54026
59	22 37464	15 59662	22 96371	15 14309	21 53954	16 68140	20 10271	16 21123	20 65377	17 73228	19 19323	17 24420	19 72157	18 74664	18 23923	18 23923
60	22 00811	15 35249	22 60716	16 89128	21 19275	16 42176	21 76547	17 94363	20 32587	17 45655	20 87447	18 96020	19 41176	18 45421	19 93820	19 93820
61	23 64158	15 10837	22 25061	16 63947	22 84596	16 16212	21 42823	17 67602	21 99797	17 18083	20 55572	18 67620	19 10196	18 16178	19 63717	19 63717
62	23 27504	16 86424	23 89407	16 38766	22 49918	17 90249	21 09099	17 40841	21 67007	18 90510	20 23696	18 39221	20 79216	19 86935	19 33614	19 33614
63	24 90851	16 62012	23 53752	16 13585	22 15239	17 64285	22 75374	17 14081	21 34217	18 62938	21 91820	18 10821	20 48235	19 57692	19 03511	19 03511
64	24 54198	16 37599	23 18097	17 88403	23 80560	17 38321	22 41650	18 87320	21 01426	18 35366	21 59944	19 82421	20 17255	19 28449	20 73408	20 73408
65	24 17545	16 13187	24 82442	17 63222	23 45881	17 12357	22 07926	18 60559	22 68636	18 07793	21 28068	19 54022	21 86275	20 99206	20 43305	20 43305
66	25 80892	17 88774	24 46788	17 38041	23 11203	18 86394	23 74202	18 33799	22 35846	19 80221	22 96192	19 25622	21 55294	20 69963	20 13202	20 13202
67	25 44239	17 64362	24 11133	17 12860	24 76524	18 60430	23 40477	18 07038	22 03056	19 52648	22 64316	20 97222	21 24314	20 40720	21 83099	21 83099
68	25 07585	17 39949	25 75478	18 87679	24 41845	18 34466	23 06753	19 80278	23 70265	19 25076	22 32440	20 68823	22 93333	20 11477	21 52996	21 52996
69	26 70932	17 15537	25 39823	18 62497	24 07166	18 08503	24 73029	19 53517	23 37475	20 97504	22 00565	20 40423	22 62353	21 82234	21 22893	21 22893
70	26 34279	18 91124	25 04169	18 37316	25 72488	19 82539	24 39305	19 26756	23 04685	20 69931	23 68689	20 12023	22 31373	21 52991	22 92790	22 92790
71	27 97626	18 66711	26 68514	18 12135	25 37809	19 56575	24 05581	20 99996	24 71895	20 42359	23 36813	21 83624	22 00392	21 23748	22 62687	22 62687
72	27 60973	18 42299	26 32859	19 86954	25 03130	19 30611	25 71856	20 73235	24 39105	20 14786	23 04937	21 55224	23 69412	22 94505	22 32584	22 32584
73	27 24320	18 17886	27 97205	19 61773	26 68451	19 04648	25 38132	20 46474	24 06314	21 87214	24 73061	21 26824	23 38431	22 65262	22 02481	22 02481
74	28 87667	19 93474	27 61550	19 36591	26 33773	20 78684	25 04408	20 19714	25 73524	21 59641	24 41185	22 98425	23 07451	22 36019	23 72378	23 72378
75	28 51013	19 69061	27 25895	19 11410	27 99094	20 52720	26 70684	21 92953	25 40734	21 32069	24 09309	22 70025	24 76471	22 06776	23 42275	23 42275
76	28 14360	19 44649	28 90240	20 86229	27 64415	20 26756	26 36960	21 66193	25 07944	21 04497	25 77433	22 41625	24 45490	23 77533	23 12172	23 12172
77	29 77707	19 20236	28 54586	20 61048	27 29736	20 00793	26 03235	21 39432	26 75154	22 76924	25 45558	22 13226	24 14510	23 48290	24 82069	24 82069
78	29 41054	20 95824	28 18931	20 35867	28 95058	21 74829	27 69511	21 12671	26 42363	22 49352	25 13682	23 84826	25 83529	23 19047	24 51966	24 51966
79	29 04401	20 71411	29 83276	20 10685	28 60379	21 48865	27 35787	22 85911	26 09573	22 21779	26 81806	23 56426	25 52549	24 89804	24 21863	24 21863
80	30 67748	20 46999	29 47621	21 85504	28 25700	21 22902	27 02063	22 59150	27 76783	23 94207	26 49930	23 28027	25 21569	24 60561	25 91760	25 91760
81	30 31094	20 22586	29 11967	21 60323	29 91021	22 96938	28 68338	22 32389	27 43993	23 66635	26 18054	24 99627	26 90588	24 31318	25 61657	25 61657
82	31 94441	21 98174	30 76312	21 35142	29 56343	22 70974	28 34614	22 05629	27 11202	23 39062	27 86178	24 71227	26 59608	24 02075	25 31554	25 31554
83	31 57788	21 73761	30 40657	21 09961	29 21664	22 45010	28 00890	23 78868	28 78412	23 11490	27 54302	24 42828	26 28627	25 72832	25 01451	25 01451
84	31 21135	21 49349	30 05002	22 84779	30 86985	22 19047	29 67166	23 52108	28 45622	24 83917	27 22426	24 14428	27 97647	25 43589	26 71348	26 71348
85	32 84482	21 24936	31 69348	22 59598	30 52306	23 93083	29 33442	23 25347	28 12832	24 56345	28 90551	25 86028	27 66667	25 14347	26 41245	26 41245
86	32 47829	21 00524	31 33693	22 34417	30 17628	23 67119	30 99717	24 98586	29 80042	24 28772	28 58675	25 57629	27 35686	26 85104	26 11142	26 11142
87	32 11176	22 76111	32 98038	22 09236	31 82949	23 41155	30 65993	24 71826	29 47251	24 01200	28 26799	25 29229	27 04706	26 55861	27 81039	27 81039
88	33 74522	22 51699	32 62384	23 84055	31 48270	23 15192	30 32269	24 45065	29 14461	25 73628	29 94923	25 00829	28 73726	26 26618	27 50936	27 50936
89	33 37869	22 27286	32 26729	23 58873	31 13591	24 89228	31 98545	24 18304	30 81671	25 46055	29 63047	26 72430	28 42745	27 97375	27 20833	27 20833
90	33 01216	22 02874	33 91074	23 33692	32 78913	24 63264	31 64820	25 91544	30 48881	25 18483	29 31171	26 44030	28 11765	27 68132	28 90730	28 90730
91	34 64563	23 78461	33 55419	23 08511	32 44234	24 37300	31 31096	25 64783	30 16091	26 90910	30 99295	26 15630	29 80784	27 38889	28 60627	28 60627
92	34 27910	23 54049	33 19765	24 83330	32 09555	24 11337	32 97372	25 38023	31 83300	26 63338	30 67419	27 87231	29 49804	27 09646	28 30524	28 30524
93	35 91257	23 29636	34 84110	24 58149	33 74876	25 85373	32 63648	25 11262	31 50510	26 35766	30 35544	27 58831	29 18824	28 80403	28 00421	28 00421
94	35 54603	23 05224	34 48455	24 32967	33 40198	25 59409	32 29924	26 84501	31 17720	26 08193	30 03668	27 30431	30 87843	28 51160	29 70318	29 70318
95	35 17950	24 80811	34 12800	24 07786	33 05519	25 33446	33 96199	26 57741	32 84930	27 80621	31 71792	27 02032	30 56863	28 21917	29 40215	29 40215
96	36 81297	24 56399	35 77146	25 82605	34 70840	25 07482	33 62475	26 30980	32 52139	27 53048	31 39916	28 73632	30 25882	29 92674	29 10112	29 10112
97	36 44644	24 31986	35 41491	25 57424	34 36161	26 81518	33 28751	26 04219	32 19349	27 25476	31 08040	28 45232	31 94902	29 63431	30 80009	30 80009
98	36 07991	24 07574	35 05836	25 32243	34 01483	26 55554	34 95027	27 77459	33 86559	28 97904	32 76164	28 16833	31 63922	29 34188	30 49906	30 49906
99	37 71338	25 83161	36 70182	25 07061	35 66804	26 29591	34 61303	27 50698	33 53769	28 70331	32 44288	29 88433	31 32941	29 04945	30 19803	30 19803
100	37 34685	25 58749	36 34527	26 81880	35 32125	26 03627	34 27578	27 23938	33 20979	28 42759	32 12412	29 60033	31 01961	30 75702	31 89700	31 89700

N = number of trials, x = number of successes, etc., $100\,p_x = 100\,x/N$

Column heads (all tables below): x; $100\,p_x$; $100(1-2\alpha)$ limits: 95% ($100p_l$–$100p_r$) and 99% ($100p_l$–$100p_r$).

$N = 2$

x	$100\,p_x$	95% $100p_l$–$100p_r$	99% $100p_l$–$100p_r$
0	0.00	0.00– 84.19	0.00– 92.93
1	50.00	1.26– 98.74	0.25– 99.75
2	100.00	15.81–100.00	7.07–100.00

$N = 3$

x	$100\,p_x$	95% $100p_l$–$100p_r$	99% $100p_l$–$100p_r$
0	0.00	0.00– 70.76	0.00– 82.90
1	33.33	0.84– 90.57	0.17– 95.86
2	66.67	9.43– 99.16	4.14– 99.83
3	100.00	29.24–100.00	17.10–100.00

$N = 4$

x	$100\,p_x$	95% $100p_l$–$100p_r$	99% $100p_l$–$100p_r$
0	0.00	0.00– 60.24	0.00– 73.41
1	25.00	0.63– 80.59	0.13– 88.91
2	50.00	6.76– 93.24	2.94– 97.06
3	75.00	19.41– 99.37	11.09– 99.87
4	100.00	39.76–100.00	26.59–100.00

$N = 5$

x	$100\,p_x$	95% $100p_l$–$100p_r$	99% $100p_l$–$100p_r$
0	0.00	0.00– 52.18	0.00– 65.34
1	20.00	0.51– 71.64	0.10– 81.49
2	40.00	5.27– 85.34	2.29– 91.72
3	60.00	14.66– 94.73	8.28– 97.71
4	80.00	28.36– 99.49	18.51– 99.90
5	100.00	47.82–100.00	34.66–100.00

$N = 6$

x	$100\,p_x$	95% $100p_l$–$100p_r$	99% $100p_l$–$100p_r$
0	0.00	0.00– 45.93	0.00– 58.65
1	16.67	0.42– 64.12	0.08– 74.60
2	33.33	4.33– 77.72	1.87– 85.64
3	50.00	11.81– 88.19	6.63– 93.37
4	66.67	22.28– 95.67	14.36– 98.13
5	83.33	35.88– 99.58	25.40– 99.92
6	100.00	54.07–100.00	41.35–100.00

$N = 7$

x	$100\,p_x$	95% $100p_l$–$100p_r$	99% $100p_l$–$100p_r$
0	0.00	0.00– 40.96	0.00– 53.09
1	14.29	0.36– 57.87	0.07– 68.49
2	28.57	3.67– 70.96	1.58– 79.70
3	42.86	9.90– 81.59	5.53– 88.23
4	57.14	18.41– 90.10	11.77– 94.47
5	71.43	29.04– 96.33	20.30– 98.42
6	85.71	42.13– 99.64	31.51– 99.93
7	100.00	59.04–100.00	46.91–100.00

$N = 8$

x	$100\,p_x$	95% $100p_l$–$100p_r$	99% $100p_l$–$100p_r$
0	0.00	0.00– 36.94	0.00– 48.43
1	12.50	0.32– 52.65	0.06– 63.15
2	25.00	3.19– 65.09	1.37– 74.22
3	37.50	8.52– 75.51	4.75– 83.03
4	50.00	15.70– 84.30	9.99– 90.01
5	62.50	24.49– 91.48	16.97– 95.25
6	75.00	34.91– 96.81	25.78– 98.63
7	87.50	47.35– 99.68	36.85– 99.94
8	100.00	63.06–100.00	51.57–100.00

$N = 9$

x	$100\,p_x$	95% $100p_l$–$100p_r$	99% $100p_l$–$100p_r$
0	0.00	0.00– 33.63	0.00– 44.50
1	11.11	0.28– 48.25	0.06– 58.50
2	22.22	2.81– 60.01	1.21– 69.26
3	33.33	7.49– 70.07	4.16– 78.09
4	44.44	13.70– 78.80	8.68– 85.39
5	55.56	21.20– 86.30	14.61– 91.32
6	66.67	29.93– 92.51	21.91– 95.84
7	77.78	39.99– 97.19	30.74– 98.79
8	88.89	51.75– 99.72	41.50– 99.94
9	100.00	66.37–100.00	55.50–100.00

$N = 10$

x	$100\,p_x$	95% $100p_l$–$100p_r$	99% $100p_l$–$100p_r$
0	0.00	0.00– 30.85	0.00– 41.13
1	10.00	0.25– 44.50	0.05– 54.43
2	20.00	2.52– 55.61	1.09– 64.82
3	30.00	6.67– 65.25	3.70– 73.51
4	40.00	12.16– 73.76	7.68– 80.91
5	50.00	18.71– 81.29	12.83– 87.17
6	60.00	26.24– 87.84	19.09– 92.32
7	70.00	34.75– 93.33	26.49– 96.30
8	80.00	44.39– 97.48	35.18– 98.91
9	90.00	55.50– 99.75	45.57– 99.95
10	100.00	69.15–100.00	58.87–100.00

$N = 11$

x	$100\,p_x$	95% $100p_l$–$100p_r$	99% $100p_l$–$100p_r$
0	0.00	0.00– 28.49	0.00– 38.22
1	9.09	0.23– 41.28	0.05– 50.86
2	18.18	2.28– 51.78	0.98– 60.85
3	27.27	6.02– 60.97	3.33– 69.33
4	36.36	10.93– 69.21	6.88– 76.68
5	45.45	16.75– 76.62	11.45– 83.07
6	54.55	23.38– 83.25	16.93– 88.55
7	63.64	30.79– 89.07	23.32– 93.12
8	72.73	39.03– 93.98	30.67– 96.67
9	81.82	48.22– 97.72	39.15– 99.02

$N = 11$ (continued)

x	$100\,p_x$	95% $100p_l$–$100p_r$	99% $100p_l$–$100p_r$
10	90.91	58.72– 99.77	49.14– 99.95
11	100.00	71.51–100.00	61.78–100.00

$N = 12$

x	$100\,p_x$	95% $100p_l$–$100p_r$	99% $100p_l$–$100p_r$
0	0.00	0.00– 26.46	0.00– 35.69
1	8.33	0.21– 38.48	0.04– 47.70
2	16.67	2.09– 48.41	0.90– 57.29
3	25.00	5.49– 57.19	3.03– 65.52
4	33.33	9.92– 65.11	6.24– 72.75
5	41.67	15.17– 72.33	10.34– 79.15
6	50.00	21.09– 78.91	15.22– 84.78
7	58.33	27.67– 84.83	20.85– 89.66
8	66.67	34.89– 90.08	27.25– 93.76
9	75.00	42.81– 94.51	34.48– 96.97
10	83.33	51.59– 97.91	42.71– 99.10
11	91.67	61.52– 99.79	52.30– 99.96
12	100.00	73.54–100.00	64.31–100.00

$N = 13$

x	$100\,p_x$	95% $100p_l$–$100p_r$	99% $100p_l$–$100p_r$
0	0.00	0.00– 24.71	0.00– 33.47
1	7.69	0.19– 36.03	0.04– 44.90
2	15.38	1.92– 45.45	0.83– 54.10
3	23.08	5.04– 53.81	2.78– 62.06
4	30.77	9.09– 61.43	5.71– 69.13
5	38.46	13.86– 68.42	9.42– 75.46
6	46.15	19.22– 74.87	13.83– 81.13
7	53.85	25.13– 80.78	18.87– 86.17
8	61.54	31.58– 86.14	24.54– 90.58
9	69.23	38.57– 90.91	30.87– 94.29
10	76.92	46.19– 94.96	37.94– 97.22
11	84.62	54.55– 98.08	45.90– 99.17
12	92.31	63.97– 99.81	55.10– 99.96
13	100.00	75.29–100.00	66.53–100.00

$N = 14$

x	$100\,p_x$	95% $100p_l$–$100p_r$	99% $100p_l$–$100p_r$
0	0.00	0.00– 23.16	0.00– 31.51
1	7.14	0.18– 33.87	0.04– 42.40
2	14.29	1.78– 42.81	0.76– 51.23
3	21.43	4.66– 50.80	2.57– 58.92
4	28.57	8.39– 58.10	5.26– 65.79
5	35.71	12.76– 64.86	8.66– 72.01
6	42.86	17.66– 71.14	12.67– 77.66
7	50.00	23.04– 76.96	17.24– 82.76
8	57.14	28.86– 82.34	22.34– 87.33
9	64.29	35.14– 87.24	27.99– 91.34
10	71.43	41.90– 91.61	34.21– 94.74
11	78.57	49.20– 95.34	41.08– 97.43
12	85.71	57.19– 98.22	48.77– 99.24
13	92.86	66.13– 99.82	57.60– 99.96
14	100.00	76.84–100.00	68.49–100.00

$N = 15$

x	$100\,p_x$	95% $100p_l$–$100p_r$	99% $100p_l$–$100p_r$
0	0.00	0.00– 21.80	0.00– 29.76
1	6.67	0.17– 31.95	0.03– 40.16
2	13.33	1.66– 40.46	0.71– 48.63
3	20.00	4.33– 48.09	2.39– 56.05
4	26.67	7.79– 55.10	4.88– 62.73
5	33.33	11.82– 61.62	8.01– 68.82
6	40.00	16.34– 67.71	11.70– 74.39
7	46.67	21.27– 73.41	15.87– 79.49
8	53.33	26.59– 78.73	20.51– 84.13
9	60.00	32.29– 83.66	25.61– 88.30
10	66.67	38.38– 88.18	31.18– 91.99
11	73.33	44.90– 92.21	37.27– 95.12
12	80.00	51.91– 95.67	43.95– 97.61
13	86.67	59.54– 98.34	51.37– 99.29
14	93.33	68.05– 99.83	59.84– 99.97
15	100.00	78.20–100.00	70.24–100.00

$N = 16$

x	$100\,p_x$	95% $100p_l$–$100p_r$	99% $100p_l$–$100p_r$
0	0.00	0.00– 20.59	0.00– 28.19
1	6.25	0.16– 30.23	0.03– 38.14
2	12.50	1.55– 38.35	0.67– 46.28
3	18.75	4.05– 45.65	2.23– 53.44
4	25.00	7.27– 52.38	4.55– 59.91
5	31.25	11.02– 58.66	7.45– 65.85
6	37.50	15.20– 64.57	10.86– 71.32
7	43.75	19.75– 70.12	14.71– 76.38
8	50.00	24.65– 75.35	18.97– 81.03
9	56.25	29.88– 80.25	23.62– 85.29
10	62.50	35.43– 84.80	28.68– 89.14
11	68.75	41.34– 88.98	34.15– 92.55
12	75.00	47.62– 92.73	40.09– 95.45
13	81.25	54.35– 95.95	46.56– 97.77
14	87.50	61.65– 98.45	53.72– 99.33
15	93.75	69.77– 99.84	61.86– 99.97
16	100.00	79.41–100.00	71.81–100.00

$N = 17$

x	$100\,p_x$	95% $100p_l$–$100p_r$	99% $100p_l$–$100p_r$
0	0.00	0.00– 19.51	0.00– 26.78
1	5.88	0.15– 28.69	0.03– 36.30
2	11.76	1.46– 36.44	0.63– 44.13
3	17.65	3.80– 43.43	2.09– 51.04
4	23.53	6.81– 49.90	4.26– 57.32

$N = 17$ (continued)

x	$100\,p_x$	95% $100p_l$–$100p_r$	99% $100p_l$–$100p_r$
5	29.41	10.31– 55.96	6.97– 63.10
6	35.29	14.21– 61.67	10.14– 68.46
7	41.18	18.44– 67.08	13.71– 73.44
8	47.06	22.98– 72.19	17.64– 78.07
9	52.94	27.81– 77.02	21.93– 82.36
10	58.82	32.92– 81.56	26.56– 86.29
11	64.71	38.33– 85.79	31.54– 89.86
12	70.59	44.04– 89.69	36.90– 93.03
13	76.47	50.10– 93.19	42.68– 95.74
14	82.35	56.57– 96.20	48.96– 97.91
15	88.24	63.56– 98.54	55.87– 99.37
16	94.12	71.31– 99.85	63.70– 99.97
17	100.00	80.49–100.00	73.22–100.00

$N = 18$

x	$100\,p_x$	95% $100p_l$–$100p_r$	99% $100p_l$–$100p_r$
0	0.00	0.00– 18.53	0.00– 25.50
1	5.56	0.14– 27.29	0.03– 34.63
2	11.11	1.38– 34.71	0.59– 42.17
3	16.67	3.58– 41.42	1.97– 48.84
4	22.22	6.41– 47.64	4.00– 54.92
5	27.78	9.69– 53.48	6.54– 60.55
6	33.33	13.34– 59.01	9.51– 65.79
7	38.89	17.30– 64.25	12.84– 70.68
8	44.44	21.53– 69.24	16.49– 75.26
9	50.00	26.02– 73.98	20.47– 79.53
10	55.56	30.76– 78.47	24.74– 83.51
11	61.11	35.75– 82.70	29.32– 87.16
12	66.67	40.99– 86.66	34.21– 90.49
13	72.22	46.52– 90.31	39.45– 93.46
14	77.78	52.36– 93.59	45.08– 96.00
15	83.33	58.58– 96.42	51.16– 98.03
16	88.89	65.29– 98.62	57.83– 99.41
17	94.44	72.71– 99.86	65.37– 99.97
18	100.00	81.47–100.00	74.50–100.00

$N = 19$

x	$100\,p_x$	95% $100p_l$–$100p_r$	99% $100p_l$–$100p_r$
0	0.00	0.00– 17.65	0.00– 24.34
1	5.26	0.13– 26.03	0.03– 33.11
2	10.53	1.30– 33.14	0.56– 40.37
3	15.79	3.38– 39.58	1.86– 46.82
4	21.05	6.05– 45.57	3.78– 52.71
5	26.32	9.15– 51.20	6.17– 58.18
6	31.58	12.58– 56.55	8.95– 63.29
7	36.84	16.29– 61.64	12.07– 68.09
8	42.11	20.25– 66.50	15.49– 72.60
9	47.37	24.45– 71.14	19.19– 76.84
10	52.63	28.86– 75.55	23.16– 80.81
11	57.89	33.50– 79.75	27.40– 84.51
12	63.16	38.36– 83.71	31.91– 87.93
13	68.42	43.45– 87.42	36.71– 91.05
14	73.68	48.80– 90.85	41.82– 93.83
15	78.95	54.43– 93.95	47.29– 96.22
16	84.21	60.42– 96.62	53.18– 98.14
17	89.47	66.86– 98.70	59.63– 99.44
18	94.74	73.97– 99.87	66.89– 99.97
19	100.00	82.35–100.00	75.66–100.00

$N = 20$

x	$100\,p_x$	95% $100p_l$–$100p_r$	99% $100p_l$–$100p_r$
0	0.00	0.00– 16.84	0.00– 23.27
1	5.00	0.13– 24.87	0.03– 31.71
2	10.00	1.23– 31.70	0.53– 38.71
3	15.00	3.21– 37.89	1.76– 44.95
4	20.00	5.73– 43.66	3.58– 50.66
5	25.00	8.66– 49.10	5.83– 55.98
6	30.00	11.89– 54.28	8.46– 60.96
7	35.00	15.39– 59.22	11.39– 65.66
8	40.00	19.12– 63.95	14.60– 70.09
9	45.00	23.06– 68.47	18.06– 74.28
10	50.00	27.20– 72.80	21.77– 78.23
11	55.00	31.53– 76.94	25.72– 81.94
12	60.00	36.05– 80.88	29.91– 85.40
13	65.00	40.78– 84.61	34.34– 88.61
14	70.00	45.72– 88.11	39.04– 91.54
15	75.00	50.90– 91.34	44.02– 94.17
16	80.00	56.34– 94.27	49.34– 96.42
17	85.00	62.11– 96.79	55.05– 98.24
18	90.00	68.30– 98.77	61.29– 99.47
19	95.00	75.13– 99.87	68.29– 99.97
20	100.00	83.16–100.00	76.73–100.00

$N = 21$

x	$100\,p_x$	95% $100p_l$–$100p_r$	99% $100p_l$–$100p_r$
0	0.00	0.00– 16.11	0.00– 22.30
1	4.76	0.12– 23.82	0.02– 30.43
2	9.52	1.17– 30.38	0.50– 37.18
3	14.29	3.05– 36.34	1.68– 43.22
4	19.05	5.45– 41.91	3.39– 48.76
5	23.81	8.22– 47.17	5.53– 53.92
6	28.57	11.28– 52.18	8.01– 58.78
7	33.33	14.59– 56.97	10.78– 63.37
8	38.10	18.11– 61.56	13.81– 67.72
9	42.86	21.82– 65.98	17.07– 71.85
10	47.62	25.71– 70.22	20.55– 75.76
11	52.38	29.78– 74.29	24.24– 79.45
12	57.14	34.02– 78.18	28.15– 82.93
13	61.90	38.44– 81.89	32.28– 86.19
14	66.67	43.03– 85.41	36.63– 89.22

$N = 21$ (continued)

x	$100\,p_x$	95% $100p_l$–$100p_r$	99% $100p_l$–$100p_r$
15	71.43	47.82– 88.72	41.22– 91.99
16	76.19	52.83– 91.78	46.08– 94.47
17	80.95	58.09– 94.55	51.24– 96.61
18	85.71	63.66– 96.95	56.78– 98.32
19	90.48	69.62– 98.83	62.82– 99.50
20	95.24	76.18– 99.88	69.57– 99.98
21	100.00	83.89–100.00	77.70–100.00

$N = 22$

x	$100\,p_x$	95% $100p_l$–$100p_r$	99% $100p_l$–$100p_r$
0	0.00	0.00– 15.44	0.00– 21.40
1	4.55	0.12– 22.84	0.02– 29.24
2	9.09	1.12– 29.16	0.48– 35.77
3	13.64	2.91– 34.91	1.60– 41.61
4	18.18	5.19– 40.28	3.23– 46.99
5	22.73	7.82– 45.37	5.26– 52.01
6	27.27	10.73– 50.22	7.61– 56.74
7	31.82	13.86– 54.87	10.24– 61.23
8	36.36	17.20– 59.34	13.10– 65.49
9	40.91	20.71– 63.65	16.18– 69.54
10	45.45	24.39– 67.79	19.46– 73.40
11	50.00	28.22– 71.78	22.93– 77.07
12	54.55	32.21– 75.61	26.60– 80.54
13	59.09	36.35– 79.29	30.46– 83.82
14	63.64	40.66– 82.80	34.51– 86.90
15	68.18	45.13– 86.14	38.77– 89.76
16	72.73	49.78– 89.27	43.26– 92.39
17	77.27	54.63– 92.18	47.99– 94.74
18	81.82	59.72– 94.81	53.01– 96.77
19	86.36	65.09– 97.09	58.39– 98.40
20	90.91	70.84– 98.88	64.23– 99.52
21	95.45	77.16– 99.88	70.76– 99.98
22	100.00	84.56–100.00	78.60–100.00

$N = 23$

x	$100\,p_x$	95% $100p_l$–$100p_r$	99% $100p_l$–$100p_r$
0	0.00	0.00– 14.82	0.00– 20.58
1	4.35	0.11– 21.95	0.02– 28.14
2	8.70	1.07– 28.04	0.46– 34.46
3	13.04	2.78– 33.59	1.53– 40.12
4	17.39	4.95– 38.78	3.08– 45.34
5	21.74	7.46– 43.70	5.02– 50.22
6	26.09	10.23– 48.41	7.25– 54.83
7	30.43	13.21– 52.92	9.74– 59.21
8	34.78	16.38– 57.27	12.46– 63.38
9	39.13	19.71– 61.46	15.37– 67.36
10	43.48	23.19– 65.51	18.48– 71.16
11	47.83	26.82– 69.41	21.76– 74.79
12	52.17	30.59– 73.18	25.21– 78.24
13	56.52	34.49– 76.81	28.84– 81.52
14	60.87	38.54– 80.29	32.64– 84.63
15	65.22	42.73– 83.62	36.62– 87.54
16	69.57	47.08– 86.79	40.79– 90.26
17	73.91	51.59– 89.77	45.17– 92.75
18	78.26	56.30– 92.54	49.78– 94.98
19	82.61	61.22– 95.05	54.66– 96.92
20	86.96	66.41– 97.22	59.88– 98.47
21	91.30	71.96– 98.93	65.54– 99.54
22	95.65	78.05– 99.89	71.86– 99.98
23	100.00	85.18–100.00	79.42–100.00

$N = 24$

x	$100\,p_x$	95% $100p_l$–$100p_r$	99% $100p_l$–$100p_r$
0	0.00	0.00– 14.25	0.00– 19.81
1	4.17	0.11– 21.12	0.02– 27.13
2	8.33	1.03– 27.00	0.44– 33.24
3	12.50	2.66– 32.36	1.46– 38.73
4	16.67	4.74– 37.38	2.95– 43.79
5	20.83	7.13– 42.15	4.79– 48.55
6	25.00	9.77– 46.71	6.92– 53.04
7	29.17	12.62– 51.09	9.30– 57.32
8	33.33	15.63– 55.32	11.88– 61.40
9	37.50	18.80– 59.41	14.65– 65.30
10	41.67	22.11– 63.36	17.59– 69.04
11	45.83	25.55– 67.18	20.70– 72.62
12	50.00	29.12– 70.88	23.96– 76.04
13	54.17	32.82– 74.45	27.38– 79.30
14	58.33	36.64– 77.89	30.96– 82.41
15	62.50	40.59– 81.20	34.70– 85.35
16	66.67	44.68– 84.37	38.60– 88.12
17	70.83	48.91– 87.38	42.68– 90.70
18	75.00	53.29– 90.23	46.96– 93.08
19	79.17	57.85– 92.87	51.45– 95.21
20	83.33	62.62– 95.26	56.21– 97.05
21	87.50	67.64– 97.34	61.27– 98.54
22	91.67	73.00– 98.97	66.76– 99.56
23	95.83	78.88– 99.89	72.87– 99.98
24	100.00	85.75–100.00	80.19–100.00

$N = 25$

x	$100\,p_x$	95% $100p_l$–$100p_r$	99% $100p_l$–$100p_r$
0	0.00	0.00– 13.72	0.00– 19.10
1	4.00	0.10– 20.35	0.02– 26.18
2	8.00	0.98– 26.03	0.42– 32.10
3	12.00	2.55– 31.22	1.40– 37.43
4	16.00	4.54– 36.08	2.82– 42.35
5	20.00	6.83– 40.70	4.59– 46.98
6	24.00	9.36– 45.13	6.63– 51.36
7	28.00	12.07– 49.39	8.89– 55.53
8	32.00	14.95– 53.50	11.35– 59.52

N = number of trials, x = number of successes, etc., $100\,p_x = 100\,x/N$

$N = 25$ (continued)

x	$100p_x$	95% $100p_l$	95% $100p_r$	99% $100p_l$	99% $100p_r$
9	36.00	17.97	57.48	13.99	63.35
10	40.00	21.13	61.33	16.79	67.02
11	44.00	24.40	65.07	19.74	70.54
12	48.00	27.80	68.69	22.83	73.93
13	52.00	31.31	72.20	26.07	77.17
14	56.00	34.93	75.60	29.46	80.26
15	60.00	38.67	78.87	32.98	83.21
16	64.00	42.52	82.03	36.65	86.01
17	68.00	46.50	85.05	40.48	88.65
18	72.00	50.61	87.93	44.47	91.11
19	76.00	54.87	90.64	48.64	93.37
20	80.00	59.30	93.17	53.02	95.41
21	84.00	63.92	95.46	57.65	97.18
22	88.00	68.78	97.45	62.57	98.60
23	92.00	73.97	99.02	67.90	99.58
24	96.00	79.65	99.90	73.82	99.98
25	100.00	86.28	100.00	80.90	100.00

$N = 26$

x	$100p_x$	95% $100p_l$	95% $100p_r$	99% $100p_l$	99% $100p_r$
0	0.00	0.00	13.23	0.00	18.44
1	3.85	0.10	19.64	0.02	25.29
2	7.69	0.95	25.13	0.41	31.04
3	11.54	2.45	30.15	1.34	36.21
4	15.38	4.36	34.87	2.71	41.00
5	19.23	6.55	39.35	4.40	45.50
6	23.08	8.97	43.65	6.35	49.77
7	26.92	11.57	47.79	8.52	53.85
8	30.77	14.33	51.79	10.87	57.75
9	34.62	17.21	55.67	13.38	61.50
10	38.46	20.23	59.43	16.05	65.10
11	42.31	23.35	63.08	18.86	68.57
12	46.15	26.59	66.63	21.81	71.91
13	50.00	29.93	70.07	24.89	75.11
14	53.85	33.37	73.41	28.09	78.19
15	57.69	36.92	76.65	31.43	81.14
16	61.54	40.57	79.77	34.90	83.95
17	65.38	44.33	82.79	38.50	86.62
18	69.23	48.21	85.67	42.25	89.13
19	73.08	52.21	88.43	46.15	91.48
20	76.92	56.35	91.03	50.23	93.65
21	80.77	60.65	93.45	54.50	95.60
22	84.62	65.13	95.64	59.00	97.29
23	88.46	69.85	97.55	63.79	98.66
24	92.31	74.87	99.05	68.96	99.59
25	96.15	80.36	99.90	74.71	99.98
26	100.00	86.77	100.00	81.56	100.00

$N = 27$

x	$100p_x$	95% $100p_l$	95% $100p_r$	99% $100p_l$	99% $100p_r$
0	0.00	0.00	12.77	0.00	17.82
1	3.70	0.09	18.97	0.02	24.46
2	7.41	0.91	24.29	0.39	30.04
3	11.11	2.35	29.16	1.29	35.07
4	14.81	4.19	33.73	2.60	39.73
5	18.52	6.30	38.08	4.23	44.11
6	22.22	8.62	42.26	6.10	48.28
7	25.93	11.11	46.28	8.17	52.26
8	29.63	13.75	50.18	10.42	56.08
9	33.33	16.52	53.96	12.83	59.75
10	37.04	19.40	57.63	15.38	63.28
11	40.74	22.39	61.20	18.07	66.69
12	44.44	25.48	64.67	20.88	69.98
13	48.15	28.67	68.05	23.81	73.14
14	51.85	31.95	71.33	26.86	76.19
15	55.56	35.33	74.52	30.02	79.12
16	59.26	38.80	77.61	33.31	81.93
17	62.96	42.37	80.60	36.72	84.62
18	66.67	46.04	83.48	40.25	87.17
19	70.37	49.82	86.25	43.92	89.58
20	74.07	53.72	88.89	47.74	91.83
21	77.78	57.74	91.38	51.72	93.90
22	81.48	61.92	93.70	55.89	95.77
23	85.19	66.27	95.81	60.27	97.40
24	88.89	70.84	97.65	64.93	98.71
25	92.59	75.71	99.09	69.96	99.61
26	96.30	81.03	99.91	75.54	99.98
27	100.00	87.23	100.00	82.18	100.00

$N = 28$

x	$100p_x$	95% $100p_l$	95% $100p_r$	99% $100p_l$	99% $100p_r$
0	0.00	0.00	12.34	0.00	17.24
1	3.57	0.09	18.35	0.02	23.69
2	7.14	0.88	23.50	0.38	29.11
3	10.71	2.27	28.23	1.25	33.99
4	14.29	4.03	32.67	2.51	38.53
5	17.86	6.06	36.89	4.07	42.80
6	21.43	8.30	40.95	5.86	46.87
7	25.00	10.69	44.87	7.86	50.76
8	28.57	13.22	48.67	10.02	54.49
9	32.14	15.88	52.35	12.32	58.08
10	35.71	18.64	55.93	14.77	61.55
11	39.29	21.50	59.42	17.33	64.90
12	42.86	24.46	62.82	20.02	68.14
13	46.43	27.51	66.13	22.82	71.26
14	50.00	30.65	69.35	25.72	74.28
15	53.57	33.87	72.49	28.74	77.18
16	57.14	37.18	75.54	31.86	79.98
17	60.71	40.58	78.50	35.10	82.67

$N = 28$ (continued)

x	$100p_x$	95% $100p_l$	95% $100p_r$	99% $100p_l$	99% $100p_r$
18	64.29	44.07	81.36	38.45	85.23
19	67.86	47.65	84.12	41.92	87.68
20	71.43	51.33	86.78	45.51	89.98
21	75.00	55.13	89.31	49.24	92.14
22	78.57	59.05	91.70	53.13	94.14
23	82.14	63.11	93.94	57.20	95.93
24	85.71	67.33	95.97	61.47	97.49
25	89.29	71.77	97.73	66.01	98.75
26	92.86	76.50	99.12	70.89	99.62
27	96.43	81.65	99.91	76.31	99.98
28	100.00	87.66	100.00	82.76	100.00

$N = 29$

x	$100p_x$	95% $100p_l$	95% $100p_r$	99% $100p_l$	99% $100p_r$
0	0.00	0.00	11.94	0.00	16.70
1	3.45	0.09	17.76	0.02	22.96
2	6.90	0.85	22.77	0.36	28.23
3	10.34	2.19	27.35	1.20	32.98
4	13.79	3.89	31.66	2.42	37.40
5	17.24	5.85	35.77	3.92	41.57
6	20.69	7.99	39.72	5.65	45.54
7	24.14	10.30	43.54	7.56	49.33
8	27.59	12.73	47.24	9.64	52.99
9	31.03	15.28	50.83	11.85	56.51
10	34.48	17.94	54.33	14.20	59.91
11	37.93	20.69	57.74	16.66	63.20
12	41.38	23.52	61.06	19.23	66.38
13	44.83	26.45	64.31	21.91	69.46
14	48.28	29.45	67.47	24.69	72.43
15	51.72	32.53	70.55	27.57	75.31
16	55.17	35.69	73.55	30.54	78.09
17	58.62	38.94	76.48	33.62	80.77
18	62.07	42.26	79.31	36.80	83.34
19	65.52	45.67	82.06	40.09	85.80
20	68.97	49.17	84.72	43.49	88.15
21	72.41	52.76	87.27	47.01	90.36
22	75.86	56.46	89.70	50.67	92.44
23	79.31	60.28	92.01	54.46	94.35
24	82.76	64.23	94.15	58.43	96.08
25	86.21	68.34	96.11	62.60	97.58
26	89.66	72.65	97.81	67.02	98.80
27	93.10	77.23	99.15	71.77	99.64
28	96.55	82.24	99.91	77.04	99.98
29	100.00	88.06	100.00	83.30	100.00

$N = 30$

x	$100p_x$	95% $100p_l$	95% $100p_r$	99% $100p_l$	99% $100p_r$
0	0.00	0.00	11.57	0.00	16.19
1	3.33	0.08	17.22	0.02	22.27
2	6.67	0.82	22.07	0.35	27.40
3	10.00	2.11	26.53	1.16	32.03
4	13.33	3.76	30.72	2.33	36.34
5	16.67	5.64	34.72	3.78	40.40
6	20.00	7.71	38.57	5.45	44.28
7	23.33	9.93	42.28	7.29	47.99
8	26.67	12.28	45.89	9.29	51.56
9	30.00	14.73	49.40	11.42	55.01
10	33.33	17.29	52.81	13.67	58.34
11	36.67	19.93	56.14	16.04	61.57
12	40.00	22.66	59.40	18.50	64.70
13	43.33	25.46	62.57	21.07	67.73
14	46.67	28.34	65.67	23.73	70.67
15	50.00	31.30	68.70	26.48	73.52
16	53.33	34.33	71.66	29.33	76.27
17	56.67	37.43	74.54	32.27	78.93
18	60.00	40.60	77.34	35.30	81.50
19	63.33	43.86	80.07	38.43	83.96
20	66.67	47.19	82.71	41.66	86.33
21	70.00	50.60	85.27	44.99	88.58
22	73.33	54.11	87.72	48.44	90.71
23	76.67	57.72	90.07	52.01	92.71
24	80.00	61.43	92.29	55.72	94.55
25	83.33	65.28	94.36	59.60	96.22
26	86.67	69.28	96.24	63.66	97.67
27	90.00	73.47	97.89	67.97	98.84
28	93.33	77.93	99.18	72.60	99.65
29	96.67	82.78	99.92	77.73	99.98
30	100.00	88.43	100.00	83.81	100.00

$N = 31$

x	$100p_x$	95% $100p_l$	95% $100p_r$	99% $100p_l$	99% $100p_r$
0	0.00	0.00	11.22	0.00	15.71
1	3.23	0.08	16.70	0.02	21.63
2	6.45	0.79	21.42	0.34	26.62
3	9.68	2.04	25.75	1.12	31.13
4	12.90	3.63	29.83	2.25	35.33
5	16.13	5.45	33.73	3.65	39.30
6	19.35	7.45	37.47	5.26	43.08
7	22.58	9.59	41.10	7.04	46.71
8	25.81	11.86	44.61	8.96	50.21
9	29.03	14.22	48.04	11.02	53.58
10	32.26	16.68	51.37	13.18	56.85
11	35.48	19.23	54.63	15.46	60.02
12	38.71	21.85	57.81	17.83	63.09
13	41.94	24.55	60.92	20.29	66.08
14	45.16	27.32	63.97	22.85	68.98
15	48.39	30.15	66.94	25.49	71.79
16	51.61	33.06	69.85	28.21	74.51
17	54.84	36.03	72.68	31.02	77.15

$N = 31$ (continued)

x	$100p_x$	95% $100p_l$	95% $100p_r$	99% $100p_l$	99% $100p_r$
18	58.06	39.08	75.45	33.92	79.71
19	61.29	42.19	78.15	36.91	82.17
20	64.52	45.37	80.77	39.98	84.54
21	67.74	48.63	83.32	43.15	86.82
22	70.97	51.96	85.78	46.42	88.98
23	74.19	55.39	88.14	49.79	91.04
24	77.42	58.90	90.41	53.29	92.96
25	80.65	62.53	92.55	56.92	94.74
26	83.87	66.27	94.55	60.70	96.35
27	87.10	70.17	96.37	64.67	97.75
28	90.32	74.25	97.96	68.87	98.88
29	93.55	78.58	99.21	73.38	99.66
30	96.77	83.30	99.92	78.37	99.98
31	100.00	88.78	100.00	84.29	100.00

$N = 32$

x	$100p_x$	95% $100p_l$	95% $100p_r$	99% $100p_l$	99% $100p_r$
0	0.00	0.00	10.89	0.00	15.26
1	3.13	0.08	16.22	0.02	21.02
2	6.25	0.77	20.81	0.33	25.88
3	9.38	1.98	25.02	1.09	30.28
4	12.50	3.51	28.99	2.18	34.38
5	15.63	5.28	32.79	3.53	38.25
6	18.75	7.21	36.44	5.09	41.95
7	21.88	9.28	39.97	6.80	45.50
8	25.00	11.46	43.40	8.66	48.92
9	28.13	13.75	46.75	10.64	52.22
10	31.25	16.12	50.01	12.73	55.43
11	34.38	18.57	53.19	14.92	58.54
12	37.50	21.10	56.31	17.20	61.56
13	40.63	23.70	59.36	19.57	64.50
14	43.75	26.36	62.34	22.03	67.35
15	46.88	29.09	65.26	24.56	70.13
16	50.00	31.89	68.11	27.18	72.82
17	53.13	34.74	70.91	29.87	75.44
18	56.25	37.66	73.64	32.65	77.97
19	59.38	40.64	76.30	35.50	80.43
20	62.50	43.69	78.90	38.44	82.80
21	65.63	46.81	81.43	41.46	85.08
22	68.75	49.99	83.88	44.57	87.27
23	71.88	53.25	86.25	47.78	89.36
24	75.00	56.60	88.54	51.08	91.34
25	78.13	60.03	90.72	54.50	93.20
26	81.25	63.56	92.79	58.05	94.91
27	84.38	67.21	94.72	61.75	96.47
28	87.50	71.01	96.49	65.62	97.82
29	90.63	74.98	98.02	69.72	98.91
30	93.75	79.19	99.23	74.12	99.67
31	96.88	83.78	99.92	78.98	99.98
32	100.00	89.11	100.00	84.74	100.00

$N = 33$

x	$100p_x$	95% $100p_l$	95% $100p_r$	99% $100p_l$	99% $100p_r$
0	0.00	0.00	10.58	0.00	14.83
1	3.03	0.08	15.76	0.02	20.44
2	6.06	0.74	20.23	0.32	25.18
3	9.09	1.92	24.33	1.05	29.47
4	12.12	3.40	28.20	2.11	33.47
5	15.15	5.11	31.90	3.42	37.26
6	18.18	6.98	35.46	4.92	40.87
7	21.21	8.98	38.91	6.58	44.34
8	24.24	11.09	42.26	8.38	47.69
9	27.27	13.30	45.52	10.29	50.93
10	30.30	15.59	48.71	12.31	54.08
11	33.33	17.96	51.83	14.42	57.13
12	36.36	20.40	54.88	16.62	60.10
13	39.39	22.91	57.86	18.90	62.98
14	42.42	25.48	60.78	21.27	65.79
15	45.45	28.11	63.65	23.71	68.53
16	48.48	30.80	66.46	26.22	71.19
17	51.52	33.54	69.20	28.81	73.78
18	54.55	36.35	71.89	31.47	76.29
19	57.58	39.22	74.52	34.21	78.73
20	60.61	42.14	77.09	37.02	81.10
21	63.64	45.12	79.60	39.90	83.38
22	66.67	48.17	82.04	42.87	85.58
23	69.70	51.29	84.41	45.92	87.69
24	72.73	54.48	86.70	49.07	89.71
25	75.76	57.74	88.91	52.31	91.62
26	78.79	61.09	91.02	55.66	93.42
27	81.82	64.54	93.02	59.13	95.08
28	84.85	68.10	94.89	62.74	96.58
29	87.88	71.80	96.60	66.53	97.89
30	90.91	75.67	98.08	70.53	98.95
31	93.94	79.77	99.26	74.82	99.68
32	96.97	84.24	99.92	79.56	99.98
33	100.00	89.42	100.00	85.17	100.00

$N = 34$

x	$100p_x$	95% $100p_l$	95% $100p_r$	99% $100p_l$	99% $100p_r$
0	0.00	0.00	10.28	0.00	14.43
1	2.94	0.07	15.33	0.01	19.90
2	5.88	0.72	19.68	0.31	24.52
3	8.82	1.86	23.68	1.02	28.71
4	11.76	3.30	27.45	2.05	32.62
5	14.71	4.95	31.06	3.32	36.31
6	17.65	6.76	34.53	4.77	39.85
7	20.59	8.70	37.90	6.38	43.24
8	23.53	10.75	41.17	8.11	46.52

$N = 34$ (continued)

x	$100p_x$	95% $100p_l$	95% $100p_r$	99% $100p_l$	99% $100p_r$
9	26.47	12.88	44.36	9.96	49.70
10	29.41	15.10	47.48	11.91	52.78
11	32.35	17.39	50.53	13.95	55.78
12	35.29	19.75	53.51	16.07	58.69
13	38.24	22.17	56.44	18.28	61.53
14	41.18	24.65	59.30	20.56	64.30
15	44.12	27.19	62.11	22.91	67.00
16	47.06	29.78	64.87	25.33	69.62
17	50.00	32.43	67.57	27.82	72.18
18	52.94	35.13	70.22	30.38	74.67
19	55.88	37.89	72.81	33.00	77.09
20	58.82	40.70	75.35	35.70	79.44
21	61.76	43.56	77.83	38.47	81.72
22	64.71	46.49	80.25	41.31	83.93
23	67.65	49.47	82.61	44.22	86.05
24	70.59	52.52	84.90	47.22	88.09
25	73.53	55.64	87.12	50.30	90.04
26	76.47	58.83	89.25	53.48	91.89
27	79.41	62.10	91.30	56.76	93.62
28	82.35	65.47	93.24	60.15	95.23
29	85.29	68.94	95.05	63.69	96.68
30	88.24	72.55	96.70	67.38	97.95
31	91.18	76.32	98.14	71.29	98.98
32	94.12	80.32	99.28	75.48	99.69
33	97.06	84.67	99.93	80.10	99.99
34	100.00	89.72	100.00	85.57	100.00

$N = 35$

x	$100p_x$	95% $100p_l$	95% $100p_r$	99% $100p_l$	99% $100p_r$
0	0.00	0.00	10.00	0.00	14.05
1	2.86	0.07	14.92	0.01	19.38
2	5.71	0.70	19.16	0.30	23.89
3	8.57	1.80	23.06	0.99	27.98
4	11.43	3.20	26.74	1.99	31.80
5	14.29	4.81	30.26	3.22	35.42
6	17.14	6.56	33.65	4.63	38.87
7	20.00	8.44	36.94	6.18	42.20
8	22.86	10.42	40.14	7.86	45.41
9	25.71	12.49	43.26	9.65	48.52
10	28.57	14.64	46.30	11.54	51.55
11	31.43	16.85	49.29	13.51	54.49
12	34.29	19.13	52.21	15.56	57.35
13	37.14	21.47	55.08	17.69	60.14
14	40.00	23.87	57.89	19.89	62.87
15	42.86	26.32	60.65	22.16	65.52
16	45.71	28.83	63.35	24.50	68.11
17	48.57	31.38	66.01	26.90	70.64
18	51.43	33.99	68.62	29.36	73.10
19	54.29	36.65	71.17	31.89	75.50
20	57.14	39.35	73.68	34.48	77.84
21	60.00	42.11	76.13	37.13	80.11
22	62.86	44.92	78.53	39.86	82.31
23	65.71	47.79	80.87	42.65	84.44
24	68.57	50.71	83.15	45.51	86.49
25	71.43	53.70	85.36	48.45	88.46
26	74.29	56.74	87.51	51.48	90.35
27	77.14	59.86	89.58	54.59	92.14
28	80.00	63.06	91.56	57.80	93.82
29	82.86	66.35	93.44	61.13	95.37
30	85.71	69.74	95.19	64.58	96.78
31	88.57	73.26	96.80	68.20	98.01
32	91.43	76.94	98.20	72.02	99.01
33	94.29	80.84	99.30	76.11	99.70
34	97.14	85.08	99.93	80.62	99.99
35	100.00	90.00	100.00	85.95	100.00

$N = 36$

x	$100p_x$	95% $100p_l$	95% $100p_r$	99% $100p_l$	99% $100p_r$
0	0.00	0.00	9.74	0.00	13.69
1	2.78	0.07	14.53	0.01	18.89
2	5.56	0.68	18.66	0.29	23.29
3	8.33	1.75	22.47	0.96	27.29
4	11.11	3.11	26.06	1.93	31.02
5	13.89	4.67	29.50	3.12	34.56
6	16.67	6.37	32.81	4.49	37.94
7	19.44	8.19	36.02	6.00	41.20
8	22.22	10.12	39.15	7.63	44.35
9	25.00	12.12	42.20	9.36	47.40
10	27.78	14.20	45.19	11.19	50.37
11	30.56	16.35	48.11	13.10	53.25
12	33.33	18.56	50.97	15.09	56.07
13	36.11	20.82	53.78	17.14	58.81
14	38.89	23.14	56.54	19.27	61.49
15	41.67	25.51	59.24	21.46	64.11
16	44.44	27.94	61.90	23.72	66.66
17	47.22	30.41	64.51	26.03	69.16
18	50.00	32.92	67.08	28.41	71.59
19	52.78	35.49	69.59	30.84	73.97
20	55.56	38.10	72.06	33.34	76.28
21	58.33	40.76	74.49	35.89	78.54
22	61.11	43.46	76.86	38.51	80.73
23	63.89	46.22	79.18	41.19	82.86
24	66.67	49.03	81.44	43.93	84.91
25	69.44	51.89	83.65	46.75	86.90
26	72.22	54.81	85.80	49.63	88.81
27	75.00	57.80	87.88	52.60	90.64
28	77.78	60.85	89.88	55.65	92.37
29	80.56	63.98	91.81	58.80	94.00

N = number of trials, x = number of successes, etc., $100\,p_x = 100\,x/N$

x	$100p_x$	95% $100p_l$	95% $100p_r$	99% $100p_l$	99% $100p_r$
		$N = 36$ (continued)			
30	83.33	67.19	93.63	62.06	95.51
31	86.11	70.50	95.33	65.44	96.88
32	88.89	73.94	96.89	68.98	98.07
33	91.67	77.53	98.25	72.71	99.04
34	94.44	81.34	99.32	76.71	99.71
35	97.22	85.47	99.93	81.11	99.99
36	100.00	90.26	100.00	86.31	100.00
		$N = 37$			
0	0.00	0.00	9.49	0.00	13.34
1	2.70	0.07	14.16	0.01	18.42
2	5.41	0.66	18.19	0.28	22.73
3	8.11	1.70	21.91	0.94	26.63
4	10.81	3.03	25.42	1.88	30.28
5	13.51	4.54	28.77	3.04	33.75
6	16.22	6.19	32.01	4.36	37.06
7	18.92	7.96	35.16	5.83	40.25
8	21.62	9.83	38.21	7.41	43.33
9	24.32	11.77	41.20	9.09	46.32
10	27.03	13.79	44.12	10.86	49.24
11	29.73	15.87	46.98	12.71	52.07
12	32.43	18.01	49.79	14.64	54.83
13	35.14	20.21	52.54	16.63	57.53
14	37.84	22.46	55.24	18.69	60.17
15	40.54	24.75	57.90	20.81	62.75
16	43.24	27.10	60.51	22.99	65.26
17	45.95	29.49	63.08	25.22	67.73
18	48.65	31.92	65.60	27.52	70.13
19	51.35	34.40	68.08	29.87	72.48
20	54.05	36.92	70.51	32.27	74.78
21	56.76	39.49	72.90	34.74	77.01
22	59.46	42.10	75.25	37.25	79.19
23	62.16	44.76	77.54	39.83	81.31
24	64.86	47.46	79.79	42.47	83.37
25	67.57	50.21	81.99	45.17	85.36
26	70.27	53.02	84.13	47.93	87.29
27	72.97	55.88	86.21	50.76	89.14
28	75.68	58.80	88.23	53.68	90.91
29	78.38	61.79	90.17	56.67	92.59
30	81.08	64.84	92.04	59.75	94.17
31	83.78	67.99	93.81	62.94	95.64
32	86.49	71.23	95.46	66.25	96.96
33	89.19	74.58	96.97	69.72	98.12
34	91.89	78.09	98.30	73.37	99.06
35	94.59	81.81	99.34	77.27	99.72
36	97.30	85.84	99.93	81.58	99.99
37	100.00	90.51	100.00	86.66	100.00
		$N = 38$			
0	0.00	0.00	9.25	0.00	13.01
1	2.63	0.07	13.81	0.01	17.98
2	5.26	0.64	17.75	0.28	22.19
3	7.89	1.66	21.38	0.91	26.01
4	10.53	2.94	24.80	1.83	29.58
5	13.16	4.41	28.09	2.95	32.97
6	15.79	6.02	31.25	4.24	36.21
7	18.42	7.74	34.33	5.67	39.34
8	21.05	9.55	37.32	7.20	42.36
9	23.68	11.44	40.24	8.83	45.30
10	26.32	13.40	43.10	10.55	48.15
11	28.95	15.42	45.90	12.35	50.94
12	31.58	17.50	48.65	14.21	53.65
13	34.21	19.63	51.35	16.14	56.31
14	36.84	21.81	54.01	18.14	58.90
15	39.47	24.04	56.61	20.19	61.44
16	42.11	26.31	59.18	22.30	63.92
17	44.74	28.62	61.70	24.47	66.35
18	47.37	30.98	64.18	26.68	68.72
19	50.00	33.38	66.62	28.95	71.05
20	52.63	35.82	69.02	31.28	73.32
21	55.26	38.30	71.38	33.65	75.53
22	57.89	40.82	73.69	36.08	77.70
23	60.53	43.39	75.96	38.56	79.81
24	63.16	45.99	78.19	41.10	81.86
25	65.79	48.65	80.37	43.69	83.86
26	68.42	51.35	82.50	46.35	85.79
27	71.05	54.10	84.58	49.06	87.65
28	73.68	56.90	86.60	51.85	89.45
29	76.32	59.76	88.56	54.70	91.17
30	78.95	62.68	90.45	57.64	92.80
31	81.58	65.67	92.26	60.66	94.33
32	84.21	68.75	93.98	63.79	95.76
33	86.84	71.91	95.59	67.03	97.05
34	89.47	75.20	97.06	70.42	98.17
35	92.11	78.62	98.34	73.99	99.09
36	94.74	82.25	99.36	77.81	99.72
37	97.37	86.19	99.93	82.02	99.99
38	100.00	90.75	100.00	86.99	100.00
		$N = 39$			
0	0.00	0.00	9.03	0.00	12.70
1	2.56	0.06	13.48	0.01	17.56
2	5.13	0.63	17.32	0.27	21.67
3	7.69	1.62	20.87	0.89	25.41
4	10.26	2.87	24.22	1.78	28.90
5	12.82	4.30	27.43	2.87	32.22
6	15.38	5.86	30.53	4.13	35.40
7	17.95	7.54	33.54	5.51	38.47
8	20.51	9.30	36.46	7.01	41.43
9	23.08	11.13	39.33	8.59	44.31
10	25.64	13.04	42.13	10.26	47.12
11	28.21	15.00	44.87	12.00	49.85
12	30.77	17.02	47.57	13.81	52.52
13	33.33	19.09	50.22	15.69	55.13
14	35.90	21.20	52.82	17.62	57.68
15	38.46	23.36	55.38	19.61	60.18
16	41.03	25.57	57.90	21.66	62.62
17	43.59	27.81	60.38	23.75	65.02
18	46.15	30.09	62.82	25.90	67.36
19	48.72	32.42	65.22	28.10	69.66
20	51.28	34.78	67.58	30.34	71.90
21	53.85	37.18	69.91	32.64	74.10
22	56.41	39.62	72.19	34.98	76.25
23	58.97	42.10	74.43	37.38	78.34
24	61.54	44.62	76.64	39.82	80.39
25	64.10	47.18	78.80	42.32	82.38
26	66.67	49.78	80.91	44.87	84.31
27	69.23	52.43	82.98	47.48	86.19
28	71.79	55.13	85.00	50.15	88.00
29	74.36	57.87	86.96	52.88	89.74
30	76.92	60.67	88.87	55.69	91.41
31	79.49	63.54	90.70	58.57	92.99
32	82.05	66.46	92.46	61.53	94.49
33	84.62	69.47	94.14	64.60	95.87
34	87.18	72.57	95.70	67.78	97.13
35	89.74	75.78	97.13	71.10	98.22
36	92.31	79.13	98.38	74.59	99.11
37	94.87	82.68	99.37	78.33	99.73
38	97.44	86.52	99.94	82.44	99.99
39	100.00	90.97	100.00	87.30	100.00
		$N = 40$			
0	0.00	0.00	8.81	0.00	12.41
1	2.50	0.06	13.16	0.01	17.15
2	5.00	0.61	16.92	0.26	21.18
3	7.50	1.57	20.39	0.86	24.84
4	10.00	2.79	23.66	1.73	28.26
5	12.50	4.19	26.80	2.80	31.51
6	15.00	5.71	29.84	4.02	34.63
7	17.50	7.34	32.78	5.37	37.63
8	20.00	9.05	35.65	6.82	40.54
9	22.50	10.84	38.45	8.36	43.37
10	25.00	12.69	41.20	9.98	46.12
11	27.50	14.60	43.89	11.68	48.81
12	30.00	16.56	46.53	13.44	51.43
13	32.50	18.57	49.13	15.26	54.00
14	35.00	20.63	51.68	17.13	56.51
15	37.50	22.73	54.20	19.06	58.97
16	40.00	24.86	56.67	21.05	61.38
17	42.50	27.04	59.11	23.08	63.74
18	45.00	29.26	61.51	25.16	66.05
19	47.50	31.51	63.87	27.29	68.32
20	50.00	33.80	66.20	29.46	70.54
21	52.50	36.13	68.49	31.68	72.71
22	55.00	38.49	70.74	33.95	74.84
23	57.50	40.89	72.96	36.26	76.92
24	60.00	43.33	75.14	38.62	78.95
25	62.50	45.80	77.27	41.03	80.94
26	65.00	48.32	79.37	43.49	82.87
27	67.50	50.87	81.43	46.00	84.74
28	70.00	53.47	83.44	48.57	86.56
29	72.50	56.11	85.40	51.19	88.32
30	75.00	58.80	87.31	53.88	90.02
31	77.50	61.55	89.16	56.63	91.64
32	80.00	64.35	90.95	59.46	93.18
33	82.50	67.22	92.66	62.37	94.63
34	85.00	70.16	94.29	65.37	95.98
35	87.50	73.20	95.81	68.49	97.20
36	90.00	76.34	97.21	71.74	98.27
37	92.50	79.61	98.43	75.16	99.14
38	95.00	83.08	99.39	78.82	99.74
39	97.50	86.84	99.94	82.85	99.99
40	100.00	91.19	100.00	87.59	100.00
		$N = 41$			
0	0.00	0.00	8.60	0.00	12.12
1	2.44	0.06	12.86	0.01	16.77
2	4.88	0.60	16.53	0.26	20.71
3	7.32	1.54	19.92	0.84	24.29
4	9.76	2.72	23.13	1.69	27.64
5	12.20	4.08	26.20	2.73	30.83
6	14.63	5.57	29.17	3.92	33.89
7	17.07	7.15	32.06	5.23	36.83
8	19.51	8.82	34.87	6.64	39.69
9	21.95	10.56	37.61	8.14	42.46
10	24.39	12.36	40.30	9.72	45.17
11	26.83	14.22	42.94	11.37	47.81
12	29.27	16.13	45.54	13.08	50.38
13	31.71	18.08	48.09	14.85	52.91
14	34.15	20.08	50.59	16.67	55.38
15	36.59	22.12	53.06	18.55	57.80
16	39.02	24.20	55.50	20.47	60.17
17	41.46	26.32	57.89	22.44	62.50
18	43.90	28.47	60.25	24.46	64.78
19	46.34	30.66	62.58	26.53	67.02
20	48.78	32.88	64.87	28.63	69.22
21	51.22	35.13	67.12	30.78	71.37
22	53.66	37.42	69.34	32.98	73.47
23	56.10	39.75	71.53	35.22	75.54
24	58.54	42.11	73.68	37.50	77.56
25	60.98	44.50	75.80	39.83	79.53
26	63.41	46.94	77.88	42.20	81.45
27	65.85	49.41	79.92	44.62	83.33
28	68.29	51.91	81.92	47.09	85.15
29	70.73	54.46	83.87	49.62	86.92
30	73.17	57.06	85.78	52.19	88.63
31	75.61	59.70	87.64	54.83	90.28
32	78.05	62.39	89.44	57.54	91.86
33	80.49	65.13	91.18	60.31	93.36
34	82.93	67.94	92.85	63.17	94.77
35	85.37	70.83	94.43	66.11	96.08
36	87.80	73.80	95.92	69.17	97.27
37	90.24	76.87	97.28	72.36	98.31
38	92.68	80.08	98.46	75.71	99.16
39	95.12	83.47	99.40	79.29	99.74
40	97.56	87.14	99.94	83.23	99.99
41	100.00	91.40	100.00	87.88	100.00
		$N = 42$			
0	0.00	0.00	8.41	0.00	11.85
1	2.38	0.06	12.57	0.01	16.40
2	4.76	0.58	16.16	0.25	20.26
3	7.14	1.50	19.48	0.82	23.77
4	9.52	2.66	22.62	1.65	27.05
5	11.90	3.98	25.63	2.66	30.18
6	14.29	5.43	28.54	3.82	33.18
7	16.67	6.97	31.36	5.10	36.07
8	19.05	8.60	34.12	6.47	38.87
9	21.43	10.30	36.81	7.94	41.59
10	23.81	12.05	39.45	9.47	44.25
11	26.19	13.86	42.04	11.08	46.84
12	28.57	15.72	44.58	12.74	49.38
13	30.95	17.62	47.09	14.46	51.86
14	33.33	19.57	49.55	16.23	54.29
15	35.71	21.55	51.97	18.06	56.68
16	38.10	23.57	54.36	19.93	59.02
17	40.48	25.63	56.72	21.84	61.31
18	42.86	27.72	59.04	23.80	63.56
19	45.24	29.85	61.33	25.81	65.77
20	47.62	32.00	63.58	27.85	67.94
21	50.00	34.19	65.81	29.93	70.07
22	52.38	36.42	68.00	32.06	72.15
23	54.76	38.67	70.15	34.23	74.19
24	57.14	40.96	72.28	36.44	76.20
25	59.52	43.28	74.37	38.69	78.16
26	61.90	45.64	76.43	40.98	80.07
27	64.29	48.03	78.45	43.32	81.94
28	66.67	50.45	80.43	45.71	83.77
29	69.05	52.91	82.38	48.14	85.54
30	71.43	55.42	84.28	50.62	87.26
31	73.81	57.96	86.14	53.16	88.92
32	76.19	60.55	87.95	55.75	90.53
33	78.57	63.19	89.70	58.41	92.06
34	80.95	65.88	91.40	61.13	93.53
35	83.33	68.64	93.03	63.93	94.90
36	85.71	71.46	94.57	66.82	96.18
37	88.10	74.37	96.02	69.82	97.34
38	90.48	77.38	97.34	72.95	98.35
39	92.86	80.52	98.50	76.23	99.18
40	95.24	83.84	99.42	79.74	99.75
41	97.62	87.43	99.94	83.60	99.99
42	100.00	91.59	100.00	88.15	100.00
		$N = 43$			
0	0.00	0.00	8.22	0.00	11.59
1	2.33	0.06	12.29	0.01	16.04
2	4.65	0.57	15.81	0.24	19.82
3	6.98	1.46	19.06	0.80	23.27
4	9.30	2.59	22.14	1.61	26.49
5	11.63	3.89	25.08	2.60	29.55
6	13.95	5.30	27.93	3.73	32.49
7	16.28	6.81	30.70	4.97	35.33
8	18.60	8.39	33.40	6.32	38.08
9	20.93	10.04	36.04	7.74	40.76
10	23.26	11.76	38.63	9.24	43.37
11	25.58	13.52	41.17	10.80	45.92
12	27.91	15.33	43.67	12.42	48.41
13	30.23	17.18	46.13	14.09	50.85
14	32.56	19.08	48.54	15.82	53.25
15	34.88	21.01	50.93	17.59	55.59
16	37.21	22.98	53.27	19.41	57.90
17	39.53	24.98	55.59	21.27	60.16
18	41.86	27.01	57.87	23.18	62.38
19	44.19	29.08	60.12	25.12	64.56
20	46.51	31.18	62.35	27.11	66.70
21	48.84	33.31	64.54	29.13	68.80
22	51.16	35.46	66.69	31.20	70.87
23	53.49	37.65	68.82	33.30	72.89
24	55.81	39.88	70.92	35.44	74.88
25	58.14	42.13	72.99	37.62	76.82
26	60.47	44.41	75.02	39.84	78.73
27	62.79	46.73	77.02	42.10	80.59
28	65.12	49.07	78.99	44.41	82.41
29	67.44	51.46	80.92	46.75	84.18
30	69.77	53.87	82.82	49.15	85.91
31	72.09	56.33	84.67	51.59	87.58
32	74.42	58.83	86.48	54.08	89.20
33	76.74	61.37	88.24	56.63	90.76
34	79.07	63.96	89.96	59.24	92.26
35	81.40	66.60	91.61	61.92	93.68
36	83.72	69.30	93.19	64.67	95.03
37	86.05	72.07	94.70	67.51	96.27
38	88.37	74.92	96.11	70.45	97.40
39	90.70	77.86	97.41	73.51	98.39
40	93.02	80.94	98.54	76.73	99.20
41	95.35	84.19	99.43	80.18	99.76
42	97.67	87.71	99.94	83.96	99.99
43	100.00	91.78	100.00	88.41	100.00
		$N = 44$			
0	0.00	0.00	8.04	0.00	11.34
1	2.27	0.06	12.02	0.01	15.70
2	4.55	0.56	15.47	0.24	19.41
3	6.82	1.43	18.66	0.78	22.79
4	9.09	2.53	21.67	1.57	25.95
5	11.36	3.79	24.56	2.54	28.95
6	13.64	5.17	27.35	3.64	31.84
7	15.91	6.64	30.07	4.85	34.62
8	18.18	8.19	32.71	6.16	37.33
9	20.45	9.80	35.30	7.55	39.96
10	22.73	11.47	37.84	9.01	42.52
11	25.00	13.19	40.34	10.53	45.03
12	27.27	14.96	42.79	12.11	47.48
13	29.55	16.76	45.20	13.74	49.88
14	31.82	18.61	47.58	15.43	52.24
15	34.09	20.49	49.92	17.15	54.55
16	36.36	22.41	52.23	18.92	56.82
17	38.64	24.36	54.50	20.73	59.05
18	40.91	26.34	56.75	22.59	61.24
19	43.18	28.35	58.97	24.48	63.39
20	45.45	30.39	61.15	26.41	65.50
21	47.73	32.46	63.31	28.37	67.58
22	50.00	34.56	65.44	30.38	69.62
23	52.27	36.69	67.54	32.42	71.63
24	54.55	38.85	69.61	34.50	73.59
25	56.82	41.03	71.65	36.61	75.52
26	59.09	43.25	73.66	38.76	77.41
27	61.36	45.50	75.64	40.95	79.27
28	63.64	47.77	77.59	43.18	81.08
29	65.91	50.08	79.51	45.45	82.85
30	68.18	52.42	81.39	47.76	84.57
31	70.45	54.80	83.24	50.12	86.26
32	72.73	57.21	85.04	52.52	87.89
33	75.00	59.66	86.81	54.97	89.47
34	77.27	62.16	88.53	57.48	90.99
35	79.55	64.70	90.20	60.04	92.45
36	81.82	67.29	91.81	62.67	93.84
37	84.09	69.93	93.36	65.38	95.15
38	86.36	72.65	94.83	68.16	96.36
39	88.64	75.44	96.21	71.05	97.46
40	90.91	78.33	97.47	74.05	98.43
41	93.18	81.34	98.57	77.21	99.22
42	95.45	84.53	99.44	80.59	99.76
43	97.73	87.98	99.94	84.30	99.99
44	100.00	91.96	100.00	88.66	100.00
		$N = 45$			
0	0.00	0.00	7.87	0.00	11.11
1	2.22	0.06	11.77	0.01	15.38
2	4.44	0.54	15.15	0.23	19.01
3	6.67	1.40	18.27	0.77	22.32
4	8.89	2.48	21.22	1.54	25.43
5	11.11	3.71	24.05	2.48	28.38
6	13.33	5.05	26.79	3.56	31.21
7	15.56	6.49	29.46	4.74	33.95
8	17.78	8.00	32.05	6.02	36.60
9	20.00	9.58	34.60	7.37	39.18
10	22.22	11.20	37.09	8.80	41.71
11	24.44	12.88	39.54	10.28	44.17
12	26.67	14.60	41.94	11.82	46.58
13	28.89	16.37	44.31	13.41	48.95
14	31.11	18.17	46.65	15.05	51.27
15	33.33	20.00	48.95	16.73	53.54
16	35.56	21.87	51.22	18.46	55.78
17	37.78	23.77	53.46	20.22	57.98
18	40.00	25.70	55.67	22.02	60.14
19	42.22	27.66	57.85	23.86	62.26
20	44.44	29.64	60.00	25.74	64.35
21	46.67	31.66	62.13	27.65	66.40
22	48.89	33.70	64.23	29.60	68.42
23	51.11	35.77	66.30	31.58	70.40
24	53.33	37.87	68.34	33.60	72.35
25	55.56	40.00	70.36	35.65	74.26
26	57.78	42.15	72.34	37.74	76.14
27	60.00	44.33	74.30	39.86	77.98

N = number of trials, x = number of successes, etc., $100\,p_x = 100\,x/N$

$N = 45$ (continued)

x	$100p_x$	$100(1-2\alpha)$ limits 95% $100p_l$	95% $100p_r$	99% $100p_l$	99% $100p_r$
28	62.22	46.54	76.23	42.02	79.78
29	64.44	48.78	78.13	44.22	81.54
30	66.67	51.05	80.00	46.46	83.27
31	68.89	53.35	81.83	48.73	84.95
32	71.11	55.69	83.63	51.05	86.59
33	73.33	58.06	85.40	53.42	88.18
34	75.56	60.46	87.12	55.83	89.72
35	77.78	62.91	88.80	58.29	91.20
36	80.00	65.40	90.42	60.82	92.63
37	82.22	67.95	92.00	63.40	93.98
38	84.44	70.54	93.51	66.05	95.26
39	86.67	73.21	94.95	68.79	96.44
40	88.89	75.95	96.29	71.62	97.52
41	91.11	78.78	97.52	74.57	98.46
42	93.33	81.73	98.60	77.68	99.23
43	95.56	84.85	99.46	80.99	99.77
44	97.78	88.23	99.94	84.62	99.99
45	100.00	92.13	100.00	88.89	100.00

$N = 46$

x	$100p_x$	95% $100p_l$	95% $100p_r$	99% $100p_l$	99% $100p_r$
0	0.00	0.00	7.71	0.00	10.88
1	2.17	0.06	11.53	0.01	15.07
2	4.35	0.53	14.84	0.23	18.63
3	6.52	1.37	17.90	0.75	21.88
4	8.70	2.42	20.79	1.50	24.93
5	10.87	3.62	23.57	2.42	27.82
6	13.04	4.94	26.26	3.47	30.60
7	15.22	6.34	28.87	4.63	33.29
8	17.39	7.82	31.42	5.88	35.90
9	19.57	9.36	33.91	7.20	38.44
10	21.74	10.95	36.36	8.59	40.92
11	23.91	12.59	38.77	10.04	43.34
12	26.09	14.27	41.13	11.54	45.72
13	28.26	15.99	43.46	13.10	48.04
14	30.43	17.74	45.75	14.69	50.33
15	32.61	19.53	48.02	16.33	52.57
16	34.78	21.35	50.25	18.01	54.77
17	36.96	23.21	52.45	19.73	56.94
18	39.13	25.09	54.63	21.49	59.07
19	41.30	27.00	56.77	23.28	61.16
20	43.48	28.93	58.89	25.11	63.23
21	45.65	30.90	60.99	26.97	65.25
22	47.83	32.89	63.05	28.86	67.25
23	50.00	34.90	65.10	30.79	69.21
24	52.17	36.95	67.11	32.75	71.14
25	54.35	39.01	69.10	34.75	73.03
26	56.52	41.11	71.07	36.77	74.89
27	58.70	43.23	73.00	38.84	76.72
28	60.87	45.37	74.91	40.93	78.51
29	63.04	47.55	76.79	43.06	80.27
30	65.22	49.75	78.65	45.23	81.99
31	67.39	51.98	80.47	47.43	83.67
32	69.57	54.25	82.26	49.67	85.31
33	71.74	56.54	84.01	51.96	86.90
34	73.91	58.87	85.73	54.28	88.46
35	76.09	61.23	87.41	56.66	89.96
36	78.26	63.64	89.05	59.08	91.41
37	80.43	66.09	90.64	61.56	92.80
38	82.61	68.58	92.18	64.10	94.12
39	84.78	71.13	93.66	66.71	95.37
40	86.96	73.74	95.06	69.40	96.53
41	89.13	76.43	96.38	72.18	97.58
42	91.30	79.21	97.58	75.07	98.50
43	93.48	82.10	98.63	78.12	99.25
44	95.65	85.16	99.47	81.37	99.77
45	97.83	88.47	99.94	84.93	99.99
46	100.00	92.29	100.00	89.12	100.00

$N = 47$

x	$100p_x$	95% $100p_l$	95% $100p_r$	99% $100p_l$	99% $100p_r$
0	0.00	0.00	7.55	0.00	10.66
1	2.13	0.05	11.29	0.01	14.77
2	4.26	0.52	14.54	0.22	18.27
3	6.38	1.34	17.54	0.73	21.45
4	8.51	2.37	20.38	1.47	24.44
5	10.64	3.55	23.10	2.37	27.29
6	12.77	4.83	25.74	3.40	30.02
7	14.89	6.20	28.31	4.53	32.66
8	17.02	7.65	30.81	5.75	35.23
9	19.15	9.15	33.26	7.04	37.72
10	21.28	10.70	35.66	8.40	40.16
11	23.40	12.30	38.03	9.81	42.55
12	25.53	13.94	40.35	11.28	44.88
13	27.66	15.62	42.64	12.79	47.17
14	29.79	17.34	44.89	14.35	49.42
15	31.91	19.09	47.12	15.95	51.63
16	34.04	20.86	49.31	17.59	53.80
17	36.17	22.67	51.48	19.27	55.94
18	38.30	24.51	53.62	20.98	58.04
19	40.43	26.37	55.73	22.73	60.11
20	42.55	28.26	57.82	24.51	62.14
21	44.68	30.17	59.88	26.32	64.14
22	46.81	32.11	61.92	28.16	66.11
23	48.94	34.08	63.94	30.04	68.05
24	51.06	36.06	65.92	31.95	69.96
25	53.19	38.08	67.89	33.89	71.84
26	55.32	40.12	69.83	35.86	73.68
27	57.45	42.18	71.74	37.86	75.49

$N = 47$ (continued)

x	$100p_x$	95% $100p_l$	95% $100p_r$	99% $100p_l$	99% $100p_r$
28	59.57	44.27	73.63	39.89	77.27
29	61.70	46.38	75.49	41.96	79.02
30	63.83	48.52	77.33	44.06	80.73
31	65.96	50.69	79.14	46.20	82.41
32	68.09	52.88	80.91	48.37	84.05
33	70.21	55.11	82.66	50.58	85.65
34	72.34	57.36	84.38	52.83	87.21
35	74.47	59.65	86.06	55.12	88.72
36	76.60	61.97	87.70	57.45	90.19
37	78.72	64.34	89.30	59.84	91.60
38	80.85	66.74	90.85	62.28	92.96
39	82.98	69.19	92.35	64.77	94.25
40	85.11	71.69	93.80	67.34	95.47
41	87.23	74.26	95.17	69.98	96.60
42	89.36	76.90	96.45	72.71	97.63
43	91.49	79.62	97.63	75.56	98.53
44	93.62	82.46	98.66	78.55	99.27
45	95.74	85.46	99.48	81.73	99.78
46	97.87	88.71	99.95	85.23	99.99
47	100.00	92.45	100.00	89.34	100.00

$N = 48$

x	$100p_x$	95% $100p_l$	95% $100p_r$	99% $100p_l$	99% $100p_r$
0	0.00	0.00	7.40	0.00	10.45
1	2.08	0.05	11.07	0.01	14.48
2	4.17	0.51	14.25	0.22	17.91
3	6.25	1.31	17.20	0.72	21.04
4	8.33	2.32	19.98	1.44	23.98
5	10.42	3.47	22.66	2.32	26.78
6	12.50	4.73	25.25	3.32	29.46
7	14.58	6.07	27.76	4.43	32.06
8	16.67	7.48	30.22	5.62	34.58
9	18.75	8.95	32.63	6.89	37.03
10	20.83	10.47	34.99	8.21	39.43
11	22.92	12.03	37.31	9.59	41.78
12	25.00	13.64	39.60	11.03	44.08
13	27.08	15.28	41.85	12.51	46.33
14	29.17	16.95	44.06	14.03	48.55
15	31.25	18.66	46.25	15.59	50.72
16	33.33	20.40	48.41	17.19	52.86
17	35.42	22.16	50.54	18.83	54.97
18	37.50	23.95	52.65	20.50	57.04
19	39.58	25.77	54.73	22.20	59.08
20	41.67	27.61	56.79	23.93	61.09
21	43.75	29.48	58.82	25.70	63.07
22	45.83	31.37	60.83	27.50	65.01
23	47.92	33.29	62.81	29.33	66.93
24	50.00	35.23	64.77	31.18	68.82
25	52.08	37.19	66.71	33.07	70.67
26	54.17	39.17	68.63	34.99	72.50
27	56.25	41.18	70.52	36.93	74.30
28	58.33	43.21	72.39	38.91	76.07
29	60.42	45.27	74.23	40.92	77.80
30	62.50	47.35	76.05	42.96	79.50
31	64.58	49.46	77.84	45.03	81.17
32	66.67	51.59	79.60	47.14	82.81
33	68.75	53.75	81.34	49.28	84.41
34	70.83	55.94	83.05	51.45	85.97
35	72.92	58.15	84.72	53.67	87.49
36	75.00	60.40	86.36	55.92	88.97
37	77.08	62.69	87.97	58.22	90.41
38	79.17	65.01	89.53	60.57	91.79
39	81.25	67.37	91.05	62.97	93.11
40	83.33	69.78	92.52	65.42	94.38
41	85.42	72.24	93.93	67.94	95.57
42	87.50	74.75	95.27	70.54	96.68
43	89.58	77.34	96.53	73.22	97.68
44	91.67	80.02	97.68	76.02	98.56
45	93.75	82.80	98.69	78.96	99.28
46	95.83	85.75	99.49	82.09	99.78
47	97.92	88.93	99.95	85.52	99.99
48	100.00	92.60	100.00	89.55	100.00

$N = 49$

x	$100p_x$	95% $100p_l$	95% $100p_r$	99% $100p_l$	99% $100p_r$
0	0.00	0.00	7.25	0.00	10.25
1	2.04	0.05	10.85	0.01	14.21
2	4.08	0.50	13.98	0.21	17.58
3	6.12	1.28	16.87	0.70	20.65
4	8.16	2.27	19.60	1.41	23.53
5	10.20	3.40	22.23	2.27	26.28
6	12.24	4.63	24.77	3.25	28.92
7	14.29	5.94	27.24	4.34	31.47
8	16.33	7.32	29.66	5.50	33.95
9	18.37	8.76	32.02	6.74	36.37
10	20.41	10.24	34.34	8.03	38.73
11	22.45	11.77	36.62	9.39	41.04
12	24.49	13.34	38.87	10.79	43.30
13	26.53	14.95	41.08	12.23	45.52
14	28.57	16.58	43.26	13.72	47.70
15	30.61	18.25	45.42	15.24	49.85
16	32.65	19.95	47.54	16.81	51.96
17	34.69	21.67	49.64	18.40	54.03
18	36.73	23.42	51.71	20.03	56.07
19	38.78	25.20	53.76	21.69	58.09
20	40.82	27.00	55.79	23.39	60.07
21	42.86	28.82	57.79	25.11	62.02
22	44.90	30.67	59.77	26.86	63.95
23	46.94	32.53	61.73	28.64	65.84

$N = 49$ (continued)

x	$100p_x$	95% $100p_l$	95% $100p_r$	99% $100p_l$	99% $100p_r$
24	48.98	34.42	63.66	30.45	67.71
25	51.02	36.34	65.58	32.29	69.55
26	53.06	38.27	67.47	34.16	71.36
27	55.10	40.23	69.33	36.05	73.14
28	57.14	42.21	71.18	37.98	74.89
29	59.18	44.21	73.00	39.93	76.61
30	61.22	46.24	74.80	41.91	78.31
31	63.27	48.29	76.58	43.93	79.97
32	65.31	50.36	78.33	45.97	81.60
33	67.35	52.46	80.05	48.04	83.19
34	69.39	54.58	81.75	50.15	84.76
35	71.43	56.74	83.42	52.30	86.28
36	73.47	58.92	85.05	54.48	87.77
37	75.51	61.13	86.66	56.70	89.21
38	77.55	63.38	88.23	58.96	90.61
39	79.59	65.66	89.76	61.27	91.97
40	81.63	67.98	91.24	63.63	93.26
41	83.67	70.34	92.68	66.05	94.50
42	85.71	72.76	94.06	68.53	95.66
43	87.76	75.23	95.37	71.08	96.75
44	89.80	77.77	96.60	73.72	97.73
45	91.84	80.40	97.73	76.47	98.59
46	93.88	83.13	98.72	79.35	99.30
47	95.92	86.02	99.50	82.42	99.79
48	97.96	89.15	99.95	85.79	99.99
49	100.00	92.75	100.00	89.75	100.00

$N = 50$

x	$100p_x$	95% $100p_l$	95% $100p_r$	99% $100p_l$	99% $100p_r$
0	0.00	0.00	7.11	0.00	10.05
1	2.00	0.05	10.65	0.01	13.94
2	4.00	0.49	13.71	0.21	17.25
3	6.00	1.25	16.55	0.69	20.27
4	8.00	2.22	19.23	1.38	23.11
5	10.00	3.33	21.81	2.22	25.80
6	12.00	4.53	24.31	3.19	28.40
7	14.00	5.82	26.74	4.25	30.91
8	16.00	7.17	29.11	5.39	33.35
9	18.00	8.58	31.44	6.60	35.73
10	20.00	10.03	33.72	7.86	38.05
11	22.00	11.53	35.96	9.19	40.32
12	24.00	13.06	38.17	10.56	42.55
13	26.00	14.63	40.34	11.97	44.74
14	28.00	16.23	42.49	13.42	46.89
15	30.00	17.86	44.61	14.91	49.00
16	32.00	19.52	46.70	16.44	51.08
17	34.00	21.21	48.77	18.00	53.12
18	36.00	22.92	50.81	19.59	55.14
19	38.00	24.65	52.83	21.21	57.13
20	40.00	26.41	54.82	22.87	59.08
21	42.00	28.19	56.79	24.55	61.01
22	44.00	29.99	58.75	26.26	62.91
23	46.00	31.81	60.68	27.99	64.78
24	48.00	33.66	62.58	29.76	66.63
25	50.00	35.53	64.47	31.55	68.45
26	52.00	37.42	66.34	33.37	70.24
27	54.00	39.32	68.19	35.22	72.01
28	56.00	41.25	70.01	37.09	73.74
29	58.00	43.21	71.81	38.99	75.45
30	60.00	45.18	73.59	40.92	77.13
31	62.00	47.17	75.35	42.87	78.79
32	64.00	49.19	77.08	44.86	80.41
33	66.00	51.23	78.79	46.88	82.00
34	68.00	53.30	80.48	48.92	83.56
35	70.00	55.39	82.14	51.00	85.09
36	72.00	57.51	83.77	53.11	86.58
37	74.00	59.66	85.37	55.26	88.03
38	76.00	61.83	86.94	57.45	89.44
39	78.00	64.04	88.47	59.68	90.81
40	80.00	66.28	89.97	61.95	92.14
41	82.00	68.56	91.42	64.27	93.40
42	84.00	70.89	92.83	66.65	94.61
43	86.00	73.26	94.18	69.09	95.75
44	88.00	75.69	95.47	71.60	96.81
45	90.00	78.19	96.67	74.20	97.78
46	92.00	80.77	97.78	76.89	98.62
47	94.00	83.45	98.75	79.73	99.31
48	96.00	86.29	99.51	82.75	99.79
49	98.00	89.35	99.95	86.06	99.99
50	100.00	92.89	100.00	89.95	100.00

$N = 51$

x	$100p_x$	95% $100p_l$	95% $100p_r$	99% $100p_l$	99% $100p_r$
0	0.00	0.00	6.98	0.00	9.87
1	1.96	0.05	10.45	0.01	13.68
2	3.92	0.48	13.46	0.20	16.94
3	5.88	1.23	16.24	0.67	19.90
4	7.84	2.18	18.88	1.35	22.69
5	9.80	3.26	21.41	2.18	25.35
6	11.76	4.44	23.87	3.12	27.90
7	13.73	5.70	26.26	4.16	30.37
8	15.69	7.02	28.59	5.28	32.77
9	17.65	8.40	30.87	6.46	35.11
10	19.61	9.82	33.12	7.70	37.39
11	21.57	11.29	35.32	8.99	39.63
12	23.53	12.79	37.49	10.33	41.82
13	25.49	14.33	39.63	11.72	43.98
14	27.45	15.89	41.74	13.14	46.09
15	29.41	17.49	43.83	14.59	48.18

$N = 51$ (continued)

x	$100p_x$	95% $100p_l$	95% $100p_r$	99% $100p_l$	99% $100p_r$
16	31.37	19.11	45.89	16.09	50.23
17	33.33	20.76	47.92	17.61	52.25
18	35.29	22.43	49.93	19.17	54.23
19	37.25	24.13	51.92	20.75	56.19
20	39.22	25.84	53.89	22.37	58.12
21	41.18	27.58	55.83	24.01	60.03
22	43.14	29.35	57.75	25.68	61.91
23	45.10	31.13	59.66	27.37	63.76
24	47.06	32.93	61.54	29.10	65.58
25	49.02	34.75	63.40	30.84	67.38
26	50.98	36.60	65.25	32.62	69.16
27	52.94	38.46	67.07	34.42	70.90
28	54.90	40.34	68.87	36.24	72.63
29	56.86	42.25	70.65	38.09	74.32
30	58.82	44.17	72.42	39.97	75.99
31	60.78	46.11	74.16	41.88	77.63
32	62.75	48.08	75.87	43.81	79.25
33	64.71	50.07	77.57	45.77	80.83
34	66.67	52.08	79.24	47.75	82.39
35	68.63	54.11	80.89	49.77	83.91
36	70.59	56.17	82.51	51.82	85.41
37	72.55	58.26	84.11	53.91	86.86
38	74.51	60.37	85.67	56.02	88.28
39	76.47	62.51	87.21	58.18	89.67
40	78.43	64.68	88.71	60.37	91.01
41	80.39	66.88	90.18	62.61	92.30
42	82.35	69.13	91.60	64.89	93.54
43	84.31	71.41	92.98	67.23	94.72
44	86.27	73.74	94.30	69.63	95.84
45	88.24	76.13	95.56	72.10	96.88
46	90.20	78.59	96.74	74.65	97.82
47	92.16	81.12	97.82	77.31	98.65
48	94.12	83.76	98.77	80.10	99.33
49	96.08	86.54	99.52	83.06	99.80
50	98.04	89.55	99.95	86.32	99.99
51	100.00	93.02	100.00	90.13	100.00

$N = 52$

x	$100p_x$	95% $100p_l$	95% $100p_r$	99% $100p_l$	99% $100p_r$
0	0.00	0.00	6.85	0.00	9.69
1	1.92	0.05	10.26	0.01	13.44
2	3.85	0.47	13.21	0.20	16.63
3	5.77	1.21	15.95	0.66	19.55
4	7.69	2.14	18.54	1.32	22.29
5	9.62	3.20	21.03	2.13	24.90
6	11.54	4.35	23.44	3.06	27.41
7	13.46	5.59	25.79	4.08	29.84
8	15.38	6.88	28.08	5.17	32.20
9	17.31	8.23	30.33	6.33	34.51
10	19.23	9.63	32.53	7.54	36.76
11	21.15	11.06	34.70	8.81	38.96
12	23.08	12.53	36.84	10.12	41.12
13	25.00	14.03	38.95	11.47	43.24
14	26.92	15.57	41.02	12.86	45.33
15	28.85	17.13	43.08	14.29	47.38
16	30.77	18.72	45.10	15.75	49.40
17	32.69	20.33	47.11	17.24	51.39
18	34.62	21.97	49.09	18.76	53.36
19	36.54	23.62	51.04	20.31	55.29
20	38.46	25.30	52.98	21.89	57.20
21	40.38	27.01	54.90	23.49	59.08
22	42.31	28.73	56.80	25.12	60.93
23	44.23	30.47	58.67	26.78	62.76
24	46.15	32.23	60.53	28.46	64.57
25	48.08	34.01	62.37	30.17	66.35
26	50.00	35.81	64.19	31.90	68.10
27	51.92	37.63	65.99	33.65	69.83
28	53.85	39.47	67.77	35.43	71.54
29	55.77	41.33	69.53	37.24	73.22
30	57.69	43.20	71.27	39.07	74.88
31	59.62	45.10	72.99	40.92	76.51
32	61.54	47.02	74.70	42.80	78.11
33	63.46	48.96	76.38	44.71	79.69
34	65.38	50.91	78.03	46.64	81.24
35	67.31	52.89	79.67	48.61	82.76
36	69.23	54.90	81.28	50.60	84.25
37	71.15	56.92	82.87	52.62	85.71
38	73.08	58.98	84.43	54.67	87.14
39	75.00	61.05	85.97	56.76	88.53
40	76.92	63.16	87.47	58.88	89.88
41	78.85	65.30	88.94	61.04	91.19
42	80.77	67.47	90.37	63.24	92.46
43	82.69	69.67	91.77	65.49	93.67
44	84.62	71.92	93.12	67.80	94.83
45	86.54	74.21	94.41	70.16	95.92
46	88.46	76.56	95.65	72.59	96.94
47	90.38	78.97	96.80	75.10	97.87
48	92.31	81.46	97.86	77.71	98.68
49	94.23	84.05	98.79	80.45	99.34
50	96.15	86.79	99.53	83.37	99.80
51	98.08	89.74	99.95	86.56	99.99
52	100.00	93.15	100.00	90.31	100.00

$N = 53$

x	$100p_x$	95% $100p_l$	95% $100p_r$	99% $100p_l$	99% $100p_r$
0	0.00	0.00	6.72	0.00	9.51
1	1.89	0.05	10.07	0.01	13.20
2	3.77	0.46	12.98	0.20	16.34
3	5.66	1.18	15.66	0.65	19.21

N = number of trials, x = number of successes, etc., $100\,p_x = 100\,x/N$

$N = 53$ (continued)

x	$100p_x$	95% $100p_l$	95% $100p_r$	99% $100p_l$	99% $100p_r$
4	7.55	2.09	18.21	1.30	21.90
5	9.43	3.13	20.66	2.09	24.47
6	11.32	4.27	23.03	3.00	26.94
7	13.21	5.48	25.34	4.00	29.33
8	15.09	6.75	27.59	5.07	31.66
9	16.98	8.07	29.80	6.20	33.93
10	18.87	9.44	31.97	7.39	36.14
11	20.75	10.84	34.11	8.63	38.31
12	22.64	12.28	36.21	9.92	40.44
13	24.53	13.76	38.28	11.24	42.53
14	26.42	15.26	40.33	12.60	44.59
15	28.30	16.79	42.35	14.00	46.61
16	30.19	18.34	44.34	15.43	48.61
17	32.08	19.92	46.32	16.89	50.57
18	33.96	21.52	48.27	18.37	52.51
19	35.85	23.14	50.20	19.89	54.41
20	37.74	24.79	52.11	21.43	56.30
21	39.62	26.45	54.00	23.00	58.15
22	41.51	28.14	55.87	24.59	59.99
23	43.40	29.84	57.72	26.21	61.79
24	45.28	31.56	59.55	27.86	63.58
25	47.17	33.30	61.36	29.52	65.34
26	49.06	35.06	63.16	31.21	67.07
27	50.94	36.84	64.94	32.93	68.79
28	52.83	38.64	66.70	34.66	70.48
29	54.72	40.45	68.44	36.42	72.14
30	56.60	42.28	70.16	38.21	73.79
31	58.49	44.13	71.86	40.01	75.41
32	60.38	46.00	73.55	41.85	77.00
33	62.26	47.89	75.21	43.70	78.57
34	64.15	49.80	76.86	45.59	80.11
35	66.04	51.73	78.48	47.49	81.63
36	67.92	53.68	80.08	49.43	83.11
37	69.81	55.66	81.66	51.39	84.57
38	71.70	57.65	83.21	53.39	86.00
39	73.58	59.67	84.74	55.41	87.40
40	75.47	61.72	86.24	57.47	88.76
41	77.36	63.79	87.72	59.56	90.08
42	79.25	65.89	89.16	61.69	91.37
43	81.13	68.03	90.56	63.86	92.61
44	83.02	70.20	91.93	66.07	93.80
45	84.91	72.41	93.25	68.34	94.93
46	86.79	74.66	94.52	70.67	96.00
47	88.68	76.97	95.73	73.06	97.00
48	90.57	79.34	96.87	75.53	97.91
49	92.45	81.79	97.91	78.10	98.70
50	94.34	84.34	98.82	80.79	99.35
51	96.23	87.02	99.54	83.66	99.80
52	98.11	89.93	99.95	86.80	99.99
53	100.00	93.28	100.00	90.49	100.00

$N = 54$

x	$100p_x$	95% $100p_l$	95% $100p_r$	99% $100p_l$	99% $100p_r$
0	0.00	0.00	6.60	0.00	9.35
1	1.85	0.05	9.89	0.01	12.97
2	3.70	0.45	12.75	0.19	16.06
3	5.56	1.16	15.39	0.64	18.88
4	7.41	2.06	17.89	1.27	21.53
5	9.26	3.08	20.30	2.05	24.06
6	11.11	4.19	22.63	2.94	26.49
7	12.96	5.37	24.90	3.92	28.84
8	14.81	6.62	27.12	4.97	31.13
9	16.67	7.92	29.29	6.08	33.36
10	18.52	9.25	31.43	7.25	35.55
11	20.37	10.63	33.53	8.46	37.69
12	22.22	12.04	35.60	9.72	39.78
13	24.07	13.49	37.64	11.02	41.85
14	25.93	14.96	39.65	12.35	43.87
15	27.78	16.46	41.64	13.72	45.87
16	29.63	17.98	43.61	15.12	47.83
17	31.48	19.52	45.55	16.55	49.77
18	33.33	21.09	47.47	18.00	51.68
19	35.19	22.68	49.38	19.49	53.56
20	37.04	24.29	51.26	20.99	55.42
21	38.89	25.92	53.12	22.53	57.26
22	40.74	27.57	54.97	24.09	59.07
23	42.59	29.23	56.79	25.67	60.85
24	44.44	30.92	58.60	27.27	62.62
25	46.30	32.62	60.39	28.90	64.36
26	48.15	34.34	62.16	30.55	66.08
27	50.00	36.08	63.92	32.23	67.77
28	51.85	37.84	65.66	33.92	69.45
29	53.70	39.61	67.38	35.64	71.10
30	55.56	41.40	69.08	37.38	72.73
31	57.41	43.21	70.77	39.15	74.33
32	59.26	45.03	72.43	40.93	75.91
33	61.11	46.88	74.08	42.74	77.47
34	62.96	48.74	75.71	44.58	79.01
35	64.81	50.62	77.32	46.44	80.51
36	66.67	52.53	78.91	48.32	82.00
37	68.52	54.45	80.48	50.23	83.45
38	70.37	56.39	82.02	52.17	84.88
39	72.22	58.36	83.54	54.13	86.28
40	74.07	60.35	85.04	56.13	87.65
41	75.93	62.36	86.51	58.15	88.98
42	77.78	64.40	87.96	60.22	90.28
43	79.63	66.47	89.37	62.31	91.54
44	81.48	68.57	90.75	64.45	92.75
45	83.33	70.71	92.08	66.64	93.92
46	85.19	72.88	93.38	68.87	95.03
47	87.04	75.10	94.63	71.16	96.08
48	88.89	77.37	95.81	73.51	97.06
49	90.74	79.70	96.92	75.94	97.95
50	92.59	82.11	97.94	78.47	98.73
51	94.44	84.61	98.84	81.12	99.36
52	96.30	87.25	99.55	83.94	99.81
53	98.15	90.11	99.95	87.03	99.99
54	100.00	93.40	100.00	90.65	100.00

$N = 55$

x	$100p_x$	95% $100p_l$	95% $100p_r$	99% $100p_l$	99% $100p_r$
0	0.00	0.00	6.49	0.00	9.18
1	1.82	0.05	9.72	0.01	12.75
2	3.64	0.44	12.53	0.19	15.79
3	5.45	1.14	15.12	0.62	18.56
4	7.27	2.02	17.59	1.25	21.17
5	9.09	3.02	19.95	2.01	23.66
6	10.91	4.11	22.25	2.89	26.05
7	12.73	5.27	24.48	3.85	28.37
8	14.55	6.50	26.66	4.88	30.62
9	16.36	7.77	28.80	5.97	32.82
10	18.18	9.08	30.90	7.11	34.97
11	20.00	10.43	32.97	8.30	37.08
12	21.82	11.81	35.01	9.53	39.15
13	23.64	13.23	37.02	10.81	41.18
14	25.45	14.67	39.00	12.11	43.18
15	27.27	16.14	40.96	13.45	45.15
16	29.09	17.63	42.90	14.82	47.08
17	30.91	19.14	44.81	16.22	49.00
18	32.73	20.68	46.71	17.64	50.88
19	34.55	22.24	48.58	19.10	52.74
20	36.36	23.81	50.44	20.57	54.57
21	38.18	25.41	52.27	22.07	56.39
22	40.00	27.02	54.09	23.60	58.17
23	41.82	28.65	55.89	25.15	59.94
24	43.64	30.30	57.68	26.72	61.68
25	45.45	31.97	59.45	28.31	63.40
26	47.27	33.65	61.20	29.92	65.10
27	49.09	35.35	62.93	31.56	66.78
28	50.91	37.07	64.65	33.22	68.44
29	52.73	38.80	66.35	34.90	70.08
30	54.55	40.55	68.03	36.60	71.69
31	56.36	42.32	69.70	38.32	73.28
32	58.18	44.11	71.35	40.06	74.85
33	60.00	45.91	72.98	41.83	76.40
34	61.82	47.73	74.59	43.61	77.93
35	63.64	49.56	76.19	45.43	79.43
36	65.45	51.42	77.76	47.26	80.90
37	67.27	53.29	79.32	49.12	82.36
38	69.09	55.19	80.86	51.00	83.78
39	70.91	57.10	82.37	52.92	85.18
40	72.73	59.04	83.86	54.85	86.55
41	74.55	61.00	85.33	56.82	87.89
42	76.36	62.98	86.77	58.82	89.19
43	78.18	64.99	88.19	60.85	90.47
44	80.00	67.03	89.57	62.92	91.70
45	81.82	69.10	90.92	65.03	92.89
46	83.64	71.20	92.23	67.18	94.03
47	85.45	73.34	93.50	69.38	95.12
48	87.27	75.52	94.73	71.63	96.15
49	89.09	77.75	95.89	73.95	97.11
50	90.91	80.05	96.98	76.34	97.99
51	92.73	82.41	97.98	78.83	98.75
52	94.55	84.88	98.86	81.44	99.38
53	96.36	87.47	99.56	84.21	99.81
54	98.18	90.28	99.95	87.25	99.99
55	100.00	93.51	100.00	90.82	100.00

$N = 56$

x	$100p_x$	95% $100p_l$	95% $100p_r$	99% $100p_l$	99% $100p_r$
0	0.00	0.00	6.38	0.00	9.03
1	1.79	0.05	9.55	0.01	12.53
2	3.57	0.44	12.31	0.19	15.52
3	5.36	1.12	14.87	0.61	18.25
4	7.14	1.98	17.29	1.23	20.82
5	8.93	2.96	19.62	1.98	23.27
6	10.71	4.03	21.88	2.83	25.63
7	12.50	5.18	24.07	3.77	27.91
8	14.29	6.38	26.22	4.79	30.13
9	16.07	7.62	28.33	5.86	32.30
10	17.86	8.91	30.40	6.98	34.42
11	19.64	10.23	32.43	8.14	36.49
12	21.43	11.59	34.44	9.35	38.53
13	23.21	12.98	36.42	10.60	40.53
14	25.00	14.39	38.37	11.88	42.50
15	26.79	15.83	40.30	13.19	44.45
16	28.57	17.30	42.21	14.53	46.36
17	30.36	18.78	44.10	15.90	48.24
18	32.14	20.29	45.96	17.30	50.10
19	33.93	21.81	47.81	18.72	51.94
20	35.71	23.36	49.64	20.17	53.75
21	37.50	24.92	51.45	21.64	55.54
22	39.29	26.50	53.25	23.13	57.31
23	41.07	28.10	55.02	24.65	59.05
24	42.86	29.71	56.78	26.18	60.77
25	44.64	31.34	58.53	27.74	62.48
26	46.43	32.99	60.26	29.32	64.16
27	48.21	34.66	61.97	30.92	65.82
28	50.00	36.34	63.66	32.54	67.46
29	51.79	38.03	65.34	34.18	69.08
30	53.57	39.74	67.01	35.84	70.68
31	55.36	41.47	68.66	37.52	72.26
32	57.14	43.22	70.29	39.23	73.82
33	58.93	44.98	71.90	40.95	75.35
34	60.71	46.75	73.50	42.69	76.87
35	62.50	48.55	75.08	44.46	78.36
36	64.29	50.36	76.64	46.25	79.83
37	66.07	52.19	78.19	48.06	81.28
38	67.86	54.04	79.71	49.90	82.70
39	69.64	55.90	81.22	51.76	84.10
40	71.43	57.79	82.70	53.64	85.47
41	73.21	59.70	84.17	55.55	86.81
42	75.00	61.63	85.61	57.50	88.12
43	76.79	63.58	87.02	59.47	89.40
44	78.57	65.56	88.41	61.47	90.65
45	80.36	67.57	89.77	63.51	91.86
46	82.14	69.60	91.09	65.58	93.02
47	83.93	71.67	92.38	67.70	94.14
48	85.71	73.78	93.62	69.87	95.21
49	87.50	75.93	94.82	72.09	96.23
50	89.29	78.12	95.97	74.37	97.17
51	91.07	80.38	97.04	76.73	98.02
52	92.86	82.71	98.02	79.18	98.77
53	94.64	85.13	98.88	81.75	99.39
54	96.43	87.69	99.56	84.48	99.81
55	98.21	90.45	99.95	87.47	99.99
56	100.00	93.62	100.00	90.97	100.00

$N = 57$

x	$100p_x$	95% $100p_l$	95% $100p_r$	99% $100p_l$	99% $100p_r$
0	0.00	0.00	6.27	0.00	8.88
1	1.75	0.04	9.39	0.01	12.32
2	3.51	0.43	12.11	0.18	15.27
3	5.26	1.10	14.62	0.60	17.96
4	7.02	1.95	17.00	1.21	20.48
5	8.77	2.91	19.30	1.94	22.90
6	10.53	3.96	21.52	2.78	25.22
7	12.28	5.08	23.68	3.71	27.47
8	14.04	6.26	25.79	4.70	29.65
9	15.79	7.48	27.87	5.75	31.79
10	17.54	8.75	29.91	6.85	33.88
11	19.30	10.05	31.91	7.99	35.92
12	21.05	11.38	33.89	9.18	37.93
13	22.81	12.74	35.84	10.40	39.91
14	24.56	14.13	37.76	11.66	41.85
15	26.32	15.54	39.66	12.94	43.77
16	28.07	16.97	41.54	14.26	45.65
17	29.82	18.43	43.40	15.60	47.51
18	31.58	19.91	45.24	16.97	49.35
19	33.33	21.40	47.06	18.36	51.16
20	35.09	22.91	48.87	19.78	52.95
21	36.84	24.45	50.66	21.22	54.72
22	38.60	26.00	52.43	22.68	56.46
23	40.35	27.56	54.18	24.17	58.19
24	42.11	29.14	55.92	25.67	59.89
25	43.86	30.74	57.64	27.20	61.57
26	45.61	32.36	59.34	28.74	63.24
27	47.37	33.98	61.03	30.31	64.88
28	49.12	35.63	62.71	31.89	66.51
29	50.88	37.29	64.37	33.49	68.11
30	52.63	38.97	66.02	35.12	69.69
31	54.39	40.66	67.64	36.76	71.26
32	56.14	42.36	69.26	38.43	72.80
33	57.89	44.08	70.86	40.11	74.33
34	59.65	45.82	72.44	41.81	75.83
35	61.40	47.57	74.00	43.54	77.32
36	63.16	49.34	75.55	45.28	78.78
37	64.91	51.13	77.09	47.05	80.22
38	66.67	52.94	78.60	48.84	81.64
39	68.42	54.76	80.09	50.65	83.03
40	70.18	56.60	81.57	52.49	84.40
41	71.93	58.46	83.03	54.35	85.74
42	73.68	60.34	84.46	56.23	87.06
43	75.44	62.24	85.87	58.15	88.34
44	77.19	64.16	87.26	60.09	89.60
45	78.95	66.11	88.62	62.07	90.82
46	80.70	68.09	89.95	64.08	92.01
47	82.46	70.09	91.25	66.12	93.15
48	84.21	72.13	92.52	68.21	94.25
49	85.96	74.21	93.74	70.35	95.30
50	87.72	76.32	94.92	72.53	96.29
51	89.47	78.48	96.04	74.78	97.22
52	91.23	80.70	97.09	77.10	98.06
53	92.98	83.00	98.05	79.52	98.79
54	94.74	85.38	98.90	82.04	99.40
55	96.49	87.89	99.57	84.73	99.82
56	98.25	90.61	99.96	87.68	99.99
57	100.00	93.73	100.00	91.12	100.00

$N = 58$

x	$100p_x$	95% $100p_l$	95% $100p_r$	99% $100p_l$	99% $100p_r$
0	0.00	0.00	6.16	0.00	8.73
1	1.72	0.04	9.24	0.01	12.12
2	3.45	0.42	11.91	0.18	15.02
3	5.17	1.08	14.38	0.59	17.67
4	6.90	1.91	16.73	1.18	20.16
5	8.62	2.86	18.98	1.91	22.53
6	10.34	3.89	21.17	2.73	24.82
7	12.07	4.99	23.30	3.64	27.03
8	13.79	6.15	25.38	4.61	29.19
9	15.52	7.35	27.42	5.64	31.29
10	17.24	8.59	29.43	6.72	33.35
11	18.97	9.87	31.41	7.85	35.37
12	20.69	11.17	33.35	9.01	37.35
13	22.41	12.51	35.27	10.21	39.30
14	24.14	13.87	37.17	11.44	41.22
15	25.86	15.26	39.04	12.70	43.11
16	27.59	16.66	40.90	13.99	44.97
17	29.31	18.09	42.73	15.31	46.80
18	31.03	19.54	44.54	16.65	48.62
19	32.76	21.01	46.34	18.02	50.41
20	34.48	22.49	48.12	19.41	52.17
21	36.21	23.99	49.88	20.82	53.92
22	37.93	25.51	51.63	22.25	55.64
23	39.66	27.05	53.36	23.70	57.35
24	41.38	28.60	55.07	25.18	59.03
25	43.10	30.16	56.77	26.67	60.70
26	44.83	31.74	58.46	28.18	62.34
27	46.55	33.34	60.13	29.72	63.97
28	48.28	34.95	61.78	31.27	65.57
29	50.00	36.58	63.42	32.84	67.16
30	51.72	38.22	65.05	34.43	68.73
31	53.45	39.87	66.66	36.03	70.28
32	55.17	41.54	68.26	37.66	71.82
33	56.90	43.23	69.84	39.30	73.33
34	58.62	44.93	71.40	40.97	74.82
35	60.34	46.64	72.95	42.65	76.30
36	62.07	48.37	74.49	44.36	77.75
37	63.79	50.12	76.01	46.08	79.18
38	65.52	51.88	77.51	47.83	80.59
39	67.24	53.66	78.99	49.59	81.98
40	68.97	55.46	80.46	51.38	83.35
41	70.69	57.27	81.91	53.20	84.69
42	72.41	59.10	83.34	55.03	86.01
43	74.14	60.96	84.74	56.89	87.30
44	75.86	62.83	86.13	58.78	88.56
45	77.59	64.73	87.49	60.70	89.79
46	79.31	66.65	88.83	62.65	90.99
47	81.03	68.59	90.13	64.63	92.15
48	82.76	70.57	91.41	66.65	93.28
49	84.48	72.58	92.65	68.71	94.36
50	86.21	74.62	93.85	70.81	95.39
51	87.93	76.70	95.01	72.97	96.36
52	89.66	78.83	96.11	75.18	97.27
53	91.38	81.02	97.14	77.47	98.09
54	93.10	83.27	98.09	79.84	98.82
55	94.83	85.62	98.92	82.33	99.41
56	96.55	88.09	99.58	84.98	99.82
57	98.28	90.76	99.96	87.88	99.99
58	100.00	93.84	100.00	91.27	100.00

$N = 59$

x	$100p_x$	95% $100p_l$	95% $100p_r$	99% $100p_l$	99% $100p_r$
0	0.00	0.00	6.06	0.00	8.59
1	1.69	0.04	9.09	0.01	11.93
2	3.39	0.41	11.71	0.18	14.78
3	5.08	1.06	14.15	0.58	17.39
4	6.78	1.88	16.46	1.16	19.84
5	8.47	2.81	18.68	1.87	22.18
6	10.17	3.82	20.83	2.69	24.43
7	11.86	4.91	22.93	3.58	26.62
8	13.56	6.04	24.98	4.53	28.74
9	15.25	7.22	26.99	5.54	30.82
10	16.95	8.44	28.97	6.60	32.84
11	18.64	9.69	30.91	7.71	34.83
12	20.34	10.98	32.83	8.85	36.79
13	22.03	12.29	34.73	10.03	38.71
14	23.73	13.62	36.60	11.24	40.60
15	25.42	14.98	38.44	12.47	42.47
16	27.12	16.36	40.27	13.74	44.30
17	28.81	17.76	42.08	15.03	46.12
18	30.51	19.19	43.87	16.35	47.91
19	32.20	20.62	45.64	17.69	49.67
20	33.90	22.08	47.39	19.05	51.42
21	35.59	23.55	49.13	20.43	53.14
22	37.29	25.04	50.85	21.84	54.84
23	38.98	26.55	52.56	23.26	56.53
24	40.68	28.07	54.25	24.70	58.19
25	42.37	29.61	55.93	26.17	59.84
26	44.07	31.16	57.60	27.65	61.47
27	45.76	32.72	59.25	29.15	63.08
28	47.46	34.30	60.88	30.67	64.67
29	49.15	35.89	62.50	32.20	66.24
30	50.85	37.50	64.11	33.76	67.80
31	52.54	39.12	65.70	35.33	69.33
32	54.24	40.75	67.28	36.92	70.85
33	55.93	42.40	68.84	38.53	72.35
34	57.63	44.07	70.39	40.16	73.83
35	59.32	45.75	71.93	41.81	75.30
36	61.02	47.44	73.45	43.47	76.74
37	62.71	49.15	74.96	45.16	78.16
38	64.41	50.87	76.45	46.86	79.57
39	66.10	52.61	77.92	48.58	80.95
40	67.80	54.36	79.38	50.33	82.31
41	69.49	56.13	80.81	52.09	83.65

N = number of trials, x = number of successes, etc., $100\,p_x = 100\,x/N$

x	$100p_x$	100(1 − 2α) limits 95%		99%	
		$100p_l$	$100p_r$	$100p_l$	$100p_r$
		N = 59 (continued)			
42	71.19	57.92	82.24	53.88	84.97
43	72.88	59.73	83.64	55.70	86.26
44	74.58	61.56	85.02	57.53	87.53
45	76.27	63.40	86.38	59.40	88.76
46	77.97	65.27	87.71	61.29	89.97
47	79.66	67.17	89.02	63.21	91.15
48	81.36	69.09	90.31	65.17	92.29
49	83.05	71.03	91.56	67.16	93.40
50	84.75	73.01	92.78	69.18	94.46
51	86.44	75.02	93.96	71.26	95.47
52	88.14	77.07	95.09	73.38	96.42
53	89.83	79.17	96.18	75.57	97.31
54	91.53	81.32	97.19	77.82	98.13
55	93.22	83.54	98.12	80.16	98.84
56	94.92	85.85	98.94	82.61	99.42
57	96.61	88.29	99.59	85.22	99.82
58	98.31	90.91	99.96	88.07	99.99
59	100.00	93.94	100.00	91.41	100.00
		N = 60			
0	0.00	0.00	5.96	0.00	8.45
1	1.67	0.04	8.94	0.01	11.74
2	3.33	0.41	11.53	0.17	14.55
3	5.00	1.04	13.92	0.57	17.12
4	6.67	1.85	16.20	1.14	19.53
5	8.33	2.76	18.39	1.84	21.84
6	10.00	3.76	20.51	2.64	24.06
7	11.67	4.82	22.57	3.51	26.21
8	13.33	5.94	24.59	4.45	28.31
9	15.00	7.10	26.57	5.45	30.35
10	16.67	8.29	28.52	6.49	32.35
11	18.33	9.52	30.44	7.57	34.31
12	20.00	10.78	32.33	8.69	36.24
13	21.67	12.07	34.20	9.85	38.14
14	23.33	13.38	36.04	11.04	40.00
15	25.00	14.72	37.86	12.25	41.84
16	26.67	16.07	39.66	13.49	43.66
17	28.33	17.45	41.44	14.76	45.45
18	30.00	18.85	43.21	16.05	47.21
19	31.67	20.26	44.96	17.37	48.96
20	33.33	21.69	46.69	18.70	50.68
21	35.00	23.13	48.40	20.06	52.39
22	36.67	24.59	50.10	21.44	54.07
23	38.33	26.07	51.79	22.83	55.73
24	40.00	27.56	53.46	24.25	57.38
25	41.67	29.07	55.12	25.68	59.01
26	43.33	30.59	56.76	27.13	60.62
27	45.00	32.12	58.39	28.60	62.21
28	46.67	33.67	60.00	30.09	63.78
29	48.33	35.23	61.61	31.60	65.34
30	50.00	36.81	63.19	33.12	66.88
31	51.67	38.39	64.77	34.66	68.40
32	53.33	40.00	66.33	36.22	69.91
33	55.00	41.61	67.88	37.79	71.40
34	56.67	43.24	69.41	39.38	72.87
35	58.33	44.88	70.93	40.99	74.32
36	60.00	46.54	72.44	42.62	75.75
37	61.67	48.21	73.93	44.27	77.17
38	63.33	49.90	75.41	45.93	78.56
39	65.00	51.60	76.87	47.61	79.94
40	66.67	53.31	78.31	49.32	81.30
41	68.33	55.04	79.74	51.04	82.63
42	70.00	56.79	81.15	52.79	83.95
43	71.67	58.56	82.55	54.55	85.24
44	73.33	60.34	83.93	56.34	86.51
45	75.00	62.14	85.28	58.16	87.75
46	76.67	63.96	86.62	60.00	88.96
47	78.33	65.80	87.93	61.86	90.15
48	80.00	67.67	89.22	63.76	91.31
49	81.67	69.56	90.48	65.69	92.43
50	83.33	71.48	91.71	67.65	93.51
51	85.00	73.43	92.90	69.65	94.55
52	86.67	75.41	94.06	71.69	95.55
53	88.33	77.43	95.18	73.79	96.49
54	90.00	79.49	96.24	75.94	97.36
55	91.67	81.61	97.24	78.16	98.16
56	93.33	83.80	98.15	80.47	98.86
57	95.00	86.08	98.96	82.88	99.43
58	96.67	88.47	99.59	85.45	99.83
59	98.33	91.06	99.96	88.26	99.99
60	100.00	94.04	100.00	91.55	100.00
		N = 61			
0	0.00	0.00	5.87	0.00	8.32
1	1.64	0.04	8.80	0.01	11.56
2	3.28	0.40	11.35	0.17	14.33
3	4.92	1.03	13.71	0.56	16.86
4	6.56	1.82	15.95	1.12	19.24
5	8.20	2.72	18.10	1.81	21.51
6	9.84	3.70	20.19	2.59	23.70
7	11.48	4.74	22.22	3.45	25.82
8	13.11	5.84	24.22	4.38	27.88
9	14.75	6.98	26.17	5.35	29.90
10	16.39	8.15	28.09	6.38	31.87
11	18.03	9.36	29.98	7.44	33.81
12	19.67	10.60	31.84	8.54	35.71
13	21.31	11.86	33.68	9.68	37.58

x	$100p_x$	100(1 − 2α) limits 95%		99%	
		$100p_l$	$100p_r$	$100p_l$	$100p_r$
		N = 61 (continued)			
14	22.95	13.15	35.50	10.84	39.42
15	24.59	14.46	37.29	12.04	41.24
16	26.23	15.80	39.07	13.26	43.03
17	27.87	17.15	40.83	14.50	44.80
18	29.51	18.52	42.57	15.77	46.54
19	31.15	19.90	44.29	17.06	48.26
20	32.79	21.31	46.00	18.37	49.97
21	34.43	22.73	47.69	19.70	51.65
22	36.07	24.16	49.37	21.05	53.31
23	37.70	25.61	51.04	22.42	54.96
24	39.34	27.07	52.69	23.81	56.59
25	40.98	28.55	54.32	25.21	58.20
26	42.62	30.04	55.94	26.64	59.79
27	44.26	31.55	57.55	28.08	61.36
28	45.90	33.06	59.15	29.54	62.92
29	47.54	34.60	60.73	31.01	64.46
30	49.18	36.14	62.30	32.50	65.99
31	50.82	37.70	63.86	34.01	67.50
32	52.46	39.27	65.40	35.54	68.99
33	54.10	40.85	66.94	37.08	70.46
34	55.74	42.45	68.45	38.64	71.92
35	57.38	44.06	69.96	40.21	73.36
36	59.02	45.68	71.45	41.80	74.79
37	60.66	47.31	72.93	43.41	76.19
38	62.30	48.96	74.39	45.04	77.58
39	63.93	50.63	75.84	46.69	78.95
40	65.57	52.31	77.27	48.35	80.30
41	67.21	54.00	78.69	50.03	81.63
42	68.85	55.71	80.10	51.74	82.94
43	70.49	57.43	81.48	53.46	84.23
44	72.13	59.17	82.85	55.20	85.50
45	73.77	60.93	84.20	56.97	86.74
46	75.41	62.71	85.54	58.76	87.96
47	77.05	64.50	86.85	60.58	89.16
48	78.69	66.32	88.14	62.42	90.32
49	80.33	68.16	89.40	64.29	91.46
50	81.97	70.02	90.64	66.19	92.56
51	83.61	71.91	91.85	68.13	93.62
52	85.25	73.83	93.02	70.10	94.65
53	86.89	75.78	94.16	72.12	95.62
54	88.52	77.78	95.26	74.18	96.55
55	90.16	79.81	96.30	76.30	97.41
56	91.80	81.90	97.28	78.49	98.19
57	93.44	84.05	98.18	80.76	98.88
58	95.08	86.29	98.97	83.14	99.44
59	96.72	88.65	99.60	85.67	99.83
60	98.36	91.20	99.96	88.44	99.99
61	100.00	94.13	100.00	91.68	100.00
		N = 62			
0	0.00	0.00	5.78	0.00	8.19
1	1.61	0.04	8.66	0.01	11.38
2	3.23	0.39	11.17	0.17	14.11
3	4.84	1.01	13.50	0.55	16.60
4	6.45	1.79	15.70	1.11	18.95
5	8.06	2.67	17.83	1.78	21.19
6	9.68	3.63	19.88	2.55	23.35
7	11.29	4.66	21.89	3.40	25.44
8	12.90	5.74	23.85	4.30	27.47
9	14.52	6.86	25.78	5.26	29.46
10	16.13	8.02	27.67	6.27	31.41
11	17.74	9.20	29.53	7.32	33.32
12	19.35	10.42	31.37	8.40	35.20
13	20.97	11.66	33.18	9.51	37.04
14	22.58	12.93	34.97	10.66	38.86
15	24.19	14.22	36.74	11.83	40.65
16	25.81	15.53	38.50	13.03	42.42
17	27.42	16.85	40.23	14.25	44.16
18	29.03	18.20	41.95	15.49	45.89
19	30.65	19.56	43.65	16.76	47.59
20	32.26	20.94	45.34	18.05	49.27
21	33.87	22.33	47.01	19.35	50.93
22	35.48	23.74	48.66	20.68	52.58
23	37.10	25.16	50.31	22.02	54.21
24	38.71	26.60	51.93	23.38	55.81
25	40.32	28.05	53.55	24.76	57.41
26	41.94	29.51	55.15	26.16	58.98
27	43.55	30.99	56.74	27.57	60.54
28	45.16	32.48	58.32	29.00	62.08
29	46.77	33.98	59.88	30.45	63.61
30	48.39	35.50	61.44	31.91	65.12
31	50.00	37.02	62.98	33.39	66.61
32	51.61	38.56	64.50	34.88	68.09
33	53.23	40.12	66.02	36.39	69.55
34	54.84	41.68	67.52	37.92	71.00
35	56.45	43.26	69.01	39.46	72.43
36	58.06	44.85	70.49	41.02	73.84
37	59.68	46.45	71.95	42.59	75.24
38	61.29	48.07	73.40	44.19	76.62
39	62.90	49.69	74.84	45.79	77.98
40	64.52	51.34	76.26	47.42	79.32
41	66.13	52.99	77.67	49.07	80.65
42	67.74	54.66	79.06	50.73	81.95
43	69.35	56.35	80.44	52.41	83.24
44	70.97	58.05	81.80	54.11	84.51
45	72.58	59.77	83.15	55.84	85.75
46	74.19	61.50	84.47	57.58	86.97
47	75.81	63.26	85.78	59.35	88.17

x	$100p_x$	100(1 − 2α) limits 95%		99%	
		$100p_l$	$100p_r$	$100p_l$	$100p_r$
		N = 62 (continued)			
48	77.42	65.03	87.07	61.14	89.34
49	79.03	66.82	88.34	62.96	90.49
50	80.65	68.63	89.58	64.80	91.60
51	82.26	70.47	90.80	66.68	92.68
52	83.87	72.33	91.98	68.59	93.73
53	85.48	74.22	93.14	70.54	94.74
54	87.10	76.15	94.26	72.53	95.70
55	88.71	78.11	95.34	74.56	96.60
56	90.32	80.12	96.37	76.65	97.45
57	91.94	82.17	97.33	78.81	98.22
58	93.55	84.30	98.21	81.05	98.89
59	95.16	86.50	98.99	83.40	99.45
60	96.77	88.83	99.61	85.89	99.83
61	98.39	91.34	99.96	88.62	99.99
62	100.00	94.22	100.00	91.81	100.00
		N = 63			
0	0.00	0.00	5.69	0.00	8.07
1	1.59	0.04	8.53	0.01	11.21
2	3.17	0.39	11.00	0.17	13.90
3	4.76	0.99	13.29	0.54	16.36
4	6.35	1.76	15.47	1.09	18.67
5	7.94	2.63	17.56	1.75	20.88
6	9.52	3.58	19.59	2.51	23.00
7	11.11	4.59	21.56	3.34	25.07
8	12.70	5.65	23.50	4.23	27.08
9	14.29	6.75	25.39	5.18	29.04
10	15.87	7.88	27.26	6.17	30.96
11	17.46	9.05	29.10	7.19	32.84
12	19.05	10.25	30.91	8.26	34.70
13	20.63	11.47	32.70	9.35	36.52
14	22.22	12.72	34.46	10.48	38.31
15	23.81	13.98	36.21	11.63	40.08
16	25.40	15.27	37.94	12.81	41.83
17	26.98	16.57	39.65	14.01	43.55
18	28.57	17.89	41.35	15.23	45.25
19	30.16	19.23	43.02	16.47	46.93
20	31.75	20.58	44.69	17.74	48.59
21	33.33	21.95	46.34	19.02	50.24
22	34.92	23.34	47.97	20.32	51.86
23	36.51	24.73	49.60	21.64	53.47
24	38.10	26.15	51.20	22.98	55.06
25	39.68	27.57	52.80	24.33	56.64
26	41.27	29.01	54.38	25.70	58.19
27	42.86	30.46	55.95	27.08	59.74
28	44.44	31.92	57.51	28.49	61.26
29	46.03	33.39	59.06	29.90	62.77
30	47.62	34.88	60.59	31.34	64.27
31	49.21	36.38	62.11	32.79	65.75
32	50.79	37.89	63.62	34.25	67.21
33	52.38	39.41	65.12	35.73	68.66
34	53.97	40.94	66.61	37.23	70.10
35	55.56	42.49	68.08	38.74	71.51
36	57.14	44.05	69.54	40.26	72.92
37	58.73	45.62	70.99	41.81	74.30
38	60.32	47.20	72.43	43.36	75.67
39	61.90	48.80	73.85	44.94	77.02
40	63.49	50.40	75.27	46.53	78.36
41	65.08	52.03	76.66	48.14	79.68
42	66.67	53.66	78.05	49.76	80.98
43	68.25	55.31	79.42	51.41	82.26
44	69.84	56.98	80.77	53.07	83.53
45	71.43	58.65	82.11	54.75	84.77
46	73.02	60.35	83.43	56.45	85.99
47	74.60	62.06	84.73	58.17	87.19
48	76.19	63.79	86.02	59.92	88.37
49	77.78	65.54	87.28	61.69	89.52
50	79.37	67.30	88.53	63.48	90.65
51	80.95	69.09	89.75	65.30	91.74
52	82.54	70.90	90.95	67.16	92.81
53	84.13	72.74	92.12	69.04	93.83
54	85.71	74.61	93.25	70.96	94.82
55	87.30	76.50	94.35	72.92	95.77
56	88.89	78.44	95.41	74.93	96.66
57	90.48	80.41	96.42	77.00	97.49
58	92.06	82.44	97.37	79.12	98.25
59	93.65	84.53	98.24	81.33	98.91
60	95.24	86.71	99.01	83.64	99.46
61	96.83	89.00	99.61	86.10	99.83
62	98.41	91.47	99.96	88.79	99.99
63	100.00	94.31	100.00	91.93	100.00
		N = 64			
0	0.00	0.00	5.60	0.00	7.95
1	1.56	0.04	8.40	0.01	11.04
2	3.13	0.38	10.84	0.16	13.69
3	4.69	0.98	13.09	0.54	16.12
4	6.25	1.73	15.24	1.07	18.40
5	7.81	2.59	17.30	1.72	20.57
6	9.38	3.52	19.30	2.47	22.67
7	10.94	4.51	21.25	3.29	24.71
8	12.50	5.55	23.15	4.17	26.69
9	14.06	6.64	25.02	5.09	28.62
10	15.63	7.76	26.86	6.07	30.52
11	17.19	8.90	28.68	7.08	32.38
12	18.75	10.08	30.46	8.12	34.21
13	20.31	11.28	32.23	9.20	36.01

x	$100p_x$	100(1 − 2α) limits 95%		99%	
		$100p_l$	$100p_r$	$100p_l$	$100p_r$
		N = 64 (continued)			
14	21.88	12.51	33.97	10.30	37.78
15	23.44	13.75	35.69	11.44	39.53
16	25.00	15.02	37.40	12.59	41.25
17	26.56	16.30	39.09	13.77	42.95
18	28.13	17.60	40.76	14.97	44.63
19	29.69	18.91	42.42	16.19	46.29
20	31.25	20.24	44.06	17.43	47.94
21	32.81	21.59	45.69	18.69	49.56
22	34.38	22.95	47.30	19.97	51.17
23	35.94	24.32	48.90	21.27	52.76
24	37.50	25.70	50.49	22.58	54.33
25	39.06	27.10	52.07	23.91	55.89
26	40.63	28.51	53.63	25.25	57.43
27	42.19	29.94	55.18	26.61	58.95
28	43.75	31.37	56.72	27.99	60.46
29	45.31	32.82	58.25	29.38	61.96
30	46.88	34.28	59.77	30.79	63.44
31	48.44	35.75	61.27	32.21	64.90
32	50.00	37.23	62.77	33.64	66.36
33	51.56	38.73	64.25	35.10	67.79
34	53.13	40.23	65.72	36.56	69.21
35	54.69	41.75	67.18	38.04	70.62
36	56.25	43.28	68.63	39.54	72.01
37	57.81	44.82	70.06	41.05	73.39
38	59.38	46.37	71.49	42.57	74.75
39	60.94	47.93	72.90	44.11	76.09
40	62.50	49.51	74.30	45.67	77.42
41	64.06	51.10	75.68	47.24	78.73
42	65.63	52.70	77.05	48.83	80.03
43	67.19	54.31	78.41	50.44	81.31
44	68.75	55.94	79.76	52.06	82.57
45	70.31	57.58	81.09	53.71	83.81
46	71.88	59.24	82.40	55.37	85.03
47	73.44	60.91	83.70	57.05	86.23
48	75.00	62.60	84.98	58.75	87.41
49	76.56	64.31	86.25	60.47	88.56
50	78.13	66.03	87.49	62.22	89.70
51	79.69	67.77	88.72	63.99	90.80
52	81.25	69.54	89.92	65.79	91.88
53	82.81	71.32	91.10	67.62	92.92
54	84.38	73.14	92.24	69.48	93.93
55	85.94	74.98	93.36	71.38	94.91
56	87.50	76.85	94.45	73.31	95.83
57	89.06	78.75	95.49	75.29	96.71
58	90.63	80.70	96.48	77.33	97.53
59	92.19	82.70	97.41	79.43	98.28
60	93.75	84.76	98.27	81.60	98.93
61	95.31	86.91	99.02	83.88	99.46
62	96.88	89.16	99.62	86.31	99.84
63	98.44	91.60	99.96	88.96	99.99
64	100.00	94.40	100.00	92.05	100.00
		N = 65			
0	0.00	0.00	5.52	0.00	7.83
1	1.54	0.04	8.28	0.01	10.88
2	3.08	0.37	10.68	0.16	13.49
3	4.62	0.96	12.90	0.53	15.88
4	6.15	1.70	15.01	1.05	18.13
5	7.69	2.54	17.05	1.70	20.28
6	9.23	3.46	19.02	2.43	22.35
7	10.77	4.44	20.94	3.24	24.36
8	12.31	5.47	22.82	4.10	26.31
9	13.85	6.53	24.66	5.01	28.22
10	15.38	7.63	26.48	5.97	30.09
11	16.92	8.76	28.27	6.96	31.93
12	18.46	9.92	30.03	7.99	33.73
13	20.00	11.10	31.77	9.05	35.51
14	21.54	12.31	33.49	10.14	37.26
15	23.08	13.53	35.19	11.25	38.98
16	24.62	14.77	36.87	12.38	40.69
17	26.15	16.03	38.54	13.54	42.37
18	27.69	17.31	40.19	14.72	44.03
19	29.23	18.60	41.83	15.93	45.67
20	30.77	19.91	43.45	17.14	47.29
21	32.31	21.23	45.05	18.38	48.90
22	33.85	22.57	46.65	19.64	50.49
23	35.38	23.92	48.23	20.91	52.06
24	36.92	25.28	49.80	22.20	53.61
25	38.46	26.65	51.36	23.50	55.15
26	40.00	28.04	52.90	24.82	56.68
27	41.54	29.44	54.44	26.16	58.19
28	43.08	30.85	55.96	27.51	59.68
29	44.62	32.27	57.47	28.88	61.16
30	46.15	33.70	58.97	30.26	62.63
31	47.69	35.15	60.46	31.65	64.08
32	49.23	36.60	61.93	33.06	65.52
33	50.77	38.07	63.40	34.48	66.94
34	52.31	39.54	64.85	35.92	68.35
35	53.85	41.03	66.30	37.37	69.74
36	55.38	42.53	67.73	38.84	71.12
37	56.92	44.04	69.15	40.32	72.49
38	58.46	45.56	70.56	41.81	73.84
39	60.00	47.10	71.96	43.32	75.18
40	61.54	48.64	73.35	44.85	76.50
41	63.08	50.20	74.72	46.39	77.80
42	64.62	51.77	76.08	47.94	79.09
43	66.15	53.35	77.43	49.51	80.36
44	67.69	54.95	78.77	51.10	81.62

N = number of trials, x = number of successes, etc., $100\,p_x = 100\,x/N$

$N = 65$ (continued)

x	$100p_x$	100 (1 − 2α) limits 95% $100p_l$ – $100p_r$	100 (1 − 2α) limits 99% $100p_l$ – $100p_r$
45	69.23	56.55– 80.09	52.71– 82.86
46	70.77	58.17– 81.40	54.33– 84.07
47	72.31	59.81– 82.69	55.97– 85.28
48	73.85	61.46– 83.97	57.63– 86.46
49	75.38	63.13– 85.23	59.31– 87.62
50	76.92	64.81– 86.47	61.02– 88.75
51	78.46	66.51– 87.69	62.74– 89.86
52	80.00	68.23– 88.90	64.49– 90.95
53	81.54	69.97– 90.08	66.27– 92.01
54	83.08	71.73– 91.24	68.07– 93.04
55	84.62	73.52– 92.37	69.91– 94.03
56	86.15	75.34– 93.47	71.78– 94.99
57	87.69	77.18– 94.53	73.69– 95.90
58	89.23	79.06– 95.56	75.64– 96.76
59	90.77	80.98– 96.54	77.65– 97.57
60	92.31	82.95– 97.46	79.72– 98.30
61	93.85	84.99– 98.30	81.87– 98.95
62	95.38	87.10– 99.04	84.12– 99.47
63	96.92	89.32– 99.63	86.51– 99.84
64	98.46	91.72– 99.96	89.12– 99.99
65	100.00	94.48–100.00	92.17–100.00

$N = 66$

x	$100p_x$	95% $100p_l$ – $100p_r$	99% $100p_l$ – $100p_r$
0	0.00	0.00– 5.44	0.00– 7.71
1	1.52	0.04– 8.16	0.01– 10.72
2	3.03	0.37– 10.52	0.16– 13.30
3	4.55	0.95– 12.71	0.52– 15.66
4	6.06	1.68– 14.80	1.04– 17.88
5	7.58	2.51– 16.80	1.67– 19.99
6	9.09	3.41– 18.74	2.39– 22.04
7	10.61	4.37– 20.64	3.19– 24.02
8	12.12	5.38– 22.49	4.03– 25.95
9	13.64	6.43– 24.31	4.93– 27.83
10	15.15	7.51– 26.10	5.87– 29.68
11	16.67	8.62– 27.87	6.85– 31.49
12	18.18	9.76– 29.61	7.86– 33.27
13	19.70	10.93– 31.32	8.90– 35.03
14	21.21	12.11– 33.02	9.97– 36.75
15	22.73	13.31– 34.70	11.07– 38.46
16	24.24	14.54– 36.36	12.18– 40.14
17	25.76	15.78– 38.01	13.32– 41.80
18	27.27	17.03– 39.64	14.49– 43.44
19	28.79	18.30– 41.25	15.67– 45.06
20	30.30	19.59– 42.85	16.86– 46.67
21	31.82	20.89– 44.44	18.08– 48.25
22	33.33	22.20– 46.01	19.31– 49.82
23	34.85	23.53– 47.58	20.56– 51.38
24	36.36	24.87– 49.13	21.83– 52.92
25	37.88	26.22– 50.66	23.11– 54.44
26	39.39	27.58– 52.19	24.41– 55.95
27	40.91	28.95– 53.71	25.72– 57.44
28	42.42	30.34– 55.21	27.05– 58.92
29	43.94	31.74– 56.70	28.39– 60.39
30	45.45	33.14– 58.19	29.74– 61.84
31	46.97	34.56– 59.66	31.11– 63.28
32	48.48	35.99– 61.12	32.49– 64.70
33	50.00	37.43– 62.57	33.89– 66.11
34	51.52	38.88– 64.01	35.30– 67.51
35	53.03	40.34– 65.44	36.72– 68.89
36	54.55	41.81– 66.86	38.16– 70.26
37	56.06	43.30– 68.26	39.61– 71.61
38	57.58	44.79– 69.66	41.08– 72.95
39	59.09	46.29– 71.05	42.56– 74.28
40	60.61	47.81– 72.42	44.05– 75.59
41	62.12	49.34– 73.78	45.56– 76.89
42	63.64	50.87– 75.13	47.08– 78.17
43	65.15	52.42– 76.47	48.62– 79.44
44	66.67	53.99– 77.80	50.18– 80.69
45	68.18	55.56– 79.11	51.75– 81.92
46	69.70	57.15– 80.41	53.33– 83.14
47	71.21	58.75– 81.70	54.94– 84.33
48	72.73	60.36– 82.97	56.56– 85.51
49	74.24	61.99– 84.22	58.20– 86.68
50	75.76	63.64– 85.46	59.86– 87.82
51	77.27	65.30– 86.69	61.54– 88.93
52	78.79	66.98– 87.89	63.25– 90.03
53	80.30	68.68– 89.07	64.97– 91.10
54	81.82	70.39– 90.24	66.73– 92.14
55	83.33	72.13– 91.38	68.51– 93.15
56	84.85	73.90– 92.49	70.32– 94.13
57	86.36	75.69– 93.57	72.17– 95.07
58	87.88	77.51– 94.62	74.05– 95.97
59	89.39	79.36– 95.63	75.98– 96.81
60	90.91	81.26– 96.59	77.96– 97.61
61	92.42	83.20– 97.49	80.01– 98.33
62	93.94	85.20– 98.32	82.12– 98.96
63	95.45	87.29– 99.05	84.34– 99.48
64	96.97	89.48– 99.63	86.70– 99.84
65	98.48	91.84– 99.96	89.28– 99.99
66	100.00	94.56–100.00	92.29–100.00

$N = 67$

x	$100p_x$	95% $100p_l$ – $100p_r$	99% $100p_l$ – $100p_r$
0	0.00	0.00– 5.36	0.00– 7.60
1	1.49	0.04– 8.04	0.01– 10.57
2	2.99	0.36– 10.37	0.16– 13.11
3	4.48	0.93– 12.53	0.51– 15.44
4	5.97	1.65– 14.59	1.02– 17.63
5	7.46	2.47– 16.56	1.65– 19.72
6	8.96	3.36– 18.48	2.36– 21.73
7	10.45	4.31– 20.35	3.14– 23.69
8	11.94	5.30– 22.18	3.97– 25.59
9	13.43	6.33– 23.97	4.86– 27.45
10	14.93	7.40– 25.74	5.78– 29.28
11	16.42	8.49– 27.48	6.74– 31.07
12	17.91	9.61– 29.20	7.74– 32.82
13	19.40	10.76– 30.89	8.76– 34.56
14	20.90	11.92– 32.57	9.82– 36.26
15	22.39	13.11– 34.22	10.89– 37.95
16	23.88	14.31– 35.86	11.99– 39.61
17	25.37	15.53– 37.49	13.11– 41.25
18	26.87	16.76– 39.10	14.25– 42.87
19	28.36	18.01– 40.69	15.41– 44.47
20	29.85	19.28– 42.27	16.59– 46.06
21	31.34	20.56– 43.84	17.79– 47.63
22	32.84	21.85– 45.40	19.00– 49.18
23	34.33	23.15– 46.94	20.23– 50.72
24	35.82	24.47– 48.47	21.47– 52.24
25	37.31	25.80– 49.99	22.73– 53.74
26	38.81	27.14– 51.50	24.01– 55.24
27	40.30	28.49– 53.00	25.30– 56.72
28	41.79	29.85– 54.48	26.60– 58.18
29	43.28	31.22– 55.96	27.92– 59.63
30	44.78	32.60– 57.42	29.25– 61.07
31	46.27	34.00– 58.88	30.59– 62.49
32	47.76	35.40– 60.33	31.95– 63.90
33	49.25	36.82– 61.76	33.32– 65.30
34	50.75	38.24– 63.18	34.70– 66.68
35	52.24	39.67– 64.60	36.10– 68.05
36	53.73	41.12– 66.00	37.51– 69.41
37	55.22	42.58– 67.40	38.93– 70.75
38	56.72	44.04– 68.78	40.37– 72.08
39	58.21	45.52– 70.15	41.82– 73.40
40	59.70	47.00– 71.51	43.28– 74.70
41	61.19	48.50– 72.86	44.76– 75.99
42	62.69	50.01– 74.20	46.26– 77.27
43	64.18	51.53– 75.53	47.76– 78.53
44	65.67	53.06– 76.85	49.28– 79.77
45	67.16	54.60– 78.15	50.82– 81.00
46	68.66	56.16– 79.44	52.37– 82.21
47	70.15	57.73– 80.72	53.94– 83.41
48	71.64	59.31– 81.99	55.53– 84.59
49	73.13	60.90– 83.24	57.13– 85.75
50	74.63	62.51– 84.47	58.75– 86.89
51	76.12	64.14– 85.69	60.39– 88.01
52	77.61	65.78– 86.89	62.05– 89.11
53	79.10	67.43– 88.08	63.74– 90.18
54	80.60	69.11– 89.24	65.44– 91.24
55	82.09	70.80– 90.39	67.18– 92.26
56	83.58	72.52– 91.51	68.93– 93.26
57	85.07	74.26– 92.60	70.72– 94.22
58	86.57	76.03– 93.67	72.55– 95.14
59	88.06	77.82– 94.70	74.41– 96.03
60	89.55	79.65– 95.69	76.31– 96.86
61	91.04	81.52– 96.64	78.27– 97.64
62	92.54	83.44– 97.53	80.28– 98.35
63	94.03	85.41– 98.35	82.37– 98.98
64	95.52	87.47– 99.07	84.56– 99.49
65	97.01	89.63– 99.64	86.89– 99.84
66	98.51	91.96– 99.96	89.43– 99.99
67	100.00	94.64–100.00	92.40–100.00

$N = 68$

x	$100p_x$	95% $100p_l$ – $100p_r$	99% $100p_l$ – $100p_r$
0	0.00	0.00– 5.28	0.00– 7.50
1	1.47	0.04– 7.92	0.01– 10.42
2	2.94	0.36– 10.22	0.15– 12.93
3	4.41	0.92– 12.36	0.50– 15.22
4	5.88	1.63– 14.38	1.01– 17.38
5	7.35	2.43– 16.33	1.62– 19.45
6	8.82	3.31– 18.22	2.32– 21.44
7	10.29	4.24– 20.07	3.09– 23.37
8	11.76	5.22– 21.87	3.91– 25.25
9	13.24	6.23– 23.64	4.78– 27.08
10	14.71	7.28– 25.39	5.69– 28.88
11	16.18	8.36– 27.10	6.64– 30.65
12	17.65	9.46– 28.80	7.62– 32.39
13	19.12	10.59– 30.47	8.63– 34.10
14	20.59	11.74– 32.12	9.66– 35.78
15	22.06	12.90– 33.76	10.72– 37.45
16	23.53	14.09– 35.38	11.80– 39.09
17	25.00	15.29– 36.98	12.91– 40.71
18	26.47	16.50– 38.57	14.03– 42.31
19	27.94	17.73– 40.15	15.17– 43.90
20	29.41	18.98– 41.71	16.33– 45.46
21	30.88	20.24– 43.26	17.51– 47.02
22	32.35	21.51– 44.79	18.70– 48.55
23	33.82	22.79– 46.32	19.91– 50.07
24	35.29	24.08– 47.83	21.13– 51.57
25	36.76	25.39– 49.33	22.37– 53.07
26	38.24	26.71– 50.82	23.62– 54.54
27	39.71	28.03– 52.30	24.89– 56.00
28	41.18	29.37– 53.77	26.17– 57.45
29	42.65	30.72– 55.23	27.46– 58.89
30	44.12	32.08– 56.68	28.77– 60.31
31	45.59	33.45– 58.12	30.09– 61.72
32	47.06	34.83– 59.55	31.42– 63.12
33	48.53	36.22– 60.97	32.77– 64.50
34	50.00	37.62– 62.38	34.12– 65.88
35	51.47	39.03– 63.78	35.50– 67.23
36	52.94	40.45– 65.17	36.88– 68.58
37	54.41	41.88– 66.55	38.28– 69.91
38	55.88	43.32– 67.92	39.69– 71.23
39	57.35	44.77– 69.28	41.11– 72.54
40	58.82	46.23– 70.63	42.55– 73.83
41	60.29	47.70– 71.97	44.00– 75.11
42	61.76	49.18– 73.29	45.46– 76.38
43	63.24	50.67– 74.61	46.93– 77.63
44	64.71	52.17– 75.92	48.43– 78.87
45	66.18	53.68– 77.21	49.93– 80.09
46	67.65	55.21– 78.49	51.45– 81.30
47	69.12	56.74– 79.76	52.98– 82.49
48	70.59	58.29– 81.02	54.54– 83.67
49	72.06	59.85– 82.27	56.10– 84.83
50	73.53	61.43– 83.50	57.69– 85.97
51	75.00	63.02– 84.71	59.29– 87.09
52	76.47	64.62– 85.91	60.91– 88.20
53	77.94	66.24– 87.10	62.55– 89.28
54	79.41	67.88– 88.26	64.22– 90.34
55	80.88	69.53– 89.41	65.90– 91.37
56	82.35	71.20– 90.54	67.61– 92.38
57	83.82	72.90– 91.64	69.35– 93.36
58	85.29	74.61– 92.72	71.12– 94.31
59	86.76	76.36– 93.77	72.92– 95.22
60	88.24	78.13– 94.78	74.75– 96.09
61	89.71	79.93– 95.76	76.63– 96.91
62	91.18	81.78– 96.69	78.56– 97.68
63	92.65	83.67– 97.57	80.55– 98.38
64	94.12	85.62– 98.37	82.62– 98.99
65	95.59	87.64– 99.08	84.78– 99.50
66	97.06	89.78– 99.64	87.07– 99.85
67	98.53	92.08– 99.96	89.58– 99.99
68	100.00	94.72–100.00	92.50–100.00

$N = 69$

x	$100p_x$	95% $100p_l$ – $100p_r$	99% $100p_l$ – $100p_r$
0	0.00	0.00– 5.21	0.00– 7.39
1	1.45	0.04– 7.81	0.01– 10.28
2	2.90	0.35– 10.08	0.15– 12.75
3	4.35	0.91– 12.18	0.50– 15.02
4	5.80	1.60– 14.18	0.99– 17.15
5	7.25	2.39– 16.11	1.60– 19.18
6	8.70	3.26– 17.97	2.29– 21.15
7	10.14	4.18– 19.79	3.04– 23.05
8	11.59	5.14– 21.57	3.85– 24.91
9	13.04	6.14– 23.32	4.71– 26.72
10	14.49	7.17– 25.04	5.61– 28.50
11	15.94	8.24– 26.74	6.54– 30.25
12	17.39	9.32– 28.41	7.50– 31.96
13	18.84	10.43– 30.06	8.50– 33.65
14	20.29	11.56– 31.69	9.51– 35.32
15	21.74	12.71– 33.31	10.56– 36.96
16	23.19	13.87– 34.91	11.62– 38.58
17	24.64	15.06– 36.49	12.71– 40.19
18	26.09	16.25– 38.06	13.81– 41.77
19	27.54	17.46– 39.62	14.93– 43.34
20	28.99	18.69– 41.16	16.07– 44.88
21	30.43	19.92– 42.69	17.23– 46.42
22	31.88	21.17– 44.21	18.40– 47.94
23	33.33	22.44– 45.71	19.59– 49.44
24	34.78	23.71– 47.21	20.80– 50.93
25	36.23	25.00– 48.69	22.01– 52.40
26	37.68	26.29– 50.16	23.24– 53.86
27	39.13	27.60– 51.63	24.49– 55.31
28	40.58	28.91– 53.08	25.75– 56.75
29	42.03	30.24– 54.52	27.02– 58.17
30	43.48	31.58– 55.96	28.30– 59.58
31	44.93	32.92– 57.38	29.60– 60.97
32	46.38	34.28– 58.80	30.91– 62.36
33	47.83	35.65– 60.20	32.23– 63.73
34	49.28	37.02– 61.59	33.57– 65.09
35	50.72	38.41– 62.98	34.91– 66.43
36	52.17	39.80– 64.35	36.27– 67.77
37	53.62	41.20– 65.72	37.64– 69.09
38	55.07	42.62– 67.08	39.03– 70.40
39	56.52	44.04– 68.42	40.42– 71.70
40	57.97	45.48– 69.76	41.83– 72.98
41	59.42	46.92– 71.09	43.25– 74.25
42	60.87	48.37– 72.40	44.69– 75.51
43	62.32	49.84– 73.71	46.14– 76.76
44	63.77	51.31– 75.00	47.60– 77.99
45	65.22	52.79– 76.29	49.07– 79.20
46	66.67	54.29– 77.56	50.56– 80.41
47	68.12	55.79– 78.83	52.06– 81.60
48	69.57	57.31– 80.08	53.58– 82.77
49	71.01	58.84– 81.31	55.12– 83.93
50	72.46	60.38– 82.54	56.66– 85.07
51	73.91	61.94– 83.75	58.23– 86.19
52	75.36	63.51– 84.94	59.81– 87.29
53	76.81	65.09– 86.13	61.42– 88.38
54	78.26	66.69– 87.29	63.04– 89.44
55	79.71	68.31– 88.44	64.68– 90.49
56	81.16	69.94– 89.57	66.35– 91.50
57	82.61	71.59– 90.68	68.04– 92.50
58	84.06	73.26– 91.76	69.75– 93.46
59	85.51	74.96– 92.83	71.50– 94.39
60	86.96	76.68– 93.86	73.28– 95.29
61	88.41	78.43– 94.86	75.09– 96.15
62	89.86	80.21– 95.82	76.95– 96.96
63	91.30	82.03– 96.74	78.85– 97.71
64	92.75	83.89– 97.61	80.82– 98.40
65	94.20	85.82– 98.40	82.85– 99.01
66	95.65	87.82– 99.09	84.98– 99.50
67	97.10	89.92– 99.65	87.25– 99.85
68	98.55	92.19– 99.96	89.72– 99.99
69	100.00	94.79–100.00	92.61–100.00

$N = 70$

x	$100p_x$	95% $100p_l$ – $100p_r$	99% $100p_l$ – $100p_r$
0	0.00	0.00– 5.13	0.00– 7.29
1	1.43	0.04– 7.70	0.01– 10.14
2	2.86	0.35– 9.94	0.15– 12.58
3	4.29	0.89– 12.02	0.49– 14.81
4	5.71	1.58– 13.99	0.98– 16.92
5	7.14	2.36– 15.89	1.57– 18.93
6	8.57	3.21– 17.73	2.25– 20.87
7	10.00	4.12– 19.52	3.00– 22.75
8	11.43	5.07– 21.28	3.80– 24.58
9	12.86	6.05– 23.01	4.64– 26.37
10	14.29	7.07– 24.71	5.52– 28.13
11	15.71	8.11– 26.38	6.44– 29.85
12	17.14	9.18– 28.03	7.39– 31.55
13	18.57	10.28– 29.66	8.37– 33.22
14	20.00	11.39– 31.27	9.37– 34.86
15	21.43	12.52– 32.87	10.40– 36.49
16	22.86	13.67– 34.45	11.45– 38.09
17	24.29	14.83– 36.01	12.51– 39.67
18	25.71	16.01– 37.56	13.60– 41.24
19	27.14	17.20– 39.10	14.71– 42.79
20	28.57	18.40– 40.62	15.83– 44.32
21	30.00	19.62– 42.13	16.97– 45.84
22	31.43	20.85– 43.63	18.12– 47.34
23	32.86	22.09– 45.12	19.29– 48.82
24	34.29	23.35– 46.60	20.47– 50.30
25	35.71	24.61– 48.07	21.67– 51.76
26	37.14	25.89– 49.52	22.88– 53.20
27	38.57	27.17– 50.97	24.11– 54.63
28	40.00	28.47– 52.41	25.34– 56.05
29	41.43	29.77– 53.83	26.59– 57.46
30	42.86	31.09– 55.25	27.85– 58.86
31	44.29	32.41– 56.66	29.13– 60.24
32	45.71	33.74– 58.06	30.42– 61.61
33	47.14	35.09– 59.45	31.72– 62.97
34	48.57	36.44– 60.83	33.03– 64.32
35	50.00	37.80– 62.20	34.35– 65.65
36	51.43	39.17– 63.56	35.68– 66.97
37	52.86	40.55– 64.91	37.03– 68.28
38	54.29	41.94– 66.26	38.39– 69.58
39	55.71	43.34– 67.59	39.76– 70.87
40	57.14	44.75– 68.91	41.14– 72.15
41	58.57	46.17– 70.23	42.54– 73.41
42	60.00	47.59– 71.53	43.95– 74.66
43	61.43	49.03– 72.83	45.37– 75.89
44	62.86	50.48– 74.11	46.80– 77.12
45	64.29	51.93– 75.39	48.24– 78.33
46	65.71	53.40– 76.65	49.70– 79.53
47	67.14	54.88– 77.91	51.18– 80.71
48	68.57	56.37– 79.15	52.66– 81.88
49	70.00	57.87– 80.38	54.16– 83.03
50	71.43	59.38– 81.60	55.68– 84.17
51	72.86	60.90– 82.80	57.21– 85.29
52	74.29	62.44– 83.99	58.76– 86.40
53	75.71	63.99– 85.17	60.33– 87.49
54	77.14	65.55– 86.33	61.91– 88.55
55	78.57	67.13– 87.48	63.51– 89.60
56	80.00	68.73– 88.61	65.14– 90.63
57	81.43	70.34– 89.72	66.78– 91.63
58	82.86	71.97– 90.82	68.45– 92.61
59	84.29	73.62– 91.89	70.15– 93.56
60	85.71	75.29– 92.93	71.87– 94.48
61	87.14	76.99– 93.95	73.63– 95.36
62	88.57	78.72– 94.93	75.42– 96.20
63	90.00	80.48– 95.88	77.25– 97.00
64	91.43	82.27– 96.79	79.13– 97.75
65	92.86	84.11– 97.64	81.07– 98.43
66	94.29	86.01– 98.42	83.08– 99.02
67	95.71	87.98– 99.11	85.19– 99.51
68	97.14	90.06– 99.65	87.42– 99.85
69	98.57	92.30– 99.96	89.86– 99.99
70	100.00	94.87–100.00	92.71–100.00

$N = 71$

x	$100p_x$	95% $100p_l$ – $100p_r$	99% $100p_l$ – $100p_r$
0	0.00	0.00– 5.06	0.00– 7.19
1	1.41	0.04– 7.60	0.01– 10.00
2	2.82	0.34– 9.81	0.15– 12.41
3	4.23	0.88– 11.86	0.48– 14.62
4	5.63	1.56– 13.80	0.96– 16.69
5	7.04	2.33– 15.67	1.55– 18.68
6	8.45	3.17– 17.49	2.22– 20.59
7	9.86	4.06– 19.26	2.95– 22.45
8	11.27	4.99– 21.00	3.74– 24.26
9	12.68	5.96– 22.70	4.57– 26.03
10	14.08	6.97– 24.38	5.44– 27.77
11	15.49	8.00– 26.03	6.35– 29.47
12	16.90	9.05– 27.66	7.28– 31.14

N = number of trials, x = number of successes, etc., $100\ p_x = 100\ x/N$

$N = 71$ (continued)

x	$100p_x$	95% $100p_l$	95% $100p_r$	99% $100p_l$	99% $100p_r$
13	18.31	10.13–	29.27	8.24–	32.79
14	19.72	11.22–	30.87	9.23–	34.42
15	21.13	12.33–	32.44	10.24–	36.02
16	22.54	13.46–	34.00	11.27–	37.61
17	23.94	14.61–	35.54	12.33–	39.17
18	25.35	15.77–	37.08	13.40–	40.72
19	26.76	16.94–	38.59	14.48–	42.25
20	28.17	18.13–	40.10	15.59–	43.77
21	29.58	19.33–	41.59	16.71–	45.27
22	30.99	20.54–	43.08	17.84–	46.75
23	32.39	21.76–	44.55	18.99–	48.22
24	33.80	23.00–	46.01	20.16–	49.68
25	35.21	24.24–	47.46	21.34–	51.12
26	36.62	25.50–	48.90	22.53–	52.55
27	38.03	26.76–	50.33	23.73–	53.97
28	39.44	28.03–	51.75	24.95–	55.38
29	40.85	29.32–	53.16	26.18–	56.77
30	42.25	30.61–	54.56	27.42–	58.15
31	43.66	31.91–	55.95	28.67–	59.52
32	45.07	33.23–	57.34	29.94–	60.88
33	46.48	34.55–	58.71	31.22–	62.23
34	47.89	35.88–	60.08	32.50–	63.56
35	49.30	37.22–	61.44	33.80–	64.88
36	50.70	38.56–	62.78	35.12–	66.20
37	52.11	39.92–	64.12	36.44–	67.50
38	53.52	41.29–	65.45	37.77–	68.78
39	54.93	42.66–	66.77	39.12–	70.06
40	56.34	44.05–	68.09	40.48–	71.33
41	57.75	45.44–	69.39	41.85–	72.58
42	59.15	46.84–	70.68	43.23–	73.82
43	60.56	48.25–	71.97	44.62–	75.05
44	61.97	49.67–	73.24	46.03–	76.27
45	63.38	51.10–	74.50	47.45–	77.47
46	64.79	52.54–	75.76	48.88–	78.66
47	66.20	53.99–	77.00	50.32–	79.84
48	67.61	55.45–	78.24	51.78–	81.01
49	69.01	56.92–	79.46	53.25–	82.16
50	70.42	58.41–	80.67	54.73–	83.29
51	71.83	59.90–	81.87	56.23–	84.41
52	73.24	61.41–	83.06	57.75–	85.52
53	74.65	62.92–	84.23	59.28–	86.60
54	76.06	64.46–	85.39	60.83–	87.67
55	77.46	66.00–	86.54	62.39–	88.73
56	78.87	67.56–	87.67	63.98–	89.76
57	80.28	69.13–	88.78	65.58–	90.77
58	81.69	70.73–	89.87	67.21–	91.76
59	83.10	72.34–	90.95	68.86–	92.72
60	84.51	73.97–	92.00	70.53–	93.65
61	85.92	75.62–	93.03	72.23–	94.56
62	87.32	77.30–	94.04	73.97–	95.43
63	88.73	79.00–	95.01	75.74–	96.26
64	90.14	80.74–	95.94	77.55–	97.05
65	91.55	82.51–	96.83	79.41–	97.78
66	92.96	84.33–	97.67	81.32–	98.45
67	94.37	86.20–	98.44	83.31–	99.04
68	95.77	88.14–	99.12	85.38–	99.52
69	97.18	90.19–	99.66	87.59–	99.85
70	98.59	92.40–	99.96	90.00–	99.99
71	100.00	94.94–	100.00	92.81–	100.00

$N = 72$

x	$100p_x$	95% $100p_l$	95% $100p_r$	99% $100p_l$	99% $100p_r$
0	0.00	0.00–	4.99	0.00–	7.09
1	1.39	0.04–	7.50	0.01–	9.87
2	2.78	0.34–	9.68	0.14–	12.25
3	4.17	0.87–	11.70	0.48–	14.42
4	5.56	1.53–	13.62	0.95–	16.48
5	6.94	2.29–	15.47	1.53–	18.44
6	8.33	3.12–	17.26	2.19–	20.33
7	9.72	4.00–	19.01	2.91–	22.16
8	11.11	4.92–	20.72	3.69–	23.95
9	12.50	5.88–	22.41	4.51–	25.70
10	13.89	6.87–	24.06	5.36–	27.41
11	15.28	7.88–	25.69	6.26–	29.09
12	16.67	8.92–	27.30	7.18–	30.75
13	18.06	9.98–	28.89	8.12–	32.38
14	19.44	11.06–	30.47	9.10–	33.99
15	20.83	12.16–	32.02	10.09–	35.57
16	22.22	13.27–	33.56	11.11–	37.14
17	23.61	14.40–	35.09	12.14–	38.69
18	25.00	15.54–	36.60	13.20–	40.22
19	26.39	16.70–	38.10	14.27–	41.73
20	27.78	17.86–	39.59	15.36–	43.23
21	29.17	19.05–	41.07	16.46–	44.71
22	30.56	20.24–	42.53	17.58–	46.18
23	31.94	21.44–	43.99	18.71–	47.64
24	33.33	22.66–	45.43	19.86–	49.08
25	34.72	23.88–	46.86	21.01–	50.51
26	36.11	25.12–	48.29	22.19–	51.92
27	37.50	26.36–	49.70	23.37–	53.33
28	38.89	27.62–	51.11	24.57–	54.72
29	40.28	28.88–	52.50	25.78–	56.10
30	41.67	30.15–	53.89	27.00–	57.47
31	43.06	31.43–	55.27	28.23–	58.82
32	44.44	32.72–	56.64	29.48–	60.17
33	45.83	34.02–	58.00	30.73–	61.50
34	47.22	35.33–	59.35	32.00–	62.82
35	48.61	36.65–	60.69	33.28–	64.13
36	50.00	37.98–	62.02	34.57–	65.43

$N = 72$ (continued)

x	$100p_x$	95% $100p_l$	95% $100p_r$	99% $100p_l$	99% $100p_r$
37	51.39	39.31–	63.35	35.87–	66.72
38	52.78	40.65–	64.67	37.18–	68.00
39	54.17	42.00–	65.98	38.50–	69.27
40	55.56	43.36–	67.28	39.83–	70.52
41	56.94	44.73–	68.57	41.18–	71.77
42	58.33	46.11–	69.85	42.53–	73.00
43	59.72	47.50–	71.12	43.90–	74.22
44	61.11	48.89–	72.38	45.28–	75.43
45	62.50	50.30–	73.64	46.67–	76.63
46	63.89	51.71–	74.88	48.08–	77.81
47	65.28	53.14–	76.12	49.49–	78.99
48	66.67	54.57–	77.34	50.92–	80.14
49	68.06	56.01–	78.56	52.36–	81.29
50	69.44	57.47–	79.76	53.82–	82.42
51	70.83	58.93–	80.95	55.29–	83.54
52	72.22	60.41–	82.14	56.77–	84.64
53	73.61	61.90–	83.30	58.27–	85.73
54	75.00	63.40–	84.46	59.78–	86.80
55	76.39	64.91–	85.60	61.31–	87.86
56	77.78	66.44–	86.73	62.86–	88.89
57	79.17	67.98–	87.84	64.43–	89.91
58	80.56	69.53–	88.94	66.01–	90.90
59	81.94	71.11–	90.02	67.62–	91.88
60	83.33	72.70–	91.08	69.25–	92.82
61	84.72	74.31–	92.12	70.91–	93.74
62	86.11	75.94–	93.13	72.59–	94.64
63	87.50	77.59–	94.12	74.30–	95.49
64	88.89	79.28–	95.08	76.05–	96.31
65	90.28	80.99–	96.00	77.84–	97.09
66	91.67	82.74–	96.88	79.67–	97.81
67	93.06	84.53–	97.71	81.56–	98.47
68	94.44	86.38–	98.47	83.52–	99.05
69	95.83	88.30–	99.13	85.58–	99.52
70	97.22	90.32–	99.66	87.75–	99.86
71	98.61	92.50–	99.96	90.13–	99.99
72	100.00	95.01–	100.00	92.91–	100.00

$N = 73$

x	$100p_x$	95% $100p_l$	95% $100p_r$	99% $100p_l$	99% $100p_r$
0	0.00	0.00–	4.93	0.00–	7.00
1	1.37	0.03–	7.40	0.01–	9.74
2	2.74	0.33–	9.55	0.14–	12.09
3	4.11	0.86–	11.54	0.47–	14.24
4	5.48	1.51–	13.44	0.94–	16.26
5	6.85	2.26–	15.26	1.51–	18.20
6	8.22	3.08–	17.04	2.16–	20.07
7	9.59	3.94–	18.76	2.87–	21.88
8	10.96	4.85–	20.46	3.63–	23.65
9	12.33	5.80–	22.12	4.44–	25.37
10	13.70	6.77–	23.75	5.29–	27.07
11	15.07	7.77–	25.36	6.17–	28.73
12	16.44	8.79–	26.95	7.07–	30.37
13	17.81	9.84–	28.53	8.01–	31.98
14	19.18	10.90–	30.08	8.97–	33.57
15	20.55	11.98–	31.62	9.95–	35.13
16	21.92	13.08–	33.14	10.95–	36.68
17	23.29	14.19–	34.65	11.97–	38.21
18	24.66	15.32–	36.14	13.01–	39.73
19	26.03	16.45–	37.62	14.06–	41.22
20	27.40	17.61–	39.09	15.13–	42.71
21	28.77	18.77–	40.55	16.22–	44.17
22	30.14	19.94–	42.00	17.32–	45.63
23	31.51	21.13–	43.44	18.43–	47.06
24	32.88	22.33–	44.87	19.56–	48.49
25	34.25	23.53–	46.28	20.70–	49.90
26	35.62	24.75–	47.69	21.86–	51.31
27	36.99	25.97–	49.09	23.02–	52.70
28	38.36	27.21–	50.48	24.20–	54.07
29	39.73	28.45–	51.86	25.39–	55.44
30	41.10	29.71–	53.23	26.59–	56.79
31	42.47	30.97–	54.59	27.80–	58.14
32	43.84	32.24–	55.95	29.03–	59.47
33	45.21	33.52–	57.30	30.26–	60.79
34	46.58	34.80–	58.63	31.51–	62.10
35	47.95	36.10–	59.96	32.77–	63.40
36	49.32	37.40–	61.28	34.03–	64.69
37	50.68	38.72–	62.60	35.31–	65.97
38	52.05	40.04–	63.90	36.60–	67.23
39	53.42	41.37–	65.20	37.90–	68.49
40	54.79	42.70–	66.48	39.21–	69.74
41	56.16	44.05–	67.76	40.53–	70.97
42	57.53	45.41–	69.03	41.86–	72.20
43	58.90	46.77–	70.29	43.21–	73.41
44	60.27	48.14–	71.55	44.56–	74.61
45	61.64	49.52–	72.79	45.93–	75.80
46	63.01	50.91–	74.03	47.30–	76.98
47	64.38	52.31–	75.25	48.69–	78.14
48	65.75	53.72–	76.47	50.10–	79.30
49	67.12	55.13–	77.67	51.51–	80.44
50	68.49	56.56–	78.87	52.94–	81.57
51	69.86	58.00–	80.06	54.37–	82.68
52	71.23	59.45–	81.23	55.83–	83.78
53	72.60	60.91–	82.39	57.29–	84.87
54	73.97	62.38–	83.55	58.78–	85.94
55	75.34	63.86–	84.68	60.27–	86.99
56	76.71	65.35–	85.81	61.79–	88.03
57	78.08	66.86–	86.92	63.32–	89.05
58	79.45	68.38–	88.02	64.87–	90.05
59	80.82	69.92–	89.10	66.43–	91.03

$N = 73$ (continued)

x	$100p_x$	95% $100p_l$	95% $100p_r$	99% $100p_l$	99% $100p_r$
60	82.19	71.47–	90.16	68.02–	91.99
61	83.56	73.05–	91.21	69.63–	92.93
62	84.93	74.64–	92.23	71.27–	93.83
63	86.30	76.25–	93.23	72.93–	94.71
64	87.67	77.88–	94.20	74.63–	95.56
65	89.04	79.54–	95.15	76.35–	96.37
66	90.41	81.24–	96.06	78.12–	97.13
67	91.78	82.96–	96.92	79.93–	97.84
68	93.15	84.74–	97.74	81.80–	98.49
69	94.52	86.56–	98.49	83.74–	99.06
70	95.89	88.46–	99.14	85.76–	99.53
71	97.26	90.45–	99.67	87.91–	99.86
72	98.63	92.60–	99.97	90.26–	99.99
73	100.00	95.07–	100.00	93.00–	100.00

$N = 74$

x	$100p_x$	95% $100p_l$	95% $100p_r$	99% $100p_l$	99% $100p_r$
0	0.00	0.00–	4.86	0.00–	6.91
1	1.35	0.03–	7.30	0.01–	9.62
2	2.70	0.33–	9.42	0.14–	11.93
3	4.05	0.84–	11.39	0.46–	14.06
4	5.41	1.49–	13.27	0.92–	16.06
5	6.76	2.23–	15.07	1.49–	17.97
6	8.11	3.03–	16.82	2.13–	19.81
7	9.46	3.89–	18.52	2.83–	21.60
8	10.81	4.78–	20.19	3.58–	23.35
9	12.16	5.71–	21.84	4.38–	25.06
10	13.51	6.68–	23.45	5.21–	26.73
11	14.86	7.66–	25.04	6.08–	28.37
12	16.22	8.67–	26.61	6.97–	29.99
13	17.57	9.70–	28.17	7.89–	31.58
14	18.92	10.75–	29.70	8.84–	33.15
15	20.27	11.81–	31.22	9.80–	34.70
16	21.62	12.89–	32.72	10.79–	36.24
17	22.97	13.99–	34.21	11.80–	37.75
18	24.32	15.10–	35.69	12.82–	39.25
19	25.68	16.22–	37.16	13.86–	40.73
20	27.03	17.35–	38.61	14.91–	42.19
21	28.38	18.50–	40.05	15.98–	43.64
22	29.73	19.66–	41.48	17.07–	45.08
23	31.08	20.83–	42.90	18.16–	46.51
24	32.43	22.00–	44.32	19.27–	47.92
25	33.78	23.19–	45.72	20.40–	49.32
26	35.14	24.39–	47.11	21.53–	50 70
27	36.49	25.60–	48.49	22.68–	52.08
28	37.84	26.81–	49.87	23.84–	53.44
29	39.19	28.04–	51.23	25.01–	54.79
30	40.54	29.27–	52.59	26.20–	56.14
31	41.89	30.51–	53.94	27.39–	57.47
32	43.24	31.77–	55.28	28.59–	58.79
33	44.59	33.02–	56.61	29.81–	60.10
34	45.95	34.29–	57.93	31.03–	61.39
35	47.30	35.57–	59.25	32.27–	62.68
36	48.65	36.85–	60.56	33.52–	63.96
37	50.00	38.14–	61.86	34.77–	65.23
38	51.35	39.44–	63.15	36.04–	66.48
39	52.70	40.75–	64.43	37.32–	67.73
40	54.05	42.07–	65.71	38.61–	68.97
41	55.41	43.39–	66.98	39.90–	70.19
42	56.76	44.72–	68.23	41.21–	71.41
43	58.11	46.06–	69.49	42.53–	72.61
44	59.46	47.41–	70.73	43.86–	73.80
45	60.81	48.77–	71.96	45.21–	74.99
46	62.16	50.13–	73.19	46.56–	76.16
47	63.51	51.51–	74.40	47.92–	77.32
48	64.86	52.89–	75.61	49.30–	78.47
49	66.22	54.28–	76.81	50.68–	79.60
50	67.57	55.68–	78.00	52.08–	80.73
51	68.92	57.10–	79.17	53.49–	81.84
52	70.27	58.52–	80.34	54.92–	82.93
53	71.62	59.95–	81.50	56.36–	84.02
54	72.97	61.39–	82.65	57.81–	85.09
55	74.32	62.84–	83.78	59.27–	86.14
56	75.68	64.31–	84.90	60.75–	87.18
57	77.03	65.79–	86.01	62.25–	88.20
58	78.38	67.28–	87.11	63.76–	89.21
59	79.73	68.78–	88.19	65.30–	90.20
60	81.08	70.30–	89.25	66.85–	91.16
61	82.43	71.83–	90.30	68.42–	92.11
62	83.78	73.39–	91.33	70.01–	93.03
63	85.14	74.96–	92.34	71.63–	93.92
64	86.49	76.55–	93.32	73.27–	94.79
65	87.84	78.16–	94.29	74.94–	95.62
66	89.19	79.81–	95.22	76.65–	96.42
67	90.54	81.48–	96.11	78.40–	97.17
68	91.89	83.18–	96.97	80.19–	97.87
69	93.24	84.93–	97.77	82.03–	98.51
70	94.59	86.73–	98.51	83.94–	99.08
71	95.95	88.61–	99.16	85.94–	99.54
72	97.30	90.58–	99.67	88.07–	99.86
73	98.65	92.70–	99.97	90.38–	99.99
74	100.00	95.14–	100.00	93.09–	100.00

$N = 75$

x	$100p_x$	95% $100p_l$	95% $100p_r$	99% $100p_l$	99% $100p_r$
0	0.00	0.00–	4.80	0.00–	6.82
1	1.33	0.03–	7.21	0.01–	9.49
2	2.67	0.32–	9.30	0.14–	11.78
3	4.00	0.83–	11.25	0.46–	13.88
4	5.33	1.47–	13.10	0.91–	15.85

$N = 75$ (continued)

x	$100p_x$	95% $100p_l$	95% $100p_r$	99% $100p_l$	99% $100p_r$
5	6.67	2.20–	14.88	1.47–	17.74
6	8.00	2.99–	16.60	2.10–	19.57
7	9.33	3.84–	18.29	2.79–	21.34
8	10.67	4.72–	19.94	3.53–	23.06
9	12.00	5.64–	21.56	4.32–	24.75
10	13.33	6.58–	23.16	5.14–	26.40
11	14.67	7.56–	24.73	5.99–	28.03
12	16.00	8.55–	26.28	6.88–	29.63
13	17.33	9.57–	27.81	7.78–	31.20
14	18.67	10.60–	29.33	8.71–	32.75
15	20.00	11.65–	30.83	9.67–	34.29
16	21.33	12.71–	32.32	10.64–	35.80
17	22.67	13.79–	33.79	11.63–	37.30
18	24.00	14.89–	35.25	12.64–	38.78
19	25.33	15.99–	36.70	13.66–	40.24
20	26.67	17.11–	38.14	14.70–	41.69
21	28.00	18.24–	39.56	15.75–	43.13
22	29.33	19.38–	40.98	16.82–	44.55
23	30.67	20.53–	42.38	17.90–	45.9[illegible]
24	32.00	21.69–	43.78	19.00–	47.3[illegible]
25	33.33	22.86–	45.17	20.10–	48.7[illegible]
26	34.67	24.04–	46.54	21.22–	50.1[illegible]
27	36.00	25.23–	47.91	22.35–	51.4[illegible]
28	37.33	26.43–	49.27	23.49–	52.8[illegible]
29	38.67	27.64–	50.62	24.65–	54.1[illegible]
30	40.00	28.85–	51.96	25.81–	55.49
31	41.33	30.08–	53.30	26.99–	56.81
32	42.67	31.31–	54.62	28.17–	58.12
33	44.00	32.55–	55.94	29.37–	59.42
34	45.33	33.79–	57.25	30.57–	60.70
35	46.67	35.05–	58.55	31.79–	61.98
36	48.00	36.31–	59.85	33.02–	63.25
37	49.33	37.58–	61.14	34.25–	64.50
38	50.67	38.86–	62.42	35.50–	65.75
39	52.00	40.15–	63.69	36.75–	66.98
40	53.33	41.45–	64.95	38.02–	68.21
41	54.67	42.75–	66.21	39.30–	69.43
42	56.00	44.06–	67.45	40.58–	70.63
43	57.33	45.38–	68.69	41.88–	71.83
44	58.67	46.70–	69.92	43.19–	73.01
45	60.00	48.04–	71.15	44.51–	74.19
46	61.33	49.38–	72.36	45.84–	75.35
47	62.67	50.73–	73.57	47.17–	76.51
48	64.00	52.09–	74.77	48.52–	77.65
49	65.33	53.46–	75.96	49.89–	78.78
50	66.67	54.83–	77.14	51.26–	79.90
51	68.00	56.22–	78.31	52.64–	81.00
52	69.33	57.62–	79.47	54.04–	82.10
53	70.67	59.02–	80.62	55.45–	83.18
54	72.00	60.44–	81.76	56.87–	84.25
55	73.33	61.86–	82.89	58.31–	85.30
56	74.67	63.30–	84.01	59.76–	86.34
57	76.00	64.75–	85.11	61.22–	87.36
58	77.33	66.21–	86.21	62.70–	88.37
59	78.67	67.68–	87.29	64.20–	89.36
60	80.00	69.17–	88.35	65.71–	90.33
61	81.33	70.67–	89.40	67.25–	91.29
62	82.67	72.19–	90.43	68.80–	92.22
63	84.00	73.72–	91.45	70.37–	93.12
64	85.33	75.27–	92.44	71.97–	94.01
65	86.67	76.84–	93.42	73.60–	94.86
66	88.00	78.44–	94.36	75.25–	95.68
67	89.33	80.06–	95.28	76.94–	96.47
68	90.67	81.71–	96.16	78.66–	97.21
69	92.00	83.40–	97.01	80.43–	97.90
70	93.33	85.12–	97.80	82.26–	98.53
71	94.67	86.90–	98.53	84.15–	99.09
72	96.00	88.75–	99.17	86.12–	99.54
73	97.33	90.70–	99.68	88.22–	99.86
74	98.67	92.79–	99.97	90.51–	99.99
75	100.00	95.20–	100.00	93.18–	100.00

$N = 76$

x	$100p_x$	95% $100p_l$	95% $100p_r$	99% $100p_l$	99% $100p_r$
0	0.00	0.00–	4.74	0.00–	6.73
1	1.32	0.03–	7.11	0.01–	9.37
2	2.63	0.32–	9.18	0.14–	11.63
3	3.95	0.82–	11.11	0.45–	13.71
4	5.26	1.45–	12.93	0.90–	15.66
5	6.58	2.17–	14.69	1.45–	17.52
6	7.89	2.95–	16.40	2.07–	19.33
7	9.21	3.78–	18.06	2.76–	21.07
8	10.53	4.66–	19.69	3.49–	22.78
9	11.84	5.56–	21.29	4.26–	24.45
10	13.16	6.49–	22.87	5.07–	26.08
11	14.47	7.45–	24.42	5.91–	27.69
12	15.79	8.43–	25.96	6.78–	29.27
13	17.11	9.43–	27.47	7.68–	30.83
14	18.42	10.45–	28.97	8.59–	32.36
15	19.74	11.49–	30.46	9.53–	33.88
16	21.05	12.54–	31.92	10.49–	35.37
17	22.37	13.60–	33.38	11.47–	36.85
18	23.68	14.68–	34.82	12.46–	38.32
19	25.00	15.77–	36.26	13.47–	39.77
20	26.32	16.87–	37.68	14.49–	41.20
21	27.63	17.99–	39.09	15.53–	42.62
22	28.95	19.11–	40.49	16.58–	44.03
23	30.26	20.25–	41.87	17.65–	45.43
24	31.58	21.39–	43.25	18.73–	46.81

N = number of trials, x = number of successes, etc., $100\,p_x = 100\,x/N$

$N = 76$ (continued)

x	$100p_x$	95% $100p_l$	95% $100p_r$	99% $100p_l$	99% $100p_r$
25	32.89	22.54	44.63	19.82	48.18
26	34.21	23.71	45.99	20.92	49.54
27	35.53	24.88	47.34	22.03	50.89
28	36.84	26.06	48.69	23.16	52.22
29	38.16	27.25	50.02	24.29	53.55
30	39.47	28.44	51.35	25.44	54.86
31	40.79	29.65	52.67	26.59	56.17
32	42.11	30.86	53.98	27.76	57.46
33	43.42	32.08	55.29	28.94	58.75
34	44.74	33.31	56.59	30.13	60.02
35	46.05	34.55	57.87	31.32	61.29
36	47.37	35.79	59.16	32.53	62.55
37	48.68	37.04	60.43	33.75	63.79
38	50.00	38.30	61.70	34.97	65.03
39	51.32	39.57	62.96	36.21	66.25
40	52.63	40.84	64.21	37.45	67.47
41	53.95	42.13	65.45	38.71	68.68
42	55.26	43.41	66.69	39.98	69.87
43	56.58	44.71	67.92	41.25	71.06
44	57.89	46.02	69.14	42.54	72.24
45	59.21	47.33	70.35	43.83	73.41
46	60.53	48.65	71.56	45.14	74.56
47	61.84	49.98	72.75	46.45	75.71
48	63.16	51.31	73.94	47.78	76.84
49	64.47	52.66	75.12	49.11	77.97
50	65.79	54.01	76.29	50.46	79.08
51	67.11	55.37	77.46	51.82	80.18
52	68.42	56.75	78.61	53.19	81.27
53	69.74	58.13	79.75	54.57	82.35
54	71.05	59.51	80.89	55.97	83.42
55	72.37	60.91	82.01	57.38	84.47
56	73.68	62.32	83.13	58.80	85.51
57	75.00	63.74	84.23	60.23	86.53
58	76.32	65.18	85.32	61.68	87.54
59	77.63	66.62	86.40	63.15	88.53
60	78.95	68.08	87.46	64.63	89.51
61	80.26	69.54	88.51	66.12	90.47
62	81.58	71.03	89.55	67.64	91.41
63	82.89	72.53	90.57	69.17	92.32
64	84.21	74.04	91.57	70.73	93.22
65	85.53	75.58	92.55	72.31	94.09
66	86.84	77.13	93.51	73.92	94.93
67	88.16	78.71	94.44	75.55	95.74
68	89.47	80.31	95.34	77.22	96.51
69	90.79	81.94	96.22	78.93	97.24
70	92.11	83.60	97.05	80.67	97.93
71	93.42	85.31	97.83	82.48	98.55
72	94.74	87.07	98.55	84.34	99.10
73	96.05	88.89	99.18	86.29	99.55
74	97.37	90.82	99.68	88.37	99.86
75	98.68	92.89	99.97	90.63	99.99
76	100.00	95.26	100.00	93.27	100.00

$N = 77$

x	$100p_x$	95% $100p_l$	95% $100p_r$	99% $100p_l$	99% $100p_r$
0	0.00	0.00	4.68	0.00	6.65
1	1.30	0.03	7.02	0.01	9.26
2	2.60	0.32	9.07	0.14	11.49
3	3.90	0.81	10.97	0.44	13.54
4	5.19	1.43	12.77	0.89	15.47
5	6.49	2.14	14.51	1.43	17.31
6	7.79	2.91	16.19	2.04	19.09
7	9.09	3.73	17.84	2.72	20.82
8	10.39	4.59	19.45	3.44	22.50
9	11.69	5.49	21.03	4.20	24.15
10	12.99	6.41	22.59	5.00	25.77
11	14.29	7.35	24.13	5.83	27.36
12	15.58	8.32	25.64	6.69	28.92
13	16.88	9.31	27.14	7.57	30.46
14	18.18	10.31	28.62	8.48	31.98
15	19.48	11.33	30.09	9.40	33.48
16	20.78	12.37	31.54	10.35	34.96
17	22.08	13.42	32.98	11.31	36.42
18	23.38	14.48	34.41	12.29	37.87
19	24.68	15.56	35.82	13.28	39.31
20	25.97	16.64	37.23	14.29	40.72
21	27.27	17.74	38.62	15.32	42.13
22	28.57	18.85	40.00	16.35	43.52
23	29.87	19.97	41.38	17.40	44.90
24	31.17	21.09	42.74	18.46	46.27
25	32.47	22.23	44.10	19.54	47.63
26	33.77	23.38	45.45	20.62	48.97
27	35.06	24.53	46.78	21.72	50.31
28	36.36	25.70	48.12	22.83	51.63
29	37.66	26.87	49.44	23.95	52.95
30	38.96	28.05	50.75	25.08	54.25
31	40.26	29.23	52.06	26.21	55.54
32	41.56	30.43	53.36	27.36	56.82
33	42.86	31.63	54.65	28.52	58.10
34	44.16	32.84	55.93	29.69	59.36
35	45.45	34.06	57.21	30.87	60.62
36	46.75	35.29	58.48	32.06	61.86
37	48.05	36.52	59.74	33.26	63.10
38	49.35	37.76	61.00	34.46	64.32
39	50.65	39.00	62.24	35.68	65.54
40	51.95	40.26	63.48	36.90	66.74
41	53.25	41.52	64.71	38.14	67.94
42	54.55	42.79	65.94	39.38	69.13
43	55.84	44.07	67.16	40.64	70.31

$N = 77$ (continued)

x	$100p_x$	95% $100p_l$	95% $100p_r$	99% $100p_l$	99% $100p_r$
44	57.14	45.35	68.37	41.90	71.48
45	58.44	46.64	69.57	43.18	72.64
46	59.74	47.94	70.77	44.46	73.79
47	61.04	49.25	71.95	45.75	74.92
48	62.34	50.56	73.13	47.05	76.05
49	63.64	51.88	74.30	48.37	77.17
50	64.94	53.22	75.47	49.69	78.28
51	66.23	54.55	76.62	51.03	79.38
52	67.53	55.90	77.77	52.37	80.46
53	68.83	57.26	78.91	53.73	81.54
54	70.13	58.62	80.03	55.10	82.60
55	71.43	60.00	81.15	56.48	83.65
56	72.73	61.38	82.26	57.87	84.68
57	74.03	62.77	83.36	59.28	85.71
58	75.32	64.18	84.44	60.69	86.72
59	76.62	65.59	85.52	62.13	87.71
60	77.92	67.02	86.58	63.58	88.69
61	79.22	68.46	87.63	65.04	89.65
62	80.52	69.91	88.67	66.52	90.60
63	81.82	71.38	89.69	68.02	91.52
64	83.12	72.86	90.69	69.54	92.43
65	84.42	74.36	91.68	71.08	93.31
66	85.71	75.87	92.65	72.64	94.17
67	87.01	77.41	93.59	74.23	95.00
68	88.31	78.97	94.51	75.85	95.80
69	89.61	80.55	95.41	77.50	96.56
70	90.91	82.16	96.27	79.18	97.28
71	92.21	83.81	97.09	80.91	97.96
72	93.51	85.49	97.86	82.69	98.57
73	94.81	87.23	98.57	84.53	99.11
74	96.10	89.03	99.19	86.46	99.56
75	97.40	90.93	99.68	88.51	99.86
76	98.70	92.98	99.97	90.74	99.99
77	100.00	95.32	100.00	93.35	100.00

$N = 78$

x	$100p_x$	95% $100p_l$	95% $100p_r$	99% $100p_l$	99% $100p_r$
0	0.00	0.00	4.62	0.00	6.57
1	1.28	0.03	6.94	0.01	9.14
2	2.56	0.31	8.96	0.13	11.35
3	3.85	0.80	10.83	0.44	13.37
4	5.13	1.41	12.61	0.88	15.28
5	6.41	2.11	14.33	1.41	17.10
6	7.69	2.88	15.99	2.02	18.86
7	8.97	3.68	17.62	2.68	20.57
8	10.26	4.53	19.21	3.39	22.24
9	11.54	5.41	20.78	4.15	23.87
10	12.82	6.32	22.32	4.94	25.46
11	14.10	7.26	23.83	5.76	27.03
12	15.38	8.21	25.33	6.60	28.58
13	16.67	9.18	26.81	7.47	30.10
14	17.95	10.17	28.28	8.36	31.60
15	19.23	11.18	29.73	9.28	33.09
16	20.51	12.20	31.16	10.21	34.55
17	21.79	13.24	32.59	11.16	36.00
18	23.08	14.29	34.00	12.12	37.43
19	24.36	15.35	35.40	13.10	38.85
20	25.64	16.42	36.79	14.10	40.26
21	26.92	17.50	38.16	15.11	41.65
22	28.21	18.59	39.53	16.13	43.03
23	29.49	19.70	40.89	17.16	44.39
24	30.77	20.81	42.24	18.21	45.75
25	32.05	21.93	43.58	19.27	47.09
26	33.33	23.06	44.92	20.34	48.42
27	34.62	24.20	46.24	21.42	49.74
28	35.90	25.34	47.56	22.51	51.05
29	37.18	26.50	48.87	23.61	52.36
30	38.46	27.66	50.17	24.72	53.65
31	39.74	28.83	51.46	25.85	54.93
32	41.03	30.01	52.75	26.98	56.20
33	42.31	31.19	54.02	28.12	57.46
34	43.59	32.39	55.30	29.27	58.71
35	44.87	33.59	56.56	30.43	59.96
36	46.15	34.79	57.82	31.60	61.19
37	47.44	36.01	59.07	32.78	62.41
38	48.72	37.23	60.31	33.97	63.63
39	50.00	38.46	61.54	35.16	64.84
40	51.28	39.69	62.77	36.37	66.03
41	52.56	40.93	63.99	37.59	67.22
42	53.85	42.18	65.21	38.81	68.40
43	55.13	43.44	66.41	40.04	69.57
44	56.41	44.70	67.61	41.29	70.73
45	57.69	45.98	68.81	42.54	71.88
46	58.97	47.25	69.99	43.80	73.02
47	60.26	48.54	71.17	45.07	74.15
48	61.54	49.83	72.34	46.35	75.28
49	62.82	51.13	73.50	47.64	76.39
50	64.10	52.44	74.66	48.95	77.49
51	65.38	53.76	75.80	50.26	78.58
52	66.67	55.08	76.94	51.58	79.66
53	67.95	56.42	78.07	52.91	80.73
54	69.23	57.76	79.19	54.25	81.79
55	70.51	59.11	80.30	55.61	82.84
56	71.79	60.47	81.41	56.97	83.87
57	73.08	61.84	82.50	58.35	84.89
58	74.36	63.21	83.58	59.74	85.90
59	75.64	64.60	84.65	61.15	86.90
60	76.92	66.00	85.71	62.57	87.88
61	78.21	67.41	86.76	64.00	88.84

$N = 78$ (continued)

x	$100p_x$	95% $100p_l$	95% $100p_r$	99% $100p_l$	99% $100p_r$
62	79.49	68.84	87.80	65.45	89.79
63	80.77	70.27	88.82	66.91	90.72
64	82.05	71.72	89.83	68.40	91.64
65	83.33	73.19	90.82	69.90	92.53
66	84.62	74.67	91.79	71.42	93.40
67	85.90	76.17	92.74	72.97	94.24
68	87.18	77.68	93.68	74.54	95.06
69	88.46	79.22	94.59	76.13	95.85
70	89.74	80.79	95.47	77.76	96.61
71	91.03	82.38	96.32	79.43	97.32
72	92.31	84.01	97.12	81.14	97.98
73	93.59	85.67	97.89	82.90	98.59
74	94.87	87.39	98.59	84.72	99.12
75	96.15	89.17	99.20	86.63	99.56
76	97.44	91.04	99.69	88.65	99.87
77	98.72	93.06	99.97	90.86	99.99
78	100.00	95.38	100.00	93.43	100.00

$N = 79$

x	$100p_x$	95% $100p_l$	95% $100p_r$	99% $100p_l$	99% $100p_r$
0	0.00	0.00	4.56	0.00	6.49
1	1.27	0.03	6.85	0.01	9.03
2	2.53	0.31	8.85	0.13	11.21
3	3.80	0.79	10.70	0.43	13.21
4	5.06	1.40	12.46	0.86	15.10
5	6.33	2.09	14.16	1.39	16.90
6	7.59	2.84	15.80	1.99	18.64
7	8.86	3.64	17.41	2.65	20.33
8	10.13	4.47	18.98	3.35	21.97
9	11.39	5.34	20.53	4.09	23.59
10	12.66	6.24	22.05	4.87	25.17
11	13.92	7.16	23.55	5.68	26.72
12	15.19	8.10	25.03	6.51	28.25
13	16.46	9.06	26.49	7.37	29.75
14	17.72	10.04	27.94	8.25	31.24
15	18.99	11.03	29.38	9.15	32.71
16	20.25	12.04	30.80	10.07	34.16
17	21.52	13.06	32.20	11.01	35.59
18	22.78	14.10	33.60	11.96	37.01
19	24.05	15.14	34.98	12.93	38.41
20	25.32	16.20	36.36	13.91	39.80
21	26.58	17.27	37.72	14.90	41.18
22	27.85	18.35	39.07	15.91	42.54
23	29.11	19.43	40.42	16.93	43.89
24	30.38	20.53	41.75	17.96	45.23
25	31.65	21.63	43.08	19.00	46.56
26	32.91	22.75	44.40	20.06	47.88
27	34.18	23.87	45.71	21.12	49.19
28	35.44	25.00	47.01	22.20	50.49
29	36.71	26.14	48.31	23.29	51.78
30	37.97	27.28	49.59	24.38	53.06
31	39.24	28.44	50.87	25.49	54.33
32	40.51	29.60	52.15	26.60	55.59
33	41.77	30.77	53.41	27.73	56.84
34	43.04	31.94	54.67	28.86	58.08
35	44.30	33.12	55.92	30.00	59.31
36	45.57	34.31	57.17	31.16	60.53
37	46.84	35.51	58.40	32.32	61.75
38	48.10	36.71	59.64	33.49	62.95
39	49.37	37.92	60.86	34.66	64.15
40	50.63	39.14	62.08	35.85	65.34
41	51.90	40.36	63.29	37.05	66.51
42	53.16	41.60	64.49	38.25	67.68
43	54.43	42.83	65.69	39.47	68.84
44	55.70	44.08	66.88	40.69	70.00
45	56.96	45.33	68.06	41.92	71.14
46	58.23	46.59	69.23	43.16	72.27
47	59.49	47.85	70.40	44.41	73.40
48	60.76	49.13	71.56	45.67	74.51
49	62.03	50.41	72.72	46.94	75.62
50	63.29	51.69	73.86	48.22	76.71
51	64.56	52.99	75.00	49.51	77.80
52	65.82	54.29	76.13	50.81	78.88
53	67.09	55.60	77.25	52.12	79.94
54	68.35	56.92	78.37	53.44	81.00
55	69.62	58.25	79.47	54.77	82.04
56	70.89	59.58	80.57	56.11	83.07
57	72.15	60.93	81.65	57.46	84.09
58	73.42	62.28	82.73	58.82	85.10
59	74.68	63.64	83.80	60.20	86.09
60	75.95	65.02	84.86	61.59	87.07
61	77.22	66.40	85.90	62.99	88.04
62	78.48	67.80	86.94	64.41	88.99
63	79.75	69.20	87.96	65.84	89.93
64	81.01	70.62	88.97	67.29	90.85
65	82.28	72.06	89.96	68.76	91.75
66	83.54	73.51	90.94	70.25	92.63
67	84.81	74.97	91.90	71.75	93.49
68	86.08	76.45	92.84	73.28	94.32
69	87.34	77.95	93.76	74.83	95.13
70	88.61	79.47	94.66	76.41	95.91
71	89.87	81.02	95.53	78.03	96.65
72	91.14	82.59	96.36	79.67	97.35
73	92.41	84.20	97.16	81.36	98.01
74	93.67	85.84	97.91	83.10	98.61
75	94.94	87.54	98.60	84.90	99.14
76	96.20	89.30	99.21	86.79	99.57
77	97.47	91.15	99.69	88.79	99.87
78	98.73	93.15	99.97	90.97	99.99
79	100.00	95.44	100.00	93.51	100.00

$N = 80$

x	$100p_x$	95% $100p_l$	95% $100p_r$	99% $100p_l$	99% $100p_r$
0	0.00	0.00	4.51	0.00	6.41
1	1.25	0.03	6.77	0.01	8.92
2	2.50	0.30	8.74	0.13	11.08
3	3.75	0.78	10.57	0.43	13.05
4	5.00	1.38	12.31	0.85	14.92
5	6.25	2.06	13.99	1.37	16.70
6	7.50	2.80	15.61	1.96	18.42
7	8.75	3.59	17.20	2.61	20.09
8	10.00	4.42	18.76	3.31	21.72
9	11.25	5.28	20.28	4.04	23.31
10	12.50	6.16	21.79	4.81	24.87
11	13.75	7.07	23.27	5.61	26.41
12	15.00	8.00	24.74	6.43	27.92
13	16.25	8.95	26.18	7.28	29.41
14	17.50	9.91	27.62	8.14	30.88
15	18.75	10.89	29.03	9.03	32.33
16	20.00	11.89	30.44	9.94	33.77
17	21.25	12.89	31.83	10.86	35.19
18	22.50	13.91	33.21	11.80	36.59
19	23.75	14.95	34.58	12.75	37.98
20	25.00	15.99	35.94	13.72	39.35
21	26.25	17.04	37.29	14.70	40.72
22	27.50	18.10	38.62	15.70	42.07
23	28.75	19.18	39.95	16.70	43.41
24	30.00	20.26	41.28	17.72	44.73
25	31.25	21.35	42.59	18.75	46.05
26	32.50	22.45	43.89	19.79	47.36
27	33.75	23.55	45.19	20.84	48.65
28	35.00	24.67	46.48	21.90	49.94
29	36.25	25.79	47.76	22.97	51.21
30	37.50	26.92	49.04	24.05	52.48
31	38.75	28.06	50.30	25.14	53.74
32	40.00	29.20	51.56	26.24	54.99
33	41.25	30.35	52.82	27.35	56.22
34	42.50	31.51	54.06	28.46	57.45
35	43.75	32.68	55.30	29.59	58.68
36	45.00	33.85	56.53	30.72	59.89
37	46.25	35.03	57.76	31.87	61.09
38	47.50	36.21	58.98	33.02	62.29
39	48.75	37.41	60.19	34.18	63.47
40	50.00	38.60	61.40	35.35	64.65
41	51.25	39.81	62.59	36.53	65.82
42	52.50	41.02	63.79	37.71	66.98
43	53.75	42.24	64.97	38.91	68.13
44	55.00	43.47	66.15	40.11	69.28
45	56.25	44.70	67.32	41.32	70.41
46	57.50	45.94	68.49	42.55	71.54
47	58.75	47.18	69.65	43.78	72.65
48	60.00	48.44	70.80	45.01	73.76
49	61.25	49.70	71.94	46.26	74.86
50	62.50	50.96	73.08	47.52	75.95
51	63.75	52.24	74.21	48.79	77.03
52	65.00	53.52	75.33	50.06	78.10
53	66.25	54.81	76.45	51.35	79.16
54	67.50	56.11	77.55	52.64	80.21
55	68.75	57.41	78.65	53.95	81.25
56	70.00	58.72	79.74	55.27	82.28
57	71.25	60.05	80.82	56.59	83.30
58	72.50	61.38	81.90	57.93	84.30
59	73.75	62.71	82.96	59.28	85.30
60	75.00	64.06	84.01	60.65	86.28
61	76.25	65.42	85.05	62.02	87.25
62	77.50	66.79	86.09	63.41	88.20
63	78.75	68.17	87.11	64.81	89.14
64	80.00	69.56	88.11	66.23	90.06
65	81.25	70.97	89.11	67.67	90.97
66	82.50	72.38	90.09	69.12	91.86
67	83.75	73.82	91.05	70.59	92.72
68	85.00	75.26	92.00	72.08	93.57
69	86.25	76.73	92.93	73.59	94.39
70	87.50	78.21	93.84	75.13	95.19
71	88.75	79.72	94.72	76.69	95.96
72	90.00	81.24	95.58	78.28	96.69
73	91.25	82.80	96.41	79.91	97.39
74	92.50	84.39	97.20	81.58	98.04
75	93.75	86.01	97.94	83.30	98.63
76	95.00	87.69	98.62	85.08	99.15
77	96.25	89.43	99.22	86.95	99.57
78	97.50	91.26	99.70	88.92	99.87
79	98.75	93.23	99.97	91.08	99.99
80	100.00	95.49	100.00	93.59	100.00

$N = 81$

x	$100p_x$	95% $100p_l$	95% $100p_r$	99% $100p_l$	99% $100p_r$
0	0.00	0.00	4.45	0.00	6.33
1	1.23	0.03	6.69	0.01	8.82
2	2.47	0.30	8.64	0.13	10.95
3	3.70	0.77	10.44	0.42	12.90
4	4.94	1.36	12.16	0.84	14.74
5	6.17	2.03	13.82	1.36	16.50
6	7.41	2.77	15.43	1.94	18.21
7	8.64	3.55	17.00	2.58	19.86
8	9.88	4.36	18.54	3.27	21.47
9	11.11	5.21	20.05	3.99	23.04
10	12.35	6.08	21.53	4.75	24.59
11	13.58	6.98	23.00	5.53	26.11
12	14.81	7.90	24.45	6.35	27.60
13	16.05	8.83	25.88	7.18	29.08
14	17.28	9.78	27.30	8.04	30.53

N = number of trials, x = number of successes, etc., $100\,p_x = 100\,x/N$

$N = 81$ (continued)

x	$100p_x$	95% $100p_l$	95% $100p_r$	99% $100p_l$	99% $100p_r$
15	18.52	10.75–	28.70	8.92–	31.97
16	19.75	11.73–	30.09	9.81–	33.39
17	20.99	12.73–	31.46	10.72–	34.79
18	22.22	13.73–	32.83	11.65–	36.18
19	23.46	14.75–	34.18	12.59–	37.55
20	24.69	15.78–	35.53	13.54–	38.92
21	25.93	16.82–	36.86	14.51–	40.27
22	27.16	17.87–	38.19	15.49–	41.60
23	28.40	18.93–	39.50	16.48–	42.93
24	29.63	19.99–	40.81	17.49–	44.24
25	30.86	21.07–	42.11	18.50–	45.55
26	32.10	22.15–	43.40	19.52–	46.84
27	33.33	23.24–	44.68	20.56–	48.12
28	34.57	24.34–	45.96	21.61–	49.40
29	35.80	25.45–	47.23	22.66–	50.66
30	37.04	26.56–	48.49	23.73–	51.92
31	38.27	27.69–	49.74	24.80–	53.16
32	39.51	28.81–	50.99	25.88–	54.40
33	40.74	29.95–	52.23	26.97–	55.62
34	41.98	31.09–	53.46	28.08–	56.84
35	43.21	32.24–	54.69	29.18–	58.05
36	44.44	33.40–	55.91	30.30–	59.26
37	45.68	34.56–	57.13	31.43–	60.45
38	46.91	35.73–	58.33	32.56–	61.64
39	48.15	36.90–	59.53	33.71–	62.81
40	49.38	38.08–	60.73	34.86–	63.98
41	50.62	39.27–	61.92	36.02–	65.14
42	51.85	40.47–	63.10	37.19–	66.29
43	53.09	41.67–	64.27	38.36–	67.44
44	54.32	42.87–	65.44	39.55–	68.57
45	55.56	44.09–	66.60	40.74–	69.70
46	56.79	45.31–	67.76	41.95–	70.82
47	58.02	46.54–	68.91	43.16–	71.92
48	59.26	47.77–	70.05	44.38–	73.03
49	60.49	49.01–	71.19	45.60–	74.12
50	61.73	50.26–	72.31	46.84–	75.20
51	62.96	51.51–	73.44	48.08–	76.27
52	64.20	52.77–	74.55	49.34–	77.34
53	65.43	54.04–	75.66	50.60–	78.39
54	66.67	55.32–	76.76	51.88–	79.44
55	67.90	56.60–	77.85	53.16–	80.48
56	69.14	57.89–	78.93	54.45–	81.50
57	70.37	59.19–	80.01	55.76–	82.51
58	71.60	60.50–	81.07	57.07–	83.52
59	72.84	61.81–	82.13	58.40–	84.51
60	74.07	63.14–	83.18	59.73–	85.49
61	75.31	64.47–	84.22	61.08–	86.46
62	76.54	65.82–	85.25	62.45–	87.41
63	77.78	67.17–	86.27	63.82–	88.35
64	79.01	68.54–	87.27	65.21–	89.28
65	80.25	69.91–	88.27	66.61–	90.19
66	81.48	71.30–	89.25	68.03–	91.08
67	82.72	72.70–	90.22	69.47–	91.96
68	83.95	74.12–	91.17	70.92–	92.82
69	85.19	75.55–	92.10	72.40–	93.65
70	86.42	77.00–	93.02	73.89–	94.47
71	87.65	78.47–	93.92	75.41–	95.25
72	88.89	79.95–	94.79	76.96–	96.01
73	90.12	81.46–	95.64	78.53–	96.73
74	91.36	83.00–	96.45	80.14–	97.42
75	92.59	84.57–	97.23	81.79–	98.06
76	93.83	86.18–	97.97	83.50–	98.64
77	95.06	87.84–	98.64	85.26–	99.16
78	96.30	89.56–	99.23	87.10–	99.58
79	97.53	91.36–	99.70	89.05–	99.87
80	98.77	93.31–	99.97	91.18–	99.99
81	100.00	95.55–	100.00	93.67–	100.00

$N = 82$

x	$100p_x$	95% $100p_l$	95% $100p_r$	99% $100p_l$	99% $100p_r$
0	0.00	0.00–	4.40	0.00–	6.26
1	1.22	0.03–	6.61	0.01–	8.71
2	2.44	0.30–	8.53	0.13–	10.82
3	3.66	0.76–	10.32	0.42–	12.75
4	4.88	1.34–	12.02	0.83–	14.57
5	6.10	2.01–	13.66	1.34–	16.31
6	7.32	2.73–	15.25	1.92–	18.00
7	8.54	3.50–	16.80	2.55–	19.63
8	9.76	4.31–	18.32	3.22–	21.22
9	10.98	5.14–	19.82	3.94–	22.78
10	12.20	6.01–	21.29	4.69–	24.31
11	13.41	6.89–	22.74	5.46–	25.81
12	14.63	7.80–	24.17	6.27–	27.29
13	15.85	8.72–	25.58	7.09–	28.75
14	17.07	9.66–	26.98	7.94–	30.19
15	18.29	10.62–	28.37	8.80–	31.61
16	19.51	11.58–	29.74	9.68–	33.02
17	20.73	12.57–	31.11	10.58–	34.41
18	21.95	13.56–	32.46	11.50–	35.78
19	23.17	14.56–	33.80	12.42–	37.14
20	24.39	15.58–	35.12	13.37–	38.49
21	25.61	16.60–	36.45	14.32–	39.82
22	26.83	17.64–	37.76	15.29–	41.15
23	28.05	18.68–	39.06	16.27–	42.46
24	29.27	19.74–	40.35	17.26–	43.76
25	30.49	20.80–	41.64	18.26–	45.05
26	31.71	21.87–	42.92	19.27–	46.33
27	32.93	22.94–	44.19	20.29–	47.61
28	34.15	24.03–	45.45	21.32–	48.87

$N = 82$ (continued)

x	$100p_x$	95% $100p_l$	95% $100p_r$	99% $100p_l$	99% $100p_r$
29	35.37	25.12–	46.70	22.36–	50.12
30	36.59	26.22–	47.95	23.41–	51.36
31	37.80	27.32–	49.19	24.47–	52.60
32	39.02	28.44–	50.43	25.54–	53.82
33	40.24	29.56–	51.66	26.61–	55.04
34	41.46	30.68–	52.88	27.70–	56.25
35	42.68	31.82–	54.09	28.79–	57.45
36	43.90	32.95–	55.30	29.89–	58.64
37	45.12	34.10–	56.51	31.00–	59.82
38	46.34	35.25–	57.70	32.12–	61.00
39	47.56	36.41–	58.89	33.25–	62.16
40	48.78	37.58–	60.08	34.38–	63.32
41	50.00	38.75–	61.25	35.53–	64.47
42	51.22	39.92–	62.42	36.68–	65.62
43	52.44	41.11–	63.59	37.84–	66.75
44	53.66	42.30–	64.75	39.00–	67.88
45	54.88	43.49–	65.90	40.18–	69.00
46	56.10	44.70–	67.05	41.36–	70.11
47	57.32	45.91–	68.18	42.55–	71.21
48	58.54	47.12–	69.32	43.75–	72.30
49	59.76	48.34–	70.44	44.96–	73.39
50	60.98	49.57–	71.56	46.18–	74.46
51	62.20	50.81–	72.68	47.40–	75.53
52	63.41	52.05–	73.78	48.64–	76.59
53	64.63	53.30–	74.88	49.88–	77.64
54	65.85	54.55–	75.97	51.13–	78.68
55	67.07	55.81–	77.06	52.39–	79.71
56	68.29	57.08–	78.13	53.67–	80.73
57	69.51	58.36–	79.20	54.95–	81.74
58	70.73	59.65–	80.26	56.24–	82.74
59	71.95	60.94–	81.32	57.54–	83.73
60	73.17	62.24–	82.36	58.85–	84.71
61	74.39	63.55–	83.40	60.18–	85.68
62	75.61	64.88–	84.42	61.51–	86.63
63	76.83	66.20–	85.44	62.86–	87.58
64	78.05	67.54–	86.44	64.22–	88.50
65	79.27	68.89–	87.43	65.59–	89.42
66	80.49	70.26–	88.42	66.98–	90.32
67	81.71	71.63–	89.38	68.39–	91.20
68	82.93	73.02–	90.34	69.81–	92.06
69	84.15	74.42–	91.28	71.25–	92.91
70	85.37	75.83–	92.20	72.71–	93.73
71	86.59	77.26–	93.11	74.19–	94.54
72	87.80	78.71–	93.99	75.69–	95.31
73	89.02	80.18–	94.86	77.22–	96.06
74	90.24	81.68–	95.69	78.78–	96.78
75	91.46	83.20–	96.50	80.37–	97.45
76	92.68	84.75–	97.27	82.00–	98.08
77	93.90	86.34–	97.99	83.69–	98.66
78	95.12	87.98–	98.66	85.43–	99.17
79	96.34	89.68–	99.24	87.25–	99.58
80	97.56	91.47–	99.70	89.18–	99.87
81	98.78	93.39–	99.97	91.29–	99.99
82	100.00	95.60–	100.00	93.74–	100.00

$N = 83$

x	$100p_x$	95% $100p_l$	95% $100p_r$	99% $100p_l$	99% $100p_r$
0	0.00	0.00–	4.35	0.00–	6.18
1	1.20	0.03–	6.53	0.01–	8.61
2	2.41	0.29–	8.43	0.13–	10.70
3	3.61	0.75–	10.20	0.41–	12.61
4	4.82	1.33–	11.88	0.82–	14.41
5	6.02	1.98–	13.50	1.32–	16.13
6	7.23	2.70–	15.07	1.89–	17.79
7	8.43	3.46–	16.61	2.52–	19.41
8	9.64	4.25–	18.11	3.18–	20.98
9	10.84	5.08–	19.59	3.89–	22.53
10	12.05	5.93–	21.04	4.63–	24.04
11	13.25	6.81–	22.48	5.40–	25.53
12	14.46	7.70–	23.89	6.19–	26.99
13	15.66	8.61–	25.29	7.00–	28.43
14	16.87	9.54–	26.68	7.84–	29.86
15	18.07	10.48–	28.05	8.69–	31.26
16	19.28	11.44–	29.41	9.56–	32.65
17	20.48	12.41–	30.76	10.45–	34.03
18	21.69	13.39–	32.09	11.35–	35.39
19	22.89	14.38–	33.42	12.27–	36.74
20	24.10	15.38–	34.73	13.20–	38.07
21	25.30	16.39–	36.04	14.14–	39.39
22	26.51	17.42–	37.34	15.09–	40.70
23	27.71	18.45–	38.62	16.06–	42.00
24	28.92	19.48–	39.91	17.03–	43.29
25	30.12	20.53–	41.18	18.02–	44.57
26	31.33	21.59–	42.44	19.02–	45.84
27	32.53	22.65–	43.70	20.03–	47.10
28	33.73	23.72–	44.95	21.04–	48.35
29	34.94	24.80–	46.19	22.07–	49.59
30	36.14	25.88–	47.43	23.10–	50.82
31	37.35	26.97–	48.66	24.15–	52.04
32	38.55	28.07–	49.88	25.20–	53.26
33	39.76	29.17–	51.10	26.26–	54.46
34	40.96	30.28–	52.31	27.33–	55.66
35	42.17	31.40–	53.51	28.41–	56.85
36	43.37	32.53–	54.71	29.50–	58.03
37	44.58	33.66–	55.90	30.59–	59.20
38	45.78	34.79–	57.08	31.69–	60.37
39	46.99	35.93–	58.26	32.80–	61.53
40	48.19	37.08–	59.44	33.92–	62.68
41	49.40	38.24–	60.60	35.05–	63.82

$N = 83$ (continued)

x	$100p_x$	95% $100p_l$	95% $100p_r$	99% $100p_l$	99% $100p_r$
42	50.60	39.40–	61.76	36.18–	64.95
43	51.81	40.56–	62.92	37.32–	66.08
44	53.01	41.74–	64.07	38.47–	67.20
45	54.22	42.92–	65.21	39.63–	68.31
46	55.42	44.10–	66.34	40.80–	69.41
47	56.63	45.29–	67.47	41.97–	70.50
48	57.83	46.49–	68.60	43.15–	71.59
49	59.04	47.69–	69.72	44.34–	72.67
50	60.24	48.90–	70.83	45.54–	73.74
51	61.45	50.12–	71.93	46.74–	74.80
52	62.65	51.34–	73.03	47.96–	75.85
53	63.86	52.57–	74.12	49.18–	76.90
54	65.06	53.81–	75.20	50.41–	77.93
55	66.27	55.05–	76.28	51.65–	78.96
56	67.47	56.30–	77.35	52.90–	79.97
57	68.67	57.56–	78.41	54.16–	80.98
58	69.88	58.82–	79.47	55.43–	81.98
59	71.08	60.09–	80.52	56.71–	82.97
60	72.29	61.38–	81.55	58.00–	83.94
61	73.49	62.66–	82.58	59.30–	84.91
62	74.70	63.96–	83.61	60.61–	85.86
63	75.90	65.27–	84.62	61.93–	86.80
64	77.11	66.58–	85.62	63.26–	87.73
65	78.31	67.91–	86.61	64.61–	88.65
66	79.52	69.24–	87.59	65.97–	89.55
67	80.72	70.59–	88.56	67.35–	90.44
68	81.93	71.95–	89.52	68.74–	91.31
69	83.13	73.32–	90.46	70.14–	92.16
70	84.34	74.71–	91.39	71.57–	93.00
71	85.54	76.11–	92.30	73.01–	93.81
72	86.75	77.52–	93.19	74.47–	94.60
73	87.95	78.96–	94.07	75.96–	95.37
74	89.16	80.41–	94.92	77.47–	96.11
75	90.36	81.89–	95.75	79.02–	96.82
76	91.57	83.39–	96.54	80.59–	97.48
77	92.77	84.93–	97.30	82.21–	98.11
78	93.98	86.50–	98.02	83.87–	98.68
79	95.18	88.12–	98.67	85.59–	99.18
80	96.39	89.80–	99.25	87.39–	99.59
81	97.59	91.57–	99.71	89.30–	99.87
82	98.80	93.47–	99.97	91.39–	99.99
83	100.00	95.65–	100.00	93.82–	100.00

$N = 84$

x	$100p_x$	95% $100p_l$	95% $100p_r$	99% $100p_l$	99% $100p_r$
0	0.00	0.00–	4.30	0.00–	6.11
1	1.19	0.03–	6.46	0.01–	8.51
2	2.38	0.29–	8.34	0.12–	10.57
3	3.57	0.74–	10.08	0.41–	12.46
4	4.76	1.31–	11.75	0.81–	14.24
5	5.95	1.96–	13.35	1.31–	15.95
6	7.14	2.67–	14.90	1.87–	17.59
7	8.33	3.42–	16.42	2.49–	19.19
8	9.52	4.20–	17.91	3.15–	20.75
9	10.71	5.02–	19.37	3.84–	22.28
10	11.90	5.86–	20.81	4.57–	23.77
11	13.10	6.72–	22.22	5.33–	25.25
12	14.29	7.61–	23.62	6.11–	26.69
13	15.48	8.51–	25.01	6.91–	28.12
14	16.67	9.42–	26.38	7.74–	29.53
15	17.86	10.35–	27.74	8.58–	30.92
16	19.05	11.30–	29.08	9.44–	32.30
17	20.24	12.25–	30.41	10.32–	33.66
18	21.43	13.22–	31.74	11.21–	35.01
19	22.62	14.20–	33.05	12.11–	36.34
20	23.81	15.19–	34.35	13.03–	37.66
21	25.00	16.19–	35.64	13.96–	38.97
22	26.19	17.20–	36.93	14.90–	40.27
23	27.38	18.21–	38.20	15.85–	41.56
24	28.57	19.24–	39.47	16.82–	42.83
25	29.76	20.27–	40.73	17.79–	44.10
26	30.95	21.31–	41.98	18.77–	45.35
27	32.14	22.36–	43.22	19.77–	46.60
28	33.33	23.42–	44.46	20.77–	47.84
29	34.52	24.48–	45.69	21.78–	49.07
30	35.71	25.55–	46.92	22.81–	50.29
31	36.90	26.63–	48.13	23.84–	51.50
32	38.10	27.71–	49.34	24.87–	52.70
33	39.29	28.80–	50.55	25.92–	53.90
34	40.48	29.90–	51.75	26.98–	55.09
35	41.67	31.00–	52.94	28.04–	56.27
36	42.86	32.11–	54.12	29.11–	57.44
37	44.05	33.22–	55.30	30.19–	58.60
38	45.24	34.34–	56.48	31.28–	59.76
39	46.43	35.47–	57.65	32.37–	60.90
40	47.62	36.60–	58.81	33.47–	62.04
41	48.81	37.74–	59.96	34.58–	63.18
42	50.00	38.88–	61.12	35.70–	64.30
43	51.19	40.04–	62.26	36.82–	65.42
44	52.38	41.19–	63.40	37.96–	66.53
45	53.57	42.35–	64.53	39.10–	67.63
46	54.76	43.52–	65.66	40.24–	68.72
47	55.95	44.70–	66.78	41.40–	69.81
48	57.14	45.88–	67.89	42.56–	70.89
49	58.33	47.06–	69.00	43.73–	71.96
50	59.52	48.25–	70.10	44.91–	73.02
51	60.71	49.45–	71.20	46.10–	74.08
52	61.90	50.66–	72.29	47.30–	75.13
53	63.10	51.87–	73.37	48.50–	76.16

$N = 84$ (continued)

x	$100p_x$	95% $100p_l$	95% $100p_r$	99% $100p_l$	99% $100p_r$
54	64.29	53.08–	74.45	49.71–	77.19
55	65.48	54.31–	75.52	50.93–	78.22
56	66.67	55.54–	76.58	52.16–	79.23
57	67.86	56.78–	77.64	53.40–	80.23
58	69.05	58.02–	78.69	54.65–	81.23
59	70.24	59.27–	79.73	55.90–	82.21
60	71.43	60.53–	80.76	57.17–	83.18
61	72.62	61.80–	81.79	58.44–	84.15
62	73.81	63.07–	82.80	59.73–	85.10
63	75.00	64.36–	83.81	61.03–	86.04
64	76.19	65.65–	84.81	62.34–	86.97
65	77.38	66.95–	85.80	63.66–	87.89
66	78.57	68.26–	86.78	64.99–	88.7
67	79.76	69.59–	87.75	66.34–	89.6
68	80.95	70.92–	88.70	67.70–	90.5
69	82.14	72.26–	89.65	69.08–	91.4
70	83.33	73.62–	90.58	70.47–	92.2
71	84.52	74.99–	91.49	71.88–	93.0
72	85.71	76.38–	92.39	73.31–	93.8
73	86.90	77.78–	93.28	74.75–	94.6
74	88.10	79.19–	94.14	76.23–	95.4
75	89.29	80.63–	94.98	77.72–	96.1
76	90.48	82.09–	95.80	79.25–	96.8
77	91.67	83.58–	96.58	80.81–	97.5
78	92.86	85.10–	97.33	82.41–	98.1
79	94.05	86.65–	98.04	84.05–	98.6
80	95.24	88.25–	98.69	85.76–	99.1
81	96.43	89.92–	99.26	87.54–	99.5
82	97.62	91.66–	99.71	89.43–	99.8
83	98.81	93.54–	99.97	91.49–	99.9
84	100.00	95.70–	100.00	93.89–	100.0

$N = 85$

x	$100p_x$	95% $100p_l$	95% $100p_r$	99% $100p_l$	99% $100p_r$
0	0.00	0.00–	4.25	0.00–	6.0
1	1.18	0.03–	6.38	0.01–	8.4
2	2.35	0.29–	8.24	0.12–	10.4
3	3.53	0.74–	9.97	0.40–	12.3
4	4.71	1.30–	11.61	0.80–	14.0
5	5.88	1.94–	13.20	1.29–	15.7
6	7.06	2.64–	14.73	1.85–	17.4
7	8.24	3.38–	16.23	2.46–	18.9
8	9.41	4.15–	17.71	3.11–	20.5
9	10.59	4.96–	19.15	3.80–	22.0
10	11.76	5.79–	20.57	4.52–	23.5
11	12.94	6.64–	21.98	5.26–	24.9
12	14.12	7.51–	23.36	6.04–	26.4
13	15.29	8.40–	24.73	6.83–	27.8
14	16.47	9.31–	26.09	7.64–	29.2
15	17.65	10.23–	27.43	8.48–	30.5
16	18.82	11.16–	28.76	9.33–	31.9
17	20.00	12.10–	30.08	10.19–	33.3
18	21.18	13.06–	31.39	11.07–	34.6
19	22.35	14.03–	32.69	11.96–	35.9
20	23.53	15.00–	33.97	12.87–	37.2
21	24.71	15.99–	35.25	13.78–	38.5
22	25.88	16.99–	36.52	14.71–	39.8
23	27.06	17.99–	37.79	15.65–	41.
24	28.24	19.00–	39.04	16.61–	42.
25	29.41	20.02–	40.29	17.57–	43.
26	30.59	21.05–	41.53	18.54–	44.
27	31.76	22.08–	42.76	19.52–	46.
28	32.94	23.13–	43.98	20.51–	47.
29	34.12	24.18–	45.20	21.51–	48.5
30	35.29	25.23–	46.41	22.51–	49.7
31	36.47	26.29–	47.62	23.53–	50.9
32	37.65	27.36–	48.82	24.55–	52.1
33	38.82	28.44–	50.01	25.59–	53.3
34	40.00	29.52–	51.20	26.63–	54.5
35	41.18	30.61–	52.38	27.68–	55.6
36	42.35	31.70–	53.55	28.73–	56.8
37	43.53	32.80–	54.72	29.80–	58.0
38	44.71	33.91–	55.89	30.87–	59.1
39	45.88	35.02–	57.04	31.95–	60.2
40	47.06	36.13–	58.19	33.03–	61.4
41	48.24	37.26–	59.34	34.13–	62.5
42	49.41	38.39–	60.48	35.23–	63.66
43	50.59	39.52–	61.61	36.34–	64.77
44	51.76	40.66–	62.74	37.45–	65.87
45	52.94	41.81–	63.87	38.58–	66.97
46	54.12	42.96–	64.98	39.71–	68.05
47	55.29	44.11–	66.09	40.85–	69.13
48	56.47	45.28–	67.20	41.99–	70.20
49	57.65	46.45–	68.30	43.15–	71.27
50	58.82	47.62–	69.39	44.31–	72.32
51	60.00	48.80–	70.48	45.48–	73.37
52	61.18	49.99–	71.56	46.65–	74.41
53	62.35	51.18–	72.64	47.84–	75.45
54	63.53	52.38–	73.71	49.03–	76.47
55	64.71	53.59–	74.77	50.23–	77.49
56	65.88	54.80–	75.82	51.44–	78.49
57	67.06	56.02–	76.87	52.66–	79.49
58	68.24	57.24–	77.92	53.88–	80.4
59	69.41	58.47–	78.95	55.12–	81.4
60	70.59	59.71–	79.98	56.37–	82.4
61	71.76	60.96–	81.00	57.62–	83.3
62	72.94	62.21–	82.01	58.88–	84.3
63	74.12	63.48–	83.01	60.16–	85.2
64	75.29	64.75–	84.01	61.44–	86.2

"Exact" Confidence Limits for p* $N = 85-90$

N = number of trials, x = number of successes, etc., $100\,p_x = 100\,x/N$

100 p_x	95% 100 p_l	95% 100 p_r	99% 100 p_l	99% 100 p_r
N = 85 (continued)				
76.47	66.03–	85.00	62.74–	87.13
77.65	67.31–	85.97	64.05–	88.04
78.82	68.61–	86.94	65.37–	88.93
80.00	69.92–	87.90	66.70–	89.81
81.18	71.24–	88.84	68.05–	90.67
82.35	72.57–	89.77	69.41–	91.52
83.53	73.91–	90.69	70.79–	92.36
84.71	75.27–	91.60	72.18–	93.17
85.88	76.64–	92.49	73.60–	93.96
87.06	78.02–	93.36	75.03–	94.74
88.24	79.43–	94.21	76.49–	95.48
89.41	80.85–	95.04	77.97–	96.20
90.59	82.29–	95.85	79.48–	96.89
91.76	83.77–	96.62	81.02–	97.54
92.94	85.27–	97.36	82.60–	98.15
94.12	86.80–	98.06	84.23–	98.71
95.29	88.39–	98.70	85.92–	99.20
96.47	90.03–	99.26	87.68–	99.60
97.65	91.76–	99.71	89.55–	99.88
98.82	93.62–	99.97	91.58–	99.99
100.00	95.75–	100.00	93.96–	100.00
N = 86				
0.00	0.00–	4.20	0.00–	5.97
1.16	0.03–	6.31	0.01–	8.32
2.33	0.28–	8.15	0.12–	10.34
3.49	0.73–	9.86	0.40–	12.19
4.65	1.28–	11.48	0.79–	13.93
5.81	1.91–	13.05	1.28–	15.60
6.98	2.60–	14.57	1.82–	17.21
8.14	3.34–	16.05	2.43–	18.77
9.30	4.10–	17.51	3.07–	20.30
10.47	4.90–	18.94	3.75–	21.79
11.63	5.72–	20.35	4.46–	23.26
12.79	6.56–	21.73	5.20–	24.70
13.95	7.42–	23.11	5.96–	26.12
15.12	8.30–	24.46	6.75–	27.52
16.28	9.20–	25.80	7.55–	28.90
17.44	10.10–	27.13	8.37–	30.26
18.60	11.02–	28.45	9.21–	31.61
19.77	11.96–	29.75	10.07–	32.94
20.93	12.90–	31.05	10.93–	34.27
22.09	13.86–	32.33	11.81–	35.57
23.26	14.82–	33.61	12.71–	36.87
24.42	15.80–	34.87	13.61–	38.15
25.58	16.78–	36.13	14.53–	39.42
26.74	17.77–	37.38	15.46–	40.69
27.91	18.77–	38.62	16.40–	41.94
29.07	19.78–	39.86	17.35–	43.18
30.23	20.79–	41.08	18.31–	44.41
31.40	21.81–	42.30	19.27–	45.64
32.56	22.84–	43.52	20.25–	46.85
33.72	23.88–	44.72	21.24–	48.06
34.88	24.92–	45.92	22.23–	49.26
36.05	25.97–	47.12	23.23–	50.45
37.21	27.02–	48.30	24.24–	51.63
38.37	28.08–	49.49	25.26–	52.80
39.53	29.15–	50.66	26.29–	53.97
40.70	30.22–	51.83	27.32–	55.13
41.86	31.30–	52.99	28.37–	56.28
43.02	32.39–	54.15	29.41–	57.43
44.19	33.48–	55.30	30.47–	58.56
45.35	34.58–	56.45	31.54–	59.69
46.51	35.68–	57.59	32.61–	60.81
47.67	36.79–	58.73	33.69–	61.93
48.84	37.90–	59.86	34.77–	63.03
50.00	39.02–	60.98	35.86–	64.14
51.16	40.14–	62.10	36.97–	65.23
52.33	41.27–	63.21	38.07–	66.31
53.49	42.41–	64.32	39.19–	67.39
54.65	43.55–	65.42	40.31–	68.46
55.81	44.70–	66.52	41.44–	69.53
56.98	45.85–	67.61	42.57–	70.59
58.14	47.01–	68.70	43.72–	71.63
59.30	48.17–	69.78	44.87–	72.68
60.47	49.34–	70.85	46.03–	73.71
61.63	50.51–	71.92	47.20–	74.74
62.79	51.70–	72.98	48.37–	75.76
63.95	52.88–	74.03	49.55–	76.77
65.12	54.08–	75.08	50.74–	77.77
66.28	55.28–	76.12	51.94–	78.76
67.44	56.48–	77.16	53.15–	79.75
68.60	57.70–	78.19	54.36–	80.73
69.77	58.92–	79.21	55.59–	81.69
70.93	60.14–	80.22	56.82–	82.65
72.09	61.38–	81.23	58.06–	83.60
73.26	62.62–	82.23	59.31–	84.54
74.42	63.87–	83.22	60.58–	85.47
75.58	65.13–	84.20	61.85–	86.39
76.74	66.39–	85.18	63.13–	87.29
77.91	67.67–	86.14	64.43–	88.19
79.07	68.95–	87.10	65.73–	89.07
80.23	70.25–	88.04	67.06–	89.93
81.40	71.55–	88.98	68.39–	90.79
82.56	72.87–	89.90	69.74–	91.63
83.72	74.20–	90.80	71.10–	92.45
84.88	75.54–	91.70	72.48–	93.25
86.05	76.89–	92.58	73.88–	94.04

x	100 p_x	95% 100 p_l	95% 100 p_r	99% 100 p_l	99% 100 p_r
N = 86 (continued)					
75	87.21	78.27–	93.44	75.30–	94.80
76	88.37	79.65–	94.28	76.74–	95.54
77	89.53	81.06–	95.10	78.21–	96.25
78	90.70	82.49–	95.90	79.70–	96.93
79	91.86	83.95–	96.66	81.23–	97.57
80	93.02	85.43–	97.40	82.79–	98.18
81	94.19	86.95–	98.09	84.40–	98.72
82	95.35	88.52–	98.72	86.07–	99.21
83	96.51	90.14–	99.27	87.81–	99.60
84	97.67	91.85–	99.72	89.66–	99.88
85	98.84	93.69–	99.97	91.68–	99.99
86	100.00	95.80–	100.00	94.03–	100.00
N = 87					
0	0.00	0.00–	4.15	0.00–	5.91
1	1.15	0.03–	6.24	0.01–	8.23
2	2.30	0.28–	8.06	0.12–	10.22
3	3.45	0.72–	9.75	0.39–	12.05
4	4.60	1.27–	11.36	0.78–	13.78
5	5.75	1.89–	12.90	1.26–	15.43
6	6.90	2.57–	14.41	1.80–	17.02
7	8.05	3.30–	15.88	2.40–	18.57
8	9.20	4.05–	17.32	3.03–	20.08
9	10.34	4.84–	18.73	3.71–	21.56
10	11.49	5.65–	20.12	4.41–	23.01
11	12.64	6.48–	21.50	5.14–	24.44
12	13.79	7.34–	22.85	5.89–	25.84
13	14.94	8.20–	24.20	6.67–	27.23
14	16.09	9.09–	25.52	7.46–	28.59
15	17.24	9.98–	26.84	8.27–	29.94
16	18.39	10.89–	28.14	9.10–	31.28
17	19.54	11.81–	29.43	9.94–	32.60
18	20.69	12.75–	30.71	10.80–	33.91
19	21.84	13.69–	31.98	11.67–	35.20
20	22.99	14.64–	33.25	12.55–	36.48
21	24.14	15.60–	34.50	13.45–	37.75
22	25.29	16.58–	35.75	14.35–	39.02
23	26.44	17.55–	36.98	15.27–	40.27
24	27.59	18.54–	38.21	16.20–	41.51
25	28.74	19.54–	39.43	17.13–	42.74
26	29.89	20.54–	40.65	18.08–	43.96
27	31.03	21.55–	41.86	19.04–	45.17
28	32.18	22.56–	43.06	20.00–	46.38
29	33.33	23.58–	44.25	20.97–	47.57
30	34.48	24.61–	45.44	21.95–	48.76
31	35.63	25.65–	46.62	22.94–	49.94
32	36.78	26.69–	47.80	23.94–	51.11
33	37.93	27.74–	48.97	24.95–	52.27
34	39.08	28.79–	50.13	25.96–	53.43
35	40.23	29.85–	51.29	26.98–	54.58
36	41.38	30.92–	52.45	28.01–	55.72
37	42.53	31.99–	53.59	29.04–	56.85
38	43.68	33.06–	54.74	30.09–	57.98
39	44.83	34.15–	55.87	31.13–	59.10
40	45.98	35.23–	57.00	32.19–	60.21
41	47.13	36.33–	58.13	33.26–	61.32
42	48.28	37.42–	59.25	34.33–	62.42
43	49.43	38.53–	60.36	35.40–	63.51
44	50.57	39.64–	61.47	36.49–	64.60
45	51.72	40.75–	62.58	37.58–	65.67
46	52.87	41.87–	63.67	38.68–	66.74
47	54.02	43.00–	64.77	39.79–	67.81
48	55.17	44.13–	65.85	40.90–	68.87
49	56.32	45.26–	66.94	42.02–	69.91
50	57.47	46.41–	68.01	43.15–	70.96
51	58.62	47.55–	69.08	44.28–	71.99
52	59.77	48.71–	70.15	45.42–	73.02
53	60.92	49.87–	71.21	46.57–	74.04
54	62.07	51.03–	72.26	47.73–	75.05
55	63.22	52.20–	73.31	48.89–	76.06
56	64.37	53.38–	74.35	50.06–	77.06
57	65.52	54.56–	75.39	51.24–	78.05
58	66.67	55.75–	76.42	52.43–	79.03
59	67.82	56.94–	77.44	53.62–	80.00
60	68.97	58.14–	78.45	54.83–	80.96
61	70.11	59.35–	79.46	56.04–	81.92
62	71.26	60.57–	80.46	57.26–	82.87
63	72.41	61.79–	81.46	58.49–	83.80
64	73.56	63.02–	82.45	59.73–	84.73
65	74.71	64.25–	83.42	60.98–	85.65
66	75.86	65.50–	84.40	62.25–	86.55
67	77.01	66.75–	85.36	63.52–	87.45
68	78.16	68.02–	86.31	64.80–	88.33
69	79.31	69.29–	87.25	66.09–	89.20
70	80.46	70.57–	88.19	67.40–	90.06
71	81.61	71.86–	89.11	68.72–	90.90
72	82.76	73.16–	90.02	70.06–	91.73
73	83.91	74.48–	90.91	71.41–	92.54
74	85.06	75.80–	91.80	72.77–	93.33
75	86.21	77.15–	92.66	74.16–	94.11
76	87.36	78.50–	93.52	75.56–	94.86
77	88.51	79.88–	94.35	76.99–	95.59
78	89.66	81.27–	95.16	78.44–	96.29
79	90.80	82.68–	95.95	79.92–	96.97
80	91.95	84.12–	96.70	81.43–	97.60
81	93.10	85.59–	97.43	82.98–	98.20
82	94.25	87.10–	98.11	84.57–	98.74
83	95.40	88.64–	98.73	86.22–	99.22

x	100 p_x	95% 100 p_l	95% 100 p_r	99% 100 p_l	99% 100 p_r
N = 87 (continued)					
84	96.55	90.25–	99.28	87.95–	99.61
85	97.70	91.94–	99.72	89.78–	99.88
86	98.85	93.76–	99.97	91.77–	99.99
87	100.00	95.85–	100.00	94.09–	100.00
N = 88					
0	0.00	0.00–	4.11	0.00–	5.84
1	1.14	0.03–	6.17	0.01–	8.14
2	2.27	0.28–	7.97	0.12–	10.11
3	3.41	0.71–	9.64	0.39–	11.92
4	4.55	1.25–	11.23	0.77–	13.63
5	5.68	1.87–	12.76	1.25–	15.26
6	6.82	2.54–	14.25	1.78–	16.84
7	7.95	3.26–	15.70	2.37–	18.37
8	9.09	4.01–	17.13	3.00–	19.87
9	10.23	4.78–	18.53	3.66–	21.33
10	11.36	5.59–	19.91	4.36–	22.77
11	12.50	6.41–	21.27	5.08–	24.18
12	13.64	7.25–	22.61	5.82–	25.57
13	14.77	8.11–	23.94	6.59–	26.94
14	15.91	8.98–	25.25	7.37–	28.29
15	17.05	9.87–	26.55	8.17–	29.63
16	18.18	10.76–	27.84	8.99–	30.95
17	19.32	11.68–	29.12	9.82–	32.26
18	20.45	12.60–	30.39	10.67–	33.55
19	21.59	13.53–	31.65	11.53–	34.84
20	22.73	14.47–	32.89	12.40–	36.11
21	23.86	15.42–	34.14	13.29–	37.37
22	25.00	16.38–	35.37	14.18–	38.61
23	26.14	17.34–	36.59	15.09–	39.85
24	27.27	18.32–	37.81	16.00–	41.08
25	28.41	19.30–	39.02	16.93–	42.30
26	29.55	20.29–	40.22	17.86–	43.51
27	30.68	21.29–	41.42	18.80–	44.71
28	31.82	22.29–	42.61	19.76–	45.91
29	32.95	23.30–	43.79	20.72–	47.09
30	34.09	24.32–	44.97	21.68–	48.27
31	35.23	25.34–	46.14	22.66–	49.44
32	36.36	26.37–	47.31	23.65–	50.60
33	37.50	27.40–	48.47	24.64–	51.75
34	38.64	28.44–	49.62	25.64–	52.90
35	39.77	29.49–	50.77	26.64–	54.04
36	40.91	30.54–	51.91	27.66–	55.17
37	42.05	31.60–	53.05	28.68–	56.29
38	43.18	32.66–	54.18	29.71–	57.41
39	44.32	33.73–	55.30	30.74–	58.52
40	45.45	34.80–	56.42	31.79–	59.63
41	46.59	35.88–	57.54	32.84–	60.72
42	47.73	36.96–	58.65	33.89–	61.81
43	48.86	38.05–	59.75	34.96–	62.90
44	50.00	39.15–	60.85	36.03–	63.97
45	51.14	40.25–	61.95	37.10–	65.04
46	52.27	41.35–	63.04	38.19–	66.11
47	53.41	42.46–	64.12	39.28–	67.16
48	54.55	43.58–	65.20	40.37–	68.21
49	55.68	44.70–	66.27	41.48–	69.26
50	56.82	45.82–	67.34	42.59–	70.29
51	57.95	46.95–	68.40	43.71–	71.32
52	59.09	48.09–	69.46	44.83–	72.34
53	60.23	49.23–	70.51	45.96–	73.36
54	61.36	50.38–	71.56	47.10–	74.36
55	62.50	51.53–	72.60	48.25–	75.36
56	63.64	52.69–	73.63	49.40–	76.35
57	64.77	53.86–	74.66	50.56–	77.34
58	65.91	55.03–	75.68	51.73–	78.32
59	67.05	56.21–	76.70	52.91–	79.28
60	68.18	57.39–	77.71	54.09–	80.24
61	69.32	58.58–	78.71	55.29–	81.20
62	70.45	59.78–	79.71	56.49–	82.14
63	71.59	60.98–	80.70	57.70–	83.07
64	72.73	62.19–	81.68	58.92–	84.00
65	73.86	63.41–	82.66	60.15–	84.91
66	75.00	64.63–	83.62	61.39–	85.82
67	76.14	65.86–	84.58	62.63–	86.71
68	77.27	67.11–	85.53	63.89–	87.60
69	78.41	68.35–	86.47	65.16–	88.47
70	79.55	69.61–	87.40	66.45–	89.33
71	80.68	70.88–	88.32	67.74–	90.18
72	81.82	72.16–	89.24	69.05–	91.01
73	82.95	73.45–	90.13	70.37–	91.83
74	84.09	74.75–	91.02	71.71–	92.63
75	85.23	76.06–	91.89	73.06–	93.41
76	86.36	77.39–	92.75	74.43–	94.18
77	87.50	78.73–	93.59	75.82–	94.92
78	88.64	80.09–	94.41	77.23–	95.64
79	89.77	81.47–	95.22	78.67–	96.34
80	90.91	82.87–	95.99	80.13–	97.00
81	92.05	84.30–	96.74	81.63–	97.63
82	93.18	85.75–	97.46	83.16–	98.22
83	94.32	87.24–	98.13	84.74–	98.75
84	95.45	88.77–	98.75	86.37–	99.23
85	96.59	90.36–	99.29	88.08–	99.61
86	97.73	92.03–	99.72	89.89–	99.88
87	98.86	93.83–	99.97	91.86–	99.99
88	100.00	95.89–	100.00	94.16–	100.00
N = 89					
0	0.00	0.00–	4.06	0.00–	5.78
1	1.12	0.03–	6.10	0.01–	8.05

x	100 p_x	95% 100 p_l	95% 100 p_r	99% 100 p_l	99% 100 p_r
N = 89 (continued)					
2	2.25	0.27–	7.88	0.12–	10.00
3	3.37	0.70–	9.54	0.38–	11.79
4	4.49	1.24–	11.11	0.77–	13.48
5	5.62	1.85–	12.63	1.23–	15.10
6	6.74	2.51–	14.10	1.76–	16.66
7	7.87	3.22–	15.54	2.34–	18.18
8	8.99	3.96–	16.95	2.96–	19.66
9	10.11	4.73–	18.33	3.62–	21.11
10	11.24	5.52–	19.69	4.31–	22.53
11	12.36	6.33–	21.04	5.02–	23.92
12	13.48	7.17–	22.37	5.75–	25.30
13	14.61	8.01–	23.68	6.51–	26.66
14	15.73	8.88–	24.98	7.29–	28.00
15	16.85	9.75–	26.27	8.08–	29.32
16	17.98	10.64–	27.55	8.89–	30.63
17	19.10	11.54–	28.81	9.71–	31.93
18	20.22	12.45–	30.07	10.55–	33.21
19	21.35	13.37–	31.31	11.39–	34.48
20	22.47	14.30–	32.55	12.26–	35.74
21	23.60	15.24–	33.78	13.13–	36.99
22	24.72	16.19–	35.00	14.01–	38.22
23	25.84	17.14–	36.21	14.91–	39.45
24	26.97	18.10–	37.42	15.81–	40.67
25	28.09	19.07–	38.62	16.72–	41.87
26	29.21	20.05–	39.81	17.65–	43.07
27	30.34	21.03–	40.99	18.58–	44.27
28	31.46	22.03–	42.17	19.52–	45.45
29	32.58	23.02–	43.34	20.47–	46.62
30	33.71	24.03–	44.51	21.42–	47.79
31	34.83	25.04–	45.67	22.39–	48.95
32	35.96	26.05–	46.82	23.36–	50.10
33	37.08	27.07–	47.97	24.34–	51.24
34	38.20	28.10–	49.11	25.32–	52.38
35	39.33	29.13–	50.25	26.32–	53.51
36	40.45	30.17–	51.38	27.32–	54.63
37	41.57	31.21–	52.51	28.33–	55.75
38	42.70	32.26–	53.63	29.34–	56.85
39	43.82	33.32–	54.75	30.36–	57.96
40	44.94	34.38–	55.86	31.39–	59.05
41	46.07	35.44–	56.96	32.43–	60.14
42	47.19	36.51–	58.06	33.47–	61.22
43	48.31	37.59–	59.16	34.52–	62.30
44	49.44	38.67–	60.25	35.57–	63.36
45	50.56	39.75–	61.33	36.64–	64.43
46	51.69	40.84–	62.41	37.70–	65.48
47	52.81	41.94–	63.49	38.78–	66.53
48	53.93	43.04–	64.56	39.86–	67.57
49	55.06	44.14–	65.62	40.95–	68.61
50	56.18	45.25–	66.68	42.04–	69.64
51	57.30	46.37–	67.74	43.15–	70.66
52	58.43	47.49–	68.79	44.25–	71.67
53	59.55	48.62–	69.83	45.37–	72.68
54	60.67	49.75–	70.87	46.49–	73.68
55	61.80	50.89–	71.90	47.62–	74.68
56	62.92	52.03–	72.93	48.76–	75.66
57	64.04	53.18–	73.95	49.90–	76.64
58	65.17	54.33–	74.96	51.05–	77.61
59	66.29	55.49–	75.97	52.21–	78.58
60	67.42	56.66–	76.98	53.38–	79.53
61	68.54	57.83–	77.97	54.55–	80.48
62	69.66	59.01–	78.97	55.73–	81.42
63	70.79	60.19–	79.95	56.93–	82.35
64	71.91	61.38–	80.93	58.13–	83.28
65	73.03	62.58–	81.90	59.33–	84.19
66	74.16	63.79–	82.86	60.55–	85.09
67	75.28	65.00–	83.81	61.78–	85.99
68	76.40	66.22–	84.76	63.01–	86.87
69	77.53	67.45–	85.70	64.26–	87.74
70	78.65	68.69–	86.63	65.52–	88.61
71	79.78	69.93–	87.55	66.79–	89.45
72	80.90	71.19–	88.46	68.07–	90.29
73	82.02	72.45–	89.36	69.37–	91.11
74	83.15	73.73–	90.25	70.68–	91.92
75	84.27	75.02–	91.12	72.00–	92.71
76	85.39	76.32–	91.99	73.34–	93.49
77	86.52	77.63–	92.83	74.70–	94.25
78	87.64	78.96–	93.67	76.08–	94.98
79	88.76	80.31–	94.48	77.47–	95.69
80	89.89	81.67–	95.27	78.89–	96.38
81	91.01	83.05–	96.04	80.34–	97.04
82	92.13	84.46–	96.78	81.82–	97.66
83	93.26	85.90–	97.49	83.34–	98.24
84	94.38	87.37–	98.15	84.90–	98.77
85	95.51	88.89–	98.76	86.52–	99.23
86	96.63	90.46–	99.30	88.21–	99.62
87	97.75	92.12–	99.73	90.00–	99.88
88	98.88	93.90–	99.97	91.95–	99.99
89	100.00	95.94–	100.00	94.22–	100.00
N = 90					
0	0.00	0.00–	4.02	0.00–	5.72
1	1.11	0.03–	6.04	0.01–	7.97
2	2.22	0.27–	7.80	0.12–	9.90
3	3.33	0.69–	9.43	0.38–	11.67
4	4.44	1.22–	10.99	0.76–	13.34
5	5.56	1.83–	12.49	1.22–	14.94
6	6.67	2.49–	13.95	1.74–	16.48
7	7.78	3.18–	15.37	2.32–	17.99
8	8.89	3.92–	16.77	2.93–	19.45

N = number of trials, x = number of successes, etc., $100\,p_x = 100\,x/N$

$100(1-2\alpha)$ limits

$N = 90$ (continued)

x	$100p_x$	95% $100p_l$	95% $100p_r$	99% $100p_l$	99% $100p_r$
9	10.00	4.68–	18.14	3.58–	20.89
10	11.11	5.46–	19.49	4.26–	22.29
11	12.22	6.26–	20.82	4.96–	23.68
12	13.33	7.08–	22.13	5.69–	25.04
13	14.44	7.92–	23.43	6.44–	26.38
14	15.56	8.77–	24.72	7.20–	27.71
15	16.67	9.64–	26.00	7.98–	29.02
16	17.78	10.52–	27.26	8.78–	30.32
17	18.89	11.41–	28.51	9.60–	31.60
18	20.00	12.31–	29.75	10.42–	32.87
19	21.11	13.22–	30.99	11.26–	34.13
20	22.22	14.13–	32.21	12.11–	35.38
21	23.33	15.06–	33.43	12.97–	36.61
22	24.44	16.00–	34.64	13.85–	37.84
23	25.56	16.94–	35.84	14.73–	39.05
24	26.67	17.89–	37.03	15.62–	40.26
25	27.78	18.85–	38.22	16.53–	41.46
26	28.89	19.82–	39.40	17.44–	42.65
27	30.00	20.79–	40.57	18.36–	43.83
28	31.11	21.77–	41.74	19.28–	45.00
29	32.22	22.75–	42.90	20.22–	46.16
30	33.33	23.74–	44.05	21.16–	47.32
31	34.44	24.74–	45.20	22.12–	48.47
32	35.56	25.74–	46.35	23.08–	49.61
33	36.67	26.75–	47.49	24.04–	50.74
34	37.78	27.77–	48.62	25.02–	51.87
35	38.89	28.79–	49.74	26.00–	52.99
36	40.00	29.81–	50.87	26.99–	54.10
37	41.11	30.84–	51.98	27.98–	55.21
38	42.22	31.88–	53.09	28.98–	56.31
39	43.33	32.92–	54.20	29.99–	57.40
40	44.44	33.96–	55.30	31.01–	58.49
41	45.56	35.02–	56.40	32.03–	59.57
42	46.67	36.07–	57.49	33.06–	60.64
43	47.78	37.13–	58.57	34.09–	61.71
44	48.89	38.20–	59.65	35.13–	62.77
45	50.00	39.27–	60.73	36.18–	63.82
46	51.11	40.35–	61.80	37.23–	64.87
47	52.22	41.43–	62.87	38.29–	65.91
48	53.33	42.51–	63.93	39.36–	66.94
49	54.44	43.60–	64.98	40.43–	67.97
50	55.56	44.70–	66.04	41.51–	68.99
51	56.67	45.80–	67.08	42.60–	70.01
52	57.78	46.91–	68.12	43.69–	71.02
53	58.89	48.02–	69.16	44.79–	72.02
54	60.00	49.13–	70.19	45.90–	73.01
55	61.11	50.26–	71.21	47.01–	74.00
56	62.22	51.38–	72.23	48.13–	74.98
57	63.33	52.51–	73.25	49.26–	75.96
58	64.44	53.65–	74.26	50.39–	76.92
59	65.56	54.80–	75.26	51.53–	77.88
60	66.67	55.95–	76.26	52.68–	78.84
61	67.78	57.10–	77.25	53.84–	79.78
62	68.89	58.26–	78.23	55.00–	80.72
63	70.00	59.43–	79.21	56.17–	81.64
64	71.11	60.60–	80.18	57.35–	82.56
65	72.22	61.78–	81.15	58.54–	83.47
66	73.33	62.97–	82.11	59.74–	84.38
67	74.44	64.16–	83.06	60.95–	85.27
68	75.56	65.36–	84.00	62.16–	86.15
69	76.67	66.57–	84.94	63.39–	87.03
70	77.78	67.79–	85.87	64.62–	87.89
71	78.89	69.01–	86.78	65.87–	88.74
72	80.00	70.25–	87.69	67.13–	89.58
73	81.11	71.49–	88.59	68.40–	90.40
74	82.22	72.74–	89.48	69.68–	91.22
75	83.33	74.00–	90.36	70.98–	92.02
76	84.44	75.28–	91.23	72.29–	92.80
77	85.56	76.57–	92.08	73.62–	93.56
78	86.67	77.87–	92.92	74.96–	94.31
79	87.78	79.18–	93.74	76.32–	95.04
80	88.89	80.51–	94.54	77.71–	95.74
81	90.00	81.86–	95.32	79.11–	96.42
82	91.11	83.23–	96.08	80.55–	97.07
83	92.22	84.63–	96.82	82.01–	97.68
84	93.33	86.05–	97.51	83.52–	98.26
85	94.44	87.51–	98.17	85.06–	98.78
86	95.56	89.01–	98.78	86.66–	99.24
87	96.67	90.57–	99.31	88.33–	99.62
88	97.78	92.20–	99.73	90.10–	99.88
89	98.89	93.96–	99.97	92.03–	99.99
90	100.00	95.98–	100.00	94.28–	100.00

$N = 91$

x	$100p_x$	95% $100p_l$	95% $100p_r$	99% $100p_l$	99% $100p_r$
0	0.00	0.00–	3.97	0.00–	5.66
1	1.10	0.03–	5.97	0.01–	7.88
2	2.20	0.27–	7.71	0.11–	9.79
3	3.30	0.69–	9.33	0.38–	11.55
4	4.40	1.21–	10.87	0.75–	13.20
5	5.49	1.81–	12.36	1.20–	14.78
6	6.59	2.46–	13.80	1.72–	16.31
7	7.69	3.15–	15.21	2.29–	17.80
8	8.79	3.87–	16.59	2.90–	19.25
9	9.89	4.62–	17.95	3.54–	20.67
10	10.99	5.40–	19.28	4.21–	22.06
11	12.09	6.19–	20.60	4.91–	23.43
12	13.19	7.00–	21.90	5.62–	24.78
13	14.29	7.83–	23.19	6.36–	26.12

$N = 91$ (continued)

x	$100p_x$	95% $100p_l$	95% $100p_r$	99% $100p_l$	99% $100p_r$
14	15.38	8.67–	24.46	7.12–	27.43
15	16.48	9.53–	25.73	7.89–	28.73
16	17.58	10.40–	26.98	8.68–	30.01
17	18.68	11.28–	28.22	9.49–	31.28
18	19.78	12.17–	29.45	10.30–	32.54
19	20.88	13.06–	30.67	11.13–	33.79
20	21.98	13.97–	31.88	11.97–	35.02
21	23.08	14.89–	33.09	12.82–	36.25
22	24.18	15.81–	34.28	13.69–	37.46
23	25.27	16.75–	35.47	14.56–	38.66
24	26.37	17.69–	36.65	15.44–	39.86
25	27.47	18.63–	37.83	16.33–	41.05
26	28.57	19.59–	39.00	17.23–	42.22
27	29.67	20.55–	40.16	18.14–	43.39
28	30.77	21.51–	41.32	19.06–	44.56
29	31.87	22.49–	42.47	19.98–	45.71
30	32.97	23.47–	43.61	20.91–	46.85
31	34.07	24.45–	44.75	21.85–	47.99
32	35.16	25.44–	45.88	22.80–	49.12
33	36.26	26.44–	47.01	23.76–	50.25
34	37.36	27.44–	48.13	24.72–	51.37
35	38.46	28.45–	49.25	25.69–	52.48
36	39.56	29.46–	50.36	26.66–	53.58
37	40.66	30.48–	51.47	27.65–	54.68
38	41.76	31.50–	52.57	28.63–	55.77
39	42.86	32.53–	53.66	29.63–	56.85
40	43.96	33.56–	54.75	30.63–	57.93
41	45.05	34.60–	55.84	31.64–	59.00
42	46.15	35.64–	56.92	32.65–	60.07
43	47.25	36.69–	58.00	33.68–	61.12
44	48.35	37.74–	59.07	34.70–	62.18
45	49.45	38.80–	60.14	35.74–	63.22
46	50.55	39.86–	61.20	36.78–	64.26
47	51.65	40.93–	62.26	37.82–	65.30
48	52.75	42.00–	63.31	38.88–	66.32
49	53.85	43.08–	64.36	39.93–	67.35
50	54.95	44.16–	65.40	41.00–	68.36
51	56.04	45.25–	66.44	42.07–	69.37
52	57.14	46.34–	67.47	43.15–	70.37
53	58.24	47.43–	68.50	44.23–	71.37
54	59.34	48.53–	69.52	45.32–	72.35
55	60.44	49.64–	70.54	46.42–	73.34
56	61.54	50.75–	71.55	47.52–	74.31
57	62.64	51.87–	72.56	48.63–	75.28
58	63.74	52.99–	73.56	49.75–	76.24
59	64.84	54.12–	74.56	50.88–	77.20
60	65.93	55.25–	75.55	52.01–	78.15
61	67.03	56.39–	76.53	53.15–	79.09
62	68.13	57.53–	77.51	54.29–	80.02
63	69.23	58.68–	78.49	55.44–	80.94
64	70.33	59.84–	79.45	56.61–	81.86
65	71.43	61.00–	80.41	57.78–	82.77
66	72.53	62.17–	81.37	58.95–	83.67
67	73.63	63.35–	82.31	60.14–	84.56
68	74.73	64.53–	83.25	61.34–	85.44
69	75.82	65.72–	84.19	62.54–	86.31
70	76.92	66.91–	85.11	63.75–	87.18
71	78.02	68.12–	86.03	64.98–	88.03
72	79.12	69.33–	86.94	66.21–	88.87
73	80.22	70.55–	87.83	67.46–	89.70
74	81.32	71.78–	88.72	68.72–	90.51
75	82.42	73.02–	89.60	69.99–	91.32
76	83.52	74.27–	90.47	71.27–	92.11
77	84.62	75.54–	91.33	72.57–	92.88
78	85.71	76.81–	92.17	73.88–	93.64
79	86.81	78.10–	93.00	75.22–	94.38
80	87.91	79.40–	93.81	76.57–	95.09
81	89.01	80.72–	94.60	77.94–	95.79
82	90.11	82.05–	95.38	79.33–	96.46
83	91.21	83.41–	96.13	80.75–	97.10
84	92.31	84.79–	96.85	82.20–	97.71
85	93.41	86.20–	97.54	83.69–	98.28
86	94.51	87.64–	98.19	85.22–	98.80
87	95.60	89.13–	98.79	86.80–	99.25
88	96.70	90.67–	99.31	88.45–	99.62
89	97.80	92.29–	99.73	90.21–	99.89
90	98.90	94.03–	99.97	92.12–	99.99
91	100.00	96.03–	100.00	94.34–	100.00

$N = 92$

x	$100p_x$	95% $100p_l$	95% $100p_r$	99% $100p_l$	99% $100p_r$
0	0.00	0.00–	3.93	0.00–	5.60
1	1.09	0.03–	5.91	0.01–	7.80
2	2.17	0.26–	7.63	0.11–	9.69
3	3.26	0.68–	9.24	0.37–	11.43
4	4.35	1.20–	10.76	0.74–	13.06
5	5.43	1.79–	12.23	1.19–	14.63
6	6.52	2.43–	13.66	1.70–	16.15
7	7.61	3.11–	15.05	2.27–	17.62
8	8.70	3.83–	16.42	2.87–	19.05
9	9.78	4.57–	17.76	3.50–	20.46
10	10.87	5.34–	19.08	4.16–	21.84
11	11.96	6.12–	20.39	4.85–	23.20
12	13.04	6.93–	21.68	5.56–	24.53
13	14.13	7.74–	22.95	6.29–	25.85
14	15.22	8.58–	24.21	7.04–	27.15
15	16.30	9.42–	25.46	7.80–	28.44
16	17.39	10.28–	26.70	8.58–	29.71
17	18.48	11.15–	27.93	9.38–	30.97

$N = 92$ (continued)

x	$100p_x$	95% $100p_l$	95% $100p_r$	99% $100p_l$	99% $100p_r$
18	19.57	12.03–	29.15	10.18–	32.22
19	20.65	12.92–	30.36	11.00–	33.45
20	21.74	13.81–	31.56	11.83–	34.67
21	22.83	14.72–	32.75	12.68–	35.89
22	23.91	15.63–	33.94	13.53–	37.09
23	25.00	16.55–	35.11	14.39–	38.28
24	26.09	17.48–	36.29	15.26–	39.47
25	27.17	18.42–	37.45	16.14–	40.64
26	28.26	19.36–	38.61	17.03–	41.81
27	29.35	20.31–	39.76	17.93–	42.97
28	30.43	21.27–	40.90	18.83–	44.12
29	31.52	22.23–	42.04	19.75–	45.27
30	32.61	23.20–	43.18	20.67–	46.40
31	33.70	24.17–	44.30	21.60–	47.53
32	34.78	25.15–	45.43	22.53–	48.65
33	35.87	26.13–	46.54	23.48–	49.77
34	36.96	27.12–	47.66	24.43–	50.87
35	38.04	28.12–	48.76	25.38–	51.98
36	39.13	29.12–	49.86	26.35–	53.07
37	40.22	30.12–	50.96	27.32–	54.16
38	41.30	31.13–	52.05	28.29–	55.24
39	42.39	32.15–	53.14	29.28–	56.32
40	43.48	33.17–	54.22	30.27–	57.38
41	44.57	34.19–	55.30	31.26–	58.45
42	45.65	35.22–	56.37	32.26–	59.50
43	46.74	36.26–	57.44	33.27–	60.55
44	47.83	37.30–	58.50	34.28–	61.60
45	48.91	38.34–	59.56	35.30–	62.64
46	50.00	39.39–	60.61	36.33–	63.67
47	51.09	40.44–	61.66	37.36–	64.70
48	52.17	41.50–	62.70	38.40–	65.72
49	53.26	42.56–	63.74	39.45–	66.73
50	54.35	43.63–	64.78	40.50–	67.74
51	55.43	44.70–	65.81	41.55–	68.74
52	56.52	45.78–	66.83	42.62–	69.73
53	57.61	46.86–	67.85	43.68–	70.72
54	58.70	47.95–	68.87	44.76–	71.71
55	59.78	49.04–	69.88	45.84–	72.68
56	60.87	50.14–	70.88	46.93–	73.65
57	61.96	51.24–	71.88	48.02–	74.62
58	63.04	52.34–	72.88	49.13–	75.57
59	64.13	53.46–	73.87	50.23–	76.52
60	65.22	54.57–	74.85	51.35–	77.47
61	66.30	55.70–	75.83	52.47–	78.40
62	67.39	56.82–	76.80	53.60–	79.33
63	68.48	57.96–	77.77	54.73–	80.25
64	69.57	59.10–	78.73	55.88–	81.17
65	70.65	60.24–	79.69	57.03–	82.07
66	71.74	61.39–	80.64	58.19–	82.97
67	72.83	62.55–	81.58	59.36–	83.86
68	73.91	63.71–	82.52	60.53–	84.74
69	75.00	64.89–	83.45	61.72–	85.61
70	76.09	66.06–	84.37	62.91–	86.47
71	77.17	67.25–	85.28	64.11–	87.32
72	78.26	68.44–	86.19	65.33–	88.17
73	79.35	69.64–	87.08	66.55–	89.00
74	80.43	70.85–	87.97	67.78–	89.82
75	81.52	72.07–	88.85	69.03–	90.62
76	82.61	73.30–	89.72	70.29–	91.42
77	83.70	74.54–	90.58	71.56–	92.20
78	84.78	75.79–	91.42	72.85–	92.96
79	85.87	77.05–	92.26	74.15–	93.71
80	86.96	78.32–	93.07	75.47–	94.44
81	88.04	79.61–	93.88	76.80–	95.15
82	89.13	80.92–	94.66	78.16–	95.84
83	90.22	82.24–	95.43	79.54–	96.50
84	91.30	83.58–	96.17	80.95–	97.13
85	92.39	84.95–	96.89	82.38–	97.73
86	93.48	86.34–	97.57	83.85–	98.30
87	94.57	87.77–	98.21	85.37–	98.81
88	95.65	89.24–	98.80	86.94–	99.26
89	96.74	90.76–	99.32	88.57–	99.63
90	97.83	92.37–	99.74	90.31–	99.89
91	98.91	94.09–	99.97	92.20–	99.99
92	100.00	96.07–	100.00	94.40–	100.00

$N = 93$

x	$100p_x$	95% $100p_l$	95% $100p_r$	99% $100p_l$	99% $100p_r$
0	0.00	0.00–	3.89	0.00–	5.54
1	1.08	0.03–	5.85	0.01–	7.72
2	2.15	0.26–	7.55	0.11–	9.59
3	3.23	0.67–	9.14	0.37–	11.31
4	4.30	1.18–	10.65	0.73–	12.93
5	5.38	1.77–	12.10	1.18–	14.48
6	6.45	2.41–	13.52	1.68–	15.98
7	7.53	3.08–	14.90	2.24–	17.44
8	8.60	3.79–	16.25	2.83–	18.86
9	9.68	4.52–	17.58	3.46–	20.25
10	10.75	5.28–	18.89	4.12–	21.62
11	11.83	6.05–	20.18	4.80–	22.96
12	12.90	6.85–	21.45	5.50–	24.29
13	13.98	7.66–	22.72	6.22–	25.59
14	15.05	8.48–	23.97	6.96–	26.88
15	16.13	9.32–	25.20	7.72–	28.16
16	17.20	10.17–	26.43	8.49–	29.42
17	18.28	11.02–	27.65	9.27–	30.66
18	19.35	11.89–	28.85	10.07–	31.90
19	20.43	12.77–	30.05	10.88–	33.12
20	21.51	13.66–	31.24	11.70–	34.33

$N = 93$ (continued)

x	$100p_x$	95% $100p_l$	95% $100p_r$	99% $100p_l$	99% $100p_r$
21	22.58	14.55–	32.42	12.53–	35.54
22	23.66	15.46–	33.60	13.37–	36.73
23	24.73	16.37–	34.76	14.23–	37.91
24	25.81	17.29–	35.92	15.09–	39.08
25	26.88	18.21–	37.08	15.96–	40.25
26	27.96	19.14–	38.22	16.84–	41.41
27	29.03	20.08–	39.36	17.72–	42.56
28	30.11	21.03–	40.50	18.62–	43.70
29	31.18	21.98–	41.63	19.52–	44.83
30	32.26	22.93–	42.75	20.43–	45.96
31	33.33	23.89–	43.87	21.35–	47.08
32	34.41	24.86–	44.98	22.27–	48.19
33	35.48	25.83–	46.09	23.20–	49.29
34	36.56	26.81–	47.19	24.14–	50.39
35	37.63	27.79–	48.28	25.09–	51.48
36	38.71	28.78–	49.38	26.04–	52.57
37	39.78	29.78–	50.46	27.00–	53.6
38	40.86	30.77–	51.54	27.96–	54.7
39	41.94	31.78–	52.62	28.93–	55.7
40	43.01	32.78–	53.69	29.91–	56.8
41	44.09	33.80–	54.76	30.89–	57.9
42	45.16	34.81–	55.83	31.88–	58.9
43	46.24	35.84–	56.88	32.87–	59.9
44	47.31	36.86–	57.94	33.88–	61.0
45	48.39	37.89–	58.99	34.88–	62.0
46	49.46	38.93–	60.03	35.90–	63.0
47	50.54	39.97–	61.07	36.91–	64.1
48	51.61	41.01–	62.11	37.94–	65.1
49	52.69	42.06–	63.14	38.97–	66.1
50	53.76	43.12–	64.16	40.01–	67.1
51	54.84	44.17–	65.19	41.05–	68.1
52	55.91	45.24–	66.20	42.10–	69.1
53	56.99	46.31–	67.22	43.15–	70.0
54	58.06	47.38–	68.22	44.21–	71.0
55	59.14	48.46–	69.23	45.28–	72.0
56	60.22	49.54–	70.22	46.35–	73.0
57	61.29	50.62–	71.22	47.43–	73.9
58	62.37	51.72–	72.21	48.52–	74.9
59	63.44	52.81–	73.19	49.61–	75.8
60	64.52	53.91–	74.17	50.71–	76.8
61	65.59	55.02–	75.14	51.81–	77.7
62	66.67	56.13–	76.11	52.92–	78.6
63	67.74	57.25–	77.07	54.04–	79.5
64	68.82	58.37–	78.02	55.17–	80.4
65	69.89	59.50–	78.97	56.30–	81.3
66	70.97	60.64–	79.92	57.44–	82.
67	72.04	61.78–	80.86	58.59–	83.
68	73.12	62.92–	81.79	59.75–	84.
69	74.19	64.08–	82.71	60.92–	84.
70	75.27	65.24–	83.63	62.09–	85.
71	76.34	66.40–	84.54	63.27–	86.
72	77.42	67.58–	85.45	64.46–	87.
73	78.49	68.76–	86.34	65.67–	88.
74	79.57	69.95–	87.23	66.88–	89.
75	80.65	71.15–	88.11	68.10–	89
76	81.72	72.35–	88.98	69.34–	90
77	82.80	73.57–	89.83	70.58–	91
78	83.87	74.80–	90.68	71.84–	92
79	84.95	76.03–	91.52	73.12–	93
80	86.02	77.28–	92.34	74.41–	93
81	87.10	78.55–	93.15	75.71–	94
82	88.17	79.82–	93.95	77.04–	95
83	89.25	81.11–	94.72	78.38–	95
84	90.32	82.42–	95.48	79.75–	96
85	91.40	83.75–	96.21	81.14–	97
86	92.47	85.10–	96.92	82.56–	97
87	93.55	86.48–	97.59	84.02–	98
88	94.62	87.90–	98.23	85.52–	98
89	95.70	89.35–	98.82	87.07–	99
90	96.77	90.86–	99.33	88.69–	99
91	97.85	92.45–	99.74	90.41–	99
92	98.92	94.15–	99.97	92.28–	99
93	100.00	96.11–	100.00	94.46–	100

$N = 94$

x	$100p_x$	95% $100p_l$	95% $100p_r$	99% $100p_l$	99% $100p_r$
0	0.00	0.00–	3.85	0.00–	5
1	1.06	0.03–	5.79	0.01–	
2	2.13	0.26–	7.48	0.11–	9
3	3.19	0.66–	9.04	0.36–	11
4	4.26	1.17–	10.54	0.72–	12
5	5.32	1.75–	11.98	1.17–	14
6	6.38	2.38–	13.38	1.67–	15
7	7.45	3.05–	14.74	2.22–	17
8	8.51	3.75–	16.08	2.80–	18
9	9.57	4.47–	17.40	3.42–	20
10	10.64	5.22–	18.70	4.07–	21
11	11.70	5.99–	19.97	4.74–	22
12	12.77	6.77–	21.24	5.44–	24
13	13.83	7.57–	22.49	6.15–	25
14	14.89	8.39–	23.72	6.88–	26
15	15.96	9.22–	24.95	7.63–	27
16	17.02	10.05–	26.16	8.39–	2
17	18.09	10.90–	27.37	9.17–	30
18	19.15	11.76–	28.56	9.96–	3
19	20.21	12.63–	29.75	10.76–	
20	21.28	13.51–	30.93	11.57–	3
21	22.34	14.39–	32.10	12.39–	3
22	23.40	15.29–	33.26	13.22–	

* Reproduction only by permission of the publishers of these *Scientific Tables*.

N = number of trials, x = number of successes, etc., $100\,p_x = 100\,x/N$

N = 94 (continued)

$100p_x$	95% $100p_l$	95% $100p_r$	99% $100p_l$	99% $100p_r$
24.47	16.19	34.42	14.07	37.54
25.53	17.09	35.57	14.92	38.71
26.60	18.01	36.71	15.78	39.86
27.66	18.93	37.85	16.65	41.01
28.72	19.86	38.98	17.52	42.15
29.79	20.79	40.10	18.41	43.28
30.85	21.73	41.22	19.30	44.40
31.91	22.67	42.33	20.20	45.52
32.98	23.62	43.44	21.10	46.63
34.04	24.58	44.54	22.02	47.73
35.11	25.54	45.64	22.94	48.83
36.17	26.51	46.73	23.86	49.92
37.23	27.48	47.82	24.80	51.00
38.30	28.46	48.90	25.74	52.08
39.36	29.44	49.98	26.68	53.15
40.43	30.42	51.05	27.64	54.21
41.49	31.41	52.12	28.59	55.27
42.55	32.41	53.18	29.56	56.32
43.62	33.41	54.24	30.53	57.37
44.68	34.41	55.29	31.51	58.41
45.74	35.42	56.34	32.49	59.44
46.81	36.44	57.39	33.48	60.47
47.87	37.46	58.43	34.47	61.50
48.94	38.48	59.46	35.47	62.51
50.00	39.51	60.49	36.48	63.52
51.06	40.54	61.52	37.49	64.53
52.13	41.57	62.54	38.50	65.53
53.19	42.61	63.56	39.53	66.52
54.26	43.66	64.58	40.56	67.51
55.32	44.71	65.59	41.59	68.49
56.38	45.76	66.59	42.63	69.47
57.45	46.82	67.59	43.68	70.44
58.51	47.88	68.59	44.73	71.41
59.57	48.95	69.58	45.79	72.36
60.64	50.02	70.56	46.85	73.32
61.70	51.10	71.54	47.92	74.26
62.77	52.18	72.52	49.00	75.20
63.83	53.27	73.49	50.08	76.14
64.89	54.36	74.46	51.17	77.06
65.96	55.46	75.42	52.27	77.98
67.02	56.56	76.38	53.37	78.90
68.09	57.67	77.33	54.48	79.80
69.15	58.78	78.27	55.60	80.70
70.21	59.90	79.21	56.72	81.59
71.28	61.02	80.14	57.85	82.48
72.34	62.15	81.07	58.99	83.35
73.40	63.29	81.99	60.14	84.22
74.47	64.43	82.91	61.29	85.08
75.53	65.58	83.81	62.46	85.93
76.60	66.74	84.71	63.63	86.78
77.66	67.90	85.61	64.81	87.61
78.72	69.07	86.49	66.00	88.43
79.79	70.25	87.37	67.20	89.24
80.85	71.44	88.24	68.41	90.04
81.91	72.63	89.10	69.64	90.83
82.98	73.84	89.95	70.87	91.61
84.04	75.05	90.78	72.12	92.37
85.11	76.28	91.61	73.38	93.12
86.17	77.51	92.43	74.66	93.85
87.23	78.76	93.23	75.95	94.56
88.30	80.03	94.01	77.26	95.26
89.36	81.30	94.78	78.60	95.93
90.43	82.60	95.53	79.95	96.58
91.49	83.92	96.25	81.33	97.20
92.55	85.26	96.95	82.74	97.78
93.62	86.62	97.62	84.18	98.33
94.68	88.02	98.25	85.67	98.83
95.74	89.46	98.83	87.20	99.28
96.81	90.96	99.34	88.81	99.64
97.87	92.52	99.74	90.51	99.89
98.94	94.21	99.97	92.36	99.99
100.00	96.15	100.00	94.52	100.00

N = 95

$100p_x$	95% $100p_l$	95% $100p_r$	99% $100p_l$	99% $100p_r$
0.00	0.00	3.81	0.00	5.42
1.05	0.03	5.73	0.01	7.56
2.11	0.26	7.40	0.11	9.40
3.16	0.66	8.95	0.36	11.08
4.21	1.16	10.43	0.72	12.67
5.26	1.73	11.86	1.15	14.19
6.32	2.35	13.24	1.65	15.66
7.37	3.01	14.59	2.19	17.09
8.42	3.71	15.92	2.77	18.49
9.47	4.42	17.22	3.39	19.85
10.53	5.16	18.51	4.03	21.19
11.58	5.92	19.77	4.69	22.51
12.63	6.70	21.03	5.38	23.81
13.68	7.49	22.26	6.08	25.09
14.74	8.30	23.49	6.81	26.36
15.79	9.12	24.70	7.55	27.61
16.84	9.94	25.90	8.30	28.84
17.89	10.78	27.10	9.07	30.07
18.95	11.63	28.28	9.85	31.28
20.00	12.49	29.46	10.64	32.48
21.05	13.36	30.62	11.44	33.67
22.11	14.23	31.78	12.25	34.85
23.16	15.12	32.94	13.08	36.02
24.21	16.01	34.08	13.91	37.18

N = 95 (continued)

x	$100p_x$	95% $100p_l$	95% $100p_r$	99% $100p_l$	99% $100p_r$
24	25.26	16.91	35.22	14.75	38.34
25	26.32	17.81	36.35	15.60	39.48
26	27.37	18.72	37.48	16.46	40.62
27	28.42	19.64	38.60	17.33	41.75
28	29.47	20.56	39.71	18.20	42.87
29	30.53	21.49	40.82	19.08	43.98
30	31.58	22.42	41.92	19.97	45.09
31	32.63	23.36	43.02	20.86	46.19
32	33.68	24.31	44.11	21.77	47.28
33	34.74	25.26	45.20	22.68	48.37
34	35.79	26.21	46.28	23.59	49.45
35	36.84	27.17	47.36	24.51	50.53
36	37.89	28.14	48.43	25.44	51.59
37	38.95	29.11	49.50	26.38	52.66
38	40.00	30.08	50.56	27.32	53.71
39	41.05	31.06	51.62	28.27	54.76
40	42.11	32.04	52.67	29.22	55.81
41	43.16	33.03	53.72	30.18	56.84
42	44.21	34.02	54.77	31.14	57.88
43	45.26	35.02	55.81	32.11	58.90
44	46.32	36.02	56.85	33.09	59.92
45	47.37	37.03	57.88	34.07	60.94
46	48.42	38.04	58.90	35.06	61.95
47	49.47	39.05	59.93	36.05	62.95
48	50.53	40.07	60.95	37.05	63.95
49	51.58	41.10	61.96	38.05	64.94
50	52.63	42.12	62.97	39.06	65.93
51	53.68	43.15	63.98	40.08	66.91
52	54.74	44.19	64.98	41.10	67.89
53	55.79	45.23	65.98	42.12	68.86
54	56.84	46.28	66.97	43.16	69.82
55	57.89	47.33	67.96	44.19	70.78
56	58.95	48.38	68.94	45.24	71.73
57	60.00	49.44	69.92	46.29	72.68
58	61.05	50.50	70.89	47.34	73.62
59	62.11	51.57	71.86	48.41	74.56
60	63.16	52.64	72.83	49.47	75.49
61	64.21	53.72	73.79	50.55	76.41
62	65.26	54.80	74.74	51.63	77.32
63	66.32	55.89	75.69	52.72	78.23
64	67.37	56.98	76.64	53.81	79.14
65	68.42	58.08	77.58	54.91	80.03
66	69.47	59.18	78.51	56.02	80.92
67	70.53	60.29	79.44	57.13	81.80
68	71.58	61.40	80.36	58.25	82.67
69	72.63	62.52	81.28	59.38	83.54
70	73.68	63.65	82.19	60.52	84.40
71	74.74	64.78	83.09	61.66	85.25
72	75.79	65.92	83.99	62.82	86.09
73	76.84	67.06	84.88	63.98	86.92
74	77.89	68.22	85.77	65.15	87.75
75	78.95	69.38	86.64	66.33	88.56
76	80.00	70.54	87.51	67.52	89.36
77	81.05	71.72	88.37	68.72	90.15
78	82.11	72.90	89.22	69.93	90.93
79	83.16	74.10	90.06	71.16	91.70
80	84.21	75.30	90.88	72.39	92.45
81	85.26	76.51	91.70	73.64	93.19
82	86.32	77.74	92.51	74.91	93.92
83	87.37	78.97	93.30	76.19	94.62
84	88.42	80.23	94.08	77.49	95.31
85	89.47	81.49	94.84	78.81	95.97
86	90.53	82.78	95.58	80.15	96.61
87	91.58	84.08	96.29	81.51	97.23
88	92.63	85.41	96.99	82.91	97.81
89	93.68	86.76	97.65	84.34	98.35
90	94.74	88.14	98.27	85.81	98.85
91	95.79	89.57	98.84	87.33	99.28
92	96.84	91.05	99.34	88.92	99.64
93	97.89	92.60	99.74	90.60	99.89
94	98.95	94.27	99.97	92.44	99.99
95	100.00	96.19	100.00	94.58	100.00

N = 96

x	$100p_x$	95% $100p_l$	95% $100p_r$	99% $100p_l$	99% $100p_r$
0	0.00	0.00	3.77	0.00	5.37
1	1.04	0.03	5.67	0.01	7.49
2	2.08	0.25	7.32	0.11	9.30
3	3.13	0.65	8.86	0.36	10.97
4	4.17	1.15	10.33	0.71	12.54
5	5.21	1.71	11.74	1.14	14.05
6	6.25	2.33	13.11	1.63	15.51
7	7.29	2.98	14.45	2.17	16.92
8	8.33	3.67	15.76	2.74	18.30
9	9.38	4.38	17.05	3.35	19.66
10	10.42	5.11	18.32	3.98	20.99
11	11.46	5.86	19.58	4.64	22.29
12	12.50	6.63	20.82	5.32	23.58
13	13.54	7.41	22.04	6.02	24.85
14	14.58	8.21	23.26	6.73	26.10
15	15.63	9.02	24.46	7.47	27.34
16	16.67	9.84	25.65	8.21	28.57
17	17.71	10.67	26.83	8.97	29.78
18	18.75	11.51	28.00	9.74	30.98
19	19.79	12.36	29.17	10.52	32.17
20	20.83	13.21	30.33	11.32	33.35
21	21.88	14.08	31.47	12.12	34.52
22	22.92	14.95	32.62	12.93	35.68
23	23.96	15.83	33.75	13.76	36.83

N = 96 (continued)

x	$100p_x$	95% $100p_l$	95% $100p_r$	99% $100p_l$	99% $100p_r$
24	25.00	16.72	34.88	14.59	37.98
25	26.04	17.62	36.00	15.43	39.11
26	27.08	18.52	37.11	16.28	40.24
27	28.13	19.42	38.22	17.13	41.36
28	29.17	20.33	39.33	18.00	42.47
29	30.21	21.25	40.43	18.87	43.57
30	31.25	22.18	41.52	19.75	44.67
31	32.29	23.10	42.61	20.63	45.76
32	33.33	24.04	43.69	21.52	46.85
33	34.38	24.98	44.77	22.42	47.92
34	35.42	25.92	45.84	23.33	48.99
35	36.46	26.87	46.91	24.24	50.06
36	37.50	27.82	47.97	25.16	51.12
37	38.54	28.78	49.03	26.08	52.17
38	39.58	29.75	50.08	27.01	53.22
39	40.63	30.71	51.13	27.94	54.26
40	41.67	31.68	52.18	28.88	55.30
41	42.71	32.66	53.22	29.83	56.33
42	43.75	33.64	54.25	30.78	57.35
43	44.79	34.63	55.29	31.74	58.37
44	45.83	35.62	56.31	32.71	59.38
45	46.88	36.61	57.34	33.68	60.39
46	47.92	37.61	58.36	34.65	61.39
47	48.96	38.61	59.37	35.63	62.39
48	50.00	39.62	60.38	36.62	63.38
49	51.04	40.63	61.39	37.61	64.37
50	52.08	41.64	62.39	38.61	65.35
51	53.13	42.66	63.39	39.61	66.32
52	54.17	43.69	64.38	40.62	67.29
53	55.21	44.71	65.37	41.63	68.26
54	56.25	45.75	66.36	42.65	69.22
55	57.29	46.78	67.34	43.67	70.17
56	58.33	47.82	68.32	44.70	71.12
57	59.38	48.87	69.29	45.74	72.06
58	60.42	49.92	70.25	46.78	72.99
59	61.46	50.97	71.22	47.83	73.92
60	62.50	52.03	72.18	48.88	74.84
61	63.54	53.09	73.13	49.94	75.76
62	64.58	54.16	74.08	51.01	76.67
63	65.63	55.23	75.02	52.08	77.58
64	66.67	56.31	75.96	53.15	78.48
65	67.71	57.39	76.90	54.24	79.37
66	68.75	58.48	77.82	55.33	80.25
67	69.79	59.57	78.75	56.43	81.13
68	70.83	60.67	79.67	57.53	82.00
69	71.88	61.78	80.58	58.64	82.87
70	72.92	62.89	81.48	59.76	83.72
71	73.96	64.00	82.38	60.89	84.57
72	75.00	65.12	83.28	62.02	85.41
73	76.04	66.25	84.17	63.17	86.24
74	77.08	67.38	85.05	64.32	87.07
75	78.13	68.53	85.92	65.48	87.88
76	79.17	69.67	86.79	66.65	88.68
77	80.21	70.83	87.64	67.83	89.48
78	81.25	72.00	88.49	69.02	90.26
79	82.29	73.17	89.33	70.22	91.03
80	83.33	74.35	90.16	71.43	91.79
81	84.38	75.54	90.98	72.66	92.53
82	85.42	76.74	91.79	73.90	93.27
83	86.46	77.96	92.59	75.15	93.98
84	87.50	79.18	93.37	76.42	94.68
85	88.54	80.42	94.14	77.71	95.36
86	89.58	81.68	94.89	79.01	96.02
87	90.63	82.95	95.62	80.34	96.65
88	91.67	84.24	96.33	81.70	97.26
89	92.71	85.55	97.02	83.08	97.83
90	93.75	86.89	97.67	84.49	98.37
91	94.79	88.26	98.29	85.95	98.86
92	95.83	89.67	98.85	87.46	99.29
93	96.88	91.14	99.35	89.03	99.64
94	97.92	92.68	99.75	90.70	99.89
95	98.96	94.33	99.97	92.51	99.99
96	100.00	96.23	100.00	94.63	100.00

N = 97

x	$100p_x$	95% $100p_l$	95% $100p_r$	99% $100p_l$	99% $100p_r$
0	0.00	0.00	3.73	0.00	5.32
1	1.03	0.03	5.61	0.01	7.41
2	2.06	0.25	7.25	0.11	9.21
3	3.09	0.64	8.77	0.35	10.86
4	4.12	1.13	10.22	0.70	12.42
5	5.15	1.69	11.62	1.13	13.91
6	6.19	2.30	12.98	1.61	15.35
7	7.22	2.95	14.30	2.15	16.76
8	8.25	3.63	15.61	2.71	18.13
9	9.28	4.33	16.88	3.31	19.47
10	10.31	5.06	18.14	3.94	20.78
11	11.34	5.80	19.39	4.59	22.08
12	12.37	6.56	20.61	5.26	23.35
13	13.40	7.33	21.83	5.95	24.61
14	14.43	8.12	23.03	6.66	25.85
15	15.46	8.92	24.22	7.39	27.08
16	16.49	9.73	25.40	8.12	28.29
17	17.53	10.55	26.57	8.87	29.50
18	18.56	11.38	27.73	9.63	30.69
19	19.59	12.22	28.89	10.41	31.87
20	20.62	13.07	30.03	11.19	33.03
21	21.65	13.93	31.17	11.99	34.19
22	22.68	14.79	32.30	12.79	35.34

N = 97 (continued)

x	$100p_x$	95% $100p_l$	95% $100p_r$	99% $100p_l$	99% $100p_r$
23	23.71	15.66	33.42	13.61	36.49
24	24.74	16.54	34.54	14.43	37.62
25	25.77	17.42	35.65	15.26	38.74
26	26.80	18.32	36.76	16.10	39.86
27	27.84	19.21	37.86	16.94	40.97
28	28.87	20.11	38.95	17.80	42.07
29	29.90	21.02	40.04	18.66	43.17
30	30.93	21.93	41.12	19.53	44.26
31	31.96	22.85	42.20	20.40	45.34
32	32.99	23.78	43.27	21.28	46.41
33	34.02	24.70	44.34	22.17	47.48
34	35.05	25.64	45.41	23.07	48.55
35	36.08	26.58	46.46	23.97	49.60
36	37.11	27.52	47.52	24.87	50.65
37	38.14	28.47	48.57	25.79	51.70
38	39.18	29.42	49.62	26.71	52.74
39	40.21	30.37	50.65	27.63	53.77
40	41.24	31.33	51.69	28.56	54.80
41	42.27	32.30	52.72	29.49	55.82
42	43.30	33.27	53.75	30.44	56.84
43	44.33	34.24	54.77	31.38	57.85
44	45.36	35.22	55.79	32.33	58.85
45	46.39	36.20	56.81	33.29	59.86
46	47.42	37.19	57.82	34.26	60.85
47	48.45	38.18	58.82	35.22	61.84
48	49.48	39.17	59.83	36.20	62.82
49	50.52	40.17	60.83	37.18	63.80
50	51.55	41.18	61.82	38.16	64.78
51	52.58	42.18	62.81	39.15	65.74
52	53.61	43.19	63.80	40.14	66.71
53	54.64	44.21	64.78	41.15	67.67
54	55.67	45.23	65.76	42.15	68.62
55	56.70	46.25	66.73	43.16	69.56
56	57.73	47.28	67.70	44.18	70.51
57	58.76	48.31	68.67	45.20	71.44
58	59.79	49.35	69.63	46.23	72.37
59	60.82	50.39	70.58	47.26	73.29
60	61.86	51.43	71.53	48.30	74.21
61	62.89	52.48	72.48	49.35	75.13
62	63.92	53.54	73.42	50.40	76.03
63	64.95	54.59	74.36	51.45	76.93
64	65.98	55.66	75.30	52.52	77.83
65	67.01	56.73	76.22	53.59	78.72
66	68.04	57.80	77.15	54.66	79.60
67	69.07	58.88	78.07	55.74	80.47
68	70.10	59.96	78.98	56.83	81.34
69	71.13	61.05	79.89	57.93	82.20
70	72.16	62.14	80.79	59.03	83.06
71	73.20	63.24	81.68	60.14	83.90
72	74.23	64.35	82.58	61.26	84.74
73	75.26	65.46	83.46	62.38	85.57
74	76.29	66.58	84.34	63.51	86.39
75	77.32	67.70	85.21	64.66	87.21
76	78.35	68.83	86.07	65.81	88.01
77	79.38	69.97	86.93	66.97	88.81
78	80.41	71.11	87.78	68.13	89.59
79	81.44	72.27	88.62	69.31	90.37
80	82.47	73.43	89.45	70.50	91.13
81	83.51	74.60	90.27	71.71	91.88
82	84.54	75.78	91.08	72.92	92.61
83	85.57	76.97	91.88	74.15	93.34
84	86.60	78.17	92.67	75.39	94.05
85	87.63	79.39	93.44	76.65	94.74
86	88.66	80.61	94.20	77.92	95.41
87	89.69	81.86	94.94	79.22	96.06
88	90.72	83.12	95.67	80.53	96.69
89	91.75	84.39	96.37	81.87	97.29
90	92.78	85.70	97.05	83.24	97.85
91	93.81	87.02	97.70	84.65	98.39
92	94.85	88.38	98.31	86.09	98.87
93	95.88	89.78	98.87	87.58	99.30
94	96.91	91.23	99.36	89.14	99.65
95	97.94	92.75	99.75	90.79	99.89
96	98.97	94.39	99.97	92.59	99.99
97	100.00	96.27	100.00	94.68	100.00

N = 98

x	$100p_x$	95% $100p_l$	95% $100p_r$	99% $100p_l$	99% $100p_r$
0	0.00	0.00	3.69	0.00	5.26
1	1.02	0.03	5.55	0.01	7.34
2	2.04	0.25	7.18	0.11	9.12
3	3.06	0.64	8.69	0.35	10.75
4	4.08	1.12	10.12	0.69	12.30
5	5.10	1.68	11.51	1.12	13.78
6	6.12	2.28	12.85	1.60	15.21
7	7.14	2.92	14.16	2.12	16.60
8	8.16	3.59	15.45	2.69	17.95
9	9.18	4.29	16.72	3.28	19.28
10	10.20	5.00	17.97	3.90	20.58
11	11.22	5.74	19.20	4.54	21.87
12	12.24	6.49	20.41	5.21	23.13
13	13.27	7.26	21.62	5.89	24.38
14	14.29	8.04	22.81	6.59	25.61
15	15.31	8.83	23.99	7.31	26.82
16	16.33	9.63	25.16	8.04	28.03
17	17.35	10.44	26.31	8.78	29.22
18	18.37	11.26	27.47	9.53	30.40
19	19.39	12.10	28.61	10.30	31.57
20	20.41	12.93	29.74	11.07	32.73

N = number of trials, x = number of successes, etc., $100\,p_x = 100\,x/N$

N = 98 (continued)

x	$100\,p_x$	95% $100p_l$	95% $100p_r$	99% $100p_l$	99% $100p_r$
21	21.43	13.78–	30.87	11.86–	33.87
22	22.45	14.64–	31.99	12.65–	35.01
23	23.47	15.50–	33.11	13.46–	36.15
24	24.49	16.36–	34.21	14.27–	37.27
25	25.51	17.24–	35.31	15.09–	38.38
26	26.53	18.12–	36.41	15.92–	39.49
27	27.55	19.01–	37.50	16.76–	40.59
28	28.57	19.90–	38.58	17.60–	41.69
29	29.59	20.79–	39.66	18.46–	42.77
30	30.61	21.70–	40.74	19.31–	43.85
31	31.63	22.61–	41.80	20.18–	44.92
32	32.65	23.52–	42.87	21.05–	45.99
33	33.67	24.44–	43.93	21.93–	47.05
34	34.69	25.36–	44.98	22.81–	48.11
35	35.71	26.29–	46.03	23.70–	49.15
36	36.73	27.22–	47.07	24.60–	50.20
37	37.76	28.16–	48.12	25.50–	51.23
38	38.78	29.10–	49.15	26.41–	52.26
39	39.80	30.04–	50.18	27.32–	53.29
40	40.82	30.99–	51.21	28.24–	54.31
41	41.84	31.95–	52.23	29.17–	55.32
42	42.86	32.90–	53.25	30.10–	56.33
43	43.88	33.87–	54.27	31.03–	57.34
44	44.90	34.83–	55.28	31.97–	58.33
45	45.92	35.80–	56.29	32.92–	59.33
46	46.94	36.78–	57.29	33.87–	60.31
47	47.96	37.76–	58.29	34.82–	61.30
48	48.98	38.74–	59.28	35.79–	62.27
49	50.00	39.73–	60.27	36.75–	63.25
50	51.02	40.72–	61.26	37.73–	64.21
51	52.04	41.71–	62.24	38.70–	65.18
52	53.06	42.71–	63.22	39.69–	66.13
53	54.08	43.71–	64.20	40.67–	67.08
54	55.10	44.72–	65.17	41.67–	68.03
55	56.12	45.73–	66.13	42.66–	68.97
56	57.14	46.75–	67.10	43.67–	69.90
57	58.16	47.77–	68.05	44.68–	70.83
58	59.18	48.79–	69.01	45.69–	71.76
59	60.20	49.82–	69.96	46.71–	72.68
60	61.22	50.85–	70.90	47.74–	73.59
61	62.24	51.88–	71.84	48.77–	74.50
62	63.27	52.93–	72.78	49.80–	75.40
63	64.29	53.97–	73.71	50.85–	76.30
64	65.31	55.02–	74.64	51.89–	77.19
65	66.33	56.07–	75.56	52.95–	78.07
66	67.35	57.13–	76.48	54.01–	78.95
67	68.37	58.20–	77.39	55.08–	79.82
68	69.39	59.26–	78.30	56.15–	80.69
69	70.41	60.34–	79.21	57.23–	81.54
70	71.43	61.42–	80.10	58.31–	82.40
71	72.45	62.50–	80.99	59.41–	83.24
72	73.47	63.59–	81.88	60.51–	84.08
73	74.49	64.69–	82.76	61.62–	84.91
74	75.51	65.79–	83.64	62.73–	85.73
75	76.53	66.89–	84.50	63.85–	86.54
76	77.55	68.01–	85.36	64.99–	87.35
77	78.57	69.13–	86.22	66.13–	88.14
78	79.59	70.26–	87.07	67.27–	88.93
79	80.61	71.39–	87.90	68.43–	89.70
80	81.63	72.53–	88.74	69.60–	90.47
81	82.65	73.69–	89.56	70.78–	91.22
82	83.67	74.84–	90.37	71.97–	91.96
83	84.69	76.01–	91.17	73.18–	92.69
84	85.71	77.19–	91.96	74.39–	93.41
85	86.73	78.38–	92.74	75.62–	94.11
86	87.76	79.59–	93.51	76.87–	94.79
87	88.78	80.80–	94.26	78.13–	95.46
88	89.80	82.03–	95.00	79.42–	96.10
89	90.82	83.28–	95.71	80.72–	96.72
90	91.84	84.55–	96.41	82.05–	97.31
91	92.86	85.84–	97.08	83.40–	97.88

N = 98 (continued)

x	$100\,p_x$	95% $100p_l$	95% $100p_r$	99% $100p_l$	99% $100p_r$
92	93.88	87.15–	97.72	84.79–	98.40
93	94.90	88.49–	98.32	86.22–	98.88
94	95.92	89.88–	98.88	87.70–	99.31
95	96.94	91.31–	99.36	89.25–	99.65
96	97.96	92.82–	99.75	90.88–	99.89
97	98.98	94.45–	99.97	92.66–	99.99
98	100.00	96.31–	100.00	94.74–	100.00

N = 99

x	$100\,p_x$	95% $100p_l$	95% $100p_r$	99% $100p_l$	99% $100p_r$
0	0.00	0.00–	3.66	0.00–	5.21
1	1.01	0.03–	5.50	0.01–	7.27
2	2.02	0.25–	7.11	0.11–	9.03
3	3.03	0.63–	8.60	0.34–	10.65
4	4.04	1.11–	10.02	0.69–	12.18
5	5.05	1.66–	11.39	1.11–	13.64
6	6.06	2.26–	12.73	1.58–	15.06
7	7.07	2.89–	14.03	2.10–	16.44
8	8.08	3.55–	15.30	2.66–	17.78
9	9.09	4.24–	16.56	3.25–	19.10
10	10.10	4.95–	17.79	3.86–	20.39
11	11.11	5.68–	19.01	4.50–	21.66
12	12.12	6.42–	20.22	5.15–	22.91
13	13.13	7.18–	21.41	5.83–	24.15
14	14.14	7.95–	22.59	6.52–	25.36
15	15.15	8.74–	23.76	7.23–	26.57
16	16.16	9.53–	24.91	7.95–	27.76
17	17.17	10.33–	26.06	8.69–	28.94
18	18.18	11.15–	27.20	9.43–	30.11
19	19.19	11.97–	28.34	10.19–	31.27
20	20.20	12.80–	29.46	10.96–	32.42
21	21.21	13.64–	30.58	11.73–	33.56
22	22.22	14.48–	31.69	12.52–	34.69
23	23.23	15.33–	32.79	13.32–	35.81
24	24.24	16.19–	33.89	14.12–	36.93
25	25.25	17.06–	34.98	14.93–	38.03
26	26.26	17.93–	36.07	15.75–	39.13
27	27.27	18.80–	37.15	16.58–	40.22
28	28.28	19.69–	38.22	17.42–	41.31
29	29.29	20.57–	39.29	18.26–	42.38
30	30.30	21.47–	40.36	19.11–	43.45
31	31.31	22.36–	41.41	19.96–	44.52
32	32.32	23.27–	42.47	20.82–	45.57
33	33.33	24.18–	43.52	21.69–	46.63
34	34.34	25.09–	44.56	22.56–	47.67
35	35.35	26.01–	45.60	23.44–	48.71
36	36.36	26.93–	46.64	24.33–	49.75
37	37.37	27.85–	47.67	25.22–	50.77
38	38.38	28.78–	48.70	26.12–	51.80
39	39.39	29.72–	49.72	27.02–	52.81
40	40.40	30.66–	50.74	27.93–	53.83
41	41.41	31.60–	51.76	28.84–	54.83
42	42.42	32.55–	52.77	29.76–	55.83
43	43.43	33.50–	53.77	30.69–	56.83
44	44.44	34.45–	54.78	31.62–	57.82
45	45.45	35.41–	55.77	32.55–	58.81
46	46.46	36.38–	56.77	33.49–	59.79
47	47.47	37.34–	57.76	34.44–	60.76
48	48.48	38.32–	58.75	35.39–	61.73
49	49.49	39.29–	59.73	36.34–	62.70
50	50.51	40.27–	60.71	37.30–	63.66
51	51.52	41.25–	61.68	38.27–	64.61
52	52.53	42.24–	62.66	39.24–	65.56
53	53.54	43.23–	63.62	40.21–	66.51
54	54.55	44.23–	64.59	41.19–	67.45
55	55.56	45.22–	65.55	42.18–	68.38
56	56.57	46.23–	66.50	43.17–	69.31
57	57.58	47.23–	67.45	44.17–	70.24
58	58.59	48.24–	68.40	45.17–	71.16
59	59.60	49.26–	69.34	46.17–	72.07
60	60.61	50.28–	70.28	47.19–	72.98
61	61.62	51.30–	71.22	48.20–	73.88

N = 99 (continued)

x	$100\,p_x$	95% $100p_l$	95% $100p_r$	99% $100p_l$	99% $100p_r$
62	62.63	52.33–	72.15	49.23–	74.78
63	63.64	53.36–	73.07	50.25–	75.67
64	64.65	54.40–	73.99	51.29–	76.56
65	65.66	55.44–	74.91	52.33–	77.44
66	66.67	56.48–	75.82	53.37–	78.31
67	67.68	57.53–	76.73	54.43–	79.18
68	68.69	58.59–	77.64	55.48–	80.04
69	69.70	59.64–	78.53	56.55–	80.89
70	70.71	60.71–	79.43	57.62–	81.74
71	71.72	61.78–	80.31	58.69–	82.58
72	72.73	62.85–	81.20	59.78–	83.42
73	73.74	63.93–	82.07	60.87–	84.25
74	74.75	65.02–	82.94	61.97–	85.07
75	75.76	66.11–	83.81	63.07–	85.88
76	76.77	67.21–	84.67	64.19–	86.68
77	77.78	68.31–	85.52	65.31–	87.48
78	78.79	69.42–	86.36	66.44–	88.27
79	79.80	70.54–	87.20	67.58–	89.04
80	80.81	71.66–	88.03	68.73–	89.81
81	81.82	72.80–	88.85	69.89–	90.57
82	82.83	73.94–	89.67	71.06–	91.31
83	83.84	75.09–	90.47	72.24–	92.05
84	84.85	76.24–	91.26	73.43–	92.77
85	85.86	77.41–	92.05	74.64–	93.48
86	86.87	78.59–	92.82	75.85–	94.17
87	87.88	79.78–	93.58	77.09–	94.85
88	88.89	80.99–	94.32	78.34–	95.50
89	89.90	82.21–	95.05	79.61–	96.14
90	90.91	83.44–	95.76	80.90–	96.75
91	91.92	84.70–	96.45	82.22–	97.34
92	92.93	85.97–	97.11	83.56–	97.90
93	93.94	87.27–	97.74	84.94–	98.42
94	94.95	88.61–	98.34	86.36–	98.89
95	95.96	89.98–	98.89	87.82–	99.31
96	96.97	91.40–	99.37	89.35–	99.66
97	97.98	92.89–	99.75	90.97–	99.89
98	98.99	94.50–	99.97	92.73–	99.99
99	100.00	96.34–	100.00	94.79–	100.00

N = 100

x	$100\,p_x$	95% $100p_l$	95% $100p_r$	99% $100p_l$	99% $100p_r$
0	0.00	0.00–	3.62	0.00–	5.16
1	1.00	0.03–	5.45	0.01–	7.20
2	2.00	0.24–	7.04	0.10–	8.94
3	3.00	0.62–	8.52	0.34–	10.55
4	4.00	1.10–	9.93	0.68–	12.06
5	5.00	1.64–	11.28	1.09–	13.51
6	6.00	2.23–	12.60	1.56–	14.92
7	7.00	2.86–	13.89	2.08–	16.28
8	8.00	3.52–	15.16	2.63–	17.61
9	9.00	4.20–	16.40	3.21–	18.92
10	10.00	4.90–	17.62	3.82–	20.20
11	11.00	5.62–	18.83	4.45–	21.45
12	12.00	6.36–	20.02	5.10–	22.70
13	13.00	7.11–	21.20	5.77–	23.92
14	14.00	7.87–	22.37	6.45–	25.13
15	15.00	8.65–	23.53	7.15–	26.32
16	16.00	9.43–	24.68	7.87–	27.51
17	17.00	10.23–	25.82	8.59–	28.68
18	18.00	11.03–	26.95	9.33–	29.84
19	19.00	11.84–	28.07	10.08–	30.98
20	20.00	12.67–	29.18	10.84–	32.12
21	21.00	13.49–	30.29	11.61–	33.25
22	22.00	14.33–	31.39	12.39–	34.37
23	23.00	15.17–	32.49	13.18–	35.49
24	24.00	16.02–	33.57	13.97–	36.59
25	25.00	16.88–	34.66	14.77–	37.69
26	26.00	17.74–	35.73	15.59–	38.77
27	27.00	18.61–	36.80	16.40–	39.86
28	28.00	19.48–	37.87	17.23–	40.93
29	29.00	20.36–	38.93	18.06–	42.00

N = 100 (continued)

x	$100\,p_x$	95% $100p_l$	95% $100p_r$	99% $100p_l$	99% $100p_r$
30	30.00	21.24–	39.98	18.90–	4
31	31.00	22.13–	41.03	19.75–	4
32	32.00	23.02–	42.08	20.60–	4
33	33.00	23.92–	43.12	21.46–	4
34	34.00	24.82–	44.15	22.32–	4
35	35.00	25.73–	45.18	23.19–	4
36	36.00	26.64–	46.21	24.07–	4
37	37.00	27.56–	47.24	24.95–	5
38	38.00	28.48–	48.25	25.84–	5
39	39.00	29.40–	49.27	26.73–	5
40	40.00	30.33–	50.28	27.63–	5
41	41.00	31.26–	51.29	28.53–	5
42	42.00	32.20–	52.29	29.44–	5
43	43.00	33.14–	53.29	30.35–	5
44	44.00	34.08–	54.28	31.27–	5
45	45.00	35.03–	55.27	32.19–	5
46	46.00	35.98–	56.26	33.12–	5
47	47.00	36.94–	57.24	34.06–	6
48	48.00	37.90–	58.22	34.99–	6
49	49.00	38.86–	59.20	35.94–	6
50	50.00	39.83–	60.17	36.89–	6
51	51.00	40.80–	61.14	37.84–	6
52	52.00	41.78–	62.10	38.80–	6
53	53.00	42.76–	63.06	39.76–	6
54	54.00	43.74–	64.02	40.73–	6
55	55.00	44.73–	64.97	41.70–	6
56	56.00	45.72–	65.92	42.68–	6
57	57.00	46.71–	66.86	43.67–	6
58	58.00	47.71–	67.80	44.65–	7
59	59.00	48.71–	68.74	45.65–	7
60	60.00	49.72–	69.67	46.65–	7
61	61.00	50.73–	70.60	47.65–	7
62	62.00	51.75–	71.52	48.66–	7
63	63.00	52.76–	72.44	49.68–	7
64	64.00	53.79–	73.36	50.70–	7
65	65.00	54.82–	74.27	51.72–	7
66	66.00	55.85–	75.18	52.75–	7
67	67.00	56.88–	76.08	53.79–	7
68	68.00	57.92–	76.98	54.83–	7
69	69.00	58.97–	77.87	55.88–	8
70	70.00	60.02–	78.76	56.94–	8
71	71.00	61.07–	79.64	58.00–	8
72	72.00	62.13–	80.52	59.07–	8
73	73.00	63.20–	81.39	60.14–	8
74	74.00	64.27–	82.26	61.23–	8
75	75.00	63.34–	83.12	62.31–	8
76	76.00	66.43–	83.98	63.41–	8
77	77.00	67.51–	84.83	64.51–	8
78	78.00	68.61–	85.67	65.63–	8
79	79.00	69.71–	86.51	66.75–	8
80	80.00	70.82–	87.33	67.88–	8
81	81.00	71.93–	88.16	69.02–	8
82	82.00	73.05–	88.97	70.16–	9
83	83.00	74.18–	89.77	71.32–	9
84	84.00	75.32–	90.57	72.49–	9
85	85.00	76.47–	91.35	73.68–	9
86	86.00	77.63–	92.13	74.87–	9
87	87.00	78.80–	92.89	76.08–	9
88	88.00	79.98–	93.64	77.30–	9
89	89.00	81.17–	94.38	78.55–	9
90	90.00	82.38–	95.10	79.80–	9
91	91.00	83.60–	95.80	81.08–	9
92	92.00	84.84–	96.48	82.39–	9
93	93.00	86.11–	97.14	83.72–	9
94	94.00	87.40–	97.77	85.08–	9
95	95.00	88.72–	98.36	86.49–	9
96	96.00	90.07–	98.90	87.94–	9
97	97.00	91.48–	99.38	89.45–	9
98	98.00	92.96–	99.76	91.06–	9
99	99.00	94.55–	99.97	92.80–	9
100	100.00	96.38–	100.00	94.84–	10

Confidence Limits for p^* $N = 105-130$

N = number of tries, x = number of successes, etc., $100\,p_x = 100\,x/N$

Values in *italics* are exact, all others have been calculated from Freeman and Tukey's approximation. For interpolation see page 185.

x	N = 105			N = 110			N = 120			N = 130		
	$100\,p_x$	100 (1 − 2α) limits 95% $100\,p_l$ $100\,p_r$	99% $100\,p_l$ $100\,p_r$	$100\,p_x$	100 (1 − 2α) limits 95% $100\,p_l$ $100\,p_r$	99% $100\,p_l$ $100\,p_r$	$100\,p_x$	100 (1 − 2α) limits 95% $100\,p_l$ $100\,p_r$	99% $100\,p_l$ $100\,p_r$	$100\,p_x$	100 (1 − 2α) limits 95% $100\,p_l$ $100\,p_r$	99% $100\,p_l$ $100\,p_r$
0	*0.00*	*0.00– 3.45*	*0.00– 4.92*	*0.00*	*0.00– 3.30*	*0.00– 4.70*	*0.00*	*0.00– 3.03*	*0.00– 4.32*	*0.00*	*0.00– 2.80*	*0.00– 3.99*
1	*0.95*	*0.02– 5.19*	*0.00– 6.86*	*0.91*	*0.02– 4.96*	*0.00– 6.56*	*0.83*	*0.02– 4.56*	*0.00– 6.03*	*0.77*	*0.02– 4.21*	*0.00– 5.58*
2	*1.90*	*0.23– 6.71*	*0.10– 8.53*	*1.82*	*0.22– 6.41*	*0.09– 8.16*	*1.67*	*0.20– 5.89*	*0.09– 7.50*	*1.54*	*0.19– 5.45*	*0.08– 6.94*
3	*2.86*	*0.59– 8.12*	*0.32–10.07*	*2.73*	*0.57– 7.76*	*0.31– 9.62*	*2.50*	*0.52– 7.13*	*0.28– 8.85*	*2.31*	*0.48– 6.60*	*0.26– 8.19*
4	*3.81*	*1.05– 9.47*	*0.65–11.51*	*3.64*	*1.00– 9.05*	*0.62–11.01*	*3.33*	*0.92– 8.31*	*0.57–10.13*	*3.08*	*0.84– 7.69*	*0.52– 9.37*
5	4.76	1.53–10.84	0.88–12.78	4.55	1.46–10.37	0.84–12.23	4.17	1.34– 9.53	0.77–11.24	3.85	1.23– 8.81	0.71–10.41
6	5.71	2.10–12.10	1.33–14.13	5.45	2.00–11.56	1.26–13.51	5.00	1.83–10.63	1.16–12.43	4.62	1.69– 9.84	1.06–11.50
7	6.67	2.70–13.32	1.81–15.43	6.36	2.58–12.74	1.73–14.76	5.83	2.36–11.71	1.58–13.58	5.38	2.17–10.84	1.46–12.57
8	7.62	3.33–14.53	2.34–16.71	7.27	3.18–13.89	2.23–15.98	6.67	2.91–12.77	2.04–14.71	6.15	2.68–11.82	1.88–13.62
9	8.57	3.99–15.71	2.90–17.96	8.18	3.80–15.02	2.76–17.18	7.50	3.48–13.81	2.52–15.81	6.92	3.20–12.79	2.32–14.64
10	9.52	4.66–16.87	3.48–19.19	9.09	4.44–16.14	3.31–18.36	8.33	4.06–14.84	3.03–16.90	7.69	3.74–13.74	2.79–15.65
11	10.48	5.35–18.03	4.08–20.40	10.00	5.10–17.24	3.89–19.52	9.17	4.66–15.86	3.55–17.97	8.46	4.30–14.68	3.27–16.65
12	11.43	6.05–19.16	4.70–21.59	10.91	5.77–18.33	4.48–20.66	10.00	5.28–16.86	4.09–19.02	9.23	4.86–15.61	3.77–17.62
13	12.38	6.77–20.29	5.34–22.76	11.82	6.45–19.41	5.09–21.79	10.83	5.90–17.86	4.65–20.06	10.00	5.43–16.53	4.28–18.59
14	13.33	7.50–21.41	6.00–23.92	12.73	7.15–20.48	5.71–22.90	11.67	6.53–18.84	5.22–21.09	10.77	6.02–17.45	4.80–19.55
15	14.29	8.24–22.51	6.67–25.07	13.64	7.85–21.54	6.35–24.00	12.50	7.18–19.82	5.80–22.11	11.54	6.61–18.35	5.34–20.49
16	15.24	8.99–23.61	7.35–26.21	14.55	8.57–22.59	7.00–25.09	13.33	7.83–20.79	6.39–23.12	12.31	7.21–19.25	5.88–21.43
17	16.19	9.75–24.69	8.04–27.33	15.45	9.29–23.63	7.66–26.17	14.17	8.49–21.75	6.99–24.11	13.08	7.82–20.15	6.43–22.36
18	17.14	10.51–25.77	8.75–28.45	16.36	10.02–24.66	8.33–27.24	15.00	9.16–22.70	7.61–25.10	13.85	8.43–21.03	7.00–23.28
19	18.10	11.29–26.85	9.47–29.55	17.27	10.76–25.69	9.01–28.30	15.83	9.83–23.65	8.23–26.08	14.62	9.05–21.91	7.57–24.19
20	19.05	12.07–27.91	10.19–30.65	18.18	11.50–26.71	9.70–29.35	16.67	10.51–24.59	8.86–27.06	15.38	9.68–22.79	8.14–25.10
21	20.00	12.86–28.97	10.93–31.74	19.09	12.25–27.73	10.40–30.39	17.50	11.20–25.53	9.49–28.02	16.15	10.31–23.66	8.73–25.99
22	20.95	13.66–30.02	11.67–32.82	20.00	13.01–28.73	11.11–31.43	18.33	11.89–26.46	10.14–28.98	16.92	10.94–24.52	9.32–26.89
23	21.90	14.46–31.07	12.42–33.89	20.91	13.78–29.74	11.83–32.46	19.17	12.58–27.39	10.79–29.93	17.69	11.58–25.39	9.92–27.77
24	22.86	15.27–32.11	13.18–34.95	21.82	14.55–30.74	12.55–33.48	20.00	13.29–28.31	11.44–30.88	18.46	12.23–26.24	10.52–28.65
25	23.81	16.09–33.14	13.95–36.01	22.73	15.32–31.73	13.28–34.49	20.83	13.99–29.23	12.11–31.82	19.23	12.88–27.09	11.13–29.53
26	24.76	16.91–34.17	14.73–37.05	23.64	16.10–32.73	14.01–35.50	21.67	14.70–30.14	12.78–32.76	20.00	13.53–27.94	11.74–30.40
27	25.71	17.73–35.20	15.51–38.10	24.55	16.89–33.70	14.76–36.50	22.50	15.42–31.05	13.45–33.68	20.77	14.19–28.79	12.36–31.27
28	26.67	18.56–36.22	16.30–39.13	25.45	17.68–34.68	15.51–37.50	23.33	16.14–31.96	14.13–34.61	21.54	14.85–29.63	12.99–32.13
29	27.62	19.40–37.23	17.09–40.16	26.36	18.47–35.65	16.26–38.49	24.17	16.86–32.86	14.82–35.53	22.31	15.51–30.47	13.62–32.98
30	28.57	20.24–38.24	17.89–41.19	27.27	19.27–36.62	17.02–39.47	25.00	17.59–33.75	15.51–36.44	23.08	16.18–31.30	14.25–33.84
31	29.52	21.08–39.25	18.70–42.20	28.18	20.08–37.59	17.79–40.45	25.83	18.32–34.65	16.21–37.35	23.85	16.85–32.13	14.89–34.68
32	30.48	21.93–40.25	19.52–43.22	29.09	20.88–38.55	18.56–41.43	26.67	19.06–35.54	16.91–38.25	24.62	17.53–32.96	15.53–35.53
33	31.43	22.79–41.25	20.33–44.22	30.00	21.69–39.50	19.34–42.39	27.50	19.80–36.42	17.62–39.15	25.38	18.20–33.79	16.18–36.37
34	32.38	23.65–42.24	21.16–45.22	30.91	22.51–40.46	20.12–43.36	28.33	20.54–37.31	18.33–40.05	26.15	18.88–34.61	16.83–37.20
35	33.33	24.51–43.23	21.99–46.22	31.82	23.33–41.41	20.91–44.32	29.17	21.28–38.19	19.04–40.94	26.92	19.57–35.43	17.48–38.03
36	34.29	25.38–44.21	22.82–47.21	32.73	24.15–42.35	21.70–45.27	30.00	22.03–39.06	19.76–41.83	27.69	20.25–36.24	18.14–38.86
37	35.24	26.25–45.19	23.66–48.20	33.64	24.98–43.30	22.50–46.22	30.83	22.78–39.94	20.48–42.71	28.46	20.94–37.06	18.80–39.69
38	36.19	27.12–46.17	24.51–49.18	34.55	25.81–44.23	23.30–47.16	31.67	23.54–40.81	21.21–43.59	29.23	21.64–37.87	19.47–40.51
39	37.14	28.00–47.14	25.36–50.15	35.45	26.64–45.17	24.11–48.10	32.50	24.30–41.68	21.94–44.46	30.00	22.33–38.68	20.13–41.33
40	38.10	28.88–48.11	26.22–51.12	36.36	27.48–46.10	24.92–49.04	33.33	25.06–42.54	22.68–45.33	30.77	23.03–39.48	20.81–42.14
41	39.05	29.77–49.08	27.08–52.09	37.27	28.32–47.03	25.74–49.97	34.17	25.82–43.40	23.42–46.20	31.54	23.73–40.29	21.48–42.95
42	40.00	30.66–50.04	27.94–53.05	38.18	29.17–47.96	26.56–50.90	35.00	26.59–44.26	24.16–47.06	32.31	24.43–41.09	22.16–43.76
43	40.95	31.55–51.00	28.81–54.01	39.09	30.01–48.88	27.38–51.82	35.83	27.36–45.12	24.90–47.92	33.08	25.14–41.89	22.84–44.56
44	41.90	32.45–51.96	29.69–54.96	40.00	30.87–49.80	28.21–52.74	36.67	28.13–45.97	25.65–48.78	33.85	25.84–42.68	23.53–45.37
45	42.86	33.35–52.91	30.57–55.91	40.91	31.72–50.71	29.04–53.65	37.50	28.90–46.82	26.41–49.63	34.62	26.55–43.48	24.22–46.17
46	43.81	34.25–53.86	31.45–56.85	41.82	32.58–51.63	29.88–54.56	38.33	29.68–47.67	27.17–50.48	35.38	27.26–44.27	24.91–46.96
47	44.76	35.16–54.80	32.34–57.79	42.73	33.44–52.54	30.72–55.47	39.17	30.46–48.52	27.93–51.33	36.15	27.98–45.06	25.60–47.75
48	45.71	36.07–55.74	33.23–58.72	43.64	34.30–53.44	31.57–56.37	40.00	31.25–49.36	28.69–52.17	36.92	28.69–45.84	26.30–48.54
49	46.67	36.98–56.68	34.13–59.65	44.55	35.17–54.35	32.42–57.27	40.83	32.03–50.20	29.46–53.01	37.69	29.41–46.63	27.00–49.33
50	47.62	37.90–57.62	35.04–60.57	45.45	36.04–55.25	33.27–58.16	41.67	32.82–51.04	30.23–53.85	38.46	30.13–47.41	27.70–50.12
51	48.57	38.82–58.55	35.94–61.49	46.36	36.91–56.14	34.13–59.05	42.50	33.61–51.87	31.00–54.68	39.23	30.86–48.19	28.41–50.90
52	49.52	39.74–59.48	36.85–62.41	47.27	37.79–57.04	34.99–59.94	43.33	34.40–52.71	31.78–55.51	40.00	31.58–48.97	29.12–51.68
53	50.48	40.52–60.26	37.59–63.15	48.18	38.67–57.93	35.86–60.82	44.17	35.20–53.54	32.56–56.34	40.77	32.31–49.75	29.83–52.45
54	51.43	41.45–61.18	38.51–64.06	49.09	39.55–58.82	36.73–61.70	45.00	36.00–54.36	33.35–57.16	41.54	33.04–50.52	30.54–53.22
55	52.38	42.38–62.10	39.43–64.96	50.00	40.36–59.64	37.51–62.49	45.83	36.80–55.19	34.13–57.98	42.31	33.77–51.30	31.26–53.99
56	53.33	43.32–63.02	40.35–65.87	50.91	41.18–60.45	38.30–63.27	46.67	37.60–56.01	34.92–58.79	43.08	34.51–52.07	31.98–54.76
57	54.29	44.26–63.93	41.28–66.77	51.82	42.07–61.33	39.18–64.14	47.50	38.41–56.83	35.72–59.61	43.85	35.24–52.83	32.70–55.53
58	55.24	45.20–64.84	42.21–67.66	52.73	42.96–62.21	40.06–65.01	48.33	39.22–57.65	36.52–60.42	44.62	35.98–53.60	33.43–56.29
59	56.19	46.14–65.75	43.15–68.55	53.64	43.86–63.09	40.95–65.87	49.17	40.03–58.47	37.32–61.23	45.38	36.72–54.36	34.16–57.05
60	57.14	47.09–66.65	44.09–69.43	54.55	44.75–63.96	41.84–66.73	50.00	40.78–59.22	38.04–61.96	46.15	37.46–55.13	34.89–57.81
61	58.10	48.04–67.55	45.04–70.31	55.45	45.65–64.83	42.73–67.58	50.83	41.53–59.97	38.77–62.68	46.92	38.21–55.89	35.62–58.56
62	59.05	49.00–68.45	45.99–71.19	56.36	46.56–65.70	43.63–68.43	51.67	42.35–60.78	39.58–63.48	47.69	38.95–56.64	36.36–59.31
63	60.00	49.96–69.34	46.95–72.06	57.27	47.46–66.56	44.53–69.28	52.50	43.17–61.59	40.39–64.28	48.46	39.70–57.40	37.10–60.06
64	60.95	50.92–70.23	47.91–72.92	58.18	48.37–67.42	45.44–70.12	53.33	43.99–62.40	41.21–65.08	49.23	40.45–58.15	37.84–60.81
65	61.90	51.89–71.12	48.88–73.78	59.09	49.29–68.28	46.35–70.96	54.17	44.81–63.20	42.02–65.87	50.00	41.14–58.86	38.51–61.51
66	62.86	52.86–72.00	49.85–74.64	60.00	50.20–69.13	47.26–71.79	55.00	45.64–64.00	42.84–66.65	50.77	41.85–59.55	39.19–62.16
67	63.81	53.83–72.88	50.82–75.49	60.91	51.12–69.99	48.18–72.62	55.83	46.46–64.80	43.66–67.44	51.54	42.60–60.30	39.94–62.90
68	64.76	54.81–73.75	51.80–76.34	61.82	52.04–70.83	49.10–73.44	56.67	47.29–65.60	44.49–68.22	52.31	43.36–61.05	40.69–63.64
69	65.71	55.79–74.62	52.79–77.18	62.73	52.97–71.68	50.03–74.26	57.50	48.13–66.39	45.32–69.00	53.08	44.11–61.79	41.44–64.38
70	66.67	56.77–75.49	53.78–78.01	63.64	53.90–72.52	50.96–75.08	58.33	48.96–67.18	46.15–69.77	53.85	44.87–62.54	42.19–65.11
71	67.62	57.76–76.35	54.78–78.84	64.55	54.83–73.36	51.90–75.89	59.17	49.80–67.97	46.99–70.54	54.62	45.64–63.28	42.95–65.84
72	68.57	58.75–77.21	55.78–79.67	65.45	55.77–74.19	52.84–76.70	60.00	50.64–68.75	47.83–71.31	55.38	46.40–64.02	43.71–66.57
73	69.52	59.75–78.07	56.78–80.48	66.36	56.70–75.02	53.78–77.50	60.83	51.48–69.54	48.67–72.07	56.15	47.17–64.76	44.47–67.30
74	70.48	60.75–78.92	57.80–81.30	67.27	57.65–75.85	54.73–78.30	61.67	52.33–70.32	49.52–72.83	56.92	47.93–65.49	45.24–68.02
75	71.43	61.76–79.76	58.81–82.11	68.18	58.59–76.67	55.68–79.09	62.50	53.18–71.10	50.37–73.59	57.69	48.70–66.23	46.01–68.74
76	72.38	62.77–80.60	59.84–82.91	69.09	59.54–77.49	56.64–79.88	63.33	54.03–71.87	51.22–74.35	58.46	49.48–66.96	46.78–69.46
77	73.33	63.78–81.44	60.87–83.70	70.00	60.50–78.31	57.61–80.66	64.17	54.88–72.64	52.08–75.10	59.23	50.25–67.69	47.55–70.17
78	74.29	64.80–82.27	61.90–84.49	70.91	61.45–79.12	58.57–81.44	65.00	55.74–73.41	52.94–75.84	60.00	51.03–68.42	48.32–70.88
79	75.24	65.83–83.09	62.95–85.27	71.82	62.41–79.92	59.55–82.21	65.83	56.60–74.18	53.80–76.58	60.77	51.81–69.14	49.10–71.59
80	76.19	66.86–83.91	63.99–86.05	72.73	63.38–80.73	60.53–82.98	66.67	57.46–74.94	54.67–77.32	61.54	52.59–69.87	49.88–72.30
81	77.14	67.89–84.73	65.05–86.82	73.64	64.35–81.53	61.51–83.74	67.50	58.32–75.70	55.54–78.06	62.31	53.37–70.59	50.67–73.00
82	78.10	68.93–85.54	66.11–87.58	74.55	65.32–82.32	62.50–84.49	68.33	59.19–76.46	56.41–78.79	63.08	54.16–71.31	51.46–73.70
83	79.05	69.98–86.34	67.18–88.33	75.45	66.30–83.11	63.50–85.24	69.17	60.06–77.22	57.29–79.52	63.85	54.94–72.02	52.25–74.40
84	80.00	71.03–87.14	68.26–89.07	76.36	67.27–83.90	64.50–85.99	70.00	60.94–77.97	58.17–80.24	64.62	55.73–72.74	53.04–75.09
85	80.95	72.09–87.93	69.35–89.81	77.27	68.27–84.68	65.51–86.72	70.83	61.81–78.72	59.06–80.96	65.38	56.52–73.45	53.83–75.78
86	81.90	73.15–88.71	70.45–90.53	78.18	69.26–85.45	66.52–87.45	71.67	62.69–79.46	59.95–81.67	66.15	57.32–74.16	54.63–76.47
87	82.86	74.23–89.49	71.55–91.25	79.09	70.26–86.22	67.54–88.17	72.50	63.58–80.20	60.85–82.38	66.92	58.11–74.86	55.44–77.16
88	83.81	75.31–90.25	72.67–91.96	80.00	71.27–86.99	68.57–88.89	73.33	64.46–80.94	61.75–83.09	67.69	58.91–75.57	56.24–77.84
89	84.76	76.39–91.01	73.79–92.65	80.91	72.27–87.75	69.61–89.60	74.17	65.35–81.68	62.65–83.79	68.46	59.71–76.27	57.05–78.52
90	85.71	77.49–91.76	74.93–93.33	81.82	73.29–88.50	70.65–90.30	75.00	66.25–82.41	63.56–84.49	69.23	60.52–76.97	57.86–79.19
91	86.67	78.59–92.50	76.08–94.00	82.73	74.31–89.24	71.70–90.99	75.83	67.14–83.14	64.47–85.18	70.00	61.32–77.67	58.67–79.87
92	87.62	79.71–93.23	77.24–94.66	83.64	75.34–89.98	72.76–91.67	76.67	68.04–83.86	65.39–85.87	70.77	62.13–78.36	59.49–80.53
93	88.57	80.84–93.95	78.41–95.30	84.55	76.37–90.71	73.83–92.34	77.50	68.95–84.58	66.32–86.55	71.54	62.94–79.06	60.31–81.20
94	89.52	81.97–94.65	79.60–95.92	85.45	77.41–91.43	74.91–93.00	78.33	69.86–85.30	67.24–87.22	72.31	63.76–79.75	61.14–81.86
95	90.48	83.13–95.34	80.81–96.52	86.36	78.46–92.15	76.00–93.65	79.17	70.77–86.01	68.18–87.89	73.08	64.57–80.43	61.97–82.52
96	91.43	84.29–96.01	82.04–97.10	87.27	79.52–92.85	77.10–94.29	80.00	71.69–86.71	69.12–88.56	73.85	65.39–81.12	62.80–83.17
97	92.38	85.47–96.67	83.29–97.66	88.18	80.59–93.55	78.21–94.91	80.83	72.61–87.42	70.07–89.21	74.62	66.21–81.80	63.63–83.82
98	93.33	86.68–97.30	84.57–98.19	89.09	81.67–94.23	79.34–95.52	81.67	73.54–88.11	71.02–89.86	75.38	67.04–82.47	64.47–84.47
99	94.29	87.90–97.90	85.87–98.67	90.00	82.76–94.90	80.48–96.11	82.50	74.47–88.80	71.98–90.51	76.15	67.87–83.15	65.32–85.11
100	95.24	89.16–98.47	87.22–99.12	90.91	83.86–95.56	81.64–96.69	83.33	75.41–89.49	72.94–91.14	76.92	68.70–83.82	66.16–85.75

N = number of tries, x = number of successes, etc., $100\ p_x = 100\ x/N$

Values in *italics* are exact, all others have been calculated from Freeman and Tukey's approximation. For interpolation see page 185.

x	$N = 140$			$N = 150$			$N = 160$			$N = 170$		
	$100\,p_x$	100 $(1-2\alpha)$ limits 95% $100\,p_l$ $100\,p_r$	99% $100\,p_l$ $100\,p_r$	$100\,p_x$	100 $(1-2\alpha)$ limits 95% $100\,p_l$ $100\,p_r$	99% $100\,p_l$ $100\,p_r$	$100\,p_x$	100 $(1-2\alpha)$ limits 95% $100\,p_l$ $100\,p_r$	99% $100\,p_l$ $100\,p_r$	$100\,p_x$	100 $(1-2\alpha)$ limits 95% $100\,p_l$ $100\,p_r$	99% $100\,p_l$ $100\,p_r$
0	*0.00*	*0.00– 2.60*	*0.00– 3.71*	*0.00*	*0.00– 2.43*	*0.00– 3.47*	*0.00*	*0.00– 2.28*	*0.00– 3.26*	*0.00*	*0.00– 2.15*	*0.00– 3.07*
1	*0.71*	*0.02– 3.92*	*0.00– 5.19*	*0.67*	*0.02– 3.66*	*0.00– 4.85*	*0.63*	*0.02– 3.43*	*0.00– 4.55*	*0.59*	*0.01– 3.23*	*0.00– 4.29*
2	*1.43*	*0.17– 5.07*	*0.07– 6.45*	*1.33*	*0.16– 4.73*	*0.07– 6.03*	*1.25*	*0.15– 4.44*	*0.07– 5.67*	*1.18*	*0.14– 4.19*	*0.06– 5.34*
3	*2.14*	*0.45– 6.13*	*0.24– 7.62*	*2.00*	*0.42– 5.73*	*0.23– 7.13*	*1.88*	*0.39– 5.38*	*0.21– 6.69*	*1.76*	*0.37– 5.07*	*0.20– 6.31*
4	*2.86*	*0.78– 7.15*	*0.49– 8.72*	*2.67*	*0.73– 6.69*	*0.45– 8.16*	*2.50*	*0.69– 6.28*	*0.42– 7.66*	*2.35*	*0.64– 5.91*	*0.40– 7.22*
5	3.57	1.14– 8.20	0.66– 9.68	3.33	1.07– 7.66	0.61– 9.06	3.13	1.00– 7.20	0.57– 8.51	2.94	0.94– 6.78	0.54– 8.02
6	4.29	1.57– 9.15	0.99–10.71	4.00	1.46– 8.56	0.92–10.02	3.75	1.37– 8.03	0.86– 9.41	3.53	1.29– 7.57	0.81– 8.87
7	5.00	2.02–10.08	1.35–11.71	4.67	1.88– 9.43	1.26–10.95	4.38	1.76– 8.85	1.18–10.29	4.12	1.66– 8.34	1.11– 9.70
8	5.71	2.48–11.00	1.74–12.68	5.33	2.32–10.28	1.62–11.86	5.00	2.17– 9.66	1.52–11.14	4.71	2.04– 9.10	1.43–10.51
9	6.43	2.97–11.90	2.15–13.64	6.00	2.77–11.13	2.00–12.76	5.63	2.59–10.45	1.88–11.99	5.29	2.44– 9.85	1.76–11.30
10	7.14	3.47–12.79	2.58–14.58	6.67	3.23–11.96	2.41–13.64	6.25	3.03–11.23	2.25–12.82	5.88	2.85–10.59	2.12–12.09
11	7.86	3.98–13.67	3.03–15.50	7.33	3.71–12.78	2.82–14.51	6.88	3.47–12.01	2.64–13.63	6.47	3.27–11.32	2.48–12.8
12	8.57	4.50–14.53	3.49–16.42	8.00	4.20–13.60	3.25–15.37	7.50	3.93–12.77	3.04–14.44	7.06	3.70–12.04	2.86–13.6
13	9.29	5.04–15.39	3.96–17.32	8.67	4.69–14.40	3.69–16.21	8.13	4.39–13.53	3.45–15.24	7.65	4.13–12.75	3.24–14.3
14	10.00	5.58–16.25	4.45–18.21	9.33	5.20–15.20	4.14–17.05	8.75	4.87–14.28	3.87–16.03	8.24	4.57–13.46	3.64–15.1
15	10.71	6.13–17.09	4.94–19.10	10.00	5.71–15.99	4.60–17.88	9.38	5.34–15.02	4.30–16.81	8.82	5.02–14.17	4.04–15.8
16	11.43	6.68–17.93	5.44–19.97	10.67	6.23–16.78	5.07–18.70	10.00	5.83–15.76	4.74–17.58	9.41	5.48–14.86	4.45–16.5
17	12.14	7.24–18.76	5.96–20.84	11.33	6.75–17.56	5.54–19.51	10.63	6.32–16.50	5.19–18.34	10.00	5.94–15.56	4.87–17.3
18	12.86	7.81–19.59	6.48–21.70	12.00	7.28–18.33	6.03–20.32	11.25	6.81–17.23	5.64–19.10	10.59	6.40–16.25	5.30–18.0
19	13.57	8.38–20.41	7.00–22.55	12.67	7.81–19.10	6.52–21.12	11.88	7.31–17.95	6.10–19.86	11.18	6.87–16.93	5.73–18.7
20	14.29	8.96–21.23	7.54–23.40	13.33	8.35–19.87	7.02–21.91	12.50	7.81–18.67	6.56–20.61	11.76	7.34–17.61	6.16–19.4
21	15.00	9.55–22.04	8.08–24.24	14.00	8.89–20.63	7.52–22.70	13.13	8.32–19.39	7.03–21.35	12.35	7.82–18.29	6.60–20.1
22	15.71	10.13–22.85	8.62–25.07	14.67	9.44–21.39	8.03–23.49	13.75	8.83–20.10	7.50–22.09	12.94	8.30–18.96	7.05–20.8
23	16.43	10.73–23.65	9.18–25.90	15.33	9.99–22.14	8.54–24.27	14.38	9.35–20.81	7.98–22.82	13.53	8.78–19.63	7.50–21.5
24	17.14	11.32–24.45	9.73–26.73	16.00	10.55–22.89	9.06–25.04	15.00	9.87–21.52	8.47–23.55	14.12	9.27–20.30	7.95–22.2
25	17.86	11.92–25.25	10.30–27.55	16.67	11.10–23.64	9.58–25.81	15.63	10.39–22.22	8.96–24.28	14.71	9.76–20.96	8.41–22.9
26	18.57	12.53–26.04	10.86–28.36	17.33	11.67–24.38	10.11–26.57	16.25	10.91–22.92	9.45–25.00	15.29	10.25–21.62	8.87–23.6
27	19.29	13.14–26.83	11.43–29.17	18.00	12.23–25.12	10.64–27.34	16.88	11.44–23.62	9.94–25.72	15.88	10.75–22.28	9.34–24.2
28	20.00	13.75–27.62	12.01–29.98	18.67	12.80–25.86	11.17–28.09	17.50	11.97–24.31	10.44–26.43	16.47	11.25–22.94	9.80–24.9
29	20.71	14.36–28.40	12.59–30.78	19.33	13.37–26.59	11.71–28.85	18.13	12.51–25.00	10.95–27.14	17.06	11.75–23.59	10.28–25.63
30	21.43	14.98–29.18	13.18–31.58	20.00	13.94–27.33	12.25–29.60	18.75	13.04–25.69	11.45–27.85	17.65	12.25–24.24	10.75–26.3
31	22.14	15.60–29.96	13.77–32.37	20.67	14.52–28.06	12.80–30.34	19.38	13.58–26.38	11.96–28.56	18.24	12.76–24.89	11.23–26.9
32	22.86	16.22–30.73	14.36–33.16	21.33	15.10–28.78	13.35–31.09	20.00	14.12–27.07	12.48–29.26	18.82	13.27–25.54	11.71–27.63
33	23.57	16.85–31.50	14.95–33.95	22.00	15.68–29.51	13.90–31.83	20.63	14.67–27.75	12.99–29.96	19.41	13.78–26.19	12.19–28.2
34	24.29	17.48–32.27	15.55–34.73	22.67	16.27–30.23	14.46–32.56	21.25	15.21–28.43	13.51–30.65	20.00	14.29–26.83	12.68–28.95
35	25.00	18.11–33.04	16.16–35.51	23.33	16.85–30.95	15.02–33.30	21.88	15.76–29.11	14.03–31.34	20.59	14.80–27.47	13.17–29.61
36	25.71	18.74–33.80	16.76–36.29	24.00	17.44–31.67	15.58–34.03	22.50	16.31–29.78	14.56–32.03	21.18	15.32–28.11	13.66–30.2
37	26.43	19.38–34.56	17.37–37.06	24.67	18.03–32.38	16.15–34.76	23.13	16.86–30.46	15.09–32.72	21.76	15.84–28.75	14.16–30.91
38	27.14	20.02–35.32	17.99–37.83	25.33	18.63–33.09	16.72–35.48	23.75	17.42–31.13	15.62–33.41	22.35	16.36–29.38	14.65–31.5
39	27.86	20.66–36.08	18.60–38.60	26.00	19.22–33.81	17.29–36.21	24.38	17.97–31.80	16.15–34.09	22.94	16.88–30.02	15.15–32.2
40	28.57	21.30–36.83	19.22–39.36	26.67	19.82–34.51	17.86–36.93	25.00	18.53–32.47	16.69–34.77	23.53	17.40–30.65	15.65–32.85
41	29.29	21.95–37.59	19.85–40.12	27.33	20.42–35.22	18.44–37.64	25.63	19.09–33.13	17.22–35.45	24.12	17.92–31.28	16.16–33.49
42	30.00	22.60–38.34	20.47–40.88	28.00	21.02–35.93	19.02–38.36	26.25	19.65–33.80	17.76–36.12	24.71	18.45–31.91	16.66–34.13
43	30.71	23.25–39.08	21.10–41.64	28.67	21.63–36.63	19.60–39.07	26.88	20.22–34.46	18.31–36.80	25.29	18.98–32.54	17.17–34.77
44	31.43	23.90–39.83	21.73–42.39	29.33	22.23–37.33	20.19–39.78	27.50	20.78–35.12	18.85–37.47	25.88	19.51–33.16	17.68–35.41
45	32.14	24.56–40.57	22.36–43.14	30.00	22.84–38.03	20.77–40.49	28.13	21.35–35.78	19.40–38.14	26.47	20.04–33.79	18.19–36.04
46	32.86	25.21–41.31	23.00–43.89	30.67	23.45–38.73	21.36–41.19	28.75	21.92–36.44	19.95–38.80	27.06	20.57–34.41	18.71–36.67
47	33.57	25.87–42.05	23.64–44.64	31.33	24.06–39.42	21.95–41.90	29.38	22.49–37.10	20.50–39.47	27.65	21.11–35.03	19.22–37.30
48	34.29	26.53–42.79	24.28–45.38	32.00	24.67–40.12	22.55–42.60	30.00	23.06–37.75	21.05–40.13	28.24	21.64–35.65	19.74–37.93
49	35.00	27.19–43.53	24.92–46.12	32.67	25.29–40.81	23.15–43.29	30.63	23.63–38.41	21.61–40.79	28.82	22.18–36.27	20.26–38.5
50	35.71	27.86–44.26	25.57–46.86	33.33	25.90–41.50	23.74–43.99	31.25	24.21–39.06	22.16–41.45	29.41	22.72–36.89	20.78–39.1
51	36.43	28.52–44.99	26.22–47.59	34.00	26.52–42.19	24.34–44.68	31.88	24.78–39.71	22.72–42.11	30.00	23.26–37.51	21.30–39.8
52	37.14	29.19–45.73	26.87–48.33	34.67	27.14–42.88	24.95–45.38	32.50	25.36–40.36	23.28–42.76	30.59	23.80–38.12	21.83–40.43
53	37.86	29.86–46.45	27.52–49.06	35.33	27.76–43.56	25.55–46.07	33.13	25.94–41.01	23.85–43.41	31.18	24.34–38.73	22.35–41.05
54	38.57	30.53–47.18	28.18–49.78	36.00	28.39–44.25	26.16–46.75	33.75	26.52–41.65	24.41–44.07	31.76	24.89–39.35	22.88–41.67
55	39.29	31.21–47.91	28.84–50.51	36.67	29.01–44.93	26.77–47.44	34.38	27.10–42.30	24.98–44.71	32.35	25.43–39.96	23.41–42.28
56	40.00	31.88–48.63	29.50–51.23	37.33	29.64–45.61	27.38–48.12	35.00	27.69–42.94	25.55–45.36	32.94	25.98–40.57	23.94–42.9
57	40.71	32.56–49.35	30.16–51.95	38.00	30.26–46.29	27.99–48.80	35.63	28.27–43.59	26.12–46.01	33.53	26.52–41.17	24.48–43.5
58	41.43	33.24–50.07	30.83–52.67	38.67	30.89–46.97	28.61–49.48	36.25	28.86–44.23	26.69–46.65	34.12	27.07–41.78	25.01–44.1
59	42.14	33.92–50.79	31.50–53.39	39.33	31.52–47.65	29.23–50.16	36.88	29.44–44.87	27.26–47.29	34.71	27.62–42.39	25.55–44.7
60	42.86	34.60–51.50	32.17–54.10	40.00	32.16–48.32	29.85–50.84	37.50	30.03–45.50	27.84–47.93	35.29	28.17–42.99	26.09–45.3
61	43.57	35.29–52.22	32.84–54.82	40.67	32.79–48.99	30.47–51.51	38.13	30.62–46.14	28.42–48.57	35.88	28.73–43.60	26.63–45.9
62	44.29	35.97–52.93	33.51–55.53	41.33	33.42–49.67	31.08–52.18	38.75	31.21–46.78	28.99–49.21	36.47	29.28–44.20	27.17–46.5
63	45.00	36.66–53.63	34.19–56.23	42.00	34.06–50.34	31.71–52.85	39.38	31.81–47.41	29.58–49.85	37.06	29.83–44.80	27.71–47.1
64	45.71	37.35–54.35	34.87–56.94	42.67	34.70–51.01	32.34–53.52	40.00	32.40–48.04	30.16–50.48	37.65	30.39–45.40	28.25–47.7
65	46.43	38.04–55.06	35.55–57.64	43.33	35.34–51.68	32.97–54.19	40.63	33.00–48.68	30.74–51.11	38.24	30.95–46.00	28.80–48.3
66	47.14	38.74–55.77	36.24–58.34	44.00	35.98–52.34	33.60–54.85	41.25	33.59–49.31	31.33–51.74	38.82	31.51–46.60	29.35–48.9
67	47.86	39.43–56.47	36.92–59.04	44.67	36.62–53.01	34.23–55.51	41.88	34.19–49.94	31.92–52.37	39.41	32.06–47.20	29.89–49.5
68	48.57	40.13–57.17	37.61–59.74	45.33	37.27–53.67	34.87–56.17	42.50	34.79–50.56	32.50–53.00	40.00	32.62–47.79	30.44–50.15
69	49.29	40.82–57.87	38.30–60.44	46.00	37.91–54.33	35.51–56.83	43.13	35.39–51.19	33.10–53.62	40.59	33.19–48.39	30.99–50.75
70	50.00	41.47–58.53	38.93–61.07	46.67	38.56–54.99	36.14–57.49	43.75	35.99–51.82	33.69–54.25	41.18	33.75–48.98	31.55–51.34
71	50.71	42.13–59.18	39.56–61.70	47.33	39.21–55.65	36.78–58.14	44.38	36.59–52.44	34.28–54.87	41.76	34.31–49.57	32.10–51.9
72	51.43	42.83–59.87	40.26–62.39	48.00	39.86–56.31	37.43–58.80	45.00	37.20–53.06	34.88–55.49	42.35	34.88–50.17	32.66–52.5
73	52.14	43.53–60.57	40.96–63.08	48.67	40.51–56.97	38.07–59.45	45.63	37.80–53.69	35.47–56.11	42.94	35.44–50.76	33.21–53.12
74	52.86	44.23–61.26	41.66–63.76	49.33	41.16–57.62	38.72–60.10	46.25	38.41–54.31	36.07–56.73	43.53	36.01–51.35	33.77–53.71
75	53.57	44.94–61.96	42.36–64.45	50.00	41.76–58.24	39.30–60.70	46.88	39.02–54.93	36.67–57.34	44.12	36.58–51.93	34.33–54.29
76	54.29	45.65–62.65	43.06–65.13	50.67	42.38–58.84	39.90–61.28	47.50	39.63–55.55	37.28–57.96	44.71	37.15–52.52	34.89–54.88
77	55.00	46.36–63.34	43.77–65.81	51.33	43.03–59.49	40.55–61.93	48.13	40.24–56.16	37.88–58.56	45.29	37.72–53.11	35.46–55.46
78	55.71	47.07–64.03	44.47–66.49	52.00	43.69–60.14	41.20–62.57	48.75	40.85–56.78	38.48–59.18	45.88	38.29–53.69	36.02–56.0
79	56.43	47.78–64.71	45.18–67.16	52.67	44.35–60.79	41.86–63.22	49.38	41.46–57.39	39.09–59.79	46.47	38.86–54.28	36.59–56.63
80	57.14	48.50–65.40	45.90–67.83	53.33	45.01–61.44	42.51–63.86	50.00	42.03–57.97	39.65–60.35	47.06	39.43–54.86	37.15–57.21
81	57.86	49.21–66.08	46.61–68.50	54.00	45.67–62.09	43.17–64.49	50.63	42.61–58.54	40.21–60.91	47.65	40.01–55.44	37.72–57.79
82	58.57	49.93–66.76	47.33–69.17	54.67	46.33–62.73	43.83–65.13	51.25	43.22–59.15	40.82–61.52	48.24	40.58–56.02	38.29–58.3
83	59.29	50.65–67.44	48.05–69.84	55.33	46.99–63.38	44.49–65.77	51.88	43.84–59.76	41.44–62.12	48.82	41.16–56.60	38.86–58.94
84	60.00	51.37–68.12	48.77–70.50	56.00	47.66–64.02	45.15–66.40	52.50	44.45–60.37	42.04–62.72	49.41	41.73–57.18	39.43–59.51
85	60.71	52.09–68.79	49.49–71.16	56.67	48.32–64.66	45.81–67.03	53.13	45.07–60.98	42.66–63.33	50.00	42.27–57.73	39.96–60.04
86	61.43	52.82–69.47	50.22–71.82	57.33	48.99–65.30	46.48–67.66	53.75	45.69–61.59	43.27–63.93	50.59	42.82–58.27	40.49–60.57
87	62.14	53.55–70.14	50.94–72.48	58.00	49.66–65.94	47.15–68.29	54.38	46.31–62.20	43.89–64.53	51.18	43.40–58.84	41.06–61.14
88	62.86	54.27–70.81	51.67–73.13	58.67	50.33–66.58	47.82–68.92	55.00	46.94–62.80	44.51–65.12	51.76	43.98–59.42	41.64–61.71
89	63.57	55.01–71.48	52.41–73.78	59.33	51.01–67.21	48.49–69.53	55.63	47.56–63.41	45.13–65.72	52.35	44.56–59.99	42.21–62.28
90	64.29	55.74–72.14	53.14–74.43	60.00	51.68–67.84	49.16–70.15	56.25	48.18–64.01	45.75–66.31	52.94	45.14–60.57	42.79–62.85
91	65.00	56.47–72.81	53.88–75.08	60.67	52.35–68.48	49.84–70.77	56.88	48.81–64.61	46.38–66.90	53.53	45.72–61.14	43.37–63.41
92	65.71	57.21–73.47	54.62–75.72	61.33	53.03–69.11	50.52–71.39	57.50	49.44–65.21	47.00–67.50	54.12	46.31–61.71	43.95–63.98
93	66.43	57.95–74.13	55.36–76.36	62.00	53.71–69.74	51.20–72.01	58.13	50.06–65.81	47.63–68.08	54.71	46.89–62.28	44.54–64.54
94	67.14	58.69–74.79	56.11–77.00	62.67	54.39–70.36	51.88–72.62	58.75	50.69–66.41	48.26–68.67	55.29	47.48–62.85	45.12–65.11
95	67.86	59.43–75.44	56.86–77.64	63.33	55.07–70.99	52.56–73.23	59.38	51.32–67.00	48.89–69.26	55.88	48.07–63.42	45.71–65.67
96	68.57	60.17–76.10	57.61–78.27	64.00	55.75–71.61	53.25–73.84	60.00	51.96–67.60	49.52–69.84	56.47	48.65–63.99	46.29–66.2
97	69.29	60.92–76.75	58.36–78.90	64.67	56.44–72.24	53.93–74.45	60.63	52.59–68.19	50.15–70.42	57.06	49.24–64.56	46.88–66.7
98	70.00	61.66–77.40	59.12–79.53	65.33	57.12–72.86	54.62–75.05	61.25	53.22–68.79	50.79–71.01	57.65	49.83–65.12	47.47–67.3
99	70.71	62.41–78.05	59.88–80.15	66.00	57.81–73.48	55.32–75.66	61.88	53.86–69.38	51.43–71.58	58.24	50.43–65.69	48.06–67.
100	71.43	63.17–78.70	60.64–80.78	66.67	58.50–74.10	56.01–76.26	62.50	54.50–69.97	52.07–72.16	58.82	51.02–66.25	48.66–68.4

N = number of tries, x = number of successes, etc., $100\ p_x = 100\ x/N$

Values in *italics* are exact, all others have been calculated from FREEMAN and TUKEY's approximation. For interpolation see page 185.

x	$N = 180$			$N = 190$		
	$100 p_x$	100 (1 − 2α) limits 95% 100 p_l 100 p_r	99% 100 p_l 100 p_r	$100 p_x$	100 (1 − 2α) limits 95% 100 p_l 100 p_r	99% 100 p_l 100 p_r
0	*0.00*	*0.00- 2.03*	*0.00- 2.90*	*0.00*	*0.00- 1.92*	*0.00- 2.75*
1	*0.56*	*0.01- 3.06*	*0.00- 4.06*	*0.53*	*0.01- 2.90*	*0.00- 3.85*
2	*1.11*	*0.14- 3.96*	*0.06- 5.05*	*1.05*	*0.13- 3.75*	*0.05- 4.79*
3	*1.67*	*0.35- 4.79*	*0.19- 5.97*	*1.58*	*0.33- 4.54*	*0.18- 5.66*
4	*2.22*	*0.61- 5.59*	*0.38- 6.83*	*2.11*	*0.58- 5.30*	*0.36- 6.48*
5	2.78	0.89- 6.41	0.51- 7.58	2.63	0.84- 6.08	0.48- 7.19
6	3.33	1.21- 7.16	0.76- 8.39	3.16	1.15- 6.79	0.72- 7.96
7	3.89	1.56- 7.89	1.04- 9.17	3.68	1.48- 7.48	0.99- 8.70
8	4.44	1.92- 8.61	1.35- 9.94	4.21	1.82- 8.17	1.27- 9.43
9	5.00	2.30- 9.32	1.66-10.69	4.74	2.18- 8.84	1.57-10.15
10	5.56	2.69-10.01	2.00-11.44	5.26	2.54- 9.50	1.89-10.85
11	6.11	3.08-10.71	2.34-12.17	5.79	2.92-10.15	2.21-11.54
12	6.67	3.49-11.39	2.69-12.89	6.32	3.30-10.80	2.55-12.23
13	7.22	3.90-12.06	3.06-13.60	6.84	3.69-11.45	2.89-12.91
14	7.78	4.31-12.74	3.43-14.31	7.37	4.08-12.08	3.25-13.58
15	8.33	4.74-13.40	3.81-15.00	7.89	4.48-12.71	3.61-14.24
16	8.89	5.17-14.06	4.20-15.70	8.42	4.89-13.34	3.97-14.90
17	9.44	5.60-14.72	4.59-16.38	8.95	5.30-13.97	4.35-15.55
18	10.00	6.04-15.37	4.99-17.06	9.47	5.71-14.58	4.72-16.20
19	10.56	6.48-16.02	5.40-17.74	10.00	6.13-15.20	5.11-16.84
20	11.11	6.93-16.66	5.81-18.41	10.53	6.55-15.81	5.49-17.48
21	11.67	7.38-17.30	6.22-19.08	11.05	6.98-16.42	5.89-18.11
22	12.22	7.83-17.94	6.64-19.74	11.58	7.41-17.03	6.28-18.74
23	12.78	8.28-18.58	7.07-20.40	12.11	7.84-17.63	6.68-19.37
24	13.33	8.74-19.21	7.49-21.05	12.63	8.27-18.23	7.09-19.99
25	13.89	9.20-19.84	7.92-21.70	13.16	8.71-18.83	7.49-20.61
26	14.44	9.67-20.47	8.36-22.35	13.68	9.15-19.43	7.90-21.22
27	15.00	10.14-21.09	8.80-22.99	14.21	9.59-20.02	8.32-21.84
28	15.56	10.61-21.71	9.24-23.64	14.74	10.03-20.61	8.73-22.45
29	16.11	11.08-22.33	9.68-24.27	15.26	10.48-21.20	9.15-23.05
30	16.67	11.55-22.95	10.13-24.91	15.79	10.93-21.79	9.58-23.66
31	17.22	12.03-23.57	10.58-25.54	16.32	11.38-22.37	10.00-24.26
32	17.78	12.51-24.18	11.03-26.17	16.84	11.83-22.95	10.43-24.86
33	18.33	12.99-24.79	11.49-26.80	17.37	12.28-23.54	10.86-25.46
34	18.89	13.47-25.40	11.95-27.43	17.89	12.74-24.12	11.29-26.05
35	19.44	13.95-26.01	12.41-28.05	18.42	13.20-24.69	11.73-26.65
36	20.00	14.44-26.62	12.87-28.67	18.95	13.65-25.27	12.16-27.24
37	20.56	14.93-27.22	13.33-29.29	19.47	14.12-25.85	12.60-27.83
38	21.11	15.42-27.82	13.80-29.90	20.00	14.58-26.42	13.04-28.41
39	21.67	15.91-28.42	14.27-30.52	20.53	15.04-26.99	13.49-29.00
40	22.22	16.40-29.02	14.74-31.13	21.05	15.51-27.56	13.93-29.58
41	22.78	16.89-29.62	15.21-31.74	21.58	15.97-28.13	14.38-30.16
42	23.33	17.39-30.22	15.69-32.35	22.11	16.44-28.70	14.83-30.74
43	23.89	17.89-30.81	16.17-32.96	22.63	16.91-29.26	15.28-31.32
44	24.44	18.38-31.41	16.65-33.56	23.16	17.38-29.83	15.73-31.89
45	25.00	18.88-32.00	17.13-34.16	23.68	17.85-30.39	16.18-32.47
46	25.56	19.39-32.59	17.61-34.76	24.21	18.33-30.96	16.64-33.04
47	26.11	19.89-33.18	18.10-35.36	24.74	18.80-31.52	17.09-33.61
48	26.67	20.39-33.77	18.58-35.96	25.26	19.28-32.08	17.55-34.18
49	27.22	20.90-34.36	19.07-36.56	25.79	19.75-32.64	18.01-34.75
50	27.78	21.40-34.94	19.56-37.15	26.32	20.23-33.19	18.48-35.32
51	28.33	21.91-35.53	20.05-37.74	26.84	20.71-33.75	18.94-35.88
52	28.89	22.42-36.11	20.54-38.33	27.37	21.19-34.31	19.40-36.44
53	29.44	22.93-36.70	21.04-38.92	27.89	21.67-34.86	19.87-37.01
54	30.00	23.44-37.28	21.53-39.51	28.42	22.16-35.41	20.34-37.57
55	30.56	23.95-37.86	22.03-40.10	28.95	22.64-35.97	20.81-38.13
56	31.11	24.47-38.44	22.53-40.68	29.47	23.13-36.52	21.28-38.68
57	31.67	24.98-39.02	23.03-41.27	30.00	23.61-37.07	21.75-39.24
58	32.22	25.50-39.59	23.53-41.85	30.53	24.10-37.62	22.22-39.80
59	32.78	26.02-40.17	24.04-42.43	31.05	24.59-38.17	22.70-40.35
60	33.33	26.53-40.74	24.54-43.01	31.58	25.07-38.71	23.17-40.90
61	33.89	27.05-41.32	25.05-43.59	32.11	25.56-39.26	23.65-41.45
62	34.44	27.57-41.89	25.56-44.16	32.63	26.05-39.81	24.13-42.00
63	35.00	28.09-42.46	26.07-44.74	33.16	26.55-40.35	24.61-42.55
64	35.56	28.62-43.03	26.58-45.31	33.68	27.04-40.89	25.09-43.10
65	36.11	29.14-43.60	27.09-45.89	34.21	27.53-41.44	25.57-43.65
66	36.67	29.66-44.17	27.60-46.46	34.74	28.03-41.98	26.05-44.19
67	37.22	30.19-44.74	28.11-47.03	35.26	28.52-42.52	26.54-44.74
68	37.78	30.72-45.30	28.63-47.60	35.79	29.02-43.06	27.02-45.28
69	38.33	31.24-45.87	29.15-48.16	36.32	29.52-43.60	27.51-45.82
70	38.89	31.77-46.44	29.67-48.73	36.84	30.01-44.14	28.00-46.36
71	39.44	32.30-47.00	30.18-49.29	37.37	30.51-44.68	28.49-46.90
72	40.00	32.83-47.56	30.71-49.86	37.89	31.01-45.21	28.98-47.44
73	40.56	33.36-48.12	31.23-50.42	38.42	31.51-45.75	29.47-47.98
74	41.11	33.89-48.68	31.75-50.98	38.95	32.01-46.28	29.96-48.52
75	41.67	34.43-49.25	32.28-51.54	39.47	32.52-46.82	30.45-49.05
76	42.22	34.96-49.80	32.80-52.10	40.00	33.02-47.35	30.95-49.59
77	42.78	35.50-50.36	33.33-52.66	40.53	33.52-47.88	31.44-50.12
78	43.33	36.03-50.92	33.86-53.21	41.05	34.03-48.41	31.94-50.65
79	43.89	36.57-51.48	34.39-53.77	41.58	34.53-48.95	32.44-51.18
80	44.44	37.11-52.03	34.92-54.32	42.11	35.04-49.48	32.94-51.71
81	45.00	37.64-52.59	35.45-54.88	42.63	35.55-50.01	33.44-52.24
82	45.56	38.18-53.14	35.98-55.43	43.16	36.06-50.53	33.94-52.77
83	46.11	38.72-53.69	36.51-55.98	43.68	36.56-51.06	34.44-53.29
84	46.67	39.26-54.25	37.05-56.53	44.21	37.07-51.59	34.94-53.82
85	47.22	39.81-54.80	37.59-57.08	44.74	37.58-52.11	35.45-54.34
86	47.78	40.35-55.35	38.12-57.62	45.26	38.10-52.64	35.95-54.87
87	48.33	40.89-55.90	38.66-58.17	45.79	38.61-53.16	36.46-55.39
88	48.89	41.44-56.44	39.20-58.71	46.32	39.12-53.69	36.96-55.91
89	49.44	41.98-56.99	39.74-59.26	46.84	39.63-54.21	37.47-56.43
90	50.00	42.49-57.51	40.24-59.76	47.37	40.15-54.73	37.98-56.95
91	50.56	43.01-58.02	40.74-60.26	47.89	40.66-55.25	38.49-57.47
92	51.11	43.56-58.56	41.29-60.80	48.42	41.18-55.78	39.00-57.99
93	51.67	44.10-59.11	41.83-61.34	48.95	41.70-56.29	39.52-58.51
94	52.22	44.65-59.65	42.38-61.88	49.47	42.21-56.81	40.03-59.02
95	52.78	45.20-60.19	42.92-62.41	50.00	42.70-57.30	40.50-59.50
96	53.33	45.75-60.74	43.47-62.95	50.53	43.19-57.79	40.98-59.97
97	53.89	46.31-61.28	44.02-63.49	51.05	43.71-58.30	41.49-60.48
98	54.44	46.86-61.82	44.57-64.02	51.58	44.22-58.82	42.01-61.00
99	55.00	47.41-62.36	45.12-64.55	52.11	44.75-59.34	42.53-61.51
100	55.56	47.97-62.89	45.68-65.08	52.63	45.27-59.85	43.05-62.02

x	$N = 200$			$N = 250$		
	$100 p_x$	100 (1 − 2α) limits 95% 100 p_l 100 p_r	99% 100 p_l 100 p_r	$100 p_x$	100 (1 − 2α) limits 95% 100 p_l 100 p_r	99% 100 p_l 100 p_r
0	*0.00*	*0.00- 1.83*	*0.00- 2.61*	*0.00*	*0.00- 1.46*	*0.00- 2.10*
1	*0.50*	*0.01- 2.75*	*0.00- 3.66*	*0.40*	*0.01- 2.21*	*0.00- 2.93*
2	*1.00*	*0.12- 3.57*	*0.05- 4.55*	*0.80*	*0.10- 2.86*	*0.04- 3.66*
3	*1.50*	*0.31- 4.32*	*0.17- 5.38*	*1.20*	*0.25- 3.47*	*0.14- 4.32*
4	*2.00*	*0.55- 5.04*	*0.34- 6.16*	*1.60*	*0.44- 4.05*	*0.27- 4.95*
5	2.50	0.80- 5.78	0.46- 6.84	2.00	0.64- 4.64	0.36- 5.49
6	3.00	1.09- 6.46	0.69- 7.57	2.40	0.87- 5.18	0.55- 6.08
7	3.50	1.40- 7.12	0.94- 8.28	2.80	1.12- 5.71	0.75- 6.65
8	4.00	1.73- 7.76	1.21- 8.97	3.20	1.38- 6.24	0.96- 7.21
9	4.50	2.07- 8.40	1.49- 9.65	3.60	1.65- 6.75	1.19- 7.76
10	5.00	2.41- 9.03	1.79- 10.32	4.00	1.93- 7.26	1.43- 8.30
11	5.50	2.77- 9.66	2.10- 10.98	4.40	2.21- 7.76	1.67- 8.84
12	6.00	3.13- 10.28	2.42- 11.64	4.80	2.50- 8.26	1.93- 9.36
13	6.50	3.50- 10.89	2.75- 12.28	5.20	2.79- 8.75	2.19- 9.88
14	7.00	3.88- 11.49	3.08- 12.92	5.60	3.09- 9.24	2.45- 10.40
15	7.50	4.26- 12.09	3.42- 13.55	6.00	3.39- 9.72	2.72- 10.91
16	8.00	4.64- 12.69	3.77- 14.18	6.40	3.70- 10.21	3.00- 11.42
17	8.50	5.03- 13.29	4.12- 14.80	6.80	4.01- 10.68	3.28- 11.92
18	9.00	5.42- 13.88	4.48- 15.42	7.20	4.32- 11.16	3.57- 12.42
19	9.50	5.82- 14.46	4.84- 16.03	7.60	4.64- 11.63	3.85- 12.91
20	10.00	6.22- 15.04	5.21- 16.63	8.00	4.96- 12.10	4.15- 13.40
21	10.50	6.62- 15.62	5.58- 17.24	8.40	5.28- 12.57	4.44- 13.89
22	11.00	7.03- 16.20	5.96- 17.84	8.80	5.60- 13.04	4.74- 14.38
23	11.50	7.44- 16.78	6.34- 18.44	9.20	5.92- 13.50	5.04- 14.86
24	12.00	7.85- 17.35	6.72- 19.03	9.60	6.25- 13.96	5.34- 15.34
25	12.50	8.26- 17.92	7.11- 19.62	10.00	6.58- 14.42	5.65- 15.82
26	13.00	8.68- 18.49	7.50- 20.21	10.40	6.91- 14.88	5.96- 16.30
27	13.50	9.10- 19.05	7.89- 20.79	10.80	7.24- 15.34	6.27- 16.77
28	14.00	9.52- 19.61	8.28- 21.37	11.20	7.58- 15.80	6.58- 17.24
29	14.50	9.94- 20.18	8.68- 21.95	11.60	7.91- 16.25	6.90- 17.71
30	15.00	10.37- 20.73	9.08- 22.53	12.00	8.25- 16.70	7.21- 18.18
31	15.50	10.79- 21.29	9.48- 23.10	12.40	8.59- 17.15	7.53- 18.65
32	16.00	11.22- 21.85	9.89- 23.67	12.80	8.93- 17.60	7.85- 19.11
33	16.50	11.65- 22.40	10.30- 24.24	13.20	9.27- 18.05	8.17- 19.57
34	17.00	12.08- 22.95	10.70- 24.81	13.60	9.61- 18.50	8.50- 20.03
35	17.50	12.52- 23.51	11.12- 25.38	14.00	9.96- 18.94	8.82- 20.49
36	18.00	12.95- 24.05	11.53- 25.94	14.40	10.30- 19.39	9.15- 20.95
37	18.50	13.39- 24.60	11.95- 26.50	14.80	10.65- 19.83	9.48- 21.41
38	19.00	13.83- 25.15	12.36- 27.06	15.20	11.00- 20.27	9.81- 21.86
39	19.50	14.27- 25.69	12.78- 27.62	15.60	11.34- 20.72	10.14- 22.32
40	20.00	14.71- 26.24	13.20- 28.18	16.00	11.69- 21.16	10.47- 22.77
41	20.50	15.15- 26.78	13.63- 28.73	16.40	12.04- 21.60	10.81- 23.22
42	21.00	15.59- 27.32	14.05- 29.28	16.80	12.40- 22.04	11.14- 23.67
43	21.50	16.04- 27.86	14.48- 29.84	17.20	12.75- 22.47	11.48- 24.12
44	22.00	16.48- 28.40	14.91- 30.39	17.60	13.10- 22.91	11.82- 24.57
45	22.50	16.93- 28.94	15.34- 30.93	18.00	13.45- 23.35	12.16- 25.01
46	23.00	17.38- 29.47	15.77- 31.48	18.40	13.81- 23.78	12.50- 25.46
47	23.50	17.83- 30.01	16.20- 32.03	18.80	14.17- 24.22	12.84- 25.90
48	24.00	18.28- 30.54	16.63- 32.57	19.20	14.52- 24.65	13.18- 26.35
49	24.50	18.73- 31.08	17.07- 33.11	19.60	14.88- 25.08	13.52- 26.79
50	25.00	19.18- 31.61	17.51- 33.65	20.00	15.24- 25.51	13.87- 27.23
60	30.00	23.77- 36.88	21.95- 38.99	24.00	18.86- 29.80	17.36- 31.59
70	35.00	28.44- 42.06	26.51- 44.21	28.00	22.55- 34.01	20.94- 35.87
80	40.00	33.19- 47.16	31.17- 49.33	32.00	26.29- 38.18	24.60- 40.08
90	45.00	38.02- 52.18	35.93- 54.36	36.00	30.07- 42.30	28.31- 44.23
100	50.00	42.89- 57.11	40.74- 59.26	40.00	33.91- 46.37	32.08- 48.31
110	55.00	47.82- 61.98	45.64- 64.07	44.00	37.78- 50.40	35.91- 52.35
120	60.00	52.84- 66.81	50.67- 68.83	48.00	41.70- 54.39	39.80- 56.33
130	65.00	57.94- 71.56	55.79- 73.49	52.00	45.61- 58.30	43.67- 60.20
140	70.00	63.12- 76.23	61.01- 78.05	56.00	49.60- 62.22	47.65- 64.09
150	75.00	68.39- 80.82	66.35- 82.49	60.00	53.63- 66.09	51.69- 67.92
160	80.00	73.76- 85.29	71.82- 86.80	64.00	57.70- 69.93	55.77- 71.69
170	85.00	79.27- 89.63	77.47- 90.92	68.00	61.82- 73.71	59.92- 75.40
180	90.00	84.96- 93.78	83.37- 94.79	72.00	65.99- 77.45	64.13- 79.06
190	95.00	90.97- 97.59	89.68- 98.21	76.00	70.20- 81.14	68.41- 82.64
200	*100.00*	*98.17-100.00*	*97.39-100.00*	80.00	74.49- 84.76	72.77- 86.13
210				84.00	78.84- 88.31	77.23- 89.53
220				88.00	83.30- 91.75	81.82- 92.79
230				92.00	87.90- 95.04	86.60- 95.85
240				96.00	92.74- 98.07	91.70- 98.57
250				*100.00*	*98.54-100.00*	*97.90-100.00*

N = number of tries, x = number of successes, etc., $100\ p_x = 100\ x/N$

Values in *italics* are exact, all others have been calculated from Freeman and Tukey's approximation. For interpolation see page 185.

x	$N = 300$			$N = 400$			$N = 500$			$N = 600$		
	$100\,p_x$	100 (1 − 2α) limits 95% $100\,\mathbf{p}_l$ $100\,\mathbf{p}_r$	99% $100\,\mathbf{p}_l$ $100\,\mathbf{p}_r$	$100\,p_x$	100 (1 − 2α) limits 95% $100\,\mathbf{p}_l$ $100\,\mathbf{p}_r$	99% $100\,\mathbf{p}_l$ $100\,\mathbf{p}_r$	$100\,p_x$	100 (1 − 2α) limits 95% $100\,\mathbf{p}_l$ $100\,\mathbf{p}_r$	99% $100\,\mathbf{p}_l$ $100\,\mathbf{p}_r$	$100\,p_x$	100 (1 − 2α) limits 95% $100\,\mathbf{p}_l$ $100\,\mathbf{p}_r$	99% $100\,\mathbf{p}_l$ $100\,\mathbf{p}_r$
0	*0.00*	*0.00– 1.22*	*0.00– 1.75*	*0.00*	*0.00– 0.92*	*0.00– 1.32*	*0.00*	*0.00– 0.74*	*0.00– 1.05*	*0.00*	*0.00– 0.61*	*0.00– 0.88*
1	*0.33*	*0.01– 1.84*	*0.00– 2.45*	*0.25*	*0.01– 1.38*	*0.00– 1.84*	*0.20*	*0.01– 1.11*	*0.00– 1.48*	*0.17*	*0.00– 0.93*	*0.00– 1.23*
2	*0.67*	*0.08– 2.39*	*0.03– 3.05*	*0.50*	*0.06– 1.79*	*0.03– 2.30*	*0.40*	*0.05– 1.44*	*0.02– 1.84*	*0.33*	*0.04– 1.20*	*0.02– 1.54*
3	*1.00*	*0.21– 2.89*	*0.11– 3.61*	*0.75*	*0.16– 2.18*	*0.08– 2.72*	*0.60*	*0.12– 1.74*	*0.07– 2.18*	*0.50*	*0.10– 1.45*	*0.06– 1.82*
4	*1.33*	*0.36– 3.38*	*0.23– 4.14*	*1.00*	*0.27– 2.54*	*0.17– 3.11*	*0.80*	*0.22– 2.04*	*0.14– 2.50*	*0.67*	*0.18– 1.70*	*0.11– 2.08*
5	1.67	0.53– 3.88	0.30– 4.59	1.25	0.40– 2.92	0.23– 3.46	1.00	0.32– 2.34	0.18– 2.77	0.83	0.26– 1.95	0.15– 2.31
6	2.00	0.73– 4.33	0.45– 5.08	1.50	0.54– 3.26	0.34– 3.83	1.20	0.43– 2.61	0.27– 3.07	1.00	0.36– 2.18	0.23– 2.56
7	2.33	0.93– 4.77	0.62– 5.56	1.75	0.70– 3.59	0.46– 4.19	1.40	0.56– 2.88	0.37– 3.36	1.17	0.46– 2.40	0.31– 2.80
8	2.67	1.15– 5.21	0.80– 6.03	2.00	0.86– 3.92	0.60– 4.54	1.60	0.69– 3.14	0.48– 3.64	1.33	0.57– 2.62	0.40– 3.04
9	3.00	1.37– 5.64	0.99– 6.49	2.25	1.03– 4.25	0.74– 4.89	1.80	0.82– 3.40	0.59– 3.92	1.50	0.68– 2.84	0.49– 3.27
10	3.33	1.60– 6.07	1.19– 6.94	2.50	1.20– 4.57	0.89– 5.23	2.00	0.96– 3.66	0.71– 4.20	1.67	0.80– 3.06	0.59– 3.5…
11	3.67	1.84– 6.49	1.39– 7.39	2.75	1.37– 4.88	1.04– 5.57	2.20	1.10– 3.92	0.83– 4.47	1.83	0.91– 3.27	0.69– 3.7…
12	4.00	2.08– 6.90	1.60– 7.83	3.00	1.55– 5.20	1.20– 5.90	2.40	1.24– 4.17	0.96– 4.74	2.00	1.03– 3.48	0.79– 3.9…
13	4.33	2.32– 7.32	1.82– 8.27	3.25	1.74– 5.51	1.36– 6.23	2.60	1.39– 4.42	1.08– 5.00	2.17	1.15– 3.69	0.90– 4.1…
14	4.67	2.57– 7.73	2.04– 8.70	3.50	1.92– 5.82	1.52– 6.56	2.80	1.54– 4.67	1.22– 5.26	2.33	1.28– 3.89	1.01– 4.3…
15	5.00	2.82– 8.13	2.26– 9.13	3.75	2.11– 6.12	1.69– 6.88	3.00	1.69– 4.91	1.35– 5.52	2.50	1.40– 4.10	1.12– 4.6…
16	5.33	3.08– 8.53	2.49– 9.55	4.00	2.30– 6.43	1.86– 7.20	3.20	1.84– 5.16	1.49– 5.78	2.67	1.53– 4.30	1.24– 4.8…
17	5.67	3.33– 8.94	2.72– 9.98	4.25	2.49– 6.73	2.03– 7.52	3.40	1.99– 5.40	1.62– 6.04	2.83	1.66– 4.51	1.35– 5.0…
18	6.00	3.59– 9.33	2.96– 10.39	4.50	2.69– 7.03	2.21– 7.84	3.60	2.14– 5.64	1.76– 6.29	3.00	1.78– 4.71	1.47– 5.2…
19	6.33	3.85– 9.73	3.20– 10.81	4.75	2.88– 7.33	2.39– 8.15	3.80	2.30– 5.88	1.91– 6.55	3.17	1.91– 4.91	1.59– 5.4…
20	6.67	4.12– 10.12	3.44– 11.22	5.00	3.08– 7.63	2.57– 8.47	4.00	2.46– 6.12	2.05– 6.80	3.33	2.05– 5.11	1.71– 5.6…
21	7.00	4.38– 10.52	3.69– 11.63	5.25	3.28– 7.93	2.75– 8.78	4.20	2.62– 6.36	2.20– 7.05	3.50	2.18– 5.31	1.83– 5.8…
22	7.33	4.65– 10.91	3.93– 12.04	5.50	3.48– 8.22	2.94– 9.09	4.40	2.78– 6.60	2.34– 7.30	3.67	2.31– 5.51	1.95– 6.0…
23	7.67	4.92– 11.30	4.18– 12.45	5.75	3.68– 8.51	3.12– 9.39	4.60	2.94– 6.83	2.49– 7.54	3.83	2.44– 5.70	2.07– 6.3…
24	8.00	5.19– 11.68	4.43– 12.85	6.00	3.88– 8.81	3.31– 9.70	4.80	3.10– 7.07	2.64– 7.79	4.00	2.58– 5.90	2.19– 6.5…
25	8.33	5.47– 12.07	4.69– 13.25	6.25	4.08– 9.10	3.50– 10.00	5.00	3.26– 7.30	2.79– 8.03	4.17	2.71– 6.10	2.32– 6.7…
26	8.67	5.74– 12.45	4.94– 13.65	6.50	4.29– 9.39	3.69– 10.31	5.20	3.42– 7.54	2.94– 8.28	4.33	2.85– 6.29	2.45– 6.9…
27	9.00	6.02– 12.84	5.20– 14.05	6.75	4.49– 9.68	3.88– 10.61	5.40	3.59– 7.77	3.09– 8.52	4.50	2.99– 6.49	2.57– 7.12
28	9.33	6.29– 13.22	5.46– 14.45	7.00	4.70– 9.97	4.07– 10.91	5.60	3.75– 8.00	3.25– 8.76	4.67	3.12– 6.68	2.70– 7.32
29	9.67	6.57– 13.60	5.72– 14.84	7.25	4.91– 10.26	4.27– 11.21	5.80	3.92– 8.23	3.40– 9.01	4.83	3.26– 6.88	2.83– 7.53
30	10.00	6.85– 13.98	5.98– 15.24	7.50	5.12– 10.54	4.46– 11.51	6.00	4.08– 8.46	3.56– 9.25	5.00	3.40– 7.07	2.96– 7.73
31	10.33	7.13– 14.36	6.25– 15.63	7.75	5.33– 10.83	4.66– 11.81	6.20	4.25– 8.69	3.71– 9.49	5.17	3.54– 7.26	3.09– 7.93
32	10.67	7.41– 14.74	6.51– 16.02	8.00	5.54– 11.12	4.85– 12.10	6.40	4.42– 8.92	3.87– 9.72	5.33	3.68– 7.45	3.22– 8.13
33	11.00	7.70– 15.11	6.78– 16.41	8.25	5.75– 11.40	5.05– 12.40	6.60	4.59– 9.15	4.03– 9.96	5.50	3.82– 7.64	3.35– 8.33
34	11.33	7.98– 15.49	7.05– 16.80	8.50	5.96– 11.69	5.25– 12.69	6.80	4.76– 9.38	4.19– 10.20	5.67	3.96– 7.84	3.48– 8.52
35	11.67	8.27– 15.86	7.32– 17.18	8.75	6.17– 11.97	5.45– 12.99	7.00	4.92– 9.61	4.35– 10.44	5.83	4.10– 8.03	3.61– 8.72
36	12.00	8.55– 16.24	7.59– 17.57	9.00	6.38– 12.25	5.65– 13.28	7.20	5.09– 9.84	4.51– 10.67	6.00	4.24– 8.22	3.75– 8.92
37	12.33	8.84– 16.61	7.86– 17.95	9.25	6.60– 12.53	5.86– 13.57	7.40	5.26– 10.06	4.67– 10.91	6.17	4.38– 8.41	3.88– 9.12
38	12.67	9.13– 16.98	8.13– 18.34	9.50	6.81– 12.82	6.06– 13.86	7.60	5.43– 10.29	4.83– 11.14	6.33	4.52– 8.60	4.01– 9.31
39	13.00	9.42– 17.35	8.41– 18.72	9.75	7.03– 13.10	6.26– 14.15	7.80	5.61– 10.52	4.99– 11.38	6.50	4.66– 8.79	4.15– 9.51
40	13.33	9.71– 17.72	8.68– 19.10	10.00	7.24– 13.38	6.47– 14.44	8.00	5.78– 10.74	5.15– 11.61	6.67	4.81– 8.97	4.28– 9.7…
41	13.67	10.00– 18.09	8.96– 19.48	10.25	7.46– 13.66	6.67– 14.73	8.20	5.95– 10.97	5.32– 11.84	6.83	4.95– 9.16	4.42– 9.9…
42	14.00	10.29– 18.46	9.23– 19.86	10.50	7.68– 13.94	6.88– 15.02	8.40	6.12– 11.19	5.48– 12.08	7.00	5.09– 9.35	4.55– 10.1…
43	14.33	10.58– 18.83	9.51– 20.24	10.75	7.89– 14.21	7.08– 15.31	8.60	6.30– 11.42	5.64– 12.31	7.17	5.24– 9.54	4.69– 10.2…
44	14.67	10.87– 19.20	9.79– 20.62	11.00	8.11– 14.49	7.29– 15.59	8.80	6.47– 11.64	5.81– 12.54	7.33	5.38– 9.73	4.83– 10.4…
45	15.00	11.16– 19.56	10.07– 20.99	11.25	8.33– 14.77	7.50– 15.88	9.00	6.64– 11.86	5.97– 12.77	7.50	5.52– 9.91	4.96– 10.6…
46	15.33	11.46– 19.93	10.35– 21.37	11.50	8.55– 15.05	7.71– 16.17	9.20	6.82– 12.09	6.14– 13.00	7.67	5.67– 10.10	5.10– 10.8…
47	15.67	11.75– 20.29	10.63– 21.74	11.75	8.77– 15.33	7.92– 16.45	9.40	6.99– 12.31	6.31– 13.23	7.83	5.81– 10.29	5.24– 11.06
48	16.00	12.05– 20.66	10.92– 22.12	12.00	8.99– 15.60	8.13– 16.74	9.60	7.17– 12.53	6.47– 13.46	8.00	5.96– 10.47	5.38– 11.2…
49	16.33	12.34– 21.02	11.20– 22.49	12.25	9.21– 15.88	8.34– 17.02	9.80	7.34– 12.76	6.64– 13.69	8.17	6.10– 10.66	5.52– 11.4…
50	16.67	12.64– 21.39	11.48– 22.86	12.50	9.43– 16.15	8.55– 17.30	10.00	7.52– 12.98	6.81– 13.92	8.33	6.25– 10.84	5.66– 11.6…
60	20.00	15.63– 24.99	14.37– 26.55	15.00	11.65– 18.89	10.68– 20.11	12.00	9.29– 15.18	8.50– 16.18	10.00	7.72– 12.69	7.06– 13.5…
70	23.33	18.68– 28.55	17.32– 30.16	17.50	13.91– 21.59	12.86– 22.87	14.00	11.08– 17.36	10.23– 18.42	11.67	9.21– 14.51	8.50– 15.4…
80	26.67	21.76– 32.06	20.32– 33.73	20.00	16.20– 24.27	15.08– 25.60	16.00	12.90– 19.52	11.99– 20.62	13.33	10.72– 16.32	9.95– 17.2…
90	30.00	24.89– 35.54	23.37– 37.25	22.50	18.51– 26.92	17.33– 28.30	18.00	14.74– 21.66	13.77– 22.80	15.00	12.24– 18.12	11.43– 19.0…
100	33.33	28.04– 38.99	26.46– 40.73	25.00	20.84– 29.55	19.61– 30.96	20.00	16.59– 23.78	15.58– 24.97	16.67	13.78– 19.90	12.92– 20.9…
110	36.67	31.22– 42.40	29.59– 44.17	27.50	23.19– 32.16	21.91– 33.61	22.00	18.45– 25.90	17.40– 27.11	18.33	15.32– 21.67	14.43– 22.7…
120	40.00	34.44– 45.79	32.76– 47.57	30.00	25.56– 34.76	24.23– 36.23	24.00	20.33– 28.00	19.23– 29.24	20.00	16.87– 23.43	15.95– 24.…
130	43.33	37.67– 49.15	35.97– 50.93	32.50	27.94– 37.34	26.57– 38.83	26.00	22.21– 30.08	21.08– 31.35	21.67	18.44– 25.19	17.47– 26.…
140	46.67	40.94– 52.49	39.20– 54.27	35.00	30.34– 39.90	28.94– 41.41	28.00	24.11– 32.16	22.95– 33.45	23.33	20.01– 26.93	19.01– 28.…
150	50.00	44.21– 55.79	42.45– 57.55	37.50	32.75– 42.45	31.32– 43.98	30.00	26.02– 34.23	24.82– 35.54	25.00	21.59– 28.67	20.56– 29.…
160	53.33	47.51– 59.06	45.73– 60.80	40.00	35.18– 44.99	33.72– 46.52	32.00	27.94– 36.29	26.71– 37.62	26.67	23.17– 30.40	22.12– 31.…
170	56.67	50.85– 62.33	49.07– 64.03	42.50	37.62– 47.51	36.14– 49.05	34.00	29.86– 38.34	28.61– 39.68	28.33	24.76– 32.13	23.69– 33.…
180	60.00	54.21– 65.56	52.43– 67.24	45.00	40.07– 50.03	38.57– 51.57	36.00	31.80– 40.38	30.52– 41.74	30.00	26.36– 33.84	25.26– 35.…
190	63.33	57.60– 68.78	55.83– 70.41	47.50	42.53– 52.52	41.02– 54.06	38.00	33.74– 42.42	32.45– 43.78	31.67	27.97– 35.56	26.85– 36.…
200	66.67	61.01– 71.96	59.27– 73.54	50.00	45.00– 55.00	43.47– 56.53	40.00	35.69– 44.45	34.38– 45.82	33.33	29.58– 37.27	28.44– 38.…
210	70.00	64.46– 75.11	62.75– 76.63	52.50	47.48– 57.47	45.94– 58.98	42.00	37.64– 46.47	36.32– 47.84	35.00	31.19– 38.97	30.03– 40.…
220	73.33	67.94– 78.24	66.27– 79.68	55.00	49.97– 59.93	48.43– 61.43	44.00	39.61– 48.48	38.27– 49.86	36.67	32.81– 40.67	31.64– 41.…
230	76.67	71.45– 81.32	69.84– 82.68	57.50	52.49– 62.38	50.95– 63.86	46.00	41.58– 50.48	40.23– 51.86	38.33	34.43– 42.36	33.25– 43.…
240	80.00	75.01– 84.37	73.45– 85.63	60.00	55.01– 64.82	53.48– 66.28	48.00	43.56– 52.48	42.20– 53.86	40.00	36.06– 44.05	34.86– 45.…
250	83.33	78.61– 87.36	77.14– 88.52	62.50	57.55– 67.25	56.02– 68.68	50.00	45.54– 54.46	44.17– 55.83	41.67	37.70– 45.73	36.49– 46.…
260	86.67	82.28– 90.29	80.90– 91.32	65.00	60.10– 69.66	58.59– 71.06	52.00	47.52– 56.44	46.14– 57.80	43.33	39.34– 47.41	38.11– 48.…
270	90.00	86.02– 93.15	84.76– 94.02	67.50	62.66– 72.06	61.17– 73.43	54.00	49.52– 58.42	48.14– 59.77	45.00	40.98– 49.08	39.75– 50…
280	93.33	89.88– 95.88	88.78– 96.56	70.00	65.24– 74.44	63.77– 75.77	56.00	51.52– 60.39	50.14– 61.73	46.67	42.63– 50.75	41.39– 52…
290	96.67	93.93– 98.40	93.06– 98.81	72.50	67.84– 76.81	66.39– 78.09	58.00	53.53– 62.36	52.16– 63.68	48.33	44.28– 52.42	43.03– 53…
300	*100.00*	*98.78–100.00*	*98.25–100.00*	75.00	70.45– 79.16	69.04– 80.39	60.00	55.55– 64.31	54.18– 65.62	50.00	45.93– 54.07	44.68– 55.…
310				77.50	73.08– 81.49	71.70– 82.67	62.00	57.58– 66.26	56.22– 67.55	51.67	47.58– 55.72	46.33– 56.…
320				80.00	75.73– 83.80	74.40– 84.92	64.00	59.62– 68.20	58.26– 69.48	53.33	49.25– 57.37	47.99– 58.…
330				82.50	78.41– 86.09	77.13– 87.14	66.00	61.66– 70.14	60.32– 71.39	55.00	50.92– 59.02	49.66– 60.…
340				85.00	81.11– 88.35	79.89– 89.32	68.00	63.71– 72.06	62.38– 73.29	56.67	52.59– 60.66	51.34– 61.…
350				87.50	83.85– 90.57	82.70– 91.45	70.00	65.77– 73.98	64.46– 75.18	58.33	54.27– 62.30	53.02– 63.…
360				90.00	86.62– 92.76	85.56– 93.53	72.00	67.84– 75.89	66.55– 77.05	60.00	55.95– 63.94	54.70– 65.…
370				92.50	89.46– 94.88	88.49– 95.54	74.00	69.92– 77.79	68.65– 78.92	61.67	57.64– 65.57	56.40– 66.…
380				95.00	92.37– 96.92	91.53– 97.43	76.00	72.00– 79.67	70.76– 80.77	63.33	59.33– 67.19	58.10– 68.3…
390				97.50	95.43– 98.80	94.77– 99.11	78.00	74.10– 81.55	72.89– 82.60	65.00	61.03– 68.81	59.80– 69.9…
400				*100.00*	*99.08–100.00*	*98.68–100.00*	80.00	76.22– 83.41	75.03– 84.42	66.67	62.73– 70.42	61.51– 71.5…
410							82.00	78.34– 85.26	77.20– 86.23	68.33	64.44– 72.03	63.23– 73.…
420							84.00	80.48– 87.10	79.38– 88.01	70.00	66.16– 73.64	64.96– 74.…
430							86.00	82.64– 88.92	81.58– 89.77	71.67	67.87– 75.24	66.69– 76.…
440							88.00	84.82– 90.71	83.82– 91.50	73.33	69.60– 76.83	68.44– 77.…
450							90.00	87.02– 92.48	86.08– 93.19	75.00	71.33– 78.41	70.19– 79.…
460							92.00	89.26– 94.22	88.39– 94.85	76.67	73.07– 79.99	71.95– 80…
470							94.00	91.54– 95.92	90.75– 96.44	78.33	74.81– 81.56	73.72– 82…
480							96.00	93.88– 97.54	93.20– 97.95	80.00	76.57– 83.13	75.49– 84…
490							98.00	96.34– 99.04	95.80– 99.29	81.67	78.33– 84.68	77.29– 8…
500							*100.00*	*99.26–100.00*	*98.95–100.00*	83.33	80.10– 86.22	79.09– 8…
510										85.00	81.88– 87.76	80.91– 8…
520										86.67	83.68– 89.28	82.74– 9…
530										88.33	85.49– 90.79	84.59– 9…
540										90.00	87.31– 92.28	86.46– 92…
550										91.67	89.16– 93.75	88.36– 9…

Confidence Limits for p* $N = 700-1000$

N = number of tries, x = number of successes, etc., $100\,p_{\bar{x}} = 100\,x/N$

Values in *italics* are exact, all others have been calculated from FREEMAN and TUKEY's approximation. For interpolation see page 185.

x	N = 700: $100\,p_x$	N = 700: 95% $100\,p_l$–$100\,p_r$	N = 700: 99% $100\,p_l$–$100\,p_r$	N = 800: $100\,p_x$	N = 800: 95% $100\,p_l$–$100\,p_r$	N = 800: 99% $100\,p_l$–$100\,p_r$	N = 900: $100\,p_x$	N = 900: 95% $100\,p_l$–$100\,p_r$	N = 900: 99% $100\,p_l$–$100\,p_r$	N = 1000: $100\,p_x$	N = 1000: 95% $100\,p_l$–$100\,p_r$	N = 1000: 99% $100\,p_l$–$100\,p_r$
0	*0.00*	*0.00– 0.53*	*0.00– 0.75*	*0.00*	*0.00– 0.46*	*0.00– 0.66*	*0.00*	*0.00– 0.41*	*0.00– 0.59*	*0.00*	*0.00– 0.37*	*0.00– 0.53*
1	*0.14*	*0.00– 0.79*	*0.00– 1.06*	*0.13*	*0.00– 0.69*	*0.00– 0.93*	*0.11*	*0.00– 0.62*	*0.00– 0.82*	*0.10*	*0.00– 0.56*	*0.00– 0.74*
2	*0.29*	*0.03– 1.03*	*0.01– 1.32*	*0.25*	*0.03– 0.90*	*0.01– 1.15*	*0.22*	*0.03– 0.80*	*0.01– 1.03*	*0.20*	*0.02– 0.72*	*0.01– 0.92*
3	*0.43*	*0.09– 1.25*	*0.05– 1.56*	*0.38*	*0.08– 1.09*	*0.04– 1.37*	*0.33*	*0.07– 0.97*	*0.04– 1.21*	*0.30*	*0.06– 0.87*	*0.03– 1.09*
4	*0.57*	*0.16– 1.46*	*0.10– 1.79*	*0.50*	*0.14– 1.28*	*0.08– 1.57*	*0.44*	*0.12– 1.13*	*0.07– 1.39*	*0.40*	*0.11– 1.02*	*0.07– 1.25*
5	0.71	0.23– 1.67	0.13– 1.98	0.63	0.20– 1.46	0.11– 1.74	0.56	0.18– 1.30	0.10– 1.54	*0.50*	0.16– 1.17	0.09– 1.39
6	0.86	0.31– 1.87	0.19– 2.20	0.75	0.27– 1.64	0.17– 1.92	0.67	0.24– 1.45	0.15– 1.71	*0.60*	0.22– 1.31	0.14– 1.54
7	1.00	0.40– 2.06	0.26– 2.40	0.88	0.35– 1.80	0.23– 2.11	0.78	0.31– 1.60	0.21– 1.87	*0.70*	0.28– 1.44	0.18– 1.69
8	1.14	0.49– 2.25	0.34– 2.61	1.00	0.43– 1.97	0.30– 2.28	0.89	0.38– 1.75	0.26– 2.03	*0.80*	0.34– 1.58	0.24– 1.83
9	1.29	0.59– 2.44	0.42– 2.81	1.13	0.51– 2.13	0.37– 2.46	1.00	0.45– 1.90	0.33– 2.19	*0.90*	0.41– 1.71	0.29– 1.97
10	1.43	0.68– 2.62	0.50– 3.01	1.25	0.60– 2.30	0.44– 2.63	1.11	0.53– 2.04	0.39– 2.34	1.00	0.48– 1.84	0.35– 2.11
11	1.57	0.78– 2.80	0.59– 3.20	1.38	0.68– 2.46	0.52– 2.80	1.22	0.61– 2.18	0.46– 2.49	1.10	0.55– 1.97	0.41– 2.25
12	1.71	0.89– 2.98	0.68– 3.39	1.50	0.77– 2.61	0.60– 2.97	1.33	0.69– 2.32	0.53– 2.64	1.20	0.62– 2.09	0.48– 2.38
13	1.86	0.99– 3.16	0.77– 3.58	1.63	0.87– 2.77	0.68– 3.14	1.44	0.77– 2.46	0.60– 2.79	1.30	0.69– 2.22	0.54– 2.51
14	2.00	1.09– 3.34	0.87– 3.77	1.75	0.96– 2.93	0.76– 3.30	1.56	0.85– 2.60	0.67– 2.94	1.40	0.77– 2.34	0.60– 2.65
15	2.14	1.20– 3.52	0.96– 3.96	1.88	1.05– 3.08	0.84– 3.47	1.67	0.93– 2.74	0.75– 3.09	1.50	0.84– 2.47	0.67– 2.78
16	2.29	1.31– 3.69	1.06– 4.15	2.00	1.14– 3.23	0.92– 3.63	1.78	1.02– 2.88	0.82– 3.23	1.60	0.92– 2.59	0.74– 2.91
17	2.43	1.42– 3.87	1.16– 4.33	2.13	1.24– 3.39	1.01– 3.79	1.89	1.10– 3.01	0.90– 3.37	1.70	0.99– 2.71	0.81– 3.04
18	2.57	1.53– 4.04	1.26– 4.51	2.25	1.34– 3.54	1.10– 3.95	2.00	1.19– 3.15	0.98– 3.52	1.80	1.07– 2.84	0.88– 3.17
19	2.71	1.64– 4.21	1.36– 4.69	2.38	1.43– 3.69	1.19– 4.11	2.11	1.27– 3.28	1.05– 3.66	1.90	1.15– 2.96	0.95– 3.30
20	2.86	1.75– 4.39	1.46– 4.87	2.50	1.53– 3.84	1.28– 4.27	2.22	1.36– 3.42	1.13– 3.80	2.00	1.22– 3.08	1.02– 3.42
21	3.00	1.86– 4.56	1.56– 5.05	2.63	1.63– 3.99	1.37– 4.43	2.33	1.45– 3.55	1.21– 3.94	2.10	1.30– 3.20	1.09– 3.55
22	3.14	1.98– 4.73	1.67– 5.23	2.75	1.73– 4.14	1.46– 4.58	2.44	1.54– 3.68	1.29– 4.08	2.20	1.38– 3.32	1.16– 3.67
23	3.29	2.09– 4.90	1.77– 5.41	2.88	1.83– 4.29	1.55– 4.74	2.56	1.63– 3.82	1.38– 4.22	2.30	1.46– 3.44	1.24– 3.80
24	3.43	2.21– 5.07	1.88– 5.59	3.00	1.93– 4.44	1.64– 4.90	2.67	1.71– 3.95	1.46– 4.36	2.40	1.54– 3.55	1.31– 3.92
25	3.57	2.32– 5.23	1.99– 5.76	3.13	2.03– 4.58	1.74– 5.05	2.78	1.80– 4.08	1.54– 4.49	2.50	1.62– 3.67	1.39– 4.05
26	3.71	2.44– 5.40	2.09– 5.94	3.25	2.13– 4.73	1.83– 5.20	2.89	1.89– 4.21	1.62– 4.63	2.60	1.70– 3.79	1.46– 4.17
27	3.86	2.56– 5.57	2.20– 6.11	3.38	2.23– 4.88	1.92– 5.36	3.00	1.99– 4.34	1.71– 4.77	2.70	1.79– 3.91	1.54– 4.29
28	4.00	2.67– 5.74	2.31– 6.29	3.50	2.34– 5.02	2.02– 5.51	3.11	2.08– 4.47	1.79– 4.90	2.80	1.87– 4.03	1.61– 4.42
29	4.14	2.79– 5.90	2.42– 6.46	3.63	2.44– 5.17	2.12– 5.66	3.22	2.17– 4.60	1.88– 5.04	2.90	1.95– 4.14	1.69– 4.54
30	4.29	2.91– 6.07	2.53– 6.64	3.75	2.54– 5.32	2.21– 5.81	3.33	2.26– 4.73	1.96– 5.17	3.00	2.03– 4.26	1.77– 4.66
31	4.43	3.03– 6.23	2.64– 6.81	3.88	2.65– 5.46	2.31– 5.97	3.44	2.35– 4.86	2.05– 5.31	3.10	2.12– 4.38	1.84– 4.78
32	4.57	3.15– 6.40	2.75– 6.98	4.00	2.75– 5.61	2.41– 6.12	3.56	2.44– 4.99	2.14– 5.44	3.20	2.20– 4.49	1.92– 4.90
33	4.71	3.27– 6.56	2.87– 7.15	4.13	2.86– 5.75	2.50– 6.27	3.67	2.54– 5.12	2.22– 5.58	3.30	2.28– 4.61	2.00– 5.02
34	4.86	3.39– 6.73	2.98– 7.32	4.25	2.96– 5.89	2.60– 6.42	3.78	2.63– 5.24	2.31– 5.71	3.40	2.37– 4.72	2.08– 5.14
35	5.00	3.51– 6.89	3.09– 7.49	4.38	3.07– 6.04	2.70– 6.57	3.89	2.72– 5.37	2.40– 5.84	3.50	2.45– 4.84	2.16– 5.26
36	5.14	3.63– 7.05	3.21– 7.66	4.50	3.17– 6.18	2.80– 6.72	4.00	2.82– 5.50	2.49– 5.98	3.60	2.53– 4.95	2.24– 5.38
37	5.29	3.75– 7.22	3.32– 7.83	4.63	3.28– 6.32	2.90– 6.86	4.11	2.91– 5.63	2.58– 6.11	3.70	2.62– 5.07	2.32– 5.50
38	5.43	3.87– 7.38	3.43– 8.00	4.75	3.38– 6.47	3.00– 7.01	4.22	3.00– 5.75	2.66– 6.24	3.80	2.70– 5.18	2.40– 5.62
39	5.57	3.99– 7.54	3.55– 8.17	4.88	3.49– 6.61	3.10– 7.16	4.33	3.10– 5.88	2.75– 6.37	3.90	2.79– 5.30	2.48– 5.74
40	5.71	4.11– 7.71	3.66– 8.34	5.00	3.60– 6.75	3.20– 7.31	4.44	3.19– 6.01	2.84– 6.50	4.00	2.87– 5.41	2.56– 5.86
41	5.86	4.24– 7.87	3.78– 8.51	5.13	3.70– 6.89	3.30– 7.46	4.56	3.29– 6.13	2.93– 6.64	4.10	2.96– 5.53	2.64– 5.98
42	6.00	4.36– 8.03	3.90– 8.67	5.25	3.81– 7.04	3.40– 7.60	4.67	3.38– 6.26	3.02– 6.77	4.20	3.04– 5.64	2.72– 6.10
43	6.14	4.48– 8.19	4.01– 8.84	5.38	3.92– 7.18	3.51– 7.75	4.78	3.48– 6.39	3.11– 6.90	4.30	3.13– 5.75	2.80– 6.21
44	6.29	4.60– 8.35	4.13– 9.01	5.50	4.02– 7.32	3.61– 7.90	4.89	3.57– 6.51	3.20– 7.03	4.40	3.21– 5.87	2.88– 6.33
45	6.43	4.73– 8.51	4.25– 9.17	5.63	4.13– 7.46	3.71– 8.04	5.00	3.67– 6.64	3.29– 7.16	4.50	3.30– 5.98	2.96– 6.45
46	6.57	4.85– 8.67	4.36– 9.34	5.75	4.24– 7.60	3.81– 8.19	5.11	3.77– 6.76	3.39– 7.29	4.60	3.39– 6.09	3.04– 6.57
47	6.71	4.98– 8.83	4.48– 9.51	5.88	4.35– 7.74	3.92– 8.33	5.22	3.86– 6.89	3.48– 7.42	4.70	3.47– 6.20	3.13– 6.68
48	6.86	5.10– 8.99	4.60– 9.67	6.00	4.46– 7.88	4.02– 8.48	5.33	3.96– 7.01	3.57– 7.55	4.80	3.56– 6.32	3.21– 6.80
49	7.00	5.22– 9.15	4.72– 9.84	6.13	4.57– 8.02	4.12– 8.62	5.44	4.05– 7.14	3.66– 7.68	4.90	3.65– 6.43	3.29– 6.92
50	7.14	5.35– 9.31	4.84–10.00	6.25	4.67– 8.16	4.23– 8.77	5.56	4.15– 7.26	3.75– 7.80	5.00	3.73– 6.54	3.37– 7.03
60	8.57	6.61–10.90	6.04–11.64	7.50	5.77– 9.55	5.28–10.20	6.67	5.13– 8.50	4.68– 9.08	6.00	4.61– 7.66	4.21– 8.19
70	10.00	7.88–12.47	7.27–13.25	8.75	6.89–10.93	6.34–11.62	7.78	6.11– 9.73	5.63–10.35	7.00	5.50– 8.76	5.06– 9.32
80	11.43	9.17–14.03	8.51–14.84	10.00	8.01–12.29	7.43–13.02	8.89	7.11–10.94	6.59–11.59	8.00	6.40– 9.86	5.93–10.45
90	12.86	10.47–15.57	9.77–16.42	11.25	9.15–13.65	8.53–14.41	10.00	8.12–12.15	7.57–12.83	9.00	7.30–10.95	6.80–11.57
100	14.29	11.78–17.10	11.04–17.99	12.50	10.29–15.00	9.64–15.78	11.11	9.13–13.35	8.55–14.06	10.00	8.21–12.03	7.69–12.67
110	15.71	13.10–18.63	12.32–19.54	13.75	11.44–16.34	10.76–17.15	12.22	10.15–14.54	9.54–15.28	11.00	9.13–13.11	8.58–13.77
120	17.14	14.43–20.15	13.62–21.09	15.00	12.60–17.67	11.89–18.51	13.33	11.18–15.73	10.54–16.49	12.00	10.05–14.18	9.47–14.87
130	18.57	15.76–21.66	14.92–22.62	16.25	13.76–19.00	13.02–19.86	14.44	12.21–16.92	11.55–17.69	13.00	10.98–15.25	10.38–15.95
140	20.00	17.10–23.16	16.23–24.15	17.50	14.93–20.32	14.16–21.20	15.56	13.25–18.09	12.56–18.89	14.00	11.91–16.31	11.29–17.03
150	21.43	18.45–24.66	17.55–25.67	18.75	16.11–21.63	15.31–22.54	16.67	14.29–19.27	13.58–20.08	15.00	12.84–17.37	12.20–18.11
160	22.86	19.80–26.15	18.88–27.18	20.00	17.28–22.95	16.47–23.87	17.78	15.34–20.44	14.60–21.27	16.00	13.78–18.42	13.12–19.18
170	24.29	21.16–27.64	20.21–28.69	21.25	18.47–24.25	17.63–25.19	18.89	16.38–21.60	15.63–22.46	17.00	14.72–19.48	14.04–20.25
180	25.71	22.52–29.12	21.55–30.19	22.50	19.65–25.56	18.80–26.51	20.00	17.44–22.77	16.66–23.63	18.00	15.67–20.53	14.97–21.32
190	27.14	23.88–30.60	22.90–31.68	23.75	20.84–26.86	19.97–27.83	21.11	18.49–23.93	17.70–24.81	19.00	16.61–21.57	15.90–22.38
200	28.57	25.25–32.08	24.25–33.17	25.00	22.04–28.15	21.14–29.14	22.22	19.55–25.08	18.74–25.98	20.00	17.56–22.64	16.83–23.44
210	30.00	26.63–33.55	25.61–34.65	26.25	23.23–29.45	22.32–30.44	23.33	20.61–26.24	19.79–27.15	21.00	18.52–23.66	17.77–24.49
220	31.43	28.01–35.01	26.97–36.13	27.50	24.44–30.74	23.51–31.75	24.44	21.67–27.39	20.83–28.31	22.00	19.47–24.70	18.71–25.54
230	32.86	29.39–36.48	28.34–37.60	28.75	25.64–32.03	24.70–33.05	25.56	22.74–28.54	21.88–29.47	23.00	20.43–25.74	19.65–26.59
240	34.29	30.78–37.94	29.71–39.07	30.00	26.85–33.31	25.89–34.34	26.67	23.81–29.69	22.94–30.63	24.00	21.39–26.77	20.59–27.64
250	35.71	32.17–39.39	31.09–40.53	31.25	28.05–34.59	27.08–35.63	27.78	24.88–30.83	24.00–31.78	25.00	22.35–27.81	21.54–28.68
260	37.14	33.56–40.84	32.47–41.99	32.50	29.27–35.87	28.28–36.92	28.89	25.95–31.97	25.06–32.93	26.00	23.31–28.84	22.49–29.72
270	38.57	34.96–42.29	33.85–43.44	33.75	30.48–37.15	29.48–38.20	30.00	27.02–33.11	26.12–34.08	27.00	24.27–29.87	23.44–30.76
280	40.00	36.36–43.74	35.24–44.89	35.00	31.70–38.42	30.69–39.48	31.11	28.10–34.25	27.18–35.23	28.00	25.24–30.90	24.40–31.80
290	41.43	37.76–45.18	36.63–46.34	36.25	32.92–39.69	31.90–40.76	32.22	29.18–35.39	28.25–36.37	29.00	26.21–31.92	25.36–32.83
300	42.86	39.16–46.62	38.03–47.78	37.50	34.14–40.96	33.11–42.03	33.33	30.26–36.52	29.32–37.51	30.00	27.18–32.95	26.31–33.87
310	44.29	40.57–48.06	39.43–49.22	38.75	35.36–42.23	34.33–43.30	34.44	31.34–37.65	30.40–38.65	31.00	28.15–33.97	27.28–34.90
320	45.71	41.99–49.49	40.84–50.65	40.00	36.59–43.49	35.55–44.57	35.56	32.43–38.78	31.47–39.79	32.00	29.12–34.99	28.24–35.92
330	47.14	43.40–50.92	42.25–52.08	41.25	37.82–44.75	36.77–45.84	36.67	33.52–39.91	32.55–40.92	33.00	30.09–36.01	29.20–36.95
340	48.57	44.82–52.35	43.66–53.51	42.50	39.05–46.01	37.99–47.10	37.78	34.60–41.04	33.63–42.05	34.00	31.07–37.03	30.17–37.97
350	50.00	46.24–53.76	45.07–54.93	43.75	40.28–47.27	39.22–48.36	38.89	35.69–42.16	34.71–43.18	35.00	32.05–38.05	31.14–39.00
360	51.43	47.65–55.18	46.49–56.34	45.00	41.52–48.52	40.45–49.61	40.00	36.79–43.29	35.80–44.30	36.00	33.02–39.06	32.11–40.02
370	52.86	49.08–56.60	47.92–57.75	46.25	42.76–49.78	41.68–50.87	41.11	37.88–44.41	36.89–45.43	37.00	34.00–40.08	33.09–41.03
380	54.29	50.51–58.01	49.35–59.16	47.50	44.00–51.03	42.92–52.12	42.22	38.97–45.53	37.98–46.55	38.00	34.98–41.09	34.06–42.05
390	55.71	51.94–59.43	50.78–60.57	48.75	45.24–52.28	44.16–53.36	43.33	40.07–46.64	39.07–47.67	39.00	35.97–42.10	35.04–43.07
400	57.14	53.38–60.84	52.22–61.97	50.00	46.49–53.51	45.39–54.61	44.44	41.17–47.76	40.16–48.79	40.00	36.95–43.11	36.01–44.08
410	58.57	54.82–62.24	53.66–63.37	51.25	47.72–54.76	46.64–55.84	45.56	42.27–48.88	41.26–49.90	41.00	37.94–44.12	36.99–45.09
420	60.00	56.26–63.64	55.11–64.76	52.50	48.97–56.00	47.88–57.08	46.67	43.37–49.99	42.36–51.02	42.00	38.92–45.13	37.98–46.10
430	61.43	57.71–65.04	56.56–66.15	53.75	50.22–57.24	49.13–58.32	47.78	44.48–51.10	43.46–52.13	43.00	39.91–46.14	38.96–47.11
440	62.86	59.16–66.44	58.01–67.53	55.00	51.48–58.48	50.39–59.55	48.89	45.58–52.21	44.56–53.24	44.00	40.90–47.14	39.95–48.11
450	64.29	60.61–67.83	59.47–68.91	56.25	52.73–59.72	51.64–60.78	50.00	46.69–53.31	45.66–54.34	45.00	41.89–48.15	40.93–49.12
460	65.71	62.06–69.22	60.93–70.29	57.50	53.99–60.95	52.90–62.01	51.11	47.79–54.42	46.76–55.44	46.00	42.88–49.15	41.92–50.12
470	67.14	63.52–70.61	62.40–71.66	58.75	55.25–62.18	54.16–63.23	52.22	48.90–55.52	47.87–56.54	47.00	43.87–50.15	42.91–51.12
480	68.57	64.99–71.99	63.87–73.03	60.00	56.51–63.41	55.43–64.45	53.33	50.01–56.63	48.98–57.64	48.00	44.87–51.15	43.90–52.12
490	70.00	66.45–73.37	65.35–74.39	61.25	57.77–64.64	56.70–65.67	54.44	51.12–57.73	50.10–58.74	49.00	45.86–52.15	44.90–53.12
500	71.43	67.92–74.75	66.83–75.75	62.50	59.04–65.86	57.97–66.89	55.56	52.24–58.83	51.21–59.84	50.00	46.85–53.15	45.88–54.12
510	72.86	69.40–76.12	68.32–77.10	63.75	60.31–67.08	59.24–68.10	56.67	53.36–59.93	52.33–60.93	51.00	47.85–54.14	46.88–55.10
520	74.29	70.88–77.48	69.81–78.45	65.00	61.58–68.30	60.52–69.31	57.78	54.47–61.03	53.45–62.02	52.00	48.85–55.13	47.88–56.10
530	75.71	72.36–78.84	71.31–79.79	66.25	62.85–69.52	61.80–70.52	58.89	55.59–62.12	54.57–63.11	53.00	49.85–56.13	48.88–57.09
540	77.14	73.85–80.20	72.82–81.12	67.50	64.13–70.73	63.08–71.72	60.00	56.71–63.21	55.70–64.20	54.00	50.85–57.12	49.88–58.08
550	78.57	75.34–81.55	74.33–82.45	68.75	65.41–71.95	64.37–72.92	61.11	57.84–64.31	56.82–65.29	55.00	51.85–58.11	50.88–59.07

Confidence Limits for Np* (sign test, etc.)

N = number of trials

Confidence limits for binomial distributions: Prob $[x_l < N\mathbf{p} < x_r] \geqq 1 - 2\alpha$; for quantiles of continuous distributions: Prob $[(x_l + 1) < N\mathbf{p} < x_r] \geqq 1 - 2\alpha$

The lack of a significant limit on one side is indicated by a period, on both sides by a single dash

$\mathbf{p}$ =	0.05		0.10		0.15		0.20		0.25		0.30		0.35		0.40		0.45		0.50	
2α =	0.05	0.01	0.05	0.01	0.05	0.01	0.05	0.01	0.05	0.01	0.05	0.01	0.05	0.01	0.05	0.01	0.05	0.01	0.05	0.01
N	$x_l\ x_r$	$x_l\ x_r$	$x_l\ x_r$	$x_l\ x_r$	$x_l\ x_r$	$x_l\ x_r$	$x_l\ x_r$	$x_l\ x_r$	$x_l\ x_r$	$x_l\ x_r$	$x_l\ x_r$	$x_l\ x_r$	$x_l\ x_r$	$x_l\ x_r$	$x_l\ x_r$	$x_l\ x_r$	$x_l\ x_r$	$x_l\ x_r$	$x_l\ x_r$	$x_l\ x_r$
5	•– 2	•– 3	•– 3	•– 4	•– 4	•– 4	•– 4	•– 5	•– 4	•– 5	•– 5	•– 5	•– 5	—	•– 5	—	•– 5	—	—	—
6	•– 3	•– 3	•– 3	•– 4	•– 4	•– 5	•– 4	•– 5	•– 5	•– 5	•– 5	•– 6	•– 5	•– 6	•– 6	•– 6	•– 6	—	0– 6	—
7	•– 3	•– 3	•– 4	•– 4	•– 4	•– 5	•– 5	•– 5	•– 5	•– 6	•– 6	•– 6	•– 6	•– 7	•– 6	•– 7	0– 7	•– 7	0– 7	—
8	•– 3	•– 4	•– 4	•– 5	•– 4	•– 5	•– 5	•– 6	•– 6	•– 6	•– 6	•– 7	•– 7	•– 7	0– 7	•– 8	0– 7	•– 8	0– 8	0– 8
9	•– 3	•– 4	•– 4	•– 5	•– 5	•– 6	•– 5	•– 6	•– 6	•– 7	•– 7	•– 7	0– 7	•– 8	0– 8	•– 8	0– 8	0– 9	1– 8	0– 9
10	•– 3	•– 4	•– 4	•– 5	•– 5	•– 6	•– 6	•– 7	•– 6	•– 7	•– 7	•– 8	0– 8	•– 8	0– 8	•– 9	1– 9	0– 9	1– 9	0–10
11	•– 3	•– 4	•– 4	•– 5	•– 5	•– 6	•– 6	•– 7	•– 7	•– 8	0– 7	•– 8	0– 8	•– 9	0– 9	0–10	1– 9	0–10	1–10	0–11
12	•– 3	•– 4	•– 5	•– 5	•– 5	•– 6	•– 6	•– 7	•– 7	•– 8	0– 8	•– 9	0– 9	•–10	1– 9	0–10	1–10	0–11	2–10	1–11
13	•– 3	•– 4	•– 5	•– 6	•– 6	•– 7	•– 7	•– 8	0– 7	•– 9	0– 8	•– 9	0– 9	0–10	1–10	0–11	1–10	1–11	2–11	1–12
14	•– 4	•– 4	•– 5	•– 6	•– 6	•– 7	•– 7	•– 8	0– 8	•– 9	0– 9	•–10	1– 9	0–11	1–10	0–11	2–11	1–12	2–12	1–13
15	•– 4	•– 5	•– 5	•– 6	•– 6	•– 7	•– 7	•– 8	0– 8	•– 9	0– 9	0–10	1–10	0–11	1–11	0–12	2–12	1–13	3–12	2–13
16	•– 4	•– 5	•– 5	•– 6	•– 6	•– 8	•– 8	•– 9	0– 9	•–10	0–10	0–11	1–10	0–12	2–11	1–12	2–12	1–13	3–13	2–14
17	•– 4	•– 5	•– 5	•– 6	•– 7	•– 8	0– 8	•– 9	0– 9	•–10	1–10	0–11	1–11	0–12	2–12	1–13	3–13	2–14	4–13	2–15
18	•– 4	•– 5	•– 6	•– 7	•– 7	•– 8	0– 8	•– 9	0– 9	•–11	1–10	0–12	2–11	1–13	2–12	1–14	3–13	2–14	4–14	3–15
19	•– 4	•– 5	•– 6	•– 7	•– 7	•– 8	0– 8	•–10	0–10	0–11	1–11	0–12	2–12	1–13	3–13	1–14	3–14	2–15	4–15	3–16
20	•– 4	•– 5	•– 6	•– 7	•– 7	•– 9	0– 9	•–10	1–10	0–11	1–11	0–13	2–12	1–14	3–13	2–15	4–14	3–16	5–15	3–17
21	•– 4	•– 5	•– 6	•– 7	•– 8	•– 9	0– 9	•–10	1–10	0–12	1–12	0–13	2–13	1–14	3–14	2–15	4–15	3–16	5–16	4–17
22	•– 4	•– 5	•– 6	•– 7	•– 8	•– 9	0– 9	•–11	1–11	0–12	2–12	1–13	3–13	1–15	3–14	2–16	4–15	3–17	5–17	4–18
23	•– 5	•– 5	•– 6	•– 8	0– 8	•– 9	0–10	•–11	1–11	0–12	2–12	1–14	3–14	2–15	4–15	2–16	5–16	3–17	6–17	4–19
24	•– 5	•– 6	•– 7	•– 8	0– 8	•–10	0–10	0–11	1–11	0–13	2–13	1–14	3–14	2–16	4–15	3–17	5–17	4–18	6–18	5–19
25	•– 5	•– 6	•– 7	•– 8	0– 9	•–10	0–10	0–12	1–12	0–13	2–13	1–15	3–15	2–16	4–16	3–17	5–17	4–19	7–18	5–20
26	•– 5	•– 6	•– 7	•– 8	0– 9	•–10	1–10	0–12	1–12	0–14	2–14	1–15	4–15	2–17	5–16	3–18	6–18	4–19	7–19	6–20
27	•– 5	•– 6	•– 7	•– 8	0– 9	•–10	1–11	0–12	2–12	1–14	3–14	1–15	4–15	2–17	5–17	4–18	6–18	5–20	7–20	6–21
28	•– 5	•– 6	•– 7	•– 8	0– 9	•–11	1–11	0–12	2–13	1–14	3–14	2–16	4–16	3–17	5–17	4–19	7–19	5–20	8–20	6–22
29	•– 5	•– 6	•– 7	•– 9	0– 9	•–11	1–11	0–13	2–13	1–15	3–15	2–16	4–16	3–18	6–18	4–19	7–19	5–21	8–21	7–22
30	•– 5	•– 6	•– 8	•– 9	0–10	•–11	1–12	0–13	2–13	1–15	3–15	2–17	5–17	3–18	6–18	4–20	7–20	6–22	9–21	7–23
31	•– 5	•– 6	•– 8	•– 9	0–10	•–11	1–12	0–13	2–14	1–15	4–15	2–17	5–17	3–19	6–19	5–21	8–20	6–22	9–22	7–24
32	•– 5	•– 6	•– 8	•– 9	0–10	•–12	1–12	0–14	2–14	1–16	4–16	2–18	5–18	4–19	7–19	5–21	8–21	6–23	9–23	8–24
33	•– 5	•– 7	•– 8	•– 9	0–10	0–12	1–12	0–14	3–14	1–16	4–16	3–18	5–18	4–20	7–20	5–22	8–21	7–23	10–23	8–25
34	•– 6	•– 7	•– 8	•–10	0–10	0–12	2–13	1–14	3–15	2–16	4–17	3–18	6–18	4–20	7–20	6–22	9–22	7–24	10–24	9–25
35	•– 6	•– 7	•– 8	•–10	1–11	0–12	2–13	1–15	3–15	2–17	4–17	3–19	6–19	4–21	7–21	6–23	9–23	7–24	11–24	9–26
36	•– 6	•– 7	0– 8	•–10	1–11	0–12	2–13	1–15	3–15	2–17	5–17	3–19	6–19	5–21	8–21	6–23	9–23	8–25	11–25	9–27
37	•– 6	•– 7	0– 9	•–10	1–11	0–13	2–13	1–15	3–16	2–17	5–18	3–20	6–20	5–22	8–22	6–24	10–24	8–25	12–25	10–27
38	•– 6	•– 7	0– 9	•–10	1–11	0–13	2–14	1–15	4–16	2–18	5–18	4–20	7–20	5–22	8–22	7–24	10–24	8–26	12–26	10–28
39	•– 6	•– 7	0– 9	•–10	1–11	0–13	2–14	1–16	4–16	2–18	5–18	4–20	7–21	5–23	9–23	7–25	11–25	9–27	12–27	11–28
40	•– 6	•– 7	0– 9	•–11	1–12	0–13	2–14	1–16	4–17	3–18	6–19	4–21	7–21	6–23	9–23	7–25	11–25	9–27	13–27	11–29
41	•– 6	•– 7	0– 9	•–11	1–12	0–14	3–14	1–16	4–17	3–19	6–19	4–21	8–21	6–23	9–24	8–26	11–26	9–28	13–28	11–30
42	•– 6	•– 7	0– 9	•–11	1–12	0–14	3–15	1–17	4–17	3–19	6–20	4–22	8–22	6–24	10–24	8–26	12–26	10–28	14–28	12–30
43	•– 6	•– 8	0– 9	•–11	1–12	0–14	3–15	2–17	4–18	3–19	6–20	5–22	8–22	6–24	10–25	8–27	12–27	10–29	14–29	12–31
44	•– 6	•– 8	0–10	•–11	1–13	0–14	3–15	2–17	5–18	3–20	6–20	5–22	8–23	7–25	10–25	9–27	12–27	10–29	15–29	13–31
45	•– 6	•– 8	0–10	•–11	1–13	0–14	3–15	2–17	5–18	3–20	7–21	5–23	9–23	7–25	11–25	9–28	13–28	11–30	15–30	13–32
46	•– 7	•– 8	0–10	•–11	2–13	0–15	3–16	2–18	5–18	4–20	7–21	5–23	9–24	7–26	11–26	9–28	13–28	11–30	15–31	13–33
47	•– 7	•– 8	0–10	•–12	2–13	1–15	3–16	2–18	5–19	4–21	7–21	5–23	9–24	7–26	11–26	9–29	14–29	12–31	16–31	14–33
48	•– 7	•– 8	0–10	•–12	2–13	1–15	4–16	2–18	5–19	4–21	7–22	6–24	10–24	8–27	12–27	10–29	14–29	12–31	16–32	14–34
49	•– 7	•– 8	0–10	•–12	2–14	1–15	4–17	2–18	6–19	4–21	8–22	6–24	10–25	8–27	12–27	10–30	14–30	12–32	17–32	15–34
50	•– 7	•– 8	0–10	•–12	2–14	1–16	4–17	2–19	6–20	4–22	8–23	6–25	10–25	8–27	12–28	10–30	15–30	13–33	17–33	15–35
51	•– 7	•– 8	0–11	0–12	2–14	1–16	4–17	3–19	6–20	4–22	8–23	6–25	10–26	8–28	13–28	11–31	15–31	13–33	18–33	15–36
52	•– 7	•– 8	0–11	0–12	2–14	1–16	4–17	3–19	6–20	5–22	8–23	7–25	11–26	9–28	13–29	11–31	15–31	13–34	18–34	16–36
53	•– 7	•– 8	0–11	0–13	2–14	1–16	4–18	3–20	6–21	5–23	9–24	7–26	11–26	9–29	13–29	11–31	16–32	14–34	18–35	16–37
54	•– 7	•– 9	1–11	0–13	2–15	1–16	4–18	3–20	7–21	5–23	9–24	7–26	11–27	9–29	14–30	12–32	16–32	14–35	19–35	17–37
55	•– 7	•– 9	1–11	0–13	2–15	1–17	5–18	3–20	7–21	5–23	9–24	7–27	11–27	10–30	14–30	12–32	17–33	14–35	19–36	17–38
56	•– 7	•– 9	1–11	0–13	3–15	1–17	5–18	3–20	7–22	5–24	9–25	7–27	12–28	10–30	14–31	12–33	17–34	15–36	20–36	17–39
57	•– 7	•– 9	1–11	0–13	3–15	1–17	5–19	3–21	7–22	5–24	10–25	8–27	12–28	10–30	15–31	13–33	17–34	15–36	20–37	18–39
58	•– 8	•– 9	1–12	0–13	3–15	1–17	5–19	3–21	7–22	6–24	10–25	8–28	12–29	10–31	15–32	13–34	18–35	16–37	21–37	18–40
59	•– 8	•– 9	1–12	0–13	3–16	2–17	5–19	4–21	8–22	6–25	10–26	8–28	13–29	11–31	15–32	13–34	18–35	16–37	21–38	19–40
60	•– 8	•– 9	1–12	0–14	3–16	2–18	5–19	4–21	8–23	6–25	10–26	8–28	13–29	11–32	16–32	13–35	19–36	16–38	21–39	19–41
61	•– 8	•– 9	1–12	0–14	3–16	2–18	5–20	4–22	8–23	6–25	11–26	9–29	13–30	11–32	16–33	14–35	19–36	17–38	22–39	20–41
62	•– 8	•– 9	1–12	0–14	3–16	2–18	6–20	4–22	8–23	6–26	11–27	9–29	14–30	11–33	16–33	14–36	19–37	17–39	22–40	20–42
63	•– 8	•– 9	1–12	0–14	3–16	2–18	6–20	4–22	8–24	6–26	11–27	9–30	14–31	12–33	17–34	14–36	20–37	17–40	23–40	20–43
64	•– 8	•– 9	1–12	0–14	3–16	2–19	6–20	4–23	8–24	7–26	11–28	9–30	14–31	12–33	17–34	15–37	20–38	18–40	23–41	21–43
65	•– 8	•– 9	1–13	0–14	3–17	2–19	6–21	4–23	9–24	7–27	11–28	9–30	14–31	12–34	17–35	15–37	20–38	18–41	24–41	21–44
66	•– 8	•–10	1–13	0–15	4–17	2–19	6–21	5–23	9–25	7–27	12–28	10–31	15–32	12–34	18–35	15–38	21–39	18–41	24–42	22–44
67	•– 8	•–10	1–13	0–15	4–17	2–19	6–21	5–23	9–25	7–27	12–29	10–31	15–32	13–35	18–36	16–38	21–39	19–42	25–42	22–45
68	•– 8	•–10	1–13	0–15	4–17	2–19	6–21	5–24	9–25	7–28	12–29	10–31	15–33	13–35	18–36	16–39	22–40	19–42	25–43	22–46
69	•– 8	•–10	1–13	0–15	4–17	2–20	7–22	5–24	9–26	8–28	12–29	10–32	16–33	13–36	19–37	16–39	22–40	20–43	25–44	23–46
70	•– 8	•–10	2–13	0–15	4–18	3–20	7–22	5–24	10–26	8–28	13–30	11–32	16–33	14–36	19–37	17–40	22–41	20–43	26–44	23–47
71	•– 9	•–10	2–13	0–15	4–18	3–20	7–22	5–24	10–26	8–29	13–30	11–33	16–34	14–36	19–38	17–40	23–41	20–44	26–45	24–47
72	0– 9	•–10	2–14	1–15	4–18	3–20	7–22	5–25	10–26	8–29	13–30	11–33	16–34	14–37	20–38	17–41	23–42	21–44	27–45	24–48
73	0– 9	•–10	2–14	1–16	4–18	3–20	7–23	5–25	10–27	8–29	13–31	11–33	17–35	14–37	20–38	18–41	24–42	21–45	27–46	25–48
74	0– 9	•–10	2–14	1–16	4–18	3–21	7–23	6–25	10–27	8–29	14–31	12–34	17–35	15–38	20–39	18–42	24–43	21–45	28–46	25–49
75	0– 9	•–10	2–14	1–16	5–19	3–21	8–23	6–25	11–27	9–30	14–31	12–34	17–35	15–38	21–39	18–42	24–43	22–46	28–47	25–50
76	0– 9	•–10	2–14	1–16	5–19	3–21	8–23	6–26	11–28	9–30	14–32	12–34	18–36	15–39	21–40	19–43	25–44	22–46	28–48	26–50
77	0– 9	•–10	2–14	1–16	5–19	3–21	8–24	6–26	11–28	9–30	14–32	12–35	18–36	16–39	21–40	19–43	25–44	23–47	29–48	26–51
78	0– 9	•–11	2–14	1–16	5–19	3–21	8–24	6–26	11–28	9–31	15–32	12–35	18–37	16–39	22–41	19–43	26–45	23–47	29–49	27–51
79	0– 9	•–11	2–14	1–16	5–19	3–22	8–24	6–26	11–28	9–31	15–33	13–35	19–37	16–40	22–41	20–44	26–45	23–48	30–49	27–52
80	0– 9	•–11	2–15	1–17	5–20	4–22	8–24	6–27	12–29	10–31	15–33	13–36	19–37	16–40	23–42	20–44	26–46	24–48	30–50	28–52
81	0– 9	•–11	2–15	1–17	5–20	4–22	8–25	7–27	12–29	10–32	15–34	13–36	19–38	17–41	23–42	20–45	27–46	24–49	31–50	28–53
82	0– 9	•–11	2–15	1–17	5–20	4–22	9–25	7–27	12–29	10–32	16–34	13–37	19–38	17–41	23–43	21–45	27–47	24–50	31–51	28–54
83	0– 9	•–11	2–15	1–17	5–20	4–22	9–25	7–27	12–30	10–32	16–34	14–37	20–39	17–41	24–43	21–46	28–47	25–50	32–51	29–54
84	0– 9	•–11	2–15	1–17	6–20	4–23	9–25	7–28	12–30	10–33	16–35	14–37	20–39	17–42	24–43	21–46	28–48	25–51	32–52	29–55
85	0–10	•–11	3–15	1–17	6–20	4–23	9–25	7–28	13–30	11–33	16–35	14–38	20–39	18–42	24–44	22–47	28–48	26–51	32–53	30–55
86	0–10	•–11	3–15	1–17	6–21	4–23	9–26	7–28	13–31	11–33	17–35	14–38	21–40	18–43	25–44	22–47	29–49	26–52	33–53	30–56
87	0–10	•–11	3–16	1–18	6–21	4–23	9–26	7–28	13–31	11–34	17–36	15–38	21–40	18–43	25–45	22–48	29–49	26–52	33–54	31–56
88	0–10	•–11	3–16	1–18	6–21	4–23	10–26	8–29	13–31	11–34	17–36	15–39	21–41	19–44	25–45	23–48	30–50	27–53	34–54	31–57
89	0–10	•–11	3–16	1–18	6–21	4–24	10–26	8–29	14–31	11–34	17–36	15–39	21–41	19–44	26–46	23–49	30–50	27–53	34–55	31–58
90	0–10	•–12	3–16	2–18	6–21	5–24	10–27	8–29	14–32	11–34	18–37	15–40	22–41	19–44	26–46	23–49	30–51	27–54	35–55	32–58
91	0–10	•–12	3–16	2–18	6–22	5–24	10–27	8–30	14–32	12–35	18–37	15–40	22–42	19–45	26–47	24–50	31–51	28–54	35–56	32–59
92	0–10	•–12	3–16	2–18	6–22	5–24	10–27	8–30	14–32	12–35	18–37	16–40	22–42	20–45	27–47	24–50	31–52	28–55	36–56	33–59
93	0–10	•–12	3–16	2–18	7–22	5–24	10–27	8–30	14–33	12–35	18–38	16–41	23–43	20–46	27–48	24–50	32–52	29–55	36–57	33–60
94	0–10	•–12	3–16	2–19	7–22	5–25	11–28	8–30	15–33	12–36	19–38	16–41	23–43	20–46	27–48	25–51	32–53	29–56	37–57	34–60
95	0–10	•–12	3–17	2–19	7–22	5–25	11–28	9–31	15–33	12–36	19–38	16–41	23–43	21–46	28–48	25–51	32–53	29–56	37–58	34–61
96	0–10	•–12	3–17	2–19	7–23	5–25	11–28	9–31	15–34	13–36	19–39	17–42	24–44	21–47	28–49	25–52	33–54	30–57	37–59	34–62
97	0–10	•–12	3–17	2–19	7–23	5–25	11–28	9–31	15–34	13–37	19–39	17–42	24–44	21–47	28–49	26–52	33–54	30–57	38–59	35–62
98	0–11	•–12	3–17	2–19	7–23	5–25	11–29	9–31	15–34	13–37	20–39	17–42	24–45	21–48	29–50	26–53	34–55	31–58	38–60	35–63
99	0–11	•–12	3–17	2–19	7–23	5–26	11–29	9–32	16–34	13–37	20–40	17–43	25–45	22–48	29–50	26–53	34–55	31–58	39–60	36–63
100	0–11	•–12	4–17	2–19	7–23	6–26	11–29	9–32	16–35	13–38	20–40	18–43	25–45	22–49	30–51	27–54	34–56	31–59	39–61	36–64

Confidence Limits for Np ($p = 0.5$, $N = 6-500$)* (sign test, etc.)

N = Number of trials. See also page 104

N	$2\alpha = 0.05$ x_l x_r	$2\alpha = 0.01$ x_l x_r	N	$2\alpha = 0.05$ x_l x_r	$2\alpha = 0.01$ x_l x_r	N	$2\alpha = 0.05$ x_l x_r	$2\alpha = 0.01$ x_l x_r	N	$2\alpha = 0.05$ x_l x_r	$2\alpha = 0.01$ x_l x_r	N	$2\alpha = 0.05$ x_l x_r	$2\alpha = 0.01$ x_l x_r
0	–	–	100	39-61	36-64	200	85-115	81-119	300	132-168	127-173	400	179-221	173-227
1	–	–	101	40-61	37-64	201	86-115	81-120	301	132-169	127-174	401	180-221	174-227
2	–	–	102	40-62	37-65	202	86-116	82-120	302	133-169	128-174	402	180-222	174-228
3	–	–	103	41-62	37-66	203	87-116	82-121	303	133-170	128-175	403	181-222	175-228
4	–	–	104	41-63	38-66	204	87-117	83-121	304	134-170	129-175	404	181-223	175-229
5	–	–	105	41-64	38-67	205	87-118	83-122	305	134-171	129-176	405	182-223	176-229
6	0-6	–	106	42-64	39-67	206	88-118	84-122	306	135-171	129-177	406	182-224	176-230
7	0-7	–	107	42-65	39-68	207	88-119	84-123	307	135-172	130-177	407	183-224	177-230
8	0-8	0-8	108	43-65	40-68	208	89-119	84-124	308	136-172	130-178	408	183-225	177-231
9	1-8	0-9	109	43-66	40-69	209	89-120	85-124	309	136-173	131-178	409	184-225	177-232
10	1-9	0-10	110	44-66	41-69	210	90-120	85-125	310	137-173	131-179	410	184-226	178-232
11	1-10	0-11	111	44-67	41-70	211	90-121	86-125	311	137-174	132-179	411	185-226	178-233
12	2-10	1-11	112	45-67	42-71	212	91-121	86-126	312	138-174	132-180	412	185-227	179-233
13	2-11	1-12	113	45-68	42-71	213	91-122	87-126	313	138-175	133-180	413	186-227	179-234
14	2-12	1-13	114	46-68	43-72	214	92-122	87-127	314	139-175	133-181	414	186-228	180-234
15	3-12	2-13	115	46-69	43-72	215	92-123	88-127	315	139-176	134-181	415	187-228	180-235
16	3-13	2-14	116	46-70	43-73	216	93-123	88-128	316	140-176	134-182	416	187-229	181-235
17	4-13	2-15	117	47-70	44-73	217	93-124	89-128	317	140-177	135-182	417	187-230	181-236
18	4-14	3-15	118	47-71	44-74	218	94-124	89-129	318	141-177	135-183	418	188-230	182-236
19	4-15	3-16	119	48-71	45-75	219	94-125	89-130	319	141-178	135-184	419	188-231	182-237
20	5-15	3-17	120	48-72	45-75	220	94-126	90-130	320	141-179	136-184	420	189-231	183-237
21	5-16	4-17	121	49-72	45-76	221	95-126	90-131	321	142-179	136-185	421	189-232	183-238
22	5-17	4-18	122	49-73	46-76	222	95-127	91-131	322	142-180	137-185	422	190-232	184-238
23	6-17	4-19	123	50-73	46-77	223	96-127	91-132	323	143-180	137-186	423	190-233	184-239
24	6-18	5-19	124	50-74	47-77	224	96-128	92-132	324	143-181	138-186	424	191-233	184-240
25	7-18	5-20	125	51-74	47-78	225	97-128	92-133	325	144-181	138-187	425	191-234	185-240
26	7-19	6-20	126	51-75	48-78	226	97-129	93-133	326	144-182	139-187	426	192-234	185-241
27	7-20	6-21	127	51-76	48-79	227	98-129	93-134	327	145-182	139-188	427	192-235	186-241
28	8-20	6-22	128	52-76	48-80	228	98-130	94-134	328	145-183	140-188	428	193-235	186-242
29	8-21	7-22	129	52-77	49-80	229	99-130	94-135	329	146-183	140-189	429	193-236	187-242
30	9-21	7-23	130	53-77	49-81	230	99-131	94-136	330	146-184	141-189	430	194-236	187-243
31	9-22	7-24	131	53-78	50-81	231	100-131	95-136	331	147-184	141-190	431	194-237	188-243
32	9-23	8-24	132	54-78	50-82	232	100-132	95-137	332	147-185	142-190	432	195-237	188-244
33	10-23	8-25	133	54-79	51-82	233	101-132	96-137	333	148-185	142-191	433	195-238	189-244
34	10-24	9-25	134	55-79	51-83	234	101-133	96-138	334	148-186	142-192	434	196-238	189-245
35	11-24	9-26	135	55-80	52-83	235	101-134	97-138	335	149-186	143-192	435	196-239	190-245
36	11-25	9-27	136	56-80	52-84	236	102-134	97-139	336	149-187	143-193	436	197-239	190-246
37	12-25	10-27	137	56-81	52-85	237	102-135	98-139	337	150-187	144-193	437	197-240	191-246
38	12-26	10-28	138	56-82	53-85	238	103-135	98-140	338	150-188	144-194	438	197-241	191-247
39	12-27	11-28	139	57-82	53-86	239	103-136	99-140	339	150-189	145-194	439	198-241	192-247
40	13-27	11-29	140	57-83	54-86	240	104-136	99-141	340	151-189	145-195	440	198-242	192-248
41	13-28	11-30	141	58-83	54-87	241	104-137	100-141	341	151-190	146-195	441	199-242	192-249
42	14-28	12-30	142	58-84	55-87	242	105-137	100-142	342	152-190	146-196	442	199-243	193-249
43	14-29	12-31	143	59-84	55-88	243	105-138	100-143	343	152-191	147-196	443	200-243	193-250
44	15-29	13-31	144	59-85	56-88	244	106-138	101-143	344	153-191	147-197	444	200-244	194-250
45	15-30	13-32	145	60-85	56-89	245	106-139	101-144	345	153-192	148-197	445	201-244	194-251
46	15-31	13-33	146	60-86	56-90	246	107-139	102-144	346	154-192	148-198	446	201-245	195-251
47	16-31	14-33	147	61-86	57-90	247	107-140	102-145	347	154-193	149-198	447	202-245	195-252
48	16-32	14-34	148	61-87	57-91	248	108-140	103-145	348	155-193	149-199	448	202-246	196-252
49	17-32	15-34	149	62-87	58-91	249	108-141	103-146	349	155-194	149-200	449	203-246	196-253
50	17-33	15-35	150	62-88	58-92	250	109-141	104-146	350	156-194	150-200	450	203-247	197-253
51	18-33	15-36	151	62-89	59-92	251	109-142	104-147	351	156-195	150-201	451	204-247	197-254
52	18-34	16-36	152	63-89	59-93	252	109-143	105-147	352	157-195	151-201	452	204-248	198-254
53	18-35	16-37	153	63-90	60-93	253	110-143	105-148	353	157-196	151-202	453	205-248	198-255
54	19-35	17-37	154	64-90	60-94	254	110-144	105-149	354	158-196	152-202	454	205-249	199-255
55	19-36	17-38	155	64-91	60-95	255	111-144	106-149	355	158-197	152-203	455	206-249	199-256
56	20-36	17-39	156	65-91	61-95	256	111-145	106-150	356	159-197	153-203	456	206-250	199-257
57	20-37	18-39	157	65-92	61-96	257	112-145	107-150	357	159-198	153-204	457	207-250	200-257
58	21-37	18-40	158	66-92	62-96	258	112-146	107-151	358	159-199	154-204	458	207-251	200-258
59	21-38	19-40	159	66-93	62-97	259	113-146	108-151	359	160-199	154-205	459	208-251	201-258
60	21-39	19-41	160	67-93	63-97	260	113-147	108-152	360	160-200	155-205	460	208-252	201-259
61	22-39	20-41	161	67-94	63-98	261	114-147	109-152	361	161-200	155-206	461	208-253	202-259
62	22-40	20-42	162	68-94	64-98	262	114-148	109-153	362	161-201	155-207	462	209-253	202-260
63	23-40	20-43	163	68-95	64-99	263	115-148	110-153	363	162-201	156-207	463	209-254	203-260
64	23-41	21-43	164	68-96	65-99	264	115-149	110-154	364	162-202	156-208	464	210-254	203-261
65	24-41	21-44	165	69-96	65-100	265	116-149	111-154	365	163-202	157-208	465	210-255	204-261
66	24-42	22-44	166	69-97	65-101	266	116-150	111-155	366	163-203	157-209	466	211-255	204-262
67	25-42	22-45	167	70-97	66-101	267	116-151	111-156	367	164-203	158-209	467	211-256	205-262
68	25-43	22-46	168	70-98	66-102	268	117-151	112-156	368	164-204	158-210	468	212-256	205-263
69	25-44	23-46	169	71-98	67-102	269	117-152	112-157	369	165-204	159-210	469	212-257	206-263
70	26-44	23-47	170	71-99	67-103	270	118-152	113-157	370	165-205	159-211	470	213-257	206-264
71	26-45	24-47	171	72-99	68-103	271	118-153	113-158	371	166-205	160-211	471	213-258	207-264
72	27-45	24-48	172	72-100	68-104	272	119-153	114-158	372	166-206	160-212	472	214-258	207-265
73	27-46	25-48	173	73-100	69-104	273	119-154	114-159	373	167-206	161-212	473	214-259	207-266
74	28-46	25-49	174	73-101	69-105	274	120-154	115-159	374	167-207	161-213	474	215-259	208-266
75	28-47	25-50	175	74-101	69-106	275	120-155	115-160	375	168-207	162-213	475	215-260	208-267
76	28-48	26-50	176	74-102	70-106	276	121-155	116-160	376	168-208	162-214	476	216-260	209-267
77	29-48	26-51	177	74-103	70-107	277	121-156	116-161	377	168-209	162-215	477	216-261	209-268
78	29-49	27-51	178	75-103	71-107	278	122-156	117-161	378	169-209	163-215	478	217-261	210-268
79	30-49	27-52	179	75-104	71-108	279	122-157	117-162	379	169-210	163-216	479	217-262	210-269
80	30-50	28-52	180	76-104	72-108	280	123-157	117-163	380	170-210	164-216	480	218-262	211-269
81	31-50	28-53	181	76-105	72-109	281	123-158	118-163	381	170-211	164-217	481	218-263	211-270
82	31-51	28-54	182	77-105	73-109	282	124-158	118-164	382	171-211	165-217	482	218-264	212-270
83	32-51	29-54	183	77-106	73-110	283	124-159	119-164	383	171-212	165-218	483	219-264	212-271
84	32-52	29-55	184	78-106	74-110	284	124-160	119-165	384	172-212	166-218	484	219-265	213-271
85	32-53	30-55	185	78-107	74-111	285	125-160	120-165	385	172-213	166-219	485	220-265	213-272
86	33-53	30-56	186	79-107	74-112	286	125-161	120-166	386	173-213	167-219	486	220-266	214-272
87	33-54	31-56	187	79-108	75-112	287	126-161	121-166	387	173-214	167-220	487	221-266	214-273
88	34-54	31-57	188	80-108	75-113	288	126-162	121-167	388	174-214	168-220	488	221-267	215-273
89	34-55	31-58	189	80-109	76-113	289	127-162	122-167	389	174-215	168-221	489	222-267	215-274
90	35-55	32-58	190	80-110	76-114	290	127-163	122-168	390	175-215	169-221	490	222-268	215-275
91	35-56	32-59	191	81-110	77-114	291	128-163	123-168	391	175-216	169-222	491	223-268	216-275
92	36-56	33-59	192	81-111	77-115	292	128-164	123-169	392	176-216	170-222	492	223-269	216-276
93	36-57	33-60	193	82-111	78-115	293	129-164	123-170	393	176-217	170-223	493	224-269	217-276
94	37-57	34-60	194	82-112	78-116	294	129-165	124-170	394	177-217	170-224	494	224-270	217-277
95	37-58	34-61	195	83-112	79-116	295	130-165	124-171	395	177-218	171-224	495	225-270	218-277
96	37-59	34-62	196	83-113	79-117	296	130-166	125-171	396	177-219	171-225	496	225-271	218-278
97	38-59	35-62	197	84-113	79-118	297	131-166	125-172	397	178-219	172-225	497	226-271	219-278
98	38-60	35-63	198	84-114	80-118	298	131-167	126-172	398	178-220	172-226	498	226-272	219-279
99	39-60	36-63	199	85-114	80-119	299	132-167	126-173	399	179-220	173-226	499	227-272	220-279
100	39-61	36-64	200	85-115	81-119	300	132-168	127-173	400	179-221	173-227	500	227-273	220-280

Confidence Limits for Np ($p=0.5$, $N=500-1000$)* (sign test, etc.)

N = Number of trials. See also page 104

N	$2\alpha=0.05$	$2\alpha=0.01$	N	$2\alpha=0.05$	$2\alpha=0.01$	N	$2\alpha=0.05$	$2\alpha=0.01$	N	$2\alpha=0.05$	$2\alpha=0.01$	N	$2\alpha=0.05$	$2\alpha=0.01$
	x_l x_r	x_l x_r		x_l x_r	x_l x_r		x_l x_r	x_l x_r		x_l x_r	x_l x_r		x_l x_r	x_l x_r
500	227–273	220–280	**600**	275–325	267–333	**700**	323–377	315–385	**800**	371–429	363–437	**900**	420–480	410–490
501	228–273	221–280	601	275–326	268–333	701	324–377	315–386	801	372–429	363–438	901	420–481	411–490
502	228–274	221–281	602	276–326	268–334	702	324–378	316–386	802	372–430	364–438	902	421–481	411–491
503	229–274	222–281	603	276–327	269–334	703	325–378	316–387	803	373–430	364–439	903	421–482	412–491
504	229–275	222–282	604	277–327	269–335	704	325–379	317–387	804	373–431	364–440	904	422–482	412–492
505	229–276	223–282	**605**	277–328	270–335	**705**	325–380	317–388	**805**	374–431	365–440	**905**	422–483	413–492
506	230–276	223–283	606	278–328	270–336	706	326–380	318–388	806	374–432	365–441	906	423–483	413–493
507	230–277	224–283	607	278–329	271–336	707	326–381	318–389	807	375–432	366–441	907	423–484	414–493
508	231–277	224–284	608	279–329	271–337	708	327–381	319–389	808	375–433	366–442	908	423–485	414–494
509	231–278	224–285	609	279–330	272–337	709	327–382	319–390	809	376–433	367–442	909	424–485	415–494
510	232–278	225–285	**610**	280–330	272–338	**710**	328–382	320–390	**810**	376–434	367–443	**910**	424–486	415–495
511	232–279	225–286	611	280–331	273–338	711	328–383	320–391	811	377–434	368–443	911	425–486	416–495
512	233–279	226–286	612	281–331	273–339	712	329–383	321–391	812	377–435	368–444	912	425–487	416–496
513	233–280	226–287	613	281–332	274–339	713	329–384	321–392	813	378–435	369–444	913	426–487	417–496
514	234–280	227–287	614	282–332	274–340	714	330–384	322–392	814	378–436	369–445	914	426–488	417–497
515	234–281	227–288	**615**	282–333	275–340	**715**	330–385	322–393	**815**	379–436	370–445	**915**	427–488	418–497
516	235–281	228–288	616	283–333	275–341	716	331–385	323–393	816	379–437	370–446	916	427–489	418–498
517	235–282	228–289	617	283–334	276–341	717	331–386	323–394	817	379–438	371–446	917	428–489	418–499
518	236–282	229–289	618	284–334	276–342	718	332–386	323–395	818	380–438	371–447	918	428–490	419–499
519	236–283	229–290	619	284–335	276–343	719	332–387	324–395	819	380–439	372–447	919	429–490	419–500
520	237–283	230–290	**620**	285–335	277–343	**720**	333–387	324–396	**820**	381–439	372–448	**920**	429–491	420–500
521	237–284	230–291	621	285–336	277–344	721	333–388	325–396	821	381–440	373–448	921	430–491	420–501
522	238–284	231–291	622	286–336	278–344	722	334–388	325–397	822	382–440	373–449	922	430–492	421–501
523	238–285	231–292	623	286–337	278–345	723	334–389	326–397	823	382–441	374–449	923	431–492	421–502
524	239–285	232–292	624	287–337	279–345	724	335–389	326–398	824	383–441	374–450	924	431–493	422–502
525	239–286	232–293	**625**	287–338	279–346	**725**	335–390	327–398	**825**	383–442	375–450	**925**	432–493	422–503
526	240–286	232–294	626	287–339	280–346	726	336–390	327–399	826	384–442	375–451	926	432–494	423–503
527	240–287	233–294	627	288–339	280–347	727	336–391	328–399	827	384–443	375–452	927	433–494	423–504
528	240–288	233–295	628	288–340	281–347	728	337–391	328–400	828	385–443	376–452	928	433–495	424–504
529	241–288	234–295	629	289–340	281–348	729	337–392	329–400	829	385–444	376–453	929	434–495	424–505
530	241–289	234–296	**630**	289–341	282–348	**730**	338–392	329–401	**830**	386–444	377–453	**930**	434–496	425–505
531	242–289	235–296	631	290–341	282–349	731	338–393	330–401	831	386–445	377–454	931	435–496	425–506
532	242–290	235–297	632	290–342	283–349	732	338–394	330–402	832	387–445	378–454	932	435–497	426–506
533	243–290	236–297	633	291–342	283–350	733	339–394	331–402	833	387–446	378–455	933	436–497	426–507
534	243–291	236–298	634	291–343	284–350	734	339–395	331–403	834	388–446	379–455	934	436–498	427–507
535	244–291	237–298	**635**	292–343	284–351	**735**	340–395	332–403	**835**	388–447	379–456	**935**	437–498	427–508
536	244–292	237–299	636	292–344	285–351	736	340–396	332–404	836	389–447	380–456	936	437–499	428–508
537	245–292	238–299	637	293–344	285–352	737	341–396	333–404	837	389–448	380–457	937	438–499	428–509
538	245–293	238–300	638	293–345	285–353	738	341–397	333–405	838	390–448	381–457	938	438–500	429–509
539	246–293	239–300	639	294–345	286–353	739	342–397	333–406	839	390–449	381–458	939	438–501	429–510
540	246–294	239–301	**640**	294–346	286–354	**740**	342–398	334–406	**840**	391–449	382–458	**940**	439–501	430–510
541	247–294	240–301	641	295–346	287–354	741	343–398	334–407	841	391–450	382–459	941	439–502	430–511
542	247–295	240–302	642	295–347	287–355	742	343–399	335–407	842	392–450	383–459	942	440–502	430–512
543	248–295	240–303	643	296–347	288–355	743	344–399	335–408	843	392–451	383–460	943	440–503	431–512
544	248–296	241–303	644	296–348	288–356	744	344–400	336–408	844	393–451	384–460	944	441–503	431–513
545	249–296	241–304	**645**	297–348	289–356	**745**	345–400	336–409	**845**	393–452	384–461	**945**	441–504	432–513
546	249–297	242–304	646	297–349	289–357	746	345–401	337–409	846	393–453	385–461	946	442–504	432–514
547	250–297	242–305	647	298–349	290–357	747	346–401	337–410	847	394–453	385–462	947	442–505	433–514
548	250–298	243–305	648	298–350	290–358	748	346–402	338–410	848	394–454	385–463	948	443–505	433–515
549	251–298	243–306	649	299–350	291–358	749	347–402	338–411	849	395–454	386–463	949	443–506	434–515
550	251–299	244–306	**650**	299–351	291–359	**750**	347–403	339–411	**850**	395–455	386–464	**950**	444–506	434–516
551	251–300	244–307	651	299–352	292–359	751	348–403	339–412	851	396–455	387–464	951	444–507	435–516
552	252–300	245–307	652	300–352	292–360	752	348–404	340–412	852	396–456	387–465	952	445–507	435–517
553	252–301	245–308	653	300–353	293–360	753	349–404	340–413	853	397–456	388–465	953	445–508	436–517
554	253–301	246–308	654	301–353	293–361	754	349–405	341–413	854	397–457	388–466	954	446–508	436–518
555	253–302	246–309	**655**	301–354	294–361	**755**	350–405	341–414	**855**	398–457	389–466	**955**	446–509	437–518
556	254–302	247–309	656	302–354	294–362	756	350–406	342–414	856	398–458	389–467	956	447–509	437–519
557	254–303	247–310	657	302–355	294–363	757	351–406	342–415	857	399–458	390–467	957	447–510	438–519
558	255–303	248–310	658	303–355	295–363	758	351–407	343–415	858	399–459	390–468	958	448–510	438–520
559	255–304	248–311	659	303–356	295–364	759	352–407	343–416	859	400–459	391–468	959	448–511	439–520
560	256–304	249–311	**660**	304–356	296–364	**760**	352–408	343–417	**860**	400–460	391–469	**960**	449–511	439–521
561	256–305	249–312	661	304–357	296–365	761	352–409	344–417	861	401–460	392–469	961	449–512	440–521
562	257–305	249–313	662	305–357	297–365	762	353–409	344–418	862	401–461	392–470	962	450–512	440–522
563	257–306	250–313	663	305–358	297–366	763	353–410	345–418	863	402–461	393–470	963	450–513	441–522
564	258–306	250–314	664	306–358	298–366	764	354–410	345–419	864	402–462	393–471	964	451–513	441–523
565	258–307	251–314	**665**	306–359	298–367	**765**	354–411	346–419	**865**	403–462	394–471	**965**	451–514	441–524
566	259–307	251–315	666	307–359	299–367	766	355–411	346–420	866	403–463	394–472	966	452–514	442–524
567	259–308	252–315	667	307–360	299–368	767	355–412	347–420	867	404–463	395–472	967	452–515	442–525
568	260–308	252–316	668	308–360	300–368	768	356–412	347–421	868	404–464	395–473	968	453–515	443–525
569	260–309	253–316	669	308–361	300–369	769	356–413	348–421	869	405–464	396–473	969	453–516	443–526
570	261–309	253–317	**670**	309–361	301–369	**770**	357–413	348–422	**870**	405–465	396–474	**970**	453–517	444–526
571	261–310	254–317	671	309–362	301–370	771	357–414	349–422	871	406–465	396–475	971	454–517	444–527
572	262–310	254–318	672	310–362	302–370	772	358–414	349–423	872	406–466	397–475	972	454–518	445–527
573	262–311	255–318	673	310–363	302–371	773	358–415	350–423	873	407–466	397–476	973	455–518	445–528
574	263–311	255–319	674	311–363	303–371	774	359–415	350–424	874	407–467	398–476	974	455–519	446–528
575	263–312	256–319	**675**	311–364	303–372	**775**	359–416	351–424	**875**	408–467	398–477	**975**	456–519	446–529
576	263–313	256–320	676	312–364	304–372	776	360–416	351–425	876	408–468	399–477	976	456–520	447–529
577	264–313	257–320	677	312–365	304–373	777	360–417	352–425	877	408–469	399–478	977	457–520	447–530
578	264–314	257–321	678	312–366	304–374	778	361–417	352–426	878	409–469	400–478	978	457–521	448–530
579	265–314	258–321	679	313–366	305–374	779	361–418	353–426	879	409–470	400–479	979	458–521	448–531
580	265–315	258–322	**680**	313–367	305–375	**780**	362–418	353–427	**880**	410–470	401–479	**980**	458–522	449–531
581	266–315	258–323	681	314–367	306–375	781	362–419	354–427	881	410–471	401–480	981	459–522	449–532
582	266–316	259–323	682	314–368	306–376	782	363–419	354–428	882	411–471	402–480	982	459–523	450–532
583	267–316	259–324	683	315–368	307–376	783	363–420	354–429	883	411–472	402–481	983	460–523	450–533
584	267–317	260–324	684	315–369	307–377	784	364–420	355–429	884	412–472	403–481	984	460–524	451–533
585	268–317	260–325	**685**	316–369	308–377	**785**	364–421	355–430	**885**	412–473	403–482	**985**	461–524	451–534
586	268–318	261–325	686	316–370	308–378	786	365–421	356–430	886	413–473	404–482	986	461–525	452–534
587	269–318	261–326	687	317–370	309–378	787	365–422	356–431	887	413–474	404–483	987	462–525	452–535
588	269–319	262–326	688	317–371	309–379	788	365–423	357–431	888	414–474	405–483	988	462–526	453–535
589	270–319	262–327	689	318–371	310–379	789	366–423	357–432	889	414–475	405–484	989	463–526	453–536
590	270–320	263–327	**690**	318–372	310–380	**790**	366–424	358–432	**890**	415–475	406–484	**990**	463–527	453–537
591	271–320	263–328	691	319–372	311–380	791	367–424	358–433	891	415–476	406–485	991	464–527	454–537
592	271–321	264–328	692	319–373	311–381	792	367–425	359–433	892	416–476	407–485	992	464–528	454–538
593	272–321	264–329	693	320–373	312–381	793	368–425	359–434	893	416–477	407–486	993	465–528	455–538
594	272–322	265–329	694	320–374	312–382	794	368–426	360–434	894	417–477	407–487	994	465–529	455–539
595	273–322	265–330	**695**	321–374	313–382	**795**	369–426	360–435	**895**	417–478	408–487	**995**	466–529	456–539
596	273–323	266–330	696	321–375	313–383	796	369–427	361–435	896	418–478	408–488	996	466–530	456–540
597	274–323	266–331	697	322–375	313–384	797	370–427	361–436	897	418–479	409–488	997	467–530	457–540
598	274–324	267–331	698	322–376	314–384	798	370–428	362–436	898	419–479	409–489	998	467–531	457–541
599	275–324	267–332	699	323–376	314–385	799	371–428	362–437	899	419–480	410–489	999	468–531	458–541
600	275–325	267–333	**700**	323–377	315–385	**800**	371–429	363–437	**900**	420–480	410–490	**1000**	468–532	458–542

95% Confidence Limits for λ*

Values from 0 to 100 are exact, all others have been calculated from FREEMAN and TUKEY's approximation (cf. page 188)

x	0	1 10 100	2 20 200	3 30 300	4 40 400	5 50 500	6 60 600	7 70 700	8 80 800	9 90 900
	λ_l λ_r	λ_l λ_r	λ_l λ_r	λ_l λ_r	λ_l λ_r	λ_l λ_r	λ_l λ_r	λ_l λ_r	λ_l λ_r	λ_l λ_r
0	0 –3.6889	0.0253–5.5716	0.2422–7.2247	0.6187–8.7673	1.0899–10.242	1.6235–11.669	2.2019–13.060	2.8144–14.423	3.4539–15.764	4.1154–17.085
10	4.7954–18.391	5.4913–19.683	6.2008–20.962	6.9223–22.231	7.6542–23.490	8.3957–24.741	9.1459–25.983	9.9037–27.219	10.668–28.448	11.440–29.671
20	12.217–30.889	13.000–32.101	13.788–33.309	14.581–34.512	15.378–35.711	16.178–36.905	16.983–38.097	17.793–39.284	18.606–40.468	19.422–41.649
30	20.241–42.827	21.063–44.002	21.888–45.175	22.715–46.345	23.545–47.512	24.378–48.677	25.213–49.840	26.050–51.000	26.890–52.158	27.732–53.315
40	28.575–54.469	29.421–55.622	30.269–56.772	31.119–57.921	31.970–59.068	32.823–60.214	33.678–61.358	34.534–62.501	35.392–63.642	36.251–64.781
50	37.112–65.919	37.973–67.056	38.837–68.192	39.701–69.326	40.567–70.459	41.433–71.591	42.301–72.721	43.171–73.851	44.041–74.979	44.912–76.106
60	45.785–77.232	46.658–78.357	47.533–79.482	48.409–80.605	49.286–81.727	50.164–82.848	51.042–83.969	51.922–85.088	52.803–86.207	53.685–87.324
70	54.567–88.441	55.451–89.557	56.335–90.673	57.220–91.787	58.106–92.901	58.993–94.014	59.880–95.126	60.768–96.237	61.657–97.348	62.547–98.458
80	63.437–99.567	64.328–100.68	65.219–101.79	66.111–102.90	67.003–104.00	67.897–105.11	68.790–106.21	69.684–107.32	70.579–108.42	71.474–109.53
90	72.370–110.63	73.267–111.73	74.164–112.83	75.061–113.94	75.959–115.04	76.858–116.14	77.757–117.24	78.657–118.34	79.557–119.44	80.458–120.53
100	81.36–121.66	90.40–132.61	99.49–143.52	108.61–154.39	117.77–165.23	126.96–176.04	136.17–186.83	145.41–197.59	154.66–208.33	163.94–219.05
200	173.24–229.75	182.56–240.43	191.89–251.10	201.24–261.75	210.60–272.39	219.97–283.01	229.36–293.62	238.75–304.23	248.16–314.82	257.58–325.39
300	267.01–335.96	276.45–346.52	285.90–357.08	295.36–367.62	304.82–378.15	314.29–388.68	323.77–399.20	333.26–409.71	342.75–420.22	352.25–430.72
400	361.76–441.21	371.27–451.69	380.79–462.18	390.32–472.65	399.85–483.12	409.38–493.58	418.92–504.04	428.47–514.50	438.02–524.95	447.57–535.39
500	457.13–545.83	466.70–556.27	476.27–566.70	485.84–577.12	495.41–587.55	505.00–597.97	514.58–608.38	524.17–618.79	533.76–629.20	543.35–639.61
600	552.95–650.01	562.55–660.41	572.16–670.80	581.77–681.19	591.38–691.58	600.99–701.97	610.61–712.35	620.23–722.73	629.85–733.11	639.48–743.48
700	649.10–753.85	658.74–764.22	668.37–774.59	678.01–784.95	687.64–795.31	697.28–805.67	706.93–816.03	716.57–826.38	726.22–836.73	735.87–847.08
800	745.52–857.43	755.18–867.78	764.84–878.12	774.49–888.46	784.16–898.80	793.82–909.14	803.48–919.47	813.15–929.80	822.82–940.14	832.49–950.46
900	842.16–960.79	851.84–971.12	861.51–981.44	871.19–991.76	880.87–1002.1	890.55–1012.5	900.23–1022.8	909.92–1033.1	919.60–1043.4	929.29–1053.7
1000	938.98–1064.0	948.67–1074.3	958.36–1084.6	968.06–1094.9	977.75–1105.2	987.45–1115.6	997.15–1125.8	1006.8–1136.1	1016.5–1146.4	1026.2–1156.7
1100	1035.9–1167.0	1045.6–1177.3	1055.3–1187.6	1065.0–1197.9	1074.7–1208.2	1084.4–1218.5	1094.2–1228.8	1103.9–1239.1	1113.6–1249.4	1123.3–1259.6
1200	1133.0–1269.9	1142.7–1280.2	1152.5–1290.5	1162.2–1300.8	1171.9–1311.1	1181.6–1321.3	1191.3–1331.6	1201.1–1341.9	1210.8–1352.2	1220.5–1362.4
1300	1230.2–1372.7	1240.0–1383.0	1249.7–1393.2	1259.4–1403.5	1269.2–1413.8	1278.9–1424.0	1288.6–1434.3	1298.4–1444.6	1308.1–1454.8	1317.8–1465.1
1400	1327.6–1475.4	1337.3–1485.6	1347.1–1495.9	1356.8–1506.1	1366.5–1516.4	1376.3–1526.7	1386.0–1536.9	1395.8–1547.2	1405.5–1557.4	1415.3–1567.7
1500	1425.0–1577.9	1434.8–1588.2	1444.5–1598.4	1454.3–1608.7	1464.0–1618.9	1473.8–1629.2	1483.5–1639.4	1493.3–1649.7	1503.0–1659.9	1512.8–1670.2
1600	1522.5–1680.4	1532.3–1690.7	1542.0–1700.9	1551.8–1711.2	1561.5–1721.4	1571.3–1731.7	1581.1–1741.9	1590.8–1752.1	1600.6–1762.4	1610.3–1772.6
1700	1620.1–1782.8	1629.9–1793.1	1639.6–1803.3	1649.4–1813.6	1659.2–1823.8	1668.9–1834.0	1678.7–1844.3	1688.5–1854.5	1698.2–1864.7	1708.0–1875.0
1800	1717.8–1885.2	1727.5–1895.4	1737.3–1905.6	1747.1–1915.9	1756.8–1926.1	1766.6–1936.3	1776.4–1946.6	1786.2–1956.8	1795.9–1967.0	1805.7–1977.2
1900	1815.5–1987.5	1825.3–1997.7	1835.0–2007.9	1844.8–2018.1	1854.6–2028.4	1864.4–2038.6	1874.1–2048.8	1883.9–2059.0	1893.7–2069.3	1903.5–2079.5
2000	1913.3–2089.7	1923.0–2099.9	1932.8–2110.1	1942.6–2120.3	1952.4–2130.6	1962.2–2140.8	1972.0–2151.0	1981.7–2161.2	1991.5–2171.4	2001.3–2181.6
2100	2011.1–2191.8	2020.9–2202.1	2030.7–2212.3	2040.5–2222.5	2050.2–2232.7	2060.0–2242.9	2069.8–2253.1	2079.6–2263.3	2089.4–2273.5	2099.2–2283.7
2200	2109.0–2294.0	2118.8–2304.2	2128.6–2314.4	2138.4–2324.6	2148.2–2334.8	2157.9–2345.0	2167.7–2355.2	2177.5–2365.4	2187.3–2375.6	2197.1–2385.8
2300	2206.9–2396.0	2216.7–2406.2	2226.5–2416.4	2236.3–2426.6	2246.1–2436.8	2255.9–2447.0	2265.7–2457.2	2275.5–2467.4	2285.3–2477.6	2295.1–2487.8
2400	2304.9–2498.0	2314.7–2508.2	2324.5–2518.4	2334.3–2528.6	2344.1–2538.8	2353.9–2549.0	2363.7–2559.2	2373.5–2569.4	2383.3–2579.6	2393.1–2589.8
2500	2402.9–2600.0	2412.7–2610.2	2422.5–2620.4	2432.3–2630.6	2442.1–2640.8	2451.9–2651.0	2461.7–2661.2	2471.6–2671.4	2481.4–2681.6	2491.2–2691.8
2600	2501.0–2702.0	2510.8–2712.2	2520.6–2722.3	2530.4–2732.5	2540.2–2742.7	2550.0–2752.9	2559.8–2763.1	2569.6–2773.3	2579.5–2783.5	2589.3–2793.7
2700	2599.1–2803.9	2608.9–2814.1	2618.7–2824.2	2628.5–2834.4	2638.3–2844.6	2648.1–2854.8	2657.9–2865.0	2667.8–2875.2	2677.6–2885.4	2687.4–2895.6
2800	2697.2–2905.7	2707.0–2915.9	2716.8–2926.1	2726.6–2936.3	2736.5–2946.5	2746.3–2956.7	2756.1–2966.8	2765.9–2977.0	2775.7–2987.2	2785.6–2997.4
2900	2795.4–3007.6	2805.2–3017.8	2815.0–3027.9	2824.8–3038.1	2834.6–3048.3	2844.5–3058.5	2854.3–3068.7	2864.1–3078.8	2873.9–3089.0	2883.7–3099.2
3000	2893.6–3109.4	2903.4–3119.6	2913.2–3129.7	2923.0–3139.9	2932.9–3150.1	2942.7–3160.3	2952.5–3170.4	2962.3–3180.6	2972.1–3190.8	2982.0–3201.0
3100	2991.8–3211.1	3001.6–3221.3	3011.4–3231.5	3021.3–3241.7	3031.1–3251.9	3040.9–3262.0	3050.7–3272.2	3060.6–3282.4	3070.4–3292.5	3080.2–3302.7
3200	3090.0–3312.9	3099.9–3323.1	3109.7–3333.2	3119.5–3343.4	3129.4–3353.6	3139.2–3363.8	3149.0–3373.9	3158.8–3384.1	3168.7–3394.3	3178.5–3404.4
3300	3188.3–3414.6	3198.2–3424.8	3208.0–3435.0	3217.8–3445.1	3227.6–3455.3	3237.5–3465.5	3247.3–3475.6	3257.1–3485.8	3267.0–3496.0	3276.8–3506.1
3400	3286.6–3516.3	3296.5–3526.5	3306.3–3536.6	3316.1–3546.8	3326.0–3557.0	3335.8–3567.1	3345.6–3577.3	3355.5–3587.5	3365.3–3597.6	3375.1–3607.8
3500	3385.0–3618.0	3394.8–3628.1	3404.6–3638.3	3414.5–3648.5	3424.3–3658.6	3434.1–3668.8	3444.0–3679.0	3453.8–3689.1	3463.6–3699.3	3473.5–3709.5
3600	3483.3–3719.6	3493.2–3729.8	3503.0–3739.9	3512.8–3750.1	3522.7–3760.3	3532.5–3770.4	3542.3–3780.6	3552.2–3790.8	3562.0–3800.9	3571.9–3811.1
3700	3581.7–3821.2	3591.5–3831.4	3601.4–3841.6	3611.2–3851.7	3621.1–3861.9	3630.9–3872.0	3640.7–3882.2	3650.6–3892.4	3660.4–3902.5	3670.3–3912.7
3800	3680.1–3922.8	3689.9–3933.0	3699.8–3943.2	3709.6–3953.3	3719.5–3963.5	3729.3–3973.6	3739.1–3983.8	3749.0–3993.9	3758.8–4004.1	3768.7–4014.3
3900	3778.5–4024.4	3788.4–4034.6	3798.2–4044.7	3808.0–4054.9	3817.9–4065.0	3827.7–4075.2	3837.6–4085.4	3847.4–4095.5	3857.3–4105.7	3867.1–4115.8
4000	3877.0–4126.0	3886.8–4136.1	3896.6–4146.3	3906.5–4156.4	3916.3–4166.6	3926.2–4176.8	3936.0–4186.9	3945.9–4197.1	3955.7–4207.2	3965.6–4217.4
4100	3975.4–4227.5	3985.3–4237.7	3995.1–4247.8	4005.0–4258.0	4014.8–4268.1	4024.7–4278.3	4034.5–4288.4	4044.3–4298.6	4054.2–4308.7	4064.0–4318.9
4200	4073.9–4329.0	4083.7–4339.2	4093.6–4349.3	4103.4–4359.5	4113.3–4369.6	4123.1–4379.8	4133.0–4389.9	4142.8–4400.1	4152.7–4410.2	4162.5–4420.4
4300	4172.4–4430.5	4182.2–4440.7	4192.1–4450.8	4201.9–4461.0	4211.8–4471.1	4221.6–4481.3	4231.5–4491.4	4241.4–4501.6	4251.2–4511.7	4261.1–4521.9
4400	4270.9–4532.0	4280.8–4542.2	4290.6–4552.3	4300.5–4562.5	4310.3–4572.6	4320.2–4582.8	4330.0–4592.9	4339.9–4603.1	4349.7–4613.2	4359.6–4623.4
4500	4369.4–4633.5	4379.3–4643.6	4389.1–4653.8	4399.0–4663.9	4408.9–4674.1	4418.7–4684.2	4428.6–4694.4	4438.4–4704.5	4448.3–4714.7	4458.1–4724.8
4600	4468.0–4735.0	4477.8–4745.1	4487.7–4755.2	4497.6–4765.4	4507.4–4775.5	4517.3–4785.7	4527.1–4795.8	4537.0–4806.0	4546.8–4816.1	4556.7–4826.2
4700	4566.5–4836.4	4576.4–4846.5	4586.3–4856.7	4596.1–4866.8	4606.0–4877.0	4615.8–4887.1	4625.7–4897.2	4635.6–4907.4	4645.4–4917.5	4655.3–4927.7
4800	4665.1–4937.8	4675.0–4948.0	4684.8–4958.1	4694.7–4968.2	4704.6–4978.4	4714.4–4988.5	4724.3–4998.7	4734.1–5008.8	4744.0–5018.9	4753.9–5029.1
4900	4763.7–5039.2	4773.6–5049.4	4783.4–5059.5	4793.3–5069.6	4803.2–5079.8	4813.0–5089.9	4822.9–5100.1	4832.7–5110.2	4842.6–5120.3	4852.5–5130.5
5000	4862.3–5140.6	4960.9–5242.0	5059.6–5343.4	5158.2–5444.7	5256.9–5546.0	5355.6–5647.4	5454.2–5748.7	5552.9–5850.0	5651.6–5951.3	5750.4–6052.6
6000	5849.1–6153.8	5947.8–6255.1	6046.6–6356.3	6145.3–6457.6	6244.1–6558.8	6342.9–6660.0	6441.7–6761.3	6540.5–6862.4	6639.3–6963.6	6738.1–7064.8
7000	6836.9–7166.0	6935.8–7267.2	7034.6–7368.3	7133.5–7469.5	7232.3–7570.6	7331.2–7671.8	7430.0–7772.9	7528.9–7874.0	7627.8–7975.1	7726.7–8076.2
8000	7825.6–8177.3	7924.5–8278.4	8023.4–8379.5	8122.4–8480.6	8221.3–8581.6	8320.2–8682.7	8419.2–8783.8	8518.1–8884.8	8617.1–8985.9	8716.0–9086.9
9000	8815.0–9188.0	8913.9–9289.0	9012.9–9390.0	9111.9–9491.0	9210.9–9592.0	9309.9–9693.0	9408.9–9794.1	9507.9–9895.0	9606.9–9996.0	9705.9–10097
10000	9804.9–10198	9903.9–10299	10003–10400	10102–10501	10201–10602	10300–10703	10399–10804	10498–10905	10597–11006	10696–11107
11000	10795–11208	10894–11309	10993–11410	11092–11511	11191–11612	11290–11713	11389–11814	11488–11914	11588–12015	11687–12116
12000	11786–12217	11885–12318	11984–12419	12083–12520	12182–12621	12281–12722	12380–12822	12480–12923	12579–13024	12678–13125
13000	12777–13226	12876–13327	12975–13428	13074–13528	13174–13629	13273–13730	13372–13831	13471–13932	13570–14033	13669–14134
14000	13769–14234	13868–14335	13967–14436	14066–14537	14165–14638	14264–14738	14364–14839	14463–14940	14562–15041	14661–15142
15000	14760–15243	14860–15343	14959–15444	15058–15545	15157–15646	15256–15746	15356–15847	15455–15948	15554–16049	15653–16150
16000	15753–16250	15852–16351	15951–16452	16050–16553	16149–16653	16249–16754	16348–16855	16447–16956	16546–17057	16646–17157
17000	16745–17258	16844–17359	16943–17460	17043–17560	17142–17661	17241–17762	17340–17862	17440–17963	17539–18064	17638–18165
18000	17738–18265	17837–18366	17936–18467	18035–18568	18135–18668	18234–18769	18333–18870	18432–18970	18532–19071	18631–19172
19000	18730–19273	18830–19373	18929–19474	19028–19575	19127–19675	19227–19778	19326–19877	19425–19978	19525–20078	19624–20179
20000	19723–20280	19823–20380	19922–20481	20021–20582	20121–20682	20220–20783	20319–20884	20418–20984	20518–21085	20617–21186
21000	20716–21286	20816–21387	20915–21488	21014–21589	21114–21689	21213–21790	21312–21891	21412–21991	21511–22092	21610–22193
22000	21710–22293	21809–22394	21908–22494	22008–22595	22107–22696	22206–22796	22306–22897	22405–22998	22505–23098	22604–23199
23000	22703–23300	22803–23400	22902–23501	23001–23602	23101–23702	23200–23803	23299–23904	23399–24004	23498–24105	23597–24205
24000	23697–24306	23796–24407	23896–24507	23995–24608	24094–24709	24194–24809	24293–24910	24392–25010	24492–25111	24591–25212
25000	24691–25312	24790–25413	24889–25514	24989–25614	25088–25715	25187–25815	25287–25916	25386–26017	25486–26117	25585–26218
26000	25684–26318	25784–26419	25883–26520	25983–26620	26082–26721	26181–26822	26281–26922	26380–27023	26480–27123	26579–27224
27000	26678–27325	26778–27425	26877–27526	26977–27626	27076–27727	27175–27827	27275–27928	27374–28029	27474–28129	27573–28230
28000	27673–28330	27772–28431	27871–28532	27971–28632	28070–28733	28170–28833	28269–28934	28368–29035	28468–29135	28567–29236
29000	28667–29336	28766–29437	28866–29537	28965–29638	29064–29739	29164–29839	29263–29940	29363–30040	29462–30141	29562–30241
30000	29661–30342	29760–30443	29860–30543	29959–30644	30059–30744	30158–30845	30258–30945	30357–31046	30456–31146	30556–31247
31000	30655–31348	30755–31448	30854–31549	30954–31649	31053–31750	31153–31850	31252–31951	31352–32051	31451–32152	31550–32253
32000	31650–32353	31749–32454	31849–32554	31948–32655	32048–32755	32147–32856	32247–32956	32346–33057	32446–33157	32545–33258
33000	32644–33359	32744–33459	32843–33560	32943–33660	33042–33761	33142–33861	33241–33962	33341–34062	33440–34163	33540–34263
34000	33639–34364	33739–34464	33838–34565	33937–34665	34037–34766	34136–34867	34236–34967	34335–35068	34435–35168	34534–35269
35000	34634–35369	34733–35470	34833–35570	34932–35671	35032–35771	35131–35872	35231–35972	35330–36073	35430–36173	35529–36274
36000	35629–36374	35728–36475	35828–36575	35927–36676	36027–36776	36126–36877	36226–36977	36325–37078	36424–37178	36524–37279
37000	36623–37379	36723–37480	36822–37580	36922–37681	37021–37781	37121–37882	37220–37983	37320–38083	37419–38184	37519–38284
38000	37618–38385	37718–38485	37817–38586	37917–38686	38016–38787	38116–38887	38215–38988	38315–39088	38414–39189	38514–39289
39000	38613–39390	38713–39490	38812–39591	38912–39691	39011–39792	39111–39892	39210–39992	39310–40093	39409–40193	39509–40294
40000	39608–40394	39708–40495	39807–40595	39907–40696	40007–40796	40106–40897	40206–40997	40305–41098	40405–41198	40504–41299
41000	40604–41399	40703–41500	40803–41600	40902–41701	41002–41801	41101–41902	41201–42002	41300–42103	41400–42203	41499–42304
42000	41599–42404	41698–42505	41798–42605	41897–42706	41997–42806	42096–42907	42196–43007	42295–43107	42395–43208	42495–43308
43000	42594–43409	42694–43509	42793–43610	42893–43710	42992–43811	43092–43911	43191–44012	43291–44112	43390–44213	43490–44313
44000	43589–44414	43689–44514	43788–44615	43888–44715	43987–44815	44087–44916	44187–45016	44286–45117	44386–45217	44485–45318

Values from 0 to 100 are exact, all others have been calculated from FREEMAN and TUKEY's approximation (cf. page 188)

x	0	1 10 100	2 20 200	3 30 300	4 40 400	5 50 500	6 60 600	7 70 700	8 80 800	9 90 900
	λ_l – λ_r	λ_l – λ_r	λ_l – λ_r	λ_l – λ_r	λ_l – λ_r	λ_l – λ_r	λ_l – λ_r	λ_l – λ_r	λ_l – λ_r	λ_l – λ_r
0	0 –5.2983	0.0050–7.4301	0.1035–9.2738	0.3379–10.978	0.6722–12.595	1.0779–14.150	1.5369–15.660	2.0374–17.134	2.5711–18.579	3.1325–19.999
10	3.7172–21.398	4.3216–22.780	4.9434–24.145	5.5807–25.497	6.2316–26.836	6.8946–28.164	7.5680–29.482	8.2518–30.791	8.9453–32.091	9.6470–33.383
20	10.355–34.668	11.072–35.947	11.795–37.219	12.525–38.485	13.260–39.745	14.000–41.001	14.745–42.251	15.495–43.497	16.244–44.739	17.003–45.976
30	17.767–47.210	18.535–48.439	19.306–49.666	20.080–50.888	20.858–52.108	21.638–53.324	22.422–54.538	23.208–55.748	23.997–56.956	24.789–58.161
40	25.583–59.363	26.381–60.564	27.181–61.761	27.983–62.957	28.788–64.150	29.596–65.341	30.406–66.530	31.218–67.717	32.032–68.902	32.848–70.085
50	33.666–71.267	34.485–72.446	35.306–73.624	36.129–74.800	36.953–75.975	37.779–77.148	38.605–78.319	39.434–79.489	40.263–80.657	41.094–81.825
60	41.926–82.990	42.759–84.155	43.594–85.317	44.430–86.479	45.267–87.640	46.106–88.799	46.946–89.957	47.787–91.114	48.630–92.269	49.475–93.424
70	50.320–94.577	51.167–95.730	52.015–96.881	52.865–98.031	53.716–99.180	54.567–100.33	55.420–101.48	56.275–102.63	57.130–103.77	57.986–104.92
80	58.844–106.06	59.701–107.20	60.559–108.34	61.419–109.49	62.279–110.63	63.140–111.77	64.001–112.90	64.863–114.04	65.725–115.18	66.587–116.31
90	67.451–117.45	68.314–118.59	69.179–119.72	70.043–120.85	70.909–121.98	71.775–123.12	72.641–124.25	73.508–125.38	74.375–126.51	75.244–127.64
100	75.90–128.55	84.64–139.80	93.44–150.99	102.29–162.14	111.18–173.24	120.11–184.31	129.08–195.34	138.07–206.34	147.10–217.31	156.15–228.26
200	165.23–239.18	174.33–250.07	183.45–260.95	192.59–271.81	201.75–282.65	210.93–293.47	220.12–304.27	229.33–315.06	238.56–325.84	247.79–336.60
300	257.04–347.35	266.31–358.08	275.58–368.81	284.87–379.52	294.16–390.22	303.47–400.92	312.79–411.60	322.11–422.27	331.45–432.94	340.79–443.59
400	350.14–454.24	359.50–464.88	368.87–475.51	378.25–486.13	387.63–496.75	397.02–507.36	406.41–517.96	415.82–528.56	425.23–539.15	434.64–549.74
500	444.06–560.31	453.49–570.89	462.92–581.45	472.36–592.01	481.80–602.57	491.25–613.12	500.70–623.67	510.16–634.21	519.62–644.75	529.09–655.28
600	538.56–665.81	548.04–676.33	557.52–686.85	567.01–697.36	576.49–707.87	585.99–718.38	595.48–728.88	604.99–739.38	614.49–749.88	624.00–760.37
700	633.51–770.86	643.02–781.34	652.54–791.82	662.06–802.30	671.59–812.78	681.12–823.25	690.65–833.72	700.18–844.18	709.72–854.64	719.26–865.10
800	728.80–875.56	738.35–886.01	747.90–896.46	757.45–906.91	767.00–917.36	776.56–927.80	786.12–938.24	795.68–948.68	805.25–959.11	814.81–969.55
900	824.38–979.98	833.96–990.40	843.53–1000.9	853.11–1011.3	862.69–1021.7	872.27–1032.1	881.85–1042.6	891.43–1053.0	901.02–1063.4	910.61–1073.8
1000	920.20–1084.2	929.80–1094.6	939.39–1105.0	948.99–1115.4	958.59–1125.8	968.19–1136.2	977.80–1146.6	987.40–1157.0	997.01–1167.4	1006.6–1177.8
1100	1016.2–1188.2	1025.8–1198.6	1035.4–1209.0	1045.0–1219.3	1054.6–1229.7	1064.3–1240.1	1073.9–1250.5	1083.5–1260.9	1093.1–1271.2	1102.8–1281.6
1200	1112.4–1292.0	1122.0–1302.3	1131.6–1312.7	1141.3–1323.1	1150.9–1333.4	1160.5–1343.8	1170.2–1354.2	1179.8–1364.5	1189.5–1374.9	1199.1–1385.3
1300	1208.7–1395.6	1218.4–1406.0	1228.0–1416.3	1237.7–1426.7	1247.3–1437.0	1257.0–1447.4	1266.6–1457.7	1276.3–1468.1	1285.9–1478.4	1295.6–1488.8
1400	1305.2–1499.1	1314.9–1509.5	1324.5–1519.8	1334.2–1530.1	1343.9–1540.5	1353.5–1550.8	1363.2–1561.2	1372.9–1571.5	1382.5–1581.8	1392.2–1592.2
1500	1401.9–1602.5	1411.5–1612.8	1421.2–1623.2	1430.9–1633.5	1440.5–1643.8	1450.2–1654.1	1459.9–1664.5	1469.6–1674.8	1479.2–1685.1	1488.9–1695.4
1600	1498.6–1705.8	1508.3–1716.1	1517.9–1726.4	1527.6–1736.7	1537.3–1747.0	1547.0–1757.4	1556.7–1767.7	1566.4–1778.0	1576.0–1788.3	1585.7–1798.6
1700	1595.4–1808.9	1605.1–1819.3	1614.8–1829.6	1624.5–1839.9	1634.2–1850.2	1643.9–1860.5	1653.6–1870.8	1663.2–1881.1	1672.9–1891.4	1682.6–1901.7
1800	1692.3–1912.0	1702.0–1922.3	1711.7–1932.6	1721.4–1942.9	1731.1–1953.2	1740.8–1963.5	1750.5–1973.8	1760.2–1984.1	1769.9–1994.4	1779.6–2004.7
1900	1789.3–2015.0	1799.0–2025.3	1808.7–2035.6	1818.5–2045.9	1828.2–2056.2	1837.9–2066.5	1847.6–2076.8	1857.3–2087.1	1867.0–2097.3	1876.7–2107.6
2000	1886.4–2117.9	1896.1–2128.2	1905.8–2138.5	1915.6–2148.8	1925.3–2159.1	1935.0–2169.4	1944.7–2179.6	1954.4–2189.9	1964.1–2200.2	1973.9–2210.5
2100	1983.6–2220.8	1993.3–2231.1	2003.0–2241.3	2012.7–2251.6	2022.5–2261.9	2032.2–2272.2	2041.9–2282.4	2051.6–2292.7	2061.3–2303.0	2071.1–2313.3
2200	2080.8–2323.5	2090.5–2333.8	2100.2–2344.1	2110.0–2354.4	2119.7–2364.6	2129.4–2374.9	2139.2–2385.2	2148.9–2395.5	2158.6–2405.7	2168.4–2416.0
2300	2178.1–2426.3	2187.8–2436.5	2197.5–2446.8	2207.3–2457.1	2217.0–2467.3	2226.7–2477.6	2236.5–2487.9	2246.2–2498.1	2256.0–2508.4	2265.7–2518.7
2400	2275.4–2528.9	2285.2–2539.2	2294.9–2549.4	2304.6–2559.7	2314.4–2570.0	2324.1–2580.2	2333.9–2590.5	2343.6–2600.7	2353.3–2611.0	2363.1–2621.3
2500	2372.8–2631.5	2382.6–2641.8	2392.3–2652.0	2402.1–2662.3	2411.8–2672.5	2421.5–2682.8	2431.3–2693.1	2441.0–2703.3	2450.8–2713.6	2460.5–2723.8
2600	2470.3–2734.1	2480.0–2744.3	2489.8–2754.6	2499.5–2764.8	2509.3–2775.1	2519.0–2785.3	2528.8–2795.6	2538.5–2805.8	2548.3–2816.1	2558.0–2826.3
2700	2567.8–2836.6	2577.5–2846.8	2587.3–2857.1	2597.0–2867.3	2606.8–2877.6	2616.5–2887.8	2626.3–2898.1	2636.0–2908.3	2645.8–2918.5	2655.6–2928.8
2800	2665.3–2939.0	2675.1–2949.3	2684.8–2959.5	2694.6–2969.8	2704.3–2980.0	2714.1–2990.2	2723.9–3000.5	2733.6–3010.7	2743.4–3021.0	2753.1–3031.2
2900	2762.9–3041.4	2772.7–3051.7	2782.4–3061.9	2792.2–3072.2	2801.9–3082.4	2811.7–3092.6	2821.5–3102.9	2831.2–3113.1	2841.0–3123.3	2850.8–3133.6
3000	2860.5–3143.8	2870.3–3154.0	2880.1–3164.3	2889.8–3174.5	2899.6–3184.7	2909.4–3195.0	2919.1–3205.2	2928.9–3215.4	2938.7–3225.7	2948.4–3235.9
3100	2958.2–3246.1	2968.0–3256.4	2977.7–3266.6	2987.5–3276.8	2997.3–3287.1	3007.0–3297.3	3016.8–3307.5	3026.6–3317.8	3036.4–3328.0	3046.1–3338.2
3200	3055.9–3348.4	3065.7–3358.7	3075.4–3368.9	3085.2–3379.1	3095.0–3389.3	3104.8–3399.6	3114.5–3409.8	3124.3–3420.0	3134.1–3430.2	3143.9–3440.5
3300	3153.6–3450.7	3163.4–3460.9	3173.2–3471.1	3183.0–3481.4	3192.7–3491.6	3202.5–3501.8	3212.3–3512.0	3222.1–3522.3	3231.9–3532.5	3241.6–3542.7
3400	3251.4–3552.9	3261.2–3563.1	3271.0–3573.4	3280.8–3583.6	3290.5–3593.8	3300.3–3604.0	3310.1–3614.2	3319.9–3624.5	3329.7–3634.7	3339.4–3644.9
3500	3349.2–3655.1	3359.0–3665.3	3368.8–3675.5	3378.6–3685.8	3388.4–3696.0	3398.1–3706.2	3407.9–3716.4	3417.7–3726.6	3427.5–3736.8	3437.3–3747.1
3600	3447.1–3757.3	3456.8–3767.5	3466.6–3777.7	3476.4–3787.9	3486.2–3798.1	3496.0–3808.3	3505.8–3818.6	3515.6–3828.8	3525.4–3839.0	3535.1–3849.2
3700	3544.9–3859.4	3554.7–3869.6	3564.5–3879.8	3574.3–3890.0	3584.1–3900.3	3593.9–3910.5	3603.7–3920.7	3613.5–3930.9	3623.2–3941.1	3633.0–3951.3
3800	3642.8–3961.5	3652.6–3971.7	3662.4–3981.9	3672.2–3992.1	3682.0–4002.3	3691.8–4012.6	3701.6–4022.8	3711.4–4033.0	3721.2–4043.2	3731.0–4053.4
3900	3740.8–4063.6	3750.5–4073.8	3760.3–4084.0	3770.1–4094.2	3779.9–4104.4	3789.7–4114.6	3799.5–4124.8	3809.3–4135.0	3819.1–4145.2	3828.9–4155.4
4000	3838.7–4165.6	3848.5–4175.8	3858.3–4186.0	3868.1–4196.2	3877.9–4206.4	3887.7–4216.6	3897.5–4226.9	3907.3–4237.1	3917.1–4247.3	3926.9–4257.5
4100	3936.7–4267.7	3946.5–4277.9	3956.3–4288.1	3966.1–4298.3	3975.9–4308.5	3985.7–4318.7	3995.5–4328.9	4005.3–4339.1	4015.1–4349.3	4024.9–4359.5
4200	4034.7–4369.7	4044.5–4379.9	4054.3–4390.1	4064.1–4400.3	4073.9–4410.4	4083.7–4420.6	4093.5–4430.8	4103.3–4441.0	4113.1–4451.2	4122.9–4461.4
4300	4132.7–4471.6	4142.5–4481.8	4152.3–4492.0	4162.1–4502.2	4171.9–4512.4	4181.7–4522.6	4191.5–4532.8	4201.3–4543.0	4211.1–4553.2	4220.9–4563.4
4400	4230.8–4573.6	4240.6–4583.8	4250.4–4594.0	4260.2–4604.2	4270.0–4614.4	4279.8–4624.6	4289.6–4634.7	4299.4–4644.9	4309.2–4655.1	4319.0–4665.3
4500	4328.8–4675.5	4338.6–4685.7	4348.4–4695.9	4358.2–4706.1	4368.1–4716.3	4377.9–4726.5	4387.7–4736.7	4397.5–4746.9	4407.3–4757.0	4417.1–4767.2
4600	4426.9–4777.4	4436.7–4787.6	4446.5–4797.8	4456.3–4808.0	4466.2–4818.2	4476.0–4828.4	4485.8–4838.6	4495.6–4848.7	4505.4–4858.9	4515.2–4869.1
4700	4525.0–4879.3	4534.8–4889.5	4544.6–4899.7	4554.5–4909.9	4564.3–4920.1	4574.1–4930.2	4583.9–4940.4	4593.7–4950.6	4603.5–4960.8	4613.3–4971.0
4800	4623.2–4981.2	4633.0–4991.4	4642.8–5001.6	4652.6–5011.7	4662.4–5021.9	4672.2–5032.1	4682.0–5042.3	4691.9–5052.5	4701.7–5062.7	4711.5–5072.8
4900	4721.3–5083.0	4731.1–5093.2	4740.9–5103.4	4750.8–5113.6	4760.6–5123.8	4770.4–5134.0	4780.2–5144.1	4790.0–5154.3	4799.8–5164.5	4809.7–5174.7
5000	4819.5–5184.9	4917.7–5286.7	5015.9–5388.5	5114.1–5490.2	5212.3–5592.0	5310.6–5693.7	5408.9–5795.5	5507.1–5897.2	5605.4–5998.9	5703.8–6100.6
6000	5802.1–6202.2	5900.4–6303.9	5998.8–6405.5	6097.2–6507.2	6195.5–6608.8	6293.9–6710.4	6392.4–6812.0	6490.8–6913.6	6589.2–7015.1	6687.6–7116.7
7000	6786.1–7218.2	6884.6–7319.8	6983.0–7421.3	7081.5–7522.8	7180.0–7624.3	7278.5–7725.8	7377.1–7827.3	7475.6–7928.7	7574.1–8030.2	7672.7–8131.7
8000	7771.2–8233.1	7869.8–8334.5	7968.4–8436.0	8066.9–8537.4	8165.5–8638.8	8264.1–8740.2	8362.7–8841.6	8461.4–8943.0	8560.0–9044.4	8658.6–9145.7
9000	8757.2–9247.1	8855.9–9348.4	8954.5–9449.8	9053.2–9551.1	9151.9–9652.5	9250.6–9753.8	9349.2–9855.1	9447.9–9956.4	9546.6–10058	9645.3–10159
10000	9744.0–10261	9842.7–10362	9941.5–10463	10040–10565	10138–10666	10237–10767	10336–10868	10435–10970	10533–11071	10632–11172
11000	10731–11273	10830–11375	10929–11476	11027–11577	11126–11678	11225–11779	11324–11881	11423–11982	11521–12083	11620–12184
12000	11719–12285	11818–12387	11917–12488	12015–12589	12114–12690	12213–12791	12312–12892	12411–12993	12510–13095	12609–13196
13000	12707–13297	12806–13398	12905–13499	13004–13600	13103–13701	13202–13802	13301–13904	13400–14005	13499–14106	13597–14207
14000	13696–14308	13795–14409	13894–14510	13993–14611	14092–14712	14191–14813	14290–14914	14389–15015	14488–15117	14587–15218
15000	14686–15319	14785–15420	14884–15521	14983–15622	15082–15723	15180–15824	15279–15925	15378–16026	15477–16127	15576–16228
16000	15675–16329	15774–16430	15873–16531	15972–16632	16071–16733	16170–16834	16269–16935	16368–17036	16467–17137	16566–17238
17000	16665–17339	16764–17440	16863–17541	16962–17642	17061–17743	17160–17844	17259–17945	17358–18046	17458–18147	17557–18248
18000	17656–18349	17755–18450	17854–18551	17953–18652	18052–18753	18151–18854	18250–18954	18349–19055	18448–19156	18547–19257
19000	18646–19358	18745–19459	18844–19560	18943–19661	19042–19762	19141–19863	19241–19964	19340–20065	19439–20166	19538–20267
20000	19637–20367	19736–20468	19835–20569	19934–20670	20033–20771	20132–20872	20231–20973	20331–21074	20430–21175	20529–21276
21000	20628–21376	20727–21477	20826–21578	20925–21679	21024–21780	21123–21881	21223–21982	21322–22083	21421–22183	21520–22284
22000	21619–22385	21718–22486	21817–22587	21917–22688	22016–22789	22115–22890	22214–22990	22313–23091	22412–23192	22511–23293
23000	22611–23394	22710–23495	22809–23596	22908–23696	23007–23797	23106–23898	23205–23999	23305–24100	23404–24201	23503–24301
24000	23602–24401	23701–24503	23800–24604	23900–24705	23999–24806	24098–24906	24197–25007	24296–25108	24396–25209	24495–25310
25000	24594–25410	24693–25511	24792–25612	24891–25713	24991–25814	25090–25914	25189–26015	25288–26116	25387–26217	25487–26318
26000	25586–26419	25685–26519	25784–26620	25883–26721	25983–26822	26082–26922	26181–27023	26280–27124	26379–27225	26479–27326
27000	26578–27426	26677–27527	26776–27628	26876–27729	26975–27830	27074–27930	27173–28031	27272–28132	27372–28233	27471–28333
28000	27570–28434	27669–28535	27769–28636	27868–28736	27967–28837	28066–28938	28166–29039	28265–29140	28364–29240	28463–29341
29000	28563–29442	28662–29543	28761–29644	28860–29744	28960–29845	29059–29946	29158–30046	29257–30147	29357–30248	29456–30349
30000	29555–30449	29654–30550	29754–30651	29853–30752	29952–30852	30051–30953	30151–31054	30250–31154	30349–31255	30448–31356
31000	30548–31457	30647–31556	30746–31658	30845–31759	30945–31860	31044–31960	31143–32061	31243–32162	31342–32263	31441–32363
32000	31540–32464	31640–32565	31739–32665	31838–32766	31938–32867	32037–32968	32136–33068	32235–33169	32335–33270	32434–33370
33000	32533–33471	32633–33572	32732–33672	32831–33773	32930–33874	33030–33975	33129–34075	33228–34176	33328–34277	33427–34377
34000	33526–34478	33626–34579	33725–34680	33824–34780	33923–34881	34023–34982	34122–35082	34221–35183	34321–35284	34420–35384
35000	34519–35485	34619–35586	34718–35686	34817–35787	34917–35888	35016–35988	35115–36089	35214–36190	35314–36291	35413–36391
36000	35512–36492	35612–36593	35711–36693	35810–36794	35910–36895	36009–36995	36108–37096	36208–37197	36307–37297	36406–37398
37000	36506–37499	36605–37599	36704–37700	36804–37801	36903–37901	37002–38002	37102–38103	37201–38203	37300–38304	37400–38405
38000	37499–38505	37598–38606	37698–38707	37797–38807	37896–38908	37996–39009	38095–39109	38194–39210	38294–39311	38393–39411
39000	38492–39512	38592–39612	38691–39713	38791–39814	38890–39914	38989–40015	39089–40116	39188–40216	39287–40317	39387–40418
40000	39486–40518	39585–40619	39685–40720	39784–40820	39883–40921	39983–41022	40082–41122	40182–41223	40281–41323	40380–41424
41000	40480–41525	40579–41625	40678–41726	40778–41827	40877–41927	40976–42028	41076–42129	41175–42229	41275–42330	41374–42430
42000	41473–42531	41573–42632	41672–42732	41771–42833	41871–42934	41970–43034	42070–43135	42169–43235	42268–43336	42368–43437
43000	42467–43537	42566–43638	42666–43739	42765–43839	42865–43940	42964–44040	43063–44141	43163–44242	43262–44342	43361–44443
44000	43461–44543	43560–44644	43660–44745	43759–44845	43858–44946	43958–45047	44057–45147	44157–45248	44256–45348	44355–45449

Significance Limits for the Fourfold Table Test*

x_1	$N_1 - x_1$	N_1
x_2	$N_2 - x_2$	N_2
X	$N - X$	N

$N = N_1 + N_2$, $X = x_1 + x_2$, $N_1 \leqq N_2$, $x_1 \leqq N_1 - x_1$

For explanation see page 123

N_1	x_1	2α = 0.20	2α = 0.10	2α = 0.05	2α = 0.02	2α = 0.01	2α = 0.002
N = 8							
4	0	•–3	•–4	•–4	–	–	–
	1	•–5	–	–	–	–	–
	2	–	–	–	–	–	–
N = 9							
4	0	•–4	•–4	•–5	•–5	–	–
	1	•–6	•–6	–	–	–	–
	2	–	–	–	–	–	–
N = 10							
4	0	•–4	•–5	•–5	•–6	•–6	–
	1	•–7	•–7	–	–	–	–
	2	–	–	–	–	–	–
5	0	•–3	•–4	•–4	•–5	•–5	–
	1	•–6	•–6	•–6	–	–	–
	2	•–7	–	–	–	–	–
N = 11							
4	0	•–5	•–5	•–6	•–7	•–7	–
	1	•–7	•–8	•–8	–	–	–
	2	–	–	–	–	–	–
5	0	•–4	•–4	•–5	•–6	•–6	–
	1	•–6	•–7	•–7	–	–	–
	2	•–8	–	–	–	–	–
N = 12							
4	0	•–5	•–6	•–7	•–8	•–8	–
	1	•–8	•–9	•–9	–	–	–
	2	2–10	–	–	–	–	–
5	0	•–4	•–5	•–6	•–6	•–7	–
	1	•–7	•–7	•–8	–	–	–
	2	•–9	•–9	–	–	–	–
6	0	•–3	•–4	•–5	•–5	•–6	–
	1	•–6	•–6	•–7	•–7	–	–
	2	•–8	•–8	–	–	–	–
	3	3–9	–	–	–	–	–
N = 13							
4	0	•–5	•–6	•–7	•–8	•–9	–
	1	•–9	•–10	•–10	–	–	–
	2	2–11	–	–	–	–	–
5	0	•–4	•–5	•–6	•–7	•–7	•–8
	1	•–7	•–8	•–9	•–9	–	–
	2	•–10	•–10	–	–	–	–
6	0	•–4	•–4	•–5	•–6	•–6	•–7
	1	•–6	•–7	•–8	•–8	•–8	–
	2	•–8	•–9	•–9	–	–	–
	3	3–10	–	–	–	–	–
N = 14							
4	0	•–6	•–7	•–8	•–9	•–9	•–10
	1	•–9	•–10	•–11	–	–	–
	2	2–12	–	–	–	–	–
5	0	•–5	•–6	•–7	•–8	•–8	•–9
	1	•–8	•–9	•–9	•–10	•–10	–
	2	•–10	•–11	–	–	–	–
6	0	•–4	•–5	•–6	•–6	•–7	•–8
	1	•–7	•–8	•–8	•–9	•–9	–
	2	•–9	•–10	•–10	–	–	–
	3	3–11	–	–	–	–	–
7	0	•–3	•–4	•–5	•–6	•–6	•–7
	1	•–6	•–7	•–7	•–8	•–8	–
	2	•–8	•–9	•–9	–	–	–
	3	3–10	•–10	–	–	–	–
N = 15							
4	0	•–6	•–8	•–9	•–10	•–10	•–11
	1	•–10	•–11	•–12	•–12	–	–
	2	2–13	–	–	–	–	–
5	0	•–5	•–6	•–7	•–8	•–9	•–10
	1	•–9	•–9	•–10	•–11	•–11	–
	2	2–11	•–12	•–12	–	–	–
6	0	•–4	•–5	•–6	•–7	•–8	•–9
	1	•–7	•–8	•–9	•–10	•–10	–
	2	•–10	•–10	•–11	–	–	–
	3	3–12	3–12	–	–	–	–
7	0	•–4	•–5	•–5	•–6	•–7	•–8
	1	•–6	•–7	•–8	•–8	•–9	–
	2	•–9	•–9	•–10	•–10	–	–
	3	3–11	•–11	–	–	–	–
N = 16							
4	0	•–7	•–8	•–9	•–10	•–11	•–12
	1	•–11	•–12	•–13	•–13	–	–
	2	2–14	–	–	–	–	–
5	0	•–6	•–7	•–8	•–9	•–9	•–11
	1	•–9	•–10	•–11	•–12	•–12	–
	2	2–12	•–13	•–13	–	–	–
N = 16 (continued)							
6	0	•–5	•–6	•–7	•–8	•–8	•–9
	1	•–8	•–9	•–9	•–10	•–11	–
	2	•–10	•–11	•–12	•–12	–	–
	3	3–13	3–13	–	–	–	–
7	0	•–4	•–5	•–6	•–7	•–7	•–8
	1	•–7	•–8	•–8	•–9	•–10	•–10
	2	•–9	•–10	•–10	•–11	•–11	–
	3	3–11	•–12	•–12	–	–	–
8	0	•–3	•–4	•–5	•–6	•–6	•–7
	1	•–6	•–7	•–7	•–8	•–9	•–9
	2	•–8	•–9	•–9	•–10	•–10	–
	3	•–10	•–11	•–11	–	–	–
	4	4–12	4–12	–	–	–	–
N = 17							
4	0	•–7	•–9	•–10	•–11	•–12	•–13
	1	•–11	•–13	•–13	•–14	–	–
	2	2–15	2–15	–	–	–	–
5	0	•–6	•–7	•–8	•–9	•–10	•–11
	1	•–10	•–11	•–12	•–12	•–13	–
	2	2–13	•–14	•–14	–	–	–
6	0	•–5	•–6	•–7	•–8	•–9	•–10
	1	•–8	•–9	•–10	•–11	•–12	•–12
	2	•–11	•–12	•–13	•–13	–	–
	3	4–13	3–14	–	–	–	–
7	0	•–4	•–5	•–6	•–7	•–8	•–9
	1	•–7	•–8	•–9	•–10	•–10	•–11
	2	•–10	•–11	•–11	•–12	•–12	–
	3	3–12	•–13	•–13	–	–	–
8	0	•–4	•–5	•–5	•–6	•–7	•–8
	1	•–6	•–7	•–8	•–9	•–9	•–10
	2	•–9	•–9	•–10	•–11	•–11	–
	3	3–11	•–11	•–12	•–12	–	–
	4	4–13	4–13	–	–	–	–
N = 18							
4	0	•–8	•–9	•–10	•–12	•–12	•–14
	1	•–12	•–13	•–14	•–15	•–15	–
	2	2–16	2–16	–	–	–	–
5	0	•–6	•–8	•–9	•–10	•–11	•–12
	1	•–10	•–11	•–12	•–13	•–14	–
	2	2–13	•–14	•–15	–	–	–
6	0	•–5	•–6	•–7	•–9	•–9	•–11
	1	•–9	•–10	•–11	•–12	•–12	•–13
	2	2–12	•–13	•–13	•–14	•–14	–
	3	4–14	3–15	3–15	–	–	–
7	0	•–5	•–6	•–6	•–8	•–8	•–10
	1	•–8	•–9	•–9	•–10	•–11	•–12
	2	•–10	•–11	•–12	•–13	•–13	–
	3	3–13	3–13	•–14	–	–	–
8	0	•–4	•–5	•–6	•–7	•–7	•–9
	1	•–7	•–8	•–8	•–9	•–10	•–11
	2	•–9	•–10	•–11	•–11	•–12	–
	3	3–11	•–12	•–13	•–13	–	–
	4	5–13	4–14	4–14	–	–	–
9	0	•–4	•–4	•–5	•–6	•–6	•–8
	1	•–6	•–7	•–7	•–8	•–9	•–10
	2	•–8	•–9	•–10	•–10	•–11	–
	3	•–10	•–11	•–11	•–12	•–12	–
	4	4–12	4–13	•–13	–	–	–
N = 19							
4	0	•–8	•–10	•–11	•–12	•–13	•–15
	1	•–13	•–14	•–15	•–16	•–16	–
	2	3–16	2–17	–	–	–	–
5	0	•–7	•–8	•–9	•–11	•–11	•–13
	1	•–11	•–12	•–13	•–14	•–15	–
	2	2–14	•–15	•–16	–	–	–
6	0	•–6	•–7	•–8	•–9	•–10	•–12
	1	•–9	•–10	•–11	•–12	•–13	•–14
	2	2–12	•–13	•–14	•–15	•–15	–
	3	4–15	3–16	3–16	–	–	–
7	0	•–5	•–6	•–7	•–8	•–9	•–10
	1	•–8	•–9	•–10	•–11	•–12	•–13
	2	•–11	•–12	•–13	•–13	•–14	–
	3	3–13	3–14	•–15	•–15	–	–
8	0	•–4	•–5	•–6	•–7	•–8	•–9
	1	•–7	•–8	•–9	•–10	•–10	•–12
	2	•–10	•–11	•–11	•–12	•–13	–
	3	3–12	•–13	•–13	•–14	•–14	–
	4	5–14	4–15	4–15	–	–	–
9	0	•–4	•–5	•–5	•–6	•–7	•–8
	1	•–6	•–7	•–8	•–9	•–9	•–10
	2	•–9	•–10	•–10	•–11	•–11	•–12
	3	3–11	•–12	•–12	•–13	•–13	–
	4	4–13	4–13	•–14	–	–	–
N = 20							
4	0	•–9	•–10	•–12	•–13	•–14	•–16
	1	•–14	•–15	•–16	•–17	•–17	–
	2	3–17	2–18	–	–	–	–
N = 20 (continued)							
5	0	•–7	•–9	•–10	•–11	•–12	•–14
	1	•–11	•–13	•–14	•–15	•–15	–
	2	2–15	•–16	•–17	•–17	–	–
6	0	•–6	•–7	•–8	•–10	•–11	•–12
	1	•–10	•–11	•–12	•–13	•–14	•–15
	2	2–13	•–14	•–15	•–16	•–16	–
	3	4–16	3–17	3–17	–	–	–
7	0	•–5	•–6	•–7	•–9	•–9	•–11
	1	•–9	•–10	•–11	•–12	•–12	•–14
	2	•–12	•–13	•–13	•–14	•–15	–
	3	3–14	3–15	•–16	•–16	–	–
8	0	•–5	•–6	•–6	•–8	•–8	•–10
	1	•–8	•–9	•–9	•–10	•–11	•–12
	2	•–10	•–11	•–12	•–13	•–13	•–14
	3	3–13	3–14	•–14	•–15	•–15	–
	4	5–15	4–16	4–16	–	–	–
9	0	•–4	•–5	•–6	•–7	•–7	•–9
	1	•–7	•–8	•–8	•–9	•–10	•–11
	2	•–9	•–10	•–11	•–12	•–12	•–13
	3	3–11	•–12	•–13	•–14	•–14	–
	4	5–14	4–14	•–15	•–15	–	–
10	0	•–4	•–4	•–5	•–6	•–7	•–8
	1	•–6	•–7	•–8	•–8	•–9	•–10
	2	•–8	•–9	•–10	•–11	•–11	•–12
	3	•–10	•–11	•–12	•–12	•–13	–
	4	4–12	4–13	•–14	•–14	–	–
	5	6–14	5–15	5–15	–	–	–
N = 21							
4	0	•–9	•–11	•–12	•–14	•–15	•–16
	1	•–14	•–16	•–17	•–18	•–18	–
	2	3–18	2–19	–	–	–	–
5	0	•–7	•–9	•–10	•–12	•–13	•–15
	1	•–12	•–13	•–15	•–16	•–16	•–17
	2	2–16	2–17	•–18	•–18	–	–
6	0	•–6	•–8	•–9	•–10	•–11	•–13
	1	•–10	•–12	•–13	•–14	•–15	•–16
	2	2–14	•–15	•–16	•–17	•–17	–
	3	4–17	3–18	3–18	–	–	–
7	0	•–5	•–7	•–8	•–9	•–10	•–12
	1	•–9	•–10	•–11	•–12	•–13	•–14
	2	•–12	•–13	•–14	•–15	•–16	–
	3	4–15	3–16	•–17	•–17	–	–
8	0	•–5	•–6	•–7	•–8	•–9	•–10
	1	•–8	•–9	•–10	•–11	•–12	•–13
	2	•–11	•–12	•–13	•–14	•–14	•–15
	3	3–13	3–14	•–15	•–16	•–16	–
	4	5–16	5–16	4–17	–	–	–
9	0	•–4	•–5	•–6	•–7	•–8	•–9
	1	•–7	•–8	•–9	•–10	•–11	•–12
	2	•–10	•–11	•–11	•–12	•–13	•–14
	3	3–12	•–13	•–14	•–14	•–15	–
	4	5–14	4–15	4–16	•–16	–	–
10	0	•–4	•–5	•–5	•–6	•–7	•–8
	1	•–6	•–7	•–8	•–9	•–10	•–11
	2	•–9	•–10	•–10	•–11	•–12	•–13
	3	3–11	•–12	•–12	•–13	•–14	–
	4	4–13	4–14	•–14	•–15	•–15	–
	5	6–15	5–16	5–16	–	–	–
N = 22							
4	0	•–9	•–11	•–13	•–14	•–15	•–17
	1	•–15	•–16	•–17	•–18	•–19	–
	2	3–19	2–20	–	–	–	–
5	0	•–8	•–9	•–11	•–12	•–13	•–15
	1	•–13	•–14	•–15	•–16	•–17	•–18
	2	2–17	2–18	•–18	•–19	–	–
6	0	•–7	•–8	•–9	•–11	•–12	•–14
	1	•–11	•–12	•–13	•–15	•–15	•–17
	2	2–14	•–16	•–17	•–17	•–18	–
	3	4–18	4–18	3–19	–	–	–
7	0	•–6	•–7	•–8	•–10	•–10	•–12
	1	•–10	•–11	•–12	•–13	•–14	•–15
	2	2–13	•–14	•–15	•–16	•–16	•–17
	3	4–16	3–17	3–17	•–18	•–18	–
8	0	•–5	•–6	•–7	•–8	•–9	•–11
	1	•–8	•–10	•–11	•–12	•–12	•–14
	2	•–11	•–12	•–13	•–14	•–15	•–16
	3	3–14	3–15	•–16	•–17	•–17	–
	4	6–16	5–17	4–18	4–18	–	–
9	0	•–4	•–5	•–6	•–8	•–8	•–10
	1	•–8	•–9	•–9	•–11	•–11	•–13
	2	•–10	•–11	•–12	•–13	•–14	•–15
	3	3–13	•–14	•–14	•–15	•–16	–
	4	5–15	4–16	4–16	•–17	•–17	–
10	0	•–4	•–5	•–6	•–7	•–7	•–9
	1	•–7	•–8	•–9	•–10	•–10	•–11
	2	•–9	•–10	•–11	•–12	•–12	•–14
	3	3–11	•–12	•–13	•–14	•–14	•–15
	4	4–14	4–14	•–15	•–16	•–16	–
	5	6–16	6–16	5–17	5–17	–	–
11	0	•–4	•–4	•–5	•–6	•–7	•–8

Significance Limits for the Fourfold Table Test*

x_1	$N_1 - x_1$	N_1
x_2	$N_2 - x_2$	N_2
X	$N - X$	N

$N = N_1 + N_2$, $X = x_1 + x_2$, $N_1 \leqq N_2$, $x_1 \leqq N_1 - x_1$

For explanation see page 123

N_1	x_1	2α = 0.20	2α = 0.10	2α = 0.05	2α = 0.02	2α = 0.01	2α = 0.002
		$N = 22$ (continued)					
11	1	•-6	•-7	•-8	•-9	•-9	•-10
	2	•-8	•-9	•-10	•-11	•-11	•-12
	3	•-10	•-11	•-12	•-13	•-13	•-14
	4	4-12	4-13	•-14	•-15	•-15	–
	5	6-14	5-15	5-16	•-16	–	–
		$N = 23$					
4	0	•-10	•-12	•-13	•-15	•-16	•-18
	1	•-16	•-17	•-18	•-19	•-20	–
	2	3-20	2-21	2-21	–	–	–
5	0	•-8	•-10	•-11	•-13	•-14	•-16
	1	•-13	•-15	•-16	•-17	•-18	•-19
	2	2-17	2-18	•-19	•-20	–	–
6	0	•-7	•-8	•-10	•-11	•-12	•-14
	1	•-11	•-13	•-14	•-15	•-16	•-18
	2	2-15	•-16	•-17	•-18	•-19	–
	3	5-18	4-19	3-20	–	–	–
7	0	•-6	•-7	•-9	•-10	•-11	•-13
	1	•-10	•-11	•-12	•-14	•-14	•-16
	2	2-13	•-15	•-16	•-17	•-17	•-18
	3	4-16	3-17	3-18	•-19	•-19	–
8	0	•-5	•-6	•-8	•-9	•-10	•-12
	1	•-9	•-10	•-11	•-12	•-13	•-15
	2	•-12	•-13	•-14	•-15	•-16	•-17
	3	3-15	3-16	•-17	•-17	•-18	–
	4	6-17	5-18	4-19	4-19	–	–
9	0	•-5	•-6	•-7	•-8	•-9	•-10
	1	•-8	•-9	•-10	•-11	•-12	•-13
	2	•-11	•-12	•-13	•-14	•-14	•-16
	3	3-13	3-14	•-15	•-16	•-16	•-17
	4	5-16	4-17	4-17	•-18	•-18	–
10	0	•-4	•-5	•-6	•-7	•-8	•-9
	1	•-7	•-8	•-9	•-10	•-11	•-12
	2	•-10	•-11	•-12	•-13	•-13	•-14
	3	3-12	•-13	•-14	•-15	•-15	•-16
	4	5-14	4-15	4-16	•-17	•-17	–
	5	7-16	6-17	5-18	5-18	–	–
11	0	•-4	•-5	•-5	•-6	•-7	•-9
	1	•-6	•-7	•-8	•-9	•-10	•-11
	2	•-9	•-10	•-11	•-11	•-12	•-13
	3	3-11	•-12	•-13	•-14	•-14	•-15
	4	4-13	4-14	•-15	•-15	•-16	–
	5	6-15	5-16	5-16	•-17	•-17	–
		$N = 24$					
4	0	•-10	•-12	•-14	•-16	•-17	•-19
	1	•-16	•-18	•-19	•-20	•-21	–
	2	3-21	2-22	2-22	–	–	–
5	0	•-9	•-10	•-12	•-14	•-15	•-17
	1	•-14	•-15	•-17	•-18	•-19	•-20
	2	3-18	2-19	•-20	•-21	•-21	–
6	0	•-7	•-9	•-10	•-12	•-13	•-15
	1	•-12	•-13	•-15	•-16	•-17	•-18
	2	2-16	•-17	•-18	•-19	•-20	–
	3	5-19	4-20	3-21	3-21	–	–
7	0	•-6	•-8	•-9	•-10	•-11	•-13
	1	•-10	•-12	•-13	•-14	•-15	•-17
	2	2-14	•-15	•-16	•-17	•-18	•-19
	3	4-17	3-18	3-19	•-20	•-20	–
8	0	•-6	•-7	•-8	•-9	•-10	•-12
	1	•-9	•-11	•-12	•-13	•-14	•-15
	2	•-12	•-14	•-15	•-16	•-16	•-18
	3	4-15	3-16	•-17	•-18	•-19	–
	4	6-18	5-19	4-20	4-20	–	–
9	0	•-5	•-6	•-7	•-8	•-9	•-11
	1	•-8	•-9	•-10	•-12	•-12	•-14
	2	•-11	•-12	•-13	•-14	•-15	•-16
	3	3-14	3-15	•-16	•-17	•-17	•-18
	4	5-16	5-17	4-18	•-19	•-19	–
10	0	•-4	•-5	•-6	•-7	•-8	•-10
	1	•-7	•-9	•-9	•-11	•-11	•-13
	2	•-10	•-11	•-12	•-13	•-14	•-15
	3	3-13	•-14	•-14	•-15	•-16	•-17
	4	5-15	4-16	4-17	•-17	•-18	–
	5	7-17	6-18	5-19	5-19	–	–
11	0	•-4	•-5	•-6	•-7	•-7	•-9
	1	•-7	•-8	•-9	•-10	•-10	•-12
	2	•-9	•-10	•-11	•-12	•-13	•-14
	3	3-12	•-12	•-13	•-14	•-15	•-16
	4	4-14	4-15	•-15	•-16	•-17	•-17
	5	6-16	6-17	5-17	•-18	•-18	–
12	0	•-4	•-4	•-5	•-6	•-7	•-8
	1	•-6	•-7	•-8	•-9	•-9	•-11
	2	•-8	•-9	•-10	•-11	•-12	•-13
	3	•-11	•-11	•-12	•-13	•-14	•-15
	4	4-13	4-13	•-14	•-15	•-15	•-16
	5	6-15	5-15	5-16	•-17	•-17	–
	6	8-16	7-17	6-18	6-18	–	–
		$N = 25$					
4	0	•-11	•-13	•-15	•-16	•-18	•-20
	1	•-17	•-19	•-20	•-21	•-22	–
	2	3-22	2-23	2-23	–	–	–
		$N = 25$ (continued)					
5	0	•-9	•-11	•-12	•-14	•-15	•-18
	1	•-14	•-16	•-17	•-19	•-20	•-21
	2	3-19	2-20	•-21	•-22	•-22	–
6	0	•-8	•-9	•-11	•-12	•-14	•-16
	1	•-12	•-14	•-15	•-17	•-18	•-19
	2	2-16	•-18	•-19	•-20	•-21	–
	3	5-20	4-21	3-22	3-22	–	–
7	0	•-7	•-8	•-9	•-11	•-12	•-14
	1	•-11	•-12	•-14	•-15	•-16	•-18
	2	2-15	•-16	•-17	•-18	•-19	•-20
	3	4-18	3-19	3-20	•-21	•-21	–
8	0	•-6	•-7	•-8	•-10	•-11	•-13
	1	•-10	•-11	•-12	•-13	•-14	•-16
	2	2-13	•-14	•-15	•-16	•-17	•-19
	3	4-16	3-17	3-18	•-19	•-20	–
	4	6-19	5-20	5-20	4-21	–	–
9	0	•-5	•-6	•-7	•-9	•-10	•-11
	1	•-9	•-10	•-11	•-12	•-13	•-15
	2	•-12	•-13	•-14	•-15	•-16	•-17
	3	3-14	3-16	•-17	•-17	•-18	•-19
	4	6-17	5-18	4-19	4-20	•-20	–
10	0	•-5	•-6	•-7	•-8	•-9	•-10
	1	•-8	•-9	•-10	•-11	•-12	•-13
	2	•-11	•-12	•-13	•-14	•-14	•-16
	3	3-13	•-14	•-15	•-16	•-17	•-18
	4	5-16	4-17	4-17	•-18	•-19	–
	5	7-18	6-19	6-19	5-20	5-20	–
11	0	•-4	•-5	•-6	•-7	•-8	•-9
	1	•-7	•-8	•-9	•-10	•-11	•-12
	2	•-10	•-11	•-12	•-13	•-13	•-15
	3	3-12	•-13	•-14	•-15	•-15	•-17
	4	5-14	4-15	•-16	•-17	•-17	•-18
	5	6-16	6-17	5-18	5-19	•-19	–
12	0	•-4	•-5	•-5	•-6	•-7	•-9
	1	•-6	•-7	•-8	•-9	•-10	•-11
	2	•-9	•-10	•-11	•-12	•-12	•-14
	3	3-11	•-12	•-13	•-14	•-14	•-15
	4	4-13	4-14	•-15	•-16	•-16	•-17
	5	6-15	5-16	5-17	•-17	•-18	–
	6	8-17	7-18	6-19	6-19	–	–
		$N = 26$					
4	0	•-11	•-13	•-15	•-17	•-18	•-21
	1	•-18	•-19	•-21	•-22	•-23	–
	2	4-22	2-24	2-24	–	–	–
5	0	•-9	•-11	•-13	•-15	•-16	•-18
	1	•-15	•-17	•-18	•-20	•-20	•-22
	2	3-20	2-21	•-22	•-23	•-23	–
6	0	•-8	•-10	•-11	•-13	•-14	•-16
	1	•-13	•-15	•-16	•-17	•-18	•-20
	2	2-17	2-19	•-20	•-21	•-21	–
	3	5-21	4-22	3-23	3-23	–	–
7	0	•-7	•-8	•-10	•-11	•-13	•-15
	1	•-11	•-13	•-14	•-16	•-17	•-18
	2	2-15	•-17	•-18	•-19	•-20	•-21
	3	4-19	4-20	3-21	•-22	•-22	–
8	0	•-6	•-7	•-9	•-10	•-11	•-13
	1	•-10	•-11	•-13	•-14	•-15	•-17
	2	2-14	•-15	•-16	•-17	•-18	•-19
	3	4-17	3-18	3-19	•-20	•-20	•-21
	4	6-20	5-21	5-21	4-22	4-22	–
9	0	•-5	•-7	•-8	•-9	•-10	•-12
	1	•-9	•-10	•-11	•-13	•-14	•-15
	2	•-12	•-13	•-15	•-16	•-16	•-18
	3	3-15	3-16	•-17	•-18	•-19	•-20
	4	6-18	5-19	4-20	4-20	•-21	–
10	0	•-5	•-6	•-7	•-8	•-9	•-11
	1	•-8	•-9	•-10	•-12	•-12	•-14
	2	•-11	•-12	•-13	•-14	•-15	•-17
	3	3-14	3-15	•-16	•-17	•-17	•-19
	4	5-16	4-17	4-18	•-19	•-20	•-20
	5	7-19	6-20	6-20	5-21	5-21	–
11	0	•-4	•-5	•-6	•-7	•-8	•-10
	1	•-7	•-8	•-9	•-11	•-11	•-13
	2	•-10	•-11	•-12	•-13	•-14	•-15
	3	3-13	•-14	•-15	•-16	•-16	•-17
	4	5-15	4-16	4-17	•-18	•-18	•-19
	5	7-17	6-18	5-19	5-20	•-20	–
12	0	•-4	•-5	•-6	•-7	•-8	•-9
	1	•-7	•-8	•-9	•-10	•-10	•-12
	2	•-9	•-10	•-11	•-12	•-13	•-14
	3	3-12	•-13	•-13	•-14	•-15	•-16
	4	4-14	4-15	•-16	•-16	•-17	•-18
	5	6-16	5-17	5-18	•-18	•-19	–
	6	8-18	7-19	7-19	6-20	6-20	–
13	0	•-4	•-4	•-5	•-6	•-7	•-8
	1	•-6	•-7	•-8	•-9	•-10	•-11
	2	•-9	•-9	•-10	•-11	•-12	•-13
	3	•-11	•-12	•-12	•-13	•-14	•-15
	4	4-13	4-14	•-14	•-15	•-16	•-17
	5	6-15	5-16	5-16	•-17	•-18	•-18
	6	7-17	7-17	6-18	6-19	•-19	–
		$N = 27$					
4	0	•-12	•-14	•-16	•-18	•-19	•-21
	1	•-18	•-20	•-21	•-23	•-24	–
	2	4-23	3-24	2-25	–	–	–
5	0	•-10	•-12	•-13	•-15	•-17	•-19
	1	•-16	•-17	•-19	•-20	•-21	•-23
	2	3-20	2-22	•-23	•-24	•-24	–
6	0	•-8	•-10	•-12	•-14	•-15	•-17
	1	•-13	•-15	•-17	•-18	•-19	•-21
	2	2-18	2-19	•-20	•-22	•-22	•-23
	3	5-22	4-23	4-23	3-24	–	–
7	0	•-7	•-9	•-10	•-12	•-13	•-15
	1	•-12	•-13	•-15	•-16	•-17	•-19
	2	2-16	•-17	•-18	•-20	•-20	•-22
	3	5-19	4-20	3-21	•-22	•-23	–
8	0	•-6	•-8	•-9	•-11	•-12	•-14
	1	•-10	•-12	•-13	•-15	•-16	•-17
	2	2-14	•-15	•-17	•-18	•-19	•-20
	3	4-17	3-19	3-20	•-21	•-21	•-22
	4	7-20	6-21	5-22	4-23	4-23	–
9	0	•-6	•-7	•-8	•-10	•-11	•-13
	1	•-9	•-11	•-12	•-13	•-14	•-16
	2	•-13	•-14	•-15	•-16	•-17	•-19
	3	4-16	3-17	•-18	•-19	•-20	•-21
	4	6-18	5-20	4-20	4-21	•-22	–
10	0	•-5	•-6	•-7	•-9	•-10	•-11
	1	•-8	•-10	•-11	•-12	•-13	•-15
	2	•-11	•-13	•-14	•-15	•-16	•-17
	3	3-14	3-15	•-16	•-18	•-18	•-19
	4	5-17	5-18	4-19	•-20	•-20	•-21
	5	8-19	7-20	6-21	5-22	5-22	–
11	0	•-5	•-6	•-7	•-8	•-9	•-10
	1	•-8	•-9	•-10	•-11	•-12	•-14
	2	•-10	•-12	•-13	•-14	•-15	•-16
	3	3-13	•-14	•-15	•-16	•-17	•-18
	4	5-16	4-17	4-17	•-18	•-19	•-20
	5	7-18	6-19	5-20	5-20	•-21	–
12	0	•-4	•-5	•-6	•-7	•-8	•-10
	1	•-7	•-8	•-9	•-10	•-11	•-12
	2	•-10	•-11	•-12	•-13	•-13	•-15
	3	3-12	•-13	•-14	•-15	•-16	•-17
	4	4-14	4-15	•-16	•-17	•-18	•-19
	5	6-17	6-17	5-18	5-19	•-20	•-20
	6	8-19	8-19	7-20	6-21	6-21	–
13	0	•-4	•-5	•-5	•-7	•-7	•-9
	1	•-6	•-7	•-8	•-9	•-10	•-12
	2	•-9	•-10	•-11	•-12	•-12	•-14
	3	3-11	•-12	•-13	•-14	•-15	•-16
	4	4-13	4-14	•-15	•-16	•-17	•-18
	5	6-15	5-16	5-17	•-18	•-18	•-19
	6	8-17	7-18	6-19	6-20	•-20	–
		$N = 28$					
4	0	•-12	•-14	•-16	•-19	•-20	•-22
	1	•-19	•-21	•-22	•-24	•-24	–
	2	4-24	3-25	2-26	–	–	–
5	0	•-10	•-12	•-14	•-16	•-17	•-20
	1	•-16	•-18	•-20	•-21	•-22	•-24
	2	3-21	2-23	•-24	•-25	•-25	–
6	0	•-9	•-10	•-12	•-14	•-15	•-18
	1	•-14	•-16	•-17	•-19	•-20	•-22
	2	2-18	2-20	•-21	•-22	•-23	•-24
	3	6-22	4-24	4-24	3-25	–	–
7	0	•-7	•-9	•-11	•-12	•-14	•-16
	1	•-12	•-14	•-15	•-17	•-18	•-20
	2	2-16	•-18	•-19	•-20	•-21	•-23
	3	5-20	4-21	3-22	•-23	•-24	–
8	0	•-7	•-8	•-9	•-11	•-12	•-14
	1	•-11	•-12	•-14	•-15	•-16	•-18
	2	2-15	•-16	•-17	•-19	•-19	•-21
	3	4-18	3-19	3-20	•-21	•-22	•-23
	4	7-21	6-22	5-23	4-24	4-24	–
9	0	•-6	•-7	•-8	•-10	•-11	•-13
	1	•-10	•-11	•-12	•-14	•-15	•-17
	2	2-13	•-15	•-16	•-17	•-18	•-19
	3	4-16	3-18	•-19	•-20	•-20	•-22
	4	6-19	5-20	4-21	4-22	•-23	–
10	0	•-5	•-6	•-8	•-9	•-10	•-12
	1	•-9	•-10	•-11	•-13	•-14	•-15
	2	•-12	•-13	•-14	•-16	•-16	•-18
	3	3-15	3-16	•-17	•-18	•-19	•-20
	4	6-18	5-19	4-20	•-21	•-21	•-22
	5	8-20	7-21	6-22	5-23	5-23	–
11	0	•-5	•-6	•-7	•-8	•-9	•-11
	1	•-8	•-9	•-10	•-12	•-12	•-14
	2	•-11	•-12	•-13	•-14	•-15	•-17
	3	3-14	•-15	•-16	•-17	•-18	•-19
	4	5-16	4-17	4-18	•-19	•-20	•-21
	5	7-19	6-20	6-20	5-21	5-22	–
12	0	•-4	•-5	•-6	•-7	•-8	•-10
	1	•-7	•-8	•-9	•-11	•-11	•-13
	2	•-10	•-11	•-12	•-13	•-14	•-16
	3	3-13	•-14	•-15	•-16	•-16	•-18
	4	5-15	4-16	4-17	•-18	•-18	•-20
	5	7-17	6-18	5-19	5-20	•-20	•-21

* Reproduction only by permission of the publishers of these *Scientific Tables*.

Significance Limits for the Fourfold Table Test*

x_1	$N_1 - x_1$	N_1
x_2	$N_2 - x_2$	N_2
X	$N - X$	N

$N = N_1 + N_2$, $X = x_1 + x_2$, $N_1 \leq N_2$, $x_1 \leq N_1 - x_1$

For explanation see page 123

N_1	x_1	2α = 0.20	2α = 0.10	2α = 0.05	2α = 0.02	2α = 0.01	2α = 0.002
N = 28 (continued)							
	6	9–19	8–20	7–21	6–22	6–22	–
13	0	•– 4	•– 5	•– 6	•– 7	•– 8	•– 9
	1	•– 7	•– 8	•– 9	•–10	•–11	•–12
	2	•– 9	•–10	•–11	•–12	•–13	•–14
	3	3–12	•–13	•–14	•–15	•–15	•–17
	4	4–14	4–15	•–16	•–17	•–17	•–18
	5	6–16	5–17	5–18	•–19	•–19	•–20
	6	8–18	7–19	7–20	6–20	6–21	–
14	0	•– 4	•– 4	•– 5	•– 6	•– 7	•– 8
	1	•– 6	•– 7	•– 8	•– 9	•–10	•–11
	2	•– 9	•–10	•–10	•–11	•–12	•–13
	3	•–11	•–12	•–13	•–14	•–14	•–15
	4	4–13	4–14	•–15	•–16	•–16	•–17
	5	6–15	5–16	5–17	•–17	•–18	•–19
	6	7–17	7–18	6–18	6–19	•–20	•–20
	7	9–19	8–20	8–20	7–21	7–21	–
N = 29							
4	0	•–13	•–15	•–17	•–19	•–21	•–23
	1	•–20	•–22	•–23	•–25	•–25	–
	2	4–25	3–26	2–27	–	–	–
5	0	•–10	•–13	•–15	•–17	•–18	•–21
	1	•–17	•–19	•–20	•–22	•–23	•–25
	2	3–22	2–23	2–24	•–26	•–26	–
6	0	•– 9	•–11	•–13	•–15	•–16	•–18
	1	•–14	•–16	•–18	•–20	•–21	•–22
	2	3–19	2–21	•–22	•–23	•–24	•–25
	3	6–23	5–24	4–25	3–26	–	–
7	0	•– 8	•– 9	•–11	•–13	•–14	•–17
	1	•–13	•–14	•–16	•–18	•–19	•–21
	2	2–17	•–19	•–20	•–21	•–22	•–23
	3	5–21	4–22	3–23	3–24	•–25	–
8	0	•– 7	•– 8	•–10	•–12	•–13	•–15
	1	•–11	•–13	•–14	•–16	•–17	•–19
	2	2–15	•–17	•–18	•–19	•–20	•–22
	3	4–19	3–20	3–21	•–22	•–23	•–24
	4	7–22	6–23	5–24	4–25	4–25	–
9	0	•– 6	•– 7	•– 9	•–10	•–11	•–14
	1	•–10	•–12	•–13	•–14	•–15	•–17
	2	2–14	•–15	•–16	•–18	•–19	•–20
	3	4–17	3–18	3–19	•–21	•–21	•–23
	4	6–20	5–21	5–22	4–23	•–24	–
10	0	•– 5	•– 7	•– 8	•– 9	•–10	•–12
	1	•– 9	•–11	•–12	•–13	•–14	•–16
	2	•–12	•–14	•–15	•–16	•–17	•–19
	3	3–15	3–17	•–18	•–19	•–20	•–21
	4	6–18	5–19	4–20	4–21	•–22	•–23
	5	8–21	7–22	6–23	5–24	5–24	–
11	0	•– 5	•– 6	•– 7	•– 9	•– 9	•–11
	1	•– 8	•–10	•–11	•–12	•–13	•–15
	2	•–11	•–13	•–14	•–15	•–16	•–17
	3	3–14	3–15	•–16	•–18	•–18	•–20
	4	5–17	4–18	4–19	•–20	•–21	•–22
	5	7–19	6–20	6–21	5–22	5–23	•–23
12	0	•– 5	•– 6	•– 7	•– 8	•– 9	•–10
	1	•– 8	•– 9	•–10	•–11	•–12	•–14
	2	•–10	•–12	•–13	•–14	•–15	•–16
	3	3–13	•–14	•–15	•–16	•–17	•–18
	4	5–15	4–17	4–18	•–19	•–19	•–20
	5	7–18	6–19	5–20	5–21	•–21	•–22
	6	9–20	8–21	7–22	6–23	6–23	–
13	0	•– 4	•– 5	•– 6	•– 7	•– 8	•–10
	1	•– 7	•– 8	•– 9	•–10	•–11	•–13
	2	•–10	•–11	•–12	•–13	•–14	•–15
	3	3–12	•–13	•–14	•–15	•–16	•–17
	4	4–14	4–15	•–16	•–17	•–18	•–19
	5	6–17	6–18	5–18	•–19	•–20	•–21
	6	8–19	7–20	7–20	6–21	6–22	–
14	0	•– 4	•– 5	•– 6	•– 7	•– 7	•– 9
	1	•– 6	•– 7	•– 8	•– 9	•–10	•–12
	2	•– 9	•–10	•–11	•–12	•–13	•–14
	3	3–11	•–12	•–13	•–14	•–15	•–16
	4	4–13	4–14	•–15	•–16	•–17	•–18
	5	6–15	5–16	5–17	•–18	•–19	•–20
	6	8–17	7–18	6–19	6–20	•–20	•–21
	7	10–19	9–20	8–21	7–22	7–22	–
N = 30							
4	0	•–13	•–15	•–18	•–20	•–21	•–24
	1	•–20	•–22	•–24	•–25	•–26	•–27
	2	4–26	3–27	2–28	–	–	–
5	0	•–11	•–13	•–15	•–17	•–19	•–21
	1	•–17	•–19	•–21	•–23	•–24	•–25
	2	3–23	2–24	2–25	•–26	•–27	–
6	0	•– 9	•–11	•–13	•–15	•–17	•–19
	1	•–15	•–17	•–19	•–20	•–21	•–23
	2	3–20	2–21	•–23	•–25	•–25	•–26
	3	6–24	5–25	4–26	3–27	3–27	–
7	0	•– 8	•–10	•–11	•–13	•–15	•–17
	1	•–13	•–15	•–17	•–18	•–19	•–21
	2	2–18	2–19	•–21	•–22	•–23	•–24
	3	5–21	4–23	3–24	3–25	•–26	–
8	0	•– 7	•– 9	•–10	•–12	•–13	•–16
	1	•–12	•–13	•–15	•–16	•–18	•–20

N_1	x_1	2α = 0.20	2α = 0.10	2α = 0.05	2α = 0.02	2α = 0.01	2α = 0.002
N = 30 (continued)							
	2	2–16	•–17	•–19	•–20	•–21	•–23
	3	4–19	4–21	3–22	•–23	•–24	•–25
	4	7–23	6–24	5–25	4–26	4–26	–
9	0	•– 6	•– 8	•– 9	•–11	•–12	•–14
	1	•–10	•–12	•–13	•–15	•–16	•–18
	2	2–14	•–16	•–17	•–18	•–19	•–21
	3	4–17	3–19	3–20	•–21	•–22	•–23
	4	7–21	6–22	5–23	4–24	4–24	•–25
10	0	•– 6	•– 7	•– 8	•–10	•–11	•–13
	1	•– 9	•–11	•–12	•–14	•–15	•–17
	2	•–13	•–14	•–16	•–17	•–18	•–19
	3	4–16	3–17	•–18	•–20	•–20	•–22
	4	6–19	5–20	4–21	4–22	•–23	•–24
	5	8–22	7–23	6–24	6–24	5–25	–
11	0	•– 5	•– 6	•– 7	•– 9	•–10	•–12
	1	•– 9	•–10	•–11	•–13	•–13	•–15
	2	•–12	•–13	•–14	•–16	•–16	•–18
	3	3–15	3–16	•–17	•–18	•–19	•–20
	4	5–17	5–19	5–19	4–20	•–21	•–23
	5	8–20	7–21	6–22	5–23	5–23	•–24
12	0	•– 5	•– 6	•– 7	•– 8	•– 9	•–11
	1	•– 8	•– 9	•–10	•–12	•–12	•–14
	2	•–11	•–12	•–13	•–14	•–15	•–17
	3	3–13	•–15	•–16	•–17	•–18	•–19
	4	5–16	4–17	4–18	•–19	•–20	•–21
	5	7–18	6–20	5–20	5–21	•–22	•–23
	6	9–21	8–22	7–23	7–23	6–24	–
13	0	•– 4	•– 5	•– 6	•– 7	•– 8	•–10
	1	•– 7	•– 8	•– 9	•–11	•–11	•–13
	2	•–10	•–11	•–12	•–13	•–14	•–16
	3	3–12	•–14	•–15	•–16	•–17	•–18
	4	5–15	4–16	•–17	•–18	•–19	•–20
	5	6–17	6–18	5–19	5–20	•–21	•–22
	6	9–19	8–20	7–21	6–22	6–23	•–23
14	0	•– 4	•– 5	•– 6	•– 7	•– 8	•– 9
	1	•– 7	•– 8	•– 9	•–10	•–11	•–12
	2	•– 9	•–10	•–11	•–12	•–13	•–15
	3	3–12	•–13	•–14	•–15	•–15	•–17
	4	4–14	4–15	•–16	•–17	•–18	•–19
	5	6–16	5–17	5–18	•–19	•–19	•–21
	6	8–18	7–19	6–20	6–21	•–21	•–22
	7	10–20	9–21	8–22	8–22	7–23	–
15	0	•– 4	•– 4	•– 5	•– 6	•– 7	•– 9
	1	•– 6	•– 7	•– 8	•– 9	•–10	•–11
	2	•– 9	•–10	•–11	•–12	•–12	•–14
	3	•–11	•–12	•–13	•–14	•–14	•–16
	4	4–13	4–14	•–15	•–16	•–16	•–18
	5	6–15	5–16	5–17	•–18	•–18	•–19
	6	7–17	7–18	6–19	6–20	•–20	•–21
	7	9–19	8–20	8–21	7–21	7–22	–
N = 31							
4	0	•–13	•–16	•–18	•–21	•–22	•–25
	1	•–21	•–23	•–25	•–26	•–27	•–28
	2	4–27	3–28	2–29	–	–	–
5	0	•–11	•–14	•–16	•–18	•–19	•–22
	1	•–18	•–20	•–22	•–23	•–25	•–26
	2	3–23	2–25	2–26	•–27	•–28	–
6	0	•–10	•–12	•–14	•–16	•–17	•–20
	1	•–15	•–18	•–19	•–21	•–22	•–24
	2	3–20	2–22	•–24	•–25	•–26	•–27
	3	6–25	5–26	4–27	3–28	3–28	–
7	0	•– 8	•–10	•–12	•–14	•–15	•–18
	1	•–14	•–16	•–17	•–19	•–20	•–22
	2	2–18	2–20	•–21	•–23	•–24	•–25
	3	5–22	4–24	3–25	3–26	•–27	–
8	0	•– 7	•– 9	•–11	•–12	•–14	•–16
	1	•–12	•–14	•–15	•–17	•–18	•–20
	2	2–16	•–18	•–19	•–21	•–22	•–23
	3	5–20	4–21	3–23	•–24	•–25	•–26
	4	8–23	6–25	5–26	5–26	4–27	–
9	0	•– 7	•– 8	•– 9	•–11	•–12	•–15
	1	•–11	•–12	•–14	•–16	•–17	•–19
	2	2–15	•–16	•–18	•–19	•–20	•–22
	3	4–18	3–20	3–21	•–22	•–23	•–24
	4	7–21	6–23	5–24	4–25	4–25	•–26
10	0	•– 6	•– 7	•– 9	•–10	•–11	•–13
	1	•–10	•–11	•–13	•–14	•–15	•–17
	2	2–13	•–15	•–16	•–17	•–18	•–20
	3	4–17	3–18	•–19	•–20	•–21	•–23
	4	6–20	5–21	4–22	4–23	•–24	•–25
	5	9–22	8–23	7–24	6–25	5–26	–
11	0	•– 5	•– 7	•– 8	•– 9	•–10	•–12
	1	•– 9	•–10	•–12	•–13	•–14	•–16
	2	•–12	•–14	•–15	•–16	•–17	•–19
	3	3–15	3–17	•–18	•–19	•–20	•–21
	4	6–18	5–19	4–20	•–21	•–22	•–23
	5	8–21	7–22	6–23	5–24	5–24	•–25
12	0	•– 5	•– 6	•– 7	•– 8	•– 9	•–11
	1	•– 8	•– 9	•–11	•–12	•–13	•–15
	2	•–11	•–12	•–14	•–15	•–16	•–18
	3	3–14	3–15	•–16	•–18	•–18	•–20
	4	5–17	4–18	4–19	•–20	•–21	•–22
	5	7–19	6–20	6–21	5–22	5–23	•–24
	6	9–22	8–23	8–23	7–24	6–25	–

N_1	x_1	2α = 0.20	2α = 0.10	2α = 0.05	2α = 0.02	2α = 0.01	2α = 0.002
N = 31 (continued)							
13	0	•– 4	•– 6	•– 7	•– 8	•– 9	•–10
	1	•– 8	•– 9	•–10	•–11	•–12	•–14
	2	•–10	•–12	•–13	•–14	•–15	•–16
	3	3–13	•–14	•–15	•–16	•–17	•–19
	4	5–15	4–17	4–18	•–19	•–19	•–21
	5	7–18	6–19	5–20	5–21	•–21	•–23
	6	9–20	8–21	7–22	6–23	6–23	•–24
14	0	•– 4	•– 5	•– 6	•– 7	•– 8	•–10
	1	•– 7	•– 8	•– 9	•–10	•–11	•–13
	2	•–10	•–11	•–12	•–13	•–14	•–15
	3	3–12	•–13	•–14	•–15	•–16	•–17
	4	4–14	4–15	•–16	•–17	•–18	•–20
	5	6–17	5–18	5–19	•–20	•–20	•–21
	6	8–19	7–20	7–21	6–21	6–22	•–23
	7	10–21	9–22	8–23	8–23	7–24	–
15	0	•– 4	•– 5	•– 6	•– 7	•– 7	•– 9
	1	•– 6	•– 8	•– 8	•–10	•–10	•–12
	2	•– 9	•–10	•–11	•–12	•–13	•–14
	3	•–11	•–12	•–13	•–14	•–15	•–16
	4	4–13	4–14	•–15	•–16	•–17	•–18
	5	6–16	5–17	5–17	•–18	•–19	•–20
	6	8–18	7–19	6–19	6–20	•–21	•–22
	7	9–20	9–21	8–21	7–22	7–23	•–23
N = 32							
4	0	•–14	•–17	•–19	•–21	•–23	•–25
	1	•–22	•–24	•–26	•–27	•–28	•–29
	2	4–28	3–29	2–30	–	–	–
5	0	•–12	•–14	•–16	•–18	•–20	•–23
	1	•–18	•–21	•–22	•–24	•–25	•–27
	2	3–24	2–26	2–27	•–28	•–29	–
6	0	•–10	•–12	•–14	•–16	•–18	•–21
	1	•–16	•–18	•–20	•–22	•–23	•–25
	2	3–21	2–23	•–24	•–26	•–27	•–28
	3	6–26	5–27	4–28	3–29	3–29	–
7	0	•– 9	•–11	•–12	•–14	•–16	•–19
	1	•–14	•–16	•–18	•–20	•–21	•–23
	2	2–19	2–21	•–22	•–24	•–24	•–26
	3	5–23	4–24	3–26	3–27	•–27	•–28
8	0	•– 8	•– 9	•–11	•–13	•–14	•–17
	1	•–13	•–14	•–16	•–18	•–19	•–21
	2	2–17	•–18	•–20	•–21	•–22	•–24
	3	5–21	4–22	3–23	•–25	•–25	•–27
	4	8–24	7–25	6–26	5–27	4–28	–
9	0	•– 7	•– 8	•–10	•–12	•–13	•–15
	1	•–11	•–13	•–14	•–16	•–17	•–19
	2	2–15	•–17	•–18	•–20	•–21	•–23
	3	4–19	3–20	3–21	•–23	•–24	•–25
	4	7–22	6–23	5–24	4–26	4–26	•–27
10	0	•– 6	•– 8	•– 9	•–11	•–12	•–14
	1	•–10	•–12	•–13	•–15	•–16	•–18
	2	2–14	•–15	•–17	•–18	•–19	•–21
	3	4–17	3–19	3–20	•–21	•–22	•–24
	4	6–20	5–22	5–23	4–24	•–24	•–26
	5	9–23	8–24	7–25	6–26	5–27	–
11	0	•– 6	•– 7	•– 8	•–10	•–11	•–13
	1	•– 9	•–11	•–12	•–13	•–14	•–17
	2	•–13	•–14	•–15	•–17	•–18	•–19
	3	3–16	3–17	•–18	•–20	•–20	•–22
	4	6–19	5–20	4–21	4–22	•–23	•–24
	5	8–21	7–23	6–23	5–24	5–25	•–26
12	0	•– 5	•– 6	•– 7	•– 9	•–10	•–12
	1	•– 9	•–10	•–11	•–12	•–13	•–15
	2	•–12	•–13	•–14	•–15	•–16	•–18
	3	3–14	3–16	•–17	•–18	•–19	•–21
	4	5–17	4–18	4–20	•–21	•–21	•–23
	5	7–20	6–21	6–22	5–23	5–24	•–25
	6	10–22	9–23	8–24	7–25	6–26	–
13	0	•– 5	•– 6	•– 7	•– 8	•– 9	•–11
	1	•– 8	•– 9	•–10	•–11	•–12	•–14
	2	•–11	•–12	•–13	•–14	•–15	•–17
	3	3–13	•–15	•–16	•–17	•–18	•–19
	4	5–16	4–17	4–18	•–19	•–20	•–21
	5	7–18	6–20	5–21	5–22	•–22	•–23
	6	9–21	8–22	7–23	6–24	6–24	•–25
14	0	•– 4	•– 5	•– 6	•– 7	•– 8	•–10
	1	•– 7	•– 8	•– 9	•–11	•–11	•–13
	2	•–10	•–11	•–12	•–13	•–14	•–16
	3	3–12	•–14	•–15	•–16	•–17	•–18
	4	5–15	4–16	•–17	•–18	•–19	•–20
	5	6–17	6–18	5–19	5–20	•–21	•–22
	6	8–19	8–20	7–21	6–22	6–23	•–24
	7	10–22	9–23	9–23	8–24	7–25	–
15	0	•– 4	•– 5	•– 6	•– 7	•– 8	•– 9
	1	•– 7	•– 8	•– 9	•–10	•–11	•–12
	2	•– 9	•–10	•–11	•–12	•–13	•–15
	3	3–12	•–13	•–14	•–15	•–16	•–17
	4	4–14	4–15	•–16	•–17	•–18	•–19
	5	6–16	5–17	5–18	•–19	•–20	•–21
	6	8–18	7–19	6–20	6–21	•–22	•–23
	7	10–20	9–21	8–22	7–23	7–23	•–24
16	0	•– 4	•– 5	•– 5	•– 6	•– 7	•– 9
	1	•– 6	•– 7	•– 8	•– 9	•–10	•–12
	2	•– 9	•–10	•–11	•–12	•–12	•–14
	3	•–11	•–12	•–13	•–14	•–15	•–16

x_1	$N_1 - x_1$	N_1
x_2	$N_2 - x_2$	N_2
X	$N - X$	N

$N = N_1 + N_2$, $X = x_1 + x_2$, $N_1 \leq N_2$, $x_1 \leq N_1 - x_1$

For explanation see page 123

N = 32 (continued)

N_1	x_1	2α = 0.20	2α = 0.10	2α = 0.05	2α = 0.02	2α = 0.01	2α = 0.002
16	4	4-13	•-14	•-15	•-16	•-17	•-18
	5	6-15	5-16	5-17	•-18	•-19	•-20
	6	7-17	7-18	6-19	6-20	•-20	•-22
	7	9-19	8-20	8-21	7-22	7-22	•-23
	8	11-21	10-22	9-23	9-23	8-24	–

N = 33

N_1	x_1	2α = 0.20	2α = 0.10	2α = 0.05	2α = 0.02	2α = 0.01	2α = 0.002
4	0	•-14	•-17	•-19	•-22	•-24	•-26
	1	•-22	•-25	•-26	•-28	•-29	•-30
	2	5-28	3-30	2-31	–	–	–
5	0	•-12	•-14	•-17	•-19	•-21	•-24
	1	•-19	•-21	•-23	•-25	•-26	•-28
	2	4-25	2-27	2-28	•-29	•-30	–
6	0	•-10	•-12	•-14	•-17	•-18	•-21
	1	•-17	•-19	•-20	•-22	•-24	•-26
	2	3-22	2-24	•-25	•-27	•-27	•-29
	3	7-26	5-28	4-29	3-30	3-30	–
7	0	•- 9	•-11	•-13	•-15	•-16	•-19
	1	•-15	•-17	•-18	•-20	•-21	•-24
	2	2-19	2-21	•-23	•-24	•-25	•-27
	3	6-24	4-25	4-26	3-28	•-28	•-29
8	0	•- 8	•-10	•-11	•-13	•-15	•-17
	1	•-13	•-15	•-16	•-18	•-19	•-22
	2	2-17	•-19	•-21	•-22	•-23	•-25
	3	5-21	4-23	3-24	•-25	•-26	•-28
	4	8-25	7-26	6-27	5-28	4-29	–
9	0	•- 7	•- 9	•-10	•-12	•-13	•-16
	1	•-12	•-13	•-15	•-17	•-18	•-20
	2	2-16	•-17	•-19	•-20	•-21	•-23
	3	4-19	3-21	3-22	•-24	•-24	•-26
	4	7-23	6-24	5-25	4-26	4-27	•-28
10	0	•- 6	•- 8	•- 9	•-11	•-12	•-14
	1	•-11	•-12	•-14	•-15	•-16	•-19
	2	2-14	•-16	•-17	•-19	•-20	•-22
	3	4-18	3-19	3-20	•-22	•-23	•-24
	4	6-21	5-22	5-23	4-25	•-25	•-27
	5	9-24	8-25	7-26	6-27	5-28	–
11	0	•- 6	•- 7	•- 8	•-10	•-11	•-13
	1	•-10	•-11	•-12	•-14	•-15	•-17
	2	•-13	•-15	•-16	•-17	•-18	•-20
	3	4-16	3-18	•-19	•-20	•-21	•-23
	4	6-19	5-21	4-22	4-23	•-24	•-25
	5	8-22	7-23	6-24	6-25	5-26	•-27
12	0	•- 5	•- 6	•- 8	•- 9	•-10	•-12
	1	•- 9	•-10	•-11	•-13	•-14	•-16
	2	•-12	•-13	•-15	•-16	•-17	•-19
	3	3-15	3-16	•-18	•-19	•-20	•-21
	4	5-18	5-19	4-20	•-21	•-22	•-24
	5	8-20	7-22	6-23	5-24	5-24	•-26
	6	10-23	9-24	8-25	7-26	7-26	6-27
13	0	•- 5	•- 6	•- 7	•- 8	•- 9	•-11
	1	•- 8	•- 9	•-11	•-12	•-13	•-15
	2	•-11	•-12	•-14	•-15	•-16	•-18
	3	3-14	•-15	•-16	•-18	•-18	•-20
	4	5-16	4-18	4-19	•-20	•-21	•-22
	5	7-19	6-20	6-21	5-22	•-23	•-24
	6	9-21	8-23	7-23	7-24	6-25	•-26
14	0	•- 4	•- 5	•- 6	•- 8	•- 9	•-10
	1	•- 8	•- 9	•-10	•-11	•-12	•-14
	2	•-10	•-12	•-13	•-14	•-15	•-16
	3	3-13	•-14	•-15	•-16	•-17	•-19
	4	5-15	4-17	4-18	•-19	•-20	•-21
	5	7-18	6-19	5-20	5-21	•-22	•-23
	6	9-20	8-21	7-22	6-23	6-24	•-25
	7	11-22	10-23	9-24	8-25	8-25	7-26
15	0	•- 4	•- 5	•- 6	•- 7	•- 8	•-10
	1	•- 7	•- 8	•- 9	•-10	•-11	•-13
	2	•-10	•-11	•-12	•-13	•-14	•-15
	3	3-12	•-13	•-14	•-15	•-16	•-18
	4	4-14	4-16	•-17	•-18	•-18	•-20
	5	6-17	5-18	5-19	•-20	•-20	•-22
	6	8-19	7-20	7-21	6-22	6-22	•-24
	7	10-21	9-22	8-23	8-24	7-24	•-25
16	0	•- 4	•- 5	•- 6	•- 7	•- 7	•- 9
	1	•- 7	•- 8	•- 8	•-10	•-10	•-12
	2	•- 9	•-10	•-11	•-12	•-13	•-14
	3	•-11	•-12	•-13	•-14	•-15	•-17
	4	4-13	4-15	•-16	•-17	•-17	•-19
	5	6-16	5-17	5-18	•-19	•-19	•-21
	6	8-18	7-19	6-20	6-21	•-21	•-22
	7	9-20	9-21	8-22	7-22	7-23	•-24
	8	11-22	10-23	10-23	9-24	8-25	8-25

N = 34

N_1	x_1	2α = 0.20	2α = 0.10	2α = 0.05	2α = 0.02	2α = 0.01	2α = 0.002
4	0	•-15	•-18	•-20	•-23	•-24	•-27
	1	•-23	•-25	•-27	•-29	•-30	•-31
	2	5-29	3-31	2-32	–	–	–
5	0	•-12	•-15	•-17	•-20	•-21	•-24
	1	•-20	•-22	•-24	•-26	•-27	•-29
	2	4-26	2-27	2-29	•-30	•-31	–
6	0	•-11	•-13	•-15	•-17	•-19	•-22
	1	•-17	•-19	•-21	•-23	•-24	•-27
	2	3-22	2-24	•-26	•-27	•-28	•-30
	3	7-27	5-29	4-30	3-31	3-31	–

N = 34 (continued)

N_1	x_1	2α = 0.20	2α = 0.10	2α = 0.05	2α = 0.02	2α = 0.01	2α = 0.002
7	0	•- 9	•-11	•-13	•-15	•-17	•-20
	1	•-15	•-17	•-19	•-21	•-22	•-24
	2	2-20	2-22	•-23	•-25	•-26	•-28
	3	6-24	5-26	4-27	3-28	•-29	•-30
8	0	•- 8	•-10	•-12	•-14	•-15	•-18
	1	•-13	•-15	•-17	•-19	•-20	•-22
	2	2-18	2-20	•-21	•-23	•-24	•-26
	3	5-22	4-24	3-25	3-26	•-27	•-29
	4	8-26	7-27	6-28	5-29	4-30	–
9	0	•- 7	•- 9	•-10	•-12	•-14	•-16
	1	•-12	•-14	•-15	•-17	•-18	•-21
	2	2-16	•-18	•-19	•-21	•-22	•-24
	3	4-20	4-22	3-23	•-24	•-25	•-27
	4	7-23	6-25	5-26	4-27	4-28	•-29
10	0	•- 7	•- 8	•- 9	•-11	•-12	•-15
	1	•-11	•-13	•-14	•-16	•-17	•-19
	2	2-15	•-16	•-18	•-19	•-20	•-22
	3	4-18	3-20	3-21	•-23	•-23	•-25
	4	7-21	6-23	5-24	4-25	4-26	•-27
	5	9-25	8-26	7-27	6-28	6-28	5-29
11	0	•- 6	•- 7	•- 9	•-10	•-11	•-14
	1	•-10	•-11	•-13	•-14	•-16	•-18
	2	2-13	•-15	•-16	•-18	•-19	•-21
	3	4-17	3-18	•-19	•-21	•-22	•-24
	4	6-20	5-21	4-22	4-24	•-24	•-26
	5	9-23	7-24	7-25	6-26	5-27	•-28
12	0	•- 5	•- 7	•- 8	•- 9	•-10	•-13
	1	•- 9	•-11	•-12	•-13	•-14	•-16
	2	•-12	•-14	•-15	•-17	•-18	•-19
	3	3-15	3-17	•-18	•-19	•-20	•-22
	4	6-18	5-20	4-21	•-22	•-23	•-24
	5	8-21	7-22	6-23	5-25	5-25	•-26
	6	10-24	9-25	8-26	7-27	7-27	6-28
13	0	•- 5	•- 6	•- 7	•- 9	•-10	•-12
	1	•- 8	•-10	•-11	•-12	•-13	•-15
	2	•-11	•-13	•-14	•-15	•-16	•-18
	3	3-14	3-16	•-17	•-18	•-19	•-21
	4	5-17	4-18	4-19	•-21	•-22	•-23
	5	7-20	6-21	6-22	5-23	5-24	•-25
	6	10-22	8-23	8-24	7-25	6-26	•-27
14	0	•- 5	•- 6	•- 7	•- 8	•- 9	•-11
	1	•- 8	•- 9	•-10	•-11	•-12	•-14
	2	•-11	•-12	•-13	•-14	•-15	•-17
	3	3-13	•-15	•-16	•-17	•-18	•-20
	4	5-16	4-17	4-18	•-19	•-20	•-22
	5	7-18	6-20	5-21	5-22	•-22	•-24
	6	9-21	8-22	7-23	6-24	6-24	•-26
	7	11-23	10-24	9-25	8-26	8-26	7-27
15	0	•- 4	•- 5	•- 6	•- 7	•- 8	•-10
	1	•- 7	•- 8	•- 9	•-11	•-12	•-13
	2	•-10	•-11	•-12	•-13	•-14	•-16
	3	3-12	•-14	•-15	•-16	•-17	•-18
	4	4-15	4-16	•-17	•-18	•-19	•-21
	5	6-17	6-18	5-19	•-20	•-21	•-22
	6	8-19	7-21	7-21	6-22	6-23	•-24
	7	10-22	9-23	9-23	8-24	7-25	•-26
16	0	•- 4	•- 5	•- 6	•- 7	•- 8	•- 9
	1	•- 7	•- 8	•- 9	•-10	•-11	•-12
	2	•- 9	•-10	•-11	•-13	•-13	•-15
	3	3-12	•-13	•-14	•-15	•-16	•-17
	4	4-14	4-15	•-16	•-17	•-18	•-19
	5	6-16	5-17	5-18	•-19	•-20	•-21
	6	7-19	7-19	6-20	6-21	•-22	•-23
	7	10-20	9-21	8-22	7-23	7-24	•-25
	8	12-22	11-23	10-24	9-25	9-25	8-26
17	0	•- 4	•- 5	•- 5	•- 6	•- 7	•- 9
	1	•- 6	•- 7	•- 8	•- 9	•-10	•-12
	2	•- 9	•-10	•-11	•-12	•-13	•-14
	3	•-11	•-12	•-13	•-14	•-15	•-16
	4	4-13	•-14	•-15	•-16	•-17	•-18
	5	6-15	5-16	5-17	•-18	•-19	•-20
	6	7-17	7-18	6-19	6-20	•-21	•-22
	7	9-19	8-20	8-21	7-22	7-23	•-24
	8	11-21	10-22	9-23	9-24	8-24	•-25

N = 35

N_1	x_1	2α = 0.20	2α = 0.10	2α = 0.05	2α = 0.02	2α = 0.01	2α = 0.002
4	0	•-15	•-18	•-21	•-23	•-25	•-28
	1	•-24	•-26	•-28	•-30	•-31	•-32
	2	5-30	3-32	2-33	–	–	–
5	0	•-13	•-15	•-18	•-20	•-22	•-25
	1	•-20	•-23	•-25	•-27	•-28	•-30
	2	4-26	3-28	2-30	•-31	•-32	–
6	0	•-11	•-13	•-15	•-18	•-19	•-23
	1	•-18	•-20	•-22	•-24	•-25	•-27
	2	3-23	2-25	•-27	•-28	•-29	•-31
	3	7-28	6-29	4-31	3-32	3-32	–
7	0	•- 9	•-12	•-14	•-16	•-17	•-20
	1	•-15	•-18	•-19	•-21	•-23	•-25
	2	3-21	2-23	•-24	•-26	•-27	•-29
	3	6-25	5-27	4-28	3-29	•-30	•-31
8	0	•- 8	•-10	•-12	•-14	•-16	•-19
	1	•-14	•-16	•-17	•-19	•-21	•-23
	2	2-18	2-20	•-22	•-24	•-25	•-27
	3	5-23	4-24	3-26	3-27	•-28	•-29
	4	9-26	7-28	6-29	5-30	4-31	–

N = 35 (continued)

N_1	x_1	2α = 0.20	2α = 0.10	2α = 0.05	2α = 0.02	2α = 0.01	2α = 0.002
9	0	•- 7	•- 9	•-11	•-13	•-14	•-17
	1	•-12	•-14	•-16	•-18	•-19	•-21
	2	2-17	•-18	•-20	•-22	•-23	•-25
	3	5-21	4-22	3-24	•-25	•-26	•-28
	4	8-24	6-26	5-27	4-28	4-29	•-30
10	0	•- 7	•- 8	•-10	•-12	•-13	•-16
	1	•-11	•-13	•-14	•-16	•-17	•-20
	2	2-15	•-17	•-18	•-20	•-21	•-23
	3	4-19	3-20	3-22	•-23	•-24	•-26
	4	7-22	6-24	5-25	4-26	4-27	•-28
	5	10-25	8-27	7-28	6-29	6-29	5-30
11	0	•- 6	•- 8	•- 9	•-11	•-12	•-14
	1	•-10	•-12	•-13	•-15	•-16	•-18
	2	2-14	•-15	•-17	•-18	•-20	•-22
	3	4-17	3-19	•-20	•-22	•-23	•-24
	4	6-20	5-22	4-23	4-24	•-25	•-27
	5	9-23	8-25	7-26	6-27	5-28	•-29
12	0	•- 6	•- 7	•- 8	•-10	•-11	•-13
	1	•- 9	•-11	•-12	•-14	•-15	•-17
	2	•-13	•-14	•-16	•-17	•-18	•-20
	3	3-16	3-17	•-19	•-20	•-21	•-23
	4	6-19	5-20	4-21	4-23	•-24	•-25
	5	8-22	7-23	6-24	5-25	5-26	•-27
	6	11-24	9-26	8-27	7-28	7-28	6-29
13	0	•- 5	•- 6	•- 8	•- 9	•-10	•-12
	1	•- 9	•-10	•-11	•-13	•-14	•-16
	2	•-12	•-13	•-14	•-16	•-17	•-19
	3	3-15	3-16	•-17	•-19	•-20	•-21
	4	5-18	4-19	4-20	•-21	•-22	•-24
	5	7-20	6-22	6-23	5-24	5-25	•-26
	6	10-23	9-24	8-25	7-26	6-27	•-28
14	0	•- 5	•- 6	•- 7	•- 8	•- 9	•-11
	1	•- 8	•- 9	•-10	•-12	•-13	•-15
	2	•-11	•-12	•-13	•-15	•-16	•-18
	3	3-14	•-15	•-16	•-18	•-18	•-20
	4	5-16	4-18	4-19	•-20	•-21	•-22
	5	7-19	6-20	5-21	5-22	•-23	•-25
	6	9-21	8-23	7-23	7-25	6-25	•-26
	7	11-24	10-25	9-26	8-27	8-27	7-28
15	0	•- 4	•- 5	•- 6	•- 8	•- 9	•-11
	1	•- 7	•- 9	•-10	•-11	•-12	•-14
	2	•-10	•-11	•-13	•-14	•-15	•-17
	3	3-13	•-14	•-15	•-16	•-17	•-19
	4	5-15	4-17	•-18	•-19	•-20	•-21
	5	6-18	6-19	5-20	5-21	•-22	•-23
	6	8-20	8-21	7-22	6-23	6-24	•-25
	7	11-22	10-23	9-24	8-25	7-26	7-27
16	0	•- 4	•- 5	•- 6	•- 7	•- 8	•-10
	1	•- 7	•- 8	•- 9	•-10	•-11	•-13
	2	•-10	•-11	•-12	•-13	•-14	•-16
	3	3-12	•-13	•-14	•-15	•-16	•-18
	4	4-14	4-16	•-17	•-18	•-19	•-20
	5	6-17	5-18	5-19	•-20	•-21	•-22
	6	8-19	7-20	7-21	6-22	6-23	•-24
	7	10-21	9-22	8-23	8-24	7-25	•-26
	8	12-23	11-24	10-25	9-26	9-26	8-27
17	0	•- 4	•- 5	•- 6	•- 7	•- 7	•- 9
	1	•- 7	•- 8	•- 8	•-10	•-10	•-12
	2	•- 9	•-10	•-11	•-12	•-13	•-15
	3	•-11	•-12	•-13	•-15	•-15	•-17
	4	4-14	4-15	•-16	•-17	•-17	•-19
	5	6-16	5-17	5-18	•-19	•-20	•-21
	6	8-18	7-19	6-20	6-21	•-21	•-23
	7	9-20	9-21	8-22	7-23	7-23	•-24
	8	11-22	10-23	10-24	9-24	8-25	•-26

N = 36

N_1	x_1	2α = 0.20	2α = 0.10	2α = 0.05	2α = 0.02	2α = 0.01	2α = 0.002
4	0	•-16	•-19	•-21	•-24	•-26	•-29
	1	•-24	•-27	•-29	•-31	•-32	•-33
	2	5-31	3-33	2-34	2-34	–	–
5	0	•-13	•-16	•-18	•-21	•-23	•-26
	1	•-21	•-23	•-25	•-27	•-29	•-31
	2	4-27	3-29	2-30	•-32	•-33	–
6	0	•-11	•-14	•-16	•-18	•-20	•-23
	1	•-18	•-20	•-22	•-25	•-26	•-28
	2	3-24	2-26	2-27	•-29	•-30	•-32
	3	7-29	6-30	5-31	3-33	3-33	–
7	0	•-10	•-12	•-14	•-16	•-18	•-21
	1	•-16	•-18	•-20	•-22	•-23	•-26
	2	3-21	2-23	•-25	•-27	•-28	•-30
	3	6-26	5-27	4-29	3-30	3-31	•-32
8	0	•- 9	•-11	•-12	•-15	•-16	•-19
	1	•-14	•-16	•-18	•-20	•-21	•-24
	2	2-19	2-21	•-23	•-24	•-25	•-28
	3	5-23	4-25	3-26	3-28	•-29	•-30
	4	9-27	7-29	6-30	5-31	4-32	–
9	0	•- 8	•- 9	•-11	•-13	•-15	•-17
	1	•-13	•-15	•-16	•-18	•-20	•-22
	2	2-17	•-19	•-21	•-22	•-23	•-26
	3	5-21	4-23	3-24	•-26	•-27	•-29
	4	8-25	7-26	6-28	5-29	4-30	•-31
10	0	•- 7	•- 9	•-10	•-12	•-13	•-16
	1	•-12	•-13	•-15	•-17	•-18	•-20
	2	2-16	•-17	•-19	•-21	•-22	•-24
	3	4-19	3-21	3-22	•-24	•-25	•-27

Significance Limits for the Fourfold Table Test*

$$\left.\begin{array}{cc|c} x_1 & N_1-x_1 & N_1 \\ x_2 & N_2-x_2 & N_2 \\ \hline X & N-X & N \end{array}\right\} \quad \left.\begin{array}{l} N = N_1+N_2 \\ X = x_1+x_2 \\ N_1 \leqq N_2 \\ x_1 \leqq N_1 - x_1 \end{array}\right\}$$

For explanation see page 123

N_1	x_1	2α= 0.20	2α= 0.10	2α= 0.05	2α= 0.02	2α= 0.01	2α= 0.002
		N = 36 (continued)					
	4	7-23	6-24	5-26	4-27	4-28	•-29
	5	10-26	9-27	8-28	6-30	6-30	5-31
11	0	•- 6	•- 8	•- 9	•-11	•-12	•-15
	1	•-11	•-12	•-14	•-15	•-17	•-19
	2	2-14	•-16	•-17	•-19	•-20	•-22
	3	4-18	3-19	3-21	•-22	•-23	•-25
	4	6-21	5-23	5-24	4-25	•-26	•-28
	5	9-24	8-25	7-27	6-28	5-28	•-30
12	0	•- 6	•- 7	•- 8	•-10	•-11	•-14
	1	•-10	•-11	•-13	•-14	•-15	•-18
	2	•-13	•-15	•-16	•-18	•-19	•-21
	3	4-16	3-18	•-19	•-21	•-22	•-24
	4	6-19	5-21	4-22	4-24	•-24	•-26
	5	8-22	7-24	6-25	5-26	5-27	•-28
	6	11-25	10-26	9-27	8-28	7-29	6-30
13	0	•- 5	•- 7	•- 8	•- 9	•-10	•-13
	1	•- 9	•-10	•-12	•-13	•-14	•-16
	2	•-12	•-14	•-15	•-16	•-17	•-19
	3	3-15	3-17	•-18	•-19	•-20	•-22
	4	5-18	5-19	4-21	•-22	•-23	•-25
	5	8-21	7-22	6-23	5-25	5-25	•-27
	6	10-23	9-25	8-26	7-27	7-27	6-29
14	0	•- 5	•- 6	•- 7	•- 9	•-10	•-12
	1	•- 8	•-10	•-11	•-12	•-13	•-15
	2	•-11	•-13	•-14	•-15	•-16	•-18
	3	3-14	•-16	•-17	•-18	•-19	•-21
	4	5-17	4-18	4-19	•-21	•-22	•-23
	5	7-19	6-21	6-22	5-23	•-24	•-25
	6	9-22	8-23	7-24	7-25	6-26	•-27
	7	12-24	10-26	10-26	9-27	8-28	7-29
15	0	•- 5	•- 6	•- 7	•- 8	•- 9	•-11
	1	•- 8	•- 9	•-10	•-11	•-12	•-14
	2	•-11	•-12	•-13	•-14	•-15	•-17
	3	3-13	•-15	•-16	•-17	•-18	•-20
	4	5-16	4-17	4-18	•-19	•-20	•-22
	5	7-18	6-20	5-21	5-22	•-23	•-24
	6	9-21	8-22	7-23	6-24	6-25	•-26
	7	11-23	10-24	9-25	8-26	8-27	7-28
16	0	•- 4	•- 5	•- 6	•- 7	•- 8	•-10
	1	•- 7	•- 8	•- 9	•-11	•-12	•-13
	2	•-10	•-11	•-12	•-13	•-14	•-16
	3	3-12	•-14	•-15	•-16	•-17	•-19
	4	4-15	4-16	•-17	•-18	•-19	•-21
	5	6-17	6-18	5-19	•-21	•-21	•-23
	6	8-19	7-21	7-22	6-23	6-23	•-25
	7	10-22	9-23	8-24	8-25	7-25	•-26
	8	12-24	11-25	10-26	9-27	9-27	8-28
17	0	•- 4	•- 5	•- 6	•- 7	•- 8	•- 9
	1	•- 7	•- 8	•- 9	•-10	•-11	•-13
	2	•- 9	•-10	•-11	•-13	•-13	•-15
	3	3-12	•-13	•-14	•-15	•-16	•-17
	4	4-14	4-15	•-16	•-17	•-18	•-20
	5	6-16	5-17	5-18	•-19	•-20	•-22
	6	8-18	7-19	6-20	6-21	•-22	•-23
	7	10-20	9-22	8-22	7-23	7-24	•-25
	8	12-22	11-23	10-24	9-25	8-26	8-27
18	0	•- 4	•- 5	•- 5	•- 6	•- 7	•- 9
	1	•- 6	•- 7	•- 8	•- 9	•-10	•-12
	2	•- 9	•-10	•-11	•-12	•-13	•-14
	3	•-11	•-12	•-13	•-14	•-15	•-17
	4	4-13	•-14	•-15	•-16	•-17	•-19
	5	6-15	5-16	5-17	•-18	•-19	•-21
	6	7-17	7-18	6-19	6-20	•-21	•-22
	7	9-19	8-20	8-21	7-22	7-23	•-24
	8	11-21	10-22	9-23	9-24	8-25	•-26
	9	13-23	12-24	11-25	10-26	10-26	9-27
		N = 37					
4	0	•-16	•-19	•-22	•-25	•-26	•-30
	1	•-25	•-28	•-30	•-31	•-32	•-34
	2	5-32	4-33	2-35	2-35	–	–
5	0	•-13	•-16	•-19	•-22	•-23	•-27
	1	•-21	•-24	•-26	•-28	•-29	•-32
	2	4-28	3-30	2-31	•-33	•-33	–
6	0	•-11	•-14	•-16	•-19	•-21	•-24
	1	•-19	•-21	•-23	•-25	•-27	•-29
	2	3-24	2-27	2-28	•-30	•-31	•-33
	3	7-30	6-31	5-32	4-33	3-34	–
7	0	•-10	•-12	•-14	•-17	•-18	•-22
	1	•-16	•-19	•-21	•-23	•-24	•-27
	2	3-22	2-24	•-26	•-27	•-28	•-30
	3	6-26	5-28	4-30	3-31	3-32	•-33
8	0	•- 9	•-11	•-13	•-15	•-17	•-20
	1	•-15	•-17	•-19	•-21	•-22	•-25
	2	2-19	2-22	•-23	•-25	•-26	•-28
	3	5-24	4-26	3-27	3-29	•-30	•-31
	4	9-28	8-29	6-31	5-32	5-32	–
9	0	•- 8	•-10	•-12	•-14	•-15	•-18
	1	•-13	•-15	•-17	•-19	•-20	•-23
	2	2-18	•-20	•-21	•-23	•-24	•-26
	3	5-22	4-24	3-25	•-27	•-28	•-29
	4	8-25	7-27	6-28	5-30	4-30	•-32
10	0	•- 7	•- 9	•-10	•-12	•-14	•-17
	1	•-12	•-14	•-15	•-17	•-19	•-21
	2	2-16	•-18	•-19	•-21	•-22	•-25

N_1	x_1	2α= 0.20	2α= 0.10	2α= 0.05	2α= 0.02	2α= 0.01	2α= 0.002
		N = 37 (continued)					
	3	4-20	3-22	3-23	•-25	•-26	•-28
	4	7-23	6-25	5-26	4-28	4-29	•-30
	5	10-27	9-28	8-29	7-30	6-31	5-32
11	0	•- 6	•- 8	•-10	•-11	•-13	•-15
	1	•-11	•-13	•-14	•-16	•-17	•-20
	2	2-15	•-16	•-18	•-20	•-21	•-23
	3	4-18	3-20	3-21	•-23	•-24	•-26
	4	7-22	5-23	5-24	4-26	4-27	•-28
	5	9-25	8-26	7-27	6-29	5-29	•-31
12	0	•- 6	•- 7	•- 9	•-10	•-12	•-14
	1	•-10	•-12	•-13	•-15	•-16	•-18
	2	2-14	•-15	•-17	•-18	•-19	•-21
	3	4-17	3-18	•-20	•-21	•-22	•-24
	4	6-20	5-22	4-23	4-24	•-25	•-27
	5	9-23	7-24	6-26	6-27	5-28	•-29
	6	11-26	10-27	9-28	8-29	7-30	6-31
13	0	•- 5	•- 7	•- 8	•-10	•-11	•-13
	1	•- 9	•-11	•-12	•-14	•-15	•-17
	2	•-13	•-14	•-15	•-17	•-18	•-20
	3	3-16	3-17	•-18	•-20	•-21	•-23
	4	6-19	5-20	4-21	•-23	•-24	•-25
	5	8-21	7-23	6-24	5-25	5-26	•-28
	6	10-24	9-25	8-26	7-28	7-28	6-30
14	0	•- 5	•- 6	•- 7	•- 9	•-10	•-12
	1	•- 9	•-10	•-11	•-13	•-14	•-16
	2	•-12	•-13	•-14	•-16	•-17	•-19
	3	3-15	3-16	•-17	•-19	•-20	•-22
	4	5-17	4-19	4-20	•-21	•-22	•-24
	5	7-20	6-21	6-23	5-24	5-25	•-26
	6	10-23	8-24	8-25	7-26	6-27	•-28
	7	12-25	11-26	10-27	9-28	8-29	7-30
15	0	•- 5	•- 6	•- 7	•- 8	•- 9	•-11
	1	•- 8	•- 9	•-10	•-12	•-13	•-15
	2	•-11	•-12	•-13	•-15	•-16	•-18
	3	3-14	•-15	•-16	•-18	•-18	•-20
	4	5-16	4-18	4-19	•-20	•-21	•-23
	5	7-19	6-20	5-21	5-22	•-23	•-25
	6	9-21	8-22	7-24	6-25	6-25	•-27
	7	11-24	10-25	9-26	8-27	8-27	7-29
16	0	•- 4	•- 5	•- 6	•- 8	•- 9	•-11
	1	•- 7	•- 9	•-10	•-11	•-12	•-14
	2	•-10	•-11	•-13	•-14	•-15	•-17
	3	3-13	•-14	•-15	•-17	•-17	•-19
	4	5-15	4-17	•-18	•-19	•-20	•-21
	5	6-18	6-19	5-20	•-21	•-22	•-24
	6	8-20	7-21	7-22	6-23	6-24	•-25
	7	10-22	9-23	9-24	8-25	7-26	•-27
	8	13-24	11-26	11-26	10-27	9-28	8-29
17	0	•- 4	•- 5	•- 6	•- 7	•- 8	•-10
	1	•- 7	•- 8	•- 9	•-10	•-11	•-13
	2	•-10	•-11	•-12	•-13	•-14	•-16
	3	3-12	•-13	•-14	•-16	•-16	•-18
	4	4-14	4-16	•-17	•-18	•-19	•-20
	5	6-17	5-18	5-19	•-20	•-21	•-22
	6	8-19	7-20	6-21	6-22	•-23	•-24
	7	10-21	9-22	8-23	7-24	7-25	•-26
	8	12-23	11-24	10-25	9-26	9-27	8-28
18	0	•- 4	•- 5	•- 6	•- 7	•- 7	•- 9
	1	•- 7	•- 8	•- 9	•-10	•-11	•-12
	2	•- 9	•-10	•-11	•-12	•-13	•-15
	3	•-11	•-12	•-13	•-15	•-15	•-17
	4	4-14	4-15	•-16	•-17	•-18	•-19
	5	6-16	5-17	5-18	•-19	•-20	•-21
	6	8-18	7-19	6-20	6-21	•-22	•-23
	7	9-20	8-21	8-22	7-23	7-24	•-25
	8	11-22	10-23	10-24	9-25	8-25	•-27
	9	13-24	12-25	11-26	10-27	10-27	9-28
		N = 38					
4	0	•-16	•-20	•-22	•-25	•-27	•-30
	1	•-26	•-28	•-30	•-32	•-33	•-35
	2	5-33	4-34	3-35	2-36	–	–
5	0	•-14	•-17	•-19	•-22	•-24	•-27
	1	•-22	•-25	•-27	•-29	•-30	•-32
	2	4-29	3-31	2-32	•-34	•-34	–
6	0	•-12	•-14	•-17	•-19	•-21	•-25
	1	•-19	•-22	•-24	•-26	•-27	•-30
	2	3-25	2-27	2-29	•-31	•-32	•-33
	3	8-30	6-32	5-33	4-34	3-35	–
7	0	•-10	•-13	•-15	•-17	•-19	•-22
	1	•-17	•-19	•-21	•-23	•-25	•-28
	2	3-22	2-24	•-26	•-28	•-29	•-31
	3	6-27	5-29	4-30	3-32	3-33	•-34
8	0	•- 9	•-11	•-13	•-16	•-17	•-20
	1	•-15	•-17	•-19	•-21	•-23	•-25
	2	2-20	2-22	•-24	•-26	•-27	•-29
	3	6-25	4-26	4-28	3-30	•-30	•-32
	4	9-29	8-30	7-31	5-33	5-33	4-34
9	0	•- 8	•-10	•-12	•-14	•-16	•-19
	1	•-13	•-16	•-17	•-19	•-21	•-23
	2	2-18	•-20	•-22	•-24	•-25	•-27
	3	5-22	4-24	3-26	3-27	•-28	•-30
	4	8-26	7-28	6-29	5-31	4-31	•-33
10	0	•- 7	•- 9	•-11	•-13	•-14	•-17
	1	•-12	•-14	•-16	•-18	•-19	•-22

N_1	x_1	2α= 0.20	2α= 0.10	2α= 0.05	2α= 0.02	2α= 0.01	2α= 0.002
		N = 38 (continued)					
	2	2-16	•-18	•-20	•-22	•-23	•-25
	3	4-20	4-22	3-24	•-25	•-26	•-28
	4	7-24	6-26	5-27	4-28	4-29	•-31
	5	11-27	9-29	8-30	7-31	6-32	5-33
11	0	•- 7	•- 8	•-10	•-12	•-13	•-16
	1	•-11	•-13	•-14	•-16	•-18	•-20
	2	2-15	•-17	•-18	•-20	•-21	•-24
	3	4-19	3-20	3-22	•-24	•-25	•-27
	4	7-22	6-24	5-25	4-27	4-28	•-29
	5	10-25	8-27	7-28	6-29	6-30	5-32
12	0	•- 6	•- 8	•- 9	•-11	•-12	•-14
	1	•-10	•-12	•-13	•-15	•-16	•-19
	2	2-14	•-16	•-17	•-19	•-20	•-22
	3	4-17	3-19	•-20	•-22	•-23	•-25
	4	6-21	5-22	4-23	4-25	•-26	•-28
	5	9-24	8-25	7-26	6-28	5-28	•-30
	6	11-27	10-28	9-29	8-30	7-31	6-32
13	0	•- 6	•- 7	•- 8	•-10	•-11	•-13
	1	•- 9	•-11	•-12	•-14	•-15	•-17
	2	•-13	•-14	•-16	•-17	•-19	•-21
	3	3-16	3-18	•-19	•-21	•-22	•-24
	4	6-19	5-21	4-22	4-23	•-24	•-26
	5	8-22	7-23	6-25	5-26	5-27	•-28
	6	11-25	9-26	8-27	7-28	7-29	6-30
14	0	•- 5	•- 6	•- 8	•- 9	•-10	•-12
	1	•- 9	•-10	•-11	•-13	•-14	•-16
	2	•-12	•-13	•-15	•-16	•-17	•-19
	3	3-15	3-16	•-18	•-19	•-20	•-22
	4	5-18	4-19	4-21	•-22	•-23	•-25
	5	7-21	7-22	6-23	5-24	5-25	•-27
	6	10-23	9-25	8-26	7-27	6-28	•-29
	7	12-26	11-27	10-28	9-29	8-30	7-31
15	0	•- 5	•- 6	•- 7	•- 9	•-10	•-12
	1	•- 8	•-10	•-11	•-12	•-13	•-15
	2	•-11	•-13	•-14	•-15	•-16	•-18
	3	3-14	•-15	•-17	•-18	•-19	•-21
	4	5-17	4-18	4-19	•-21	•-22	•-23
	5	7-19	6-21	5-22	5-23	•-24	•-26
	6	9-22	8-23	7-24	7-25	6-26	•-28
	7	11-24	10-25	9-26	8-28	8-28	7-29
16	0	•- 4	•- 6	•- 7	•- 8	•- 9	•-11
	1	•- 8	•- 9	•-10	•-11	•-12	•-14
	2	•-10	•-12	•-13	•-14	•-15	•-17
	3	3-13	•-14	•-16	•-17	•-18	•-20
	4	5-16	4-17	4-18	•-20	•-20	•-22
	5	7-18	6-19	5-21	5-22	•-23	•-24
	6	9-21	8-22	7-23	6-24	6-25	•-26
	7	11-23	10-24	9-25	8-26	7-27	7-28
	8	13-25	12-26	11-27	10-28	9-29	8-30
17	0	•- 4	•- 5	•- 6	•- 7	•- 8	•-10
	1	•- 7	•- 8	•- 9	•-11	•-12	•-13
	2	•-10	•-11	•-12	•-13	•-14	•-16
	3	3-12	•-14	•-15	•-16	•-17	•-19
	4	4-15	4-16	•-17	•-18	•-19	•-21
	5	6-17	5-18	5-19	•-21	•-21	•-23
	6	8-19	7-21	7-22	6-23	6-24	•-25
	7	10-22	9-23	8-24	8-25	7-26	•-27
	8	12-24	11-25	10-26	9-27	9-27	8-29
18	0	•- 4	•- 5	•- 6	•- 7	•- 8	•-10
	1	•- 7	•- 8	•- 9	•-10	•-11	•-13
	2	•- 9	•-10	•-11	•-13	•-14	•-15
	3	3-12	•-13	•-14	•-15	•-16	•-18
	4	4-14	4-15	•-16	•-17	•-18	•-20
	5	6-16	5-17	5-18	•-20	•-20	•-22
	6	8-18	7-20	6-21	6-22	•-22	•-24
	7	10-20	9-22	8-23	7-24	7-24	•-26
	8	11-23	11-24	10-25	9-26	8-26	8-27
	9	13-25	12-26	12-26	11-27	10-28	9-29
19	0	•- 4	•- 5	•- 5	•- 6	•- 7	•- 9
	1	•- 6	•- 7	•- 8	•- 9	•-10	•-12
	2	•- 9	•-10	•-11	•-12	•-13	•-14
	3	•-11	•-12	•-13	•-14	•-15	•-17
	4	4-13	•-14	•-15	•-17	•-17	•-19
	5	6-15	5-16	5-17	•-19	•-19	•-21
	6	7-17	7-19	6-20	6-21	•-21	•-23
	7	9-19	8-21	8-21	7-23	7-23	•-24
	8	11-21	10-22	9-23	9-24	8-25	•-26
	9	13-23	12-24	11-25	10-26	10-27	9-28
		N = 39					
4	0	•-17	•-20	•-23	•-26	•-28	•-31
	1	•-26	•-29	•-31	•-33	•-34	•-36
	2	5-34	4-35	3-36	2-37	–	–
5	0	•-14	•-17	•-20	•-23	•-25	•-28
	1	•-23	•-25	•-27	•-30	•-31	•-33
	2	4-29	3-31	2-33	•-35	•-35	–
6	0	•-12	•-15	•-17	•-20	•-22	•-25
	1	•-20	•-22	•-24	•-27	•-28	•-31
	2	3-26	2-28	2-30	•-32	•-33	•-34
	3	8-31	6-33	5-34	4-35	3-36	–
7	0	•-11	•-13	•-15	•-18	•-20	•-23
	1	•-17	•-20	•-22	•-24	•-26	•-28
	2	3-23	2-25	•-27	•-29	•-30	•-32
	3	7-28	5-30	4-31	3-33	3-34	•-35
8	0	•- 9	•-12	•-14	•-16	•-18	•-21
	1	•-15	•-18	•-20	•-22	•-23	•-26

* Reproduction only by permission of the publishers of these *Scientific Tables.*

Significance Limits for the Fourfold Table Test*

x_1	$N_1 - x_1$	N_1
x_2	$N_2 - x_2$	N_2
X	$N - X$	N

$$N = N_1 + N_2,\quad X = x_1 + x_2,\quad N_1 \leqq N_2,\quad x_1 \leqq N_1 - x_1$$

For explanation see page 123

N_1	x_1	$2\alpha =$ 0.20	$2\alpha =$ 0.10	$2\alpha =$ 0.05	$2\alpha =$ 0.02	$2\alpha =$ 0.01	$2\alpha =$ 0.002
$N = 39$ (continued)							
	2	2–21	2–23	•–25	•–26	•–28	•–30
	3	6–25	5–27	4–29	3–30	•–31	•–33
	4	10–29	8–31	7–32	5–34	5–34	4–35
9	0	•–8	•–10	•–12	•–14	•–16	•–19
	1	•–14	•–16	•–18	•–20	•–21	•–24
	2	2–19	2–21	•–22	•–24	•–26	•–28
	3	5–23	4–25	3–26	3–28	•–29	•–31
	4	8–27	7–29	6–30	5–31	4–32	•–34
10	0	•–8	•–9	•–11	•–13	•–15	•–18
	1	•–13	•–15	•–16	•–18	•–20	•–22
	2	2–17	•–19	•–21	•–22	•–24	•–26
	3	5–21	4–23	3–24	•–26	•–27	•–29
	4	8–25	6–26	5–28	4–29	4–30	•–32
	5	11–28	9–30	8–31	7–32	6–33	5–34
11	0	•–7	•–9	•–10	•–12	•–13	•–16
	1	•–11	•–13	•–15	•–17	•–18	•–21
	2	2–16	•–17	•–19	•–21	•–22	•–24
	3	4–19	3–21	3–23	•–24	•–25	•–27
	4	7–23	6–24	5–26	4–27	4–28	•–30
	5	10–26	8–28	7–29	6–30	6–31	5–32
12	0	•–6	•–8	•–9	•–11	•–12	•–15
	1	•–11	•–12	•–14	•–16	•–17	•–19
	2	2–14	•–16	•–18	•–19	•–20	•–23
	3	4–18	3–20	3–21	•–23	•–24	•–26
	4	6–21	5–23	5–24	4–26	•–27	•–28
	5	9–24	8–26	7–27	6–28	5–29	•–31
	6	12–27	10–29	9–30	8–31	7–32	6–33
13	0	•–6	•–7	•–9	•–10	•–11	•–14
	1	•–10	•–11	•–13	•–14	•–16	•–18
	2	•–13	•–15	•–16	•–18	•–19	•–21
	3	4–17	3–18	•–20	•–21	•–22	•–24
	4	6–20	5–21	4–23	4–24	•–25	•–27
	5	8–23	7–24	6–25	5–27	5–28	•–29
	6	11–25	10–27	9–28	8–29	7–30	6–31
14	0	•–5	•–7	•–8	•–9	•–11	•–13
	1	•–9	•–11	•–12	•–13	•–15	•–17
	2	•–12	•–14	•–15	•–17	•–18	•–20
	3	3–15	3–17	•–18	•–20	•–21	•–23
	4	5–18	5–20	4–21	•–23	•–24	•–25
	5	8–21	7–23	6–24	5–25	5–26	•–28
	6	10–24	9–25	8–26	7–28	6–28	6–30
	7	13–26	11–28	10–29	9–30	8–31	7–32
15	0	•–5	•–6	•–7	•–9	•–10	•–12
	1	•–8	•–10	•–11	•–13	•–14	•–16
	2	•–12	•–13	•–14	•–16	•–17	•–19
	3	3–14	3–16	•–17	•–19	•–20	•–22
	4	5–17	4–19	4–20	•–21	•–22	•–24
	5	7–20	6–21	6–22	5–24	•–25	•–26
	6	9–22	8–24	7–25	7–26	6–27	•–28
	7	12–25	11–26	10–27	9–28	8–29	7–30
16	0	•–5	•–6	•–7	•–8	•–9	•–11
	1	•–8	•–9	•–10	•–12	•–13	•–15
	2	•–11	•–12	•–13	•–15	•–16	•–18
	3	3–14	•–15	•–16	•–18	•–18	•–20
	4	5–16	4–18	4–19	•–20	•–21	•–23
	5	7–19	6–20	5–21	5–22	•–23	•–25
	6	9–21	8–22	7–24	6–25	6–26	•–27
	7	11–24	10–25	9–26	8–27	8–28	7–29
	8	13–26	12–27	11–28	10–29	9–30	8–31
17	0	•–4	•–5	•–6	•–8	•–9	•–11
	1	•–7	•–9	•–10	•–11	•–12	•–14
	2	•–10	•–11	•–13	•–14	•–15	•–17
	3	3–13	•–14	•–15	•–17	•–17	•–19
	4	4–15	4–17	•–18	•–19	•–20	•–22
	5	6–18	6–19	5–20	•–21	•–22	•–24
	6	8–20	7–21	7–22	6–23	6–24	•–26
	7	10–22	9–23	9–24	8–26	7–26	•–28
	8	12–24	11–26	10–27	10–28	9–28	8–29
18	0	•–4	•–5	•–6	•–7	•–8	•–10
	1	•–7	•–8	•–9	•–10	•–11	•–13
	2	•–10	•–11	•–12	•–13	•–14	•–16
	3	3–12	•–13	•–14	•–16	•–16	•–18
	4	4–14	4–16	•–17	•–18	•–19	•–20
	5	6–17	5–18	5–19	•–20	•–21	•–23
	6	8–19	7–20	6–21	6–22	•–23	•–25
	7	10–21	9–22	8–23	7–24	7–25	•–26
	8	12–23	11–24	10–25	9–26	9–27	8–28
	9	14–25	13–26	12–27	11–28	10–29	9–30
19	0	•–4	•–5	•–6	•–7	•–8	•–9
	1	•–7	•–8	•–9	•–10	•–11	•–12
	2	•–9	•–10	•–11	•–12	•–13	•–15
	3	•–11	•–13	•–14	•–15	•–16	•–17
	4	4–14	4–15	•–16	•–17	•–18	•–19
	5	6–16	5–17	5–18	•–19	•–20	•–21
	6	7–18	7–19	6–20	6–21	•–22	•–23
	7	9–20	8–21	8–22	7–23	7–24	•–25
	8	11–22	10–23	9–24	9–25	8–26	•–27
	9	13–24	12–25	11–26	10–27	10–27	9–29
$N = 40$							
4	0	•–17	•–21	•–24	•–27	•–29	•–32
	1	•–27	•–30	•–32	•–34	•–35	•–37
	2	6–34	4–36	3–37	2–38	–	–
5	0	•–14	•–18	•–20	•–23	•–25	•–29
	1	•–23	•–26	•–28	•–30	•–32	•–34
	2	4–30	3–32	2–34	•–35	•–36	–
$N = 40$ (continued)							
6	0	•–12	•–15	•–18	•–21	•–22	•–26
	1	•–20	•–23	•–25	•–27	•–29	•–32
	2	4–26	2–29	2–31	•–32	•–33	•–35
	3	8–32	6–34	5–35	4–36	3–37	–
7	0	•–11	•–13	•–16	•–18	•–20	•–24
	1	•–18	•–20	•–22	•–25	•–26	•–29
	2	3–24	2–26	•–28	•–30	•–31	•–33
	3	7–29	5–31	4–32	3–34	3–34	•–36
8	0	•–10	•–12	•–14	•–16	•–18	•–21
	1	•–16	•–18	•–20	•–22	•–24	•–27
	2	3–21	2–23	•–25	•–27	•–28	•–31
	3	6–26	5–28	4–29	3–31	•–32	•–34
	4	10–30	8–32	7–33	6–34	5–35	4–36
9	0	•–9	•–11	•–13	•–15	•–16	•–20
	1	•–14	•–16	•–18	•–20	•–22	•–25
	2	2–19	2–21	•–23	•–25	•–26	•–29
	3	5–24	4–25	3–27	3–29	•–30	•–32
	4	9–28	7–29	6–31	5–32	4–33	•–35
10	0	•–8	•–10	•–11	•–13	•–15	•–18
	1	•–13	•–15	•–17	•–19	•–20	•–23
	2	2–17	•–19	•–21	•–23	•–24	•–27
	3	5–22	4–23	3–25	•–27	•–28	•–30
	4	8–25	6–27	5–29	5–30	4–31	•–33
	5	11–29	10–30	8–32	7–33	6–34	5–35
11	0	•–7	•–9	•–10	•–12	•–14	•–17
	1	•–12	•–14	•–15	•–17	•–19	•–21
	2	2–16	•–18	•–19	•–21	•–23	•–25
	3	4–20	3–22	3–23	•–25	•–26	•–28
	4	7–23	6–25	5–27	4–28	4–29	•–31
	5	10–27	9–28	8–30	6–31	6–32	5–33
12	0	•–6	•–8	•–10	•–11	•–13	•–15
	1	•–11	•–13	•–14	•–16	•–17	•–20
	2	2–15	•–16	•–18	•–20	•–21	•–23
	3	4–18	3–20	3–22	•–23	•–24	•–26
	4	6–22	5–23	5–25	4–26	•–27	•–29
	5	9–25	8–26	7–28	6–29	5–30	•–32
	6	12–28	11–29	9–31	8–32	8–32	6–34
13	0	•–6	•–7	•–9	•–10	•–12	•–14
	1	•–10	•–12	•–13	•–15	•–16	•–19
	2	•–14	•–15	•–17	•–18	•–20	•–22
	3	4–17	3–19	•–20	•–22	•–23	•–25
	4	6–20	5–22	4–23	4–25	•–26	•–28
	5	8–23	7–25	6–26	6–27	5–28	•–30
	6	11–26	10–28	9–29	8–30	7–31	6–32
14	0	•–5	•–7	•–8	•–10	•–11	•–13
	1	•–9	•–11	•–12	•–14	•–15	•–17
	2	•–13	•–14	•–16	•–17	•–18	•–21
	3	3–16	3–17	•–19	•–20	•–21	•–24
	4	6–19	5–20	4–22	•–23	•–24	•–26
	5	8–22	7–23	6–25	5–26	5–27	•–28
	6	10–24	9–26	8–27	7–28	7–29	6–31
	7	13–27	12–28	10–30	9–31	9–31	7–33
15	0	•–5	•–6	•–8	•–9	•–10	•–12
	1	•–9	•–10	•–11	•–13	•–14	•–16
	2	•–12	•–13	•–15	•–16	•–17	•–19
	3	3–15	3–16	•–18	•–19	•–20	•–22
	4	5–18	4–19	4–20	•–22	•–23	•–25
	5	7–20	6–22	6–23	5–24	5–25	•–27
	6	10–23	9–24	8–26	7–27	6–28	•–29
	7	12–26	11–27	10–28	9–29	8–30	7–31
16	0	•–5	•–6	•–7	•–8	•–9	•–12
	1	•–8	•–9	•–11	•–12	•–13	•–15
	2	•–11	•–12	•–14	•–15	•–16	•–18
	3	3–14	•–15	•–17	•–18	•–19	•–21
	4	5–17	4–18	4–19	•–21	•–22	•–23
	5	7–19	6–21	5–22	5–23	•–24	•–26
	6	9–22	8–23	7–24	6–25	6–26	•–28
	7	11–24	10–25	9–27	8–28	8–28	7–30
	8	14–26	12–28	11–29	10–30	10–30	8–32
17	0	•–4	•–6	•–7	•–8	•–9	•–11
	1	•–8	•–9	•–10	•–11	•–12	•–14
	2	•–10	•–12	•–13	•–14	•–15	•–17
	3	3–13	•–14	•–16	•–17	•–18	•–20
	4	5–16	4–17	•–18	•–20	•–20	•–22
	5	6–18	6–19	5–21	5–22	•–23	•–24
	6	8–21	8–22	7–23	6–24	6–25	•–27
	7	11–23	10–24	9–25	8–26	7–27	•–28
	8	13–25	12–26	11–27	10–28	9–29	8–30
18	0	•–4	•–5	•–6	•–7	•–8	•–10
	1	•–7	•–8	•–9	•–11	•–12	•–14
	2	•–10	•–11	•–12	•–13	•–14	•–16
	3	3–12	•–14	•–15	•–16	•–17	•–19
	4	4–15	4–16	•–17	•–18	•–19	•–21
	5	6–17	5–18	5–20	•–21	•–22	•–23
	6	8–19	7–21	7–22	6–23	6–24	•–25
	7	10–22	9–23	8–24	8–25	7–26	•–27
	8	12–24	11–25	10–26	9–27	9–28	8–29
	9	14–26	13–27	12–28	11–29	10–30	9–31
19	0	•–4	•–5	•–6	•–7	•–8	•–10
	1	•–7	•–8	•–9	•–10	•–11	•–13
	2	•–9	•–10	•–11	•–13	•–14	•–15
	3	3–12	•–13	•–14	•–15	•–16	•–18
	4	4–14	4–15	•–16	•–18	•–18	•–20
	5	6–16	5–17	5–19	•–20	•–21	•–22
	6	8–18	7–20	6–21	6–22	•–23	•–24
	7	9–21	9–22	8–23	7–24	7–25	•–26
	8	11–23	10–24	10–25	9–26	8–26	8–28
$N = 40$ (continued)							
	9	13–25	12–26	11–27	11–28	10–28	9–29
20	0	•–4	•–5	•–5	•–7	•–7	•–9
	1	•–6	•–7	•–8	•–9	•–10	•–12
	2	•–9	•–10	•–11	•–12	•–13	•–15
	3	•–11	•–12	•–13	•–14	•–15	•–17
	4	4–13	•–14	•–15	•–17	•–17	•–19
	5	6–15	5–17	5–18	•–19	•–20	•–21
	6	7–18	7–19	6–20	•–21	•–22	•–23
	7	9–20	8–21	8–22	7–23	7–23	•–25
	8	11–22	10–23	9–24	9–25	8–25	•–27
	9	13–24	12–25	11–25	10–26	10–27	9–28
	10	15–25	14–26	13–27	12–28	11–29	10–30
$N = 41$							
4	0	•–18	•–21	•–24	•–27	•–29	•–33
	1	1–28	•–31	•–33	•–35	•–36	•–38
	2	6–35	4–37	3–38	2–39	–	–
5	0	•–15	•–18	•–21	•–24	•–26	•–30
	1	•–24	•–27	•–29	•–31	•–33	•–35
	2	4–31	3–33	2–35	•–36	•–37	•–38
6	0	•–13	•–16	•–18	•–21	•–23	•–27
	1	•–21	•–23	•–26	•–28	•–30	•–32
	2	4–27	2–30	2–31	•–33	•–34	•–36
	3	8–33	6–35	5–36	4–37	3–38	–
7	0	•–11	•–14	•–16	•–19	•–21	•–24
	1	•–18	•–21	•–23	•–25	•–27	•–30
	2	3–24	2–26	•–28	•–30	•–32	•–34
	3	7–29	5–31	4–33	3–34	3–35	•–37
8	0	•–10	•–12	•–14	•–17	•–19	•–22
	1	•–16	•–19	•–21	•–23	•–25	•–28
	2	3–22	2–24	•–26	•–28	•–29	•–32
	3	6–27	5–29	4–30	3–32	•–33	•–35
	4	10–31	8–33	7–34	6–35	5–36	4–37
9	0	•–9	•–11	•–13	•–15	•–17	•–20
	1	•–15	•–17	•–19	•–21	•–23	•–25
	2	2–20	2–22	•–24	•–26	•–27	•–29
	3	5–24	4–26	3–28	3–30	•–31	•–33
	4	9–28	7–30	6–32	5–33	4–34	•–35
10	0	•–8	•–10	•–12	•–14	•–15	•–19
	1	•–13	•–15	•–17	•–19	•–21	•–24
	2	2–18	•–20	•–22	•–24	•–25	•–27
	3	5–22	4–24	3–26	•–27	•–29	•–31
	4	8–26	7–28	6–29	5–31	4–32	•–34
	5	11–30	10–31	8–33	7–34	6–35	5–36
11	0	•–7	•–9	•–11	•–13	•–14	•–17
	1	•–12	•–14	•–16	•–18	•–19	•–22
	2	2–16	•–18	•–20	•–22	•–23	•–26
	3	4–20	3–22	3–24	•–26	•–27	•–29
	4	7–24	6–26	5–27	4–29	4–30	•–32
	5	10–27	9–29	8–30	7–32	6–33	5–34
12	0	•–7	•–8	•–10	•–12	•–13	•–16
	1	•–11	•–13	•–15	•–16	•–18	•–20
	2	2–15	•–17	•–19	•–20	•–22	•–24
	3	4–19	3–21	3–22	•–24	•–25	•–27
	4	7–22	5–24	5–25	4–27	4–28	•–30
	5	9–26	8–27	7–28	6–30	5–31	•–32
	6	12–29	11–30	10–31	8–33	8–33	6–35
13	0	•–6	•–8	•–9	•–11	•–12	•–15
	1	•–10	•–12	•–13	•–15	•–17	•–19
	2	2–14	•–16	•–17	•–19	•–20	•–23
	3	4–17	3–19	•–21	•–22	•–23	•–26
	4	6–21	5–22	4–24	4–25	•–26	•–28
	5	9–24	7–25	7–27	6–28	5–29	•–31
	6	11–27	10–28	9–29	8–31	7–32	6–33
14	0	•–6	•–7	•–8	•–10	•–11	•–14
	1	•–10	•–11	•–13	•–14	•–15	•–18
	2	•–13	•–15	•–16	•–18	•–19	•–21
	3	3–16	3–18	•–19	•–21	•–22	•–24
	4	6–19	5–21	4–22	4–24	•–25	•–27
	5	8–22	7–24	6–25	5–27	5–28	•–29
	6	11–25	9–27	8–28	7–29	7–30	6–31
	7	13–28	12–29	11–30	10–31	9–32	7–34
15	0	•–5	•–7	•–8	•–9	•–10	•–13
	1	•–9	•–10	•–12	•–13	•–14	•–17
	2	•–12	•–14	•–15	•–17	•–18	•–20
	3	3–15	3–17	•–18	•–20	•–21	•–23
	4	5–18	4–20	4–21	•–23	•–23	•–25
	5	7–21	7–22	6–24	5–25	5–26	•–28
	6	10–24	9–25	8–26	7–28	6–28	•–30
	7	12–26	11–28	10–29	9–30	8–31	7–32
16	0	•–5	•–6	•–7	•–9	•–10	•–12
	1	•–8	•–10	•–11	•–12	•–14	•–16
	2	•–11	•–13	•–14	•–16	•–17	•–19
	3	3–14	•–16	•–17	•–19	•–20	•–22
	4	5–17	4–19	4–20	•–21	•–22	•–24
	5	7–20	6–21	5–22	5–24	•–25	•–26
	6	9–22	8–24	7–25	7–26	6–27	•–29
	7	11–25	10–26	9–27	8–28	8–29	7–31
	8	14–27	13–28	12–29	10–31	10–31	9–32
17	0	•–5	•–6	•–7	•–8	•–9	•–11
	1	•–8	•–9	•–10	•–12	•–13	•–15
	2	•–11	•–12	•–13	•–15	•–16	•–18
	3	3–13	•–15	•–16	•–18	•–18	•–20
	4	5–16	4–17	4–19	•–20	•–21	•–23
	5	7–19	6–20	5–21	5–23	•–23	•–25
	6	9–21	8–22	7–24	6–25	6–26	•–27

Significance Limits for the Fourfold Table Test*

$$\begin{array}{ccc|c} x_1 & N_1 - x_1 & & N_1 \\ x_2 & N_2 - x_2 & & N_2 \\ \hline X & N - X & & N \end{array} \quad \left\} \begin{array}{l} N = N_1 + N_2 \\ X = x_1 + x_2 \\ N_1 \leqq N_2 \\ x_1 \leqq N_1 - x_1 \end{array} \right\}$$

For explanation see page 123

N_1	x_1	2α = 0.20	2α = 0.10	2α = 0.05	2α = 0.02	2α = 0.01	2α = 0.002
			$N = 41$ (continued)				
	7	11–23	10–25	9–26	8–27	7–28	7–29
	8	13–26	12–27	11–28	10–29	9–30	8–31
18	0	•– 4	•– 5	•– 6	•– 8	•– 9	•–11
	1	•– 7	•– 9	•–10	•–11	•–12	•–14
	2	•–10	•–11	•–13	•–14	•–15	•–17
	3	3–13	•–14	•–15	•–17	•–17	•–19
	4	4–15	4–17	•–18	•–19	•–20	•–22
	5	6–18	6–19	5–20	•–21	•–22	•–24
	6	8–20	7–21	7–22	6–24	6–24	•–26
	7	10–22	9–23	8–25	8–26	7–26	•–28
	8	12–24	11–26	10–27	9–28	9–28	8–30
	9	14–27	13–28	12–29	11–30	11–30	9–32
19	0	•– 4	•– 5	•– 6	•– 7	•– 8	•–10
	1	•– 7	•– 8	•– 9	•–10	•–11	•–13
	2	•–10	•–11	•–12	•–13	•–14	•–16
	3	3–12	•–13	•–14	•–16	•–17	•–18
	4	4–14	4–16	•–17	•–18	•–19	•–21
	5	6–17	5–18	5–19	•–20	•–21	•–23
	6	8–19	7–20	6–21	6–22	•–23	•–25
	7	10–21	9–22	8–23	7–25	7–25	•–27
	8	12–23	11–24	10–25	9–27	8–27	8–29
	9	14–25	13–26	12–27	11–28	10–29	9–30
20	0	•– 4	•– 5	•– 6	•– 7	•– 8	•– 9
	1	•– 7	•– 8	•– 9	•–10	•–11	•–12
	2	•– 9	•–10	•–11	•–12	•–13	•–15
	3	•–11	•–13	•–14	•–15	•–16	•–17
	4	4–14	4–15	•–16	•–17	•–18	•–20
	5	6–16	5–17	5–18	•–19	•–20	•–22
	6	7–18	7–19	6–20	6–21	•–22	•–24
	7	9–20	8–21	8–22	7–23	7–24	•–26
	8	11–22	10–23	9–24	9–25	8–26	•–27
	9	13–24	12–25	11–26	10–27	10–28	9–29
	10	15–26	14–27	13–28	12–29	11–30	10–31
			$N = 42$				
4	0	•–18	•–22	•–25	•–28	•–30	•–34
	1	1–28	•–31	•–34	•–36	•–37	•–39
	2	6–36	4–38	3–39	2–40	–	–
5	0	•–15	•–18	•–21	•–25	•–27	•–30
	1	•–24	•–27	•–30	•–32	•–34	•–36
	2	5–32	3–34	2–36	•–37	•–38	•–39
6	0	•–13	•–16	•–19	•–22	•–24	•–27
	1	•–21	•–24	•–26	•–29	•–30	•–33
	2	4–28	3–30	2–32	•–34	•–35	•–37
	3	8–34	7–35	5–37	4–38	3–39	–
7	0	•–11	•–14	•–16	•–19	•–21	•–25
	1	•–19	•–21	•–23	•–26	•–28	•–31
	2	3–25	2–27	2–29	•–31	•–32	•–35
	3	7–30	6–32	4–34	3–35	3–36	•–38
8	0	•–10	•–12	•–15	•–17	•–19	•–23
	1	•–17	•–19	•–21	•–24	•–25	•–28
	2	3–22	2–25	•–26	•–29	•–30	•–32
	3	6–27	5–29	4–31	3–33	3–34	•–36
	4	10–32	9–33	7–35	6–36	5–37	4–38
9	0	•– 9	•–11	•–13	•–16	•–17	•–21
	1	•–15	•–17	•–19	•–22	•–23	•–26
	2	2–20	2–22	•–24	•–26	•–28	•–30
	3	5–25	4–27	3–29	3–30	•–32	•–34
	4	9–29	8–31	6–32	5–34	4–35	•–36
10	0	•– 8	•–10	•–12	•–14	•–16	•–19
	1	•–14	•–16	•–18	•–20	•–21	•–24
	2	2–18	•–20	•–22	•–24	•–26	•–28
	3	5–23	4–25	3–26	•–28	•–29	•–32
	4	8–27	7–29	6–30	5–32	4–33	•–34
	5	12–30	10–32	9–33	7–35	7–35	5–37
11	0	•– 7	•– 9	•–11	•–13	•–15	•–18
	1	•–12	•–14	•–16	•–18	•–20	•–22
	2	2–17	•–19	•–21	•–23	•–24	•–26
	3	4–21	4–23	3–24	•–26	•–27	•–30
	4	7–25	6–26	5–28	4–30	4–31	•–33
	5	10–28	9–30	8–31	7–33	6–34	5–35
12	0	•– 7	•– 8	•–10	•–12	•–13	•–16
	1	•–11	•–13	•–15	•–17	•–18	•–21
	2	2–15	•–17	•–19	•–21	•–22	•–25
	3	4–19	3–21	3–23	•–25	•–26	•–28
	4	7–23	6–25	5–26	4–28	4–29	•–31
	5	10–26	8–28	7–29	6–31	6–32	5–33
	6	13–29	11–31	10–32	9–33	8–34	6–36
13	0	•– 6	•– 8	•– 9	•–11	•–12	•–15
	1	•–11	•–12	•–14	•–16	•–17	•–20
	2	2–14	•–16	•–18	•–20	•–21	•–23
	3	4–18	3–20	3–21	•–23	•–24	•–26
	4	6–21	5–23	4–24	4–26	•–27	•–29
	5	9–24	8–26	7–27	6–29	5–30	•–32
	6	12–27	10–29	9–30	8–32	7–32	6–34
14	0	•– 6	•– 7	•– 9	•–10	•–12	•–14
	1	•–10	•–11	•–13	•–15	•–16	•–18
	2	•–13	•–15	•–17	•–18	•–19	•–22
	3	4–17	3–18	•–20	•–22	•–23	•–25
	4	6–20	5–22	4–23	4–25	•–26	•–28
	5	8–23	7–24	6–26	5–27	5–28	•–30
	6	11–26	9–27	8–29	7–30	7–31	6–32
	7	13–29	12–30	11–31	10–32	9–33	8–34
15	0	•– 5	•– 7	•– 8	•–10	•–11	•–13
	1	•– 9	•–11	•–12	•–14	•–15	•–17

N_1	x_1	2α = 0.20	2α = 0.10	2α = 0.05	2α = 0.02	2α = 0.01	2α = 0.002
			$N = 42$ (continued)				
	2	•–12	•–14	•–15	•–17	•–18	•–21
	3	3–16	3–17	•–19	•–20	•–21	•–23
	4	5–19	5–20	4–22	•–23	•–24	•–26
	5	8–21	7–23	6–24	5–26	5–27	•–29
	6	10–24	9–26	8–27	7–28	6–29	6–31
	7	13–27	11–28	10–29	9–31	8–31	7–33
16	0	•– 5	•– 6	•– 7	•– 9	•–10	•–12
	1	•– 9	•–10	•–11	•–13	•–14	•–16
	2	•–12	•–13	•–15	•–16	•–17	•–19
	3	3–15	3–16	•–18	•–19	•–20	•–22
	4	5–17	4–19	4–20	•–22	•–23	•–25
	5	7–20	6–22	6–23	5–24	•–25	•–27
	6	9–23	8–24	8–26	7–27	6–28	•–29
	7	12–25	11–27	10–28	9–29	8–30	7–31
	8	14–28	13–29	12–30	11–31	10–32	9–33
17	0	•– 5	•– 6	•– 7	•– 8	•– 9	•–12
	1	•– 8	•– 9	•–11	•–12	•–13	•–15
	2	•–11	•–12	•–14	•–15	•–16	•–18
	3	3–14	•–15	•–17	•–18	•–19	•–21
	4	5–16	4–18	4–19	•–21	•–22	•–24
	5	7–19	6–21	5–22	5–23	•–24	•–26
	6	9–22	8–23	7–24	6–26	6–26	•–28
	7	11–24	10–25	9–27	8–28	8–29	7–30
	8	13–26	12–28	11–29	10–30	9–31	8–32
18	0	•– 4	•– 5	•– 7	•– 8	•– 9	•–11
	1	•– 8	•– 9	•–10	•–11	•–12	•–14
	2	•–10	•–12	•–13	•–14	•–15	•–17
	3	3–13	•–14	•–16	•–17	•–18	•–20
	4	5–16	4–17	•–18	•–20	•–20	•–22
	5	6–18	6–19	5–21	•–22	•–23	•–25
	6	8–20	7–22	7–23	6–24	6–25	•–27
	7	10–23	9–24	9–25	8–26	7–27	•–29
	8	13–25	11–26	11–27	10–29	9–29	8–31
	9	15–27	14–28	13–29	11–31	11–31	10–32
19	0	•– 4	•– 5	•– 6	•– 7	•– 8	•–10
	1	•– 7	•– 8	•– 9	•–11	•–12	•–14
	2	•–10	•–11	•–12	•–14	•–14	•–16
	3	3–12	•–14	•–15	•–16	•–17	•–19
	4	4–15	4–16	•–17	•–19	•–19	•–21
	5	6–17	5–18	5–20	•–21	•–22	•–23
	6	8–19	7–21	7–22	6–23	•–24	•–26
	7	10–22	9–23	8–24	7–25	7–26	•–27
	8	12–24	11–25	10–26	9–27	9–28	8–29
	9	14–26	13–27	12–28	11–29	10–30	9–31
20	0	•– 4	•– 5	•– 6	•– 7	•– 8	•–10
	1	•– 7	•– 8	•– 9	•–10	•–11	•–13
	2	•– 9	•–10	•–12	•–13	•–14	•–16
	3	3–12	•–13	•–14	•–15	•–16	•–18
	4	4–14	4–15	•–16	•–18	•–18	•–20
	5	6–16	5–18	5–19	•–20	•–21	•–22
	6	8–18	7–20	6–21	6–22	•–23	•–24
	7	9–21	9–22	8–23	7–24	7–25	•–26
	8	11–23	10–24	10–25	9–26	8–27	•–28
	9	13–25	12–26	11–27	10–28	10–29	9–30
	10	15–27	14–28	13–29	12–30	12–30	11–31
21	0	•– 4	•– 5	•– 5	•– 7	•– 7	•– 9
	1	•– 6	•– 7	•– 8	•–10	•–10	•–12
	2	•– 9	•–10	•–11	•–12	•–13	•–15
	3	•–11	•–12	•–13	•–15	•–15	•–17
	4	4–13	•–15	•–16	•–17	•–18	•–19
	5	6–15	5–17	5–18	•–19	•–20	•–21
	6	7–18	7–19	6–20	•–21	•–22	•–23
	7	9–20	8–21	8–22	7–23	7–24	•–25
	8	11–22	10–23	9–24	8–25	8–26	•–27
	9	13–24	12–25	11–26	10–27	10–27	9–29
	10	15–26	13–27	13–28	12–29	11–29	10–30
			$N = 43$				
4	0	•–19	•–22	•–25	•–29	•–31	•–35
	1	1–29	•–32	•–34	•–37	•–38	•–40
	2	6–37	4–39	3–40	2–41	–	–
5	0	•–16	•–19	•–22	•–25	•–27	•–31
	1	•–25	•–28	•–30	•–33	•–34	•–37
	2	5–32	3–35	2–36	•–38	•–39	•–40
6	0	•–13	•–16	•–19	•–22	•–24	•–28
	1	•–22	•–25	•–27	•–30	•–31	•–34
	2	4–28	3–31	2–33	•–35	•–36	•–38
	3	9–34	7–36	5–38	4–39	3–40	–
7	0	•–12	•–14	•–17	•–20	•–22	•–25
	1	•–19	•–22	•–24	•–27	•–28	•–31
	2	3–25	2–28	2–30	•–32	•–33	•–36
	3	7–31	6–33	5–35	3–36	3–37	•–39
8	0	•–10	•–13	•–15	•–18	•–20	•–23
	1	•–17	•–20	•–22	•–24	•–26	•–29
	2	3–23	2–25	•–27	•–29	•–31	•–33
	3	6–28	5–30	4–32	3–34	3–35	•–37
	4	11–32	9–34	7–36	6–37	5–38	4–39
9	0	•– 9	•–11	•–14	•–16	•–18	•–21
	1	•–15	•–18	•–20	•–22	•–24	•–27
	2	2–21	2–23	•–25	•–27	•–28	•–31
	3	6–25	4–27	4–29	3–31	•–32	•–34
	4	9–30	8–32	6–33	5–35	5–36	•–37
10	0	•– 8	•–10	•–12	•–15	•–16	•–20
	1	•–14	•–16	•–18	•–20	•–22	•–25
	2	2–19	2–21	•–23	•–25	•–26	•–29
	3	5–23	4–25	3–27	3–29	•–30	•–32

N_1	x_1	2α = 0.20	2α = 0.10	2α = 0.05	2α = 0.02	2α = 0.01	2α = 0.002
			$N = 43$ (continued)				
	4	8–27	7–29	6–31	5–32	4–33	•–35
	5	12–31	10–33	9–34	7–36	7–36	5–38
11	0	•– 8	•– 9	•–11	•–13	•–15	•–18
	1	•–13	•–15	•–17	•–19	•–20	•–23
	2	2–17	•–19	•–21	•–23	•–24	•–27
	3	5–21	4–23	3–25	•–27	•–28	•–30
	4	8–25	6–27	5–29	4–30	4–31	•–33
	5	11–29	9–31	8–32	7–33	6–34	5–36
12	0	•– 7	•– 9	•–10	•–12	•–14	•–17
	1	•–12	•–14	•–15	•–17	•–19	•–22
	2	2–16	•–18	•–20	•–21	•–23	•–25
	3	4–20	3–22	3–23	•–25	•–26	•–29
	4	7–23	6–25	5–27	4–28	4–30	•–32
	5	10–27	8–29	7–30	6–31	6–32	5–34
	6	13–30	11–32	10–33	9–34	8–35	7–36
13	0	•– 6	•– 8	•–10	•–11	•–13	•–16
	1	•–11	•–13	•–14	•–16	•–17	•–20
	2	2–15	•–17	•–18	•–20	•–21	•–24
	3	4–18	3–20	3–22	•–24	•–25	•–27
	4	6–22	5–24	5–25	4–27	•–28	•–30
	5	9–25	8–27	7–28	6–30	5–31	•–32
	6	12–28	10–30	9–31	8–32	7–33	6–35
14	0	•– 6	•– 7	•– 9	•–11	•–12	•–14
	1	•–10	•–12	•–13	•–15	•–16	•–19
	2	•–14	•–15	•–17	•–19	•–20	•–22
	3	4–17	3–19	•–20	•–22	•–23	•–26
	4	6–20	5–22	4–24	4–25	•–26	•–28
	5	8–23	7–25	6–26	5–28	5–29	•–31
	6	11–26	10–28	9–29	8–31	7–32	6–33
	7	14–29	12–31	11–32	10–33	9–34	8–35
15	0	•– 6	•– 7	•– 8	•–10	•–11	•–14
	1	•– 9	•–11	•–12	•–14	•–15	•–18
	2	•–13	•–14	•–16	•–18	•–19	•–21
	3	3–16	3–18	•–19	•–21	•–22	•–24
	4	6–19	5–21	4–22	•–24	•–25	•–27
	5	8–22	7–24	6–25	5–26	5–27	•–29
	6	10–25	9–26	8–28	7–29	7–30	6–32
	7	13–28	11–29	10–30	9–31	9–32	7–34
16	0	•– 5	•– 6	•– 8	•– 9	•–10	•–13
	1	•– 9	•–10	•–12	•–13	•–14	•–17
	2	•–12	•–14	•–15	•–17	•–18	•–20
	3	3–15	3–17	•–18	•–20	•–21	•–23
	4	5–18	4–20	4–21	•–22	•–23	•–25
	5	7–21	6–22	6–24	5–25	5–26	•–28
	6	10–23	9–25	8–26	7–28	6–28	•–30
	7	12–26	11–27	10–29	9–30	8–31	7–32
	8	14–29	13–30	12–31	11–32	10–33	9–34
17	0	•– 5	•– 6	•– 7	•– 9	•–10	•–12
	1	•– 8	•–10	•–11	•–12	•–13	•–16
	2	•–11	•–13	•–14	•–16	•–17	•–19
	3	3–14	•–16	•–17	•–18	•–20	•–22
	4	5–17	4–18	4–20	•–21	•–22	•–24
	5	7–20	6–21	5–22	5–24	•–25	•–27
	6	9–22	8–24	7–25	6–26	6–27	•–29
	7	11–25	10–26	9–27	8–28	8–29	7–31
	8	14–27	12–28	11–29	10–31	10–31	8–33
18	0	•– 5	•– 6	•– 7	•– 8	•– 9	•–11
	1	•– 8	•– 9	•–10	•–12	•–13	•–15
	2	•–11	•–12	•–13	•–15	•–16	•–18
	3	3–13	•–15	•–16	•–17	•–18	•–20
	4	5–16	4–17	4–19	•–20	•–21	•–23
	5	7–19	6–20	5–21	5–23	•–23	•–25
	6	9–21	8–22	7–24	6–25	6–26	•–27
	7	11–23	10–25	9–26	8–27	7–28	7–30
	8	13–26	12–27	11–28	10–29	9–30	8–31
	9	15–28	14–29	13–30	12–31	11–32	10–33
19	0	•– 4	•– 5	•– 6	•– 8	•– 9	•–11
	1	•– 7	•– 9	•–10	•–11	•–12	•–14
	2	•–10	•–11	•–13	•–14	•–15	•–17
	3	3–13	•–14	•–15	•–17	•–18	•–19
	4	4–15	4–17	•–18	•–19	•–20	•–22
	5	6–18	5–19	5–20	•–21	•–22	•–24
	6	8–20	7–21	7–22	6–24	6–25	•–26
	7	10–22	9–24	8–25	8–26	7–27	•–28
	8	12–24	11–26	10–27	9–28	9–29	8–30
	9	14–27	13–28	12–29	11–30	11–31	9–32
20	0	•– 4	•– 5	•– 6	•– 7	•– 8	•–10
	1	•– 7	•– 8	•– 9	•–10	•–11	•–13
	2	•–10	•–11	•–12	•–13	•–14	•–16
	3	3–12	•–13	•–14	•–16	•–17	•–18
	4	4–14	4–16	•–17	•–18	•–19	•–21
	5	6–17	5–18	5–19	•–20	•–21	•–23
	6	8–19	7–20	6–21	6–23	•–23	•–25
	7	10–21	9–22	8–23	7–25	7–25	•–27
	8	12–23	11–25	10–26	9–27	8–27	8–29
	9	14–25	12–27	12–28	11–29	10–29	9–31
	10	16–27	14–29	13–30	12–31	12–31	11–32
21	0	•– 4	•– 5	•– 6	•– 7	•– 8	•– 9
	1	•– 7	•– 8	•– 9	•–10	•–11	•–13
	2	•– 9	•–10	•–11	•–12	•–13	•–15
	3	•–11	•–13	•–14	•–15	•–16	•–18
	4	4–14	4–15	•–16	•–17	•–18	•–20
	5	6–16	5–17	5–18	•–19	•–20	•–22
	6	7–18	7–19	6–20	6–22	•–22	•–24
	7	9–20	8–21	8–22	7–24	7–24	•–26
	8	11–22	10–23	9–24	9–26	8–26	•–28
	9	13–24	12–25	11–26	10–27	10–28	9–29
	10	15–26	14–27	13–28	12–29	11–30	10–31

x_1	$N_1 - x_1$	N_1
x_2	$N_2 - x_2$	N_2
X	$N - X$	N

$N = N_1 + N_2$, $X = x_1 + x_2$, $N_1 \leq N_2$, $x_1 \leq N_1 - x_1$

For explanation see page 123

N_1	x_1	2α = 0.20	2α = 0.10	2α = 0.05	2α = 0.02	2α = 0.01	2α = 0.002
				N = 44			
4	0	•–19	•–23	•–26	•–30	•–32	•–35
	1	1–30	•–33	•–35	•–37	•–39	•–41
	2	6–38	4–40	3–41	2–42	–	–
5	0	•–16	•–19	•–22	•–26	•–28	•–32
	1	•–25	•–29	•–31	•–34	•–35	•–38
	2	5–33	3–36	2–37	•–39	•–40	•–41
6	0	•–14	•–17	•–20	•–23	•–25	•–29
	1	•–22	•–25	•–28	•–30	•–32	•–35
	2	4–29	3–32	2–34	•–36	•–37	•–39
	3	9–35	7–37	5–39	4–40	3–41	–
7	0	•–12	•–15	•–17	•–20	•–22	•–26
	1	•–20	•–22	•–25	•–27	•–29	•–32
	2	3–26	2–28	2–31	•–33	•–34	•–36
	3	7–32	6–34	5–35	4–37	3–38	•–40
8	0	•–11	•–13	•–15	•–18	•–20	•–24
	1	•–17	•–20	•–22	•–25	•–26	•–30
	2	3–23	2–26	•–28	•–30	•–31	•–34
	3	6–28	5–31	4–32	3–34	3–35	•–37
	4	11–33	9–35	7–37	6–38	5–39	4–40
9	0	•– 9	•–12	•–14	•–16	•–18	•–22
	1	•–16	•–18	•–20	•–23	•–24	•–27
	2	2–21	2–23	•–25	•–28	•–29	•–32
	3	6–26	4–28	4–30	3–32	•–33	•–35
	4	9–30	8–32	7–34	5–36	5–36	4–38
10	0	•– 9	•–11	•–13	•–15	•–17	•–20
	1	•–14	•–16	•–18	•–21	•–22	•–25
	2	2–19	2–21	•–23	•–26	•–27	•–30
	3	5–24	4–26	3–28	3–30	•–31	•–33
	4	8–28	7–30	6–32	5–33	4–34	•–36
	5	12–32	10–34	9–35	8–36	7–37	5–39
11	0	•– 8	•–10	•–12	•–14	•–15	•–19
	1	•–13	•–15	•–17	•–19	•–21	•–24
	2	2–18	•–20	•–22	•–24	•–25	•–28
	3	5–22	4–24	3–26	•–28	•–29	•–31
	4	8–26	6–28	5–29	4–31	4–32	•–34
	5	11–30	9–31	8–33	7–34	6–35	5–37
12	0	•– 7	•– 9	•–11	•–13	•–14	•–17
	1	•–12	•–14	•–16	•–18	•–19	•–22
	2	2–16	•–18	•–20	•–22	•–23	•–26
	3	4–20	3–22	3–24	•–26	•–27	•–29
	4	7–24	6–26	5–27	4–29	4–30	•–32
	5	10–27	9–29	8–31	6–32	6–33	5–35
	6	13–31	12–32	10–34	9–35	8–36	7–37
13	0	•– 7	•– 8	•–10	•–12	•–13	•–16
	1	•–11	•–13	•–15	•–17	•–18	•–21
	2	2–15	•–17	•–19	•–21	•–22	•–24
	3	4–19	3–21	3–22	•–24	•–25	•–28
	4	6–22	5–24	5–26	4–27	•–29	•–31
	5	9–26	8–27	7–29	6–30	5–31	•–33
	6	12–29	11–30	9–32	8–33	8–34	6–36
14	0	•– 6	•– 8	•– 9	•–11	•–12	•–15
	1	•–10	•–12	•–14	•–15	•–17	•–19
	2	2–14	•–16	•–17	•–19	•–20	•–23
	3	4–18	3–19	•–21	•–23	•–24	•–26
	4	6–21	5–23	4–24	4–26	•–27	•–29
	5	9–24	7–26	6–27	6–29	5–30	•–32
	6	11–27	10–29	9–30	8–31	7–32	6–34
	7	14–30	13–31	11–33	10–34	9–35	8–36
15	0	•– 6	•– 7	•– 8	•–10	•–11	•–14
	1	•–10	•–11	•–13	•–14	•–16	•–18
	2	•–13	•–15	•–16	•–18	•–19	•–22
	3	3–16	3–18	•–20	•–21	•–22	•–25
	4	6–20	5–21	4–23	•–24	•–25	•–28
	5	8–23	7–24	6–26	5–27	5–28	•–30
	6	10–25	9–27	8–28	7–30	7–31	6–32
	7	13–28	12–30	11–31	9–32	9–33	7–35
16	0	•– 5	•– 7	•– 8	•– 9	•–11	•–13
	1	•– 9	•–10	•–12	•–14	•–15	•–17
	2	•–12	•–14	•–15	•–17	•–18	•–20
	3	3–15	3–17	•–18	•–20	•–21	•–23
	4	5–18	4–20	4–21	•–23	•–24	•–26
	5	8–21	7–23	6–24	5–26	5–27	•–29
	6	10–24	9–26	8–27	7–28	6–29	•–31
	7	12–27	11–28	10–29	9–31	8–32	7–33
	8	15–29	13–31	12–32	11–33	10–34	9–35
17	0	•– 5	•– 6	•– 7	•– 9	•–10	•–12
	1	•– 8	•–10	•–11	•–13	•–14	•–16
	2	•–12	•–13	•–14	•–16	•–17	•–19
	3	3–15	•–16	•–17	•–19	•–20	•–22
	4	5–17	4–19	4–20	•–22	•–23	•–25
	5	7–20	6–22	5–23	5–24	•–25	•–27
	6	9–23	8–24	7–25	7–27	6–28	•–30
	7	12–25	10–27	9–28	8–29	8–30	7–32
	8	14–28	13–29	12–30	10–31	10–32	9–34
18	0	•– 5	•– 6	•– 7	•– 8	•– 9	•–12
	1	•– 8	•– 9	•–10	•–12	•–13	•–15
	2	•–11	•–12	•–14	•–15	•–16	•–18
	3	3–14	•–15	•–16	•–18	•–19	•–21
	4	5–16	4–18	4–19	•–21	•–22	•–24
	5	7–19	6–20	5–22	5–23	•–24	•–26
	6	9–21	8–23	7–24	6–26	6–26	•–28
	7	11–24	10–25	9–27	8–28	8–29	7–30
	8	13–26	12–28	11–29	10–30	9–31	8–32
	9	15–29	14–30	13–31	12–32	11–33	10–34
19	0	•– 4	•– 5	•– 7	•– 8	•– 9	•–11
	1	•– 8	•– 9	•–10	•–11	•–12	•–14

N_1	x_1	2α = 0.20	2α = 0.10	2α = 0.05	2α = 0.02	2α = 0.01	2α = 0.002
				N = 44 (continued)			
	2	•–10	•–12	•–13	•–14	•–15	•–17
	3	3–13	•–14	•–16	•–17	•–18	•–20
	4	5–16	4–17	•–18	•–20	•–21	•–22
	5	6–18	6–19	5–21	•–22	•–23	•–25
	6	8–20	7–22	7–23	6–24	6–25	•–27
	7	10–23	9–24	9–25	8–27	7–27	•–29
	8	12–25	11–26	10–27	9–29	9–29	8–31
	9	15–27	13–29	12–30	11–31	11–31	10–33
20	0	•– 4	•– 5	•– 6	•– 7	•– 8	•–10
	1	•– 7	•– 8	•– 9	•–11	•–12	•–14
	2	•–10	•–11	•–12	•–14	•–14	•–16
	3	3–12	•–14	•–15	•–16	•–17	•–19
	4	4–15	4–16	•–17	•–19	•–20	•–21
	5	6–17	5–18	5–20	•–21	•–22	•–24
	6	8–19	7–21	6–22	6–23	•–24	•–26
	7	10–22	9–23	8–24	7–25	7–26	•–28
	8	12–24	11–25	10–26	9–27	9–28	8–30
	9	14–26	13–27	12–28	11–29	10–30	9–31
	10	16–28	15–29	14–30	13–31	12–32	11–33
21	0	•– 4	•– 5	•– 6	•– 7	•– 8	•–10
	1	•– 7	•– 8	•– 9	•–10	•–11	•–13
	2	•– 9	•–10	•–12	•–13	•–14	•–16
	3	•–12	•–13	•–14	•–15	•–16	•–18
	4	4–14	4–15	•–16	•–18	•–19	•–20
	5	6–16	5–18	5–19	•–20	•–21	•–23
	6	8–18	7–20	6–21	6–22	•–23	•–25
	7	9–21	9–22	8–23	7–24	7–25	•–27
	8	11–23	10–24	10–25	9–26	8–27	•–28
	9	13–25	12–26	11–27	10–28	10–29	9–30
	10	15–27	14–28	13–29	12–30	12–31	10–32
22	0	•– 4	•– 5	•– 5	•– 7	•– 7	•– 9
	1	•– 6	•– 7	•– 8	•–10	•–10	•–12
	2	•– 9	•–10	•–11	•–12	•–13	•–15
	3	•–11	•–12	•–13	•–15	•–15	•–17
	4	4–13	•–15	•–16	•–17	•–18	•–19
	5	6–16	5–17	5–18	•–19	•–20	•–22
	6	7–18	7–19	6–20	•–21	•–22	•–24
	7	9–20	8–21	8–22	7–23	7–24	•–25
	8	11–22	10–23	9–24	8–25	8–26	•–27
	9	13–24	12–25	11–26	10–27	10–28	9–29
	10	14–26	13–27	13–28	12–29	11–29	10–31
	11	16–28	15–29	14–30	13–31	13–31	12–32
				N = 45			
4	0	•–20	•–23	•–27	•–30	•–32	•–36
	1	1–31	•–34	•–36	•–38	•–40	•–42
	2	6–39	4–41	3–42	2–43	–	–
5	0	•–16	•–20	•–23	•–26	•–29	•–33
	1	•–26	•–29	•–32	•–34	•–36	•–39
	2	5–34	3–36	2–38	•–40	•–41	•–42
6	0	•–14	•–17	•–20	•–23	•–25	•–29
	1	•–23	•–26	•–28	•–31	•–33	•–36
	2	4–30	3–32	2–34	•–37	•–38	•–40
	3	9–36	7–38	6–39	4–41	3–42	–
7	0	•–12	•–15	•–18	•–21	•–23	•–27
	1	•–20	•–23	•–25	•–28	•–30	•–33
	2	3–26	2–29	2–31	•–33	•–35	•–37
	3	8–32	6–34	5–36	4–38	3–39	•–41
8	0	•–11	•–13	•–16	•–19	•–21	•–24
	1	•–18	•–20	•–23	•–25	•–27	•–30
	2	3–24	2–26	•–28	•–31	•–32	•–35
	3	7–29	5–31	4–33	3–35	3–36	•–38
	4	11–34	9–36	8–37	6–39	5–40	4–41
9	0	•–10	•–12	•–14	•–17	•–19	•–22
	1	•–16	•–19	•–21	•–23	•–25	•–28
	2	3–22	2–24	•–26	•–28	•–30	•–33
	3	6–27	5–29	4–31	3–33	•–34	•–36
	4	10–31	8–33	7–35	5–36	5–37	4–39
10	0	•– 9	•–11	•–13	•–15	•–17	•–21
	1	•–15	•–17	•–19	•–21	•–23	•–26
	2	2–20	2–22	•–24	•–26	•–28	•–30
	3	5–24	4–26	3–28	3–30	•–32	•–34
	4	9–29	7–31	6–32	5–34	4–35	•–37
	5	12–33	11–34	9–36	8–37	7–38	5–40
11	0	•– 8	•–10	•–12	•–14	•–16	•–19
	1	•–13	•–15	•–17	•–20	•–21	•–24
	2	2–18	•–20	•–22	•–24	•–26	•–28
	3	5–22	4–24	3–26	•–28	•–30	•–32
	4	8–26	7–28	6–30	5–32	4–33	•–35
	5	11–30	10–32	8–34	7–35	6–36	5–38
12	0	•– 7	•– 9	•–11	•–13	•–14	•–18
	1	•–12	•–14	•–16	•–18	•–20	•–23
	2	2–17	•–19	•–20	•–23	•–24	•–27
	3	4–21	3–23	3–24	•–26	•–28	•–30
	4	7–24	6–26	5–28	4–30	4–31	•–33
	5	10–28	9–30	8–31	7–33	6–34	5–36
	6	13–32	12–33	10–35	9–36	8–37	7–38
13	0	•– 7	•– 8	•–10	•–12	•–13	•–16
	1	•–11	•–13	•–15	•–17	•–18	•–21
	2	2–15	•–17	•–19	•–21	•–22	•–25
	3	4–19	3–21	3–23	•–25	•–26	•–28
	4	7–23	6–25	5–26	4–28	4–29	•–31
	5	9–26	8–28	7–30	6–31	5–32	•–34
	6	12–29	11–31	10–33	8–34	8–35	6–37
14	0	•– 6	•– 8	•– 9	•–11	•–12	•–15
	1	•–11	•–12	•–14	•–16	•–17	•–20

N_1	x_1	2α = 0.20	2α = 0.10	2α = 0.05	2α = 0.02	2α = 0.01	2α = 0.002
				N = 45 (continued)			
	2	2–14	•–16	•–18	•–20	•–21	•–24
	3	4–18	3–20	•–21	•–23	•–24	•–27
	4	6–21	5–23	4–25	4–26	•–28	•–30
	5	9–25	8–26	7–28	6–29	5–30	•–32
	6	11–28	10–29	9–31	8–32	7–33	6–35
	7	14–31	13–32	12–33	10–35	9–36	8–37
15	0	•– 6	•– 7	•– 9	•–10	•–12	•–14
	1	•–10	•–11	•–13	•–15	•–16	•–19
	2	•–13	•–15	•–17	•–18	•–20	•–22
	3	3–17	3–19	•–20	•–22	•–23	•–25
	4	6–20	5–22	4–23	4–25	•–26	•–28
	5	8–23	7–25	6–26	5–28	5–29	•–31
	6	11–26	9–28	8–29	7–30	7–31	6–33
	7	13–29	12–30	11–32	10–33	9–34	8–35
16	0	•– 5	•– 7	•– 8	•–10	•–11	•–13
	1	•– 9	•–11	•–12	•–14	•–15	•–18
	2	•–13	•–14	•–16	•–17	•–19	•–21
	3	3–16	3–17	•–19	•–21	•–22	•–24
	4	5–19	5–20	4–22	•–24	•–25	•–27
	5	8–22	7–23	6–25	5–26	5–27	•–29
	6	10–25	9–26	8–27	7–29	6–30	6–32
	7	13–27	11–29	10–30	9–31	8–32	7–34
	8	15–30	14–31	12–33	11–34	10–35	9–36
17	0	•– 5	•– 6	•– 8	•– 9	•–10	•–13
	1	•– 9	•–10	•–11	•–13	•–14	•–17
	2	•–12	•–13	•–15	•–16	•–18	•–20
	3	3–15	3–16	•–18	•–19	•–21	•–23
	4	5–18	4–19	4–21	•–22	•–23	•–25
	5	7–21	6–22	6–23	5–25	•–26	•–28
	6	9–23	8–25	8–26	7–28	6–28	•–30
	7	12–26	11–27	10–29	9–30	8–31	7–32
	8	14–28	13–30	12–31	11–32	10–33	9–34
18	0	•– 5	•– 6	•– 7	•– 9	•–10	•–12
	1	•– 8	•–10	•–11	•–12	•–13	•–16
	2	•–11	•–13	•–14	•–15	•–17	•–19
	3	3–14	•–16	•–17	•–18	•–19	•–22
	4	5–17	4–18	4–20	•–21	•–22	•–24
	5	7–19	6–21	5–22	5–24	•–25	•–27
	6	9–22	8–23	7–25	6–26	6–27	•–29
	7	11–25	10–26	9–27	8–29	8–29	7–31
	8	13–27	12–28	11–29	10–31	9–32	8–33
	9	16–29	14–31	13–32	12–33	11–34	10–35
19	0	•– 5	•– 6	•– 7	•– 8	•– 9	•–11
	1	•– 8	•– 9	•–10	•–12	•–13	•–15
	2	•–11	•–12	•–13	•–15	•–16	•–18
	3	3–13	•–15	•–16	•–17	•–18	•–21
	4	5–16	4–17	•–19	•–20	•–21	•–23
	5	7–18	6–20	5–21	5–23	•–24	•–25
	6	8–21	8–22	7–24	6–25	6–26	•–28
	7	11–23	10–25	9–26	8–27	7–28	•–30
	8	13–26	12–27	11–28	10–29	9–30	8–32
	9	15–28	14–29	13–30	12–31	11–32	10–34
20	0	•– 4	•– 5	•– 6	•– 8	•– 9	•–11
	1	•– 7	•– 8	•–10	•–11	•–12	•–14
	2	•–10	•–11	•–12	•–14	•–15	•–17
	3	3–13	•–14	•–15	•–17	•–18	•–20
	4	4–15	4–16	•–18	•–19	•–20	•–22
	5	6–18	5–19	5–20	•–21	•–22	•–24
	6	8–20	7–21	7–22	6–24	6–25	•–26
	7	10–22	9–24	8–25	8–26	7–27	•–28
	8	12–24	11–26	10–27	9–28	9–29	8–30
	9	14–27	13–28	12–29	11–30	10–31	9–32
	10	16–29	15–30	14–31	13–32	12–33	11–34
21	0	•– 4	•– 5	•– 6	•– 7	•– 8	•–10
	1	•– 7	•– 8	•– 9	•–10	•–11	•–13
	2	•–10	•–11	•–12	•–13	•–14	•–16
	3	3–12	•–13	•–14	•–16	•–17	•–19
	4	4–14	4–16	•–17	•–18	•–19	•–21
	5	6–17	5–18	5–19	•–20	•–21	•–23
	6	8–19	7–20	6–21	6–23	•–24	•–25
	7	10–21	9–22	8–24	7–25	7–26	•–27
	8	12–23	11–25	10–26	9–27	8–28	8–29
	9	13–25	12–27	12–28	11–29	10–30	9–31
	10	15–28	14–29	13–30	12–31	12–31	11–33
22	0	•– 4	•– 5	•– 6	•– 7	•– 8	•– 9
	1	•– 7	•– 8	•– 9	•–10	•–11	•–13
	2	•– 9	•–10	•–11	•–13	•–13	•–15
	3	•–11	•–13	•–14	•–15	•–16	•–18
	4	4–14	4–15	•–16	•–17	•–18	•–20
	5	6–16	5–17	5–18	•–20	•–20	•–22
	6	7–18	7–19	6–20	6–22	•–23	•–24
	7	9–20	8–21	8–23	7–24	7–25	•–26
	8	11–22	10–24	9–25	9–26	8–27	•–28
	9	13–24	12–26	11–27	10–28	10–28	9–30
	10	15–26	14–27	13–28	12–30	11–30	10–32
	11	17–28	16–29	15–30	14–31	13–32	12–33
				N = 46			
4	0	•–20	•–24	•–27	•–31	•–33	•–37
	1	1–31	•–34	•–37	•–39	•–40	•–43
	2	6–40	4–42	3–43	2–44	–	–
5	0	•–17	•–20	•–23	•–27	•–29	•–33
	1	•–27	•–30	•–32	•–35	•–37	•–40
	2	5–35	3–37	2–39	2–41	•–42	•–43
6	0	•–14	•–18	•–20	•–24	•–26	•–30
	1	•–23	•–26	•–29	•–32	•–33	•–36
	2	4–30	3–33	2–35	•–37	•–39	•–41

Significance Limits for the Fourfold Table Test*

x_1	$N_1 - x_1$	N_1	
x_2	$N_2 - x_2$	N_2	
X	$N - X$	N	

$N = N_1 + N_2$, $X = x_1 + x_2$, $N_1 \leqq N_2$, $x_1 \leqq N_1 - x_1$

For explanation see page 123

$N = 46$ (continued)

N_1	x_1	2α = 0.20	2α = 0.10	2α = 0.05	2α = 0.02	2α = 0.01	2α = 0.002
	3	9-37	7-39	6-40	4-42	4-42	–
7	0	•-13	•-15	•-18	•-21	•-23	•-27
	1	•-20	•-23	•-26	•-29	•-30	•-34
	2	3-27	2-30	2-32	•-34	•-36	•-38
	3	8-33	6-35	5-37	4-39	3-40	•-42
8	0	•-11	•-14	•-16	•-19	•-21	•-25
	1	•-18	•-21	•-23	•-26	•-28	•-31
	2	3-24	2-27	•-29	•-31	•-33	•-36
	3	7-30	5-32	4-34	3-36	3-37	•-39
	4	11-35	9-37	8-38	6-40	5-41	4-42
9	0	•-10	•-12	•-15	•-17	•-19	•-23
	1	•-16	•-19	•-21	•-24	•-25	•-29
	2	3-22	2-25	•-27	•-29	•-30	•-33
	3	6-27	5-29	4-31	3-33	•-35	•-37
	4	10-32	8-34	7-35	6-37	5-38	4-40
10	0	•-9	•-11	•-13	•-16	•-17	•-21
	1	•-15	•-17	•-19	•-22	•-23	•-27
	2	2-20	2-22	•-24	•-27	•-28	•-31
	3	5-25	4-27	3-29	3-31	•-32	•-35
	4	9-29	7-31	6-33	5-35	4-36	•-38
	5	13-33	11-35	9-37	8-38	7-39	6-40
11	0	•-8	•-10	•-12	•-14	•-16	•-19
	1	•-14	•-16	•-18	•-20	•-22	•-25
	2	2-18	•-21	•-23	•-25	•-26	•-29
	3	5-23	4-25	3-27	•-29	•-30	•-33
	4	8-27	7-29	6-31	5-33	4-34	•-36
	5	11-31	10-33	9-34	7-36	6-37	5-39
12	0	•-8	•-9	•-11	•-13	•-15	•-18
	1	•-13	•-15	•-16	•-19	•-20	•-23
	2	2-17	•-19	•-21	•-23	•-25	•-27
	3	4-21	4-23	3-25	•-27	•-28	•-31
	4	7-25	6-27	5-29	4-31	4-32	•-34
	5	10-29	9-31	8-32	7-34	6-35	5-37
	6	14-32	12-34	11-35	9-37	8-38	7-39
13	0	•-7	•-9	•-10	•-12	•-14	•-17
	1	•-12	•-14	•-15	•-17	•-19	•-22
	2	2-16	•-18	•-20	•-22	•-23	•-26
	3	4-20	3-22	3-23	•-25	•-27	•-29
	4	7-23	6-25	5-27	4-29	4-30	•-32
	5	10-27	8-29	7-30	6-32	6-33	5-35
	6	13-30	11-32	10-33	9-35	8-36	6-37
14	0	•-6	•-8	•-10	•-11	•-13	•-16
	1	•-11	•-13	•-14	•-16	•-18	•-20
	2	2-15	•-17	•-18	•-20	•-22	•-24
	3	4-18	3-20	3-22	•-24	•-25	•-27
	4	6-22	5-24	5-25	4-27	•-28	•-30
	5	9-25	8-27	7-28	6-30	5-31	•-33
	6	12-28	10-30	9-31	8-33	7-34	6-36
	7	15-31	13-33	12-34	10-36	10-36	8-38
15	0	•-6	•-7	•-9	•-11	•-12	•-15
	1	•-10	•-12	•-13	•-15	•-16	•-19
	2	•-14	•-16	•-17	•-19	•-20	•-23
	3	4-17	3-19	•-21	•-22	•-24	•-26
	4	6-20	5-22	4-24	4-26	•-27	•-29
	5	8-24	7-25	6-27	5-28	5-30	•-32
	6	11-27	10-28	9-30	8-31	7-32	6-34
	7	14-30	12-31	11-32	10-34	9-35	8-36
16	0	•-6	•-7	•-8	•-10	•-11	•-14
	1	•-9	•-11	•-12	•-14	•-15	•-18
	2	•-13	•-15	•-16	•-18	•-19	•-22
	3	3-16	3-18	•-19	•-21	•-22	•-25
	4	6-19	5-21	4-22	•-24	•-25	•-27
	5	8-22	7-24	6-25	5-27	5-28	•-30
	6	10-25	9-27	8-28	7-30	7-31	6-32
	7	13-28	11-29	10-31	9-32	9-33	7-35
	8	15-31	14-32	13-33	11-35	11-35	9-37
17	0	•-5	•-7	•-8	•-9	•-10	•-13
	1	•-9	•-10	•-12	•-13	•-15	•-17
	2	•-12	•-14	•-15	•-17	•-18	•-20
	3	3-15	3-17	•-18	•-20	•-21	•-23
	4	5-18	4-20	4-21	•-23	•-24	•-26
	5	7-21	6-23	6-24	5-26	5-27	•-29
	6	10-24	9-25	8-27	7-28	6-29	•-31
	7	12-26	11-28	10-29	9-31	8-32	7-33
	8	14-29	13-30	12-32	11-33	10-34	9-35
18	0	•-5	•-6	•-7	•-9	•-10	•-12
	1	•-8	•-10	•-11	•-13	•-14	•-16
	2	•-11	•-13	•-14	•-16	•-17	•-19
	3	3-14	•-16	•-17	•-19	•-20	•-22
	4	5-17	4-19	4-20	•-22	•-23	•-25
	5	7-20	6-21	5-23	5-24	•-25	•-27
	6	9-23	8-24	7-25	6-27	6-28	•-30
	7	11-25	10-27	9-28	8-29	8-30	7-32
	8	14-28	12-29	11-30	10-31	10-32	8-34
	9	16-30	15-31	14-32	12-34	12-34	10-36
19	0	•-5	•-6	•-7	•-8	•-9	•-11
	1	•-8	•-9	•-10	•-12	•-13	•-15
	2	•-11	•-12	•-14	•-15	•-16	•-18
	3	3-14	•-15	•-16	•-18	•-19	•-21
	4	5-16	4-18	4-19	•-21	•-22	•-24
	5	7-19	6-20	5-22	5-23	•-24	•-26
	6	9-21	8-23	7-24	6-26	6-26	•-28
	7	11-24	10-25	9-26	8-28	7-29	7-30
	8	13-26	12-28	11-29	10-30	9-31	8-32
	9	15-29	14-30	13-31	12-32	11-33	10-34
20	0	•-4	•-5	•-6	•-8	•-9	•-11

$N = 46$ (continued)

N_1	x_1	2α = 0.20	2α = 0.10	2α = 0.05	2α = 0.02	2α = 0.01	2α = 0.002
	1	•-7	•-9	•-10	•-11	•-12	•-14
	2	•-10	•-12	•-13	•-14	•-15	•-17
	3	3-13	•-14	•-16	•-17	•-18	•-20
	4	4-15	4-17	•-18	•-20	•-21	•-23
	5	6-18	6-19	5-21	•-22	•-23	•-25
	6	8-20	7-22	7-23	6-24	6-25	•-27
	7	10-23	9-24	8-25	8-27	7-27	•-29
	8	12-25	11-26	10-27	9-29	9-30	8-31
	9	14-27	13-29	12-30	11-31	11-32	9-33
	10	17-29	15-31	14-32	13-33	12-34	11-35
21	0	•-4	•-5	•-6	•-7	•-8	•-10
	1	•-7	•-8	•-9	•-11	•-12	•-14
	2	•-10	•-11	•-12	•-14	•-15	•-17
	3	3-12	•-14	•-15	•-16	•-17	•-19
	4	4-15	4-16	•-17	•-19	•-20	•-22
	5	6-17	5-18	5-20	•-21	•-22	•-24
	6	8-19	7-21	6-22	6-23	•-24	•-26
	7	10-22	9-23	8-24	7-25	7-26	•-28
	8	12-24	11-25	10-26	9-28	9-28	8-30
	9	14-26	13-27	12-28	11-30	10-30	9-32
	10	16-28	15-29	14-30	13-32	12-32	11-34
22	0	•-4	•-5	•-6	•-7	•-8	•-10
	1	•-7	•-8	•-9	•-10	•-11	•-13
	2	•-9	•-10	•-12	•-13	•-14	•-16
	3	•-12	•-13	•-14	•-15	•-16	•-18
	4	4-14	4-15	•-16	•-18	•-19	•-21
	5	6-16	5-18	5-19	•-20	•-21	•-23
	6	8-19	7-20	6-21	6-22	•-23	•-25
	7	9-21	8-22	8-23	7-24	7-25	•-27
	8	11-23	10-24	10-25	9-26	8-27	•-29
	9	13-25	12-26	11-27	10-28	10-29	9-31
	10	15-27	14-28	13-29	12-30	11-31	10-32
	11	17-29	16-30	15-31	14-32	13-33	12-34
23	0	•-4	•-5	•-5	•-7	•-7	•-9
	1	•-6	•-7	•-8	•-10	•-10	•-12
	2	•-10	•-10	•-11	•-12	•-13	•-15
	3	•-11	•-12	•-13	•-15	•-16	•-17
	4	4-13	•-15	•-16	•-17	•-18	•-20
	5	6-16	5-17	5-18	•-19	•-20	•-22
	6	7-18	7-19	6-20	•-21	•-22	•-24
	7	9-20	8-21	8-22	7-23	7-24	•-26
	8	11-22	10-23	9-24	8-25	8-26	•-28
	9	13-24	12-25	11-26	10-27	10-28	9-29
	10	14-26	13-27	13-28	12-29	11-30	10-31
	11	16-28	15-29	14-30	13-31	13-32	12-33

$N = 47$

N_1	x_1	2α = 0.20	2α = 0.10	2α = 0.05	2α = 0.02	2α = 0.01	2α = 0.002
4	0	•-20	•-24	•-28	•-32	•-34	•-38
	1	1-32	•-35	•-38	•-40	•-41	•-43
	2	7-40	4-43	3-44	2-45	–	–
5	0	•-17	•-21	•-24	•-28	•-30	•-34
	1	•-27	•-31	•-33	•-36	•-38	•-40
	2	5-35	3-38	2-40	2-42	•-43	•-44
6	0	•-15	•-18	•-21	•-24	•-27	•-31
	1	•-24	•-27	•-29	•-32	•-34	•-37
	2	4-31	3-34	2-36	•-38	•-40	•-42
	3	9-38	7-40	6-41	4-43	4-43	–
7	0	•-13	•-16	•-18	•-22	•-24	•-28
	1	•-21	•-24	•-26	•-29	•-31	•-34
	2	4-28	2-30	2-33	•-35	•-36	•-39
	3	8-34	6-36	5-38	4-40	3-41	•-42
8	0	•-11	•-14	•-17	•-19	•-21	•-26
	1	•-19	•-21	•-24	•-27	•-28	•-32
	2	3-25	2-28	•-30	•-32	•-34	•-36
	3	7-30	5-33	4-35	3-37	3-38	•-40
	4	11-36	9-38	8-39	6-41	5-42	4-43
9	0	•-10	•-13	•-15	•-18	•-20	•-23
	1	•-17	•-19	•-22	•-24	•-26	•-29
	2	3-23	2-25	•-27	•-30	•-31	•-34
	3	6-28	5-30	4-32	3-34	•-35	•-38
	4	10-32	8-35	7-36	6-38	5-39	4-41
10	0	•-9	•-11	•-14	•-16	•-18	•-22
	1	•-15	•-18	•-20	•-22	•-24	•-27
	2	2-21	2-23	•-25	•-27	•-29	•-32
	3	5-25	4-28	3-30	3-32	•-33	•-36
	4	9-30	7-32	6-34	5-36	4-37	•-39
	5	13-34	11-36	10-37	8-39	7-40	6-41
11	0	•-8	•-10	•-12	•-15	•-16	•-20
	1	•-14	•-16	•-18	•-21	•-22	•-25
	2	2-19	•-21	•-23	•-25	•-27	•-30
	3	5-23	4-26	3-27	•-30	•-31	•-34
	4	8-28	7-30	6-31	5-33	4-35	•-37
	5	12-32	10-33	9-35	7-37	7-38	5-39
12	0	•-8	•-10	•-11	•-14	•-15	•-18
	1	•-13	•-15	•-17	•-19	•-21	•-24
	2	2-17	•-20	•-21	•-24	•-25	•-28
	3	5-22	4-24	3-26	•-28	•-29	•-32
	4	7-26	6-28	5-29	4-31	4-32	•-35
	5	11-29	9-31	8-33	7-35	6-36	5-38
	6	14-33	12-35	11-36	9-38	9-38	7-40
13	0	•-7	•-9	•-11	•-13	•-14	•-17
	1	•-12	•-14	•-16	•-18	•-19	•-22
	2	2-16	•-18	•-20	•-22	•-23	•-26
	3	4-20	3-22	3-24	•-26	•-27	•-30
	4	7-24	6-26	5-28	4-29	4-31	•-33
	5	10-27	8-29	7-31	6-33	6-34	5-36

$N = 47$ (continued)

N_1	x_1	2α = 0.20	2α = 0.10	2α = 0.05	2α = 0.02	2α = 0.01	2α = 0.002
	6	13-31	11-33	10-34	9-36	8-37	7-38
14	0	•-7	•-8	•-10	•-12	•-13	•-16
	1	•-11	•-13	•-15	•-17	•-18	•-21
	2	2-15	•-17	•-19	•-21	•-22	•-25
	3	4-19	3-21	3-22	•-24	•-26	•-28
	4	6-22	5-24	5-26	4-28	•-29	•-31
	5	9-26	8-28	7-29	6-31	5-32	•-34
	6	12-29	11-31	9-32	8-34	7-35	6-37
	7	15-32	13-34	12-35	11-36	10-37	8-39
15	0	•-6	•-8	•-9	•-11	•-12	•-15
	1	•-10	•-12	•-14	•-16	•-17	•-20
	2	2-14	•-16	•-18	•-19	•-21	•-23
	3	4-18	3-19	•-21	•-23	•-24	•-27
	4	6-21	5-23	4-24	4-26	•-27	•-30
	5	9-24	7-26	6-27	6-29	5-30	•-32
	6	11-27	10-29	9-30	8-32	7-33	6-35
	7	14-30	12-32	11-33	10-35	9-35	8-37
16	0	•-6	•-7	•-9	•-10	•-11	•-14
	1	•-10	•-11	•-13	•-15	•-16	•-18
	2	•-13	•-15	•-16	•-18	•-20	•-22
	3	3-17	3-18	•-20	•-22	•-23	•-25
	4	6-20	5-21	4-23	•-25	•-26	•-28
	5	8-23	7-24	6-26	5-28	5-29	•-31
	6	10-26	9-27	8-29	7-30	7-31	6-33
	7	13-29	12-30	11-31	9-33	9-34	7-36
	8	16-31	14-33	13-34	12-35	11-36	9-38
17	0	•-5	•-7	•-8	•-10	•-11	•-13
	1	•-9	•-11	•-12	•-14	•-15	•-17
	2	•-12	•-14	•-16	•-17	•-18	•-21
	3	3-16	3-17	•-19	•-20	•-22	•-24
	4	5-19	4-20	4-22	•-23	•-25	•-27
	5	8-21	7-23	6-25	5-26	5-27	•-29
	6	10-24	9-26	8-27	7-29	6-30	•-32
	7	12-27	11-29	10-30	9-31	8-32	7-34
	8	15-30	13-31	12-32	11-34	10-35	9-36
18	0	•-5	•-6	•-7	•-9	•-10	•-12
	1	•-9	•-10	•-11	•-13	•-14	•-16
	2	•-12	•-13	•-15	•-16	•-17	•-20
	3	3-15	•-16	•-18	•-19	•-20	•-23
	4	5-18	4-19	4-21	•-22	•-23	•-25
	5	7-20	6-22	6-23	5-25	•-26	•-28
	6	9-23	8-25	7-26	7-27	6-28	•-30
	7	12-26	10-27	9-28	8-30	8-31	7-33
	8	14-28	13-30	12-31	10-32	10-33	9-35
	9	16-31	15-32	14-33	13-34	12-35	10-37
19	0	•-5	•-6	•-7	•-8	•-10	•-12
	1	•-8	•-9	•-11	•-12	•-13	•-16
	2	•-11	•-13	•-14	•-15	•-17	•-19
	3	3-14	•-15	•-17	•-18	•-19	•-22
	4	5-17	4-18	4-20	•-21	•-22	•-24
	5	7-19	6-21	5-22	5-24	•-25	•-27
	6	9-22	8-23	7-25	6-26	6-27	•-29
	7	11-24	10-26	9-27	8-29	8-29	7-31
	8	13-27	12-28	11-29	10-31	9-32	8-33
	9	15-29	14-31	13-32	12-33	11-34	10-35
20	0	•-4	•-6	•-7	•-8	•-9	•-11
	1	•-8	•-9	•-10	•-12	•-13	•-15
	2	•-11	•-12	•-13	•-15	•-16	•-18
	3	3-13	•-15	•-16	•-17	•-18	•-21
	4	5-16	4-17	•-19	•-20	•-21	•-23
	5	6-18	6-20	5-21	•-23	•-24	•-26
	6	8-21	7-22	7-24	6-25	6-26	•-28
	7	10-23	9-25	9-26	8-27	7-28	•-30
	8	13-26	11-27	11-28	10-29	9-30	8-32
	9	15-28	13-29	12-30	11-32	11-32	10-34
	10	17-30	16-31	15-32	13-34	13-34	11-36
21	0	•-4	•-5	•-6	•-8	•-8	•-11
	1	•-7	•-8	•-10	•-11	•-12	•-14
	2	•-10	•-11	•-12	•-14	•-15	•-17
	3	3-13	•-14	•-15	•-17	•-18	•-20
	4	4-15	4-16	•-18	•-19	•-20	•-22
	5	6-17	5-19	5-20	•-22	•-22	•-24
	6	8-20	7-21	7-22	6-24	•-25	•-27
	7	10-22	9-24	8-25	7-26	7-27	•-29
	8	12-24	11-26	10-27	9-28	9-29	8-31
	9	14-27	13-28	12-29	11-30	10-31	9-33
	10	16-29	15-30	14-31	13-32	12-33	11-34
22	0	•-4	•-5	•-6	•-7	•-8	•-10
	1	•-7	•-8	•-9	•-10	•-11	•-13
	2	•-10	•-11	•-12	•-13	•-14	•-16
	3	3-12	•-13	•-14	•-16	•-17	•-19
	4	4-14	4-16	•-17	•-18	•-19	•-21
	5	6-17	5-18	5-19	•-21	•-21	•-23
	6	8-19	7-20	6-21	6-23	•-24	•-25
	7	10-21	9-23	8-24	7-25	7-26	•-28
	8	11-23	10-25	10-26	9-27	8-28	•-29
	9	13-25	12-27	11-28	11-29	10-30	9-31
	10	15-28	14-29	13-30	12-31	12-32	11-33
	11	17-30	16-31	15-32	14-33	13-34	12-35
23	0	•-4	•-5	•-6	•-7	•-8	•-9
	1	•-7	•-8	•-9	•-10	•-11	•-13
	2	•-9	•-10	•-11	•-13	•-13	•-15
	3	•-11	•-13	•-14	•-15	•-16	•-18
	4	4-14	4-15	•-16	•-17	•-18	•-20
	5	6-16	5-17	5-18	•-20	•-21	•-22
	6	7-18	7-19	6-21	6-22	•-23	•-24
	7	9-20	8-22	8-23	7-24	7-25	•-26
	8	11-22	10-24	9-25	9-26	8-27	•-28

x_1	$N_1 - x_1$	N_1
x_2	$N_2 - x_2$	N_2
X	$N - X$	N

$N = N_1 + N_2$, $X = x_1 + x_2$, $N_1 \leqq N_2$, $x_1 \leqq N_1 - x_1$

For explanation see page 123

N = 47 (continued)

N_1	x_1	2α = 0.20	2α = 0.10	2α = 0.05	2α = 0.02	2α = 0.01	2α = 0.002
23	9	13–24	12–26	11–27	10–28	10–29	9–30
	10	15–26	14–28	13–29	12–30	11–31	10–32
	11	17–28	16–30	15–31	14–32	13–32	12–34

N = 48

N_1	x_1	2α = 0.20	2α = 0.10	2α = 0.05	2α = 0.02	2α = 0.01	2α = 0.002
4	0	•–21	•–25	•–28	•–32	•–35	•–39
	1	1–33	•–36	•–38	•–41	•–42	•–44
	2	7–41	5–43	3–45	2–46	–	–
5	0	•–17	•–21	•–24	•–28	•–31	•–35
	1	•–28	•–31	•–34	•–37	•–38	•–41
	2	5–36	4–39	2–41	2–43	•–44	•–45
6	0	•–15	•–18	•–21	•–25	•–27	•–32
	1	•–24	•–27	•–30	•–33	•–35	•–38
	2	4–32	3–35	2–37	•–39	•–40	•–43
	3	10–38	8–40	6–42	4–44	4–44	–
7	0	•–13	•–16	•–19	•–22	•–24	•–29
	1	•–21	•–24	•–27	•–30	•–32	•–35
	2	4–28	2–31	2–33	•–36	•–37	•–40
	3	8–34	6–37	5–39	4–41	3–42	•–43
8	0	•–12	•–14	•–17	•–20	•–22	•–26
	1	•–19	•–22	•–24	•–27	•–29	•–33
	2	3–25	2–28	2–30	•–33	•–34	•–37
	3	7–31	6–34	4–36	3–38	3–39	•–41
	4	12–36	10–38	8–40	6–42	6–42	4–44
9	0	•–10	•–13	•–15	•–18	•–20	•–24
	1	•–17	•–20	•–22	•–25	•–27	•–30
	2	3–23	2–26	•–28	•–30	•–32	•–35
	3	6–28	5–31	4–33	3–35	3–36	•–39
	4	10–33	9–35	7–37	6–39	5–40	4–42
10	0	•– 9	•–12	•–14	•–16	•–18	•–22
	1	•–16	•–18	•–20	•–23	•–25	•–28
	2	2–21	2–23	•–26	•–28	•–30	•–33
	3	6–26	4–28	4–30	3–32	•–34	•–36
	4	9–31	8–33	6–34	5–36	5–38	•–40
	5	13–35	11–37	10–38	8–40	7–41	6–42
11	0	•– 9	•–11	•–13	•–15	•–17	•–20
	1	•–14	•–17	•–19	•–21	•–23	•–26
	2	2–19	2–22	•–24	•–26	•–28	•–30
	3	5–24	4–26	3–28	3–30	•–32	•–34
	4	8–28	7–30	6–32	5–34	4–35	•–38
	5	12–32	10–34	9–36	7–37	7–39	5–40
12	0	•– 8	•–10	•–12	•–14	•–16	•–19
	1	•–13	•–15	•–17	•–20	•–21	•–24
	2	2–18	•–20	•–22	•–24	•–26	•–29
	3	5–22	4–24	3–26	•–28	•–30	•–32
	4	8–26	6–28	5–30	4–32	4–33	•–36
	5	11–30	9–32	8–34	7–35	6–36	5–38
	6	14–34	13–35	11–37	10–38	9–39	7–41
13	0	•– 7	•– 9	•–11	•–13	•–14	•–18
	1	•–12	•–14	•–16	•–18	•–20	•–23
	2	2–17	•–19	•–20	•–23	•–24	•–27
	3	4–21	3–23	3–24	•–26	•–28	•–30
	4	7–24	6–26	5–28	4–30	4–31	•–34
	5	10–28	9–30	7–32	6–33	6–34	5–37
	6	13–32	12–33	10–35	9–36	8–37	7–39
14	0	•– 7	•– 8	•–10	•–12	•–13	•–16
	1	•–11	•–13	•–15	•–17	•–18	•–21
	2	2–15	•–17	•–19	•–21	•–23	•–25
	3	4–19	3–21	3–23	•–25	•–26	•–29
	4	7–23	5–25	5–26	4–28	•–30	•–32
	5	9–26	8–28	7–30	6–31	5–33	•–35
	6	12–30	11–31	10–33	8–34	8–35	6–37
	7	15–33	14–34	12–36	11–37	10–38	8–40
15	0	•– 6	•– 8	•– 9	•–11	•–13	•–15
	1	•–11	•–12	•–14	•–16	•–17	•–20
	2	2–14	•–16	•–18	•–20	•–21	•–24
	3	4–18	3–20	•–22	•–23	•–25	•–27
	4	6–21	5–23	4–25	4–27	•–28	•–30
	5	9–25	7–27	7–28	6–30	5–31	•–33
	6	11–28	10–30	9–31	8–33	7–34	6–36
	7	14–31	13–33	11–34	10–35	9–36	8–38
16	0	•– 6	•– 7	•– 9	•–10	•–12	•–14
	1	•–10	•–12	•–13	•–15	•–16	•–19
	2	•–14	•–15	•–17	•–19	•–20	•–23
	3	3–17	3–19	•–20	•–22	•–23	•–26
	4	6–20	5–22	4–24	4–25	•–26	•–29
	5	8–23	7–25	6–27	5–28	5–29	•–32
	6	11–26	9–28	8–29	7–31	7–32	6–34
	7	13–29	12–31	11–32	10–34	9–35	7–36
	8	16–32	14–34	13–35	12–36	11–37	9–39
17	0	•– 5	•– 7	•– 8	•–10	•–11	•–14
	1	•– 9	•–11	•–12	•–14	•–15	•–18
	2	•–13	•–14	•–16	•–18	•–19	•–21
	3	3–16	3–18	•–19	•–21	•–22	•–25
	4	5–19	5–21	4–22	•–24	•–25	•–27
	5	8–22	7–24	6–25	5–27	5–28	•–30
	6	10–25	9–27	8–28	7–30	6–31	•–33
	7	12–28	11–29	10–31	9–32	8–33	7–35
	8	15–30	14–32	12–33	11–34	10–35	9–37
18	0	•– 5	•– 6	•– 8	•– 9	•–10	•–13
	1	•– 9	•–10	•–12	•–13	•–14	•–17
	2	•–12	•–14	•–15	•–17	•–18	•–20
	3	3–15	3–17	•–18	•–20	•–21	•–23
	4	5–18	4–20	4–21	•–23	•–24	•–26
	5	7–21	6–22	6–24	5–25	•–27	•–29

N = 48 (continued)

N_1	x_1	2α = 0.20	2α = 0.10	2α = 0.05	2α = 0.02	2α = 0.01	2α = 0.002
	6	9–24	8–25	8–27	7–28	6–29	•–31
	7	12–26	11–28	10–29	9–31	8–32	7–33
	8	14–29	13–30	12–32	11–33	10–34	9–35
	9	17–31	15–33	14–34	13–35	12–36	11–37
19	0	•– 5	•– 6	•– 7	•– 9	•–10	•–12
	1	•– 8	•–10	•–11	•–13	•–14	•–16
	2	•–11	•–13	•–14	•–16	•–17	•–19
	3	3–14	•–16	•–17	•–19	•–20	•–22
	4	5–17	4–19	4–20	•–22	•–23	•–25
	5	7–20	6–21	5–23	5–24	•–25	•–27
	6	9–22	8–24	7–25	6–27	6–28	•–30
	7	11–25	10–26	9–28	8–29	8–30	7–32
	8	13–27	12–29	11–30	10–32	9–32	8–34
	9	16–30	14–31	13–32	12–34	11–35	10–36
20	0	•– 5	•– 6	•– 7	•– 8	•– 9	•–11
	1	•– 8	•– 9	•–10	•–12	•–13	•–15
	2	•–11	•–12	•–13	•–15	•–16	•–18
	3	3–14	•–15	•–16	•–18	•–19	•–21
	4	5–16	4–18	4–19	•–21	•–22	•–24
	5	7–19	6–20	5–22	5–23	•–24	•–26
	6	9–21	8–23	7–24	6–26	6–27	•–28
	7	11–24	10–25	9–26	8–28	7–29	•–31
	8	13–26	12–28	11–29	10–30	9–31	8–33
	9	15–28	14–30	13–31	12–32	11–33	10–35
	10	17–31	16–32	15–33	14–34	13–35	11–37
21	0	•– 4	•– 5	•– 6	•– 8	•– 9	•–11
	1	•– 7	•– 9	•–10	•–11	•–12	•–14
	2	•–10	•–12	•–13	•–14	•–15	•–17
	3	3–13	•–14	•–16	•–17	•–18	•–20
	4	4–15	4–17	•–18	•–20	•–21	•–23
	5	6–18	6–19	5–21	•–22	•–23	•–25
	6	8–20	7–22	7–23	6–24	6–25	•–27
	7	10–23	9–24	8–25	8–27	7–28	•–29
	8	12–25	11–26	10–28	9–29	9–30	8–31
	9	14–27	13–29	12–30	11–31	10–32	9–33
	10	16–29	15–31	14–32	13–33	12–34	11–35
22	0	•– 4	•– 5	•– 6	•– 7	•– 8	•–10
	1	•– 7	•– 8	•– 9	•–11	•–12	•–14
	2	•–10	•–11	•–12	•–14	•–15	•–17
	3	3–12	•–14	•–15	•–16	•–17	•–19
	4	4–15	4–16	•–17	•–19	•–20	•–22
	5	6–17	5–18	5–20	•–21	•–22	•–24
	6	8–19	7–21	6–22	6–23	•–24	•–26
	7	10–22	9–23	8–24	7–26	7–26	•–28
	8	12–24	11–25	10–26	9–28	8–29	8–30
	9	14–26	13–27	12–28	11–30	10–31	9–32
	10	16–28	14–29	14–31	13–32	12–32	11–34
	11	18–30	16–32	15–33	14–34	14–34	12–36
23	0	•– 4	•– 5	•– 6	•– 7	•– 8	•–10
	1	•– 7	•– 8	•– 9	•–10	•–11	•–13
	2	•– 9	•–10	•–12	•–13	•–14	•–16
	3	•–12	•–13	•–14	•–15	•–16	•–18
	4	4–14	4–15	•–17	•–18	•–19	•–21
	5	6–16	5–18	5–19	•–20	•–21	•–23
	6	8–19	7–20	6–21	6–22	•–23	•–25
	7	9–21	8–22	8–23	7–24	7–25	•–27
	8	11–23	10–24	9–25	9–27	8–27	•–29
	9	13–25	12–26	11–27	10–29	10–29	9–31
	10	15–27	14–28	13–29	12–30	11–31	10–33
	11	17–29	16–30	15–31	14–32	13–33	12–34
24	0	•– 4	•– 5	•– 5	•– 7	•– 7	•– 9
	1	•– 6	•– 7	•– 8	•–10	•–11	•–12
	2	•– 9	•–10	•–11	•–12	•–13	•–15
	3	•–11	•–12	•–13	•–15	•–16	•–18
	4	4–13	•–15	•–16	•–17	•–18	•–20
	5	6–16	5–17	5–18	•–19	•–20	•–22
	6	7–18	7–19	6–20	•–21	•–22	•–24
	7	9–20	8–21	8–22	7–23	7–24	•–26
	8	11–22	10–23	9–24	8–25	8–26	•–28
	9	13–24	12–25	11–26	10–27	9–28	9–30
	10	14–26	13–27	13–28	12–29	11–30	10–32
	11	16–28	15–29	14–30	13–31	13–32	12–33
	12	18–30	17–31	16–32	15–33	14–34	13–35

N = 49

N_1	x_1	2α = 0.20	2α = 0.10	2α = 0.05	2α = 0.02	2α = 0.01	2α = 0.002
4	0	•–21	•–26	•–29	•–33	•–35	•–39
	1	1–33	•–37	•–39	•–42	•–43	•–45
	2	7–42	5–44	3–46	2–47	–	–
5	0	•–18	•–22	•–25	•–29	•–31	•–36
	1	•–28	•–32	•–35	•–38	•–39	•–42
	2	5–37	4–40	3–42	2–43	•–45	•–46
6	0	•–15	•–19	•–22	•–25	•–28	•–32
	1	•–25	•–28	•–31	•–34	•–36	•–39
	2	4–32	3–35	2–38	•–40	•–41	•–43
	3	10–39	8–41	6–43	5–44	4–45	–
7	0	•–13	•–16	•–19	•–23	•–25	•–29
	1	•–22	•–25	•–28	•–31	•–32	•–36
	2	4–29	3–32	2–34	•–37	•–38	•–41
	3	8–35	6–38	5–39	4–41	3–42	•–44
8	0	•–12	•–15	•–17	•–20	•–22	•–27
	1	•–19	•–22	•–25	•–28	•–30	•–33
	2	3–26	2–29	2–31	•–34	•–35	•–38
	3	7–32	6–34	4–36	3–38	3–40	•–42
	4	12–37	10–39	8–41	7–42	6–43	4–45
9	0	•–11	•–13	•–16	•–18	•–20	•–24
	1	•–18	•–20	•–23	•–25	•–27	•–31

N = 49 (continued)

N_1	x_1	2α = 0.20	2α = 0.10	2α = 0.05	2α = 0.02	2α = 0.01	2α = 0.002
	2	3–24	2–26	•–28	•–31	•–33	•–36
	3	6–29	5–31	4–33	3–36	3–37	•–39
	4	11–34	9–36	7–38	6–40	5–41	4–43
10	0	•–10	•–12	•–14	•–17	•–19	•–23
	1	•–16	•–18	•–21	•–23	•–25	•–29
	2	2–21	2–24	•–26	•–29	•–30	•–33
	3	6–26	4–29	4–31	3–33	•–35	•–37
	4	9–31	8–33	7–35	5–37	5–38	4–40
	5	13–36	11–38	10–39	8–41	7–42	6–43
11	0	•– 9	•–11	•–13	•–15	•–17	•–21
	1	•–15	•–17	•–19	•–22	•–23	•–27
	2	2–20	2–22	•–24	•–27	•–28	•–31
	3	5–24	4–27	3–29	3–31	•–32	•–35
	4	9–29	7–31	6–33	5–35	4–36	•–38
	5	12–33	10–35	9–37	8–38	7–39	5–41
12	0	•– 8	•–10	•–12	•–14	•–16	•–19
	1	•–13	•–16	•–18	•–20	•–22	•–25
	2	2–18	•–20	•–22	•–25	•–26	•–29
	3	5–23	4–25	3–27	•–29	•–30	•–33
	4	8–27	6–29	5–31	4–33	4–34	•–36
	5	11–31	9–33	8–34	7–36	6–37	5–39
	6	15–34	13–36	11–38	10–39	9–40	7–42
13	0	•– 7	•– 9	•–11	•–13	•–15	•–18
	1	•–12	•–15	•–16	•–19	•–20	•–23
	2	2–17	•–19	•–21	•–23	•–25	•–28
	3	4–21	3–23	3–25	•–27	•–28	•–31
	4	7–25	6–27	5–29	4–31	4–32	•–34
	5	10–29	9–31	8–32	6–34	6–35	5–37
	6	13–32	12–34	10–36	9–37	8–38	7–40
14	0	•– 7	•– 9	•–10	•–12	•–14	•–17
	1	•–12	•–14	•–15	•–17	•–19	•–22
	2	2–16	•–18	•–20	•–22	•–23	•–26
	3	4–20	3–22	3–23	•–25	•–27	•–29
	4	7–23	6–25	5–27	4–29	4–30	•–33
	5	9–27	8–29	7–30	6–32	5–33	•–36
	6	12–30	11–32	10–34	8–35	8–36	6–38
	7	16–33	14–35	12–37	11–38	10–39	8–41
15	0	•– 6	•– 8	•–10	•–11	•–13	•–16
	1	•–11	•–13	•–14	•–16	•–18	•–21
	2	2–15	•–17	•–18	•–20	•–22	•–24
	3	4–18	3–20	3–22	•–24	•–25	•–28
	4	6–22	5–24	4–25	4–27	•–29	•–31
	5	9–25	8–27	7–29	6–30	5–32	•–34
	6	12–28	10–30	9–32	8–33	7–34	6–36
	7	14–32	13–33	12–35	10–36	9–37	8–39
16	0	•– 6	•– 7	•– 9	•–11	•–12	•–15
	1	•–10	•–12	•–13	•–15	•–17	•–19
	2	•–14	•–16	•–17	•–19	•–20	•–23
	3	4–17	3–19	•–21	•–23	•–24	•–26
	4	6–21	5–22	4–24	4–26	•–27	•–29
	5	8–24	7–26	6–27	5–29	5–30	•–32
	6	11–27	10–29	9–30	7–32	7–33	6–35
	7	14–30	12–31	11–33	10–34	9–35	8–37
	8	16–33	15–34	13–36	12–37	11–38	10–39
17	0	•– 6	•– 7	•– 8	•–10	•–11	•–14
	1	•–10	•–11	•–13	•–14	•–16	•–18
	2	•–13	•–15	•–16	•–18	•–19	•–22
	3	3–16	3–18	•–20	•–21	•–23	•–25
	4	6–19	5–21	4–23	•–25	•–26	•–28
	5	8–22	7–24	6–26	5–27	5–29	•–31
	6	10–25	9–27	8–29	7–30	7–31	6–33
	7	13–28	11–30	10–31	9–33	8–34	7–36
	8	15–31	14–33	13–34	11–35	11–36	9–38
18	0	•– 5	•– 7	•– 8	•– 9	•–11	•–13
	1	•– 9	•–10	•–12	•–14	•–15	•–17
	2	•–12	•–14	•–15	•–17	•–18	•–21
	3	3–15	3–17	•–19	•–20	•–21	•–24
	4	5–18	4–20	4–22	•–23	•–24	•–27
	5	7–21	6–23	6–24	5–26	5–27	•–29
	6	10–24	9–26	8–27	7–29	6–30	•–32
	7	12–27	11–28	10–30	9–31	8–32	7–34
	8	14–29	13–31	12–32	11–34	10–35	9–36
	9	17–32	16–33	14–35	13–36	12–37	11–38
19	0	•– 5	•– 6	•– 7	•– 9	•–10	•–12
	1	•– 8	•–10	•–11	•–13	•–14	•–16
	2	•–12	•–13	•–15	•–16	•–17	•–20
	3	3–15	•–16	•–18	•–19	•–20	•–23
	4	5–17	4–19	4–20	•–22	•–23	•–25
	5	7–20	6–22	5–23	5–25	•–26	•–28
	6	9–23	8–24	7–26	6–27	6–28	•–30
	7	11–25	10–27	9–28	8–30	8–31	7–33
	8	14–28	12–30	11–31	10–32	10–33	8–35
	9	16–30	15–32	14–33	12–34	12–35	10–37
20	0	•– 5	•– 6	•– 7	•– 8	•– 9	•–12
	1	•– 8	•– 9	•–11	•–12	•–13	•–16
	2	•–11	•–12	•–14	•–15	•–16	•–19
	3	3–14	•–15	•–17	•–18	•–19	•–22
	4	5–17	4–18	4–19	•–21	•–22	•–24
	5	7–19	6–21	5–22	5–24	•–25	•–27
	6	9–22	8–23	7–25	6–26	6–27	•–29
	7	11–24	10–26	9–27	8–29	7–29	7–31
	8	13–27	12–28	11–29	10–31	9–32	8–33
	9	15–29	14–31	13–32	12–33	11–34	10–35
	10	18–31	16–33	15–34	14–35	13–36	12–37
21	0	•– 4	•– 6	•– 7	•– 8	•– 9	•–11
	1	•– 8	•– 9	•–10	•–12	•–13	•–15
	2	•–10	•–12	•–13	•–15	•–16	•–18

Significance Limits for the Fourfold Table Test*

$$\begin{array}{cc|c} x_1 & N_1-x_1 & N_1 \\ x_2 & N_2-x_2 & N_2 \\ \hline X & N-X & N \end{array} \quad \left\} \begin{array}{l} N=N_1+N_2 \\ X=x_1+x_2 \\ N_1 \leqq N_2 \\ x_1 \leqq N_1-x_1 \end{array} \right\}$$

For explanation see page 123

N = 49 (continued)

N_1	x_1	2α = 0.20	2α = 0.10	2α = 0.05	2α = 0.02	2α = 0.01	2α = 0.002
	3	3–13	•–15	•–16	•–17	•–18	•–21
	4	5–16	4–17	•–19	•–20	•–21	•–23
	5	6–18	6–20	5–21	•–23	•–24	•–26
	6	8–21	7–22	7–24	6–25	6–26	•–28
	7	10–23	9–25	9–26	8–27	7–28	•–30
	8	12–26	11–27	10–28	9–30	9–30	8–32
	9	15–28	13–29	12–30	11–32	11–33	9–34
	10	17–30	15–31	14–33	13–34	13–35	11–36
22	0	•–4	•–5	•–6	•–8	•–8	•–11
	1	•–7	•–8	•–10	•–11	•–12	•–14
	2	•–10	•–11	•–12	•–14	•–15	•–17
	3	3–13	•–14	•–15	•–17	•–18	•–20
	4	4–15	4–16	•–18	•–19	•–20	•–22
	5	6–17	5–19	5–20	•–22	•–23	•–25
	6	8–20	7–21	6–22	6–24	•–25	•–27
	7	10–22	9–24	8–25	7–26	7–27	•–29
	8	12–24	11–26	10–27	9–28	9–29	8–31
	9	14–27	13–28	12–29	11–30	10–31	9–33
	10	16–29	15–30	14–31	13–32	12–33	11–35
	11	18–31	17–32	16–33	15–34	14–35	12–37
23	0	•–4	•–5	•–6	•–7	•–8	•–10
	1	•–7	•–8	•–9	•–10	•–11	•–13
	2	•–10	•–11	•–12	•–13	•–14	•–16
	3	3–12	•–13	•–14	•–16	•–17	•–19
	4	4–14	4–16	•–17	•–18	•–19	•–21
	5	6–17	5–18	5–19	•–21	•–22	•–24
	6	8–19	7–20	6–22	6–23	•–24	•–26
	7	10–21	9–23	8–24	7–25	7–26	•–28
	8	11–23	10–25	10–26	9–27	8–28	•–30
	9	13–26	12–27	11–28	10–29	10–30	9–32
	10	15–28	14–29	13–30	12–31	12–32	10–33
	11	17–30	16–31	15–32	14–33	13–34	12–35
24	0	•–4	•–5	•–6	•–7	•–8	•–9
	1	•–7	•–8	•–9	•–10	•–11	•–13
	2	•–9	•–10	•–11	•–13	•–14	•–15
	3	•–11	•–13	•–14	•–15	•–16	•–18
	4	4–14	•–15	•–16	•–18	•–18	•–20
	5	6–16	5–17	5–18	•–20	•–21	•–23
	6	7–18	7–19	6–21	6–22	•–23	•–25
	7	9–20	8–22	8–23	7–24	7–25	•–27
	8	11–22	10–24	9–25	9–26	8–27	•–29
	9	13–24	12–26	11–27	10–28	10–29	9–30
	10	15–27	14–28	13–29	12–30	11–31	10–32
	11	17–29	15–30	15–31	14–32	13–33	12–34
	12	19–30	17–32	16–33	15–34	15–34	13–36

N = 50

N_1	x_1	2α = 0.20	2α = 0.10	2α = 0.05	2α = 0.02	2α = 0.01	2α = 0.002
4	0	•–22	•–26	•–30	•–34	•–36	•–40
	1	1–34	•–37	•–40	•–43	•–44	•–46
	2	7–43	5–45	3–47	2–48	2–48	–
5	0	•–18	•–22	•–26	•–29	•–32	•–36
	1	•–29	•–33	•–35	•–38	•–40	•–43
	2	5–38	4–40	3–42	2–44	•–45	•–47
6	0	•–16	•–19	•–22	•–26	•–28	•–33
	1	•–25	•–29	•–31	•–34	•–36	•–40
	2	4–33	3–36	2–38	•–41	•–42	•–44
	3	10–40	8–42	6–44	5–45	4–46	–
7	0	•–14	•–17	•–20	•–23	•–25	•–30
	1	•–22	•–25	•–28	•–31	•–33	•–37
	2	4–29	3–32	2–35	•–37	•–39	•–42
	3	9–36	7–38	5–40	4–42	3–43	•–45
8	0	•–12	•–15	•–18	•–21	•–23	•–27
	1	•–20	•–23	•–25	•–28	•–30	•–34
	2	3–26	2–29	2–32	•–34	•–36	•–39
	3	7–32	6–35	5–37	3–39	3–40	•–43
	4	12–38	10–40	8–42	7–43	6–44	4–46
9	0	•–11	•–13	•–16	•–19	•–21	•–25
	1	•–18	•–21	•–23	•–26	•–28	•–31
	2	3–24	2–27	•–29	•–32	•–33	•–36
	3	7–30	5–32	4–34	3–36	3–38	•–40
	4	11–35	9–37	7–39	6–41	5–42	4–44
10	0	•–10	•–12	•–14	•–17	•–19	•–23
	1	•–16	•–19	•–21	•–24	•–26	•–29
	2	3–22	2–24	•–27	•–29	•–31	•–34
	3	6–27	5–30	4–32	3–34	•–35	•–38
	4	10–32	8–34	7–36	5–38	5–39	4–41
	5	14–36	12–38	10–40	8–42	8–42	6–44
11	0	•–9	•–11	•–13	•–16	•–18	•–21
	1	•–15	•–17	•–19	•–22	•–24	•–27
	2	2–20	2–23	•–25	•–27	•–29	•–32
	3	5–25	4–27	3–29	3–32	•–33	•–36
	4	9–29	7–32	6–34	5–36	4–37	•–39
	5	12–34	11–36	9–37	8–39	7–40	5–42
12	0	•–8	•–10	•–12	•–15	•–16	•–20
	1	•–14	•–16	•–18	•–20	•–22	•–25
	2	2–19	•–21	•–23	•–25	•–27	•–30
	3	5–23	4–25	3–27	•–30	•–31	•–34
	4	8–27	7–29	6–31	5–33	4–35	•–37
	5	11–31	10–33	8–35	7–37	6–38	5–40
	6	15–35	13–37	12–38	10–40	9–41	7–43
13	0	•–8	•–9	•–11	•–14	•–15	•–18
	1	•–13	•–15	•–17	•–19	•–21	•–24
	2	2–17	•–19	•–21	•–24	•–25	•–28
	3	4–21	4–24	3–26	•–28	•–29	•–32
	4	7–25	6–28	5–29	4–31	4–33	•–35
	5	10–29	9–31	8–33	7–35	6–36	5–38

N = 50 (continued)

N_1	x_1	2α = 0.20	2α = 0.10	2α = 0.05	2α = 0.02	2α = 0.01	2α = 0.002
	6	14–33	12–35	11–36	9–38	8–39	7–41
14	0	•–7	•–9	•–10	•–13	•–14	•–17
	1	•–12	•–14	•–16	•–18	•–19	•–22
	2	2–16	•–18	•–20	•–22	•–24	•–27
	3	4–20	3–22	3–24	•–26	•–27	•–30
	4	7–24	6–26	5–28	4–30	4–31	•–33
	5	10–27	8–29	7–31	6–33	6–34	5–36
	6	13–31	11–33	10–34	9–36	8–37	6–39
	7	16–34	14–36	13–37	11–39	10–40	9–41
15	0	•–7	•–8	•–10	•–12	•–13	•–16
	1	•–11	•–13	•–15	•–17	•–18	•–21
	2	2–15	•–17	•–19	•–21	•–22	•–25
	3	4–19	3–21	3–23	•–25	•–26	•–29
	4	6–22	5–24	5–26	4–28	•–29	•–32
	5	9–26	8–28	7–29	6–31	5–32	•–35
	6	12–29	10–31	9–32	8–34	7–35	6–37
	7	15–32	13–34	12–35	10–37	10–38	8–40
16	0	•–6	•–8	•–9	•–11	•–12	•–15
	1	•–10	•–12	•–14	•–16	•–17	•–20
	2	2–14	•–16	•–18	•–20	•–21	•–24
	3	4–18	3–20	•–21	•–23	•–24	•–27
	4	6–21	5–23	4–25	4–26	•–28	•–30
	5	8–24	7–26	6–28	6–30	5–31	•–33
	6	11–27	10–29	9–31	8–32	7–34	6–36
	7	14–30	12–32	11–34	10–35	9–36	8–38
	8	17–33	15–35	14–36	12–38	11–39	10–40
17	0	•–6	•–7	•–9	•–10	•–12	•–14
	1	•–10	•–11	•–13	•–15	•–16	•–19
	2	•–13	•–15	•–17	•–18	•–20	•–22
	3	3–17	3–18	•–20	•–22	•–23	•–26
	4	6–20	5–22	4–23	•–25	•–26	•–29
	5	8–23	7–25	6–26	5–28	5–29	•–31
	6	10–26	9–28	8–29	7–31	7–32	6–34
	7	13–29	12–31	10–32	9–33	9–35	7–36
	8	16–32	14–33	13–35	12–36	11–37	9–39
18	0	•–5	•–7	•–8	•–10	•–11	•–13
	1	•–9	•–11	•–12	•–14	•–15	•–18
	2	•–13	•–14	•–16	•–17	•–19	•–21
	3	3–16	3–17	•–19	•–21	•–22	•–24
	4	5–19	4–21	4–22	•–24	•–25	•–27
	5	8–22	7–23	6–25	5–27	5–28	•–30
	6	10–25	9–26	8–28	7–29	6–30	•–33
	7	12–27	11–29	10–30	9–32	8–33	7–35
	8	15–30	13–32	12–33	11–34	10–35	9–37
	9	17–33	16–34	15–35	13–37	12–38	11–39
19	0	•–5	•–6	•–8	•–9	•–10	•–13
	1	•–9	•–10	•–11	•–13	•–14	•–17
	2	•–12	•–13	•–15	•–17	•–18	•–20
	3	3–15	3–17	•–18	•–20	•–21	•–23
	4	5–18	4–19	4–21	•–23	•–24	•–26
	5	7–21	6–22	6–24	5–25	•–26	•–29
	6	9–23	8–25	7–26	7–28	6–29	•–31
	7	12–26	10–28	9–29	8–31	8–32	7–33
	8	14–29	13–30	12–31	10–33	10–34	9–36
	9	16–31	15–33	14–34	13–35	12–36	10–38
20	0	•–5	•–6	•–7	•–9	•–10	•–12
	1	•–8	•–10	•–11	•–12	•–14	•–16
	2	•–11	•–13	•–14	•–16	•–17	•–19
	3	3–14	•–16	•–17	•–19	•–20	•–22
	4	5–17	4–19	4–20	•–22	•–23	•–25
	5	7–20	6–21	5–23	5–24	•–25	•–27
	6	9–22	8–24	7–25	6–27	6–28	•–30
	7	11–25	10–26	9–28	8–29	8–30	7–32
	8	13–27	12–29	11–30	10–32	9–32	8–34
	9	16–30	14–31	13–32	12–34	11–35	10–36
	10	18–32	16–34	15–35	14–36	13–37	12–38
21	0	•–5	•–6	•–7	•–8	•–9	•–11
	1	•–8	•–9	•–10	•–12	•–13	•–15
	2	•–11	•–12	•–13	•–15	•–16	•–18
	3	3–13	•–15	•–16	•–18	•–19	•–21
	4	5–16	4–18	•–19	•–21	•–22	•–24
	5	7–19	6–20	5–22	5–23	•–24	•–26
	6	8–21	8–23	7–24	6–26	6–27	•–29
	7	11–24	9–25	9–26	8–28	7–29	•–31
	8	13–26	12–28	11–29	10–30	9–31	8–33
	9	15–28	14–30	13–31	11–32	11–33	10–35
	10	17–31	16–32	15–33	13–35	13–35	11–37
22	0	•–4	•–5	•–6	•–8	•–9	•–11
	1	•–7	•–9	•–10	•–11	•–12	•–14
	2	•–10	•–12	•–13	•–14	•–15	•–17
	3	3–13	•–14	•–16	•–17	•–18	•–20
	4	4–15	4–17	•–18	•–20	•–21	•–23
	5	6–18	5–19	5–21	•–22	•–23	•–25
	6	8–20	7–22	7–23	6–24	6–25	•–27
	7	10–23	9–24	8–25	8–27	7–28	•–30
	8	12–25	11–26	10–28	9–29	9–30	8–32
	9	14–27	13–29	12–30	11–31	10–32	9–34
	10	16–29	15–31	14–32	13–33	12–34	11–36
	11	18–32	17–33	16–34	15–35	14–36	13–37
23	0	•–4	•–5	•–6	•–7	•–8	•–10
	1	•–7	•–8	•–9	•–11	•–12	•–14
	2	•–10	•–11	•–12	•–14	•–15	•–17
	3	3–12	•–14	•–15	•–16	•–17	•–19
	4	4–15	4–16	•–17	•–19	•–20	•–22
	5	6–17	5–18	5–20	•–21	•–22	•–24
	6	8–19	7–21	6–22	6–23	•–24	•–26
	7	10–22	9–23	8–24	7–26	7–27	•–28
	8	12–24	11–25	10–26	9–28	8–29	8–30
	9	14–26	12–27	12–29	11–30	10–31	9–32
	10	16–28	14–30	13–31	12–32	12–33	11–34
	11	18–30	16–32	15–33	14–34	14–35	12–36
24	0	•–4	•–5	•–6	•–7	•–8	•–10
	1	•–7	•–8	•–9	•–10	•–11	•–13
	2	•–9	•–10	•–12	•–13	•–14	•–16
	3	•–12	•–13	•–14	•–16	•–16	•–18
	4	4–14	4–15	•–17	•–18	•–19	•–21
	5	6–16	5–18	5–19	•–20	•–21	•–23
	6	8–19	7–20	6–21	6–22	•–23	•–25
	7	9–21	8–22	8–23	7–25	7–26	•–27
	8	11–23	10–24	9–25	9–27	8–28	•–29
	9	13–25	12–26	11–27	10–29	10–30	9–31
	10	15–27	14–28	13–29	12–31	11–31	10–33
	11	17–29	16–30	15–31	14–33	13–33	12–35
	12	19–31	18–32	17–33	16–34	15–35	13–37
25	0	•–4	•–5	•–6	•–7	•–7	•–9
	1	•–6	•–7	•–8	•–10	•–11	•–12
	2	•–9	•–10	•–11	•–12	•–13	•–15
	3	•–11	•–12	•–14	•–15	•–16	•–18
	4	4–13	•–15	•–16	•–17	•–18	•–20
	5	6–16	5–17	•–18	•–19	•–20	•–22
	6	7–18	7–19	6–20	•–22	•–22	•–24
	7	9–20	8–21	8–22	7–24	7–25	•–26
	8	11–22	10–23	9–24	8–26	8–27	•–28
	9	13–24	12–25	11–26	10–28	9–28	9–30
	10	14–26	13–27	12–28	12–30	11–30	10–32
	11	16–28	15–29	14–30	13–31	13–32	12–34
	12	18–30	17–31	16–32	15–33	14–34	13–35

N = 52

N_1	x_1	2α = 0.20	2α = 0.10	2α = 0.05	2α = 0.02	2α = 0.01	2α = 0.002
4	0	•–23	•–27	•–31	•–35	•–38	•–42
	1	1–35	•–39	•–42	•–44	•–46	•–48
	2	7–45	5–47	3–49	2–50	2–50	–
5	0	•–19	•–23	•–27	•–31	•–33	•–38
	1	1–30	•–34	•–37	•–40	•–42	•–45
	2	6–39	4–42	3–44	2–46	•–47	•–49
6	0	•–16	•–20	•–23	•–27	•–29	•–34
	1	•–26	•–30	•–33	•–36	•–38	•–41
	2	5–34	3–38	2–40	•–42	•–44	•–46
	3	10–42	8–44	6–46	5–47	4–48	3–49
7	0	•–14	•–18	•–21	•–24	•–26	•–31
	1	•–23	•–26	•–29	•–32	•–34	•–38
	2	4–31	3–34	2–36	•–39	•–40	•–43
	3	9–37	7–40	5–42	4–44	3–45	•–47
8	0	•–13	•–16	•–18	•–22	•–24	•–28
	1	•–21	•–24	•–26	•–30	•–32	•–35
	2	3–28	2–31	2–33	•–36	•–37	•–41
	3	8–34	6–36	5–39	4–41	3–42	•–45
	4	13–39	10–42	9–43	7–45	6–46	4–48
9	0	•–11	•–14	•–17	•–20	•–22	•–26
	1	•–19	•–22	•–24	•–27	•–29	•–33
	2	3–25	2–28	•–30	•–33	•–35	•–38
	3	7–31	5–33	4–36	3–38	3–39	•–42
	4	11–36	9–38	8–40	6–42	5–43	4–45
10	0	•–10	•–13	•–15	•–18	•–20	•–24
	1	•–17	•–20	•–22	•–25	•–27	•–30
	2	3–23	2–26	•–28	•–30	•–32	•–35
	3	6–28	5–31	4–33	3–35	•–37	•–40
	4	10–33	8–35	7–37	6–39	5–41	4–43
	5	14–38	12–40	10–42	9–43	8–44	6–46
11	0	•–9	•–12	•–14	•–16	•–18	•–22
	1	•–16	•–18	•–20	•–23	•–25	•–28
	2	2–21	2–24	•–26	•–28	•–30	•–33
	3	5–26	4–28	3–31	3–33	•–34	•–37
	4	9–31	7–33	6–35	5–37	4–38	•–41
	5	13–35	11–37	9–39	8–41	7–42	6–44
12	0	•–9	•–11	•–13	•–15	•–17	•–21
	1	•–14	•–17	•–19	•–21	•–23	•–27
	2	2–19	2–22	•–24	•–26	•–28	•–31
	3	5–24	4–26	3–28	3–31	•–32	•–35
	4	8–28	7–31	6–33	5–35	4–36	•–39
	5	12–33	10–35	9–36	7–38	7–40	5–42
	6	15–37	14–38	12–40	10–42	9–43	7–45
13	0	•–8	•–10	•–12	•–14	•–16	•–19
	1	•–13	•–15	•–17	•–20	•–21	•–25
	2	2–18	•–20	•–22	•–25	•–26	•–29
	3	5–22	4–25	3–27	•–29	•–30	•–33
	4	8–26	6–29	5–31	4–33	4–34	•–37
	5	11–30	9–33	8–34	7–36	6–37	5–40
	6	14–34	12–36	11–38	10–40	9–41	7–43
14	0	•–7	•–9	•–11	•–13	•–15	•–18
	1	•–12	•–14	•–16	•–19	•–20	•–23
	2	2–17	•–19	•–21	•–23	•–25	•–28
	3	4–21	3–23	3–25	•–27	•–29	•–31
	4	7–25	6–27	5–29	4–31	4–32	•–35
	5	10–29	9–31	7–32	6–34	6–36	5–38
	6	13–32	12–34	10–36	9–37	8–39	7–41
	7	16–36	15–37	13–39	12–40	11–41	9–43
15	0	•–7	•–9	•–10	•–12	•–14	•–17
	1	•–12	•–13	•–15	•–17	•–19	•–22
	2	2–16	•–18	•–20	•–22	•–23	•–26
	3	4–20	3–22	3–23	•–26	•–27	•–30
	4	7–23	5–25	5–27	4–29	•–30	•–33
	5	9–27	8–29	7–31	6–32	5–34	•–36
	6	12–30	11–32	10–34	8–36	8–37	6–39

Significance Limits for the Fourfold Table Test*

$$\begin{array}{cc|c} x_1 & N_1 - x_1 & N_1 \\ x_2 & N_2 - x_2 & N_2 \\ \hline X & N - X & N \end{array} \quad \left\} \begin{array}{l} N = N_1 + N_2 \\ X = x_1 + x_2 \\ N_1 \leqq N_2 \\ x_1 \leqq N_1 - x_1 \end{array} \right\}$$

For explanation see page 123

N = 52 (continued)

N_1	x_1	$2\alpha=$ 0.20	$2\alpha=$ 0.10	$2\alpha=$ 0.05	$2\alpha=$ 0.02	$2\alpha=$ 0.01	$2\alpha=$ 0.002
	7	15–34	14–35	12–37	11–38	10–39	8–41
16	0	•– 6	•– 8	•–10	•–11	•–13	•–16
	1	•–11	•–13	•–14	•–16	•–18	•–21
	2	2–15	•–17	•–18	•–20	•–22	•–25
	3	4–18	3–20	•–22	•–24	•–26	•–28
	4	6–22	5–24	4–26	4–28	•–29	•–31
	5	9–25	8–27	7–29	6–31	5–32	•–34
	6	11–29	10–30	9–32	8–34	7–35	6–37
	7	14–32	13–33	12–35	10–37	9–38	8–40
	8	17–35	16–36	14–38	13–39	12–40	10–42
17	0	•– 6	•– 8	•– 9	•–11	•–12	•–15
	1	•–10	•–12	•–13	•–15	•–17	•–20
	2	•–14	•–16	•–17	•–19	•–21	•–23
	3	4–17	3–19	•–21	•–23	•–24	•–27
	4	6–21	5–23	4–24	4–26	•–27	•–30
	5	8–24	7–26	6–27	5–29	5–30	•–33
	6	11–27	10–29	8–30	7–32	7–33	6–36
	7	13–30	12–32	11–33	10–35	9–36	8–38
	8	16–33	15–35	13–36	12–38	11–39	10–40
18	0	•– 6	•– 7	•– 8	•–10	•–11	•–14
	1	•–10	•–11	•–13	•–15	•–16	•–19
	2	•–13	•–15	•–16	•–18	•–20	•–22
	3	3–16	3–18	•–20	•–22	•–23	•–26
	4	6–20	5–21	4–23	•–25	•–26	•–29
	5	8–23	7–24	6–26	5–28	5–29	•–31
	6	10–26	9–27	8–29	7–31	7–32	6–34
	7	13–28	11–30	10–32	9–33	8–34	7–36
	8	15–31	14–33	13–34	11–36	11–37	9–39
	9	18–34	16–36	15–37	14–38	13–39	11–41
19	0	•– 5	•– 7	•– 8	•–10	•–11	•–13
	1	•– 9	•–11	•–12	•–14	•–15	•–18
	2	•–12	•–14	•–16	•–17	•–19	•–21
	3	3–16	3–17	•–19	•–21	•–22	•–24
	4	5–19	4–20	4–22	•–24	•–25	•–27
	5	7–22	6–23	6–25	5–27	5–28	•–30
	6	10–24	9–26	8–28	7–29	6–30	•–33
	7	12–27	11–29	10–30	9–32	8–33	7–35
	8	14–30	13–31	12–33	11–34	10–35	9–37
	9	17–32	16–34	14–35	13–37	12–38	11–39
20	0	•– 5	•– 6	•– 8	•– 9	•–10	•–13
	1	•– 9	•–10	•–11	•–13	•–14	•–17
	2	•–12	•–13	•–15	•–16	•–18	•–20
	3	3–15	•–16	•–18	•–20	•–21	•–23
	4	5–18	4–19	4–21	•–23	•–24	•–26
	5	7–20	6–22	5–24	5–25	•–26	•–29
	6	9–23	8–25	7–26	7–28	6–29	•–31
	7	11–26	10–27	9–29	8–30	8–32	7–34
	8	14–28	12–30	11–31	10–33	10–34	8–36
	9	16–31	15–33	14–34	12–35	12–36	10–38
	10	19–33	17–35	16–36	15–37	14–38	12–40
21	0	•– 5	•– 6	•– 7	•– 9	•–10	•–12
	1	•– 8	•–10	•–11	•–12	•–13	•–16
	2	•–11	•–13	•–14	•–16	•–17	•–19
	3	3–14	•–16	•–17	•–19	•–20	•–22
	4	5–17	4–18	4–20	•–21	•–23	•–25
	5	7–20	6–21	5–23	5–24	•–25	•–27
	6	9–22	8–24	7–25	6–27	6–28	•–30
	7	11–25	10–26	9–28	8–29	7–30	7–32
	8	13–27	12–29	11–30	10–32	9–33	8–34
	9	15–30	14–31	13–32	12–34	11–35	10–36
	10	18–32	16–33	15–35	14–36	13–37	12–38
22	0	•– 5	•– 6	•– 7	•– 8	•– 9	•–11
	1	•– 8	•– 9	•–10	•–12	•–13	•–15
	2	•–11	•–12	•–13	•–15	•–16	•–18
	3	3–13	•–15	•–16	•–18	•–19	•–21
	4	5–16	4–18	•–19	•–21	•–22	•–24
	5	6–19	6–20	5–22	•–23	•–24	•–26
	6	8–21	7–23	7–24	6–26	6–27	•–29
	7	10–24	9–25	9–26	8–28	7–29	•–31
	8	13–26	11–27	10–29	10–30	9–31	8–33
	9	15–28	13–30	12–31	11–32	11–33	10–35
	10	17–31	16–32	14–33	13–35	13–35	11–37
	11	19–33	18–34	17–35	15–37	15–37	13–39
23	0	•– 4	•– 5	•– 6	•– 8	•– 9	•–11
	1	•– 7	•– 9	•–10	•–11	•–12	•–14
	2	•–10	•–12	•–13	•–14	•–15	•–17
	3	3–13	•–14	•–15	•–17	•–18	•–20
	4	4–15	4–17	•–18	•–20	•–21	•–23
	5	6–18	5–19	5–21	•–22	•–23	•–25
	6	8–20	7–22	7–23	6–24	6–26	•–28
	7	10–23	9–24	8–25	7–27	7–28	•–30
	8	12–25	11–26	10–28	9–29	9–30	8–32
	9	14–27	13–29	12–30	11–31	10–32	9–34
	10	16–29	15–31	14–32	13–33	12–34	11–36
	11	18–32	17–33	16–34	15–35	14–36	13–38
24	0	•– 4	•– 5	•– 6	•– 7	•– 8	•–10
	1	•– 7	•– 8	•– 9	•–11	•–12	•–14
	2	•–10	•–11	•–12	•–14	•–15	•–17
	3	3–12	•–14	•–15	•–16	•–17	•–19
	4	4–15	4–16	•–17	•–19	•–20	•–22
	5	6–17	5–18	5–20	•–21	•–22	•–24
	6	8–19	7–21	6–22	6–23	•–24	•–26
	7	10–22	9–23	8–24	7–26	7–27	•–29
	8	12–24	11–25	10–27	9–28	8–29	8–31
	9	13–26	12–27	12–29	11–30	10–31	9–33
	10	15–28	14–30	13–31	12–32	12–33	11–35
	11	18–30	16–32	15–33	14–34	13–35	12–36
	12	20–32	18–34	17–35	16–36	15–37	14–38

N = 52 (continued)

N_1	x_1	$2\alpha=$ 0.20	$2\alpha=$ 0.10	$2\alpha=$ 0.05	$2\alpha=$ 0.02	$2\alpha=$ 0.01	$2\alpha=$ 0.002
25	0	•– 4	•– 5	•– 6	•– 7	•– 8	•–10
	1	•– 7	•– 8	•– 9	•–10	•–11	•–13
	2	•– 9	•–11	•–12	•–13	•–14	•–16
	3	•–12	•–13	•–14	•–16	•–17	•–19
	4	4–14	4–15	•–17	•–18	•–19	•–21
	5	6–16	5–18	5–19	•–20	•–21	•–23
	6	7–19	7–20	6–21	6–23	•–24	•–25
	7	9–21	8–22	8–23	7–25	7–26	•–28
	8	11–23	10–24	9–25	9–27	8–28	•–30
	9	13–25	12–26	11–28	10–29	10–30	9–31
	10	15–27	14–28	13–30	12–31	11–32	10–33
	11	17–29	16–30	15–32	14–33	13–34	12–35
	12	19–31	18–32	17–34	15–35	15–35	13–37
26	0	•– 4	•– 5	•– 6	•– 7	•– 7	•– 9
	1	•– 6	•– 7	•– 8	•–10	•–11	•–13
	2	•– 9	•–10	•–11	•–12	•–13	•–15
	3	•–11	•–12	•–14	•–15	•–16	•–18
	4	4–13	•–15	•–16	•–17	•–18	•–20
	5	6–16	5–17	•–18	•–20	•–20	•–22
	6	7–18	7–19	6–20	•–22	•–23	•–24
	7	9–20	8–21	8–22	7–24	7–25	•–26
	8	11–22	10–23	9–25	8–26	8–27	•–28
	9	13–24	12–25	11–27	10–28	9–29	9–30
	10	14–26	13–27	12–29	12–30	11–31	10–32
	11	16–28	15–29	14–30	13–32	13–32	11–34
	12	18–30	17–31	16–32	15–34	14–34	13–36
	13	20–32	19–33	18–34	17–35	16–36	15–37

N = 54

N_1	x_1	$2\alpha=$ 0.20	$2\alpha=$ 0.10	$2\alpha=$ 0.05	$2\alpha=$ 0.02	$2\alpha=$ 0.01	$2\alpha=$ 0.002
4	0	•–23	•–28	•–32	•–36	•–39	•–44
	1	1–37	•–40	•–43	•–46	•–48	•–50
	2	7–47	5–49	4–50	2–52	2–52	–
5	0	•–20	•–24	•–28	•–32	•–34	•–39
	1	1–31	•–35	•–38	•–41	•–43	•–47
	2	6–41	4–44	3–46	2–48	•–49	•–51
6	0	•–17	•–21	•–24	•–28	•–31	•–36
	1	•–27	•–31	•–34	•–37	•–39	•–43
	2	5–36	3–39	2–41	•–44	•–46	•–48
	3	11–43	8–46	7–47	5–49	4–50	3–51
7	0	•–15	•–18	•–21	•–25	•–28	•–32
	1	•–24	•–28	•–30	•–34	•–36	•–40
	2	4–32	3–35	2–38	•–40	•–42	•–45
	3	9–39	7–41	6–44	4–46	3–47	•–49
8	0	•–13	•–16	•–19	•–23	•–25	•–30
	1	•–21	•–25	•–28	•–31	•–33	•–37
	2	3–29	2–32	2–34	•–37	•–39	•–42
	3	8–35	6–38	5–40	4–42	3–44	•–46
	4	13–41	11–43	9–45	7–47	6–48	4–50
9	0	•–12	•–15	•–17	•–20	•–23	•–27
	1	•–19	•–22	•–25	•–28	•–30	•–34
	2	3–26	2–29	•–31	•–34	•–36	•–39
	3	7–32	5–35	4–37	3–39	3–41	•–44
	4	12–37	10–40	8–42	6–44	5–45	4–47
10	0	•–11	•–13	•–16	•–19	•–21	•–25
	1	•–18	•–20	•–23	•–26	•–28	•–32
	2	3–24	2–27	•–29	•–32	•–33	•–37
	3	6–29	5–32	4–34	3–37	3–38	•–41
	4	10–34	9–37	7–39	6–41	5–42	4–45
	5	15–39	13–41	11–43	9–45	8–46	6–48
11	0	•–10	•–12	•–14	•–17	•–19	•–23
	1	•–16	•–19	•–21	•–24	•–26	•–30
	2	2–22	2–24	•–27	•–29	•–31	•–35
	3	6–27	4–30	4–32	3–34	•–36	•–39
	4	9–32	8–34	6–36	5–39	5–40	•–42
	5	13–36	11–39	10–40	8–42	7–44	6–46
12	0	•– 9	•–11	•–13	•–16	•–18	•–22
	1	•–15	•–17	•–20	•–22	•–24	•–28
	2	2–20	2–23	•–25	•–27	•–29	•–33
	3	5–25	4–27	3–30	3–32	•–34	•–37
	4	9–30	7–32	6–34	5–36	4–38	•–40
	5	12–34	10–36	9–38	8–40	7–41	5–43
	6	16–38	14–40	12–42	11–43	10–44	8–46
13	0	•– 8	•–10	•–12	•–15	•–16	•–20
	1	•–14	•–16	•–18	•–21	•–22	•–26
	2	2–19	•–21	•–23	•–26	•–27	•–31
	3	5–23	4–26	3–28	•–30	•–32	•–35
	4	8–28	7–30	6–32	5–34	4–35	•–38
	5	11–32	10–34	8–36	7–38	6–39	5–41
	6	15–36	13–38	11–39	10–41	9–42	7–44
14	0	•– 8	•–10	•–11	•–14	•–15	•–19
	1	•–13	•–15	•–17	•–19	•–21	•–24
	2	2–17	•–20	•–22	•–24	•–26	•–29
	3	4–22	4–24	3–26	•–28	•–30	•–33
	4	7–26	6–28	5–30	4–32	4–34	•–36
	5	10–30	9–32	8–34	7–36	6–37	5–39
	6	14–33	12–35	11–37	9–39	8–40	7–42
	7	17–37	15–39	14–40	12–42	11–43	9–45
15	0	•– 7	•– 9	•–11	•–13	•–14	•–18
	1	•–12	•–14	•–16	•–18	•–20	•–23
	2	2–16	•–18	•–20	•–23	•–24	•–27
	3	4–20	3–23	3–24	•–27	•–28	•–31
	4	7–24	6–26	5–28	4–30	4–32	•–34
	5	10–28	8–30	7–32	6–34	6–35	5–38
	6	13–31	11–33	10–35	9–37	8–38	6–40
	7	16–35	14–37	13–38	11–40	10–41	9–43
16	0	•– 7	•– 8	•–10	•–12	•–13	•–17

N = 54 (continued)

N_1	x_1	$2\alpha=$ 0.20	$2\alpha=$ 0.10	$2\alpha=$ 0.05	$2\alpha=$ 0.02	$2\alpha=$ 0.01	$2\alpha=$ 0.002
	1	•–11	•–13	•–15	•–17	•–19	•–22
	2	2–15	•–17	•–19	•–21	•–23	•–26
	3	4–19	3–21	3–23	•–25	•–27	•–29
	4	6–23	5–25	5–27	4–29	•–30	•–33
	5	9–26	8–28	7–30	6–32	5–33	•–36
	6	12–30	10–32	9–33	8–35	7–36	6–39
	7	15–33	13–35	12–36	10–38	10–39	8–41
	8	18–36	16–38	15–39	13–41	12–42	10–44
17	0	•– 6	•– 8	•– 9	•–11	•–13	•–16
	1	•–11	•–12	•–14	•–16	•–17	•–20
	2	2–14	•–16	•–18	•–20	•–22	•–24
	3	4–18	3–20	•–22	•–24	•–25	•–28
	4	6–22	5–24	4–25	4–27	•–29	•–31
	5	9–25	7–27	6–29	6–30	5–32	•–34
	6	11–28	10–30	9–32	8–33	7–35	6–37
	7	14–31	12–33	11–35	10–36	9–37	8–40
	8	17–34	15–36	14–37	12–39	11–40	10–42
18	0	•– 6	•– 7	•– 9	•–11	•–12	•–15
	1	•–10	•–12	•–13	•–15	•–17	•–19
	2	•–14	•–15	•–17	•–19	•–20	•–23
	3	3–17	3–19	•–21	•–23	•–24	•–27
	4	6–20	5–22	4–24	4–26	•–27	•–30
	5	8–24	7–25	6–27	5–29	5–30	•–33
	6	11–27	9–29	8–30	7–32	7–33	6–35
	7	13–30	12–31	11–33	9–35	9–36	7–38
	8	16–33	14–34	13–36	12–37	11–38	9–40
	9	19–35	17–37	16–38	14–40	13–41	11–43
19	0	•– 6	•– 7	•– 8	•–10	•–11	•–14
	1	•– 9	•–11	•–13	•–14	•–16	•–18
	2	•–13	•–15	•–16	•–18	•–19	•–22
	3	3–16	3–18	•–20	•–21	•–23	•–25
	4	5–19	5–21	4–23	•–25	•–26	•–28
	5	8–22	7–24	6–26	5–28	5–29	•–31
	6	10–25	9–27	8–29	7–30	6–32	•–34
	7	12–28	11–30	10–31	9–33	8–34	7–36
	8	15–31	14–33	12–34	11–36	10–37	9–39
	9	18–34	16–35	15–37	13–38	13–39	11–41
20	0	•– 5	•– 7	•– 8	•– 9	•–11	•–13
	1	•– 9	•–10	•–12	•–14	•–15	•–17
	2	•–12	•–14	•–15	•–17	•–18	•–21
	3	3–15	3–17	•–19	•–20	•–22	•–24
	4	5–18	4–20	4–22	•–23	•–25	•–27
	5	7–21	6–23	6–25	5–26	5–28	•–30
	6	10–24	8–26	8–27	7–29	6–30	•–33
	7	12–27	11–29	10–30	9–32	8–33	7–35
	8	14–30	13–31	12–33	11–34	10–35	9–37
	9	17–32	15–34	14–35	13–37	12–38	10–39
	10	19–35	18–36	16–38	15–39	14–40	12–42
21	0	•– 5	•– 6	•– 7	•– 9	•–10	•–13
	1	•– 8	•–10	•–11	•–13	•–14	•–17
	2	•–12	•–13	•–15	•–16	•–18	•–20
	3	3–15	•–16	•–18	•–19	•–21	•–23
	4	5–18	4–19	4–21	•–22	•–24	•–26
	5	7–20	6–22	5–23	5–25	•–26	•–29
	6	9–23	8–25	7–26	6–28	6–29	•–31
	7	11–26	10–27	9–29	8–30	8–31	7–34
	8	14–28	12–30	11–31	10–33	10–34	8–36
	9	16–31	15–32	13–34	12–35	11–36	10–38
	10	18–33	17–35	16–36	14–37	13–38	12–40
22	0	•– 5	•– 6	•– 7	•– 9	•–10	•–12
	1	•– 8	•– 9	•–11	•–12	•–13	•–16
	2	•–11	•–13	•–14	•–16	•–17	•–19
	3	3–14	•–16	•–17	•–19	•–20	•–22
	4	5–17	4–18	4–20	•–21	•–23	•–25
	5	7–19	6–21	5–22	5–24	•–25	•–27
	6	9–22	8–24	7–25	6–27	6–28	•–30
	7	11–25	10–26	9–28	8–29	7–30	7–32
	8	13–27	12–29	11–30	10–32	9–33	8–35
	9	15–29	14–31	13–32	12–34	11–35	10–37
	10	17–32	16–33	15–35	14–36	13–37	11–39
	11	20–34	18–36	17–37	16–38	15–39	13–41
23	0	•– 4	•– 6	•– 7	•– 8	•– 9	•–11
	1	•– 8	•– 9	•–10	•–12	•–13	•–15
	2	•–11	•–12	•–13	•–15	•–16	•–18
	3	3–13	•–15	•–16	•–18	•–19	•–21
	4	5–16	4–18	•–19	•–20	•–22	•–24
	5	6–19	6–20	5–21	•–23	•–24	•–26
	6	8–21	7–23	7–24	6–26	6–27	•–29
	7	10–24	9–25	9–26	8–28	7–29	•–31
	8	12–26	11–27	10–29	9–30	9–31	8–33
	9	15–28	13–30	12–31	11–33	11–33	9–35
	10	17–31	15–32	14–33	13–35	12–36	11–37
	11	19–33	18–34	16–35	15–37	14–38	13–39
24	0	•– 4	•– 5	•– 6	•– 8	•– 9	•–11
	1	•– 7	•– 9	•–10	•–11	•–12	•–14
	2	•–10	•–11	•–13	•–14	•–15	•–17
	3	3–13	•–14	•–15	•–17	•–18	•–20
	4	4–15	4–17	•–18	•–20	•–21	•–23
	5	6–18	5–19	5–21	•–22	•–23	•–25
	6	8–20	7–22	7–23	6–25	•–26	•–28
	7	10–23	9–24	8–25	7–27	7–28	•–30
	8	12–25	11–26	10–28	9–29	9–30	8–32
	9	14–27	13–29	12–30	11–31	10–32	9–34
	10	16–29	15–31	14–32	13–33	12–34	11–36
	11	18–32	17–33	16–34	15–35	14–36	12–38
	12	20–34	19–35	18–36	17–37	16–38	14–40
25	0	•– 4	•– 5	•– 6	•– 7	•– 8	•–10
	1	•– 7	•– 8	•– 9	•–11	•–12	•–14

Significance Limits for the Fourfold Table Test*

x_1	$N_1 - x_1$	N_1
x_2	$N_2 - x_2$	N_2
X	$N - X$	N

$N = N_1 + N_2$, $X = x_1 + x_2$, $N_1 \leq N_2$, $x_1 \leq N_1 - x_1$

For explanation see page 123

N_1	x_1	2α = 0.20	2α = 0.10	2α = 0.05	2α = 0.02	2α = 0.01	2α = 0.002
		N = 54 (continued)					
	2	•-10	•-11	•-12	•-14	•-15	•-17
	3	3-12	•-14	•-15	•-16	•-17	•-19
	4	4-15	4-16	•-17	•-19	•-20	•-22
	5	6-17	5-18	5-20	•-21	•-22	•-24
	6	8-19	7-21	6-22	6-24	•-25	•-27
	7	10-22	9-23	8-24	7-26	7-27	•-29
	8	11-24	10-25	10-27	9-28	8-29	•-31
	9	13-26	12-28	11-29	11-30	10-31	9-33
	10	15-28	14-30	13-31	12-32	12-33	10-35
	11	17-30	16-32	15-33	14-34	13-35	12-37
	12	19-32	18-34	17-35	16-36	15-37	14-38
26	0	•- 4	•- 5	•- 6	•- 7	•- 8	•-10
	1	•- 7	•- 8	•- 9	•-10	•-11	•-13
	2	•- 9	•-11	•-12	•-13	•-14	•-16
	3	•-12	•-13	•-14	•-16	•-17	•-19
	4	4-14	4-15	•-17	•-18	•-19	•-21
	5	6-16	5-18	5-19	•-20	•-21	•-23
	6	7-19	7-20	6-21	6-23	•-24	•-26
	7	9-21	8-22	8-23	7-25	7-26	•-28
	8	11-23	10-24	9-26	9-27	8-28	•-30
	9	13-25	12-26	11-28	10-29	10-30	9-32
	10	15-27	14-29	13-30	12-31	11-32	10-34
	11	17-29	16-31	15-32	14-33	13-34	12-35
	12	19-31	17-33	16-34	15-35	15-36	13-37
	13	21-33	19-35	18-36	17-37	16-38	15-39
27	0	•- 4	•- 5	•- 6	•- 7	•- 8	•- 9
	1	•- 6	•- 8	•- 9	•-10	•-11	•-13
	2	•- 9	•-10	•-11	•-12	•-13	•-15
	3	•-11	•-12	•-14	•-15	•-16	•-18
	4	4-14	•-15	•-16	•-17	•-18	•-20
	5	6-16	5-17	•-18	•-20	•-21	•-22
	6	7-18	6-19	6-20	•-22	•-23	•-25
	7	9-20	8-21	7-23	7-24	•-25	•-27
	8	11-22	10-23	9-25	8-26	8-27	•-29
	9	12-24	12-26	11-27	10-28	9-29	9-31
	10	14-26	13-28	12-29	12-30	11-31	10-32
	11	16-28	15-30	14-31	13-32	13-33	11-34
	12	18-30	17-31	16-33	15-34	14-35	13-36
	13	20-32	19-33	18-34	17-36	16-36	15-38
		N = 56					
4	0	•-24	•-29	•-33	•-38	•-40	•-45
	1	1-38	•-42	•-45	•-48	•-49	•-52
	2	8-48	5-51	4-52	2-54	2-54	–
5	0	•-20	•-25	•-29	•-33	•-36	•-41
	1	1-33	•-36	•-40	•-43	•-45	•-48
	2	6-42	4-45	3-48	2-50	•-51	•-53
6	0	•-18	•-21	•-25	•-29	•-32	•-37
	1	•-28	•-32	•-35	•-39	•-41	•-45
	2	5-37	3-40	2-43	2-46	•-47	•-50
	3	11-45	9-47	7-49	5-51	4-52	3-53
7	0	•-15	•-19	•-22	•-26	•-29	•-34
	1	•-25	•-29	•-32	•-35	•-37	•-41
	2	4-33	3-36	2-39	•-42	•-44	•-47
	3	10-40	7-43	6-45	4-47	4-49	•-51
8	0	•-14	•-17	•-20	•-23	•-26	•-31
	1	•-22	•-26	•-29	•-32	•-34	•-38
	2	4-30	2-33	2-36	•-39	•-40	•-44
	3	8-36	6-39	5-42	4-44	3-45	•-48
	4	14-42	11-45	9-47	7-49	6-50	5-51
9	0	•-12	•-15	•-18	•-21	•-24	•-28
	1	•-20	•-23	•-26	•-29	•-31	•-35
	2	3-27	2-30	2-33	•-36	•-37	•-41
	3	7-33	6-36	4-38	3-41	3-42	•-45
	4	12-39	10-41	8-43	7-45	6-47	4-49
10	0	•-11	•-14	•-16	•-19	•-22	•-26
	1	•-18	•-21	•-24	•-27	•-29	•-33
	2	3-25	2-28	•-30	•-33	•-35	•-38
	3	7-30	5-33	4-36	3-38	3-40	•-43
	4	11-36	9-38	7-40	6-43	5-44	4-47
	5	15-41	13-43	11-45	9-47	8-48	6-50
11	0	•-10	•-13	•-15	•-18	•-20	•-24
	1	•-17	•-20	•-22	•-25	•-27	•-31
	2	3-23	2-25	•-28	•-31	•-32	•-36
	3	6-28	5-31	4-33	3-36	•-37	•-40
	4	10-33	8-36	7-38	5-40	5-41	4-44
	5	14-38	12-40	10-42	9-44	8-45	6-47
12	0	•- 9	•-12	•-14	•-17	•-18	•-22
	1	•-15	•-18	•-20	•-23	•-25	•-29
	2	2-21	2-24	•-26	•-29	•-30	•-34
	3	5-26	4-29	3-31	3-33	•-35	•-38
	4	9-31	7-33	6-35	5-38	4-39	•-42
	5	13-35	11-37	9-39	8-41	7-43	5-45
	6	17-39	14-42	13-43	11-45	10-46	8-48
13	0	•- 9	•-11	•-13	•-15	•-17	•-21
	1	•-14	•-17	•-19	•-22	•-23	•-27
	2	2-19	•-22	•-24	•-27	•-28	•-32
	3	5-24	4-27	3-29	•-31	•-33	•-36
	4	8-29	7-31	6-33	5-35	4-37	•-40
	5	12-33	10-35	9-37	7-39	6-41	5-43
	6	15-37	13-39	12-41	10-43	9-44	7-46
14	0	•- 8	•-10	•-12	•-14	•-16	•-20
	1	•-13	•-16	•-18	•-20	•-22	•-25
	2	2-18	•-20	•-23	•-25	•-27	•-30
	3	5-23	4-25	3-27	•-29	•-31	•-34
	4	8-27	6-29	5-31	4-33	4-35	•-38

N_1	x_1	2α = 0.20	2α = 0.10	2α = 0.05	2α = 0.02	2α = 0.01	2α = 0.002
		N = 56 (continued)					
	5	11-31	9-33	8-35	7-37	6-38	5-41
	6	14-35	12-37	11-39	9-40	9-42	7-44
	7	18-38	16-40	14-42	12-44	11-45	9-47
15	0	•- 7	•- 9	•-11	•-13	•-15	•-18
	1	•-12	•-15	•-17	•-19	•-21	•-24
	2	2-17	•-19	•-21	•-24	•-25	•-28
	3	4-21	3-23	3-25	•-28	•-29	•-32
	4	7-25	6-27	5-29	4-32	4-33	•-36
	5	10-29	9-31	7-33	6-35	6-36	5-39
	6	13-33	11-35	10-37	9-38	8-40	7-42
	7	16-36	15-38	13-40	12-42	11-43	9-45
16	0	•- 7	•- 9	•-10	•-13	•-14	•-17
	1	•-12	•-14	•-16	•-18	•-19	•-23
	2	2-16	•-18	•-20	•-22	•-24	•-27
	3	4-20	3-22	3-24	•-26	•-28	•-31
	4	7-24	6-26	5-28	4-30	4-31	•-34
	5	9-27	8-29	7-31	6-33	5-35	•-37
	6	12-31	11-33	10-35	8-37	8-38	6-40
	7	15-34	14-36	12-38	11-40	10-41	8-43
	8	19-37	17-39	15-41	14-42	12-44	11-45
17	0	•- 7	•- 8	•-10	•-12	•-13	•-16
	1	•-11	•-13	•-15	•-17	•-18	•-21
	2	2-15	•-17	•-19	•-21	•-22	•-25
	3	4-19	3-21	3-23	•-25	•-26	•-29
	4	6-22	5-24	4-26	4-28	•-30	•-33
	5	9-26	8-28	7-30	6-32	5-33	•-36
	6	12-29	10-31	9-33	8-35	7-36	6-38
	7	14-32	13-34	12-36	10-38	9-39	8-41
	8	17-36	16-37	14-39	13-41	12-42	10-44
18	0	•- 6	•- 8	•- 9	•-11	•-12	•-15
	1	•-10	•-12	•-14	•-16	•-17	•-20
	2	2-14	•-16	•-18	•-20	•-21	•-24
	3	4-18	3-20	•-21	•-24	•-25	•-28
	4	6-21	5-23	4-25	4-27	•-28	•-31
	5	8-24	7-26	6-28	5-30	5-31	•-34
	6	11-28	10-30	9-31	7-33	7-34	6-37
	7	14-31	12-33	11-34	10-36	9-37	8-39
	8	16-34	15-36	13-37	12-39	11-40	10-42
	9	19-37	18-38	16-40	15-41	14-42	12-44
19	0	•- 6	•- 7	•- 9	•-10	•-12	•-15
	1	•-10	•-12	•-13	•-15	•-16	•-19
	2	•-13	•-15	•-17	•-19	•-20	•-23
	3	3-17	3-19	•-20	•-22	•-24	•-26
	4	6-20	5-22	4-24	•-26	•-27	•-30
	5	8-23	7-25	6-27	5-29	5-30	•-33
	6	10-26	9-28	8-30	7-32	7-33	6-35
	7	13-29	12-31	10-33	9-34	9-36	7-38
	8	16-32	14-34	13-36	11-37	11-38	9-40
	9	18-35	17-37	15-38	14-40	13-41	11-43
20	0	•- 5	•- 7	•- 8	•-10	•-11	•-14
	1	•- 9	•-11	•-12	•-14	•-16	•-18
	2	•-13	•-14	•-16	•-18	•-19	•-22
	3	3-16	3-18	•-19	•-21	•-23	•-25
	4	5-19	5-21	4-23	•-24	•-26	•-28
	5	8-22	7-24	6-26	5-27	5-29	•-31
	6	10-25	9-27	8-28	7-30	6-31	•-34
	7	12-28	11-30	10-31	9-33	8-34	7-36
	8	15-31	13-32	12-34	11-36	10-37	9-39
	9	17-33	16-35	14-37	13-38	12-39	11-41
	10	20-36	18-38	17-39	15-41	15-41	13-43
21	0	•- 5	•- 6	•- 8	•- 9	•-11	•-13
	1	•- 9	•-10	•-12	•-14	•-15	•-17
	2	•-12	•-14	•-15	•-17	•-18	•-21
	3	3-15	3-17	•-18	•-20	•-22	•-24
	4	5-18	4-20	4-22	•-23	•-25	•-27
	5	7-21	6-23	6-24	5-26	•-27	•-30
	6	9-24	8-26	7-27	7-29	6-30	•-32
	7	12-27	10-28	9-30	8-32	8-33	7-35
	8	14-29	13-31	12-33	10-34	10-35	9-37
	9	16-32	15-34	14-35	13-37	12-38	10-40
	10	19-35	17-36	16-38	15-39	14-40	12-42
22	0	•- 5	•- 6	•- 7	•- 9	•-10	•-12
	1	•- 8	•-10	•-11	•-13	•-14	•-17
	2	•-12	•-13	•-15	•-16	•-17	•-20
	3	3-15	•-16	•-18	•-19	•-21	•-23
	4	5-17	4-19	4-21	•-22	•-24	•-26
	5	7-20	6-22	5-23	5-25	•-26	•-29
	6	9-23	8-25	7-26	6-28	6-29	•-31
	7	11-26	10-27	9-29	8-30	8-31	7-34
	8	13-28	12-30	11-31	10-33	9-34	8-36
	9	16-31	14-32	13-34	12-35	11-36	10-38
	10	18-33	17-35	15-36	14-37	13-38	12-40
	11	20-36	19-37	18-38	16-40	15-41	14-42
23	0	•- 5	•- 6	•- 7	•- 8	•-10	•-12
	1	•- 8	•- 9	•-11	•-12	•-13	•-16
	2	•-11	•-13	•-14	•-16	•-17	•-19
	3	3-14	•-15	•-17	•-19	•-20	•-22
	4	5-17	4-18	4-20	•-21	•-23	•-25
	5	7-19	6-21	5-22	5-24	•-25	•-28
	6	9-22	8-24	7-25	6-27	6-28	•-30
	7	11-24	10-26	9-27	8-29	7-30	•-32
	8	13-27	12-29	11-30	10-32	9-33	8-35
	9	15-29	14-31	13-32	12-34	11-35	10-37
	10	17-32	16-33	15-35	14-36	13-37	11-39
	11	20-34	18-36	17-37	16-38	15-39	13-41
24	0	•- 4	•- 6	•- 7	•- 8	•- 9	•-11
	1	•- 8	•- 9	•-10	•-12	•-13	•-15
	2	•-11	•-12	•-13	•-15	•-16	•-18

N_1	x_1	2α = 0.20	2α = 0.10	2α = 0.05	2α = 0.02	2α = 0.01	2α = 0.002
		N = 56 (continued)					
	3	3-13	•-15	•-16	•-18	•-19	•-21
	4	4-16	4-17	•-19	•-20	•-22	•-24
	5	6-18	6-20	5-21	•-23	•-24	•-26
	6	8-21	7-23	7-24	6-26	6-27	•-29
	7	10-23	9-25	8-26	8-28	7-29	•-31
	8	12-26	11-27	10-29	9-30	9-31	8-33
	9	14-28	13-30	12-31	11-33	11-34	9-35
	10	17-31	15-32	14-33	13-35	12-36	11-38
	11	19-33	17-34	16-36	15-37	14-38	13-40
	12	21-35	20-36	18-38	17-39	16-40	15-41
25	0	•- 4	•- 5	•- 6	•- 8	•- 9	•-11
	1	•- 7	•- 9	•-10	•-11	•-12	•-14
	2	•-10	•-11	•-13	•-14	•-15	•-17
	3	3-13	•-14	•-15	•-17	•-18	•-20
	4	4-15	4-17	•-18	•-20	•-21	•-23
	5	6-18	5-19	5-21	•-22	•-23	•-25
	6	8-20	7-22	6-23	6-25	•-26	•-28
	7	10-23	9-24	8-25	7-27	7-28	•-30
	8	12-25	11-26	10-28	9-29	9-30	8-32
	9	14-27	13-29	12-30	11-31	10-32	9-34
	10	16-29	15-31	14-32	13-34	12-34	11-36
	11	18-32	17-33	16-34	14-36	14-36	12-38
	12	20-34	19-35	18-36	16-38	16-38	14-40
26	0	•- 4	•- 5	•- 6	•- 7	•- 8	•-10
	1	•- 7	•- 8	•- 9	•-11	•-12	•-14
	2	•-10	•-11	•-12	•-14	•-15	•-17
	3	3-12	•-14	•-15	•-16	•-17	•-19
	4	4-15	4-16	•-17	•-19	•-20	•-22
	5	6-17	5-18	5-20	•-21	•-22	•-24
	6	8-19	7-21	6-22	6-24	•-25	•-27
	7	10-22	9-23	8-24	7-26	7-27	•-29
	8	11-24	10-25	10-27	9-28	8-29	•-31
	9	13-26	12-28	11-29	10-30	10-31	9-33
	10	15-28	14-30	13-31	12-32	12-33	10-35
	11	17-30	16-32	15-33	14-34	13-35	12-37
	12	19-33	18-34	17-35	16-36	15-37	14-39
	13	21-35	20-36	19-37	18-38	17-39	15-41
27	0	•- 4	•- 5	•- 6	•- 7	•- 8	•-10
	1	•- 7	•- 8	•- 9	•-10	•-11	•-13
	2	•- 9	•-11	•-12	•-13	•-14	•-16
	3	•-12	•-13	•-14	•-16	•-17	•-19
	4	4-14	4-15	•-17	•-18	•-19	•-21
	5	6-16	5-18	5-19	•-20	•-21	•-24
	6	7-19	7-20	6-21	6-23	•-24	•-26
	7	9-21	8-22	8-23	7-25	7-26	•-28
	8	11-23	10-24	9-26	9-27	8-28	•-30
	9	13-25	12-27	11-28	10-29	10-30	9-32
	10	15-27	14-29	13-30	12-31	11-32	10-34
	11	17-29	16-31	15-32	14-33	13-34	12-36
	12	19-31	17-33	16-34	15-35	15-36	13-38
	13	21-33	19-35	18-36	17-37	16-38	15-39
28	0	•- 4	•- 5	•- 6	•- 7	•- 8	•- 9
	1	•- 6	•- 8	•- 9	•-10	•-11	•-13
	2	•- 9	•-10	•-11	•-13	•-13	•-15
	3	•-11	•-13	•-14	•-15	•-16	•-18
	4	4-14	•-15	•-16	•-17	•-18	•-20
	5	6-16	5-17	•-18	•-20	•-21	•-23
	6	7-18	6-19	6-20	•-22	•-23	•-25
	7	9-20	8-21	7-23	7-24	•-25	•-27
	8	11-22	10-24	9-25	8-26	8-27	•-29
	9	12-24	11-26	11-27	10-28	9-29	9-31
	10	14-26	13-28	12-29	11-30	11-31	10-33
	11	16-28	15-30	14-31	13-32	13-33	11-35
	12	18-30	17-32	16-33	15-34	14-35	13-36
	13	20-32	19-34	18-35	17-36	16-37	15-38
	14	22-34	21-35	20-36	18-38	18-38	16-40
		N = 58					
4	0	•-25	•-30	•-35	•-39	•-42	•-47
	1	1-39	•-43	•-47	•-49	•-51	•-54
	2	8-50	6-52	4-54	2-56	2-56	–
5	0	•-21	•-26	•-30	•-34	•-37	•-42
	1	1-34	•-38	•-41	•-45	•-47	•-50
	2	6-44	4-47	3-49	2-52	•-53	•-55
6	0	•-18	•-22	•-26	•-30	•-33	•-38
	1	•-29	•-33	•-37	•-40	•-42	•-46
	2	5-38	4-42	2-45	2-47	•-49	•-52
	3	12-46	9-49	7-51	5-53	4-54	3-55
7	0	•-16	•-20	•-23	•-27	•-30	•-35
	1	•-26	•-30	•-33	•-36	•-39	•-43
	2	4-34	3-38	2-40	•-43	•-45	•-48
	3	10-42	8-45	6-47	4-49	4-50	•-53
8	0	•-14	•-17	•-21	•-24	•-27	•-32
	1	•-23	•-27	•-30	•-33	•-35	•-40
	2	4-31	3-34	2-37	•-40	•-42	•-45
	3	9-38	7-41	5-43	4-46	3-47	•-50
	4	14-44	12-46	10-48	8-50	7-51	5-53
9	0	•-13	•-16	•-19	•-22	•-24	•-29
	1	•-21	•-24	•-27	•-30	•-32	•-37
	2	3-28	2-31	2-34	•-37	•-39	•-42
	3	8-34	6-37	5-40	4-42	3-44	•-47
	4	12-40	10-43	8-45	7-47	6-48	4-51
10	0	•-11	•-14	•-17	•-20	•-22	•-27
	1	•-19	•-22	•-25	•-28	•-30	•-34
	2	3-26	2-29	•-31	•-34	•-36	•-40
	3	7-31	5-34	4-37	3-39	3-41	•-44
	4	11-37	9-40	8-42	6-44	5-46	4-48

Significance Limits for the Fourfold Table Test*

$$\begin{array}{cc|c} x_1 & N_1 - x_1 & N_1 \\ x_2 & N_2 - x_2 & N_2 \\ \hline X & N - X & N \end{array} \quad \left\{ \begin{array}{l} N = N_1 + N_2 \\ X = x_1 + x_2 \\ N_1 \leq N_2 \\ x_1 \leq N_1 - x_1 \end{array} \right\}$$

For explanation see page 123

N_1	x_1	$2\alpha=$ 0.20	$2\alpha=$ 0.10	$2\alpha=$ 0.05	$2\alpha=$ 0.02	$2\alpha=$ 0.01	$2\alpha=$ 0.002
$N = 58$ (continued)							
	5	16–42	13–45	12–46	10–48	9–49	7–51
11	0	•–10	•–13	•–16	•–19	•–21	•–25
	1	•–17	•–20	•–23	•–26	•–28	•–32
	2	3–23	2–26	•–29	•–32	•–34	•–37
	3	6–29	5–32	4–34	3–37	•–39	•–42
	4	10–34	8–37	7–39	6–41	5–43	4–46
	5	14–39	12–42	10–44	9–46	8–47	6–49
12	0	•–10	•–12	•–14	•–17	•–19	•–23
	1	•–16	•–19	•–21	•–24	•–26	•–30
	2	2–22	2–24	•–27	•–30	•–31	•–35
	3	6–27	4–30	3–32	3–35	•–36	•–40
	4	9–32	8–34	6–37	5–39	4–41	•–43
	5	13–36	11–39	10–41	8–43	7–44	6–47
	6	17–41	15–43	13–45	11–47	10–48	8–50
13	0	•–9	•–11	•–13	•–16	•–18	•–22
	1	•–15	•–17	•–20	•–22	•–24	•–28
	2	2–20	2–23	•–25	•–28	•–29	•–33
	3	5–25	4–28	3–30	3–32	•–34	•–37
	4	8–30	7–32	6–34	5–37	4–38	•–41
	5	12–34	10–36	9–38	7–41	7–42	5–45
	6	16–38	14–40	12–42	10–44	9–45	8–48
14	0	•–8	•–10	•–12	•–15	•–17	•–20
	1	•–14	•–16	•–18	•–21	•–23	•–26
	2	2–19	•–21	•–23	•–26	•–28	•–31
	3	5–23	4–26	3–28	•–31	•–32	•–35
	4	8–28	6–30	5–32	4–35	4–36	•–39
	5	11–32	9–34	8–36	7–38	6–40	5–43
	6	15–36	13–38	11–40	10–42	9–43	7–46
	7	18–40	16–42	15–43	13–45	12–46	10–48
15	0	•–8	•–10	•–12	•–14	•–16	•–19
	1	•–13	•–15	•–17	•–20	•–21	•–25
	2	2–18	•–20	•–22	•–24	•–26	•–30
	3	4–22	4–24	3–26	•–29	•–30	•–34
	4	7–26	6–28	5–30	4–33	4–34	•–37
	5	10–30	9–32	8–34	7–36	6–38	5–41
	6	14–34	12–36	10–38	9–40	8–41	7–44
	7	17–37	15–40	14–41	12–43	11–44	9–46
16	0	•–7	•–9	•–11	•–13	•–15	•–18
	1	•–12	•–14	•–16	•–18	•–20	•–23
	2	2–17	•–19	•–21	•–23	•–25	•–28
	3	4–21	3–23	3–25	•–27	•–29	•–32
	4	7–25	6–27	5–29	4–31	4–33	•–35
	5	10–28	8–31	7–32	6–35	6–36	5–39
	6	13–32	11–34	10–36	9–38	8–39	6–42
	7	16–35	14–38	13–39	11–41	10–42	9–45
	8	19–39	17–41	16–42	14–44	13–45	11–47
17	0	•–7	•–8	•–10	•–12	•–14	•–17
	1	•–11	•–13	•–15	•–17	•–19	•–22
	2	2–16	•–18	•–20	•–22	•–23	•–27
	3	4–19	3–22	3–24	•–26	•–27	•–30
	4	6–23	5–25	5–27	4–29	•–31	•–34
	5	9–27	8–29	7–31	6–33	5–34	•–37
	6	12–30	10–32	9–34	8–36	7–37	6–40
	7	15–34	13–36	12–37	11–39	10–40	8–43
	8	18–37	16–39	15–40	13–42	12–43	10–45
18	0	•–6	•–8	•–10	•–12	•–13	•–16
	1	•–11	•–13	•–14	•–16	•–18	•–21
	2	2–15	•–17	•–19	•–21	•–22	•–25
	3	4–18	3–20	•–22	•–24	•–26	•–29
	4	6–22	5–24	4–26	4–28	•–29	•–32
	5	9–25	7–27	7–29	6–31	5–33	•–35
	6	11–29	10–31	9–32	8–34	7–36	6–38
	7	14–32	13–34	11–36	10–37	9–39	8–41
	8	17–35	15–37	14–39	12–40	11–41	10–44
	9	20–38	18–40	17–41	15–43	14–44	12–46
19	0	•–6	•–8	•–9	•–11	•–12	•–15
	1	•–10	•–12	•–14	•–16	•–17	•–20
	2	•–14	•–16	•–18	•–20	•–21	•–24
	3	4–17	3–19	•–21	•–23	•–25	•–28
	4	6–21	5–23	4–25	4–27	•–28	•–31
	5	8–24	7–26	6–28	5–30	5–31	•–34
	6	11–27	9–29	8–31	7–33	7–34	6–37
	7	13–30	12–32	11–34	10–36	9–37	7–39
	8	16–33	14–35	13–37	12–39	11–40	9–42
	9	19–36	17–38	16–40	14–41	13–42	11–44
20	0	•–6	•–7	•–9	•–10	•–12	•–14
	1	•–10	•–11	•–13	•–15	•–16	•–19
	2	•–13	•–15	•–17	•–19	•–20	•–23
	3	3–17	3–18	•–20	•–22	•–24	•–26
	4	6–20	5–22	4–23	•–25	•–27	•–29
	5	8–23	7–25	6–27	5–29	5–30	•–32
	6	10–26	9–28	8–30	7–31	6–33	6–35
	7	13–29	11–31	10–32	9–34	8–35	7–38
	8	15–32	14–34	13–35	11–37	10–38	9–40
	9	18–35	16–36	15–38	14–40	13–41	11–43
	10	21–37	19–39	17–41	16–42	15–43	13–45
21	0	•–5	•–7	•–8	•–10	•–11	•–14
	1	•–9	•–11	•–12	•–14	•–15	•–18
	2	•–13	•–14	•–16	•–18	•–19	•–22
	3	3–16	3–18	•–19	•–21	•–22	•–25
	4	5–19	4–21	4–22	•–24	•–26	•–28
	5	7–22	6–24	6–25	5–27	5–29	•–31
	6	10–25	9–27	8–28	7–30	6–31	•–34
	7	12–28	11–30	10–31	9–33	8–34	7–36
	8	15–30	13–32	12–34	11–35	10–37	9–39
	9	17–33	15–35	14–36	13–38	12–39	11–41
	10	20–36	18–38	17–39	15–40	14–41	13–43
22	0	•–5	•–6	•–8	•–9	•–10	•–13
	1	•–9	•–10	•–12	•–13	•–15	•–17
	2	•–12	•–14	•–15	•–17	•–18	•–21
	3	3–15	3–17	•–18	•–20	•–21	•–24
	4	5–18	4–20	4–21	•–23	•–24	•–27
	5	7–21	6–23	5–24	5–26	•–27	•–30
	6	9–24	8–26	7–27	7–29	6–30	•–32
	7	12–26	10–28	9–30	8–32	8–33	7–35
	8	14–29	13–31	11–32	10–34	10–35	8–37
	9	16–32	15–33	14–35	12–37	12–38	10–40
	10	19–34	17–36	16–37	15–39	14–40	12–42
	11	21–37	20–38	18–40	17–41	16–42	14–44
23	0	•–5	•–6	•–7	•–9	•–10	•–12
	1	•–8	•–10	•–11	•–13	•–14	•–16
	2	•–11	•–13	•–14	•–16	•–17	•–20
	3	3–14	•–16	•–18	•–19	•–21	•–23
	4	5–17	4–19	4–20	•–22	•–23	•–26
	5	7–20	6–22	5–23	5–25	•–26	•–29
	6	9–23	8–24	7–26	6–28	6–29	•–31
	7	11–25	10–27	9–29	8–30	8–31	7–34
	8	13–28	12–30	11–31	10–33	9–34	8–36
	9	16–30	14–32	13–34	12–35	11–36	10–38
	10	18–33	16–35	15–36	14–37	13–38	12–40
	11	20–35	19–37	17–38	16–40	15–41	14–42
24	0	•–5	•–6	•–7	•–8	•–9	•–12
	1	•–8	•–9	•–11	•–12	•–13	•–16
	2	•–11	•–12	•–14	•–15	•–17	•–19
	3	3–14	•–15	•–17	•–18	•–20	•–22
	4	5–17	4–18	•–20	•–21	•–22	•–25
	5	7–19	6–21	5–22	5–24	•–25	•–28
	6	9–22	8–23	7–25	6–27	6–28	•–30
	7	11–24	10–26	9–27	8–29	7–30	•–32
	8	13–27	12–28	11–30	10–32	9–33	8–35
	9	15–29	14–31	13–32	11–34	11–35	10–37
	10	17–32	16–33	15–35	13–36	13–37	11–39
	11	19–34	18–36	17–37	15–38	15–39	13–41
	12	22–36	20–38	19–39	18–40	17–41	15–43
25	0	•–4	•–6	•–7	•–8	•–9	•–11
	1	•–8	•–9	•–10	•–12	•–13	•–15
	2	•–11	•–12	•–13	•–15	•–16	•–18
	3	3–13	•–15	•–16	•–18	•–19	•–21
	4	4–16	4–17	•–19	•–20	•–22	•–24
	5	6–18	6–20	5–21	•–23	•–24	•–26
	6	8–21	7–23	7–24	6–26	6–27	•–29
	7	10–23	9–25	8–26	8–28	7–29	•–31
	8	12–26	11–27	10–29	9–30	9–31	8–33
	9	14–28	13–30	12–31	11–33	10–34	9–36
	10	16–30	15–32	14–33	13–35	12–36	11–38
	11	19–33	17–34	16–36	15–37	14–38	13–40
	12	21–35	19–36	18–38	17–39	16–40	14–42
26	0	•–4	•–5	•–6	•–8	•–9	•–11
	1	•–7	•–9	•–10	•–11	•–12	•–14
	2	•–10	•–11	•–13	•–14	•–15	•–18
	3	3–13	•–14	•–15	•–17	•–18	•–20
	4	4–15	4–17	•–18	•–20	•–21	•–23
	5	6–18	5–19	5–21	•–22	•–23	•–25
	6	8–20	7–22	6–23	6–25	•–26	•–28
	7	10–22	9–24	8–25	7–27	7–28	•–30
	8	12–25	11–26	10–28	9–29	9–30	8–32
	9	14–27	13–29	12–30	11–31	10–32	9–34
	10	16–29	15–31	14–32	13–34	12–35	11–36
	11	18–32	17–33	16–34	14–36	14–37	12–38
	12	20–34	19–35	18–36	16–38	15–39	14–40
	13	22–36	21–37	20–38	18–40	17–41	16–42
27	0	•–4	•–5	•–6	•–7	•–8	•–10
	1	•–7	•–8	•–9	•–11	•–12	•–14
	2	•–10	•–11	•–12	•–14	•–15	•–17
	3	3–12	•–14	•–15	•–16	•–17	•–20
	4	4–15	4–16	•–17	•–19	•–20	•–22
	5	6–17	5–18	5–20	•–21	•–22	•–25
	6	8–19	7–21	6–22	6–24	•–25	•–27
	7	10–22	9–23	8–24	7–26	7–27	•–29
	8	11–24	10–25	10–27	9–28	8–29	•–31
	9	13–26	12–28	11–29	10–30	10–31	9–33
	10	15–28	14–30	13–31	12–32	12–33	10–35
	11	17–30	16–32	15–33	14–35	13–35	12–37
	12	19–33	18–34	17–35	16–37	15–37	14–39
	13	21–35	20–36	19–37	18–38	17–39	15–41
28	0	•–4	•–5	•–6	•–7	•–8	•–10
	1	•–7	•–8	•–9	•–10	•–11	•–13
	2	•–9	•–11	•–12	•–13	•–14	•–16
	3	•–12	•–13	•–14	•–16	•–17	•–19
	4	4–14	4–15	•–17	•–18	•–19	•–21
	5	6–16	5–18	5–19	•–21	•–22	•–24
	6	7–19	7–20	6–21	6–23	•–24	•–26
	7	9–21	8–22	8–24	7–25	7–26	•–28
	8	11–23	10–24	9–26	9–27	8–28	•–30
	9	13–25	12–27	11–28	10–29	10–30	9–32
	10	15–27	14–29	13–30	12–31	11–32	10–34
	11	17–29	15–31	15–32	13–33	13–34	12–36
	12	19–31	17–33	16–34	15–35	15–36	13–38
	13	21–33	19–35	18–36	17–37	16–38	15–40
	14	23–35	21–37	20–38	19–39	18–40	17–41
29	0	•–4	•–5	•–6	•–7	•–8	•–9
	1	•–6	•–8	•–9	•–10	•–11	•–13
	2	•–9	•–10	•–11	•–13	•–13	•–16
	3	•–11	•–13	•–14	•–15	•–16	•–18
	4	4–14	•–15	•–16	•–17	•–18	•–20
	5	6–16	5–17	•–18	•–20	•–21	•–23
	6	7–18	6–19	6–21	•–22	•–23	•–25
	7	9–20	8–22	7–23	7–24	•–25	•–27
	8	11–22	10–24	9–25	8–26	8–27	•–29
	9	12–24	11–26	11–27	10–28	9–29	9–31
	10	14–26	13–28	12–29	11–30	11–31	10–33
	11	16–28	15–30	14–31	13–32	13–33	11–35
	12	18–30	17–32	16–33	15–34	14–35	13–37
	13	20–32	19–34	18–35	17–36	16–37	14–38
	14	22–34	20–36	19–37	18–38	18–39	16–40
$N = 60$							
4	0	•–26	•–31	•–36	•–40	•–43	•–49
	1	1–41	•–45	•–48	•–51	•–53	•–56
	2	8–52	6–54	4–56	3–57	2–58	–
5	0	•–22	•–27	•–31	•–35	•–38	•–44
	1	1–35	•–39	•–43	•–46	•–48	•–52
	2	7–45	4–48	3–51	2–53	•–55	•–57
6	0	•–19	•–23	•–27	•–31	•–34	•–40
	1	•–30	•–34	•–38	•–42	•–44	•–48
	2	5–40	4–43	3–46	2–49	•–51	•–53
	3	12–48	9–51	7–53	5–55	4–56	3–57
7	0	•–16	•–20	•–24	•–28	•–31	•–36
	1	•–27	•–31	•–34	•–38	•–40	•–44
	2	5–35	3–39	2–42	•–45	•–47	•–50
	3	10–43	8–46	6–48	5–51	4–52	•–54
8	0	•–15	•–18	•–21	•–25	•–28	•–33
	1	•–24	•–28	•–31	•–34	•–37	•–41
	2	4–32	3–35	2–38	•–41	•–43	•–47
	3	9–39	7–42	5–45	4–47	3–49	•–52
	4	15–45	12–48	10–50	8–52	7–53	5–55
9	0	•–13	•–16	•–19	•–23	•–25	•–30
	1	•–22	•–25	•–28	•–31	•–34	•–38
	2	3–29	2–32	2–35	•–38	•–40	•–44
	3	8–36	6–39	5–41	4–44	3–46	•–49
	4	13–42	11–44	9–47	7–49	6–50	4–53
10	0	•–12	•–15	•–18	•–21	•–23	•–28
	1	•–20	•–23	•–26	•–29	•–31	•–35
	2	3–26	2–30	•–32	•–35	•–37	•–41
	3	7–33	5–36	4–38	3–41	3–43	•–46
	4	11–38	9–41	8–43	6–46	5–47	4–50
	5	16–44	14–46	12–48	10–50	9–51	7–53
11	0	•–11	•–14	•–16	•–19	•–21	•–26
	1	•–18	•–21	•–24	•–27	•–29	•–33
	2	3–24	2–27	•–30	•–33	•–35	•–39
	3	6–30	5–33	4–35	3–38	3–40	•–43
	4	10–35	9–38	7–40	6–43	5–45	4–47
	5	15–40	13–43	11–45	9–47	8–49	6–51
12	0	•–10	•–12	•–15	•–18	•–20	•–24
	1	•–17	•–19	•–22	•–25	•–27	•–31
	2	3–22	2–25	•–28	•–31	•–33	•–36
	3	6–28	5–31	4–33	3–36	•–38	•–41
	4	9–33	8–36	7–38	5–40	5–42	•–45
	5	13–38	11–40	10–42	8–45	7–46	6–49
	6	18–42	15–45	14–46	12–48	10–50	8–52
13	0	•–9	•–12	•–14	•–17	•–18	•–23
	1	•–15	•–18	•–20	•–23	•–25	•–29
	2	2–21	2–24	•–26	•–29	•–31	•–34
	3	5–26	4–29	3–31	3–34	•–35	•–39
	4	9–31	7–33	6–36	5–38	4–40	•–43
	5	12–35	11–38	9–40	8–42	7–44	5–46
	6	16–40	14–42	13–44	11–46	10–47	8–49
14	0	•–9	•–11	•–13	•–15	•–17	•–21
	1	•–14	•–17	•–19	•–22	•–24	•–27
	2	2–19	•–22	•–24	•–27	•–29	•–32
	3	5–24	4–27	3–29	•–32	•–33	•–37
	4	8–29	7–31	6–33	5–36	4–38	•–41
	5	11–33	10–35	8–38	7–40	6–41	5–44
	6	15–37	13–39	12–41	10–44	9–45	7–47
	7	19–41	17–43	15–45	13–47	12–48	10–50
15	0	•–8	•–10	•–12	•–14	•–16	•–20
	1	•–13	•–16	•–18	•–20	•–22	•–26
	2	2–18	•–21	•–23	•–25	•–27	•–31
	3	5–23	4–25	3–27	•–30	•–32	•–35
	4	8–27	6–29	5–32	4–34	4–36	•–39
	5	11–31	9–33	8–36	7–38	6–39	5–42
	6	14–35	12–37	11–39	9–41	8–43	7–45
	7	18–39	16–41	14–43	12–45	11–46	9–48
16	0	•–7	•–9	•–11	•–14	•–15	•–19
	1	•–13	•–15	•–17	•–19	•–21	•–24
	2	2–17	•–19	•–21	•–24	•–26	•–29
	3	4–21	3–24	3–26	•–28	•–30	•–33
	4	7–25	6–28	5–30	4–32	4–34	•–37
	5	10–29	9–32	7–34	6–36	6–37	5–40
	6	13–33	11–35	10–37	9–39	8–41	7–43
	7	16–37	15–39	13–41	11–43	10–44	9–46
	8	20–40	18–42	16–44	14–46	13–47	11–49
17	0	•–7	•–9	•–11	•–13	•–14	•–18
	1	•–12	•–14	•–16	•–18	•–20	•–23
	2	2–16	•–18	•–20	•–23	•–24	•–28
	3	4–20	3–22	3–24	•–27	•–28	•–31
	4	7–24	6–26	5–28	4–31	4–32	•–35
	5	9–28	8–30	7–32	6–34	5–36	•–38
	6	12–31	11–34	10–35	8–37	8–39	6–41
	7	15–35	14–37	12–39	11–41	10–42	8–44
	8	19–38	17–40	15–42	13–44	12–45	11–47

$$\begin{array}{ccc} x_1 & N_1 - x_1 & N_1 \\ x_2 & N_2 - x_2 & N_2 \\ \hline X & N - X & N \end{array} \left.\begin{array}{l} N = N_1 + N_2 \\ X = x_1 + x_2 \\ N_1 \leqq N_2 \\ x_1 \leqq N_1 - x_1 \end{array}\right\}$$ For explanation see below

N_1	x_1	$2\alpha=$ 0.20	$2\alpha=$ 0.10	$2\alpha=$ 0.05	$2\alpha=$ 0.02	$2\alpha=$ 0.01	$2\alpha=$ 0.002
				$N=60$ (continued)			
18	0	•– 7	•– 8	•–10	•–12	•–13	•–17
	1	•–11	•–13	•–15	•–17	•–19	•–22
	2	2–15	•–17	•–19	•–21	•–23	•–26
	3	4–19	3–21	3–23	•–25	•–27	•–30
	4	6–23	5–25	4–27	4–29	•–31	•–33
	5	9–26	8–28	7–30	6–32	5–34	•–37
	6	12–30	10–32	9–34	8–36	7–37	6–40
	7	15–33	13–35	12–37	10–39	9–40	8–43
	8	18–36	16–38	14–40	13–42	12–43	10–45
	9	21–39	19–41	17–43	15–45	14–46	12–48
19	0	•– 6	•– 8	•– 9	•–11	•–13	•–16
	1	•–11	•–12	•–14	•–16	•–18	•–21
	2	2–14	•–16	•–18	•–20	•–22	•–25
	3	4–18	3–20	•–22	•–24	•–26	•–29
	4	6–22	5–24	4–26	4–28	•–29	•–32
	5	8–25	7–27	6–29	5–31	5–32	•–35
	6	11–28	10–30	9–32	8–34	7–35	6–38
	7	14–31	12–33	11–35	10–37	9–38	8–41
	8	17–35	15–37	14–38	12–40	11–41	10–43
	9	19–38	18–39	16–41	15–43	14–44	12–46
20	0	•– 6	•– 7	•– 9	•–11	•–12	•–15
	1	•–10	•–12	•–13	•–15	•–17	•–20
	2	•–14	•–16	•–17	•–19	•–21	•–24
	3	3–17	3–19	•–21	•–23	•–24	•–27
	4	6–21	5–23	4–24	4–26	•–28	•–31
	5	8–24	7–26	6–28	5–30	5–31	•–34
	6	11–27	9–29	8–31	7–33	7–34	6–37
	7	13–30	12–32	11–34	9–36	9–37	7–39
	8	16–33	14–35	13–37	12–38	11–40	9–42
	9	18–36	17–38	15–39	14–41	13–42	11–44
	10	21–39	19–41	18–42	16–44	15–45	13–47
21	0	•– 6	•– 7	•– 8	•–10	•–11	•–14
	1	•–10	•–11	•–13	•–15	•–16	•–19
	2	•–13	•–15	•–16	•–18	•–20	•–23
	3	3–16	3–18	•–20	•–22	•–23	•–26
	4	5–20	5–22	4–23	•–25	•–27	•–29
	5	8–23	7–25	6–26	5–28	5–30	•–32
	6	10–26	9–28	8–29	7–31	6–33	•–35
	7	12–29	11–31	10–32	9–34	8–35	7–38
	8	15–32	14–33	12–35	11–37	10–38	9–40
	9	18–34	16–36	15–38	13–39	12–41	11–43
	10	20–37	19–39	17–40	16–42	15–43	13–45
22	0	•– 5	•– 7	•– 8	•–10	•–11	•–14
	1	•– 9	•–11	•–12	•–14	•–15	•–18
	2	•–12	•–14	•–16	•–18	•–19	•–22
	3	3–16	3–17	•–19	•–21	•–22	•–25
	4	5–19	4–21	4–22	•–24	•–25	•–28
	5	7–22	6–24	6–25	5–27	5–28	•–31
	6	10–25	8–26	8–28	7–30	6–31	•–34
	7	12–27	11–29	10–31	9–33	8–34	7–36
	8	14–30	13–32	12–34	11–35	10–37	9–39
	9	17–33	15–35	14–36	13–38	12–39	10–41
	10	19–36	18–37	16–39	15–40	14–41	12–43
	11	22–38	20–40	19–41	17–43	16–44	14–46
23	0	•– 5	•– 6	•– 8	•– 9	•–10	•–13
	1	•– 9	•–10	•–12	•–13	•–15	•–17
	2	•–12	•–14	•–15	•–17	•–18	•–21
	3	3–15	•–17	•–18	•–20	•–21	•–24
	4	5–18	4–20	4–21	•–23	•–24	•–27
	5	7–21	6–23	5–24	5–26	•–27	•–30
	6	9–24	8–25	7–27	6–29	6–30	•–32
	7	11–26	10–28	9–30	8–31	8–33	7–35
	8	14–29	12–31	11–32	10–34	10–35	8–37
	9	16–32	15–33	13–35	12–36	11–38	10–40
	10	18–34	17–36	16–37	14–39	13–40	12–42
	11	21–37	19–38	18–40	17–41	16–42	14–44
24	0	•– 5	•– 6	•– 7	•– 9	•–10	•–12
	1	•– 8	•–10	•–11	•–13	•–14	•–16
	2	•–11	•–13	•–14	•–16	•–17	•–20
	3	3–14	•–16	•–17	•–19	•–20	•–23
	4	5–17	4–19	4–20	•–22	•–23	•–26
	5	7–20	6–22	5–23	5–25	•–26	•–29
	6	9–23	8–24	7–26	6–28	6–29	•–31
	7	11–25	10–27	9–28	8–30	7–31	7–34
	8	13–28	12–30	11–31	10–33	9–34	8–36
	9	15–30	14–32	13–33	12–35	11–36	10–38
	10	18–33	16–34	15–36	14–37	13–39	12–41
	11	20–35	18–37	17–38	16–40	15–41	13–43
	12	22–38	21–39	19–41	18–42	17–43	15–45
25	0	•– 5	•– 6	•– 7	•– 8	•– 9	•–12
	1	•– 8	•– 9	•–11	•–12	•–13	•–16
	2	•–11	•–12	•–14	•–15	•–17	•–19
	3	3–14	•–15	•–17	•–18	•–20	•–22
	4	5–16	4–18	•–20	•–21	•–22	•–25
	5	7–19	6–21	5–22	5–24	•–25	•–28
	6	8–22	8–23	7–25	6–27	6–28	•–30
	7	11–24	9–26	9–27	8–29	7–30	•–32
	8	13–27	11–28	11–30	10–31	9–33	8–35
	9	15–29	14–31	12–32	11–34	11–35	10–37
	10	17–32	16–33	14–35	13–36	13–37	11–39
	11	19–34	18–36	17–37	15–38	14–39	13–41
	12	21–36	20–38	19–39	17–41	16–41	15–43
26	0	•– 4	•– 6	•– 7	•– 8	•– 9	•–11
	1	•– 8	•– 9	•–10	•–12	•–13	•–15
	2	•–10	•–12	•–13	•–15	•–16	•–18
	3	3–13	•–15	•–16	•–18	•–19	•–21
	4	4–16	4–17	•–19	•–20	•–22	•–24
	5	6–18	6–20	5–21	•–23	•–24	•–27
	6	8–21	7–22	7–24	6–26	6–27	•–29
	7	10–23	9–25	8–26	8–28	7–29	•–31
	8	12–26	11–27	10–29	9–30	9–31	8–34
	9	14–28	13–30	12–31	11–33	10–34	9–36
	10	16–30	15–32	14–33	13–35	12–36	11–38
	11	18–33	17–34	16–36	15–37	14–38	13–40
	12	21–35	19–36	18–38	17–39	16–40	14–42
	13	23–37	21–39	20–40	19–41	18–42	16–44
27	0	•– 4	•– 5	•– 6	•– 8	•– 9	•–11
	1	•– 7	•– 9	•–10	•–11	•–12	•–14
	2	•–10	•–11	•–13	•–14	•–15	•–18
	3	3–13	•–14	•–15	•–17	•–18	•–20
	4	4–15	4–17	•–18	•–20	•–21	•–23
	5	6–18	5–19	5–21	•–22	•–23	•–26
	6	8–20	7–22	6–23	6–25	•–26	•–28
	7	10–22	9–24	8–25	7–27	7–28	•–30
	8	12–25	11–26	10–28	9–29	8–30	8–32
	9	14–27	13–29	12–30	11–32	10–33	9–35
	10	16–29	15–31	14–32	12–34	12–35	11–37
	11	18–32	16–33	15–34	14–36	14–37	12–39
	12	20–34	19–35	17–36	16–38	15–39	14–41
	13	22–36	21–37	19–39	18–40	17–41	16–42
28	0	•– 4	•– 5	•– 6	•– 7	•– 8	•–10
	1	•– 7	•– 8	•– 9	•–11	•–12	•–14
	2	•–10	•–11	•–12	•–14	•–15	•–17
	3	3–12	•–14	•–15	•–16	•–17	•–20
	4	4–15	4–16	•–17	•–19	•–20	•–22
	5	6–17	5–18	5–20	•–21	•–22	•–25
	6	8–19	7–21	6–22	6–24	•–25	•–27
	7	9–22	9–23	8–24	7–26	7–27	•–29
	8	11–24	10–25	10–27	9–28	8–29	•–31
	9	13–26	12–28	11–29	10–30	10–31	9–33
	10	15–28	14–30	13–31	12–33	11–34	10–35
	11	17–30	16–32	15–33	14–35	13–36	12–37
	12	19–33	18–34	17–35	16–37	15–38	14–39
	13	21–35	20–36	19–37	18–39	17–40	15–41
	14	23–37	22–38	21–39	19–41	19–41	17–43
29	0	•– 4	•– 5	•– 6	•– 7	•– 8	•–10
	1	•– 7	•– 8	•– 9	•–10	•–11	•–13
	2	•– 9	•–11	•–12	•–13	•–14	•–16
	3	•–12	•–13	•–14	•–16	•–17	•–19
	4	4–14	4–15	•–17	•–18	•–19	•–21
	5	6–16	5–18	5–19	•–21	•–22	•–24
	6	7–19	7–20	6–21	6–23	•–24	•–26
	7	9–21	8–22	8–24	7–25	7–26	•–28
	8	11–23	10–25	9–26	9–27	8–28	•–30
	9	13–25	12–27	11–28	10–29	10–30	9–32
	10	15–27	14–29	13–30	12–31	11–32	10–34
	11	17–29	15–31	14–32	13–34	13–34	12–36
	12	19–31	17–33	16–34	15–35	14–36	13–38
	13	20–34	19–35	18–36	17–37	16–38	15–40
	14	22–36	21–37	20–38	19–39	18–40	17–42
30	0	•– 4	•– 5	•– 6	•– 7	•– 8	•– 9
	1	•– 6	•– 8	•– 9	•–10	•–11	•–13
	2	•– 9	•–10	•–11	•–13	•–14	•–16
	3	•–11	•–13	•–14	•–15	•–16	•–18
	4	4–14	•–15	•–16	•–18	•–19	•–21
	5	6–16	5–17	•–18	•–20	•–21	•–23
	6	7–18	6–19	6–21	•–22	•–23	•–25
	7	9–20	8–22	7–23	7–24	•–25	•–27
	8	11–22	10–24	9–25	8–26	8–27	•–29
	9	12–24	11–26	11–27	10–28	9–29	9–31
	10	14–26	13–28	12–29	11–30	11–31	10–33
	11	16–28	15–30	14–31	13–32	12–33	11–35
	12	18–30	17–32	16–33	15–34	14–35	13–37
	13	20–32	19–34	18–35	16–36	16–37	14–39
	14	22–34	20–36	19–37	18–38	17–39	16–41
	15	24–36	22–38	21–39	20–40	19–41	18–42

Explanation of the tables on pages 109–123

Any statistical test can be put in the form of a fourfold table

$$\begin{array}{ccc} x_1 & (N_1 - x_1) & N_1 \\ x_2 & (N_2 - x_2) & N_2 \end{array}$$

which is so arranged that $N_1 \leqq N_2$ and $x_1 \leqq (N_1 - x_1)$. The sum of $N_1 + N_2 = N$, of $x_1 + x_2 = X$. N and N_1 are looked for in the table, where against x_1 will be found the limits X_l and X_r for any desired significance. Putting $x_1/N_1 = p_1$ and $x_2/N_2 = p_2$, then if $X \leqq X_l$, the significance limit when testing for

$$p_1 > p_2 \text{ is } P_l \leqq \alpha$$

and for $p_1 \neq p_2$ is $2P_l \leqq 2\alpha$

If $X \geqq X_r$, the significance limit when testing for

$$p_1 < p_2 \text{ is } P_r \leqq \alpha$$

and for $p_1 \neq p_2$ is $2P_r \leqq 2\alpha$

If X lies between X_l and X_r, the null hypothesis $p_1 = p_2$ cannot be rejected.

Prob $[T_l < T < T_r] \geqq 1 - 2\alpha$. For explanation see page 191. The italic values are 'exact' limits[1], the others approximate limits[2]
The limits for $N_1 = N_2$ are in bold figures

$2\alpha = 0.10$ (each cell: T_l–T_r)

N_2 \ N_1	4	5	6	7	8	9	10	11	12	13	14	15	16	17	18	19	20	21	22	23	24	25
4	**11–25**	17–33	24–42	32–52	41–63	51–75	62–88	74–102	87–117	101–133	116–150	132–168	150–186	168–206	187–227	207–249	228–272	250–296	273–321	297–347	322–374	348–402
5	12–28	**19–36**	26–46	34–57	44–68	54–81	66–94	78–109	91–125	106–141	121–159	138–177	155–197	173–218	193–239	213–262	235–285	257–310	281–335	305–362	330–390	357–418
6	13–31	20–40	**28–50**	36–62	46–74	57–87	69–101	82–116	95–133	110–150	126–168	143–187	161–207	179–229	199–251	220–274	242–298	265–323	289–349	313–377	339–405	366–434
7	14–34	21–44	29–55	**39–66**	49–79	60–93	72–108	85–124	99–141	115–158	131–177	148–197	166–218	186–239	206–262	227–286	249–311	272–337	297–363	322–391	348–420	375–450
8	15–37	23–47	31–59	41–71	**51–85**	63–99	75–115	89–131	104–148	119–167	136–186	153–207	172–228	192–250	212–274	234–298	257–323	280–350	305–377	330–406	357–435	385–465
9	16–40	24–51	33–63	43–76	54–90	**66–105**	79–121	93–138	108–156	124–178	141–195	159–216	178–238	198–261	219–285	241–310	264–336	288–363	313–391	339–420	366–450	394–481
10	17–43	26–54	35–67	45–81	56–96	69–111	**82–128**	97–145	112–164	128–184	146–204	164–226	184–248	204–272	226–297	248–322	272–348	296–376	321–405	348–434	375–465	403–497
11	18–46	27–58	37–71	47–86	59–101	72–117	86–134	**100–153**	116–172	133–192	151–213	170–235	190–258	210–283	232–308	255–334	279–361	304–389	329–419	356–449	384–480	413–512
12	19–49	28–62	38–76	49–91	62–106	75–123	89–141	104–160	**120–180**	138–200	156–222	175–245	196–268	217–293	239–319	262–346	286–374	312–402	338–432	365–463	393–495	423–527
13	20–52	30–65	40–80	52–95	64–112	78–129	92–148	108–167	125–187	**142–209**	161–231	181–254	201–279	223–304	245–331	269–358	294–386	320–415	346–446	374–477	403–509	433–542
14	21–55	31–69	42–84	54–100	67–117	81–135	96–154	112–174	129–195	147–217	**166–240**	186–264	207–289	229–315	252–342	276–370	301–399	328–428	355–459	383–491	412–524	442–558
15	22–58	33–72	44–88	56–105	69–123	84–141	99–161	116–181	133–203	152–225	171–249	**191–274**	213–299	235–326	259–353	284–381	309–411	336–441	363–473	392–505	422–538	452–573
16	24–60	34–76	46–92	58–110	72–128	87–147	103–167	120–188	138–210	156–234	176–258	197–283	**219–309**	242–336	266–364	291–393	317–423	344–454	372–486	401–519	431–553	462–588
17	25–63	35–80	47–97	61–114	75–133	90–153	106–174	123–196	142–218	161–242	181–267	202–293	225–319	**248–347**	273–375	298–405	325–435	352–467	380–500	410–533	440–568	472–603
18	26–66	37–83	49–101	63–119	77–139	93–159	110–180	127–203	146–226	165–251	186–276	208–302	231–329	255–357	**280–386**	305–417	332–448	360–480	389–513	419–547	450–582	482–618
19	27–69	38–87	51–105	65–124	80–144	96–165	113–187	131–210	150–234	170–259	191–285	214–311	237–339	261–368	286–398	**313–428**	340–460	368–493	398–526	428–561	459–597	492–633
20	28–72	40–90	53–109	67–129	83–149	99–171	117–193	135–217	154–242	175–267	196–294	219–321	243–349	268–378	293–409	320–440	**348–472**	376–506	406–540	437–575	469–611	501–649
21	29–75	41–94	55–113	69–134	85–155	102–177	120–200	139–224	159–249	180–275	202–302	225–330	249–359	274–389	300–420	327–452	355–485	**385–518**	415–553	446–589	478–626	511–664
22	30–78	43–97	57–117	72–138	88–160	105–183	123–207	142–232	163–257	184–284	207–311	230–340	255–369	280–400	307–431	335–463	363–497	393–531	**423–567**	455–603	488–640	521–679
23	31–81	44–101	58–122	74–143	90–166	108–189	127–213	146–239	167–265	189–292	212–320	236–349	261–379	287–410	314–442	342–475	371–509	401–544	432–580	**464–617**	497–655	531–694
24	32–84	45–105	60–126	76–148	93–171	111–195	130–220	150–246	171–273	194–300	217–329	242–358	267–389	293–421	321–453	349–487	379–521	409–557	441–593	473–631	**507–669**	541–709
25	33–87	47–108	62–130	78–153	96–176	114–201	133–227	154–253	176–280	199–308	222–338	247–368	273–399	300–431	328–464	357–498	386–534	417–570	449–607	482–645	516–684	**551–724**
26	34–90	48–112	64–134	81–157	98–182	117–207	137–233	158–260	180–288	203–317	227–347	253–377	279–409	306–442	335–475	364–510	394–546	426–582	458–620	491–659	526–698	561–739
27	35–93	50–115	66–138	83–162	101–187	120–213	140–240	162–267	184–296	208–325	233–355	258–387	285–419	313–452	342–486	371–522	402–558	434–595	467–633	500–673	535–713	571–754
28	36–96	51–119	67–143	85–167	103–193	123–219	144–246	166–274	189–303	213–333	238–364	264–396	291–429	319–463	348–498	379–533	410–570	442–608	475–647	510–686	545–727	581–769
29	37–99	53–122	69–147	87–172	106–198	126–225	147–253	170–281	193–311	218–341	243–373	270–405	297–439	326–473	355–509	386–545	418–582	450–621	484–660	519–700	554–742	591–784
30	38–102	54–126	71–151	89–177	109–203	129–231	151–259	174–288	197–319	222–350	248–382	275–415	303–449	332–484	362–520	393–557	425–595	459–633	493–673	528–714	564–756	601–799
31	39–105	55–130	73–155	92–181	111–209	132–237	154–266	178–295	202–326	227–358	253–391	281–424	309–459	339–494	369–531	401–568	433–607	467–646	501–687	537–728	574–770	611–814
32	40–108	57–133	75–159	94–186	114–214	135–243	158–272	181–303	206–334	232–366	259–399	286–434	315–469	345–505	376–542	408–580	441–619	475–659	510–700	546–742	583–785	621–829
33	41–111	58–137	77–163	96–191	117–219	138–249	161–279	185–310	210–342	237–374	264–408	292–443	321–479	352–515	383–553	415–592	449–631	483–672	519–713	555–756	593–799	631–844
34	42–114	60–140	78–168	98–196	119–225	141–255	165–285	189–317	215–349	241–383	269–417	298–452	327–489	358–526	390–564	423–603	457–643	492–684	527–727	564–770	602–814	641–859
35	43–117	61–144	80–172	100–201	122–230	144–261	168–292	193–324	219–357	246–391	274–426	303–462	333–499	365–536	397–575	430–615	464–656	500–697	536–740	574–783	612–828	651–874
36	44–120	62–148	82–176	102–206	124–236	148–266	172–298	197–331	223–365	251–399	279–435	309–471	340–508	371–547	404–586	438–626	472–668	508–710	545–753	583–797	621–843	661–889
37	45–123	64–151	84–180	105–210	127–241	151–272	175–305	201–338	228–372	256–407	285–443	315–480	346–518	378–557	411–597	445–638	480–680	516–723	554–766	592–811	631–857	671–904
38	46–126	65–155	85–185	107–215	130–246	154–278	179–311	205–345	232–380	260–416	290–452	320–490	352–528	384–568	418–608	452–650	488–692	525–735	562–780	601–825	641–871	681–919
39	47–129	67–158	87–189	109–220	132–252	157–284	182–318	209–352	236–388	265–424	295–461	326–499	358–538	391–578	425–619	460–661	496–704	533–748	571–793	610–839	650–886	691–934
40	48–132	68–162	89–193	111–225	135–257	160–290	186–324	213–359	241–395	270–432	300–470	331–509	364–548	397–589	432–630	467–673	504–716	541–761	580–806	619–853	660–900	702–948
41	49–135	69–166	91–197	114–229	138–262	163–296	189–331	217–366	245–403	275–440	305–479	337–518	370–558	404–599	439–641	474–685	511–729	549–774	588–820	628–867	669–915	712–963
42	50–138	71–169	93–201	116–234	140–268	166–302	193–337	221–373	249–411	279–449	311–487	343–527	376–568	410–610	446–652	482–696	519–741	558–786	597–833	638–880	679–929	722–978
43	51–141	72–173	95–205	118–239	143–273	169–308	196–344	224–381	254–418	284–457	316–496	348–537	382–578	417–620	452–664	489–708	527–753	566–799	606–846	647–894	689–943	732–993
44	52–144	74–176	96–210	120–244	146–278	172–314	200–350	228–388	258–426	289–465	321–505	354–546	388–588	423–631	459–675	497–719	535–765	574–812	615–859	656–908	698–958	742–1008
45	53–147	75–180	98–214	123–248	148–284	175–320	203–357	232–395	262–434	294–473	326–514	360–555	394–598	430–641	466–686	504–731	543–777	583–824	623–873	665–922	708–972	752–1023
46	55–149	77–183	100–218	125–253	151–289	178–326	207–363	236–402	267–441	299–481	331–523	365–565	400–608	436–652	473–697	511–743	551–789	591–837	632–886	674–936	718–986	762–1038
47	56–152	78–187	102–222	127–258	154–294	181–332	210–370	240–409	271–449	303–490	337–531	371–574	406–618	443–662	480–708	519–754	558–802	599–850	641–899	683–950	727–1001	772–1053
48	57–155	79–191	104–226	129–263	156–300	184–338	214–376	244–416	275–457	308–498	342–540	377–583	412–628	449–673	487–719	526–766	566–814	607–863	649–913	693–963	737–1015	782–1068
49	58–158	81–194	106–230	132–267	159–305	187–344	217–383	248–423	280–464	313–506	347–549	382–593	418–638	456–683	494–730	534–777	574–826	616–875	658–926	702–977	746–1030	792–1083
50	59–161	82–198	107–235	134–272	162–310	190–350	221–387	252–430	284–472	318–514	352–558	388–602	425–647	462–694	501–741	541–789	582–838	624–888	667–939	711–991	756–1044	802–1098

1) Based on the exact limits for $W = 2U$ in WABEKE and VAN EEDEN, *Handleiding voor de toets van Wilcoxon*, Report S 176 (M 65), Mathematisch Centrum, Statistische Afdeling (Prof. D. VAN DANTZIG), Amsterdam, 1955, by kind permission of the authors and publishers. *2)* Based on the normal approximation with empirical continuity correction.

Significance Limits for the Rank Sum T, $2\alpha = 0.05$

Prob $[T_l < \boldsymbol{T} < T_r] \geqq 1 - 2\alpha$. For explanation see page 191. The italic values are 'exact' limits[1], the others approximate limits[2]
The limits for $N_1 = N_2$ are in bold figures

$2\alpha = 0.05$ — each cell gives T_l–T_r

N_2 \ N_1	4	5	6	7	8	9	10	11	12	13	14	15	16	17	18	19	20	21	22	23	24	25
4	**10–26**	16–34	23–43	31–53	40–64	49–77	60–90	72–104	85–119	99–135	114–152	130–170	147–189	164–210	183–231	203–253	224–276	246–300	269–325	293–351	317–379	343–407
5	11–29	**17–38**	24–48	33–58	42–70	52–83	63–97	75–112	89–127	103–144	118–162	134–181	151–201	170–221	189–243	209–266	230–290	253–314	276–340	300–367	325–395	352–423
6	12–32	18–42	**26–52**	34–64	44–76	55–89	66–104	79–119	92–136	107–153	122–172	139–191	157–211	175–233	195–255	215–279	237–303	260–328	283–355	308–382	333–411	360–440
7	13–35	20–45	27–57	**36–69**	46–82	57–96	69–111	82–127	96–144	111–162	127–181	144–201	162–222	181–244	201–267	222–291	244–316	267–342	291–369	316–397	342–426	369–456
8	14–38	21–49	29–61	38–74	**49–87**	60–102	72–118	85–135	100–152	115–171	131–191	149–211	167–233	187–255	207–279	228–304	251–329	274–356	298–384	324–412	350–442	378–472
9	14–42	22–53	31–65	40–79	51–93	**62–109**	75–125	89–142	104–160	119–180	136–200	154–221	173–243	192–267	213–291	235–316	258–342	281–370	306–398	332–427	359–457	387–488
10	15–45	23–57	32–70	42–84	53–99	65–115	**78–132**	92–150	107–169	124–188	141–209	159–231	178–254	198–278	219–303	242–328	265–355	289–383	314–412	340–442	368–472	396–504
11	16–48	24–61	34–74	44–89	55–105	68–121	81–139	**96–157**	111–177	128–197	145–219	164–241	183–265	204–289	226–314	248–341	272–368	296–397	322–426	349–456	376–488	405–520
12	17–51	26–64	35–79	46–94	58–110	71–127	84–146	99–165	**115–185**	132–206	150–228	169–251	189–275	210–300	232–326	255–353	279–381	304–410	330–440	357–471	385–503	414–536
13	18–54	27–68	37–83	48–99	60–116	73–134	88–152	103–172	119–193	**136–215**	155–237	174–261	195–285	216–311	239–337	262–365	286–394	312–423	338–454	365–486	394–518	423–552
14	19–57	28–72	38–88	50–104	62–122	76–140	91–159	106–180	123–201	141–223	**160–246**	179–271	200–296	222–322	245–349	269–377	293–407	319–437	346–468	374–500	403–533	433–567
15	20–60	29–76	40–92	52–109	65–127	79–146	94–166	110–187	127–209	145–232	164–256	**184–281**	206–306	228–333	251–361	275–390	301–419	327–450	354–482	382–515	412–548	442–583
16	21–63	30–80	42–96	54–114	67–133	82–152	97–173	113–195	131–217	150–240	169–265	190–290	**211–317**	234–344	258–372	282–402	308–432	335–463	362–496	391–529	421–563	451–599
17	21–67	32–83	43–101	56–119	70–138	84–159	100–180	117–202	135–225	154–249	174–274	195–300	217–327	**240–355**	264–384	289–414	315–445	342–477	370–510	399–544	429–579	461–614
18	22–70	33–87	45–105	58–124	72–144	87–165	103–187	121–209	139–233	159–257	179–283	200–310	223–337	246–366	**271–395**	296–426	322–458	350–490	378–524	408–558	438–594	470–630
19	23–73	34–91	46–110	60–129	74–150	90–171	107–193	124–217	143–241	163–266	184–292	205–320	228–348	252–377	277–407	**303–438**	330–470	358–503	387–537	416–573	447–609	479–646
20	24–76	35–95	48–114	62–134	77–155	93–177	110–200	128–224	147–249	167–275	188–302	211–329	234–358	258–388	283–419	310–450	**337–483**	365–517	395–551	425–587	456–624	489–661
21	25–79	37–98	50–118	64–139	79–161	95–184	113–207	131–232	151–257	172–283	193–311	216–339	240–368	264–399	290–430	317–462	344–496	**373–530**	403–565	434–601	465–639	498–677
22	26–82	38–102	51–123	66–144	81–167	98–190	116–214	135–239	155–265	176–292	198–320	221–349	245–379	270–410	296–442	324–474	352–508	381–543	**411–579**	442–616	474–654	508–692
23	27–85	39–106	53–127	68–149	84–172	101–196	119–221	139–246	159–273	180–301	203–329	226–359	251–389	276–421	303–453	330–487	359–521	389–556	419–593	**451–630**	483–669	517–708
24	27–89	40–110	54–132	70–154	86–178	104–202	123–227	142–254	163–281	185–309	208–338	232–368	257–399	282–432	309–465	337–499	366–534	396–570	427–607	459–645	**492–684**	527–723
25	28–92	42–113	56–136	72–159	89–183	107–208	126–234	146–261	167–289	189–318	213–347	237–378	262–410	289–442	316–476	344–511	374–546	404–583	436–620	468–659	502–698	**536–739**
26	29–95	43–117	58–140	74–164	91–189	109–215	129–241	150–268	171–297	194–326	217–357	242–388	268–420	295–453	322–488	351–523	381–559	412–596	444–634	477–673	511–713	545–755
27	30–98	44–121	59–145	76–169	93–195	112–221	132–248	153–276	175–305	198–335	222–366	247–398	273–431	301–464	329–499	358–535	388–572	420–609	452–648	485–688	520–728	555–770
28	31–101	45–125	61–149	78–174	96–200	115–227	135–255	157–283	179–313	203–343	227–375	253–407	279–441	307–475	335–511	365–547	396–584	427–623	460–662	494–702	529–743	564–786
29	32–104	47–128	63–153	80–179	98–206	118–233	139–261	160–291	183–321	207–352	232–384	258–417	285–451	313–486	342–522	372–559	403–597	435–636	468–676	503–716	538–758	574–801
30	33–107	48–132	64–158	82–184	101–211	121–239	142–268	164–298	187–329	211–361	237–393	263–427	291–461	319–497	348–534	379–571	411–609	443–649	477–689	511–731	547–773	584–816
31	34–110	49–136	66–162	84–189	103–217	123–246	145–275	167–306	191–337	216–369	242–402	268–437	296–472	325–508	355–545	386–583	418–622	451–662	485–703	520–745	556–788	593–832
32	34–114	50–140	67–167	86–194	106–222	126–252	148–282	171–313	195–345	220–378	246–412	274–446	302–482	331–519	362–556	393–595	425–635	459–675	493–717	529–759	565–803	603–847
33	35–117	52–143	69–171	88–199	108–228	129–258	151–289	175–320	199–353	225–386	251–421	279–456	308–492	337–530	368–568	400–607	433–647	467–688	501–731	537–774	574–818	612–863
34	36–120	53–147	71–175	90–204	110–234	132–264	155–295	178–328	203–361	229–395	256–430	284–466	313–503	343–541	375–579	407–619	440–660	474–702	510–744	546–788	583–833	622–878
35	37–123	54–151	72–180	92–209	113–239	135–270	158–302	182–335	207–369	234–403	261–439	289–476	319–513	350–551	381–591	414–631	447–673	482–715	518–758	555–802	592–848	631–894
36	38–126	55–155	74–184	94–214	115–245	137–277	161–309	185–343	211–377	238–412	266–448	295–485	325–523	356–562	388–602	421–643	455–685	490–728	526–772	563–817	602–862	641–909
37	39–129	57–158	76–188	96–219	117–251	140–283	164–316	189–350	215–385	242–421	271–457	300–495	330–534	362–573	394–614	428–655	462–698	498–741	534–786	572–831	611–877	650–925
38	40–132	58–162	77–193	98–224	120–256	143–289	167–323	193–357	219–393	247–429	275–467	305–505	336–544	368–584	401–625	435–667	470–710	506–754	543–799	581–845	620–892	660–940
39	41–135	59–166	79–197	100–229	122–262	146–295	170–330	196–365	223–401	251–438	280–476	311–514	342–554	374–595	407–637	442–679	477–723	514–767	551–813	589–860	629–907	670–955
40	41–139	60–170	80–202	102–234	125–267	149–301	174–336	200–372	227–409	256–446	285–485	316–524	347–565	380–606	414–648	449–691	485–735	521–781	559–827	598–874	638–922	679–971
41	42–142	61–174	82–206	104–239	127–273	151–308	177–343	204–379	231–417	260–455	290–494	321–534	353–575	386–617	420–660	456–703	492–748	529–794	568–840	607–888	647–937	689–986
42	43–145	63–177	84–210	106–244	129–279	154–314	180–350	207–387	235–425	265–463	295–503	326–544	359–585	392–628	427–671	463–715	499–761	537–807	576–854	616–902	656–952	698–1002
43	44–148	64–181	85–215	108–249	132–284	157–320	183–357	211–394	239–433	269–472	300–512	332–553	365–595	399–638	434–682	470–727	507–773	545–820	584–868	624–917	666–966	708–1017
44	45–151	65–185	87–219	110–254	134–290	160–326	186–364	214–402	243–441	273–481	305–521	337–563	370–606	405–649	440–694	477–739	514–786	553–833	592–882	633–931	675–981	717–1033
45	46–154	66–189	88–224	112–259	137–295	163–332	190–370	218–409	247–449	278–489	309–531	342–573	376–616	411–660	447–705	484–751	522–798	561–846	601–895	642–945	684–996	727–1048
46	47–157	68–192	90–228	114–264	139–301	165–339	193–377	222–416	251–457	282–498	314–540	347–583	382–626	417–671	453–717	491–763	529–811	568–860	609–909	651–959	693–1011	737–1063
47	48–160	69–196	92–232	116–269	141–307	168–345	196–384	225–424	255–465	287–506	319–549	353–592	387–637	423–682	460–728	498–775	536–824	576–873	617–923	659–974	702–1026	746–1079
48	48–164	70–200	93–237	118–274	144–312	171–351	199–391	229–431	259–473	291–515	324–558	358–602	393–647	429–693	466–740	505–787	544–836	584–886	626–936	668–988	711–1041	756–1094
49	49–167	71–204	95–241	120–279	146–318	174–357	202–398	232–439	263–481	296–523	329–567	363–612	399–657	435–704	473–751	512–799	551–849	592–899	634–950	677–1002	721–1055	766–1109
50	50–170	73–207	97–245	122–284	149–323	177–363	206–404	236–446	267–489	300–532	334–576	369–621	405–667	441–715	480–762	519–811	559–861	600–912	642–964	685–1017	730–1070	775–1125

1) Based on the exact limits for $W = 2U$ in WABEKE and VAN EEDEN, *Handleiding voor de toets van Wilcoxon*, Report S 176 (M 65), Mathematisch Centrum, Statistische Afdeling (Prof. D. VAN DANTZIG), Amsterdam, 1955, by kind permission of the authors and publishers. *2)* Based on the normal approximation with empirical continuity correction.

Prob $[T_l < \boldsymbol{T} < T_r] \geqq 1 - 2\alpha$. For explanation see page 191. The italic values are 'exact' limits[1], the others approximate limits[2]
The limits for $N_1 = N_2$ are in bold figures

$2\alpha = 0.02$ (each cell: T_l–T_r)

N_2 \ N_1	4	5	6	7	8	9	10	11	12	13	14	15	16	17	18	19	20	21	22	23	24	25
4	—	15–35	22–44	29–55	38–66	48–78	58–92	70–106	83–121	96–138	111–155	127–173	143–193	161–213	180–234	199–257	220–280	242–304	264–330	288–356	313–383	338–412
5	10–30	**16–39**	23–49	31–60	40–72	50–85	61–99	73–114	86–130	100–147	115–165	131–184	148–204	166–225	185–247	205–270	226–294	248–319	271–345	295–372	320–400	346–429
6	11–33	17–43	**24–54**	32–66	42–78	52–92	63–107	75–123	89–139	103–157	118–176	135–195	152–216	171–237	190–260	210–284	232–308	254–334	277–361	302–388	327–417	354–446
7	11–37	18–47	25–59	**34–71**	43–85	54–99	66–114	78–131	92–148	107–166	122–186	139–206	157–227	176–249	195–273	216–297	238–322	261–348	284–376	309–404	335–433	361–464
8	12–40	19–51	27–63	35–77	**45–91**	56–106	68–122	81–139	95–157	111–175	127–195	144–216	162–238	181–261	201–285	222–310	244–336	267–363	291–391	316–420	342–450	370–480
9	13–43	20–55	28–68	37–82	47–97	**59–112**	71–129	84–147	99–165	114–185	131–205	148–227	167–249	186–273	207–297	228–323	250–350	274–377	298–406	324–435	350–466	378–497
10	13–47	21–59	29–73	39–87	49–103	61–119	**74–136**	88–154	102–174	118–194	135–215	153–237	172–260	191–285	212–310	234–336	257–363	281–391	306–420	331–451	358–482	386–514
11	14–50	22–63	30–78	40–93	51–109	63–126	77–143	**91–162**	106–182	122–203	139–225	157–248	177–271	197–296	218–322	240–349	263–377	288–405	313–435	339–466	366–498	394–531
12	15–53	23–67	32–82	42–98	53–115	66–132	79–151	94–170	**109–191**	126–212	143–235	162–258	182–282	202–308	224–334	246–362	270–390	295–419	320–450	347–481	374–514	403–547
13	15–57	24–71	33–87	44–103	56–120	68–139	82–158	97–178	113–199	**130–221**	148–244	167–268	187–293	208–319	230–346	253–374	276–404	301–434	327–465	354–497	382–530	411–564
14	16–60	25–75	34–92	45–109	58–126	71–145	85–165	100–186	116–208	134–230	**152–254**	171–279	192–304	213–331	235–359	259–387	283–417	308–448	335–479	362–512	391–545	420–580
15	17–63	26–79	36–96	47–114	60–132	73–152	88–172	103–194	120–216	138–239	156–264	**176–289**	197–315	218–343	241–371	265–400	290–430	315–462	342–494	370–527	399–561	429–596
16	17–67	27–83	37–101	49–119	62–138	76–158	91–179	107–201	124–224	142–248	161–273	181–299	**202–326**	224–354	247–383	271–413	296–444	323–475	350–508	378–542	407–577	437–613
17	18–70	28–87	39–105	51–124	64–144	78–165	93–187	110–209	127–233	146–257	165–283	185–310	207–337	**229–366**	253–395	278–425	303–457	330–489	357–523	386–557	416–592	446–629
18	19–73	29–91	40–110	52–130	66–150	81–171	96–194	113–217	131–241	150–266	169–293	190–320	212–348	235–377	**259–407**	284–438	310–470	337–503	365–537	394–572	424–608	455–645
19	19–77	30–95	41–115	54–135	68–156	83–178	99–201	116–225	134–250	154–275	174–302	195–330	217–359	241–388	265–419	**290–451**	317–483	344–517	373–551	402–587	432–624	464–661
20	20–80	31–99	43–119	56–140	70–162	85–185	102–208	119–233	138–258	157–285	178–312	200–340	222–370	246–400	271–431	297–463	**323–497**	351–531	380–566	410–602	441–639	473–677
21	21–83	32–103	44–124	58–145	72–168	88–191	105–215	123–240	142–266	161–294	182–322	204–351	228–380	252–411	277–443	303–476	330–510	**359–544**	388–580	418–617	449–655	482–693
22	21–87	33–107	45–129	59–151	74–174	90–198	108–222	126–248	145–275	165–303	187–331	209–361	233–391	257–423	283–455	310–488	337–523	366–558	**395–595**	426–632	458–670	490–710
23	22–90	34–111	47–133	61–156	76–180	93–204	110–230	129–256	149–283	169–312	191–341	214–371	238–402	263–434	289–467	316–501	344–536	373–572	403–609	**434–647**	466–686	499–726
24	23–93	35–115	48–138	63–161	78–186	95–211	113–237	132–264	152–292	173–321	196–350	219–381	243–413	269–445	295–479	322–514	351–549	380–586	411–623	442–662	**475–701**	508–742
25	23–97	36–119	50–142	64–167	81–191	98–217	116–244	135–272	156–300	177–330	200–360	224–391	248–424	274–457	301–491	329–526	358–562	388–599	418–638	450–677	483–717	**517–758**
26	24–100	37–123	51–147	66–172	83–197	100–224	119–251	138–280	159–309	181–339	204–370	229–401	254–434	280–468	307–503	335–539	365–575	395–613	426–652	458–692	492–732	526–774
27	25–103	38–127	52–152	68–177	85–203	103–230	121–259	142–287	163–317	185–348	209–379	233–412	259–445	285–480	313–515	342–551	371–589	402–627	434–666	466–707	500–748	535–790
28	26–106	39–131	54–156	70–182	87–209	105–237	124–266	145–295	167–325	189–357	213–389	238–422	264–456	291–491	319–527	348–564	378–602	409–641	441–681	475–721	509–763	544–806
29	26–110	40–135	55–161	71–188	89–215	108–243	127–273	148–303	170–334	193–366	218–398	243–432	269–467	297–502	325–539	355–576	385–615	417–654	449–695	483–736	517–779	553–822
30	27–113	41–139	56–166	73–193	91–221	110–250	130–280	151–311	174–342	198–374	222–408	248–442	275–477	302–514	331–551	361–589	392–628	424–668	457–709	491–751	526–794	562–838
31	28–116	42–143	58–170	75–198	93–227	112–257	133–287	155–318	178–350	202–383	227–417	253–452	280–488	308–525	337–563	368–601	399–641	431–682	465–723	499–766	534–810	571–854
32	28–120	43–147	59–175	77–203	95–233	115–263	136–294	158–326	181–359	206–392	231–427	258–462	285–499	314–536	343–575	374–614	406–654	439–695	472–738	507–781	543–825	580–870
33	29–123	44–151	61–179	78–209	97–239	117–270	139–301	161–334	185–367	210–401	235–437	262–473	290–510	319–548	349–587	381–626	413–667	446–709	480–752	515–796	552–840	589–886
34	30–126	45–155	62–184	79–215	99–245	120–276	141–309	164–342	189–375	214–410	240–446	267–483	296–520	325–559	356–598	387–639	420–680	453–723	488–766	523–811	560–856	598–902
35	30–130	46–159	63–189	81–220	101–251	122–283	144–316	168–349	192–384	218–419	244–456	272–493	301–531	331–570	362–610	394–651	427–693	461–736	496–780	532–825	569–871	607–918
36	31–133	47–163	65–193	83–225	103–257	125–289	147–323	171–357	196–392	222–428	249–465	277–503	306–542	336–582	368–622	400–664	433–707	468–750	503–795	540–840	577–887	616–934
37	32–136	48–167	66–198	84–231	105–263	127–296	150–330	174–365	199–401	226–437	253–475	282–513	311–553	342–593	374–634	407–676	440–720	475–764	511–809	548–855	586–902	625–950
38	32–140	49–171	67–203	86–236	107–269	129–303	153–337	177–373	203–409	230–446	258–484	287–523	317–563	348–604	380–646	413–689	447–733	483–777	519–823	556–870	595–917	634–966
39	33–143	50–175	69–207	88–241	109–275	132–309	156–344	181–380	207–417	234–455	262–494	292–533	322–574	353–616	386–658	420–701	454–746	490–791	527–837	564–885	603–933	643–982
40	34–146	51–179	70–212	90–246	111–281	134–316	159–351	184–388	210–426	238–464	267–503	296–544	327–585	359–627	392–670	426–714	461–759	497–805	534–852	573–899	612–948	652–998
41	34–150	52–183	72–216	91–252	113–287	137–322	161–359	187–396	214–434	242–473	271–513	301–554	333–595	365–638	398–682	433–726	468–772	505–818	542–866	581–914	620–964	661–1014
42	35–153	53–187	73–221	93–257	116–292	139–329	164–366	190–404	218–442	246–482	276–522	306–564	338–606	371–649	404–694	439–739	475–785	512–832	550–880	589–929	629–979	670–1030
43	35–157	54–191	74–226	95–262	118–298	142–335	167–373	194–411	221–451	250–491	280–532	311–574	343–617	376–661	410–706	446–751	482–798	519–846	558–894	597–944	638–994	679–1046
44	36–160	55–195	76–230	97–267	120–304	144–342	170–380	197–419	225–459	254–500	284–542	316–584	348–628	382–672	416–718	452–764	489–811	527–859	565–909	605–959	646–1010	688–1062
45	37–163	56–199	77–235	98–273	122–310	147–348	173–387	200–427	229–467	258–509	289–551	321–594	354–638	388–683	423–729	459–776	496–824	534–873	573–923	614–973	655–1025	697–1078
46	37–167	57–203	78–240	100–278	124–316	149–355	176–394	203–435	232–476	262–518	293–561	326–604	359–649	393–695	429–741	465–789	503–837	541–887	581–937	622–988	663–1041	706–1094
47	38–170	58–207	80–244	102–283	126–322	152–361	179–401	207–442	236–484	266–527	298–570	330–615	364–660	399–706	435–753	472–801	510–850	549–900	589–951	630–1003	672–1056	715–1110
48	39–173	59–211	81–249	103–289	128–328	154–368	181–409	210–450	240–492	270–536	302–580	335–625	369–671	405–717	441–765	478–814	517–863	556–914	597–965	638–1018	681–1071	724–1126
49	39–177	60–215	82–254	105–294	130–334	157–374	184–416	213–458	243–501	274–545	307–589	340–635	375–681	410–729	447–777	485–826	524–876	563–928	604–980	646–1033	689–1087	733–1142
50	40–180	61–219	84–258	107–299	132–340	159–381	187–423	216–466	247–509	279–553	311–599	345–645	380–692	416–740	453–789	491–839	531–889	571–941	612–994	655–1047	698–1102	743–1157

1) Based on the exact limits for $W = 2U$ in WABEKE and VAN EEDEN, *Handleiding voor de toets van Wilcoxon*, Report S 176 (M 65), Mathematisch Centrum, Statistische Afdeling (Prof. D. VAN DANTZIG), Amsterdam, 1955, by kind permission of the authors and publishers. *2)* Based on the normal approximation with empirical continuity correction.

Significance Limits for the Rank Sum T, $2\alpha = 0.01$

Prob $[T_l < \boldsymbol{T} < T_r] \geqq 1 - 2\alpha$. For explanation see page 191. The italic values are 'exact' limits[1], the others approximate limits[2]
The limits for $N_1 = N_2$ are in bold figures

$2\alpha = 0.01$ — entries are T_l–T_r

N_2 \ N_1	4	5	6	7	8	9	10	11	12	13	14
4	—	—	21–45	28–56	37–67	46–80	57–93	68–108	81–123	94–140	109–157
5	—	**15–40**	22–50	29–62	38–74	48–87	59–101	71–116	84–132	98–149	112–168
6	10–34	16–44	**23–55**	31–67	40–80	50–94	61–109	73–125	87–141	101–159	116–178
7	10–38	16–49	24–60	**32–73**	42–86	52–101	64–116	76–133	90–150	104–169	120–188
8	11–41	17–53	25–65	34–78	**43–93**	54–108	66–124	79–141	93–159	108–178	123–199
9	11–45	18–57	26–70	35–84	45–99	**56–115**	68–132	82–149	96–168	111–188	127–209
10	12–48	19–61	27–75	37–89	47–105	58–122	**71–139**	84–158	99–177	115–197	131–219
11	12–52	20–65	28–80	38–95	49–111	61–128	73–147	**87–166**	102–186	118–207	135–229
12	13–55	21–69	30–84	40–100	51–117	63–135	76–154	90–174	**105–195**	122–216	139–239
13	13–59	22–73	31–89	41–106	53–123	65–142	79–161	93–182	109–203	**125–226**	143–249
14	14–62	22–78	32–94	43–111	54–130	67–149	81–169	96–190	112–212	129–235	**147–259**
15	15–65	23–82	33–99	44–117	56–136	69–156	84–176	99–198	115–221	133–244	151–269
16	15–69	24–86	34–104	46–122	58–142	72–162	86–184	102–206	119–229	136–254	155–279
17	16–72	25–90	36–108	47–128	60–148	74–169	89–191	105–214	122–238	140–263	160–288
18	16–76	26–94	37–113	49–133	62–154	76–176	92–198	108–222	125–247	144–272	164–298
19	17–79	27–98	38–118	50–139	64–160	78–183	94–206	111–230	129–255	148–281	168–308
20	18–82	28–102	39–123	52–144	66–166	81–189	97–213	114–238	132–264	152–290	172–318
21	18–86	29–106	40–128	53–150	68–172	83–196	99–221	117–246	136–272	155–300	176–328
22	19–89	29–111	42–132	55–155	70–178	85–203	102–228	120–254	139–281	159–309	180–338
23	19–93	30–115	43–137	57–160	71–185	88–209	105–235	123–262	142–290	163–318	184–348
24	20–96	31–119	44–142	58–166	73–191	90–216	107–243	126–270	146–298	167–327	188–358
25	20–100	32–123	45–147	60–171	75–197	92–223	110–250	129–278	149–307	170–337	193–367
26	21–103	33–127	46–152	61–177	77–203	94–230	113–257	132–286	152–316	174–346	197–377
27	22–106	34–131	48–156	63–182	79–209	97–236	115–265	135–294	156–324	178–355	201–387
28	22–110	35–135	49–161	64–188	81–215	99–243	118–272	138–302	159–333	182–364	205–397
29	23–113	36–139	50–166	66–193	83–221	101–250	120–280	141–310	163–341	185–374	209–407
30	23–117	37–143	51–171	68–198	85–227	103–257	123–287	144–318	166–350	189–383	213–417
31	24–120	37–148	53–175	69–204	87–233	106–263	126–294	147–326	169–359	193–392	217–427
32	24–124	38–152	54–180	71–209	89–239	108–270	128–302	150–334	173–367	197–401	222–436
33	25–127	39–156	55–185	72–215	90–246	110–277	131–309	153–342	176–376	200–411	226–446
34	26–130	40–160	56–190	73–221	92–252	112–284	134–316	156–350	180–384	204–420	230–456
35	26–134	41–164	57–195	75–226	94–258	114–291	136–324	159–358	183–393	208–429	234–466
36	27–137	42–168	58–200	76–232	96–264	117–297	139–331	162–366	186–402	212–438	238–476
37	28–140	43–172	60–204	78–237	98–270	119–304	141–339	165–374	190–410	216–447	242–486
38	28–144	44–176	61–209	79–243	100–276	121–311	144–346	168–382	193–419	219–457	247–495
39	29–147	45–180	62–214	81–248	102–282	123–318	147–353	171–390	197–427	223–466	251–505
40	29–151	46–184	63–219	82–254	103–289	126–324	149–361	174–398	200–436	227–475	255–515
41	30–154	46–189	65–223	84–259	105–295	128–331	152–368	177–406	203–445	231–484	259–525
42	31–157	47–193	66–228	85–265	107–301	130–338	155–375	180–414	207–453	234–494	263–535
43	31–161	48–197	67–233	87–270	109–307	133–344	157–383	183–422	210–462	238–503	268–544
44	32–164	49–201	68–238	88–276	111–313	135–351	160–390	186–430	214–470	242–512	272–554
45	32–168	50–205	69–243	90–281	113–319	137–358	162–398	189–438	217–479	246–521	276–564
46	33–171	51–209	71–247	91–287	115–325	139–365	165–405	192–446	220–488	250–530	280–574
47	34–174	52–213	72–252	93–292	117–331	142–371	168–412	195–454	224–496	253–540	284–584
48	34–178	53–217	73–257	95–297	118–338	144–378	170–420	198–462	227–505	257–549	289–593
49	35–181	54–221	74–262	96–303	120–344	146–385	173–427	201–470	231–513	261–558	293–603
50	36–184	55–225	76–266	98–308	122–350	148–392	176–434	204–478	234–522	265–567	297–613

N_2 \ N_1	15	16	17	18	19	20	21	22	23	24	25
4	125–175	141–195	159–215	177–237	197–259	218–282	239–307	262–332	285–359	310–386	335–415
5	128–187	145–207	163–228	182–250	202–273	223–297	245–322	267–349	291–376	316–404	342–433
6	132–198	149–219	168–240	187–263	207–287	228–312	250–338	274–364	298–392	323–421	349–451
7	136–209	154–230	172–253	192–276	212–301	234–326	256–353	280–380	305–408	330–438	357–468
8	140–220	158–242	177–265	197–289	218–314	240–340	263–367	287–395	311–425	337–455	364–486
9	144–231	163–253	182–277	202–302	223–328	246–354	269–382	293–411	319–440	345–471	372–503
10	149–241	167–265	187–289	208–314	229–341	252–368	275–397	300–426	326–456	352–488	380–520
11	153–252	172–276	192–301	213–327	235–354	258–382	282–411	307–441	333–472	360–504	388–537
12	157–263	177–287	197–313	218–340	241–367	264–396	289–425	314–456	340–488	368–520	396–554
13	162–273	181–299	202–325	224–352	247–380	271–409	295–440	321–471	348–503	376–536	404–571
14	166–284	186–310	208–336	230–364	253–393	277–423	302–454	328–486	355–519	383–553	413–587
15	**171–294**	191–321	213–348	235–377	259–406	283–437	309–468	335–501	363–534	391–569	421–604
16	175–305	**196–332**	218–360	241–389	265–419	290–450	315–483	342–516	370–550	399–585	429–621
17	180–315	201–343	**223–372**	246–402	271–432	296–464	322–497	350–530	378–565	407–601	437–638
18	184–326	206–354	228–384	**252–414**	277–445	302–478	329–511	357–545	385–581	415–617	446–654
19	189–336	211–365	234–395	258–426	**283–458**	309–491	336–525	364–560	393–596	423–633	454–671
20	193–347	216–376	239–407	263–439	289–471	**315–505**	343–539	371–575	401–611	431–649	463–687
21	198–357	220–388	244–419	269–451	295–484	322–518	**350–553**	378–590	408–627	439–665	471–704
22	202–368	225–399	250–430	275–463	301–497	328–532	356–568	**386–604**	416–642	447–681	480–720
23	207–378	230–410	255–442	280–476	307–510	335–545	363–582	393–619	**424–657**	455–697	488–737
24	211–389	235–421	260–454	286–488	313–523	341–559	370–596	400–634	431–673	**464–712**	497–753
25	216–399	240–432	265–466	292–500	319–536	348–572	377–610	408–648	439–688	472–728	**505–770**
26	220–410	245–443	271–477	298–512	325–549	354–586	384–624	415–663	447–703	480–744	514–786
27	225–420	250–454	276–489	303–525	332–561	361–599	391–638	422–678	455–718	488–760	522–803
28	229–431	255–465	281–501	309–537	338–574	367–613	398–652	430–692	462–734	496–776	531–819
29	234–441	260–476	287–512	315–549	344–587	374–626	405–666	437–707	470–749	504–792	540–835
30	239–451	265–487	292–524	321–561	350–600	380–640	412–680	444–722	478–764	513–807	548–852
31	243–462	270–498	298–535	326–574	356–613	387–653	419–694	452–736	486–779	521–823	557–868
32	248–472	275–509	303–547	332–586	362–626	394–666	426–708	459–751	494–794	529–839	565–885
33	252–483	280–520	308–559	338–598	368–639	400–680	433–722	467–765	501–810	537–855	574–901
34	257–493	285–531	314–570	344–610	375–651	407–693	440–736	474–780	509–825	545–871	583–917
35	261–504	290–542	319–582	349–623	381–664	413–707	447–750	481–795	517–840	554–886	591–934
36	266–514	295–553	324–594	355–635	387–677	420–720	454–764	489–809	525–855	562–902	600–950
37	270–525	300–564	330–605	361–647	393–690	426–734	461–778	496–824	533–870	570–918	608–967
38	275–535	305–575	335–617	367–659	399–703	433–747	468–792	504–838	540–886	578–934	617–983
39	280–545	310–586	340–629	372–672	406–715	440–760	475–806	511–853	548–901	587–949	626–999
40	284–556	314–598	346–640	378–684	412–728	446–774	482–820	518–868	556–916	595–965	634–1016
41	289–566	319–609	351–652	384–696	418–741	453–787	489–834	526–882	564–931	603–981	643–1032
42	293–577	324–620	357–663	390–708	424–754	459–801	496–848	533–897	572–946	611–997	652–1048
43	298–587	329–631	362–675	396–720	430–767	466–814	503–862	541–911	580–961	620–1012	660–1065
44	303–597	334–642	367–687	401–733	437–779	473–827	510–876	548–926	587–977	628–1028	669–1081
45	307–608	339–653	373–698	407–745	443–792	479–841	517–890	556–940	595–992	636–1044	678–1097
46	312–618	344–664	378–710	413–757	449–805	486–854	524–904	563–955	603–1007	644–1060	687–1113
47	316–629	349–675	384–721	419–769	455–818	493–867	531–918	570–970	611–1022	653–1075	695–1130
48	321–639	354–686	389–733	425–781	461–831	499–881	538–932	578–984	619–1037	661–1091	704–1146
49	325–650	359–697	394–745	430–794	468–843	506–894	545–946	585–999	627–1052	669–1107	713–1162
50	330–660	364–708	400–756	436–806	474–856	512–908	552–960	593–1013	635–1067	677–1123	721–1179

1) The lower exact limits are based on data kindly supplied by Prof. C. WHITE, Department of Public Health, Yale University, New Haven, Connecticut, and published in part in *Biometrics*, **8**, 33 (1952). *2)* Based on the normal approximation with empirical continuity correction.

Distribution-Free Tolerance Limits*

(Values in *italics* are approximate)

The table gives the minimum size N of the sample for which it can be assumed with a confidence probability of β_t that 100 β_p% of the *values* in the population

($x = 0$) lie either above the lowest or below the highest value of the sample;

($x = 1$) lie between the lowest and highest values of the sample;

($x = 2$) lie between the second lowest and second highest values of the sample, etc.

Example: How large must a sample be if, with a confidence probability of $\beta_t = 0.99$, $100\,\beta_p = 95\%$ of the values in the population

(a) are to lie either above the lowest or below the highest value of the sample? With $x = 0$ the table gives $N = 90$;

(b) are to lie between the fifth lowest and fifth highest values of the sample? With $x = 5$ the table gives $N = 371$.

$\beta_t = 0.999$

x \ β_p	0.999	0.990	0.950	0.90	0.80	0.70	0.60	0.50	0.40	0.30
0	6 905	688	135	66	31	20	14	10	8	6
1	9 230	919	181	88	42	27	19	14	11	9
2	13 058	1301	256	126	60	38	27	21	16	13
3	16 450	1640	324	159	77	49	35	27	21	17
4	19 620	1957	387	190	92	59	43	33	26	21
5	22 651	2260	447	220	107	69	50	38	30	25
6	25 583	2552	505	249	121	78	57	44	35	28
7		2838	562	277	135	87	63	49	39	32
8		*3116*	617	305	148	96	70	54	43	35
9		*3390*	672	332	162	105	76	59	47	39
10		*3661*	*725*	359	175	113	83	64	51	42

$\beta_t = 0.990$

x \ β_p	0.999	0.990	0.950	0.90	0.80	0.70	0.60	0.50	0.40	0.30
0	4 603	459	90	44	21	13	10	7	6	4
1	6 636	661	130	64	31	20	14	10	8	6
2	10 042	1001	197	97	46	30	21	16	13	10
3	13 105	1307	259	128	62	40	29	22	18	14
4	15 996	1596	316	156	76	49	36	28	22	18
5	18 779	1874	371	184	90	58	42	33	26	21
6	21 486	2145	425	210	103	67	49	38	30	25
7		2409	478	237	116	75	55	43	34	28
8		*2668*	530	262	128	83	61	47	38	31
9		*2924*	581	288	141	92	67	52	42	35
10		*3178*	*630*	313	153	100	73	57	46	38

$\beta_t = 0.980$

x \ β_p	0.999	0.990	0.950	0.90	0.80	0.70	0.60	0.50	0.40	0.30
0	3 911	390	77	38	18	11	8	6	5	4
1	5 832	581	115	56	27	17	12	9	7	6
2	9 081	906	179	88	43	27	19	15	12	9
3	12 024	1200	238	117	57	37	27	21	16	13
4	14 813	1478	293	145	71	46	34	26	21	17
5	17 506	1747	347	172	84	55	40	31	25	20
6	20 131	2010	399	198	97	63	46	36	29	24
7		2267	450	223	109	71	52	40	33	27
8			501	248	122	79	58	45	37	30
9			551	273	134	87	64	50	40	33
10				297	146	95	70	55	44	37

$\beta_t = 0.950$

x \ β_p	0.999	0.990	0.950	0.90	0.80	0.70	0.60	0.50	0.40	0.30
0	2 995	299	59	29	14	9	6	5	4	3
1	4 742	473	93	45	22	14	10	7	6	5
2	7 751	773	153	75	36	23	17	13	10	8
3	10 511	1049	208	103	50	33	24	18	15	12
4	13 146	1313	261	129	63	41	30	24	19	16
5	15 703	1568	312	154	76	50	36	28	23	19
6	18 205	1818	362	179	88	58	42	33	27	22
7		2064	410	204	100	65	48	38	30	25
8		*2305*	459	228	112	73	54	42	34	28
9		*2545*	507	252	124	81	60	47	38	32
10		*2783*	*553*	275	135	89	65	51	42	35

$\beta_t = 0.900$

x \ β_p	0.999	0.990	0.950	0.90	0.80	0.70	0.60	0.50	0.40	0.30
0	2 302	230	45	22	11	7	5	4	3	2
1	3 889	388	77	38	18	12	8	6	5	4
2	6 679	666	132	65	32	20	14	11	9	7
3	9 273	926	184	91	45	29	21	17	13	11
4	11 770	1176	234	116	57	38	28	21	17	14
5	14 204	1419	283	140	69	45	33	26	21	18
6	16 596	1658	330	164	81	53	39	31	25	21
7		1894	377	188	92	61	45	35	29	24
8		*2126*	424	211	104	68	50	40	32	27
9		*2347*	470	234	115	76	56	44	36	30
10		*2586*	*514*	256	127	83	61	48	40	33

Wilcoxon's Test for Pair Differences[1]

n = number of pairs. For explanation see page 191.

n	$2\alpha \leqq 0.10$	$2\alpha \leqq 0.05$	$2\alpha \leqq 0.02$	$2\alpha \leqq 0.01$
5	0– 15	–	–	–
6	2– 19	0– 21	–	–
7	3– 25	2– 26	0– 28	–
8	5– 31	3– 33	1– 35	0– 36
9	8– 37	5– 40	3– 42	1– 44
10	10– 45	8– 47	5– 50	3– 52
11	13– 53	10– 56	7– 59	5– 61
12	17– 61	13– 65	9– 69	7– 71
13	21– 70	17– 74	12– 79	9– 82
14	25– 80	21– 84	15– 90	12– 93
15	30– 90	25– 95	19–101	15–105
16	35–101	29–107	23–113	19–117
17	41–112	34–119	28–125	23–130
18	47–124	40–131	32–139	27–144
19	53–137	46–144	37–153	32–158
20	60–150	52–158	43–167	37–173
21	67–164	58–173	49–182	42–189
22	75–178	66–187	55–198	48–205
23	83–193	73–203	62–214	54–222
24	91–209	81–219	69–231	61–239
25	100–225	89–236	76–249	68–257

Poisson Distribution

Significance limits* for x when λ is given. **For explanation see page 188**

λ	$2\alpha \leqq 0.05$	$2\alpha \leqq 0.01$	λ	$2\alpha \leqq 0.05$	$2\alpha \leqq 0.01$
0	–	–	50	36– 65	32– 70
1	•– 4	•– 5	51	36– 66	33– 71
2	•– 6	•– 7	52	37– 68	33– 72
3	•– 8	•– 9	53	38– 69	34– 74
4	0– 9	•–11	54	39– 70	35– 75
5	0–11	•–13	55	40– 71	36– 76
6	1–12	0–14	56	41– 72	37– 77
7	1–14	0–16	57	42– 73	38– 78
8	2–15	1–17	58	43– 74	38– 80
9	3–16	1–19	59	43– 76	39– 81
10	3–18	2–20	60	44– 77	40– 82
11	4–19	3–21	61	45– 78	41– 83
12	5–20	3–23	62	46– 79	42– 84
13	5–21	4–24	63	47– 80	43– 85
14	6–23	4–25	64	48– 81	43– 86
15	7–24	5–27	65	49– 82	44– 88
16	8–25	6–28	66	50– 83	45– 89
17	8–27	6–29	67	50– 84	46– 90
18	9–28	7–31	68	51– 86	47– 91
19	10–29	8–32	69	52– 87	48– 92
20	11–30	9–33	70	53– 88	48– 93
21	12–31	9–35	71	54– 89	49– 95
22	12–33	10–36	72	55– 90	50– 96
23	13–34	11–37	73	56– 91	51– 97
24	14–35	11–39	74	57– 92	52– 98
25	15–36	12–40	75	58– 93	53– 99
26	16–37	13–41	76	58– 95	54–101
27	16–39	14–42	77	59– 96	54–102
28	17–40	14–44	78	60– 97	55–103
29	18–41	15–45	79	61– 98	56–104
30	19–42	16–46	80	62– 99	57–105
31	20–43	17–47	81	63–100	58–106
32	20–45	17–48	82	64–101	59–107
33	21–46	18–50	83	65–102	60–109
34	22–47	19–51	84	66–103	60–110
35	23–48	20–52	85	66–105	61–111
36	24–49	21–53	86	67–106	62–112
37	25–50	21–55	87	68–107	63–113
38	25–52	22–56	88	69–108	64–114
39	26–53	23–57	89	70–109	65–115
40	27–54	24–58	90	71–110	66–117
41	28–55	24–59	91	72–111	66–118
42	29–56	25–61	92	73–112	67–119
43	30–57	26–62	93	74–113	68–120
44	30–58	27–63	94	74–114	69–121
45	31–60	28–64	95	75–116	70–122
46	32–61	29–65	96	76–117	71–123
47	33–62	29–67	97	77–118	72–125
48	34–63	30–68	98	78–119	72–126
49	35–64	31–69	99	79–120	73–127
50	36–65	32–70	100	80–121	74–128

1) Values (rounded off outwards) are from Tukey, J. W., *Memorandum Report 17*, Statistical Research Group, Princeton University, 1949. Reprinted by kind permission of the author.

Runs: Significance Limits for the Total Number *I*[1]

For explanation see below
The lack of a significant limit on one side is indicated by a period, on both sides by a single dash

$N_1 = N_2 = ½N \leqq 100$

½N	2α = 0.10	2α = 0.05	2α = 0.02	2α = 0.01
4	2– 8	–	–	–
5	3– 9	2– 10	2– 10	–
6	3– 11	3– 11	2– 12	2– 12
7	4– 12	3– 13	3– 13	3– 13
8	5– 13	4– 14	4– 14	3– 15
9	6– 14	5– 15	4– 16	4– 16
10	6– 16	6– 16	5– 17	5– 17
11	7– 17	7– 17	6– 18	5– 19
12	8– 18	7– 19	7– 19	6– 20
13	9– 19	8– 20	7– 21	7– 21
14	10– 20	9– 21	8– 22	7– 23
15	11– 21	10– 22	9– 23	8– 24
16	11– 23	11– 23	10– 24	9– 25
17	12– 24	11– 25	10– 26	10– 26
18	13– 25	12– 26	11– 27	11– 27
19	14– 26	13– 27	12– 28	11– 29
20	15– 27	14– 28	13– 29	12– 30
21	16– 28	15– 29	14– 30	13– 31
22	17– 29	16– 30	14– 32	14– 32
23	17– 31	16– 32	15– 33	14– 34
24	18– 32	17– 33	16– 34	15– 35
25	19– 33	18– 34	17– 35	16– 36
26	20– 34	19– 35	18– 36	17– 37
27	21– 35	20– 36	19– 37	18– 38
28	22– 36	21– 37	19– 39	18– 40
29	23– 37	22– 38	20– 40	19– 41
30	24– 38	22– 40	21– 41	20– 42
31	25– 39	23– 41	22– 42	21– 43
32	25– 41	24– 42	23– 43	22– 44
33	26– 42	25– 43	24– 44	23– 45
34	27– 43	26– 44	24– 46	23– 47
35	28– 44	27– 45	25– 47	24– 48
36	29– 45	28– 46	26– 48	25– 49
37	30– 46	29– 47	27– 49	26– 50
38	31– 47	30– 48	28– 50	27– 51
39	32– 48	30– 50	29– 51	28– 52
40	33– 49	31– 51	30– 52	29– 53
41	34– 50	32– 52	31– 53	29– 55
42	35– 51	33– 53	31– 54	30– 56
43	35– 53	34– 54	32– 56	31– 57
44	36– 54	35– 55	33– 57	32– 58
45	37– 55	36– 56	34– 58	33– 59
46	38– 56	37– 57	35– 59	34– 60
47	39– 57	38– 58	36– 60	35– 61
48	40– 58	38– 60	37– 61	36– 63
49	41– 59	39– 61	38– 62	36– 64
50	42– 60	40– 62	38– 64	37– 65
51	43– 61	41– 63	39– 65	38– 66
52	44– 62	42– 64	40– 66	39– 67
53	45– 63	43– 65	41– 67	40– 68
54	45– 65	44– 66	42– 68	41– 69
55	46– 66	45– 67	43– 69	42– 70
56	47– 67	46– 68	44– 70	42– 72
57	48– 68	47– 69	45– 71	43– 73
58	49– 69	47– 71	46– 72	44– 74
59	50– 70	48– 72	46– 74	45– 75
60	51– 71	49– 73	47– 75	46– 76
61	52– 72	50– 74	48– 76	47– 77
62	53– 73	51– 75	49– 77	48– 78
63	54– 74	52– 76	50– 78	49– 79
64	55– 75	53– 77	51– 79	49– 81
65	56– 76	54– 78	52– 80	50– 82
66	57– 77	55– 79	53– 81	51– 83
67	58– 78	56– 80	54– 82	52– 84
68	58– 80	57– 81	54– 84	53– 85
69	59– 81	58– 82	55– 85	54– 86
70	60– 82	58– 84	56– 86	55– 87
71	61– 83	59– 85	57– 87	56– 88
72	62– 84	60– 86	58– 88	57– 89
73	63– 85	61– 87	59– 89	57– 91
74	64– 86	62– 88	60– 90	58– 92
75	65– 87	63– 89	61– 91	59– 93
76	66– 88	64– 90	62– 92	60– 94
77	67– 89	65– 91	63– 93	61– 95
78	68– 90	66– 92	64– 94	62– 96
79	69– 91	67– 93	64– 96	63– 97
80	70– 92	68– 94	65– 97	64– 98
81	71– 93	69– 95	66– 98	65– 99
82	71– 95	69– 97	67– 99	66–100
83	72– 96	70– 98	68–100	66–102
84	73– 97	71– 99	69–101	67–103
85	74– 98	72–100	70–102	68–104
86	75– 99	73–101	71–103	69–105
87	76–100	74–102	72–104	70–106
88	77–101	75–103	73–105	71–107
89	78–102	76–104	74–106	72–108
90	79–103	77–105	74–108	73–109
91	80–104	78–106	75–109	74–110
92	81–105	79–107	76–110	75–111
93	82–106	80–108	77–111	75–113
94	83–107	81–109	78–112	76–114
95	84–108	82–110	79–113	77–115
96	85–109	82–112	80–114	78–116
97	86–110	83–113	81–115	79–117
98	87–111	84–114	82–116	80–118
99	87–113	85–115	83–117	81–119
100	88–114	86–116	84–118	82–120

$N_1 < N_2,\ N_2 \leqq 20$

N_2	2α = 0.10	2α = 0.05	2α = 0.02	2α = 0.01
$N_1 = 2$				
2	–	–	–	–
3	–	–	–	–
4	–	–	–	–
5	–	–	–	–
6	–	–	–	–
7	–	–	–	–
8	2– •	–	–	–
9	2– •	–	–	–
10	2– •	–	–	–
11	2– •	–	–	–
12	2– •	2– •	–	–
13	2– •	2– •	–	–
14	2– •	2– •	–	–
15	2– •	2– •	–	–
16	2– •	2– •	–	–
17	2– •	2– •	–	–
18	2– •	2– •	–	–
19	2– •	2– •	2– •	–
20	2– •	2– •	2– •	–
$N_1 = 3$				
3	–	–	–	–
4	•– 7	–	–	–
5	2– •	–	–	–
6	2– •	2– •	–	–
7	2– •	2– •	–	–
8	2– •	2– •	–	–
9	2– •	2– •	2– •	–
10	3– •	2– •	2– •	–
11	3– •	2– •	2– •	–
12	3– •	2– •	2– •	2– •
13	3– •	2– •	2– •	2– •
14	3– •	2– •	2– •	2– •
15	3– •	3– •	2– •	2– •
16	3– •	3– •	2– •	2– •
17	3– •	3– •	2– •	2– •
18	3– •	3– •	2– •	2– •
19	3– •	3– •	2– •	2– •
20	3– •	3– •	2– •	2– •
$N_1 = 4$				
4	2– 8	–	–	–
5	2– 9	2– 9	•– 9	–
6	3– 9	2– 9	2– •	–
7	3– 9	2– •	2– •	–
8	3– •	3– •	2– •	2– •
9	3– •	3– •	2– •	2– •
10	3– •	3– •	2– •	2– •
11	3– •	3– •	2– •	2– •
12	4– •	3– •	3– •	2– •
13	4– •	3– •	3– •	2– •
14	4– •	3– •	3– •	2– •
15	4– •	3– •	3– •	3– •
16	4– •	4– •	3– •	3– •
17	4– •	4– •	3– •	3– •
18	4– •	4– •	3– •	3– •
19	4– •	4– •	3– •	3– •
20	4– •	4– •	3– •	3– •
$N_1 = 5$				
5	3– 9	2–10	2–10	–
6	3–10	3–10	2–11	2– •
7	3–10	3–11	2–11	2–11
8	3–11	3–11	2– •	2– •
9	4–11	3– •	3– •	2– •
10	4–11	3– •	3– •	3– •
11	4– •	4– •	3– •	3– •
12	4– •	4– •	3– •	3– •
13	4– •	4– •	3– •	3– •
14	5– •	4– •	3– •	3– •
15	5– •	4– •	4– •	3– •
16	5– •	4– •	4– •	3– •
17	5– •	4– •	4– •	3– •
18	5– •	5– •	4– •	4– •
19	5– •	5– •	4– •	4– •
20	5– •	5– •	4– •	4– •
$N_1 = 6$				
6	3–11	3–11	2–12	2–12
7	4–11	3–12	3–12	2–13
8	4–12	3–12	3–13	3–13
9	4–12	4–13	3–13	3– •
10	5–12	4–13	3– •	3– •
11	5–13	4–13	4– •	3– •
12	5–13	4–13	4– •	3– •
13	5–13	5– •	4– •	3– •
14	5–13	5– •	4– •	4– •
15	6– •	5– •	4– •	4– •
16	6– •	5– •	4– •	4– •
17	6– •	5– •	5– •	4– •
18	6– •	5– •	5– •	4– •
19	6– •	6– •	5– •	4– •
20	6– •	6– •	5– •	4– •
$N_1 = 7$				
7	4–12	3–13	3–13	3–13
8	4–13	4–13	3–14	3–14
9	5–13	4–14	4–14	3–15
10	5–13	5–14	4–15	3–15
11	5–14	5–14	4–15	4–15
12	6–14	5–14	4–15	4– •
13	6–14	5–15	5– •	4– •
14	6–14	5–15	5– •	4– •
15	6–15	6–15	5– •	4– •
16	6–15	6– •	5– •	5– •
17	7–15	6– •	5– •	5– •
18	7–15	6– •	5– •	5– •
19	7–15	6– •	6– •	5– •
20	7–15	6– •	6– •	5– •
$N_1 = 8$				
8	5–13	4–14	4–14	3–15
9	5–14	5–14	4–15	3–15
10	6–14	5–15	4–15	4–16
11	6–15	5–15	5–16	4–16
12	6–15	6–16	5–16	4–17
13	6–15	6–16	5–17	5–17
14	7–16	6–16	5–17	5–17
15	7–16	6–16	5–17	5– •
16	7–16	6–17	6–17	5– •
17	7–16	7–17	6– •	5– •
18	8–16	7–17	6– •	6– •
19	8–16	7–17	6– •	6– •
20	8–17	7–17	6– •	6– •
$N_1 = 9$				
9	6–14	5–15	4–16	4–16
10	6–15	5–16	5–16	4–17
11	6–15	6–16	5–17	5–17
12	7–16	6–16	5–17	5–18
13	7–16	6–17	6–18	5–18
14	7–17	7–17	6–18	5–18
15	8–17	7–18	6–18	6–19
16	8–17	7–18	6–18	6–19
17	8–17	7–18	7–19	6–19
18	8–18	8–18	7–19	6– •
19	8–18	8–18	7–19	6– •
20	9–18	8–18	7–19	7– •
$N_1 = 10$				
10	6–16	6–16	5–17	5–17
11	7–16	6–17	5–18	5–18
12	7–17	7–17	6–18	5–19
13	8–17	7–18	6–19	5–19
14	8–17	7–18	6–19	6–19
15	8–18	7–18	7–19	6–20
16	8–18	8–19	7–20	6–20
17	9–18	8–19	7–20	7–20
18	9–19	8–19	7–20	7–21
19	9–19	8–20	8–20	7–21
20	9–19	9–20	8–20	7–21
$N_1 = 11$				
11	7–17	7–17	6–18	5–19
12	8–17	7–18	6–19	6–19
13	8–18	7–19	6–19	6–20
14	8–18	8–19	7–20	6–20
15	9–19	8–19	7–20	7–21
16	9–19	8–20	7–21	7–21
17	9–19	9–20	8–21	7–22
18	10–20	9–20	8–21	7–22
19	10–20	9–21	8–22	8–22
20	10–20	9–21	8–22	8–22
$N_1 = 12$				
12	8–18	7–19	7–19	6–20
13	9–18	8–19	7–20	6–21
14	9–19	8–20	7–21	7–21
15	9–19	8–20	8–21	7–22
16	10–20	9–21	8–22	7–22
17	10–20	9–21	8–22	8–22
18	10–21	9–21	8–22	8–23
19	10–21	10–22	9–23	8–23
20	11–21	10–22	9–23	8–23
$N_1 = 13$				
13	9–19	8–20	7–21	7–21
14	9–20	9–20	8–21	7–22
15	10–20	9–21	8–22	7–22
16	10–21	9–21	8–22	8–23
17	10–21	10–22	9–23	8–23
18	11–21	10–22	9–23	8–24
19	11–22	10–23	9–24	9–24
20	11–22	10–23	10–24	9–24
$N_1 = 14$				
14	10–20	9–21	8–22	7–23
15	10–21	9–22	8–23	8–23
16	11–21	10–22	9–23	8–24
17	11–22	10–23	9–24	8–24
18	11–22	10–23	9–24	9–25
19	12–23	11–23	10–24	9–25
20	12–23	11–24	10–25	9–25
$N_1 = 15$				
15	11–21	10–22	9–23	8–24
16	11–22	10–23	9–24	9–24
17	11–22	11–23	10–24	9–25
18	12–23	11–24	10–25	9–25
19	12–23	11–24	10–25	10–26
20	12–24	12–25	11–26	10–26
$N_1 = 16$				
16	11–23	11–23	10–24	9–25
17	12–23	11–24	10–25	9–26
18	12–24	11–25	10–26	10–26
19	13–24	12–25	11–26	10–27
20	13–25	12–25	11–26	10–27
$N_1 = 17$				
17	12–24	11–25	10–26	10–26
18	13–24	12–25	11–26	10–27
19	13–25	12–26	11–27	10–27
20	13–25	13–26	11–27	11–28
$N_1 = 18$				
18	13–25	12–26	11–27	11–27
19	14–25	13–26	12–27	11–28
20	14–26	13–27	12–28	11–29
$N_1 = 19$				
19	14–26	13–27	12–28	11–29
20	14–27	13–27	12–29	12–29

Explanation

(Time)	1	2	3	4	5	6	7	8	9	10
Series (I)	A	B	A	A	A	B	B	A	B	A
Series (II)	A	B	A	B	A	A	B	A	B	A
Series (III)	A	A	A	A	A	A	B	B	B	B

Each of the series (I), (II), (III) has a size $N = 10$ and contains $N_1 = 4$ *B*'s and $N_2 = 6$ *A*'s (provided that $N = N_1 + N_2 < 40$, the smaller number is denoted by N_1). In these series the underscored letters in each case form a run. The total number of runs *I* is 7 in series (I), 9 in series (II), 2 in series (III).

The table gives the significance limits for the estimate *I* (total | N_1, N_2) of the expectation **I** (total) under the condition (N_1, N_2).

(a) If the left limit is *attained*, then *I* is significantly less than **I** (significance probability α) or *I* differs significantly from **I** (significance probability 2α).

(b) If the right limit is *attained*, then *I* significantly exceeds **I** (significance probability α) or *I* differs significantly from **I** (significance probability 2α).

(c) If *I* lies between the limits and *attains neither*, then the null hypothesis cannot be rejected. See also pages 193 and 194.

1) Values from SWED and EISENHART, *Ann. math. Statist.*, **14**, 66 (1943). Reprinted by kind permission of the authors and publishers.

The table[1] gives the probability α that for the size of sample given in the table the longest run above or below the median will attain or exceed the length *l*. The choice of which side of the median is to be tested must be made beforehand.

Example: Size of sample = 28. Longest run above = 4. Result: $0.50 < \alpha < 0.90$.

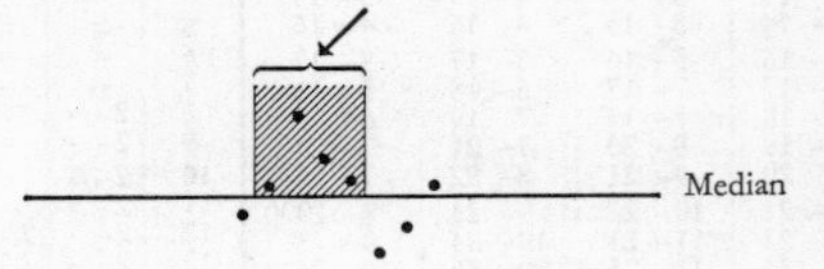

l	α ≦ 0.01	α ≦ 0.10	α ≦ 0.50	α ≦ 0.90	α ≦ 0.99
1	2	2	2	2	2
2	4	4	6	8	12
3	6	6	12	22	38
4	8	10	22	54	100
5	10	16	46	116	230
6	14	26	92	260	490
7	18	44	182	530	1 044
8	26	78	360	1 104	2 140
9	38	142	714	2 240	4 370
10	56	256	1 424	4 530	8 980
11	86	480	2 850	9 190	18 240
12	140	930	5 680	18 540	37 200
13	234	1 838	11 330	37 600	75 500
14	410	3 630	22 700	75 700	151 700
15	748	7 160	45 300	151 700	303 000
16	1 446	14 190	90 600	303 000	607 000
17	2 830	28 100	181 200	607 000	1 214 000
18	5 530	56 100	362 000	1 214 000	2 430 000
19	10 860	117 300	725 000	2 430 000	4 850 000
20	21 500	235 000	1450 000	4 850 000	9 710 000

The table[1] gives the probability α that for the size of sample given in the table the *shorter* of the two runs which are respectively the longest above and the longest below the median will attain or exceed the length *l*.

Example: Size of sample = 28. Longest run above = 4, below = 9. Result: $0.10 < \alpha < 0.50$.

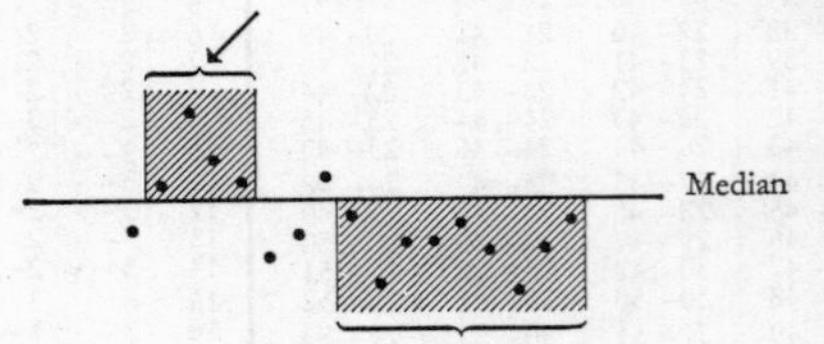

l	α ≦ 0.01	α ≦ 0.10	α ≦ 0.50	α ≦ 0.90	α ≦ 0.99
1	2	2	2	2	2
2	4	4	6	10	14
3	6	8	14	26	44
4	8	14	30	68	116
5	12	26	68	152	252
6	20	50	140	322	552
7	34	98	290	676	1 164
8	62	194	596	1 390	2 390
9	116	390	1 208	2 830	4 930
10	216	782	2 440	5 650	10 140
11	446	1 182	4 910	11 750	20 700
12	884	2 360	9 840	23 800	42 500
13	1 762	4 720	19 890	48 600	86 700
14	3 510	9 450	39 900	98 600	174 200
15	6 990	18 900	80 500	197 300	348 000
16	13 930	37 800	161 300	395 000	697 000
17	27 900	75 600	323 000	789 000	1 394 000
18	55 500	151 200	645 000	1 578 000	2 790 000
19	111 000	302 000	1 290 000	3 160 000	5 570 000
20	222 000	605 000	2 580 000	6 310 000	11 150 000

The table[1] gives the probability α that for the size of sample given in the table the *longer* of the two runs which are respectively the longest above and the longest below the median will attain or exceed the length *l*.

Example: Size of sample = 28. Longest run above = 4, below = 9. Result: $\alpha < 0.01$.

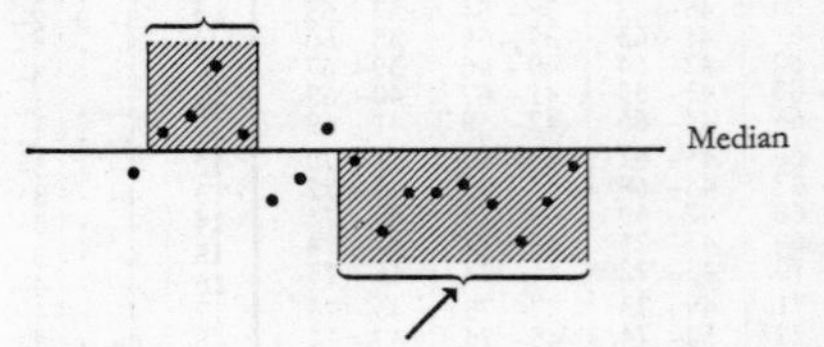

l	α ≦ 0.01	α ≦ 0.10	α ≦ 0.50	α ≦ 0.90	α ≦ 0.99
1	2	2	2	2	2
2	4	4	4	8	10
3	6	6	8	16	28
4	8	8	16	36	64
5	10	14	30	76	136
6	12	20	58	152	282
7	16	32	106	296	568
8	22	52	200	580	1 150
9	32	86	388	1 174	2 310
10	42	150	758	2 350	4 640
11	62	262	1 488	4 720	9 330
12	94	500	2 920	9 460	18 730
13	156	962	5 860	10 660	37 700
14	256	1 876	11 250	21 300	75 700
15	418	3 670	22 600	42 600	151 600
16	766	7 330	45 200	85 300	303 000
17	1 472	14 090	90 100	170 500	606 000
18	2 860	27 900	180 300	341 000	1 213 000
19	5 570	55 500	361 000	682 000	2 430 000
20	10 860	111 100	721 000	1 364 000	4 850 000

The table[1] gives the probability α that for the size of sample given in the table the *shorter* of the two runs which are respectively the longest run above and the longest run below a maximal cut will attain or exceed the length *l*. The maximal cut is so made that this particular run is maximalized.

Example: Size of sample = 28. Longest run above the maximal cut = 8, below = 9. Result: $\alpha < 0.01$.

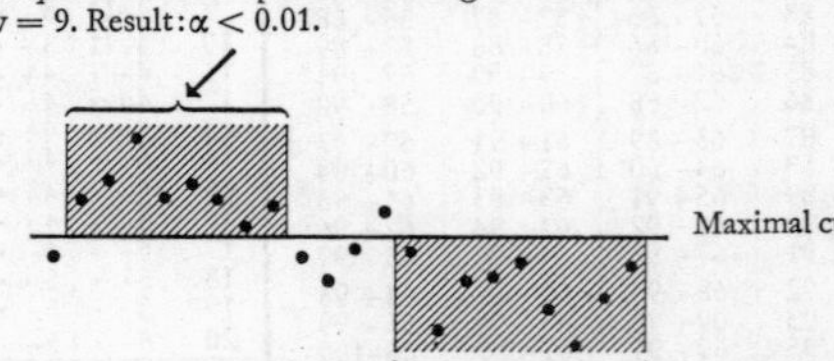

l	α ≦ 0.01	α ≦ 0.10	α ≦ 0.50	α ≦ 0.90	α ≦ 0.99
1	2	2	2	2	2
2	4	4	6	8	12
3	6	8	12	22	34
4	8	12	22	48	76
5	12	18	46	96	162
6	16	34	86	192	380
7	24	58	166	382	668
8	38	108	324	760	1 342
9	66	204	638	1 518	2 690
10	118	400	1 266	3 030	5 410
11	228	790	2 530	6 070	10 870
12	444	1 568	5 050	12 130	21 500
13	878	3 130	10 070	24 300	43 100
14	1 750	6 220	20 100	48 500	86 200
15	3 480	12 490	40 300	97 000	172 300
16	6 790	25 000	80 600	194 100	345 000
17	13 860	49 900	161 100	388 000	689 000
18	27 700	99 900	322 000	776 000	1 379 000
19	55 400	199 800	644 000	1 553 000	2 760 000
20	110 800	400 000	1 289 000	3 110 000	5 510 000

The table[2,3] gives the probability α that for the size of sample given in the table at least one run up or down of length *l* or longer will occur.

Example: Size of sample = 28. Up-run to be tested = 5. Result: $0.05 < \alpha < 0.10$.

l	α ≦ 0.01	α ≦ 0.05	α ≦ 0.10	α ≦ 0.90	α ≦ 0.95	α ≦ 0.99
2	—	—	—	7	8	12
3	—	—	4	32	40	61
4	—	7	11	162	210	321
5	9	26	48	964	1 253	1 923
6	34	153	309	6 637	8 633	13 268
7	234	1 170	2 396	52 229	67 950	104 452
8	2 034	10 348	21 248	464 209	603 947	928 410
9	20 067	102 382	210 291	4 595 600	5 979 012	9 191 191
10	218 833	1 116 808	2 294 003	50 133 734	65 225 489	100 267 459

Illustration of up- and down-runs:

Time sequence:	1	2	3	4	5	6
Values:	1.14	1.17	1.20	1.19	1.21	1.16
	up (1–3)			down (3–4)	up (4–5)	down (5–6)
Length *l*:	3			1	1	1

1) Values from Olmstead, P.S., *Runs Determined in a Sample by an Arbitrary Cut*, Bell Telephone System Technical Publications, Monograph 2937, New York, 1958. *2)* Values of *l* from 2 to 5 from Olmstead, P.S., *Distribution of Sample Arrangements for Runs Up and Down*, Bell Telephone System Technical Publications, Monograph 2289, New York, 1946; and *Ann. math. Statist.*, **17**, 24 (1946). Reprinted by kind permission of the author, publishers and Bell Telephone Laboratories, Inc., New York. *3)* Values of *l* from 6 to 10 calculated with Poisson approximation by the editors of these *Scientific Tables*.

Random Numbers[1]

72137	73850	32733	35321	80647	39713	61060	57865	88049	20557	43375	50914	83628	73935	72502	48174	62551	96122	22375	96488
04254	60099	50584	10961	57642	19101	30613	01549	96531	83936	45842	78222	88481	44933	12839	20750	47116	58973	99018	22769
48083	50731	81250	57995	41467	29834	08059	22945	72193	36077	82577	16210	76092	87730	90049	02115	37096	20505	91937	69776
16602	26772	89693	92558	38394	84119	68486	17622	30953	78267	31568	58297	88922	50436	86135	42726	54307	29170	13045	65527
29910	55480	47184	79775	09779	08718	45822	17643	63252	00232	98059	07255	90786	95246	15280	61692	45137	17539	31799	64780
77708	83761	89238	86521	82711	79266	47763	26173	36183	65869	64355	91271	49295	98354	28005	69792	01480	51557	70726	35862
90715	65115	12870	89922	24926	44062	94896	97561	96490	35454	51623	98381	11055	32951	28363	16451	67912	66404	76254	75495
79666	48119	38525	82189	34921	49838	47558	92343	47408	99542	44247	12762	54488	74321	36224	95619	16238	25374	13653	25345
53294	49761	76235	55814	29900	03796	73326	94291	10739	36087	32326	52225	72447	77804	57045	27552	72387	34001	83792	66764
44422	78305	76369	20601	39701	80769	17322	78280	42376	64899	62390	68375	42921	28545	33167	85710	11035	40171	04840	69848
12601	54432	65017	91131	50515	97477	80691	31834	32401	11994	97820	06653	27477	61364	22681	02280	53815	47479	44017	37563
65664	73669	24910	25458	23699	86413	19985	49355	24358	02915	81553	92012	50435	73814	96290	86827	81430	45597	82296	28947
18363	66515	23098	22384	87756	66396	63646	50963	99099	62895	09202	48494	95974	33534	94657	71126	71770	16092	03942	90111
00491	53688	72033	68063	86104	90576	04119	65531	30304	39202	82110	82254	03669	03281	11613	36336	98297	48100	71594	52667
02878	83197	94318	47901	85252	91124	32939	75043	40325	53252	18175	09457	83810	46392	02705	85591	33192	65127	80852	42030
79920	22780	43100	83886	26378	66010	00020	80666	66861	17820	50756	80608	35695	72641	26306	76298	32532	22644	96853	18610
97556	54260	42361	12741	56996	48177	85725	36668	45531	85245	12710	60264	74650	92126	08152	32147	17457	56298	48964	64733
79435	52143	12322	12254	04314	98550	58315	78036	24355	85822	44424	88508	66190	74060	93206	92840	44833	81146	64060	62975
93903	78220	09178	33676	58996	78675	11648	96220	54127	24804	24720	66501	74157	42246	41688	72835	87258	89384	11251	34329
04758	50961	90230	72006	24268	77817	10524	60304	79352	31942	85419	93017	28087	78323	77109	56832	78400	24190	37978	85863
53841	28758	93442	42983	25254	96336	16570	89358	36619	72838	10933	99964	13468	17211	48046	51122	92668	96750	11139	06275
07626	78473	17708	59059	33584	52451	11575	55992	83228	38546	49559	71671	53603	24491	57570	90789	32932	67449	05115	45941
40645	27008	16341	05870	42604	79286	08720	13175	89573	38051	39391	92039	71664	40219	97707	93975	66981	19556	24605	52169
82666	14127	94390	07069	39152	10357	94612	56748	75428	28101	38543	54214	48928	32818	51963	87353	15094	29529	87305	01361
60147	99378	58310	34655	48242	58656	30544	01860	08322	70476	44242	54227	28598	64422	29361	20359	48577	05971	92373	22765
61557	43927	11643	65522	76713	95782	34956	67384	47654	64999	11468	74149	81386	94127	67342	38010	92522	57728	39432	27914
71522	16545	68464	62540	76143	06328	94718	58404	84099	73641	52165	54336	89196	40042	37889	06003	58033	59082	94988	62152
05366	66273	49518	25413	20346	22719	18255	47685	78475	67421	83093	77038	55399	67893	89597	85630	08059	35757	49479	63531
72668	62720	08971	97908	15905	86615	97559	68107	10649	30976	66455	90708	08450	50120	17795	55604	51222	17900	55553	02980
51497	78491	83680	08319	51223	19735	72708	82599	28127	29660	30790	65154	19582	20942	81439	83917	90452	64753	99645	19799
66170	68781	91423	86645	02925	51327	41022	76893	29200	82747	97297	74420	18783	93471	89055	56413	77817	10655	52915	68198
23361	60672	52451	03774	06365	94880	70978	57385	70532	46978	87390	53319	90155	03154	20301	47831	86786	11284	49160	79852
53608	59661	70966	24937	56559	98856	19207	41684	20288	19783	82215	35810	39852	43795	21530	96315	55657	76473	08217	46810
24079	01177	02666	35515	24819	73382	50172	23114	28745	12249	35844	63265	26451	06986	08707	99251	06260	74779	96285	31998
50495	87947	20592	91917	59595	55083	43112	94833	72864	58785	53473	06308	56778	30474	57277	23425	27092	47759	18422	56074
93550	48308	20282	92711	74402	51335	64031	41740	69680	69373	73674	97914	77989	47280	71804	74587	70563	77813	50242	60398
16269	03381	09798	89487	33632	47073	92357	38870	73784	95662	83923	90790	49474	11901	30322	80254	99608	17019	17892	76813
32868	72831	55156	90166	91599	09471	79945	42580	86605	97758	08206	54199	41327	01170	21745	71318	07978	35440	26128	10545
80722	21328	19977	82161	29385	62151	48030	05125	70866	72154	86385	39490	57482	32921	33795	43155	30432	48384	85430	51828
67362	87389	09559	98456	70498	40173	80016	81500	48061	25583	74101	87573	01556	89183	64830	16779	35724	82103	61658	20296
83452	92994	85019	57720	36951	03383	34265	65728	89776	04006	06089	84076	12445	47416	83620	59151	97420	23689	74515	55211
51168	41624	94768	53124	95920	04777	82534	76335	21108	42302	79496	21054	80132	67719	72662	58360	57384	65406	63918	17046
83805	28803	63272	65480	08764	16379	72055	61146	82780	89411	53131	57879	39099	42715	24830	60045	23250	39847	46616	17817
59782	50488	77081	10186	86577	28581	26999	96294	20431	30114	23035	30380	76272	60343	57573	42492	47962	21439	54664	97968
09627	26695	79373	09119	79765	99918	01628	47335	17893	53176	07436	14799	78197	48601	97557	83918	20530	61565	69344	71964
20160	50603	71684	34875	60617	77991	66322	27390	73834	73494	21527	93579	20949	85666	25102	64733	93872	72698	87520	43340
04375	15463	49139	17369	71179	77472	96239	18521	67354	41883	58939	36222	43935	36272	47817	90287	91434	86453	84477	03559
67163	48629	25607	27003	09721	70206	10497	83617	39176	45062	63903	33862	14903	38996	60027	41702	78189	28598	12707	91191
49380	42273	93835	32621	60848	67721	69712	33438	85908	58620	50646	47857	96024	58568	67614	44370	40276	85964	71604	05691
56013	02278	53110	33235	62949	53799	51375	42451	76889	68096	80657	91046	95340	70209	23825	46031	45306	64476	31460	61553
46596	51960	02957	56574	18672	02994	39960	02489	53079	72789	22562	39359	38220	13972	86115	17196	24569	26820	66299	50962
52928	66296	15570	31407	54988	78749	16135	82797	31296	93268	10104	95616	82618	85756	51156	74037	12501	94162	42006	99213
09403	50848	71088	31308	35677	49046	10870	72107	11550	61175	33345	56717	07896	74085	59886	03051	78702	13402	74318	20992
30328	72163	66728	81091	52307	78952	60261	11207	73065	48286	57057	49472	95241	84360	13960	95736	43637	60399	19080	72417
78707	57821	28410	64908	30432	78760	36880	02564	96978	62332	77321	92228	53849	26578	39954	86726	91039	13884	25376	60187
73597	94657	72927	46459	61325	50908	25601	30038	78786	65197	65283	18169	72967	53031	47906	99501	27753	69946	66875	31598
07446	66408	19958	65159	11338	39231	72802	70630	87336	16385	32784	38073	87910	89260	66444	15979	83469	76952	50065	89540
47870	55448	14158	83451	58729	42430	42234	04905	83274	22459	75032	93544	10482	34277	40177	01081	57788	08612	39886	33050
84269	35324	35508	49481	56478	30246	41771	61398	98154	61644	12405	45037	68034	98561	46747	30655	41878	93610	51745	97527
52704	71441	50581	65679	37597	17182	60733	11765	09293	70076	40751	95846	80277	92450	60888	18689	45966	25837	70906	62841
19020	09999	08316	32781	89731	52148	09111	64205	77930	32391	69076	13459	59896	78185	60268	03650	36814	88460	34049	19544
19442	94873	36976	30366	65815	66895	27222	17378	59359	00055	66780	54939	78369	04163	77673	73342	78915	20537	06126	92480
39523	74227	51895	39733	29426	76685	93548	87546	07687	47338	12240	32277	23015	54261	95020	77705	81682	96907	37411	90717
01201	85057	93409	81200	21176	78459	18960	85182	02245	11566	52527	62992	55171	85448	12545	75992	08790	88992	69756	46722
51725	60273	84903	84374	31438	36959	83719	40702	79038	68639	63329	93821	58095	62204	69319	00672	96037	78680	98734	92743
91045	72642	42684	32419	12825	58785	84563	62071	17799	96994	41635	52830	19700	98193	37600	70617	58959	45486	58338	12464
54896	95603	17290	91508	95605	82514	32257	15699	02654	83110	44278	95523	12666	87597	23190	26243	36690	75829	71060	91605
92324	88115	77848	38006	45600	02181	79261	49705	31491	25318	52586	72494	66685	05344	71633	68536	18786	28575	08455	93825
88397	78035	06366	37342	62070	74459	62026	13032	14048	16304	11959	78684	72590	47283	45445	35611	98354	53680	45747	87442
52118	65337	13461	18438	16099	57330	05018	92605	10316	07351	78020	86361	30286	06434	50229	09070	44848	09996	77753	49227
37202	05623	23595	79677	59772	37141	63390	48093	02366	05407	08325	52046	87494	95585	25547	53500	45047	08406	66984	71128
71637	80269	83299	89743	94628	26784	17792	09214	53781	90102	25774	92525	32301	25923	76556	13274	39776	97027	56919	88547
35790	19603	31212	34419	34728	47391	93272	09887	34196	98251	62453	37703	70711	37921	54989	17828	60976	57662	61757	71249
99087	72525	34402	50115	09825	54728	37514	24437	01316	04770	06534	17768	36086	05468	41631	95632	78154	38634	47463	99728
89768	36608	49108	92337	79809	81934	06370	18703	90858	55130	40869	88243	37403	42231	17073	49097	54147	03656	14735	78351
83816	00718	94663	39629	27812	28250	44983	33834	54280	67850	96025	96117	00768	14821	69029	25453	48798	15486	73835	51776
00806	20667	81224	24296	39967	60239	89494	34431	44890	59892	79682	20308	82510	53609	13258	89631	80497	49167	81559	47202
65733	03902	29140	05414	62087	65727	54430	52632	94126	95597	48338	67645	44676	14730	22642	21919	21050	87791	76192	56686
60671	23190	47433	86979	45281	69750	96999	42104	34377	63309	82181	00278	28209	95629	75818	09043	48564	87355	27209	09827
45326	86280	74876	51858	03263	10215	87947	09427	32380	43636	58578	07761	28456	46570	11623	50417	37763	30136	58254	71090
54419	65493	88741	89069	10789	00973	30238	46126	85306	37114	22718	50584	92291	56575	24075	43889	40909	18741	86154	20843
72845	68939	06483	40835	16564	75047	22938	13073	32066	43098	75738	94910	15403	89151	73322	18370	90586	46115	87375	79147
01828	48113	60005	87083	90000	22346	89182	27750	63314	87302	49472	24885	79506	60638	07132	00908	92035	75518	30878	14979
89871	81320	05251	25930	37320	11895	16187	03303	40287	52435	23926	92544	54099	31497	03863	22864	72620	74169	25311	80669
74883	93005	77888	64673	19302	54669	21526	07401	30925	46148	20138	33874	56715	38424	38273	11361	15203	64912	62494	31231
25493	56247	46907	25634	84761	76421	42907	95158	27146	37012	43361	03173	97911	71313	44256	66609	42504	76799	46790	28464
28278	93841	13134	25129	65536	19838	21479	48265	01674	47274	56350	37512	14883	99673	62298	33948	32456	28675	04242	20735
44834	89816	52509	85192	32114	83770	90076	70233	76730	25043	16686	54737	57431	01786	20803	69465	37970	05673	49516	98035
23329	74767	85661	54449	76606	02131	93202	25355	93941	84434	22384	13240	93617	51549	28532	57150	77261	62643	74966	08777
33176	16108	98145	27652	76918	41000	46059	72208	90475	10341	39703	83224	37858	61657	04184	15597	29448	01922	05709	77900
44597	28074	92908	22392	38034	83739	32876	98604	75652	95680	51386	48724	76069	94867	93570	20306	31712	96238	57864	86267
81456	81110	94771	13664	07478	80992	58485	18882	13238	59865	55644	05528	94935	58972	43340	94718	97397	92197	57257	73187
91503	59589	22803	18122	17790	00236	93750	20468	92189	66781	06210	18208	13973	57905	66878	55721	67437	61709	88182	92769
63651	64109	13207	68346	42140	00052	04099	48767	23355	42505	34539	51129	48580	59386	62209	29754	77409	48146	50411	50511
30709	25869	68851	65221	69392	35106	36393	27129	17326	86452	69952	68433	72332	62502	76323	38379	07293	76788	84281	58581
50664	89487	41973	98456	51147	51327	26590	94684	58103	96936	71276	30275	22753	46046	67196	65135	54879	71903	23541	92400
80089	83750	36605	85343	26090	28447	33179	69730	09683	08770	50381	43130	88108	64709	15191	68718	38375	46747	19860	76129
19293	91304	37043	82077	42231	31534	54358	52939	26655	72687	26616	09608	59223	74533	64986	49667	78039	61030	46122	54941
97754	28401	62553	98641	48553	35996	08033	91811	70471	81538	20017	19613	81103	37642	41866	96777	08667	74544	92903	58427
47923	38366	81939	61526	27691	13988	21630	00957	50599	91260	72832	89364	14158	71740	91289	61204	91185	23485	18424	65084

1) From LINDER, A., *Planen und Auswerten von Versuchen,* Birkhäuser, Basle, 1953, pages 177 et seq. Reprinted by kind permission of the author and publishers.

I. Symbols

$a \to b$	a tending toward b
∞	infinity
lim	limiting value
$a \sim b$	a approximately equal to b
$a \approx b$	a very nearly equal to b
$a = b$	a equal to b. Cf. section II, equation **(1)**
$a \equiv b$	a identical with b (for formulas only)
$a > b$	a greater than b } Cf. section II, formulas **(2)** and **(3)**
$a < b$	a smaller than b } Cf. section II, formulas **(2)** and **(3)**
$a \gg b$	a much greater than b
$a \ll b$	a much smaller than b
$a \neq b$, $a \lessgtr b$	a not equal to b
$b < a < c$	a greater than b and smaller than c
$a \geqq b$	a equal to or greater than b, i.e. a at least as great as b
$a \leqq b$	a equal to or smaller than b, i.e. a at most as great as b
$b \leqq a \leqq c$	a lying between b and c
$\lvert a \rvert$	absolute value of a; this is always positive, for example $\lvert -5 \rvert = 5$
$+$	addition sign, plus, positive
$-$	subtraction sign, minus, negative
$\times$ or $\cdot$	multiplication sign, times (the period is not used in these *Tables*)
: or $\div$	division sign, divided by (the sign $\div$ is not used in these *Tables*)
$a + b = c$	$a + b$, read as a plus b, denotes the sum of a and b. The result of the addition, c, is also known as the sum
$\sum_1^k x_i$	sum of all values $x_1, x_2, x_3, \ldots$, i.e. of all values x_i, from $i = 1$ to $i = k$ inclusive, or $\sum_1^k x_i = x_1 + x_2 + x_3 + \cdots + x_k$ (the limits of the summation above and below the sign $\sum$ are usually omitted if there is no possibility of confusion)
$\int$	indefinite integral
$\int_a^b$	definite integral, or integral between $x = a$ and $x = b$
$a - b = c$	$a - b$, read as a minus b, denotes subtraction of b from a. a is the minuend, b the subtrahend; $a - b$, or c, is the difference. Subtraction is the opposite of addition
$a \times b = c$, $a\,b = c$, $a \cdot b = c$	$a \times b$, read as a times b, denotes multiplication of a by b. a and b are the multiplicands or factors; $a \times b$, or c, is the product. The period sign is not used in these *Tables* owing to the possibility of confusion
$a : b = c$	$a : b$, read as a divided by b, denotes division. a is the dividend, b the divisor; $a : b$, or c, is the quotient. Division is the opposite of multiplication and can also be represented by the fraction $\frac{a}{b}$ or a/b. In fractions, a is the numerator (= dividend), b the denominator (= divisor)
$a^b = c$	a^b, read as a to the power b, is known as involution. a is the base, b the exponent; a^b, or c, is the bth power of a. In the special case of $a^2 = c$, a^2 or c is the square of a; in that of $a^3 = c$, a^3 or c is the cube of a
$\sqrt[b]{a} = c$	$\sqrt[b]{a}$, is the bth root of a, b being known as the root exponent. In the special case of $\sqrt[2]{a} = c$, $\sqrt[2]{a}$ or c is known as the square root of a, and the root exponent is usually omitted, i.e. $\sqrt[2]{a} = \sqrt{a}$. In the special case of $\sqrt[3]{a} = c$, $\sqrt[3]{a}$ or c is known as the cube root of a. Extraction of a root is the opposite of involution. Cf. also Logarithms, page 134
log, ln	see Logarithms, page 134
e	base of natural (Napierian) logarithms $= 2.718\,281\,828\,4\ldots$
π	ratio of the circumference of a circle to its diameter $= 3.141\,592\,653\,5\ldots$
sin, cos, tan, tg	see page 138
arc sin	see page 139

II. Numbers

The *natural numbers* consist of all positive whole numbers (positive integers). Zero and negative numbers are not natural numbers.

The *rational numbers* consist of all positive and negative integers, the fractions formed from them, and zero.

The *irrational numbers* are incommensurable quantities which cannot be expressed as quotients either of integers or of rational fractions. Examples are $\sqrt{2}$ and $\sqrt{5}$. π and e are also irrational numbers.

The *real numbers* consist of all rational and irrational numbers. The fundamental laws of real numbers are the following:

1. The four fundamental operations

Addition, subtraction, multiplication and division (except division by zero) can always and without ambiguity be carried out with real numbers.

2. The order of numbers

Between any two real numbers a and b there can exist *only one* of the three relationships

$a = b$ or $a > b$ or $a < b$

where

$$a = b \quad \text{when} \quad a - b = 0 \qquad (1)$$

$$a > b \quad \text{when} \quad a - b > 0 \qquad (2)$$

$$a < b \quad \text{when} \quad a - b < 0 \qquad (3)$$

Examples of equations **(2)** and **(3)** are

$$\cdots > \quad 10 > \quad 9 > \cdots > \quad 1 > 0 > -1 > \cdots > -10 > \cdots$$

$$\cdots < -10 < -9 < \cdots < -1 < 0 < \quad 1 < \cdots < \quad 10 < \cdots$$

3. The commutative law

$$a + b = b + a \qquad (4)$$

$$a\,b = b\,a \qquad (5)$$

4. The associative law

$$(a + b) + c = a + (b + c) \qquad (6)$$

$$(a\,b)\,c = a\,(b\,c) \qquad (7)$$

5. The distributive law

$$a\,(b + c) = a\,b + a\,c \qquad (8)$$

III. Calculations with zero and infinity

$$a - a = 0 \qquad (9)$$

$$\lvert 0 \rvert = 0 \qquad (10)$$

$$0 \times a = 0 \qquad (11)$$

$$\frac{a}{\infty} = 0 \quad (a \neq \infty) \qquad (12)$$

$$\frac{0}{a} = 0 \quad (a \neq 0) \qquad (13)$$

$\frac{a}{0}$ is not defined **(14)**

$0^a = 0 \quad (a > 0)$ **(15)**

$a^0 = 1 \quad (a \neq 0)$ **(16)**

$$\lim_{n \to \infty} a^n = \begin{cases} \infty & \text{for } a > 1 \\ 1 & \text{for } a = 1 \\ 0 & \text{for } -1 < a < 1 \text{ and } a \neq 0 \\ \text{nonconvergent} & \text{for } a \leqq -1 \end{cases}$$ **(17)**

$\log_c 0 = -\infty \quad (c > 1)$ **(18)**

$\log_c \infty = +\infty \quad (c > 1)$ **(19)**

$\log_c 1 = 0$ **(20)**

$0! = 1$ **(21)**

$\binom{n}{0} = 1$ **(22)**

IV. Addition, subtraction, multiplication, division

1. Algebraic signs

If a, b, c are positive numbers, then

$a \pm b = a \mp (-b)$ **(23)**

$a(-b) = (-a)\,b = -(a\,b) = -c$ **(24)**

$(-a)(-b) = +a\,b = +c$ **(25)**

$\frac{-b}{a} = \frac{b}{-a} = -\frac{b}{a} = -c$ **(26)**

$\frac{-b}{-a} = +\frac{a}{b} = +c$ **(27)**

2. Brackets

$a - b - c - d - \cdots = a - (b + c + d + \cdots)$ **(28)**

$\pm a\,b \pm a\,c \pm a\,d \pm \cdots = a\,(\pm b \pm c \pm d \pm \cdots)$ **(29)**

$= \pm a\,(b + c + d + \cdots)$

3. Conversion of divisions into multiplications

$\frac{b}{a} = \frac{1}{a} \times b$ **(30)**

For values of $1/a$ for numbers from 1 to 999 see page 18. Equation **(30)** is particularly useful in mechanical calculation with a constant divisor.

4. Conversion of multiplications and divisions into additions

If b is an integer (or can be converted into an integer), then

$$\left.\begin{aligned} a\,b &= a + a + a + \cdots \\ \frac{b}{a} &= \frac{1}{a} + \frac{1}{a} + \frac{1}{a} + \cdots \end{aligned}\right\} b \text{ components}$$ **(31)**

Equation **(31)** is particularly useful in the mechanical tabulation of linear functions.

5. Fractions

$\frac{a}{a} = 1 \quad (a \neq 0)$ **(32)**

$\frac{m\,a}{m\,b} = \frac{a}{b} \quad (m \neq 0)$ **(33)**

$\frac{a}{b} + \frac{c}{b} = \frac{a + c}{b}$ (can also be used from right to left) **(34)**

$\frac{a}{b} + \frac{c}{d} = \frac{a\,d + b\,c}{b\,d}$ (can also be used from right to left) **(35)**

$\frac{a}{b} \times \frac{c}{d} = \frac{a}{d} \times \frac{c}{b} = \frac{a\,c}{b\,d}$ **(36)**

$\frac{a}{b} : \frac{c}{d} = \frac{a}{b} \times \frac{d}{c} = \frac{a}{c} \times \frac{d}{b} = \frac{a}{c} : \frac{b}{d}$ **(37)**

6. Proportions

The equation

$a : b = c : d$ **(38)**

read as: a is to b as c is to d, is known as a proportion. a and d are the extremes, b and c the means of the proportion. The product of the extremes equals the product of the means:

$a\,d = b\,c$ **(39)**

If a constant proportion is of the type expressed by

$a : b = b : c$ **(40)**

then in accordance with equation **(39)**, $a\,c = b^2$, that is, $b = \sqrt{a\,c}$ **(41)**

b is known as the mean proportional between a and c, or the geometric mean of a and c. c is known as the third proportional to a and b.

A special case of proportions of type **(40)** is the so-called "golden section" (extreme and mean ratio)

$\frac{a}{b} = \frac{b}{a - b}$, that is

$b = \frac{a\left(\sqrt{5} - 1\right)}{2} = 0.618\,034\,a \quad \text{or} \quad \frac{a}{b} = 1.618\,034$ **(42)**

Another special case is that of the European "Normformate", expressed by

$\frac{a}{b} = \frac{b}{a/2}$, that is

$b = a/\sqrt{2} = 0.707\,107\,a \quad \text{or} \quad \frac{a}{b} = 1.414\,214$ **(43)**

If the individual values of two related variables x, y are such that

$\frac{y_1}{x_1} = \frac{y_2}{x_2} = \frac{y_3}{x_3} = \cdots = k$ **(44)**

then

$y = k\,x$ **(45)**

read as: y is proportional to x in the ratio k. k is known as the proportionality constant. As x increases, y increases in proportion when k is positive, decreases when k is negative. The graphical representation of a proportional relationship on rectangular coordinates results in a straight line, whence the expression linear relationship. On the other hand, a linear relationship between x and y does not necessarily mean that they are proportional to one another since there are many straight lines which do not correspond to equation **(45)**. For example, $y = a + k\,x$ is *not* a proportional relationship between x and y. In this case $(y - a)$ is proportional to x.

If the individual values of two related variables x, y are such that

$$\left.\begin{aligned} &\frac{y_1}{1/x_1} = \frac{y_2}{1/x_2} = \frac{y_3}{1/x_3} = \cdots = k \\ &\text{that is} \\ &y_1 x_1 = y_2 x_2 = y_3 x_3 = \cdots = k \end{aligned}\right\}$$ **(46)**

then

$y = \frac{k}{x}$ **(47)**

read as: y is inversely proportional to x in the ratio k. The graphical representation of an inversely proportional relationship on rectangular coordinates results in a hyperbola. Such a relationship is therefore a nonlinear one.

V. Powers and roots

1. Powers with integral exponents

If a and b are any real numbers, m and r positive integers, then

$0^m = 0 \quad (m > 0)$ **(15)**

$$a^0 = 1 \quad (a \neq 0) \tag{16}$$

$$\lim_{m \to \infty} a^m = \begin{cases} \infty & \text{for } a > 1 \\ 1 & \text{for } a = 1 \\ 0 & \text{for } -1 < a < 1 \text{ and } a \neq 0 \\ \text{nonconvergent for } a \leqq -1 \end{cases} \tag{17}$$

$$a \times a \times a \times \cdots (m \text{ factors}) = a^m \tag{48}$$

$$\frac{1}{a} \times \frac{1}{a} \times \frac{1}{a} \times \cdots (m \text{ factors}) = \frac{1}{a^m} = a^{-m} \quad (a \neq 0) \tag{49}$$

$$a^m \times b^m = (a\,b)^m \tag{50}$$

$$\frac{a^m}{b^m} = \left(\frac{a}{b}\right)^m = a^m\,b^{-m} \quad (b \neq 0) \tag{51}$$

$$a^m \times a^r = a^{m+r} \tag{52}$$

$$\frac{a^m}{a^r} = a^m\,a^{-r} = a^{m-r} \quad (a \neq 0) \tag{53}$$

$$(a^m)^r = (a^r)^m = a^{m\,r} \tag{54}$$

Algebraic signs: If in equations (**48**) to (**54**) R is the resulting *absolute value* of the base, c the absolute value of the power, $2\,m$ or $2\,m - 1$ the resulting even or uneven exponent, then

$$(\pm R)^{2m} = +c \tag{55}$$

$$(\pm R)^{2m-1} = \pm c \tag{56}$$

2. Extraction of roots with integral exponents

If a and b are any real numbers, n and s positive integers but not zero, then

$$\sqrt[n]{a} = a^{\frac{1}{n}} \tag{57}$$

$$\frac{1}{\sqrt[n]{a}} = a^{-\frac{1}{n}} \quad (a \neq 0) \tag{58}$$

$$\sqrt[n]{a\,b} = \sqrt[n]{a}\,\sqrt[n]{b} = (a\,b)^{\frac{1}{n}} \tag{59}$$

$$\sqrt[n]{\frac{a}{b}} = \frac{\sqrt[n]{a}}{\sqrt[n]{b}} = \left(\frac{a}{b}\right)^{\frac{1}{n}} \quad (b \neq 0) \tag{60}$$

$$\sqrt[s]{\sqrt[n]{a}} = \sqrt[n]{\sqrt[s]{a}} = a^{\frac{1}{n\,s}} \tag{61}$$

Algebraic signs: If in equations (**57**) to (**61**) R is the resulting *absolute value* of the base, c the absolute value of the power, $2\,n$ or $2\,n - 1$ the resulting even or uneven exponent, then

$$\sqrt[2n]{(+R)} = (+R)^{\frac{1}{2n}} = +c \tag{62}$$

$$\sqrt[2n]{(-R)} = (-R)^{\frac{1}{2n}} \quad \text{has no real solution} \tag{63}$$

$$\sqrt[2n-1]{(\pm R)} = (\pm R)^{\frac{1}{2n-1}} = \pm c \tag{64}$$

3. Mixed powers and roots

If a and b are any real numbers, m and r positive integers, k, n and s likewise positive integers but not zero, then

$$\sqrt[n]{a^m} = a^{\frac{m}{n}} \tag{65}$$

$$\frac{1}{\sqrt[n]{a^m}} = a^{-\frac{m}{n}} \quad (a \neq 0) \tag{66}$$

$$\sqrt[kn]{a^{k\,m}} = \sqrt[n]{a^m} = a^{\frac{m}{n}} \tag{67}$$

If in equation (**67**) a is negative it is important that all other necessary conversion operations on the exponent should be performed *before* reduction is carried out. If the resulting numerator in the exponent is even, then a negative a is made positive and reduction carried out.

$$\sqrt[n]{(a\,b)^m} = \sqrt[n]{a^m} \times \sqrt[n]{b^m} = (a\,b)^{\frac{m}{n}} \tag{68}$$

$$\frac{\sqrt[n]{a^m}}{\sqrt[n]{b^m}} = \sqrt[n]{\left(\frac{a}{b}\right)^m} = \left(\frac{a}{b}\right)^{\frac{m}{n}} \quad (b \neq 0) \tag{69}$$

$$\sqrt[n]{a} \times \sqrt[s]{a} = a^{\frac{1}{n}+\frac{1}{s}} = a^{\frac{n+s}{ns}} = \sqrt[ns]{a^{n+s}} \tag{70}$$

$$\sqrt[n]{a^m} \times \sqrt[s]{a^r} = a^{\frac{m}{n}+\frac{r}{s}} = a^{\frac{ms+nr}{ns}} = \sqrt[ns]{a^{ms+nr}} \tag{71}$$

$$\left(a^{\frac{m}{n}}\right)^{\frac{r}{s}} = \left(a^{\frac{r}{s}}\right)^{\frac{m}{n}} = a^{\frac{mr}{ns}} \tag{72}$$

Algebraic signs: If in equations (**65**) to (**72**) R is the resulting *absolute value* of the base, c the absolute value of the power, $2\,m$, $2\,n$, or $2\,m - 1$, $2\,n - 1$ respectively the resulting even or uneven numerator and denominator of the exponent, then

$$\sqrt[2n]{(\pm R)^{2m}} = (\pm R)^{\frac{2m}{2n}} = (+R)^{\frac{2m}{2n}} = +c \tag{73}$$

(always to be used in any reduction of an exponent)

$$\sqrt[2n]{(+R)^{2m-1}} = (+R)^{\frac{2m-1}{2n}} = +c \tag{74}$$

$$\sqrt[2n]{(-R)^{2m-1}} = (-R)^{\frac{2m-1}{2n}} \quad \text{has no real solution} \tag{75}$$

$$\sqrt[2n-1]{(\pm R)^{2m}} = (\pm R)^{\frac{2m}{2n-1}} = +c \tag{76}$$

$$\sqrt[2n-1]{(\pm R)^{2m-1}} = (\pm R)^{\frac{2m-1}{2n-1}} = \pm c \tag{77}$$

VI. Logarithms

In accordance with the equation

$$a = c^{\log_c a} \tag{78}$$

(a = number or antilogarithm, c = base, $\log_c a$ = logarithm of a to the base c)

the logarithm of a to the base c is defined as the exponent of the power of the base c which equals the number a. The usual bases are 10 (common or Briggsian logarithms) and $e = 2.718\,281\,8285$ (natural, Napierian or hyperbolic logarithms). In these *Tables* the symbol log is used for common logarithms and the symbol ln for natural logarithms. The relation between the two is given by

$$\ln a = \frac{\log a}{\log e} = 2.302\,585\,0930 \log a = \ln 10 \times \log a \tag{79}$$

$$\log a = \frac{\ln a}{\ln 10} = 0.434\,294\,4819 \ln a = \log e \times \ln a \tag{80}$$

In general the relation is expressed by

$$\log_c a = \frac{\log_{10} a}{\log_{10} c} \tag{81}$$

Example: It is required to find the logarithm of 20 to the base 2. From equation (**81**)

$$\log_2 20 = \frac{\log_{10} 20}{\log_{10} 2} = \frac{1.301\,0300}{0.301\,0300} = 4.321\,928$$

With the aid of logarithms, multiplication, division, raising to powers and the extraction of roots are reduced to addition, subtraction, multiplication and division respectively.

For common logarithms equation (**78**) gives

$$a = 10^{\log a} \quad \text{and} \quad b = 10^{\log b}$$

so that according to equation (**52**)

$$a \times b = 10^{\log a} \times 10^{\log b} = 10^{\log a + \log b}$$

that is $\quad \log(a \times b) = \log a + \log b$

whence $\quad (a \times b) = \text{antilog}(\log a + \log b)$

All the principles of logarithmic calculation can be deduced from section V in an analogous manner. The most important are:

$$\log(a \times b) = \log a + \log b \tag{82}$$

$$\log\left(\frac{a}{b}\right) = \log a - \log b \tag{83}$$

$$\log a^b = b \log a \quad \textbf{(84)}$$

$$\log \sqrt[b]{a} = \frac{\log a}{b} \quad \textbf{(85)}$$

Since by definition there are only logarithms of positive numbers, logarithmic calculation is made without regard to the algebraic sign of $a, b, \ldots$ and the result assigned the appropriate sign according to the rules already given.

A logarithmic calculation falls into three parts:

1. Finding the logarithms,
2. Operating with them according to the above rules,
3. Finding the antilogarithms.

1. Finding the logarithm

The number of which the logarithm is required is first converted into a product as follows:

$$a = 10^x \times \frac{a}{10^x} = K' \times M' \quad \textbf{(86)}$$

x is determined for $|a| \geqq 1$ by counting the number b of places to the left of the decimal point, for $|a| < 1$ by counting the number b of ciphers to the right of the decimal point, so that

$$x = b - 1 \quad \text{when} \quad |a| \geqq 1 \quad \textbf{(87)}$$

and

$$x = -b - 1 \quad \text{when} \quad |a| < 1 \quad \textbf{(88)}$$

Examples:

a	b	x	K'	$K' \times M'$
1566.3	4	3	10^3	$10^3 \times 1.5663$
1.2	1	0	10^0	$10^0 \times 1.2$
0.12	0	−1	10^{-1}	$10^{-1} \times 1.2$
0.00034	−3	−4	10^{-4}	$10^{-4} \times 3.4$

In accordance with equation (**82**)

$$\log a = \log(K' \times M') = \log K' + \log M' = K + M \quad \textbf{(89)}$$

K is known as the characteristic, M as the mantissa of the logarithm of a.

The characteristic K is the positive or negative exponent x of K' in equation (**86**). The mantissa M must be looked for in a table of logarithms. For this purpose M' is first rounded off so that it contains the same number of figures as the logarithms in the table used. In the following examples four-figure logarithms are used:

For $M' < 1.1$, round off M' to 5 significant places

For $M' \geqq 1.1$, round off M' to 4 significant places

Example:

$\log 1.0993 = ?$ $\quad \log 1.5663 \approx \log 1.566 = ?$

From the table on page 10:

x	$\log x$		Proportional parts	
↓→	6	9	3	6
109		0410	1	
15	1931			17

$$\log 1.0993 = 0.0410 + 0.0001 = 0.0411$$

$$\log 1.566 = 0.1931 + 0.0017 = 0.1948$$

Further examples:

(a) $\log 3048 = \log(10^3 \times 3.048) = 3 + 0.4829 + 0.0011 = 3.4840$

(b) $\log 0.2130 = \log(10^{-1} \times 2.130) = -1 + 0.3284 + 0 = 0.3284 - 1$

(c) $\log 1/3048 = \log(10^{-3} \times 3.048^{-1}) = -3 - (0.4829 + 0.0011) = -0.4840 - 3$

(d) $\log 1/0.2130 = \log(10^1 \times 2.13^{-1}) = 1 - 0.3284 = 0.6716$

In example (c) the mantissa as well as the characteristic is negative. A negative mantissa must be converted into a positive one by adding 1 to the mantissa and subtracting 1 from the characteristic. For example: $-0.4840 - 3 = 0.5160 - 4$.

2. Operating with logarithms

This is done in accordance with equations (**82**) to (**85**) and the following rules observed:

1. Calculations are so made that no negative mantissas arise.
2. In extracting the roots of fractions, the difference between the root exponent and the characteristic is subtracted from the characteristic and added to the mantissa (examples e and f).
3. When the logarithmic calculation is complete, positive and negative characteristics are added together. The resulting characteristic x gives the number b of places to the left of the decimal point (when $x \geqq 0$) or the number b of ciphers to the right of the decimal point (when $x < 0$), as follows:

$$b = x + 1 \quad \text{when } x \geqq 0 \quad \textbf{(90)}$$

$$b = -(x + 1) \quad \text{when } x < 0 \quad \textbf{(91)}$$

Examples:

(a) $\log(3048 \times 0.2130) = \begin{array}{r} 3.4840 \\ +\,0.3284 - 1 \\ \hline 3.8124 - 1 \end{array} = 2.8124$

(b) $\log(0.2130 : 3048) = \begin{array}{r} 0.3284 - 1 \\ +\,0.5160 - 4 \\ \hline 0.8444 - 5 \end{array} = 0.8444 - 5$

(c) $\log(0.2130 : 0.000\,3281) = \begin{array}{r} 0.3284 - 1 \\ -(0.5160 - 4) \end{array} = \begin{array}{r} 1.3284 - 2 \\ -\,0.5160 + 4 \\ \hline 0.8124 + 2 \end{array} = 2.8124$

(d) $\log(0.2130^5) = 5 \log 0.2130 = 5 \times (0.3284 - 1) = 1.6420 - 5 = 0.6420 - 4$

(e) $\log(\sqrt[6]{0.2130}) = \frac{\log 0.2130}{6} = \frac{0.3284 - 1}{6} = \frac{5.3284 - 6}{6} = 0.8881 - 1$

(f) $\log(\sqrt[1.5]{0.2130}) = \frac{\log 0.2130}{1.5} = \frac{0.3284 - 1}{1.5} = \frac{0.8284 - 1.5}{1.5} = 0.5523 - 1$

3. Finding the antilogarithm

The antilogarithm corresponding to a mantissa is looked for in a table of antilogarithms (see page 11) in the same way as a logarithm is looked for in a table of logarithms. (Care should be taken not to confuse the two tables.) The position of the decimal point is determined by means of equations (**90**) and (**91**).

Examples: antilog $2.8124 = 649.2$

antilog $(0.8881 - 1) = 0.7729$

antilog $(0.6420 - 4) = 0.000\,4385$

VII. Factorials and binomial coefficients

1. $n^{(r)}$

For a positive integer r and any real number n the symbol $n^{(r)}$ represents the product

$$n^{(r)} = n(n-1)(n-2)\cdots(n-r+1) \quad \textbf{(92)}$$

where

$$n^{(0)} = 1 \quad \textbf{(93)}$$

by definition.

Examples:

(a) $10^{(4)} = ?$

In this case, $(n - r + 1) = 10 - 4 + 1 = 7$, so that
$10^{(4)} = 10 \times 9 \times 8 \times 7 = 5040$

(b) $4^{(5)} = ?$

In this case, $(n - r + 1) = 4 - 5 + 1 = 0$, so that
$4^{(5)} = 4 \times 3 \times 2 \times 1 \times 0 = 0$

From example (b) it can be seen that

$$n^{(r)} = 0 \qquad \textbf{(94)}$$

when $r > n$ and n is a positive integer.

2. Factorials

The factorial of a positive integer n, symbol $n!$, is defined as

$$n! = n(n-1)(n-2)\ldots 3 \times 2 \times 1 \qquad \textbf{(95)}$$

where

$$0! = 1 \qquad \textbf{(96)}$$

by definition.

For positive integers n, the factorial $n!$ can be expressed as $n^{(n)}$, in which case equation (**92**) can be written

$$n^{(r)} = \frac{n!}{(n-r)!} \qquad \textbf{(97)}$$

Equations (**93**) and (**94**) remain valid.

Logarithms of the factorials of numbers n between 1 and 999 and of their reciprocals are given on pages 26 and 27. For the factorials of numbers $n \geqq 1000$ the STIRLING approximation is used:

$$\underset{(n\to\infty)}{n!} \to n^n e^{-n} \sqrt{2\pi n} \qquad \textbf{(98)}$$

or

$$\log n! \to 0.5 \times \left[2n(\log n - 0.4342944819) + \log n + 0.798178\right] \qquad \textbf{(99)}$$

3. Binomial coefficients

In its general form the binomial coefficient $\binom{n}{r}$ or $C(n, r)$ is defined as

$$\binom{n}{r} = \frac{n^{(r)}}{r!} \qquad \textbf{(100)}$$

For $n^{(r)}$ and $r!$ see subsections 1 and 2 above.

When n is a positive integer equations (**97**) and (**100**) give

$$\binom{n}{r} = \frac{n!}{r!\,(n-r)!} \qquad \textbf{(101)}$$

From equations (**93**), (**94**) and (**96**) it follows that

$$\binom{n}{0} = 1 \qquad \textbf{(102)}$$

$$\binom{0}{0} = 1 \qquad \textbf{(103)}$$

$$\binom{n}{r} = 0 \quad \text{when } r > n \text{ and } n \text{ is a positive integer} \qquad \textbf{(104)}$$

It is also clear that

$$\binom{n}{n} = 1 \qquad \textbf{(105)}$$

Example: For $n = 9$ and $n = 10$ all the coefficients for values of r between zero and n are tabulated:

	0	1	2	3	4	5	6	7	8	9	10
r (n = 9; $n/2$ between 4 and 5)	0	1	2	3	4	5	6	7	8	9	
$n = 9$	1	9	36	84	126	126	84	36	9	1	
$n = 10$	1	10	45	120	210	252	210	120	45	10	1
r (n = 10; $n/2$ at 5)	0	1	2	3	4	5	6	7	8	9	10

It will be seen that as r increases, the values of $\binom{n}{r}$ increase up to $n/2$ and then decrease again in symmetrical fashion:

$$\binom{n}{r} = \binom{n}{n-r} \qquad \textbf{(106)}$$

For uneven numbers n, the median falls between the two highest values of the series, for even numbers n it is at the highest value.

Binomial coefficients for n from zero to 39 and for r from zero to 15 are given on page 25. Logarithms of the binomial coefficients for n from 2 to 100 and for r from zero to $n/2$ are given on pages 70–77. For $101 \leqq n \leqq 999$ the binomial coefficients are calculated from equation (**101**) using the logarithms of factorials and their reciprocals given on pages 26 and 27.

VIII. Series

The sum $a_1 + a_2 + a_3 + \cdots + a_n$ of a sequence of numbers $a_1, a_2, a_3, \ldots a_n$ formed according to some fixed rule or law is known as a series.

1. Arithmetic series of the 1st order

This is a series in which the difference d between successive terms is constant:

$$a_2 - a_1 = a_3 - a_2$$

The individual terms are therefore

$$\left.\begin{matrix} a_1 & a_2 & a_3 & \ldots & a_n \\ a_1 & (a_1 + d) & (a_1 + 2d) & \ldots & a_1 + (n-1)\,d \end{matrix}\right\} \qquad \textbf{(107)}$$

The sum of the first n terms is

$$S = \frac{n(a_1 + a_n)}{2} \qquad \textbf{(108)}$$

A special case of (**108**) is the sum of the natural sequence of numbers $1, 2, 3, \ldots, n$

$$1 + 2 + 3 + \cdots + n = \frac{n(n+1)}{2} \qquad \textbf{(109)}$$

Example: The sum of all numbers from 1 to 81 is

$$(81 \times 82)/2 = 3321$$

2. Geometric series

A geometric series is one in which there is a constant ratio q between successive terms

$$\left.\begin{matrix} a_1 & a_2 & a_3 & \ldots & a_n \\ a_1 & a_1 q & a_1 q^2 & \ldots & a_1 q^{n-1} \end{matrix}\right\} \qquad \textbf{(110)}$$

The sum of the first n terms is

$$S = a_1 \frac{1 - q^n}{1 - q} = a_1 \frac{q^n - 1}{q - 1} \quad (q \neq 1) \qquad \textbf{(111)}$$

When $-1 < q < 1$, $q^\infty = 0$ in accordance with (**17**), and (**111**) becomes

$$S_\infty = \frac{a_1}{1 - q} \quad (-1 < q < 1) \qquad \textbf{(112)}$$

With the aid of equation (**112**) infinite periodic decimal fractions, for example, can be converted into true fractions.

Examples:

(a) $$0.333\,\dot{3} = \frac{3}{10} + \frac{3}{100} + \frac{3}{1000} \cdots$$

$$q = \frac{1}{10} \qquad a_1 = \frac{3}{10}$$

$$0.333\,\dot{3} = \frac{3}{10} \Big/ \frac{9}{10} = \frac{3}{9} = \frac{1}{3}$$

(b) $$0.033\,\dot{3} = \frac{3}{100} + \frac{3}{1000} + \cdots$$

$$q = \frac{1}{10} \quad a_1 = \frac{3}{100}$$

$$0.033\,3\dot{3} = \frac{3}{100} \Big/ \frac{9}{10} = \frac{3}{90} = \frac{1}{30}$$

(c) $$0.233\,3\dot{3} = \frac{2}{10} + \frac{3}{100} + \frac{3}{1000} + \cdots$$

The infinite series begins with 3/100, whence $q = 1/10$, $a_1 = 3/100$, etc., as in the previous example. There remains 2/10 to be added to it.

$$0.233\,3\dot{3} = \frac{2}{10} + \frac{1}{30} = \frac{60+10}{300} = \frac{7}{30}$$

(d) $$0.123\,123\,\dot{1}2\dot{3} = \frac{123}{1000} + \frac{123}{1\,000\,000} + \cdots$$

$$q = \frac{1}{1000} \qquad a_1 = \frac{123}{1000}$$

$$0.123\,\dot{1}2\dot{3} = \frac{123}{1000} \Big/ \frac{999}{1000} = \frac{123}{999} = \frac{41}{333}$$

3. Binomial series for positive integers n

$$\left.\begin{aligned}(a+b)^n &= \binom{n}{0} a^n b^0 + \binom{n}{1} a^{n-1} b^1 + \binom{n}{2} a^{n-2} b^2 \\ &+ \binom{n}{3} a^{n-3} b^3 + \cdots + \binom{n}{n} a^0 b^n\end{aligned}\right\} \quad (113)$$

Algebraic signs: When b is negative, all terms in which the exponent of b is uneven are negative.

Examples: $(a+b)^2 = a^2 + 2ab + b^2$

$(a+b)^3 = a^3 + 3a^2 b + 3ab^2 + b^3$ etc.

IX. Means

For n positive variates $x_1, x_2, \ldots, x_n$

(a) the arithmetic mean $$m_a = \frac{x_1 + x_2 + \cdots + x_n}{n} = \frac{\sum_1^n x_i}{n} \quad (114)$$

(b) the geometric mean $$m_g = \sqrt[n]{x_1 \times x_2 \times \cdots \times x_n} \quad (115)$$

(c) the harmonic mean $$m_h = 1 : \frac{1}{n}\left(\frac{1}{x_1} + \frac{1}{x_2} + \cdots + \frac{1}{x_n}\right) \quad (116)$$

When $n = 2$, then

$$m_a = \frac{x_1 + x_2}{2} \quad (117)$$

$$m_g = \sqrt{x_1 x_2} \quad (118)$$

$$m_h = \frac{2 x_1 x_2}{x_1 + x_2} \quad (119)$$

CAUCHY's principle: $m_a \geqq m_g \geqq m_h$ **(120)**

where the equality signs are valid only when

$x_1 = x_2 = \cdots = x_n$

X. Solutions of equations

Solutions of equations exist only when all the denominators differ from zero.

Required is x:

$$ax \pm b = 0; \quad x = \mp \frac{b}{a} \quad (121)$$

$$\frac{a}{x} \pm b = 0; \quad x = \mp \frac{a}{b} \quad (122)$$

1. Simplification of equations of higher degree

$$(ax \pm b)^m \pm c = 0; \quad x = \frac{\sqrt[m]{\mp c} \mp b}{a} \quad (123)$$

$$\sqrt[n]{ax \pm b} \pm c = 0; \quad x = \frac{(\mp c)^n \mp b}{a} \quad (124)$$

2. Equations of the first degree with two unknowns

x and y are required:

$$\left.\begin{aligned} &a_1 x + b_1 y + c_1 = 0 \\ &a_2 x + b_2 y + c_2 = 0 \\ &x = \frac{b_1 c_2 - b_2 c_1}{a_1 b_2 - a_2 b_1} \\ &y = -\frac{(a_1 x + c_1)}{b_1} = -\frac{(a_2 x + c_2)}{b_2}\end{aligned}\right\} \quad (125)$$

3. Equations of the first degree with three unknowns

x, y, z are required:

$$a_1 x + b_1 y + c_1 z + d_1 = 0$$
$$a_2 x + b_2 y + c_2 z + d_2 = 0$$
$$a_3 x + b_3 y + c_3 z + d_3 = 0$$

Let

$$\left.\begin{aligned} A &= c_2 a_1 - c_1 a_2 \\ B &= c_2 b_1 - c_1 b_2 \\ C &= c_2 d_1 - c_1 d_2 \\ D &= c_2 a_3 - c_3 a_2 \\ E &= c_2 b_3 - c_3 b_2 \\ F &= c_2 d_3 - c_3 d_2 \end{aligned}\right\} \quad (126)$$

then

$$x = \frac{BF - CE}{AE - BD}$$

$$y = -\frac{(C + Ax)}{B} = -\frac{(F + Dx)}{E}$$

$$z = -\frac{(a_1 x + b_1 y + d_1)}{c_1} = -\frac{(a_2 x + b_2 y + d_2)}{c_2}$$

$$= -\frac{(a_3 x + b_3 y + d_3)}{c_3}$$

4. Quadratic equations with one unknown

$$ax^2 + bx + c = 0$$

$$x_{(1,2)} = \frac{-b \pm \sqrt{b^2 - 4ac}}{2a} = \frac{-b}{2a} \pm \sqrt{\left(\frac{b}{2a}\right)^2 - \frac{c}{a}} \quad (127)$$

The magnitude $D = b^2 - 4ac$ is known as the discriminant of the equation. When

$D > 0$ there are two real solutions,

$D = 0$ there is only one real solution,

$D < 0$ there is no real solution.

5. Exponential equations in common use

$$x = 1 - e^{-\lambda}; \quad x = 1 - \text{antilog}\,(-0.4342944819\,\lambda) \quad (128)$$

$$a = 1 - e^{-z}; \quad z = -2.3025850930 \log(1 - a) \quad [0 \leqq a \leqq 1] \quad (129)$$

If in equation (**129**)

$$z = \frac{a x^b \pm c}{d}, \text{ then } \log x = \frac{\log\left(\frac{dz \mp c}{a}\right)}{b} \quad (130)$$

when $b = 1$ the log sign disappears on both sides

$$z = \frac{a b^x \pm c}{d}, \text{ then } \quad x = \frac{\log\left(\frac{dz \mp c}{a}\right)}{\log b} \quad (b \neq 1) \quad (131)$$

$$z = \frac{d}{a x^b \pm c}, \text{ then } \log x = \frac{\log\left(\frac{d/z \mp c}{a}\right)}{b} \quad (132)$$

when $b = 1$ the log sign disappears on both sides

$$z = \frac{d}{a\,b^x \pm c}, \text{ then } x = \frac{\log\left(\dfrac{d/z \mp c}{a}\right)}{\log b} \qquad (b \neq 1) \qquad \textbf{(133)}$$

Equations (**130**) to (**133**) have no solution when

$(d\,z \mp c) < 0$ or $(d/z \mp c) < 0$

This is true for equations (**130**) and (**132**), however, only when $b \neq 1$.

The following table gives z-values [solutions of equation (**129**)] for various numbers a in common use

a	$1-a$	$\log(1-a)$	$z = -\ln 10 \times \log(1-a) = -\ln(1-a)$
0.999	0.001	− 3	6.907 755 279
0.995	0.005	0.698 970 0043 − 3	5.298 317 367
0.99	0.01	− 2	4.605 170 186
0.975	0.025	0.397 940 0087 − 2	3.688 879 453
0.95	0.05	0.698 970 0043 − 2	2.995 732 274
0.90	0.10	− 1	2.302 585 093
0.85	0.15	0.176 091 2591 − 1	1.897 119 985
0.80	0.20	0.301 029 9957 − 1	1.609 437 912
0.75	0.25	0.397 940 0087 − 1	1.386 294 361
0.70	0.30	0.477 121 2547 − 1	1.203 972 804
0.65	0.35	0.544 068 0444 − 1	1.049 822 124
0.60	0.40	0.602 059 9913 − 1	0.916 290 731 9
0.55	0.45	0.653 212 5138 − 1	0.798 507 696 2
0.50	0.50	0.698 970 0043 − 1	0.693 147 180 4
0.45	0.55	0.740 362 6895 − 1	0.597 837 000 7
0.40	0.60	0.778 151 2504 − 1	0.510 825 623 7
0.35	0.65	0.812 913 3566 − 1	0.430 782 916 2
0.30	0.70	0.845 098 0400 − 1	0.356 674 944 0
0.25	0.75	0.875 061 2634 − 1	0.287 682 072 4
0.20	0.80	0.903 089 9870 − 1	0.223 143 551 5
0.15	0.85	0.929 418 9257 − 1	0.162 518 929 5
0.10	0.90	0.954 242 5094 − 1	0.105 360 515 7
0.05	0.95	0.977 723 6053 − 1	0.051 293 294 39
0.025	0.975	0.989 004 6157 − 1	0.025 317 807 98
0.01	0.99	0.995 635 1946 − 1	0.010 050 335 85
0.005	0.995	0.997 823 0807 − 1	0.005 012 541 823
0.001	0.999	0.999 565 4882 − 1	0.001 000 500 333

XI. Rectangular coordinate system

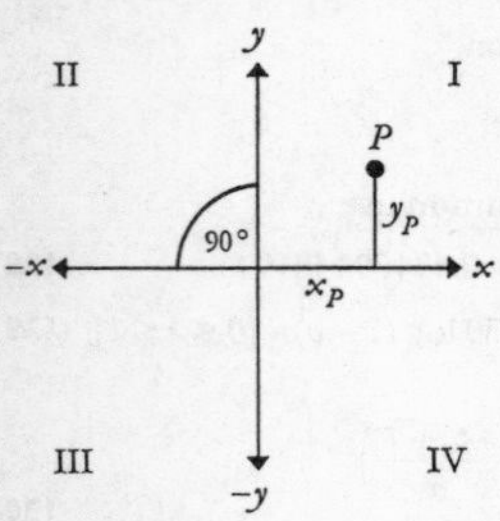

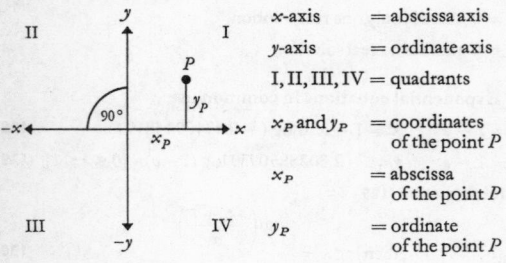

x-axis = abscissa axis
y-axis = ordinate axis
I, II, III, IV = quadrants
x_P and y_P = coordinates of the point P
x_P = abscissa of the point P
y_P = ordinate of the point P

Signs of the coordinates of points in each of the 4 quadrants

Quadrant	x	y
I	+	+
II	−	+
III	−	−
IV	+	−

XII. Angles, trigonometrical functions, inverse trigonometric functions

1. Positive and negative angles

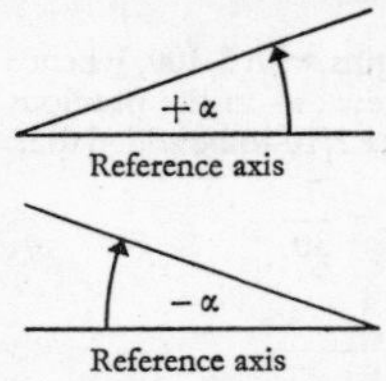

Rotation in an *anti*clockwise direction is defined as positive rotation, rotation in a clockwise direction as negative rotation. Similarly an angle measured by positive rotation is a positive angle, one measured by negative rotation a negative angle.

By angle of inclination of a straight line a is usually meant the *acute* angle between the straight line and the x-axis.

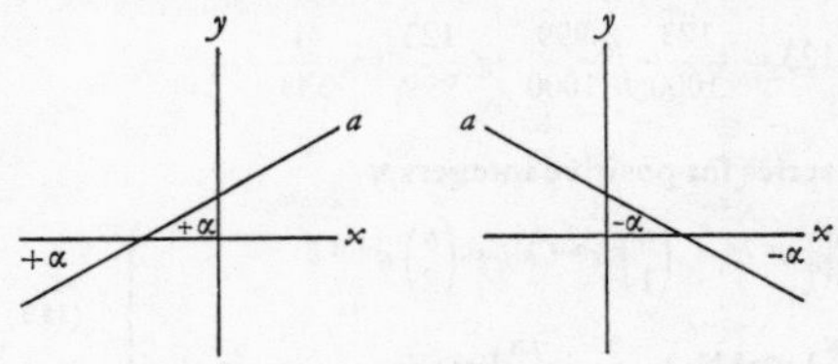

2. Angle units (see also under Units of measurement, page 209)

The basis of all angle units is the circumference of a circle drawn with its center at the point of intersection of the lines forming the angle. This is divided into 360 equal parts (degrees, the unit normally used) or into 400 equal parts (grades), or measured in terms of its own radius (arc, circular or radian measure). Since the circumference of a circle is 2 π times its radius, angles are often expressed as fractions or multiples of π. The arc measure of the angle α is designated arcus α (arc α).

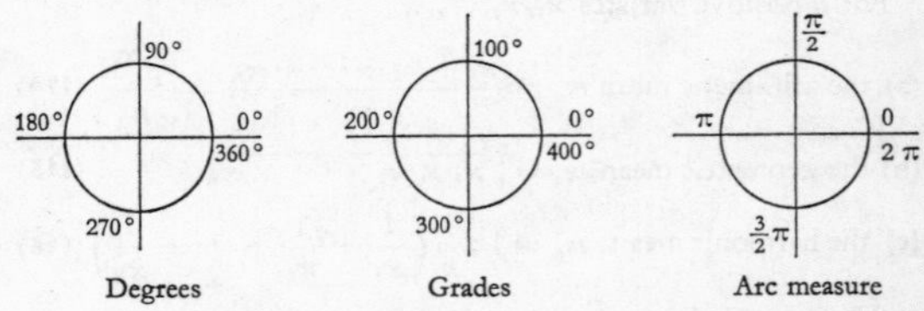

Degrees	0°	1°	30°	57°17′45″	60°	90°	180°	270°	360°
Arc measure	0	0.01745	$\frac{\pi}{6}$	1	$\frac{\pi}{3}$	$\frac{\pi}{2}$	π	$\frac{3}{2}\pi$	2π

3. Trigonometric functions
(other than secant and cosecant)

The definitions are based on the right triangle and are valid only for acute angles between 0 and 90°:

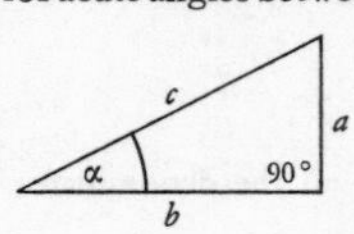

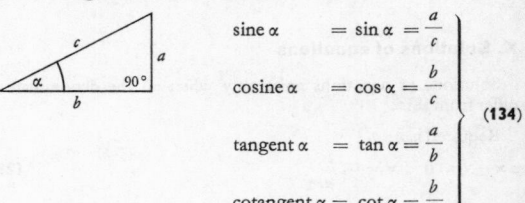

$$\left.\begin{aligned} &\text{sine } \alpha &&= \sin\alpha = \frac{a}{c} \\ &\text{cosine } \alpha &&= \cos\alpha = \frac{b}{c} \\ &\text{tangent } \alpha &&= \tan\alpha = \frac{a}{b} \\ &\text{cotangent } \alpha &&= \cot\alpha = \frac{b}{a} \end{aligned}\right\} \qquad \textbf{(134)}$$

(the tangent is also sometimes abbreviated to tg, the cotangent to ctg or ctn)

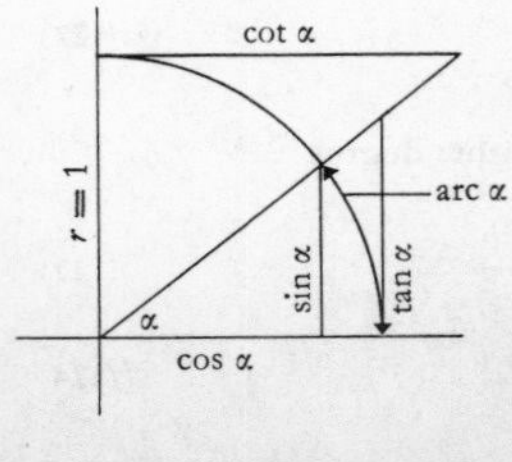

Representation of trigonometric functions on the unit circle (circle with radius = 1)

Algebraic signs of trigonometric functions in the 4 quadrants

Function	Quadrant I	II	III	IV
sin	+	+	−	−
cos	+	−	−	+
tan	+	−	+	−
cot	+	−	+	−

(135)

Ranges of trigonometric functions in the 4 quadrants

Function	Quadrant I	II	III	IV
sin	0 to 1	1 to 0	0 to −1	−1 to 0
cos	1 to 0	0 to −1	−1 to 0	0 to 1
tan	0 to ∞	−∞ to 0	0 to ∞	−∞ to 0
cot	∞ to 0	0 to −∞	∞ to 0	0 to −∞

(136)

Behavior of trigonometric functions

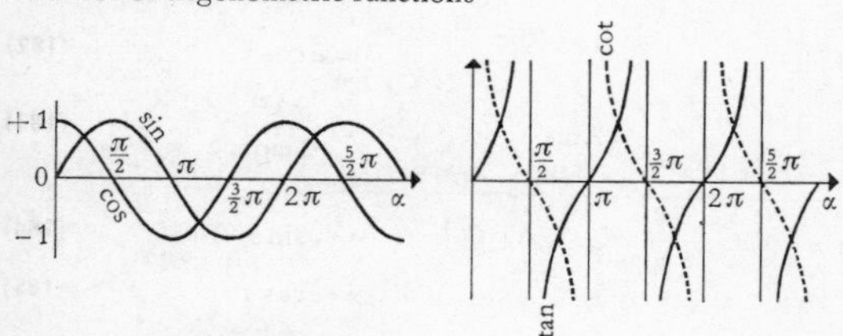

Functions of negative angles

$$\left.\begin{aligned}\sin(-\alpha) &= -\sin\alpha\\ \cos(-\alpha) &= +\cos\alpha\\ \tan(-\alpha) &= -\tan\alpha\\ \cot(-\alpha) &= -\cot\alpha\end{aligned}\right\}\quad \textbf{(137)}$$

Conversion of the functions of obtuse angles into those of acute angles

	$90°\pm\alpha$	$180°\pm\alpha$	$270°\pm\alpha$	$n^*(360°)\pm\alpha$
sin	$+\cos\alpha$	$\mp\sin\alpha$	$-\cos\alpha$	$\pm\sin\alpha$
cos	$\mp\sin\alpha$	$-\cos\alpha$	$\pm\sin\alpha$	$+\cos\alpha$
tan	$\mp\cot\alpha$	$\pm\tan\alpha$	$\mp\cot\alpha$	$\pm\tan\alpha$
cot	$\mp\tan\alpha$	$\pm\cot\alpha$	$\mp\tan\alpha$	$\pm\cot\alpha$

* n = positive integer

(138)

Example: sin 125° = cos 35°

Relationships between trigonometric functions

Function	$\sin\alpha$	$\cos\alpha$	$\tan\alpha$	$\cot\alpha$
$\sin\alpha$	$\sin\alpha$	$\pm\sqrt{1-\cos^2\alpha}$	$\frac{\tan\alpha}{\pm\sqrt{1+\tan^2\alpha}}$	$\frac{1}{\pm\sqrt{1+\cot^2\alpha}}$
$\cos\alpha$	$\pm\sqrt{1-\sin^2\alpha}$	$\cos\alpha$	$\frac{1}{\pm\sqrt{1+\tan^2\alpha}}$	$\frac{\cot\alpha}{\pm\sqrt{1+\cot^2\alpha}}$
$\tan\alpha$	$\frac{\sin\alpha}{\pm\sqrt{1-\sin^2\alpha}}$	$\frac{\pm\sqrt{1-\cos^2\alpha}}{\cos\alpha}$	$\tan\alpha$	$\frac{1}{\cot\alpha}$
$\cot\alpha$	$\frac{\pm\sqrt{1-\sin^2\alpha}}{\sin\alpha}$	$\frac{\cos\alpha}{\pm\sqrt{1-\cos^2\alpha}}$	$\frac{1}{\tan\alpha}$	$\cot\alpha$

(139)

Algebraic sign of the square root: This is determined by the quadrant into which the angle falls. For algebraic signs in the quadrants see (**135**).

Functions of half the angle and of twice the angle

$$\left.\begin{aligned}\sin\frac{\alpha}{2} &= \pm\tfrac{1}{2}\left(\sqrt{1+\sin\alpha}-\sqrt{1-\sin\alpha}\right)\\ &= \pm\sqrt{\frac{1-\cos\alpha}{2}}\end{aligned}\right\}\quad \textbf{(140)}$$

$$\cos\frac{\alpha}{2} = \pm\sqrt{\frac{1+\cos\alpha}{2}} \quad \textbf{(141)}$$

$$\left.\begin{aligned}\tan\frac{\alpha}{2} &= \frac{-1\pm\sqrt{1+\tan^2\alpha}}{\tan\alpha} = \frac{1-\cos\alpha}{\sin\alpha}\\ &= \frac{\sin\alpha}{1+\cos\alpha} = \pm\sqrt{\frac{1-\cos\alpha}{1+\sin\alpha}}\end{aligned}\right\}\quad \textbf{(142)}$$

$$\sin 2\alpha = 2\sin\alpha\cos\alpha \quad \textbf{(143)}$$

$$\cos 2\alpha = 2\cos^2\alpha - 1 = 1 - 2\sin^2\alpha = \cos^2\alpha - \sin^2\alpha \quad \textbf{(144)}$$

$$\tan 2\alpha = \frac{2\tan\alpha}{1-\tan^2\alpha} \quad \textbf{(145)}$$

Algebraic signs: ± indicates that the algebraic sign is determined by the quadrant into which the *required* angle falls. For algebraic signs in the quadrants see (**135**).

Relationships between the functions of two angles

$$\sin(\alpha\pm\beta) = \sin\alpha\cos\beta \pm \cos\alpha\sin\beta \quad \textbf{(146)}$$

$$\cos(\alpha\pm\beta) = \cos\alpha\cos\beta \mp \sin\alpha\sin\beta \quad \textbf{(147)}$$

$$\operatorname{tg}(\alpha\pm\beta) = \frac{\operatorname{tg}\alpha\pm\operatorname{tg}\beta}{1\mp\operatorname{tg}\alpha\operatorname{tg}\beta} = \frac{\sin(\alpha\pm\beta)}{\cos(\alpha\pm\beta)} \quad \textbf{(148)}$$

$$\sin\alpha+\sin\beta = 2\sin\left(\frac{\alpha+\beta}{2}\right)\cos\left(\frac{\alpha-\beta}{2}\right) \quad \textbf{(149)}$$

$$\sin\alpha-\sin\beta = 2\cos\left(\frac{\alpha+\beta}{2}\right)\sin\left(\frac{\alpha-\beta}{2}\right) \quad \textbf{(150)}$$

$$\cos\alpha+\cos\beta = 2\cos\left(\frac{\alpha+\beta}{2}\right)\cos\left(\frac{\alpha-\beta}{2}\right) \quad \textbf{(151)}$$

$$\cos\alpha-\cos\beta = -2\sin\left(\frac{\alpha+\beta}{2}\right)\sin\left(\frac{\alpha-\beta}{2}\right) \quad \textbf{(152)}$$

$$\tan\alpha\pm\tan\beta = \frac{\sin(\alpha\pm\beta)}{\cos\alpha\cos\beta} \quad \textbf{(153)}$$

$$\sin\alpha\sin\beta = \tfrac{1}{2}\cos(\alpha-\beta) - \tfrac{1}{2}\cos(\alpha+\beta) \quad \textbf{(154)}$$

$$\cos\alpha\cos\beta = \tfrac{1}{2}\cos(\alpha-\beta) + \tfrac{1}{2}\cos(\alpha+\beta) \quad \textbf{(155)}$$

$$\sin\alpha\cos\beta = \tfrac{1}{2}\sin(\alpha+\beta) + \tfrac{1}{2}\sin(\alpha-\beta) \quad \textbf{(156)}$$

4. Inverse trigonometric functions

These are also known as arc or cyclometric functions. Only the inverse sine (arc sine) function will be described here, since this is used for the stabilization of the variance of binomial distributions (see page 186).

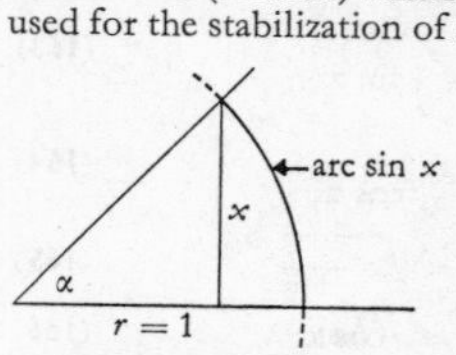

Arc sine x, abbreviated to $\sin^{-1}x$ or arc sin x, is the arc or degree measure of the angle with sine = x. An arc sine table in arc measure for the range $0 \leqq x \leqq 1$ is given on page 69. If the value of an arc sine in degrees is required, the value given in this table must be multiplied by $180/\pi = 57.295\,779\,513$.

Behavior of the function arc sin x in the range $0 \leqq x \leqq 1$

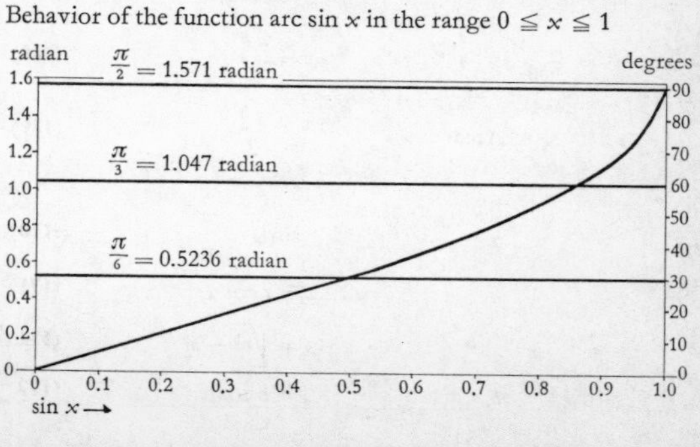

XIII. Hyperbolic functions

These derive their name from their geometric representation in relation to a rectangular hyperbola in a manner similar to that in which the trigonometric functions are related to a circle. Here only the hyperbolic tangent ($\tanh z$) and the corresponding inverse function ($\tanh^{-1} r$) will be dealt with, since these functions are required for the transformation of the correlation coefficient r (see page 179). They are defined as follows:

$$\tanh z = r = \frac{e^{2z}-1}{e^{2z}+1} \qquad \textbf{(157)}$$

$$\tanh^{-1} r = z = \tfrac{1}{2} \ln \frac{1+r}{1-r} = 1.151\,292\,55 \log_{10} \frac{1+r}{1-r} \qquad \textbf{(158)}$$

Only the following two relationships are required:

$$\tanh(-z) = -\tanh z \qquad \textbf{(159)}$$

$$\tanh^{-1}(-r) = -\tanh^{-1} r \qquad \textbf{(160)}$$

The range of variation of $\tanh z$ is -1 to $+1$ for values of z from $-\infty$ to $+\infty$.

Behavior of the function $\tanh z$ in the range $-3.2 \leqq z \leqq +3.2$

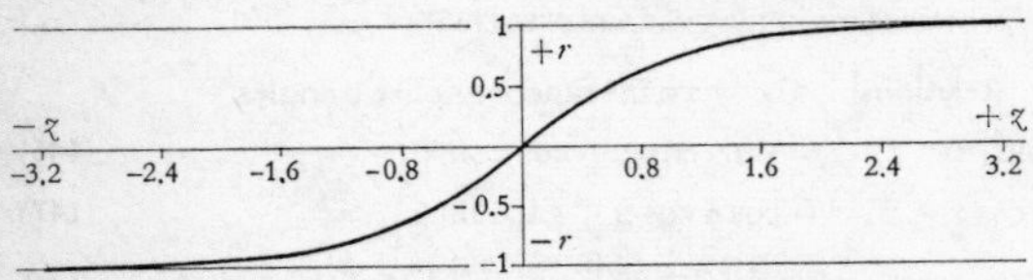

Tables of $\tanh z$ are given on pages 64 and 65, of $\tanh^{-1} r$ on page 62.

XIV. Geometric calculations

1. Right triangle *ABC*

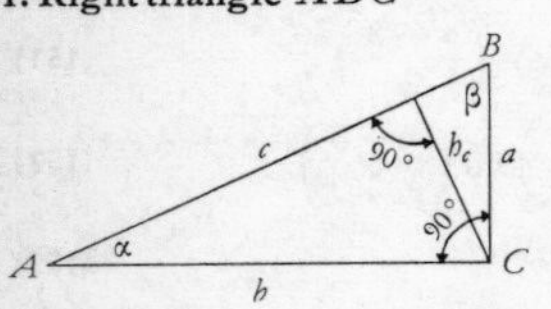

a = perpendicular } sides
b = base } sides
c = hypotenuse
h_c = altitude above hypotenuse

Given	Required	Solution	
β	α	$= 90° - \beta$	**(161)**
a, b	α	$\tan\alpha = \frac{a}{b}$	**(162)**
	c	$= \frac{a}{\sin\alpha}$	**(163)**
		$= \frac{b}{\cos\alpha}$	**(164)**
		$= \sqrt[+]{a^2+b^2}$	**(165)**
	h_c	$= a\cos\alpha$	**(166)**
		$= b\sin\alpha$	**(167)**
		$= \frac{ab}{c}$	**(168)**
	Area	$= \frac{ab}{2}$	**(169)**
a, c	α	$\sin\alpha = \frac{a}{c}$	**(170)**
	b	$= c\cos\alpha$	**(171)**
		$= \sqrt[+]{c^2-a^2}$	**(172)**
	h_c	$= a\cos\alpha$	**(173)**
	Area	$= \frac{ac\cos\alpha}{2}$	**(174)**
b, c	α	$\cos\alpha = \frac{b}{c}$	**(175)**
	a	$= c\sin\alpha$	**(176)**
		$= \sqrt[+]{c^2-b^2}$	**(177)**
	h_c	$= b\sin\alpha$	**(178)**
	Area	$= \frac{bc\sin\alpha}{2}$	**(179)**
a, α	b	$= \frac{a}{\tan\alpha}$	**(180)**
	c	$= \frac{a}{\sin\alpha}$	**(181)**
	h_c	$= a\cos\alpha$	**(182)**
	Area	$= \frac{a^2}{2\tan\alpha}$	**(183)**
c, α	a	$= c\sin\alpha$	**(184)**
	b	$= c\cos\alpha$	**(185)**
	h_c	$= \frac{c\sin 2\alpha}{2}$	**(186)**
	Area	$= \frac{c^2\sin 2\alpha}{4}$	**(187)**
c, h_c	α	$\sin 2\alpha = \frac{2h_c}{c}$	**(188)**
	a	$= \frac{h_c}{\cos\alpha}$	**(189)**
	b	$= \frac{h_c}{\sin\alpha}$	**(190)**
	Area	$= \frac{c\,h_c}{2}$	**(191)**

2. Obtuse triangle

All the sides are of equal value in the obtuse triangle, and permutation of a, b, c, etc. in a cyclic fashion results in different formulas which are equally valid. When one of the symbols in any formula in a group is permuted, the symbols in all the other formulas of the group must be permuted in accordance with the following scheme:

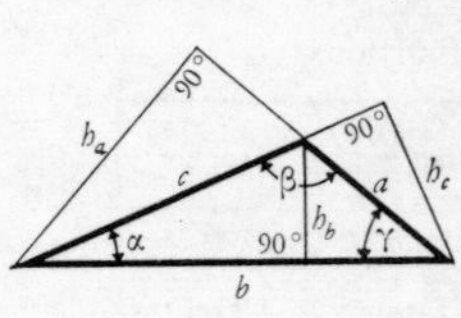

Permutation by one step	Permutation by two steps	
$a \rightarrow b$	$a \rightarrow c$	
$b \rightarrow c$	$b \rightarrow a$	
$c \rightarrow a$	$c \rightarrow b$	
$\alpha \rightarrow \beta$	$\alpha \rightarrow \gamma$	**(192)**
$\beta \rightarrow \gamma$	$\beta \rightarrow \alpha$	
$\gamma \rightarrow \alpha$	$\gamma \rightarrow \beta$	
$h_a \rightarrow h_b$	$h_a \rightarrow h_c$	

Altitudes and areas

$h_a = b \sin\gamma$ **(193)**

$ = c \sin\beta$ **(194)**

$ = a \dfrac{\sin\beta \sin\gamma}{\sin\alpha}$ **(195)**

Area $A = \dfrac{a\,h_a}{2}$ **(196)**

Given	Required	Solution	
$\beta + \gamma$	α	$= 180° - (\beta + \gamma)$	**(197)**
$\sin\alpha$	$\sin(\beta+\gamma) = \sin\alpha$		
$\cos\alpha$	$\cos(\beta+\gamma) = -\cos\alpha$		**(198)**
$\tan\alpha$	$\tan(\beta+\gamma) = -\tan\alpha$		
a, b, c	α	$\cos\alpha = \dfrac{b^2 + c^2 - a^2}{2\,b\,c}$	**(199)**
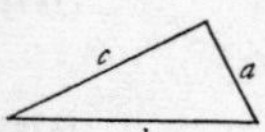	h_a	$= b \sin\gamma$	**(200)**
		$= \dfrac{2A}{a}$	**(201)**
	Area A	$= \dfrac{b\,c \sin\alpha}{2}$	**(202)**
		$= \sqrt[+]{s(s-a)(s-b)(s-c)}$ where $s = \dfrac{a+b+c}{2}$	**(203)**
a, b, γ	α	$\tan\alpha = \dfrac{a \sin\gamma}{b - a\cos\gamma}$	**(204)**
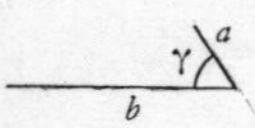	c	$= \dfrac{a \sin\gamma}{\sin\alpha}$	**(205)**
		$= \sqrt[+]{a^2 + b^2 - 2\,a\,b\cos\gamma}$	**(206)**
	h_a	$= b \sin\gamma$	**(207)**
	h_b	$= a \sin\gamma$	**(208)**
	Area A	$= \dfrac{a\,b \sin\gamma}{2}$	**(209)**
a, b, α	β	$\sin\beta = \dfrac{b \sin\alpha}{a}$	**(210)**
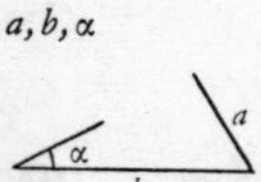	c	$= \dfrac{a \sin\gamma}{\sin\alpha}$	**(211)**
		$= b\cos\alpha \pm \sqrt{a^2 - b^2 \sin\alpha}$	**(212)**
	h_a	$= b \sin\gamma$	**(213)**
	h_b	$= a \sin\gamma$	**(214)**
	h_c	$= b \sin\alpha$	**(215)**
	Area A	$= \dfrac{b}{2} \sin\alpha \times \left(b\cos\alpha \pm \sqrt{a^2 - b^2 \sin\alpha}\right)$	**(216)**
a, b, β	α	$\sin\alpha = \dfrac{a \sin\beta}{b}$	**(217)**
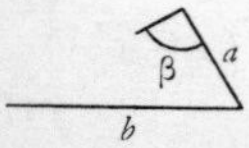	c	$= \dfrac{b \sin\gamma}{\sin\beta}$	**(218)**
	h_a	$= b \sin\gamma$	**(219)**
	h_b	$= a \sin\gamma$	**(220)**
a, b, β	h_c	$= a \sin\beta$	**(221)**
	Area A	$= \dfrac{a}{2} \sin\beta \times \left(a\cos\beta \pm \sqrt{b^2 - a^2 \sin\beta}\right)$	**(222)**

Note that in the above group of equations (given two sides and the angle they enclose), the following conditions hold:

	Equations **(210)** – **(216)**	Equations **(217)** – **(222)**
solution is only possible when	$b\sin\alpha \leqq a$	$a\sin\beta \leqq b$
If	$b\sin\alpha = a$	$a\sin\beta = b$
then	$\beta = 90°$	$\alpha = 90°$
If	$b\sin\alpha < a$ and $a < b$	$a\sin\beta < b$ and $b < a$
two solutions are possible:	β_1 and $\beta_2 = 180° - \beta_1$	α_1 and $\alpha_2 = 180° - \alpha_1$
If	$b\sin\alpha < a$ and $a \geqq b$	$a\sin\beta < a$ and $b \geqq a$
no solution is possible.		

Given	Required	Solution	
a, β, γ	b	$= \dfrac{a \sin\beta}{\sin(\beta+\gamma)}$	**(223)**
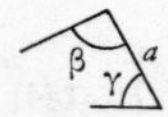	c	$= \dfrac{a \sin\gamma}{\sin(\beta+\gamma)}$	**(224)**
(Note that if two angles are given, the third is also given)	h_a	$= \dfrac{a \sin\beta \sin\gamma}{\sin(\beta+\gamma)}$	**(225)**
	h_b	$= a \sin\gamma$	**(226)**
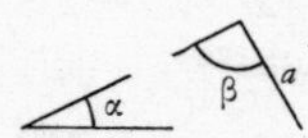	h_c	$= a \sin\beta$	**(227)**
$\gamma = 180 - (\alpha + \beta)$	Area A	$= \dfrac{a^2}{2} \times \dfrac{\sin\beta \sin\gamma}{\sin(\beta+\gamma)}$	**(228)**

3. Quadrilateral

In general the area of any quadrilateral can be calculated from the diagonals and the angle θ (or $\theta' = 180° - \theta$) enclosed by them:

Any quadrilateral

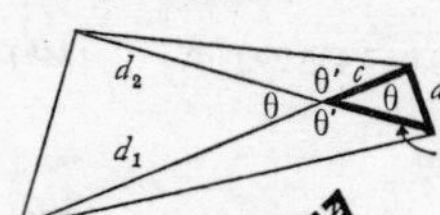

$\sin\theta = \sin\theta'$

$= \dfrac{2}{b\,c}\sqrt{s(s-a)(s-b)(s-c)}$ **(229)**

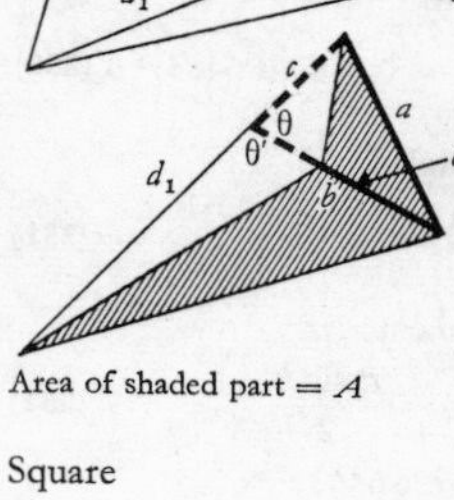

Area of shaded part $= A$

where $s = ½\,(a + b + c)$ is half the circumference of the triangle bounded by the two diagonals and the side a. Any triangle can be chosen, but the sides indicated by b, c must *enclose* the angle θ or θ'.

Area $A = \dfrac{d_1\,d_2 \sin\theta}{2}$ **(230)**

Square

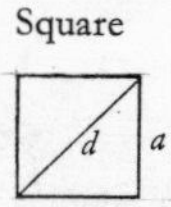

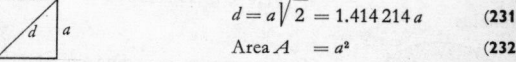

$d = a\sqrt{2} = 1.414\,214\,a$ **(231)**

Area $A = a^2$ **(232)**

Rectangle

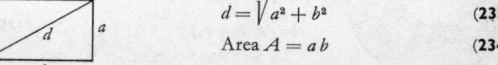

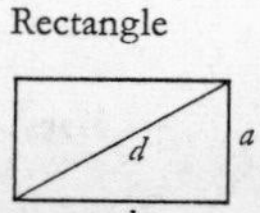

$d = \sqrt{a^2 + b^2}$ **(233)**

Area $A = a\,b$ **(234)**

Parallelogram

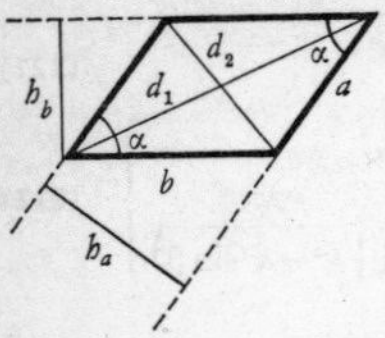

$$d_1, d_2 = \sqrt{a^2 + b^2 \pm 2\,a\,b\cos\alpha} \quad (235)$$

$$= \sqrt{a^2 + b^2 \pm 2\,a\sqrt{b^2 - h_a^2}} \quad (236)$$

$$h_a = b\sin\alpha \quad (237)$$

$$h_b = a\sin\alpha \quad (238)$$

$$\text{Area } A = a\,h_a = b\,h_b = a\,b\sin\alpha \quad (239)$$

Trapezoid

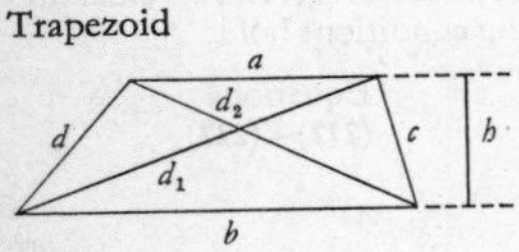

a, b are parallel, c, d non-parallel sides; d_1 = diagonal drawn between the point of intersection of d with b and that of a with c.

$$d_1 = \sqrt{a\,b + \frac{a\,c^2 - b\,d^2}{a - b}} \quad (240)$$

$$d_2 = \sqrt{a\,b + \frac{a\,d^2 - b\,c^2}{a - b}} \quad (241)$$

$$h = \frac{2}{a-b} \times \sqrt{s(s-a+b)(s-c)(s-d)} \quad (242)$$

where $s = \frac{1}{2}(a + b + c + d)$

$$\text{Area } A = \frac{(a+b)\,h}{2} \quad (243)$$

4. Circle

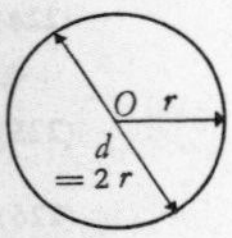

$$\left.\begin{aligned}\text{Circumference } c &= 2\pi r\\ &= 6.283\,1853\,r\\ &= 3.141\,592\,65\,d\end{aligned}\right\} \quad (244)$$

$$\left.\begin{aligned}\text{Area } A &= \pi r^2 = 3.141\,592\,65\,r^2\\ &= 0.785\,398\,16\,d^2\end{aligned}\right\} \quad (245)$$

Sector

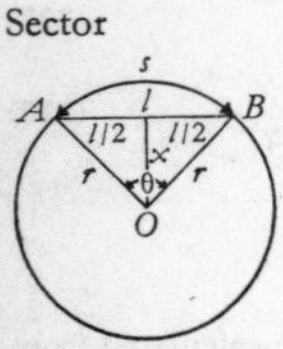

Angle θ between the radii r

$$\cos\theta = 1 - \frac{l^2}{2\,r^2} \quad (246)$$

or

$$\theta = 180° - 2\,\text{arc}\sin(x/r) \quad (247)$$

Length of a chord

$$l = 2\,r\sin\frac{\theta}{2} \quad (248)$$

Length of an arc

$$s = \frac{\pi\,r\,\theta}{180} = 0.017\,453\,293\,r\,\theta \quad (249)$$

Area of a sector

$$A_{Se} = \frac{\pi\,r^2\,\theta}{360} = 0.008\,726\,6463\,r^2\,\theta \quad (250)$$

Area of a triangle OAB

$$A_\triangle = \frac{r^2\sin\theta}{2} \quad (251)$$

Area of a segment AsB

$$A_{Sg} = \frac{\pi\,r^2\,\theta}{360} - \frac{r^2\sin\theta}{2} \quad (252)$$

$$= 0.008\,726\,6463\,r^2 \times (\theta - 57.295\,7795\sin\theta)$$

Annulus

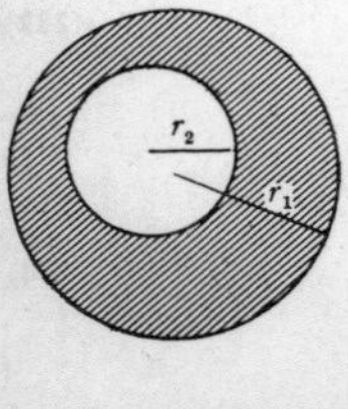

(The two circles bounding an annulus need not be concentric)

Area of shaded part

$$A = \pi(r_1 + r_2)(r_1 - r_2) \quad [r_1 \geqq r_2] \quad (253)$$

$$= 3.141\,592\,65\,(r_1 + r_2)(r_1 - r_2)$$

Annular segment (concentric)

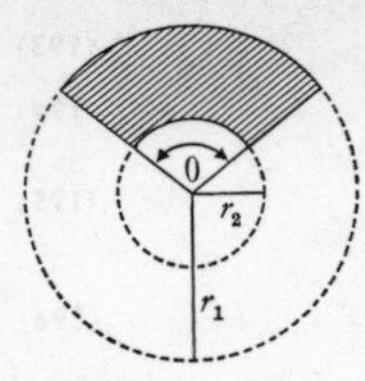

Area of shaded part

$$A = \frac{\pi\,\theta}{360}(r_1 + r_2)(r_1 - r_2) \quad [r_1 \geqq r_2] \quad (254)$$

$$\frac{\pi}{360} = 0.008\,726\,646\,26$$

For the angle θ see equations (**246**) and (**247**)

5. Ellipse

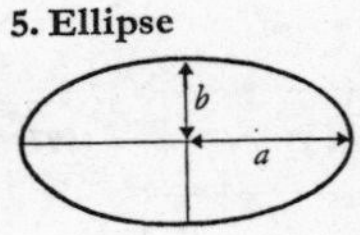

$$\text{Circumference} \sim 2\pi\sqrt{\frac{a^2 + b^2}{2}} \quad (255)$$

$$\sim 4.443\sqrt{a^2 + b^2}$$

$$\text{Area } A = \pi\,a\,b = 3.141\,592\,65\,a\,b \quad (256)$$

XV. Solid geometry

1. Rectangular parallelepiped

(all edges at right angles to the adjacent ones)

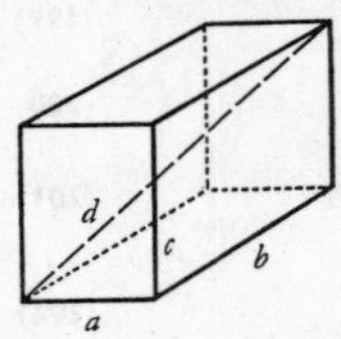

Surface area

$$A = 2\,(a\,b + b\,c + c\,a) \quad (257)$$

Internal diagonal

$$d = \sqrt{a^2 + b^2 + c^2} \quad (258)$$

Volume

$$V = a\,b\,c \quad (259)$$

In the case of the cube, equations (**257**) to (**259**) become

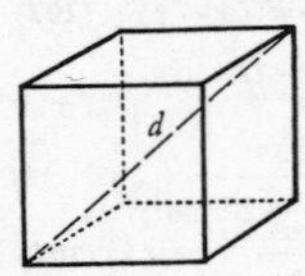

$$A = 6\,a^2 \quad (260)$$

$$d = a\sqrt{3} = 1.732\,051\,a \quad (261)$$

$$V = a^3 \quad (262)$$

2. Pyramid (any base)

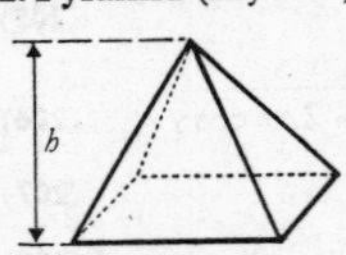

Volume

$$V = \frac{h}{3}A_B \quad (263)$$

(A_B = area of base)

3. Right circular cylinder

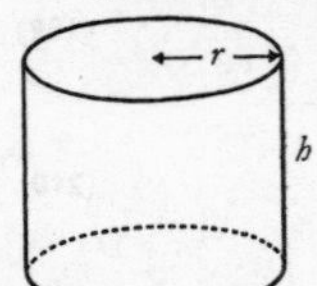

Area of convex surface

$$A_C = 2\pi\,r\,h = 6.283\,1853\,r\,h \quad (264)$$

Total surface area

$$A = 2\pi\,r\,(r + h) \quad (265)$$

$$= 6.283\,1853\,r\,(r + h)$$

Volume

$$V = \pi\,r^2\,h = 3.141\,592\,65\,r^2\,h \quad (266)$$

Hollow cylinder

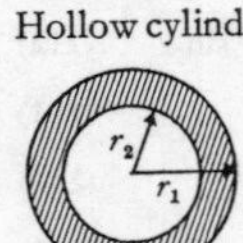

Internal volume

$$V_I = \pi\,(r_1^2 - r_2^2)\,h \quad [r_1 \geqq r_2] \quad (267)$$

$$= 3.141\,592\,65\,(r_1^2 - r_2^2)\,h$$

4. Right circular cone

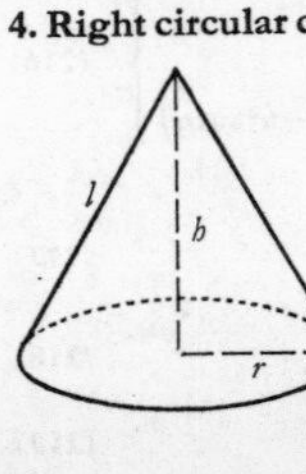

Area of convex surface

$$A_C = \pi\,r\,l = 3.141\,592\,65\,r\,l \quad (268)$$

(l = slant height = $\sqrt{r^2 + h^2}$)

Total surface area

$$A = \pi\,r\,(r + l) \quad (269)$$

$$= 3.141\,592\,65\,r\,(r + l)$$

Volume

$$V = \frac{1}{3}\pi\,r^2\,h = 1.047\,197\,55\,r^2\,h \quad (270)$$

Truncated cone (right circular, plane surfaces parallel)

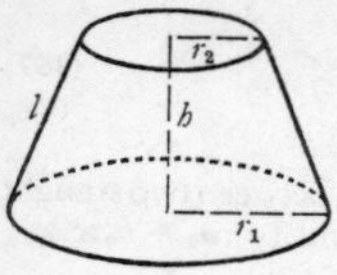

Area of convex surface

$$A_C = \pi\, l\,(r_1 + r_2) = 3.141\,592\,65\, l\,(r_1 + r_2) \quad \textbf{(271)}$$

Total surface area

$$A = \pi\left[r_1(r_1 + l) + r_2(r_2 + l)\right] \quad \textbf{(272)}$$

Volume

$$V = \frac{\pi h}{3}(r_1^2 + r_1 r_2 + r_2^2) = 1.047\,197\,55\, h\,(r_1^2 + r_1 r_2 + r_2^2) \quad \textbf{(273)}$$

5. Sphere

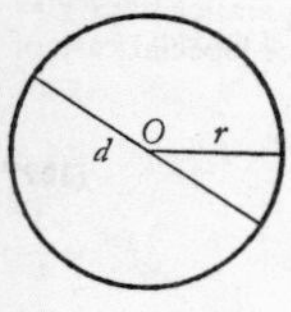

Surface area

$$A = 4\pi r^2 = \pi d^2 = 12.566\,3706\, r^2 = 3.141\,592\,65\, d^2 \quad \textbf{(274)}$$

Volume

$$V = \frac{4\pi r^3}{3} = \frac{\pi d^3}{6} = 4.188\,790\,20\, r^3 = 0.523\,598\,78\, d^3 \quad \textbf{(275)}$$

Segment of a sphere (cut by a single plane)

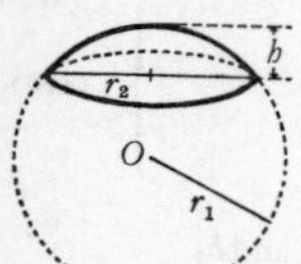

Area of convex surface

$$A_C = \pi(r_2^2 + h^2) = 2\pi r_1 h \quad \textbf{(276)}$$

Total surface area

$$A = \pi(2r_2^2 + h^2) \quad \textbf{(277)}$$

Volume

$$\left.\begin{aligned} V &= \frac{\pi h}{6}(3r_2^2 + h^2)\\ &= \frac{\pi h^2}{3}(3r_1 - h)\end{aligned}\right\} \quad \textbf{(278)}$$

($\pi = 3.141\,592\,65$; $\pi/6 = 0.523\,598\,78$; $\pi/3 = 1.047\,197\,55$)

Segment of a sphere (cut by two parallel planes)

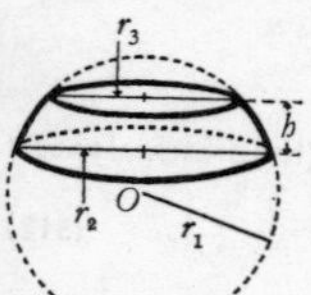

Area of convex surface

$$A_C = 2\pi r_1 h = 6.283\,1853\, r_1 h \quad \textbf{(279)}$$

Total surface area

$$A = \pi(r_2^2 + 2r_1 h + r_3^2) \quad \textbf{(280)}$$

Volume

$$V = \frac{\pi h}{6}(3r_2^2 + 3r_3^2 + h^2) = 0.523\,598\,78\, h\,(3r_2^2 + 3r_3^2 + h^2) \quad \textbf{(281)}$$

Wedge segment of a sphere

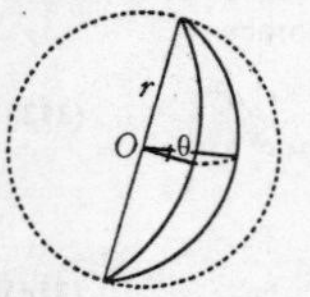

Volume

$$V = \frac{\pi r^3 \theta}{270} = 0.011\,635\,528\, r^3 \theta \quad \textbf{(282)}$$

[for θ (= angle between the two planes passing through the center of the sphere) see (**246**) and (**247**)]

6. Bodies of the same shape

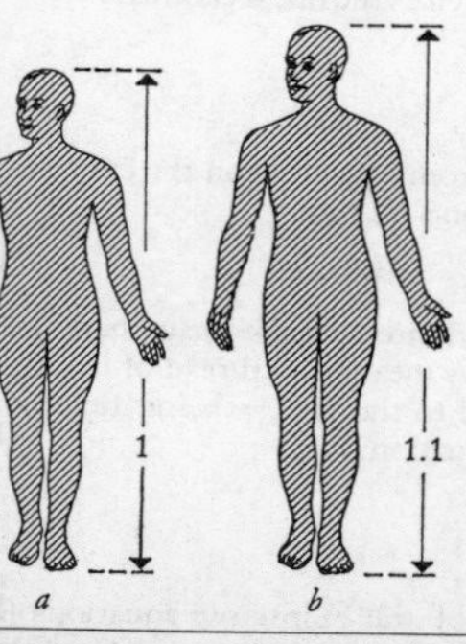

Bodies of the same shape, i.e. those in which *all corresponding linear measurements bear the same ratio* $a : b$*, have surface areas in the ratio $a^2 : b^2$ and weights in the ratio $a^3 : b^3$. **(283)**

All dimensions of body b are 10% greater than those of body a; b has 21% more surface area and 33% more weight

* Note that this is usually not true of human bodies of different *heights*.

XVI. Formulas of analytic geometry

1. Transformation of rectangular coordinates

The new coordinates are indicated by C, the transformed variables by X, Y, the old coordinates and variables by c, x, y. For the sake of simplicity the transformation is illustrated in the first quadrant (see section XI, page 138) but the equations are valid for all quadrants.

(*a*) Translation of coordinate axes

The origin is translated from O to O', i.e. a distance a in the direction x and a distance b in the direction y.

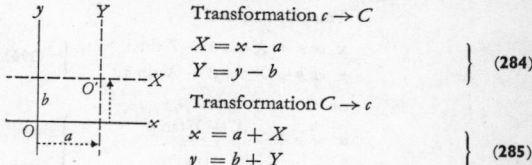

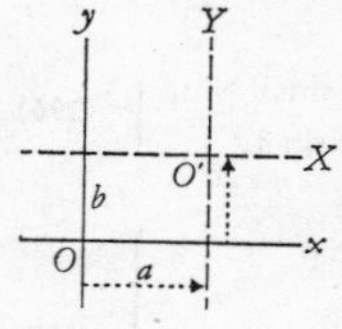

Transformation $c \to C$

$$\left.\begin{aligned} X &= x - a\\ Y &= y - b\end{aligned}\right\} \quad \textbf{(284)}$$

Transformation $C \to c$

$$\left.\begin{aligned} x &= a + X\\ y &= b + Y\end{aligned}\right\} \quad \textbf{(285)}$$

(*b*) Alteration of linear scale

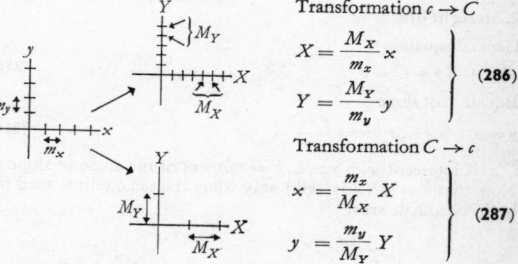

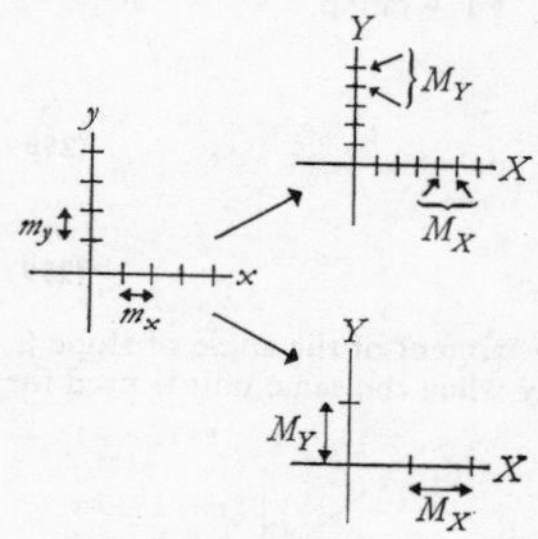

Transformation $c \to C$

$$\left.\begin{aligned} X &= \frac{M_X}{m_x}\, x\\ Y &= \frac{M_Y}{m_y}\, y\end{aligned}\right\} \quad \textbf{(286)}$$

Transformation $C \to c$

$$\left.\begin{aligned} x &= \frac{m_x}{M_X}\, X\\ y &= \frac{m_y}{M_Y}\, Y\end{aligned}\right\} \quad \textbf{(287)}$$

(*c*) Translation of axes and alteration of linear scale

Transformation $c \to C$

$$\left.\begin{aligned} X &= \frac{M_X}{m_x}(x - a)\\ Y &= \frac{M_Y}{m_y}(y - b)\end{aligned}\right\} \quad \textbf{(288)}$$

Transformation $C \to c$

$$\left.\begin{aligned} x &= a + \frac{m_x}{M_X}\, X\\ y &= b + \frac{m_y}{M_Y}\, Y\end{aligned}\right\} \quad \textbf{(289)}$$

(*d*) Rotation of coordinate axes

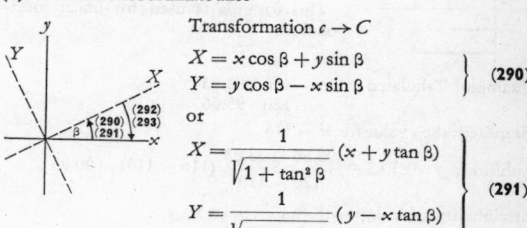

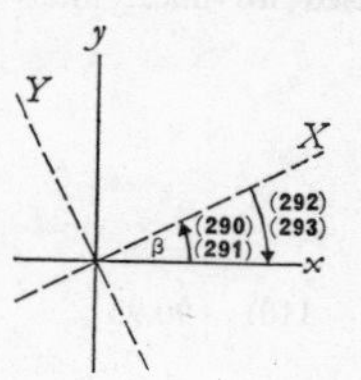

Transformation $c \to C$

$$\left.\begin{aligned} X &= x\cos\beta + y\sin\beta\\ Y &= y\cos\beta - x\sin\beta\end{aligned}\right\} \quad \textbf{(290)}$$

or

$$\left.\begin{aligned} X &= \frac{1}{\sqrt{1 + \tan^2\beta}}(x + y\tan\beta)\\ Y &= \frac{1}{\sqrt{1 + \tan^2\beta}}(y - x\tan\beta)\end{aligned}\right\} \quad \textbf{(291)}$$

Transformation $C \to c$

$$\left.\begin{aligned} x &= X\cos\beta - Y\sin\beta\\ y &= X\sin\beta + Y\cos\beta\end{aligned}\right\} \quad \textbf{(292)}$$

or

$$\left.\begin{aligned} x &= \frac{1}{\sqrt{1 + \tan^2\beta}}(X - Y\tan\beta)\\ y &= \frac{1}{\sqrt{1 + \tan^2\beta}}(Y + X\tan\beta)\end{aligned}\right\} \quad \textbf{(293)}$$

(*e*) Rotation and translation of the coordinate axes

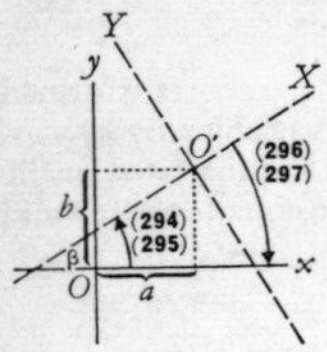

Transformation $c \to C$

$$\left.\begin{aligned} X &= (x-a)\cos\beta + (y-b)\sin\beta \\ Y &= (y-b)\cos\beta - (x-a)\sin\beta \end{aligned}\right\} \quad (294)$$

or

$$\left.\begin{aligned} X &= \frac{x-a+(y-b)\tan\beta}{\sqrt{1+\tan^2\beta}} \\ Y &= \frac{y-b-(x-a)\tan\beta}{\sqrt{1+\tan^2\beta}} \end{aligned}\right\} \quad (295)$$

Transformation $C \to c$

$$\left.\begin{aligned} x &= a + X\cos\beta - Y\sin\beta \\ y &= b + Y\cos\beta + X\sin\beta \end{aligned}\right\} \quad (296)$$

or

$$\left.\begin{aligned} x &= a + \frac{X - Y\tan\beta}{\sqrt{1+\tan^2\beta}} \\ y &= b + \frac{Y + X\tan\beta}{\sqrt{1+\tan^2\beta}} \end{aligned}\right\} \quad (297)$$

2. Straight line

General equation

$$Ax + By + C = 0 \quad (298)$$

Equation of slope

$$y = a + bx \quad \text{or} \quad x = \frac{y-a}{b} \quad (299)$$

a = intercept with y axis, b = tangent of the angle of slope β. Note that $b = \tan\beta$ is valid only when the same unit is used for both coordinate axes.

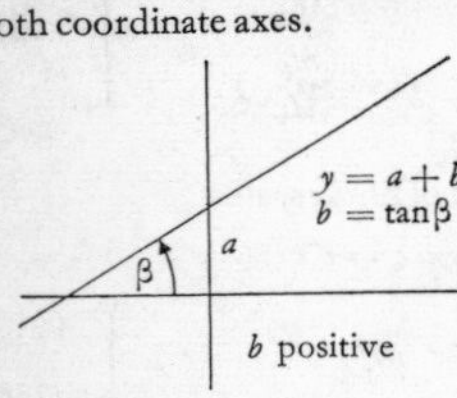

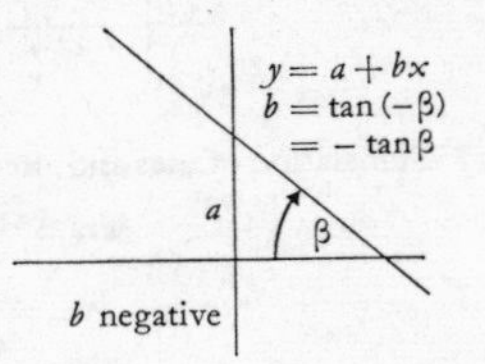

Special cases

$x = a$ is the equation of a line parallel to the y axis (300)

$y = c$ is the equation of a line parallel to the x axis (301)

A straight line is at right angles to another straight line with slope b when its slope is $-1/b$. (302)

Straight line through two points with coordinates x_1, y_1; x_2, y_2

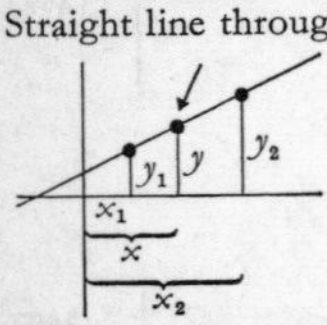

$$y = y_1 + \frac{y_2 - y_1}{x_2 - x_1}(x - x_1) \quad (303)$$

This formula is used for linear interpolation.

Example: Tabulated values

x	y
110	83.83
120	95.66

Required: the y value for $x = 116$

$$\text{Solution: } y = 83.83 + \frac{95.66 - 83.83}{120 - 110}(116 - 110) = 90.93$$

Straight line with slope b through a point x_1, y_1

$$y = y_1 + b(x - x_1) \quad (304)$$

Straight line through the origin and a point x_1, y_1

$$y = \frac{y_1}{x_1}x \quad (305)$$

Length p of the straight line parallel to the y axis between a point x_1, y_1 and the straight line $y = a + bx$

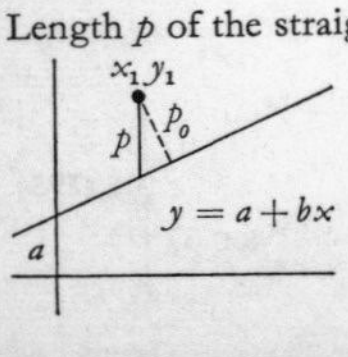

$$p = y_1 - a - bx_1 \quad (306)$$

Shortest (orthogonal) distance p_0 between a point and the straight line $y = a + bx$

$$p_0 = \frac{y_1 - a - bx_1}{\sqrt{1+b^2}} \quad (307)$$

Distance p_x parallel to the x axis at a height y_p between two straight lines $y = a_1 + b_1x$ and $y = a_2 + b_2x$

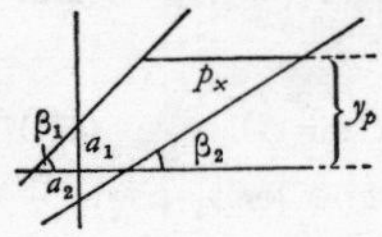

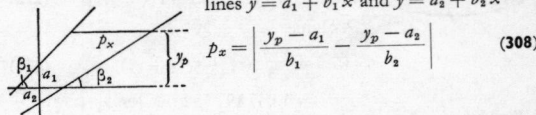

$$p_x = \left| \frac{y_p - a_1}{b_1} - \frac{y_p - a_2}{b_2} \right| \quad (308)$$

Distance p_x parallel to the x axis between two parallel lines $y = a_1 + bx$ and $y = a_2 + bx$ [special case of (**308**) with $b_1 = b_2$]

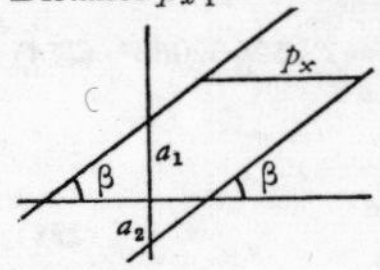

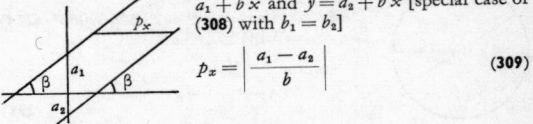

$$p_x = \left| \frac{a_1 - a_2}{b} \right| \quad (309)$$

Coordinates of the intersection of two straight lines $y = a_1 + b_1x$ and $y = a_2 + b_2x$

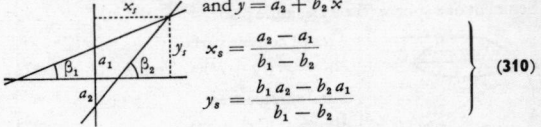

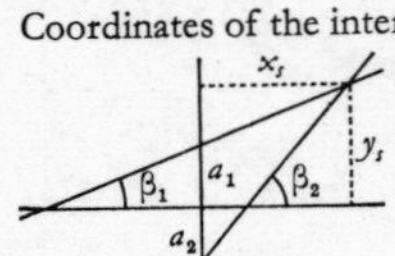

$$\left.\begin{aligned} x_s &= \frac{a_2 - a_1}{b_1 - b_2} \\ y_s &= \frac{b_1a_2 - b_2a_1}{b_1 - b_2} \end{aligned}\right\} \quad (310)$$

Angle θ between two straight lines with slopes b_1 and b_2

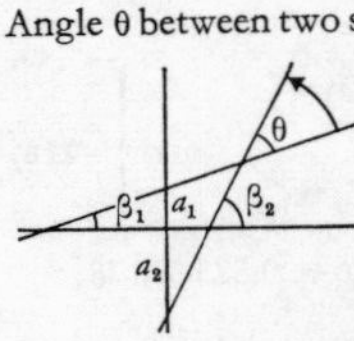

$$\tan\theta = \frac{b_1 - b_2}{b_1b_2 + 1} \quad (311)$$

By the angle θ is understood the positive angle through which the first straight line must be rotated in order that it shall coincide with the second straight line. Note that equation (**311**) is valid only when the same unit is used for both coordinate axes.

3. Ellipse

Standard equation in rectangular coordinates (the principal axes):

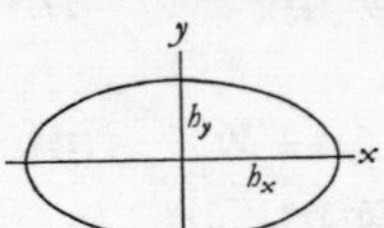

$$\frac{x^2}{a^2} + \frac{y^2}{b^2} = c^2 \quad (312)$$

a and b determine the relation between the two semi-axes and thus the shape of the ellipse.

If b_x is the semi-major, b_y the semi-minor axis, equation (**312**) becomes

$$\frac{x^2}{b_x^2} + \frac{y^2}{b_y^2} = 1 \quad \left\{ \begin{aligned} b_x^2 &= c^2a^2 \\ b_y^2 &= c^2b^2 \end{aligned} \right. \quad (313)$$

The focal width F_1F_2 is given by

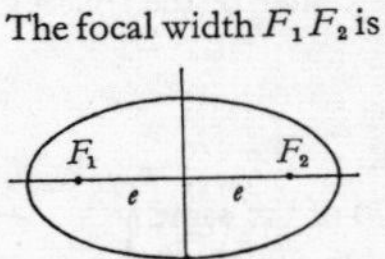

$$2e = 2\sqrt{b_x^2 - b_y^2} \quad (314)$$

e is known as the linear eccentricity.

If s is the sum of the distances from a point P on the curve to the foci F_1 and F_2, then

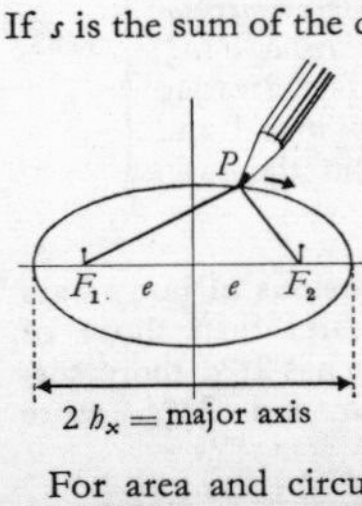

$$s = 2b_x = \text{major axis} \quad (315)$$

Any desired ellipse may therefore be drawn by means of a thread of length $2b_x$ attached to the foci, e being determined from equation (**314**).

For area and circumference of the ellipse see equations (**255**) and (**256**) on page 142.

Statistical Methods

For bibliographical references in this chapter see page 195; for contents and index see pages 196–198

In the limited space here available it is impossible to give more than a brief explanation of the many additional statistical tables which have been included in the 6th edition of these *Scientific Tables*. The following description is in consequence limited to those fundamentals which the non-mathematician requires to enable him to solve simple statistical problems.

The calculation of probabilities by statistical methods is an essential step in the proper interpretation of experimental results which conform to certain basic laws but are at the same time subject to modification by unknown factors, in other words, to so-called "chance" variation. This holds not only for the empirical sciences, the exact as well as the biological, but in a wider sense also for the abstract sciences:

On peut même dire à parler en rigueur, que presque toutes nos connaissances ne sont que probables; et dans le petit nombre des choses que nous pouvons savoir avec certitude, dans les sciences mathématiques elles-mêmes, les principaux moyens de parvenir à la vérité, l'induction et l'analogie, se fondent sur les probabilités... (De Laplace, 1820)[1].

One reason for the physician's frequent mistrust of statistical methods is epitomized in the well-known allegation that "you can prove anything with statistics". Some prejudice against mathematics is also understandable in a profession in which intuitive reasoning is generally preferred. These are sentiments without any logical basis. Statistics is one of the most vigorous branches of mathematics, and its techniques for the disciplined assessment of observational data can be readily mastered. Furthermore, it should not be forgotten that every medical diagnosis represents the result of an intentional or unintentional calculation of probabilities.

The disparaging view of statistics quoted above has its origin in their improper use as well as in their wrong or exaggerated interpretation. The statistical method is no more than another scientific method and cannot by its nature provide proof or disproof. On the other hand it constitutes the only method of subjecting values liable to chance variation (stochastic variables) to fixed and reproducible criteria based on logical mathematical considerations. The converse of the saying quoted is therefore much nearer the truth, namely that *no scientific investigation is capable of proving anything without the aid of statistics*. Human judgment is influenced to a very large extent by the subconscious wish and by the deep-rooted tendency – even in the worst of pessimists – to overrate one's own chances. The most careful investigator can be led astray by these psychological factors if he fails to arm himself against them with an adequate measure of self-control:

Le sentiment par lequel l'homme s'est placé longtemps au centre de l'univers en se considérant comme l'objet spécial des soins de la nature, porte chaque individu à se faire le centre d'une sphère plus ou moins étendue, et à croire que le hasard a pour lui des préférences. Soutenus par cette opinion, les joueurs exposent souvent des sommes considérables à des jeux dont ils savent que les chances leur sont contraires. Dans la conduite de la vie, une semblable opinion peut quelquefois avoir des avantages; mais le plus souvent elle conduit à des entreprises funestes. Ici, comme en tout, les illusions sont dangereuses et la vérité seule est généralement utile.

Un des grands avantages du Calcul des Probabilités est d'apprendre à se défier des premiers aperçus. Comme on reconnaît qu'ils trompent souvent lorsqu'on peut les soumettre au calcul, on doit en conclure que sur d'autres objets il ne faut s'y livrer qu'avec une circonspection extrême (De Laplace, 1820)[1].

"The wish" as "father to the thought" may be an indispensable stimulus to research, but it has also been responsible – in the guise of "our experience" or "our opinion" backed by a few percentages – for much misunderstanding. One need only reflect on the wealth of new treatments and new drugs which after an enthusiastic reception have been allowed to fall quietly into oblivion.

Many a research worker in the past could have spared himself much wasted time and effort had he submitted his observations and hypotheses to statistical test before publication. Recognition of this fact has clearly become general during the last few years, and close links have now been established between clinical medicine and statistics.

The growing use of statistical methods, however, is not without its own dangers. The general tendency is to overrate any new research tool, particularly when it is unfamiliar and complicated in operation. Too much uncritical dependence is placed on the results obtained; the limitations of the method may not be clearly recognized and the experimental data may be inadequately checked. Statistical methods clearly allow of no such dispensation. On the other hand, the beginner will find that with increasing experience statistical ways of thinking will not only render him more circumspect but give him a deeper insight.

1. Introductory definitions*

An experiment subject to chance influences may be compared to an operation such as the drawing of numbers in a lottery. Imagine a box containing balls bearing the numbers 0, 1, 2, …, 9. These are thoroughly mixed before the draw is commenced. The player drawing the balls is supposed to have no influence on the selection.

Using this analogy, we can designate

– the mixing of the balls as the *randomization* of the experimental material; **(316)**

– the numbers 0, 1, 2, …, 9 distinguishing the balls as *variables* or *attributes*; **(317)**

– the aggregate number of balls in the box as the *parent population*; **(318)**

– a draw as a *trial*; **(319)**

– N trials as *random sampling*; **(320)**

– the result of the trial which is represented by the drawing of the number 5 as the *random event* 5; **(321)**

– the result of N trials as a *random sample* of size N, or briefly as a sample N; **(322)**

– the succession of events as a *random sequence* (in the numbered ball analogy it is the random series of numbers, or *random numbers*); **(323)**

– the relative frequency of the variate values in the population as the *probabilities* with which these values will be drawn; **(324)**

– the relative frequency of the variate values in the sample as *estimate* of their probability; **(325)**

– the distribution of the probabilities of the different variate values as probability distribution, or briefly as *distribution*. **(326)**

Some of these definitions will be discussed in more detail later in this chapter.

2. Population and sample

A population is finite or infinite when the trials (draws) can be repeated a finite or infinite number of times. **(327)**

A finite population, such as a finite number of balls in a box, can be converted into an effectively infinite one by putting the balls back into the box after each draw. Such an operation is known as *sampling with replacement*. **(328)**

From an infinite population an infinite number of samples can be taken, for example all of the same size N. The totality of such samples of size N is known as the *sampling population* N and their probability distribution as the *sampling distribution* N. **(329)**

An infinite sampling population can also be taken from a finite population in a manner similar to that in **(328)**, i.e. by returning the whole of the first sample to the box, drawing a second sample of the same size, returning this sample also to the box, and so on. *All sampling populations can therefore be regarded as infinite*. This is one of the fundamental concepts of mathematical statistics. **(330)**

Quantities such as mean value and variance which relate to the population are known as *parameters*, their counterparts in the sample as *statistics*. **(331)**

Symbols which relate to the population are here printed in bold type whenever it is necessary to distinguish them from symbols relating to samples. Exceptions are the symbols for mean value and variance: these are respectively μ and σ^2 for the population and $\bar{x}$ and s^2 for the sample. **(332)**

* The mathematician will appreciate that this presentation is more readily understandable by the non-mathematician than a strictly mathematical one.

3. Variable and event

Variables are accumulated (possible) events in the box, events variables which have been drawn from the box. Where no possibility of confusion exists, the word "event" is therefore here also used for "variable", for example in the expression "population of red and black events". **(333)**

If A is an event, then the non-occurrence of A is its *complementary event*, designated here as non-A. Examples are success or failure, alive or dead, 6 or non-6 in die throwing, etc. **(334)**

The complementary event non-A is often an event B. For example, a girl can be born instead of a boy. Such events are known as *mutually exclusive events*, denoted by A or B, or by A, B. A and non-A in (**334**) are therefore by definition mutually exclusive events. **(335)**

Simultaneously occurring events can be treated as *successive* events. Whether the events $A, B, C, \ldots$ occur simultaneously or successively, they are denoted by A and B and C ... or by $ABC \ldots$ **(336)**

If the occurrence (or non-occurrence) of an event A is restricted by the condition that an event B has occurred [or occurs simultaneously, cf. (**336**)], then event A is known as a *conditioned event*, denoted by $A \mid B$ and read as event A under the condition B. B can represent several conditions. **(337)**

An event which is made up of several different events is known as a *compound event*. **(338)**

Qualitative variables can be denoted by numbers, for example 1 for success, 0 for failure. **(339)**

If the events are already numbers they are here denoted by x provided that other symbols are not in general use, as in the case of some sampling distributions. **(340)**

If x (within a finite interval) takes only a finite number of values it is known as a *discontinuous random variable* or *variate*. In this case x changes by *discrete* amounts. Examples are 0, 1, 2, 3, ... successes, 25, 26, 27, ... respirations, etc. **(341)**

If the numbers 1, 2, 3, ... denote the smallest, second smallest, third smallest value, etc., the series is said to be ordered (by magnitude) and is known as a *ranked series*. In such a series the *exact* magnitudes which determine the ranks of the smallest, second smallest, etc., may be unknown. *Example 1:* a group of persons can be arranged in order of height without their exact heights being known. **(342)**

If x can take all possible values in some interval it is known as a *continuous random variable* or *variate*. In this case x changes *continuously*. Examples of continuous variates are length, area, volume, weight, temperature, time, concentration, etc., i.e. variables which can be *measured*. **(343)**

In practice, continuous variates do not exist since all measured values are rounded values. For example, when the smallest interval which a balance can measure is a milligram, any weight measured will be rounded off to the nearest milligram. In this case x changes by discrete intervals of one milligram. Such a variable can be called a "*granulated*" (or "*atomic*") *variable*. "Granulated" variables are actually continuous variables which have been converted into discrete variables by rounding off. **(344)**

In the case of discrete variables the same value may occur two or more times in a sample from two or more tests. This is an almost impossible event in the case of continuous variables [cf. (**352**)], but occurs all the more often the more "coarsely granulated" they are. Cf. (**344**). **(345)**

If two or more identical values occur in a sample of a "granulated" variable they are known as *ties* or tied values. Cf. (**344**) and (**345**). **(346)**

4. Frequency, probability, compound events

If in a group of N individuals there are x females and $N - x$ males, then x and $N - x$ are the *absolute* and x/N and $(N - x)/N$ the *relative frequencies* of females and males in the group. Here the expression frequency will be used to mean the relative frequency. **(347)**

The relative frequency multiplied by 100 is known as the *percentage frequency*. *Example 2:* In 81 operations there are 3 fatalities. The percentage frequency is then $(3/81) \times 100 = 3.7\%$. **(348)**

The percentage frequencies for values of N between 2 and 100 and for any values of $x \leq N$ are given in the column $100\ p_x$ (column 2) of the tables on pages 85–98. For the above example see page 93, $N = 81, x = 3$.

The following symbols are used here for probability: **(349)**

"Probability" in general .... Prob

Probabilities of mutually exclusive events ...... $\dot{\boldsymbol{P}}$

Probabilities of two complementary events .... $\boldsymbol{p}$ and $\boldsymbol{q}$

In a later section the symbols α and $\boldsymbol{P}$ will also be used [cf. (**378**) and (**379**)].

In (**324**) *probability* was defined as the *relative frequency of a variable* [or of an event, cf. (**333**)] *in the population*. Propositions (**350**)–(**355**) follow directly from this definition:

Every probability is a number between zero and one: $0 \leq \text{Prob} \leq 1$ **(350)**

An impossible event has a probability of zero, a certain event a probability of one. **(351)**

The converse of (**351**) *is not valid:*

An event with a probability of zero is an *almost* impossible event, an event with a probability of one an *almost* certain event. *Example 3:* A box contains all the positive integers 1, 2, 3, ..., ∞. The probability of drawing, say, the number 1960 is $1/\infty = 0$. Nevertheless the possibility exists of drawing this number since it is present in the population. **(352)**

The sum of the probabilities of *all* mutually exclusive events $E_0, E_1, \ldots, E_T$ in a single population is equal to one: **(353)**

$$\text{Prob}\,(E_0 \text{ or } E_1 \text{ or} \ldots E_T) = \dot{\boldsymbol{P}}_0 + \dot{\boldsymbol{P}}_1 + \ldots + \dot{\boldsymbol{P}}_T = 1$$

where the total of all mutually exclusive events is $T + 1$, and [cf. (**335**)]

$$\text{Prob}\,(E \text{ or non-}E) = \boldsymbol{p} + \boldsymbol{q} = 1$$

It follows from (**353**) that a population with many mutually exclusive events can be converted in various ways into one with two complementary events. **(354)**

For example:

$$\text{Prob}\left[\underbrace{(E_0 \text{ or } E_1)}_{=E} \text{ or } \underbrace{(E_2 \text{ or} \ldots E_T)}_{=\text{non-}E}\right]$$

$$= \underbrace{(\dot{\boldsymbol{P}}_0 + \dot{\boldsymbol{P}}_1)}_{=\boldsymbol{p}} + \underbrace{(\dot{\boldsymbol{P}}_2 + \cdots + \dot{\boldsymbol{P}}_T)}_{=\boldsymbol{q}}$$

where the total number of mutually exclusive events is $T + 1$.

Example (4) of (**354**). With a true die the probability of throwing any one number is 1/6. The probability of throwing a 6 is 1/6, of throwing a non-6 (1 or 2 or ... 5) 5/6. The probability of throwing an even number (2 or 4 or 6) is $1/6 + 1/6 + 1/6 = 1/2$, of throwing an odd number likewise 1/2.

From (**353**) it follows that:

Of the mutually exclusive events $A, B, \ldots$, the probability that either the event A or the event B will occur is equal to the sum of their probabilities, *provided that the events are from one and the same population.* **(355)**

$$\text{Prob}\,(A \text{ or } B \text{ or} \ldots) = \dot{\boldsymbol{P}}_A + \dot{\boldsymbol{P}}_B + \cdots$$

Example (5) of (**355**). *Correct application.* Assuming that the probability of an 85-year-old person dying of pneumonia is 0.2 and of dying of cancer also 0.2, then the probability that he will die either of pneumonia or cancer is $0.2 + 0.2 = 0.4$.

Example (6) of (**355**). *Incorrect application.* Assuming that the mortality of 85-year-olds is 0.5 and that of 86-year-olds 0.6, then the statement that the probability of an 85-year-old dying either at 85 or at 86 is 1.1 is false. Here the error is already indicated by the probability figure of 1.1, which according to (**350**) is an impossibility, but it might well have been overlooked had the figure been 0.4, as in example 5. The error arises from the fact that mutually exclusive events from *different* populations, that of the 85-year-olds and that of the 86-year-olds, have been added together.

The probability of two simultaneous or successive events A and B is equal to the probability of the event A multiplied by the probability of the event B under the condition A, or to the probability of the event B multiplied by the probability of the event A under the condition B. On conditioned events see (**337**).

$$\text{Prob}(A \text{ and } B) = \text{Prob}(A) \times \text{Prob}(B \mid A) = \text{Prob}(B) \times \text{Prob}(A \mid B)$$ (**356**)

Example (7) of (**356**). A box contains N balls, x red and $N-x$ white. A sample consisting of two balls is drawn *without replacement*. What is the probability of drawing (*a*) two red balls, (*b*) a red and then a white ball, (*c*) a red and a white ball in any order?

(*a*) The probability of a red ball at the first draw is x/N. The conditioned probability of a red ball at the second draw – when there is one red ball less in the box – is $(x-1)/(N-1)$. The probability of drawing two red balls is therefore

$$\text{Prob (red, red)} = \frac{x}{N} \times \frac{x-1}{N-1}$$

(*b*) $$\text{Prob (red, white)} = \frac{x}{N} \times \frac{N-x}{N-1} = \frac{N-x}{N-1} \times \frac{x}{N} = \text{Prob (white, red)}$$

(*c*) $$\text{Prob (red and white)} = \text{Prob (red, white)} + \text{Prob (white, red)} = 2x(N-x)/(N^2-N)$$

Example (8) of (**356**). From the same box as in example 7 a sample of the same size is taken, but *with replacement*. In this case the probabilities are as follows:

(*a*) The probability of a red ball at the first draw remains x/N. Since this ball is replaced in the box, the probability of a red ball at the second draw is the same:

$$\text{Prob (red, red)} = \frac{x}{N} \times \frac{x}{N}$$

(*b*) $$\text{Prob (red, white)} = \frac{x}{N} \times \frac{N-x}{N} = \frac{N-x}{N} \times \frac{x}{N} = \text{Prob (white, red)}$$

(*c*) $$\text{Prob (red and white)} = \text{Prob (red, white)} + \text{Prob (white, red)} = 2x(N-x)/N^2$$

From example 7 it will be seen that the probabilities change with each draw, i.e. each successive draw is *dependent* on the previous one. The corresponding statistical expressions are *dependent trials* and *dependent events*. In example 8 the second draw is unaffected by the previous one, in which case the trials and events are *independent*.

In other words, in the collection of samples from *finite* populations (no replacement), the trials and events are *dependent* on one another; in the collection of samples from *infinite* populations (replacement), they are *independent* of one another. (**357**)

Two simultaneous or successive events are known as stochastically *dependent* events when in (**356**) the conditioned and the absolute probability of an event are *not the same*, i.e. when
$\text{Prob}(A \mid B) \neq \text{Prob}(A)$ or $\text{Prob}(B \mid A) \neq \text{Prob}(B)$. (**358**)

Two simultaneous or successive events are known as stochastically *independent* events when in (**356**) the conditioned and the absolute probability of an event are *the same*, i.e. when
$\text{Prob}(A \mid B) = \text{Prob}(A)$ or $\text{Prob}(B \mid A) = \text{Prob}(B)$. (**359**)

From (**356**) and (**359**) it follows that the two events A and B are stochastically independent of one another when the probability of their simultaneous or successive occurrence is equal to the product of their probabilities:
If $\text{Prob}(A \text{ and } B) = \text{Prob}(A) \times \text{Prob}(B)$
then A and B are stochastically independent of one another. (**360**)

In (**358**)–(**360**) the expressions "dependent" and "independent" are coupled with the qualification "stochastic". This is a precautionary measure of the statistician. *In* (**358**)–(**360**) *a factual conclusion is reached on the basis of a mathematical result.* If such conclusions lie wholly within the domain of the probability calculation the expressions "dependent" and "independent" are completely valid, as in examples 7 and 8 under (**356**). However, if they are extended beyond the mathematical domain into those of physics, chemistry, physiology, etc., then the qualification "stochastic" is necessary since the conceptions "dependent" and "independent" do not necessarily imply a *causal* connection. Stochastically independent events can very well be dependent on one another in reality. *The conclusion "independent" implies only actual independence of the events.* It can be accepted if it is not incompatible with the physical circumstances. *On the other hand it can be regarded as proof* if independence was *presumable* from the physical circumstances and the mathematical treatment led to the *same* result. For this reason the converse of (**360**) should also be noted: (**361**)

If A and B are events independent of one another, then the probability of their simultaneous or successive occurrence is equal to the product of their probabilities:
$\text{Prob}(A \text{ and } B) = \text{Prob}(A) \times \text{Prob}(B)$
(*when* A and B are independent of one another) (**362**)

Example (9) of (**362**). A box contains the events '+' and '−' in equal numbers, so that the probabilities are 1/2. Samples are collected with replacement, so that in accordance with (**357**) the events are independent of one another. What is the probability of drawing a '+' 5, 6 or 7 times in succession? The respective probabilities are $(1/2)^5$, $(1/2)^6$, $(1/2)^7$, or 0.031 25, 0.015 625, 0.007 8125.

Example (10) of (**362**). An infinite population contains the events A and B with the probabilities $\boldsymbol{p}$ and $\boldsymbol{q}$ respectively. What are the probabilities of the events AA, AB, BA, BB in two draws?

Event	Probability	
AA	$\boldsymbol{p} \times \boldsymbol{p} = \boldsymbol{p}^2$	
AB	$\boldsymbol{p} \times \boldsymbol{q}$ } $= 2\boldsymbol{pq}$	$= \boldsymbol{p}^2 + 2\boldsymbol{pq} + \boldsymbol{q}^2 = (\boldsymbol{p}+\boldsymbol{q})^2$
BA	$\boldsymbol{q} \times \boldsymbol{p}$	$= 1^2 = 1$, as it should be according to (**353**)
BB	$\boldsymbol{q} \times \boldsymbol{q} = \boldsymbol{q}^2$	

In the expression $\boldsymbol{p}^2 + 2\boldsymbol{pq} + \boldsymbol{q}^2$ the individual terms represent the *probability distribution* for the events two As, one A, and no As (provided that no importance is attached to the order in the event one A). A *sampling distribution* [cf. (**329**)] is thus obtained for samples of size 2 from an infinite population, the complementary variables A or B, and the probabilities $\boldsymbol{p}$ and $\boldsymbol{q}$. From this example it will be seen intuitively how samples with 3, 4, ... draws can be dealt with: the sampling distributions can be written in accordance with (**113**) as developments of $(\boldsymbol{p}+\boldsymbol{q})^3$, $(\boldsymbol{p}+\boldsymbol{q})^4$, ... Cf. Binomial distribution, page 182.

5. Discrete probability distribution

Example 10 under (**362**) demonstrated a simple sampling distribution of practical importance which will be further discussed later in this chapter. At this point, discussion will be limited to a few conceptions related to such a distribution.

Given an infinite population with the events $x = 0, 1, 2, \ldots, 10$ and the probabilities $\dot{\boldsymbol{P}}_x$, then:

x	$\dot{\boldsymbol{P}}_x = f(x)$	$\sum_0^x \dot{\boldsymbol{P}}_x = F(x)$
0	0.0010	$0.0010 = \dot{\boldsymbol{P}}_0$
1	0.0098	$0.0108 = \dot{\boldsymbol{P}}_0 + \dot{\boldsymbol{P}}_1$
2	0.0439	$0.0547 = \dot{\boldsymbol{P}}_0 + \dot{\boldsymbol{P}}_1 + \dot{\boldsymbol{P}}_2$
3	0.1172	$0.1719 = \dot{\boldsymbol{P}}_0 + \dot{\boldsymbol{P}}_1 + \dot{\boldsymbol{P}}_2 + \dot{\boldsymbol{P}}_3$
4	0.2051	0.3770 etc.
5	0.2460	0.6230
6	0.2051	0.8281
7	0.1172	0.9453
8	0.0439	0.9892
9	0.0098	0.9990
10	0.0010	1.0000

The column $\dot{\boldsymbol{P}}_x = f(x)$ gives the probabilities for the events $x = 0, x = 1, x = 2$, etc.:

According to (**326**) this is the *probability distribution* for the events $x = 0, x = 1, x = 2$, etc., denoted by $f(x)$. **(363)**

In column $\sum\limits_{0}^{x} \dot{\boldsymbol{P}}_x = F(x)$ the probabilities $\dot{\boldsymbol{P}}_x$ are continously summed, thus giving the probabilities for $x = 0$, $x = 0$ or 1, $x = 0$ or 1 or 2, etc. This is the *cumulative probability distribution* of x, denoted by $F(x)$. **(364)**

These data may be represented graphically:

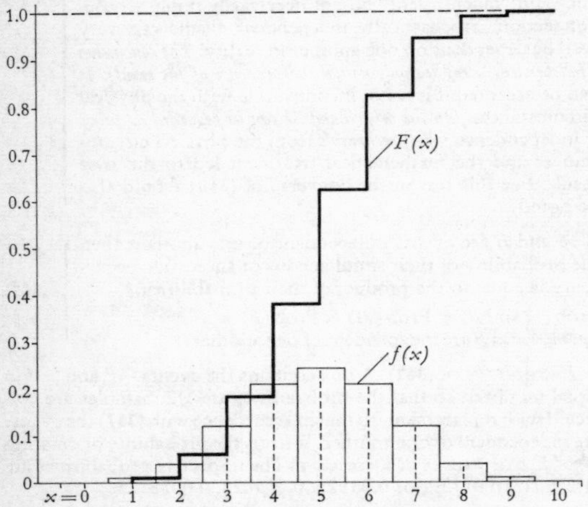

Fig. 1 Abscissas: x; ordinates: probabilities $f(x)$ and $F(x)$.

Since x is a discrete variable [cf. (**341**)] the distributions $f(x)$ and $F(x)$ give stepped curves. It follows that:

A discrete random variable has a discrete probability distribution. **(365)**

The probabilities are dependent on x, i.e. *for every value of x there is a definite probability*: $f(x)$ and $F(x)$ are *functions* of x, whence the use of the symbols f and F (the Greek letters φ and Φ are also frequently used). The pattern of probabilities can be expressed by a mathematical formula or in some other appropriate manner. **(366)**

In Figure 1 the probabilities $f(x)$ and $F(x)$ are shown as stepped lines in order to emphasize the similarity between discrete and continuous distributions (cf. Fig. 8). In fact, such a stepped curve could represent a "*granulated*" distribution [cf. (**344**)] in which the values of x have been rounded off to whole numbers. In this case all events between 4.5 and 5.5, for example, would be assigned to event 5. For this reason, another method is preferred here for representing discrete distributions which shows clearly that the events x are *discrete*:

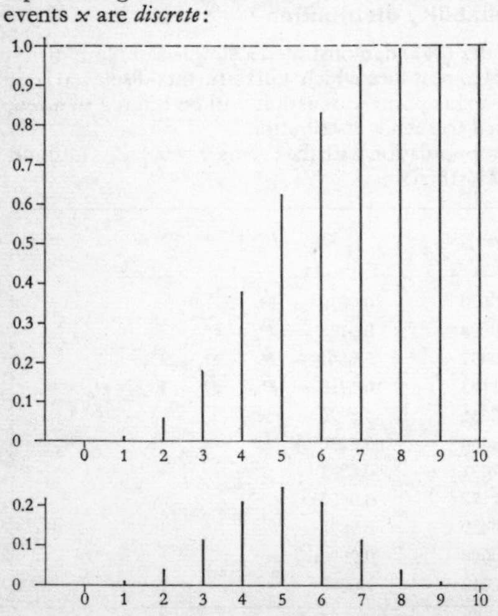

Fig. 2

In the cumulative distribution $F(x)$ representing the probabilities of the events $x = 0$, $x = 0$ or 1, $x = 0$ or 1 or 2, etc., the expression $x = 0, 1$ will in future be used in place of $x = 0$ or 1. Prob $(x = 0, 1)$ can also be written as Prob $(x \leqq 1)$. From (**364**) another notation is Prob $(x < 2, 3, \ldots, N)$, equivalent to Prob $(x < 2)$.

In general, the following expressions are valid for such discrete distributions:

Prob $(x < k + 1) =$ Prob $(x \leqq k)$, or
Prob $(x < k) =$ Prob $(x \leqq k - 1)$
and Prob $(x > k - 1) =$ Prob $(x \geqq k)$, or
Prob $(x > k) =$ Prob $(x \geqq k + 1)$ **(367)**

With increasing values of k, the distribution $F(x)$ thus produces continuously the probabilities for $x \leqq k$ or $x < k + 1$. **(368)**

Conversely, with decreasing values of k the cumulative distribution $\sum\limits_{x=k}^{N} \dot{\boldsymbol{P}}_x$ from N in the direction of zero produces continuously the probabilities for $x \geqq k$ or $x > k - 1$. **(369)**

For discrete distributions in general the following should be noted:

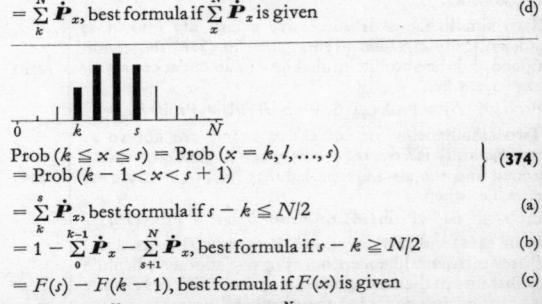

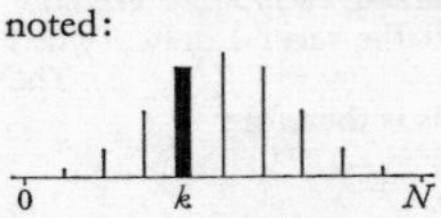

Prob $(x = k) = \dot{\boldsymbol{P}}_k = f(k)$ **(370)**

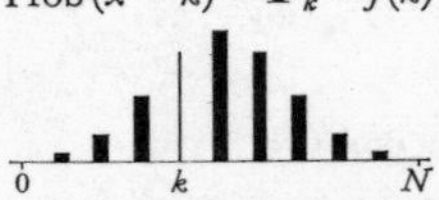

Prob $(x \neq k) = 1 - \dot{\boldsymbol{P}}_k = 1 - f(k)$ **(371)**

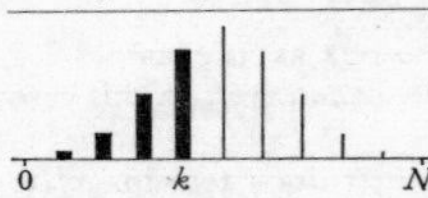

Prob $(x \leqq k) =$ Prob $(x < k + 1)$ **(372)**

$= \sum\limits_{0}^{k} \dot{\boldsymbol{P}}_x$, best formula if $k \leqq N/2$ (a)

$= 1 - \sum\limits_{k+1}^{N} \dot{\boldsymbol{P}}_x$, best formula if $k \geqq N/2$ (b)

$= F(x)$, best formula if $F(x)$ is given (c)

$= 1 - \sum\limits_{k+1}^{N} \dot{\boldsymbol{P}}_x$, best formula if $\sum\limits_{x}^{N} \dot{\boldsymbol{P}}_x$ is given (d)

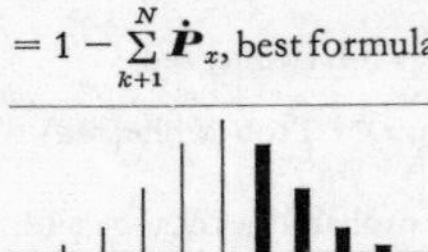

Prob $(x \geqq k) =$ Prob $(x > k - 1)$ **(373)**

$= 1 - \sum\limits_{0}^{k-1} \dot{\boldsymbol{P}}_x$, best formula if $k \leqq N/2$ (a)

$= \sum\limits_{k}^{N} \dot{\boldsymbol{P}}_x$, best formula if $k \geqq N/2$ (b)

$= 1 - F(k - 1)$, best formula if $F(x)$ is given (c)

$= \sum\limits_{k}^{N} \dot{\boldsymbol{P}}_x$, best formula if $\sum\limits_{x}^{N} \dot{\boldsymbol{P}}_x$ is given (d)

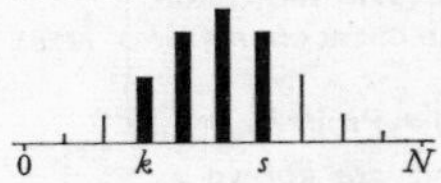

Prob $(k \leqq x \leqq s) =$ Prob $(x = k, l, \ldots, s)$
$=$ Prob $(k - 1 < x < s + 1)$ **(374)**

$= \sum\limits_{k}^{s} \dot{\boldsymbol{P}}_x$, best formula if $s - k \leqq N/2$ (a)

$= 1 - \sum\limits_{0}^{k-1} \dot{\boldsymbol{P}}_x - \sum\limits_{s+1}^{N} \dot{\boldsymbol{P}}_x$, best formula if $s - k \geqq N/2$ (b)

$= F(s) - F(k - 1)$, best formula if $F(x)$ is given (c)

$= \sum\limits_{k}^{N} \dot{\boldsymbol{P}}_x - \sum\limits_{s+1}^{N} \dot{\boldsymbol{P}}_x$, best formula if $\sum\limits_{x}^{N} \dot{\boldsymbol{P}}_x$ is given (d)

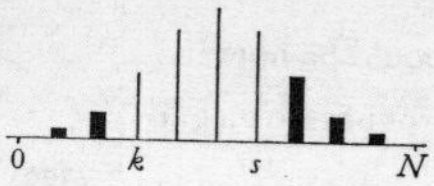

$$\left.\begin{aligned}&\text{Prob}\,(x \leqq k-1) + \text{Prob}\,(x \geqq s+1)\\ &= \text{Prob}\,(x < k) + \text{Prob}\,(x > k)\\ &= \text{Prob}\,(x \neq k, l, \ldots, s)\end{aligned}\right\} \quad \textbf{(375)}$$

$$= 1 - \sum_k^s \dot{\boldsymbol{P}}_x, \text{ best formula if } s - k \leqq N/2 \qquad \text{(a)}$$

$$= \sum_0^{k-1} \dot{\boldsymbol{P}}_x + \sum_{s+1}^N \dot{\boldsymbol{P}}_x, \text{ best formula if } s - k \geqq N/2 \qquad \text{(b)}$$

$$= 1 - F(s) + F(k-1), \text{ best formula if } F(x) \text{ is given} \qquad \text{(c)}$$

$$= 1 - \sum_k^N \dot{\boldsymbol{P}}_x + \sum_{s+1}^N \dot{\boldsymbol{P}}_x, \text{ best formula if } \sum_x^N \dot{\boldsymbol{P}}_x \text{ is given} \qquad \text{(d)}$$

In (**370**)–(**375**) the best formulas for use in each particular case are indicated. As a rule, the user must calculate $\dot{\boldsymbol{P}}_x$ himself and then proceed with the formulas (a) or (b). The editors know of extensive tabulations of $\sum_x^\infty \dot{\boldsymbol{P}}_x$ only for the POISSON distribution[2], of $\sum_x^N \dot{\boldsymbol{P}}_x$ only for the binomial distribution[3, 4, 63], of $\sum_0^x \dot{\boldsymbol{P}}_x \mid N, n, k$ only for the hypergeometric probability distribution[64]. The tabulations[2, 3, 4, 64] include also values of $f(x)$.

Example 11. Using the formulas (a) or (b) in (**370**)–(**375**), the probabilities for $k = 2$ and $s = 8$ are calculated from the values of $f(x)$ given in the table on page 147.

(**370**): $\text{Prob}\,(x = 2) = \dot{\boldsymbol{P}}_2 = 0.0439$

(**371**): $\text{Prob}\,(x \neq 2) = 1 - \dot{\boldsymbol{P}}_2 = 0.9561$

(**372**): $\text{Prob}\,(x \leqq 2) = \dot{\boldsymbol{P}}_0 + \dot{\boldsymbol{P}}_1 + \dot{\boldsymbol{P}}_2 = 0.0547$
[by formula (a), since $k < N/2$]

(**373**): $\text{Prob}\,(x \geqq 2) = 1 - (\dot{\boldsymbol{P}}_0 + \dot{\boldsymbol{P}}_1) = 0.9892$
[by formula (a), since $k < N/2$]

(**374**): $\text{Prob}\,(2 \leqq x \leqq 8) = \text{Prob}\,(x = 2, 3, \ldots, 8)$
$= 1 - (\dot{\boldsymbol{P}}_0 + \dot{\boldsymbol{P}}_1) - (\dot{\boldsymbol{P}}_9 + \dot{\boldsymbol{P}}_{10}) = 0.9784$
[by formula (b), since $s - k > N/2$]

(**375**): $\text{Prob}\,(x \neq 2, 3, \ldots, 8) = (\dot{\boldsymbol{P}}_0 + \dot{\boldsymbol{P}}_1) + (\dot{\boldsymbol{P}}_9 + \dot{\boldsymbol{P}}_{10}) = 0.0216$
[by formula (b), since $s - k > N/2$]

Example 12. What is the probability of the event "x at least equal to 1"? This is the same as saying "x equal to 1 or more" (cf. page 132), and calculation using (**373**a) gives

$\text{Prob}\,(x \geqq 1) = 1 - \dot{\boldsymbol{P}}_0 = 0.9990$

Example 13.

Confidence intervals* and significance limits

Cf. also sections 8 and 9, pages 153–158.

A. *One-sided significance limits*

Given α, where $0 < \alpha \leqq 0.5$, determine x_l and x_r in such a way that

$$\left.\begin{aligned}&\text{Prob}\,(x \leqq x_l) = \boldsymbol{P}_l = \sum_0^{x_l} \dot{\boldsymbol{P}}_x \leqq \alpha \quad \text{and}\\ &\text{Prob}\,(x \leqq x_l + 1) = \sum_0^{x_l+1} \dot{\boldsymbol{P}}_x > \alpha\end{aligned}\right\} \quad \textbf{(376)}$$

$$\left.\begin{aligned}&\text{Prob}\,(x \geqq x_r) = \boldsymbol{P}_r = \sum_{x_r}^{N} \dot{\boldsymbol{P}}_x \leqq \alpha \quad \text{and}\\ &\text{Prob}\,(x \geqq x_r - 1) = \sum_{x_r-1}^{N} \dot{\boldsymbol{P}}_x > \alpha\end{aligned}\right\} \quad \textbf{(377)}$$

For $\alpha = 0.10$, $x_l = 2$ and $x_r = 8$; for $\alpha = 0.025$, $x_l = 1$ and $x_r = 9$.

The following definitions follow from the above example:

– α as *postulated* or *nominal one-sided significance probability.* (**378**)

– $\boldsymbol{P}$ as *actual one-sided significance probability*, $\boldsymbol{P}_l$ being the *left* (*lower*) and $\boldsymbol{P}_r$ the *right* (*upper*) level, with $\boldsymbol{P}_l$ and $\boldsymbol{P}_r \leqq \alpha$. (**379**)

– x_l as *left* (*lower*) and x_r as *right* (*upper*) significance limit (**380**)

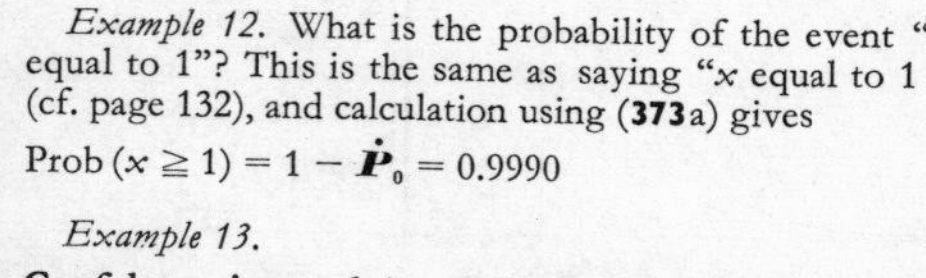

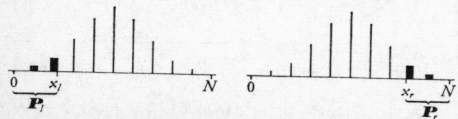

Fig. 3 One-sided significance limit of discrete distributions.

* Also known as "tolerance intervals". Cf. section 8, page 153.

It should be noted that

– if x *attains or exceeds* (to the left) the *left* (lower) significance limit x_l, then in a *one-tailed* test x is *smaller* than $x_l + 1, x_l + 2, \ldots, N$ with a significance probability $\leqq \alpha$:
$\text{Prob}\,(x < x_l + 1) \leqq \alpha$, when $x \leqq x_l$ (**381**)

– if x *attains or exceeds* (to the right) the *right* (upper) significance limit x_r, then in a *one-tailed* test x is *greater* than $x_r - 1, x_r - 2, \ldots, N$ with a significance probability $\leqq \alpha$:
$\text{Prob}\,(x > x_r - 1) \leqq \alpha$, when $x \geqq x_r$ (**382**)

– rules (**381**) and (**382**) are valid for *all* significance limits of *discrete* distributions tabulated in these *Scientific Tables*. Elsewhere, significance limits of discrete distributions may be found which must be exceeded in an *outward* direction in order to satisfy, for example, the rule $\boldsymbol{P}_l \leqq \alpha$. (**383**)

– as a rule the *actual* significance probability $\boldsymbol{P}$ in *discrete* distributions is *smaller* than the *nominal* α, for small values of N often considerably smaller. With increasing values of N this difference decreases rapidly. (In example 13 with $\alpha = 0.10$ or 0.025, the corresponding values of $\boldsymbol{P}$ are 0.0547 or 0.0108. In this case the actual significance probability amounts to only about 50% of the nominal.) (**384**)

The following definitions should also be noted:

– the range between x_l and N or between zero and x_r as *one-sided confidence interval.* (**385**)

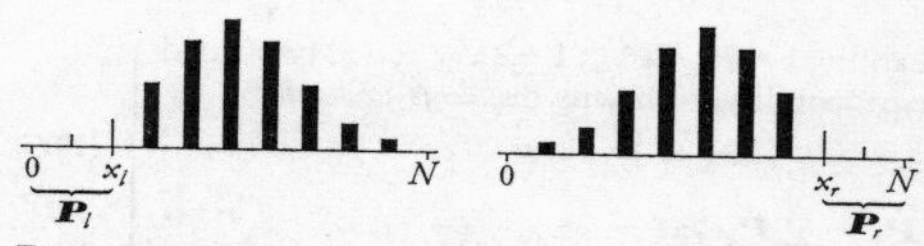

Fig. 4 One-sided confidence intervals for discrete distributions.

– x_l or x_r as *one-sided confidence limits* when the other limit lies at N or zero. (**386**)

– the probability $1 - \boldsymbol{P}_l \geqq 1 - \alpha$ and $1 - \boldsymbol{P}_r \geqq 1 - \alpha$ as *one-sided confidence probability*:

$$\text{Prob}\,(x_l < x \leqq N) = 1 - \boldsymbol{P}_l = 1 - \sum_0^{x_l} \dot{\boldsymbol{P}}_x \geqq 1 - \alpha \qquad \textbf{(387)}$$

$$\text{Prob}\,(0 \leqq x < x_r) = 1 - \boldsymbol{P}_r = 1 - \sum_{x_r}^{N} \dot{\boldsymbol{P}}_x \geqq 1 - \alpha \qquad \textbf{(388)}$$

From (**380**) and (**386**) it will be seen that significance limits and confidence intervals are determined mathematically according to the same principles. (**389**)

B. *Two-sided significance limits*

If a left and a right significance limit are determined jointly for a discrete distribution according to rules (**376**) and (**377**), then for the two together $\boldsymbol{P}_l + \boldsymbol{P}_r \leqq 2\alpha$. (**390**)

In this case the following definitions apply:

– 2α as *postulated* or *nominal two-sided significance probability.* (**391**)

– $\boldsymbol{P}_l + \boldsymbol{P}_r$ as *actual two-sided significance probability* [note also (**384**)], where $\boldsymbol{P}_l = \boldsymbol{P}_r$ in symmetrical distributions and $\boldsymbol{P}_l \neq \boldsymbol{P}_r$ in unsymmetrical distributions, although both satisfy rules (**376**) and (**377**) (cf. Fig. 5). (**392**)

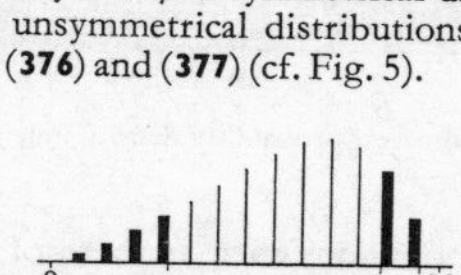

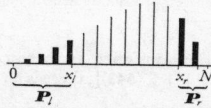

Fig. 5 Two-sided significance limits for discrete (unsymmetrical) distributions.

– x_l and x_r together as *two-sided* significance limits (with symmetrical probability), or briefly *significance limits.* (**393**)

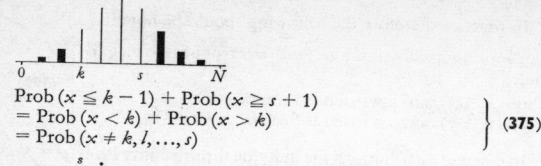

It should be noted that

– when x *attains or exceeds* (outwards) *one of the two* significance limits x_l or x_r, then in a *two-sided* test x is *not equal* to $x_l+1, x_l+2, \ldots, x_r-1$ with a significance probability $\leqq 2\alpha$:

$\text{Prob}\,(x \neq x_l+1, x_l+2, \ldots, x_r-1) \leqq 2\alpha$,
when $x \leqq x_l$ or $x \geqq x_r$. **(394)**

Fig. 6 Two-sided significance limits for discrete (symmetrical) distributions.

The following definitions should also be noted:

– the range between x_l+1 and x_r-1 as two-sided confidence interval, or briefly *confidence interval*. **(395)**

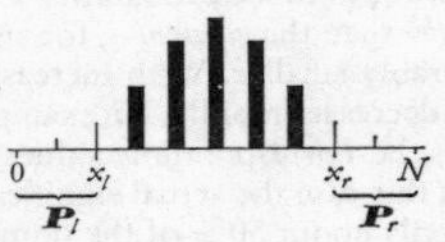

Fig. 7 Two-sided confidence interval for discrete distributions.

– x_l and x_r as two-sided confidence limits, or briefly *confidence limits*, whereby it should again be noted that significance limits and confidence intervals are determined mathematically according to the same principles. **(396)**

– the probability $1-P_l-P_r \geqq 1-2\alpha$ as actual two-sided confidence probability, or briefly *confidence probability*:

$\text{Prob}\,(x_l < x < x_r) = 1 - P_l - P_r$
$= 1 - \sum_0^{x_l} \dot{P}_x - \sum_{x_r}^{N} \dot{P}_x \geqq 1 - 2\alpha$ **(397)**

6. Continuous probability distribution

A comparison of Figures 1 and 8 reveals the similarity between discrete and continuous distributions. When the distribution shown at the beginning of the previous section (page 147) is worked out for increasing values of N, the steps in the $f(x)$ and $F(x)$ curves will become smaller and smaller until finally, with infinite N, a continuous curve such as that shown in Figure 8 is obtained. This will be further discussed in a later section.

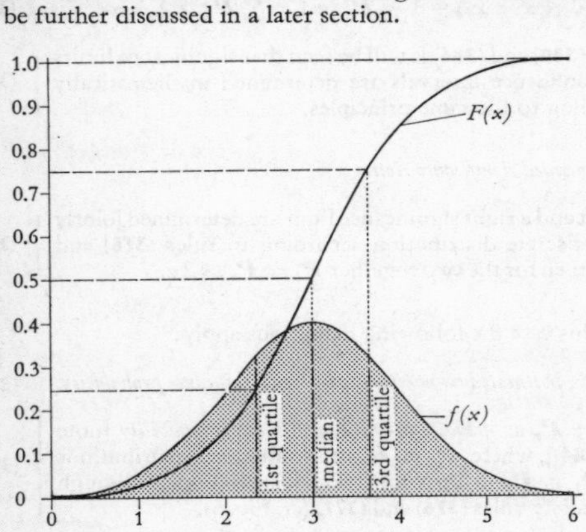

Fig. 8 Abscissas: x; ordinates: probability density function $f(x)$ and probability $F(x)$.

In probability distributions such as those of Figure 8, x is a *continuous* random variable [cf. **(343)**]; there is an infinite number of events x, so that

$\text{Prob}\,(x = k) = 1/\infty = 0$ **(398)**

and

$\text{Prob}\,(x \leqq k) = \text{Prob}\,(x < k) + \text{Prob}\,(x = k) = \text{Prob}\,(x < k) + 0$

In practice therefore the following should be noted:

For continuous distributions (with an error of zero magnitude)
$\text{Prob}\,(x \leqq k)$ can be written as $\text{Prob}\,(x < k)$
$\text{Prob}\,(x \geqq k)$ can be written as $\text{Prob}\,(x > k)$ **(399)**

In discrete distributions the individual probability $\text{Prob}\,(x = k)$ can be read from $f(x)$ but this no longer applies in continuous distributions:

In a continuous distribution, $f(x)$ is the *probability density function* at the point x. **(400)**

The cumulative probability distribution $F(x)$ has the same significance in continuous distributions, however, as in discrete distributions: it represents the probabilities of the events $x \leqq k$. In contrast to the case with discrete distributions, the latter are equivalent to the events $x < k$ [cf. **(399)**]. **(401)**

In discrete distributions, $F(x)$ is the *sum* of the individual probabilities [cf. **(372)**]. In continuous distributions, $F(x)$ is an *integral*:

$F(x) = \int_{-\infty}^{x} f(x)\,dx$ **(402)**

i.e. $F(x)$ corresponds to the area between the abscissa and the curve $f(x)$ from $-\infty$ to x:

Fig. 9

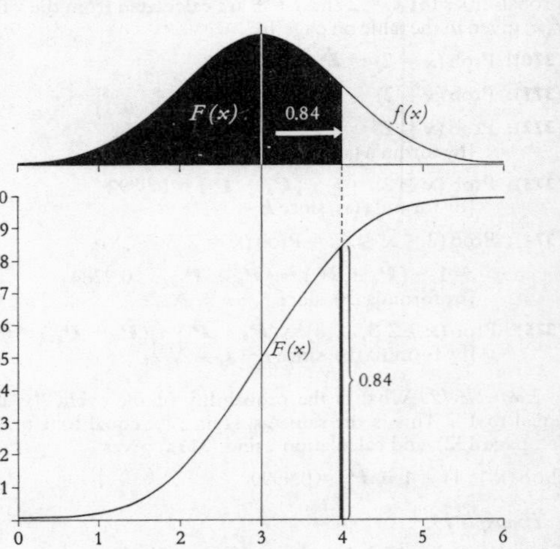

The total area between the abscissa and the curve $f(x)$ from $-\infty$ to $+\infty$ amounts to unity [cf. **(353)**]:

$F(\infty) = 1;\ F(-\infty) = 0$ **(403)**

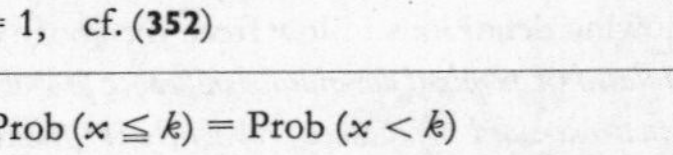

Fig. 10

For continuous distributions the equations analogous to **(370)**–**(375)** are the following:

$\text{Prob}\,(x = k) = 0$, cf. **(352)** and **(398)**

$\text{Prob}\,(x \neq k) = 1$, cf. **(352)** **(404)**

$\text{Prob}\,(x \leqq k) = \text{Prob}\,(x < k)$ **(405)**

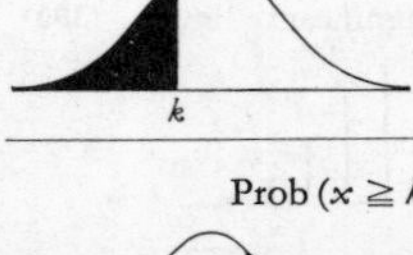

$= \int_{-\infty}^{k} f(x)\,dx = F(k)$ (a)

$= 1 - \int_{k}^{\infty} f(x)\,dx$ (b)

$\text{Prob}\,(x \geqq k) = \text{Prob}\,(x > k)$ **(406)**

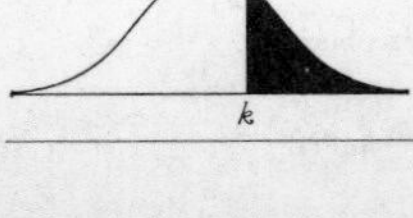

$= 1 - \int_{-\infty}^{k} f(x)\,dx = 1 - F(k)$ (a)

$= \int_{k}^{\infty} f(x)\,dx$ (b)

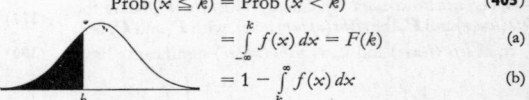

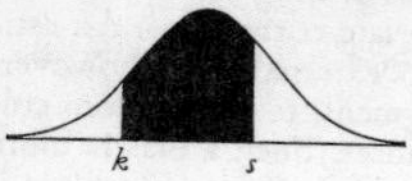

$$\left.\begin{aligned}\text{Prob}\,(k \leqq x \leqq s) &= \int_{-\infty}^{s} f(x)\,dx - \int_{-\infty}^{k} f(x)\,dx \\ &= F(s) - F(k)\end{aligned}\right\}\quad \textbf{(407a)}$$

$$= 1 - \int_{-\infty}^{k} f(x)\,dx - \int_{s}^{\infty} f(x)\,dx \quad \textbf{(407b)}$$

$$= \int_{k}^{s} f(x)\,dx \quad \textbf{(407c)}$$

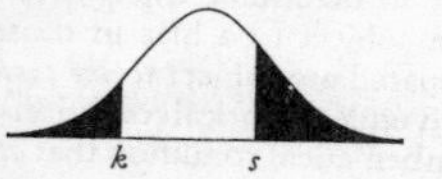

$$\left.\begin{aligned}\text{Prob}\,(x < k) + \text{Prob}\,(x > s) &= \text{Prob}\,(x \neq k \text{ to } s)^* \\ &= 1 - \int_{-\infty}^{s} f(x)\,dx + \int_{-\infty}^{k} f(x)\,dx \\ &= 1 - F(s) + F(k)\end{aligned}\right\}\quad \textbf{(408a)}$$

$$= \int_{-\infty}^{k} f(x)\,dx + \int_{s}^{\infty} f(x)\,dx \quad \textbf{(408b)}$$

$$= 1 - \int_{k}^{s} f(x)\,dx \quad \textbf{(408c)}$$

* In this text the expression Prob ($x \neq k$ to s) is used in place of the mathematically correct Prob ($x < k$) + Prob ($x > s$) since it demonstrates the significant inequality more clearly and is formulated in the same manner as **(375)**.

In equations **(405)**–**(408)**, comparison with **(399)** shows for example that Prob ($k \leqq x \leqq s$) is the same as Prob ($k < x \leqq s$), Prob ($k \leqq x < s$) and Prob ($k < x < s$).

The numerical values of the various integrals in **(405)**–**(408)** for the most important distributions will be found in the statistical tables on pages 28 onward. They will be discussed further under the headings of the individual distributions later in this chapter. In the examples below in which probabilities in the normal distribution are calculated, the abscissas x are designated deviations c. In the table on page 28, $F(c)$ values are tabulated on the right (deviation→ integral), i.e. *the probabilities $F(c)$ for given deviations c.* On the left (integral→ deviation) are deviations c for given probabilities, so that here the deviation c is a function of $F(c)$, known as the quantile c (cf. section 10 E, page 159). Such a function is known as an *inverse function.* Tables of inverse functions are useful but not absolutely necessary. The values required can also be obtained from tables of basic functions by interpolation.

Example 14. The probabilities for $k = -1.65$ and $s = 1.96$ are calculated for the normal distribution using the form (a) of equations **(405)** to **(408)**.

The right-hand side of the table on page 28 gives $F(-1.65) = 0.04947$ and $F(1.96) = 0.97500$, so that

(405): Prob ($c \leqq -1.65$) = 0.04947
(406): Prob ($c \geqq -1.65$) = 1 − 0.04947 = 0.95053
(407): Prob ($-1.65 \leqq c \leqq 1.96$) = 0.97500 − 0.04947 = 0.92553
(408): Prob ($c \neq -1.65$ to 1.96) = 1 − 0.97500 + 0.04947 = 0.07447

Example 15. Given the probabilities $F(c) = 0.001$ and 0.995 it is required to find the corresponding deviations c. The left-hand side of the table on page 28 gives $c = -3.0902$ and 2.5758. The corresponding values taken from the right-hand side without interpolation are 3.09 and 2.58.

Example 16.

Confidence intervals* and significance limits

Cf. also sections 8 and 9, pages 153–158.

A. *One-sided significance limits*

Given α, where $0 < \alpha \leqq 0.5$, determine x_l and x_r in such a way that

$$\text{Prob}\,(x < x_l) = \boldsymbol{P}_l = \int_{-\infty}^{x_l} f(x)\,dx = F(x_l) = \alpha \quad \textbf{(409)}$$

$$\left.\begin{aligned}\text{Prob}\,(x > x_r) = \boldsymbol{P}_r &= \int_{x_r}^{\infty} f(x)\,dx = 1 - \int_{-\infty}^{x_r} f(x)\,dx \\ &= 1 - F(x_r) = \alpha\end{aligned}\right\}\quad \textbf{(410)}$$

From **(410)** it follows that $F(x_r) = 1 - \alpha$ **(411)**

For the normal distribution, the table on page 28, left-hand side, gives for $\alpha = 0.025$, $x_l = -1.96$ and $x_r = 1.96$.

* Also known as "tolerance intervals". Cf. section 8, page 153.

The definitions of the symbols α, $\boldsymbol{P}_l$, $\boldsymbol{P}_r$, x_l and x_r in **(409)** and **(410)** are the same as in **(378)**, **(379)** and **(380)**.

It will be noted, however, that in contrast to discrete distributions [cf. **(384)**], the actual and nominal significance probabilities in continuous distributions are of the same magnitude. In continuous distributions therefore, the simple expression "significance probability" is used, the symbols $\boldsymbol{P}$ and α becoming synonymous. **(412)**

As in the case of discrete distributions it follows that:

If x *attains or exceeds* (to the left) the *left* (lower) significance limit x_l, then in a *one-tailed* test x is *smaller* than x_l with a significance probability $\leqq \alpha$:
Prob ($x < x_l$) $\leqq \alpha$ **(413)**

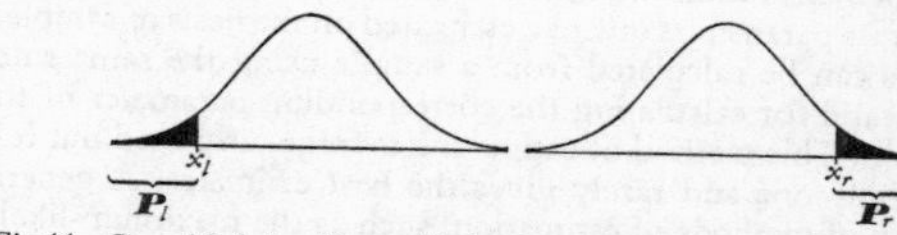

Fig. 11 One-sided significance limits for continuous distributions.

If x *attains or exceeds* (to the right) the *right* (upper) significance limit x_r, then in a *one-tailed* test x is *greater* than x_r with a significance probability $\leqq \alpha$:
Prob ($x > x_r$) $\leqq \alpha$, when $x \geqq x_r$ **(414)**

The following definitions should also be noted:

– the range between x_l and ∞ or between $-\infty$ and x_r as *one-sided confidence interval.* **(415)**

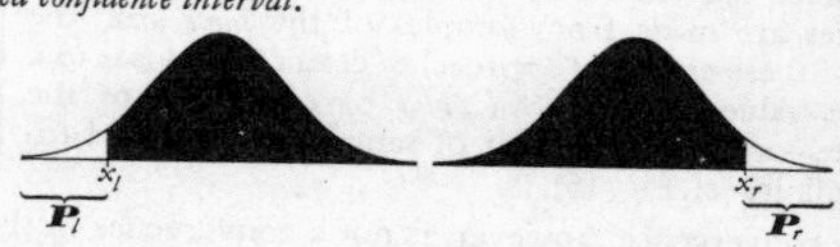

Fig. 12 One-sided confidence intervals for continuous distributions.

– x_l and x_r as *one-sided confidence limits* when the other limit lies at ∞ and $-\infty$ respectively. Again, significance limits and confidence intervals for continuous distributions are determined according to the same mathematical principles. **(416)**

B. *Two-sided significance limits*

When a left and a right significance limit are jointly determined for a continuous distribution according to rules **(409)** and **(410)**, then for the two together $\boldsymbol{P}_l + \boldsymbol{P}_r = 2\,\boldsymbol{P} = 2\alpha$. **(417)**

In this case

– $2\,\boldsymbol{P} = 2\,\alpha$ is known as the *two-sided significance level.* **(418)**

– x_l and x_r together are known as *two-sided* significance limits, or briefly as *significance limits.* **(419)**

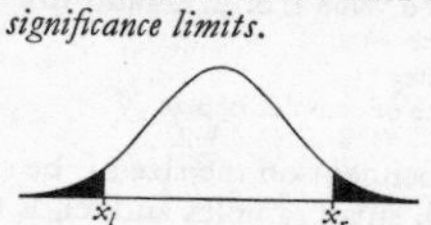

Fig. 13 Two-sided significance limits for continuous distributions.

It should be noted that

– if x *attains or exceeds* (outwards) *one of the two* significance limits x_l or x_r, then in a *two-tailed* test x is *unequal* to x_l to x_r with a significance probability $\leqq 2\alpha$:
Prob ($x \neq x_l$ to x_r) $\leqq 2\,\alpha$ **(420)**

The following definitions should also be noted:

– the range between x_l and x_r as *two-sided* confidence interval, or briefly as *confidence interval.* **(421)**

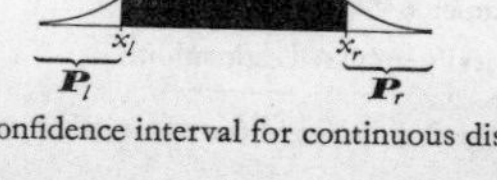

Fig. 14 Two-sided confidence interval for continuous distributions.

– x_l and x_r as *two-sided* confidence limits (with symmetrical probability), or briefly as *confidence limits*. **(422)**

– the probability $1 - 2\,\boldsymbol{P} = 1 - 2\alpha$ as two-sided confidence probability, or briefly as *confidence probability*:

$$\begin{aligned} &\text{Prob}\,(x_l \leqq x \leqq x_r) = 1 - 2\,\boldsymbol{P} \\ &= 1 - \int_{-\infty}^{x_l} f(x)\,dx - \int_{x_r}^{\infty} f(x)\,dx = \int_{x_l}^{x_r} f(x)\,dx \\ &= \int_{-\infty}^{x_r} f(x)\,dx - \int_{-\infty}^{x_l} f(x)\,dx = F(x_r) - F(x_l) = 1 - 2\alpha \end{aligned} \qquad \textbf{(423)}$$

7. Estimation

The variables of a population are usually known but not always the type of distribution and rarely the parameters, so that the distribution or its parameters must be estimated on the basis of samples. Estimates can be calculated from a sample using the same rules that are valid for calculating the corresponding parameter of the population. This method of estimating is frequently used but it is not the only one and rarely gives the best estimates. A general discussion of methods of estimation, such as the maximum-likelihood method of R. A. Fisher, would not be appropriate here since their understanding requires a knowledge of higher mathematics*. It is also unnecessary in practice since for the commonest cases a recognized estimating formula can be used.

7A. Expectation and bias

It is assumed that it is required to estimate some parameter P from a sample of size N.

Experience has shown that when a number of similar estimates are made from samples of the *same* size, the mean of these estimates approaches closer and closer to a definite value – the *expected value* or *expectation* of the estimate – when the number of samples is increased toward infinity (cf. Fig. 15). **(424)**

This convergence, however, is not a convergence in the usual mathematical sense but a *convergence in probability* or *stochastic convergence*, i.e. "*the probability that...*" *converges toward unity or zero* [cf. **(427)**].

When the expectation of an estimate is equal to the parameter, the estimate is said to be *unbiased*. When this is not the case, the estimate has *bias*. **(425)**

Fig. 15 Estimation with bias.

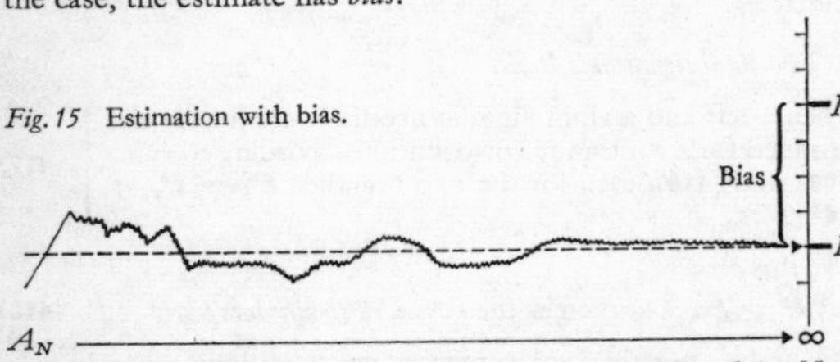

Broken line = Expected value E of an estimate from samples of size N
Full line = Estimate
P = Parameter
A_N = Number of samples of size N

The bias can be dependent on the size of the sample. As a rule it is larger with small samples and tends toward zero when the sample size N approaches infinity. Such estimates are known as *asymptotically unbiased* estimates (cf. Fig. 16). **(426)**

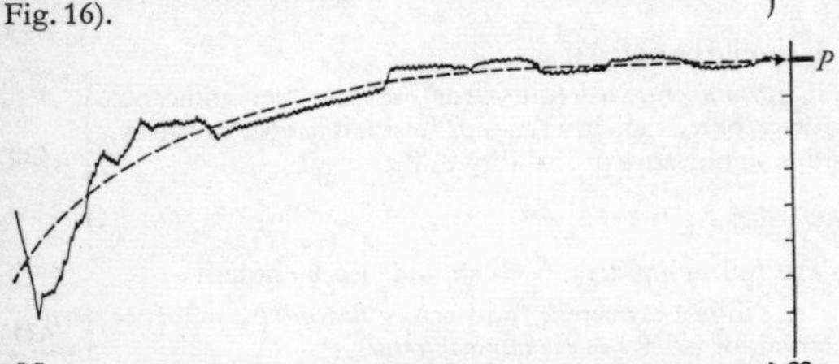

Broken line = Expected value E of an estimate from samples of size N
Full line = Estimate
P = Parameter

Fig. 16 Asymptotically unbiased estimation.

* "Higher" from the standpoint of the non-mathematician.

The bias described above is a mathematical one, that is, one inherent in the estimation. If the magnitude of this "internal" bias is known, it can be eliminated by appropriate corrections. An estimate can also have a non-mathematical, "external" bias, however, due to errors of measurement or judgment, to nonrandom collection of samples, or to both these causes. Such a bias is more dangerous than a mathematical one since only in rare cases can it be eliminated by recognition of its extent and direction. External bias can be avoided only by careful experimental design. For further information the reader is referred to the literature.

When estimates are made in order to determine the *difference between samples*, the results will *not* be subject to a bias in those cases in which the samples being compared are subject to *the same* bias, e.g. when the samples are collected under identical conditions. To this must be added the obvious mathematical condition that *all estimates to be compared are calculated according to the same rule.*

7B. Consistency

As in **(424)**, experience has shown that with increasing sample size, estimates also usually tend toward a definite value, the expected value in *infinitely large* samples:

If with increasing sample size N a parameter remains *constant*, then
Prob (| estimate minus expectation | $< \varepsilon) \to 1$
$(\varepsilon > 0)$, as the sample size $N \to \infty$. (a)

(a) is also valid for parameters which with increasing sample size N increase in proportion to N, N^2, etc. when the absolute value of the difference between estimate and expected value is divided by N, N^2, etc. (b) **(427)**

(427) is interpreted as follows: The probability that the absolute difference between estimate and expectation will not exceed any chosen small number ε tends toward unity as the sample size N tends toward infinity. This is the so-called (weak) *law of large numbers*.

Estimates which satisfy **(427)**, i.e. which follow the law of large numbers, are known as *consistent estimates*.

7C. Efficiency

Estimates are the result of calculations based on random events and are therefore themselves *random variables* which fluctuate from sample to sample around their expected value within a range dependent on the sample size; in other words, they exhibit *variance*. It is apparent that the accuracy of the estimate will increase or decrease with the range of this fluctuation, i.e. with the magnitude of the standard deviation or of its square, the variance:

The estimate with the *lowest* variance is known as the *most efficient estimate*. The variance of the most efficient estimate, provided that one exists for the parameter concerned, may be calculated by means of the Rao-Cramér Inequality[5,6], for details of which the reader is referred to the original publications.

Here the *most efficient estimate* is defined as that unbiased estimate of a parameter with variance equal to the lower bound of Rao-Cramér. This will be assigned an efficiency of 100%. **(428)**

Estimates which fulfil condition **(428)** for every size of sample are rare. However, there are estimates which meet this condition when the sample size tends toward infinity. Such estimates are known as *asymptotically most efficient estimates* (with an asymptotic efficiency of 100%). **(429)**

Asymptotically most efficient estimates of **(429)** are suitable for χ^2 tests, others not. **(430)**

(430) must be qualified to the extent that such estimates do not always exist. In this case, the asymptotically most efficient estimate should be selected from those known, and this one used for χ^2 tests even though its asymptotic efficiency according to **(429)** does not amount to 100%. **(431)**

As a rule, the standard deviation of an estimate decreases either absolutely or relatively (to the magnitude of the estimate) as the sample size increases (cf. Fig. 17):

If a parameter remains *constant* with increasing sample size, the standard deviation of its estimate shows stochastic convergence toward zero of the order of $1/\sqrt{N}$ with increasing sample size N. (a) **(432)**

(a) is also valid for parameters which with increasing sample size N *increase* in proportion to N, N^2, etc. when the parameter, the estimate and its standard deviation are divided by N, N^2, etc. (b) **(432)**

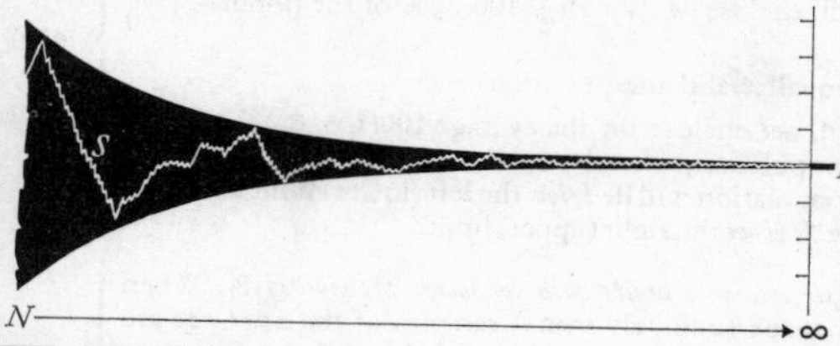

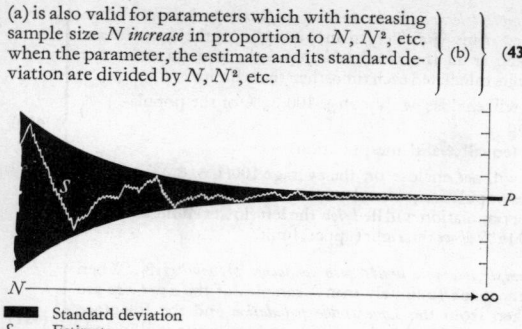

Standard deviation
S Estimate
P Parameter

Fig. 17

If the efficiency of the estimate A is 100%, that of the estimate B for the same parameter 75%, then the sample size when using method B must be 100/75 times larger (⅓ as large again) than when using method A if the same degree of precision is to be obtained [provided that (**432**) applies]. **(433)**

Thus by increasing the size of the sample a less efficient estimate can be given the same precision as a more efficient one,

or conversely, for a given degree of precision the sample size can be smaller when a more efficient method of estimation is used (cf. Fig. 18). **(434)**

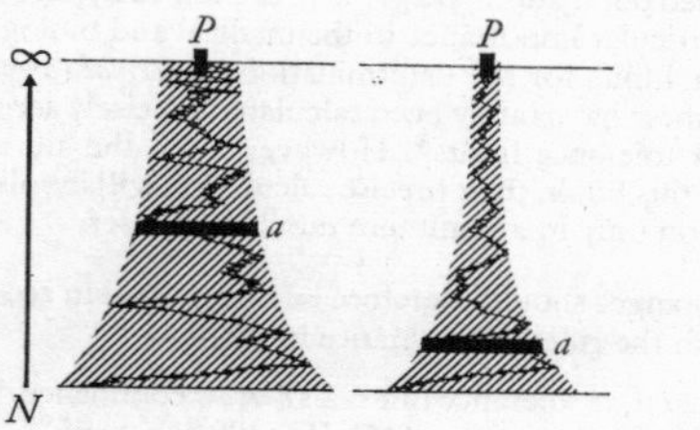

Fig. 18 a = precision of the estimate.

The question arises of which method to use in estimating a parameter when several formulas are available: that which yields the most efficient estimate but is more complicated, or a simpler but less efficient method? Theoretically, only the most efficient method should be used; in practice, however, the niceties of mathematical usage must be tempered by other considerations.

The most efficient of the known estimates of a parameter should be used
- when tests are expensive in comparison with simple counting [cf. (**434**)],
- when the tests cannot be repeated,
- when χ^2 tests are planned,
- when the result must be as exact and informative as possible,
- when the most efficient estimate has been used in similar studies by other investigators (thus offering the possibility of mutual comparisons and significance tests).

(435)

Where none of the reasons given in (**435**) apply, a less efficient but rapid method of estimating should be used
- when simple counting is more costly than the tests [cf. (**434**)],
- when the precision of the method suffices for the purpose in mind,
- when the object is simply a rapid preliminary check of the results,
- when the investigations are of a routine nature,
- when it is necessary to check more efficient estimates in the calculation of which there is a high possibility of error.

(436)

7D. Sufficient estimates

An estimate or combination of estimates which in any given case yields *all the information* which it is possible to obtain is known as a *sufficient estimate*. **(437)**

Information may be imagined (more or less) as the reciprocal of the variance. **(438)**

In conclusion it should be noted that as in the case of bias, the variance of an estimate is dependent on the experimental conditions and can be reduced by suitable planning of the investigation.

The designations "consistent", "efficient" and "sufficient" are due to R. A. Fisher. However, Fisher reserves the term "efficient" for those estimates which have been described here as suitable for χ^2 tests [cf. (**430**) and (**431**)].

8. Confidence limits and tolerance limits

8A. Confidence limits for continuous and discrete distributions

In this subsection it is assumed that the reader is familiar with examples 13 and 16, pages 149 and 151.

The estimation of a parameter alone does not yield a great deal of information. In a continuous distribution, for example, as (**398**) shows, the probability that the estimate [x in (**398**)] and parameter [k in (**398**)] agree is equal to zero. More information is provided by calculating from the sample the two values x_l and x_r which with a *high probability* enclose the parameter between them. Such limits are known as *confidence limits*. The associated terminology and mathematical definitions are given in examples 13 and 16 (sections 5 and 6).

The confidence limits used here are characterized as follows:

They are identical with the confidence limits of J. Neyman[7–9]. **(439)**

The parameter to which they relate is a *constant*. **(440)**

They are *estimates* and therefore *random variables*. Moreover, the *position of the limits* as well as the *width of the confidence interval* are random variables (cf. Fig. 19). **(441)**

Fig. 19 95% confidence intervals for the parameter p of a binomially distributed population, calculated from 20 samples of size 40.

For a given sample size, *more efficient* estimates result in a *narrower* confidence interval than less efficient ones. **(442)**

In analogy with (**432**), the confidence interval becomes absolutely or relatively (to the magnitude of the estimate) narrower with increasing sample size:

When a parameter remains *constant* with increasing sample size N, the confidence limits show stochastic convergence of the order of $1/\sqrt{N}$ toward the parameter, and the width of the confidence interval shows stochastic convergence toward zero (cf. Fig. 20). (a)

When the parameter is divided by N, N^2, etc. and its confidence limits by N, N^2, etc., (a) is also valid for parameters which with increasing sample size N *increase* in proportion to N, N^2, etc. (b) **(443)**

Confidence limits are to be interpreted as follows [see also (**456**)]: When very many (infinitely many) samples *of the same size* are taken *from the same stable population* and the confidence limits calculated for each, then these limits

(*one-sided confidence intervals*)

- will enclose the true value of the parameter on the average in $\geqq 100\,(1-\alpha)\%$ of cases* (a)

or (an equally valid interpretation)

- will *not* enclose the true value of the parameter on the average in $\leqq 100\,\alpha\%$ of cases* (b) **(444)**

* The "greater than" and "smaller than" signs apply to discrete distributions, the "equals" sign to continuous distributions.

(two-sided confidence intervals)

– will enclose the true value of the parameter on the average in $\geqq 100\,(1-2\alpha)\,\%$ of cases* (c)

or (an equally valid interpretation)

– will *not* enclose the true value of the parameter on the average in $\leqq 100\,(2\,\alpha)\,\%$ of cases*. Further, in an average of $\leqq 100\alpha\,\%$ of cases*, x_l (the lower limit) will lie *above* the parameter; and in an average of $\leqq 100\alpha\,\%$ of cases*, x_r (the upper limit) will lie *below* the parameter. (d) **(444)**

As a rule, the confidence probability 0.95 (more rarely 0.99) is used in the medical and biological field, i.e. α (one-sided intervals) or $2\,\alpha$ (two-sided intervals) is equal to 0.05 (more rarely 0.01). **(445)**

Formulas for the calculation of confidence intervals are given later for individual cases.

When the object of a statistical test is the estimation of a parameter, the corresponding confidence limits should always be determined as well. When these are known, an estimate (the result of a series of investigations) gives information worthy of confidence; without confidence limits it gives no such information. The statistical tables given in this book permit the calculation of confidence limits with *little* or *no* additional calculation.

In conclusion it should be noted that R. A. Fisher uses the term *fiducial limits*, logically a conception differing from that of J. Neyman's *confidence limits*. *Fiducial limits* can be precisely determined only for certain continuous distributions. For discrete distributions they can be determined approximately, but then only when the sample size is large. *Confidence limits* are not subject to these limitations and their use is therefore preferred here.

8B. Tolerance limits for continuous distributions

Limits for a percentage of a population are known as tolerance limits. **(446)**

The percentage of the population is expressed as $100\,\beta_p\,\%$, the confidence probabilities associated with tolerance limits as β_t. **(447)**

(**441**) and (**442**) are also valid for tolerance limits. **(448)**

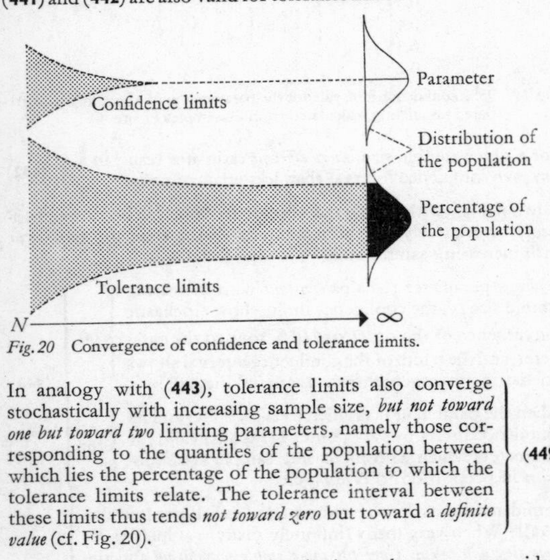

Fig. 20 Convergence of confidence and tolerance limits.

In analogy with (**443**), tolerance limits also converge stochastically with increasing sample size, *but not toward one but toward two* limiting parameters, namely those corresponding to the quantiles of the population between which lies the percentage of the population to which the tolerance limits relate. The tolerance interval between these limits thus tends *not toward zero* but toward a *definite value* (cf. Fig. 20). **(449)**

Like confidence limits, tolerance limits can be one- or two-sided. The following statements refer to two-sided tolerance limits in which

$$\beta_p = 1 - 2\alpha, \text{ and } \alpha\,(\text{left}) = \alpha\,(\text{right}) = \int_{-\infty}^{x_l} f(x)\,dx = \int_{x_r}^{\infty} f(x)\,dx.$$

Tolerance limits with confidence probability β_t must be distinguished from those without. They are interpreted as follows [note also (**456**)]:

Sample tolerance limits without confidence probability. When very many (infinitely many) samples of the *same size* are taken from the *same stable population* and the tolerance limits calculated each time, then these limits

– will enclose *on the average* $100\,\beta_p\,\%$ of the population (a)

or (equally valid interpretation)

– will *not* enclose on the average $100(1-\beta_p)\,\%$ of the population, whereby on the average $100\,\alpha\,\%$ of the population will lie *below* the left (lower) limit and $100\,\alpha\,\%$ *above* the right (upper) limit. (b) **(450)**

Sample tolerance limits with confidence probability β_t. When very many (infinitely many) samples of the *same size* are taken from the *same stable population* and the tolerance limits calculated each time, then these limits will include *at least* $100\beta_p\,\%$ of the population in an average of $100\beta_t\,\%$ of cases. **(451)**

The tolerance factors for tolerance intervals without confidence probability [interpretation (**450**)] given in the left-hand table on page 44 are valid for *normally distributed* populations. These tolerance intervals are identical with the confidence limits for the difference between the mean of a sample and a later single observation[10]. **(452)**

Tolerance intervals *with* confidence probability [interpretation (**450**)] are wider than those *without*, as would be intuitively expected. With increasing sample size, however, both intervals converge toward the limiting interval of (**449**). **(453)**

Formulas for the calculation of tolerance intervals for normally distributed populations are given in section 13B, page 168.

Of particular importance in the medical and biological field are tolerance limits for the determination of *normal ranges*. Up to the present these have rarely been calculated precisely according to the rules for tolerance limits*. However, with the aid of the tables given in this book, their precise calculation will involve additional calculation only in a minimum number of cases.

Normal ranges should therefore be determined in accordance with the rules for tolerance limits, and

– in general, as tolerance intervals *without* confidence probability [interpretation (**450**)] for $100\,\beta_p\,\% = 95\,\%$ of the population [cf. (**452**)]. (a)

– in special cases (usually industrial, where for example the wastage must be kept as low as possible), as tolerance intervals *with* confidence probability β_t [interpretation (**451**)]. (b) **(454)**

In the above text the word "normal" has been used – in "normally distributed" and "normal range" – in two different senses:

In "normally distributed", the expression is used in its conventional sense and has no deeper significance. The normal distribution is so named because it is frequently encountered and important, although it is not the only distribution which has these attributes.

In "normal range", the expression is used deliberately to denote that range which embraces the "normals" of a population. In the medical and biological field this range is conventionally the 95% tolerance interval without confidence probability [cf. (**450**)]. **(455)**

8C. Distribution-free confidence and tolerance limits

Cf. also section 10F, page 160.

Statements (**444**), (**450**) and (**451**) are correct only when the sample in fact originates from the population for whose parameter or percentage the limits were calculated. The formulas for calculating these limits are specific for the individual types of population. **(456)**

If the distribution type of a population is unknown, as is often the case, it is pointless – particularly with *small* samples – to

* The "greater than" and "smaller than" signs apply to discrete distributions, the "equals" sign to continuous distributions.

* With large samples this is in any case pointless.

calculate confidence and tolerance limits on the basis of *assumptions* concerning the distribution which are not justified by experience, the experimental conditions, and so on.

In such cases the so-called *distribution-free* confidence and tolerance limits are used, provided that these are available for the case concerned. Statements (**444**), (**450**) and (**451**) are then valid *without any stipulation as to the distribution* of the population*, i.e. they are valid for *all* populations with the sole provision that these are *continuous*. (**457**)

Distribution-free confidence and tolerance limits are *wider* than those calculated for populations of a specific type. This is understandable in view of the fact that they must satisfy (**444**), (**450**) and (**451**) for populations of widely differing kinds.

Distribution-free confidence limits for quantiles (median, quartile, percentile, etc.) for small samples (up to $N = 100$) of continuous populations can be read off *without* calculation from the tables on pages 104 et seq. An introduction to the calculation of distribution-free confidence and tolerance limits will be found, together with formulas, in sections 10 F (page 160) and 20 (page 182).

The table of distribution-free tolerance limits on page 128 can be used to solve problems of the following type without the need of calculation: At the start of a series of tests it is often necessary to decide the size of the sample to be taken *when it is impossible to know the form of the population distribution*. On the one hand the sample must be large enough to be reasonably representative of the population, on the other hand not unnecessarily large and wasteful. The answer is provided by distribution-free tolerance limits and for most purposes these can be read off directly from the table mentioned. For example, if the two extreme values of the sample are to include 90% of the population with the high probability of 0.999, then the table gives a sample size of 88. In other words, if a sample of size 88 is taken, then with a probability of 0.999, 90% of the population will lie between the 1st and 88th values of the sample.

9. Statistical significance tests

9A. Introduction

With a "true" die the probability of throwing the number 1, 2, ..., 6 is by definition exactly 1/6, and the probability of throwing an even number is exactly ½. In accordance with (**331**), the probability ½ is a parameter of the population of events "even number" and "uneven number" produced by throwing the die.

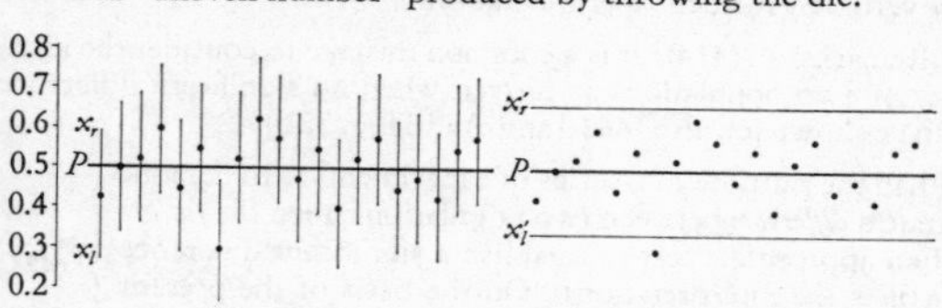

Fig. 21 95% confidence limits (left) and corresponding 5% significance limits (right) for a given sample size (cf. legend of Fig. 19). The points are estimates p of the probability $\boldsymbol{p} = ½$ (shown here as the parameter P).

Such a die can be used to check statement (**444** d). 20 samples of 40 throws each are made and in each sample the uneven numbers thrown used to determine the 95% confidence limits given in Figure 21 (left) for the parameter ½. In accordance with (**444** d), one confidence interval out of 20 does not include the parameter (note arrow).

Supposing now that these confidence limits had been obtained not with samples consisting of *twenty throws of a known die* but with separate samples from *each of twenty unknown dice*. The suspicion would immediately arise that "something was wrong" with that die for which the confidence interval did not include the parameter ½. Only one sample has been thrown with this die, and in this first solitary sample a rare event occurs which according to (**444** d) should only occur in the long run in 5% of cases**. The suspected die is therefore declared to be loaded, but with the reservation that this assertion may err with a significance probability of 0.05.

---

* Hence the expression "distribution-free".

** Further consideration will show that such an occurrence is possible, although with a much lower probability, since (**444** d) gives no indication *when* a rare event has to occur in a series of tests. *With random events no such forecast can be made when the tests are independent.*

This is the principle on which, mutatis mutandis, all statistical tests are based.

9B. Significance limits

The example given above demonstrates that significance tests can be performed with the aid of confidence limits:

In a significance test based on *confidence or tolerance limits*, 1 or 2 *randomly variable limiting values* are compared with a known or hypothetical *fixed parameter value* (cf. Fig. 21, left). (**458**)

Many significance tests are performed with the aid of significance limits:

In a significance test based on *significance limits* in the usual sense, 1 or 2 *constant limiting values* are compared with a *randomly variable test statistic* (cf. Fig. 21, right). (**459**)

It is *immaterial* whether significance tests are made on the basis of confidence and tolerance limits or on the basis of significance limits in the usual sense: the result is the same (cf. Fig. 21, left and right). With both methods it is valid to deduce a significant difference [cf. (**381**), (**382**), (**394**), (**413**), (**414**) and (**420**)] *when the test statistic lies at or outside the limits.* (**460**)

Confidence limits, tolerance limits and significance limits are intimately bound up with one another: (**461**)

– either they differ from one another merely symbolically and are numerically identical (a)

– or they differ in respect of formula and numerical value, with the formulas mutually interconvertible. (b)

Example (17) of (**461** a). In the binomial distribution

$\boldsymbol{p}_l < p < \boldsymbol{p}_r$ are significance limits for p

$p_l < \boldsymbol{p} < p_r$ are confidence limits for $\boldsymbol{p}$

where $\boldsymbol{p}$ are constants and p random variables. When $p = \boldsymbol{p}$, then $\boldsymbol{p}_l = p_l$ and $\boldsymbol{p}_r = p_r$ (for the same sample size).

Example (18) of (**461** b). $\bar{x}$ is the mean, $s_{\bar{x}}$ the estimated standard deviation of the mean of a sample from a normally distributed population. μ_1 is the mean of the hypothetical population, t the significance limit (corresponding to the sample size and desired significance probability) of the STUDENT distribution. Then

$\bar{x} - t\,s_{\bar{x}} < \mu_1 < \bar{x} + t\,s_{\bar{x}}$ are confidence limits for μ_1

$-t\,s_{\bar{x}} < \bar{x} - \mu_1 < +t\,s_{\bar{x}}$ are neither confidence limits nor significance limits in the usual sense (like the test statistic, the limits are random variables)

$-t < \dfrac{\bar{x} - \mu_1}{s_{\bar{x}}} < +t$ are significance limits for $\dfrac{\bar{x} - \mu_1}{s_{\bar{x}}}$

All three formulas are suitable for testing the null hypothesis $\mu_0 = \mu_1$. This is done by replacing μ_1 by the hypothetical comparison parameter μ_0 and noting the position of the latter with regard to the limits. The simplest formula (for beginners) is the first, the second allows the quickest calculation, while the third is that most commonly used.

When the simple term "limits" is used here in connection with significance tests [cf. (**460**) and (**461**) and their examples], then those limits are meant which conform with rules (**376**) and (**377**) or (**409**) and (**410**), depending on the population under consideration.

All limits suitable for significance tests converge absolutely or relatively with increasing sample size or with increasing numbers of samples of the same size [when (**432**) holds]. The statements in (**443**) and (**449**) concerning confidence and tolerance limits are valid for all such limits. (**462**)

It follows from (**462**) that:

With increasing sample size, any difference existing can be demonstrated more and more significantly. (a) (**463**)

With increasing sample size, smaller and smaller differences can be demonstrated for any given significance probability. (b)

When there is a real difference, shown with small samples to be significant, between a real and a hypothetical population, then with increasing sample size the assumption that the real population *differs* from the hypothetical will be *confirmed* (as a rule) with increasing significance (cf. Fig. 22a). (c)

When there is a real difference, which *cannot* be shown with small samples to be significant, between a real and a hypothetical population, then with increasing sample size the assumption that the real population is *the same* as the hypothetical will be *controverted* (as a rule) (cf. Fig. 22b). (d) **(463)**

When there is in fact *no* difference between a real and a hypothetical population, then it *may* be possible to demonstrate this with some certainty with very large samples (with complete certainty only with infinitely large samples). (e)

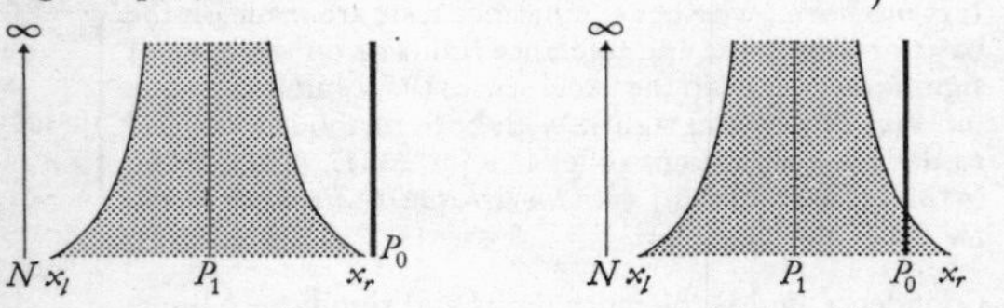

a [cf. (**463**c)] b [cf. (**463**d)]

Fig. 22 P_0 is the hypothetical parameter, P_1 that to be tested; x_l and x_r are the confidence limits of P_1 converging with increasing sample size.

9C. Significance tests

General

All statistical tests are based on the fundamental principle of comparing an *unknown population* from which the sample originates with a *known or hypothetical population*. **(464)**

All statistical tests provide confirmation with precise significance probability only of differences between the populations compared, *not* of their identity [cf. also (**463**)]. **(465)**

The hypothesis H_0 that 2 populations are identical is known as the *null hypothesis*. As implied in (**465**), it is usually postulated in order to be *disproved*. **(466)**

The expression "null hypothesis" is derived from the postulated identity of the population P_1 from which the sample originates with the hypothetical population P_0, whence $P_1 = P_0$, so that $P_1 - P_0 = 0$ (null).

When a statistical test* "demonstrates" a difference between the populations compared with a significance probability α or 2α [cf. (**460**)], then if α is sufficiently small, the null hypothesis may be regarded as provisionally disproved, and the alternative hypothesis – that the populations are different – is provisionally accepted. The probability of making an *error of the first kind* in this *decision*, i.e. of rejecting the null hypothesis when it is true, in other words of determining a difference where none exists, is α or 2α. **(467)**

The probability of making an *error of the second kind*, i.e. of accepting the null hypothesis when it is untrue, in other words of not determining a difference where one exists, is β. The probabilities α and β are closely related: as α decreases β increases, and vice versa (note however that β is *not* $1 - \alpha$ or $1 - 2\alpha$; the reader is referred to more advanced statistical treatises for a detailed discussion of this relationship). **(468)**

With increasing sample size it can be arranged that the probabilities of making an error of the first or second kind both decrease. **(469)**

Remarks on (**467**) and (**468**): When it is important to avoid making an error of the first kind, i.e. when it is necessary to be quite certain that a difference exists before accepting it, then a small value of α or 2α is chosen, say between 10^{-2} and 10^{-6} or more, according to the risk which it is permissible to take.

On the other hand, in a series of experiments designed to *uncover* a difference, larger values of α or 2α are chosen, say between 0.2 and 0.05. In any later and more elaborate experiments the significance probability can always be reduced in order to increase the certainty of a difference already disclosed. However, even though a difference has a significance probability in large samples of only 0.1 it is permissible in some circumstances (for example, with drugs which are life-saving) to reject the null hypothesis. The physician would willingly take the risk that in one case out of ten he has failed to administer a better drug. The tendency in medical and biological investigations is to use *too small* a significance probability.

* In the subsequent text the word "test" is used to mean "statistical test".

Power of a test

The probability $1 - \beta$, i.e. the probability of disclosing a difference when one actually exists, is known as the *power* of a test. **(470)**

From (**469**) it follows that the power of a test can be increased (as a rule) by increasing the sample size. **(471)**

The *more* that is *known* about the populations being compared, the *more powerful* are the tests which can (but need not necessarily) be carried out on the basis of this knowledge. (Less powerful tests can be used in such cases if they are adequate to meet the purpose in hand.) **(472)**

Remarks on (**472**): A useful analogy is that of the police searching for a delinquent: the more that is known about him, the more effective (more powerful) will the search (the test) be.

The *relative* power of different tests having the same object can *only* be decided by their use on *known* populations. **(473)**

Remarks on (**473**): The relative power of a test (previously calculated on the basis of some specific situation) is thus useless as a criterion in any situation in which the populations to be compared are unknown. In such cases care should be taken not to confuse known facts with *assumptions*. The results of statistical tests based on assumptions may not be reliable (see also below).

Interpretations

[Cf. also (**476**)]

When the purpose of a series of experiments is to demonstrate the *identity* of two populations, then the *failure* of an appropriate test to establish a significant difference justifies acceptance of the null hypothesis so long as it is not controverted by further experimentation. **(474)**

Remarks on (**474**): It is a common mistake to consider the identity of two populations as proven when no significant difference can be shown [cf. also (**463**d and e) and Fig. 22b].

When the purpose of a series of experiments is to demonstrate a *difference* between two populations, then the *failure* of an appropriate test to establish a significant difference justifies the interpretation: "On the basis of the present sample a difference cannot (with the significance probability used) be statistically guaranteed." **(475)**

Remarks on (**475**): The interpretation: "There is *no* difference" would be incorrect [cf. also (**463**d and e) and Fig. 22b].

One-tailed and two-tailed tests

When from previous experience or on theoretical grounds the direction of an assumed difference in magnitude between two parameters is known or thought to be known, then a *one-tailed* test should be made after deciding on the assumed direction of the difference in magnitude ($A < B$ or $A > B$) and on the significance probability α, conventionally 0.05 or 0.01* [cf. remarks on (**468**)]. The one-tailed test checks only one of the limits, either the left or the right, in accordance with the prearranged direction of the test, whence its name. One-tailed tests are more sensitive (more powerful) than two-tailed as far as the disclosure of a difference is concerned. However, they are justified only when the direction of the assumed difference in magnitude is fairly certain for reasons other than those connected with the sample. On the interpretation of one-tailed tests see (**476**).

* When α or 2α serves as a criterion of *decision* (rejection or acceptance of the null hypothesis), then the decision as to its magnitude must be made *independently* of the sample being tested, that is to say, if the investigator is in direct contact with the sample then *before* it is taken, if he is not in direct contact with it then *before* starting the statistical analysis.

Interpretation of one-tailed tests*

Required significance	Situation of the test statistic: hypothetical	Situation of the test statistic: test	Interpretation and significance (in brackets): one-tailed	Interpretation and significance (in brackets): two-tailed
α	$x < x_l$	$x \leqq x_l$ $x > x_l$	$x < x_l \, (\leqq \alpha)$ **(475)**	none
α	$x > x_r$	$x \geqq x_r$ $x < x_r$	$x > x_r \, (\leqq \alpha)$ **(475)**	none

Interpretation of two-tailed tests*

2α	uncertain	$x \leqq x_l$ $x \geqq x_r$ $x_l < x < x_r$	$x < x_l \, (\leqq 2\alpha)$ $x > x_r \, (\leqq 2\alpha)$ **(475)** or **(474)**	not equal (2α)

(476)

In general however, particularly at the start of an investigation, there will be considerable doubt as to which of the populations is the smaller and which the larger, even if they can be distinguished at all. In this case a *two-tailed test* should be made. If before samples were taken no decision was made as to a one-tailed or two-tailed test, then no alternative to the latter remains. The significance probability is 2α, conventionally 0.05 or 0.01**, i.e. $\alpha = 0.025$ or 0.005 [cf. remarks on **(467)** and **(468)**]. Note that even when the two-tailed test is interpreted as a one-tailed test, the significance probability of this interpretation is still 2α.

It should also be noted that the interpretation referred to here relates to the *test statistic*. The *real* interpretation based on this may be different. **(476)** is merely a summarized form of **(381)**, **(382)**, **(392)**, **(413)**, **(414)**, **(420)**, **(474)** and **(475)**.

Conditions which require to be fulfilled

It follows from **(472)** that in a situation in which several tests are available the one chosen will usually be that with the greatest power. According to **(473)**, however, the choice is only possible when the form of the populations to be compared is known. The form may be known from *previous experience* or from *theoretical considerations* (game of chance, central limit theorem), or may be deduced from the sample itself when it is very large. When the samples are small, however, particularly in complex fields such as biology, medicine and psychology, the form of the population is often unknown. In such cases, *assumptions* concerning the form are only too often made simply for the purpose of being able to apply a "more powerful" test [which in actual fact it may not be, cf. **(473)**]. For the following reasons this should be avoided (as far as it is possible):

In regard to the *reliability* of a statistical test result, it is wiser to risk losing a little of the information contained in the sample and to use a test contingent on fewer conditions which involves fewer assumptions or even none at all. A possibly more powerful test would require assumptions to be made which may result in illusory information not contained in the sample. **(477)**

When the conditions on which a test is based are not, or only partly, fulfilled, then the probabilities of making an error of the first or second kind are modified in a manner which it is difficult to judge. The one certainty is that the probabilities *valid* when the conditions are *fulfilled* are *no longer precise* or may be misleading when the conditions are not, or only partly, fulfilled. **(478)**

First of all therefore, in situations where several tests are available, care should be taken to choose a test in which (if possible) all the conditions which it involves are *actually* fulfilled in the case under consideration. **(479)**

Situations are often encountered in which a choice according to **(479)** is impossible because in none of the available tests (sometimes there is only one) can all the conditions be fulfilled. In such a case the test result should be interpreted with a degree of *caution* depending on the effects which the nonfulfillment of the conditions could have in the case concerned. It is advisable to *specify the conditions which cannot be fulfilled*, for example as follows: "On condition that both samples originate from the same normally distributed population, there exists..." **(480)**

The importance of the form of the population as a condition of many tests has already been stressed, but in **(477)**–**(480)** it will be noted that conditions are mentioned in a quite general sense. The number of conditions and their "severity" varies from test to test: obviously as many as possible should be fulfilled and not only those concerned with the form of the population. One condition which is fundamental to *all* tests is the following:

All statistical tests require that the samples should be *random* samples, that is to say, that they should be drawn by means of an operation fundamentally similar to that described in section 1, page 145. **(481)**

While this condition **(481)** is probably the most important condition in the whole field of statistics it is a very difficult one to fulfill completely in practice, especially in medical and biological studies. When an investigation has developed to the stage of statistical testing, any nonrandom samples can probably be discarded provided that testing for nonrandomness is possible in the case concerned. Although this guards against making an erroneous decision, both time and money will have been wasted. For this reason it is advisable – *before* starting the investigation – to take all possible measures to ensure (maximum) randomness of sampling.

When as in **(479)** there are several permissible tests, no generally valid rules can be laid down as to how the choice should be made. Usually the first tests adopted will be those involving the least amount of calculation. If these do not give the postulated level of significance, they will be followed by more powerful tests from among those permissible. Such a procedure is in order* provided that it does not result in the mistake of assuming that a significance is doubly (or more than doubly) guaranteed when two (or more) tests give a significant result. The reason for this is that between many tests there exist correlations which are not always apparent even to the statistician: to some extent they test in the same manner but with different degrees of acuity. An analogy is provided by the viewing of an object under the microscope at three different magnifications: one is unlikely to fall into the error of assuming that its existence is guaranteed three times. Similar but less easily recognized relationships hold for tests between which there are correlations.

Example 19. Given the sample (in chronological order)

1 hour
– 0.7 "
0.5 "
1.1 "
3 hours
1.2 hour
1.4 "

mean $\bar{x} = 1.07$ hour
median $M = 1.1$ hour

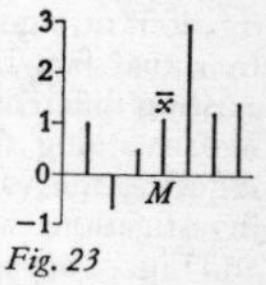

Fig. 23

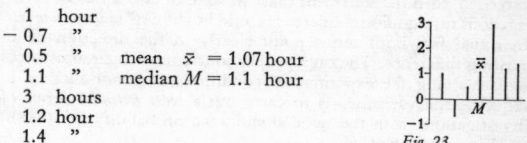

representing the differences between pairs of observations on the same subject, for example after the administration of two barbiturates. The question is whether these differences differ significantly from zero ($2\alpha = 0.05$).

In such a case the following 7 tests are available (these are all given in the statistical tables preceding this chapter with the exception of the maximum test, for which the significance limits can be memorized):

Test	Conditional form of the population	Calculation involved
1 Student (*t*-test)	Normally distributed	Among these tests the most
2 Lord	Normally distributed	About ¼ of that in 1
3 Midrange (Walsh)	Normally distributed	Less than in 2
4 Walsh	Symmetrical	About the same as in 2
5 Sign	None	None
6 Maximum (Walter)	None	Arrangement only
7 Wilcoxon	None	About the same as in 2

If it is known that the sample is from a normally distributed population, then *all* of these tests can be tried. In this case the

* For discrete distributions $x < x_l + 1$ and $x > x_r - 1$ are used.
** See footnote, page 156, right-hand column.

* The editors know of no precise indications in this respect.

most powerful is the STUDENT test, followed by the LORD and midrange tests, which are only slightly less powerful with samples of this small size. For normally distributed populations the WILCOXON test is also little inferior to the STUDENT test.

If nothing is known of the form of the population, then tests 5, 6 and 7 must be used, in accordance with (**479**). In the event of failure of all these only the interpretation given in (**475**) remains.

In the above example the tests yield the following significances:

Test	Significance
STUDENT	$0.025 \leqslant 2\alpha < 0.05$
LORD	$0.05 < 2\alpha < 0.1$
Midrange	$0.05 \approx 2\alpha$
WALSH	–
Sign	$0.05 < 2\alpha$
Maximum	$0.05 < 2\alpha \leqslant 0.1$
WILCOXON	$2\alpha < 0.05$

The STUDENT, midrange and WILCOXON tests yield the desired significance while the others more or less fail. This reflects the fact that when two samples are to be tested with respect to a difference in location between their populations, then as a rule for normally distributed populations the STUDENT test is the most powerful, for populations of doubtful form the WILCOXON test is the most powerful (of the available tests as given in the table above).

As stated in (**481**), all tests are conditional upon the samples being random samples. However, a test of the randomness of this sample made on the basis of runs on the median indicates marked nonrandomness with $\alpha \leqq 0.01$. In spite of the obvious significance, the result of the STUDENT and WILCOXON tests is therefore merely accepted as evidence of a possible difference which requires closer investigation by further experiment.

Common sense in statistical testing

Division of the sample values in the above example by 10 leaves the significances resulting from the tests unchanged. This would result in a statistically "guaranteed" difference in the action of the two barbiturates of 6 minutes on the average – in practice a meaningless difference. This illustrates the importance of looking at the *real* meaning of statistically "guaranteed" differences before drawing conclusions from them.

If often happens that a significance probability is *almost* but not quite reached, 0.054 or 0.06 say, instead of the required 0.05. The line drawn in making decisions must of course be a hard and fast one, but nevertheless in a case such as this the "commonsense" course is to investigate further. However, in the event that the postulated significance is once again not obtained but only *slightly* exceeded, then the statement that "in spite of two series of investigations no significant difference could be shown" is *inappropriate*. In actual fact both series point clearly in the direction of an existing difference. The only proper course in such circumstances – if changing the experimental conditions does not succeed in reducing the variance – is to carry out a *more extensive* series of investigations with the same significance probability [cf. (**463**b) and Fig. 22b, page 156].

10. Parameters

In this section means, variances and quantiles are dealt with in a general manner. Special formulas for calculating means and variances of various distributions are given in the sections dealing with these distributions.

10A. Mean and variance of the population

μ_x symbolizes the *mean*, σ_x^2 the *variance* of a distribution. In this text the index x will be omitted when there is no danger of confusion arising. The variance is also known as the mean-square deviation. (**482**)

The square root of the variance is known as the *standard deviation* (σ). (**483**)

The variance and standard deviation *of the mean* are expressed respectively by σ^2/N and $\sigma/\sqrt{N}$ and symbolized by $\sigma_{\bar{x}}^2$ and $\sigma_{\bar{x}}$. (**484**)

The quotient σ/μ is known as the coefficient of variance V. It is therefore the standard deviation with the mean expressed as unity. V has meaning only for *positive* values of x. (**485**)

The standard deviation is a measure of the variance. The smaller it is, the steeper the curve of the distribution, the larger it is, the flatter the curve (cf. Fig. 25). This relationship is the basis of the CHEBYSHEF Inequality:

$$\text{Prob}\,(|x-\mu| \geqq k\sigma) \leqq 1/k^2 = 2\alpha \quad (k > 0)$$

For $1/k^2 = 2\alpha = 0.05$ and 0.01, $k \sim 4.5$ and $= 10$ respectively. This inequality is valid for *any* population. (**486**)

10B. Transformations

If the variable x is subject to a constant increment a, then

$$X = x \pm a$$

so that

$$\mu_X = \mu_x \pm a \qquad \sigma_X^2 = \sigma_x^2 \quad \text{(a)}$$

The inverse transformation is

$$\mu_x = \mu_X \mp a \qquad \sigma_x^2 = \sigma_X^2 \quad \text{(b)}$$

(**487**)

The variance is *unaffected* by a lateral displacement, i.e. it is translation-invariant.

If the variable x is increased or decreased by a constant factor a, then

$$X = ax$$

so that

$$\mu_X = a\,\mu_x \qquad \sigma_X^2 = a^2\sigma_x^2 \quad \text{(a)}$$

The inverse transformation is

$$\mu_x = \mu_X/a \qquad \sigma_x^2 = \sigma_X^2/a^2 \quad \text{(b)}$$

(**488**)

(**487**) and (**488**) are also valid for the estimates $\bar{x}$ and s of μ and σ, the calculation of which they often render easier.

Example 20.

(*a*) Given

$x = 145 \quad 145.5 \quad 147 \quad 147.3$ Then with $X = x - 145$

$X = \ \ 0 \quad 0.5 \quad 2 \quad 2.3$ from which values $\bar{x}_X$ and s_X^2 are calculated, when

$$\bar{x}_x = \bar{x}_X + 145 = 1.2 + 145 = 146.2$$
$$s_x^2 = s_X^2 = 1.26$$

(*b*) Given

$x = 0.00325 \quad 0.00160 \quad 0.00320$ Then with $X = 10^5\,x$

$X = 325 \quad 160 \quad 320$ from which values $\bar{x}_X$ and s_X^2 are calculated, when

$$\bar{x}_x = \bar{x}_X/10^5 = 268.\dot{3} \times 10^{-5} = 0.002\,68\dot{3}$$
$$s_x^2 = s_X^2/10^{10} = 8\,808.1\dot{6} \times 10^{-10} = 8.808\,1\dot{6} \times 10^{-7}$$

A variable x whose distribution has

mean $= 0$

and variance $= 1$

is known as a *standardized* variable, or variable in *standard measure*. (**489**)

If a variable x has the mean μ and the variance σ^2, then the variable

$$X = \frac{x-\mu}{\sigma} \quad \text{(a)}$$

is in standard measure.

From the standardized variable X the original variable

$$x = \sigma X + \mu \quad \text{(b)}$$

is obtained. (**490**)

(**489**) and (**490**) are in common use in statistics.

10C. Estimates of μ and σ based on ungrouped samples

The *most efficient*, *unbiased* estimate of the mean μ based on a sample from a normal population with the values $x_1, x_2, \ldots, x_N$ is

$$\bar{x} = \frac{x_1 + x_2 + \cdots + x_N}{N} = \frac{\sum x}{N} \quad \textbf{(491)}$$

$\bar{x}$ is read as "x bar".

The *most efficient, unbiased* estimate of the variance σ^2 is

(a) when μ is known

$$s^2 = \frac{\sum (x-\mu)^2}{N} = \frac{S'_x}{N} \quad \text{(a)}$$

(b) when μ is unknown

$$s^2 = \frac{\sum (x-\bar{x})^2}{N-1} = \frac{S_x}{N-1} \quad \text{(b)}$$

for S_x see **(493)** **(492)**

The calculation of S_x (this symbol should be noted) is facilitated by the use of the following sums:

$$S_x = \sum (x-\bar{x})^2 \quad \text{(a)}$$
$$= \sum x^2 - N\bar{x}^2 \quad \text{(b)}$$
$$= \sum x^2 - \bar{x}\sum x \quad \text{(c)} \quad \textbf{(493)}$$
$$= \sum x^2 - (\sum x)^2/N \quad \text{(d)}$$
$$[= s^2(N-1)] \quad \text{(e)}$$

The most efficient, *asymptotically* unbiased estimate of σ is s. In practice the bias of s can usually be neglected. Correction factors for eliminating this bias in samples from normally distributed populations are given on page 47. **(494)**

The most efficient, unbiased estimate of $\sigma^2_{\bar{x}}$ is $s^2_{\bar{x}} = s^2/N$, the most efficient, asymptotically unbiased estimate of $\sigma_{\bar{x}}$ is $s_{\bar{x}} = s/\sqrt{N}$. Cf. also **(494)**. **(495)**

Other estimates of σ will be dealt with later.

Example (21) of **(491)**–**(495)**. Given the sample 19, page 157, then according to formula **(491)** $\bar{x} = 7.5/7 = 1.0714$

(493) $S_x = 15.35 - 8.0357 = 7.3143$

(492) $s^2 = 7.3143/6 = 1.2190$

(494) $s = \sqrt{1.2190} = 1.1041$

(495) $s_{\bar{x}} = 1.1041/\sqrt{7} = 0.4173$

The results should finally be rounded off to a few decimal places in order not to imply an accuracy which the estimates do not possess.

10D. Estimates of μ and σ based on grouped samples

Given the classes $x_1, x_2, \ldots, x_n$ with the same class width for all classes $d = x_{i+1} - x_i$ and the frequencies $f_1, f_2, \ldots, f_n$ $(N = \sum f_i)$, a provisional mean $\bar{x}'$ is chosen which falls in one class. The classes are now numbered. $\bar{x}'$ receives the number $z = 0$, the classes downwards receive the numbers $z = -1, -2, \ldots$, the classes upwards the numbers $z = 1, 2, \ldots$

Classes ... $(\bar{x}'-2)$ $(\bar{x}'-1)$ $\bar{x}'$ $(\bar{x}'+1)$ $(\bar{x}'+2)$ ...
z ... -2 -1 0 1 2 ...

Then

$$\bar{x} = \bar{x}' + d\frac{\sum fz}{N} \quad \textbf{(496)}$$

$$s^2 = \frac{d^2}{N-1}\left(\sum (fz^2) - \frac{(\sum fz)^2}{N}\right) \quad \textbf{(497)}$$

SHEPPARD's *correction*

In the grouping of the individual values into classes a small error arises as a result of the random choice of the individual values. This introduces a small error into the estimate of the variance which can be corrected by subtraction of $k = 0.08\dot{3}$ (that is, of 1/12) from the variance estimated in class units. This correction (SHEPPARD's correction) can be dispensed with in the testing of differences for significance but is otherwise to be recommended.

SHEPPARD's correction: $s^2_{\text{korr.}} = s^2 - \dfrac{d^2}{12}$ **(498)**

Example 22. Diameter of erythrocytes. Class width $d = 0.4$ μm.

Class	Frequency f	Deviation z	Frequency × deviation fz	Frequency × square of deviation $fz^2 = fz \cdot z$
5.6	5	− 4	− 20	80
6.0	78	− 3	− 234	702
6.4	144	− 2	− 288	576
6.8	479	− 1	− 479	479
7.2 = $\bar{x}'$	542	0	0	0
7.6	358	+ 1	+ 358	358
8.0	279	+ 2	+ 558	1114
8.4	99	+ 3	+ 297	891
8.8	15	+ 4	+ 60	240
9.2	1	+ 5	+ 5	25
	$\Sigma(f) = N = 2000$		$\Sigma(fz) = 257$	$\Sigma(fz^2) = 4467$

$$\bar{x} = 7.2 + 0.4\frac{257}{2000} = 7.251 \text{ μm}$$

$$s^2 = 0.4^2\frac{4467 - 33.0}{1999} = 0.4^2 \times 2.218;$$

$s = 0.4\sqrt{2.218} = 0.596$ μm without SHEPPARD's correction

$s^2 = 0.4^2(2.218 - 0.0833) = 0.4^2(2.135);$

$s = 0.4\sqrt{2.135} = 0.584$ μm with SHEPPARD's correction.

10E. Quantiles of continuous distributions

Definition: In $p = F(x)$, x is known as the *quantile* (p), here given the symbol $Q(p)$ or x_p. Quantiles are thus the *inverse function* of $F(x)$; they are so-called parameters of position. The quantile has also been given the name fractile. On $F(x)$ see also **(401)** and **(402)**.

The quantiles most commonly used are given special names: **(499)**

Quantile	Probability p
Quartile	$0.25 \times n$ $(n = 1, 2, 3, 4)$
Median	0.5 (= 2nd quartile)
Decile	$0.1 \times n$ $(n = 1, 2, \ldots, 10)$
Percentile	$0.01 \times n$ $(n = 1, 2, \ldots, 100)$

Interpretation of a quantile (p) of a continuous population: $100p\%$ of the population lie below the quantile p, $100(1-p)\%$ above it. **(500)**

Example 23. See Figure 8 (quartiles and median of a normal distribution), page 150.

Estimation

(a) *Ungrouped samples.* The quantile $Q(p)$ of a population is estimated by calculating the corresponding quantile $Q(p)$ of a sample taken from it. The sample values x are arranged in order of magnitude [cf. **(342)**] and numbered serially, the smallest value receiving the number 1. These *order numbers* are known as the *ranks* of the sample values x, so that

$$x_1 < x_2 < x_3 < \cdots < x_N$$

The quantile $Q(p)$ thus corresponds to the sample value with the rank $O(p)$:

$$O(p) = Np + 0.5\left(\text{for } \frac{1}{N} \leq p \leq \frac{N-1}{N}\right) \quad \textbf{(501 a)}$$

If $O(p)$ is a whole number, the quantile $Q(p)$ *coincides with* the sample value; if $O(p)$ is a fraction, the quantile $Q(p)$ *lies between* the sample values with ranks adjacent to $O(p)$, i.e. between x_i and x_{i+1}. There would be little point in interpolating between these two values.

If the sequence of ordered sample values contains ties [cf. **(346)**] and $O(p)$ falls on or between the ranks of tied values, then $Q(p)$ is given the magnitude of these tied values provided that the number of such ties is small compared with the sample size. In samples with very many ties (few classes and high frequencies) there is no point in determining quantiles in accordance with **(501 a)**.

Example 24. Given the ranked sample

x:	1.75	1.76	1.76	1.77	1.78	1.79	1.80	1.81	1.82	1.84	1.86
O:	1	2	3	4	5	6	7	8	9	10	11
x:	1.86	1.93	1.95	2.00	2.07	2.18	2.35	2.68	3.56	4.41	
O:	12	13	14	15	16	17	18	19	20	21	

it is required to find the 1st quartile, median and percentile (0.7). In accordance with (**501** a)

$O(0.25) = 0.25 \times 21 + 0.5 = 5.75$; $Q(0.25)$ lies between 1.78 and 1.79

$O(0.5) = 0.5 \times 21 + 0.5 = 11$; $Q(0.5) = 1.86$ (note the tie)

$O(0.7) = 0.7 \times 21 + 0.5 = 15.2$; $Q(0.7)$ lies between 2.00 and 2.07

(*b*) *Grouped samples.* Given are the ranked classes $x_1 < x_2 < x_3 < \ldots < x_n$, with class width $d = x_{i+1} - x_i$, and class frequencies $f_1, f_2, \ldots, f_n$, where $f_1 + f_2 + \ldots + f_n = N$, the sample size.
The cumulative frequencies are written as follows: $f_1 = F(1), f_1 + f_2 = F(2), f_1 + f_2 + f_3 = F(3)$, up to $f_1 + f_2 + \ldots + f_n = F(i)$. Np is now compared with $F(i)$:
If $Np = F(i)$, then $Q(p) = x_i + \frac{1}{2} d$.
If Np lies between $F(i)$ and $F(i+1)$, then $Q(p)$ lies between $x_i + \frac{1}{2} d$ and $x_{i+1} + \frac{1}{2} d$. (**501** b)

10F. Distribution-free confidence limits for quantiles of continuous distributions

Cf. also section 8 C, page 154.

Apart from their importance as the inverse function of $F(x)$, quantiles are useful in practice for two reasons: on the one hand their estimates $Q(p)$ can be obtained with a minimum of calculation*; on the other hand, exact confidence limits can be constructed for the parameter $\boldsymbol{Q}(p)$ without any knowledge of the form of the distribution from which the sample is drawn. The mathematical definition and method of calculating distribution-free confidence limits for quantiles are given in section 20 F (c), page 186.

The ranks $O(p)$ for distribution-free confidence limits for quantiles with various values of $p \leq 0.5$ and samples of size up to $N = 100$ can be read directly from the table on page 104. The ranks $O(p)$ for the median and sample sizes up to $N = 1000$ are given in the tables on pages 105 and 106.

The procedure is as follows: The limits x_l and x_r corresponding to the sample size N and the probability $p \leq 0.5$ are looked for in the table. If $p > 0.5$ it is subtracted from 1, giving $p' = (1 - p) < 0.5$. For p' the limits x_l and x_r, symbolized by x_l' and x_r', are looked for in the same way. The ranks $O(p)$ which fix the confidence limits in the sample are then

for $p \leq 0.5$: $O(p)_l = x_l + 1$ and $O(p)_r = x_r$
for $p > 0.5$: $O(p)_l = N - x_r' + 1$ and $O(p)_r = N - x_l'$ (**502**)

Example 25. For the sample in example 24 the 95% confidence limits are as follows:

Quantile	Ranks		95% confidence limits
1st quartile	$1 + 1 = 2$	and 10	$1.76 < \boldsymbol{Q}(p) < 1.84$
Median	$5 + 1 = 6$	and 16	$1.79 < \boldsymbol{Q}(p) < 2.07$
Percentile (0.7)	$21 - 12 + 1 = 10$	and $21 - 1 = 20$	$1.84 < \boldsymbol{Q}(p) < 3.56$

10G. Relations between mode, median and mean

The abscissa x of the maximum value of the density function $f(x)$ is known as the *mode*. (**503**)

In practice the mode is of little importance. On $f(x)$ see (**400**).

In *symmetrical* continuous distributions the *mode, median and mean are coincident*, but not in unsymmetrical distributions (cf. Fig. 31, page 164). The relationship between the three parameters is expressed by
Median $\sim \frac{2}{3}$ mean $+ \frac{1}{3}$ mode (**504**)

Of main importance in practice is the *identity* of the *median* and the *mean* in *symmetrical* continuous distributions: the distribution-free confidence limits for the median are valid also for the mean. It follows that:

If the population mean $\bar{x}$ of a sample coincides with either of the distribution-free confidence limits for the population median or lies outside them, then with a significance probability $\leq 2\,\alpha$, the sample *does not* originate from a symmetrical distribution. (**505**)

This is the basis of the sign test, which is easily carried out and also independent of the form of the population.

10H. The sign test

(*a*) *Testing a sample for symmetry.* $\bar{x}$ is calculated, and the sample values, including $\bar{x}$, are ranked. The number $N(-)$ of samples smaller than $\bar{x}$ is then counted, and the levels x_l and x_r corresponding to the sample size N and the significance probability $2\,\alpha$ looked for in the table on pages 105 and 106. If the number $N(-)$ coincides with either of these levels or lies outside them, then interpretation (**505**) applies.

Example 26. In example 24 in section 10 E, $\bar{x} = 2.130$, $N(-) = 16$. For $N = 21$ and $2\,\alpha = 0.05$, the table on page 105 gives the levels 5–16. With a significance probability of 0.05, the sample *does not* originate from a symmetrical distribution.

(*b*) *Testing of pair differences* (*differences between pairs of observations*). In such cases the null hypothesis is that the differences do not on the average differ from zero, or rather that there is the same number of differences smaller and larger than zero. The median is therefore zero. As in (*a*) above, the number $N(-)$ of differences which are smaller than zero, i.e. negative, is counted; in other words, the number $N(-)$ of *minus signs* is counted. The further procedure is as in (*a*).

Example 27. Of 500 pair differences, 210 are negative. Do these 500 differences differ on the average from zero ($2\,\alpha = 0.05$)? For $2\,\alpha = 0.05$ and $N = 500$ the table on page 105 gives the levels 227–273, so that the difference from zero is confirmed with the desired significance.

Note that if in (*a*) above $\bar{x}$ *coincides* with one of the sample values (or in the case of ties, with 2, 3, ... sample values), or if in (*b*) above 1, 2, ... of the pair differences are equal to zero, then the sample size with which the table is entered must be reduced by 1, 2, ... More powerful, but involving somewhat more calculation, is the Wilcoxon test for pair differences. For *small* samples a desired significance can be more easily reached with this test than with the sign test. Cf. also example 19 on page 157. For samples of over 50 there is no longer much difference between the two tests (as far as power is concerned; in the Wilcoxon test the amount of calculation involved increases rapidly with increasing sample size). Pair differences can also be examined by sequential analysis (cf. section 26, page 195).

11. The normal distribution

Cf. also section 6, page 150. For the meaning of "normal" see (**455**).

11A. Definition and characteristics

The normal distribution is a *continuous* distribution, the probability density function for which is defined by

$$f(x) = \frac{1}{\sigma\sqrt{2\pi}}\, e^{-\frac{1}{2}\left(\frac{x-\mu}{\sigma}\right)^2} \qquad (\mathbf{506})$$

(μ = mean, σ = standard deviation; for π and e see page 132)

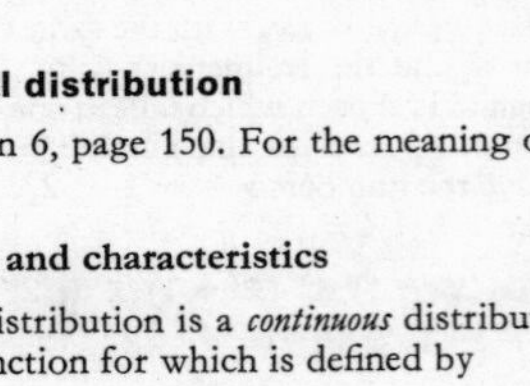

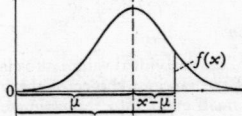

Fig. 24

The curve of the probability density function is *symmetrical* and bell-shaped, that of the cumulative probability distribution $F(x)$ is sigmoid (cf. Figs. 8 and 9). The range of variation of the variable x is from $-\infty$ to ∞. The normal distribution is often criticized on this score since it implies, for example, that the existence of human

* In the case of large samples the time saved here will be offset by that lost in ranking the sample.

beings 9 feet tall or more should be "possible"*. However, the word "possible" is here inappropriate. "Almost impossible" would be better, since the probability of extreme deviations from the mean decreases rapidly in the normal distribution.

If Prob $(|x - \mu| \geqq k\sigma) \leqq 2\alpha$, 2α changes with increasing k as follows[11]: **(507)**

k	2α	k	2α
1	$3.173\,105 \times 10^{-1}$	6	$1.973\,175 \times 10^{-9}$
2	$4.550\,026 \times 10^{-2}$	7	$2.559\,625 \times 10^{-12}$
3	$2.699\,796 \times 10^{-3}$	8	$1.244\,192 \times 10^{-15}$
4	$6.334\,248 \times 10^{-5}$	9	$2.257\,177 \times 10^{-19}$
5	$5.733\,031 \times 10^{-7}$	10	$1.523\,971 \times 10^{-23}$

Remarks on **(507)**: In accordance with the CHEBYSHEF Inequality [cf. **(486)**], the probability that in *any* distribution the variable x falls outside the limit $\mu \pm 3\,\sigma$, for example, is less than 1/9; as **(507)** shows, however, in the normal distribution it is only 3/1000. On the other hand, these much closer limits are valid *only* when the population is *in fact* normal. The inverse deduction should therefore also be noted, namely that should a distribution for which the $3\,\sigma$ limits are regarded as adequate *not* be normal, then the probability that the variable x falls outside these limits is *not* 3/1000 but may be as large as 1/9. This is an excellent illustration of **(478)**.

As with all symmetrical distributions, the mode, median and mean of the normal distribution are coincident. Their ordinate is the axis of symmetry of the curve of the probability density function [cf. Fig. 24 and **(504)**]. The most important consequences in practice are the following:

With a significance probability $\leqq 2\,\alpha$, a sample which fails to pass the test for symmetry *does not* originate from a normally distributed population. **(508)**

If a *fairly small* sample passes the symmetry test [cf. also **(474)**], then the population from which it is drawn may still not be normal**. However, in significance tests (cf. page 157, "Conditions which require to be fulfilled") the condition of normality may be regarded as *almost* fulfilled. **(509)**

For *small* samples the sign test used for testing symmetry is relatively insensitive, that is, it will disclose an actual lack of symmetry in a population much more rarely with small samples than with large ones. For this reason **(509)** is valid only for *fairly small* samples. For small samples therefore, significance tests should be used – provided they are available – in which there are no conditions regarding symmetry or normality.

As **(506)** shows, the normal distribution is *fully* characterized by the two parameters μ and σ. The mean determines the *position* of the distribution with respect to the x axis, the standard deviation the *shape* of the curve: the larger σ is, the flatter the curve (cf. Fig. 25).

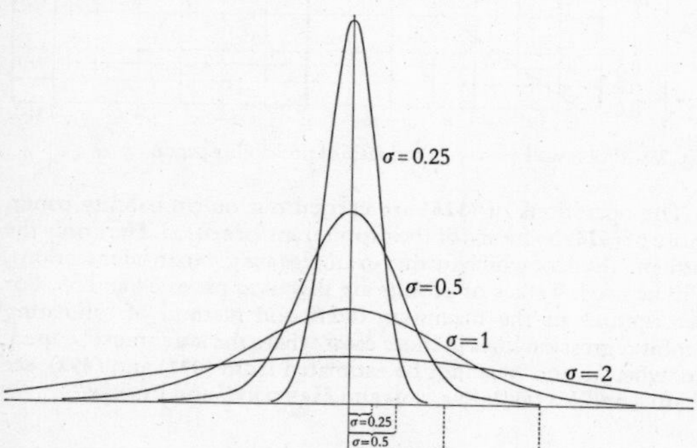

Fig. 25 Normal distributions with various standard deviations.

Since μ and σ can have any values, the number of possible normally distributed populations is infinite. If these are standardized according to **(490a)**, they are *all* transformed into a *single* standardized normal distribution.

* Although they may appear absurd, limits according to probability are more logical than absolute limits. What is the absolute limit, for example, for the height of a man – at 8′ 3″, 9′ 2″, 10′ 3″, or where ?

** Symmetrical distributions also exist which are not normal.

11 B. The standardized normal distribution

If the quotient $(x - \mu)/\sigma$ in **(490a)** is denoted by c, then **(506)** becomes the *standardized normal distribution* (with *zero mean* and *unit standard deviation*):

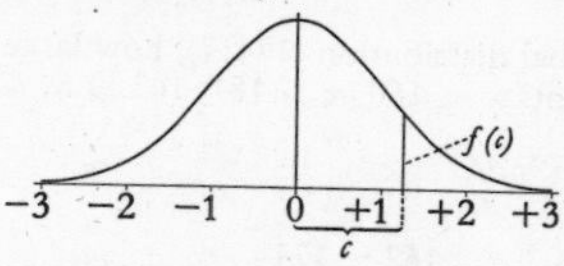

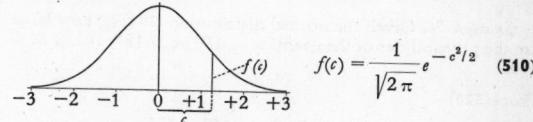

$$f(c) = \frac{1}{\sqrt{2\pi}}\, e^{-c^2/2} \quad \textbf{(510)}$$

Fig. 26 Standardized normal distribution.

The symmetry of the distribution has the following consequences, namely in relation to

Probability density function

$$f(0) = \max f(c) = 0.398\,942 \quad \textbf{(511)}$$

$$f(-c) = f(c) \quad \textbf{(512)}$$

Probabilities

$$F(0) = \text{Prob}\,(c < 0) = \text{Prob}\,(c > 0) = \tfrac{1}{2} \quad \textbf{(513)}$$

$$\text{Prob}\,(c < -k) = \text{Prob}\,(c > k) \quad \text{(a)}$$

$$= F(-k) = 1 - F(k) \quad \text{(b)} \quad \textbf{(514)}$$

$$\text{Prob}\,(-k \leqq c \leqq 0) = \text{Prob}\,(0 \leqq c \leqq k) \quad \textbf{(515)}$$

Quantiles

$$Q(\tfrac{1}{2}) = 0 \quad \textbf{(516)}$$

$$Q(p) = -Q(1-p) \quad \textbf{(517)}$$

11 C. Tables of the standardized normal distribution (pages 28–31)

Page	Table relates to	Left-hand side	Right-hand side
28	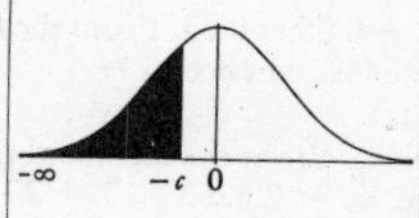 −∞ −c 0	Inverse function of the integral → = Quantile $Q(p)$ = $c(p)$ Argument p	$\int_{-\infty}^{c} f(c)\,dc$ $= F(c) = p(c)$ Argument c
29	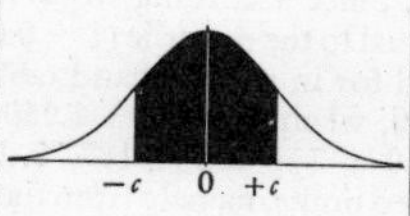 −c 0 +c	Inverse function of the integral → = $c(p')$ Argument p'	$\int_{-c}^{c} f(c)\,dc$ $= p'(c)$ Argument c
30	Left-hand side 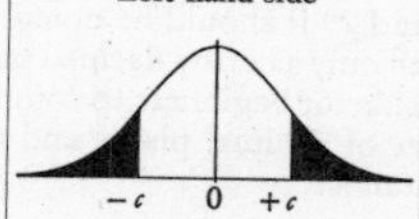 −c 0 +c	$1 - \int_{-c}^{c} f(c)\,dc$ $= 2P$ Argument c *	
	Right-hand side 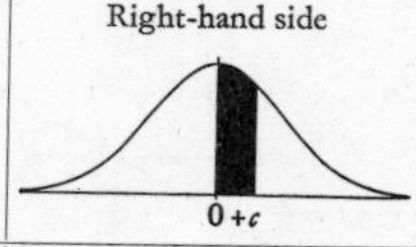 0 +c		$\int_{0}^{c} f(c)\,dc$ $= \int_{-c}^{0} f(c)\,dc$ Argument c
31	Upper: ordinate $f(c)$, argument c. Cf. Fig. 26. Lower: inverse function of $1 - \int_{-c}^{c} f(c)\,dc$		

* For inverse function see page 31.

11 D. Conversion of a normal distribution into the standardized form and vice versa

Cf. also section 10B, page 158.

The statement "normal distribution with mean μ and standard deviation σ" is here abbreviated to "normal distribution $(\mu; \sigma)$". **(518)**

The normal distribution $(\mu; \sigma)$ of the variable x is converted into the standardized normal distribution $(0; 1)$ of the variable c (and vice versa) by substituting X of (**490**) by c. **(519)**

In this conversion the probabilities of the converted values remain *unchanged*, so that

$\text{Prob}\,(x < x_k) = \text{Prob}\,(c < c_k)$ **(520)**

Example 28. Given the normal distribution (174;7), how large are the probabilities of the events $x < 160$, $x > 181$, $162 \leqq x \leqq 179$?

From (**520**)

$$\frac{160-174}{7} = -2, \quad \frac{181-174}{7} = 1, \quad \frac{162-174}{7} \sim -1.71,$$

$$\frac{179-174}{7} \sim 0.71$$

whence

$\text{Prob}\,(c < -2) = F(-2) = 0.02275$ (from the right-hand table on page 28).

$\text{Prob}\,(c > 1) = \text{Prob}\,(c < -1)$ [cf. (**514**a)] $= 0.15866$ (from the same table)

$\text{Prob}\,(-1.71 \leqq c \leqq 0.71)$: $\text{Prob}\,(0 \geqq c \geqq -1.71)$, from (**515**),
$= \text{Prob}\,(0 \leqq c \leqq 1.71)$, whence the total probability, $\text{Prob}\,(-1.71 \leqq c \leqq 0.71)$
$= \text{Prob}\,(0 \leqq c \leqq 1.71) + \text{Prob}\,(0 \leqq c \leqq 0.71)$
$= 0.48214 + 0.26115 = 0.74329$ (from the right-hand table on page 30).

Example 29. Given the normal distribution of example 28, it is required to find

(*a*) the one-sided confidence limit x_l for $1 - \alpha_l = 0.95$;
(*b*) the one-sided confidence limit x_r for $1 - \alpha_r = 0.99$;
(*c*) the two-sided confidence limits x_l and x_r for $1 - 2\alpha = 0.95$.

Solution:

All confidence limits or significance limits are quantiles (α):

(*a*) c_l is the quantile (α_l), where $\alpha_l = 1 - 0.95 = 0.05$. From the left-hand table on page 28, $c_l = -1.6449$, whence $x_l = -1.6449 \times 7 + 174 = 162.4857$;

(*b*) c_r is the quantile $(1 - \alpha_r) = Q(0.99)$. From the left-hand table on page 28, $c_r = 2.3263$, whence $x_r = 2.3263 \times 7 + 174 = 190.2841$;

(*c*) α is here $(1 - 0.95)/2 = 0.025$. Since according to (**517**) the quantile (0.025) is numerically equal to the quantile $(1 - 0.025)$, only the former need be looked for in the left-hand table on page 28. This gives $c = -1.960$, whence $x_l = -1.960 \times 7 + 174 = 160.28$, and $x_r = 1.960 \times 7 + 174 = 187.72$. Even simpler to obtain are the two-sided limits, namely from the left-hand table on page 30, using the deviation c, which can be read off directly by entering with the probability $1 - 2\alpha$.

In connection with examples 28 and 29 it should be noted that in practice, calculations are made with only as many decimal places as are required. However, it is advisable for beginners to complete the calculation with the full number of decimal places and then round off the result to the required number.

11 E. The probit transformation

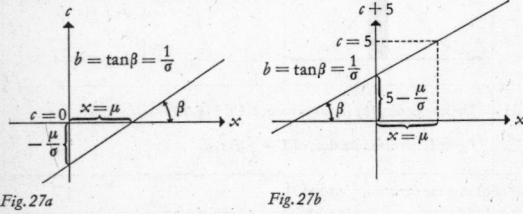

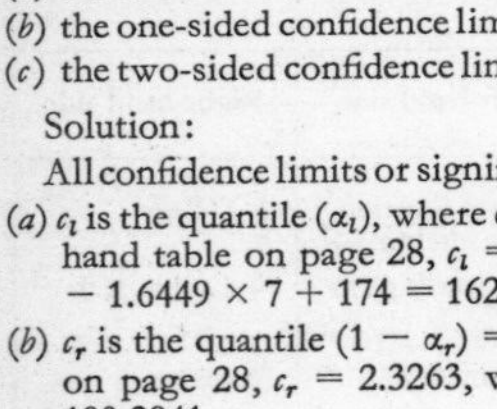

Fig. 27a

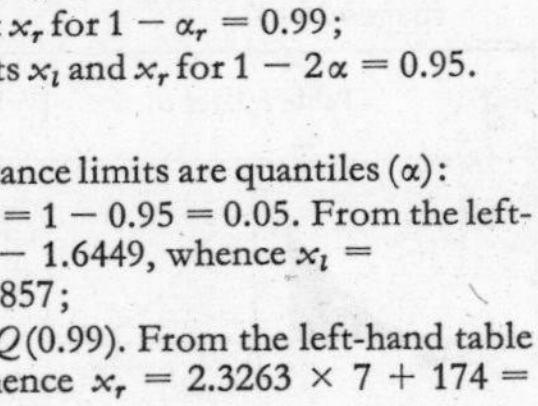

Fig. 27b

The standardized variable $(x - \mu)/\sigma$ can be broken down in accordance with (**34**) into the fractions $-\mu/\sigma$ and x/σ. If $-\mu/\sigma = a$ and $1/\sigma = b$, then

$c = a + bx$, where $a = -b\mu$ and $b = 1/\sigma$ **(521)**

In accordance with (**299**), the curve of (**521**) is a *straight line* (cf. Fig. 27a).

The straight line of (**521**) passes through the point $(\mu; 0)$. When μ and σ are known its construction therefore only requires *one* other point to be calculated from (**521**). **(522)**

If the straight line in Fig. 27b is displaced 5 units in the direction of the ordinate axis, then

$c + 5 = \text{probit}$[12] $= a + bx = 5 + b\,(x - \mu)$, whence $a = 5 - b\mu$ and $b = 1/\sigma$ **(523)**

The straight line of (**523**) passes through the point $(\mu; 5)$. When μ and σ are known its construction therefore only requires *one* other point to be calculated from (**523**). **(524)**

Since deviations of more than 5 σ are rare, the displacement of (**521**)–(**523**) means that in practice the majority of probit calculations can be carried out in the upper right quadrant (i.e. $c + 5 > 0$).

If the corresponding $F(c)$ values, which in accordance with (**520**) have the same magnitude as the $F(x)$ values, are now inscribed on the ordinate axis alongside the c or $(c + 5)$ scale it will be seen at once that the sigmoid curve can be transformed in this way into a straight line. The following therefore apply to probit calculations on samples:

If the ordinate and abscissa scales are linear scales (cf. the extreme left-hand scale in Fig. 28) and if now in place of $F(x_p)$ the quantiles c_p or probits $c_p + 5$ are plotted in the ordinate direction and x_p in the abscissa direction, then with increasing sample size the points $[x_p;\, c_p]$ or $[x_p;$ probit$]$ will converge stochastically toward the straight line (**521**) or (**523**) provided that the random variable x is normally distributed. **(525)**

If the abscissa axis is divided linearly and the ordinate axis in percentiles $c\,(0.01 \times n)$ or probits $(0.01 \times n)$, where $n = 1, 2, \ldots, 100$, and if the probabilities $F(c)$ or percentages $100F(c)\%$ corresponding to the latter are entered on the ordinate scale (cf. Fig. 28, right-hand vertical scale) and $F(x_p)$ or $100F(x_p)\%$ plotted in the ordinate direction and x_p in the abscissa direction, then with increasing sample size the points $[x_p;\, F(x_p)]$ or $[x_p;\, 100\,F(x_p)\%]$ will converge stochastically toward a straight line provided that the random variable x is normally distributed. **(526)**

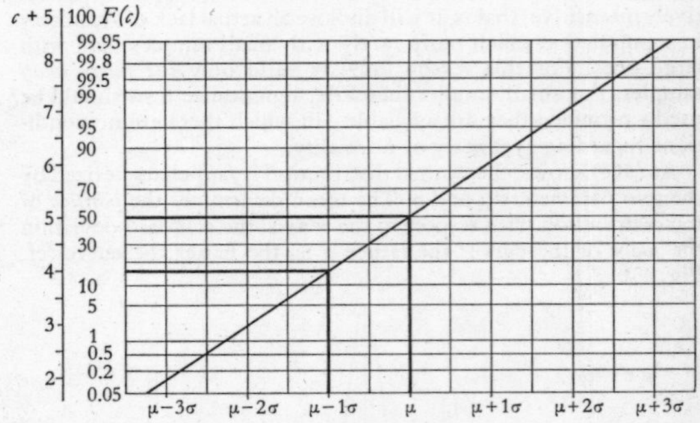

Fig. 28 Probit scale $(= c + 5)$ and scale of probability paper.

The operations of (**526**) are carried out on probability paper, those of (**525**) by means of the probit transformation. Here only the latter method, of which further examples are given in later sections, will be used. Tables of probits are given on pages 54 and 55. For descriptions of the maximum likelihood method of estimating probit regression lines in those cases where the latter must be used, i.e. when μ and σ cannot be estimated from (**491**) and (**492**), see Fisher and Yates[13], Pearson and Hartley[14] and Finney[15].

11 F. Fitting of normal curves to samples

Normal curves which are *fitted* to the sample are required when it is desired either to make a test of non-normality (either by eye or exactly) or to illustrate this condition. The above-mentioned exact tests for non-normality are more powerful than for example the equally exact symmetry test, since the *whole* of the empirical curve of the sample is compared with the normal curve fitted to it, with the result that these tests utilize *all* the information which can be extracted from the sample. For this reason such tests are known as tests of *goodness of fit*. If the test is to be carried out exactly, which here amounts to a χ^2 test, two conditions must be met: the sample must be grouped, and the parameters μ and σ must be estimated by means of $\bar{x}$ and s in accordance with (**491**) and (**492**) [cf. the remarks on these equations and also (**430**)]. *In equations used in testing for goodness of fit, μ and σ are replaced by $\bar{x}$ and s.*

(a) *Ungrouped samples*

With ungrouped samples, empirical and fitted probit values can be compared only by eye. From (**499**) and (**501** a) it follows that

$$p_i = F(x_i) = \frac{O_i - 0.5}{N} \qquad (\mathbf{527})$$

(O_i = rank of the individual sample value x_i; cf. section 10E, page 159)

The empirical and fitted probits can then be calculated from (**527**) in conjunction with (**523**)–(**525**).

Example 30. Given is the sample of example 24, section 10 E, page 160. The mean $\bar{x}$ is 2.130, and the standard deviation s is 0.6713. The $F(x_i)$ values are first calculated according to (**527**): $F(x_1) = 0.5/21$, $F(x_2) = 1.5/21$, etc. [equation (**31**) is used here: $0.5/21 + 1/21 + \cdots$]. By multiplying by 100, these values are converted into percentages, which are then used in the table on pages 54 and 55 to obtain the probits. For $x_1, x_2, \ldots$ this gives the empirical probits 3.0, 3.5, 3.8, 4.0, etc. These values are plotted on millimeter paper in accordance with (**525**) to give the result shown in Figure 29.

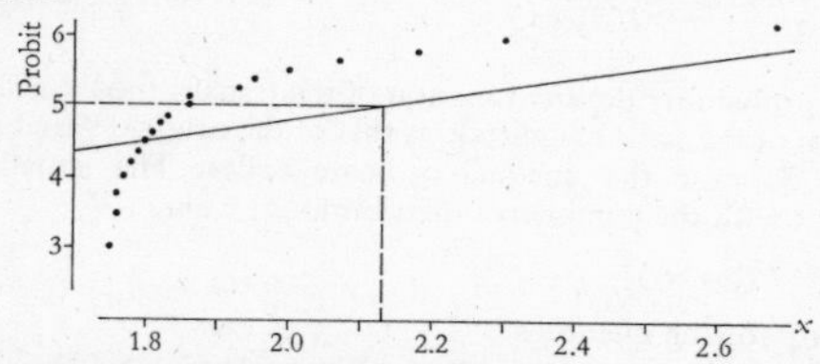

Fig. 29 Empirical probits and fitted probit line for the ungrouped sample of example 24, section 10E, page 160.

It will at once be seen that the points plotted deviate systematically from a straight line, indicating that it is very unlikely that the sample originates from a normally distributed population (as indeed was already clear from the result of the symmetry test of section 10H, page 160). If the sample had originated from a normal population, the points would have been distributed stochastically around the fitted probit line calculated in accordance with (**523**) and (**524**) from $\bar{x}$ and s in place of μ and σ.

(b) *Grouped samples*

In this case

$$f(x_i) = \frac{Nd}{\sigma} f(c_i), \quad c_i = \frac{x_i - \mu}{\sigma} \qquad (\mathbf{528})$$

$$F(x_i + \tfrac{1}{2} d) = \Big(\sum_{1}^{i} f_i\Big)/N \qquad (\mathbf{529})$$

(i = ranks of the classes x, $d = x_{i+1} - x_i$ = class width, f_i = frequency of the class i)

If both the fitted probability density *and* the cumulative distribution are to be calculated, then $x_i + \tfrac{1}{2} d$ is also used in (**528**) and the calculated ordinates plotted against $x_i + \tfrac{1}{2} d$, that is to say, at the *upper* limit of the class i. (**528**) gives the ordinates for the *middle* of the classes.

Example 31. Given is the sample of example 22, section 10D, page 159, with $\bar{x} = 7.251$, $s = 0.584$.

Table 1

$x+\frac{1}{2}d$	$x+\frac{1}{2}d-\bar{x}$	$(x+\frac{1}{2}d-\bar{x})/s = c$	$f(c)$	$f(c)\times Nd/s = f(x+\frac{1}{2}d)$
5.4	− 1.851	− 3.17	0.002 62	3.6
5.8	− 1.451	− 2.48	0.018 42	25.2
6.2	− 1.051	− 1.80	0.078 95	108.2
6.6	− 0.651	− 1.11	0.215 46	295.2
7.0	− 0.251	− 0.429	0.363 87	498.5
7.4	0.149	0.255	0.386 18	529.0
7.8	0.549	0.939	0.256 71	351.7
8.2	0.949	1.62	0.107 41	147.1
8.6	1.349	2.31	0.027 68	37.9
9.0	1.749	2.99	0.004 57	6.3
9.4	2.149	3.68	0.000 46	0.6

Calculation of the fitted probability density

The calculation is made as follows: The differences $x_i + \tfrac{1}{2} d - \bar{x}$ are multiplied by $1/s$ to obtain the fitted c_i values [this can also be carried out as a simple addition by using equation (**31**)]. For these deviations c, the corresponding ordinates $f(c)$ are obtained from the upper table on page 31 [in this connection see also (**512**)]. Multiplication of these ordinates by Nd/s gives the required ordinates $f(x_i + \tfrac{1}{2} d)$. (Cf. Fig. 30, left.)

Calculation of the empirical probits

The values of $F(x_i + \tfrac{1}{2} d)$ are calculated from (**529**), multiplied by 100, and the table on pages 54 and 55 entered to obtain the corresponding probits. The latter are plotted against $x_i + \tfrac{1}{2} d$ as ordinates, giving the points of Figure 30, right.

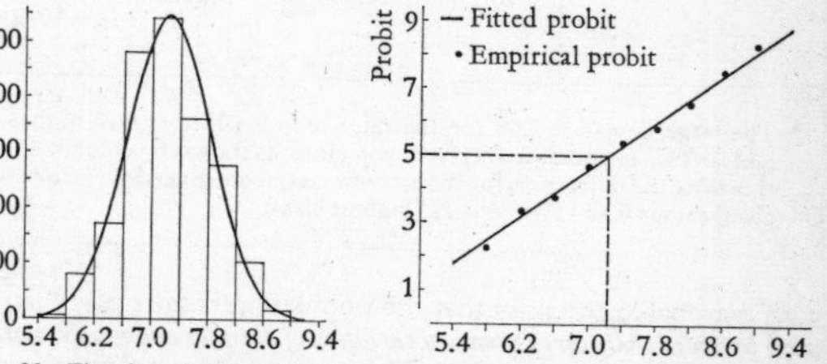

Fig. 30 Fitted probability density, empirical probits and fitted probit line for the sample of example 22 in section 10D, page 159.

Calculation of the fitted probit line

The probit line is constructed according to (**524**). In this example it first passes through the point (7.25; 5). If the value $x = 5.4$, say, is taken as the abscissa of the other necessary point, then from (**523**) the corresponding probit is $5 + 1.712\,(5.4 - 7.25) = 1.8$. When a straight line is drawn between these two points it is seen that the empirical probits all lie very close to it. The immediate impression given by Figure 30, right, is hardly such as to raise doubts that the population from which the sample is taken is other than a normally distributed one. That this impression is misleading, however, is demonstrated below.

Note that when the probability density is calculated as shown above, the two points required for the construction of the fitted probit line can be obtained by taking two remotely separated values from the column headed c of Table 1 and increasing them by 5.

Exact testing for non-normality by the χ^2 test

In this case the test is carried out by means of the c transformation, without probits, as follows (cf. Table 2 on the next page):

1. For calculation of the fitted c values for $x_i + \tfrac{1}{2} d$ according to (**521**) see column c of Table 1, which contains these values.
2. The $F(c)$ values corresponding to these fitted c values are obtained from the table on page 28. These are the fitted $F(c)$ values.
3. Multiplication of the fitted $F(c)$ values by the sample size N gives the fitted distribution of the cumulative absolute frequencies $H(x_i + \tfrac{1}{2} d)$.
4. From the differences $H(x_{i+1} + \tfrac{1}{2} d) - H(x_i + \tfrac{1}{2} d)$, the fitted absolute class frequencies f_i' are obtained.
5. From these the values of $(f_i - f_i')^2/f_i' = \chi_i^2$ are calculated.
6. The sum of all the χ_i^2 values is the required test statistic χ^2 with degrees of freedom $\nu = n - 2 - 1$, where n = number of classes.

The significance probability 2α of the χ^2 value obtained (cf. the table on page 36) is considerably smaller than 0.0005. Hence the population from which the sample originates is definitely not normally distributed, a result completely contrary to the impression gained by eye from the empirical probits (above).

Note that in the above calculation the sequence of the signs of the differences $f_i - f_i'$ should be looked at closely. The occurrence of pluses and minuses should vary randomly and not follow any systematic cycle. If there are enough classes a test of randomness of runs should be made (cf. section 25C, page 193). The reason for this is that if the χ^2 test gives no significant result when the number of classes is large – as in the above example – then it can be assumed

Table 2

$x+\frac{1}{2}d$	$F(c)$	$F(c)\times N = H(x+\frac{1}{2}d)$	$H(x_{i+1}+\frac{1}{2}d)$ minus $H(x_i+\frac{1}{2}d) = f_i'$	f_i [cf. (**501**b)]	$(f_i-f_i')^2/f_i' = \chi_i^2$
			1.5* } =		
5.4	0.00076	1.5	11.6 } 13.1	5	5.01
5.8	0.00657	13.1	58.8	78	6.27
6.2	0.03593	71.9	195.1	144	13.38
6.6	0.13350	267.0	400.2	479	15.52
7.0	0.33360	667.2	537.9	542	0.03
7.4	0.60257	1205.1	447.7	358	17.97
7.8	0.82639	1652.8	242.0	279	5.66
8.2	0.94738	1894.8	84.3	99	2.56
8.6	0.98956	1979.1	18.1	15	0.53
9.0	0.99861	1997.2	2.8	1	1.16
9.4	—*	—*	2000.0	2000	$\chi^2 = 68.09$
					$\nu = 10-2-1 = 7$

* The large deviation 3.68 for the value $x = 9.4$ is not given in these tables. This is unimportant, however, since as shown by column 4 of this table the differences for the extreme classes are given by H (lowest class) minus 0 and N minus H (highest class).

with reasonable certainty that the population is normally distributed *provided that there is random variation of the plus and minus runs*. If the latter is not the case then the χ^2 test needs supplementation. The test is also conditional on the classes being *independent* of one another. This is doubtful if the signs follow any systematic cycle.

11 G. Standard deviations of the quantiles of samples from normally distributed populations

The formulas given here are only *asymptotically* correct and should therefore only be used for *large* samples (the more extreme the position of the quantile the larger the sample should be), so that in practice they are seldom applicable. When confidence limits for the quantiles of small and medium samples are required it is better to use the procedure given in section 10 F, page 160 (distribution-free confidence limits) and *not* calculate them by means of the standard deviations defined in the formulas given here.

(Asymptotic)

$$\text{Standard deviation of } x_p = \sigma_{x_p} = \frac{1}{f(x_p)}\sqrt{\frac{p(1-p)}{N}} \qquad \textbf{(530)}$$

From (**530**) and (**506**) it follows that

$$\left.\begin{array}{l}\text{Standard}\\ \text{deviation}\\ \text{of the median}\end{array}\right\} x_{0.5} = \sigma_{x_{0.5}} = \sigma\sqrt{\frac{\pi}{2N}} = 1.2533\,\sigma\sqrt{\frac{1}{N}} \qquad \textbf{(531)}$$

In a normal distribution the median is identical with the mean μ. The median of a sample is therefore also an estimate of μ. The relative asymptotic efficiency of this estimate according to (**433**), (**484**) and (**531**) is

$$\frac{\sigma/\sqrt{N}}{\sigma\sqrt{\pi/2N}} = \sqrt{\frac{2}{\pi}} \sim 0.8$$

that is to say, about 80% of the efficiency of the estimate of μ made from $\bar{x}$ according to (**491**).

11 H. The logarithmic-normal (lognormal) distribution

The probability density function of this distribution is

$$f(x) = \frac{0.4343}{x \times \sigma_{\log x}} \times f(c),$$

$$c = \frac{\log x - \mu_{\log x}}{\sigma_{\log x}}, \quad (0 < x < \infty) \qquad \textbf{(532)}$$

The estimates of $\mu_{\log x}$ and $\sigma_{\log x}$ are $\bar{x}_{\log x}$ and $s_{\log x}$, calculated according to (**491**) and (**492** a and b) by substituting $\log x$ for x and $(\log x)^2$ for x^2.

The logarithmic-normal distribution is unsymmetrical (cf. Fig. 31 a) and has the following characteristics:

$$\text{Mode} = \text{antilog}\,(\mu_{\log x} - 2.3026\,\sigma^2_{\log x}) \qquad \textbf{(533)}$$

$$\text{Median} = \text{antilog}\,\mu_{\log x} \qquad \textbf{(534)}$$

$$\text{Mean} = \text{antilog}\,(\mu_{\log x} + 1.1513\,\sigma^2_{\log x}) \qquad \textbf{(535)}$$

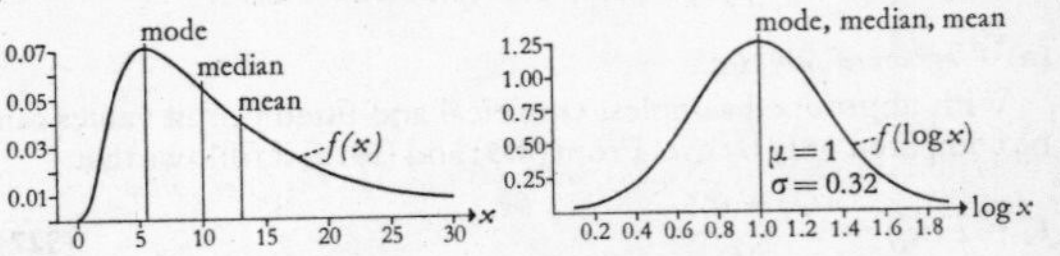

Fig. 31 (*a*) Lognormal distribution. (*b*) Transformation of (*a*).

If x is plotted on a logarithmic abscissa scale or – what amounts to the same process – $\log x$ is plotted on a linear abscissa scale, the unsymmetrical distribution (**532**) is transformed into the symmetrical normal distribution

$$f(\log x) = \frac{1}{\sigma_{\log x}} \times f(c), \qquad \textbf{(536)}$$

$$c = \frac{\log x - \mu_{\log x}}{\sigma_{\log x}}, \quad (0 < x < \infty)$$

[for $\mu_{\log x}$ and $\sigma_{\log x}$ see (**532**)]

From (**532**) and (**536**) it follows that

$$f(x) = \frac{0.4343}{x} \times f(\log x) \qquad \textbf{(537)}$$

The probability density function of the transformed variables is thus not of the same magnitude as that of the original variables. In Figure 31 note the unequal ordinate scales. The situation is different with the cumulative distribution*, where

$$F(x_p) = F(\log x_p) = p \qquad \textbf{(538)}$$

Similarly for the quantiles

$$x_p = \text{antilog}\,(\log x_p) \qquad \textbf{(539)}$$

and for ungrouped samples

$$O(x_p) = O(\log x_p) \qquad \textbf{(540)}$$

(O = ranks of the individual sample values, cf. section 10 E, page 159)

From (**536**) and (**538**)–(**540**) it follows that [for (**541**)–(**543**)]:

If an unsymmetrical continuous distribution can be converted into a normal distribution by transformation of the individual values in the manner described in (**536**), then this distribution is a lognormal distribution. (**541**)

If the transformation in (**536**) yields samples from a normally distributed population [cf. (**508**) and section 11 F, page 162], then any *tests* valid for the latter may be applied to these samples. *The results of these tests will also be valid for the untransformed samples.* (**542**)

For the estimation of the quantiles and their confidence limits in *ungrouped* samples from lognormal populations whose individual values have *not* been transformed, the procedures described in sections 10 E and 10 F on pages 159–160 are applicable *without any modification.* (**543**)

For *grouped* samples the following should be noted: the transformation $x \rightarrow \log x$ may only be carried out with the *individual values*. If a sample is grouped into classes it must first be rearranged into an ungrouped sample. The logarithms of the individual values are then obtained, when these may be re-formed into a grouped sample, but with *equidistant logarithmic* class limits. If a grouped sample cannot be rearranged because the individual values were not noted, then a logarithmic transformation is *no longer possible*. In taking samples, the individual values should therefore always be noted before they are grouped. (**544**)

In natural processes many random variables are lognormally distributed. In all cases where the reaction of a body to a given stimulus is proportional to the intensity of the stimulus and to the

* The quantiles of a transformed variable are given by the transformed quantiles of the original variable provided that the transformation was made with an *increasing* function [$f(\log x)$ is an increasing function of x].

size of the body, the form of the distribution is lognormal. In practice, this applies particularly to toxicological and other similar biological studies, where logarithmic transformation of the variable x (dose) is a matter of routine.

11 I. The addition theorem for the normal distribution

If $x_1, x_2, \ldots, x_k$ are stochastically independent, normally distributed variables with mean values $\mu_1, \mu_2, \ldots, \mu_k$ and variances $\sigma_1^2, \sigma_2^2, \ldots, \sigma_k^2$, then the variable

$$x = x_1 \pm x_2 \pm \cdots \pm x_k$$

is also normally distributed with mean **(545)**

$$\mu = \mu_1 \pm \mu_2 \pm \cdots \pm \mu_k$$

and variance

$$\sigma^2 = \sigma_1^2 + \sigma_2^2 + \cdots + \sigma_k^2$$

In (**545**) it should be noted that the variances are also *additive* when the mean μ is obtained from *differences*.

11 J. The central limit theorem

The importance of the normal distribution lies in the fact that under fairly general conditions, the sum of k stochastically independent variables *of any sort* converges stochastically with increasing k toward a normal distribution with mean **(546)**

$$\mu = \mu_1 + \mu_2 + \cdots + \mu_k$$

and variance

$$\sigma^2 = \sigma_1^2 + \sigma_2^2 + \cdots + \sigma_k^2$$

From (**545**) the sum of normally distributed variables is *always* normally distributed, even when k is small. (**546**) is valid for variables distributed in *any* form, however, only when k approaches infinity. In practice, the expression "infinity" is interpreted liberally. Thus, if for example in (**546**) the distributions all have the *same*, not too unsymmetrical form, then practically speaking their sum is normally distributed even when k is fairly small (50, 100, 200, ...). In other words, there will be a negligible error if the sample distributions are treated as normal.

In this publication, the statistical tables relating to sample distributions are so arranged that samples which exceed the tabulated sizes can for practical purposes be regarded as normally distributed. **(547)**

With *one* exception, *all* the sample distributions dealt with in this chapter converge toward the normal distribution in accordance with (**546**). The exception is the distribution of the extreme range (and of course that of the extreme deviations).

12. Distributions closely allied to the normal distribution

12 A. The STUDENT distribution

If in the standardized *normal* deviation $c = (x - \mu)/\sigma$ the standard deviation σ has to be replaced by its estimate s because σ is unknown and thus has to be estimated from the sample, then the standardized variable

$$t_\nu = \frac{x - \mu}{s_\nu} \ (s_\nu \text{ independent of } x) \qquad \textbf{(548)}$$

has a probability density function

$$f(t|\nu) = \frac{\Gamma\left(\frac{\nu+1}{2}\right)}{\Gamma(\nu/2)\sqrt{\nu\pi}}\left(1 + \frac{t^2}{\nu}\right)^{-(\nu+1)/2}$$

(549)

$$\text{where } \Gamma(x/2) = \begin{cases} (x/2-1)(x/2-2)\ldots 3 \times 2 \times 1 & \text{when } x \text{ is even} \\ (x/2-1)(x/2-2)\ldots 3/2 \times 1/2 \times \sqrt{\pi} & \text{when } x \text{ is odd} \end{cases}$$

ν is the number of *degrees of freedom* of t.

The STUDENT distribution is independent of μ and σ; its form is determined only by the number of degrees of freedom ν. The determination of the degrees of freedom will be described later for various individual cases.

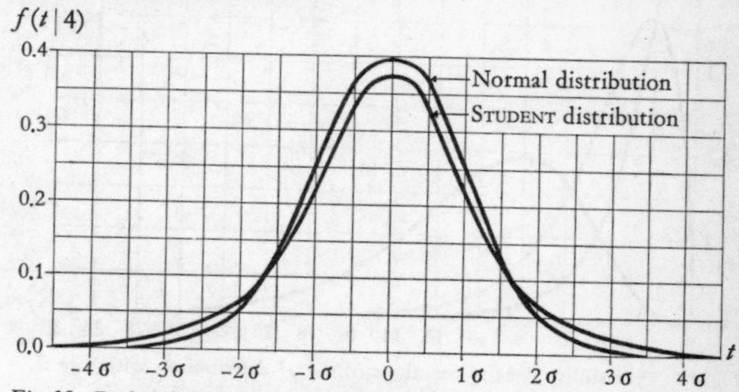

Fig. 32 Probability density of the normal distribution and of the STUDENT distribution with degrees of freedom $\nu = 4$.

The STUDENT distribution (or t-distribution) is very similar to the normal distribution and converges toward it rapidly with increasing degrees of freedom. Its range of variation is from minus infinity to infinity. It is continuous, *symmetrical* and bell-shaped, but in contrast to the normal distribution has more probability concentrated in the tails and less in the central part.

Equations (**512**)–(**517**) for the standardized normal distribution derived from the symmetry are also valid for the STUDENT distribution when c is replaced by t in these equations. **(550)**

Tables

In the tables on pages 32–35 the exact deviations t_0 for degrees of freedom ν between 1 and 200 are given for the following integrals:

$$P \text{ (of the table)} = \int_{t_0}^{\infty} f(t)\,dt = \text{Prob}(t > t_0) \qquad \text{(a)}$$

$$\begin{aligned} 2P \text{ (of the table)} &= \int_{-\infty}^{-t_0} f(t)\,dt + \int_{t_0}^{\infty} f(t)\,dt \\ &= \text{Prob}(t < -t_0) + \text{Prob}(t > t_0) \\ &= \text{Prob}(t \text{ not between } -t_0 \text{ and } t_0) \end{aligned} \qquad \text{(b)}$$

In *one-tailed* tests (confidence limits) $\alpha = P$, in *two-tailed* tests (confidence limits) $2\alpha = 2P$. (c) **(551)**

In accordance with (**405**b), the cumulative distribution of t is $F(t) = \text{Prob}(t \leqq t_0)$

$$F(t_0) = 1 - \text{Prob}(t > t_0) = 1 - P = 1 - \textbf{(551a)} \qquad \text{(d)}$$

In the table on page 42 the exact deviations t_0^2 for degrees of freedom between 1 and 200 are given for the following integral:

$$P_r = \int_{t_0^2}^{\infty} f(t^2)\,dt^2 = \text{Prob}(t^2 > t_0^2) = 2\,\text{Prob}(t > t_0) \qquad \text{(a)}$$

$$\tfrac{1}{2} P_r = \tfrac{1}{2}\,\textbf{(552a)} \qquad \text{(b)} \quad \textbf{(552)}$$

For *one-tailed* tests $\alpha = \frac{1}{2} P$, for *two-tailed* tests $2\alpha = P$. (c)

For the relationship between the STUDENT and F-distributions see (**575**).

12 B. The χ^2 distribution

If $x_1, x_2, \ldots$ are stochastically independent observations from the *same normally distributed* population with mean μ and standard deviation σ, then the sum

$$\chi_\nu^2 = c_1^2 + c_2^2 + \cdots + c_i^2 + \cdots + c_\nu^2 = \sum_1^\nu c_i^2 \qquad \textbf{(553)}$$

of the squares of the standardized deviations

$$c_i^2 = \left(\frac{x_i - \mu}{\sigma}\right)^2$$

has the probability density function

$$f(\chi^2|\nu) = \frac{1}{2^{\nu/2}\,\Gamma(\nu/2)}\, e^{-\chi^2/2} (\chi^2)^{\nu/2-1}; \ (0 \leqq \chi^2 < \infty) \qquad \textbf{(554)}$$

[ν is the number of degrees of freedom of χ^2; for Γ see (**549**)]

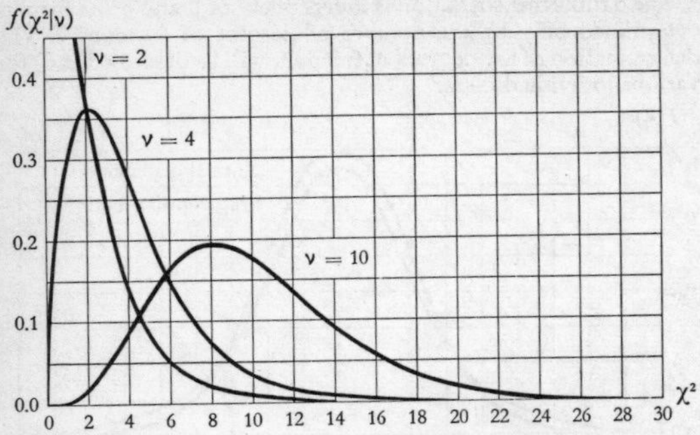

Fig. 33 Probability density functions of the χ^2 distribution with $\nu = 2$, 4 and 10.

The χ^2 distribution is a continuous, *unsymmetrical* distribution which like the STUDENT distribution – but more slowly – converges toward the normal distribution with increasing degrees of freedom (see Fig. 33). Its range of variation is from zero to infinity, its form dependent only on the degrees of freedom. The determination of the latter will be described later for various individual cases [see also **(566)** and **(569)**].

Parameters

Mode $= \nu - 2$ (a)
Mean $\mu = \nu$ (b) **(555)**
Variance $\sigma^2 = 2\nu$ (c)

Stochastic convergence when $\nu \to \infty$:

$\chi^2/\nu \to 1$ (a)
χ^2 Distribution $\to$ Normal distribution $(\nu; \sqrt{2\nu})$; fairly slowly (b) **(556)**
$\sqrt{2\chi^2}$ Distribution $\to$ Normal distribution $(\sqrt{2\nu - 1}; 1)$*; faster than (b) (c)

Approximations for quantiles

More centrally positioned quantiles [in accordance with **(556** c)]:

$$\chi^2_p \sim \tfrac{1}{2}(c_p + \sqrt{2\nu - 1})^2;\ \nu > 30 \qquad \text{(a)}$$

More extreme quantiles[*]: **(557)**

$$\chi^2_p \approx \nu \left(1 - \frac{2}{9\nu} + c_p \sqrt{\frac{2}{9\nu}}\right)^3;\ \nu > 30 \qquad \text{(b)}$$

For calculation of the quantiles 0.005, 0.025, 0.975 and 0.995 from the confidence limits for λ of the POISSON distribution see **(563)**.

Example (32) of **(557)**. Comparison between (a) and (b): The quantile $\chi^2_{0.975;\,\nu=50}$ is required.

(a) $\chi^2_p \sim \tfrac{1}{2}(1.96 + \sqrt{100 - 1})^2 = 70.922$

(b) $\chi^2_p \approx 50\left(1 - \frac{2}{450} + 1.96\sqrt{\frac{2}{450}}\right)^3 = 71.424$

The exact value is 71.420.

Tables

In the tables on pages 36–39 the exact deviations χ^2_0 for degrees of freedom between 1 and 200 are given for the following integrals:

$1\ \int_r$ (of the table) $= \int_{\chi^2_0}^{\infty} f(\chi^2)\, d\chi^2 = \text{Prob}\,(\chi^2 > \chi^2_0)$ (a)

$\tfrac{1}{2}\int_r$ (of the table) $= \tfrac{1}{2}$ **(558** a) (b) **(558)**

$1\ \int_l$ (of the table) $= \int_0^{\chi^2_0} f(\chi^2)\, d\chi^2 = \text{Prob}\,(\chi^2 < \chi^2_0) = F(\chi^2_0)$ (c)

* According to R.A. FISHER.

$\tfrac{1}{2}\int_l$ (of the table) $= \tfrac{1}{2}$ **(558** c) (d)

For *one-tailed* χ^2 tests $\alpha = \tfrac{1}{2}\int_r$
For *two-tailed* χ^2 tests $2\alpha = 1\int_r$ (e)

With *one-sided* confidence limits for σ:
for *upper* limits $\alpha = 1\int_r$
for *lower* limits $\alpha = 1\int_l$ (f) **(558)**
With *two-sided* confidence limits for σ:
for the *upper* limit $\alpha = \tfrac{1}{2}\int_r$
for the *lower* limit $\alpha = \tfrac{1}{2}\int_l$ } $\alpha < 0.5$

The useful square root $\sqrt{\nu/\chi^2_p}$ for degrees of freedom between 1 and 200 is given on page 47 (*confidence factors for* σ) for the following quantiles **(559)**

χ^2_p	Column $1-2\alpha$	χ^2_p	Column $1-2\alpha$
0.05 and 0.95	0.90	0.01 and 0.99	0.98
0.025 and 0.975	0.95	0.005 and 0.995	0.99

Relationships with other distributions

Normal distribution:

when $\nu = 1$, then $\chi^2_p = c^2_{(1+p)/2}$, that is
$\text{Prob}\,(\chi^2 < \chi^2_0) = 2\,\text{Prob}\,(0 < c < \chi^2)$ **(560)**

F-Distribution: see **(576)** and **(577)**.

POISSON distribution:

The probability that a POISSON variable with mean $\tfrac{1}{2}\chi^2_0$ takes the value x is **(561)**

$$\frac{e^{-\chi^2_0/2}\,(\chi^2_0/2)^x}{x!}$$

This distribution is shown diagrammatically in Figure 44, page 184, with $\lambda = \tfrac{1}{2}\chi^2_0$.

It can be shown that if ν is even

$$\text{Prob}\,(\chi^2 > \chi^2_0 \mid \nu) = \sum_{x=0}^{(\nu/2)-1} \frac{e^{-\chi^2_0/2}\,(\chi^2_0/2)^x}{x!} \qquad \textbf{(562)}$$

For even numbers of degrees of freedom ν the following quantiles can be calculated on the basis of **(562)** from the confidence limits for λ of the POISSON distribution, pages 107 and 108: **(563)**

Prob $(\chi^2 \leq \chi^2_p) = p$	Argument (table on pp. 107 and 108)	Page	χ^2_p equals	
0.005	$x = \nu/2$	108	$2\lambda_l$	ν an even number
0.025	$x = \nu/2$	107	$2\lambda_l$	
0.975	$x = (\nu/2) - 1$	107	$2\lambda_r$	
0.995	$x = (\nu/2) - 1$	108	$2\lambda_r$	

Example (33) of **(563)**. Required	Solution
$\chi^2_{0.025,\ \nu=260}$	$x = 130;\ \lambda_l = 108.61;\ \chi^2_p = 217.22$
$\chi^2_{0.975,\ \nu=260}$	$x = 129;\ \lambda_r = 153.30;\ \chi^2_p = 306.60$

The value $\lambda_r = 153.30$ has been interpolated linearly:

$154.39 - {}^1/_{10}\,(154.39 - 143.52) = 153.30$

The addition theorem for the χ^2 *distribution*

In equation **(553)** the sum can be broken up into any number of parts, for example

$$\chi^2 = \underbrace{c_1^2 + c_2^2}_{=\chi^2_1\,(\nu=2)} + \underbrace{c_3^2 + c_4^2 + c_5^2 + c_6^2}_{=\chi^2_2\,(\nu=4)} + \underbrace{c_7^2 + \cdots}_{=\chi^2_3\,(\nu=\ldots)} \text{ etc.}$$

It follows that

If $\chi^2_1, \chi^2_2, \ldots, \chi^2_n$ are stochastically independent and the χ^2 distributions have the degrees of freedom $\nu_1, \nu_2, \ldots, \nu_n$ respectively, then the sum $\chi^2 = \chi^2_1 + \chi^2_2 + \cdots + \chi^2_n$ likewise has a χ^2 distribution with $\nu = \nu_1 + \nu_2 + \cdots + \nu_n$ degrees of freedom. **(564)**

There is also a division theorem for χ^2 on which the analysis of regression and variance is based. For further details the reader is referred to the literature.

χ^2 and sample variance

In accordance with (**553**), $\chi^2 = [\sum (x-\mu)^2]/\sigma^2$. If μ is replaced by $\bar{x}$, then from (**493**e), $\sum (x-\bar{x})^2 = (N-1)\, s^2$. If now $N-1$ is replaced by ν, $\nu\, s^2$ is finally obtained in place of $\sum (x-\mu)^2$. Intuitively it is surmised that

$$\chi_\nu^2 = \frac{\nu\, s_\nu^2}{\sigma^2}, \text{ where } \nu = \text{degrees of freedom of } s^2 \qquad \textbf{(565)}$$

and this is a good guess. It should be noted that (**565**) is a second definition of χ^2 equivalent to (**553**) but valid *only* for *normally* distributed populations.

An important asymptotic property of χ^2

Given is a sample divided into n classes from a population *of any desired form*. If f_i is the observed frequency of the class i, where $f_1+f_2+\cdots+f_i+\cdots+f_n = N$, then f_i is known as the *empirical* (absolute) *frequency*. If p_i is the *given* or a *hypothetical* probability that the variable x will fall in the class i, where $p_1+p_2+\cdots+p_i+\cdots+p_n = 1$, then Np_i is known as the *given* or the *hypothetical* (absolute) *frequency*. The empirical frequencies in the individual classes are random variables. If they are stochastically *independent* of each other, then

$$\sum_1^n \frac{(f_i - Np_i)^2}{Np_i} \to \chi_\nu^2; \text{ where } \nu = n-1$$

when $\nu \to \infty$. **(566)**

(**566**) was discovered by K. Pearson. The fact that it is exactly valid only when $\nu \to \infty$ is of little consequence in practice but gives rise to certain restrictions:

In tests for goodness of fit based on (**566**), the *samples* as a whole should *not* be *too small*, the *hypothetical* (absolute) *frequencies in the individual classes not below* $Np_i = 4$. If they are less than this, they should be increased to the required level by combining 2, 3, . . . neighboring classes. This is only necessary, however, when the number of classes is small. If ν is greater than (about) 8 and the sample size over 40, then it is permissible for Np_i in isolated classes to be as low as 1. **(567)**

As a rule the hypothetical frequencies are not given:

Theoretical (absolute) frequencies Np_i which have been calculated on the basis of *estimated* parameters are known as *fitted frequencies*; the theoretical distribution corresponding to them is known as the *fitted distribution*. **(568)**

(569)

(a) If k parameters must be estimated in the calculation of fitted frequencies, then the number of degrees of freedom for χ^2 defined by (**566**) is $\nu = n-1-k$, where n = number of classes.

(b) If m samples each grouped into n classes (in an $m \times n$ contingency table) are submitted to a χ^2 test based on (**566**), then the number of degrees of freedom for χ^2 is $\nu = (n-1)(m-1)$.

(c) In the frequently encountered special case of the 2×2 table, $\nu = 1$.

For an example of a χ^2 test with estimation of parameters see section 11 F (a), page 163. Another χ^2 test is described in section 23, page 190, in which further tests for frequency are dealt with.

In conclusion it should be noted that definitions (**543**) and (**565**) differ *fundamentally* from definition (**566**) in spite of the fact that the formulas are very similar: (**543**) and (**565**) are valid only for *normally distributed* populations, (**566**) is valid for populations of *any* form; in (**543**) and (**565**), $\bar{x}$ and s are *continuous* variables, while in (**566**), f_i is a *discrete* variable.

When χ^2 tests are carried out with the aid of fitted distributions, care must be taken that the estimates made satisfy condition (**430**) or (**431**).

12 C. The F-distribution (variance-ratio distribution)

In the expression F-distribution, the letter F symbolizes *not* a cumulative distribution but the name of R. A. Fisher, the discoverer of the z-distribution which is equivalent to the F-distribution[17].

If s_1^2 and s_2^2 are two stochastically independent estimates of the variance σ^2 of the *same normally distributed* population, then in accordance with (**565**)

$$s_1^2 = \sigma^2 \frac{\chi_1^2}{\nu_1} \text{ and } s_2^2 = \sigma^2 \frac{\chi_2^2}{\nu_2}$$

It follows that the quotient

$$F = \frac{s_1^2}{s_2^2} = \frac{\chi_1^2/\nu_1}{\chi_2^2/\nu_2}; \; 0 \leq F < \infty;$$

(ν_1 and ν_2 are the degrees of freedom of s_1 and s_2 respectively) **(570)**

has the probability density function

$$f(F) = \frac{\Gamma\left(\frac{\nu_1+\nu_2}{2}\right)}{\Gamma\left(\frac{\nu_1}{2}\right)\Gamma\left(\frac{\nu_2}{2}\right)} \nu_1^{\frac{\nu_1}{2}} \nu_2^{\frac{\nu_2}{2}} \frac{F^{\frac{\nu_1}{2}-1}}{(\nu_2+\nu_1 F)^{\frac{\nu_1+\nu_2}{2}}} \quad \begin{pmatrix} 0 \leq F \\ < \infty \end{pmatrix} \qquad \textbf{(571)}$$

[for Γ see (**549**)]

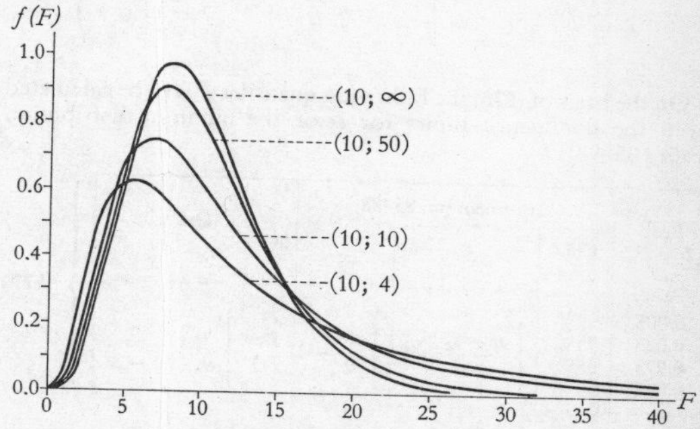

Fig. 34 Probability density functions of the F-distribution with various degrees of freedom (ν_1; ν_2).

The F-distribution is a continuous *unsymmetrical* distribution with a range of variation from zero to infinity.

Parameters

$$\text{Mean} \quad \mu = \nu_2/(\nu_2 - 2); \; \nu_2 > 2 \qquad \text{(a)}$$

$$\text{Variance } \sigma^2 = \left(\frac{\nu_2}{\nu_2 - 2}\right)^2 \times \frac{2(\nu_1+\nu_2-2)}{\nu_1(\nu_2-4)}; \; \nu_2 > 4 \qquad \text{(b)}$$

(572)

Interchange of ν_1 and ν_2

$$F_0(p; \nu_1; \nu_2) = 1/[F_0(1-p; \nu_2; \nu_1)] \qquad \textbf{(573)}$$

In (**573**), p can be Prob $(F > F_0)$ just as well as Prob $(F < F_0)$.

Tables

The values of F_0 given on pages 40 and 41 satisfy the following equation:

$$P \text{ (of the table)} = P_r = \int_{F_0}^{\infty} f(F)\, dF = \text{Prob}\,(F > F_0) \qquad \text{(a)}$$

In one-tailed tests $\alpha = \frac{1}{2} P$, in two-tailed tests $2\alpha = P$ (b)

On the t^2 table of page 42 see (**575**) and (**552**) (c)

(574)

Relationships to other distributions

Student distribution:

$$\text{Prob}\,[(F > F_0) \mid 1; \nu_2] = \text{Prob}\,(t^2 > t_0^2 \mid \nu_2) = 2\,\text{Prob}\,(t > t_0 \mid \nu_2) \qquad \textbf{(575)}$$

For $F(1; \nu_2)$ with ν_2 values between 1 and 200, the more comprehensive t^2 table on page 42 should therefore be used. For explanation see (**552**).

χ^2 distribution:

When F_p and χ_p^2 denote quantiles

$$F_p(\nu_1; \infty) = \frac{\chi^2_{p,\nu_1}}{\nu_1} \quad \text{(a)}$$

$$F_p(\infty; \nu_2) = \frac{\nu_2}{\chi^2_{1-p,\nu_2}} \quad \text{(b)} \qquad \textbf{(576)}$$

From (**576**) and (**556**a) it follows that

$$\left.\begin{aligned} F(\nu_1; \infty) &\to 1, \text{ when } \nu_1 \to \infty \\ F(\infty; \nu_2) &\to 1, \text{ when } \nu_2 \to \infty \end{aligned}\right\} \text{ that is, } F(\infty; \infty) = 1 \qquad \textbf{(577)}$$

Binomial distribution:

$$\text{Prob}\left[F(\nu_1; \nu_2) < \frac{N-x}{x+1} \times \frac{p}{1-p}\right]$$

$$= \sum_{x+1}^{N} \binom{N}{k} p^k (1-p)^{N-k} \qquad \textbf{(578)}$$

$$\left.\begin{aligned} \text{where } N &= \frac{\nu_1 + \nu_2}{2} - 1 \\ x &= \frac{\nu_1}{2} - 1 \end{aligned}\right\} \nu_1 \text{ and } \nu_2 \text{ are even numbers}$$

On the basis of (**578**) the following quantiles F_0 can be calculated from the confidence limits for p of the binomial distribution (pages 85–98):

Prob $(F < F_0)$	Argument pp. 85–98: Column	N	x	p	Quantile F_0
0.005	99%	$\frac{\nu_1+\nu_2}{2} - 1$	$\frac{\nu_1}{2} - 1$	p_l	$\frac{\nu_2}{\nu_1} \times \frac{p}{1-p}$
0.025	95%			p_l	
0.975	95%			p_r	
0.995	99%			p_r	

(579)

Example 34. $F_{0.995}$ (152; 36) is required. We have $N = 93$; $x = 75$; $p_r = 0.8993$ (from page 96); $p/(1-p) = 8.930\,49$; $\nu_2/\nu_1 = 0.236\,842$; $F_{0.995}$ (152; 36) = 2.12.

13. The normally distributed population: Confidence and tolerance intervals

Cf. also section 8, page 153.

13 A. Confidence intervals for the mean μ

One-sided confidence interval with *single upper* limit

$\text{Prob}(-\infty < \mu < \bar{x} + k \times Sd) = 1 - \alpha$; cf. also (**580**d) (a)

One-sided confidence interval with *single lower* limit

$\text{Prob}(\bar{x} - k \times Sd < \mu < \infty) = 1 - \alpha$; cf. also (**580**d) (b)

Two-sided confidence interval with symmetrical limits

$\text{Prob}(\bar{x} - k \times Sd < \mu < \bar{x} + k \times Sd) = 1 - 2\alpha$; cf. also (**580**d) (c)

Factors $k \times Sd$ for (**580**a, b, c) (d)

Equation	Degrees of freedom ν of s	k	Sd	Page (c, t or k)
(a) and (b)	> 200	$\lvert c_\alpha \rvert / \sqrt{N}$	σ or s	28
(a) and (b)	≦ 200	$t_{\nu,\alpha}/\sqrt{N}$	s_ν	32–35
(c)	> 200	k_2 or $\lvert c_\alpha \rvert / \sqrt{N}$	σ or s	k_2: 43; c: 28
(c)	≦ 200	k_2 or $t_{\nu,2\alpha}/\sqrt{N}$	s_ν	k_2: 43; t: 32–35

(580)

In the table on page 43 (for k_2) the number of degrees of freedom $\nu = N - 1$ is contained in the argument N. In this table the transition from t to c takes place at $N = 201$.

13 B. Tolerance intervals

Tolerance intervals without confidence probability

One-sided tolerance interval with *single upper* limit

$\text{Prob}(-\infty < x < m + k \times Sd) = 1 - \alpha = \beta_p$; cf. also (**581**d) (a)

One-sided tolerance interval with *single lower* limit

$\text{Prob}(m - k \times Sd < x < \infty) = 1 - \alpha = \beta_p$; cf. also (**581**d) (b)

Two-sided tolerance interval with symmetrical limits

$\text{Prob}(m - k \times Sd < x < m + k \times Sd) = 1 - 2\alpha = \beta_p$; cf. also (**581**d) (c)

m, k and Sd for (**581**a, b, c) (d)

Equation	Degrees of freedom ν of s	Known parameters or estimates	m	k	Sd	Page (c, t, k)
(a) and (b)	> 200	μ, σ or $\bar{x}, s$	μ or $\bar{x}$	$\lvert c_\alpha \rvert$	σ or s	28
(a) and (b)	≦ 100	$\bar{x}, \sigma$	$\bar{x}$	k_3*	σ	44, col. 1
(a) and (b)	≦ 100	μ, s	μ	$t_{\nu,\alpha}$	s	32–35
(a) and (b)	≦ 100	$\bar{x}, s$	$\bar{x}$	k_4*	s	44, col. 2
(c)	> 200	μ, σ or $\bar{x}, s$	μ or $\bar{x}$	$\lvert c_\alpha \rvert$	σ or s	28
(c)	≦ 100	$\bar{x}, \sigma$	$\bar{x}$	k_3	σ	44, col. 1
(c)	≦ 100	μ, s	μ	$t_{\nu,2\alpha}$	s	32–35
(c)	≦ 100	$\bar{x}, s$	$\bar{x}$	k_4	s	44, col. 2

* β_p in the table is selected as follows: β_p (required) = $1 - 2\alpha$; α is given.

(581)

Tolerance intervals with confidence probability β_t

Equations (**581**a, b, c) are applicable with the following complementary equation [example of (**581**d)]:

$$\text{Prob}\left[\text{Prob}(m - k \times Sd < x < m + k \times Sd) \geqq 1 - 2\alpha\right] = \beta_t.$$

m, k and Sd for (**581**a, b, c)

Equation	Degrees of freedom ν of s	Known parameters or estimates	m	k	Sd	Page (c, t, k)
(a) and (b)	≦ 100	$\bar{x}, \sigma$	$\bar{x}$	k_5*	σ	44, col. 3
(a) and (b)	≦ 100	μ, s	μ	k_6*	s	44, col. 4
(a) and (b)	≦ 1000	$\bar{x}, s$	$\bar{x}$	k_7	s	45–46
(c)	≦ 100	$\bar{x}, \sigma$	$\bar{x}$	k_5	σ	44, col. 3
(c)	≦ 100	μ, s	μ	k_6	s	44, col. 4
(c)	≦ 1000	$\bar{x}, s$	$\bar{x}$	k_7	s	45–46

* β_p in the table is selected as follows: $\beta_p = 1 - 2\alpha$; α is given.

(582)

The following equations are valid for the confidence and tolerance factors

$$k_2 = t_{2\alpha, N-1} \times 1/\sqrt{N} \text{ for } N \leqq 201 \quad \text{(a)}$$

$$= \lvert c_\alpha \rvert \times 1/\sqrt{N} \text{ for } N > 201 \quad \text{(b)}$$

$$k_3 = \lvert c_\alpha \rvert \times \sqrt{1 + 1/N} \quad \text{(c)}$$

$$k_4 = t_{2\alpha, N-1} \times \sqrt{1 + 1/N} \quad \text{(d)}$$

$$k_5 \quad \text{solution of } \int_{c'-k_5}^{c'+k_5} f(c)\,dc = \beta_p;\ (c' = c_{\beta_t}) \quad \text{(e)}$$

$$k_6 = \lvert c_{\alpha_p} \rvert \times \sqrt{(N-1)/\chi^2_{1-\beta_t, N-1}} \quad \text{(f)}$$

k_7 cf. EISENHART et al.[18], pages 108–109.

(583)

13 C. Confidence intervals for the standard deviation σ

From (**565**) it follows that

$$\left.\begin{aligned} &\text{Prob}(k_l s_\nu < \sigma < k_r s_\nu) = 1 - 2\alpha \\ &\text{where } k_l = \sqrt{\nu/\chi^2_{\nu, 1-\alpha}} \text{ and } k_r = \sqrt{\nu/\chi^2_{\nu,\alpha}} \end{aligned}\right\} \qquad \textbf{(584)}$$

Values of k_l and k_r for degrees of freedom between 1 and 100 are given in the left-hand table on page 47.

14. The normally distributed population: Extreme range and extreme deviations

14 A. The extreme range

Definition

If x_1 is the lowest and x_n the highest value of a sample of size n, then $(x_n - x_1)$ is the extreme range w_n of this sample. **(585)**

The standardized extreme range of a sample of size n from a population with standard deviation σ is

$$W_n = \frac{w_n}{\sigma} = \frac{x_n - x_1}{\sigma} \qquad \textbf{(586)}$$

The mean extreme range of m samples of size n from one and the same population is

$$\bar{w}_{m,n} = \frac{\sum_1^m w_n}{m} = \frac{\sum_1^m (x_n - x_1)}{m} \qquad \textbf{(587)}$$

and the standardized mean extreme range is

$$\bar{W}_{m,n} = \frac{\bar{w}_{m,n}}{\sigma} = \frac{\sum_1^m w_n}{m\,\sigma} = \frac{\sum_1^m (x_n - x_1)}{m\,\sigma} \qquad \textbf{(588)}$$

Since the extreme range w_n is merely a special case of the mean extreme range $\bar{w}_{m,n}$ with $m = 1$, only the mean extreme range will be referred to in the text which follows.

Mean extreme range as a multiple of σ

The expected value $\bar{\boldsymbol{W}}_n$ of the extreme range of random samples of size n from a normally distributed population with unit standard deviation satisfies the relation

$$\bar{W}_{m,n} \underset{m\to\infty}{\to} \bar{\boldsymbol{W}}_n \qquad \textbf{(589)}$$

The upper right-hand table on page 47 gives values of $\bar{\boldsymbol{W}}_n$ for the standardized normal distribution as multiples of σ[19]. (Many authors use the symbol d_n in place of $\bar{\boldsymbol{W}}_n$.)

σ as a fraction of the mean extreme range

The quotient

$$\frac{\bar{w}_{m,n}}{\bar{\boldsymbol{W}}_n} = \bar{w}_{m,n} \times \boldsymbol{A}_n \qquad \textbf{(590)}$$

gives an unbiased estimate of σ. Values of this quotient are given in the lower right-hand table on page 47.

The relative efficiency of (**590**) compared with that of the estimate s [s^2 from (**492**a)] when $m = 1$ is[20]

n	2	3	4	5	6	10	15	20	50	100	∞
Efficiency	1.00	0.99	0.98	0.96	0.93	0.85	0.77	0.70	0.49	0.34	0

For sample sizes between 2 and 10 there is thus little difference between the two estimates. Within this range (**590**) is useful as a *rapid method of estimating σ* but *it should not be used in place of s in a standard t test.*

For larger samples the extreme range of σ can likewise be accurately estimated, namely by dividing the sample into a number m of *independent* subgroups of the same size between 2 and 10 and determining their extreme ranges. In accordance with (**588**), the mean of these ranges is then the mean extreme range. However, such a subdivision must be effected by a *random selection* among the available sample values. If there is no natural method of doing this (such as, for example, using the order in time of obtaining the sample values), random numbers may be used, but the time needed to carry out the subdivision will tend to nullify the advantages of the more rapid calculation.

Example 35. A sample of size 24, $x_1, x_2, \ldots, x_{24}$, can be subdivided into 12 groups of 2, 8 groups of 3, 6 groups of 4, or 3 groups of 8:

Groups of 2: $x_1 - x_2, x_3 - x_4, \ldots, x_{23} - x_{24}$

Groups of 3: $x_1 - x_3, x_4 - x_6, \ldots, x_{22} - x_{24}$

Overlapping groups must of course be avoided, for example $x_1 - x_2, x_2 - x_3, \ldots$, since these would obviously no longer be independent.

$\sigma_{\bar{x}}$ as a fraction of the mean extreme range

The quotient

$$\frac{\bar{w}_{m,n}}{\bar{\boldsymbol{W}}_n \sqrt{m\,n}} = \bar{w}_{m,n} \times \boldsymbol{A}_{m,n} \qquad \textbf{(591)}$$

where $m\,n$ = sample size N, gives an unbiased estimate of the standard deviation $\sigma_{\bar{x}}$ of the estimate $\bar{x}$. Values of the factor $\boldsymbol{A}_{m,n} = 1/(\bar{\boldsymbol{W}}_n \times \sqrt{m\,n})$ are given in the table on page 48.

Example 36 (section 14 A)

Given is the sample 3.00, 1.56, 1.34, 2.08, 2.10, 2.67. The estimates of σ and $\sigma_{\bar{x}}$ on the basis of the extreme range or mean extreme range are

(a) 1 extreme range

1.34 − 3.00: range = 1.66 $\sigma' = 1.66 \times 0.39457 = 0.655$, $\sigma'_{\bar{x}} = 1.66 \times 0.16108 = 0.267$

(b) 2 extreme ranges

1.34 − 3.00, 2.08 − 2.67: mean range = 1.125 $\sigma' = 1.125 \times 0.59082 = 0.665$, $\sigma'_{\bar{x}} = 1.125 \times 0.24120 = 0.271$

(c) 3 extreme ranges

1.56 − 3.00, 1.34 − 2.08, 2.10 − 2.67: mean range = $0.91\dot{6}$ $\sigma' = 0.91\dot{6} \times 0.88623 = 0.812$, $\sigma'_{\bar{x}} = 0.91\dot{6} \times 0.36180 = 0.332$

For comparison, σ can be estimated using (**492**a) with the result $s = 0.63257$. In order to correct the bias of this estimate it must be multiplied by the factor $k_s = 1.0509$ (see the left-hand table on page 47, column k_s), giving the result $s = 0.665$ and $s_{\bar{x}} = 0.271$.

All the above estimates may be regarded as equally valid. Although the agreement between s and the estimates (a) and (b) is striking, this does not mean that estimate (c) is not as good. A further sample from the same population could result in estimates nearer to (c).

14 B. Testing extreme ranges and extreme deviations

The studentized extreme range

Table on page 51, sample size 2–20.

In the test quotients

$$\frac{x_N - x_1}{s_\nu}; \quad \nu = \text{degrees of freedom of } s; \quad x_1 < x_2 < \cdots < x_N \qquad \textbf{(592)}$$

s is an estimate calculated from a sample *different* from and *independent* of the sample to be tested but originating from the *same* population. If the test quotient attains or exceeds the level in the table corresponding to the degrees of freedom ν_s and the sample size N, then the extreme range in question is *too large* (significance probability α).

If σ is known, the levels at $\nu = \infty$ should be used. If the sample size exceeds the range of the table, testing should be carried out according to (**596**d) for sample sizes between 21 and 25 and according to (**595**) for still larger samples, *if it is desired to test extreme values.*

The studentized extreme deviation

Table on page 52, sample size 3–9.

In the test quotients

$$\frac{x_N - \bar{x}}{s_\nu} \text{ or } \frac{\bar{x} - x_1}{s_\nu}; \quad \nu = \text{degrees of freedom of } s; \quad x_1 < x_2 < \cdots < x_N \qquad \textbf{(593)}$$

s has the same meaning as in (**592**). If σ is known, the levels at $\nu = \infty$ should be used. If the test quotient attains or exceeds the level in the table corresponding to the degrees of freedom ν_s and the sample size N, then the extreme range in question is *too large* (significance probability α).

If the sample size exceeds the range of the table, testing should be carried out according to (**596**c and d) for sample sizes between 10 and 25 and according to (**595**) for still larger samples.

The standardized extreme deviation

Upper table on page 52.

We have

$$\left.\begin{aligned}&\text{Prob}\,(c \leq c_e) = \left[\int_{-\infty}^{c_e} f(c)\,dc\right]^N; \text{ for } c_e \text{ see } (\mathbf{595}) &\text{(a)}\\ &\text{Prob}\,(-c_e \leq c \leq c_e) = \left[\int_{-c_e}^{c_e} f(c)\,dc\right]^N &\text{(b)}\end{aligned}\right\}\ (\mathbf{594})^*$$

(c_e = standardized extreme deviation; N = sample size)

(**594**a) gives the probability that no deviation from the mean μ is greater than c_e; (**594**b) gives the probability that no deviation from the mean μ is greater than c_e *in absolute value*. In accordance with (**408**b), the corresponding significance probabilities are 1 − (**594**). The table on page 52 gives the probabilities 1 − (**594**a).

In the test quotients

$$\frac{x_N - \mu}{\sigma} \text{ or } \frac{\mu - x_1}{\sigma} = c_e \qquad (\mathbf{595})$$

the symbols have the customary meaning. For sample sizes over 25, μ and σ can be replaced by $\bar{x}$ and s. For smaller samples (**593**) should be used.

Testing extreme values of a sample on the basis of their own attributes[21–23]

Upper left-hand table on page 53, sample size 3–25.

When no independent information on the standard deviation of the population is available, extreme deviations in samples up to a size of 25 can be tested by means of the following quotients:

Sample size N	Quotient		Sample size N	Quotient		
3–7	$\left\lvert\frac{x_N - x_{N-1}}{x_N - x_1}\right\rvert$	(a)	11–13	$\left\lvert\frac{x_N - x_{N-2}}{x_N - x_2}\right\rvert$	(c)	(**596**)
8–10	$\left\lvert\frac{x_N - x_{N-1}}{x_N - x_{N-2}}\right\rvert$	(b)	14–25	$\left\lvert\frac{x_N - x_{N-2}}{x_N - x_3}\right\rvert$	(d)	

where $x_1 < x_2 < \cdots < x_N$, when a right-hand extreme value is tested,
$x_N < x_{N-1} < \cdots < x_1$, when a left-hand extreme value is tested.

With samples of over 25, (**595**) should be used with μ and σ replaced by $\bar{x}$ and s.

General considerations in testing extreme values

It is common for extreme values to be ignored, often without comment by the author and without their first being tested statistically. Occasionally they are even eliminated *before* the experimental data are put into the hands of the statistician. This is clearly undesirable, for in some situations extreme values are often the most informative ones in the sample.

If an extreme value is found to be significantly too large after proper statistical testing in accordance with (**593**), (**595**) or (**596**), its rejection is actually only justifiable when a check on the experiment reveals a causal circumstance which accounts for its existence. Examples would be an error made in measurements or calculations, the unwitting inclusion of a sick person among healthy persons being investigated, and so on. In such cases the extreme values originate from *other* populations and *ought to be rejected.*

If, however, there is a high degree of probability that the extreme value originates from the same population, the following considerations apply: The smaller the sample the more unlikely it is to contain extreme values of the population. A small sample containing an extreme value can give a completely false picture of the population it represents. In such cases the extreme value *may be ignored*. However, it is advisable to use a small significance probability, at least with larger samples.

A third important consideration to be borne in mind in judging extreme values is that the validity of the tests described above is conditional on the population being *normally distributed*. If this is not the case, the tests are practically *worthless* since they are very peculiarly dependent on this condition of normality.

* This formula is derived from (**362**) and (**405**a) or (**407**c).

Special considerations in testing extreme values

If testing in accordance with (**592**) results in the postulated significance, then at least one of the two extreme values, left or right (*or* possibly the *whole* sample, depending on the situation) must be rejected since they do not originate from that population from which the sample with the calculated s was taken.

It is permissible to test extreme values more than once in the same sample. In this case the sample size must be reduced by one after each rejection before a new test is made. The resulting level of significance α_{res} for the total number k of significant tests then has the *very approximate* order of magnitude

$$\alpha_{res} \sim 1 - (1 - \alpha_1)(1 - \alpha_2)\dots(1 - \alpha_k)$$

Example 37. The sample of example 24 in section 10E, page 159, is to be tested using (**596**d) ($\alpha_{res} = 0.05$).

1st test ($N = 21$)

right-hand extreme deviate $\dfrac{4.41 - 2.68}{4.41 - 1.76} = 0.653$; Deviate is too large ($\alpha \ll 0.005$)

2nd test ($N = 20$)

right-hand extreme deviate $\dfrac{3.56 - 2.35}{4.41 - 1.76} = 0.457$; Deviate is too large ($\alpha < 0.05$)

The *3rd test* gives no further significant deviation.

$\alpha_{res} \sim 1 - (\gg 0.995)(> 0.95) < 0.05475$, if the sample were from a normally distributed population.

15. The normally distributed population: Comparison of a sample with the hypothetical population

15 A. Comparison of the sample and population standard deviations s and σ (or of the variances s^2 and σ^2)

The confidence limits for σ are obtained from (**584**), those for σ^2 analogously by replacing s by s^2 and k by k^2. The hypothetical σ or σ^2 is then compared with these limits and the result interpreted in accordance with (**476**).

15 B. Comparison of the sample and population means $\bar{x}$ and μ

Comparison of the estimate $\bar{x}$ with the hypothetical mean is made by means of the test quotients given in (**598**)–(**602**), the numerical value of the quotient being compared with the limit given:

If the test quotient is *smaller* than the limit, then the result is interpreted in accordance with (**474**) or (**475**). If it attains or exceeds the limit, then (**597**)

	Significance in brackets	
	one-tailed test	two-tailed test
when $\bar{x} - \mu < 0$	$\bar{x} < \mu\,(\alpha)$	$\bar{x} \neq \mu\,(2\alpha)$
when $\bar{x} - \mu > 0$	$\bar{x} > \mu\,(\alpha)$	

The c-test (normal distribution)

Applicability:

When σ is known or when the degrees of freedom of $s = N-1 > 200$

Test quotient	Significance limit		
$\dfrac{\lvert\bar{x} - \mu\rvert\sqrt{N}}{\sigma}$; or $\dfrac{\lvert\bar{x} - \mu\rvert\sqrt{N}}{s_{N-1}}$; $N > 201$	$\lvert c_\alpha\rvert$, page 28	(a)	(**598**)
$\dfrac{(\bar{x} - \mu)^2 N}{\sigma^2}$; or $\dfrac{(\bar{x} - \mu)^2 N}{s_{N-1}^2}$; $N > 201$	$\chi^2_{\nu=1}$, page 36; $\alpha = \tfrac{1}{2} \int_r, 2\alpha = 1 \int_r$	(b)	
$\dfrac{\lvert\bar{x} - \mu\rvert}{s_{N-1}}$; $N > 201$	$c/\sqrt{N}$ = confidence factor k_2, page 43	(c)	

The t-test (STUDENT distribution)

Applicability: When σ is unknown and the degrees of freedom of $s = N - 1 \leq 200$

Test quotient	Significance limit		
$\frac{\lvert\bar{x}-\mu\rvert\sqrt{N}}{s_{N-1}}$; $N \leq 201$	t_{N-1}, pages 32–35; $\alpha = P, 2\alpha = 2P$	(a)	(599)
$\frac{(\bar{x}-\mu)^2 N}{s^2_{N-1}}$; $N \leq 201$	t^2_{N-1}, page 42; $\alpha = \frac{1}{2}P, 2\alpha = P$	(b)	
$\frac{\lvert\bar{x}-\mu\rvert}{s_{N-1}}$; $N \leq 201$	$t_{N-1}/\sqrt{N}$ = confidence factor k_2, page 43	(c)	

LORD's test based on the extreme range[24]

Applicability: Samples of size $N \leq 20$ (a) and $N > 20$ (b)

$\frac{\lvert\bar{x}-\mu\rvert}{x_N - x_1}$; $N \leq 20$; $x_1 < x_2 < \cdots < x_N$	page 53, middle left-hand table	(a)	(600)
$\frac{\lvert\bar{x}-\mu\rvert m}{[\sum(x_n - x_1)]\,\boldsymbol{A}_{m,n}}$; $m \times n = N$	page 49; $\boldsymbol{A}_{m,n}$ page 48	(b)	

m = number of subgroups of size n (cf. section 14A, page 169) in which $x_1 < x_2 < \cdots < x_n$

The mid-range test based on the extreme range[25]

Applicability: Samples of size $N \leq 10$

$\frac{\lvert x_N + x_1 - 2\mu\rvert}{x_N - x_1}$; $N \leq 10$	page 53, upper right-hand table	(601)

WALSH's test[25,26]

Applicability: Samples of size $4 \leq N \leq 14$ from *any symmetrical* population

page 53, lower right-hand table	page 53, lower right-hand table	(602)

Note that the use of (**598**b) and (**599**b) involves the squaring of $(\bar{x} - \mu)$ but on the other hand obviates extracting the square root of s^2 (provided s is not required). The use of (**598**c) and (**599**c) avoids the multiplication by $\sqrt{N}$, with the further advantage that the transition from t to c in using the table on page 43 is quite "automatic".

(**600**)–**602**) are straightforward *rapid tests* [especially (**601**)] in which even $\bar{x}$ does not need to be calculated. Within the tabulated range their power is practically the same as that of (**599**). The WALSH test is suitable not only for normal but also for *any* other symmetrical distribution. In this case, the significance probability for N up to 8 is somewhat higher than that in the table. For $N > 8$ the values in the table are exact.

When a calculating machine is not available, multiplication is faster than division. In this event, the significance limit should be multiplied by the divisor of the test quotient in order to obtain the limit for the dividend.

Example 38. When t is the limit for $\frac{\lvert x-\mu\rvert\sqrt{N}}{s}$, then ts is the limit for $\lvert x-\mu\rvert\sqrt{N}$.

16. The normally distributed population: Comparison of two samples

In comparing two samples, the following hypotheses concerning the parameters of the original populations must be taken into consideration:

$$\sigma_1^2 = \sigma_2^2 \quad \begin{cases} \mu_1 = \mu_2 & \text{(a)} \\ \mu_1 \neq \mu_2 & \text{(b)} \end{cases} \quad (603)$$

$$\sigma_1^2 \neq \sigma_2^2 \quad \begin{cases} \mu_1 = \mu_2 & \text{(a)} \\ \mu_1 \neq \mu_2 & \text{(b)} \end{cases} \quad (604)$$

16 A. Comparison of variances

The test quotient for the hypothesis $(\sigma_1^2 = \sigma_2^2)$ (**603**) is (**570**), in which the *larger of the two sample variances must always be made the numerator*. This means that renumbering of the variances with respect to the *indices of the table* is necessary when s_1^2 (from sample 1) is smaller than s_2^2. *The number of degrees of freedom* ν_1 *in the tables on pages 40 and 41 is always that of the numerator of* (**570**). (**605**)

s_1^2 and s_2^2 must be calculated from (**492**). Their degrees of freedom are $\nu_1 = N_1 - 1$ and $\nu_2 = N_2 - 1$.

If the test quotient is *smaller* than the significance limit F in the table on pages 40 and 41, then in accordance with (**474**) it can be assumed that $\sigma_1^2 = \sigma_2^2$. In this case the means are tested by the procedure given in section 16B below. If the test quotient *attains* or *exceeds* the significance limit F, then $\sigma_1^2 \neq \sigma_2^2$. The means are tested by the procedure given in section 16C, page 172.

16 B. Comparison of means when $\sigma_1^2 = \sigma_2^2$

The following symbols are used here:

$$\lvert\bar{x}_1 - \bar{x}_2\rvert = d \text{ and } \lvert\mu_1 - \mu_2\rvert = \boldsymbol{d} \quad (606)$$

The estimate of the common standard deviation $\sigma = \sigma_1 = \sigma_2$ is

$$s_\nu = \sqrt{\frac{S_1 + S_2}{N_1 + N_2 - 2}}; \; S_1 \text{ and } S_2 \text{ from (493)} \qquad \nu_s = \nu_1 + \nu_2 = N_1 + N_2 - 2 \quad (607)$$

The estimate of the standard deviation of the difference $\boldsymbol{d}$ is

$$s_{\nu d} = s_\nu \sqrt{\frac{1}{N_1} + \frac{1}{N_2}}; \; s_\nu \text{ from (607)}; \; \nu_{s_{\nu d}} = N_1 + N_2 - 2 \quad (608)$$

If σ is known, s_ν is replaced by σ in (**608**). If $N_1 = 1$, then $s_{\nu d} = s_\nu\sqrt{1 + 1/N_2}$, $\nu = N_2 - 1$; cf. also (**452**) and (**583**c and e).

The test quotients for the hypotheses $(\mu_1 = \mu_2 \mid \sigma_1^2 = \sigma_2^2)$ are (**609**)

(a) if σ is known or $\nu > 200$: d/σ_d or $d/s_{\nu d}$; limit $\lvert c_\alpha\rvert$, page 28

(b) when $\nu \leq 200$: $d/s_{\nu d}$; limit t_ν; pages 32–35; $\alpha = P, 2\alpha = 2P$

or

(c) $d^2/s^2_{\nu d}$; limit $t_\nu^2 [= F(1;\nu)]$; page 42; $\alpha = \frac{1}{2}P$, $2\alpha = P$

If the test quotient *attains* or *exceeds* the significance limit, then this is considered evidence that $\mu_1 \neq \mu_2$. In this case it is often desirable to test the hypothesis $(\mu_1 - \mu_2 = \boldsymbol{d} \mid \sigma_1^2 = \sigma_2^2)$:

The test quotients are obtained by replacing d in (**609**) by $\lvert d - \boldsymbol{d}\rvert$. If the quotient exceeds the significance limit, then this is considered evidence that $\mu_1 - \mu_2 \neq \boldsymbol{d}$. (**610**)

The confidence limits for $\boldsymbol{d}$ are (**611**)

two-sided

$$\text{Prob}(d - t_{\nu,\alpha} \times s_{\nu d} \leq \boldsymbol{d} \leq d + t_{\nu,\alpha} \times s_{\nu d}) = 1 - 2\alpha \quad \text{(a)}$$

one-sided with a single upper limit

$$\text{Prob}(\boldsymbol{d} \leq d + t_{\nu,\alpha} \times s_{\nu d}) = 1 - \alpha \quad \text{(b)}$$

If the test quotient in (**609**) is *smaller* than the significance limit, then it may be assumed in accordance with (**474**) that $\mu_1 = \mu_2$. Since also $\sigma_1^2 = \sigma_2^2$, the conclusion may be drawn that the two samples 1 and 2 originated from the same population with mean μ and variance σ^2. Estimates of these parameters are

$$\bar{x} = \frac{\sum_1^{N_1} x_1 + \sum_1^{N_2} x_2}{N_1 + N_2} = \frac{N_1\bar{x}_1 + N_2\bar{x}_2}{N_1 + N_2} \quad (612)$$

$$s^2 = \frac{S_1 + S_2 + \frac{\left(\sum_1^{N_1} x_1\right)^2}{N_1} + \frac{\left(\sum_1^{N_2} x_2\right)^2}{N_2} - \frac{\left(\sum_1^{N_1} x_1 + \sum_1^{N_2} x_2\right)^2}{N_1 + N_2}}{N_1 + N_2 - 1}$$

$$= \frac{\nu_1 s_1^2 + \nu_2 s_2^2 + N_1\bar{x}_1^2 + N_2\bar{x}_2^2 - \frac{(N_1\bar{x}_1 + N_2\bar{x}_2)^2}{N_1 + N_2}}{N_1 + N_2 - 1} \quad (613)$$

where $\nu_s = N_1 + N_2 - 1$; S_1 and S_2 from (**493**).

16 C. Comparison of means when $\sigma_1^2 \neq \sigma_2^2$

If σ_1 and σ_2 are known, or $N_1 + N_2 > 200$, then

$$\sigma_{\boldsymbol{d}} = \sqrt{\frac{\sigma_1^2}{N_1} + \frac{\sigma_2^2}{N_2}} \text{ and } s_d = \sqrt{\frac{s_1^2}{N_1} + \frac{s_2^2}{N_2}} \quad \textbf{(614)}$$

and the test quotients

$$\frac{d}{\sigma_{\boldsymbol{d}}} \text{ and } \frac{d}{s_d} \text{ or } \frac{|d - \boldsymbol{d}|}{\sigma_{\boldsymbol{d}}} \text{ and } \frac{|d - \boldsymbol{d}|}{s_d} \quad \textbf{(615)}$$

have the same limits as (**609**a).

If σ_1 and σ_2 are unknown, then the test quotients

$$\frac{d}{s_{vd}} \text{ and } \frac{|d - \boldsymbol{d}|}{s_{vd}} \quad \textbf{(616)}$$

have the same limits as (**609**b)[27], where

$$s_{vd} = \sqrt{\frac{s_1^2}{N_1} + \frac{s_2^2}{N_2}} \quad \text{(a)}$$

$$\nu = \frac{1}{\dfrac{k^2}{\nu_1} + \dfrac{(1-k)^2}{\nu_2}}; \ \nu_1 \text{ and } \nu_2 \text{ are degrees of freedom of } s_1 \text{ and } s_2 \text{ respectively} \quad \text{(b)} \quad \textbf{(617)}$$

$$k = \frac{N_2 s_1^2}{N_2 s_1^2 + N_1 s_2^2} \quad \text{(c)}$$

16 D. Testing pair differences

When two analytical methods can be tried out on the same substrate, or two methods of treatment on the same individual, then the *power of a test is considerably greater* if in place of the difference between *two* means, *one* mean calculated from the sum of the pair differences is tested.

Let A and B be the methods to be compared, $A_i - B_i = d_i$ the difference between the results given by these methods with the object i, N the total number of objects. A sample of size N of all pair differences d_i is thus obtained which can be tested in accordance with (**598**)–(**602**), usually with a hypothetical mean $\mu = 0$. Other even simpler methods of testing pair differences are the sign test (see section 10H, page 160), the Wilcoxon test, and in certain cases appropriate sequential analysis (cf. section 26, page 195).

16 E. Tests for two samples using the extreme range[24]

(a) *Two samples of the same size* $N' = N'' = N \leq 20$:

$x'_N - x'_1$ and $x''_N - x''_1$ are the extreme ranges of these samples; the test quotient is then

$$\frac{|\bar{x}' - \bar{x}''|}{x'_N - x'_1 + x''_N - x''_1}; \text{ for limit see page 53, bottom left-hand table} \quad \textbf{(618)}$$

(b) *Two samples of unequal size*, or of the same size but larger than in (a):

The samples are divided respectively into m' and m'' random subgroups of the same size n (cf. section 14A, page 169). The sum of all the extreme ranges of these subgroups from both samples is denoted by S_E. The test quotient is then

$$\frac{|\bar{x}' - \bar{x}''| \sqrt{m' m''}}{S_E \times \boldsymbol{A}_{m,n}}; \quad m = m' + m''; \text{ for limit see page 49, for } \boldsymbol{A}_{m,n} \text{ page 48} \quad \textbf{(619)}$$

17. The normally distributed population: Testing several samples

Given are n samples of sizes

$$N_1, N_2, \ldots, N_i, \ldots, N_n, \text{ where } \sum_1^n N_i = N \quad \text{(a)}$$

The sums of the individual values x are

$$\sum_1^{N_1} x_1, \sum_1^{N_2} x_2, \ldots, \sum_1^{N_i} x_i, \ldots, \sum_1^{N_n} x_n, \text{ where } \sum_1^n \sum_1^{N_i} x_i = \sum_1^N x \quad \text{(b)} \quad \textbf{(620)}$$

The sums of the individual squares x^2 are

$$\sum_1^{N_1} x_1^2, \sum_1^{N_2} x_2^2, \ldots, \sum_1^{N_i} x_i^2, \ldots, \sum_1^{N_n} x_n^2, \text{ where } \sum_1^n \sum_1^{N_i} x_i = \sum_1^N x^2 \quad \text{(c)}$$

The sums of squares calculated in accordance with (**493**) are

$$S_1, S_2, \ldots, S_i, \ldots, S_n, \text{ where } \sum_1^n S_i = S \quad \text{(d)}$$

The degrees of freedom are

$$N_1 - 1, N_2 - 1, \ldots, N_i - 1, \ldots, N_n - 1, \text{ where } \sum_1^n \left(N_i - 1\right) = N - n \quad \text{(e)} \quad \textbf{(620)}$$

symbolized by $\nu_1, \nu_2, \ldots, \nu_i, \ldots, \nu_n$, where $\sum_1^n \nu_i = \nu$

The means $\bar{x}_1, \bar{x}_2, \ldots, \bar{x}_i, \ldots, \bar{x}_n$ are defined by (**491**) (f)

and the variances $s_1^2, s_2^2, \ldots, s_i^2, \ldots, s_n^2$ by (**492**) (g)

17 A. Testing variances

The hypothesis $\sigma_1^2 = \sigma_2^2 = \cdots = \sigma_i^2 = \cdots = \sigma_n^2 = \sigma^2$ is tested by means of Bartlett's test[28].

An estimate of the common variance σ^2 is

$$s_\nu^2 = S/\nu \text{ where } \nu_s = N - n \quad S, \nu \text{ and } N \text{ from (620d, e and a)} \quad \textbf{(621)}$$

The test statistic is

$$2.3026\,(\nu \log s^2 - \sum_1^n \nu_i \log s_i^2)/k; \quad s^2 \text{ from (621)}, \nu, \nu_i \text{ and } s_i^2 \text{ from (620e and g)} \quad \text{(a)}$$

where

$$k = 1 + \left(\sum_1^n \frac{1}{\nu_i} - \frac{1}{\nu}\right) / 3\,(n-1); \ \nu \text{ and } \nu_i \text{ from (620e)} \quad \text{(b)} \quad \textbf{(622)}$$

When $\nu_1 = \nu_2 = \cdots = \nu_i = \cdots = \nu_n = \nu/n$, (**622**a and b) become

$$2.3026\,\nu \left[\log s^2 - (1/n) \sum_1^n \log s_i^2\right] / k; \text{ see (a)} \quad \text{(c)}$$

and

$$k = 1 + (n+1)/3\,\nu; \text{ see (b)} \quad \text{(d)}$$

The significance limit for the test statistics (**622**a) and (**622**c) is found from the χ^2 distribution with degrees of freedom $\nu = n - 1$ (tables on pages 36–39, $2\,\alpha = 1 \int_r$). If the test statistic *attains* or *exceeds* the significance limit, then we may suspect that populations with discrepant variances are among those being compared. If the test statistic is *smaller* than the limit, then in accordance with (**474**) it can be assumed that all the populations have the same variance. In this case the means can be further tested as described in section 17B below.

17 B. Testing means: simple analysis of variance

In testing the hypothesis $\mu_1 = \mu_2 = \cdots = \mu_i = \cdots = \mu_n = \mu$ the following tabulation is first made [cf. also (**620**)]:

	Sums of squares	Degrees of freedom	Variance
Variance between the samples	S_2	$n - 1$	$s_2^2 = S_2/(n-1)$
Variance within the samples	S_1	$N - n$	$s_1^2 = S_1/(N-n)$
Total	S_T	$N - 1$	$s_T^2 = S_T/(N-1)$

(623)

$$\text{where } S_2 = \sum_1^n (\bar{x}_i - \bar{x}) = \sum_1^n \left(\sum_1^{N_i} x_i\right)^2 / N_i - \left(\sum_1^N x\right)^2 / N \quad \text{(a)}$$

$$S_1 = S\,[\text{from (620d)}] = S_T - S_2 \quad \text{(b)} \quad \textbf{(624)}$$

$$S_T = S_1 + S_2 = \sum_1^N x^2 - \left(\sum_1^N x\right)^2 / N \quad \text{(c)}$$

$$\text{and } \bar{x} = \left(\sum_1^N x\right) / N \quad \text{(d)}$$

Calculations are based on the identities (**624**a, b and c).

In (**623**), s_2^2 represents the dispersion of the sample means $\bar{x}_i$ around the common mean $\bar{x}$, s_1^2 the dispersion of the individual values around the sample means. If all the samples originate from the same population, so that $\mu_1 = \mu_2 = \cdots = \mu_i = \cdots = \mu_n = \mu$ (the hypothesis in the light of which the variances have been tested), then the variances s_2^2 and s_1^2 should be approximately of the same magnitude. If they are not, then among the samples are some with discrepant means, in which case s_2^2 must be greater than s_1^2. The necessity of carrying out the appropriate F test is thus avoided when $s_2^2 \leq s_1^2$.

The test quotient is s_2^2/s_1^2, limit F; pages 40–41, $2\,\alpha = P$ with $s_2^2 > s_1^2$. **(625)**

If the test quotient is smaller than the significance limit, then in accordance with **(474)** it can be assumed that all the samples originate from the same population. The estimates of their mean μ and variance σ^2 are

$\bar{x}$ = **(624 d)**; s_v^2 = **(621)**, with $\nu = N - n$ **(626)**

and confidence and tolerance intervals constructed as described in **(580)**–**(584)**.

If the test quotient attains or exceeds the significance limit F, then among the means there must be some of discrepant magnitude. Various methods of analyzing this situation have been proposed[29]. Here that of DUNCAN[29] will be used.

The method is dependent on *all samples having the same size* N_0. The standard deviation of a mean $\bar{x}_i$ is first calculated

$s_{\bar{x}_i} = \sqrt{s_v^2/N_0}$; s from **(621)** **(627)**

$\nu_{s\bar{x}_i} = N - n$

The means $\bar{x}_i$ are now ranked

$\bar{x}_1 < \bar{x}_2 < \cdots < \bar{x}_i < \cdots < \bar{x}_n$;
$1, 2, \ldots, i, \ldots, n$ = ranks O **(628)**

and the n extreme ranges W_i corresponding to the degrees of freedom $\nu_{s\bar{x}_i}$ and the ranks $O = 2, 3, \ldots, n$ looked for in the table on page 50. Multiplication of these by the standard deviation of a mean $s_{\bar{x}_i}$ [cf. **(627)**] gives the extreme ranges of the means $W_{\bar{x}_i}$. Subtraction of these from the means $\bar{x}_i$ gives the "localized extreme ranges" $\bar{x}_i - W_{\bar{x}_i}$. The following conclusions can now be drawn:

The means falling in a "localized extreme range" $\bar{x}_i - W_{\bar{x}_i}$ cannot be distinguished from each other significantly. **(629)**

The means not distinguishable in **(629)** are underscored in the order of **(628)**, with the result that

two means which are not underscored with a common line differ from one another significantly (significance probability α of the table). **(630)**

Example 39. Given are 7 samples with the means $\bar{x}_i$ shown below. $N_0 = 5$, $N = 35$, $s_v = 0.099$, $\nu_s = 28$. Significance probability = 0.05.

From **(627)** the estimated standard deviation of a mean is $s_{\bar{x}_i} = \sqrt{0.099/5} \approx 0.1407$. The extreme ranges W_i and $W_{\bar{x}_i} = W_i \times s_{\bar{x}_i}$ are given in the table below. The differences $\bar{x}_i - W_{\bar{x}_i}$ are then calculated up to the point where the corresponding underscoring reaches or passes the lowest mean.

O	1	2	3	4	5	6	7
$\bar{x}$	1.34	1.36	1.48	1.62	1.74	1.88	2.04
W_i		2.90	3.04	3.13	3.20	3.26	3.30
$W_{\bar{x}_i}$		0.408	0.428	0.440	0.450	0.569	0.464
$\bar{x}_i - W_{\bar{x}_i}$					1.290	1.421	1.576
(629)	1.34	1.36	1.48	1.62	1.74	1.88	2.04

The final result is given by **(630)**: 2.04 > 1.34 to 1.48; 1.88 > 1.34 to 1.36.

18. The normally distributed population: Regressions of the first kind

Discussion will be limited here to *linear* regression functions. For the transformation of nonlinear into linear functions see under Lognormal distribution (page 164) and Probit transformation (page 162).

The functional relationships between two or more variables are often more or less obscured by random influences. Thus the effect of a dose of a drug, for example, will change in a certain way as the dose is increased. The effect will never be an exact function of the dosage, however, but even in the same subject will fluctuate around a curve – the *regression function* – in a random manner. Using statistical methods it is possible to estimate the parameters of the regression function and the required variances.

Although in the above example the dose is *not* a random variable, the effect which it brings about is. In this case the regression is one of the *first kind*. In cases where *both* variables are random variables the regression is one of the *second kind*. A regression of the second kind can be treated as a regression of the first kind when the range of variation of the dependent variable as well as the points at which it is measured are arbitrarily decided beforehand.

In regressions of the first kind there is a *single* regression line, that of y on x, which is used for calculations in both directions – from y to x as well as from x to y. Cf. also section 19, page 178.

18 A. Estimation of the parameters of the regression line Y

Cf. also **(298)**–**(311)**.

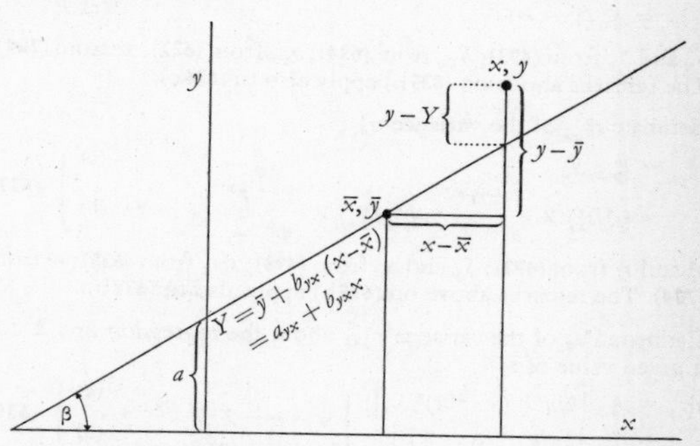

Fig. 35 Linear regression, ungrouped sample.

Ungrouped samples, two variables

Given are n pairs of observations x, y. x is the *independent, nonrandom* variable, y the *dependent, random* variable.

Estimate Y of the regression line $\boldsymbol{Y}$

$$Y = \bar{y} + b_{yx}(x - \bar{x}) \quad \text{(a)}$$
$$= a_{yx} + b_{yx}x \quad \text{(b)} \qquad \textbf{(631)}$$

where $a_{yx} = \bar{y} - b_{yx}\bar{x}$
with $\bar{y}$ and $\bar{x}$ calculated from **(491)**, b_{yx} from **(632)**.

Estimate b_{yx} of the regression coefficient $\boldsymbol{b}_{yx}$

$$b_{yx} = \frac{s_{xy}}{s_x^2} = \frac{S_{xy}}{S_x} \qquad \textbf{(632)}$$

with s_x^2 and S_x from **(492)** and **(493)**. For s_{xy} see **(633)**. Cf. also **(299)**. b_{yx} is the tangent of the angle of inclination β_{yx} of the regression line Y.

Estimate s_{xy} of the covariance σ_{xy}

$$s_{xy} = \frac{\sum(x - \bar{x})(y - \bar{y})}{n - 1} = \frac{S_{xy}}{n - 1} \qquad \textbf{(633)}$$

For S_{xy} see **(634)**.

The calculation of S_{xy} is facilitated by the use of the following sums:

$$S_{xy} = \sum(x - \bar{x})(y - \bar{y}) \quad \text{(a)}$$
$$= \sum xy - \bar{x}\sum y \quad \text{(b)}$$
$$= \sum xy - \bar{y}\sum x \quad \text{(c)} \qquad \textbf{(634)}$$
$$= \sum xy - \sum x \sum y/n \quad \text{(d)}$$
$$[= s_{xy}(n - 1)] \quad \text{(e)}$$

Estimate $s^2_{y\cdot x}$ of the residual variance $\sigma^2_{y\cdot x}$

$$s^2_{y\cdot x} = \frac{\sum(Y-y)^2}{n-2} = \frac{S_{y\cdot x}}{n-2} \quad \text{(a)}$$
$$= s^2_y(1-r^2)\frac{n-1}{n-2} \quad \text{(b)} \qquad \textbf{(635)}$$

For $S_{y\cdot x}$ and r^2 see (**636**) and (**704**).

$\sigma^2_{y\cdot x}$ is the variance of y when x is fixed. It is *smaller* than the variance σ^2_y. In very rare cases (with very small correlation or regression coefficients) we can have

$$(1-r^2)\frac{n-1}{n-2} > \frac{1}{n-1}, \text{ in which case } s^2_{y\cdot x} > s^2_y.$$

Formula (**635**b) belongs properly in section 19, page 178, but has been included here for the reader's convenience.

If r is known, values of $1 - r^2$ and of its square root can be taken from the table on page 59. Values of $(n-1)/(n-2)$ and of its square root for n between 1 and 200 are given in the table on page 60.

$$S_{y\cdot x} = S_y - b_{yx}S_{xy} \quad \text{(a)}$$
$$= S_y - b^2_{yx}S_x \quad \text{(b)} \qquad \textbf{(636)}$$
$$= S_y(1-r^2) \quad \text{(c)}$$

S_y and S_x from (**493**); S_{xy} from (**634**); b_{yx} from (**632**); r^2 from (**704**). The remarks above on (**635**b) apply also to (**636**c).

Estimate $s^2_{b_{yx}}$ of the variance $\sigma^2_{b_{yx}}$

$$s^2_{b_{yx}} = s^2_{y\cdot x}/S_x \quad \text{(a)}$$
$$= (s^2_y/s^2_x) \times \frac{1-r^2}{n-2} = (S_y/S_x) \times \frac{1-r^2}{n-2} \quad \text{(b)} \qquad \textbf{(637)}$$

s^2_y and s^2_x from (**492**); S_y and S_x from (**493**); $s^2_{y\cdot x}$ from (**635**); r^2 from (**704**). The remarks above on (**635**b) apply also to (**637**b).

Estimate $s^2_{Y|x}$ of the variance $\sigma^2_{Y|x}$ about the regression line $\mathbf{Y}$ for a given value of x

$$s^2_{Y|x} = s^2_{y\cdot x}\left[1/n + (x-\bar{x})^2/S_x\right]; \quad \text{(a)}$$
$$= s^2_{b_{yx}}\left[S_x/n + (x-\bar{x})^2\right] \quad \text{(b)} \qquad \nu = n-2 \qquad \textbf{(638)}$$

S_x from (**493**); $s^2_{y\cdot x}$ from (**635**).

Special cases of (**638**) are:

Estimate $s^2_{\bar{y}}$ of the variance $\sigma^2_{\bar{y}}$ of the mean $\bar{y}$

$$s^2_{\bar{y}} = s^2_{y\cdot x}/n; \; \nu = n-2 \qquad \textbf{(639)}$$

Estimate $s^2_{a_{yx}}$ of the variance $\sigma^2_{a_{yx}}$ of the intercept a

$$s^2_{a_{yx}} = s^2_{y\cdot x}\left[1/n + \bar{x}^2/S_x\right] \quad \text{(a)}$$
$$= s^2_{b_{yx}}\sqrt{(\textstyle\sum x^2)/n} \quad \text{(b)} \qquad \nu = n-2 \qquad \textbf{(640)}$$

$s^2_{b_{yx}}$ from (**637**).

Example 40. Given is the sample

x	y	x	y	x	y
5.8	2.19	7.0	4.62	8.2	6.58
6.2	3.27	7.4	5.32	8.6	7.41
6.6	3.79	7.8	5.85	9.0	8.29

The y values in this example correspond to the empirical probits of example 31 in section 11F, page 162.

It follows that

$\bar{x} = 7.4$ from (**491**)

$S_x = 9.6$ from (**493**)

$\bar{y} = 47.32/9 = 5.25\dot{7}$ from (**491**)

$S_y = 280.651 - 248.798 = 31.853$ from (**493**)

$s^2_y = S_y/8 = 3.981\,625$; $s_y = 1.9954$ from (**492**b)

$S_{xy} = 367.620 - 350.168 = 17.452$ from (**634**)

$b_{yx} = 17.452/9.6 = 1.817\,91\dot{6}$ from (**632**)

$S_{y\cdot x} = 31.8530 - 31.7263 = 0.1267$ from (**636**a or b)

$s^2_{y\cdot x} = 0.1267/7 = 0.0181$; $s_{y\cdot x} = 0.134\,54$ from (**635**a)

$s^2_{b_{yx}} = 0.0181/9.6 = 0.001\,885\,42$; $s_{b_{yx}} = 0.043\,421$ from (**637**a)

$s^2_{\bar{y}} = 0.0181/9 = 0.002\,0\dot{1}$; $s_{\bar{y}} = 0.044\,843$ from (**639**)

$s^2_{a_{yx}} = 0.0181\left(0.\dot{1} + \dfrac{(7.4)^2}{9.6}\right) = 0.105\,257$; $s_{a_{yx}} = 0.324\,43$ from (**640**a)

$Y = 5.25\dot{7} + 1.817\,91\dot{6}\,(x - 7.4)$ from (**631**a)
$\;\; = -8.1948 + 1.8179\,x$ from (**631**b)

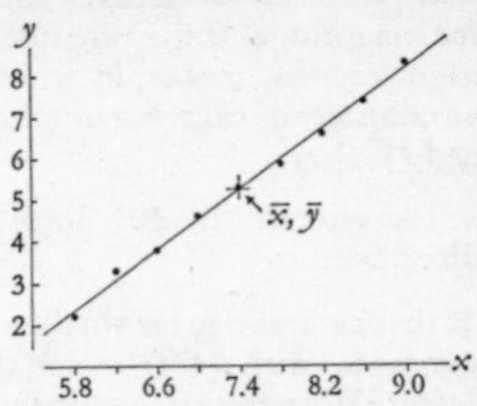

Fig. 36 Probit line of example 40.

A comparison of Figure 36 with Figure 30 (page 163) shows that the two probit lines – obtained by basically different methods – are hardly distinguishable by eye. The slope of the line of Figure 30 is $1/0.584 = 1.7123$. As will be shown in section 18D, page 176, this differs significantly from the slope 1.8179 of Figure 36.

Grouped samples, two variables

Given are $1, 2, \ldots, i, \ldots, k$ points of measurement (columns) x_i with $m_1, m_2, \ldots, m_i, \ldots, m_k$ observations y_{ij}. x is the *independent, nonrandom* variable, y the *dependent, random* variable.

(641)

x	1	2	$\ldots i$	$\ldots k$	
y	11	21	$\ldots i1$	$\ldots k1$	
	12	22	$\ldots i2$	$\ldots k2$	
	⋮	⋮	⋮	⋮	
	$1j$	$2j$	ij	kj	
	⋮	⋮	⋮	⋮	
	$1\,m_1$	$2\,m_2$	$i\,m_i$	$k\,m_k$	
	$\sum_{j=1}^{m_1} y_{1j}$	$\sum_{j=1}^{m_2} y_{2j}$	$\sum_{j=1}^{m_i} y_{ij}$	$\sum_{j=1}^{m_k} y_{kj}$	
	overall sum: $\sum y$;		column sum $\sum y_i$		(a) (b)
	$(\sum_{j=1}^{m_1} y_{1j})^2 / m_1$	$(\sum_{j=1}^{m_2} y_{2j})^2 / m_2$	$\ldots (\sum_{j=1}^{m_i} y_{ij})^2 / m_i$	$(\sum_{j=1}^{m_k} y_{kj})^2 / m_k$	
	overall sum $\sum(\sum y_i)^2/m_i$				(c)
xy	$x_1\sum_{j=1}^{m_1} y_{1j}$	$x_2\sum_{j=1}^{m_2} y_{2j}$	$\ldots x_i\sum_{j=1}^{m_i} y_{ij}$	$\ldots x_k\sum_{j=1}^{m_k} y_{kj}$	
	overall sum $\sum xy$				(d)
x	1	2	$\ldots i$	$\ldots k$	
y^2	$(11)^2$	$(21)^2$	$\ldots (i1)^2$	$\ldots (k1)^2$	
	$(12)^2$	$(22)^2$	$\ldots (i2)^2$	$\ldots (k2)^2$	
	⋮	⋮	⋮	⋮	
	$(1j)^2$	$(2j)^2$	$\ldots (ij)^2$	$\ldots (kj)^2$	
	⋮	⋮	⋮	⋮	
	$(1\,m_1)^2$	$(2\,m_2)^2$	$\ldots (i\,m_i)^2$	$\ldots (k\,m_k)^2$	
	$\sum_{j=1}^{m_1} y^2_{1j}$	$\sum_{j=1}^{m_2} y^2_{2j}$	$\ldots \sum_{j=1}^{m_i} y^2_{ij}$	$\ldots \sum_{j=1}^{m_k} y^2_{kj}$	
	overall sum: $\sum y^2$		column sum $\sum y_i^2$		(e) (f)
x	$m_1 x_1$	$m_2 x_2$	$\ldots m_i x_i$	$\ldots m_k x_k$	
	overall sum: $\sum x$				(g)
	$m_1 x_1^2$	$m_2 x_2^2$	$\ldots m_i x_i^2$	$\ldots m_k x_k^2$	
	overall sum: $\sum x^2$				(h)
n	$= m_1$	$+ m_2 + \cdots$	$+ m_i + \cdots$	$+ m_k$	(i)

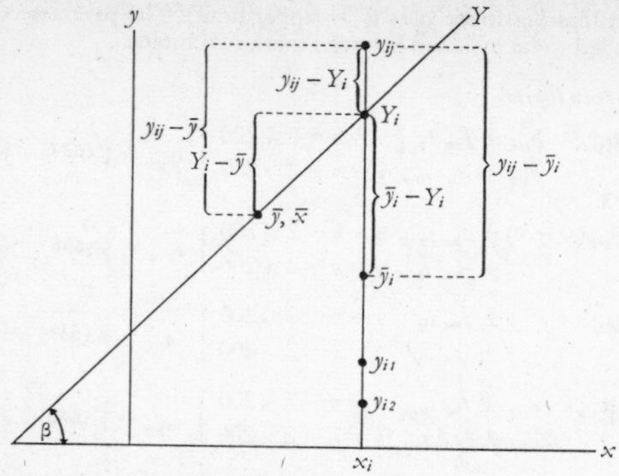

Fig. 37 Linear regression, grouped sample.

(**641**) allows the following to be calculated:

Column means

$\bar{y}_i = (\sum y_i)/m_i = (\mathbf{641}\,\mathrm{b})/m_i$ (**642**)

Sums of the squares of the deviations of the individual column values from the column means

$Sy_i = \sum y_i^2 - (\sum y_i)^2/m_i = (\mathbf{641}\,\mathrm{f}) - (\mathbf{641}\,\mathrm{b})^2/m_i$ (**643**)

Overall mean

$\bar{y} = (\sum y)/n = (\mathbf{641}\,\mathrm{a})/(\mathbf{641}\,\mathrm{i})$ (**644**)

Mean of the independent variables

$\bar{x} = (\sum x)/n = (\mathbf{641}\,\mathrm{g})/(\mathbf{641}\,\mathrm{i})$ (**645**)

Sums of the squares of the deviations of x from $\bar{x}$

$S_x = \sum x^2 - (\sum x)^2/n = (\mathbf{641}\,\mathrm{h}) - (\mathbf{641}\,\mathrm{g})^2/(\mathbf{641}\,\mathrm{i})$ (**646**)

Sums of products

$S_{xy} = \sum xy - \sum x \sum y/n = (\mathbf{641}\,\mathrm{d}) - (\mathbf{641}\,\mathrm{g})\,(\mathbf{641}\,\mathrm{a})/(\mathbf{641}\,\mathrm{i})$ (**647**)

Regression coefficient

$b_{yx} = S_{xy}/S_x = (\mathbf{647})/(\mathbf{646})$ (**648**)

Sums of the squares for variation within columns

$$\left.\begin{aligned} S_1 &= \sum_1^k Sy_i = \sum_1^k (\mathbf{643}) \\ &\left[= \sum_{i=1}^{k}\sum_{j=1}^{m_i} (y_{ij} - \bar{y}_i)^2\right] \end{aligned}\right\} \quad (\mathbf{649})$$

Sums of the squares of the deviations of the column means from the regression line Y

$$\left.\begin{aligned} S_2 &= \sum (\sum y_i)^2\, m_i - (\sum y)^2/n - S_3 \\ &= (\mathbf{641}\,\mathrm{d}) - (\mathbf{641}\,\mathrm{a})^2/(\mathbf{641}\,\mathrm{i}) - (\mathbf{651}) \\ &\left[= \sum_{i=1}^{k} m_i (\bar{y}_i - Y_i)^2\right] \end{aligned}\right\} \quad (\mathbf{650})$$

S_3 from (**651**)

Sums of the squares of the deviations of the regression line from the overall mean

$$\left.\begin{aligned} S_3 &= b_{yx} S_{xy} = b_{yx}^2 S_x = (\mathbf{648})\,(\mathbf{647}) = (\mathbf{648})^2\,(\mathbf{646}) \\ &\left[= \sum_{i=1}^{k} m_i (Y_i - \bar{y})^2\right] \end{aligned}\right\} \quad (\mathbf{651})$$

Sums of the squares of the deviations of the individual values from the overall mean

$$\left.\begin{aligned} S_y &= \sum y^2 - (\sum y)^2/n = (\mathbf{641}\,\mathrm{e}) - (\mathbf{641}\,\mathrm{a})^2/(\mathbf{641}\,\mathrm{i}) \\ &\left[= \sum (y_{ij} - \bar{y})^2\right] \end{aligned}\right\} \quad (\mathbf{652})$$

Check:

$S_1 + S_2 + S_3 = S_y$ (**653**)

Sums of the squares of the residual variations

$S_{y\cdot x} = S_1 + S_2 = S_y - S_3 = (\mathbf{649}) + (\mathbf{650}) = (\mathbf{652}) - (\mathbf{651})$ (**654**)

Estimated variances

$s_1^2 = S_1/(n-k) = (\mathbf{649})/(n-k);\ \nu = n-k$ (**655**)

$s_2^2 = S_2/(k-2) = (\mathbf{650})/(k-2);\ \nu = k-2$ (**656**)

$s_3^2 = S_3 = (\mathbf{651});\ \nu = 1$ (**657**)

$s_y^2 = S_y/(n-1) = (\mathbf{652})/(n-1);\ \nu = n-1$ (**658**)

$s_{y\cdot x}^2 = S_{y\cdot x}/(n-2) = (\mathbf{654})/(n-2);\ \nu = n-2$ (**659**)

The equation of the regression line Y and the estimated variances $s_{b_{yx}}^2$, $s_{\bar{Y}x}^2$, $s_{\bar{y}}^2$, $s_{a_{yx}}^2$ are obtained from (**631**), (**637**), (**638**), (**639**) and (**640**) by replacing b_{yx} by (**648**), $s_{y\cdot x}^2$ by (**659**) and S_x by (**646**).

Example 41. Given is the sample

x	7	8	9
y	1.0 1.4 2.0 2.2	2.0 2.5 2.8 3.1 3.7 4.0	2.9 3.2 3.4 3.9 4.4
$\bar{y}_i$	$6.6/4 = 1.65$	$18.1/6 = 3.01\dot{6}$	$17.8/5 = 3.56$ from (**642**)
Sy_i	$11.8 - 10.89 = 0.91$	$57.39 - 54.601\dot{6} = 2.788\dot{3}$	$64.78 - 63.368 = 1.412$ from (**643**)

$n = 15$ from (**641** i)

$\bar{y} = 42.5/15 = 2.8\dot{3}$ from (**644**); $\bar{x} = (28 + 48 + 45)/15 = 8.0\dot{6}$ from (**645**)

$S_x = (196 + 384 + 405) - (28 + 48 + 45)^2/15 = 8.9\dot{3}$ from (**646**)

$S_{xy} = 46.2 + 144.8 + 160.2 - 8.06 \times 42.5 = 8.3\dot{6}$ from (**647**)

$b_{yx} = 8.3\dot{6}/8.9\dot{3} = 0.936\,567\,164$ from (**648**)

$S_1 = 0.91 + 2.788\dot{3} + 1.412 = 5.110\dot{3}$ from (**649**)

$S_2 = 6.6^2/4 + 18.1^2/6 + 17.8^2/5 - 42.5^2/15 - S_3 = 0.607\,054\,728$ from (**650**)

$S_3 = 0.936\,567\,164 \times 8.3\dot{6} = 7.835\,945\,272$ from (**651**)

$S_y = 133.97 - 42.5^2/15 = 13.55\dot{3}$ from (**652**)

Check: $5.110\dot{3} + 0.607\,054\,728 + 7.835\,945\,272 = 13.55\dot{3}$ from (**653**)

$S_{x\cdot y} = 5.110\dot{3} + 0.607\,055 = 5.717\,388$ from (**654**)

$s_{y\cdot x}^2 = 5.717\,388/13 = 0.439\,799$; $s_{y\cdot x} = 0.663\,173$ from (**659**)

$s_{b_{yx}}^2 = 0.439\,799/8.9\dot{3} = 0.049\,2312$; $s_{b_{yx}} = 0.221\,881$ from (**637** a)

$Y = 2.8\dot{3} + 0.936\,567\,(x - 8.0\dot{6}) = -4.721\,64 + 0.936\,567\,x$ from (**631**)

$s_1^2 = S_1/12 = 0.425\,861$ from (**655**); $s_2^2 = S_2/1$ from (**656**); $s_3^2 = S_3$ from (**657**)

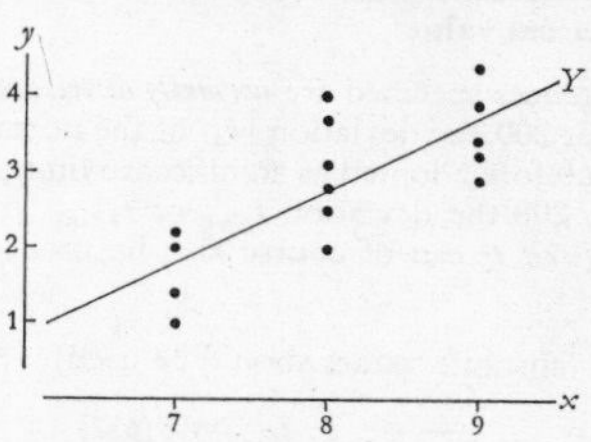

Fig. 38 Regression line of example 41.

18 B. Testing the linearity of the regression function

With *ungrouped* samples, general departure from linearity of the regression function can be tested only by eye. The deviations $Y_i - y_i$ should give an impression of randomness and not show any systematic trend (cf. for example Fig. 29 [systematic deviations] with Fig. 30, right [apparently random deviations], on page 163).

With *grouped* samples an exact test is possible, namely by comparing the variance of the column means about the regression line with the variance within the columns.

Test quotient:

$s_2^2/s_1^2 = (\mathbf{656})/(\mathbf{655})$; significance limit $F \begin{Bmatrix} \nu_2 = k-2 \\ \nu_1 = n-k \end{Bmatrix}$; (**660**)

$P = 2\,\alpha$; table on pages 40 and 41

(ν_1 of the table $= \nu_2$ of the test quotient)

If the test quotient *attains* or *exceeds* the significance limit, then the regression function is quite possibly nonlinear (significance probability $2\,\alpha = P$). If the test quotient is *smaller* than the significance limit, then in accordance with (**474**) it can be assumed that the regression is linear. Extrapolation of this interpretation beyond the range of variation of x in the samples should only be done with the greatest caution.

Example 42. In example 41, $s_1^2 = 0.425861$ and $s_2^2 = 0.607055$. From (**660**) the value of the test quotient is 1.43, that of the significance limit $F(1; 12)$ for $P = 0.05$ is 4.75. The statistical test therefore does not disprove the linearity of the regression function.

18 C. Testing the regression coefficient against zero

If the linearity of the regression function is not disproved by the test (**660**), the next step is to test the regression coefficient against zero, that is, to test the hypothesis $\boldsymbol{b}_{yx} = 0$. In other words, the estimate of the regression coefficient is tested for a significant difference from zero.

Test statistics:

$$\left.\begin{array}{l} b_{yx}/s_{b_{yx}};\ \text{significance limit } t;\ 2P = 2\alpha; \\ \nu = n - 2, \text{ pages 32–35} \end{array}\right\} \quad (\mathbf{661})$$

b_{yx} from (**632**) or (**648**), $s_{b_{yx}} = \sqrt{(\mathbf{637}\,\text{a})}$

or

$$\left.\begin{array}{ll} b_{yx}^2/s_{b_{yx}}^2 = b\,S_{xy}/s_{y\cdot x}^2;\ \text{significance limit } t^2; & \text{(a)} \\ P = 2\alpha,\ \nu = n-2, \text{ pages 32–35} & \\ \text{or} & \\ b\,S_{xy} - t_{2\alpha}^2\, s_{y\cdot x}^2;\ \text{significance limit null};\ t^2 \text{ as in } (\mathbf{662}\text{a}) & \text{(b)} \end{array}\right\} \quad (\mathbf{662})$$

With ungrouped samples, $b\,S_{xy}$ is obtained from (**632**) and (**634**), with grouped samples from (**651**). $s_{y\cdot x}^2$ is obtained from (**635**) or (**659**)

or

if the correlation coefficient r has been calculated (cf. section 19 A, page 178), then

$$\text{when } \boldsymbol{r} = 0, \text{ it follows that } \boldsymbol{b}_{yx} \text{ (and } \boldsymbol{b}_{xy}) = 0 \quad (\mathbf{663})$$

and vice versa. The hypothesis $\boldsymbol{b}_{yx} = 0$ can be tested using r. Significance limit for $|r|$, see page 61; $\nu = n - 2$.

If any of the test statistics in (**661**)–(**663**) attains or exceeds the corresponding significance limit, then b_{yx} differs significantly from zero. The above tests are special cases of (**664**a) for $\boldsymbol{b}_{yx} = 0$.

18 D. Testing the difference between estimate and hypothetical value

All the differences specified are *normally distributed.* For degrees of freedom over 200, the deviation $|c_\alpha|$ of the normal distribution (page 28) is therefore adopted as significance limit, for degrees of freedom up to 200 the deviation $t_{p=\alpha}$ or $t_{2P=2\alpha}$ of the STUDENT distribution [χ^2 or t^2 can of course also be used; cf. (**598**b) and (**599**b)].

Test quotients (absolute values should be used)

$$\left.\begin{array}{lll} (b_{yx} - \boldsymbol{b}_{yx})/s_{b_{yx}} & ;\ \nu = n-2;\ s_{b_{yx}} = \sqrt{(\mathbf{637})} & \text{(a)} \\ (Y|x - \boldsymbol{Y}|x)/s_{Y|x}; & \nu = n-2;\ s_{Y|x} = \sqrt{(\mathbf{638})} & \text{(b)} \\ (\bar{y} - \boldsymbol{\mu}_y)/s_{\bar{y}} & ;\ \nu = n-2;\ s_{\bar{y}} = \sqrt{(\mathbf{639})} & \text{(c)} \\ (a_{yx} - \boldsymbol{a}_{yx})/s_{a_{yx}} & ;\ \nu = n-2;\ s_{a_{yx}} = \sqrt{(\mathbf{640})} & \text{(d)} \end{array}\right\} \quad (\mathbf{664})$$

Example (43) of (**664**a). Comparison between the regression coefficients of examples 31 (page 163) and 40 (page 174), which have the values 1.7123 and 1.8179 respectively. Since the former was not calculated from (**632**), it will be considered here as a hypothetical value. The test quotient has the value

$$\frac{1.8179 - 1.7123}{0.04342} = 2.432;\ \nu = 7$$

The corresponding significance limit $t_{2\alpha=0.05}$, page 32, is 2.3646. The two regression coefficients, and therefore the regression lines, thus differ significantly.

18 E. Confidence and tolerance limits

Here only the formulas for the two-sided limits will be given, and these in the form of "estimate $\pm$ G" (estimate minus G = lower limit, estimate plus G = upper limit). The parameters are intended to be included between these two limits.

Confidence limits

For $\boldsymbol{b}_{yx}$:

$$\left.\begin{array}{ll} b_{yx} \pm t_{2\alpha}\, s_{b_{yx}} & \nu = n-2 \leqq 200 \\ b_{yx} \pm |c_\alpha|\, s_{b_{yx}} & \nu = n-2 > 200 \end{array}\right\} s_{b_{yx}} = \sqrt{(\mathbf{637})} \quad (\mathbf{665})$$

For $\boldsymbol{Y}|x$:

$$\left.\begin{array}{ll} \bar{y} + b_{yx}(x - \bar{x}) \pm t_{2\alpha}\, s_{Y|x} & \nu = n-2 \leqq 200 \\ \pm |c_\alpha|\, s_{Y|x} & \nu = n-2 > 200 \end{array}\right\} s_{Y|x} = \sqrt{(\mathbf{638})} \quad (\mathbf{666})$$

For $\boldsymbol{\mu}_y$:

$$\left.\begin{array}{ll} \bar{y} \pm t_{2\alpha}\, s_{\bar{y}} & \nu = n-2 \leqq 200 \\ \bar{y} \pm |c_\alpha|\, s_{\bar{y}} & \nu = n-2 > 200 \end{array}\right\} s_{\bar{y}} = \sqrt{(\mathbf{639})} \quad (\mathbf{667})$$

For $\boldsymbol{a}_{yx}$:

$$\left.\begin{array}{ll} a_{yx} \pm t_{2\alpha}\, s_{a_{yx}} & \nu = n-2 \leqq 200 \\ a_{yx} \pm |c_\alpha|\, s_{a_{yx}} & \nu = n-2 > 200 \end{array}\right\} s_{a_{yx}} = \sqrt{(\mathbf{640})} \quad (\mathbf{668})$$

(**666**) is a hyperbola (cf. Fig. 39).

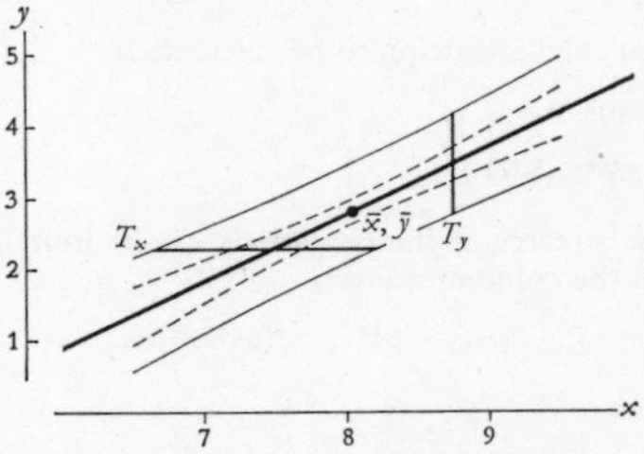

Fig. 39 Confidence and tolerance limits for the regression of Figure 38. - - - confidence limits for $\boldsymbol{Y}$, —— tolerance limits for $\boldsymbol{Y}$, T_y = tolerance interval for $Y|x$, T_x = tolerance interval for $x|y$.

Tolerance limits for $\boldsymbol{Y}|x$

$$\left.\begin{array}{l} = \bar{y} + b_{yx}(x - \bar{x}) \pm t_{2\alpha}\, s_T;\ \nu_t = n-2; \\ \quad b_{yx} \text{ from } (\mathbf{632}) \text{ or } (\mathbf{648}) \end{array}\right\} \quad (\mathbf{669})$$

where

$$\left.\begin{array}{lll} s_T = s_{y\cdot x}\sqrt{1 + 1/n + (x-\bar{x})^2/S_x}\,; & \nu = n-2 & \text{(a)} \\ \quad = s_{b_{yx}}\sqrt{(1 + 1/n)\,S_x + (x - \bar{x})^2}; & \nu = n-2 & \text{(b)} \end{array}\right\} \quad (\mathbf{670})$$

S_x from (**493**) or (**646**); $s_{y\cdot x} = \sqrt{(\mathbf{635})}$ or $\sqrt{(\mathbf{659})}$;

$s_{b_{yx}} = \sqrt{(\mathbf{637}\,\text{a})}$; $\bar{x} = (\mathbf{491})$ or (**645**)

18 F. Estimation of x when y is given

$$x|y = \bar{x} + \frac{y - \bar{y}}{b_{yx}} \quad (\mathbf{671})$$

Confidence limits for the expected value of x, given y [solution from (**666**) for x]

$$\left.\begin{array}{l} \bar{x} + \dfrac{y - \bar{y}}{b_{yx}(1-k^2)} \pm \\ \pm \dfrac{k}{b_{yx}(1-k^2)}\sqrt{(1/n)\,b_{yx}^2(1-k^2)\,S_x + (y - \bar{y})^2} \end{array}\right\} \quad (\mathbf{672})$$

where for ungrouped samples b_{yx} and S_x are obtained from (**632**) and (**493**), for grouped samples from (**648**) and (**646**)

$$k^2 = \frac{t_{2\alpha}^2\, s_{b_{yx}}^2}{b_{yx}^2}\ ;\ \nu_t = n - 2 \quad (\mathbf{673})$$

where $s_{b_{yx}}^2 = (\mathbf{637})$.

If $k^2 \leqq 0.05$, then $1 - k^2$ can be taken as 1 in (**672**).

Tolerance limits for $x|y$ [solution from (**669**) for x]

(**672**) is used, but with $(1 + 1/n)$ in place of $1/n$ in the term under the root. } (**674**)

Example 44. In example 40, it is required to calculate x for $y = 5$ and the corresponding confidence and tolerance limits $x|y = 5$.

$$x = 7.4 + \frac{5 - 5.25\dot{7}}{1.81791\dot{6}} = 7.2582 \text{ from } (\mathbf{671})$$

Confidence limits: k^2 is first calculated from (**673**), giving

$$k^2 = \frac{2.3646^2 \times 0.001\,885\,42}{1.817\,916} = 0.003\,190;\; k = 0.056\,48$$

k^2 is less than 0.05, so that $1 - k^2$ can be taken as 1 in (**672**). For purposes of comparison, however, (**672**) is calculated with both values:

	Confidence limits	Tolerance limits
$1 - k^2 = 1$	$= 7.2582 \pm 0.0589$	7.2582 ± 0.5534
	$= 7.1993$ to 7.3171	$= 6.7048$ to 7.8116
$1 - k^2 = 0.996\,810$	7.2577 ± 0.0590	7.2577 ± 0.5545
	$= 7.1987$ to 7.3167	$= 6.7032$ to 7.8122
	from (**672**)	from (**674**)

18 G. Comparison of two regression lines of the first kind

Given are the following ungrouped and grouped samples

$(x, y)_1$	and $(x, y)_2$	
with n_1	and n_2	pairs of observations
$\bar{x}_1$	and $\bar{x}_2$	from (**491**) or (**645**)
$\bar{y}_1$	and $\bar{y}_2$	from (**491**) or (**644**)
S_{x_1}	and S_{x_2}	from (**493**) or (**646**)
S_{y_1}	and S_{y_2}	from (**493**) or (**652**)
$(S_{xy})_1$	and $(S_{xy})_2$	from (**634**) or (**647**)
$(S_{y \cdot x})_1$	and $(S_{y \cdot x})_2$	from (**636**) or (**654**)
$(s^2_{y \cdot x})_1$	and $(s^2_{y \cdot x})_2$	from (**635**) or (**659**)
$(b_{yx})_1 = b_1$	and $(b_{yx})_2 = b_2$	from (**632**) or (**648**)
Y_1	and Y_2	from (**631**)

In analogy with section 16 (page 171), the following hypotheses must be considered in comparing two linear regressions:

$$(\sigma^2_{y\cdot x})_1 = (\sigma^2_{y\cdot x})_2 \begin{cases} \boldsymbol{b}_1 = \boldsymbol{b}_2 \begin{cases} \boldsymbol{Y}_1 = \boldsymbol{Y}_2 \\ \boldsymbol{Y}_1 \neq \boldsymbol{Y}_2 \end{cases} \text{(a)} \begin{cases} \text{(a c)} \\ \text{(a d)} \end{cases} \\ \boldsymbol{b}_1 \neq \boldsymbol{b}_2 \quad \text{(b)} \end{cases} \qquad \textbf{(675)}$$

$$(\sigma^2_{y\cdot x})_1 \neq (\sigma^2_{y\cdot x})_2 \begin{cases} \boldsymbol{b}_1 = \boldsymbol{b}_2 \begin{cases} \boldsymbol{Y}_1 = \boldsymbol{Y}_2 \\ \boldsymbol{Y}_1 \neq \boldsymbol{Y}_2 \end{cases} \text{(a)} \begin{cases} \text{(a c)} \\ \text{(a d)} \end{cases} \\ \boldsymbol{b}_1 \neq \boldsymbol{b}_2 \quad \text{(b)} \end{cases} \qquad \textbf{(676)}$$

The hypothesis $(\sigma^2_{y\cdot x})_1 = (\sigma^2_{y\cdot x})_2$ is tested by means of the quotient

$$\frac{(s^2_{y\cdot x})_1}{(s^2_{y\cdot x})_2};\; \begin{cases} \text{significance limit } F; \\ P = 2\alpha; \end{cases} \begin{cases} \nu_1 = n_1 - 2 \\ \nu_2 = n_2 - 2 \end{cases};\; \text{pages 40 and 41} \qquad \textbf{(677)}$$

where the *greater* of the variances is given the index 1.

If the test quotient is *smaller* than the significance limit, then (**681**)–(**693**) are valid; if the quotient attains or exceeds the significance limit, then (**694**)–(**701**) are valid.

If the test quotient is smaller than the significance limit (**677**), then it is reasonable to assume that $(\sigma^2_{y\cdot x})_1 = (\sigma^2_{y\cdot x})_2$. The common variance $\bar{\sigma}^2_{y\cdot x}$ of the two regression lines can then be estimated under the conditions of (**675**) as

$$\bar{\sigma}^2_{y\cdot x} = \frac{(S_{y\cdot x})_1 + (S_{y\cdot x})_2}{n_1 + n_2 - 4};\; \nu = n_1 + n_2 - 4 \qquad \textbf{(678)}$$

(**678**) is used to test the hypothesis (**675** a). The test quotient for the difference between the two regression coefficients under the conditions of (**675**) is

$$\frac{b_1 - b_2}{s_{D_b}};\; \text{significance limit } t;\, 2P = 2\alpha;\; \nu_t = n_1 + n_2 - 4 \qquad \textbf{(679)}$$

$$\text{where } s^2_{D_b} = \textbf{(678)} \times \left(\frac{1}{S_{x_1}} + \frac{1}{S_{x_2}}\right) \qquad \textbf{(680)}$$

If the test quotient (**679**) is *smaller* than the significance limit, then (**681**)–(**693**) are valid. If the quotient *attains* or *exceeds* the significance limit, then the regression lines are not parallel. In other words

if the test quotient is *smaller* than the significance limit, then the two regression lines may be regarded as *parallel*. (**681**)

The estimate of the common residual variance $\bar{\sigma}^2_{y\cdot x}$ when the conditions of (**675** a) are fulfilled is

$$\bar{s}^2_{y\cdot x} \approx \textbf{(678)};\; \nu = n_1 + n_2 - 4$$
$$= \frac{(S_{y\cdot x})_1 + (S_{y\cdot x})_2 + \dfrac{(b_1 - b_2)^2}{1/S_{x_1} + 1/S_{x_2}}}{n_1 + n_2 - 3};\; \nu = n_1 + n_2 - 3 \qquad \textbf{(682)}$$

The estimate of the common regression coefficient b_{yx} when the conditions of (**675** a) are fulfilled is

$$\bar{b}_{yx} = \frac{(S_{xy})_1 + (S_{xy})_2}{S_{x_1} + S_{x_2}} \qquad \textbf{(683)}$$

The estimate of the variance $\sigma^2_{\bar{b}_{yx}}$ of the estimate b_{yx} of the common regression coefficient when the conditions of (**675** a) are fulfilled is

$$s^2_{\bar{b}_{yx}} \approx \frac{\textbf{(678)}}{S_{x_1} + S_{x_2}};\; \nu = n_1 + n_2 - 4 \quad \text{(a)}$$
$$= \frac{\textbf{(682)}}{S_{x_1} + S_{x_2}};\; \nu = n_1 + n_2 - 3 \quad \text{(b)} \qquad \textbf{(684)}$$

The two lines may be considered as *identical* [hypothesis (**675** a c)] when the test quotient

$$\frac{\hat{b} - \bar{b}}{s_{\hat{b}-\bar{b}}},\; \begin{matrix} \nu = n_1 + n_2 - 4, \text{ when } s_{\hat{b}-\bar{b}} = \sqrt{\textbf{(687 a)}} \;\; \bar{b} = \textbf{(686)} \\ \nu = n_1 + n_2 - 3, \text{ when } s_{\hat{b}-\bar{b}} = \sqrt{\textbf{(687 b)}} \;\; \bar{b} = \textbf{(683)} \end{matrix} \qquad \textbf{(685)}$$

is *smaller* than the significance limit t, $2P = 2\alpha$, pages 32–35.

$$\hat{b} = \frac{\bar{y}_1 - \bar{y}_2}{\bar{x}_1 - \bar{x}_2} \qquad \textbf{(686)}$$

$$s^2_{\hat{b}-\bar{b}} \approx \textbf{(678)} \times K \quad \text{(a)}$$
$$= \textbf{(682)} \times K \quad \text{(b)} \qquad K = \textbf{(688)} \qquad \textbf{(687)}$$

where

$$K = \frac{1}{(\bar{x}_1 - \bar{x}_2)^2}\left(\frac{1}{n_1} + \frac{1}{n_2}\right) + \frac{1}{S_{x_1} + S_{x_2}} \qquad \textbf{(688)}$$

The two parallel regression lines do not coincide [hypothesis (**675** a d)] when the test quotient (**685**) *attains* or *exceeds* the significance limit. In this case the vertical and horizontal distances p_y and p_x are often of interest.

The *vertical distance* p_y and its confidence limits, when the conditions of (**675** a c) are fulfilled, are

$$p_y = |\bar{y}_1 - \bar{y}_2 - \bar{b}_{yx}(\bar{x}_1 - \bar{x}_2)|;\; \bar{b}_{yx} = \textbf{(683)} \qquad \textbf{(689)}$$

Confidence limits for $\boldsymbol{p}_{Y|x}$

$$\approx \textbf{(689)} \pm t_{2\alpha}\sqrt{\textbf{(684a)} \times [(1/n_1 + 1/n_2)(S_{x_1} + S_{x_2}) + (\bar{x}_1 - \bar{x}_2)^2]} \quad \text{(a)}$$
$$\text{where } \nu_t = n_1 + n_2 - 4$$
$$= \textbf{(689)} \pm t_{2\alpha}\sqrt{\textbf{(684b)} \times [(1/n_1 + 1/n_2)(S_{x_1} + S_{x_2}) + (\bar{x}_1 - \bar{x}_2)^2]} \quad \text{(b)}$$
$$\text{where } \nu_t = n_1 + n_2 - 3 \qquad \textbf{(690)}$$

The *horizontal distance* p_x and its confidence limits, when the conditions of (**675** a d) are fulfilled, are

$$p_x = \left|\bar{x}_1 - \bar{x}_2 - \frac{\bar{y}_1 - \bar{y}_2}{\bar{b}_{yx}}\right|;\; \bar{b}_{yx} \text{ from } \textbf{(683)} \qquad \textbf{(691)}$$

Confidence limits for $\boldsymbol{p}_x$

$$\approx \text{or} = \left|\bar{x}_1 - \bar{x}_2 - \frac{\bar{y}_1 - \bar{y}_2}{\bar{b}_{yx}(1 - k^2)}\right| \pm \frac{k}{\bar{b}_{yx}(1 - k^2)} \times \sqrt{\left(\frac{1}{n_1} + \frac{1}{n_2}\right)\left(\bar{b}_{yx}\right)^2\left(1 - k^2\right)\left(S_{x_1} + S_{x_2}\right) + \left(\bar{y}_1 - \bar{y}_2\right)^2} \qquad \textbf{(692)}$$

where $\bar{b}_{yx} = \textbf{(683)}$ and either $k = k_1 = \textbf{(693a)}$ or $k = k_2 = \textbf{(693b)}$. The approximation sign is for $k = k_1$, the equality sign for $k = k_2$.

$$\begin{matrix} k_1^2 \\ k_2^2 \end{matrix} = \frac{t^2_{2\alpha}\, s^2_{\bar{b}_{yx}}}{(\bar{b}_{yx})^2} \begin{cases} s^2_{\bar{b}_{yx}} = \textbf{684a};\; \nu_t = n_1 + n_2 - 4 \quad \text{(a)} \\ s^2_{\bar{b}_{yx}} = \textbf{684b};\; \nu_t = n_1 + n_2 - 3 \quad \text{(b)} \end{cases} \qquad \textbf{(693)}$$

When $k \leq 0.05$, the term $1 - k^2$ in (**692**) can be taken as 1.

If the test quotient (**677**) *attains* or *exceeds* the significance limit, then hypothesis (**676**) is valid, that is to say, $(\sigma^2_{y\cdot x})_1 \neq (\sigma^2_{y\cdot x})_2$.

Hypothesis (**676**a), that $b_1 = b_2$, is then tested by means of the quotient (**679**), where

$$s^2_{D_b} = \frac{(s^2_{y\cdot x})_1}{S_{x_1}} + \frac{(s^2_{y\cdot x})_2}{S_{x_2}} \quad \text{(a)}$$

Degrees of freedom ν_t = (**617**b) **(694)**

$$\text{with } k = \frac{(s^2_{y\cdot x})_1 S_{x_2}}{(s^2_{y\cdot x})_1 S_{x_2} + (s^2_{y\cdot x})_2 S_{x_1}} \quad \text{(b)}$$

Significance limit $t_{2\alpha}$, with ν_t from (**617**b) and k from (**694**b).

If the test quotient (**679**) fitted to (**694**) is *smaller* than the significance limit, then it can be assumed that $b_1 = b_2$. The common regression coefficient is then

$$\bar{b}_{yx} = \frac{\dfrac{(S_{xy})_1}{(s^2_{y\cdot x})_1} + \dfrac{(S_{xy})_2}{(s^2_{y\cdot x})_2}}{\dfrac{S_{x_1}}{(s^2_{y\cdot x})_1} + \dfrac{S_{x_2}}{(s^2_{y\cdot x})_2}} \quad \textbf{(695)}$$

with the estimated variance

$$s^2_{\bar{b}_{yx}} = \frac{1}{\dfrac{S_{x_1}}{(s^2_{y\cdot x})_1} + \dfrac{S_{x_2}}{(s^2_{y\cdot x})_2}} \quad \textbf{(696)}$$

Provided that the sample sizes n_1 and n_2 are *large*, the hypothesis (**676**a c) that the two parallel regression lines are *identical* can be tested approximately by means of the quotient (**685**), where

$$\hat{b} = \textbf{(686)}$$

$$s^2_{\hat{b}-\bar{b}} = \frac{1}{(\bar{x}_1 - \bar{x}_2)^2}\left[\frac{(s^2_{y\cdot x})_1}{n_1} + \frac{(s^2_{y\cdot x})_2}{n_2} + \textbf{(696)}\right] \quad \textbf{(697)}$$

Significance limit $|c_\alpha|$, page 28.

If the test quotient (**685**) fitted to (**697**) *attains* or *exceeds* the significance limit, then the two parallel regression lines probably do *not* coincide. In this case, when the conditions of (**676**a d) are fulfilled,

the *vertical* distance is

$$p_y = \textbf{(689)}; \text{ where } \bar{b}_{yx} = \textbf{(695)} \quad \textbf{(698)}$$

with confidence limits

$$\approx \textbf{(698)} \pm |c_\alpha| \times \sqrt{\frac{(s^2_{y\cdot x})_1}{n_1} + \frac{(s^2_{y\cdot x})_2}{n_2} + (\bar{x}_1 - \bar{x}_2)^2 \times \textbf{(696)}} \quad \textbf{(699)}$$

the *horizontal* distance is

$$p_x = \textbf{(691)}; \text{ where } \bar{b}_{yx} = \textbf{(695)} \quad \textbf{(700)}$$

with confidence limits

$$\approx \left|\bar{x}_1 - \bar{x}_2 - \frac{\bar{y}_1 - \bar{y}_2}{\bar{b}_{yx}(1-k^2)}\right| \pm \frac{k}{\bar{b}_{yx}(1-k^2)} \times \sqrt{\left[\frac{(s^2_{y\cdot x})_1}{n_1} + \frac{(s^2_{y\cdot x})_2}{n_2}\right]\frac{(\bar{b}_{yx})^2(1-k^2)}{\textbf{(696)}} + (\bar{y}_1 - \bar{y}_2)^2} \quad \textbf{(701)}$$

where $k^2 = \dfrac{c^2_\alpha \times \textbf{(696)}}{(\bar{b}_{yx})^2}$; c_α, page 28; $c^2_\alpha = \chi^2$, $\nu = 1$, $1 \int_r = 2\alpha$, page 36

and $\bar{b}_{yx}$ = (**695**)

When $k \leqq 0.05$, the term $1 - k^2$ in (**701**) can be taken as 1.

Probit and logit regressions

With appropriate modifications, many of the formulas given in section 18 can be applied to probit and logit regressions. For further details the reader is referred to the literature.

Probit regression[12–15, 30]: tables on pages 54 and 55

Logit regression[31, 32]: tables on pages 56 and 57

19. Regressions of the second kind: The bivariate normal distribution

Cf. introduction to section 18, page 173.

Given are n pairs of observations x, y. Both x and y are *random*, normally distributed variables.

Regressions of the second kind are distinguished from those of the first kind by the existence of *two* regression lines

$$Y = \bar{y} + b_{yx}(x - \bar{x}) \quad \text{(a)}$$
$$X = \bar{x} + b_{xy}(y - \bar{y}) \quad \text{(b)} \quad \textbf{(702)}$$

In regressions of the first kind, inferences both from x to y and from y to x are made on the basis of (**702**a) = (**631**), while in regressions of the second kind they are made from x to y on the basis of (**702**a) and from y to x on the basis of (**702**b).

Estimates of the parameters of (**702**) and their variances are made by means of the appropriate formulas in section 18. In estimating the parameters of (**702**b), x and y in these formulas must be transposed.

19 A. The correlation coefficient

A further parameter of regressions of the second kind is the correlation coefficient r, a measure of the stochastic dependence of the two variables x and y. Its value can lie between -1 and $+1$. If it amounts to either -1 or $+1$, the two variables are (mathematically speaking) totally dependent upon one another, and the two regression lines Y and X coincide. If its value is zero, the variables are (stochastically) independent of one another, and the two regression lines Y and X are at right angles to one another and parallel to the coordinate axes. The remarks in (**361**) apply here too to the expressions "dependent" and "independent", so that a realistic interpretation of the correlation coefficient is often difficult or even impossible.

When the correlation coefficient is less than, equal to, or greater than zero, the two regression coefficients b_{yx} and b_{xy} are likewise less than, equal to, or greater than zero. **(703)**

The following relationships are valid for the correlation coefficient

$$\boldsymbol{r} = \frac{\sigma_{xy}}{\sigma_x \sigma_y} \quad \text{(a)}$$

and for its estimate **(704)**

$$r = \frac{s_{xy}}{s_x s_y} = \frac{S_{xy}}{\sqrt{S_x S_y}}; \quad S_x \text{ and } S_y \text{ from (493)}, \; S_{xy} \text{ from (634)} \quad \text{(b)}$$

The square of the correlation coefficient r^2 is also known as the coefficient (or index) of determination.

From (**704**) it follows that

$$r = \sqrt{\frac{s_{xy}}{s^2_x} \times \frac{s_{xy}}{s^2_y}} = \sqrt{b_{yx} \times b_{xy}} \quad \textbf{(705)}$$

From (**115**) it therefore follows that the correlation coefficient is also the *geometrical mean* of the two regression coefficients b_{yx} and b_{xy}.

Under the hypothesis $\boldsymbol{r} = 0$, the correlation coefficient is related to the STUDENT distribution. In fact

$$\frac{r\sqrt{(n-2)}}{\sqrt{(1-r^2)}} \text{ is distributed as } t \text{ with } \nu = n - 2 \text{ degrees of freedom} \quad \textbf{(706)}$$

The hypothesis can therefore be tested by means of the quotient

$$\frac{r\sqrt{(n-2)}}{\sqrt{(1-r^2)}}; \text{ significance limit } \begin{cases} t_{2\alpha} \text{ for } n \leqq 202 & \text{(a)} \\ |c_\alpha| \text{ for } n > 202 & \text{(b)} \end{cases} \quad \textbf{(707)}$$

where $\nu = n - 2$

(**706**) does not need to be calculated for $\nu \leqq 200$ since the significance limits for r can be taken directly from the table on page 61. They are based on the following formula identical with (**706**a):

$$|r| = \frac{t_{2\alpha}}{\sqrt{\nu + t^2_{2\alpha}}}; \quad \nu_t = n - 2 \quad \textbf{(708)}$$

If the test statistics from (**706**) or (**708**) are *smaller* than the corresponding significance limits, then it can be assumed that the correlation coefficient, and in accordance with (**703**) also the two regression coefficients b_{yx} and b_{xy}, do *not* differ significantly from zero.

If the test statistics from **(706)** or **(708)** *attain* or *exceed* the corresponding significance limits, then the correlation coefficient and the two regression coefficients *differ* significantly from zero. If $r \neq 0$, then the distribution of the sample correlation coefficient r is complicated in form. However, its distribution can be approximately normalized by means of R. A. FISHER's z-transformation, as follows:

$$z = \tanh^{-1} r = \tfrac{1}{2} \ln \frac{1+r}{1-r} \quad \text{(a)}$$

and

$$r = \tanh z = \frac{e^{2z}-1}{e^{2z}+1} \quad \text{(b)} \qquad \textbf{(709)}$$

Cf. also Hyperbolic functions, page 140. Tables for (**709**a) are to be found on page 62 and for (**709**b) on pages 64 and 65.

The variance of z (2 variables x, y) is

$$\sigma_z^2 \approx \frac{1}{n-3}; \text{ cf. also page 62} \qquad \textbf{(710)}$$

The expectation $\boldsymbol{z}$ of z is

$$\boldsymbol{z} \approx \tanh^{-1} \boldsymbol{r} \quad \text{(a)}$$

$$\approx \frac{\boldsymbol{r}}{2(n-1)} + \tanh^{-1} \boldsymbol{r} \quad \text{(b)} \qquad \textbf{(711)}$$

(**711**b) can as a rule be neglected (see below).

The following is derived from **(709)**–**(711)**:

Testing the difference between an estimate r and a hypothetical correlation coefficient $\boldsymbol{r}$

Test quotient

$$\frac{|z-\boldsymbol{z}|}{\sigma_z} = |z-\boldsymbol{z}|\sqrt{n-3}\,; \; z \text{ and } \boldsymbol{z} \text{ from (709a) and (711a)} \qquad \textbf{(712)}$$

Significance limit $|c_\alpha|$, page 28, or $c_{2\alpha}$, page 31, lower table.

If the test quotient **(712)** is *smaller* than the significance limit, then there is no evidence that the population correlation coefficient differs from $\boldsymbol{r}$.

Confidence limits for $\boldsymbol{r}$

$$\text{Prob}\left[\tanh\left(z - \frac{|c_\alpha|}{\sqrt{n-3}}\right) \leq \boldsymbol{r} \leq \tanh\left(z + \frac{|c_\alpha|}{\sqrt{n-3}}\right)\right] \approx 1 - 2\alpha \qquad \textbf{(713)}$$

Values for $\dfrac{|c_\alpha|}{\sqrt{n-3}}$ for $1-2\alpha = 0.95$ and 0.99 are given on page 63.

Comparison of two correlation coefficients $\boldsymbol{r}_1$ *and* $\boldsymbol{r}_2$

Testing the hypothesis $\boldsymbol{r}_1 = \boldsymbol{r}_2$ on the basis of the estimates r_1 and r_2 is effected by means of the following quotient:

$$\frac{|z_1 - z_2|}{\sqrt{\dfrac{1}{n_1-3} + \dfrac{1}{n_2-3}}}; \text{ significance limit } |c_\alpha|, \text{ page 28, or } c_{2\alpha}, \text{ page 31} \qquad \textbf{(714)}$$

If the test quotient **(714)** is *smaller* than the significance limit, then it can be assumed that $\boldsymbol{r}_1 = \boldsymbol{r}_2$. The estimate of the common correlation coefficient is then

$$\bar{r} = \tanh \bar{z} = \tanh \frac{(n_1-3)z_1 + (n_2-3)z_2}{n_1+n_2-6} \qquad \textbf{(715)}$$

$$\text{and } \sigma_{\bar{z}}^2 = \frac{1}{n_1+n_2-6} \qquad \textbf{(716)}$$

The confidence limits for the common correlation coefficient are

$$\text{Prob}\left[\tanh(\bar{z} - |c_\alpha|\sigma_{\bar{z}}) \leq \bar{\boldsymbol{r}} \leq \tanh(\bar{z} + |c_\alpha|\sigma_{\bar{z}})\right] = 1 - 2\alpha; \text{ where } \sigma_{\bar{z}} = \sqrt{(716)} \qquad \textbf{(717)}$$

Comparison of several correlation coefficients

Given are k estimates $r_1, r_2, \ldots, r_i, \ldots, r_k$ from k bivariate samples of sizes $n_1, n_2, \ldots, n_i, \ldots, n_k$ respectively.

Testing the hypothesis $\boldsymbol{r}_1 = \boldsymbol{r}_2 = \cdots = \boldsymbol{r}_k = \boldsymbol{r}$, where $\boldsymbol{r}$ is a hypothetical value, is effected by means of the test statistic

$$\sum_1^k (n_i-3)(z_i-\boldsymbol{z})^2; \text{ significance limit } \chi^2; \; 1\textstyle\int_r = 2\alpha; \; \nu_{\chi^2} = k; \text{ pages 36–39} \qquad \textbf{(718)}$$

z_i and $\boldsymbol{z}$ from (**709**a) and (**711**a).

If the hypothetical value is unknown, then its estimate is

$$\bar{z} = \frac{\sum_1^k (n_i-3) z_i}{\sum_1^k (n_i-3)} \qquad \textbf{(719)}$$

with variance

$$\sigma_{\bar{z}}^2 \approx \frac{1}{\sum_1^k (n_i-3)} \qquad \textbf{(720)}$$

Testing the hypothesis $\boldsymbol{r}_1 = \boldsymbol{r}_2 = \cdots = \boldsymbol{r}_k = \bar{\boldsymbol{r}}$ is effected by means of the test statistic

$$\sum_1^k (n_i-3)(z_i-\bar{z})^2; \text{ significance limit } \chi^2; \; 1\textstyle\int_r = 2\alpha; \; \nu_{\chi^2} = k-1; \text{ pages 36–39} \qquad \textbf{(721)}$$

If the test statistic **(721)** is *smaller* than the significance limit, then it can be assumed that $\boldsymbol{r}_1 = \boldsymbol{r}_2 = \cdots = \boldsymbol{r}_k = \bar{\boldsymbol{r}}$. The estimate $\bar{r}$ of the common correlation coefficient $\bar{\boldsymbol{r}}$ is then approximately

$$\bar{r} \approx \tanh(\bar{z} - a \tanh \bar{z}) \qquad \textbf{(722)}$$

where $\bar{z}$ is from **(719)** and

$$a = \frac{\sum_1^k \left(\dfrac{n_i-3}{n_i-1}\right)}{2\sum_1^k (n_i-3)} \qquad \textbf{(723)}$$

The *confidence limits* for the common correlation coefficient $\bar{\boldsymbol{r}}$ are then approximately

$$\text{Prob}\left[\tanh(\bar{z} - a\tanh\bar{z} - |c_\alpha|\sigma_{\bar{z}}) \leq \bar{\boldsymbol{r}} \leq \tanh(\bar{z} - a\tanh\bar{z} + |c_\alpha|\sigma_{\bar{z}})\right] \approx 1 - 2\alpha \qquad \textbf{(724)}$$

$\bar{z}$ from **(719)**; a from **(723)**, $\sigma_{\bar{z}} = \sqrt{(720)}$, and significance limit $|c_\alpha|$, page 28.

Examples, section 19 A

Example 45. Given are $r = 0.3223$, $n = 34$. Does r differ from zero ($2\alpha = 0.05$)? Since $\nu = 32$ and the corresponding limit (page 61) is 0.3388, the hypothesis $r = 0$ cannot be rejected.

Example 46. Given are $r = 0.613$, $n = 42$. Required are the 95% confidence limits for $\boldsymbol{r}$:

$z = 0.713\,71$ (page 62)

$c_\alpha \sigma_z = 0.313\,58$ (page 63)

$z \pm c_\alpha \sigma_z = 0.400$ to 1.027

whence $\text{Prob}(\underbrace{0.380}_{\text{page 64}} \leq \boldsymbol{r} \leq \underbrace{0.773}_{\text{page 64}}) = 0.95$

Example 47.

Given are		whence are obtained		
r_i	n_i	z_i	$n_i - 3$	$n_i - 1$
0.555	12	0.625 58	9	11
0.590	20	0.677 67	17	19
0.670	15	0.810 74	12	14
0.621	9	0.726 63	6	8
0.733	26	0.935 18	23	25
0.800	13	1.098 61	10	12
		page 62		

$\bar{z} = 63.734\,51/77 = 0.828$ [from **(719)**]; $\tanh \bar{z} = \underbrace{0.6793}_{\text{page 64}}$

$\chi^2 = 1.815$; $\nu = 6 - 1 = 5$ [from **(721)**]

The 0.05 significance limit for χ^2, $\nu = 5$, is 11.07 (page 36), whence it follows that the hypothesis $\boldsymbol{r}_1 = \boldsymbol{r}_2 = \cdots = \boldsymbol{r}_k = \bar{\boldsymbol{r}}$ cannot be rejected.

$a = 5.0734/144 = 0.0352$; from **(723)**

$\bar{r} = \tanh(0.828 - 0.0352 \times 0.6794) = \tanh 0.804 = \underbrace{0.666}_{\text{page 64}}$; from **(722)**

$\sigma_{\bar{z}}^2 = 1/77 = 0.012\,987$; $\sigma_{\bar{z}} = 0.113\,96$ [from **(720)**]

For $2\alpha = 0.05$, $|c_\alpha| = 1.96$ (page 28). It follows that $|c_\alpha|\,\sigma_{\bar{z}} = 0.223$ and that the 95% confidence limits for $\boldsymbol{r}$ are

$$\tanh\underbrace{(0.804 - 0.223)}_{\substack{=0.523\\ \text{(page 64)}}} \leq \boldsymbol{r} \leq \tanh\underbrace{(0.804 + 0.223)}_{\substack{=0.773\\ \text{(page 64)}}} \quad \text{[from (724)]}$$

19 B. SPEARMAN's coefficient of rank correlation

(The SPEARMAN coefficient is dealt with here since it is suitable for estimating the correlation coefficient r discussed in section 19 A.)

If the bivariate sample x, y originates from *any continuous* distribution and its values have been not measured but *ranked* [cf. **(342)**], then the interdependence of y and x can be assessed by means of SPEARMAN's coefficient of rank correlation $\boldsymbol{R}$. (There is another correlation coefficient τ due to KENDALL[33] which has some advantages and some disadvantages[34].)

The SPEARMAN coefficient can be calculated for ranked samples from distributions of any form. When the distribution is a bivariate normal one, the interpretation of this coefficient corresponds to that of the correlation coefficient r (see below). How it should be interpreted for other distributions is not clear.

Given are n pairs of observations $(x, y)_i$. The pairs are first separated to form two samples x_i and y_i. The x and y values are then ranked by magnitude, so that for example x_{i5} is the fifth smallest of all x values, y_{i3} the third smallest of all y values. The original pairs of observations are now re-formed, giving for example $(x_5, y_3)_i$. The rank numbers (order numbers), such as here 5 and 3, are given the symbol O as before. The difference between the rank numbers of each pair of observations is now calculated and squared:

$$D_i^2 = (O_{x_i} - O_{y_i})^2 \qquad \textbf{(725)}$$

For the pair $(x_5, y_3)_i$ for example, $D_i^2 = (5-3)^2 = 4$.

The estimate of the SPEARMAN coefficient $\boldsymbol{R}$ is then

$$R = 1 - \frac{6\sum_1^n D_i^2}{n^3 - n} \qquad \textbf{(726)}$$

Values of the factor $6/(n^3 - n)$ are given in the table on page 68.

(726) is only exactly valid when no ties [cf. **(346)**] occur. However, when the number of ties is small it can still be used. For the procedure when there is a large number of ties see KENDALL[33].

The testing of R against zero is made with the significance limits given in the tables on pages 66 and 67. It is not necessary to calculate R, but only $\sum D^2$:

If the sum $\sum D^2$ *attains* or *falls outside* the significance limits, then R differs significantly from zero. (a)

If $\sum D^2$ *falls inside* the significance limits, R does not differ from zero. (b) **(727)**

The calculation of R is therefore only proceeded with in the case of **(727 a)**.

The exact significance limits in the tables are from KENDALL[33]. For higher values of n the limits have been calculated approximately from the normal distribution as follows:

Significance limits for $\sum D^2$

$$\sim \frac{n^3 - n}{6}\left(1 \pm \frac{|c_\alpha|}{\sqrt{n-1}}\right) \qquad \text{(a)}$$

Significance limits for $|R|$ **(728)**

$$\sim \pm \frac{|c_\alpha|}{\sqrt{n-1}} \qquad \text{(b)}$$

whereby the user remains on the safe side[34].

If the ranked samples originate from *normally distributed* populations, then according to K. PEARSON $\boldsymbol{r}$ and $\boldsymbol{R}$ have the following relationship

$$\boldsymbol{r} = 2 \sin \frac{\pi}{6} \boldsymbol{R} \qquad \textbf{(729)}$$

For estimates, **(729)** is only approximately valid. A table for calculating r from R is given on page 68.

Example 48. Given is the sample of example 49, section 19 D. This sample has 4 ties with x and 6 with y, an acceptable number with a sample size $n = 20$. The pairs of observations and corresponding ranks O_x and O_y are

x	O_x	y	O_y	D^2	x	O_x	y	O_y	D^2
2.6	1	2.3	1	0	6.0	11	5.7	8	9
3.0	2.5	2.7	3.5	1	6.5	12.5	6.0	12.5	0
3.0	2.5	3.5	5	6.25	6.5	12.5	6.0	19	42.25
3.5	4	3.5	3.5	0.25	7.0	14.5	6.5	12.5	4
3.8	5	4.0	6.5	2.25	7.0	14.5	7.0	15.5	1
4.2	6	4.5	2	16	7.5	16	7.0	17	1
4.5	7	4.5	9	4	8.0	18	7.7	14	16
4.7	8	5.2	10.5	6.25	8.0	18	8.0	15.5	6.25
5.5	9	5.5	6.5	6.25	8.0	18	8.0	19	1
5.7	10	5.7	10.5	0.25	10.0	20	8.0	19	1

$\sum D^2 = 124$, a sum which lies far outside the 0.001 limit of the table on page 66. R therefore differs from zero, and calculation is proceeded with in accordance with **(726)**. From the upper table on page 68, the factor $6/(20^3 - 20) = 10^{-4} \times 7.518\,80$, whence it follows that $R = 1 - (10^{-4} \times 7.518\,80 \times 124) = 0.906\,767 \sim 0.907$. Assuming that the sample originates from a normally distributed population, $r \sim 0.915$ from **(729)** (lower table, page 68). The estimate of r from **(704)** is 0.881.

19 C. Significance tests

For significance tests for correlation coefficients see section 19 A, page 178.

Comparisons between estimates and hypothetical values are made by means of the following test quotients

Estimate	Hypothetical value	Test quotient	
b_{yx}	0	**(706)**–**(708)** on the basis of **(703)**	**(730)**
b_{xy}	0		
b_{yx}	$\boldsymbol{b}_{yx}$	**(664 a)**	
b_{xy}	$\boldsymbol{b}_{xy}$	**(664 a)***	
$Y\|x$	$\boldsymbol{Y}\|x$	**(664 b)**	
$X\|y$	$\boldsymbol{X}\|y$	**(664 b)***	
$\bar{y}$	μ_y	**(664 c)**	
$\bar{x}$	μ_x	**(664 c)***	
a_{yx}	$\boldsymbol{a}_{yx}$	**(664 d)**	
a_{xy}	$\boldsymbol{a}_{xy}$	**(664 d)***	

* With x and y transposed.

It will be seen that for comparisons of a *single* estimate with a *hypothetical* value, the appropriate formulas for a regression of the first kind are valid also for a regression of the second kind. However, when two estimates from two *different* samples [as for example with $(b_{yx})_1 - (b_{yx})_2$] are to be compared, then the formulas for a regression of the first kind are no longer valid, although for *high values* of n they are approximately so.

Comparison of μ_y with μ_x, that is to say, testing the hypothesis $\mu_y = \mu_x$, is made by means of the test quotient

$$\frac{(\bar{y} - \bar{x})\sqrt{n}}{\sqrt{s_y^2 + s_x^2 - 2\,s_{xy}}};\ \text{significance limit } t;\ 2P = 2\alpha;\ \nu = n - 1;\ \text{pages 32–35} \qquad \textbf{(731)}$$

s_y^2 and s_x^2 from **(492)**, s_{xy} from **(633)**

Simultaneous comparison of $\bar{y}$ with μ_y *and* of $\bar{x}$ with μ_x, that is to say, testing the hypothesis (mean $y = \mu_y$, mean $x = \mu_x$), is made by means of the test statistic

$$\frac{n(n-2)}{2(1-r^2)} \times \left[\frac{(\bar{x}-\mu_x)^2}{S_x} + \frac{(\bar{y}-\mu_y)^2}{S_y} - \frac{2\,S_{xy}(\bar{x}-\mu_x)(\bar{y}-\mu_y)}{\sqrt{S_x S_y}}\right] \qquad \textbf{(732)}$$

Significance limit F; $P = 2\alpha$; $\nu_1 = 2$, $\nu_2 = n - 2$; pages 40 and 41

S_x and S_y are from **(493)**, S_{xy} from **(634)**, r from **(704)**. Calculation is facilitated by using the relationship

$$r^2 = \frac{S_{xy}}{S_x S_y} \times S_{xy}$$

Comparison of a bivariate sample with means $\bar{y}$ and $\bar{x}$ with an *independent* pair of observations x, y, that is to say, testing the hypothesis that (x, y) come from the same (normal) population $(\bar{x}, \bar{y})$, is made by means of the test statistic

$$\frac{n(n-2)}{2(n+1)(1-r^2)} \times \left[\frac{(x-\bar{x})^2}{S_x} + \frac{(y-\bar{y})^2}{S_y} - \frac{2S_{xy}(x-\bar{x})(y-\bar{y})}{\sqrt{S_x S_y}}\right] \qquad \textbf{(733)}$$

Significance limits, degrees of freedom, etc. are all as in **(732)**. **(733)** is a special case of **(734)** with $n_1 = 1$.

Simultaneous comparison of the means of *two* bivariate samples $(x, y)_1$ and $(x, y)_2$, that is to say, testing the hypothesis $(\mu_{y_1} = \mu_{y_2};\ \mu_{x_1} = \mu_{x_2})$, is made by means of the following test statistic *when* $\sigma^2_{y_1} = \sigma^2_{y_2}, \sigma^2_{x_1} = \sigma^2_{x_2}$,

$$\frac{n_1 n_2(n_1+n_2-3)}{2(n_1+n_2)(1-r^2)} \times \left\{\frac{(\bar{x}_1-\bar{x}_2)^2}{S_{x_1}+S_{x_2}} + \frac{(\bar{y}_1-\bar{y}_2)^2}{S_{y_1}+S_{y_2}} - \frac{2\left[(S_{xy})_1+(S_{xy})_2\right](\bar{x}_1-\bar{x}_2)(\bar{y}_1-\bar{y}_2)}{\sqrt{(S_{x_1}+S_{x_2})(S_{y_1}+S_{y_2})}}\right\} \qquad \textbf{(734)}$$

where

$$r^2 = \frac{\left[(S_{xy})_1+(S_{xy})_2\right]^2}{(S_{x_1}+S_{x_2})(S_{y_1}+S_{y_2})}, \text{ for calculation cf. } \textbf{(732)} \qquad \textbf{(735)}$$

Significance limit F; $P = 2\alpha$; $\nu_1 = 2$, $\nu_2 = n_1 + n_2 - 3$; pages 40 and 41. Otherwise as in **(732)**.

Approximate tests, preliminary to **(734)**, can be made as follows:
Testing the hypothesis $\sigma^2_{x_1} = \sigma^2_{x_2}$ and $\sigma^2_{y_1} = \sigma^2_{y_2}$ from **(605)**
Testing the hypothesis $r_1 = r_2$ from **(714)**.

For further discussion of tests of the above hypotheses see Pearson and Wilks[35].

19 D. Confidence and tolerance limits

The *confidence limits* for μ_y, given μ_x, and for μ_x, given μ_y, are

for $\mu_y \mid \mu_x$

$$= \bar{y} + b_{yx}(x-\bar{x}) \pm s_{b_{yx}}\sqrt{2FS_x/n - (n-2)(\bar{x}-\mu_x)^2} \quad \text{(a)}$$

for $\mu_x \mid \mu_y$

$$= \bar{x} + b_{xy}(y-\bar{y}) \pm s_{b_{xy}}\sqrt{2FS_y/n - (n-2)(\bar{y}-\mu_y)^2} \quad \text{(b)} \qquad \textbf{(736)}$$

Degrees of freedom of F: $\nu_1 = 2$, $\nu_2 = n-2$; $s_{b_{yx}}$ from **(637)**, $s_{b_{xy}}$ likewise but with x and y transposed.

(736a) and **(736b)** are solutions of **(732)** for y and x respectively. The corresponding *confidence ellipses* (see below) are identical.

The *tolerance limits* for y, given x, and for x, given y, are as follows:

for $\mathbf{Y} \mid x$

$$= \bar{y} + b_{yx}(x-\bar{x}) \pm \pm s_{b_{yx}}\sqrt{2(n+1)FS_x/n - (n-2)(x-\bar{x})^2} \quad \text{(a)}$$

for $\mathbf{X} \mid y$

$$= \bar{x} + b_{xy}(y-\bar{y}) \pm \pm s_{b_{xy}}\sqrt{2(n+1)FS_y/n - (n-2)(y-\bar{y})^2} \quad \text{(b)} \qquad \textbf{(737)}$$

For degrees of freedom of F, etc., see **(736)**.

(737a) and **(737b)** are solutions of **(733)** for y and x respectively. The corresponding *tolerance ellipses* (see below) are identical.

The *slopes* of the main axes of the ellipses of **(736)** and **(737)**, the so-called *orthogonal* regression coefficients, are

$$b_o, -\frac{1}{b_o} = \frac{S_y - S_x}{2S_{xy}} \pm \sqrt{1 + \left(\frac{S_y - S_x}{2S_{xy}}\right)^2} \qquad \textbf{(738)}$$

The lengths of the *semi-axes* of the ellipses of **(736)** and **(737)** are

$$l_1, l_2 = \sqrt{k}\sqrt{S_x + S_y \pm \sqrt{(S_x+S_y)^2 - 4(S_xS_y - S^2_{xy})}} \qquad \textbf{(739)}$$

where

$$k = \frac{F}{n(n-2)} \text{ for confidence ellipse } \textbf{(736)} \quad \text{(a)}$$
$$k = \frac{F(n+1)}{n(n-2)} \text{ for tolerance ellipse } \textbf{(737)} \quad \text{(b)}$$
degrees of freedom of F: $\nu_1 = 2$, $\nu_2 = n-2$ **(740)**

Construction of ellipses

Rapid method: Calculation from **(738)** and **(739)** and construction from **(315)**.

Exact method: From **(736)** or **(737a)** and/or **(737b)** in conjunction with **(738)** and **(739)**, according to the accuracy required.

The equations of tangents to the confidence or tolerance ellipses parallel to the coordinate axes are

Horizontal tangents: $y = \bar{y} \pm \sqrt{kS_y}$
Abscissas of the points of contact: $x = \bar{x} \pm b_{xy}\sqrt{kS_y}$ (a)

Vertical tangents: $x = \bar{x} \pm \sqrt{kS_x}$
Ordinates of the points of contact: $y = \bar{y} \pm b_{yx}\sqrt{kS_x}$ (b) **(741)**

where

$$k \begin{cases} = 2F/n(n-2) \text{ for confidence ellipse } \textbf{(736)} & \text{(a)} \\ = 2F(n+1)/n(n-2) \text{ for tolerance ellipse } \textbf{(737)} & \text{(b)} \end{cases} \qquad \textbf{(742)}$$

Degrees of freedom of F: $\nu_1 = 2$, $\nu_2 = n-2$.

The lengths of the sides of the rectangle formed by these tangents which circumscribes the ellipse are:

Horizontal sides

$$l_h = 2\sqrt{kS_x} \quad \text{(a)}$$

Vertical sides

$$l_v = 2\sqrt{kS_y} \quad \text{(b)} \qquad \textbf{(743)}$$

where $k =$ **(742)**

Example 49. Given is the bivariate sample (Figs. 40 and 41)

x	y	x	y	x	y	x	y
2.6	2.3	4.2	2.7	6.0	5.2	7.5	7.7
3.0	3.5	4.5	5.5	6.5	6.0	8.0	6.5
3.0	4.0	4.7	5.7	6.5	8.0	8.0	7.0
3.5	3.5	5.5	4.5	7.0	6.0	8.0	8.0
3.8	4.5	5.7	5.7	7.0	7.0	10.0	8.0

(a) The parameters are estimated.
(b) Using the formulas for the regression lines Y and X, for the orthogonal regression lines Y_o and X_o, for the tolerance ellipse for $\mathbf{Y} \mid x$ or $\mathbf{X} \mid y$, and for the horizontal and vertical tangents to the latter, the lengths of the sides of the rectangle formed by the tangents and the lengths of the semi-axes of the ellipse are calculated.
(c) For purposes of comparison, the tolerance limits for $\mathbf{Y} \mid x$ and $\mathbf{X} \mid y$ are calculated using the appropriate formulas for a regression of the first kind.
(d) A comparison is made of the tolerance limits for $\mathbf{Y} \mid \bar{x}$ and $\mathbf{X} \mid \bar{y}$ of regressions of the second and first kind.
(e) $\bar{x}$ and $\bar{y}$ are compared.

If a significance probability is required, then $2\alpha = 0.05$.

(a) Estimates of parameters

$\bar{x} = 115.0/20 = 5.75$	$\bar{y} = 111.3/20 = 5.565$
$S_x = 740.92 - 5.75 \times 115 = 79.67$	$S_y = 679.39 - 5.565 \times 111.3 = 60.0055$
$s^2_x = 79.67/19 = 4.193\,158$	$s^2_y = 60.0055$
$s_x = 2.047\,72$	$s_y = 1.777\,13$

$S_{xy} = 700.90 - 5.75 \times 111.3 = 60.925$ from **(634)**
$s_{xy} = 60.925/19 = 3.206\,579$
$r^2 = 60.925^2\,(79.67 \times 60.0055) = 0.776435170 =$ **(704b)**^{2}
$1 - r^2 = 0.223\,564\,830$
$r = 0.881\,155$
$b_{yx} = 60.925/79.67 = 0.764\,7170$ from **(632)**
$b_{xy} = 60.925/60.0055 = 1.015\,3236$ from **(632)***

* With x and y transposed.

$b_0, -1/b_0 = (60.0055 - 79.67)/2 \times 60.925 \pm \sqrt{1 + (-0.161\,382\,848)^2} = 0.851\,56$ and $-1.174\,32$ from **(738)**

$S_{y \cdot x} = 60.0055 \times 0.223\,564\,83 = 13.415\,1194$ from **(636c)**

$s^2_{y \cdot x} = 13.415\,1194/18 = 0.745\,284\,411$ from **(635a)**

$s^2_{b_{yx}} = 0.745\,284\,411/79.67 = 0.009\,354\,643$ from **(637a)**

$s_{b_{yx}} = 0.096\,7224$

$S_{x \cdot y} = 79.67 \times 0.223\,564\,83 = 17.811\,4100$ from **(636c)***

$s^2_{x \cdot y} = 17.811\,4100/18 = 0.989\,522\,777$ from **(635a)***

$s^2_{b_{xy}} = 0.989\,522\,777/60.0055 = 0.016\,490\,53$ from **(637a)***

$s_{b_{xy}} = 0.128\,416$

(b) Formulas

Regression lines

$Y = 5.565 + 0.7647\,(x - 5.75) = 1.1679 + 0.7647\,x$ from **(702a)**

$X = 5.75 + 1.0153\,(y - 5.565) = 0.0997 + 1.0153\,y$ from **(702b)**

$Y_0 = 5.565 + 0.8516\,(x - 5.75) = 0.6686 + 0.8516\,x$

$X_0 = 5.75 - 1.1743\,(y - 5.565) = 12.1001 - 1.1743\,y$

Tolerance ellipse

Tolerance limits for $\boldsymbol{Y}\,|\,x$

$= 5.565 + 0.7647\,(x - 5.75) \pm 0.096\,72 \times \sqrt{593.94 - 18\,(x - 5.75)^2}$ from **(737a)**

Tolerance limits for $\boldsymbol{X}\,|\,y$

$= 5.75 + 1.0153\,(y - 5.565) \pm 0.128\,42 \times \sqrt{447.34 - 18\,(y - 5.565)^2}$ from **(737b)**

Horizontal tangents y and abscissas of the points of contact

$$\left.\begin{array}{l} y = 5.565 \pm 4.99 = 0.58 \text{ and } 10.55 \\ x = 5.75 \pm 5.06 = 0.69 \text{ and } 10.81 \end{array}\right\} \text{ from } \textbf{(741a)} \text{ and } \textbf{(742b)}$$

Vertical tangents x and ordinates of the points of contact

$$\left.\begin{array}{l} x = 5.75 \pm 5.74 = 0.01 \text{ and } 11.49 \\ y = 5.565 \pm 4.39 = 1.18 \text{ and } 9.96 \end{array}\right\} \text{ from } \textbf{(741b)} \text{ and } \textbf{(742b)}$$

Lengths of the sides of the resulting rectangle

$$\left.\begin{array}{l} \text{Horizontal sides } l_h = 11.48 \\ \text{Vertical sides } l_v = 9.98 \end{array}\right\} \text{ from } \textbf{(743)} \text{ and } \textbf{(742b)}$$

Lengths of the semi-axes of the ellipse [$F_{0.05}\,(2; 18) = 3.55$; page 40]

$$= \sqrt{\frac{3.55 \times 21}{20 \times 18}} \times \sqrt{79.67 + 60.0055 \pm \sqrt{139.6755^2 - 4\,(4780.6382 - 60.925)^2}}$$

$= 7.38$ and 1.83 from **(739)** and **(740b)**

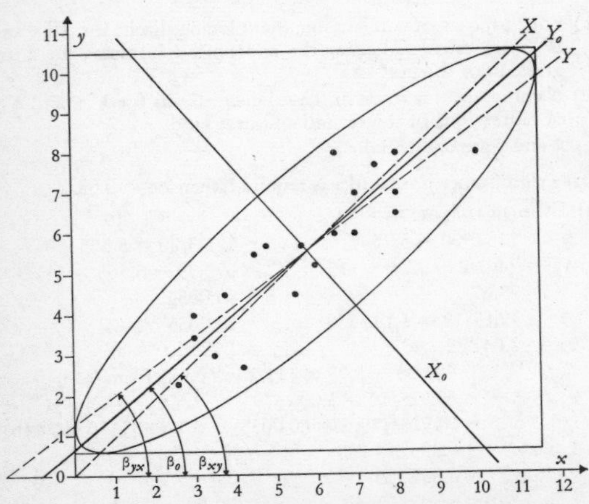

Fig. 40 Tolerance ellipse, example 49.

* With x and y transposed.

(c) Tolerance limits for $\boldsymbol{Y}\,|\,x$ and $\boldsymbol{X}\,|\,y$ calculated from the formulas for a regression of the first kind ($t_{2\alpha=0.05,\ \nu=18} = 2.1009$, page 32)

for $\boldsymbol{Y}\,|\,x$

$= 5.565 + 0.7647\,(x - 5.75) \pm 0.2032 \times \sqrt{83.6535 + (x - 5.75)^2}$ from **(669)**

for $\boldsymbol{X}\,|\,y$

$= 5.75 + 1.4070\,(y - 5.565) \pm 0.3739 \times \sqrt{45.4659 + (y - 5.565)^2}$ from **(674)**

(d) Tolerance limits for $\boldsymbol{Y}\,|\,\bar{x}$ and $\boldsymbol{X}\,|\,\bar{y}$ calculated from the formulas for

	Regression of 2nd kind	Regression of 1st kind
$Y\,\vert\,\bar{x}$	5.565 ± 2.3572 from **(737a)**	5.565 ± 1.8585 from **(669)**
$X\,\vert\,\bar{y}$	5.75 ± 2.7161 from **(737b)**	5.75 ± 2.5213 from **(674)**

(e) Comparison of $\bar{x}$ and $\bar{y}$ ($t_{2\alpha=0.05,\ \nu=19} \sim 2.09$)

$$\frac{5.75 - 5.565}{\sqrt{4.1932 + 3.1582 - 2 \times 3.2066}} = 0.191 \text{ from } \textbf{(731)}$$

The test statistic is smaller than the significance limit, so that the hypothesis $\bar{x} = \bar{y}$ cannot be rejected.

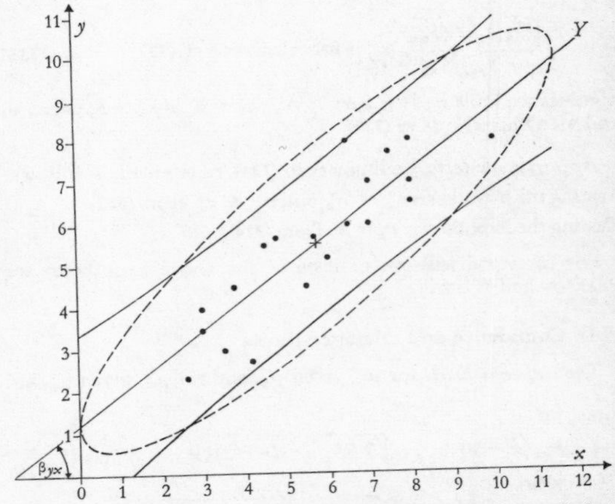

Fig. 41 Regression line of y on x, example 49. Tolerance limits calculated from the formula for a regression of the first kind (hyperbolas) and second kind (ellipse).

20. The binomial distribution

(Cf. also section 5, page 147)

20 A. General

E and non-E are two *complementary* events [cf. **(334)** and **(335)**] with the probabilities $\boldsymbol{p}$ and $\boldsymbol{q} = 1 - \boldsymbol{p}$ [cf. **(339)**]. The probability that in N *independent* trials [cf. **(328)**, **(357)**, and example 10 under **(362)**] the event E will occur exactly $x = 0, 1, 2, \ldots, N$ times is

$$\left.\begin{array}{l} f(x) = \dot{\boldsymbol{P}}_x = \binom{N}{x} \boldsymbol{p}^x \boldsymbol{q}^{N-x} \\ \dot{\boldsymbol{P}}_0 = \binom{N}{0} \boldsymbol{p}^0 \boldsymbol{q}^N = \boldsymbol{q}^N \\ \dot{\boldsymbol{P}}_1 = \binom{N}{1} \boldsymbol{p}^1 \boldsymbol{q}^{N-1}; \ldots \\ \dot{\boldsymbol{P}}_N = \binom{N}{N} \boldsymbol{p}^N \boldsymbol{q}^0 = \boldsymbol{p}^N \end{array}\right\} \quad \textbf{(744)}$$

where $0 \leq \boldsymbol{p} \leq 1$ and $\boldsymbol{q} = 1 - \boldsymbol{p}$.

The individual probabilities $\dot{\boldsymbol{P}}_x$ of **(744)** correspond to the terms of the binomial series developed from $(q + p)^N$ [cf. **(113)**]. On the binomial coefficient $\binom{N}{x}$ cf. **(100)**–**(106)**, page 136.

From (**744**) follow the recursion formulas

$$\left.\begin{aligned} \dot{\boldsymbol{P}}_{x+1} &= \dot{\boldsymbol{P}}_x \times \frac{\boldsymbol{p}}{\boldsymbol{q}} \times \frac{N-x}{x+1} \qquad \text{(a)} \\ \dot{\boldsymbol{P}}_{x-1} &= \dot{\boldsymbol{P}}_x \times \frac{\boldsymbol{q}}{\boldsymbol{p}} \times \frac{x}{N-x+1} \qquad \text{(b)} \end{aligned}\right\} \quad \textbf{(745)}$$

Example 50. Calculate all the individual probabilities $\dot{\boldsymbol{P}}_x$ for $\boldsymbol{p} = 0.3$ and $N = 7$.

Calculations are made from (**745**a) starting from $x = 0$. $\boldsymbol{p}/\boldsymbol{q} = 3/7$.

$$\dot{\boldsymbol{P}}_0 = \left(\frac{7}{10}\right)^7 = 0.0823543$$

$$\dot{\boldsymbol{P}}_1 = \dot{\boldsymbol{P}}_0 \times \frac{3}{7} \times \frac{7}{1} = \dot{\boldsymbol{P}}_0 \times \frac{21}{7} = 0.2470629$$

$$\dot{\boldsymbol{P}}_2 = \dot{\boldsymbol{P}}_1 \times \frac{3}{7} \times \frac{6}{2} = \dot{\boldsymbol{P}}_1 \times \frac{18}{14} = 0.3176523$$

$$\dot{\boldsymbol{P}}_3 = \dot{\boldsymbol{P}}_2 \times \frac{3}{7} \times \frac{5}{3} = \dot{\boldsymbol{P}}_2 \times \frac{15}{21} = 0.2268945$$

A study of the series 21/7, 18/14, 15/21 at once reveals the regular manner in which the numerators and denominators of the recursion factors decrease and increase respectively. The further factors for calculating $\dot{\boldsymbol{P}}_4, \dot{\boldsymbol{P}}_5, \ldots$ can therefore be assumed to be 12/28, 9/35, 6/42 and 3/49, giving

$\dot{\boldsymbol{P}}_4 = 0.0972405$
$\dot{\boldsymbol{P}}_5 = 0.0250047$
$\dot{\boldsymbol{P}}_6 = 0.0035721$
$\dot{\boldsymbol{P}}_7 = 0.0002187$

Check: $\sum_1^N \dot{\boldsymbol{P}}_x = 1$

The individual probabilities for $N = 1, 2, \ldots, 99, 100$ and $\boldsymbol{p} = 0.01, 0.02, \ldots, 0.49, 0.50$ can be obtained in a different manner using the tables on pages 70–77 (logarithms of binomial coefficients) and 78–84 (logarithms of powers of $\boldsymbol{p}$ and $\boldsymbol{q}$).

Example 51. Calculate $\dot{\boldsymbol{P}}_1$ for $\boldsymbol{p} = 0.3$ and $N = 7$.

$\log \binom{7}{1} = 0.84510$ (page 70)

$\log \boldsymbol{p}^1 = 0.47712 - 1$ (page 82)

$\log \boldsymbol{q}^6 = 0.07059 - 1$ (page 82)

$\log \dot{\boldsymbol{P}}_1 = 1.39281 - 2 = 0.3928 - 1$

$\dot{\boldsymbol{P}}_1 = 0.2471$ (page 11)

For binomial coefficients with $N > 100$ see under Binomial Coefficients, page 136. For calculating powers of $\boldsymbol{p}$ and $\boldsymbol{q}$, logarithms with 7 or more places should be used*.

The binomial distribution is a *discrete* distribution. It is *symmetrical* when $\boldsymbol{p} = 0.5$, *asymmetrical* when $\boldsymbol{p} \neq 0.5$.

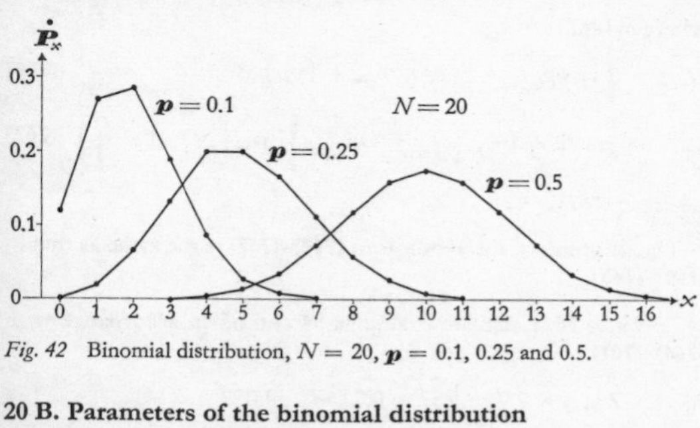

Fig. 42 Binomial distribution, $N = 20$, $\boldsymbol{p} = 0.1$, 0.25 and 0.5.

20 B. Parameters of the binomial distribution

As shown by (**744**), the binomial distribution is fully characterized by the probability $\boldsymbol{p}$ and the number of trials N, so that it can be represented by the expression "binomial distribution ($\boldsymbol{p}$; N)". Its mean and variance are respectively

$$\mu_x = N\boldsymbol{p} = \text{expectation of } \textbf{(749)} \qquad \textbf{(746)}$$

$$\sigma_x^2 = N\boldsymbol{p}\boldsymbol{q} = \boldsymbol{q}\mu_x = \text{expectation of } \textbf{(750)} \times \frac{N}{N-1} \qquad \textbf{(747)}$$

For any given sample size N (N trials) the variance of the binomial distribution is greatest when $\boldsymbol{p} = 0.5$, least when $\boldsymbol{p} = 0$ or $\boldsymbol{q} = 0$.

The best estimate of $\boldsymbol{p}$ from a sample of size N in which the event E occurs x times is

$$p = x/N \qquad \textbf{(748)}$$

The following are derived from (**746**)–(**748**):

Estimate of μ_x

$$\bar{x} = Np = x \qquad \textbf{(749)}$$

Estimate of σ_x^2

$$s_x^2 = Npq = \frac{x(N-x)}{N} \qquad \textbf{(750)}$$

The mean and variance of the *relative* frequency x/N are

$$\mu_{x/N} = \boldsymbol{p} = \text{expectation of } \textbf{(748)} \qquad \textbf{(751)}$$

$$\sigma_{x/N}^2 = \frac{\boldsymbol{p}\boldsymbol{q}}{N} = \text{expectation of } \textbf{(753)} \times \frac{N}{N-1} \qquad \textbf{(752)}$$

The corresponding estimates are

for the mean = (**748**)

$$\text{for the variance: } s_p^2 = \frac{pq}{N} = \frac{x(N-x)}{N^3} = \frac{1}{N^2} s_x^2 \qquad \textbf{(753)}$$

Example 52. In 64 trials the event x occurs 6 times. Estimate $\boldsymbol{p}$, σ_x^2 and σ_p^2.

$p = 6/64 = 0.09375$ from (**748**)
$s_x^2 = 0.09375 \times 58 = 5.4375$ from (**750**)
$s_p^2 = 5.4375/64^2 = 0.001327515$ from (**753**)

20 C. Cumulative probabilities of the binomial distribution

The calculation of cumulative probabilities in discrete distributions has been dealt with fully in section 5 (page 148). Here some practical applications are indicated.

Let $\boldsymbol{p}$ be the probability of the event E, $\boldsymbol{q}$ that of the event non-E. $\dot{\boldsymbol{P}}_x$ is defined in (**744**).

The probability that the event E

- will occur exactly $x = k$ times is given by (**370**) (a)
- will *not* occur exactly $x = k$ times is given by (**371**) (b)
- will occur *at the most* or *less* than $x = k$ times is given by (**372**) (c)
- will occur *at least* or *more* than $x = k$ times is given by (**373**) (d)
- will occur at least $x = k$ times *but at the most* $x = s$ times ($k < s$) is given by (**374**) (e)
- will occur less than $x = k$ times *or more* than $x = s$ times ($k < s$) is given by (**375**) (f)

(**754**)

Examples of the calculation of probabilities of this kind are given in section 5, page 149. The following is an additional example.

Example 53. Let $\boldsymbol{p}$ be the probability of the occurrence of an event E in a population. What size N must a sample have if the probability that the event E occurs *at least once* is $\mathfrak{p}^*$?

From (**754**d) and (**373**) it follows that

$$\text{Prob}(x \geq 1) = \sum_1^N \dot{\boldsymbol{P}}_x \qquad (\text{from } \textbf{373}\text{b})$$
$$= 1 - \dot{\boldsymbol{P}}_0 \qquad (\text{from } \textbf{373}\text{a})$$

In accordance with (**744**), $\dot{\boldsymbol{P}}_0 = \boldsymbol{q}^N$, whence

$$\mathfrak{p}^* = 1 - \boldsymbol{q}^N$$

$$\text{that is, } N = \frac{\log(1-\mathfrak{p}^*)}{\log \boldsymbol{q}} = \frac{\log(1-\mathfrak{p}^*)}{\log(1-\boldsymbol{p})} \qquad \textbf{(755)}$$

Application. Let the probability of throwing a six with a die be 1/6. How many throws must be made in order to throw a six at least once with a probability $\mathfrak{p}^* \geq 0.99$?

* Tables of $f(x)$ and the cumulative distribution $\sum_x^N f(x)$ for $N = 2, 3, \ldots, 49$ and $\boldsymbol{p} = 0.01, 0.02, \ldots, 0.5$ are to be found in the literature[3,4,63].

From **(755)**

$$N = \frac{\log(1-0.99)}{\log(1-1/6)} = \frac{\log 0.01}{\log 5/6} \sim \frac{-2}{-0.0792} \sim 25.2\dot{5}$$

It follows that 26 throws must be made in order that, with a probability $\mathfrak{p}^* \geqq 0.99$, at least one six will be thrown (with 25 throws $\mathfrak{p}^*$ would be a little under 0.99).

20 D. The binomial and the normal distribution

As shown by Figure 42, with $\boldsymbol{p} = \frac{1}{2}$, the binomial distribution closely resembles the normal distribution even with *fairly small* samples. This is not the case with more extreme values of $\boldsymbol{p}$ (cf. $\boldsymbol{p} = 0.1$). As shown by Figure 43, however, with increasing sample size the binomial distribution approximates to the normal distribution even with more extreme values of $\boldsymbol{p}$. In other words:

With increasing sample size N the binomial distribution $(\boldsymbol{p}, N)$ tends toward the normal distribution $\left(N\boldsymbol{p}, \sqrt{N\boldsymbol{pq}}\right)$. The closer $\boldsymbol{p}$ lies to 0.5, the greater is this tendency:

$$\binom{N}{x} \boldsymbol{p}^x \boldsymbol{q}^{N-x} \to \frac{1}{\sqrt{2\pi N\boldsymbol{pq}}} e^{-\frac{(x-N\boldsymbol{p})^2}{2N\boldsymbol{pq}}} \qquad \textbf{(756)}$$

as $N \to \infty$

With large sample sizes N, it follows from **(756)** in accordance with the definitions

$$\text{Prob}\,(x \leqq x_{\mathfrak{p}}) = \sum_0^{x_{\mathfrak{p}}} \mathring{\boldsymbol{P}}_x = \mathfrak{p}$$

$\text{Prob}\,(c \leqq c_{\mathfrak{p}}) = \int_{-\infty}^{c_{\mathfrak{p}}}$ of the standardized normal distribution

that

$$\text{Prob}\,(x \leqq x_{\mathfrak{p}}) \sim \text{Prob}\,(c \leqq c_{\mathfrak{p}}) \qquad \textbf{(757)}$$

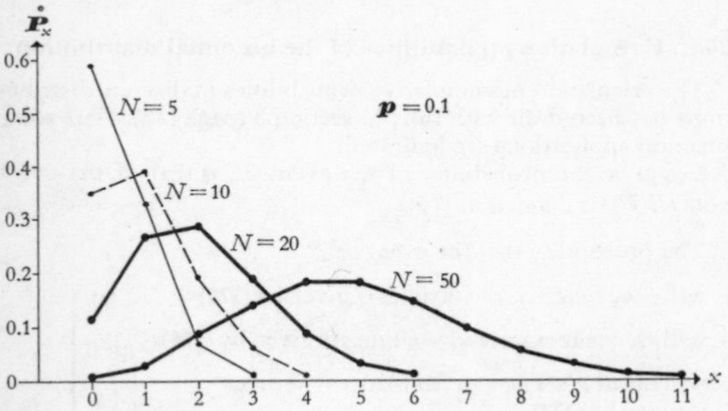

Fig. 43 Binomial distribution, $\boldsymbol{p} = 0.1$, $N = 5, 10, 20, 50$.

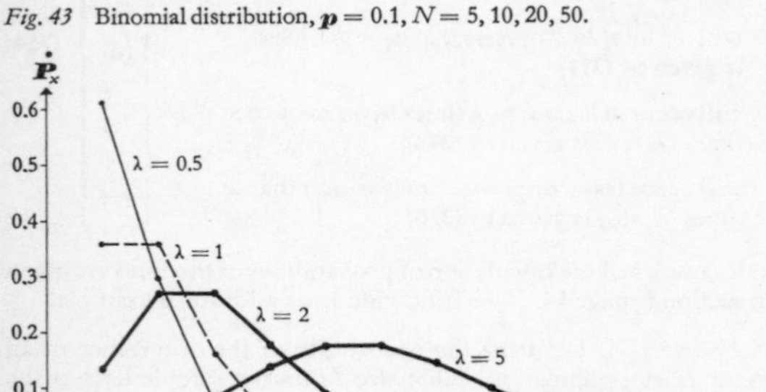

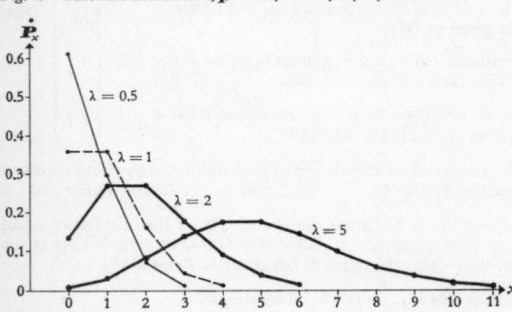

Fig. 44 Poisson distribution, $\lambda = 0.5, 1, 2, 5$.

where

$$c_{\mathfrak{p}} = \frac{x_{\mathfrak{p}} - N\boldsymbol{p}}{\sqrt{N\boldsymbol{pq}}}; \text{ (for } c \text{ see page 28, right-hand table)} \qquad \textbf{(758)}$$

or

$$x_{\mathfrak{p}} = N\boldsymbol{p} + c_{\mathfrak{p}}\sqrt{N\boldsymbol{pq}} \text{ (for } c \text{ see page 28, left-hand table)} \qquad \textbf{(759)}$$

With smaller samples, the transformations **(757)** and **(758)** can be improved by using the so-called correction for continuity. In this case, $x + \frac{1}{2}$ is used in place of x, whence

$$c_{\mathfrak{p}} = \frac{x_{\mathfrak{p}} + \frac{1}{2} - N\boldsymbol{p}}{\sqrt{N\boldsymbol{pq}}}; \text{ (for } c \text{ see page 28, right-hand table)} \qquad \textbf{(760)}$$

$$x_{\mathfrak{p}} = N\boldsymbol{p} - \tfrac{1}{2} + c_{\mathfrak{p}}\sqrt{N\boldsymbol{pq}}; \text{ (for } c \text{ see page 28, left-hand table)} \qquad \textbf{(761)}$$

From the definitions

$$\text{Prob}\,(x \geqq x_{\mathfrak{p}*}) = 1 - \text{Prob}\,(x \leqq x_{\mathfrak{p}*} - 1) = \mathfrak{p}^*$$

$$\text{Prob}\,(c \leqq c_{1-\mathfrak{p}*}) = \int_{-\infty}^{c_{1-\mathfrak{p}*}} = 1 - \mathfrak{p}^*$$

it follows from **(760)** and **(761)** that

$$c_{1-\mathfrak{p}*} = \frac{x_{\mathfrak{p}*} - \frac{1}{2} - N\boldsymbol{p}}{\sqrt{N\boldsymbol{pq}}}; \text{ (for } c \text{ see page 28, right-hand table)} \qquad \textbf{(762)}$$

$$x_{\mathfrak{p}*} = N\boldsymbol{p} + \tfrac{1}{2} + c_{1-\mathfrak{p}*}\sqrt{N\boldsymbol{pq}}; \text{ (for } c \text{ see page 28, left-hand table)} \qquad \textbf{(763)}$$

Example 54. Given the binomial distribution ($\boldsymbol{p} = 0.1$, $N = 40$), calculate the probabilities $\text{Prob}\,(x \leqq 3) = \mathfrak{p}$ and $\text{Prob}\,(x \geqq 6) = \mathfrak{p}^*$ using the approximate formulas **(760)**–**(763)**.

$c_{\mathfrak{p}} = \dfrac{3.5 - 4}{\sqrt{3.6}} = -0.264$ [from **(760)**]

$\mathfrak{p} = 0.396$ (by linear interpolation in right-hand table, page 28)

$c_{1-\mathfrak{p}*} = \dfrac{5.5 - 4}{\sqrt{3.6}} = 0.791$ [from **(761)**]

$1 - \mathfrak{p}^* = 0.786$ (as before)

$\mathfrak{p}^* = 0.214$

The exact values of $\mathfrak{p}$ and $\mathfrak{p}^*$, rounded off to 3 decimal places, are 0.423 and 0.206.

Example 55. For the binomial distribution of example 54, calculate $x_{\mathfrak{p}}$ for $\mathfrak{p} = 0.1$ and $x_{\mathfrak{p}*}$ for $\mathfrak{p}^* = 0.05$ using the approximate formulas **(760)**–**(763)**.

$$\left.\begin{aligned} c_{\mathfrak{p}} &= -1.2816 \\ c_{1-\mathfrak{p}*} &= 1.6449 \end{aligned}\right\} \text{ page 28, left-hand table}$$

whence

$x_{\mathfrak{p}} = 3.5 - 1.2816\sqrt{3.6} = 1.07$ [from **(761)**]

$x_{\mathfrak{p}*} = 4.5 + 1.6449\sqrt{3.6} = 7.62$ [from **(763)**]

Since x must be a whole number, this gives the results $x_{\mathfrak{p}} = 1$ and $x_{\mathfrak{p}*} = 8$, which agree with the nearest exact values.

A further and, if $\boldsymbol{p} < \boldsymbol{q}$, rather better approximation[36] is

$$c_{\mathfrak{p}} = 2\left(\sqrt{(x_{\mathfrak{p}}+1)\,\boldsymbol{q}} - \sqrt{(N - x_{\mathfrak{p}})\,\boldsymbol{p}}\right) \qquad \textbf{(764)}$$

$$x_{\mathfrak{p}} = \boldsymbol{p}\left(N + 1 - \frac{c^2}{4}\right) + \frac{c^2}{4}\boldsymbol{q} - 1 + c\sqrt{\boldsymbol{pq}\left(N + 1 - \frac{c^2}{4}\right)} \qquad \textbf{(765)}$$

where in **(765)** $c = c_{\mathfrak{p}}$

$$c_{1-\mathfrak{p}*} = 2\left(\sqrt{x_{\mathfrak{p}*}\,\boldsymbol{q}} - \sqrt{(N - x_{\mathfrak{p}*} + 1)\,\boldsymbol{p}}\right) \qquad \textbf{(766)}$$

$$x_{\mathfrak{p}*} = \boldsymbol{p}\left(N + 1 - \frac{c^2}{4}\right) + \frac{c^2}{4}\boldsymbol{q} + c\sqrt{\boldsymbol{pq}\left(N + 1 - \frac{c^2}{4}\right)} \qquad \textbf{(767)}$$

where in **(767)** $c = c_{1-\mathfrak{p}*}$

The meaning of the symbols in **(764)**–**(767)** is the same as that in **(760)**–**(763)**.

Example 56. Calculate examples 54 and 55 in accordance with **(764)**–**(767)**.

$c_{\mathfrak{p}} = 2\left(\sqrt{4 \times 0.9} - \sqrt{37 \times 0.1}\right) = -0.052$

$\mathfrak{p} = 0.479$

$c_{1-\mathfrak{p}*} = 2\left(\sqrt{6 \times 0.9} - \sqrt{35 \times 0.1}\right) = 0.906$

$\mathfrak{p}^* = -1 - 0.817 = 0.183$

$x_{\mathfrak{p}} = 0.979$

$x_{\mathfrak{p}*} = 8.00$

20 E. The binomial and the POISSON distribution

As shown by Figure 43, with small values of $\boldsymbol{p}$ the binomial distribution closely resembles the POISSON distribution. The following rule of thumb should be noted:

$$\left.\begin{aligned}&\binom{N}{x}\boldsymbol{p}^x\boldsymbol{q}^{N-x}\approx\frac{e^{-\lambda}\lambda^x}{x!},\text{ where }\lambda=N\boldsymbol{p}\\&\text{if}\\&\frac{N\boldsymbol{pq}}{N\boldsymbol{p}}\approx 1\end{aligned}\right\}\quad\textbf{(768)}$$

20 F. Confidence limits and significance limits

(a) *Confidence limits for* $\boldsymbol{p}$ (tables on pages 85–103)
(or significance limits for $p = x/N$, cf. example 17, page 155)

In N trials, the event E occurs $x = k$ times. According to CLOPPER and PEARSON[37], the confidence limits which satisfy the equation

$\text{Prob}\,(p_l < \boldsymbol{p} < p_r \mid x = k, N) = 1 - 2\alpha$

are the solutions of

$$\left.\begin{aligned}&\sum_{x=k}^{N}\binom{N}{x}p_l^x(1-p_l)^{N-x}=\alpha\text{ for }p_l &&\text{(a)}\\&\text{and}\\&\sum_{x=0}^{k}\binom{N}{x}p_r^x(1-p_r)^{N-x}=\alpha\text{ for }p_r &&\text{(b)}\end{aligned}\right\}\quad\textbf{(769)}$$

For $x = 0$ and $x = N$, only *one-sided* $1 - \alpha$ limits are possible:

$$\left.\begin{aligned}&\text{for }x=0\\&0\text{ and }p_r=1-\text{antilog}\left(\frac{\log\alpha}{N}\right) &&\text{(a)}\\&\text{for }x=N\\&p_l=\text{antilog}\left(\frac{\log\alpha}{N}\right)\text{ and }N &&\text{(b)}\end{aligned}\right\}\quad\textbf{(770)}$$

For $x = 0$ and $x = N$, the confidence limits for $\boldsymbol{p}$ given in the tables on pages 85–103 thus correspond not to $1 - 2\alpha$ but to $1 - \alpha$ limits.

For $0 < x < N$ an exact solution of **(769)** is only possible by means of an iterative process. The tables on pages 85–98 were calculated in this way by means of an electronic computer.

Approximate solutions are

$$p_l, p_r = \frac{x \mp \tfrac{1}{2} + \dfrac{c^2}{2} \mp |c|\sqrt{(x \mp \tfrac{1}{2})\left(1 - \dfrac{x \mp \tfrac{1}{2}}{N}\right) + \dfrac{c^2}{4}}}{N + c^2}\quad\textbf{(771)}$$

where $c = c_\alpha$, page 28, left-hand table,

or, if $x \leq N/2$

$$\left.\begin{aligned}&p_l, p_r = (A-B) \mp \sqrt{B\,[2-(A-B)-A]}\\&\text{where}\\&Ap_l, Ap_r = \frac{x+\tfrac{1}{2}\mp\tfrac{1}{2}+\dfrac{c^2}{4}}{N+1}\\&Bp_l, Bp_r = \frac{c^2}{2}\left(\frac{x+\tfrac{1}{2}\mp\tfrac{1}{2}}{(N+1)^2}\right)\end{aligned}\right\}\quad\textbf{(772)}$$

$c = c_\alpha$, page 28, left-hand table.

With larger samples, $\mp \tfrac{1}{2}$ in **(771)** and **(772)** can be ignored. **(771)** is the solution of **(760)** and **(762)** for p, **(772)** that of **(764)** and **(766)**. The tables on pages 99–103 were calculated from **(772)** (for $x > 4$). In practice, **(771)** and **(772)** will seldom be required since the range of the tables is sufficient for most cases.

Figure 45 shows the confidence intervals for $\boldsymbol{p}$ for all possible values of x for sample sizes $N = 30$ and $N = 10$.

Interpolation and extrapolation for limits not contained in the tables on pages 99–103 are carried out as follows:
(The examples are all for 95% limits.)

Four different situations will be considered, of which 1) can be combined with 2), 3) or 4). In the latter case, calculation should begin with 1) and be continued with 2) or 3) or 4) as the case may be.

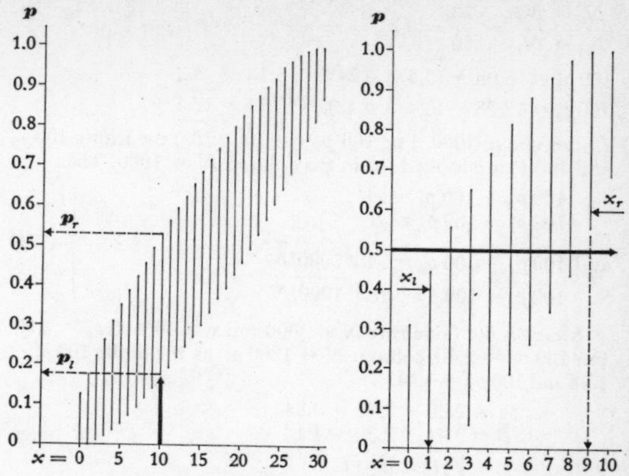

Fig. 45 Binomial distribution. Confidence limits for $\boldsymbol{p}$; $N = 30$ and $N = 10$.

1) x or $100\,p_x$ $(= 100\,x/N)$ lies *above* the tabulated values in an N column.

$N - x = x'$, or $100 - 100\,p_x = 100p'_x$, is first calculated and the corresponding limits $100\,p'_l$ and $100\,p'_r$ looked for in the table. The required limits are:
lower $p_l = 100 - 100\,p'_r$
upper $p_r = 100 - 100\,p'_l$ **(773)**

Example 57. $N = 150$, $x = 125$. $x' = 150 - 125 = 25$, or $100\,p'_x = 100 - 83.33 = 16.67$. For this the table gives $100\,p'_l = 11.10$ and $100\,p'_r = 23.64$, whence from **(773)** the required limits are $76.36 - 88.90$.

2) x or $100\,p_x$ $(= 100\,x/N)$ lies between two values in an N column. $100\,p_x$ lies between $100\,p'_x$ and $100\,p''_x$ $(p'_x < p''_x)$.

The limits $100\,p'_l$ and $100\,p'_r$ for $100\,p'_x$ and the limits $100\,p''_l$ and $100\,p''_r$ for $100\,p''_x$ are looked for in the table:

$$\left.\begin{aligned}&\begin{array}{ccc}100\,p''_x & 100\,p''_l & 100\,p''_r\\ 100\,p'_x & 100\,p'_l & 100\,p'_r\\ \hline (100\,p''_x - 100\,p'_x) & (100\,p''_l - 100\,p'_l) & (100\,p''_r - 100\,p'_r)\\ & = B_l & = B_r\end{array}\\&\text{If the quotient }\frac{100\,p_x - 100\,p'_x}{100\,p''_x - 100\,p'_x} = A\\&\text{then the required limits are}\\&100\,p_l = 100\,p'_l + (A \times B_l)\\&100\,p_r = 100\,p'_r + (A \times B_r)\end{aligned}\right\}\quad\textbf{(774)}$$

Example 58. $N = 500$, $x = 427$, $100\,p_x = 85.40$

$100\,p''_x = 86.00$	$100\,p''_l = 82.64$	$100\,p''_r = 88.92$
$100\,p'_x = 84.00$	$100\,p'_l = 80.48$	$100\,p'_r = 87.10$
Difference 2.00	2.16	1.82

$100\,p_x - 100\,p'_x = 85.40 - 84.00 = 1.40$
$A = 1.40 / 2.00 \quad = 0.70$
$100\,p_l = 80.48 + (0.7 \times 2.16) = 81.99 = \underline{82.0}$
$100\,p_r = 87.10 + (0.7 \times 1.92) = 88.44 = \underline{88.4}$

3) N lies between N_1 and N_2 $(N_1 < N_2)$. For $100\,p_x$ $(= 100\,x/N)$ interpolation is made in column N_1 to give the limits $100\,p_l^*$ and $100\,p_r^*$, in column N_2 to give the limits $100\,p_l^{**}$ and $100\,p_r^{**}$, in accordance with **(774)**. The required limits are then

$$\left.\begin{aligned}&100\,p_l = 100\,p_l^* + \frac{N - N_1}{N_2 - N_1}(100\,p_l^{**} - 100\,p_l^*)\\&100\,p_r = 100\,p_r^* + \frac{N - N_1}{N_2 - N_1}(100\,p_r^{**} - 100\,p_r^*)\end{aligned}\right\}\quad\textbf{(775)}$$

Example 59. $N = 270$, $x = 22$, $100\,p_x = 8.15$. $N = 270$ lies between $N_1 = 250$ and $N_2 = 300$. The interpolated limits for $100\,p_x = 8.15$ in accordance with **(774)** are in column

$N_2 = 300$	$100\,p_l^{**} = 5.32$	$100\,p_r^{**} = 11.86$
$N_1 = 250$	$100\,p_l^* = 5.08$	$100\,p_r^* = 12.28$
Difference 50	0.24	− 0.42

$$\frac{N - N_1}{N_2 - N_1} = \frac{20}{50} = 0.4$$

$$100\,p_l = 5.08 + (0.4 \times 0.24) = 5.18 = \underline{5.2}$$
$$100\,p_r = 12.28 - (0.4 \times 0.42) = 12.11 = \underline{12.1}$$

4) N lies above 1000. For $100\,p_x$ ($= 100\,x/N$) the limits $100\,p'_l$ and $100\,p'_r$ are looked for in the column $N = 1000$. Then

$$\left.\begin{aligned} &100\,p_x - 100\,p'_l = A \\ &100\,p'_r - 100\,p_x = B \\ \text{and } &100\,p_l = 100\,p_x - A\sqrt{1000/N} \\ &100\,p_r = 100\,p_x + B\sqrt{1000/N} \end{aligned}\right\} \quad \textbf{(776)}$$

Example 60. Given are $N = 3000$ and $x = 69$, $100\,p_x = 2.30$. For $100\,p_x = 2.30$, column $N = 1000$ gives the limits $100\,p'_l = 1.46$ and $100\,p'_r = 3.44$.

$$A = 2.30 - 1.46 = 0.84$$
$$B = 3.44 - 2.30 = 1.14$$
$$\sqrt{1000/3000} = \sqrt{1/3} \sim 0.577$$
$$100\,p_l = 2.3 - (0.84 \times 0.577) = 1.82 = \underline{1.8}$$
$$100\,p_r = 2.3 + (1.14 \times 0.577) = 2.96 = \underline{3.0}$$

(b) *Significance limits for* x (tables on pages 104–106) (and confidence limits for $N\boldsymbol{p}$)

It is assumed that the probability $\boldsymbol{p}$ is known (either on theoretical grounds or from large samples). In a sample which *possibly* originates from this population the event E occurs x times. The significance limits for x are in accordance with the conditions (**376**) and (**377**).

The table on page 104 gives limits of this nature for samples of size up to $N = 100$ and for $\boldsymbol{p} = 0.05; 0.1; \ldots; 0.45; 0.5$, that on pages 105 and 106 for samples of size up to $N = 1000$ and $\boldsymbol{p} = 0.5$. As shown in Figure 45, right, the significance limits for x can be obtained from the confidence limits for $\boldsymbol{p}$ without calculation.

Example 61. Required are the 95% confidence limits for x for a sample of size $N = 10$ and a given $\boldsymbol{p} = 0.5$.

As shown by Figure 45, right, the *lower* limit x_l is fixed by that confidence interval for $\boldsymbol{p}$ whose *upper* limit p_r lies *closest* to the given $\boldsymbol{p}$ *without exceeding it.* (a)

The *upper* limit x_r is fixed by that confidence interval for $\boldsymbol{p}$ whose *lower* limit p_l lies *closest* to the given $\boldsymbol{p}$ *without falling below it.* (b) **(777)**

In the table on page 85, $p_r = 44.50$ is in accordance with (**777**a) and $p_l = 55.50$ in accordance with (**777**b). The required limits for x are therefore $x_l = 1$ and $x_r = 9$.

According to WILKS[38], the above significance limits correspond to the *distribution-free confidence limits for quantiles* $Q(p)$ (cf. section 10F, page 160) when x_l is replaced by $x_l + 1$ and when p in the table is so chosen that it is of the same magnitude as p in $Q(p)$.

In this connection it should be noted [cf. (**383**)] that the postulated significance probability is attained when x *attains* or exceeds in an outward direction from $N\boldsymbol{p}$ the limits x_l or x_r.

Example 62. The hypothetical probability $\boldsymbol{p}$ is 0.05. In 48 trials the event E occurs 7 times. Does this sample originate from the hypothetical population ($2\,\alpha = 0.05$)? The table on page 104 gives as upper level $x = 7$, so that:

(one-tailed test) the sample originates from a population with $\boldsymbol{p} > 0.05$ ($\alpha = 0.025$).
(two-tailed test) the sample originates from a population with $\boldsymbol{p} \neq 0.05$ ($2\,\alpha = 0.05$).

On the basis of (**760**) and (**762**) or of (**764**) and (**766**) the following approximations are suitable for calculating the significance limits for x:

$$x_l, x_r = N\boldsymbol{p} \mp \left(\tfrac{1}{2} + |c_\alpha|\sqrt{N\boldsymbol{p}\boldsymbol{q}}\right) \quad \textbf{(778)}$$

(c_α, page 28, left-hand table)

or, if $\boldsymbol{p} < \boldsymbol{q}$

$$\left.\begin{aligned} x_l + 1, x_r &= \boldsymbol{p}\left(N + 1 - \frac{c^2}{4}\right) + \\ &+ \frac{c^2}{4}\,q \mp |c|\sqrt{\boldsymbol{p}\boldsymbol{q}\left(N + 1 - \frac{c^2}{4}\right)} \end{aligned}\right\} \quad \textbf{(779)}$$

($c = c_\alpha$, page 28, left-hand table)

(c) *Distribution-free tolerance limits for continuous distributions* (table on page 128)

(Cf. also sections 8C, page 154, and 10F, page 160.)

The values of N in this table have been calculated by an iterative process based on a formula of WILKS[38] so that

$$\sum_{x=N-2k+1}^{N} \binom{N}{x} \beta_p^x (1 - \beta_p)^{N-x} \leqq 1 - \beta_t \quad \textbf{(780)}$$

The rounded-off values are based on the approximations[39]

$$\left.\begin{aligned} N &\sim 1.03\,x + 4.74\,\chi^2 - 1 \quad \text{for } \beta_p = 0.90 \\ N &\sim 1.01\,x + 9.75\,\chi^2 - 1 \quad \text{for } \beta_p = 0.95 \\ N &\sim 1.00\,x + 49.75\,\chi^2 - 1 \quad \text{for } \beta_p = 0.99 \end{aligned}\right\} \quad \textbf{(781)}$$

where χ^2 is so chosen that $1\int_r$ of the table on pages 36–39 equals $1 - \beta_t$ for $\nu = 4\,x$.

The approximation to N obtained from (**781**) is very close to (**780**).

20 G. Binomial distribution: miscellaneous

(a) *Arc-sine transformation* (table on page 69)

(Cf. also Inverse trigonometric functions, page 139.)

According to FREEMAN and TUKEY[36], the best transformation $x \to X$ for stabilizing the variance of the binomial distribution when $N\boldsymbol{p} \geqq 1$ is in most cases

$$\left.\begin{aligned} &X = \arcsin\sqrt{\frac{x}{N+1}} + \arcsin\sqrt{\frac{x+1}{N+1}} \\ &\text{with a variance within } \pm\,6\% \text{ of} \\ &s_X^2 = \frac{1}{N + \frac{1}{2}}\begin{pmatrix}\text{angle in}\\ \text{radians}\end{pmatrix} \text{ or } \frac{821}{N + \frac{1}{2}}\begin{pmatrix}\text{angle in}\\ \text{degrees}\end{pmatrix} \end{aligned}\right\} \quad \textbf{(782)}$$

The mean $\bar{\boldsymbol{X}}$ of the values thus transformed is approximately $2 \arcsin\sqrt{\boldsymbol{p}}$.

This transformation can be used in variance-analysis and other operations.

(b) With a given $\boldsymbol{p} < \boldsymbol{q}$, how large must the sample size N be for the event E to occur at least x times with a probability $\mathfrak{p}^*$? The solution of this problem for $x = 1$ is given in (**755**).

The simplest approximate solution for $x > 1$, on the basis of (**766**), is (when $\boldsymbol{p} < \boldsymbol{q}$)

$$N \sim \frac{1}{\boldsymbol{p}}\left(\frac{c^2}{4} + x + c\sqrt{x\,\boldsymbol{q}}\right) - 1 \quad \textbf{(783)}$$

where $c = c_{\mathfrak{p}*}$

21. The Poisson distribution

21 A. General

E is a random event which over a long period of observation* can occur an infinite number of times but which in a relatively short time* (in general the *observation unit* t) occurs only rarely. The probability that in an observation unit t the event will occur $0, 1, 2, \ldots, x$ times is then

$$f(x) = \dot{\boldsymbol{P}}_x = \frac{e^{-\lambda}\lambda^x}{x!} = \underbrace{\frac{e^{-\lambda}\lambda^0}{0!}}_{=\,e^{-\lambda}}, \frac{e^{-\lambda}\lambda^1}{1!}, \frac{e^{-\lambda}\lambda^2}{2!} \ldots \quad \textbf{(784)}$$

e = base of natural logarithms, t = observation unit

The POISSON distribution is a discrete asymmetrical distribution in which, with increasing x, the individual probabilities decrease in a regular manner when $\lambda < 1$, and first increase but then decrease when $\lambda > 1$. Cf. Figure 44, page 184.

As shown by (**784**), the POISSON distribution is characterized completely by the parameter λ. For this reason it will be written here as POISSON distribution (λ).

Tables of $f(x)$ and the cumulative distribution $\sum_x^\infty \dot{\boldsymbol{P}}_x$ are given by MOLINA[2].

* Time has been chosen as an example. The same argument applies to surfaces and volumes.

The simplest calculation of several successive individual probabilities is from the recursion formula

$$\dot{P}_{x+1} = \dot{P}_x \times \frac{\lambda}{x+1} \qquad (785)$$

Example 63. For the POISSON distribution ($\lambda = 1$) calculate the individual probabilities for x from 0 to 5.

$\dot{P}_0 = 1/e = 0.367879$ $\quad \dot{P}_3 = \dot{P}_2 \times {}^1/_3 = 0.061313$

$\dot{P}_1 = \dot{P}_0 \times 1 = 0.367879$ $\quad \dot{P}_4 = \dot{P}_3 \times {}^1/_4 = 0.015328$

$\dot{P}_2 = \dot{P}_1 \times ½ = 0.183940$ $\quad \dot{P}_5 = \dot{P}_4 \times {}^1/_5 = 0.003066$

Calculation of the *cumulative probabilities* is carried out according to the procedure given in section 5, page 147, with N replaced by infinity. It should also be noted that in the POISSON distribution the probability Prob ($x \geq k$) can be calculated only from the probability Prob ($x \leq k - 1$), i.e. Prob ($x \geq k$) = 1 − Prob ($x \leq k - 1$).

Example 64. How large must λ be for the event E to occur at least once during the observation unit t with a probability $\mathfrak{p}^*$? (This is an unusual problem in the POISSON distribution but sometimes occurs when the latter is used as an approximation to other distributions.)

The solution is obtained by using equation (**129**) on page 137. Here numerical values for various probabilities $\mathfrak{p}^*$ can also be found. For $\mathfrak{p}^* = 0.999$, λ for example is 6.9.

21 B. The addition theorem for the POISSON distribution

If $x_{t_1}, x_{t_2}, \ldots, x_{t_k}$ are stochastically independent* random variables with POISSON distributions $(\lambda_{t_1}), (\lambda_{t_2}), \ldots, (\lambda_{t_k})$ respectively, then their sum $x = x_{t_1} + x_{t_2} + \cdots + x_{t_k}$ is likewise a POISSON distribution (λ) with $\lambda = \lambda_{t_1} + \lambda_{t_2} + \cdots + \lambda_{t_k}$. (**786**)

21 C. Parameters and their estimates

The mean of the POISSON distribution is

$\mu_{x_t} = \lambda_t$ = expectation of x_t (a)

and the variance (**787**)

$\sigma^2_{x_t} = \lambda_t$ = expectation of x_t (b)

where t = observation unit to which x and λ_t relate.

If from a POISSON distribution with observation unit t another POISSON distribution with observation unit kt is calculated, then the mean and variance of the latter are

$$\mu_{x_{kt}}, \sigma^2_{x_{kt}} = k\lambda_t; (k > 0) \qquad (788)$$

The equal magnitude of mean and variance in the POISSON distribution results in the following rule of thumb:

If in a *discrete* distribution the ratio of mean to variance is approximately unity (say between ${}^{10}/_9$ and ${}^9/_{10}$), then the distribution is likely to be approximated to by a POISSON distribution provided that the variable x can assume high (theoretically, infinitely high) values. (**789**)

Unbiased estimates of λ_t based on n *equal* observation units t are

$$\bar{x}_t = \frac{\sum x_t}{n} = \frac{\sum x_i f_i}{n} \qquad \text{(a)}$$

or (**790**)

$$s_t^2 = \frac{\sum x_t^2 - (\sum x_t)^2/n}{n-1} = \frac{\sum x_i^2 f_i - (\sum x_i f_i)^2/n}{n-1} = \frac{S_t}{n-1} \qquad \text{(b)}$$

$\bar{x}_t$ is the *better* (more efficient) estimate. Since it is also more quickly calculated it is the one always used. With higher values of n (say $n > 5$), however, the additional calculation of $(n-1)\,s^2$ [the numerator in (**790**b)] offers the advantage of being able to test whether the ratio $s^2/\bar{x}$ differs significantly from 1. The test quotient is

$$\frac{(n-1)\,s_t^2}{\bar{x}_t} = \frac{S_t}{\bar{x}_t} \qquad (791)$$

Significance limit χ^2 with $\nu = n - 1$, $2\alpha = 1\int_r$, pages 36–39.

If the test quotient (**791**) attains or exceeds the significance limit, then the sample probably does not originate from a POISSON distribution. This leads to the following rule of thumb:

* For example, the observation units $t_1, t_2, \ldots, t_k$ must not overlap.

When (**791**) is significant, the sample could originate from a binomial distribution when $s^2 < \bar{x}$, from a binomial distribution with negative index when $s^2 > \bar{x}$. Cf. also BLISS[40]. (**792**)

Example 65. In 60 minutes 12 events are observed. $\lambda_{60\,\text{min}} \sim 12/1 = 12$. In accordance with (**788**), the estimate of $\lambda_{1\,\text{min}}$ is then $12/60 \sim 1/5$.

Example 66. In 60 minutes 12 events are observed, in 30 minutes 8. In accordance with (**786**), $\lambda_{90\,\text{min}} \sim 12 + 8 = 20$, $\lambda_{1\,\text{min}} \sim 20/90$.

Example 67. In 100 observation periods of 1 minute each, the event E is observed x_i times in f_i observation periods, as follows:

x_i	f_i	$x_i f_i$	$x_i^2 f_i$		
0	5	0	0	$\bar{x}_t = 2.36$	from (**790**a)
1	30	30	30		
2	24	48	96	$S_t = 778 - 556.96$	
3	20	60	180	$= 221.04$	from (**790**b)
4	12	48	192		
5	4	20	100	$\chi^2 = 93.661$,	
6	5	30	180	$\nu = 99$	from (**791**)
7	0				
8	0				
	$n = 100$	$\sum x = 236$ $\sim \lambda_{100\,\text{min}}$	$\sum x^2 = 778$		

In this case χ^2 lies far inside the significance limit of 0.05 ($0.30 < \alpha < 0.35$), so that the distribution *could* be a POISSON distribution. A *more efficient* test is provided by calculation of the *fitted* POISSON distribution in accordance with (**784**) with $\lambda = 2.36$, multiplication of the value obtained by n and then testing with χ^2 in accordance with (**566**) with degrees of freedom $\nu = k - 1$ from (**569**a), where k = number of classes i.

21 D. Transformations

As shown by Figure 44 (page 184), with increasing λ the form of the POISSON distribution approaches closer and closer (and fairly rapidly) to that of the normal distribution.

$$\frac{e^{-\lambda}\lambda^x}{x!} \to \frac{1}{\sqrt{2\pi\lambda}}\, e^{-\frac{(x-\lambda)^2}{2\lambda}} \qquad (793)$$

as $\lambda \to \infty$.

The corresponding transformations are analogous to the transformations of the binomial distribution to the normal distribution using (**760**) to (**763**), with $N\mathfrak{p}$ replaced by λ.

The following approximations are better[36]

$$c_p = 2\left(\sqrt{x_p + 1} - \sqrt{\lambda}\right) \qquad (794)$$

$$x_p = \lambda + c_p\sqrt{\lambda} + \frac{c^2}{4} - 1 \qquad (795)$$

$$c_{1-p*} = 2\left(\sqrt{x_{p*}} - \sqrt{\lambda}\right) \qquad (796)$$

$$x_{p*} = \lambda + c_{1-p*}\sqrt{\lambda} + \frac{c^2}{4} \qquad (797)$$

$\lambda \geq 1$

Example 68. Calculate x_p and x_{p*} for $\mathfrak{p} = \mathfrak{p}^* = 0.025$ of the POISSON distribution ($\lambda = 99$).

$$x_p = 99 - 1.96\sqrt{99} + \frac{1.96^2}{4} - 1 = 79.46 \text{ from (795)}$$

$$x_{p*} = 99 + 1.96\sqrt{99} + \frac{1.96^2}{4} = 119.46 \text{ from (797)}$$

Since x can have only discrete values, these results are rounded off to give 79 and 119. The exact values are 79 and 120. In this connection it should be noted that in such cases it is better to be on the safe side and round off outwards:

In order more adequately to meet the requirements Prob ($x \leq x_p$) $\leq \mathfrak{p}$ and Prob ($x \geq x_{p*}$) $\leq \mathfrak{p}^*$, x_p should always be rounded off downwards, x_{p*} always upwards. This also applies to approximations to other discrete distributions. (**798**)

If rule (**798**) had been adhered to in example 68, the correct result would have been obtained. However, this is not necessarily always the case when (**798**) is adhered to.

The following transformation[36] is suitable for stabilizing the variance

$$\left.\begin{aligned} X &= \sqrt{x} + \sqrt{x+1} \\ \text{with variance } \sigma_X^2 &\approx 1 \\ \text{and mean } \bar{X} &\sim \sqrt{4\lambda + 1} \end{aligned}\right\} \quad (799)$$

The relationship between the POISSON and χ^2 distributions is given in (**561**) and (**562**), whence the following procedure for determining the *exact* values of x_p and x_{p*}:

(a) x_p is required. The value $\chi^2 \leq 2\lambda$ is looked for in the column $1\int_l = 1 - p$ of the χ^2 table on pages 36–39. From the degrees of freedom ν of this χ^2 it follows that

$$\left.\begin{aligned} x_p &= \frac{\nu}{2} - 1, \text{ when } \nu \text{ is even} \\ &= \frac{\nu}{2} - 1.5, \text{ when } \nu \text{ is odd} \end{aligned}\right\} \quad (800)$$

(b) x_{p*} is required. The value $\chi^2 \geq 2\lambda$ is looked for in the column $1\int_l = p^*$ of the χ^2 table on pages 36–39. From the degrees of freedom ν of this χ^2 it follows that

$$\left.\begin{aligned} x_{p*} &= \frac{\nu}{2}, \text{ when } \nu \text{ is even} \\ &= \frac{\nu}{2} + 0.5, \text{ when } \nu \text{ is odd} \end{aligned}\right\} \quad (801)$$

Example 69. Required are the $(1 - 2\alpha)$ limits for x when $\lambda = 32$ and $\alpha = 0.0005$. The left limit is obtained from (**800**) and is $\chi^2_{0.9995} \leq 64 = 63.582$ with $\nu = 31$. $x_l = 31/2 - 1.5 = 14$. The right limit is obtained from (**801**) and is $\chi^2_{0.0005} \geq 64 = 64.526$ with $\nu = 106$. $x_r = 106/2 = 53$.

21 E. Confidence limits and significance limits

(a) *Confidence limits* for λ (tables on pages 107 and 108)

In analogy with the binomial distribution, confidence limits for λ are solutions of the equations

$$\sum_x^{\infty} \frac{e^{-\lambda_l}\lambda_l^x}{x!} = \alpha \quad \text{and} \quad \sum_0^x \frac{e^{-\lambda_r}\lambda_r^x}{x!} = \alpha \qquad \text{(a) (b)} \quad (802)$$

for λ_l and λ_r.

For $x = 0$ there is only one $(1 - \alpha)$ confidence interval with the solution $\lambda_r = z$ [equation (**129**), page 137]. The left limit λ_l is zero.

For $x > 0$ only iterative solutions are possible. The tables on pages 107 and 108 were calculated in this way by electronic computer for values of λ up to 100. For values of $x > 100$ the formulas (**804**) were used (from FREEMAN and TUKEY's approximation[36]).

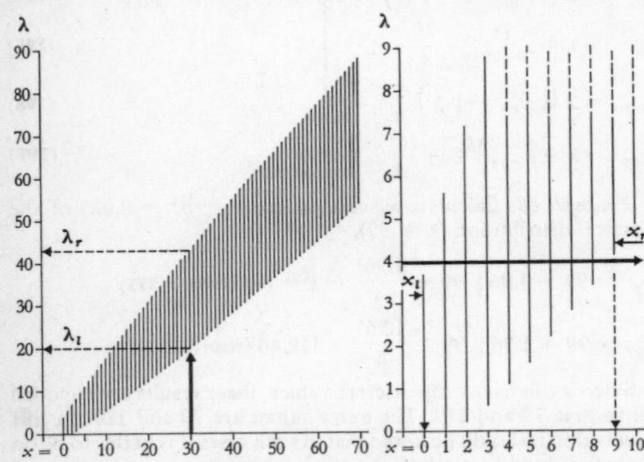

Fig. 46 POISSON distribution, confidence limits for λ.

For significance probabilities other than those in the tables on pages 107 and 108, *exact* limits for x up to 100 (or 99) can be calculated from the χ^2 table on pages 36–39, as follows:

Given x and α, then

$$\left.\begin{aligned} \tfrac{1}{2}\,[\chi^2_{\alpha,\, \nu=2x}] &= \lambda_l \quad \text{(a)} \\ \tfrac{1}{2}\,[\chi^2_{1-\alpha,\, \nu=2(x+1)}] &= \lambda_r \quad \text{(b)} \end{aligned}\right\} \quad (803)$$

where χ^2_α and $\chi^2_{1-\alpha}$ denote the α and $1 - \alpha$ quantiles, and α and $1 - \alpha$ are to be found under $1\int_l$.

Example 70. Required are the $(1 - 2\alpha)$ limits for λ when $x = 98$ and $\alpha = 0.05$. For λ_l the table is entered at $\nu = 2 \times 98 = 196$ and $1\int_l = 0.05$, giving $\chi^2_l = 164.10$. $\lambda_l = 164.10/2 = 82.05$. For λ_r the table is entered at $\nu = 2\,(98 + 1) = 198$ and $1\int_l = 0.95$, giving $\chi^2_r = 231.829$. $\lambda_r = 231.829/2 = 115.915$.

For higher values of x, very good approximations are obtained from (**794**) and (**796**):

$$\lambda_l, \lambda_r = \left(\frac{|c_\alpha|}{2} \mp \sqrt{x + \tfrac{1}{2} \mp \tfrac{1}{2}}\right)^2 \quad (804)$$

Example 71. Required are the $(1 - 2\alpha)$ confidence limits for λ when $x = 99$ and $\alpha = 0.025$.

$$\lambda_l = \left(\frac{1.96}{2} - \sqrt{99 + \tfrac{1}{2} - \tfrac{1}{2}}\right)^2 = 80.459$$

$$\lambda_r = \left(\frac{1.96}{2} + \sqrt{99 + \tfrac{1}{2} + \tfrac{1}{2}}\right)^2 = 120.56$$

The exact values are 80.458 and 120.53.

Example 72. In 12 minutes 24 events are observed. Calculate the 95% limits for $\lambda_{12\,\text{min}}$, $\lambda_{1\,\text{min}}$, $\lambda_{1\,\text{h}}$. For $x = 24$ in the table on page 107 the limits 15.378 and 35.711 are given. In accordance with (**788**) these give the following further limits

for $\lambda_{1\,\text{min}} = 15.378/12$ and $35.711/12 = 1.2815$ and 2.9759
for $\lambda_{1\,\text{h}} \;\; = 15.378 \times 5$ and $35.711 \times 5 = 76.890$ and 178.56

The estimate of the limits for λ_{kt} must always be made on the basis of the number of events x observed during the observation unit t, and *not* on the basis of this number multiplied by k. The following calculation in the case of example 72 would be ***wrong:***

$x_{1\,\text{min}} = 24/12 = 2$; limits $0.2422 - 7.2247$
or $x_{1\,\text{h}} \;\; = 24 \times 5 = 120$; limits $99.49 - 143.52$

(b) *Significance limits for x when λ is given* (table on page 128)

These limits meet the condition (**390**) with N replaced by ∞. They can be obtained without calculation from the confidence limits for λ, as shown in Figure 46, left. The procedure is exactly analogous to that for determining the corresponding limits for the binomial distribution. For $\alpha \neq 0.025$ or 0.005, the left limit is obtained from (**800**), the right limit from (**801**). Cf. example 69 on this page. For $n > 100$ (or 99), approximations are obtained from (**795**) and (**797**).

22. The hypergeometric distribution

22 A. General

Given are N balls, of which X are white and $N - X$ red. The probability of drawing exactly x_1 white balls in N_1 draws is then

$$\left.\begin{aligned} f(x_1 \mid X, N, N_1) &= \frac{\binom{X}{x_1}\binom{N-X}{N_1-x_1}}{\binom{N}{N_1}} \quad \text{(a)} \\ &= \frac{N_1!\,(N-N_1)!\,X!\,(N-X)!}{N!\,x_1!\,(N_1-x_1)!\,(X-x_1)!\,(N-X-N_1+x_1)!} \quad \text{(b)} \end{aligned}\right\} \quad (805)$$

$f(x_1 \mid X, N, N_1)$ is known as the hypergeometric distribution of x_1 (X, N, N_1 constant).

The corresponding fourfold table (cf. section 22D, page 190) is

White	x_1	$N_1 - x_1$	N_1	=	x_1	$N_1 - x_1$	N_1
Red	$X - x_1$	$N - X - N_1 + x_1$	$N - N_1$		x_2	$N_2 - x_2$	N_2
	X	$N - X$	N		X	$N - X$	N

(806)

For $N \leq 100$ the calculation of (**805**) is best made from (a) by means of the tables on pages 70–77 (cf. explanation on page 77), for $N > 100$ from (b) by means of the tables on pages 26 and 27. The calculation can also be made with the aid of the recursion formulas

$$f(x_1 + 1 \mid X) = [f(x_1 \mid X)] \times \frac{(N_1 - x_1)(X - x_1)}{(x_1 + 1)(N - X - N_1 + x_1 + 1)} \quad (807)$$

or

$$f(x_1 \mid X + 1) = [f(x_1 \mid X)] \times \frac{(N - X - N_1 + x_1)(X + 1)}{(N - X)(X + 1 - x_1)} \quad (808)$$

Hypergeometric distribution, $N = 20$, $N_1 = 5$, individual probabilities Prob $(x_1 = k_1 \mid X = K)$

x_1 \ $X=K$	0	1	2	3	4	5	6	7	8	9	10	11	12	13	14	15	16	17	18	19	20
0	1	0.75	0.5526	0.3991	0.2817	0.1937	0.1291	0.0830	0.0511	0.0298	0.0163	0.0081	0.0036	0.0014	0.0004	0.0001					
1		0.25	0.3947	0.4605	0.4696	0.4402	0.3874	0.3228	0.2554	0.1916	0.1354	0.0894	0.0542	0.0293	0.0135	0.0048	0.0010				
2			0.0526	0.1316	0.2167	0.2935	0.3522	0.3874	0.3973	0.3831	0.3483	0.2980	0.2384	0.1761	0.1174	0.0677	0.0310	0.0088			
3				0.0088	0.0310	0.0677	0.1174	0.1761	0.2384	0.2980	0.3483	0.3831	0.3973	0.3874	0.3522	0.2935	0.2167	0.1316	0.0526		
4					0.0010	0.0048	0.0135	0.0293	0.0542	0.0894	0.1354	0.1916	0.2554	0.3228	0.3874	0.4402	0.4696	0.4605	0.3947	0.25	
5						0.0001	0.0004	0.0014	0.0036	0.0081	0.0163	0.0298	0.0511	0.0830	0.1291	0.1937	0.2817	0.3991	0.5526	0.75	1

Hypergeometric distribution, $N = 20$, $N_1 = 5$, cumulative probabilities Prob $(x_1 \leqq k_1 \mid X = K)$

x_1 \ $X=K$	0	1	2	3	4	5	6	7	8	9	10	11	12	13	14	15	16	17	18	19	20
0	1	0.75	0.5526	0.3991	0.2817	0.1937	0.1291	0.0830	0.0511	0.0298	0.0163	0.0081	0.0036	0.0011	0.0004	0.0001					
1		1	0.9474	0.8596	0.7513	0.6339	0.5165	0.4058	0.3065	0.2214	0.1517	0.0975	0.0578	0.0307	0.0139	0.0049	0.0010				
2			1	0.9912	0.9680	0.9274	0.8687	0.7932	0.7038	0.6045	0.5000	0.3955	0.2962	0.2068	0.1313	0.0726	0.0320	0.0088			
3				1	0.9990	0.9951	0.9861	0.9693	0.9422	0.9025	0.8483	0.7786	0.6935	0.5942	0.4835	0.3661	0.2487	0.1404	0.0526		
4					1	0.9999	0.9996	0.9986	0.9964	0.9919	0.9837	0.9702	0.9489	0.9170	0.8709	0.8063	0.7183	0.6009	0.4474	0.25	
5						1	1	1	1	1	1	1	1	1	1	1	1	1	1	1	1

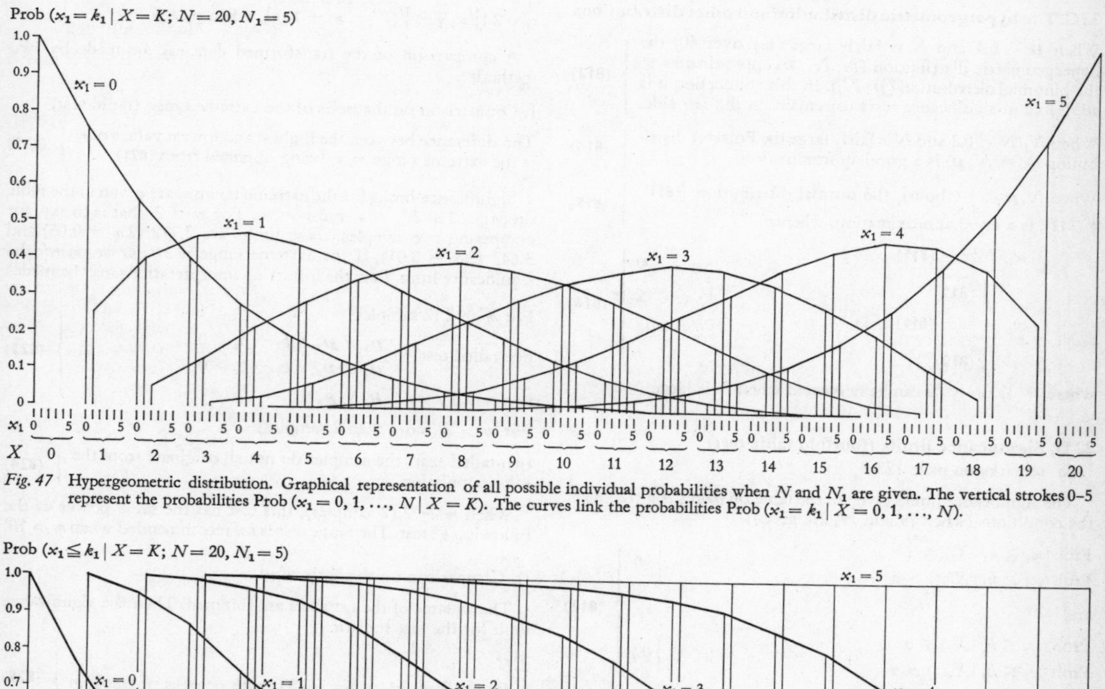

Fig. 47 Hypergeometric distribution. Graphical representation of all possible individual probabilities when N and N_1 are given. The vertical strokes 0–5 represent the probabilities Prob $(x_1 = 0, 1, \ldots, N \mid X = K)$. The curves link the probabilities Prob $(x_1 = k_1 \mid X = 0, 1, \ldots, N)$.

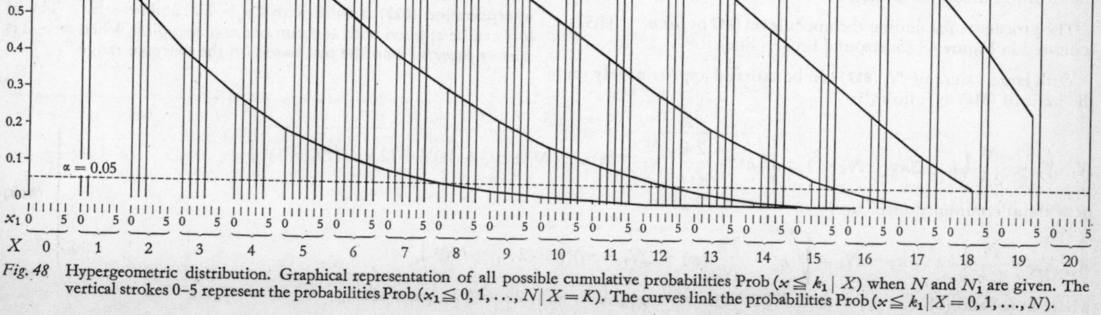

Fig. 48 Hypergeometric distribution. Graphical representation of all possible cumulative probabilities Prob $(x \leqq k_1 \mid X)$ when N and N_1 are given. The vertical strokes 0–5 represent the probabilities Prob $(x_1 \leqq 0, 1, \ldots, N \mid X = K)$. The curves link the probabilities Prob $(x \leqq k_1 \mid X = 0, 1, \ldots, N)$.

All the probabilities $f(x_1 \mid X, N = 20, N_1 = 5)$ and cumulative probabilities $F(x_1 \mid X)$ are given in the tables on page 189, where the same probabilities are shown graphically in Figures 47 and 48.

A check on calculations of this kind is provided by

$$\sum_{x_1=0}^{x_1=N_1} \text{Prob}\,(x_1 \mid X = K) = 1 \qquad \textbf{(809)}$$

Figure 47 clearly demonstrates the symmetry of the relationship

$$\left.\begin{array}{l} \text{Prob}\,(x_1 = k_1 \mid X = K) = \text{Prob}\,(x_1 = N_1 - k_1 \mid X = N - K) \quad \text{(a)} \\ \text{whence} \\ \text{Prob}\,(x_1 \leqq k_1 \mid X = K) = \text{Prob}\,(x_1 \geqq N_1 - k_1 \mid X = N - k) \quad \text{(b)} \end{array}\right\} \quad \textbf{(810)}$$

22 B. Parameters

The mean of x when X, N and N_1 are given is (putting $X/N = \boldsymbol{p}$)

$$\mu_x = N_1 \boldsymbol{p} \qquad \textbf{(811)}$$

and the variance is

$$\sigma_x^2 = N_1 \boldsymbol{p}\boldsymbol{q} \left(\frac{N - N_1}{N - 1}\right) \qquad X/N = \boldsymbol{p},\ \boldsymbol{q} = 1 - \boldsymbol{p} \qquad \textbf{(812)}$$

The variance of the hypergeometric distribution $(N, N_1, \boldsymbol{p})$ is thus *smaller* than that of the binomial distribution $(\boldsymbol{p}; N_1)$ by the factor $(N - N_1)/(N - 1)$.

22 C. The hypergeometric distribution and other distributions

When $\boldsymbol{p} < 0.1$ and N is fairly large (say over 60) the hypergeometric distribution $(N, N_1, \boldsymbol{p})$ approximates to the binomial distribution $(\boldsymbol{p}; N_1)$. In this connection it is advisable in significance tests to remain on the *safe* side. **(813)**

When $N_1/N < 0.1$ and N is fairly large the POISSON distribution $(\lambda = N_1 \boldsymbol{p})$ is a good approximation. **(814)**

When $N_1 \boldsymbol{p} \geqq 4$ (about), the normal distribution [(**811**), $\sqrt{(\textbf{812})}$] is a good approximation, whence **(815)**

$$\left.\begin{array}{ll} c_{\text{p}} = \dfrac{x_1 + \frac12 - (\textbf{811})}{\sqrt{(\textbf{812})}} & \text{(a)} \\[2ex] c_{1-\text{p}*} = \dfrac{x_1 - \frac12 - (\textbf{811})}{\sqrt{(\textbf{812})}} & \text{(b)} \end{array}\right\} \quad \textbf{(816)}$$

where $+\frac12$ or $-\frac12$ can be neglected when N is large.

22 D. Significance limits (fourfold table test)

Cf. remarks on page 123

The significance limits given in the table on pages 109–123 meet the conditions (when N and N_1 are given)

$$\left.\begin{array}{l} \left.\begin{array}{l} \text{Prob}\,(x_1 \geqq k_1 \mid X_l) \leqq \alpha \\ \text{Prob}\,(x_1 \geqq k_1 \mid X_{l+1}) > \alpha \end{array}\right\} \text{(a)} \\ \text{and} \\ \left.\begin{array}{l} \text{Prob}\,(x_1 \leqq k_1 \mid X_r) \leqq \alpha \\ \text{Prob}\,(x_1 \leqq k_1 \mid X_{r-1}) > \alpha \end{array}\right\} \text{(b)} \end{array}\right\} \quad \textbf{(817)}$$

This form of presentation is preferred since it is also convenient in situations in which X is unknown (these do *not* correspond to the situation described at the start of section 22 A, page 188).

The procedure for finding the upper level (**817** b) for $\alpha = 0.05$ is indicated in Figure 48 (horizontal broken line).

With large values of N, (**817**) can be satisfied approximately on the basis of (**816**) as follows[41]:

$$X_l, X_r = \frac{N}{2k}\left(k + 2x_1 - N_1 - 1 \mp \sqrt{k^2 - \frac{2k}{N_1}\left[(x_1 \mp \tfrac12)^2 + (N_1 - x_1 \pm \tfrac12)^2\right] + (2x_1 - N_1 \mp 1)^2}\right) \quad \text{(a)}$$

or without continuity correction

$$X_l, X_r = \frac{N}{2k}\left(k + 2x_1 - N_1 \mp \sqrt{k^2 - \frac{2k}{N_1}\left[x_1^2 + (N_1 - x_1)^2\right] + (2x_1 - N_1)^2}\right) \quad \text{(b)} \qquad \textbf{(818)}$$

where in (a) and (b) $k = N_1 + (1 - N_1/N)\, c_\alpha^2$. $c_\alpha^2 = \chi^2_{2\alpha}$ for $\nu = 1$; $2\alpha = 1\int_r$, page 36.

When $N > 60$, $N_1 \boldsymbol{p} \geqq 4$, $N_2 \boldsymbol{p} \geqq 4$ (about), the $(1 - 2\alpha)$ significance limits for x_1 with X given can be obtained approximately as follows:

$$X_l, X_r = N_1 \boldsymbol{p} \mp \left(\tfrac12 + |c_\alpha| \sqrt{N_1 \boldsymbol{p}\boldsymbol{q}\,(N - N_1)/(N - 1)}\right) \qquad \textbf{(819)}$$

For $\boldsymbol{p}$ and $\boldsymbol{q}$ see (**811**).

23. Testing frequencies

23 A. Samples from binomially distributed populations

(a) Given *2 samples* of sizes N_1 and N_2 in which the event E occurs x_1 and x_2 times respectively. If $N_1 + N_2 \leqq 60$ the procedure is as given on page 123. If $N_1 + N_2 > 60$ proceed as in (b) below. **(820)**

(b) Given *several* (*m*) *samples* of sizes $N_1, N_2, \ldots, N_i, \ldots, N_m$ in which the event E occurs $x_1, x_2, \ldots, x_i, \ldots, x_m$ times respectively. The following are calculated:

$$p_i = \frac{x_i}{N_i};\ q_i = 1 - p_i;\ \bar{p} = (\Sigma x_i)/(\Sigma N_i);\ \bar{q} = 1 - \bar{p}$$

The x_i values are now transformed as follows in accordance with (**764**) and (**766**):

$$\left.\begin{array}{l} c_i = 2\left(\sqrt{(x_i + 1)\,\bar{q}} - \sqrt{(N_i - x_i)\,\bar{p}}\right), \text{ when } p_i < \bar{p} \\ \text{or} \\ c_i = 2\left(\sqrt{x_i \bar{q}} - \sqrt{(N_i - x_i + 1)\,\bar{p}}\right), \text{ when } p_i > \bar{p} \end{array}\right\} \quad \textbf{(821)}$$

A comparison of the transformed data can be made by two methods:

I. Comparison on the basis of the extreme range (rapid test)

The difference between the highest and lowest values of c_i is the extreme range m, c_i being obtained from (**821**). **(822)**

Significance limits for the extreme range m are given in the table on page 51 at $N_1 = m$ and $\nu = \infty$. For $m = 2$, that is to say, for comparing two samples, these limits are 2.772 $(2\alpha = 0.05)$ and 3.643 $(2\alpha = 0.01)$. If the extreme range m *attains* or *exceeds* the significance limit, then the following interpretations may be made:

$$\left.\begin{array}{l} \text{For } m = 2 \text{ (2 samples)} \\ \text{one-tailed test: } \left\{\begin{array}{l} \boldsymbol{p}_1 < \boldsymbol{p}_2, \text{ if } p_1 - p_2 < 0 \\ \boldsymbol{p}_1 > \boldsymbol{p}_2, \text{ if } p_1 - p_2 > 0 \end{array}\right. \\ \text{two-tailed test: } \boldsymbol{p}_1 \neq \boldsymbol{p}_2 \end{array}\right\} \quad \textbf{(823)}$$

For $m > 2$ (more than 2 samples)

two-tailed test: the samples do not all originate from the same population. **(824)**

When $m = 2$ (2 samples), this test has the same power as the following χ^2 test. The range test is *not* recommended when $m > 10$.

II. Comparison on the basis of χ^2

The squares of the c_i values are summed. Then the significance limit for the test statistic

Σc_i^2

is found from χ^2, pages 36–39, with degrees of freedom $\nu = m - 1$ (cf. section 12 B, page 165). **(825)**

If the test statistic *attains* or *exceeds* the significance limit, then interpretation (**823**) is valid with $2\alpha = 1\int_r$ and $\alpha = \frac12\int_r$. The χ^2 test can be applied with any number m of samples. When $m > 2$ it is *more powerful* than the test based on the extreme range.

23 B. Samples from multinomially distributed populations

Given are m samples of sizes $N_1, N_2, \ldots, N_i, \ldots, N_m$, in which the events $E_1, E_2, \ldots, E_j, \ldots, E_n$ occur $x_{1j}, x_{2j}, \ldots, x_{ij}, \ldots, x_{mn}$ times respectively, and

$$\left.\begin{array}{l} \sum_{j=1}^{n} x_{ij} = N_i,\ \sum_{i=1}^{m} x_{ij} = X_j \text{ and } \sum_{j=1}^{n} X_j = \sum_{i=1}^{m} N_i = N: \\ \begin{array}{ccccccc|c} x_{11} & x_{12} & \ldots & x_{1j} & \ldots & x_{1n} & & N_1 \\ x_{21} & x_{22} & \ldots & x_{2j} & \ldots & x_{2n} & & N_2 \\ \vdots & \vdots & & \vdots & & \vdots & & \vdots \\ x_{i1} & x_{i2} & \ldots & x_{ij} & \ldots & x_{in} & & N_i \\ \vdots & \vdots & & \vdots & & \vdots & & \vdots \\ x_{m1} & x_{m2} & \ldots & x_{mj} & \ldots & x_{mn} & & N_m \\ \hline X_1 & X_2 & & X_j & & X_n & & N \end{array} \end{array}\right\} \quad (826)$$

The expected values $E_{ij} = N_i X_j / N$ of x_{ij} on the assumption of constant probabilities and independence are now calculated. The expected value of x_{11} (event 1 in sample 1), for example, is $N_1 X_1 / N$. With these expected values the following quotient is calculated for each observation x_{ij}:

$$\frac{(x_{ij} - E_{ij})^2}{E_{ij}} \quad \text{or} \quad \left[\frac{x_{ij}^2}{X_j N_i} - \frac{1}{m\,n}\right] \qquad \text{(a) (b)} \qquad (827)$$

and the values summed. The significance limit for the sum

$$\sum_1^n \sum_1^m \text{ (827 a)} \quad \text{or} \quad N \sum_1^n \sum_1^m \text{ (827 b)} \qquad (828)$$

is found from χ^2, pages 36–39, with degrees of freedom $\nu = (n-1)(m-1)$ and $2\alpha = 1 \int_r$. If the test statistic (**828**) *attains* or *exceeds* the significance limit, then interpretation (**825**) is valid.

23 C. Samples from POISSON distributions

(a) *2 samples from two observation units of equal magnitude* $t_1 = t_2 = t$

Given are 2 samples with the *same* observation unit $t_1 = t_2 = t$, in which the event E occurs x_1 and x_2 times respectively.

The sums $x_1 + x_2 = N$ are calculated. The significance limits for x_1 and x_2 are then x_l and x_r of the table on pages 105 and 106 for $N = x_1 + x_2$. If x_1 and x_2 *attain* or *exceed* these limits (in an outward direction from ½ N), then the following interpretations may be made:

$$\left.\begin{array}{ll} \text{one-tailed test:} & \begin{cases} \lambda_1 < \lambda_2, \text{ if } x_1 \leqq x_l \text{ (significance } \alpha) \\ \lambda_1 > \lambda_2, \text{ if } x_1 \geqq x_r \text{ (significance } \alpha) \end{cases} \\ \text{two-tailed test:} & \lambda_1 \neq \lambda_2, \text{ if } x_1 \text{ and } x_2 \text{ attain or exceed (outwards) the levels } x_l \text{ and } x_r \text{ (significance } 2\alpha) \end{array}\right\} \quad (829)$$

For samples with $x_1 + x_2 > 1000$ or $t_1 \neq t_2$ see (b) below.

(b) *One sample from each of m observation units* t_i

Given are m samples from any number of observation units $t_1, t_2, \ldots, t_i, \ldots, t_m$ in which the event E occurs $x_1, x_2, \ldots, x_i, \ldots, x_m$ times. The following are calculated:

$$\lambda_i^* = \frac{x_i}{t_i} \text{ and } \bar{\lambda} = (\Sigma x_i)/(\Sigma t_i)$$

and the x_i values transformed into c_i values as follows in accordance with (**794**) and (**796**):

$$\left.\begin{array}{l} c_i = 2\left(\sqrt{x_i + 1} - \sqrt{t_i \bar{\lambda}}\right), \text{ if } \lambda_i^* < \bar{\lambda} \\ c_i = 2\left(\sqrt{x_i} - \sqrt{t_i \bar{\lambda}}\right), \text{ if } \lambda_i^* > \bar{\lambda} \end{array}\right\} \quad (830)$$

Comparison of these transformed data and their interpretations are as in section 23 A, (b), I and II, with $\bar{\lambda}$ and λ_i^* in place of $\bar{p}$ and p_i.

(c) *Confidence limits for the increase in frequency of a rare event*[42]

Given are two samples of sizes N_1 and N_2 in which the fairly *rare* event E occurs with a relative frequency of $p_1 = x_1/N_1$ and $p_2 = x_2/N_2$ respectively. *The samples should be so numbered that* $p_1 < p_2$. The estimate of the proportionate *increase* in relative frequency from sample 1 to sample 2 is then

$$Proc_{1\to 2} = \frac{p_2 - p_1}{p_1} \qquad (831)$$

with the $(1 - 2\alpha)$ confidence limits for $\boldsymbol{Proc}_{1\to 2}$

$$k\left(\frac{1}{p_r} - 1\right) - 1 < \boldsymbol{Proc}_{1\to 2} < k\left(\frac{1}{p_l} - 1\right) - 1 \qquad (832)$$

where $k = N_1/N_2$ and p_r and p_l are obtained from the table of confidence limits for $\boldsymbol{p}$ of the binomial distribution on pages 85–103 for $N = x_1 + x_2$ and $x = x_1$. (**831**) and (**832**) are converted to percentages by multiplying by 100. (**832**) can also be calculated in this way when only the *ratio* N_1/N_2 and the absolute numbers x_1 and x_2 are known. *Interpretation:* When the left limit of (**832**) $\leqq$ zero, then no increase in frequency is indicated.

24. Rank tests

24 A. Ranking

(a) *By magnitude* (continuous distributions). Given are two samples 1 and 2 with the x_1 values 1.06, 1.53, 1.68, 1.68, 1.69, 1.69 and the x_2 values 1.30, 1.55, 1.69, 1.80. These values are ranked as follows:

$$\left.\begin{array}{lcccccccccc} x_1 & 1.06 & & 1.53 & & 1.68 & 1.68 & & 1.69 & 1.69 & \\ x_2 & & 1.30 & & 1.55 & & & 1.69 & & & 1.80 \\ O_{1,2} & 1 & 2 & 3 & 4 & 5 & 6 & \underbrace{8 \quad 8 \quad 8}_{=(7+8+9)/3} & & & 10 \end{array}\right\} \quad (833)$$

With ties [cf. (**346**)], the procedure is as in (**833**): tied values *within* a sample receive *successive* rank numbers, those *between* the samples the *mean* of the two rank numbers at the position concerned. (**834**)

In the above example, the rank numbers O_1 of the x_1 values are $O_1 = 1, 3, 5, 6, 8$ and 8, and their sum $T_1 = \Sigma O_1 = 31$. (**835**)

With *paired observations*, the n pair differences d_i are calculated as in section 16 D, page 172, with all d_i values equal to zero ignored and N reduced accordingly. The *absolute values* of these differences are then ranked and either the rank numbers of all negative differences summed to give T_- or those of all positive differences summed to give T_+. (**836**)

(b) *By order in a series* (discrete distributions). If in a series of N trials the event E occurs once each in the 2nd, 3rd, 8th and 13th trials, in all N_1 times (for example 4 times), then $O_E = 2, 3, 8$ and 13 respectively and the sum of the O_E numbers $= T_E = 26$. (**837**)

24 B. The WILCOXON test for two samples[43, 44]

Given are two samples from *continuous* distributions of *any* form with means μ_1 and μ_2 respectively. These are so numbered that $N_1 \leqq 25$ and $N_2 \leqq 50$. The x_1 values are now ranked as in (**833**) and (**834**) to give the sum T_1 of (**835**).

The significance limits for T_1 are given in the tables on pages 124–127. If T_1 *attains* the significance levels or *exceeds them in the outward direction* from its expected value, then this may be regarded as evidence that

$$\left.\begin{array}{ll} \text{one-tailed test:} & \begin{cases} \mu_1 < \mu_2, \text{ if } T_1 \leqq T_l\ (\leqq \alpha) \\ \mu_1 > \mu_2, \text{ if } T_1 \geqq T_r\ (\leqq \alpha) \end{cases} \\ \text{two-tailed test:} & \mu_1 \neq \mu_2, \text{ if } T_1 \leqq T_l \text{ or } T_1 \geqq T_r\ (\leqq 2\alpha) \end{array}\right\} \quad (838)$$

Cf. also section 9 C, page 156.

Under the null hypothesis, the expectation $\boldsymbol{T}_1$ of the estimate T_1 is

$$\left.\begin{array}{lr} \boldsymbol{T}_1 = N_1(N_1 + N_2 + 1)/2 \quad \text{or} & \text{(a)} \\ 6\,\boldsymbol{T}_1 = 3\,N_1(N_1 + N_2 + 1) & \text{(b)} \end{array}\right\} \quad (839)$$

$$\left.\begin{array}{lr} \text{and the variance } \sigma_{T_1}^2 = N_2 \boldsymbol{T}_1/12 \quad \text{or} & \text{(a)} \\ \sigma_{6T_1}^2 = 3\,N_2 \boldsymbol{T}_1 & \text{(b)} \end{array}\right\} \quad (840)$$

For samples outside the scope of the tables the following test quotient can be used

$$(T_1 - \boldsymbol{T}_1) / \sqrt{\sigma_{T_1}^2} \quad \text{or} \quad (6\,T_1 - 6\,\boldsymbol{T}_1) / \sqrt{\sigma_{6T_1}^2} \qquad \text{(a) (b)} \qquad (841)$$

Significance limit c_α, page 28.

24 C. The WILCOXON test for pair differences[44]

Cf. sections 9 C, page 157, and 24 B, above.

The sum T_- is calculated in accordance with (**836**). The number of ranked pair differences is denoted by n (all zero values are ignored).

Significance limits for the sum T_- are given in the table on page 128. If the differences have been calculated as $d_i = x_{1i} - x_{2i}$ and the sum T_- *attains* the significance limits or *exceeds them in the outward direction* from the expected value of T_-, then it follows that

one-tailed test: $\begin{cases} \mu_1 > \mu_2, \text{ when } T_- \leqq T_l\ (\leqq \alpha) \\ \mu_1 < \mu_2, \text{ when } T_- \geqq T_r\ (\leqq \alpha) \end{cases}$

two-tailed test: $\mu_1 \neq \mu_2$, when $T_- \leqq T_l$ or $T_- \geqq T_r$ $(\leqq 2\alpha)$ **(842)**

Under the null hypothesis, the expectation $\boldsymbol{T}_-$ of the estimate T_- is

$$\boldsymbol{T}_- = n\,(n+1)/4 \qquad \textbf{(843)}$$

and the variance is

$$\sigma^2_{T_-} = n\,\boldsymbol{T}/3 \qquad \textbf{(844)}$$

For samples outside the scope of the tables the following test quotient can be used:

$$(T_- - \boldsymbol{T}_-)\,/\sqrt{\sigma^2_{T_-}} \qquad \textbf{(845)}$$

Significance limit c_α, page 28.

24 D. HALDANE's test for chronological order effect[45]

The WILCOXON test can also be used for testing exactly for the possibility that an event E is affected by the chronological order in which it occurs. Examples of this situation are the possibility that the later children of *one* mother may be more liable to a certain disease, the question whether the mortality in, or success of, a particular operation in the *same* hospital is increasing or decreasing, and so on. The test was developed by HALDANE for such problems independently of WILCOXON.

(a) *Investigation of a chronological series.* T_E is calculated as in (**837**). N_1 is the number of trials (births, operations, etc.) in which the event E has occurred. N_2 is $N - N_1$, where N is the total number of trials in the series being investigated.

The significance limits for T_E are the same as those in section 24B; the interpretation, however, is completely different. *One-tailed test:* If T_E attains or exceeds the *left* limit, then the frequency *decreases* with time; if it attains or exceeds the *right* limit, the *opposite* is the case. *Two-tailed test:* The chronological order has an influence on the frequency. **(846)**

If all the events in the series cannot be specified, the following sequence, for example, may arise:

Trial	2	3	4	5	6	7	8	9	10	11	12
	+	+	?	−	+	?	+	−	+	?	+
O_E				5				9			
$O_?$			4			7				11	

(847)

and the tables on pages 124–127 can no longer be used. In such cases, the test criterion (**841** b) is used, with

$$\begin{aligned} 6\,T_E &= 6\,\Sigma\, O_E && \text{(a)} \\ 6\,\boldsymbol{T}_E &= 6\,N_1 A/N && \text{(b)} \\ \sigma^2_{6T_E} &= 36\,N_1 N_2\,(NB - A^2)/N^2(N-1) && \text{(c)} \\ A &= N(N+1)/2 - \Sigma\, O_? && \text{(d)} \\ B &= N[1 + N(2N+3)]/6 - \Sigma\, O_?^2 && \text{(e)} \end{aligned} \qquad \textbf{(848)}$$

If all the events are specified but the sample exceeds the scope of the table, then equations (**839** b) and (**840** b) can be used in conjunction with (**841** b).

(b) *Investigation of several chronological series as samples from the same population.* The successive offspring of 1, 2, 3, ..., *i*, ..., *m* mothers, for example, are to be investigated in respect of a childhood disease which appears to be commoner among later births.

The test criterion (**841** b) is used, with

$$\begin{aligned} 6\,T &= \Sigma\, 6\,T_i \\ 6\,\boldsymbol{T} &= \Sigma\, 6\,\boldsymbol{T}_i \\ \sigma^2_{6T} &= \Sigma\, \sigma^2_{6T_i} \end{aligned} \qquad \textbf{(849)}$$

and 6 $\boldsymbol{T}_i$ and $\sigma^2_{6T_i}$ are calculated from (**839** b) and (**840** b) or from (**848** b) and (**848** c) respectively, according to whether all the events in the series i are specified or not.

24 E. The maximum test for pair differences[26, 46–48]

(This name has been proposed by E. WALTER. The test is described here since it is also useful for assessing series but by a method different to that of the WILCOXON test.)

With paired observations from *continuous* populations of *any* form the pair differences d_i are calculated as in section 16D, page 172. All zero values of d_i are excluded and the remainder arranged in the order of their *absolute magnitudes*. If two differences of equal absolute magnitude but opposite sign appear, then in order to be on the safe side these are so arranged that any runs of the same sign are as small as possible. The k differences with the highest absolute magnitude and the *same* sign are then counted.

The significance probability for a difference between the two series of measurements (two-tailed test) is then $2\,\alpha = (\tfrac{1}{2})^{k-1}$, that is,

$k =$	$2\alpha =$	$\alpha =$
5	0.0625 ∼ 0.1	0.031 25 ∼ 0.05
6	0.031 25 ∼ 0.05	0.015 625 ∼ 0.02
8	0.007 8125 ∼ 0.01	0.003 906 25 ∼ 0.005
11	0.000 9725 ∼ 0.001	0.000 486 25 ∼ 0.0005

(850)

Example 73. The series +3.2, +2.0, +1.0, +1.0, +0.7, +0.5, −0.3, +0.3 (note the awkward position of −0.3) results in a significance probability of $2\,\alpha \sim 0.05$.

25. Testing for nonrandomness

All statistical tests for nonrandomness depend on the *chronological* order in which the values $x_1, x_2, \ldots, x_N$ occur in the series of tries 1, 2, ..., N. Here the indices 1, 2, ..., i, ..., N denote *not the rank but the chronological order.*

25 A. The mean-square successive difference[49]

The mean-square successive difference δ^2 is defined as

$$\delta^2 = \frac{1}{N-1}\sum_1^{N-1}(x_{i+1} - x_i)^2;\ N = \text{size of the sample} \qquad \textbf{(851)}$$

If the sample originates from a normally distributed population, then the

$$\text{expectation of } \delta^2 = 2\,\sigma^2 \qquad \textbf{(852)}$$

$\delta^2/2$ is thus an unbiased estimate of σ^2 with an

$$\text{efficiency} = 2/3\,[1 + 1/(3\,N - 4)] \qquad \textbf{(853)}$$

For $N = 2$, the efficiency is therefore unity; for $N \to \infty$ (asymptotically) it is $^2/_3$.

Since the mean-square successive difference is calculated on the basis of the successive differences $x_{i+1} - x_i$, it is *less sensitive* to *long-term* displacements of the mean and *more sensitive* to rapid *cyclic* influences on the mean than the estimate s^2, which is calculated on the basis of the differences $x_i - \bar{x}_i$.

$$\text{The ratio } \eta = \frac{\delta^2}{s^2} = \frac{\sum_1^{N-1}(x_{i+1} - x_i)^2}{\sum_1^{N}(x_i - \bar{x}_i)^2} \qquad \textbf{(854)}$$

is therefore an indication of a possible nonrandom influence on the mean of a *normally distributed* population.

Significance limits for η are given in the left-hand table on page 58. *Interpretation:* If η attains or exceeds the *left* limit, then the mean of the population is influenced* by *nonrandom* long-term factors; if it attains or exceeds the *right* limit, the population mean is influenced* by *short-term cyclic* factors (significance α). **(855)**

The approximate limits ($N > 60$) in the table on page 58 have been calculated from

$$\eta_l, \eta_r = 2 \mp 2\,|c_\alpha|\sqrt{\frac{N-2}{(N-1)(N+1)}} \qquad \textbf{(856)}$$

with empirical correction at the transition from exact to approximate values.

25 B. Serial correlation[50, 51]

Given is the sample $x_1, x_2, \ldots, x_N$. Serial correlation is defined as the correlation between the pairs of observations x_i and x_{i+h}. h is known as the lag. For $i + h > N$, $x_{i+h} = x_{i+h-N}$ in the *cyclic* definition. For further details the reader is referred to the literature[50–52].

* The influences can be linear or nonlinear.

Expected value $\mathbf{I}(l \mid N)$ and variance of runs up and down of length l

Length	Expected value $\mathbf{I}(l \mid N)$ exact: $\mathbf{I}(l \mid N) = aN - b$		asymptotic $\mathbf{I}(l \mid N) \to \mathbf{I}(1+ \mid N) \times c$ $(N \to \infty)$	Variance $\sigma_I^2 = d \times \mathbf{I}(l \mid N) + e$		Remarks
l	a	b	c	d	e	Note
1	$4.1\dot{6} \times 10^{-1}$	$-8.\dot{3} \times 10^{-2}$	6.25×10^{-1}	$1.01\dot{6}$	$-0.397\dot{2}$	— for b and e
2	$1.8\dot{3} \times 10^{-1}$	$2.\dot{3} \times 10^{-1}$	2.75×10^{-1}	0.614 550	−0.019 433 42	— for e
3	$5.2\dot{7} \times 10^{-2}$	$1.30\dot{5} \times 10^{-1}$	$7.91\dot{6} \times 10^{-2}$	0.794 215	0.006 782 18	
4	$1.150\,793\,65 \times 10^{-2}$	$4.126\,984\,13 \times 10^{-2}$	$1.726\,190\,48 \times 10^{-2}$	0.935 800	0.000 839 24	
5	$2.033\,730\,16 \times 10^{-3}$	$9.474\,206\,34 \times 10^{-3}$	$3.050\,595\,24 \times 10^{-3}$	0.985 361	0.000 046 29	
6	$3.031\,305\,11 \times 10^{-4}$	$1.730\,599\,65 \times 10^{-3}$	$4.546\,957\,67 \times 10^{-4}$	0.997 338	0.000 001 56	
7	$3.913\,139\,33 \times 10^{-5}$	$2.639\,991\,18 \times 10^{-4}$	$5.869\,708\,99 \times 10^{-5}$	0.999 595	0.000 000 04	
8	$4.459\,275\,29 \times 10^{-6}$	$3.467\,211\,80 \times 10^{-5}$	$6.688\,912\,94 \times 10^{-6}$	0.999 947	0.000 000 00	
9	$4.551\,133\,02 \times 10^{-7}$	$4.004\,161\,99 \times 10^{-6}$	$6.826\,699\,53 \times 10^{-7}$	0.999 994	0.000 000 00	
10	$4.207\,469\,48 \times 10^{-8}$	$4.130\,386\,07 \times 10^{-7}$	$6.311\,204\,22 \times 10^{-8}$	0.999 999	0.000 000 00	

(**860**)

Expected value $\mathbf{I}(l+ \mid N)$ and variance of runs up and down of length l and longer

Length	Expected value $\mathbf{I}(l+ \mid N)$ exact: $\mathbf{I}(l+ \mid N) = aN - b$		asymptotic $\mathbf{I}(l+ \mid N) \to \mathbf{I}(1+ \mid N) \times c$ $(N \to \infty)$	Variance $\sigma_I^2 = d \times \mathbf{I}(l+ \mid N) + e$		Remarks
$l+$	a	b	c	d	e	Note
1	$6.\dot{6} \times 10^{-1}$	$3.\dot{3} \times 10^{-1}$	1	$0.2\dot{6}$	$-0.2\dot{3}$	— for e
2	$2.\dot{5} \times 10^{-1}$	$4.1\dot{6} \times 10^{-1}$	3.75×10^{-1}	$0.31\dot{6}$	$0.07\dot{2}$	
3	$6.\dot{6} \times 10^{-2}$	$1.8\dot{3} \times 10^{-1}$	1×10^{-1}	0.710 847	0.017 294 97	
4	$1.3\dot{8} \times 10^{-2}$	$5.2\dot{7} \times 10^{-2}$	$2.08\dot{3} \times 10^{-2}$	0.917 857	0.001 478 17	
5	$\dot{2}.3809\dot{5} \times 10^{-3}$	$1.150\,793\,65 \times 10^{-2}$	$3.571\,428\,57 \times 10^{-3}$	0.982 145	0.000 070 53	
6	$3.47\dot{2} \times 10^{-4}$	$2.033\,730\,16 \times 10^{-3}$	$5.208\dot{3} \times 10^{-4}$	0.996 871	0.000 002 20	
7	$4.409\,171\,08 \times 10^{-5}$	$3.031\,305\,11 \times 10^{-4}$	$6.613\,756\,61 \times 10^{-5}$	0.999 535	0.000 000 05	
8	$4.960\,317\,46 \times 10^{-6}$	$3.913\,139\,33 \times 10^{-5}$	$7.440\,476\,19 \times 10^{-6}$	0.999 940	0.000 000 00	
9	$5.010\,421\,67 \times 10^{-7}$	$4.459\,275\,29 \times 10^{-6}$	$7.515\,632\,51 \times 10^{-7}$	0.999 993	0.000 000 00	
10	$4.592\,886\,53 \times 10^{-8}$	$4.551\,133\,02 \times 10^{-7}$	$6.889\,329\,80 \times 10^{-8}$	0.999 999	0.000 000 00	
11	$3.854\,170\,52 \times 10^{-9}$	$4.207\,469\,48 \times 10^{-8}$	$5.781\,255\,78 \times 10^{-9}$	0.999 999	0.000 000 00	

(**861**)

With the cyclic definition, serial correlation is a sensitive instrument for revealing periodic influences on a population (or sample when the population is stable).

A measure of the serial correlation with lag h is the serial correlation coefficient $\mathbf{R}_h$. Its estimate is

$$R_h = \frac{\Sigma\, x_i x_{i+h} - \bar{x}_i\, \Sigma\, x_i}{\Sigma\,(x_i - \bar{x}_i)^2} \qquad \textbf{(857)}$$

As with other correlation coefficients, its value lies between -1 and $+1$.

The right-hand table on page 58 gives the significance limits for R_h (when $h = 1$) on the assumption that the samples are random samples from a normally distributed population. The approximate limits ($N > 75$) have been calculated from

$$R_l, R_r = \frac{-1 \mp |c_\alpha| \sqrt{N-2}}{N-1}\,;\ N = \text{sample size} \qquad \textbf{(858)}$$

with empirical correction at the transition from exact to approximate values. With this approximation the user remains on the safe side.

For lags other than 1 the same levels can be used, provided that h and N do not possess a common factor. The latter is always the case when N is a prime number. In practice these conditions can be met by deleting one or more individual sample values.

25 C. Runs up and down[53–55]

If $x_1, x_2, \ldots, x_i, \ldots, x_N$ are individual sample values from a *continuous* population of *any* form, then a run "up" of length 1 is defined as the sequence $x_i \to x_{i+1}$ when $x_{i+1} - x_i > 0$. For runs "down", $x_{i+1} - x_i < 0$. A sequence of three runs "up" of length 1 is called a run "up" of length 3, and so on.

If the sample is a random one not subject to cyclic or constant nonrandom influences, then the runs up and down should present a random picture, that is to say, there should be no regular runs and not too many long ones or too few short ones.

Testing of runs up and down can be effected by means of the table at the foot of page 130. Thus a run of length 5 in a sample of size $N = 9$, for example, is not likely to be random ($\alpha = 0.01$). In the same way, a sample of size $N = 12$ is not likely to be a random sample when no run of length 2 is present (significance probability $1 - 0.99 = 0.01$).

The number $I\,(l \mid N)$ of runs up and down of length l and the number $I\,(l+ \mid N)$ of runs of length l and *longer* can be regarded as normally distributed from $N = 20$ onwards. This can be tested by means of the quotient

$$(I - \mathbf{I}) / \sqrt{\sigma_I^2}\,;\ \text{significance level } |c_\alpha|, \text{page 28} \qquad \textbf{(859)}$$

The expected value $\mathbf{I}$ and the variance σ_I^2 are functions of N; appropriate formulas are to be found in the literature[53]. To some extent their calculation is a tedious operation. The two tables (**860**) and (**861**) above give values up to lengths which practically no longer occur; they also show clearly how σ^2 for greater lengths converges rapidly toward the expected value. It follows from (**789**) that the distribution of runs up and down very closely approximates, for runs of greater length, to a Poisson distribution (or to approximations to a Poisson distribution) with $\lambda = \mathbf{I}$.

25 D. Runs above or below the median[56]

Runs above and/or below the median can be tested by means of the table on page 130, where a brief explanation of the method will be found.

25 E. Runs in samples from binomially distributed populations in which the probabilities p and q are unknown

The definition is as follows:

(Time)	1	2	3	4	5	6	7	8	9	10
Series (I)	A	B	A	A	A	B	B	A	B	A
Series (II)	A	B	A	B	A	A	B	A	B	A
Series (III)	A	A	A	A	A	A	B	B	B	B

Each of the series (I), (II), (III) has a size $N = 10$ and contains $N_1 = 4$ B's and $N_2 = 6$ A's (provided that $N = N_1 + N_2 < 40$, the smaller number is denoted by N_1). In these series the underscored letters in each case form a run. The total number of runs I is 7 in series (I), 9 in series (II), 2 in series (III).

The table on page 129 gives the significance limits for the estimate I (total | N_1, N_2) of the expectation $\boldsymbol{I}$ (total | N_1, N_2) of the total number of all runs of events 1 and 2.

(a) If the left limit is *attained*, then
I is significantly less than $\boldsymbol{I}$ (significance probability α) or
I differs significantly from $\boldsymbol{I}$ (significance probability 2α).

(b) If the right limit is *attained*, then
I significantly exceeds $\boldsymbol{I}$ (significance probability α) or
I differs significantly from $\boldsymbol{I}$ (significance probability 2α).

(c) If I lies between the limits and *attains neither*, then the null hypothesis cannot be rejected.

For N_1 and N_2 values outside the scope of the table, the test quotient (**859**) can be used in conjunction with (**868**a) and (**868**b).

Expected values and variances

– for the number of runs of length l of the event 1, which has occurred a total of N_1 times (N_2 = number of events 2; $N = N_1 + N_2$)

$$\boldsymbol{I}_1(l \mid N_1, N_2) = N_2(N_2+1)\frac{N_1!\,(N-l-1)!}{N!\,(N_1-l)!} \quad \text{(a)}$$

$$\sigma^2 = \boldsymbol{I}\left[1 - \boldsymbol{I} + N_2(N_2-1)\frac{(N-2l-2)!\,(N_1-l)!}{(N-l-1)!\,(N_1-2l)!}\right] \quad \text{(b)}$$

(862)[57]

and asymptotically for higher values of N

$$\boldsymbol{I}_1(l \mid N_1, N_2) = Np^l q^2 \quad \text{(a)}$$

$$\sigma^2 = \boldsymbol{I}\left\{1 - \frac{\boldsymbol{I}}{N}\left[\frac{l^2}{p} + \frac{2}{q} - (l+1)^2\right]\right\} \quad \text{(b)}$$

$$p = N_1/N, \quad q = N_2/N$$

(863)[57]

– for the number of runs of length l and *longer* of the event 1

$$\boldsymbol{I}_1(l+ \mid N_1, N_2) = (N_2+1)\frac{N_1!\,(N-l)!}{N!\,(N_1-l)!} \quad \text{(a)}$$

$$\sigma^2 = \boldsymbol{I}\left[1 - \boldsymbol{I} + N_2\frac{(N-2l)!\,(N_1-l)!}{(N-l)!\,(N_1-2l)!}\right] \quad \text{(b)}$$

(864)[57]

and asymptotically

$$\boldsymbol{I}_1(l+ \mid N_1, N_2) = Np^l q \quad \text{(a)}$$

$$\sigma^2 = \boldsymbol{I}\left\{1 - \frac{\boldsymbol{I}}{N}\left[\frac{l^2 q}{p} + \frac{1}{q}\right]\right\} \quad \text{(b)}$$

p and q as in (**863**)

(865)[57]

– for the total number of all runs of the event 1

$$\boldsymbol{I}_1(\text{total} \mid N_1, N_2) = \boldsymbol{I}_1(1+ \mid N_1, N_2) = \frac{N_1(N_2+1)}{N} \quad \text{(a)}$$

$$\sigma^2 = \frac{\boldsymbol{I}(\boldsymbol{I}-1)}{N-1} \quad \text{(b)}$$

(866)[58]

and asymptotically

$$\boldsymbol{I}_1(\text{total} \mid N_1, N_2) = \boldsymbol{I}(1+ \mid N_1, N_2) = Npq \quad \text{(a)}$$

$$\sigma^2 = \boldsymbol{I}^2/N \quad \text{(b)}$$

p and q as in (**863**)

(867)[57]

– for the total number of all runs of events 1 and 2

$$\boldsymbol{I}_{1+2}(\text{total} \mid N_1, N_2) = \frac{2N_1N_2}{N} + 1 \quad \text{(a)}$$

$$\sigma^2 = \frac{(\boldsymbol{I}-1)(\boldsymbol{I}-2)}{N-1} \quad \text{(b)}$$

(868)[59]

and asymptotically

$$\boldsymbol{I}_{1+2}(\text{total} \mid N_1, N_2) = 2Npq \quad \text{(a)}$$

$$\sigma^2 = \boldsymbol{I}^2/N \quad \text{(b)}$$

p and q as in (**863**)

(869)[59]

The total number of all runs of the event 1 can be tested exactly (within the scope of the tables on pages 109–123) by means of the fourfold table test[58]:

I_1	$N_1 - I_1$	N_1
$N_2 + 1 - I_1$	$I_1 - 1$	N_2
$N_2 + 1$	$N_1 - 1$	N

(870)

25 F. The WALD-WOLFOWITZ test[59]

Given are 2 samples from *continuous* populations of *any* form. These are ranked as in (**833**) and the total number of all runs (a run being defined as the occurrence of *successive* rank numbers in a sample) counted. Testing is carried out by means of the table on page 129 (cf. section 25 E) or, for samples outside the scope of this table, by means of the test quotient (**859**) in conjunction with (**868**a and b) or (**869**a and b).

Example 74. Ranking and determination of runs (1, 2, ... is here a rank order):

Sample 1	1.55	1.58	1.70		1.92			2.20	2.21		
Sample 2				1.91		1.93	2.00			2.30	2.40
$O_{1,2}$	1	2	3	4	5	6	7	8	9	10	11
Run 1 and 2		1		1	1	1		1		1	

Total runs: 6, $N = 11$, $N_1 = 6$, $N_2 = 5$

If the total number of runs *attains* or *passes* the *left* limit (only this limit can be used in this test), then the samples do not originate from the same population (significance probability 2α).

25 G. Runs in samples from binomially distributed populations in which the probabilities $\boldsymbol{p}$ and $\boldsymbol{q}$ are known

Expected values and variances

– for the number of runs of the event 1 the probability of whose occurrence is $\boldsymbol{p}$

$$\boldsymbol{I}_1(l \mid N, \boldsymbol{p}) = \boldsymbol{p}^l\boldsymbol{q}\left[(N-l-1)\boldsymbol{q} + 2\right]; \ (l < N)$$
$$= \boldsymbol{p}^l; \ (l = N)$$

σ^2 no correct formula known

(871)[60]

and asymptotically

$$\boldsymbol{I}_1(l \mid N, \boldsymbol{p}) = N\boldsymbol{p}^l\boldsymbol{q}^2 \quad \text{(a)[60]}$$

$$\sigma^2 = \boldsymbol{I}\left\{1 - \boldsymbol{p}^l\boldsymbol{q}^2\left[2\left(l - \frac{\boldsymbol{p}}{\boldsymbol{q}}\right) + 1\right]\right\} \quad \text{(b)[57]}$$

(872)

– for the number of runs of length l and *longer*

$$\boldsymbol{I}_1(l+ \mid N, \boldsymbol{p}) = \boldsymbol{p}^l\left[(N-l)\boldsymbol{q} + 1\right]$$

σ^2 no correct formula known

(873)[60]

and asymptotically

$$\boldsymbol{I}_1(l+ \mid N, \boldsymbol{p}) = N\boldsymbol{p}^l\boldsymbol{q} \quad \text{(a)[60]}$$

$$\sigma^2 = \boldsymbol{I}\left[1 - \boldsymbol{p}^l\boldsymbol{q}(2l+1)\right] \quad \text{(b)[57]}$$

(874)

– for the total number of runs of the event 1

$$\boldsymbol{I}_1(\text{total} \mid N, \boldsymbol{p}) = \boldsymbol{p}\left[(N-1)\boldsymbol{q} + 1\right] \quad \text{(a)[60]}$$

$$\sigma^2 = \boldsymbol{I}(1-\boldsymbol{I}) + (N-2)\boldsymbol{p}^2\boldsymbol{q}\left[(N-3)\boldsymbol{q} + 2\right] \quad \text{(b)[57]}$$

(875)

and asymptotically

$$\boldsymbol{I}_1(\text{total} \mid N, \boldsymbol{p}) = N\boldsymbol{p}\boldsymbol{q} \quad \text{(a)}$$

$$\sigma^2 = \boldsymbol{I}(1 - 3\boldsymbol{p}\boldsymbol{q}) \quad \text{(b)}$$

(876)[60]

– for the total number of runs of events 1 and 2

$$\boldsymbol{I}_{1+2}(\text{total} \mid N, \boldsymbol{p}) = 2(N-1)\boldsymbol{p}\boldsymbol{q} + 1 \quad \text{(a)}$$

$$\sigma^2 = 2\boldsymbol{p}\boldsymbol{q}\left\{2\left[N - (3N-5)\boldsymbol{p}\boldsymbol{q}\right] - 3\right\} \quad \text{(b)}$$

(877)[60]

and asymptotically

$$\boldsymbol{I}_{1+2}(\text{total} \mid N, \boldsymbol{p}) = 2N\boldsymbol{p}\boldsymbol{q} \quad \text{(a)}$$

$$\sigma^2 = \boldsymbol{I}(2 - 3\boldsymbol{p}\boldsymbol{q}) \quad \text{(b)}$$

(878)[60]

25 H. Runs in samples from multinomially distributed populations

(a) *The probabilities $\boldsymbol{p}_1, \boldsymbol{p}_2, \ldots, \boldsymbol{p}_i, \ldots, \boldsymbol{p}_k$ are unknown.*

Expected values and variances

– for the total number of runs of the event i, given that this event occurs N_i times

$$\boldsymbol{I}_i(\text{total} \mid N_i, N) = \frac{N_i(N - N_i - 1)}{N} \quad \text{(a)}$$

$$\sigma^2 = \frac{\boldsymbol{I}(\boldsymbol{I}-1)}{N-1} \quad \text{(b)}$$

(879)[57]

and asymptotically

$$\boldsymbol{I}_i(\text{total} \mid N_i, N) = Np_i(1-p_i) \quad \text{(a)}$$

$$\sigma^2 = \boldsymbol{I}^2/N \quad \text{(b)}$$

$$p_i = \frac{N_i}{N}$$

(880)[57]

– for the total number of runs of all events asymptotically

$$\left.\begin{aligned} \boldsymbol{I}(\text{total}, N) &= N\left(1 - \sum_{1}^{k} p_i^2\right) & \text{(a)} \\ \sigma^2 &= N\left[\sum p_i^2 - 2\sum p_i^3 - \left(\sum p_i^2\right)^2\right] & \text{(b)} \end{aligned}\right\} p_i \text{ as in } \mathbf{(880)} \quad \mathbf{(881)}^{57}$$

When $N_1 = N_2 = \cdots = N_k = N$, **(877)** becomes

$$\left.\begin{aligned} \boldsymbol{I}(\text{total}) &= N(1-p) & \text{(a)} \\ \sigma^2 &= p\boldsymbol{I} & \text{(b)} \end{aligned}\right\} p = 1/k \quad \mathbf{(882)}$$

(b) *The probabilities* $\boldsymbol{p}_i$ *are known.*

$\boldsymbol{p}_i$ is the probability that the event i will occur.

Expected values and variances

– for the total number of runs of the event i

$$\left.\begin{aligned} \boldsymbol{I}_i(\text{total} \mid N, \boldsymbol{p}_i) &= \boldsymbol{p}_i\left[(N-1)(1-\boldsymbol{p}_i)+1\right] & \text{(a)} \\ \sigma^2 &= N\boldsymbol{p}_i(1 - 4\boldsymbol{p}_i + 6\boldsymbol{p}_i^2 - 3\boldsymbol{p}_i^3) + \\ &\quad + \boldsymbol{p}_i^2(3 - 8\boldsymbol{p}_i + 5\boldsymbol{p}_i^2) & \text{(b)} \end{aligned}\right\} \mathbf{(883)}^{57}$$

[Formula **(883)** is identical with **(875)** when in the latter, $\boldsymbol{p}$ is replaced by $\boldsymbol{p}_i$ and $\boldsymbol{q}$ is replaced by $1 - \boldsymbol{p}_i$]

and asymptotically

$$\left.\begin{aligned} \boldsymbol{I}_i(\text{total} \mid N, \boldsymbol{p}_i) &= N\boldsymbol{p}_i(1-\boldsymbol{p}_i) & \text{(a)} \\ \sigma^2 &= \boldsymbol{I}\left[1 - 3\boldsymbol{p}_i(1-\boldsymbol{p}_i)\right] & \text{(b)} \end{aligned}\right\} \mathbf{(884)}^{57}$$

– for the total number of runs of all events asymptotically

$$\left.\begin{aligned} \boldsymbol{I}(\text{total}) &= N\left(1 - \sum \boldsymbol{p}_i^2\right) & \text{(a)} \\ \sigma^2 &= N\left[\sum \boldsymbol{p}_i^2 + 2\sum \boldsymbol{p}_i^3 - 3\left(\sum \boldsymbol{p}_i^2\right)^2\right] & \text{(b)} \end{aligned}\right\} \mathbf{(885)}^{57}$$

When $\boldsymbol{p}_1 = \boldsymbol{p}_2 = \cdots \boldsymbol{p}_k = \boldsymbol{p} = 1/k$, **(885)** becomes

$$\left.\begin{aligned} \boldsymbol{I}(\text{total}) &= N(1-\boldsymbol{p}) & \text{(a)} \\ \sigma^2 &= \boldsymbol{p}\boldsymbol{I} & \text{(b)} \end{aligned}\right\} \mathbf{(886)}^{57}$$

26. Sequential analysis

Sequential analysis is one of the more recently developed statistical methods, and its use in medical trials is increasing[61]

The method is illustrated here by two charts[62] which enable a comparison to be made between two drugs, for example, without calculation.

Example 75. The effect on patients of drug A is to be compared with that of drug B. Two patients are selected, the toss of a coin deciding which one is to receive drug A and which drug B. They should receive the drugs *simultaneously or in quick succession.* The result is given one of the three ratings

Drug A better Drug B better No difference

If drug A is better, a cross is made in the square immediately *above* the black square in the charts (Figs. 49 and 50). If drug B is better, a cross is made in the square immediately *to the right* of the black square. If there is no difference, no entry is made in the charts. A second test is then made in exactly the same way with two different patients and the result entered in the square above or to the right of that marked in the first test, and so on for successive tests. As soon as a barrier is overstepped one of the following decisions can be made:

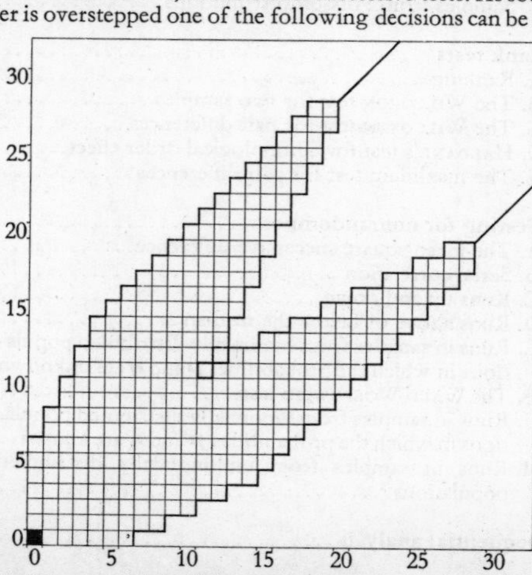

Fig. 49 Sequential analysis chart ($2\alpha = 0.2$).

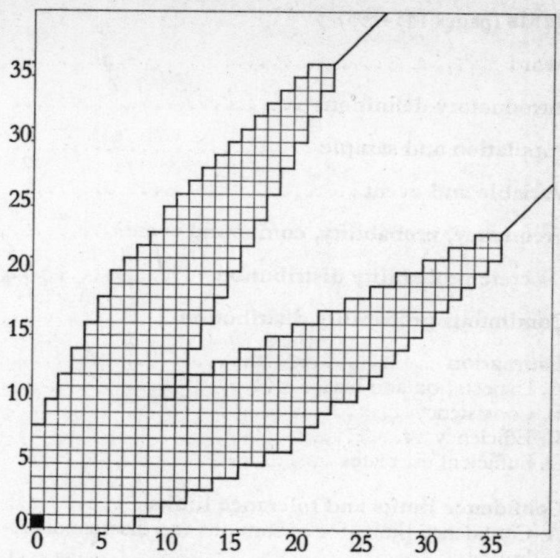

Fig. 50 Sequential analysis chart ($2\alpha = 0.1$).

(a) upper barrier overstepped: drug A is better
(b) lower barrier overstepped: drug B is better
(c) middle barrier overstepped: no difference demonstrated

The significance probability for (a) and (b) combined is 2α.

References

1) De Laplace, M., *Théorie analytique des probabilités*, 3rd ed., Paris, 1820. *2)* Molina, E. C., *Poisson's Exponential Binomial Limit*, Princeton, 1942. *3)* Pearson, K., *Tables of the Incomplete Beta-Function*, Cambridge, 1934. *4) Tables of the Binomial Probability Distribution*, National Bureau of Standards, Applied Mathematics Series 6, Washington, 1949. *5)* Rao, C. R., *Bull. Calcutta math. Soc.*, **37**, 81 (1945). *6)* Cramér, H., *Mathematical Methods of Statistics*, Princeton, 1946. *7)* Neyman, J., *Ann. math. Statist.*, **6**, 111 (1935). *8)* Neyman, J., *Phil. Trans. A*, **236**, 333 (1937). *9)* Neyman, J., *Biometrika*, **32**, 128 (1941/42). *10)* Proschan, F., *J. Amer. statist. Ass.*, **48**, 550 (1953). *11) Tables of Normal Probability Functions*, National Bureau of Standards, Applied Mathematics Series 23, Washington, 1953. *12)* Bliss, C. I., *Ann. appl. Biol.*, **22**, 134 (1935). *13)* Fisher and Yates, *Statistical Tables for Biological, Agricultural and Medical Research*, 4th ed., Edinburgh, 1953. *14)* Pearson and Hartley, *Biometrika Tables for Statisticians*, vol. I, Cambridge, 1954. *15)* Finney, D. J., *Probit Analysis*, 2nd ed., Cambridge, 1952. *16)* Wilson and Hilferty, *Proc. nat. Acad. Sci. (Wash.)*, **17**, 684 (1931). *17)* Fisher, R. A., On a distribution yielding the error function of several well-known statistics, *Proceedings of the International Mathematical Congress*, vol. II, Toronto, 1924, page 805. *18)* Eisenhart et al. (Eds.), *Selected Techniques of Statistical Analysis for Scientific and Industrial Research and Production and Management Engineering*, New York and London, 1947, page 108. *19)* Cf. Tippett, L. H. C., *Biometrika*, **17**, 364, (1925). *20)* Davies and Pearson, Suppl. to *J. roy. statist. Soc.*, **1**, 76 (1934). *21)* Dixon, W. J., *Ann. math. Statist.*, **21**, 488 (1950). *22)* Dixon, W. J., *Ann. math. Statist.*, **22**, 68 (1951). *23)* Dixon, W. J., *Biometrics*, **9**, 74 (1953). *24)* Lord, E., *Biometrika*, **34**, 41 (1947). *25)* Walsh, J. E., *Ann. math. Statist.*, **20**, 257 (1949). *26)* Walsh, J. E., *J. Amer. statist. Ass.*, **44**, 342 (1949). *27)* Welch, B. L., *Biometrika*, **36**, 293 (1949). *28)* Bartlett, M. S., *Proc. roy. Soc. A*, **160**, 268 (1937). *29)* Duncan, D. B., *Biometrics*, **11**, 1 (1955). *30)* Bliss, C. I., *Biometrics*, **1**, 57 (1945). *31)* Berkson, J. *Biometrics*, **7**, 327 (1951). *32)* Berkson, J., *J. Amer. statist. Ass.*, **48**, 565 (1953). *33)* Kendall, M. G., *Rank Correlation Methods*, 2nd ed., London, 1955. *34)* Van der Waerden, B. L., *Mathematische Statistik*, Berlin, 1957. *35)* Pearson and Wilks, *Biometrika*, **25**, 353 (1933). *36)* Freeman and Tukey, *Ann. math. Statist.*, **21**, 607 (1950). *37)* Clopper and Pearson, *Biometrika*, **26**, 404 (1934). *38)* Wilks, S. S., *Bull. Amer. math. Soc.*, **54**, 6 (1948). *39)* Scheffé and Tukey, *Memorandum Report 28*, Statistical Research Group, Princeton University, 1949. *40)* Bliss, C. I., *Biometrics*, **9**, 176 (1953). *41)* Katz, L., *J. Amer. statist. Ass.*, **48**, 256 (1953). *42)* Bross, I., *Biometrics*, **10**, 245 (1954). *43)* Wilcoxon, F., *Biometrics*, **1**, 80 (1945). *44)* Wilcoxon, F., *Biometrics*, **3**, 119 (1947). *45)* Haldane and Smith, *Ann. Eugen. (Lond.)*, **14**, 117 (1947–1949). *46)* Walter, E., *Mittbl. math. Statist.*, **6**, 92 (1954). *47)* Walter, E., *Mittbl. math. Statist.*, **6**, 170 (1954). *48)* Walter, E., *Metrika*, **1**, 81 (1958). *49)* Neumann et al., *Ann. math. Statist.*, **12**, 153 (1941). *50)* Anderson, R. L., *Ann. math. Statist.*, **13**, 1 (1942). *51)* Wald and Wolfowitz, *Ann. math. Statist.*, **14**, 378 (1943). *52)* Bennett and Franklin, *Statistical Analysis in Chemistry and the Chemical Industry*, New York, 1954. *53)* Levene and Wolfowitz, *Ann. math. Statist.*, **15**, 58 (1944). *54)* Wolfowitz, J., *Ann. math. Statist.*, **15**, 163 (1944). *55)* Olmstead, P. S., *Ann. math. Statist.*, **17**, 24 (1946). *56)* Olmstead, P. S., *Runs Determined in a Sample by an Arbitrary Cut*, Bell Telephone System Technical Publications, Monograph 2937, New York, 1958. *57)* Mood, A. M., *Ann. math. Statist.*, **11**, 367 (1940). *58)* Stevens, W. L., *Ann. Eugen. (Lond.)*, **9**, 10 (1939). *59)* Wald and Wolfowitz, *Ann. math. Statist.*, **11**, 147 (1940). *60)* von Bortkiewicz, L., *Die Iterationen*, Berlin, 1917. *61)* Armitage, P., *Sequential Medical Trials*, Oxford, 1960. *62)* Bross, I., *Biometrics*, **8**, 188 (1952). *63)* Harvard University Computation Laboratory, *Tables of the Cumulative Binomial Probability Distribution*, Cambridge, Mass., 1955. *64)* Lieberman and Owen, *Tables of the Hypergeometric Probability Distribution*, Stanford, Cal., 1961.

Contents (pages 145–195)

Index (pages 145–195)

Page numbers are in roman type, proposition numbers in **bold** type

Qualities, physical magnitudes, dimensions[1]

The representation of physical phenomena requires among other things the use of purely qualitative concepts such as length, mass, time, acceleration, force, velocity and so on. These concepts are known as *physical qualities* (or *quantities*) and are established and defined by means of appropriate methods of measurement.

When the abstract quality is combined with a measurement, as in "velocity of light" or "radius of the electron", the result is known as a *physical magnitude*. Such physical magnitudes are thus divisible into a qualitative and a quantitative component. It follows that their measurement requires the establishment not only of a *method* but also of a *unit*, that is to say of a known and easily reproducible amount of the quality concerned.

In physics, qualities are related to each other both in an abstract and a mathematical way by means of equations. By a process of substitution most qualities, and therefore their magnitudes, can thus be expressed in terms of a small number of fundamental qualities which in the present state of scientific knowledge cannot be related to each other by natural laws. These fundamental qualities are known as *dimensions*. Their definition rests a priori on an agreed basic method of measurement. Purely numerical values such as ½, ¼, π, as well as the ratios of two like qualities such as angles and specific gravity, are dimensionless.

The number of dimensions required for the complete representation of the various fields of physics varies from field to field. Two are sufficient in kinematics, three in mechanics, while additional dimensions are necessary in thermodynamics, electrodynamics and photometry.

In theoretical physics the analysis of the dimensions of physical qualities plays an important role. If physical magnitudes are to be equated, added or subtracted, clearly they must have the same dimensional formula. This principle of dimensional equivalence is used in testing the validity of equations expressing relationships between physical magnitudes, where all the terms of the equation must have identical dimensions.

Systems of measurement

The *nature* of a system of measurement is determined unequivocally by the combination of fundamental dimensions on which it is based. Systems of measurement with differing dimensions are known as *unlike* systems, for example the Length-Mass-Time systems (LMT-systems) in physics and the corresponding Length-Force-Time systems (LFT-systems) in technology. The interconversion of two unlike systems may be effected by replacing the differing dimension (or fundamental quality) in the one system by the dimensional formula of the *derived quality* in the other system. In the case of the LFT- and LMT-systems, for example, the dimension F (force) has the dimensional formula LMT^{-2} in the LMT-system, so that any dimensional formula in the LFT-system may be converted to the LMT-system simply by substituting LMT^{-2} for F.

The various fundamental qualities or dimensions are assigned appropriate *basic units*. The choice of the size of the basic units is merely a matter of expediency, so that various LMT-systems exist side by side: the CGS-system (basic units: centimeter, gram, mean solar second), the MKS-system (basic units: meter, kilogram, mean solar second), the MTS-system (basic units: meter, metric ton, mean solar second), the FPS-system (basic units: foot, pound, second), and others. Systems such as these, with like dimensions but employing different basic units, are known as *like systems*.

In order to arrive at the units of derived qualities within any system of measurement, the individual dimensions in the dimensional formula concerned are simply replaced by the appropriate basic units of the system. For example, the dimensional formula of force in the LMT-systems is LMT^{-2}. The unit of force in the CGS-system is therefore cm g s^{-2}, in the MKS-system m kg s^{-2}, in the MTS-system m t sec^{-2}, in the FPS-system ft lb sec^{-2}, and so on. When such derived units are in frequent use they usually acquire special names, like the following units of force in the LMT-systems: cm g s^{-2} = dyne (CGS-system), m kg s^{-2} = newton (MKS-system), m t sec^{-2} = sthene (MTS-system), ft lb sec^{-2} = poundal (FPS-system).

The LMT-systems with decimal division of the units (except time units) are all based on the metric system and have long been used internationally in science and technology. In the United States, British Commonwealth and other English-speaking countries the FPS-system continues to be very largely used in technology, but its gradual replacement by the metric system is under consideration. The CGS- or absolute system, up till now that most extensively used in physics, has given place in recent years to the MKS-system, since the absolute electrical system of measurement (basic units: m-s-V_{abs}-I_{abs}), which has enjoyed international recognition since 1948, is integrated with this system. As part of the GIORGI system, which except for the use of other dimensions conforms with the absolute electrical system, it has for example been the statutory system in Switzerland since 1950. In France the MTS-system has been the statutory system since 1919. Also internationally recognized are the LFT-systems of technology, namely the cm-p-s-system (basic units: centimeter, gram-force [pond], second, corresponding to the CGS-system) and the m-kp-s-system (basic units: meter, kilogram-force [kilopond], second, corresponding to the MKS-system).

Symbols for dimensions, units and constants

The following conventions are accepted internationally: Symbols for units are written in perpendicular script, symbols for qualities and physical magnitudes in italic script. Lower case letters are used for the symbols of all units with the exception of some of those named after famous scientists.

For the symbols of dimensions the modern tendency is to use sans-serif capital letters in place of the lower case italics earlier customary.

The Metric Convention

The decisions of the Metric Convention, to which 33 countries now subscribe, are to be found in the *Procès-Verbaux des Séances, Comité international des Poids et Mesures,* and in the *Comptes rendus de la Conférence générale des Poids et Mesures,* both published in Paris.

---

1) Cf. FOCKEN, C. M., *Dimensional Methods and Their Applications*, London, 1953; FLEISCHMANN, R., *Z. phys.*, **129**, 377 (1951); HÄBERLI, F., *Schweiz. Arch. angew. Wiss. Techn.*, **13**, 65, 113, 136 (1947).

Where there is a difference between US and British units, the equivalents of the latter are given in *italics*

Length

Inches (in)	Feet (ft)	Yards (yd)	Rods (rd)	Miles (mi)
1	1/12 = 0.083 333	1/36 = 0.027 778	1/198 = 0.005 050 51	1/63360 = 0.000 015 782 8
12	1	1/3 = 0.333 333	2/33 = 0.060 606 1	1/5280 = 0.000 189 394
36	3	1	2/11 = 0.181 818	1/1760 = 0.000 568 182
198	16.5	5.5	1	1/320 = 0.003 125
63,360	5280	1760	320	1

Area

Square inches (sq.in)	Square feet (sq.ft)	Square yards (sq.yd)	Square rods (sq.rd)	Acres (A.)	Square miles (sq.mi)
1	1/144 = 0.006 944 4	1/1296 = 0.000 771 6	1/39204 = $2.550\,8 \times 10^{-5}$	$1.594\,2 \times 10^{-7}$	$2.490\,41 \times 10^{-10}$
144	1	1/9 = 0.111 1	4/1089 = 0.003 673 1	1/43560 = $2.295\,68 \times 10^{-5}$	$3.587\,01 \times 10^{-8}$
1,296	9	1	4/121 = 0.033 057 85	1/4840 = $2.066\,12 \times 10^{-4}$	$3.228\,31 \times 10^{-7}$
39,204	272.25	30.25	1	1/160 = 0.006 25	$9.765\,625 \times 10^{-6}$
6,272,640	43,560	4 840	160	1	1/640 = 0.001 5625
4.0154×10^{9}	27,878,400	3,097,600	102,400	640	1

Volume

Cubic inches (cu.in)	Cubic feet (cu.ft)	Cubic yards (cu.yd)
1	1/1728 = 0.000 578 704	1/46656 = $2.143\,347 \times 10^{-5}$
1,728	1	1/27 = 0.037 037 0
46,656	27	1

Capacity — Liquid Measure

Gills (gi)	Pints (pt)	Quarts (qt)	Gallons (gal)	Cubic inches (cu.in)
1	1/4 = 0.25	1/8 = 0.125	1/32 = 0.031 25	7.218 75 (*8.669*)
4	1	1/2 = 0.5	1/8 = 0.125	28.875 (*34.678*)
8	2	1	1/4 = 0.25	57.75 (*69.355*)
32	8	4	1	231 (*277.421*)

Apothecaries' Fluid Measure

Minims (min or ♏)	Fluid drams (Brit.: fluid drachms) (fl.dr or ʒ fl.)	Fluid ounces (fl.oz or ℥ fl.)	Pints (pt)
1	1/60 = 0.016 667	1/480 = 0.002 083 3	(1/7680 = 0.000 130 21 1/9600 = *0.000 104 17*)
60	1	1/8 = 0.125	(1/128 = 0.007 812 5 1/160 = *0.006 25*)
480	8	1	(1/16 = 0.062 5 1/20 = *0.05*)
7680 (*9600*)	128 (*160*)	16 (*20*)	1

Dry Measure

Pints (pt)	Quarts (qt)	Pecks (pk)	Bushels (bu)	Cubic inches (cu. in)
1	1/2 = 0.5	1/16 = 0.062 5	1/64 = 0.015 625	33.600 3
2	1	1/8 = 0.125	1/32 = 0.031 25	67.200 6
16	8	1	1/4 = 0.25	537.605 (*554.6*)
64	32	4	1	2150.42 (*2219.3*)

Mass — Avoirdupois (commercial)

Grains (gr)	Drams (dr.av.)	Ounces (oz.av.)	Pounds (lb.av.)	Tons (short) (sh.tn)
1	0.036 571 43	0.002 285 7	1/7000 = 0.000 142 86	7.1429×10^{-7}
27.343 75	1	1/16 = 0.062 5	1/256 = 0.003 906 25	1.9531×10^{-6}
437.5	16	1	1/16 = 0.062 5	1/32000 = 0.000 031 25
7000	256	16	1	1/2000 = 0.0005
1,400,000	512,000	32,000	2000	1

Mass — Troy Weight

Grains (gr)	Pennyweights (dwt)	Ounces (oz.t.)	Pounds (lb.t.)
1	1/24 = 0.041 667	1/480 = 0.002 0833	1/5760 = 0.000 173 611 1
24	1	1/20 = 0.05	1/240 = 0.004 166 7
480	20	1	1/12 = 0.083 333
5760	240	12	1

Mass — Apothecaries' Weight

Grains (gr)	Scruples (℈ or s.ap.)	Drams (Brit: drachms) (ʒ or dr.ap.)	Ounces (℥ or oz.ap.)	Pounds (lb.ap.)
1	1/20 = 0.05	1/60 = 0.016 667	1/480 = 0.002 083 3	1/5760 = 0.000 173 611 1
20	1	1/3 = 0.333 333	1/24 = 0.041 667	1/288 = 0.003 472 2
60	3	1	1/8 = 0.125	1/96 = 0.010 416 7
480	24	8	1	1/12 = 0.083 333
5760	288	96	12	1

Conversion Table for Apothecaries' and Metric Weights for Use in Prescribing[1]

Grains	Milligrams	Grains	Milligrams	Grains	Milligrams	Grains	Milligrams
10	600	1/2	30	1/20	3	1/150, 1/160 }	0.4
7 1/2	450	2/5	25	1/25	2.5	1/200	0.3
5	300	1/3	20	1/30	2	1/240	0.25
4	250	1/4	15	1/40	1.5	1/300, 1/320 }	0.2
3	200	1/5	12.5	1/50	1.25	1/480	0.125
2 1/2	150	1/6	10	1/60	1	1/600	0.1
2	125	1/8	7.5	1/75	0.8		
1 1/2	100	1/10	6	1/100	0.6		
1	60	1/12	5	1/120, 1/130 }	0.5		
3/4	50	1/15	4				

1) Approved by the British Medical Association and the Pharmaceutical Society of Great Britain. Cf. Editorial, *Brit. med. J.*, 2, 794 (1960).

Length

Dimension in all systems of measurement = L

Basic units

MKS-system: meter (m)
CGS-system: centimeter (cm)
MTS-system: meter (m)
ft-lb-s-system: foot (ft)

Metric system

The fundamental standard of length in the metric system is the *meter* (m)[1], formerly the distance at 0°C between two marks engraved on a platinum-iridium bar, the international prototype meter, preserved at the International Bureau of Weights and Measures at Sèvres (France). Agreement has recently been reached in the International Metric Convention[2] on the replacement of this definition by one based on the wave length of a particular spectral line, as follows:

1 meter = $1.650\,763\,73 \times 10^{6}\,\lambda_{\mathrm{Kr\text{-}86}}$

where $\lambda_{\mathrm{Kr\text{-}86}} = 6.057\,802\,1 \times 10^{-7}$ m is the wave length in vacuo of the orange-red radiation corresponding to the transition between two specific energy levels of the krypton-86 atom.

United States and British (imperial) system

The fundamental standard of length in the system in use in the English-speaking countries (the "English" system) is the *yard* (yd). In the United States this is legally defined in terms of the meter (the National Bureau of Standards holds a National Prototype Meter which is identical, within the uncertainty of the measurements, with the international prototype) as follows[3]:

$$1\ \text{US yard} = \frac{3600}{393\mathbf{7}}\ \text{meter} = 0.914\,401\,829\ \text{meter}$$

$$1\ \text{US inch} = 25.400\,051\ \text{millimeters} = 4.192\,939\,9 \times 10^{4}\,\lambda_{\mathrm{Kr\text{-}86}}$$

In the United Kingdom the yard is defined[4] as the distance at 62° F between two lines ruled on a bronze bar, the Imperial Standard Yard, held in the Standards Department of the Board of Trade in London. For the imperial yard there exist two differing accepted relations to the meter, viz., the legally defined relation[5]:

1 imperial yard = 0.914 399 208 meter
1 imperial inch = 25.399 978 millimeters

and the more recently determined relation used in precise scientific measurements[6]:

1 imperial yard = 0.914 398 416 meter
1 imperial inch = 25.399 956 millimeters

In addition, both in the United States[7] and United Kingdom[5], the following *standardized* relation is accepted for industrial purposes:

1 yard = 0.914**4** meter
1 inch = 25.**4** millimeters

It has recently been agreed by the major English-speaking countries that this standardized yard shall be established as an "international yard" for use generally in science and technology, thus finally eliminating the discrepancies between the present units[8].

The relationships *between corresponding length units* in the "English" system of measurement are shown in the left-hand table on the opposite page.

Nautical and geodetic length units

The *nautical mile* is defined as the length of the mean minute of arc on the meridian of the earth (mean minute of latitude). Using the values of the earth's polar and equatorial radii derived from the international terrestrial geoid[9]

$$1\ \text{nautical mile} = \frac{\text{Meridian quadrant } Q_{♁}^{Me}}{90 \times 60} = 1852.276\ \text{meters}$$

In 1928 an international *standard* value was proposed[10]:

1 international nautical mile = 185**2** meters = 2025.368 US yards

This value has been accepted by all maritime nations (United States, 1954[11]) with the exception of the United Kingdom, where the nautical mile is based on the British value of the *knot* (nautical mile per hour) of 608**0** imperial feet per hour, whence

1 imp. nautical mile (n. mi.) = 608**0** imp. feet = 1853.181 meters

The *geographical mile* (not to be confused with the land, or statute, mile) is defined as the length of 4 minutes of arc on the equator. Using the value of the earth's equatorial radius $a_{♁}$ derived from the international reference ellipsoid[9]

$$1\ \text{geographical mile} = 4 \times \frac{\text{Equatorial quadrant } Q_{♁}^{E}}{90 \times 60} = 7421.591\ \text{meters} = 8116.335\ \text{US yards}$$

Astronomical length units

The *astronomical unit* (AU)[20] is defined as the distance between the sun and a hypothetical planet (its weight can be disregarded) which rotates around the sun in a circular path with a period of 365.256 898 326 mean days. In other words, a planet is situated at a distance of 1 AU from the sun when it rotates around the latter with a uniform angular velocity of 0.985 607 668 601° per mean day[12]. The AU is thus defined in terms of angle and time and not of length, and is accordingly regarded by astronomers as a *relative magnitude* and not as a length. Physically, this relative magnitude corresponds (≙) to the radius of the circular path of the above hypothetical planet; in practice it is regarded as being equal to the major semiaxis a of the earth's orbit, which differs only slightly from this radius. It may be calculated from the daily solar parallax $\pi_{\odot}$ (the angle subtended by the equatorial radius of the earth $a_{♁}$ at the distance a of the sun) and the equatorial radius as follows:

$$a = \frac{a_{♁}}{\sin \pi_{\odot}} \cong \frac{a_{♁}}{\pi_{\odot}}$$

Using the standard values for the solar parallax $\pi_{\odot} = 8.8\mathbf{0}''$[13] and equatorial radius $a_{♁} = 6378.38\mathbf{8}$ km[9]

$$1\ \text{AU} ≙ \frac{6378.388 \times 60 \times 60 \times 180}{8.8 \times \pi}\ \text{km} ≙ 1.495\,042 \times 10^{8}\ \text{km}$$

The 10^{6} multiple of the astronomical unit is known as the *siriometer*:

1 siriometer ≡ 10^{6} AU ≙ $1.495\,042 \times 10^{14}$ km

The *parsec* (pc) is defined as the distance of a fixed star possessing an annual stellar parallax p (the angle subtended by 1 AU at the distance of the star) equal to 1″[13]:

$$1\ \text{pc} = \frac{1\ \text{AU}}{p} = \frac{1\ \text{AU}}{\sin 1''} \cong \frac{1\ \text{AU}}{1''} = \frac{60 \times 60 \times 180}{\pi}\ \text{AU} = 2.062\,648 \times 10^{5}\ \text{AU} ≙ 3.083\,745 \times 10^{13}\ \text{km}$$

The distance of 5 parsec is known as the *distance of Sirius*:

1 distance of Sirius = 5 pc = $1.031\,324 \times 10^{6}$ AU ≙ $1.541\,873 \times 10^{14}$ km

In astrophysics it has become usual to express distances in terms of the *light year* (ly). This is the distance traveled by light at the vacuum velocity c_0 in one tropical year (a_{trop})[14]:

$$1\ \text{light year} = c_0 \times 1\,a_{\mathrm{trop}} = (299\,792.50 \pm 0.04)\ \text{km s}^{-1} \times 3.155\,692\,97 \times 10^{7}\ \text{s} = (9.460\,530 \pm 0.000\,001) \times 10^{12}\ \text{km}$$

Spectrometric length units

The unit of wave length in X-ray spectrometry, the Siegbahn *X-unit* (XU)[15] is related to the lattice constant of calcite and is defined by the relation:

$d_{\infty}^{18^{\circ}\mathrm{C}}\,(CaCO_3) = 3029.4\mathbf{5}$ X-units

The XU has been evaluated experimentally in metric units. The following value has been agreed upon by the X-Ray Analysis Group of the Institute of Physics (England), the American Society for X-Ray and Electron Diffraction, and Professor Siegbahn[16]:

1 XU = $(1.002\,02 \pm 0.000\,03) \times 10^{-13}$ meter

The value in ångströms (Å; see below) (when the uncertainty in the conversion Å→ m is ignored) is therefore

1 XU = $(1.002\,02 \pm 0.000\,03) \times 10^{-3}$ ångström

DuMond[17] (1959) has calculated a value of $1.002\,031 \times 10^{-3}$ for XU/Å, in agreement with the value of Birge[18] (1945) of $1.002\,030 \pm 0.000\,02 \times 10^{-3}$ Å for 1 XU.

The *ångström* is the unit of wave length in optical spectrometry. It is defined by the relation[19]:

Wave length of the red cadmium line ($\lambda_{n\mathrm{Cd}}$) = 6438.469**6** ångströms

The measured wave length[13] of the red cadmium line is

$\lambda_{n\mathrm{Cd}} = (6.438\,469_{6} \pm 0.000\,003) \times 10^{-7}$ meter

whence[13]

1 ångström = $(1.000\,000 \pm 0.000\,000\,5) \times 10^{-10}$ meter

Under the new definition of the meter (above) this relation becomes
1 ångström = **1** × 10^{-10} meter

---

1) *Comptes rendus de la 1re Conférence générale des Poids et Mesures*, Paris, 1889, page 100. *2)* Barrell, H., *Nature*, **180**, 1387 (1957); Froome, K.D., *Proc. roy. Soc. A*, **247**, 109 (1958); Editorial, *Science*, **132**, 1384 (1960). *3)* *U.S. Coast and Geodetic Survey, Treasury Department*, Bull. **26** (1893) (Mendenhall Order). *4)* *Weights and Measures Act*, 1878. *5)* British Standards Institution, *BS 350* (1944) (*Conversion Factors and Tables*). *6)* Sears et al., *Phil. Trans. A*, **227**, 281 (1928). *7)* American Standards Association, *ASA B 48.1* (1933) (*Inch-Millimeter Conversion Tables for Industrial Use*). *8)* Gould, F. A., *Nature*, **182**, 1767 (1958); Editorial, *Nature*, **183**, 80 (1959); Editorial, *Science*, **129**, 260 (1959). *9)* International Union of Geodesy and Geophysics, *Bull. géod. int.*, **1925**, 157, 540, 552. *10)* International Hydrographic Bureau, *Abridged Manual of the Symbols and Abbreviations used on Charts*, Special Publ. 22, Monaco, 1928; also in *Hydrogr. Rev.*, **5**, 227 (1928). *11)* National Bureau of Standards, *Techn. News Bull. U.S. Bur. Stand.*, **38**, 122 (1954). *12)* International Astronomical Union, *Trans. int. astr. Un.*, **6**, 20, 336 (1938); Bureau des Longitudes, *Annuaire pour l'an 1954*, Paris, 1954, page 189. *13)* Cf. Stille, U., *Messen und Rechnen in der Physik*, Braunschweig, 1955. *14)* c_0-Value of the *International Scientific Radio Union* and *International Union of Geodesy and Geophysics*, mentioned in *17)*. *15)* Siegbahn, M., *Ann. Phys.*, **59** (4th Series), 56 (1919); *Spektroskopie der Röntgenstrahlen*, Berlin, 1932. *16)* Wood, E.A., *Phys. Rev.*, **72**, 436 (1947); Bragg, W. L., *J. sci. Instrum.*, **24**, 27 (1947). *17)* DuMond, J.W.M., *Ann. Phys. (N.Y.)*, **7**, 365 (1959). *18)* Birge, R. T., *Amer. J. Phys.*, **13**, 69 (1945.) *19)* The International Union for Co-operation in Solar Research, *Trans. int. Un. solar Res.*, **2**, 20 (1908); **3**, 135 (1911). *20)* For a review see Thomson, J. H., *The Times Science Review*, Autumn 1961, page 5.

Conversion factors for length, area and volume units in the United States and British (Imperial) system

Imperial	Units of length				Units of area				Units of volume			
	Imp. comm.	Imp. scientific	United States	Standardized	Imp. comm.	Imp. scientific	United States	Standardized	Imp. comm.	Imp. scientific	United States	Standardized
commercial	**1**	1.000 000 866	0.999 997 133	0.999 999 133	**1**	1.000 001 732	0.999 994 266	0.999 998 266	**1**	1.000 002 598	0.999 991 399	0.999 997 399
scientific ...	0.999 999 133	**1**	0.999 996 267	0.999 998 267	0.999 998 266	**1**	0.999 992 534	0.999 996 534	0.999 997 399	**1**	0.999 988 801	0.999 994 801
United States .	1.000 002 866	1.000 003 732	**1**	1.000 002 000	1.000 005 732	1.000 007 464	**1**	1.000 004 000	1.000 008 598	1.000 011 196	**1**	1.000 006 000
Standardized .	1.000 000 866	1.000 001 732	0.999 998 000	**1**	1.000 001 732	1.000 003 464	0.999 996 000	**1**	1.000 002 598	1.000 005 196	0.999 994 000	**1**

Conversion factors for length units*

To convert from a unit in col. **A** into any unit under **C**, multiply by the factor in col. **B** and by the power of 10 given in the appropriate col. under **C**

A		B	C: nm	µm	mm	cm	dm	m	km
Nanometer (millimicron)	nm(mµ)	**1** ×	1	10^{-3}	10^{-6}	10^{-7}	10^{-8}	10^{-9}	10^{-12}
Micrometer (micron) ...	µm (µ)	**1** ×	10^{3}	1	10^{-3}	10^{-4}	10^{-5}	10^{-6}	10^{-9}
Millimeter	mm	**1** ×	10^{6}	10^{3}	1	10^{-1}	10^{-2}	10^{-3}	10^{-6}
Centimeter	cm	**1** ×	10^{7}	10^{4}	10	1	10^{-1}	10^{-2}	10^{-5}
Decimeter	dm	**1** ×	10^{8}	10^{5}	10^{2}	10	1	10^{-1}	10^{-4}
Meter	m	**1** ×	10^{9}	10^{6}	10^{3}	10^{2}	10	1	10^{-3}
Decameter	dkm	**1** ×	10^{10}	10^{7}	10^{4}	10^{3}	10^{2}	10	10^{-2}
Hectometer	hm	**1** ×	10^{11}	10^{8}	10^{5}	10^{4}	10^{3}	10^{2}	10^{-1}
Kilometer..........	km	**1** ×	10^{12}	10^{9}	10^{6}	10^{5}	10^{4}	10^{3}	1
X-unit (Siegbahn unit).	XU	1.002 02 ×	10^{-4}	10^{-7}	10^{-10}	10^{-11}	10^{-12}	10^{-13}	10^{-16}
Ångström	Å	1.000 000×	10^{-1}	10^{-4}	10^{-7}	10^{-8}	10^{-9}	10^{-10}	10^{-13}
Astronomical unit	AU	1.495 042×	10^{20}	10^{17}	10^{14}	10^{13}	10^{12}	10^{11}	10^{8}
Siriometer..........		1.495 042×	10^{26}	10^{23}	10^{20}	10^{19}	10^{18}	10^{17}	10^{14}
Parsec..............	pc	3.083 745×	10^{25}	10^{22}	10^{19}	10^{18}	10^{17}	10^{16}	10^{13}
Distance of Sirius		1.541 873×	10^{26}	10^{23}	10^{20}	10^{19}	10^{18}	10^{17}	10^{14}
Light year	ly	9.460 530×	10^{24}	10^{21}	10^{18}	10^{17}	10^{16}	10^{15}	10^{12}
Mil .... (US)	mil	2.540 005×	10^{4}	10	10^{-2}	10^{-3}	10^{-4}	10^{-5}	10^{-8}
Mil .... (imp.)	mil	2.539 996×	10^{4}	10	10^{-2}	10^{-3}	10^{-4}	10^{-5}	10^{-8}
Inch .... (US)	in	2.540 005×	10^{7}	10^{4}	10	1	10^{-1}	10^{-2}	10^{-5}
Inch .... (imp.)	in	2.539 996×	10^{7}	10^{4}	10	1	10^{-1}	10^{-2}	10^{-5}
Foot .... (US)	ft	3.048 006×	10^{8}	10^{5}	10^{2}	10	1	10^{-1}	10^{-4}
Foot .... (imp.)	ft	3.047 995×	10^{8}	10^{5}	10^{2}	10	1	10^{-1}	10^{-4}
Yard .... (US)	yd	9.144 018×	10^{8}	10^{5}	10^{2}	10	1	10^{-1}	10^{-4}
Yard .... (imp.)	yd	9.143 984×	10^{8}	10^{5}	10^{2}	10	1	10^{-1}	10^{-4}
Mile .... (US)	mi	1.609 347×	10^{12}	10^{9}	10^{6}	10^{5}	10^{4}	10^{3}	1
Mile .... (imp.)	mi	1.609 341×	10^{12}	10^{9}	10^{6}	10^{5}	10^{4}	10^{3}	1
Nautical mile . (int.)	n. mi	**1.852** ×	10^{12}	10^{9}	10^{6}	10^{5}	10^{4}	10^{3}	1
Nautical mile . (imp.)	n. mi	1.853 181×	10^{12}	10^{9}	10^{6}	10^{5}	10^{4}	10^{3}	1

To convert from a unit in column **A** into any unit under **D**, multiply by the factor given in the appropriate column under **D**

A		D: XU	Å	AU	pc	ly	mi (US)	yd (US)	ft (US)	in (US)
Nanometer (millimicron)	nm(mµ)	9.979 84 $\times10^{5}$	1.000 000 $\times10$	6.688 775 $\times10^{-21}$	3.242 810 $\times10^{-26}$	1.057 023 $\times10^{-25}$	6.213 699 $\times10^{-13}$	1.093 611 $\times10^{-9}$	3.280 8$\dot{3}$ $\times10^{-9}$	**3.937** $\times10^{-8}$
Micrometer (micron) ...	µm (µ)	9.979 84 $\times10^{8}$	1.000 000 $\times10^{4}$	6.688 775 $\times10^{-18}$	3.242 810 $\times10^{-23}$	1.057 023 $\times10^{-22}$	6.213 699 $\times10^{-10}$	1.093 611 $\times10^{-6}$	3.280 8$\dot{3}$ $\times10^{-6}$	**3.937** $\times10^{-5}$
Millimeter	mm	9.979 84 $\times10^{11}$	1.000 000 $\times10^{7}$	6.688 775 $\times10^{-15}$	3.242 810 $\times10^{-20}$	1.057 023 $\times10^{-19}$	6.213 699 $\times10^{-7}$	1.093 611 $\times10^{-3}$	3.280 8$\dot{3}$ $\times10^{-3}$	**3.937** $\times10^{-2}$
Centimeter	cm	9.979 84 $\times10^{12}$	1.000 000 $\times10^{8}$	6.688 775 $\times10^{-14}$	3.242 810 $\times10^{-19}$	1.057 023 $\times10^{-18}$	6.213 699 $\times10^{-6}$	1.093 611 $\times10^{-2}$	3.280 8$\dot{3}$ $\times10^{-2}$	**3.937** $\times10^{-1}$
Decimeter	dm	9.979 84 $\times10^{13}$	1.000 000 $\times10^{9}$	6.688 775 $\times10^{-13}$	3.242 810 $\times10^{-18}$	1.057 023 $\times10^{-17}$	6.213 699 $\times10^{-5}$	1.093 611 $\times10^{-1}$	3.280 8$\dot{3}$ $\times10^{-1}$	**3.937** × 1
Meter	m	9.979 84 $\times10^{14}$	1.000 000 $\times10^{10}$	6.688 775 $\times10^{-12}$	3.242 810 $\times10^{-17}$	1.057 023 $\times10^{-16}$	6.213 699 $\times10^{-4}$	1.093 611 × 1	3.280 8$\dot{3}$ × 1	**3.937** × 10
Decameter	dkm	9.979 84 $\times10^{15}$	1.000 000 $\times10^{11}$	6.688 775 $\times10^{-11}$	3.242 810 $\times10^{-16}$	1.057 023 $\times10^{-15}$	6.213 699 $\times10^{-3}$	1.093 611 × 10	3.280 8$\dot{3}$ × 10	**3.937** $\times10^{2}$
Hectometer	hm	9.979 84 $\times10^{16}$	1.000 000 $\times10^{12}$	6.688 775 $\times10^{-10}$	3.242 810 $\times10^{-15}$	1.057 023 $\times10^{-14}$	6.213 699 $\times10^{-2}$	1.093 611 $\times10^{2}$	3.280 8$\dot{3}$ $\times10^{2}$	**3.937** $\times10^{3}$
Kilometer..........	km	9.979 84 $\times10^{17}$	1.000 000 $\times10^{13}$	6.688 775 $\times10^{-9}$	3.242 810 $\times10^{-14}$	1.057 023 $\times10^{-13}$	6.213 699 $\times10^{-1}$	1.093 611 $\times10^{3}$	3.280 8$\dot{3}$ $\times10^{3}$	**3.937** $\times10^{4}$
X-unit (Siegbahn unit).	XU	**1** × 1	1.002 02 $\times10^{-3}$	6.702 29 $\times10^{-25}$	3.249 36 $\times10^{-30}$	1.059 16 $\times10^{-29}$	6.226 25 $\times10^{-17}$	1.095 82 $\times10^{-13}$	3.287 46 $\times10^{-13}$	3.944 95 $\times10^{-12}$
Ångström	Å	9.979 84 $\times10^{2}$	**1** × 1	6.688 775 $\times10^{-22}$	3.242 810 $\times10^{-27}$	1.057 023 $\times10^{-26}$	6.213 699 $\times10^{-14}$	1.093 611 $\times10^{-10}$	3.280 833 $\times10^{-10}$	3.937 000 $\times10^{-9}$
Astronomical unit	AU	1.492 03 $\times10^{24}$	1.495 042 $\times10^{21}$	**1** × 1	4.848 137 $\times10^{-6}$	1.580 294 $\times10^{-5}$	9.289 742 $\times10^{9}$	1.634 995 $\times10^{11}$	4.904 984 $\times10^{11}$	5.885 980 $\times10^{12}$
Siriometer..........		1.492 03 $\times10^{30}$	1.495 042 $\times10^{27}$	**1** $\times10^{6}$	4.848 137 × 1	1.580 294 × 10	9.289 742 $\times10^{15}$	1.634 995 $\times10^{17}$	4.904 984 $\times10^{17}$	5.885 980 $\times10^{18}$
Parsec..............	pc	3.077 53 $\times10^{29}$	3.083 745 $\times10^{26}$	2.062 648 $\times10^{5}$	**1** × 1	3.259 591 × 1	1.916 147 $\times10^{13}$	3.372 418 $\times10^{16}$	1.011 726 $\times10^{17}$	1.214 071 $\times10^{17}$
Distance of Sirius		1.538 76 $\times10^{30}$	1.541 873 $\times10^{27}$	1.031 324 $\times10^{6}$	**5** × 1	1.629 795 × 10	9.580 734 $\times10^{13}$	1.686 209 $\times10^{17}$	5.058 628 $\times10^{17}$	6.070 353 $\times10^{17}$
Light year	ly	9.441 46 $\times10^{28}$	9.460 530 $\times10^{25}$	6.327 936 $\times10^{4}$	3.067 870 $\times10^{-1}$	**1** × 1	5.878 489 $\times10^{12}$	1.034 614 $\times10^{16}$	3.103 842 $\times10^{16}$	3.724 611 $\times10^{17}$
Mil .... (US)	mil	2.534 88 $\times10^{8}$	2.540 005 $\times10^{5}$	1.698 952 $\times10^{-16}$	8.236 753 $\times10^{-22}$	2.684 844 $\times10^{-21}$	1.578 $\dot{2}$ $\times10^{-8}$	2.$\dot{7}$ $\times10^{-5}$	8.$\dot{3}$ $\times10^{-5}$	**1** $\times10^{-3}$
Mil .... (imp.)	mil	2.534 88 $\times10^{8}$	2.539 996 $\times10^{5}$	1.698 946 $\times10^{-16}$	8.236 723 $\times10^{-22}$	2.684 834 $\times10^{-21}$	1.578 277 $\times10^{-8}$	2.777 767 $\times10^{-5}$	8.333 302 $\times10^{-5}$	9.999 963 $\times10^{-4}$
Inch .... (US)	in	2.534 88 $\times10^{11}$	2.540 005 $\times10^{8}$	1.698 952 $\times10^{-13}$	8.236 753 $\times10^{-19}$	2.684 844 $\times10^{-18}$	1.578 $\dot{2}$ $\times10^{-5}$	2.$\dot{7}$ $\times10^{-2}$	8.$\dot{3}$ $\times10^{-2}$	**1** × 1
Inch .... (imp.)	in	2.534 88 $\times10^{11}$	2.539 996 $\times10^{8}$	1.698 946 $\times10^{-13}$	8.236 723 $\times10^{-19}$	2.684 834 $\times10^{-18}$	1.578 277 $\times10^{-5}$	2.777 767 $\times10^{-2}$	8.333 302 $\times10^{-2}$	9.999 963 $\times10^{-1}$
Foot .... (US)	ft	3.041 86 $\times10^{12}$	3.048 006 $\times10^{9}$	2.038 743 $\times10^{-12}$	9.884 104 $\times10^{-18}$	3.221 813 $\times10^{-17}$	1.8$\dot{9}\dot{3}$ $\times10^{-4}$	3.$\dot{3}$ $\times10^{-1}$	**1** × 1	**1.2** × 10
Foot .... (imp.)	ft	3.041 85 $\times10^{12}$	3.047 995 $\times10^{9}$	2.038 735 $\times10^{-12}$	9.884 067 $\times10^{-18}$	3.221 801 $\times10^{-17}$	1.893 932 $\times10^{-4}$	3.333 321 $\times10^{-1}$	9.999 963 $\times10^{-1}$	1.199 996 × 10
Yard .... (US)	yd	9.125 58 $\times10^{12}$	9.144 018 $\times10^{9}$	6.116 228 $\times10^{-12}$	2.965 231 $\times10^{-17}$	9.665 440 $\times10^{-17}$	5.6$\dot{8}\dot{1}$ $\times10^{-4}$	**1** × 1	**3** × 1	**3.6** × 10
Yard .... (imp.)	yd	9.125 55 $\times10^{12}$	9.143 984 $\times10^{9}$	6.116 206 $\times10^{-12}$	2.965 220 $\times10^{-17}$	9.665 404 $\times10^{-17}$	5.681 797 $\times10^{-4}$	9.999 963 × 1	2.999 992 × 1	3.599 987 × 10
Mile .... (US)	mi	1.606 10 $\times10^{16}$	1.609 347 $\times10^{13}$	1.076 456 $\times10^{-8}$	5.218 807 $\times10^{-14}$	1.701 117 $\times10^{-13}$	**1** × 1	**1.76** $\times10^{3}$	**5.28** $\times10^{3}$	**6.336** $\times10^{4}$
Mile .... (imp.)	mi	1.606 10 $\times10^{16}$	1.609 341 $\times10^{13}$	1.076 452 $\times10^{-8}$	5.218 787 $\times10^{-14}$	1.701 111 $\times10^{-13}$	9.999 963 × 1	1.759 993 $\times10^{3}$	5.279 980 $\times10^{3}$	6.335 976 $\times10^{4}$
Nautical mile . (int.)	n. mi	1.848 27 $\times10^{16}$	1.852 000 $\times10^{13}$	1.238 761 $\times10^{-8}$	6.005 684 $\times10^{-14}$	1.957 607 $\times10^{-13}$	1.150 777 × 1	2.025 368 $\times10^{3}$	6.076 103 $\times10^{3}$	7.291 324 $\times10^{4}$
Nautical mile . (imp.)	n. mi	1.849 44 $\times10^{16}$	1.853 181 $\times10^{13}$	1.239 551 $\times10^{-8}$	6.009 513 $\times10^{-14}$	1.958 855 $\times10^{-13}$	1.151 511 × 1	2.026 659 $\times10^{3}$	6.079 977 $\times10^{3}$	7.295 973 $\times10^{4}$

* Note that the metric conversions in this table are based in the case of US units on the statutory relation, in the case of imperial units on the relation most recently determined (cf. remarks on the opposite page).

Area

Dimension

(derived from length in all systems of measurement) = L^2

Basic units

MKS-system: square meter (m^2)
CGS-system: square centimeter (cm^2)
MTS-system: square meter (m^2)
ft-lb-s-system: square foot (ft^2 or sq.ft) = $^1/_9$ square yard

United States and British (imperial) area units

Conversion factors for the United States, British (commercial and scientific) and standardized area units are obtained by squaring those for the corresponding length units and are given in the table on this page.

Circular inch. This unit is defined as the area of a circle of 1 inch diameter:

1 circular inch = $\pi/4$ in^2 = 10^6 circular mils

Volume and capacity

Dimension

(derived from length and area in all systems of measurement) = L^3

Basic units

MKS-system: cubic meter (m^3);
CGS-system: cubic centimeter (cm^3 or ccm)
MTS-system: cubic meter (m^3)
ft-lb-s-system: cubic foot (ft^3 or cu.ft) = $^1/_{27}$ cubic yard

Units of volume and of capacity

Physically, there is no theoretical difference between the units of volume and of capacity, the dimension of both being L^3. The units of volume are defined as the third power of the corresponding units of length, e.g. m^3, in^3, etc. However, the practical realization of this geometrical definition presents difficulties. The units of capacity, on the other hand, are based on a physical definition which can be readily and precisely realized in practice. This definition uses a measurement of *weight* instead of one of volume: the units of capacity are those volumes which under certain defined conditions will contain particular weights of water.

Metric system

The *basic unit of capacity* in the metric system is the liter, defined as the volume of one kilogram of pure, air-free water at its maximum density (at 3.98° C) under normal atmospheric pressure (1 atm = 760 mm Hg)[1]. In 1950, the International Committee of Weights and Measures established the following relation between the liter and metric *units of volume*[2]:

1 liter = 1.000 028 dm^3 = 1000.028 cm^3, etc.

The factor of 1.000 028 is now accepted as an absolute value for the conversion of capacity into volume units in the metric system.

"English" system

Units of volume (in^3, ft^3, etc.). Conversion factors for the United States, British (commercial and scientific) and standardized volume units are obtained by raising to the third power those for the corresponding length units and are given in the table on the opposite page.

Units of capacity. In the "English" system the usual capacity measures for liquids are the gallon (gal) and the units derived from it, for dry commodities the bushel (bu) and the units derived from it. It should be noted that in the United States the gallon and derived units may only be used for liquids, the bushel and derived units only for dry commodities. In the United Kingdom, on the other hand, the two sets of units are admissible both for liquid and dry commodities.

In the United States the following relations define the units of liquid and of dry measure:

1 US gallon = 231 US cubic inches
1 US bushel = 2150.42 US cubic inches

In the United Kingdom the gallon is defined by the Weights and Measures Act of 1878 as the volume occupied at 62° F by 10 imperial pounds of distilled water weighed in air with brass weights at a barometric pressure of 30 inches of mercury. Since this definition is lacking in precision, the following relations were established by an Order in Council of May 19th 1898:

1 imperial gallon = 4.545 9631 liters
1 imperial bushel = 8 imperial gallons

(continued on page 207)

1) *Comptes rendus de la 3e Conférence générale des Poids et Mesures*, Paris, 1901, page 37. 2) Comité international des Poids et Mesures, *P. V. Com. int. Poids Mes.*, **22**, 77, 94 (1950).

Conversion factors for area units

To convert from a unit in column **A** into any unit under **C**, multiply by the factor in column **B** and by the power of 10 given in the appropriate column under **C**

To convert from a unit in column **A** into any unit under **D**, multiply by the factor given in the appropriate column under **D**

A		B	C: µm²	C: mm²	C: cm²	C: dm²	C: m²	C: km²	D: circ.inch (US)	D: in² (US)	D: ft² (US)	D: yd² (US)	D: acre (US)	D: mi² (US)
Square micrometer	µm²	1	1	10⁻⁶	10⁻⁸	10⁻¹⁰	10⁻¹²	10⁻¹⁸	1.973 517×10⁻⁹	1.549 997×10⁻⁹	1.076 387×10⁻¹¹	1.195 985×10⁻¹²	2.471 044×10⁻¹⁶	3.861 006×10⁻¹⁹
Square millimeter	mm²	1	10⁶	1	10⁻²	10⁻⁴	10⁻⁶	10⁻¹²	1.973 517×10⁻³	1.549 997×10⁻³	1.076 387×10⁻⁵	1.195 985×10⁻⁶	2.471 044×10⁻¹⁰	3.861 006×10⁻¹³
Square centimeter	cm²	1	10⁸	10²	1	10⁻²	10⁻⁴	10⁻¹⁰	1.973 517×10⁻¹	1.549 997×10⁻¹	1.076 387×10⁻³	1.195 985×10⁻⁴	2.471 044×10⁻⁸	3.861 006×10⁻¹¹
Square decimeter	dm²	1	10¹⁰	10⁴	10²	1	10⁻²	10⁻⁸	1.973 517×10	1.549 997×10	1.076 387×10⁻¹	1.195 985×10⁻²	2.471 044×10⁻⁶	3.861 006×10⁻⁹
Square meter	m²	1	10¹²	10⁶	10⁴	10²	1	10⁻⁶	1.973 517×10³	1.549 997×10³	1.076 387×10	1.195 985× 1	2.471 044×10⁻⁴	3.861 006×10⁻⁷
Square decameter (are)	dam² (a)	1	10¹⁴	10⁸	10⁶	10⁴	10²	10⁻⁴	1.973 517×10⁵	1.549 997×10⁵	1.076 387×10³	1.195 985×10²	2.471 044×10⁻²	3.861 006×10⁻⁵
Square hectometer (hectare)	hm² (ha)	1	10¹⁶	10¹⁰	10⁸	10⁶	10⁴	10⁻²	1.973 517×10⁷	1.549 997×10⁷	1.076 387×10⁵	1.195 985×10⁴	2.471 044× 1	3.861 006×10⁻³
Square kilometer	km²	1	10¹⁸	10¹²	10¹⁰	10⁸	10⁶	1	1.973 517×10⁹	1.549 997×10⁹	1.076 387×10⁷	1.195 985×10⁶	2.471 044×10²	3.861 006×10⁻¹
Circular inch (US)	circ.in	5.067 095	10⁸	10²	1	10⁻²	10⁻⁴	10⁻¹⁰	1 × 1	7.853 982×10⁻¹	5.454 154×10⁻³	6.060 171×10⁻⁴	1.252 101×10⁻⁷	1.956 409×10⁻¹⁰
Circular inch (imp.)	circ.in	5.067 057	10⁸	10²	1	10⁻²	10⁻⁴	10⁻¹⁰	9.999 925×10⁻¹	7.853 923×10⁻¹	5.454 113×10⁻³	6.060 126×10⁻⁴	1.252 092×10⁻⁷	1.956 394×10⁻¹⁰
Square inch (US)	sq.in or in²	6.451 626	10⁸	10²	1	10⁻²	10⁻⁴	10⁻¹⁰	1.273 240× 1	1 × 1	6.94 ×10⁻³	7.716 049×10⁻⁴	1.594 225×10⁻⁷	2.490 977×10⁻¹⁰
Square inch (imp.)	sq.in or in²	6.451 578	10⁸	10²	1	10⁻²	10⁻⁴	10⁻¹⁰	1.273 230× 1	9.999 925×10⁻¹	6.944 393×10⁻³	7.715 992×10⁻⁴	1.594 213×10⁻⁷	2.490 958×10⁻¹⁰
Square foot (US)	sq.ft or ft²	9.290 341	10¹⁰	10⁴	10²	1	10⁻²	10⁻⁸	1.833 465×10²	1.44 ×10²	1 × 1	1.1 ×10⁻¹	2.295 684×10⁻⁵	3.587 006×10⁻⁸
Square foot (imp.)	sq.ft or ft²	9.290 272	10¹⁰	10⁴	10²	1	10⁻²	10⁻⁸	1.833 451×10²	1.439 989×10²	9.999 925×10⁻¹	1.111 103×10⁻¹	2.295 667×10⁻⁵	3.586 980×10⁻⁸
Square yard (US)	sq.yd or yd²	8.361 307	10¹¹	10⁵	10³	10	10⁻¹	10⁻⁷	1.650 118×10³	1.296 ×10³	9 × 1	1 × 1	2.066 116×10⁻⁴	3.228 306×10⁻⁷
Square yard (imp.)	sq.yd or yd²	8.361 245	10¹¹	10⁵	10³	10	10⁻¹	10⁻⁷	1.650 106×10³	1.295 990×10³	8.999 933× 1	9.999 925×10⁻¹	2.066 101×10⁻⁴	3.228 282×10⁻⁷
Acre (US)	A. or ac	4.046 873	10¹⁵	10⁹	10⁷	10⁵	10³	10⁻³	7.986 573×10⁶	6.272 64 ×10⁶	4.356 ×10⁴	4.84 ×10³	1 × 1	1.5625 ×10⁻³
Acre (imp.)	A. or ac	4.046 842	10¹⁵	10⁹	10⁷	10⁵	10³	10⁻³	7.986 514×10⁶	6.272 593×10⁶	4.355 967×10⁴	4.839 964×10³	9.999 925×10⁻¹	1.562 488×10⁻³
Square mile (US)	sq.mi or mi²	2.589 998	10¹⁸	10¹²	10¹⁰	10⁸	10⁶	1	5.111 407×10⁹	4.014 490×10⁹	2.787 84 ×10⁷	3.0976 ×10⁶	6.4 ×10²	1 × 1
Square mile (imp.)	sq.mi or mi²	2.589 979	10¹⁸	10¹²	10¹⁰	10⁸	10⁶	1	5.111 369×10⁹	4.014 460×10⁹	2.787 819×10⁷	3.097 577×10⁶	6.399 952×10²	9.999 925×10⁻¹

Conversion factors for units of volume and capacity

To convert from a unit in column **A** into any unit under **C**, multiply by the factor in column **B** and by the power of 10 given in the appropriate column under **C**

To convert from a unit in column **A** into any unit under **D**, multiply by the factor given in the appropriate column under **D**

A		B	C					D							
			µm³	mm³	cm³	dm³	m³	µl	ml	dl	l	hl	in³ (US)	ft³ (US)	yd³ (US)
Cubic micrometer	µm³	**1**	1	10^{-9}	10^{-12}	10^{-15}	10^{-18}	9.999 720$\times10^{-10}$	9.999 720$\times10^{-13}$	9.999 720$\times10^{-15}$	9.999 720$\times10^{-16}$	9.999 720$\times10^{-18}$	6.102 338$\times10^{-14}$	3.531 445$\times10^{-17}$	1.307 943$\times10^{-18}$
Cubic millimeter	mm³	**1**	10^{9}	1	10^{-3}	10^{-6}	10^{-9}	9.999 720$\times10^{-1}$	9.999 720$\times10^{-4}$	9.999 720$\times10^{-6}$	9.999 720$\times10^{-7}$	9.999 720$\times10^{-9}$	6.102 338$\times10^{-5}$	3.531 445$\times10^{-8}$	1.307 943$\times10^{-9}$
Cubic centimeter	cm³ (ccm)	**1**	10^{12}	10^{3}	1	10^{-3}	10^{-6}	9.999 720$\times10^{2}$	9.999 720$\times10^{-1}$	9.999 720$\times10^{-3}$	9.999 720$\times10^{-4}$	9.999 720$\times10^{-6}$	6.102 338$\times10^{-2}$	3.531 445$\times10^{-5}$	1.307 943$\times10^{-6}$
Cubic decimeter	dm³	**1**	10^{15}	10^{6}	10^{3}	1	10^{-3}	9.999 720$\times10^{5}$	9.999 720$\times10^{2}$	9.999 720$\times$ 1	9.999 720$\times10^{-1}$	9.999 720$\times10^{-3}$	6.102 338$\times10$	3.531 445$\times10^{-2}$	1.307 943$\times10^{-3}$
Cubic meter (stere)	m³	**1**	10^{18}	10^{9}	10^{6}	10^{3}	1	9.999 720$\times10^{8}$	9.999 720$\times10^{5}$	9.999 720$\times10^{3}$	9.999 720$\times10^{2}$	9.999 720$\times$ 1	6.102 338$\times10^{4}$	3.531 445$\times10$	1.307 943$\times$ 1
Microliter	µl	1.000 028	10^{9}	1	10^{-3}	10^{-6}	10^{-9}	**1** $\times$ 1	**1** $\times10^{-3}$	**1** $\times10^{-5}$	**1** $\times10^{-6}$	**1** $\times10^{-8}$	6.102 509$\times10^{-5}$	3.531 544$\times10^{-8}$	1.307 979$\times10^{-9}$
Milliliter	ml	1.000 028	10^{12}	10^{3}	1	10^{-3}	10^{-6}	**1** $\times10^{3}$	**1** $\times$ 1	**1** $\times10^{-2}$	**1** $\times10^{-3}$	**1** $\times10^{-5}$	6.102 509$\times10^{-2}$	3.531 544$\times10^{-5}$	1.307 979$\times10^{-6}$
Deciliter	dl	1.000 028	10^{14}	10^{5}	10^{2}	10^{-1}	10^{-4}	**1** $\times10^{5}$	**1** $\times10^{2}$	**1** $\times$ 1	**1** $\times10^{-1}$	**1** $\times10^{-3}$	6.102 509$\times$ 1	3.531 544$\times10^{-3}$	1.307 979$\times10^{-4}$
Liter	l	1.000 028	10^{15}	10^{6}	10^{3}	1	10^{-3}	**1** $\times10^{6}$	**1** $\times10^{3}$	**1** $\times10$	**1** $\times$ 1	**1** $\times10^{-2}$	6.102 509$\times10$	3.531 544$\times10^{-2}$	1.307 979$\times10^{-3}$
Hectoliter	hl	1.000 028	10^{17}	10^{8}	10^{5}	10^{2}	10^{-1}	**1** $\times10^{8}$	**1** $\times10^{5}$	**1** $\times10^{3}$	**1** $\times10^{2}$	**1** $\times$ 1	6.102 509$\times10^{3}$	3.531 544$\times$ 1	1.307 979$\times10^{-1}$
Cubic inch (US)	cu.in or in³	1.638 716	10^{13}	10^{4}	10	10^{-2}	10^{-5}	1.638 670$\times10^{4}$	1.638 670$\times10$	1.638 670$\times10^{-1}$	1.638 670$\times10^{-2}$	1.638 670$\times10^{-4}$	**1** $\times$ 1	5.787 0̇3̇ $\times10^{-4}$	2.143 347$\times10^{-5}$
Cubic inch (imp.)	cu.in or in³	1.638 698	10^{13}	10^{4}	10	10^{-2}	10^{-5}	1.638 652$\times10^{4}$	1.638 652$\times10$	1.638 652$\times10^{-1}$	1.638 652$\times10^{-2}$	1.638 652$\times10^{-4}$	9.999 888$\times10^{-1}$	5.786 972$\times10^{-4}$	2.143 323$\times10^{-5}$
Cubic foot (US)	cu.ft or ft³	2.831 702	10^{16}	10^{7}	10^{4}	10	10^{-2}	2.831 622$\times10^{7}$	2.831 622$\times10^{4}$	2.831 622$\times10^{2}$	2.831 622$\times10$	2.831 622$\times10^{-1}$	**1.728** $\times10^{3}$	**1** $\times$ 1	3.7̇0̇3̇ $\times10^{-2}$
Cubic foot (imp.)	cu.ft or ft³	2.831 670	10^{16}	10^{7}	10^{4}	10	10^{-2}	2.831 591$\times10^{7}$	2.831 591$\times10^{4}$	2.831 591$\times10^{2}$	2.831 591$\times10$	2.831 591$\times10^{-1}$	1.727 981$\times10^{3}$	9.999 888$\times10^{-1}$	3.703 662$\times10^{-2}$
Cubic yard (US)	cu.yd or yd³	7.645 594	10^{17}	10^{8}	10^{5}	10^{2}	10^{-1}	7.645 380$\times10^{8}$	7.645 380$\times10^{5}$	7.645 380$\times10^{3}$	7.645 380$\times10^{2}$	7.645 380$\times$ 1	4.665 **6** $\times10^{4}$	**2.7** $\times10$	**1** $\times$ 1
Cubic yard (imp.)	cu.yd or yd³	7.645 509	10^{17}	10^{8}	10^{5}	10^{2}	10^{-1}	7.645 295$\times10^{8}$	7.645 295$\times10^{5}$	7.645 295$\times10^{3}$	7.645 295$\times10^{2}$	7.645 295$\times$ 1	4.665 548$\times10^{4}$	2.699 970$\times10$	9.999 888$\times10^{-1}$
Register ton (US)	reg.tn	2.831 702	10^{18}	10^{9}	10^{6}	10^{3}	1	2.831 622$\times10^{9}$	2.831 622$\times10^{6}$	2.831 622$\times10^{4}$	2.831 622$\times10^{3}$	2.831 622$\times10$	**1.728** $\times10^{5}$	**1** $\times10^{2}$	3.7̇0̇3̇ $\times$ 1
Register ton (imp.)	reg.tn	2.831 670	10^{18}	10^{9}	10^{6}	10^{3}	1	2.831 591$\times10^{9}$	2.831 591$\times10^{6}$	2.831 591$\times10^{4}$	2.831 591$\times10^{3}$	2.831 591$\times10$	1.727 981$\times10^{5}$	9.999 888$\times10$	3.703 662$\times$ 1

Conversion factors for US dry capacity measures

To convert from a unit in column **A** into any unit under **B**, multiply by the factor given in the appropriate column under **B**

A		B							C (see footnote)
		m³	l	in³ (US)	dry pt (US)	dry qt (US)	pk	bu	Imperial
Cubic meter	m³	**1** $\times$ 1	9.999 720$\times10^{2}$	6.102 338$\times10^{4}$	1.816 155$\times10^{3}$	9.080 775$\times10^{2}$	1.135 097$\times10^{2}$	2.837 742$\times10$	
Liter	l	1.000 028$\times10^{-3}$	**1** $\times$ 1	6.102 509$\times10$	1.816 206$\times$ 1	9.081 030$\times10^{-1}$	1.135 129$\times10^{-1}$	2.837 822$\times10^{-2}$	—
Cubic inch (US)	cu.in or in³	1.638 716$\times10^{-5}$	1.638 670$\times10^{-2}$	**1** $\times$ 1	2.976 163$\times10^{-2}$	1.488 081$\times10^{-2}$	1.860 102$\times10^{-3}$	4.650 254$\times10^{-4}$	1.000 011 20
Dry pint (US)	dry pt	5.506 138$\times10^{-4}$	5.505 984$\times10^{-1}$	3.360 031$\times10$	**1** $\times$ 1	**5** $\times10^{-1}$	**6.25** $\times10^{-2}$	**1.5625** $\times10^{-2}$	0.968 944 72
Dry quart (US)	dry qt	1.101 228$\times10^{-3}$	1.101 197$\times$ 1	6.720 062$\times10$	**2** $\times$ 1	**1** $\times$ 1	**1.25** $\times10^{-1}$	**3.125** $\times10^{-2}$	0.968 944 72
Peck (US)	pk	8.809 820$\times10^{-3}$	8.809 574$\times$ 1	5.376 **05** $\times10^{2}$	**1.6** $\times10$	**8** $\times$ 1	**1** $\times$ 1	**2.5** $\times10^{-1}$	0.968 944 72
Bushel (US)	bu	3.523 928$\times10^{-2}$	3.523 829$\times10$	2.150 **42** $\times10^{3}$	**6.4** $\times10$	**3.2** $\times10$	**4** $\times$ 1	**1** $\times$ 1	0.968 944 72

To convert a US (or imperial) unit under **A** into the corresponding imperial (or US) unit, multiply (or divide) by the appropriate factor under **C**. The same applies to any of the equivalents given under **B**; for an example see the footnote on the following page.

Conversion factors for US liquid capacity measures

To convert from a unit in column **A** into any unit under **B**, multiply by the factor given in the appropriate column under **B**

A		B: m^3	l	in^3 (US)	min (US)	fl.dr. (US)	fl.oz (US)	gi (US)	liq.pt (US)	liq.qt (US)	gal (US)	C (see footnote): Imperial
Cubic meter	m^3	1×1	$9.999\,720\times10^{2}$	$6.102\,338\times10^{4}$	$1.623\,063\times10^{7}$	$2.705\,106\times10^{5}$	$3.381\,382\times10^{4}$	$8.453\,455\times10^{3}$	$2.113\,364\times10^{3}$	$1.056\,682\times10^{3}$	$2.641\,705\times10^{2}$	—
Liter	l	$1.000\,028\times10^{-3}$	1×1	$6.102\,509\times10$	$1.623\,109\times10^{4}$	$2.705\,181\times10^{2}$	$3.381\,477\times10$	$8.453\,692\times1$	$2.113\,423\times1$	$1.056\,711\times1$	$2.641\,779\times10^{-1}$	—
Cubic inch (US)	cu.in or in^3	$1.638\,716\times10^{-5}$	$1.638\,670\times10^{-2}$	1×1	$2.659\,740\times10^{2}$	$4.432\,900\times1$	$5.541\,126\times10^{-1}$	$1.385\,281\times10^{-1}$	$3.463\,203\times10^{-2}$	$1.731\,602\times10^{-2}$	$4.329\,004\times10^{-3}$	1.000 011 20
Minim (US)	min	$6.161\,189\times10^{-8}$	$6.161\,016\times10^{-5}$	$3.759\,766\times10^{-3}$	1×1	$1.\dot{6}\times10^{-2}$	$2.08\dot{3}\times10^{-3}$	$5.208\,\dot{3}\times10^{-4}$	$1.302\,08\dot{3}\times10^{-4}$	$6.510\,41\dot{6}\times10^{-5}$	$1.627\,604\times10^{-5}$	0.960 754 24
Fluid dram (US)	fl.dr	$3.696\,713\times10^{-6}$	$3.696\,610\times10^{-3}$	$2.255\,859\times10^{-1}$	6×10	1×1	1.25×10^{-1}	3.125×10^{-2}	$7.812\,5\times10^{-3}$	$3.906\,25\times10^{-3}$	$9.765\,625\times10^{-4}$	0.960 754 24
Fluid ounce (US)	fl.oz	$2.957\,371\times10^{-5}$	$2.957\,288\times10^{-2}$	$1.804\,688\times1$	4.8×10^{2}	8×1	1×1	2.5×10^{-1}	6.25×10^{-2}	3.125×10^{-2}	$7.812\,5\times10^{-3}$	0.960 754 24
Gill (US)	gi	$1.182\,948\times10^{-4}$	$1.182\,915\times10^{-1}$	$7.218\,75\times1$	1.92×10^{3}	3.2×10	4×1	1×1	2.5×10^{-1}	1.25×10^{-1}	3.125×10^{-2}	0.832 679 13
Liquid pint (US)	liq.pt	$4.731\,793\times10^{-4}$	$4.731\,661\times10^{-1}$	$2.887\,5\times10$	7.68×10^{3}	1.28×10^{2}	1.6×10	4×1	1×1	5×10^{-1}	1.25×10^{-1}	0.832 679 13
Liquid quart (US)	liq.qt	$9.463\,586\times10^{-4}$	$9.463\,321\times10^{-1}$	5.775×10	1.536×10^{4}	2.56×10^{2}	3.2×10	8×1	2×1	1×1	2.5×10^{-1}	0.832 679 13
Gallon (US)	gal	$3.785\,434\times10^{-3}$	$3.785\,329\times1$	2.31×10^{2}	6.144×10^{4}	1.024×10^{3}	1.28×10^{2}	3.2×10	8×1	4×1	1×1	0.832 679 13

To convert a US (for imperial) unit under **A** into the corresponding imperial (or US) unit, multiply (or divide) by the appropriate factor under **C**. The same applies to any of the equivalents given under **B**, for example: 1 fl.dr (US) = 0.960 754 24 fl.dr (imp.); 1 fl.dr (imp.) = $(3.696\,610\times10^{-3})\times0.960\,754\,24$ l = $3.551\,534\times10^{-3}$ l.

Conversion factors for British (imperial) capacity measures (admissible for both liquid and dry commodities)

To convert from a unit in column **A** into any unit under **B**, multiply by the factor given in the appropriate column under **B**

A		B: m^3	l	in^3 (imp.)	min (imp.)	fl.dr (imp.)	fl.oz (imp.)	gi (imp.)	pt (imp.)	qt (imp.)	gal (imp.)	pk (imp.)	bu (imp.)	C (see footnote): US liquid	US dry
Cubic meter	m^3	1×1	$9.999\,720\times10^{2}$	$6.102\,406\times10^{4}$	$1.689\,364\times10^{7}$	$2.815\,606\times10^{5}$	$3.519\,508\times10^{4}$	$7.039\,015\times10^{3}$	$1.759\,754\times10^{3}$	$8.798\,769\times10^{2}$	$2.199\,692\times10^{2}$	$1.099\,846\times10^{2}$	$2.749\,615\times10$	—	—
Liter	l	$1.000\,028\times10^{-3}$	1×1	$6.102\,577\times10$	$1.689\,411\times10^{4}$	$2.815\,685\times10^{2}$	$3.519\,606\times10$	$7.039\,213\times1$	$1.759\,803\times1$	$8.799\,016\times10^{-1}$	$2.199\,754\times10^{-1}$	$1.099\,877\times10^{-1}$	$2.749\,692\times10^{-2}$	—	—
Cubic inch (imp.)	cu.in or in^3	$1.638\,698\times10^{-5}$	$1.638\,652\times10^{-2}$	1×1	$2.768\,357\times10^{2}$	$4.613\,928\times1$	$5.767\,410\times10^{-1}$	$1.153\,482\times10^{-1}$	$2.883\,705\times10^{-2}$	$1.441\,852\times10^{-2}$	$3.604\,631\times10^{-3}$	$1.802\,316\times10^{-3}$	$4.505\,789\times10^{-4}$	0.999 988 80	0.999 988 80
Minim (imp.)	min	$5.919\,388\times10^{-8}$	$5.919\,223\times10^{-5}$	$3.612\,251\times10^{-3}$	1×1	$1.\dot{6}\times10^{-2}$	$2.08\dot{3}\times10^{-3}$	$4.1\dot{6}\times10^{-4}$	$1.041\,\dot{6}\times10^{-4}$	$5.208\,\dot{3}\times10^{-5}$	$1.302\,08\dot{3}\times10^{-5}$	$6.510\,41\dot{6}\times10^{-6}$	$1.627\,604\times10^{-6}$	1.040 848 91	—
Fluid drachm (imp.)	fl.dr	$3.551\,633\times10^{-6}$	$3.551\,534\times10^{-3}$	$2.167\,351\times10^{-1}$	6×10	1×1	1.25×10^{-1}	2.5×10^{-2}	6.25×10^{-3}	3.125×10^{-3}	$7.812\,5\times10^{-4}$	$3.906\,25\times10^{-4}$	$9.765\,625\times10^{-5}$	1.040 848 91	—
Fluid ounce (imp.)	fl.oz	$2.841\,306\times10^{-5}$	$2.841\,227\times10^{-2}$	$1.733\,881\times1$	4.8×10^{2}	8×1	1×1	2×10^{-1}	5×10^{-2}	2.5×10^{-2}	6.25×10^{-3}	3.125×10^{-3}	$7.812\,5\times10^{-4}$	1.040 848 91	—
Gill (imp.)	gi	$1.420\,653\times10^{-4}$	$1.420\,613\times10^{-1}$	$8.669\,403\times1$	2.4×10^{3}	4×10	5×1	1×1	2.5×10^{-1}	1.25×10^{-1}	3.125×10^{-2}	$1.562\,5\times10^{-2}$	$3.906\,25\times10^{-3}$	1.200 942 80	—
Pint (imp.)	pt	$5.682\,613\times10^{-4}$	$5.682\,454\times10^{-1}$	$3.467\,761\times10$	9.6×10^{3}	1.6×10^{2}	2×10	4×1	1×1	5×10^{-1}	1.25×10^{-1}	6.25×10^{-2}	$1.562\,5\times10^{-2}$	1.200 942 80	1.032 050 62
Quart (imp.)	qt	$1.136\,523\times10^{-3}$	$1.136\,491\times1$	$6.935\,522\times10$	1.92×10^{4}	3.2×10^{2}	4×10	8×1	2×1	1×1	2.5×10^{-1}	1.25×10^{-1}	3.125×10^{-2}	1.200 942 80	1.032 050 62
Gallon (imp.)	gal	$4.546\,090\times10^{-3}$	$4.545\,963\times1$	$2.774\,209\times10^{2}$	7.68×10^{4}	1.28×10^{3}	1.6×10^{2}	3.2×10	8×1	4×1	1×1	5×10^{-1}	1.25×10^{-1}	1.200 942 80	—
Peck (imp.)	pk	$9.092\,181\times10^{-3}$	$9.091\,926\times1$	$5.548\,418\times10^{2}$	1.536×10^{5}	2.56×10^{3}	3.2×10^{2}	6.4×10	1.6×10	8×1	2×1	1×1	2.5×10^{-1}	—	1.032 050 62
Bushel (imp.)	bu	$3.636\,872\times10^{-2}$	$3.636\,770\times10$	$2.219\,367\times10^{3}$	6.144×10^{5}	1.024×10^{4}	1.28×10^{3}	2.56×10^{2}	6.4×10	3.2×10	8×1	4×1	1×1	—	1.032 050 62

To convert a US (or imperial) unit under **A** into the corresponding imperial (or US) unit, multiply (or divide) by the appropriate factor under **C**. The same applies to any of the equivalents given under **B**, for example: 1 fl.dr (US) = 0.960 754 24 fl.dr (imp.); 1fl.dr (imp.) = $(3.696\,610\times10^{-3})\times0.960\,754\,24$ l = $3.551\,534\times10^{-3}$ l.

(continued from page 204)

The following further relations are obtained by using the conversion factors for liter and cubic meter and for cubic meter and cubic inch (see the table on the opposite page):

1 imperial gallon (commercial)
= 277.420 imperial cubic inches (commercial)
1 imperial gallon (scientific)
= 277.421 imperial cubic inches (scientific)

There are considerable differences between the United States and imperial capacity measures (the latter are in use throughout the British Commonwealth including Canada) which can best be appreciated from the conversion tables on pages 205 and 206. The capacity units minim, fluid scruple (the latter is not included in the conversion tables since it is in use only in the United Kingdom), fluid dram (US) or fluid drachm (imp.), and fluid ounce are apothecaries' measures and are based on the corresponding units of mass, viz., 1 minim : 1 fluid scruple : 1 fluid dram or drachm : 1 fluid ounce = 1 grain : 1 scruple : 1 dram or drachm : 1 ounce = 1 : 20 : 60 : 480.

Mass

Dimension

in the length-mass-time systems (LMT-systems) = M
in the length-force-time systems (LFT-systems) = $L^{-1}FT^2$

Basic units

LMT-systems: MKS-system: kilogram (kg); CGS-system: gram (g); MTS-system: metric ton (t); ft-lb-s-system: pound (lb).

LFT-systems: In the meter-kilopond-second- (m-kp-s-) system, which finds considerable application in technology, the unit of mass is a derived unit with the formula $m^{-1}kp\ s^2$, corresponding to 9.806 **65** kg. This unit has not been named and is becoming of less and less importance with the rapid spread of the MKS-system. It has so far been little used, having been usually replaced by a unit derived from the relation weight/gravitational acceleration = kp/9.806 **65** m s^{-2}, corresponding to the kilogram of the MKS-system.

Metric system

The fundamental standard of mass in the metric system is the *kilogram* (kg), defined as the mass of the international prototype kilogram, a platinum-iridium cylinder preserved at the International Bureau of Weights and Measures at Sèvres (France)[1].

United States and British (Imperial) system

In the English-speaking countries, in addition to the *avoirdupois* system of mass units in common use in commerce and technology, there are two other systems of restricted application: the *troy* system for precious metals, precious stones and coins, and the *apothecaries'* system. The only unit common to all three systems is the grain (gr), which is defined as the 7000th part of the pound avoirdupois (lb.av.).

In the United States the pound avoirdupois is legally defined in terms of the kilogram (the National Bureau of Standards holds a national prototype kilogram which is identical, within the uncertainty of the measurements, with the international prototype) as follows[2]:

1 US pound avoirdupois = 1/2.204**6** kilogram

This relation gives a conversion factor of 0.453 597 024. More precise measurements made by the National Bureau of Standards later led to the adoption of the following definition:

1 US pound avoirdupois = 0.453 592 42**77** kilogram

In the United Kingdom the pound avoirdupois is defined by the Weights and Measures Act, 1878, as the mass of the Imperial Standard Pound, a platinum cylinder preserved in the Standards Department of the Board of Trade in London. An Order in Council of May 19th 1898 laid down the following legal relation for commercial purposes:

1 imperial pound = 0.453 592 43 kilogram

For very precise scientific measurements the National Physical Laboratory has established the following relation:

1 imperial pound = 0.453 592 338 kilogram

It has recently been agreed by the major English-speaking countries that an "international pound" defined as

1 international pound = 0.453 592 37 kg

shall be established for use generally in science and technology[3].

In the United States the troy pound is the legal basic unit for coins:

1 US pound troy = 5760/7000 US pound avoirdupois

1) *Comptes rendus de la 3e Conférence générale des Poids et Mesures*, Paris, 1901, page 68. 2) *U. S. Coast and Geodetic Survey, Treasury Department*, Bull. **26** (1893) (Mendenhall Order). 3) Editorial, *Nature*, **183**, 80 (1959).

Conversion factors for units of mass

To convert from a unit in column **A** into any unit under **C**, multiply by the factor in column **B** and by the power of 10 given in the appropriate column under **C**. To convert from a unit in column **A** into any unit under **D**, multiply by the factor given in the appropriate column under **D**.

A		B	C					D							
			μg	mg	g	kg	t	gr	dr.av.	oz.av.	lb.av.	ctl (imp.), sh.cwt (US)	cwt (imp.), l.cwt (US)	sh.tn (US)	tn (imp.), l.tn (US)
Microgram (gamma) *(The term gamma should no longer be used)*	μg(γ)	**1** ×	1	10^{-3}	10^{-6}	10^{-9}	10^{-12}	1.543 236×10^{-5}	5.643 833×10^{-7}	3.527 396×10^{-8}	2.204 622×10^{-9}	2.204 622×10^{-11}	1.968 413×10^{-11}	1.102 311×10^{-12}	9.842 064×10^{-13}
Milligram	mg	**1** ×	10^{3}	1	10^{-3}	10^{-6}	10^{-9}	1.543 236×10^{-2}	5.643 833×10^{-4}	3.527 396×10^{-5}	2.204 622×10^{-6}	2.204 622×10^{-8}	1.968 413×10^{-8}	1.102 311×10^{-9}	9.842 064×10^{-10}
Gram	g	**1** ×	10^{6}	10^{3}	1	10^{-3}	10^{-6}	1.543 236×10	5.643 833×10^{-1}	3.527 396×10^{-2}	2.204 622×10^{-3}	2.204 622×10^{-5}	1.968 413×10^{-5}	1.102 311×10^{-6}	9.842 064×10^{-7}
Kilogram	kg	**1** ×	10^{9}	10^{6}	10^{3}	1	10^{-3}	1.543 236×10^{4}	5.643 833×10^{2}	3.527 396×10	2.204 622× 1	2.204 622×10^{-2}	1.968 413×10^{-2}	1.102 311×10^{-3}	9.842 064×10^{-4}
Metric ton	t	**1** ×	10^{12}	10^{9}	10^{6}	10^{3}	1	1.543 236×10^{7}	5.643 833×10^{5}	3.527 396×10^{4}	2.204 622×10^{3}	2.204 622×10	1.968 413×10	1.102 311× 1	9.842 064×10^{-1}
Grain, avoirdupois, ap. or troy (US/imp.)	gr	6.479 892×	10^{4}	10	10^{-2}	10^{-5}	10^{-8}	**1** × 1	3.657 143×10^{-2}	2.285 714×10^{-3}	1.428 571×10^{-4}	1.428 571×10^{-6}	1.275 511×10^{-6}	7.142 587×10^{-8}	6.377 551×10^{-8}
Dram, avoirdupois (US/imp.)	dr.av.	1.771 845×	10^{6}	10^{3}	1	10^{-3}	10^{-6}	2.734 37**5**×10	**1** × 1	**6.25** ×10^{-2}	3.906 **25** ×10^{-3}	3.906 **25** ×10^{-5}	3.487 723×10^{-5}	1.953 1**25**×10^{-6}	1.743 862×10^{-6}
Ounce, avoirdupois (US/imp.)	oz.av.	2.834 953×	10^{7}	10^{4}	10	10^{-2}	10^{-5}	4.37**5** ×10^{2}	**1.6** ×10	**1** × 1	**6.25** ×10^{-2}	**6.25** ×10^{-4}	5.580 357×10^{-4}	3.1**25** ×10^{-5}	2.790 179×10^{-5}
Pound, avoirdupois (US/imp.)	lb.av.	4.535 924×	10^{8}	10^{5}	10^{2}	10^{-1}	10^{-4}	**7** ×10^{3}	2.5**6** ×10^{2}	**1.6** ×10	**1** × 1	**1** ×10^{-2}	8.928 571×10^{-3}	**5** ×10^{-4}	4.464 286×10^{-4}
Cental (imp.) / Hundredweight, short (US)	ctl / sh.cwt	4.535 924×	10^{10}	10^{7}	10^{4}	10	10^{-2}	**7** ×10^{5}	2.5**6** ×10^{4}	**1.6** ×10^{3}	**1** ×10^{2}	**1** × 1	8.928 571×10^{-1}	**5** ×10^{-2}	4.464 286×10^{-2}
Hundredweight (imp.) / Hundredweight, long (US)	cwt / l.cwt	5.080 235×	10^{10}	10^{7}	10^{4}	10	10^{-2}	7.8**4** ×10^{5}	2.867 **2** ×10^{4}	1.79**2** ×10^{3}	1.1**2** ×10^{2}	1.1**2** × 1	**1** × 1	5.**6** ×10^{-2}	**5** ×10^{-2}
Ton, short (US)	sh.tn	9.071 849×	10^{11}	10^{8}	10^{5}	10^{2}	10^{-1}	1.**4** ×10^{6}	5.1**2** ×10^{5}	3.**2** ×10^{4}	**2** ×10^{3}	**2** ×10	1.785 714×10	**1** × 1	8.928 571×10^{-1}
Ton (imp.) / Ton, long (US)	tn / l.tn	1.016 047×	10^{12}	10^{9}	10^{6}	10^{3}	1	1.56**8** ×10^{6}	5.734 **4** ×10^{5}	3.58**4** ×10^{4}	2.2**4** ×10^{3}	2.2**4** ×10	**2** ×10	1.1**2** × 1	**1** × 1

Conversion factors for units of troy weight

To convert from a unit in column **A** into any unit under **B**, multiply by the factor given in the appropriate column under **B**

A		g	c	gr	s.ap	dwt	dr.ap.	oz.ap., oz.t.	lb.ap., lb.t.	lb.av.
Gram	g	**1** × 1	**5** × 1	1.543 236×10	$7.716\,179\times10^{-1}$	$6.430\,149\times10^{-1}$	$2.572\,059\times10^{-1}$	$3.215\,074\times10^{-2}$	$2.679\,229\times10^{-3}$	$2.204\,622\times10^{-3}$
Carat	c	**2** $\times10^{-1}$	**1** × 1	3.086 471×10	—	$1.286\,030\times10^{-1}$	—	$6.430\,148\times10^{-2}$	$5.358\,457\times10^{-3}$	$4.409\,245\times10^{-3}$
Grain, avoirdupois, apoth. or troy (US/imp.)	gr	$6.479\,892\times10^{-2}$	$3.239\,946\times10^{-1}$	**1** × 1	**5** $\times10^{-2}$	$4.1\dot{6}\times10^{-2}$	$1.\dot{6}\times10^{-2}$	$2.08\dot{3}\times10^{-3}$	$1.736\,\dot{1}\times10^{-4}$	$1.428\,571\times10^{-4}$
Scruple, apothecary ....(US/imp.)	s.ap.	1.295 978× 1	—	**2** ×10	**1** × 1	—	$3.\dot{3}\times10^{-1}$	$4.1\dot{6}\times10^{-2}$	$3.47\dot{2}\times10^{-3}$	$2.857\,143\times10^{-3}$
Pennyweight, troy ....(US/imp.)	dwt	1.555 174× 1	7.775 870× 1	2.**4** ×10	—	**1** × 1	—	**5** $\times10^{-2}$	$4.1\dot{6}\times10^{-3}$	$3.428\,571\times10^{-3}$
Dram, apothecary ....(US) / Drachm, apothecary............(imp.)	dr.ap.	3.887 935× 1	—	**6** ×10	**3** × 1	—	**1** × 1	1.2**5** $\times10^{-1}$	$1.041\,6\times10^{-2}$	$8.571\,429\times10^{-3}$
Ounce, apothecary or troy.......(US/imp.)	oz.ap. or oz.t.	3.110 348×10	$1.555\,174\times10^{2}$	4.**8** $\times10^{2}$	2.**4** ×10	**2** ×10	**8** × 1	**1** × 1	$8.\dot{3}\times10^{-2}$	$6.857\,143\times10^{-2}$
Pound, apothecary or troy.......(US)	lb.ap. or lb.t.	$3.732\,418\times10^{2}$	$1.866\,209\times10^{3}$	5.7**6** $\times10^{3}$	2.8**8** $\times10^{2}$	2.**4** $\times10^{2}$	9.**6** ×10	1.**2** ×10	**1** × 1	$8.228\,571\times10^{-1}$
Pound, avoirdupois.............(US/imp.)	lb.av.	$4.535\,924\times10^{2}$	$2.267\,962\times10^{3}$	**7** $\times10^{3}$	3.**5** $\times10^{2}$	$2.91\dot{6}\times10^{2}$	$1.1\dot{6}\times10^{2}$	$1.458\,\dot{3}$ ×10	$1.215\,2\dot{7}$ × 1	**1** × 1

In the United Kingdom the troy pound is no longer legal, although a number of the smaller units derived from it are still in use for precious metals and precious stones (see the conversion table on this page).

This conversion table is based on the National Bureau of Standards metric equivalent for the US pound avoirdupois.

International unit for precious metals and precious stones

1 carat (c) = 0.0002 kilogram = 0.2 gram = 200 milligrams

Time

Dimension in all systems of measurement = T

Basic unit in all systems of measurement: mean solar second = second (s, sec, or ^{s}).

The units in which time is measured[1] are derived both from the earth's axial rotation (second, minute, hour, day) and from its orbital passage around the sun (year). Both axial rotation and orbital passage can be defined and measured only in relation to a point situated outside the earth. In everyday life the sun is used as the reference point, giving *apparent solar time*, and in astronomy the system of the fixed stars, particularly the vernal point or vernal equinox, giving *sidereal time*.

Time units derived from the earth's rotation

The ellipticity of the earth's orbit and the inclination of the ecliptic cause irregularities in the apparent motion of the true sun, which is thus unsuitable as a basis for uniform measurements of time. The true sun is therefore replaced by an imaginary body, known as the mean sun, which is assumed to describe a uniform path along the celestial meridian in the course of one year and in such a way that its distance from the true sun remains a minimum and its passage through the vernal equinox coincides with that of a sun moving uniformly in the ecliptic.

The apparent solar day is the period of time between two successive lower transits of the true sun over the meridian, while the mean solar day (d) is the time interval between two successive transits of the mean sun. The difference between apparent and mean solar time (or the difference in right ascension of the true and mean suns) is known as the equation of time. Its values for the days of the year may be found tabulated in astronomical and nautical yearbooks.

The day, i.e. the time occupied by one rotation of the earth, is divided into 24 hours (h or ^{h}) of 60 minutes (min or ^{m}) of 60 seconds (s, sec or ^{s}). Other equivalents and the relation between solar and sidereal time are given in the conversion table on the opposite page.

The mean solar second, the 86,400th part of the mean solar day, was formerly the primary standard of time in the metric system. In practice, astronomical determinations of the mean solar second (second of Universal Time, called UT 2) lead to varying results owing to the circumstance that the earth's rotational velocity not only undergoes seasonal variations but is also diminishing slowly with the course of time (due among other unknown causes to tidal friction)[2]. For this reason the International Metric Convention has recently agreed[6] that the second be defined as a fixed fraction of the length of the tropical year for 1900.**0** (Universal Time, January 1, noon), based on the orbital motion of the moon, as follows:

$$1 \text{ second} = 1/31\,556\,925.9747\ a_{trop}\ (1900.\mathbf{0})$$

This definition (second of Ephemeris Time) was adopted in 1955 by the International Astronomical Union[3]. The above value has been used in the conversion table opposite.

Neither the second of Universal Time nor that of Ephemeris Time is realizable with the accuracy necessary for some precise scientific measurements, and more accurate systems of time measurement have recently been developed based on measurements of atomic frequencies, notably that of cesium[4].

The length of the day and the time units derived from it are independent of the meridian of the observer. This is not the case in the establishment of local time since the day begins later as the observer moves from east to west, with the result that the earth has been divided into a number of differing standard-time zones in each of which the time related to the central meridian is used. The reference meridian for astronomical purposes as well as the fixing of local time is the meridian of Greenwich, England. Universal Time is based on mean solar time related to this meridian[5]. The various local standard times are shown in the time zone map on pages 218 and 219.

Time units derived from the earth's orbital movement

The time unit *year* (a) is defined as the time taken for the earth to make one revolution round the sun. The three principal definitions of this unit in use in astronomy are as follows:

The *sidereal year* (a_{sid}) is related to the fixed stars and is defined as the time interval between two successive passages of the sun past a fixed star, on the assumption that the latter does not change its position in the meantime. The sidereal year is 4.7 (mean solar) minutes shorter than the anomalistic year, and respectively 20.4, 9.2 and 20.0 minutes longer than the tropical, Julian and Gregorian years.

The *tropical year* (a_{trop}) is defined as the time interval between two successive passages of the true sun through the mean vernal equinox. The astronomical year (a_{astr}), also known as the Besselian or fictitious year, is defined analogously by the apparent movement of the mean sun. The difference between the tropical and astronomical years is so small that for all purposes they may be regarded as equal. Owing to the precession of the vernal equinox the tropical year is shorter than the sidereal year.

1) Cf. Westphal, H.W., (Ed.), *Physikalisches Wörterbuch*, Berlin, 1952. *2)* Essen et al., *Nature*, **181**, 1054 (1958). *3)* Jones, H. Spencer, *Nature*, **176**, 669 (1955); Essen, L., *Nature*, **178**, 34 (1956). *4)* Essen and Parry, *Nature*, **176**, 280 (1955); Bullard, E.C., *Nature*, **176**, 282, 381 (1955); Essen, L., *Nature*, **178**, 34 (1956). For a review see Essen and Parry, *The Times Science Review*, Autumn 1957, page 4. *5)* International Astronomical Union, *Trans. int. astr. Un.*, **3**, 300 (1928). *6)* Editorial, *Science*, **132**, 1384 (1960).

It is respectively 20.4, 25.1, 11.2, and 0.4 minutes shorter than the sidereal, anomalistic, Julian and Gregorian years.

The *anomalistic year* (a_{anom}) is based on the earth's elliptical orbit and is defined as the time interval between two successive passages of the earth through the perihelion. It is longer than the sidereal year owing to the eastward precession of the line of apsides of the earth's orbit. The anomalistic year is respectively 4.7, 25.1, 13.9 and 24.7 minutes longer than the sidereal, tropical, Julian and Gregorian years.

Of the above three time units, the sidereal year does not alter noticeably with the passage of time; in the course of 100 years the tropical year decreases by 0.5303 second and the anomalistic year increases by 0.27 second in the same period of time. In the conversion table below, the length of these units is given at the time point 1900.**0** (Universal Time, January 1, noon).

It is important to distinguish these three kinds of year, with their differing astronomical definitions, from the calendar or civil year used in everyday life for the fixing of dates. The first precise system of dating was introduced in 45 B.C. by Julius Caesar, and the Julian year remained in use until 1581. It consists on the average of 365.2**5** days, i.e. three years of 365 days followed by a leap year of 366 days:

$$1 \text{ Julian year} = (3 \times 365 + 366)/4 \text{ days} = 365.2\mathbf{5} \text{ days}$$

The leap years have numbers divisible by 4, and the intercalated day is February 29.

As already mentioned, the Julian year is some 11 minutes longer than the tropical year corresponding to the earth's actual orbital motion. This resulted in the Julian calendar showing earlier and earlier dates for natural events such as the seasons. The growing discrepancy was finally rectified by the calendar reform introduced by Pope Gregory XIII's bull of February 24 1582. Under this reform, 10 days were to be dropped from the calendar of the year 1582, October 5–14 inclusive, in order to restore the vernal equinox to March 21. France adopted the reform the same year, dropping the days from December 10 to 19 1582. In England, the Gregorian calendar was not adopted until 1752, when 11 days, September 3–13, had to be dropped. In order to keep the Gregorian calendar in step with the sidereal years, the reform also laid down that three out of every four century years were to be ordinary years instead of leap years, i.e. that only those century years divisible by 400 were to be leap years. The mean length of the Gregorian year is therefore:

$$1 \text{ Gregorian year} = (400\ a_{jul} - 3 \text{ days})/400 \text{ days} = 365.242\mathbf{5} \text{ days}$$

It is thus only 0.4 minute longer than the tropical year, and ensures agreement between actual and calendar dates for a considerable time to come.

Conversion table for time units

To convert from a unit in column **A** into any unit under **B**, multiply by the factor given in the appropriate column under **B**

	A		**B**: Mean solar time 1900.**0**				**A**
		Symbol	Second	Minute	Hour	Day	Symbol
	Second	s	**1** × 1	$1.\dot{6}$ × 10^{-2}	$2.\dot{7}$ × 10^{-4}	$1.15\dot{7}4\dot{0}$ × 10^{-5}	s
Mean solar time	Minute	min	**6** × 10	**1** × 1	$1.\dot{6}$ × 10^{-2}	$6.9\dot{4}$ × 10^{-4}	min
Mean solar time	Hour	h	3.**6** × 10^{3}	**6** × 10	**1** × 1	$4.1\dot{6}$ × 10^{-2}	h
Mean solar time	Day	d	8.6**4** × 10^{4}	1.4**4** × 10^{3}	2.**4** × 10	**1** × 1	d
Mean solar time	Month (28 days)		2.419 **2** × 10^{6}	4.03**2** × 10^{4}	6.7**2** × 10^{2}	2.**8** × 10	Month (28 d)
Mean solar time	Month (29 days)		2.505 **6** × 10^{6}	4.17**6** × 10^{4}	6.9**6** × 10^{2}	2.**9** × 10	Month (29 d)
Mean solar time	Month (30 days)		2.59**2** × 10^{6}	4.3**2** × 10^{4}	7.**2** × 10^{2}	**3** × 10	Month (30 d)
Mean solar time	Month (31 days)		2.678 **4** × 10^{6}	4.46**4** × 10^{4}	7.4**4** × 10^{2}	3.**1** × 10	Month (31 d)
Mean solar time	Year (365 days)	a_{365}	3.153 **6** × 10^{7}	5.25**6** × 10^{5}	8.7**6** × 10^{3}	3.6**5** × 10^{2}	a_{365}
Mean solar time	Year (366 days)	a_{366}	3.162 2**4** × 10^{7}	5.270 **4** × 10^{5}	8.78**4** × 10^{3}	3.6**6** × 10^{2}	a_{366}
Sidereal time	Sidereal second[1]	s*	9.972 695 66 × 10^{-1}	1.662 115 94 × 10^{-2}	2.770 193 24 × 10^{-4}	1.154 247 18 × 10^{-5}	s*
Sidereal time	Sidereal minute[1]	min*	5.983 617 40 × 10	9.972 695 66 × 10^{-1}	1.662 115 94 × 10^{-2}	6.925 483 10 × 10^{-4}	min*
Sidereal time	Sidereal hour[1]	h*	3.590 170 44 × 10^{3}	5.983 617 40 × 10	9.972 695 66 × 10^{-1}	4.155 289 86 × 10^{-2}	h*
Sidereal time	Sidereal day[1]	d*	8.616 409 05 × 10^{4}	1.436 068 18 × 10^{3}	2.393 446 96 × 10	9.972 695 66 × 10^{-1}	d*
At time point 1900.**0**	Sidereal year[1]	a_{sid}	3.155 814 95 × 10^{7}	5.259 691 58 × 10^{5}	8.766 152 64 × 10^{3}	3.652 563 60 × 10^{2}	a_{sid}
At time point 1900.**0**	Tropical year[1]	a_{trop}	3.155 692 60 × 10^{7}	5.259 487 66 × 10^{5}	8.765 812 77 × 10^{3}	3.652 421 99 × 10^{2}	a_{trop}
At time point 1900.**0**	Anomalistic year[1]	a_{anom}	3.155 843 30 × 10^{7}	5.259 738 83 × 10^{5}	8.766 231 38 × 10^{3}	3.652 596 41 × 10^{2}	a_{anom}
Calendar years	Julian year	a_{jul}	3.155 7**6** × 10^{7}	5.259 **6** × 10^{5}	8.76**6** × 10^{3}	3.652 **5** × 10^{2}	a_{jul}
Calendar years	Gregorian year	a_{greg}	3.155 695 **2** × 10^{7}	5.259 49**2** × 10^{5}	8.765 8**2** × 10^{3}	3.652 42**5** × 10^{2}	a_{greg}

1) Values from (or calculated from) Newcomb's *Tables of the Sun* (Newcomb, S., *Tables of the Motion of the Earth on its Axis and Around the Sun*, U.S. Nautical Almanac Office, Washington, 1895).

Angles

Plane angles

The plane angle φ between two half-lines *a* and *b* is defined as the ratio of the arc *s* to the radius *r* of a circle whose center lies at the point of intersection of the two half-lines.

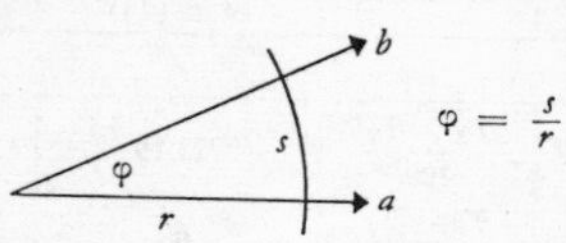

$$\varphi = \frac{s}{r}$$

Since the angle φ is the ratio of two lengths it is a dimensionless quantity.

The *radian* (symbol: rad) is the angle for which the ratio $s/r \equiv 1$. The *right angle* (symbol: ∟) is defined by $\pi/2$, the *degree* (symbol: °) as $\pi/180$, and the *grade* (symbol: ^{g}) as $\pi/200$. The whole circular angle, or *revolution* (symbol: rev) is defined by 2π rad = 4 ∟ = 360° = 400^g.

The subdivision of the unit of angle is sexagesimal in the case of the degree:

1 degree = 60 minutes = 60 × 60 seconds
1° = 60′ = 60 × 60″

The grade is subdivided centesimally:

1 grade = 100 centesimal minutes = 100 × 100 centesimal seconds
1^g = 100^c = 100 × 100^{cc}

The radian, the right angle and the revolution are subdivided decimally without special designation.

Spherical angles

The spherical angle Ω is defined as the ratio F/r^2, where F is that part of the surface of a sphere of radius *r* which is cut out by a cone whose apex coincides with the center of the sphere.

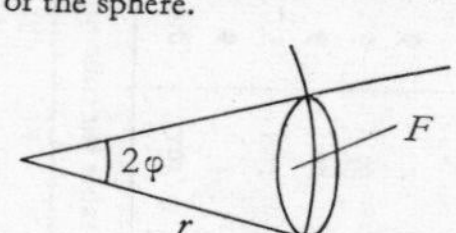

$$\Omega = \frac{F}{r^2}$$

Since the spherical angle is the ratio of two areas it is likewise a dimensionless quantity. When the apical angle of the cone is 2φ the following relation holds:

$$\Omega = 2\pi(1 - \cos\varphi)$$

The *steradian* (symbol: sr) is the spherical angle for which $F/r^2 \equiv 1$. The *square degree* [symbol: □° or (°)²] is defined by $(\pi/180)^2$, the *square grade* [symbol: $(^g)^2$] by $(\pi/200)^2$.

Conversion table for plane angles

To convert from a unit in column **A** into any unit under **B**, multiply by the factor given in the appropriate column under **B**

A		Degree	Minute	Second	Grade	Centesimal minute	Centesimal second	Radian	Right angle	Revolution
Degree*........	°	**1** ×1	**6** ×10	**3.6** ×10³	1.$\dot{1}$ ×1	1.$\dot{1}$ ×10²	1.$\dot{1}$ ×10⁴	1.745 329×10⁻²	1.$\dot{1}$ ×10⁻²	2.$\dot{7}$ ×10⁻³
Minute*........	′	1.$\dot{6}$ ×10⁻²	**1** ×1	**6** ×10	1.851 $\dot{8}\dot{5}$ ×10⁻²	1.851 $\dot{8}\dot{5}$ ×1	1.851 $\dot{8}\dot{5}$ ×10²	2.908 882×10⁻⁴	1.851 $\dot{8}\dot{5}$ ×10⁻⁴	4.$\dot{6}2\dot{9}$ ×10⁻⁵
Second*........	″	2.$\dot{7}$ ×10⁻⁴	1.$\dot{6}$ ×10⁻²	**1** ×1	3.086 420×10⁻⁴	3.086 420×10⁻²	3.086 420×1	4.848 137×10⁻⁶	3.086 420×10⁻⁶	7.716 049×10⁻⁷
Grade..........	g	**9** ×10⁻¹	5.4 ×10	3.24 ×10³	**1** ×1	**1** ×10²	**1** ×10⁴	1.570 796×10⁻²	**1** ×10⁻²	**2.5** ×10⁻³
Centesimal minute...	c	**9** ×10⁻³	5.4 ×10⁻¹	3.24 ×10	**1** ×10⁻²	**1** ×1	**1** ×10²	1.570 796×10⁻⁴	**1** ×10⁻⁴	**2.5** ×10⁻⁵
Centesimal second...	cc	**9** ×10⁻⁵	5.4 ×10⁻³	3.24 ×10⁻¹	**1** ×10⁻⁴	**1** ×10⁻²	**1** ×1	1.570 796×10⁻⁶	**1** ×10⁻⁶	**2.5** ×10⁻⁷
Radian.........	rad	5.729 578×10	3.437 747×10³	2.062 648×10⁵	6.366 198×10	6.366 198×10³	6.366 198×10⁵	**1** ×1	6.366 198×10⁻¹	1.591 549×10⁻¹
Right angle......	∟	**9** ×10	5.4 ×10³	3.24 ×10⁵	**1** ×10²	**1** ×10⁴	**1** ×10⁶	1.570 796	**1** ×1	**2.5** ×10⁻¹
Revolution.......	rev	**3.6** ×10²	**2.16** ×10⁴	**1.296** ×10⁶	**4** ×10²	**4** ×10⁴	**4** ×10⁶	6.283 185	**4**	**1** ×1

* See also conversion table for time units on the previous page.

Conversion table for spherical angles

To convert from a unit in column **A** into any unit under **B**, multiply by the factor given in the appropriate column under **B**

A		B: Square degree	Square grade	Steradian
Square degree ...	□° or (°)²	**1** × 1	1.234 568× 1	3.046 174×10⁻⁴
Square grade.....	(ᵍ)²	8.1 ×10⁻¹	**1** × 1	2.467 401×10⁻⁴
Steradian........	sr	3.826 806×10³	4.052 847×10³	**1** × 1

Temperature

Dimension in all systems of measurement = degree or Θ

Basic units

In metric (MKS-, CGS-, MTS-) systems: degree Centigrade (°C) (known as degree Celsius in continental European countries) or degree Kelvin (°K). In English-speaking countries (technical and commercial usage): degree Fahrenheit (°F) or degree Rankine (°R).

The concepts *temperature* and *heat* (quantity of heat) are rigorously differentiated in physics. The same quantity of heat can be distributed over a larger or smaller quantity of the same material, which will have a lower temperature in the former case than in the latter. Heat itself can thus be said to have a higher or lower temperature.

Heat is a form of energy (see Energy, page 216), whilst the temperature of a body is a measure of the average kinetic energy per degree of freedom of the constituent molecules. Since it is related to the average movement of the latter, the concept of temperature can be applied only to bodies consisting of a large number of molecules. This simple relationship no longer applies at very low temperatures.

Thermodynamic temperature and temperature scales

Thermodynamic temperature is defined by the laws of thermodynamics, for example by the equation of state of ideal gases:

$$T = \frac{pv}{R_0}$$ where T = temperature, p = pressure, v = volume, R_0 = universal gas constant,

so that it is independent of the properties of the material concerned. From the laws of thermodynamics it also follows that there is a zero temperature below which it is impossible to go. This point is known as the *absolute zero*[1], and temperature scales which commence at this point as absolute temperature scales. The commonest scale of absolute temperatures is that due to Kelvin (1848), (Centigrade) the *Kelvin scale*. The absolute *Rankine scale*, corresponding to the Fahrenheit scale is now little used. Other thermodynamic Centigrade and Fahrenheit scales, with zero points not coinciding with the absolute zero, have been adopted for special purposes.

Although the thermodynamic scales are thus all based on the fundamental interval $T_S - T_I$, they possess only *one* fundamental point with an assigned temperature value, the melting point of ice. The present accepted value was agreed upon internationally in 1954[2].

1) Dalton, J., *Mem. Manchr lit. phil. Soc.*, Series 1, 601 (1802). 2) *Comptes rendus de la 10e Conférence générale des Poids et Mesures*, Paris, 1955.

Thermodynamic temperature scales

	Degree symbol	Degree definition	Temperature value at melting point of ice (T_I)*	Temperature value at condensing point of steam (T_S)**
Kelvin	°K	$\frac{T_S - T_I}{100}$	**273.15**	373.15
Centigrade	°C$_{\text{therm.}}$	$\frac{T_S - T_I}{100}$	**0**	100
Rankine	°R	$\frac{T_S - T_I}{180}$	491.67	671.67
Fahrenheit	°F$_{\text{therm.}}$	$\frac{T_S - T_I}{180}$	**32**	212

* Also known as the ice point. ** Measured thermodynamically.

Empirical temperature scales

	Degree symbol	Degree definition	Temperature value at melting point of ice (T_I)	Temperature value at condensing point of steam (T_S)
International scales 1948[1,2]				
Kelvin	°K$_{\text{int.}}$	$\frac{T_S - T_I}{100}$	**273.15**	**373.15**
Centigrade	°C	$\frac{T_S - T_I}{100}$	**0**	**100**
Technical and commercial scale in English-speaking countries				
Fahrenheit	°F	$\frac{T_S - T_I}{180}$	**32**	**212**
Old French scale				
Réaumur	°R	$\frac{T_S - T_I}{80}$	**0**	**80**

1) Comité international des Poids et Mesures, *P. V. Com. int. Poids Mes.*, **21**, 16 (1948).
2) *Comptes rendus de la 9e Conférence générale des Poids et Mesures*, Paris, 1949.

Conversion table for temperature scales

To convert from a scale in column **A** to any scale under **B**, use the formula given in the appropriate column under **B**

A		B				
		Degrees Kelvin	Degrees Centigrade	Degrees Rankine	Degrees Fahrenheit	Degrees Réaumur
Degrees Kelvin	°K	°K	°K − 273.15	**1.8** °K	**1.8** °K − 459.6**7**	0.**8** °K − 218.5**2**
Degrees Centigrade	°C	°C + 273.1**5**	°C	**1.8** °C + 491.6**7**	**1.8** °C + **32**	0.**8** °C
Degrees Rankine	°R	$0.\dot{5}$ °R	$0.\dot{5}$ °R − 273.15	°R	°R − 459.6**7**	$0.\dot{4}$ °R − 218.5**2**
Degrees Fahrenheit	°F	$0.\dot{5}$ °F + $255.37\dot{2}$	$0.\dot{5}$ °F − $17.\dot{7}$	°F + 459.6**7**	°F	$0.\dot{4}$ °F − $14.\dot{2}$
Degrees Réaumur	°R	1.2**5** °R + 273.1**5**	1.2**5** °R	2.2**5** °R + 491.67	2.2**5** °R + **32**	°R

For Centigrade-Fahrenheit and Fahrenheit-Centigrade conversions see page 224.

Empirical temperature and temperature scales

Empirical temperatures are defined on the basis of temperature-dependent properties of certain materials, such as length changes of liquid columns, the freezing and boiling points of water, resistance changes of metals, etc. There is neither analytic nor algebraic connection between empirical and thermodynamic temperature but this is not of practical significance since with present-day accuracy of measurement they can be made to approximate closely to one another. The international empirical temperature scales may thus be regarded as approximations of the thermodynamic scales which are adequate for most practical purposes.

The fundamental interval of all modern empirical temperature scales is the same as that of the thermodynamic scales, viz. the difference between the melting point of ice and the condensing point of steam. In the empirical scales, however, *both* these points have assigned values. Over and above these fundamental points, other primary and secondary fixed points have been established for the International Practical Temperature Scale. The present values of these were agreed upon in 1948[1-3] and are given in the table below.

The Kelvin and Centigrade scales, which use the same degree unit, are adapted to the decimal systems of measurement, the Fahrenheit scale (and the Rankine scale which uses the same degree) to the "hexagesimal" system of measurement in common use in English-speaking countries. The Réaumur scale is no longer used to any significant extent.

1) Comité international des Poids et Mesures, *P. V. Com. int. Poids Mes.*, **21**, 16 (1948). *2) Comptes rendues de la 9e Conférence générale des Poids et Mesures*, Paris, 1949. *3)* National Bureau of Standards, *Nat. Bur. Stand. Techn. News Bull.*, **45**, 65 (1961).

Comparison of empirical temperature scales

The table gives the international fundamental points (in bold type) and the international primary and secondary fixed points of the International Practical Temperature Scale of 1948 (at normal pressure of 1 atm = 760 mm Hg = 1 013 25 dyn/cm²).

	Temperature in degrees				
	Kelvin	Centigrade	Rankine	Fahrenheit	Réaumur
Absolute zero (theoretical)	0	−273.15	0	−459.67	−218.52
Oxygen point (equilibrium temperature between liquid oxygen and its vapor; *primary fixed point*)	90.180	−182.970	162.324	−297.346	−146.376
Sublimation point of carbon dioxide (secondary fixed point)	194.65	− 78.5	350.37	−109.3	− 62.8
Freezing point of mercury (secondary fixed point)	234.28	− 38.87	421.704	− 37.966	− 31.096
Ice point (equilibrium temperature between ice and water saturated with air; **fundamental point**)	273.1**5**	**0**	491.6**7**	**32**	**0**
Triple point of water (primary fixed point)	273.1600	0.0100	491.6880	32.0180	0.0080
Transition point of sodium sulfate decahydrate (secondary fixed point)	305.53	32.38	549.954	90.284	25.904
Steam point (equilibrium temperature between liquid water and water vapor; **fundamental point**; *primary fixed point*)	373.1**5**	10**0**	671.6**7**	21**2**	8**0**
Triple point of benzoic acid (secondary fixed point)	395.51	122.36	711.918	252.248	97.888
Boiling point of naphthalene (secondary fixed point)	491.15	218.0	884.07	424.40	174.40
Freezing point of tin (secondary fixed point)	505.05	231.9	909.09	449.42	185.52
Boiling point of benzophenone (secondary fixed point)	579.05	305.9	1042.29	582.62	244.72
Freezing point of cadmium (secondary fixed point)	594.05	320.9	1069.29	609.62	256.72
Freezing point of lead (secondary fixed point)	600.45	327.3	1080.81	621.14	261.84
Boiling point of mercury (secondary fixed point)	629.73	356.58	1133.514	673.844	285.264
Freezing point of zinc (secondary fixed point)	692.65	419.5	1246.77	787.1	335.6
Sulfur point (equilibrium temperature between liquid sulfur and its vapor; *primary fixed point*)	717.750	444.600	1291.950	832.280	355.680
Freezing point of antimony (secondary fixed point)	903.65	630.5	1626.57	1166.9	504.4
Freezing point of aluminum (secondary fixed point)	933.25	660.1	1679.85	1220.18	528.08
Silver point (equilibrium temperature between solid and liquid silver; *primary fixed point*)	1233.95	960.8	2221.11	1761.44	768.64
Gold point (equilibrium temperature between solid and liquid gold; *primary fixed point*)	1336.15	1063.0	2405.07	1945.4	850.4
Freezing point of copper in a reducing atmosphere (secondary fixed point)	1356.15	1083	2441.07	1981.4	866.4
Freezing point of nickel (secondary fixed point)	1726.15	1453	3107.07	2647.4	1162.4
Freezing point of cobalt (secondary fixed point)	1765.15	1492	3177.27	2717.6	1193.6
Freezing point of palladium (secondary fixed point)	1825.15	1552	3285.27	2825.6	1241.6
Freezing point of platinum (secondary fixed point)	2042.15	1769	3675.87	3216.2	1415.2
Freezing point of rhodium (secondary fixed point)	2233.15	1960	4019.67	3560	1568
Freezing point of iridium (secondary fixed point)	2716.15	2443	4889.07	4429.4	1954.4
Freezing point of tungsten (secondary fixed point)	3653.15	3380	6575.67	6116	2704

Conversion factors for units of density

A		B	C					D	E					F					
		Multiply the given unit under **A** by the factor under **B** and by the power of ten in the appropriate column under **C**						Multiply the given unit under **A** by the factor under **D** and by the power of ten in the appropriate column under **E**						Multiply the given unit under **A** by the factor in the appropriate column under **F**					
			µg/100 cm^3	µg cm^{-3} mg dm^{-3} g m^{-3}	mg/100 cm^3	mg cm^{-3} g dm^{-3} kg m^{-3}	g cm^{-3} kg dm^{-3} t m^{-3}		µg/100 ml	µg ml^{-1} mg l^{-1} g hl^{-1}	mg/100 ml	mg ml^{-1} g l^{-1} kg hl^{-1}	g ml^{-1} kg l^{-1} t hl^{-1}	gr ft^{-3}*	gr in^{-3} (US)	lb ft^{-3}*	lb gal^{-1} (imp.)	lb gal^{-1} (US)	lb in^{-3}*
Micrograms per 100 cubic centimeters .	µg/100 cm^3	**1** ×	1	10^{-2}	10^{-3}	10^{-5}	10^{-8}	1.000 02**8**×	1	10^{-2}	10^{-3}	10^{-5}	10^{-8}	4.369 957×10^{-3}	2.528 925×10^{-6}	6.242 795×10^{-7}	1.002 241×10^{-7}	8.345 453×10^{-8}	3.612 729×10^{-10}
Micrograms per cubic centimeter . . Milligrams per cubic decimeter . . . Grams per cubic meter	µg cm^{-3} mg dm^{-3} g m^{-3}	**1** ×	10^2	1	10^{-1}	10^{-3}	10^{-6}	1.000 02**8**×	10^2	1	10^{-1}	10^{-3}	10^{-6}	4.369 957×10^{-1}	2.528 925×10^{-4}	6.242 795×10^{-5}	1.002 241×10^{-5}	8.345 453×10^{-6}	3.612 729×10^{-8}
Milligrams per 100 cubic centimeters .	mg/100 cm^3	**1** ×	10^3	10	1	10^{-2}	10^{-5}	1.000 02**8**×	10^3	10	1	10^{-2}	10^{-5}	4.369 957× 1	2.528 925×10^{-3}	6.242 795×10^{-4}	1.002 241×10^{-4}	8.345 453×10^{-5}	3.612 729×10^{-7}
Milligrams per cubic centimeter . . Grams per cubic decimeter . . Kilograms per cubic meter	mg cm^{-3} g dm^{-3} kg m^{-3}	**1** ×	10^5	10^3	10^2	1	10^{-3}	1.000 02**8**×	10^5	10^3	10^2	1	10^{-3}	4.369 957×10^2	2.528 925×10^{-1}	6.242 795×10^{-2}	1.002 241×10^{-2}	8.345 453×10^{-3}	3.612 729×10^{-5}
Grams per cubic centimeter . . Kilograms per cubic decimeter . . . Metric tons per cubic meter . . .	g cm^{-3} kg dm^{-3} t m^{-3}	**1** ×	10^8	10^6	10^5	10^{-3}	1	1.000 02**8**×	10^8	10^6	10^5	10^3	1	4.369 957×10^5	2.528 925×10^{-2}	6.242 795×10^{-1}	1.002 241×10^{-1}	8.345 453× 1	3.612 729×10^{-2}
Micrograms per 100 milliliters .	µg/100 ml	9.999 270×	10^{-1}	10^{-3}	10^{-4}	10^{-6}	10^{-9}	**1** ×	1	10^{-2}	10^{-3}	10^{-5}	10^{-8}	4.369 834×10^{-3}	2.528 854×10^{-6}	6.242 620×10^{-7}	1.002 213×10^{-7}	8.345 220×10^{-8}	3.612 628×10^{-10}
Micrograms p. milliliter Milligrams per liter . . . . Grams per 100 liters . . .	µg ml^{-1} mg l^{-1} g hl^{-1}	9.999 270×	10	10^{-1}	10^{-2}	10^{-4}	10^{-7}	**1** ×	10^2	1	10^{-1}	10^{-3}	10^{-6}	4.369 834×10^{-1}	2.528 854×10^{-4}	6.242 620×10^{-5}	1.002 213×10^{-5}	8.345 220×10^{-6}	3.612 628×10^{-8}
Milligrams per 100 milliliters .	mg/100 ml	9.999 270×	10^2	1	10^{-1}	10^{-3}	10^{-6}	**1** ×	10^3	10	1	10^{-2}	10^{-5}	4.369 834× 1	2.528 854×10^{-3}	6.242 620×10^{-4}	1.002 213×10^{-4}	8.345 220×10^{-5}	3.612 628×10^{-7}
Milligrams p. milliliter . Grams per liter . . . . Kilograms per 100 liters	mg ml^{-1} g l^{-1} kg hl^{-1}	9.999 270×	10^4	10^2	10	10^{-1}	10^{-4}	**1** ×	10^5	10^3	10^2	1	10^{-3}	4.369 834×10^2	2.528 854×10^{-1}	6.242 620×10^{-2}	1.002 213×10^{-2}	8.345 220×10^{-3}	3.612 628×10^{-5}
Grams per milliliter . . . Kilograms per liter . . . . Metric tons p. 100 liters	g ml^{-1} kg l^{-1} t hl^{-1}	9.999 270×	10^7	10^5	10^4	10^2	10^{-1}	**1** ×	10^8	10^6	10^5	10^3	1	4.369 834×10^5	2.528 854×10^2	6.242 620×10	1.002 213×10	8.345 220× 1	3.612 628×10^{-2}
Grains per cubic foot* .	gr ft^{-3}	2.288 352×	10^2	1	10^{-1}	10^{-3}	10^{-6}	2.288 416×	10^2	1	10^{-1}	10^{-3}	10^{-6}	**1** × 1	5.787 072×10^{-4}	1.428 571×10^{-4}	2.293 481×10^{-5}	1.909 734×10^{-5}	8.267 196×10^{-8}
Grains per cubic inch (US) . . .	gr in^{-3} (US)	3.954 249×	10^5	10^3	10^2	1	10^{-3}	3.954 360×	10^5	10^3	10^2	1	10^{-3}	1.727 990×10^3	**1** × 1	2.468 557×10^{-1}	3.963 112×10^{-2}	**3.3** ×10^{-2}	1.428 563×10^{-4}
Pounds (av.)																			
per cubic foot*	lb ft^{-3}	1.601 847×	10^6	10^4	10^3	10	10^{-2}	1.601 891×	10^6	10^4	10^3	10	10^{-2}	**7** ×10^3	4.050 950× 1	**1** × 1	1.605 437×10^{-1}	1.336 814×10^{-1}	5.787 037×10^{-4}
per gallon (imp.)	lb gal^{-1} (imp.)	9.977 636×	10^6	10^4	10^3	10^2	10^{-2}	9.977 915×	10^6	10^4	10^3	10	10^{-2}	4.360 184×10^4	2.523 270×10	6.228 834× 1	**1** × 1	8.326 789×10^{-1}	3.604 649×10^{-3}
per gallon (US)	lb gal^{-1} (US)	1.198 257×	10^7	10^5	10^4	10^2	10^{-1}	1.198 291×	10^7	10^5	10^4	10^2	10^{-1}	5.236 332×10^4	3.03 ×10	7.480 475× 1	1.200 943× 1	**1** × 1	4.328 978×10^{-3}
per cubic inch*	lb in^{-3}	2.767 991×	10^9	10^7	10^6	10^4	10	2.768 068×	10^9	10^7	10^6	10^4	10	1.209 **6** ×10^7	7.000 042×10^3	1.72**8** ×10^3	2.774 195×10^2	2.310 01 ×10^2	**1** ×1

* Based on the relation 1 inch = 25.**4** millimeters (see page 202).

Density

Dimensional formulas

In the length-mass-time (LMT-) systems: $L^{-3}M$. Derived units in these systems:

MKS-system: kilogram per cubic meter (kg m^{-3});

CGS-system: gram per cubic centimeter (g cm^{-3});

MTS-system: metric ton per cubic meter (t m^{-3}).

In the length-force-time (LFT-) systems: $L^{-4}KT^2$.

The density of a substance is the ratio of its mass to its volume and for this reason has also been given the name *specific weight*. (This latter name has also been given to the product of density and gravitational acceleration.) Density is dependent on both temperature and pressure, so that these must be specified when giving density data.

The *normal density* of a material is its density at normal temperature and pressure (0°C, 760 mm Hg).

Important standard densities are the maximum density of air-free water* (at 4°C and 760 mm Hg: $\rho_{m\,(H_2O)}$ = 0.999 972 g/cm³ = 1 g/ml) and the normal density of mercury[1] ($\rho_{n\,(Hg)}$ = 13.59505 g/cm³ = 13.59543 g/ml).

The *relative density* of a material is the ratio of its density to that of a reference substance and is commonly known as the *specific gravity*, a dimensionless quantity since it is the ratio of two quantities with the same dimensions. The reference substance for solids and liquids is usually water at its maximum density, for gases dry air containing 0.04% of carbon dioxide at normal temperature and pressure (density ρ_n=1.293 0$_7$ g/l; cf. page 245).

Since the maximum density of water in metric units is 1 g/ml and very nearly 1 g/cm³ (see above), specific gravity can be numerically equated with density for most practical purposes. A given specific gravity, being the ratio of two densities, must be related to two particular temperatures; thus the "specific gravity at 20°/4°C" of a substance is the ratio

$$\frac{\text{Density of the substance at 20°C}}{\text{Density of water at 4°C}}$$

and is usually written as d_4^{20}.

The adjacent conversion table for density units can also be used for concentration units. For this reason some units have been included which are used for expressing concentrations but are unusual as density units.

* Cf. definition of the liter, page 204.

1) After Stille, U., *Messen und Rechnen in der Physik*, Braunschweig, 1955.

Linear velocity

Dimension in all systems of measurement: LT^{-1}

Derived unit in the MKS- and MTS-systems: meters per second (meters/second, m s^{-1})

Derived unit in CGS-system: centimeters per second (centimeters/second, cm s^{-1})

Angular velocity

Dimension in all systems of measurement: T^{-1}

Conversion table for units of linear velocity

To convert from a unit in column **A** into any unit under **B**, multiply by the factor given in the appropriate column under **B**

A		B: cm s^{-1}	m min^{-1}	km h^{-1}	m s^{-1}	km s^{-1}	ft min^{-1}*	ft s^{-1}*	mi h^{-1}*	Knots (int.)	Knots (imp.)	mi s^{-1}*
Centimeters per second	cm s^{-1}	**1** $\times1$	**6** $\times10^{-1}$	**3.6** $\times10^{-2}$	**1** $\times10^{-2}$	**1** $\times10^{-5}$	1.968 504 $\times1$	3.280 840 $\times10^{-2}$	2.236 936 $\times10^{-2}$	1.943 844 $\times10^{-2}$	1.942 606 $\times10^{-2}$	6.213 712 $\times10^{-6}$
Meters per minute	m min^{-1}	1.6̇ $\times1$	**1** $\times1$	**6** $\times10^{-2}$	1.6̇ $\times10^{-2}$	1.6̇ $\times10^{-5}$	3.280 840 $\times1$	5.468 066 $\times10^{-2}$	3.728 227 $\times10^{-2}$	3.239 741 $\times10^{-2}$	3.237 677 $\times10^{-2}$	1.035 619 $\times10^{-5}$
Kilometers per hour	km h^{-1}	2.7̇ $\times10$	1.6̇ $\times10$	**1** $\times1$	2.7̇ $\times10^{-1}$	2.7̇ $\times10^{-4}$	5.468 066 $\times10$	9.113 444 $\times10^{-1}$	6.213 712 $\times10^{-1}$	5.399 568 $\times10^{-1}$	5.396 128 $\times10^{-1}$	1.726 031 $\times10^{-4}$
Meters per second	m s^{-1}	**1** $\times10^{2}$	**6** $\times10$	**3.6** $\times1$	**1** $\times1$	**1** $\times10^{-3}$	1.968 504 $\times10^{2}$	3.280 840 $\times1$	2.236 936 $\times1$	1.943 844 $\times1$	1.942 606 $\times1$	6.213 712 $\times10^{-4}$
Kilometers per second	km s^{-1}	**1** $\times10^{5}$	**6** $\times10^{4}$	**3.6** $\times10^{3}$	**1** $\times10^{3}$	**1** $\times1$	1.968 504 $\times10^{5}$	3.280 840 $\times10^{3}$	2.236 936 $\times10^{3}$	1.943 844 $\times10^{3}$	1.942 606 $\times10^{3}$	6.213 712 $\times10^{-1}$
Feet per minute*	ft min^{-1}*	5.08 $\times10^{-1}$	3.048 $\times10^{-1}$	1.828 8 $\times10^{-2}$	5.08 $\times10^{-3}$	5.08 $\times10^{-6}$	**1** $\times1$	1.6̇ $\times10^{-2}$	1.13̇6̇ $\times10^{-2}$	9.874 730 $\times10^{-3}$	9.868 438 $\times10^{-3}$	3.15̇6̇ $\times10^{-6}$
Feet per second*	ft s^{-1}*	3.048 $\times10$	1.828 8 $\times10$	1.097 28 $\times1$	3.048 $\times10^{-1}$	3.048 $\times10^{-4}$	**6** $\times10$	**1** $\times1$	6.8̇1̇ $\times10^{-1}$	5.924 838 $\times10^{-1}$	5.921 063 $\times10^{-1}$	1.89̇3̇ $\times10^{-4}$
Miles per hour*	mi h^{-1}*	4.470 4 $\times10$	2.682 24 $\times10$	1.609 344 $\times1$	4.470 4 $\times10^{-1}$	4.470 4 $\times10^{-4}$	8.8 $\times10$	1.46̇ $\times1$	**1** $\times1$	8.689 762 $\times10^{-1}$	8.684 226 $\times10^{-1}$	2.7̇ $\times10^{-4}$
Knots (international) / Nautical miles (int.) per hour	Knots int.	5.14̇ $\times10$	3.08̇6̇ $\times10$	1.852 $\times1$	5.14̇ $\times10^{-1}$	5.14̇ $\times10^{-4}$	1.012 686 $\times10^{2}$	1.687 810 $\times1$	1.150 779 $\times1$	**1** $\times1$	9.993 628 $\times10^{-1}$	3.196 610 $\times10^{-4}$
Knots (imperial) / Nautical miles (imp.) per hour	Knots imp.	5.147 724 $\times10$	3.088 635 $\times10$	1.853 181 $\times1$	5.147 724 $\times10^{-1}$	5.147 724 $\times10^{-4}$	1.013 332 $\times10^{2}$	1.688 886 $\times1$	1.151 513 $\times1$	1.000 638 $\times1$	**1** $\times1$	3.198 648 $\times10^{-4}$
Miles per second*	mi s^{-1}*	1.609 344 $\times10^{5}$	9.656 064 $\times10^{4}$	5.793 638 $\times10^{3}$	1.609 344 $\times10^{3}$	1.609 344 $\times1$	3.168 $\times10^{5}$	5.28 $\times10^{3}$	3.6 $\times10^{3}$	3.128 314 $\times10^{3}$	3.126 321 $\times10^{3}$	**1** $\times1$

* Based on the relation 1 inch = 25.4 millimeters (see page 202).

Conversion table for units of angular velocity

To convert from a unit in column **A** into any unit under **B**, multiply by the factor given in the appropriate column under **B**

A		B: rev d^{-1}	^{g} min^{-1}	° min^{-1}	rev h^{-1}	^{g} s^{-1}	rad min^{-1}	° s^{-1}	rev min^{-1}	rad s^{-1}	rev s^{-1}
Revolutions per day	rev d^{-1}	**1** $\times1$	2.7̇ $\times10^{-1}$	**2.5** $\times10^{-1}$	4.16̇ $\times10^{-2}$	4.6̇29̇ $\times10^{-3}$	4.363 323 $\times10^{-3}$	4.16̇ $\times10^{-3}$	6.94̇ $\times10^{-4}$	7.272 005 $\times10^{-5}$	1.157 40̇7̇ $\times10^{-5}$
Grades per minute	^{g} min^{-1}	**3.6** $\times1$	**1** $\times1$	**9** $\times10^{-1}$	**1.5** $\times10^{-1}$	1.6̇ $\times10^{-2}$	1.570 796 $\times10^{-2}$	**1.5** $\times10^{-2}$	**2.5** $\times10^{-3}$	2.617 994 $\times10^{-4}$	4.16̇ $\times10^{-5}$
Degrees per minute	° min^{-1}	**4** $\times1$	1.1̇ $\times1$	**1** $\times1$	1.6̇ $\times10^{-1}$	1.8̇5̇1̇ $\times10^{-2}$	1.745 329 $\times10^{-2}$	1.6̇ $\times10^{-2}$	2.7̇ $\times10^{-3}$	2.908 882 $\times10^{-4}$	4.6̇29̇ $\times10^{-5}$
Revolutions per hour	rev h^{-1}	**2.4** $\times10$	6.6̇ $\times1$	**6** $\times1$	**1** $\times1$	1.1̇ $\times10^{-1}$	1.047 198 $\times10^{-1}$	**1** $\times10^{-1}$	1.6̇ $\times10^{-2}$	1.745 329 $\times10^{-3}$	2.7̇ $\times10^{-4}$
Grades per second	^{g} s^{-1}	**2.16** $\times10^{2}$	**6** $\times10$	**5.4** $\times10$	**9** $\times1$	**1** $\times1$	9.424 778 $\times10^{-1}$	**9** $\times10^{-1}$	**1.5** $\times10^{-1}$	1.570 796 $\times10^{-2}$	**2.5** $\times10^{-3}$
Radians per minute	rad min^{-1}	2.291 831 $\times10^{2}$	6.366 198 $\times10$	5.729 578 $\times10$	9.549 297 $\times1$	1.061 033 $\times1$	**1** $\times1$	9.549 297 $\times10^{-1}$	1.591 549 $\times10^{-1}$	1.6̇ $\times10^{-2}$	2.652 582 $\times10^{-3}$
Degrees per second	° s^{-1}	**2.4** $\times10^{2}$	6.6̇ $\times10$	**6** $\times10$	**1** $\times10$	1.1̇ $\times1$	1.047 198 $\times1$	**1** $\times1$	1.6̇ $\times10^{-1}$	1.745 329 $\times10^{-2}$	2.7̇ $\times10^{-3}$
Revolutions per minute	rev min^{-1}	**1.44** $\times10^{3}$	**4** $\times10^{2}$	**3.6** $\times10^{2}$	**6** $\times10$	6.6̇ $\times1$	6.283 185 $\times1$	**6** $\times1$	**1** $\times1$	1.047 198 $\times10^{-1}$	1.6̇ $\times10^{-2}$
Radians per second	rad s^{-1}	1.375 099 $\times10^{4}$	3.819 719 $\times10^{3}$	3.437 747 $\times10^{3}$	5.729 578 $\times10^{2}$	6.366 198 $\times10$	**6** $\times10$	5.729 578 $\times10$	9.549 297 $\times1$	**1** $\times1$	1.591 549 $\times10^{-1}$
Revolutions per second	rev s^{-1}	**8.64** $\times10^{4}$	**2.4** $\times10^{4}$	**2.16** $\times10^{4}$	**3.6** $\times10^{3}$	**4** $\times10^{2}$	3.769 911 $\times10^{2}$	**3.6** $\times10^{2}$	**6** $\times10$	6.283 185 $\times1$	**1** $\times1$

Frequency – Acceleration
Angular Acceleration – Force, Weight

Frequency

Dimension in all systems of measurement: T^{-1}
Fundamental unit in all systems of measurement: s^{-1} = cycle per second (cps), also written simply as cycle (c). In German-speaking countries this unit is called the Hertz (Hz). 1000 cycles = 1 kilocycle (kc) = 1 Kilohertz (kHz).

Acceleration

Dimension in all systems of measurement: LT^{-2}

Derived unit in the MKS- and MTS-systems: meter per second per second (m s^{-2}). Derived unit in the CGS-system: centimeter per second per second (cm s^{-2}) = galilei (gal).

The international standard value[1] for gravitational acceleration g_n = 9.806 65 m s^{-2} = 980.665 gal (cms^{-2}) = 32.17396 ft s^{-2} (US) = 32.17405 ft s^{-2}*. For values of gravity in various latitudes see page 245.

* Based on the relation 1 inch = 25.4 millimeters (see page 202).
1) *Comptes rendus de la 3e Conférence générale des Poids et Mesures*, Paris, 1901.

Conversion table for acceleration units

To convert from a unit in column **A** into any unit under **B**, multiply by the factor given in the appropriate column under **B**

A		B: gal, cm s^{-2}		km h^{-1} s^{-1}		m s^{-2}		ft s^{-2}*	mi h^{-1} s^{-1}*
Galilei / Centimeter/second per second	gal / cm s^{-2}	1	× 1	3.6	×10^{-2}	1	×10^{-2}	3.280 840×10^{-2}	2.236 936×10^{-2}
Kilometer/hour per second	km h^{-1} s^{-1}	2.7̇	×10	1	× 1	2.7̇	×10^{-1}	9.113 444×10^{-1}	6.213 712×10^{-1}
Meter/second per second	m s^{-2}	1	×10^{2}	3.6	× 1	1	× 1	3.280 840× 1	2.236 936× 1
Foot/second per second*	ft s^{-2}*	3.048	×10	1.097 28	× 1	3.048	×10^{-1}	1 × 1	6.81̇ ×10^{-1}
Mile/hour per second*	mi h^{-1} s^{-1}*	4.470 4	×10	1.609 344	× 1	4.470 4	×10^{-1}	1.46̇ × 1	1 × 1

* Based on the relation 1 inch = 25.4 millimeters (see page 202).

Angular acceleration

Dimension in all systems of measurement: T^{-2}

Conversion table for units of angular acceleration

To convert from a unit in column **A** into any unit under **B**, multiply by the factor given in the appropriate column under **B**

A		B: rev min^{-2}		g s^{-2}		° s^{-2}		rev min^{-1} s^{-1}		rad s^{-2}	rev s^{-2}	
Revolution/minute per minute	rev min^{-2}	1	× 1	1.1̇	×10^{-1}	1	×10^{-1}	1.6̇	×10^{-2}	1.745 329×10^{-3}	2.7̇	×10^{-4}
Grade/second per second	g s^{-2}	9	× 1	1	× 1	9	×10^{-1}	1.5	×10^{-1}	1.570 796×10^{-2}	2.5	×10^{-3}
Degree/second per second	° s^{-2}	1	×10	1.1̇	× 1	1	× 1	1.6̇	×10^{-1}	1.745 329×10^{-2}	2.7̇	×10^{-3}
Revolution/minute per second	rev min^{-1} s^{-1}	6	×10	6.6̇	× 1	6	× 1	1	× 1	1.047 198×10^{-1}	1.6̇	×10^{-2}
Radian/second per second	rad s^{-2}	5.729 578×10^{2}		6.366 198×10		5.729 578×10		9.549 297× 1		1 × 1	1.591 549×10^{-1}	
Revolution/second per second	rev s^{-2}	3.6	×10^{3}	4	×10^{2}	3.6	×10^{2}	6	×10	6.283 185× 1	1	× 1

Force, Weight

Dimensional formula in the LMT-systems = LMT^{-2}

Derived units in the corresponding systems of measurement:

MKS-system: newton (N) m kg s^{-2}
CGS-system: dyne (dyn) cm g s^{-2}
MTS-system: sthene (sn) m t s^{-2}

Dimension in the LFT-system = F

Fundamental unit in the associated m-kp-s-system of technology: 9.806 65 newtons = the weight of one kilogram at the standard acceleration of gravity g_n. This unit is known as the kilopond (kp) in Germany, Austria and Sweden, but owing to the possibility of confusion with the English 'pound' and Dutch 'pond' it has not received international recognition. The names

Conversion table for units of force

To convert from a unit in column **A** into any unit under **B**, multiply by the factor given in the appropriate column under **B**

A		B: dyn	p	N	kp	Gr*	Pdl (US)**	Lb***
Dyne	dyn cm g s^{-2}	1 × 1	1.019 716×10^{-3}	1 ×10^{-5}	1.019 716×10^{-6}	1.573 662×10^{-2}	7.232 998×10^{-5}	2.248 089×10^{-6}
Gram-force / Pond	p	9.806 65 ×10^{2}	1 × 1	9.806 65 ×10^{-3}	1 ×10^{3}	1.543 236×10	7.093 148×10^{-2}	2.204 622×10^{-3}
Newton	N / m kg s^{-2}	1 ×10^{5}	1.019 716×10^{2}	1 × 1	1.019 716×10^{-1}	1.573 662×10^{3}	7.232 998× 1	2.248 089×10^{-1}
Kilogram-force / Kilopond	kp	9.806 65 ×10^{5}	1 ×10^{3}	9.806 65 × 1	1 × 1	1.543 236×10^{4}	7.093 148×10	2.204 622× 1
Grain-force* (grain-weight)	Gr (gr wt)	6.354 603×10	6.479 892×10^{-1}	6.354 603×10^{-4}	6.479 892×10^{-5}	1 × 1	4.596 283×10^{-3}	1.428 571×10^{-4}
Poundal** (US)	Pdl (US)	1.382 552×10^{4}	1.409 811×10	1.382 552×10^{-1}	1.409 811×10^{-2}	2.175 671×10^{2}	1 × 1	3.108 101×10^{-2}
Pound-force*** (pound-weight)	Lb (lb wt)	4.448 222×10^{5}	4.535 924×10^{2}	4.448 222× 1	4.535 924×10^{-1}	7 ×10^{3}	3.217 398× 1	1 × 1

* 1 Gr = 9.806 65 m s^{-2} gr ** 1 Poundal = 1 ft lb s^{-2} (US) *** 1 Lb = 9.806 65 m s^{-2} lb

of mass units (page 207) should in any case not be used as such for units of force. The following distinction is recommended:

Definition	Name
Weight of one kilogram at the standard acceleration of gravity (technical unit of force) $= g_n \times$ kg	Kilogram-force (French: kilogramme-force) (German: Kilogramm-Kraft)
Weight of one kilogram at a locality with acceleration of gravity g_l (local weight) $= g_l \times$ kg	Kilogram-weight (French: kilogramme-poids) (German: Kilogramm-Gewicht)

Pressure

Dimensional formula in the LMT-systems $= L^{-1}MT^{-2}$.

Derived units in the corresponding systems of measurement:

MKS-system: newton per square meter ($N\,m^{-2}$) $\equiv m^{-1}\,kg\,s^{-2}$

CGS-system: dyne per square centimeter (dyn cm^{-2}) $\equiv cm^{-1}\,g\,s^{-2} \equiv$ microbar (μb)

MTS-system: pièze (pz) $\equiv m^{-1}\,t\,s^{-2}$

Dimensional formula in the LFT-systems of technology $= L^{-2}F$

Derived unit in the corresponding m-kp-s-system of technology: kilogram-force per square meter (kp m^{-2}) = 9.806 65 N m^{-2}. The 10^4 multiple of the kp cm^{-2} is known as the **technical atmosphere** (at), and is the pressure unit mainly used in technology: 1 at = 9.806 65 × 10^4 N m^{-2}.

The 10^6 multiple of the dyn cm^{-2} is known as the bar (b or bar). The millibar (mb) is the present international unit of pressure in meteorology. The microbar (μb) is used in the measurement of sound pressures (see page 240).

The following special pressure units do not conform to the CGS-, MKS- or m-kp-s-systems:

Standard physical atmosphere (atm): defined in accordance with the international temperature scale of 1948[1,2]:

1 atm = 1 013 250 dyn/cm^2

Torricelli (Torr): defined as 1/760th of the standard atmosphere:

1 Torr = 1 atm/760 = 1333.223 68 dyn/cm^2

Millimeter of water (mm H_2O): defined as the weight of a column of water 1 mm in height and 1 cm^2 in cross-section at 4° C, 760 mm Hg and the standard acceleration of gravity:

1 mm H_2O = 0.1 cm × 0.999 972 g/cm^3 × 980.665 cm/s^2 = 98.0638 dyn/cm^2

Millimeter of mercury (mm Hg): defined[3] as 1/760th of the old standard atmosphere of 1927. The latter was defined as the pressure exerted by a column of mercury 760 mm in height at the standard acceleration of gravity when the density of mercury is 13.5951 g/cm^3:

$1\ atm_{1927}$ = 76 cm × 13.5951 g/cm^3 × 980.665 cm/s^2 = 1.013 250 144 dyn/cm^2 = 1.000 000 14 atm

whence

1 mm Hg = $1\ atm_{1927}$/760 = 1333.223 87 dyn/cm^2 = 1.000 000 14 Torr

For very precise measurements the unit Torr is preferable to the mm Hg since unlike the latter it is independent of material properties.

Normal pressure in both physics and meteorology is 1 atm (= 760 Torr) and represents the mean atmospheric pressure at sea level and the standard acceleration of gravity.

Pressure units occasionally used in technology in English-speaking countries are inch of water, foot of water, and inch of mercury. They are obtained from the above formulas for millimeter of water and standard atmosphere 1927 by substituting 1 inch or 1 foot for the metric lengths 0.1 cm and 76 cm.

1) *Comptes rendus de la 9e Conférence générale des Poids et Mesures*, Paris, 1949. 2) *Comptes rendus de la 10e Conférence générale des Poids et Mesures*, Paris, 1955. 3) *Comptes rendus de la 7e Conférence générale des Poids et Mesures*, Paris, 1927.

Conversion table for pressure units

A		B: Multiply the given unit under **A** by the factor under **B** and by the power of ten in the appropriate column under **C**	C				D: Multiply the given unit under **A** by the factor under **D** and by the power of ten in the appropriate column under **E**	E			F: Multiply the given unit under **A** by the factor in the appropriate column under **F**								
			μb	N m^{-2}	mb	b		kp m^{-2}	p cm^{-2}	at	mm H_2O	mm Hg	atm	Lb ft^{-2}*	in H_2O (US)	ft H_2O*	in Hg (US)	Lb in^{-2}*	Tn ft^{-2}*
Microbar	μb	1 ×	1	10^{-1}	10^{-3}	10^{-6}	1.019 716×	10^{-2}	10^{-3}	10^{-6}	1.019745×10^{-2}	7.500617×10^{-4}	9.869233×10^{-7}	2.088543×10^{-3}	4.014735×10^{-4}	3.345619×10^{-5}	2.952992×10^{-5}	1.450377×10^{-5}	9.323853×10^{-7}
Newton per square meter	N m^{-2}	1 ×	10	1	10^{-2}	10^{-5}	1.019 716×	10^{-1}	10^{-2}	10^{-5}	1.019745×10^{-1}	7.500617×10^{-3}	9.869233×10^{-6}	2.088543×10^{-2}	4.014735×10^{-3}	3.345619×10^{-4}	2.952992×10^{-4}	1.450377×10^{-4}	9.323853×10^{-6}
Millibar	mb	1 ×	10^{3}	10^{2}	1	10^{-3}	1.019 716×	10	1	10^{-3}	1.019745×10	7.500617×10^{-1}	9.869233×10^{-4}	2.088543×1	4.014735×10^{-1}	3.345619×10^{-2}	2.952992×10^{-2}	1.450377×10^{-2}	9.323853×10^{-4}
Bar	b	1 ×	10^{6}	10^{5}	10^{3}	1	1.019 716×	10^{4}	10^{3}	1	1.019745×10^{4}	7.500617×10^{2}	9.869233×10^{-1}	2.088543×10^{3}	4.014735×10^{2}	3.345619×10	2.952992×10	1.450377×10	9.323853×10^{-1}
Kilogram-force per square meter	kp m^{-2}	9.806 65 ×	10	1	10^{-2}	10^{-5}	1 ×	1	10^{-1}	10^{-4}	1.000028×1	7.355592×10^{-2}	9.678411×10^{-5}	2.048161×10^{-1}	3.937110×10^{-2}	3.280932×10^{-3}	2.895896×10^{-3}	1.422334×10^{-3}	9.143577×10^{-5}
Gram-force per square centimeter	p cm^{-2}	9.806 65 ×	10^{2}	10	10^{-1}	10^{-4}	1 ×	10	1	10^{-3}	1.000028×10	7.355592×10^{-1}	9.678411×10^{-4}	2.048161×1	3.937110×10^{-1}	3.280932×10^{-2}	2.895896×10^{-2}	1.422334×10^{-2}	9.143577×10^{-4}
Atmosphere (techn.)	at	9.806 65 ×	10^{5}	10^{4}	10^{2}	10^{-1}	1 ×	10^{4}	10^{3}	1	1.000028×10^{4}	7.355592×10^{2}	9.678411×10^{-1}	2.048161×10^{3}	3.937110×10^{2}	3.280932×10	2.895896×10	1.422334×10	9.143577×10^{-1}
Millimeter of water	mm H_2O	9.806 375×	10	1	10^{-2}	10^{-5}	9.999 720×	10^{-1}	10^{-2}	10^{-5}	1×1	7.355386×10^{-2}	9.678140×10^{-5}	2.048104×10^{-1}	3.937×10^{-2}	3.280840×10^{-3}	2.895815×10^{-3}	1.422294×10^{-3}	9.143207×10^{-5}
Millimeter of mercury	mm Hg	1.333 224×	10^{3}	10^{2}	1	10^{-3}	1.359 510×	10	1	10^{-3}	1.359548×10	1×1	1.315789×10^{-3}	2.784495×1	5.352540×10^{-1}	4.460459×10^{-2}	3.936999×10^{-2}	1.933677×10^{-2}	1.243078×10^{-3}
Atmosphere (physical)	atm	1.013 25 ×	10^{6}	10^{5}	10^{3}	1	1.033 227×	10^{4}	10^{3}	1	1.033256×10^{4}	7.6×10^{2}	1×1	2.116216×10^{3}	4.067930×10^{2}	3.389949×10	2.992120×10	1.469595×10	9.447394×10^{-1}
Pound force per square foot*	Lb ft^{-2}	4.788 027×	10^{2}	10	10^{-1}	10^{-4}	4.882 428×	1	10^{-1}	10^{-4}	4.882565×1	3.591315×10^{-1}	4.725415×10^{-4}	1×1	1.922266×10^{-1}	1.601891×10^{-2}	1.413901×10^{-2}	$6.9\dot{4}\times10^{-3}$	4.464286×10^{-4}
Inch of water (US)	in H_2O	2.490 824×	10^{3}	10^{2}	1	10^{-3}	2.539 934×	10	1	10^{-3}	2.540005×10	1.868272×1	2.458252×10^{-3}	5.202194×1	1×1	8.333350×10^{-2}	7.355385×10^{-2}	3.612635×10^{-2}	2.322408×10^{-3}
Foot of water*	ft H_2O	2.988 983×	10^{4}	10^{3}	10	10^{-2}	3.047 915×	10^{2}	10	10^{-2}	3.048×10^{2}	2.241922×10	2.949897×10^{-2}	6.242620×10	1.199998×10	1×1	8.826445×10^{-1}	4.335153×10^{-1}	2.786884×10^{-2}
Inch of mercury (US)	in Hg	3.386 395×	10^{4}	10^{3}	10	10^{-2}	3.453 162×	10^{2}	10	10^{-2}	3.453259×10^{2}	2.540005×10	3.342112×10^{-2}	7.072633×10	1.359548×10	1.132959×1	1×1	4.911551×10^{-1}	3.157425×10^{-2}
Pound-force per square inch*	Lb in^{-2}	6.894 758×	10^{4}	10^{3}	10	10^{-2}	7.030 697×	10^{2}	10	10^{-2}	7.030894×10^{2}	5.171494×10	6.804597×10^{-2}	1.44×10^{2}	2.768063×10	2.306724×1	2.036017×1	1×1	6.428571×10^{-2}
Ton-force per square foot*	Tn ft^{-2}	1.072 518×	10^{6}	10^{5}	10^{3}	1	1.093 664×	10^{4}	10^{3}	1	1.093695×10^{4}	8.044546×10^{2}	1.058493×1	2.24×10^{3}	4.305875×10^{2}	3.588237×10	3.167137×10	$1.\dot{5}\times10$	1×1

* Based on the relation 1 inch = 25.4 millimeters (cf. page 202).

Energy (amount of work or heat)

Dimensional formula in the LMT-systems = $L^2\,MT^{-2}$

Derived units in the corresponding systems of measurement:

MKS-system: joule (J) ≡ newton × meter ≡ $m^2\,kg\,s^{-2}$
CGS-system: erg (erg) ≡ dyne × centimeter ≡ $cm^2\,g\,s^{-2}$

Dimensional formula in the LFT-systems = LF

Derived unit in the corresponding m-kp-s-system: meter-kilogram-force (mkp) ≡ meter × kilogram-force = 9.806 **65** joules.

Energy is "*stored*" *work*, or the *capacity to do work*, and is therefore measured in the same units as work.

Fundamentally, a body can possess energy in two ways: either as a result of its position with respect to surrounding bodies (potential energy) or as a result of its motion (energy of motion). In addition all bodies possess the potential energy E in the form of their mass m given by the relation $E = m\,c^2$ (where c = velocity of light in vacuum), whence the use of the Mass Unit (MU) as energy unit in atomic physics. Heat (amount of heat) is the energy of motion of molecules and was originally measured in calories, now in joules. The relationship between these two units (1 cal_{15} = 4.1855 joules) is the so-called heat equivalent, a constant now rendered redundant by the measurement of heat in joules.

Energy units in atomic and nuclear physics. All the energy units used in atomic and nuclear physics contain one or more physical constants as factors: velocity of light in vacuum (c), charge of the electron (e), PLANCK's constant (h), AVOGADRO's constant (N), the BOLTZMANN entropy constant (k), and the RYDBERG constant for hydrogen (R_H). In contrast to the usual energy units, the units derived from these constants are based not on a definition but on the measurement of the constants, and are thus *natural* energy units. For values of the constants concerned and formulas for calculation of the units see pages 246–248.

Conversion factors for energy units of atomic physics

To convert from a unit in column **A** into any unit under **B**, multiply by the factor given in the appropriate column under **B**

A		B								
		g	J	erg	MU	Ry	eV	cm^{-1}	°K	s^{-1}
Gram	g	**1** × 1	$8.987\,55\times10^{13}$	$8.987\,55\times10^{20}$	$6.025\,02\times10^{23}$	$4.125\,94\times10^{31}$	$5.610\,15\times10^{32}$	$4.525\,23\times10^{36}$	$6.510\,82\times10^{36}$	$1.356\,63\times10^{47}$
Joule........	J	$1.112\,65\times10^{-14}$	**1** × 1	**1** $\times10^{7}$	$6.703\,74\times10^{9}$	$4.590\,73\times10^{17}$	$6.242\,13\times10^{18}$	$5.035\,00\times10^{22}$	$7.244\,26\times10^{22}$	$1.509\,45\times10^{33}$
Erg	erg	$1.112\,65\times10^{-21}$	**1** $\times10^{-7}$	**1** × 1	$6.703\,74\times10^{2}$	$4.590\,73\times10^{10}$	$6.242\,13\times10^{11}$	$5.035\,00\times10^{15}$	$7.244\,26\times10^{15}$	$1.509\,45\times10^{26}$
Mass unit	MU	$1.659\,75\times10^{-24}$	$1.491\,71\times10^{-10}$	$1.491\,71\times10^{-3}$	**1** × 1	$6.848\,01\times10^{7}$	$9.311\,41\times10^{8}$	$7.510\,73\times10^{12}$	$1.080\,63\times10^{13}$	$2.251\,66\times10^{23}$
Rydberg	Ry	$2.423\,69\times10^{-32}$	$2.178\,30\times10^{-18}$	$2.178\,30\times10^{-11}$	$1.460\,28\times10^{-8}$	**1** × 1	$1.359\,73\times10$	$1.096\,78\times10^{5}$	$1.578\,02\times10^{5}$	$3.288\,05\times10^{15}$
Electron volt .	eV	$1.782\,48\times10^{-33}$	$1.602\,02\times10^{-19}$	$1.602\,02\times10^{-12}$	$1.073\,95\times10^{-9}$	$7.354\,43\times10^{-2}$	**1** × 1	$8.066\,16\times10^{3}$	$1.160\,54\times10^{4}$	$2.418\,17\times10^{14}$
Centimeter^{-1} .	cm^{-1}	$2.209\,83\times10^{-37}$	$1.986\,10\times10^{-23}$	$1.986\,10\times10^{-16}$	$1.331\,43\times10^{-13}$	$9.117\,63\times10^{-6}$	$1.239\,74\times10^{-4}$	**1** × 1	$1.438\,78\times 1$	$2.997\,93\times10^{10}$
Degree Kelvin	°K	$1.535\,91\times10^{-37}$	$1.380\,40\times10^{-23}$	$1.380\,40\times10^{-16}$	$9.253\,86\times10^{-14}$	$6.337\,05\times10^{-6}$	$8.616\,65\times10^{-5}$	$6.950\,33\times10^{-1}$	**1** × 1	$2.083\,66\times10^{10}$
Second^{-1}	s^{-1}	$7.371\,20\times10^{-48}$	$6.624\,91\times10^{-34}$	$6.624\,91\times10^{-27}$	$4.441\,17\times10^{-24}$	$3.041\,31\times10^{-6}$	$4.135\,35\times10^{-15}$	$3.335\,64\times10^{-11}$	$4.799\,26\times10^{-11}$	**1** × 1

Conversion factors for energy units of ordinary physics

To convert from a unit in column **A** into any unit under **B**, multiply by the factor given in the appropriate column under **B**

A		B								
		J	erg	kWh	HPh (int.)	mkp	latm	cal_{15}	$kcal_{15}$	BTU_{mean}
Joule........	J	**1** × 1	**1** $\times10^{7}$	$2.\dot{7}\times10^{-7}$	3.776727×10^{-7}	1.019716×10^{-1}	9.868956×10^{-3}	2.3892×10^{-1}	2.3892×10^{-4}	9.4716×10^{-4}
Erg	erg	**1** $\times10^{-7}$	**1** × 1	$2.\dot{7}\times10^{-14}$	3.776727×10^{-14}	1.019716×10^{-8}	9.868956×10^{-10}	2.3892×10^{-8}	2.3892×10^{-11}	9.4716×10^{-11}
Kilowatt-hour	kWh	3.**6** $\times10^{6}$	3.**6** $\times10^{13}$	**1** × 1	1.359622×1	3.670978×10^{5}	3.552824×10^{4}	8.6011×10^{5}	8.6011×10^{2}	3.4098×10^{3}
Horsepower-hour (int.)	HPh (int.)	2.647796×10^{6}	2.647796×10^{13}	7.354989×10^{-1}	**1** × 1	2.**7** $\times10^{5}$	2.613098×10^{4}	6.3261×10^{5}	6.3261×10^{2}	2.5079×10^{3}
Meter-kilogram-force	mkp	9.8066**5** × 1	9.8066**5** $\times10^{7}$	2.724069×10^{-6}	3.703704×10^{-6}	**1** × 1	9.678140×10^{-2}	2.3430×1	2.3430×10^{-3}	9.2885×10^{-3}
Liter-atmosphere	latm	1.013278×10^{2}	1.013278×10^{9}	2.814662×10^{-5}	3.826875×10^{-5}	1.033256×10	**1** × 1	2.4209×10	2.4209×10^{-2}	9.5974×10^{-2}
15° calorie ...	cal_{15}	4.1855×1	4.1855×10^{7}	1.1626×10^{-6}	1.5808×10^{-6}	4.2680×10^{-1}	4.1307×10^{-2}	**1** × 1	**1** $\times10^{-3}$	3.9643×10^{-3}
15° kilogram calorie ...	$kcal_{15}$	4.1855×10^{3}	4.1855×10^{10}	1.1626×10^{-3}	1.5808×10^{-3}	4.2680×10^{2}	4.1307×10	**1** $\times10^{3}$	**1** × 1	3.9643×1
Brit. thermal $unit_{mean}$.	BTU_{mean}	1.0558×10^{3}	1.0558×10^{10}	2.9328×10^{-4}	3.9874×10^{-4}	1.0766×10^{2}	1.0420×10	2.5225×10^{2}	2.5225×10^{-1}	**1** × 1

Power

Dimensional formula in the LMT-systems = $L^2\,MT^{-3}$

Derived units in the corresponding systems of measurement:

MKS-system: watt (W) ≡ 1 joule per second ≡ newton × meter per second ≡ $m^2\,kg\,s^{-3}$

CGS-system: erg/second (erg s^{-1}) ≡ dyne × centimeter per second ≡ $cm^2\,g\,s^{-3}$

Dimensional formula in the LFT-systems = LFT^{-1}

Derived unit in the corresponding m-kp-s-system of technology:
meter kilogram-force per second (mkp s^{-1}).

In the British Commonwealth and USA the technical power unit is the horsepower (HP), defined as 55**0** foot-pounds per second (= 76.0402 mkp s^{-2}). The international or metric horsepower (HP [int.]) = 75 mkp s^{-2}.

Work (energy × time)

Dimensional formula in the LMT-systems = $L^2\,MT^{-1}$

Derived units in the corresponding systems of measurement:

MKS-system: joule × second (J s) ≡ newton × meter × second ≡ $m^2\,kg\,s^{-1}$

CGS-system: erg × second (erg s) ≡ dyne × centimeter × second ≡ $cm^2\,g\,s^{-1}$

Dimensional formula in the LFT-systems = LFT

Derived unit in the corresponding m-kp-s-system of technology:
mkp s = 9.806 **65** J s.

Units of atomic physics:
Electron volt × second (eV s); PLANCK's constant (h).

Dynamic Viscosity – Kinematic Viscosity – Surface Tension
Thermal Conductivity – Coefficient of Heat Transfer

Conversion factors for power units

To convert from a unit in column **A** into any unit under **B**, multiply by the factor given in the appropriate column under **B**

A		B						
		erg s^{-1}	W	kW	mkp s^{-1}	HP (int.)	cal_{15} s^{-1}	BTU_{mean} s^{-1}
Erg per second	erg s^{-1}	**1** $\times 1$	**1** $\times 10^{-7}$	**1** $\times 10^{-10}$	$1.019\,716\times10^{-8}$	$1.359\,622\times10^{-10}$	$2.389\,2\times10^{-8}$	$9.471\,6\times10^{-11}$
Watt	W	**1** $\times 10^{7}$	**1** $\times 1$	**1** $\times 10^{-3}$	$1.019\,716\times10^{-1}$	$1.359\,622\times10^{-3}$	$2.389\,2\times10^{-1}$	$9.471\,6\times10^{-4}$
Kilowatt	kW	**1** $\times 10^{10}$	**1** $\times 10^{3}$	**1** $\times 1$	$1.019\,716\times10^{2}$	$1.359\,622\times 1$	$2.389\,2\times10^{2}$	$9.471\,6\times10^{-1}$
Meter-kilogram-force per second	mkp s^{-1}	9.806 6**5** $\times10^{7}$	9.806 6**5** $\times 1$	9.806 6**5** $\times10^{-3}$	**1** $\times 1$	$1.\dot{3}$ $\times10^{-2}$	$2.343\,0\times 1$	$9.288\,4\times10^{-3}$
Horsepower (international)	HP (int.)	$7.354\,988\times10^{9}$	$7.354\,988\times10^{2}$	$7.354\,988\times10^{-1}$	7.**5** $\times 10$	**1** $\times 1$	$1.757\,3\times10^{2}$	$6.966\,3\times10^{-1}$
15° calorie per second	cal_{15} s^{-1}	$4.185\,5\times10^{7}$	$4.185\,5\times 1$	$4.185\,5\times10^{-3}$	$4.268\,0\times10^{-1}$	$5.690\,7\times10^{-3}$	**1** $\times 1$	$3.964\,3\times10^{-3}$
British thermal $unit_{mean}$ per second	BTU_{mean} s^{-1}	$1.055\,8\times10^{10}$	$1.055\,8\times10^{3}$	$1.055\,8\times 1$	$1.076\,6\times10^{2}$	$1.435\,5\times 1$	$2.522\,5\times10^{2}$	**1** $\times 1$

Conversion factors for work units

To convert from a unit in column **A** into any unit under **B**, multiply by the factor given in the appropriate column under **B**

A		B						
		erg s	J s	mkp s	cal_{15} s	BTU_{mean} s	eV s	*h*
Erg × second	erg s	**1** $\times 1$	**1** $\times10^{-7}$	$1.019\,716\times10^{-8}$	$2.389\,2\times10^{-8}$	$9.471\,6\times10^{-11}$	$6.242\,13\times10^{11}$	$1.509\,45\times10^{26}$
Joule × second	J s	**1** $\times10^{7}$	**1** $\times 1$	$1.019\,716\times10^{-1}$	$2.389\,2\times10^{-1}$	$9.471\,6\times10^{-4}$	$6.242\,13\times10^{18}$	$1.509\,45\times10^{33}$
Meter-kilogram-force × second	mkp s	9.806 6**5** $\times10^{7}$	9.806 6**5** $\times 1$	**1** $\times 1$	$2.343\,0\times 1$	$9.288\,4\times10^{-3}$	$6.121\,44\times10^{19}$	$1.480\,27\times10^{34}$
15° calorie × second	cal_{15} s	$4.185\,5\times10^{7}$	$4.185\,5\times 1$	$4.268\,0\times10^{-1}$	**1** $\times 1$	$3.964\,3\times10^{-3}$	$2.612\,6\times10^{19}$	$6.317\,8\times10^{33}$
British thermal $unit_{mean}$ × second	BTU_{mean} s	$1.055\,8\times10^{10}$	$1.055\,8\times10^{3}$	$1.076\,6\times10^{2}$	$2.522\,5\times10^{2}$	**1** $\times 1$	$6.590\,4\times10^{21}$	$1.593\,7\times10^{36}$
Electron volt × second	eV s	$1.602\,02\times10^{-12}$	$1.602\,02\times10^{-19}$	$1.633\,60\times10^{-20}$	$3.827\,5\times10^{-20}$	$1.517\,4\times10^{-22}$	**1** $\times 1$	$2.418\,17\times10^{14}$
PLANCK's constant	*h*	$6.624\,91\times10^{-27}$	$6.624\,91\times10^{-34}$	$6.755\,53\times10^{-35}$	$1.582\,8\times10^{-34}$	$6.274\,8\times10^{-37}$	$4.135\,35\times10^{-15}$	**1** $\times 1$

Entropy

Dimensional formula in the LMT-systems = L^2MT^{-2}degree^{-1}

Derived units in the corresponding systems of measurement:

MKS-system: joule per degree Kelvin (J °K^{-1}) ≡ m^2 kg s^{-2} °K^{-1} ≡ 10^{-7} erg °K^{-1}

CGS-system: erg per degree Kelvin (erg °K^{-1}) ≡ cm^2 kg s^{-2} °K^{-1} ≡ 10^{-7} J °K^{-1}

Dimensional formula in the LFT-systems = LF degree^{-1}

Derived unit in the corresponding m-kp-s-system of technology: meter-kilogram-force per degree Kelvin (mkp °K^{-1}) = 9.806 6**5** J °K^{-1}

The special entropy unit clausius (Cl) = 15° calorie per degree Kelvin (cal_{15} °K^{-1}) has become less important since the introduction of the joule as the unit of quantity of heat in place of the calorie.

1 J °K^{-1} ≡ 10^7 erg °K^{-1} = 0.2389 Cl; 1 Cl = 4.1854 J °K^{-1} = 4.1854 × 10^7 erg °K^{-1}

Dynamic viscosity

Dimensional formula in the LMT-systems = $L^{-1}MT^{-1}$

Derived units in the corresponding systems of measurement:

MKS-system: newton × second per square meter (N s m^{-2}) ≡ m^{-1} kg s^{-1} ≡ 10 poises

CGS-system: poise (P) = dyne × second per square centimeter (dyn cm^{-2}) ≡ cm^{-1} g s^{1} ≡ 0.1 N s m^{-2}

Foot-Pound-Second-system (avoirdupois): pound per foot per second (lb ft^{-1} s^{-1}) = poundal second per square foot = 1.488 1612 N s m^{-2} = 14.881 612 P (US measures)

Dimensional formula in the LFT-systems = $L^{-2}FT$

Derived units in the corresponding systems of measurement in technology:

m-kp-s-system: kilogram-force × second per square meter (kp s m^{-2}) = 9.806 6**5** N s m^{-2}

Foot-Pound-Second-system (avoirdupois): $pound_{wt}$ × second per square foot (Lb s ft^{-2}) = 14.59391 N s m^{-2} = 1.488 164 kp s m^{-2}

Kinematic viscosity

Dimensional formula in all systems of measurement = L^2T^{-1}

Derived units:

MKS-system and m-kp-s-system: square meter per second (m^2 s^{-1}) ≡ 10^4 stokes; square meter per hour (m^2 h^{-1}) = $2.\dot{7}$ m^2 s^{-1}

CGS-system: stokes (St) ≡ square centimeter per second (cm^2 s^{-1}) ≡ 10^{-4} m^2 s^{-1}

Foot-Pound-Second-system (avoirdupois): square foot per second (ft^2 s^{-1}) = 0.092 9034 (US measures) m^2 s^{-1}; square foot per hour (ft^2 h^{-1}) = 2.580 650 (US measures) × 10^{-5} m^2 s^{-1}

Surface tension

Dimensional formula in the LMT-systems = MT^{-2}

Derived units in the corresponding systems of measurement:

MKS-system: newton per meter (N m^{-1}) ≡ kg s^{-2} ≡ 10^3 dyn cm^{-1} = 1.019 716 × 10^{-1} kp m^{-1}

CGS-system: dyne per centimeter (dyn cm^{-1}) ≡ g s^{-2} ≡ 10^{-3} N m^{-1} = 1.019 716 × 10^{-4} kp m^{-1}

Dimensional formula in the LFT-systems = $L^{-1}F$

Derived unit in the corresponding m-kp-s-system of technology: kilogram-force per meter (kp m^{-1}) = 9.806 6**5** N m^{-1}

Thermal conductivity

Dimensional formula in the LMT-systems = LMT^{-3}degree^{-1}

Derived units in the corresponding systems of measurement:

MKS-system: watt per meter per degree ≡ m kg s^{-3} °K^{-1} ≡ 10^5 erg cm^{-1} s^{-1} °K^{-1} = 2.3892 × 10^{-3} cal_{15} cm^{-1} s^{-1} °K^{-1}

CGS-system: erg per centimeter per second per degree Kelvin (erg cm^{-1} s^{-1} °K^{-1}) ≡ cm g s^{-3} °K^{-1} ≡ 10^{-5} W m^{-1} °K^{-1} = 2.3892 × 10^{-8} cal_{15} cm^{-1} s^{-1} °K^{-1}

Foot-Pound-Second-system (avoirdupois): British thermal $unit_{mean}$ per foot per second per degree Fahrenheit (BTU_{mean} ft^{-1} s^{-1} °F^{-1}) = 1.5587 × 10^4 W m^{-1} °K^{-1}

Special unit: 15° calorie per centimeter per second per degree Kelvin (cal_{15} cm^{-1} s^{-1} °K^{-1}) = 4.1855 × 10^7 erg cm^{-1} s^{-1} °K^{-1} = 4.1855 × 10^2 W m^{-1} °K^{-1}

Dimensional formula in the LFT-systems = FT^{-1}degree^{-1}

Coefficient of heat transfer

Dimensional formula in the LMT-systems = MT^{-3}degree^{-1}

Derived units in the corresponding systems of measurement:

MKS-system: watt per square meter per degree Kelvin (W m^{-2} °K^{-1} ≡ kg s^{-3} °K^{-1} ≡ 10^{-7} W cm^{-2} °K^{-1} ≡ 10^3 erg s^{-1} cm^{-2} °K^{-1} = 2.3892 × 10^{-5} cal_{15} cm^{-2} s^{-1} °K^{-1}

CGS-system: erg per second per square centimeter per degree Kelvin (erg s^{-1} cm^{-2} °K^{-1}) ≡ g s^{-3} °K^{-1} ≡ 10^{-3} W m^{-2} °K^{-1} ≡ 10^{-7} W cm^{-2} °K^{-1} = 2.3892 × 10^{-8} cal_{15} cm^{-2} s^{-1} °K^{-1}

Foot-Pound-Second-system (avoirdupois): British thermal $unit_{mean}$ per square foot per second per degree Fahrenheit (BTU_{mean} ft^{-2} s^{-1} °F^{-1}) = 5.1140 × 10^4 W m^{-2} °K^{-1}

Dimensional formula in the LFT-systems = $L^{-1}FT^{-1}$degree^{-1}

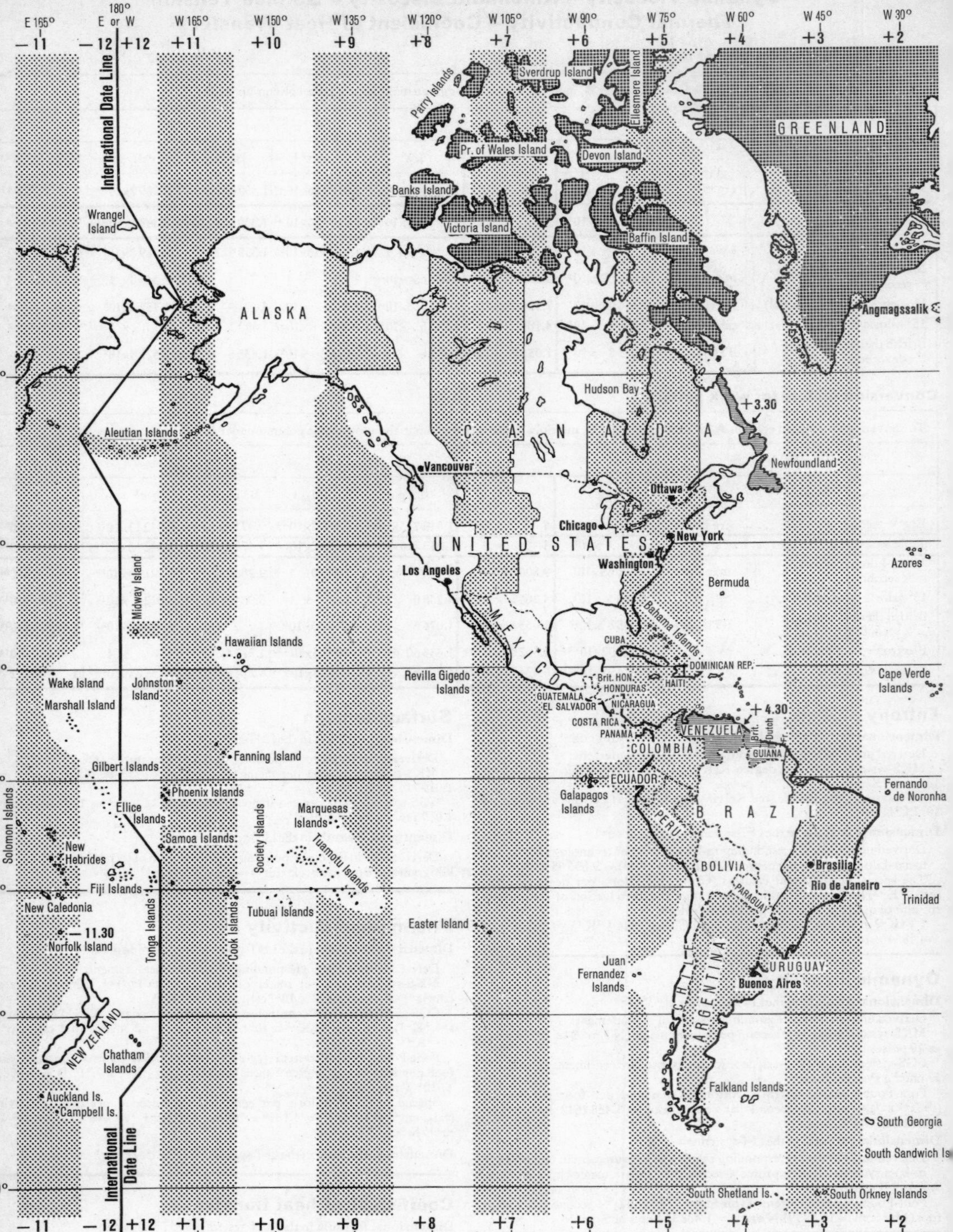

Map of Time Zones

The zone of Greenwich Time is indicated by the index figure "**0**".

= Zones in which the time differs from Greenwich Time by a whole number of hours

= Zones in which the time difference from Greenwich Time involves half-an-hour

= Zones in which the zone time has not yet been officially accepted

= Zones without legal time

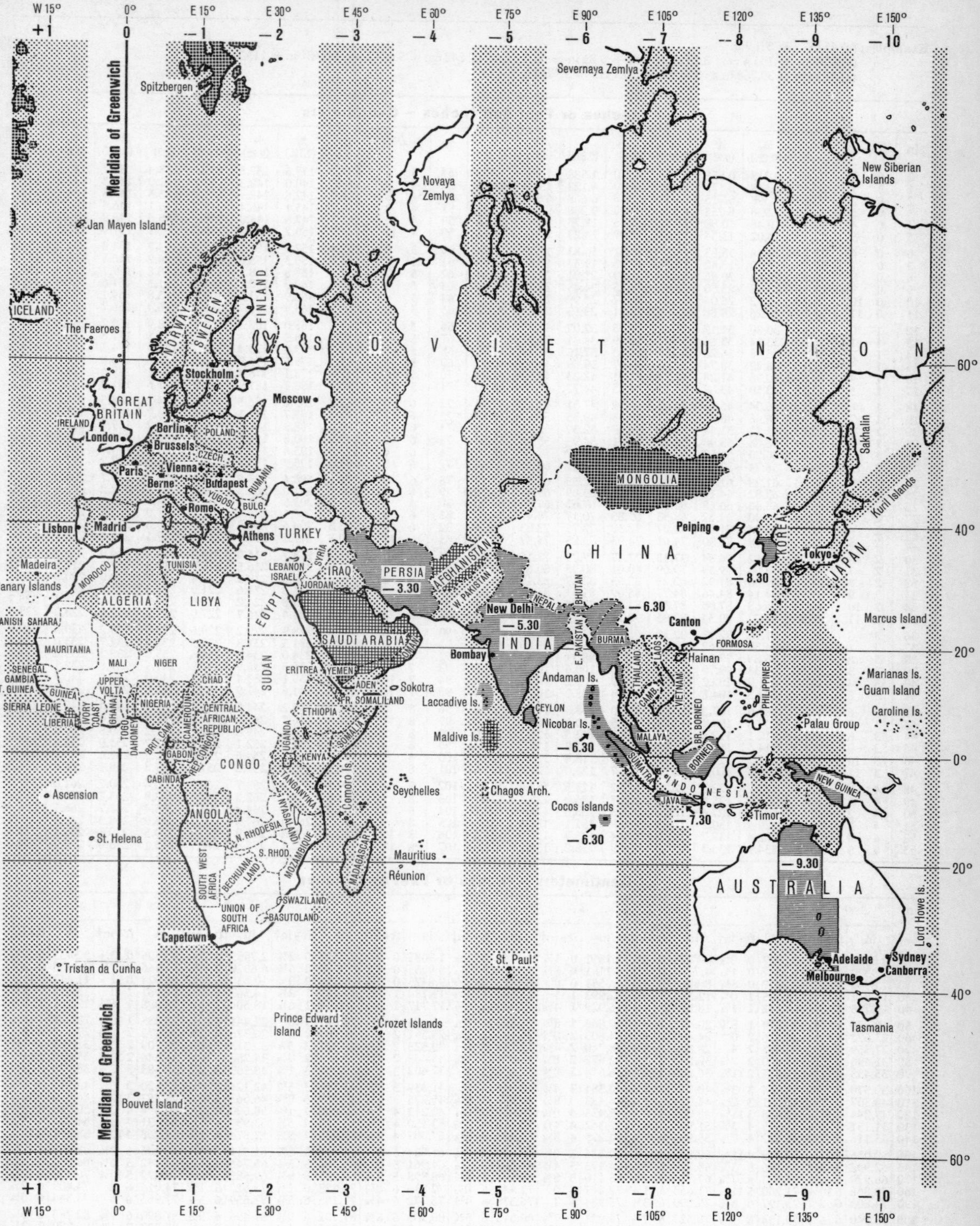

Conversion of Time

It is required to find the time in a Zone B when the time in Zone A is known. The index figure of Zone B is subtracted from that of Zone A to give the difference C. Then

Time in Zone B = (time in Zone A) + C

Examples:

(*a*) Given the time in Zone + **5**, what is the time in Zone + **6**?
C = **5** − **6** = − 1

(*b*) Given the time in Zone − **5**, what is the time in Zone − **6**?
C = − **5** − (− **6**) = + 1

(*c*) Given the time in Zone + **5**, what is the time in Zone − **6.30**?
C = + **5** − (− **6.30**) = + 11.30

(*d*) Given the time in Zone − **12**, what is the time in Zone + **12**?
C = − **12** − **12** = − 24

Examples: (*a*) 45 in = 3 ft 9 in
(*b*) 60⅜ in = 153.4 cm; 2.23 in = 2 in + 0.23 in = 5.08 cm + 0.5842 cm = 5.6642 cm; 3 ft 8¾ in = 113.7 cm
(*c*) 101 cm = 39.764 in ≈ 3 ft 3¾ in; 10.1 cm = 3.9764 in

Inches or Feet and Inches – Centimeters

in	ft + in	0	⅛ (0.125)	¼ (0.25)	⅜ (0.375)	½ (0.5)	⅝ (0.625)	¾ (0.75)	⅞ (0.875)	in	ft + in	0	⅛ (0.125)	¼ (0.25)	⅜ (0.375)	½ (0.5)	⅝ (0.625)	¾ (0.75)	⅞ (0.875)
0	0 0	0.000	0.318	0.635	0.953	1.270	1.588	1.905	2.223	**54**	4 6	137.2	137.5	137.8	138.1	138.4	138.7	139.1	139.4
1	0 1	2.540	2.858	3.175	3.493	3.810	4.128	4.445	4.763	55	4 7	139.7	140.0	140.3	140.7	141.0	141.3	141.6	141.9
2	0 2	5.080	5.398	5.715	6.033	6.350	6.668	6.985	7.303	56	4 8	142.2	142.6	142.9	143.2	143.5	143.8	144.1	144.5
3	0 3	7.620	7.938	8.255	8.573	8.890	9.208	9.525	9.843	57	4 9	144.8	145.1	145.4	145.7	146.1	146.4	146.7	147.0
4	0 4	10.16	10.48	10.80	11.11	11.43	11.75	12.07	12.38	58	4 10	147.3	147.6	148.0	148.3	148.6	148.9	149.2	149.5
5	0 5	12.70	13.02	13.34	13.65	13.97	14.29	14.61	14.92	59	4 11	149.9	150.2	150.5	150.8	151.1	151.4	151.8	152.1
6	0 6	15.24	15.56	15.88	16.19	16.51	16.83	17.15	17.46	**60**	5 0	152.4	152.7	153.0	153.4	153.7	154.0	154.3	154.6
7	0 7	17.78	18.10	18.42	18.73	19.05	19.37	19.69	20.00	61	5 1	154.9	155.3	155.6	155.9	156.2	156.5	156.8	157.2
8	0 8	20.32	20.64	20.96	21.27	21.59	21.91	22.23	22.54	62	5 2	157.5	157.8	158.1	158.4	158.8	159.1	159.4	159.7
9	0 9	22.86	23.18	23.50	23.81	24.13	24.45	24.77	25.08	63	5 3	160.0	160.3	160.7	161.0	161.3	161.6	161.9	162.2
10	0 10	25.40	25.72	26.04	26.35	26.67	26.99	27.31	27.62	64	5 4	162.6	162.9	163.2	163.5	163.8	164.1	164.5	164.8
11	0 11	27.94	28.26	28.58	28.89	29.21	29.53	29.85	30.16	65	5 5	165.1	165.4	165.7	166.1	166.4	166.7	167.0	167.3
12	1 0	30.48	30.80	31.12	31.43	31.75	32.07	32.39	32.70	**66**	5 6	167.6	168.0	168.3	168.6	168.9	169.2	169.5	169.9
13	1 1	33.02	33.34	33.66	33.97	34.29	34.61	34.93	35.24	67	5 7	170.2	170.5	170.8	171.1	171.5	171.8	172.1	172.4
14	1 2	35.56	35.88	36.20	36.51	36.83	37.15	37.47	37.78	68	5 8	172.7	173.0	173.4	173.7	174.0	174.3	174.6	174.9
15	1 3	38.10	38.42	38.74	39.05	39.37	39.69	40.01	40.32	69	5 9	175.3	175.6	175.9	176.2	176.5	176.8	177.2	177.5
16	1 4	40.64	40.96	41.28	41.59	41.91	42.23	42.55	42.86	70	5 10	177.8	178.1	178.4	178.8	179.1	179.4	179.7	180.0
17	1 5	43.18	43.50	43.82	44.13	44.45	44.77	45.09	45.40	71	5 11	180.3	180.7	181.0	181.3	181.6	181.9	182.2	182.6
18	1 6	45.72	46.04	46.36	46.67	46.99	47.31	47.63	47.94	**72**	6 0	182.9	183.2	183.5	183.8	184.2	184.5	184.8	185.1
19	1 7	48.26	48.58	48.90	49.21	49.53	49.85	50.17	50.48	73	6 1	185.4	185.7	186.1	186.4	186.7	187.0	187.3	187.6
20	1 8	50.80	51.12	51.44	51.75	52.07	52.39	52.71	53.02	74	6 2	188.0	188.3	188.6	188.9	189.2	189.5	189.9	190.2
21	1 9	53.34	53.66	53.98	54.29	54.61	54.93	55.25	55.56	75	6 3	190.5	190.8	191.1	191.5	191.8	192.1	192.4	192.7
22	1 10	55.88	56.20	56.52	56.83	57.15	57.47	57.79	58.10	76	6 4	193.0	193.4	193.7	194.0	194.3	194.6	194.9	195.3
23	1 11	58.42	58.74	59.06	59.37	59.69	60.01	60.33	60.64	77	6 5	195.6	195.9	196.2	196.5	196.9	197.2	197.5	197.8
24	2 0	60.96	61.28	61.60	61.91	62.23	62.55	62.87	63.18	**78**	6 6	198.1	198.4	198.8	199.1	199.4	199.7	200.0	200.3
25	2 1	63.50	63.82	64.14	64.45	64.77	65.09	65.41	65.72	79	6 7	200.7	201.0	201.3	201.6	201.9	202.2	202.6	202.9
26	2 2	66.04	66.36	66.68	66.99	67.31	67.63	67.95	68.26	80	6 8	203.2	203.5	203.8	204.2	204.5	204.8	205.1	205.4
27	2 3	68.58	68.90	69.22	69.53	69.85	70.17	70.49	70.80	81	6 9	205.7	206.1	206.4	206.7	207.0	207.3	207.6	208.0
28	2 4	71.12	71.44	71.76	72.07	72.39	72.71	73.03	73.34	82	6 10	208.3	208.6	208.9	209.2	209.6	209.9	210.2	210.5
29	2 5	73.66	73.98	74.30	74.61	74.93	75.25	75.57	75.88	83	6 11	210.8	211.1	211.5	211.8	212.1	212.4	212.7	213.0
30	2 6	76.20	76.52	76.84	77.15	77.47	77.79	78.11	78.42	**84**	7 0	213.4	213.7	214.0	214.3	214.6	214.9	215.3	215.6
31	2 7	78.74	79.06	79.38	79.69	80.01	80.33	80.65	80.96	85	7 1	215.9	216.2	216.5	216.9	217.2	217.5	217.8	218.1
32	2 8	81.28	81.60	81.92	82.23	82.55	82.87	83.19	83.50	86	7 2	218.4	218.8	219.1	219.4	219.7	220.0	220.3	220.7
33	2 9	83.82	84.14	84.46	84.77	85.09	85.41	85.73	86.04	87	7 3	221.0	221.3	221.6	221.9	222.3	222.6	222.9	223.2
34	2 10	86.36	86.68	87.00	87.31	87.63	87.95	88.27	88.58	88	7 4	223.5	223.8	224.2	224.5	224.8	225.1	225.4	225.7
35	2 11	88.90	89.22	89.54	89.85	90.17	90.49	90.81	91.12	89	7 5	226.1	226.4	226.7	227.0	227.3	227.6	228.0	228.3
36	3 0	91.44	91.76	92.08	92.39	92.71	93.03	93.35	93.66	**90**	7 6	228.6	228.9	229.2	229.6	229.9	230.2	230.5	230.8
37	3 1	93.98	94.30	94.62	94.93	95.25	95.57	95.89	96.20	91	7 7	231.1	231.5	231.8	232.1	232.4	232.7	233.0	233.4
38	3 2	96.52	96.84	97.16	97.47	97.79	98.11	98.43	98.74	92	7 8	233.7	234.0	234.3	234.6	235.0	235.3	235.6	235.9
39	3 3	99.06	99.38	99.70	100.0	100.3	100.6	101.0	101.3	93	7 9	236.2	236.5	236.9	237.2	237.5	237.8	238.1	238.4
40	3 4	101.6	101.9	102.2	102.6	102.9	103.2	103.5	103.8	94	7 10	238.8	239.1	239.4	239.7	240.0	240.3	240.7	241.0
41	3 5	104.1	104.5	104.8	105.1	105.4	105.7	106.0	106.4	95	7 11	241.3	241.6	241.9	242.3	242.6	242.9	243.2	243.5
42	3 6	106.7	107.0	107.3	107.6	108.0	108.3	108.6	108.9	**96**	8 0	243.8	244.2	244.5	244.8	245.1	245.4	245.7	246.1
43	3 7	109.2	109.5	109.9	110.2	110.5	110.8	111.1	111.4	97	8 1	246.4	246.7	247.0	247.3	247.7	248.0	248.3	248.6
44	3 8	111.8	112.1	112.4	112.7	113.0	113.3	113.7	114.0	98	8 2	248.9	249.2	249.6	249.9	250.2	250.5	250.8	251.1
45	3 9	114.3	114.6	114.9	115.3	115.6	115.9	116.2	116.5	99	8 3	251.5	251.8	252.1	252.4	252.7	253.0	253.4	253.7
46	3 10	116.8	117.2	117.4	117.8	118.1	118.4	118.7	119.1	100	8 4	254.0	254.3	254.6	255.0	255.3	255.6	255.9	256.2
47	3 11	119.4	119.7	120.0	120.3	120.7	121.0	121.3	121.6	101	8 5	256.5	256.9	257.2	257.5	257.8	258.1	258.4	258.8
48	4 0	121.9	122.2	122.6	122.9	123.2	123.5	123.8	124.1	**102**	8 6	259.1	259.4	259.7	260.0	260.4	260.7	261.0	261.3
49	4 1	124.5	124.8	125.1	125.4	125.7	126.0	126.4	126.7	103	8 7	261.6	261.9	262.3	262.6	262.9	263.2	263.5	263.8
50	4 2	127.0	127.3	127.6	128.0	128.3	128.6	128.9	129.2	104	8 8	264.2	264.5	264.8	265.1	265.4	265.7	266.1	266.4
51	4 3	129.5	129.9	130.2	130.5	130.8	131.1	131.4	131.8	105	8 9	266.7	267.0	267.3	267.7	268.0	268.3	268.6	268.9
52	4 4	132.1	132.4	132.7	133.0	133.4	133.7	134.0	134.3	106	8 10	269.2	269.6	269.9	270.2	270.5	270.8	271.1	271.5
53	4 5	134.6	134.9	135.3	135.6	135.9	136.2	136.5	136.8	107	8 11	271.8	272.1	272.4	272.7	273.1	273.4	273.7	274.0

Centimeters – Inches or Feet and Inches

cm	0		1		2		3		4		5		6		7		8		9	
	in	ft+in†	in	ft+in†	in	ft+in†	in	ft+in†	in	ft+in†	in	ft+in†	in	ft+in†	in	ft+in†	in	ft+in†	in	ft+in†
0	0.0000	0 0	0.3937	0 0⅜	0.7874	0 0¾	1.1811	0 1⅛	1.5748	0 1⅝	1.9685	0 2	2.3622	0 2⅜	2.7559	0 2¾	3.1496	0 3⅛	3.5433	0 3½
10	3.9370	0 3⅞	4.3307	0 4⅜	4.7244	0 4¾	5.1181	0 5⅛	5.5118	0 5½	5.9055	0 5⅞	6.2992	0 6¼	6.6929	0 6¾	7.0866	0 7⅛	7.4803	0 7½
20	7.8740	0 7⅞	8.2677	0 8¼	8.6614	0 8⅝	9.0551	0 9	9.4488	0 9½	9.8425	0 9⅞	10.236	0 10¼	10.630	0 10⅝	11.024	0 11	11.417	0 11⅜
30	11.811	0 11¾	12.205	1 0¼	12.598	1 0⅝	12.992	1 1	13.386	1 1⅜	13.780	1 1¾	14.173	1 2⅛	14.567	1 2⅝	14.961	1 3	15.354	1 3⅜
40	15.748	1 3¾	16.142	1 4⅛	16.535	1 4½	16.929	1 4⅞	17.323	1 5⅜	17.717	1 5¾	18.110	1 6⅛	18.504	1 6½	18.898	1 6⅞	19.291	1 7¼
50	19.685	1 7⅝	20.079	1 8⅛	20.472	1 8½	20.866	1 8⅞	21.260	1 9¼	21.654	1 9⅝	22.047	1 10	22.441	1 10½	22.835	1 10⅞	23.228	1 11¼
60	23.622	1 11⅝	24.016	2 0	24.409	2 0⅜	24.803	2 0¾	25.197	2 1¼	25.591	2 1⅝	25.984	2 2	26.378	2 2⅜	26.772	2 2¾	27.165	2 3⅛
70	27.559	2 3½	27.953	2 4	28.346	2 4⅜	28.740	2 4¾	29.134	2 5⅛	29.528	2 5½	29.921	2 5⅞	30.315	2 6⅜	30.709	2 6¾	31.102	2 7⅛
80	31.496	2 7½	31.890	2 7⅞	32.283	2 8¼	32.677	2 8⅝	33.071	2 9⅛	33.465	2 9½	33.858	2 9⅞	34.252	2 10¼	34.646	2 10⅝	35.039	2 11
90	35.433	2 11⅜	35.827	2 11⅞	36.220	3 0¼	36.614	3 0⅝	37.008	3 1	37.402	3 1⅜	37.795	3 1¾	38.189	3 2¼	38.583	3 2⅝	38.976	3 3
100	39.370	3 3⅜	39.764	3 3¾	40.157	3 4⅛	40.551	3 4½	40.945	3 5	41.339	3 5⅜	41.732	3 5¾	42.126	3 6⅛	42.520	3 6½	42.913	3 6⅞
110	43.307	3 7¼	43.701	3 7¾	44.094	3 8⅛	44.488	3 8½	44.882	3 8⅞	45.276	3 9¼	45.669	3 9⅝	46.063	3 10⅛	46.457	3 10½	46.850	3 10⅞
120	47.244	3 11¼	47.638	3 11⅝	48.031	4 0	48.425	4 0⅜	48.819	4 0⅞	49.213	4 1¼	49.606	4 1⅝	50.000	4 2	50.394	4 2⅜	50.787	4 2¾
130	51.181	4 3⅛	51.575	4 3⅝	51.968	4 4	52.362	4 4⅜	52.756	4 4¾	53.150	4 5⅛	53.543	4 5½	53.937	4 5⅞	54.331	4 6⅜	54.724	4 6¾
140	55.118	4 7⅛	55.512	4 7½	55.905	4 7⅞	56.299	4 8¼	56.693	4 8¾	57.087	4 9⅛	57.480	4 9½	57.874	4 9⅞	58.268	4 10¼	58.661	4 10⅝
150	59.055	4 11	59.449	4 11½	59.842	4 11⅞	60.236	5 0¼	60.630	5 0⅝	61.024	5 1	61.417	5 1⅜	61.811	5 1¾	62.205	5 2¼	62.598	5 2⅝
160	62.992	5 3	63.386	5 3⅜	63.779	5 3¾	64.173	5 4⅛	64.567	5 4⅝	64.961	5 5	65.354	5 5⅜	65.748	5 5¾	66.142	5 6⅛	66.535	5 6½
170	66.929	5 6⅞	67.323	5 7⅜	67.716	5 7¾	68.110	5 8⅛	68.504	5 8½	68.898	5 8⅞	69.291	5 9¼	69.685	5 9⅝	70.079	5 10⅛	70.472	5 10½
180	70.866	5 10⅞	71.260	5 11¼	71.653	5 11⅝	72.047	6 0	72.441	6 0½	72.835	6 0⅞	73.228	6 1¼	73.622	6 1⅝	74.016	6 2	74.409	6 2⅜
190	74.803	6 2¾	75.197	6 3¼	75.590	6 3⅝	75.984	6 4	76.378	6 4⅜	76.772	6 4¾	77.165	6 5⅛	77.559	6 5½	77.953	6 6	78.346	6 6⅜
200	78.740	6 6¾	79.134	6 7⅛	79.527	6 7½	79.921	6 7⅞	80.315	6 8⅜	80.709	6 8¾	81.102	6 9⅛	81.496	6 9½	81.890	6 9⅞	82.283	6 10¼
210	82.677	6 10⅝	83.071	6 11⅛	83.464	6 11½	83.858	6 11⅞	84.252	7 0¼	84.646	7 0⅝	85.039	7 1	85.433	7 1⅜	85.827	7 1⅞	86.220	7 2¼
220	86.614	7 2⅝	87.008	7 3	87.401	7 3⅜	87.795	7 3¾	88.189	7 4¼	88.583	7 4⅝	88.976	7 5	89.370	7 5⅜	89.764	7 5¾	90.157	7 6⅛
230	90.551	7 6½	90.945	7 7	91.338	7 7⅜	91.732	7 7¾	92.126	7 8⅛	92.520	7 8½	92.913	7 8⅞	93.307	7 9¼	93.701	7 9¾	94.094	7 10⅛
240	94.488	7 10½	94.882	7 10⅞	95.275	7 11¼	95.669	7 11⅝	96.063	8 0⅛	96.457	8 0½	96.850	8 0⅞	97.244	8 1¼	97.638	8 1⅝	98.031	8 2
250	98.425	8 2⅜	98.819	8 2⅞	99.212	8 3¼	99.606	8 3⅝	100.00	8 4	100.39	8 4⅜	100.79	8 4¾	101.18	8 5⅛	101.57	8 5⅝	101.97	8 6
260	102.36	8 6⅜	102.76	8 6¾	103.15	8 7⅛	103.54	8 7½	103.94	8 8	104.33	8 8⅜	104.72	8 8¾	105.12	8 9⅛	105.51	8 9½	105.91	8 9⅞
270	106.30	8 10¼	106.69	8 10¾	107.09	8 11⅛	107.48	8 11½	107.87	8 11⅞	108.27	9 0¼	108.66	9 0⅝	109.05	9 1	109.45	9 1½	109.84	9 1⅞
280	110.24	9 2¼	110.63	9 2⅝	111.02	9 3	111.42	9 3⅜	111.81	9 3¾	112.20	9 4¼	112.60	9 4⅝	112.99	9 5	113.39	9 5⅜	113.78	9 5¾
290	114.17	9 6⅛	114.57	9 6⅝	114.96	9 7	115.35	9 7⅜	115.75	9 7¾	116.14	9 8⅛	116.54	9 8½	116.93	9 8⅞	117.32	9 9⅜	117.72	9 9¾

 † Rounded off to the nearest one-eighth inch.

Conversion of Mass and Capacity Units*

Ounces (avoirdupois) – Grams

	0	1	2	3	4	5	6	7	8	9
0	00.000	28.350	56.699	85.049	113.40	141.75	170.10	198.45	226.80	255.15
10	283.50	311.84	340.19	368.54	396.89	425.24	453.59	481.94	510.29	538.64
20	566.99	595.34	623.69	652.04	680.39	708.74	737.09	765.44	793.79	822.14
30	850.49	878.84	907.18	935.53	963.88	992.23	1020.6	1048.9	1077.3	1105.6
40	1134.0	1162.3	1190.7	1219.0	1247.4	1275.7	1304.1	1332.4	1360.8	1389.1
50	1417.5	1445.8	1474.2	1502.5	1530.9	1559.2	1587.6	1615.9	1644.3	1672.6
60	1701.0	1729.3	1757.7	1786.0	1814.4	1842.7	1871.1	1899.4	1927.8	1956.1
70	1984.5	2012.8	2041.2	2069.5	2097.9	2126.2	2154.6	2182.9	2211.3	2239.6
80	2268.0	2296.3	2324.7	2353.0	2381.4	2409.7	2438.1	2466.4	2494.8	2523.1
90	2551.5	2579.8	2608.2	2636.5	2664.9	2693.2	2721.6	2749.9	2778.3	2806.6

Ounces (apothecary) – Grams

	0	1	2	3	4	5	6	7	8	9
0	00.000	31.103	62.207	93.310	124.41	155.52	186.62	217.72	248.83	279.93
10	311.03	342.14	373.24	404.35	435.45	466.55	497.66	528.76	559.86	590.97
20	622.07	653.17	684.28	715.38	746.48	777.59	808.69	839.79	870.90	902.00
30	933.10	964.21	995.31	1026.4	1057.5	1088.6	1119.7	1150.8	1181.9	1213.0
40	1244.1	1275.2	1306.3	1337.4	1368.6	1399.7	1430.8	1461.9	1493.0	1524.1
50	1555.2	1586.3	1617.4	1648.5	1679.6	1710.7	1741.8	1772.9	1804.0	1835.1
60	1866.2	1897.3	1928.4	1959.5	1990.6	2021.7	2052.8	2083.9	2115.0	2146.1
70	2177.2	2208.3	2239.5	2270.6	2301.7	2332.8	2363.9	2395.0	2426.1	2457.2
80	2488.3	2519.4	2550.5	2581.6	2612.7	2643.8	2674.9	2706.0	2737.1	2768.2
90	2799.3	2830.4	2861.5	2892.6	2923.7	2954.8	2985.9	3017.0	3048.1	3079.2

Fluid ounces (Brit.) – Milliliters

	0	1	2	3	4	5	6	7	8	9
0	00.000	28.412	56.825	85.237	113.65	142.06	170.47	198.89	227.30	255.71
10	284.12	312.53	340.95	369.36	397.77	426.18	454.60	483.01	511.42	539.83
20	568.25	596.66	625.07	653.48	681.89	710.31	738.72	767.13	795.54	823.96
30	852.37	880.78	909.19	937.60	966.02	994.43	1022.8	1051.3	1079.7	1108.1
40	1136.5	1164.9	1193.3	1221.7	1250.1	1278.6	1307.0	1335.4	1363.8	1392.2
50	1420.6	1449.0	1477.4	1505.9	1534.3	1562.7	1591.1	1619.5	1647.9	1676.3
60	1704.7	1733.1	1761.6	1790.0	1818.4	1846.8	1875.2	1903.6	1932.0	1960.4
70	1988.9	2017.3	2045.7	2074.1	2102.5	2130.9	2159.3	2187.7	2216.2	2244.6
80	2273.0	2301.4	2329.8	2358.2	2386.6	2415.0	2443.5	2471.9	2500.3	2528.7
90	2557.1	2585.5	2613.9	2642.3	2670.8	2699.2	2727.6	2756.0	2784.4	2812.8

Fluid ounces (US) – Milliliters

	0	1	2	3	4	5	6	7	8	9
0	00.000	29.573	59.146	88.719	118.29	147.86	177.44	207.01	236.58	266.16
10	295.73	325.30	354.87	384.45	414.02	443.59	473.17	502.74	532.31	561.88
20	591.46	621.03	650.60	680.18	709.75	739.32	768.89	798.47	828.04	857.61
30	887.19	916.76	946.33	975.91	1005.5	1035.1	1064.6	1094.2	1123.8	1153.3
40	1182.9	1212.5	1242.1	1271.6	1301.2	1330.8	1360.4	1389.9	1419.5	1449.1
50	1478.6	1508.2	1537.8	1567.4	1596.9	1626.5	1656.1	1685.7	1715.2	1744.8
60	1774.4	1803.9	1833.5	1863.1	1892.7	1922.2	1951.8	1981.4	2011.0	2040.5
70	2070.1	2099.7	2129.2	2158.8	2188.4	2218.0	2247.5	2277.1	2306.7	2336.3
80	2365.8	2395.4	2425.0	2454.5	2484.1	2513.7	2543.3	2572.8	2602.4	2632.0
90	2661.6	2691.1	2720.7	2750.3	2779.9	2809.4	2839.0	2868.6	2898.1	2927.7

Pints (Brit.) – Liters

	0	1	2	3	4	5	6	7	8	9
0	0.0000	0.5682	1.1365	1.7047	2.2730	2.8412	3.4095	3.9777	4.5460	5.1142
10	5.6825	6.2507	6.8189	7.3872	7.9554	8.5237	9.0919	9.6602	10.228	10.797
20	11.365	11.933	12.501	13.070	13.638	14.206	14.774	15.343	15.911	16.479
30	17.047	17.616	18.184	18.752	19.320	19.889	20.457	21.025	21.593	22.162
40	22.730	23.298	23.866	24.435	25.003	25.571	26.139	26.708	27.276	27.844
50	28.412	28.981	29.549	30.117	30.685	31.253	31.822	32.390	32.958	33.526
60	34.095	34.663	35.231	35.799	36.368	36.936	37.504	38.072	38.641	39.209
70	39.777	40.345	40.914	41.482	42.050	42.618	43.187	43.755	44.323	44.891
80	45.460	46.028	46.596	47.164	47.733	48.301	48.869	49.437	50.006	50.574
90	51.142	51.710	52.279	52.847	53.415	53.983	54.552	55.120	55.688	56.256

Pints (US) – Liters

	0	1	2	3	4	5	6	7	8	9
0	0.0000	0.4732	0.9463	1.4195	1.8927	2.3658	2.8390	3.3122	3.7853	4.2585
10	4.7317	5.2048	5.6780	6.1512	6.6243	7.0975	7.5707	8.0438	8.5170	8.9902
20	9.4633	9.9365	10.410	10.883	11.356	11.829	12.302	12.775	13.249	13.722
30	14.195	14.668	15.141	15.614	16.088	16.561	17.034	17.507	17.980	18.453
40	18.927	19.400	19.873	20.346	20.819	21.292	21.766	22.239	22.712	23.185
50	23.658	24.131	24.605	25.078	25.551	26.024	26.497	26.970	27.444	27.917
60	28.390	28.863	29.336	29.809	30.283	30.756	31.229	31.702	32.175	32.648
70	33.122	33.595	34.068	34.541	35.014	35.487	35.961	36.434	36.907	37.380
80	37.853	38.326	38.800	39.273	39.746	40.219	40.692	41.165	41.639	42.112
90	42.585	43.058	43.531	44.004	44.478	44.951	45.424	45.897	46.370	46.843

Gallons (Brit.) – Liters

	0	1	2	3	4	5	6	7	8	9
0	0.0000	4.5460	9.0919	13.638	18.184	22.730	27.276	31.822	36.368	40.914
10	45.460	50.006	54.552	59.098	63.643	68.189	72.735	77.281	81.827	86.373
20	90.919	95.465	100.01	104.56	109.10	113.65	118.20	122.74	127.29	131.83
30	136.38	140.92	145.47	150.02	154.56	159.11	163.65	168.20	172.75	177.29
40	181.84	186.38	190.93	195.48	200.02	204.57	209.11	213.66	218.21	222.75
50	227.30	231.84	236.39	240.94	245.48	250.03	254.57	259.12	263.67	268.21
60	272.76	277.30	281.85	286.40	290.94	295.49	300.03	304.58	309.13	313.67
70	318.22	322.76	327.31	331.86	336.40	340.95	345.49	350.04	354.59	359.13
80	363.68	368.22	372.77	377.31	381.86	386.41	390.95	395.50	400.04	404.59
90	409.14	413.68	418.23	422.77	427.32	431.87	436.41	440.96	445.50	450.05

Gallons (US) – Liters

	0	1	2	3	4	5	6	7	8	9
0	0.0000	3.7853	7.5707	11.356	15.141	18.927	22.712	26.497	30.283	34.068
10	37.853	41.639	45.424	49.209	52.995	56.780	60.565	64.351	68.136	71.921
20	75.707	79.492	83.277	87.063	90.848	94.633	98.419	102.20	105.99	109.77
30	113.56	117.35	121.13	124.92	128.70	132.49	136.27	140.06	143.84	147.63
40	151.41	155.20	158.98	162.77	166.55	170.34	174.13	177.91	181.70	185.48
50	189.27	193.05	196.84	200.62	204.41	208.19	211.98	215.76	219.55	223.33
60	227.12	230.91	234.69	238.48	242.26	246.05	249.83	253.62	257.40	261.19
70	264.97	268.76	272.54	276.33	280.11	283.90	287.69	291.47	295.26	299.04
80	302.83	306.61	310.40	314.18	317.97	321.75	325.54	329.32	333.11	336.89
90	340.68	344.46	348.25	352.04	355.82	359.61	363.39	367.18	370.96	374.75

Grams – Ounces (avoirdupois)

	0	1	2	3	4	5	6	7	8	9
0	0.0000	0.0353	0.0705	0.1058	0.1411	0.1764	0.2116	0.2469	0.2822	0.3175
10	0.3527	0.3880	0.4233	0.4586	0.4938	0.5291	0.5644	0.5997	0.6349	0.6702
20	0.7055	0.7408	0.7760	0.8113	0.8466	0.8818	0.9171	0.9524	0.9877	1.0229
30	1.0582	1.0935	1.1288	1.1640	1.1993	1.2346	1.2699	1.3051	1.3404	1.3757
40	1.4110	1.4462	1.4815	1.5168	1.5521	1.5873	1.6226	1.6579	1.6932	1.7284
50	1.7637	1.7990	1.8342	1.8695	1.9048	1.9401	1.9753	2.0106	2.0459	2.0812
60	2.1164	2.1517	2.1870	2.2223	2.2575	2.2928	2.3281	2.3634	2.3986	2.4339
70	2.4692	2.5045	2.5397	2.5750	2.6103	2.6455	2.6808	2.7161	2.7514	2.7866
80	2.8219	2.8572	2.8925	2.9277	2.9630	2.9983	3.0336	3.0688	3.1041	3.1394
90	3.1747	3.2099	3.2452	3.2805	3.3158	3.3510	3.3863	3.4216	3.4568	3.4921

Grams – Ounces (apothecary)

	0	1	2	3	4	5	6	7	8	9
0	0.0000	0.0322	0.0643	0.0965	0.1286	0.1608	0.1929	0.2251	0.2572	0.2894
10	0.3215	0.3537	0.3858	0.4180	0.4501	0.4823	0.5144	0.5466	0.5787	0.6109
20	0.6430	0.6752	0.7073	0.7395	0.7716	0.8038	0.8359	0.8681	0.9002	0.9324
30	0.9645	0.9967	1.0288	1.0610	1.0931	1.1253	1.1574	1.1896	1.2217	1.2539
40	1.2860	1.3182	1.3503	1.3825	1.4146	1.4468	1.4789	1.5111	1.5432	1.5754
50	1.6075	1.6397	1.6718	1.7040	1.7361	1.7683	1.8004	1.8326	1.8647	1.8969
60	1.9290	1.9612	1.9933	2.0255	2.0576	2.0898	2.1219	2.1541	2.1863	2.2184
70	2.2506	2.2827	2.3149	2.3470	2.3792	2.4113	2.4435	2.4756	2.5078	2.5399
80	2.5721	2.6042	2.6364	2.6685	2.7007	2.7328	2.7650	2.7971	2.8293	2.8614
90	2.8936	2.9257	2.9579	2.9900	3.0222	3.0543	3.0865	3.1186	3.1508	3.1829

Milliliters – Fluid ounces (Brit.)

	0	1	2	3	4	5	6	7	8	9
0	0.0000	0.0352	0.0704	0.1056	0.1408	0.1760	0.2112	0.2464	0.2816	0.3168
10	0.3520	0.3872	0.4224	0.4575	0.4927	0.5279	0.5631	0.5983	0.6335	0.6687
20	0.7039	0.7391	0.7743	0.8095	0.8447	0.8799	0.9151	0.9503	0.9855	1.0207
30	1.0559	1.0911	1.1263	1.1615	1.1967	1.2319	1.2671	1.3023	1.3375	1.3726
40	1.4078	1.4430	1.4782	1.5134	1.5486	1.5838	1.6190	1.6542	1.6894	1.7246
50	1.7598	1.7950	1.8302	1.8654	1.9006	1.9358	1.9710	2.0062	2.0414	2.0766
60	2.1118	2.1470	2.1822	2.2174	2.2525	2.2877	2.3229	2.3581	2.3933	2.4285
70	2.4637	2.4989	2.5341	2.5693	2.6045	2.6397	2.6749	2.7101	2.7453	2.7805
80	2.8157	2.8509	2.8861	2.9213	2.9565	2.9917	3.0269	3.0621	3.0973	3.1324
90	3.1676	3.2028	3.2380	3.2732	3.3084	3.3436	3.3788	3.4140	3.4492	3.4844

Milliliters – Fluid ounces (US)

	0	1	2	3	4	5	6	7	8	9
0	0.0000	0.0338	0.0676	0.1014	0.1353	0.1691	0.2029	0.2367	0.2705	0.3043
10	0.3381	0.3720	0.4058	0.4396	0.4734	0.5072	0.5410	0.5749	0.6087	0.6425
20	0.6763	0.7101	0.7439	0.7777	0.8116	0.8454	0.8792	0.9130	0.9468	0.9806
30	1.0144	1.0483	1.0821	1.1159	1.1497	1.1835	1.2173	1.2511	1.2850	1.3188
40	1.3526	1.3864	1.4202	1.4540	1.4878	1.5217	1.5555	1.5893	1.6231	1.6569
50	1.6907	1.7246	1.7584	1.7922	1.8260	1.8598	1.8936	1.9274	1.9613	1.9951
60	2.0289	2.0627	2.0965	2.1303	2.1641	2.1980	2.2318	2.2656	2.2994	2.3332
70	2.3670	2.4008	2.4347	2.4685	2.5023	2.5361	2.5699	2.6037	2.6376	2.6714
80	2.7052	2.7390	2.7728	2.8066	2.8404	2.8743	2.9081	2.9419	2.9757	3.0095
90	3.0433	3.0771	3.1110	3.1448	3.1786	3.2124	3.2462	3.2800	3.3138	3.3477

Liters – Pints (Brit.)

	0	1	2	3	4	5	6	7	8	9
0	0.0000	1.7598	3.5196	5.2794	7.0392	8.7990	10.559	12.319	14.078	15.838
10	17.598	19.358	21.118	22.877	24.637	26.397	28.157	29.917	31.676	33.436
20	35.196	36.956	38.716	40.475	42.235	43.995	45.755	47.515	49.274	51.034
30	52.794	54.554	56.314	58.073	59.833	61.593	63.353	65.113	66.873	68.632
40	70.392	72.152	73.912	75.672	77.431	79.191	80.951	82.711	84.471	86.230
50	87.990	89.750	91.510	93.270	95.029	96.789	98.549	100.31	102.07	103.83
60	105.59	107.35	109.11	110.87	112.63	114.39	116.15	117.91	119.67	121.43
70	123.19	124.95	126.71	128.47	130.23	131.99	133.75	135.50	137.26	139.02
80	140.78	142.54	144.30	146.06	147.82	149.58	151.34	153.10	154.86	156.62
90	158.38	160.14	161.90	163.66	165.42	167.18	168.94	170.70	172.46	174.22

Liters – Pints (US)

	0	1	2	3	4	5	6	7	8	9
0	0.0000	2.1134	4.2268	6.3403	8.4537	10.567	12.681	14.794	16.907	19.021
10	21.134	23.248	25.361	27.474	29.588	31.701	33.815	35.928	38.042	40.155
20	42.268	44.382	46.495	48.609	50.722	52.836	54.949	57.062	59.176	61.289
30	63.403	65.516	67.630	69.743	71.856	73.970	76.083	78.197	80.310	82.423
40	84.537	86.650	88.764	90.877	92.991	95.104	97.217	99.331	101.44	103.56
50	105.67	107.78	109.90	112.01	114.12	116.24	118.35	120.47	122.58	124.69
60	126.81	128.92	131.03	133.15	135.26	137.37	139.49	141.60	143.71	145.83
70	147.94	150.05	152.17	154.28	156.39	158.51	160.62	162.73	164.85	166.96
80	169.07	171.19	173.30	175.41	177.53	179.64	181.75	183.87	185.98	188.09
90	190.21	192.32	194.43	196.55	198.66	200.78	202.89	205.00	207.12	209.23

Liters – Gallons (Brit.)

	0	1	2	3	4	5	6	7	8	9
0	0.0000	0.2200	0.4400	0.6599	0.8799	1.0999	1.3199	1.5398	1.7598	1.9798
10	2.1998	2.4197	2.6397	2.8597	3.0797	3.2996	3.5196	3.7396	3.9596	4.1795
20	4.3995	4.6195	4.8395	5.0594	5.2794	5.4994	5.7194	5.9393	6.1593	6.3793
30	6.5993	6.8192	7.0392	7.2592	7.4792	7.6991	7.9191	8.1391	8.3591	8.5790
40	8.7990	9.0190	9.2390	9.4589	9.6789	9.8989	10.119	10.339	10.559	10.779
50	10.999	11.219	11.439	11.659	11.879	12.099	12.319	12.539	12.759	12.979
60	13.199	13.418	13.638	13.858	14.078	14.298	14.518	14.738	14.958	15.178
70	15.398	15.618	15.838	16.058	16.278	16.498	16.718	16.938	17.158	17.378
80	17.598	17.818	18.038	18.258	18.478	18.698	18.918	19.138	19.358	19.578
90	19.798	20.018	20.238	20.458	20.678	20.898	21.118	21.338	21.558	21.778

Liters – Gallons (US)

	0	1	2	3	4	5	6	7	8	9
0	0.0000	0.2642	0.5284	0.7925	1.0567	1.3209	1.5851	1.8492	2.1134	2.3776
10	2.6418	2.9060	3.1701	3.4343	3.6985	3.9627	4.2268	4.4910	4.7552	5.0194
20	5.2836	5.5477	5.8119	6.0761	6.3403	6.6044	6.8686	7.1328	7.3970	7.6612
30	7.9253	8.1895	8.4537	8.7179	8.9820	9.2462	9.5104	9.7746	10.039	10.303
40	10.567	10.831	11.095	11.360	11.624	11.888	12.152	12.416	12.681	12.945
50	13.209	13.473	13.737	14.001	14.266	14.530	14.794	15.058	15.322	15.586
60	15.851	16.115	16.379	16.643	16.907	17.172	17.436	17.700	17.964	18.228
70	18.492	18.757	19.021	19.285	19.549	19.813	20.078	20.342	20.606	20.870
80	21.134	21.398	21.663	21.927	22.191	22.455	22.719	22.983	23.248	23.512
90	23.776	24.040	24.304	24.569	24.833	25.097	25.361	25.625	25.889	26.154

Examples: 445 gr = 28 836 mg; 44.5 gr = 2883.6 mg; 4.45 gr = 288.36 mg; 0.445 gr = 28.84 mg

Examples: 445 mg = 6.8674 gr; 44.5 mg = 0.6867 gr; 4.45 mg = 0.0687 gr; 0.445 mg = 0.006 87 gr

Grains – Milligrams

gr	0	0.1	0.2	0.3	0.4	0.5	0.6	0.7	0.8	0.9
10	647.99	654.47	660.95	667.43	673.91	680.39	686.87	693.35	699.83	706.31
11	712.79	719.27	725.75	732.23	738.71	745.19	751.67	758.15	764.63	771.11
12	777.59	784.07	790.55	797.03	803.51	809.99	816.47	822.95	829.43	835.91
13	842.39	848.87	855.35	861.83	868.31	874.79	881.27	887.75	894.23	900.70
14	907.18	913.66	920.14	926.62	933.10	939.58	946.06	952.54	959.02	965.50
15	971.98	978.46	984.94	991.42	997.90	1004.4	1010.9	1017.3	1023.8	1030.3
16	1036.8	1043.3	1049.7	1056.2	1062.7	1069.2	1075.7	1082.1	1088.6	1095.1
17	1101.6	1108.1	1114.5	1121.0	1127.5	1134.0	1140.5	1146.9	1153.4	1159.9
18	1166.4	1172.9	1179.3	1185.8	1192.3	1198.8	1205.3	1211.7	1218.2	1224.7
19	1231.2	1237.7	1244.1	1250.6	1257.1	1263.6	1270.1	1276.5	1283.0	1289.5
20	1296.0	1302.5	1308.9	1315.4	1321.9	1328.4	1334.9	1341.3	1347.8	1354.3
21	1360.8	1367.3	1373.7	1380.2	1386.7	1393.2	1399.7	1406.1	1412.6	1419.1
22	1425.6	1432.1	1438.5	1445.0	1451.5	1458.0	1464.5	1470.9	1477.4	1483.9
23	1490.4	1496.9	1503.3	1509.8	1516.3	1522.8	1529.3	1535.7	1542.2	1548.7
24	1555.2	1561.7	1568.1	1574.6	1581.1	1587.6	1594.1	1600.5	1607.0	1613.5
25	1620.0	1626.5	1632.9	1639.4	1645.9	1652.4	1658.9	1665.3	1671.8	1678.3
26	1684.8	1691.3	1697.7	1704.2	1710.7	1717.2	1723.7	1730.1	1736.6	1743.1
27	1749.6	1756.1	1762.5	1769.0	1775.5	1782.0	1788.5	1794.9	1801.4	1807.9
28	1814.4	1820.8	1827.3	1833.8	1840.3	1846.8	1853.2	1859.7	1866.2	1872.7
29	1879.2	1885.6	1892.1	1898.6	1905.1	1911.6	1918.0	1924.5	1931.0	1937.5
30	1944.0	1950.4	1956.9	1963.4	1969.9	1976.4	1982.8	1989.3	1995.8	2002.3
31	2008.8	2015.2	2021.7	2028.2	2034.7	2041.2	2047.6	2054.1	2060.6	2067.1
32	2073.6	2080.0	2086.5	2093.0	2099.5	2106.0	2112.4	2118.9	2125.4	2131.9
33	2138.4	2144.8	2151.3	2157.8	2164.3	2170.8	2177.2	2183.7	2190.2	2196.7
34	2203.2	2209.6	2216.1	2222.6	2229.1	2235.6	2242.0	2248.5	2255.0	2261.5
35	2268.0	2274.4	2280.9	2287.4	2293.9	2300.4	2306.8	2313.3	2319.8	2326.3
36	2332.8	2339.2	2345.7	2352.2	2358.7	2365.2	2371.6	2378.1	2384.6	2391.1
37	2397.6	2404.0	2410.5	2417.0	2423.5	2430.0	2436.4	2442.9	2449.4	2455.9
38	2462.4	2468.8	2475.3	2481.8	2488.3	2494.8	2501.2	2507.7	2514.2	2520.7
39	2527.2	2533.6	2540.1	2546.6	2553.1	2559.6	2566.0	2572.5	2579.0	2585.5
40	2592.0	2598.4	2604.9	2611.4	2617.9	2624.4	2630.8	2637.3	2643.8	2650.3
41	2656.8	2663.2	2669.7	2676.2	2682.7	2689.2	2695.6	2702.1	2708.6	2715.1
42	2721.6	2728.0	2734.5	2741.0	2747.5	2754.0	2760.4	2766.9	2773.4	2779.9
43	2786.4	2792.8	2799.3	2805.8	2812.3	2818.8	2825.2	2831.7	2838.2	2844.7
44	2851.2	2857.6	2864.1	2870.6	2877.1	2883.6	2890.0	2896.5	2903.0	2909.5
45	2916.0	2922.4	2928.9	2935.4	2941.9	2948.4	2954.8	2961.3	2967.8	2974.3
46	2980.8	2987.2	2993.7	3000.2	3006.7	3013.1	3019.6	3026.1	3032.6	3039.1
47	3045.5	3052.0	3058.5	3065.0	3071.5	3077.9	3084.4	3090.9	3097.4	3103.9
48	3110.3	3116.8	3123.3	3129.8	3136.3	3142.7	3149.2	3155.7	3162.2	3168.7
49	3175.1	3181.6	3188.1	3194.6	3201.1	3207.5	3214.0	3220.5	3227.0	3233.5
50	3239.9	3246.4	3252.9	3259.4	3265.9	3272.3	3278.8	3285.3	3291.8	3298.3
51	3304.7	3311.2	3317.7	3324.2	3330.7	3337.1	3343.6	3350.1	3356.6	3363.1
52	3369.5	3376.0	3382.5	3389.0	3395.5	3401.9	3408.4	3414.9	3421.4	3427.9
53	3434.3	3440.8	3447.3	3453.8	3460.3	3466.7	3473.2	3479.7	3486.2	3492.7
54	3499.1	3505.6	3512.1	3518.6	3525.1	3531.5	3538.0	3544.5	3551.0	3557.5
55	3563.9	3570.4	3576.9	3583.4	3589.9	3596.3	3602.8	3609.3	3615.8	3622.3
56	3628.7	3635.2	3641.7	3648.2	3654.7	3661.1	3667.6	3674.1	3680.6	3687.1
57	3693.5	3700.0	3706.5	3713.0	3719.5	3725.9	3732.4	3738.9	3745.4	3751.9
58	3758.3	3764.8	3771.3	3777.8	3784.3	3790.7	3797.2	3803.7	3810.2	3816.7
59	3823.1	3829.6	3836.1	3842.6	3849.1	3855.5	3862.0	3868.5	3875.0	3881.5
60	3887.9	3894.4	3900.9	3907.4	3913.9	3920.3	3926.8	3933.3	3939.8	3946.3
61	3952.7	3959.2	3965.7	3972.2	3978.7	3985.1	3991.6	3998.1	4004.6	4011.1
62	4017.5	4024.0	4030.5	4037.0	4043.5	4049.9	4056.4	4062.9	4069.4	4075.9
63	4082.3	4088.8	4095.3	4101.8	4108.3	4114.7	4121.2	4127.7	4134.2	4140.7
64	4147.1	4153.6	4160.1	4166.6	4173.1	4179.5	4186.0	4192.5	4199.0	4205.4
65	4211.9	4218.4	4224.9	4231.4	4237.8	4244.3	4250.8	4257.3	4263.8	4270.2
66	4276.7	4283.2	4289.7	4296.2	4302.6	4309.1	4315.6	4322.1	4328.6	4335.0
67	4341.5	4348.0	4354.5	4361.0	4367.4	4373.9	4380.4	4386.9	4393.4	4399.8
68	4406.3	4412.8	4419.3	4425.8	4432.2	4438.7	4445.2	4451.7	4458.2	4464.6
69	4471.1	4477.6	4484.1	4490.6	4497.0	4503.5	4510.0	4516.5	4523.0	4529.4
70	4535.9	4542.4	4548.9	4555.4	4561.8	4568.3	4574.8	4581.3	4587.8	4594.2
71	4600.7	4607.2	4613.7	4620.2	4626.6	4633.1	4639.6	4646.1	4652.6	4659.0
72	4665.5	4672.0	4678.5	4685.0	4691.4	4697.9	4704.4	4710.9	4717.4	4723.8
73	4730.3	4736.8	4743.3	4749.8	4756.2	4762.7	4769.2	4775.7	4782.2	4788.6
74	4795.1	4801.6	4808.1	4814.6	4821.0	4827.5	4834.0	4840.5	4847.0	4853.4
75	4859.9	4866.4	4872.9	4879.4	4885.8	4892.3	4898.8	4905.3	4911.8	4918.2
76	4924.7	4931.2	4937.7	4944.2	4950.6	4957.1	4963.6	4970.1	4976.6	4983.0
77	4989.5	4996.0	5002.5	5009.0	5015.4	5021.9	5028.4	5034.9	5041.4	5047.8
78	5054.3	5060.8	5067.3	5073.8	5080.2	5086.7	5093.2	5099.7	5106.2	5112.6
79	5119.1	5125.6	5132.1	5138.6	5145.0	5151.5	5158.0	5164.5	5171.0	5177.4
80	5183.9	5190.4	5196.9	5203.4	5209.8	5216.3	5222.8	5229.3	5235.8	5242.2
81	5248.7	5255.2	5261.7	5268.2	5274.6	5281.1	5287.6	5294.1	5300.6	5307.0
82	5313.5	5320.0	5326.5	5333.0	5339.4	5345.9	5352.4	5358.9	5365.4	5371.8
83	5378.3	5384.8	5391.3	5397.8	5404.2	5410.7	5417.2	5423.7	5430.1	5436.6
84	5443.1	5449.6	5456.1	5462.5	5469.0	5475.5	5482.0	5488.5	5494.9	5501.4
85	5507.9	5514.4	5520.9	5527.3	5533.8	5540.3	5546.8	5553.3	5559.7	5566.2
86	5572.7	5579.2	5585.7	5592.1	5598.6	5605.1	5611.6	5618.1	5624.5	5631.0
87	5637.5	5644.0	5650.5	5656.9	5663.4	5669.9	5676.4	5682.9	5689.3	5695.8
88	5702.3	5708.8	5715.3	5721.7	5728.2	5734.7	5741.2	5747.7	5754.1	5760.6
89	5767.1	5773.6	5780.1	5786.5	5793.0	5799.5	5806.0	5812.5	5818.9	5825.4
90	5831.9	5838.4	5844.9	5851.3	5857.8	5864.3	5870.8	5877.3	5883.7	5890.2
91	5896.7	5903.2	5909.7	5916.1	5922.6	5929.1	5935.6	5942.1	5948.5	5955.0
92	5961.5	5968.0	5974.5	5980.9	5987.4	5993.9	6000.4	6006.9	6013.3	6019.8
93	6026.3	6032.8	6039.3	6045.7	6052.2	6058.7	6065.2	6071.7	6078.1	6084.6
94	6091.1	6097.6	6104.1	6110.5	6117.0	6123.5	6130.0	6136.5	6142.9	6149.4
95	6155.9	6162.4	6168.9	6175.3	6181.8	6188.3	6194.8	6201.3	6207.7	6214.2
96	6220.7	6227.2	6233.7	6240.1	6246.6	6253.1	6259.6	6266.1	6272.5	6279.0
97	6285.5	6292.0	6298.5	6304.9	6311.4	6317.9	6324.4	6330.9	6337.3	6343.8
98	6350.3	6356.8	6363.3	6369.7	6376.2	6382.7	6389.2	6395.7	6402.1	6408.6
99	6415.1	6421.6	6428.1	6434.5	6441.0	6447.5	6454.0	6460.5	6466.9	6473.4

Milligrams – Grains

mg	0	1	2	3	4	5	6	7	8	9
100	1.5432	1.5587	1.5741	1.5895	1.6050	1.6204	1.6358	1.6513	1.6667	1.6821
110	1.6976	1.7130	1.7284	1.7439	1.7593	1.7747	1.7902	1.8056	1.8210	1.8365
120	1.8519	1.8673	1.8827	1.8982	1.9136	1.9290	1.9445	1.9599	1.9753	1.9908
130	2.0062	2.0216	2.0371	2.0525	2.0679	2.0834	2.0988	2.1142	2.1297	2.1451
140	2.1605	2.1760	2.1914	2.2068	2.2223	2.2377	2.2531	2.2686	2.2840	2.2994
150	2.3149	2.3303	2.3457	2.3612	2.3766	2.3920	2.4074	2.4229	2.4383	2.4537
160	2.4692	2.4846	2.5000	2.5155	2.5309	2.5463	2.5618	2.5772	2.5926	2.6081
170	2.6235	2.6389	2.6544	2.6698	2.6852	2.7007	2.7161	2.7315	2.7470	2.7624
180	2.7778	2.7933	2.8087	2.8241	2.8396	2.8550	2.8704	2.8859	2.9013	2.9167
190	2.9321	2.9476	2.9630	2.9784	2.9939	3.0093	3.0247	3.0402	3.0556	3.0710
200	3.0865	3.1019	3.1173	3.1328	3.1482	3.1636	3.1791	3.1945	3.2099	3.2254
210	3.2408	3.2562	3.2717	3.2871	3.3025	3.3180	3.3334	3.3488	3.3643	3.3797
220	3.3951	3.4106	3.4260	3.4414	3.4568	3.4723	3.4877	3.5031	3.5186	3.5340
230	3.5494	3.5649	3.5803	3.5957	3.6112	3.6266	3.6420	3.6575	3.6729	3.6883
240	3.7038	3.7192	3.7346	3.7501	3.7655	3.7809	3.7964	3.8118	3.8272	3.8427
250	3.8581	3.8735	3.8890	3.9044	3.9198	3.9353	3.9507	3.9661	3.9815	3.9970
260	4.0124	4.0278	4.0433	4.0587	4.0741	4.0896	4.1050	4.1204	4.1359	4.1513
270	4.1667	4.1822	4.1976	4.2130	4.2285	4.2439	4.2593	4.2748	4.2902	4.3056
280	4.3211	4.3365	4.3519	4.3674	4.3828	4.3982	4.4137	4.4291	4.4445	4.4600
290	4.4754	4.4908	4.5062	4.5217	4.5371	4.5525	4.5680	4.5834	4.5988	4.6143
300	4.6297	4.6451	4.6606	4.6760	4.6914	4.7069	4.7223	4.7377	4.7532	4.7686
310	4.7840	4.7995	4.8149	4.8303	4.8458	4.8612	4.8766	4.8921	4.9075	4.9229
320	4.9384	4.9538	4.9692	4.9847	5.0001	5.0155	5.0309	5.0464	5.0618	5.0772
330	5.0927	5.1081	5.1235	5.1390	5.1544	5.1698	5.1853	5.2007	5.2161	5.2316
340	5.2470	5.2624	5.2779	5.2933	5.3087	5.3242	5.3396	5.3550	5.3705	5.3859
350	5.4013	5.4168	5.4322	5.4476	5.4631	5.4785	5.4939	5.5094	5.5248	5.5402
360	5.5556	5.5711	5.5865	5.6019	5.6174	5.6328	5.6482	5.6637	5.6791	5.6945
370	5.7100	5.7254	5.7408	5.7563	5.7717	5.7871	5.8026	5.8180	5.8334	5.8489
380	5.8643	5.8797	5.8952	5.9106	5.9260	5.9415	5.9569	5.9723	5.9878	6.0032
390	6.0186	6.0341	6.0495	6.0649	6.0803	6.0958	6.1112	6.1266	6.1421	6.1575
400	6.1729	6.1884	6.2038	6.2192	6.2347	6.2501	6.2655	6.2810	6.2964	6.3118
410	6.3273	6.3427	6.3581	6.3736	6.3890	6.4044	6.4199	6.4353	6.4507	6.4662
420	6.4816	6.4970	6.5125	6.5279	6.5433	6.5588	6.5742	6.5896	6.6051	6.6205
430	6.6359	6.6513	6.6668	6.6822	6.6976	6.7131	6.7285	6.7439	6.7594	6.7748
440	6.7902	6.8057	6.8211	6.8365	6.8520	6.8674	6.8828	6.8983	6.9137	6.9291
450	6.9446	6.9600	6.9754	6.9909	7.0063	7.0217	7.0372	7.0526	7.0680	7.0835
460	7.0989	7.1143	7.1298	7.1452	7.1606	7.1760	7.1915	7.2069	7.2223	7.2378
470	7.2532	7.2686	7.2841	7.2995	7.3149	7.3304	7.3458	7.3612	7.3767	7.3921
480	7.4075	7.4230	7.4384	7.4538	7.4693	7.4847	7.5001	7.5156	7.5310	7.5464
490	7.5619	7.5773	7.5927	7.6082	7.6236	7.6390	7.6545	7.6699	7.6853	7.7007
500	7.7162	7.7316	7.7470	7.7625	7.7779	7.7933	7.8088	7.8242	7.8396	7.8551
510	7.8705	7.8859	7.9014	7.9168	7.9322	7.9477	7.9631	7.9785	7.9940	8.0094
520	8.0248	8.0403	8.0557	8.0711	8.0866	8.1020	8.1174	8.1329	8.1483	8.1637
530	8.1792	8.1946	8.2100	8.2254	8.2409	8.2563	8.2717	8.2872	8.3026	8.3180
540	8.3335	8.3489	8.3643	8.3798	8.3952	8.4106	8.4261	8.4415	8.4569	8.4724
550	8.4878	8.5032	8.5187	8.5341	8.5495	8.5650	8.5804	8.5958	8.6113	8.6267
560	8.6421	8.6576	8.6730	8.6884	8.7039	8.7193	8.7347	8.7501	8.7656	8.7810
570	8.7964	8.8119	8.8273	8.8427	8.8582	8.8736	8.8890	8.9045	8.9199	8.9353
580	8.9508	8.9662	8.9816	8.9971	9.0125	9.0279	9.0434	9.0588	9.0742	9.0897
590	9.1051	9.1205	9.1360	9.1514	9.1668	9.1823	9.1977	9.2131	9.2286	9.2440
600	9.2594	9.2748	9.2903	9.3057	9.3211	9.3366	9.3520	9.3674	9.3829	9.3983
610	9.4137	9.4292	9.4446	9.4600	9.4755	9.4909	9.5063	9.5218	9.5372	9.5526
620	9.5681	9.5835	9.5989	9.6144	9.6298	9.6452	9.6607	9.6761	9.6915	9.7070
630	9.7224	9.7378	9.7533	9.7687	9.7841	9.7995	9.8150	9.8304	9.8458	9.8613
640	9.8767	9.8921	9.9076	9.9230	9.9384	9.9539	9.9693	9.9847	10.000	10.016
650	10.031	10.046	10.062	10.077	10.093	10.108	10.124	10.139	10.154	10.170
660	10.185	10.201	10.216	10.232	10.247	10.263	10.278	10.293	10.309	10.324
670	10.340	10.355	10.371	10.386	10.401	10.417	10.432	10.448	10.463	10.479
680	10.494	10.509	10.525	10.540	10.556	10.571	10.587	10.602	10.617	10.633
690	10.648	10.664	10.679	10.695	10.710	10.725	10.741	10.756	10.772	10.787
700	10.803	10.818	10.834	10.849	10.864	10.880	10.895	10.911	10.926	10.942
710	10.957	10.972	10.988	11.003	11.019	11.034	11.050	11.065	11.080	11.096
720	11.111	11.127	11.142	11.158	11.173	11.188	11.204	11.219	11.235	11.250
730	11.266	11.281	11.296	11.312	11.327	11.343	11.358	11.374	11.389	11.405
740	11.420	11.435	11.451	11.466	11.482	11.497	11.513	11.528	11.543	11.559
750	11.574	11.590	11.605	11.621	11.636	11.651	11.667	11.682	11.698	11.713
760	11.729	11.744	11.759	11.775	11.790	11.806	11.821	11.837	11.852	11.867
770	11.883	11.898	11.914	11.929	11.945	11.960	11.976	11.991	12.006	12.022
780	12.037	12.053	12.068	12.084	12.099	12.114	12.130	12.145	12.161	12.176
790	12.192	12.207	12.222	12.238	12.253	12.269	12.284	12.300	12.315	12.330
800	12.346	12.361	12.377	12.392	12.408	12.423	12.438	12.454	12.469	12.485
810	12.500	12.516	12.531	12.547	12.562	12.577	12.593	12.608	12.624	12.639
820	12.655	12.670	12.685	12.701	12.716	12.732	12.747	12.763	12.778	12.793
830	12.809	12.824	12.840	12.855	12.871	12.886	12.901	12.917	12.932	12.948
840	12.963	12.979	12.994	13.009	13.025	13.040	13.056	13.071	13.087	13.102
850	13.118	13.133	13.148	13.164	13.179	13.195	13.210	13.226	13.241	13.256
860	13.272	13.287	13.303	13.318	13.334	13.349	13.364	13.380	13.395	13.411
870	13.426	13.442	13.457	13.472	13.488	13.503	13.519	13.534	13.550	13.565
880	13.580	13.596	13.611	13.627	13.642	13.658	13.673	13.689	13.704	13.719
890	13.735	13.750	13.766	13.781	13.797	13.812	13.827	13.843	13.858	13.874
900	13.889	13.905	13.920	13.935	13.951	13.966	13.982	13.997	14.013	14.028
910	14.043	14.059	14.074	14.090	14.105	14.121	14.136	14.151	14.167	14.182
920	14.198	14.213	14.229	14.244	14.260	14.275	14.290	14.306	14.321	14.337
930	14.352	14.368	14.383	14.398	14.414	14.429	14.445	14.460	14.476	14.491
940	14.506	14.522	14.537	14.553	14.568	14.584	14.599	14.614	14.630	14.645
950	14.661	14.676	14.692	14.707	14.722	14.738	14.753	14.769	14.784	14.800
960	14.815	14.830	14.846	14.861	14.877	14.892	14.908	14.923	14.939	14.954
970	14.969	14.985	15.000	15.016	15.031	15.047	15.062	15.077	15.093	15.108
980	15.124	15.139	15.155	15.170	15.185	15.201	15.216	15.232	15.247	15.263
990	15.278	15.293	15.309	15.324	15.340	15.355	15.371	15.386	15.401	15.417

Examples: 300 lb = 136.08 kg; 30 lb = 13.608 kg; 3 lb = 1.361 kg; 0.3 lb = 0.136 kg

Pounds (avoirdupois) – Kilograms

lb	0	1	2	3	4	5	6	7	8	9
100	45.359	45.813	46.266	46.720	47.174	47.627	48.081	48.534	48.988	49.442
110	49.895	50.349	50.802	51.256	51.710	52.163	52.617	53.070	53.524	53.977
120	54.431	54.885	55.338	55.792	56.245	56.699	57.153	57.606	58.060	58.513
130	58.967	59.421	59.874	60.328	60.781	61.235	61.689	62.142	62.596	63.049
140	63.503	63.957	64.410	64.864	65.317	65.771	66.224	66.678	67.132	67.585
150	68.039	68.492	68.946	69.400	69.853	70.307	70.760	71.214	71.668	72.121
160	72.575	73.028	73.482	73.936	74.389	74.843	75.296	75.750	76.204	76.657
170	77.111	77.564	78.018	78.471	78.925	79.379	79.832	80.286	80.739	81.193
180	81.647	82.100	82.554	83.007	83.461	83.915	84.368	84.822	85.275	85.729
190	86.183	86.636	87.090	87.543	87.997	88.451	88.904	89.358	89.811	90.265
200	90.718	91.172	91.626	92.079	92.533	92.986	93.440	93.894	94.347	94.801
210	95.254	95.708	96.162	96.615	97.069	97.522	97.976	98.430	98.883	99.337
220	99.790	100.24	100.70	101.15	101.60	102.06	102.51	102.97	103.42	103.87
230	104.33	104.78	105.23	105.69	106.14	106.59	107.05	107.50	107.95	108.41
240	108.86	109.32	109.77	110.22	110.68	111.13	111.58	112.04	112.49	112.94
250	113.40	113.85	114.31	114.76	115.21	115.67	116.12	116.57	117.03	117.48
260	117.93	118.39	118.84	119.29	119.75	120.20	120.66	121.11	121.56	122.02
270	122.47	122.92	123.38	123.83	124.28	124.74	125.19	125.65	126.10	126.55
280	127.01	127.46	127.91	128.37	128.82	129.27	129.73	130.18	130.63	131.09
290	131.54	132.00	132.45	132.90	133.36	133.81	134.26	134.72	135.17	135.62
300	136.08	136.53	136.98	137.44	137.89	138.35	138.80	139.25	139.71	140.16
310	140.61	141.07	141.52	141.97	142.43	142.88	143.34	143.79	144.24	144.70
320	145.15	145.60	146.06	146.51	146.96	147.42	147.87	148.32	148.78	149.23
330	149.69	150.14	150.59	151.05	151.50	151.95	152.41	152.86	153.31	153.77
340	154.22	154.68	155.13	155.58	156.04	156.49	156.94	157.40	157.85	158.30
350	158.76	159.21	159.66	160.12	160.57	161.03	161.48	161.93	162.39	162.84
360	163.29	163.75	164.20	164.65	165.11	165.56	166.01	166.47	166.92	167.38
370	167.83	168.28	168.74	169.19	169.64	170.10	170.55	171.00	171.46	171.91
380	172.37	172.82	173.27	173.73	174.18	174.63	175.09	175.54	175.99	176.45
390	176.90	177.35	177.81	178.26	178.72	179.17	179.62	180.08	180.53	180.98
400	181.44	181.89	182.34	182.80	183.25	183.70	184.16	184.61	185.07	185.52
410	185.97	186.43	186.88	187.33	187.79	188.24	188.69	189.15	189.60	190.06
420	190.51	190.96	191.42	191.87	192.32	192.78	193.23	193.68	194.14	194.59
430	195.04	195.50	195.95	196.41	196.86	197.31	197.77	198.22	198.67	199.13
440	199.58	200.03	200.49	200.94	201.40	201.85	202.30	202.76	203.21	203.66
450	204.12	204.57	205.02	205.48	205.93	206.38	206.84	207.29	207.75	208.20
460	208.65	209.11	209.56	210.01	210.47	210.92	211.37	211.83	212.28	212.73
470	213.19	213.64	214.10	214.55	215.00	215.46	215.91	216.36	216.82	217.27
480	217.72	218.18	218.63	219.09	219.54	219.99	220.45	220.90	221.35	221.81
490	222.26	222.71	223.17	223.62	224.07	224.53	224.98	225.44	225.89	226.34
500	226.80	227.25	227.70	228.16	228.61	229.06	229.52	229.97	230.42	230.88
510	231.33	231.79	232.24	232.69	233.15	233.60	234.05	234.51	234.96	235.41
520	235.87	236.32	236.78	237.23	237.68	238.14	238.59	239.04	239.50	239.95
530	240.40	240.86	241.31	241.76	242.22	242.67	243.13	243.58	244.03	244.49
540	244.94	245.39	245.85	246.30	246.75	247.21	247.66	248.12	248.57	249.02
550	249.48	249.93	250.38	250.84	251.29	251.74	252.20	252.65	253.10	253.56
560	254.01	254.47	254.92	255.37	255.83	256.28	256.73	257.19	257.64	258.09
570	258.55	259.00	259.45	259.91	260.36	260.82	261.27	261.72	262.18	262.63
580	263.08	263.54	263.99	264.44	264.90	265.35	265.81	266.26	266.71	267.17
590	267.62	268.07	268.53	268.98	269.43	269.89	270.34	270.79	271.25	271.70
600	272.16	272.61	273.06	273.52	273.97	274.42	274.88	275.33	275.78	276.24
610	276.69	277.14	277.60	278.05	278.51	278.96	279.41	279.87	280.32	280.77
620	281.23	281.68	282.13	282.59	283.04	283.50	283.95	284.40	284.86	285.31
630	285.76	286.22	286.67	287.12	287.58	288.03	288.48	288.94	289.39	289.85
640	290.30	290.75	291.21	291.66	292.11	292.57	293.02	293.47	293.93	294.38
650	294.84	295.29	295.74	296.20	296.65	297.10	297.56	298.01	298.46	298.92
660	299.37	299.82	300.28	300.73	301.19	301.64	302.09	302.55	303.00	303.45
670	303.91	304.36	304.81	305.27	305.72	306.17	306.63	307.08	307.54	307.99
680	308.44	308.90	309.35	309.80	310.26	310.71	311.16	311.62	312.07	312.53
690	312.98	313.43	313.89	314.34	314.79	315.25	315.70	316.15	316.61	317.06
700	317.51	317.97	318.42	318.88	319.33	319.78	320.24	320.69	321.14	321.60
710	322.05	322.50	322.96	323.41	323.86	324.32	324.77	325.23	325.68	326.13
720	326.59	327.04	327.49	327.95	328.40	328.85	329.31	329.76	330.22	330.67
730	331.12	331.58	332.03	332.48	332.94	333.39	333.84	334.30	334.75	335.20
740	335.66	336.11	336.57	337.02	337.47	337.93	338.38	338.83	339.29	339.74
750	340.19	340.65	341.10	341.56	342.01	342.46	342.92	343.37	343.82	344.28
760	344.73	345.18	345.64	346.09	346.54	347.00	347.45	347.91	348.36	348.81
770	349.27	349.72	350.17	350.63	351.08	351.53	351.99	352.44	352.89	353.35
780	353.80	354.26	354.71	355.16	355.62	356.07	356.52	356.98	357.43	357.88
790	358.34	358.79	359.25	359.70	360.15	360.61	361.06	361.51	361.97	362.42
800	362.87	363.33	363.78	364.23	364.69	365.14	365.60	366.05	366.50	366.96
810	367.41	367.86	368.32	368.77	369.22	369.68	370.13	370.58	371.04	371.49
820	371.95	372.40	372.85	373.31	373.76	374.21	374.67	375.12	375.57	376.03
830	376.48	376.94	377.39	377.84	378.30	378.75	379.20	379.66	380.11	380.56
840	381.02	381.47	381.92	382.38	382.83	383.29	383.74	384.19	384.65	385.10
850	385.55	386.01	386.46	386.91	387.37	387.82	388.28	388.73	389.18	389.64
860	390.09	390.54	391.00	391.45	391.90	392.36	392.81	393.26	393.72	394.17
870	394.63	395.08	395.53	395.99	396.44	396.89	397.35	397.80	398.25	398.71
880	399.16	399.61	400.07	400.52	400.98	401.43	401.88	402.34	402.79	403.24
890	403.70	404.15	404.60	405.06	405.51	405.97	406.42	406.87	407.33	407.78
900	408.23	408.69	409.14	409.59	410.05	410.50	410.95	411.41	411.86	412.32
910	412.77	413.22	413.68	414.13	414.58	415.04	415.49	415.94	416.40	416.85
920	417.31	417.76	418.21	418.67	419.12	419.57	420.03	420.48	420.93	421.39
930	421.84	422.29	422.75	423.20	423.66	424.11	424.56	425.02	425.47	425.92
940	426.38	426.83	427.28	427.74	428.19	428.64	429.10	429.55	430.01	430.46
950	430.91	431.37	431.82	432.27	432.73	433.18	433.63	434.09	434.54	435.00
960	435.45	435.90	436.36	436.81	437.26	437.72	438.17	438.62	439.08	439.53
970	439.98	440.44	440.89	441.35	441.80	442.25	442.71	443.16	443.61	444.07
980	444.52	444.97	445.43	445.88	446.33	446.79	447.24	447.70	448.15	448.60
990	449.06	449.51	449.96	450.42	450.87	451.32	451.78	452.23	452.69	453.14

Examples: 152 kg = 335.10 lb; 15.2 kg = 33.510 lb; 1.52 kg = 3.351 lb; 0.152 kg = 0.335 lb

Kilograms – Pounds (avoirdupois)

kg	0	1	2	3	4	5	6	7	8	9
100	220.46	222.67	224.87	227.08	229.28	231.49	233.69	235.89	238.10	240.30
110	242.51	244.71	246.92	249.12	251.33	253.53	255.74	257.94	260.15	262.35
120	264.55	266.76	268.96	271.17	273.37	275.58	277.78	279.99	282.19	284.40
130	286.60	288.81	291.01	293.21	295.42	297.62	299.83	302.03	304.24	306.44
140	308.65	310.85	313.06	315.26	317.47	319.67	321.87	324.08	326.28	328.49
150	330.69	332.90	335.10	337.31	339.51	341.72	343.92	346.13	348.33	350.53
160	352.74	354.94	357.15	359.35	361.56	363.76	365.97	368.17	370.38	372.58
170	374.79	376.99	379.19	381.40	383.60	385.81	388.01	390.22	392.42	394.63
180	396.83	399.04	401.24	403.45	405.65	407.86	410.06	412.26	414.47	416.67
190	418.88	421.08	423.29	425.49	427.70	429.90	432.11	434.31	436.52	438.72
200	440.92	443.13	445.33	447.54	449.74	451.95	454.15	456.36	458.56	460.77
210	462.97	465.18	467.38	469.58	471.79	473.99	476.20	478.40	480.61	482.81
220	485.02	487.22	489.43	491.63	493.84	496.04	498.24	500.45	502.65	504.86
230	507.06	509.27	511.47	513.68	515.88	518.09	520.29	522.50	524.70	526.90
240	529.11	531.31	533.52	535.72	537.93	540.13	542.34	544.54	546.75	548.95
250	551.16	553.36	555.56	557.77	559.97	562.18	564.38	566.59	568.79	571.00
260	573.20	575.41	577.61	579.82	582.02	584.22	586.43	588.63	590.84	593.04
270	595.25	597.45	599.66	601.86	604.07	606.27	608.48	610.68	612.88	615.09
280	617.29	619.50	621.70	623.91	626.11	628.32	630.52	632.73	634.93	637.14
290	639.34	641.55	643.75	645.95	648.16	650.36	652.57	654.77	656.98	659.18
300	661.39	663.59	665.80	668.00	670.21	672.41	674.61	676.82	679.02	681.23
310	683.43	685.64	687.84	690.05	692.25	694.46	696.66	698.87	701.07	703.27
320	705.48	707.68	709.89	712.09	714.30	716.50	718.71	720.91	723.12	725.32
330	727.53	729.73	731.93	734.14	736.34	738.55	740.75	742.96	745.16	747.37
340	749.57	751.78	753.98	756.19	758.39	760.59	762.80	765.00	767.21	769.41
350	771.62	773.82	776.03	778.23	780.44	782.64	784.85	787.05	789.25	791.46
360	793.66	795.87	798.07	800.28	802.48	804.69	806.89	809.10	811.30	813.51
370	815.71	817.91	820.12	822.32	824.53	826.73	828.94	831.14	833.35	835.55
380	837.76	839.96	842.17	844.37	846.57	848.78	850.98	853.19	855.39	857.60
390	859.80	862.01	864.21	866.42	868.62	870.83	873.03	875.23	877.44	879.64
400	881.85	884.05	886.26	888.46	890.67	892.87	895.08	897.28	899.49	901.69
410	903.90	906.10	908.30	910.51	912.71	914.92	917.12	919.33	921.53	923.74
420	925.94	928.15	930.35	932.56	934.76	936.96	939.17	941.37	943.58	945.78
430	947.99	950.19	952.40	954.60	956.81	959.01	961.22	963.42	965.62	967.83
440	970.03	972.24	974.44	976.65	978.85	981.06	983.26	985.47	987.67	989.88
450	992.08	994.28	996.49	998.69	1000.9	1003.1	1005.3	1007.5	1009.7	1011.9
460	1014.1	1016.3	1018.5	1020.7	1022.9	1025.1	1027.4	1029.6	1031.8	1034.0
470	1036.2	1038.4	1040.6	1042.8	1045.0	1047.2	1049.4	1051.6	1053.8	1056.0
480	1058.2	1060.4	1062.6	1064.8	1067.0	1069.2	1071.4	1073.7	1075.9	1078.1
490	1080.3	1082.5	1084.7	1086.9	1089.1	1091.3	1093.5	1095.7	1097.9	1100.1
500	1102.3	1104.5	1106.7	1108.9	1111.1	1113.3	1115.5	1117.7	1119.9	1122.2
510	1124.4	1126.6	1128.8	1131.0	1133.2	1135.4	1137.6	1139.8	1142.0	1144.2
520	1146.4	1148.6	1150.8	1153.0	1155.2	1157.4	1159.6	1161.8	1164.0	1166.2
530	1168.4	1170.7	1172.9	1175.1	1177.3	1179.5	1181.7	1183.9	1186.1	1188.3
540	1190.5	1192.7	1194.9	1197.1	1199.3	1201.5	1203.7	1205.9	1208.1	1210.3
550	1212.5	1214.7	1217.0	1219.2	1221.4	1223.6	1225.8	1228.0	1230.2	1232.4
560	1234.6	1236.8	1239.0	1241.2	1243.4	1245.6	1247.8	1250.0	1252.2	1254.4
570	1256.6	1258.8	1261.0	1263.2	1265.5	1267.7	1269.9	1272.1	1274.3	1276.5
580	1278.7	1280.9	1283.1	1285.3	1287.5	1289.7	1291.9	1294.1	1296.3	1298.5
590	1300.7	1302.9	1305.1	1307.3	1309.5	1311.8	1314.0	1316.2	1318.4	1320.6
600	1322.8	1325.0	1327.2	1329.4	1331.6	1333.8	1336.0	1338.2	1340.4	1342.6
610	1344.8	1347.0	1349.2	1351.4	1353.6	1355.8	1358.0	1360.3	1362.5	1364.7
620	1366.9	1369.1	1371.3	1373.5	1375.7	1377.9	1380.1	1382.3	1384.5	1386.7
630	1388.9	1391.1	1393.3	1395.5	1397.7	1399.9	1402.1	1404.3	1406.5	1408.8
640	1411.0	1413.2	1415.4	1417.6	1419.8	1422.0	1424.2	1426.4	1428.6	1430.8
650	1433.0	1435.2	1437.4	1439.6	1441.8	1444.0	1446.2	1448.4	1450.6	1452.8
660	1455.1	1457.3	1459.5	1461.7	1463.9	1466.1	1468.3	1470.5	1472.7	1474.9
670	1477.1	1479.3	1481.5	1483.7	1485.9	1488.1	1490.3	1492.5	1494.7	1496.9
680	1499.1	1501.3	1503.6	1505.8	1508.0	1510.2	1512.4	1514.6	1516.8	1519.0
690	1521.2	1523.4	1525.6	1527.8	1530.0	1532.2	1534.4	1536.6	1538.8	1541.0
700	1543.2	1545.4	1547.6	1549.8	1552.1	1554.3	1556.5	1558.7	1560.9	1563.1
710	1565.3	1567.5	1569.7	1571.9	1574.1	1576.3	1578.5	1580.7	1582.9	1585.1
720	1587.3	1589.5	1591.7	1593.9	1596.1	1598.4	1600.6	1602.8	1605.0	1607.2
730	1609.4	1611.6	1613.8	1616.0	1618.2	1620.4	1622.6	1624.8	1627.0	1629.2
740	1631.4	1633.6	1635.8	1638.0	1640.2	1642.4	1644.6	1646.9	1649.1	1651.3
750	1653.5	1655.7	1657.9	1660.1	1662.3	1664.5	1666.7	1668.9	1671.1	1673.3
760	1675.5	1677.7	1679.9	1682.1	1684.3	1686.5	1688.7	1690.9	1693.1	1695.4
770	1697.6	1699.8	1702.0	1704.2	1706.4	1708.6	1710.8	1713.0	1715.2	1717.4
780	1719.6	1721.8	1724.0	1726.2	1728.4	1730.6	1732.8	1735.0	1737.2	1739.4
790	1741.7	1743.9	1746.1	1748.3	1750.5	1752.7	1754.9	1757.1	1759.3	1761.5
800	1763.7	1765.9	1768.1	1770.3	1772.5	1774.7	1776.9	1779.1	1781.3	1783.5
810	1785.7	1787.9	1790.2	1792.4	1794.6	1796.8	1799.0	1801.2	1803.4	1805.6
820	1807.8	1810.0	1812.2	1814.4	1816.6	1818.8	1821.0	1823.2	1825.4	1827.6
830	1829.8	1832.0	1834.2	1836.5	1838.7	1840.9	1843.1	1845.3	1847.5	1849.7
840	1851.9	1854.1	1856.3	1858.5	1860.7	1862.9	1865.1	1867.3	1869.5	1871.7
850	1873.9	1876.1	1878.3	1880.5	1882.7	1885.0	1887.2	1889.4	1891.6	1893.8
860	1896.0	1898.2	1900.4	1902.6	1904.8	1907.0	1909.2	1911.4	1913.6	1915.8
870	1918.0	1920.2	1922.4	1924.6	1926.8	1929.0	1931.2	1933.5	1935.7	1937.9
880	1940.1	1942.3	1944.5	1946.7	1948.9	1951.1	1953.3	1955.5	1957.7	1959.9
890	1962.1	1964.3	1966.5	1968.7	1970.9	1973.1	1975.3	1977.5	1979.8	1982.0
900	1984.2	1986.4	1988.6	1990.8	1993.0	1995.2	1997.4	1999.6	2001.8	2004.0
910	2006.2	2008.4	2010.6	2012.8	2015.0	2017.2	2019.4	2021.6	2023.8	2026.0
920	2028.3	2030.5	2032.7	2034.9	2037.1	2039.3	2041.5	2043.7	2045.9	2048.1
930	2050.3	2052.5	2054.7	2056.9	2059.1	2061.3	2063.5	2065.7	2067.9	2070.1
940	2072.3	2074.5	2076.8	2079.0	2081.2	2083.4	2085.6	2087.8	2090.0	2092.2
950	2094.4	2096.6	2098.8	2101.0	2103.2	2105.4	2107.6	2109.8	2112.0	2114.2
960	2116.4	2118.6	2120.8	2123.1	2125.3	2127.5	2129.7	2131.9	2134.1	2136.3
970	2138.5	2140.7	2142.9	2145.1	2147.3	2149.5	2151.7	2153.9	2156.1	2158.3
980	2160.5	2162.7	2164.9	2167.1	2169.3	2171.6	2173.8	2176.0	2178.2	2180.4
990	2182.6	2184.8	2187.0	2189.2	2191.4	2193.6	2195.8	2198.0	2200.2	2202.4

Examples: +23°F = -5.00°C; 99.4°F = 37.44°C; 117°F = 47.22°C; 1210°F = 654.4°C

Fahrenheit – Centigrade

- 59 to +79°F (1°F intervals)

	0	1	2	3	4	5	6	7	8	9
-50	-45.56	-46.11	-46.67	-47.22	-47.78	-48.33	-48.89	-49.44	-50.00	-50.56
-40	-40.00	-40.56	-41.11	-41.67	-42.22	-42.78	-43.33	-43.89	-44.44	-45.00
-30	-34.44	-35.00	-35.56	-36.11	-36.67	-37.22	-37.78	-38.33	-38.89	-39.44
-20	-28.89	-29.44	-30.00	-30.56	-31.11	-31.67	-32.22	-32.78	-33.33	-33.89
-10	-23.33	-23.89	-24.44	-25.00	-25.56	-26.11	-26.67	-27.22	-27.78	-28.33
-00	-17.78	-18.33	-18.89	-19.44	-20.00	-20.56	-21.11	-21.67	-22.22	-22.78
+00	-17.78	-17.22	-16.67	-16.11	-15.56	-15.00	-14.44	-13.89	-13.33	-12.78
10	-12.22	-11.67	-11.11	-10.56	-10.00	- 9.44	- 8.89	- 8.33	- 7.78	- 7.22
20	- 6.67	- 6.11	- 5.56	- 5.00	- 4.44	- 3.89	- 3.33	- 2.78	- 2.22	- 1.67
30	- 1.11	- 0.56	0.00	+ 0.56	+ 1.11	+ 1.67	+ 2.22	+ 2.78	+ 3.33	+ 3.89
40	+ 4.44	+ 5.00	+ 5.56	+ 6.11	+ 6.67	+ 7.22	+ 7.78	+ 8.33	+ 8.89	+ 9.44
50	+10.00	+10.56	+11.11	+11.67	+12.22	+12.78	+13.33	+13.89	+14.44	+15.00
60	+15.56	+16.11	+16.67	+17.22	+17.78	+18.33	+18.89	+19.44	+20.00	+20.56
70	+21.11	+21.67	+22.22	+22.78	+23.33	+23.89	+24.44	+25.00	+25.56	+26.11

80.0 to 109.9°F ($^1/_{10}$°F intervals)

	0	0.1	0.2	0.3	0.4	0.5	0.6	0.7	0.8	0.9
80.	26.67	26.72	26.78	26.83	26.89	26.94	27.00	27.06	27.11	27.17
81.	27.22	27.28	27.33	27.39	27.44	27.50	27.56	27.61	27.67	27.72
82.	27.78	27.83	27.89	27.94	28.00	28.06	28.11	28.17	28.22	28.28
83.	28.33	28.39	28.44	28.50	28.56	28.61	28.67	28.72	28.78	28.83
84.	28.89	28.94	29.00	29.06	29.11	29.17	29.22	29.28	29.33	29.39
85.	29.44	29.50	29.56	29.61	29.67	29.72	29.78	29.83	29.89	29.94
86.	30.00	30.06	30.11	30.17	30.22	30.28	30.33	30.39	30.44	30.50
87.	30.56	30.61	30.67	30.72	30.78	30.83	30.89	30.94	31.00	31.06
88.	31.11	31.17	31.22	31.28	31.33	31.39	31.44	31.50	31.56	31.61
89.	31.67	31.72	31.78	31.83	31.89	31.94	32.00	32.06	32.11	32.17
90.	32.22	32.28	32.33	32.39	32.44	32.50	32.56	32.61	32.67	32.72
91.	32.78	32.83	32.89	32.94	33.00	33.06	33.11	33.17	33.22	33.28
92.	33.33	33.39	33.44	33.50	33.56	33.61	33.67	33.72	33.78	33.83
93.	33.89	33.94	34.00	34.06	34.11	34.17	34.22	34.28	34.33	34.39
94.	34.44	34.50	34.56	34.61	34.67	34.72	34.78	34.83	34.89	34.94
95.	35.00	35.06	35.11	35.17	35.22	35.28	35.33	35.39	35.44	35.50
96.	35.56	35.61	35.67	35.72	35.78	35.83	35.89	35.94	36.00	36.06
97.	36.11	36.17	36.22	36.28	36.33	36.39	36.44	36.50	36.56	36.61
98.	36.67	36.72	36.78	36.83	36.89	36.94	37.00	37.06	37.11	37.17
99.	37.22	37.28	37.33	37.39	37.44	37.50	37.56	37.61	37.67	37.72
100.	37.78	37.83	37.89	37.94	38.00	38.06	38.11	38.17	38.22	38.28
101.	38.33	38.39	38.44	38.50	38.56	38.61	38.67	38.72	38.78	38.83
102.	38.89	38.94	39.00	39.06	39.11	39.17	39.22	39.28	39.33	39.39
103.	39.44	39.50	39.56	39.61	39.67	39.72	39.78	39.83	39.89	39.94
104.	40.00	40.06	40.11	40.17	40.22	40.28	40.33	40.39	40.44	40.50
105.	40.56	40.61	40.67	40.72	40.78	40.83	40.89	40.94	41.00	41.06
106.	41.11	41.17	41.22	41.28	41.33	41.39	41.44	41.50	41.56	41.61
107.	41.67	41.72	41.78	41.83	41.89	41.94	42.00	42.06	42.11	42.17
108.	42.22	42.28	42.33	42.39	42.44	42.50	42.56	42.61	42.67	42.72
109.	42.78	42.83	42.89	42.94	43.00	43.06	43.11	43.17	43.22	43.28

110 to 299°F (1°F intervals)

	0	1	2	3	4	5	6	7	8	9
110	43.33	43.89	44.44	45.00	45.56	46.11	46.67	47.22	47.78	48.33
120	48.89	49.44	50.00	50.56	51.11	51.67	52.22	52.78	53.33	53.89
130	54.44	55.00	55.56	56.11	56.67	57.22	57.78	58.33	58.89	59.44
140	60.00	60.56	61.11	61.67	62.22	62.78	63.33	63.89	64.44	65.00
150	65.56	66.11	66.67	67.22	67.78	68.33	68.89	69.44	70.00	70.56
160	71.11	71.67	72.22	72.78	73.33	73.89	74.44	75.00	75.56	76.11
170	76.67	77.22	77.78	78.33	78.89	79.44	80.00	80.56	81.11	81.67
180	82.22	82.78	83.33	83.89	84.44	85.00	85.56	86.11	86.67	87.22
190	87.78	88.33	88.89	89.44	90.00	90.56	91.11	91.67	92.22	92.78
200	93.33	93.89	94.44	95.00	95.56	96.11	96.67	97.22	97.78	98.33
210	98.89	99.44	100.0	100.6	101.1	101.7	102.2	102.8	103.3	103.9
220	104.4	105.0	105.6	106.1	106.7	107.2	107.8	108.3	108.9	109.4
230	110.0	110.6	111.1	111.7	112.2	112.8	113.3	113.9	114.4	115.0
240	115.6	116.1	116.7	117.2	117.8	118.3	118.9	119.4	120.0	120.6
250	121.1	121.7	122.2	122.8	123.3	123.9	124.4	125.0	125.6	126.1
260	126.7	127.2	127.8	128.3	128.9	129.4	130.0	130.6	131.1	131.7
270	132.2	132.8	133.3	133.9	134.4	135.0	135.6	136.1	136.7	137.2
280	137.8	138.3	138.9	139.4	140.0	140.6	141.1	141.7	142.2	142.8
290	143.3	143.9	144.4	145.0	145.6	146.1	146.7	147.2	147.8	148.3

300 to 1890°F (10°F intervals)

	0	10	20	30	40	50	60	70	80	90
300	148.9	154.4	160.0	165.6	171.1	176.7	182.2	187.8	193.3	198.9
400	204.4	210.0	215.6	221.1	226.7	232.2	237.8	243.3	248.9	254.4
500	260.0	265.6	271.1	276.7	282.2	287.8	293.3	298.9	304.4	310.0
600	315.6	321.1	326.7	332.2	337.8	343.3	348.9	354.4	360.0	365.6
700	371.1	376.7	382.2	387.8	393.3	398.9	404.4	410.0	415.6	421.1
800	426.7	432.2	437.8	443.3	448.9	454.4	460.0	465.6	471.1	476.7
900	482.2	487.8	493.3	498.9	504.4	510.0	515.6	521.1	526.7	532.2
1000	537.8	543.3	548.9	554.4	560.0	565.6	571.1	576.7	582.2	587.8
1100	593.3	598.9	604.4	610.0	615.6	621.1	626.7	632.2	637.8	643.3
1200	648.9	654.4	660.0	665.6	671.1	676.7	682.2	687.8	693.3	698.9
1300	704.4	710.0	715.6	721.1	726.7	732.2	737.8	743.3	748.9	754.4
1400	760.0	765.6	771.1	776.7	782.2	787.8	793.3	798.9	804.4	810.0
1500	815.6	821.1	826.7	832.2	837.8	843.3	848.9	854.4	860.0	865.6
1600	871.1	876.7	882.2	887.8	893.3	898.9	904.4	910.0	915.6	921.1
1700	926.7	932.2	937.8	943.3	948.9	954.4	960.0	965.6	971.1	976.7
1800	982.2	987.8	993.3	998.9	1004	1010	1016	1021	1027	1032

Examples: -14°C = +6.8°F; 38.3°C = 100.9°F; 89°C = 192.2°F; 550°C = 1022°F

Centigrade – Fahrenheit

- 59 to 0°C (1°C intervals)

	0	1	2	3	4	5	6	7	8	9
-50	-58.0	-59.8	-61.6	-63.4	-65.2	-67.0	-68.8	-70.6	-72.4	-74.2
-40	-40.0	-41.8	-43.6	-45.4	-47.2	-49.0	-50.8	-52.6	-54.4	-56.2
-30	-22.0	-23.8	-25.6	-27.4	-29.2	-31.0	-32.8	-34.6	-36.4	-38.2
-20	- 4.0	- 5.8	- 7.6	- 9.4	-11.2	-13.0	-14.8	-16.6	-18.4	-20.2
-10	+14.0	+12.2	+10.4	+ 8.6	+ 6.8	+ 5.0	+ 3.2	+ 1.4	- 0.4	- 2.2
-00	+32.0	+30.2	+28.4	+26.6	+24.8	+23.0	+21.2	+19.4	+17.6	+15.8

0 to 49.9°C ($^1/_{10}$°C intervals)

	0	0.1	0.2	0.3	0.4	0.5	0.6	0.7	0.8	0.9
+0.	32.00	32.18	32.36	32.54	32.72	32.90	33.08	33.26	33.44	33.62
1.	33.80	33.98	34.16	34.34	34.52	34.70	34.88	35.06	35.24	35.42
2.	35.60	35.78	35.96	36.14	36.32	36.50	36.68	36.86	37.04	37.22
3.	37.40	37.58	37.76	37.94	38.12	38.30	38.48	38.66	38.84	39.02
4.	39.20	39.38	39.56	39.74	39.92	40.10	40.28	40.46	40.64	40.82
5.	41.00	41.18	41.36	41.54	41.72	41.90	42.08	42.26	42.44	42.62
6.	42.80	42.98	43.16	43.34	43.52	43.70	43.88	44.06	44.24	44.42
7.	44.60	44.78	44.96	45.14	45.32	45.50	45.68	45.86	46.04	46.22
8.	46.40	46.58	46.76	46.94	47.12	47.30	47.48	47.66	47.84	48.02
9.	48.20	48.38	48.56	48.74	48.92	49.10	49.28	49.46	49.64	49.82
10.	50.00	50.18	50.36	50.54	50.72	50.90	51.08	51.26	51.44	51.62
11.	51.80	51.98	52.16	52.34	52.52	52.70	52.88	53.06	53.24	53.42
12.	53.60	53.78	53.96	54.14	54.32	54.50	54.68	54.86	55.04	55.22
13.	55.40	55.58	55.76	55.94	56.12	56.30	56.48	56.66	56.84	57.02
14.	57.20	57.38	57.56	57.74	57.92	58.10	58.28	58.46	58.64	58.82
15.	59.00	59.18	59.36	59.54	59.72	59.90	60.08	60.26	60.44	60.62
16.	60.80	60.98	61.16	61.34	61.52	61.70	61.88	62.06	62.24	62.42
17.	62.60	62.78	62.96	63.14	63.32	63.50	63.68	63.86	64.04	64.22
18.	64.40	64.58	64.76	64.94	65.12	65.30	65.48	65.66	65.84	66.02
19.	66.20	66.38	66.56	66.74	66.92	67.10	67.28	67.46	67.64	67.82
20.	68.00	68.18	68.36	68.54	68.72	68.90	69.08	69.26	69.44	69.62
21.	69.80	69.98	70.16	70.34	70.52	70.70	70.88	71.06	71.24	71.42
22.	71.60	71.78	71.96	72.14	72.32	72.50	72.68	72.86	73.04	73.22
23.	73.40	73.58	73.76	73.94	74.12	74.30	74.48	74.66	74.84	75.02
24.	75.20	75.38	75.56	75.74	75.92	76.10	76.28	76.46	76.64	76.82
25.	77.00	77.18	77.36	77.54	77.72	77.90	78.08	78.26	78.44	78.62
26.	78.80	78.98	79.16	79.34	79.52	79.70	79.88	80.06	80.24	80.42
27.	80.60	80.78	80.96	81.14	81.32	81.50	81.68	81.86	82.04	82.22
28.	82.40	82.58	82.76	82.94	83.12	83.30	83.48	83.66	83.84	84.02
29.	84.20	84.38	84.56	84.74	84.92	85.10	85.28	85.46	85.64	85.82
30.	86.00	86.18	86.36	86.54	86.72	86.90	87.08	87.26	87.44	87.62
31.	87.80	87.98	88.16	88.34	88.52	88.70	88.88	89.06	89.24	89.42
32.	89.60	89.78	89.96	90.14	90.32	90.50	90.68	90.86	91.04	91.22
33.	91.40	91.58	91.76	91.94	92.12	92.30	92.48	92.66	92.84	93.02
34.	93.20	93.38	93.56	93.74	93.92	94.10	94.28	94.46	94.64	94.82
35.	95.00	95.18	95.36	95.54	95.72	95.90	96.08	96.26	96.44	96.62
36.	96.80	96.98	97.16	97.34	97.52	97.70	97.88	98.06	98.24	98.42
37.	98.60	98.78	98.96	99.14	99.32	99.50	99.68	99.86	100.0	100.2
38.	100.4	100.6	100.8	100.9	101.1	101.3	101.5	101.7	101.8	102.0
39.	102.2	102.4	102.6	102.7	102.9	103.1	103.3	103.5	103.6	103.8
40.	104.0	104.2	104.4	104.5	104.7	104.9	105.1	105.3	105.4	105.6
41.	105.8	106.0	106.2	106.3	106.5	106.7	106.9	107.1	107.2	107.4
42.	107.6	107.8	108.0	108.1	108.3	108.5	108.7	108.9	109.0	109.2
43.	109.4	109.6	109.8	109.9	110.1	110.3	110.5	110.7	110.8	111.0
44.	111.2	111.4	111.6	111.7	111.9	112.1	112.3	112.5	112.6	112.8
45.	113.0	113.2	113.4	113.5	113.7	113.9	114.1	114.3	114.4	114.6
46.	114.8	115.0	115.2	115.3	115.5	115.7	115.9	116.1	116.2	116.4
47.	116.6	116.8	117.0	117.1	117.3	117.5	117.7	117.9	118.0	118.2
48.	118.4	118.6	118.8	118.9	119.1	119.3	119.5	119.7	119.8	120.0
49.	120.2	120.4	120.6	120.7	120.9	121.1	121.3	121.5	121.6	121.8

50 to 199°C (1°C intervals)

	0	1	2	3	4	5	6	7	8	9
50	122.0	123.8	125.6	127.4	129.2	131.0	132.8	134.6	136.4	138.2
60	140.0	141.8	143.6	145.4	147.2	149.0	150.8	152.6	154.4	156.2
70	158.0	159.8	161.6	163.4	165.2	167.0	168.8	170.6	172.4	174.2
80	176.0	177.8	179.6	181.4	183.2	185.0	186.8	188.6	190.4	192.2
90	194.0	195.8	197.6	199.4	201.2	203.0	204.8	206.6	208.4	210.2
100	212.0	213.8	215.6	217.4	219.2	221.0	222.8	224.6	226.4	228.2
110	230.0	231.8	233.6	235.4	237.2	239.0	240.8	242.6	244.4	246.2
120	248.0	249.8	251.6	253.4	255.2	257.0	258.8	260.6	262.4	264.2
130	266.0	267.8	269.6	271.4	273.2	275.0	276.8	278.6	280.4	282.2
140	284.0	285.8	287.6	289.4	291.2	293.0	294.8	296.6	298.4	300.2
150	302.0	303.8	305.6	307.4	309.2	311.0	312.8	314.6	316.4	318.2
160	320.0	321.8	323.6	325.4	327.2	329.0	330.8	332.6	334.4	336.2
170	338.0	339.8	341.6	343.4	345.2	347.0	348.8	350.6	352.4	354.2
180	356.0	357.8	359.6	361.4	363.2	365.0	366.8	368.6	370.4	372.2
190	374.0	375.8	377.6	379.4	381.2	383.0	384.8	386.6	388.4	390.2

100 to 990°C (10°C intervals)

	0	10	20	30	40	50	60	70	80	90
100	212	230	248	266	284	302	320	338	356	374
200	392	410	428	446	464	482	500	518	536	554
300	572	590	608	626	644	662	680	698	716	734
400	752	770	788	806	824	842	860	878	896	914
500	932	950	968	986	1004	1022	1040	1058	1076	1094
600	1112	1130	1148	1166	1184	1202	1220	1238	1256	1274
700	1292	1310	1328	1346	1364	1382	1400	1418	1436	1454
800	1472	1490	1508	1526	1544	1562	1580	1598	1616	1634
900	1652	1670	1688	1706	1724	1742	1760	1778	1796	1814

Conversion of Time and Angle Units*

Example: 1.2367 h = how many hours, minutes, seconds?

0.236 h = 14.16 min
0.0007 h = 0.042 min

i.e. 1.2367 h = 1 h 14.202 min

0.202 min = 12.12 s

i.e. 1.2367 h = 1 h 14 min 12.12 s

Example: 68 min 26.3 s = how many hours?

26.3 s = 0.438 33... min
68 min 26.3 s = 68.438 33... min

68.4 min = 1.140 000 00 h
0.0383 min = 0.000 638 33... h
0.00003... min = 0.000 000 55... h

68.43833... min = 1.140 638 88... h

Note that the figures given in the table below *have not been rounded off*. In each case the last decimal is *recurring*.

Hours or Degrees – Minutes (or Minutes – Seconds)

h, ° / min	0	0.001	0.002	0.003	0.004	0.005	0.006	0.007	0.008	0.009
0.10	6.00	6.06	6.12	6.18	6.24	6.30	6.36	6.42	6.48	6.54
0.11	6.60	6.66	6.72	6.78	6.84	6.90	6.96	7.02	7.08	7.14
0.12	7.20	7.26	7.32	7.38	7.44	7.50	7.56	7.62	7.68	7.74
0.13	7.80	7.86	7.92	7.98	8.04	8.10	8.16	8.22	8.28	8.34
0.14	8.40	8.46	8.52	8.58	8.64	8.70	8.76	8.82	8.88	8.94
0.15	9.00	9.06	9.12	9.18	9.24	9.30	9.36	9.42	9.48	9.54
0.16	9.60	9.66	9.72	9.78	9.84	9.90	9.96	10.02	10.08	10.14
0.17	10.20	10.26	10.32	10.38	10.44	10.50	10.56	10.62	10.68	10.74
0.18	10.80	10.86	10.92	10.98	11.04	11.10	11.16	11.22	11.28	11.34
0.19	11.40	11.46	11.52	11.58	11.64	11.70	11.76	11.82	11.88	11.94
0.20	12.00	12.06	12.12	12.18	12.24	12.30	12.36	12.42	12.48	12.54
0.21	12.60	12.66	12.72	12.78	12.84	12.90	12.96	13.02	13.08	13.14
0.22	13.20	13.26	13.32	13.38	13.44	13.50	13.56	13.62	13.68	13.74
0.23	13.80	13.86	13.92	13.98	14.04	14.10	14.16	14.22	14.28	14.34
0.24	14.40	14.46	14.52	14.58	14.64	14.70	14.76	14.82	14.88	14.94
0.25	15.00	15.06	15.12	15.18	15.24	15.30	15.36	15.42	15.48	15.54
0.26	15.60	15.66	15.72	15.78	15.84	15.90	15.96	16.02	16.08	16.14
0.27	16.20	16.26	16.32	16.38	16.44	16.50	16.56	16.62	16.68	16.74
0.28	16.80	16.86	16.92	16.98	17.04	17.10	17.16	17.22	17.28	17.34
0.29	17.40	17.46	17.52	17.58	17.64	17.70	17.76	17.82	17.88	17.94
0.30	18.00	18.06	18.12	18.18	18.24	18.30	18.36	18.42	18.48	18.54
0.31	18.60	18.66	18.72	18.78	18.84	18.90	18.96	19.02	19.08	19.14
0.32	19.20	19.26	19.32	19.38	19.44	19.50	19.56	19.62	19.68	19.74
0.33	19.80	19.86	19.92	19.98	20.04	20.10	20.16	20.22	20.28	20.34
0.34	20.40	20.46	20.52	20.58	20.64	20.70	20.76	20.82	20.88	20.94
0.35	21.00	21.06	21.12	21.18	21.24	21.30	21.36	21.42	21.48	21.54
0.36	21.60	21.66	21.72	21.78	21.84	21.90	21.96	22.02	22.08	22.14
0.37	22.20	22.26	22.32	22.38	22.44	22.50	22.56	22.62	22.68	22.74
0.38	22.80	22.86	22.92	22.98	23.04	23.10	23.16	23.22	23.28	23.34
0.39	23.40	23.46	23.52	23.58	23.64	23.70	23.76	23.82	23.88	23.94
0.40	24.00	24.06	24.12	24.18	24.24	24.30	24.36	24.42	24.48	24.54
0.41	24.60	24.66	24.72	24.78	24.84	24.90	24.96	25.02	25.08	25.14
0.42	25.20	25.26	25.32	25.38	25.44	25.50	25.56	25.62	25.68	25.74
0.43	25.80	25.86	25.92	25.98	26.04	26.10	26.16	26.22	26.28	26.34
0.44	26.40	26.46	26.52	26.58	26.64	26.70	26.76	26.82	26.88	26.94
0.45	27.00	27.06	27.12	27.18	27.24	27.30	27.36	27.42	27.48	27.54
0.46	27.60	27.66	27.72	27.78	27.84	27.90	27.96	28.02	28.08	28.14
0.47	28.20	28.26	28.32	28.38	28.44	28.50	28.56	28.62	28.68	28.74
0.48	28.80	28.86	28.92	28.98	29.04	29.10	29.16	29.22	29.28	29.34
0.49	29.40	29.46	29.52	29.58	29.64	29.70	29.76	29.82	29.88	29.94
0.50	30.00	30.06	30.12	30.18	30.24	30.30	30.36	30.42	30.48	30.54
0.51	30.60	30.66	30.72	30.78	30.84	30.90	30.96	31.02	31.08	31.14
0.52	31.20	31.26	31.32	31.38	31.44	31.50	31.56	31.62	31.68	31.74
0.53	31.80	31.86	31.92	31.98	32.04	32.10	32.16	32.22	32.28	32.34
0.54	32.40	32.46	32.52	32.58	32.64	32.70	32.76	32.82	32.88	32.94
0.55	33.00	33.06	33.12	33.18	33.24	33.30	33.36	33.42	33.48	33.54
0.56	33.60	33.66	33.72	33.78	33.84	33.90	33.96	34.02	34.08	34.14
0.57	34.20	34.26	34.32	34.38	34.44	34.50	34.56	34.62	34.68	34.74
0.58	34.80	34.86	34.92	34.98	35.04	35.10	35.16	35.22	35.28	35.34
0.59	35.40	35.46	35.52	35.58	35.64	35.70	35.76	35.82	35.88	35.94
0.60	36.00	36.06	36.12	36.18	36.24	36.30	36.36	36.42	36.48	36.54
0.61	36.60	36.66	36.72	36.78	36.84	36.90	36.96	37.02	37.08	37.14
0.62	37.20	37.26	37.32	37.38	37.44	37.50	37.56	37.62	37.68	37.74
0.63	37.80	37.86	37.92	37.98	38.04	38.10	38.16	38.22	38.28	38.34
0.64	38.40	38.46	38.52	38.58	38.64	38.70	38.76	38.82	38.88	38.94
0.65	39.00	39.06	39.12	39.18	39.24	39.30	39.36	39.42	39.48	39.54
0.66	39.60	39.66	39.72	39.78	39.84	39.90	39.96	40.02	40.08	40.14
0.67	40.20	40.26	40.32	40.38	40.44	40.50	40.56	40.62	40.68	40.74
0.68	40.80	40.86	40.92	40.98	41.04	41.10	41.16	41.22	41.28	41.34
0.69	41.40	41.46	41.52	41.58	41.64	41.70	41.76	41.82	41.88	41.94
0.70	42.00	42.06	42.12	42.18	42.24	42.30	42.36	42.42	42.48	42.54
0.71	42.60	42.66	42.72	42.78	42.84	42.90	42.96	43.02	43.08	43.14
0.72	43.20	43.26	43.32	43.38	43.44	43.50	43.56	43.62	43.68	43.74
0.73	43.80	43.86	43.92	43.98	44.04	44.10	44.16	44.22	44.28	44.34
0.74	44.40	44.46	44.52	44.58	44.64	44.70	44.76	44.82	44.88	44.94
0.75	45.00	45.06	45.12	45.18	45.24	45.30	45.36	45.42	45.48	45.54
0.76	45.60	45.66	45.72	45.78	45.84	45.90	45.96	46.02	46.08	46.14
0.77	46.20	46.26	46.32	46.38	46.44	46.50	46.56	46.62	46.68	46.74
0.78	46.80	46.86	46.92	46.98	47.04	47.10	47.16	47.22	47.28	47.34
0.79	47.40	47.46	47.52	47.58	47.64	47.70	47.76	47.82	47.88	47.94
0.80	48.00	48.06	48.12	48.18	48.24	48.30	48.36	48.42	48.48	48.54
0.81	48.60	48.66	48.72	48.78	48.84	48.90	48.96	49.02	49.08	49.14
0.82	49.20	49.26	49.32	49.38	49.44	49.50	49.56	49.62	49.68	49.74
0.83	49.80	49.86	49.92	49.98	50.04	50.10	50.16	50.22	50.28	50.34
0.84	50.40	50.46	50.52	50.58	50.64	50.70	50.76	50.82	50.88	50.94
0.85	51.00	51.06	51.12	51.18	51.24	51.30	51.36	51.42	51.48	51.54
0.86	51.60	51.66	51.72	51.78	51.84	51.90	51.96	52.02	52.08	52.14
0.87	52.20	52.26	52.32	52.38	52.44	52.50	52.56	52.62	52.68	52.74
0.88	52.80	52.86	52.92	52.98	53.04	53.10	53.16	53.22	53.28	53.34
0.89	53.40	53.46	53.52	53.58	53.64	53.70	53.76	53.82	53.88	53.94
0.90	54.00	54.06	54.12	54.18	54.24	54.30	54.36	54.42	54.48	54.54
0.91	54.60	54.66	54.72	54.78	54.84	54.90	54.96	55.02	55.08	55.14
0.92	55.20	55.26	55.32	55.38	55.44	55.50	55.56	55.62	55.68	55.74
0.93	55.80	55.86	55.92	55.98	56.04	56.10	56.16	56.22	56.28	56.34
0.94	56.40	56.46	56.52	56.58	56.64	56.70	56.76	56.82	56.88	56.94
0.95	57.00	57.06	57.12	57.18	57.24	57.30	57.36	57.42	57.48	57.54
0.96	57.60	57.66	57.72	57.78	57.84	57.90	57.96	58.02	58.08	58.14
0.97	58.20	58.26	58.32	58.38	58.44	58.50	58.56	58.62	58.68	58.74
0.98	58.80	58.86	58.92	58.98	59.04	59.10	59.16	59.22	59.28	59.34
0.99	59.40	59.46	59.52	59.58	59.64	59.70	59.76	59.82	59.88	59.94

Minutes – Hours or Degrees (or Seconds – Minutes)

min / s	0	1	2	3	4	5	6	7	8	9
100	1.6666	1.6833	1.7000	1.7166	1.7333	1.7500	1.7666	1.7833	1.8000	1.8166
110	1.8333	1.8500	1.8666	1.8833	1.9000	1.9166	1.9333	1.9500	1.9666	1.9833
120	2.0000	2.0166	2.0333	2.0500	2.0666	2.0833	2.1000	2.1166	2.1333	2.1500
130	2.1666	2.1833	2.2000	2.2166	2.2333	2.2500	2.2666	2.2833	2.3000	2.3166
140	2.3333	2.3500	2.3666	2.3833	2.4000	2.4166	2.4333	2.4500	2.4666	2.4833
150	2.5000	2.5166	2.5333	2.5500	2.5666	2.5833	2.6000	2.6166	2.6333	2.6500
160	2.6666	2.6833	2.7000	2.7166	2.7333	2.7500	2.7666	2.7833	2.8000	2.8166
170	2.8333	2.8500	2.8666	2.8833	2.9000	2.9166	2.9333	2.9500	2.9666	2.9833
180	3.0000	3.0166	3.0333	3.0500	3.0666	3.0833	3.1000	3.1166	3.1333	3.1500
190	3.1666	3.1833	3.2000	3.2166	3.2333	3.2500	3.2666	3.2833	3.3000	3.3166
200	3.3333	3.3500	3.3666	3.3833	3.4000	3.4166	3.4333	3.4500	3.4666	3.4833
210	3.5000	3.5166	3.5333	3.5500	3.5666	3.5833	3.6000	3.6166	3.6333	3.6500
220	3.6666	3.6833	3.7000	3.7166	3.7333	3.7500	3.7666	3.7833	3.8000	3.8166
230	3.8333	3.8500	3.8666	3.8833	3.9000	3.9166	3.9333	3.9500	3.9666	3.9833
240	4.0000	4.0166	4.0333	4.0500	4.0666	4.0833	4.1000	4.1166	4.1333	4.1500
250	4.1666	4.1833	4.2000	4.2166	4.2333	4.2500	4.2666	4.2833	4.3000	4.3166
260	4.3333	4.3500	4.3666	4.3833	4.4000	4.4166	4.4333	4.4500	4.4666	4.4833
270	4.5000	4.5166	4.5333	4.5500	4.5666	4.5833	4.6000	4.6166	4.6333	4.6500
280	4.6666	4.6833	4.7000	4.7166	4.7333	4.7500	4.7666	4.7833	4.8000	4.8166
290	4.8333	4.8500	4.8666	4.8833	4.9000	4.9166	4.9333	4.9500	4.9666	4.9833
300	5.0000	5.0166	5.0333	5.0500	5.0666	5.0833	5.1000	5.1166	5.1333	5.1500
310	5.1666	5.1833	5.2000	5.2166	5.2333	5.2500	5.2666	5.2833	5.3000	5.3166
320	5.3333	5.3500	5.3666	5.3833	5.4000	5.4166	5.4333	5.4500	5.4666	5.4833
330	5.5000	5.5166	5.5333	5.5500	5.5666	5.5833	5.6000	5.6166	5.6333	5.6500
340	5.6666	5.6833	5.7000	5.7166	5.7333	5.7500	5.7666	5.7833	5.8000	5.8166
350	5.8333	5.8500	5.8666	5.8833	5.9000	5.9166	5.9333	5.9500	5.9666	5.9833
360	6.0000	6.0166	6.0333	6.0500	6.0666	6 0833	6.1000	6.1166	6.1333	6.1500
370	6.1666	6.1833	6.2000	6.2166	6.2333	6.2500	6.2666	6.2833	6.3000	6.3166
380	6.3333	6.3500	6.3666	6.3833	6.4000	6.4166	6.4333	6.4500	6.4666	6.4833
390	6.5000	6.5166	6.5333	6.5500	6.5666	6.5833	6.6000	6.6166	6.6333	6.6500
400	6.6666	6.6833	6.7000	6.7166	6.7333	6.7500	6.7666	6.7833	6.8000	6.8166
410	6.8333	6.8500	6.8666	6.8833	6.9000	6.9166	6.9333	6.9500	6.9666	6.9833
420	7.0000	7.0166	7.0333	7.0500	7.0666	7.0833	7.1000	7.1166	7.1333	7.1500
430	7.1666	7.1833	7.2000	7.2166	7.2333	7.2500	7.2666	7.2833	7.3000	7.3166
440	7.3333	7.3500	7.3666	7.3833	7.4000	7.4166	7.4333	7.4500	7.4666	7.4833
450	7.5000	7.5166	7.5333	7.5500	7.5666	7.5833	7.6000	7.6166	7.6333	7.6500
460	7.6666	7.6833	7.7000	7.7166	7.7333	7.7500	7.7666	7.7833	7.8000	7.8166
470	7.8333	7.8500	7.8666	7.8833	7.9000	7.9166	7.9333	7.9500	7.9666	7.9833
480	8.0000	8.0166	8.0333	8.0500	8.0666	8.0833	8.1000	8.1166	8.1333	8.1500
490	8.1666	8.1833	8.2000	8.2166	8.2333	8.2500	8.2666	8.2833	8.3000	8.3166
500	8.3333	8.3500	8.3666	8.3833	8.4000	8.4166	8.4333	8.4500	8.4666	8.4833
510	8.5000	8.5166	8.5333	8.5500	8.5666	8.5833	8.6000	8.6166	8.6333	8.6500
520	8.6666	8.6833	8.7000	8.7166	8.7333	8.7500	8.7666	8.7833	8.8000	8.8166
530	8.8333	8.8500	8.8666	8.8833	8.9000	8.9166	8.9333	8.9500	8.9666	8.9833
540	9.0000	9.0166	9.0333	9.0500	9.0666	9.0833	9.1000	9.1166	9.1333	9.1500
550	9.1666	9.1833	9.2000	9.2166	9.2333	9.2500	9.2666	9.2833	9.3000	9.3166
560	9.3333	9.3500	9.3666	9.3833	9.4000	9.4166	9.4333	9.4500	9.4666	9.4833
570	9.5000	9.5166	9.5333	9.5500	9.5666	9.5833	9.6000	9.6166	9.6333	9.6500
580	9.6666	9.6833	9.7000	9.7166	9.7333	9.7500	9.7666	9.7833	9.8000	9.8166
590	9.8333	9.8500	9.8666	9.8833	9.9000	9.9166	9.9333	9.9500	9.9666	9.9833
600	10.000	10.016	10.033	10.050	10.066	10.083	10.100	10.116	10.133	10.150
610	10.166	10.183	10.200	10.216	10.233	10.250	10.266	10.283	10.300	10.316
620	10.333	10.350	10.366	10.383	10.400	10.416	10.433	10.450	10.466	10.483
630	10.500	10.516	10.533	10.550	10.566	10.583	10.600	10.616	10.633	10.650
640	10.666	10.683	10.700	10.716	10.733	10.750	10.766	10.783	10.800	10.816
650	10.833	10.850	10.866	10.883	10.900	10.916	10.933	10.950	10.966	10.983
660	11.000	11.016	11.033	11.050	11.066	11.083	11.100	11.116	11.133	11.150
670	11.166	11.183	11.200	11.216	11.233	11.250	11.266	11.283	11.300	11.316
680	11.333	11.350	11.366	11.383	11.400	11.416	11.433	11.450	11.466	11.483
690	11.500	11.516	11.533	11.550	11.566	11.583	11.600	11.616	11.633	11.650
700	11.666	11.683	11.700	11.716	11.733	11.750	11.766	11.783	11.800	11.816
710	11.833	11.850	11.866	11.883	11.900	11.916	11.933	11.950	11.966	11.983
720	12.000	12.016	12.033	12.050	12.066	12.083	12.100	12.116	12.133	12.150
730	12.166	12.183	12.200	12.216	12.233	12.250	12.266	12.283	12.300	12.316
740	12.333	12.350	12.366	12.383	12.400	12.416	12.433	12.450	12.466	12.483
750	12.500	12.516	12.533	12.550	12.566	12.583	12.600	12.616	12.633	12.650
760	12.666	12.683	12.700	12.716	12.733	12.750	12.766	12.783	12.800	12.816
770	12.833	12.850	12.866	12.883	12.900	12.916	12.933	12.950	12.966	12.983
780	13.000	13.016	13.033	13.050	13.066	13.083	13.100	13.116	13.133	13.150
790	13.166	13.183	13.200	13.216	13.233	13.250	13.266	13.283	13.300	13.316
800	13.333	13.350	13.366	13.383	13.400	13.416	13.433	13.450	13.466	13.483
810	13.500	13.516	13.533	13.550	13.566	13.583	13.600	13.616	13.633	13.650
820	13.666	13.683	13.700	13.716	13.733	13.750	13.766	13.783	13.800	13.816
830	13.833	13.850	13.866	13.883	13.900	13.916	13.933	13.950	13.966	13.983
840	14.000	14.016	14.033	14.050	14.066	14.083	14.100	14.116	14.133	14.150
850	14.166	14.183	14.200	14.216	14.233	14.250	14.266	14.283	14.300	14.316
860	14.333	14.350	14.366	14.383	14.400	14.416	14.433	14.450	14.466	14.483
870	14.500	14.516	14.533	14.550	14.566	14.583	14.600	14.616	14.633	14.650
880	14.666	14.683	14.700	14.716	14.733	14.750	14.766	14.783	14.800	14.816
890	14.833	14.850	14.866	14.883	14.900	14.916	14.933	14.950	14.966	14.983
900	15.000	15.016	15.033	15.050	15.066	15.083	15.100	15.116	15.133	15.150
910	15.166	15.183	15.200	15.216	15.233	15.250	15.266	15.283	15.300	15.316
920	15.333	15.350	15.366	15.383	15.400	15.416	15.433	15.450	15.466	15.483
930	15.500	15.516	15.533	15.550	15.566	15.583	15.600	15.616	15.633	15.650
940	15.666	15.683	15.700	15.716	15.733	15.750	15.766	15.783	15.800	15.816
950	15.833	15.850	15.866	15.883	15.900	15.916	15.933	15.950	15.966	15.983
960	16.000	16.016	16.033	16.050	16.066	16.083	16.100	16.116	16.133	16.150
970	16.166	16.183	16.200	16.216	16.233	16.250	16.266	16.283	16.300	16.316
980	16.333	16.350	16.366	16.383	16.400	16.416	16.433	16.450	16.466	16.483
990	16.500	16.516	16.533	16.550	16.566	16.583	16.600	16.616	16.633	16.650

Examples: 512 mm Hg = 682.61 mb
51.2 mm Hg = 68.261 mb

Conversion of millibars into MKS pressure units, newtons per square meter :
1 mb = 100 N/m² (i.e. multiply the millibar value by 100 to obtain the value in N/m²)

Millimeters of mercury (mm Hg) – Millibars (mb)

mm Hg	0	1	2	3	4	5	6	7	8	9
100	133.32	134.66	135.99	137.32	138.66	139.99	141.32	142.65	143.99	145.32
110	146.65	147.99	149.32	150.65	151.99	153.32	154.65	155.99	157.32	158.65
120	159.99	161.32	162.65	163.99	165.32	166.65	167.99	169.32	170.65	171.99
130	173.32	174.65	175.99	177.32	178.65	179.99	181.32	182.65	183.98	185.32
140	186.65	187.98	189.32	190.65	191.98	193.32	194.65	195.98	197.32	198.65
150	199.98	201.32	202.65	203.98	205.32	206.65	207.98	209.32	210.65	211.98
160	213.32	214.65	215.98	217.32	218.65	219.98	221.32	222.65	223.98	225.31
170	226.65	227.98	229.31	230.65	231.98	233.31	234.65	235.98	237.31	238.65
180	239.98	241.31	242.65	243.98	245.31	246.65	247.98	249.31	250.65	251.98
190	253.31	254.65	255.98	257.31	258.65	259.98	261.31	262.65	263.98	265.31
200	266.64	267.98	269.31	270.64	271.98	273.31	274.64	275.98	277.31	278.64
210	279.98	281.31	282.64	283.98	285.31	286.64	287.98	289.31	290.64	291.98
220	293.31	294.64	295.98	297.31	298.64	299.98	301.31	302.64	303.97	305.31
230	306.64	307.97	309.31	310.64	311.97	313.31	314.64	315.97	317.31	318.64
240	319.97	321.31	322.64	323.97	325.31	326.64	327.97	329.31	330.64	331.97
250	333.31	334.64	335.97	337.31	338.64	339.97	341.31	342.64	343.97	345.30
260	346.64	347.97	349.30	350.64	351.97	353.30	354.64	355.97	357.30	358.64
270	359.97	361.30	362.64	363.97	365.30	366.64	367.97	369.30	370.64	371.97
280	373.30	374.64	375.97	377.30	378.64	379.97	381.30	382.64	383.97	385.30
290	386.63	387.97	389.30	390.63	391.97	393.30	394.63	395.97	397.30	398.63
300	399.97	401.30	402.63	403.97	405.30	406.63	407.97	409.30	410.63	411.97
310	413.30	414.63	415.97	417.30	418.63	419.97	421.30	422.63	423.97	425.30
320	426.63	427.96	429.30	430.63	431.96	433.30	434.63	435.96	437.30	438.63
330	439.96	441.30	442.63	443.96	445.30	446.63	447.96	449.30	450.63	451.96
340	453.30	454.63	455.96	457.30	458.63	459.96	461.30	462.63	463.96	465.30
350	466.63	467.96	469.29	470.63	471.96	473.29	474.63	475.96	477.29	478.63
360	479.96	481.29	482.63	483.96	485.29	486.63	487.96	489.29	490.63	491.96
370	493.29	494.63	495.96	497.29	498.63	499.96	501.29	502.63	503.96	505.29
380	506.62	507.96	509.29	510.62	511.96	513.29	514.62	515.96	517.29	518.62
390	519.96	521.29	522.62	523.96	525.29	526.62	527.96	529.29	530.62	531.96
400	533.29	534.62	535.96	537.29	538.62	539.96	541.29	542.62	543.96	545.29
410	546.62	547.95	549.29	550.62	551.95	553.29	554.62	555.95	557.29	558.62
420	559.95	561.29	562.62	563.95	565.29	566.62	567.95	569.29	570.62	571.95
430	573.29	574.62	575.95	577.29	578.62	579.95	581.29	582.62	583.95	585.29
440	586.62	587.95	589.28	590.62	591.95	593.28	594.62	595.95	597.28	598.62
450	599.95	601.28	602.62	603.95	605.28	606.62	607.95	609.28	610.62	611.95
460	613.28	614.62	615.95	617.28	618.62	619.95	621.28	622.62	623.95	625.28
470	626.62	627.95	629.28	630.61	631.95	633.28	634.61	635.95	637.28	638.61
480	639.95	641.28	642.61	643.95	645.28	646.61	647.95	649.28	650.61	651.95
490	653.28	654.61	655.95	657.28	658.61	659.95	661.28	662.61	663.95	665.28
500	666.61	667.95	669.28	670.61	671.94	673.28	674.61	675.94	677.28	678.61
510	679.94	681.28	682.61	683.94	685.28	686.61	687.94	689.28	690.61	691.94
520	693.28	694.61	695.94	697.28	698.61	699.94	701.28	702.61	703.94	705.28
530	706.61	707.94	709.27	710.61	711.94	713.27	714.61	715.94	717.27	718.61
540	719.94	721.27	722.61	723.94	725.27	726.61	727.94	729.27	730.61	731.94
550	733.27	734.61	735.94	737.27	738.61	739.94	741.27	742.61	743.94	745.27
560	746.61	747.94	749.27	750.60	751.94	753.27	754.60	755.94	757.27	758.60
570	759.94	761.27	762.60	763.94	765.27	766.60	767.94	769.27	770.60	771.94
580	773.27	774.60	775.94	777.27	778.60	779.94	781.27	782.60	783.94	785.27
590	786.60	787.94	789.27	790.60	791.93	793.27	794.60	795.93	797.27	798.60
600	799.93	801.27	802.60	803.93	805.27	806.60	807.93	809.27	810.60	811.93
610	813.27	814.60	815.93	817.27	818.60	819.93	821.27	822.60	823.93	825.27
620	826.60	827.93	829.27	830.60	831.93	833.26	834.60	835.93	837.26	838.60
630	839.93	841.26	842.60	843.93	845.26	846.60	847.93	849.26	850.60	851.93
640	853.26	854.60	855.93	857.26	858.60	859.93	861.26	862.60	863.93	865.26
650	866.60	867.93	869.26	870.60	871.93	873.26	874.59	875.93	877.26	878.59
660	879.93	881.26	882.59	883.93	885.26	886.59	887.93	889.26	890.59	891.93
670	893.26	894.59	895.93	897.26	898.59	899.93	901.26	902.59	903.93	905.26
680	906.59	907.93	909.26	910.59	911.92	913.26	914.59	915.92	917.26	918.59
690	919.92	921.26	922.59	923.92	925.26	926.59	927.92	929.26	930.59	931.92
700	933.26	934.59	935.92	937.26	938.59	939.92	941.26	942.59	943.92	945.26
710	946.59	947.92	949.26	950.59	951.92	953.25	954.59	955.92	957.25	958.59
720	959.92	961.25	962.59	963.92	965.25	966.59	967.92	969.25	970.59	971.92
730	973.25	974.59	975.92	977.25	978.59	979.92	981.25	982.59	983.92	985.25
740	986.59	987.92	989.25	990.59	991.92	993.25	994.58	995.92	997.25	998.58
750	999.92	1001.3	1002.6	1003.9	1005.3	1006.6	1007.9	1009.3	1010.6	1011.9
760	1013.2	1014.6	1015.9	1017.2	1018.6	1019.9	1021.2	1022.6	1023.9	1025.2
770	1026.6	1027.9	1029.2	1030.6	1031.9	1033.2	1034.6	1035.9	1037.2	1038.6
780	1039.9	1041.2	1042.6	1043.9	1045.2	1046.6	1047.9	1049.2	1050.6	1051.9
790	1053.2	1054.6	1055.9	1057.2	1058.6	1059.9	1061.2	1062.6	1063.9	1065.2
800	1066.6	1067.9	1069.2	1070.6	1071.9	1073.2	1074.6	1075.9	1077.2	1078.6
810	1079.9	1081.2	1082.6	1083.9	1085.2	1086.6	1087.9	1089.2	1090.6	1091.9
820	1093.2	1094.6	1095.9	1097.2	1098.6	1099.9	1101.2	1102.6	1103.9	1105.2
830	1106.6	1107.9	1109.2	1110.6	1111.9	1113.2	1114.6	1115.9	1117.2	1118.6
840	1119.9	1121.2	1122.6	1123.9	1125.2	1126.6	1127.9	1129.2	1130.6	1131.9
850	1133.2	1134.6	1135.9	1137.2	1138.6	1139.9	1141.2	1142.6	1143.9	1145.2
860	1146.6	1147.9	1149.2	1150.6	1151.9	1153.2	1154.6	1155.9	1157.2	1158.6
870	1159.9	1161.2	1162.6	1163.9	1165.2	1166.6	1167.9	1169.2	1170.6	1171.9
880	1173.2	1174.6	1175.9	1177.2	1178.6	1179.9	1181.2	1182.6	1183.9	1185.2
890	1186.6	1187.9	1189.2	1190.6	1191.9	1193.2	1194.6	1195.9	1197.2	1198.6
900	1199.9	1201.2	1202.6	1203.9	1205.2	1206.6	1207.9	1209.2	1210.6	1211.9
910	1213.2	1214.6	1215.9	1217.2	1218.6	1219.9	1221.2	1222.6	1223.9	1225.2
920	1226.6	1227.9	1229.2	1230.6	1231.9	1233.2	1234.6	1235.9	1237.2	1238.6
930	1239.9	1241.2	1242.6	1243.9	1245.2	1246.6	1247.9	1249.2	1250.6	1251.9
940	1253.2	1254.6	1255.9	1257.2	1258.6	1259.9	1261.2	1262.6	1263.9	1265.2
950	1266.6	1267.9	1269.2	1270.6	1271.9	1273.2	1274.6	1275.9	1277.2	1278.6
960	1279.9	1281.2	1282.6	1283.9	1285.2	1286.6	1287.9	1289.2	1290.6	1291.9
970	1293.2	1294.6	1295.9	1297.2	1298.6	1299.9	1301.2	1302.6	1303.9	1305.2
980	1306.6	1307.9	1309.2	1310.6	1311.9	1313.2	1314.6	1315.9	1317.2	1318.6
990	1319.9	1321.2	1322.6	1323.9	1325.2	1326.6	1327.9	1329.2	1330.6	1331.9
1000	1333.2	1334.6	1335.9	1337.2	1338.6	1339.9	1341.2	1342.6	1343.9	1345.2
1010	1346.6	1347.9	1349.2	1350.6	1351.9	1353.2	1354.6	1355.9	1357.2	1358.6
1020	1359.9	1361.2	1362.6	1363.9	1365.2	1366.6	1367.9	1369.2	1370.6	1371.9
1030	1373.2	1374.6	1375.9	1377.2	1378.6	1379.9	1381.2	1382.6	1383.9	1385.2
1040	1386.6	1387.9	1389.2	1390.6	1391.9	1393.2	1394.6	1395.9	1397.2	1398.6

Millibars (mb) – Millimeters of mercury (mm Hg)

mb	0	1	2	3	4	5	6	7	8	9
100	75.006	75.756	76.506	77.256	78.006	78.756	79.507	80.257	81.007	81.757
110	82.507	83.257	84.007	84.757	85.507	86.257	87.007	87.757	88.507	89.257
120	90.007	90.757	91.508	92.258	93.008	93.758	94.508	95.258	96.008	96.758
130	97.508	98.258	99.008	99.758	100.51	101.26	102.01	102.76	103.51	104.26
140	105.01	105.76	106.51	107.26	108.01	108.76	109.51	110.26	111.01	111.76
150	112.51	113.26	114.01	114.76	115.51	116.26	117.01	117.76	118.51	119.26
160	120.01	120.76	121.51	122.26	123.01	123.76	124.51	125.26	126.01	126.76
170	127.51	128.26	129.01	129.76	130.51	131.26	132.01	132.76	133.51	134.26
180	135.01	135.76	136.51	137.26	138.01	138.76	139.51	140.26	141.01	141.76
190	142.51	143.26	144.01	144.76	145.51	146.26	147.01	147.76	148.51	149.26
200	150.01	150.76	151.51	152.26	153.01	153.76	154.51	155.26	156.01	156.76
210	157.51	158.26	159.01	159.76	160.51	161.26	162.01	162.76	163.51	164.26
220	165.01	165.76	166.51	167.26	168.01	168.76	169.51	170.26	171.01	171.76
230	172.51	173.26	174.01	174.76	175.51	176.26	177.01	177.76	178.51	179.26
240	180.01	180.76	181.51	182.26	183.02	183.77	184.52	185.27	186.02	186.77
250	187.52	188.27	189.02	189.77	190.52	191.27	192.02	192.77	193.52	194.27
260	195.02	195.77	196.52	197.27	198.02	198.77	199.52	200.27	201.02	201.77
270	202.52	203.27	204.02	204.77	205.52	206.27	207.02	207.77	208.52	209.27
280	210.02	210.77	211.52	212.27	213.02	213.77	214.52	215.27	216.02	216.77
290	217.52	218.27	219.02	219.77	220.52	221.27	222.02	222.77	223.52	224.27
300	225.02	225.77	226.52	227.27	228.02	228.77	229.52	230.27	231.02	231.77
310	232.52	233.27	234.02	234.77	235.52	236.27	237.02	237.77	238.52	239.27
320	240.02	240.77	241.52	242.27	243.02	243.77	244.52	245.27	246.02	246.77
330	247.52	248.27	249.02	249.77	250.52	251.27	252.02	252.77	253.52	254.27
340	255.02	255.77	256.52	257.27	258.02	258.77	259.52	260.27	261.02	261.77
350	262.52	263.27	264.02	264.77	265.52	266.27	267.02	267.77	268.52	269.27
360	270.02	270.77	271.52	272.27	273.02	273.77	274.52	275.27	276.02	276.77
370	277.52	278.27	279.02	279.77	280.52	281.27	282.02	282.77	283.52	284.27
380	285.02	285.77	286.52	287.27	288.02	288.77	289.52	290.27	291.02	291.77
390	292.52	293.27	294.02	294.77	295.52	296.27	297.02	297.77	298.52	299.27
400	300.02	300.77	301.52	302.27	303.02	303.77	304.53	305.28	306.03	306.78
410	307.53	308.28	309.03	309.78	310.53	311.28	312.03	312.78	313.53	314.28
420	315.03	315.78	316.53	317.28	318.03	318.78	319.53	320.28	321.03	321.78
430	322.53	323.28	324.03	324.78	325.53	326.28	327.03	327.78	328.53	329.28
440	330.03	330.78	331.53	332.28	333.03	333.78	334.53	335.28	336.03	336.78
450	337.53	338.28	339.03	339.78	340.53	341.28	342.03	342.78	343.53	344.28
460	345.03	345.78	346.53	347.28	348.03	348.78	349.53	350.28	351.03	351.78
470	352.53	353.28	354.03	354.78	355.53	356.28	357.03	357.78	358.53	359.28
480	360.03	360.78	361.53	362.28	363.03	363.78	364.53	365.28	366.03	366.78
490	367.53	368.28	369.03	369.78	370.53	371.28	372.03	372.78	373.53	374.28
500	375.03	375.78	376.53	377.28	378.03	378.78	379.53	380.28	381.03	381.78
510	382.53	383.28	384.03	384.78	385.53	386.28	387.03	387.78	388.53	389.28
520	390.03	390.78	391.53	392.28	393.03	393.78	394.53	395.28	396.03	396.78
530	397.53	398.28	399.03	399.78	400.53	401.28	402.03	402.78	403.53	404.28
540	405.03	405.78	406.53	407.28	408.03	408.78	409.53	410.28	411.03	411.78
550	412.53	413.28	414.03	414.78	415.53	416.28	417.03	417.78	418.53	419.28
560	420.03	420.78	421.53	422.28	423.03	423.78	424.53	425.28	426.04	426.79
570	427.54	428.29	429.04	429.79	430.54	431.29	432.04	432.79	433.54	434.29
580	435.04	435.79	436.54	437.29	438.04	438.79	439.54	440.29	441.04	441.79
590	442.54	443.29	444.04	444.79	445.54	446.29	447.04	447.79	448.54	449.29
600	450.04	450.79	451.54	452.29	453.04	453.79	454.54	455.29	456.04	456.79
610	457.54	458.29	459.04	459.79	460.54	461.29	462.04	462.79	463.54	464.29
620	465.04	465.79	466.54	467.29	468.04	468.79	469.54	470.29	471.04	471.79
630	472.54	473.29	474.04	474.79	475.54	476.29	477.04	477.79	478.54	479.29
640	480.04	480.79	481.54	482.29	483.04	483.79	484.54	485.29	486.04	486.79
650	487.54	488.29	489.04	489.79	490.54	491.29	492.04	492.79	493.54	494.29
660	495.04	495.79	496.54	497.29	498.04	498.79	499.54	500.29	501.04	501.79
670	502.54	503.29	504.04	504.79	505.54	506.29	507.04	507.79	508.54	509.29
680	510.04	510.79	511.54	512.29	513.04	513.79	514.54	515.29	516.04	516.79
690	517.54	518.29	519.04	519.79	520.54	521.29	522.04	522.79	523.54	524.29
700	525.04	525.79	526.54	527.29	528.04	528.79	529.54	530.29	531.04	531.79
710	532.54	533.29	534.04	534.79	535.54	536.29	537.04	537.79	538.54	539.29
720	540.04	540.79	541.54	542.29	543.04	543.79	544.54	545.29	546.04	546.79
730	547.55	548.30	549.05	549.80	550.55	551.30	552.05	552.80	553.55	554.30
740	555.05	555.80	556.55	557.30	558.05	558.80	559.55	560.30	561.05	561.80
750	562.55	563.30	564.05	564.80	565.55	566.30	567.05	567.80	568.55	569.30
760	570.05	570.80	571.55	572 30	573.05	573.80	574.55	575.30	576.05	576.80
770	577.55	578.30	579.05	579.80	580.55	581.30	582.05	582.80	583.55	584.30
780	585.05	585.80	586.55	587.30	588.05	588.80	589.55	590.30	591.05	591.80
790	592.55	593.30	594.05	594.80	595.55	596.30	597.05	597.80	598.55	599.30
800	600.05	600.80	601.55	602.30	603.05	603.80	604.55	605.30	606.05	606.80
810	607.55	608.30	609.05	609.80	610.55	611.30	612.05	612.80	613.55	614.30
820	615.05	615.80	616.55	617.30	618.05	618.80	619.55	620.30	621.05	621.80
830	622.55	623.30	624.05	624.80	625.55	626.30	627.05	627.80	628.55	629.30
840	630.05	630.80	631.55	632.30	633.05	633.80	634.55	635.30	636.05	636.80
850	637.55	638.30	639.05	639.80	640.55	641.30	642.05	642.80	643.55	644.30
860	645.05	645.80	646.55	647.30	648.05	648.80	649.55	650.30	651.05	651.80
870	652.55	653.30	654.05	654.80	655.55	656.30	657.05	657.80	658.55	659.30
880	660.05	660.80	661.55	662.30	663.05	663.80	664.55	665.30	666.05	666.80
890	667.55	668.30	669.06	669.81	670.56	671.31	672.06	672.81	673.56	674.31
900	675.06	675.81	676.56	677.31	678.06	678.81	679.56	680.31	681.06	681.81
910	682.56	683.31	684.06	684.81	685.56	686.31	687.06	687.81	688.56	689.31
920	690.06	690.81	691.56	692.31	693.06	693.81	694.56	695.31	696.06	696.81
930	697.56	698.31	699.06	699.81	700.56	701.31	702.06	702.81	703.56	704.31
940	705.06	705.81	706.56	707.31	708.06	708.81	709.56	710.31	711.06	711.81
950	712.56	713.31	714.06	714.81	715.56	716.31	717.06	717.81	718.56	719.31
960	720.06	720.81	721.56	722.31	723.06	723.81	724.56	725.31	726.06	726.81
970	727.56	728.31	729.06	729.81	730.56	731.31	732.06	732.81	733.56	734.31
980	735.06	735.81	736.56	737.31	738.06	738.81	739.56	740.31	741.06	741.81
990	742.56	743.31	744.06	744.81	745.56	746.31	747.06	747.81	748.56	749.31
1000	750.06	750.81	751.56	752.31	753.06	753.81	754.56	755.31	756.06	756.81
1010	757.56	758.31	759.06	759.81	760.56	761.31	762.06	762.81	763.56	764.31
1020	765.06	765.81	766.56	767.31	768.06	768.81	769.56	770.31	771.06	771.81
1030	772.56	773.31	774.06	774.81	775.56	776.31	777.06	777.81	778.56	779.31
1040	780.06	780.81	781.56	782.31	783.06	783.81	784.56	785.31	786.06	786.81

Millimeters of water (mm H_2O) – Millibars (mb)

	0	100	200	300	400	500	600	700	800	900
0	0.0000	9.8064	19.613	29.419	39.226	49.032	58.838	68.645	78.451	88.257
1000	98.064	107.87	117.68	127.48	137.29	147.10	156.90	166.71	176.51	186.32
2000	196.13	205.93	215.74	225.55	235.35	245.16	254.97	264.77	274.58	284.38
3000	294.19	304.00	313.80	323.61	333.42	343.22	353.03	362.84	372.64	382.45
4000	392.26	402.06	411.87	421.67	431.48	441.29	451.09	460.90	470.71	480.51
5000	490.32	500.13	509.93	519.74	529.54	539.35	549.16	558.96	568.77	578.58
6000	588.38	598.19	608.00	617.80	627.61	637.41	647.22	657.03	666.83	676.64
7000	686.45	696.25	706.06	715.87	725.67	735.48	745.28	755.09	764.90	774.70
8000	784.51	794.32	804.12	813.93	823.74	833.54	843.35	853.15	862.96	872.77
9000	882.57	892.38	902.19	911.99	921.80	931.61	941.41	951.22	961.02	970.83

Millimeters of water (mm H_2O) – Millimeters of mercury (mm Hg)

	0	100	200	300	400	500	600	700	800	900
0	0.0000	7.3554	14.711	22.066	29.422	36.777	44.132	51.488	58.843	66.198
1000	73.554	80.909	88.265	95.620	102.98	110.33	117.69	125.04	132.40	139.75
2000	147.11	154.46	161.82	169.17	176.53	183.88	191.24	198.60	205.95	213.31
3000	220.66	228.02	235.37	242.73	250.08	257.44	264.79	272.15	279.50	286.86
4000	294.22	301.57	308.93	316.28	323.64	330.99	338.35	345.70	353.06	360.41
5000	367.77	375.12	382.48	389.84	397.19	404.55	411.90	419.26	426.61	433.97
6000	441.32	448.68	456.03	463.39	470.74	478.10	485.46	492.81	500.17	507.52
7000	514.88	522.23	529.59	536.94	544.30	551.65	559.01	566.36	573.72	581.08
8000	588.43	595.79	603.14	610.50	617.85	625.21	632.56	639.92	647.27	654.63
9000	661.98	669.34	676.70	684.05	691.41	698.76	706.12	713.47	720.83	728.18

Physical atmospheres (atm) – Bars (b)

	0	100	200	300	400	500	600	700	800	900
0	000.00	101.33	202.65	303.98	405.30	506.63	607.95	709.28	810.60	911.93
1000	1013.3	1114.6	1215.9	1317.2	1418.6	1519.9	1621.2	1722.5	1823.9	1925.2
2000	2026.5	2127.8	2229.2	2330.5	2431.8	2533.1	2634.5	2735.8	2837.1	2938.4
3000	3039.8	3141.1	3242.4	3343.7	3445.1	3546.4	3647.7	3749.0	3850.4	3951.7
4000	4053.0	4154.3	4255.7	4357.0	4458.3	4559.6	4661.0	4762.3	4863.6	4964.9
5000	5066.3	5167.6	5268.9	5370.2	5471.6	5572.9	5674.2	5775.5	5876.9	5978.2
6000	6079.5	6180.8	6282.2	6383.5	6484.8	6586.1	6687.5	6788.8	6890.1	6991.4
7000	7092.8	7194.1	7295.4	7396.7	7498.1	7599.4	7700.7	7802.0	7903.4	8004.7
8000	8106.0	8207.3	8308.7	8410.0	8511.3	8612.6	8714.0	8815.3	8916.6	9017.9
9000	9119.3	9220.6	9321.9	9423.2	9524.6	9625.9	9727.2	9828.5	9929.9	10031.

Millimeters of mercury (mm Hg) – Physical atmospheres (atm)

	0	100	200	300	400	500	600	700	800	900
0	0.0000	0.1316	0.2632	0.3947	0.5263	0.6579	0.7895	0.9211	1.0526	1.1842
1000	1.3158	1.4474	1.5789	1.7105	1.8421	1.9737	2.1053	2.2368	2.3684	2.5000
2000	2.6316	2.7632	2.8947	3.0263	3.1579	3.2895	3.4211	3.5526	3.6842	3.8158
3000	3.9474	4.0789	4.2105	4.3421	4.4737	4.6053	4.7368	4.8684	5.0000	5.1316
4000	5.2632	5.3947	5.5263	5.6579	5.7895	5.9211	6.0526	6.1842	6.3158	6.4474
5000	6.5789	6.7105	6.8421	6.9737	7.1053	7.2368	7.3684	7.5000	7.6316	7.7632
6000	7.8947	8.0263	8.1579	8.2895	8.4210	8.5526	8.6842	8.8158	8.9474	9.0789
7000	9.2105	9.3421	9.4737	9.6053	9.7368	9.8684	10.000	10.132	10.263	10.395
8000	10.526	10.658	10.789	10.921	11.053	11.184	11.316	11.447	11.579	11.711
9000	11.842	11.974	12.105	12.237	12.368	12.500	12.632	12.763	12.895	13.026

Physical atmospheres (atm) – Technical atmospheres (at)

	0	100	200	300	400	500	600	700	800	900
0	000.00	103.32	206.65	309.97	413.29	516.61	619.94	723.26	826.58	929.90
1000	1033.2	1136.6	1239.9	1343.2	1446.5	1549.8	1653.2	1756.5	1859.8	1963.1
2000	2066.5	2169.8	2273.1	2376.4	2479.7	2583.1	2686.4	2789.7	2893.0	2996.4
3000	3099.7	3203.0	3306.3	3409.7	3513.0	3616.3	3719.6	3822.9	3926.3	4029.6
4000	4132.9	4236.2	4339.6	4442.9	4546.2	4649.5	4752.8	4856.2	4959.5	5062.8
5000	5166.1	5269.5	5372.8	5476.1	5579.4	5682.8	5786.1	5889.4	5992.7	6096.0
6000	6199.4	6302.7	6406.0	6509.3	6612.7	6716.0	6819.3	6922.6	7025.9	7129.3
7000	7232.6	7335.9	7439.2	7542.6	7645.9	7749.2	7852.5	7955.9	8059.2	8162.5
8000	8265.8	8369.1	8472.5	8575.8	8679.1	8782.4	8885.8	8989.1	9092.4	9195.7
9000	9299.0	9402.4	9505.7	9609.0	9712.3	9815.7	9919.0	10022.	10126.	10229.

Millimeters of mercury (mm Hg) – Technical atmospheres (at)

	0	100	200	300	400	500	600	700	800	900
0	0.0000	0.1359	0.2718	0.4077	0.5436	0.6795	0.8155	0.9514	1.0873	1.2232
1000	1.3591	1.4950	1.6309	1.7668	1.9027	2.0386	2.1746	2.3105	2.4464	2.5823
2000	2.7182	2.8541	2.9900	3.1259	3.2618	3.3977	3.5337	3.6696	3.8055	3.9414
3000	4.0773	4.2132	4.3491	4.4850	4.6209	4.7568	4.8928	5.0287	5.1646	5.3005
4000	5.4364	5.5723	5.7082	5.8441	5.9800	6.1159	6.2519	6.3878	6.5237	6.6596
5000	6.7955	6.9314	7.0673	7.2032	7.3391	7.4750	7.6109	7.7469	7.8828	8.0187
6000	8.1546	8.2905	8.4264	8.5623	8.6982	8.8341	8.9700	9.1060	9.2419	9.3778
7000	9.5137	9.6496	9.7855	9.9214	10.057	10.193	10.329	10.465	10.601	10.737
8000	10.873	11.009	11.145	11.281	11.416	11.552	11.688	11.824	11.960	12.096
9000	12.232	12.368	12.504	12.640	12.776	12.911	13.047	13.183	13.319	13.455

Inches of water at 3.96° C (in. H_2O) – Millimeters of mercury (mm Hg)

	0	100	200	300	400	500	600	700	800	900
0	000.00	186.83	373.65	560.48	747.31	934.13	1121.0	1307.8	1494.6	1681.4
1000	1868.3	2055.1	2241.9	2428.7	2615.6	2802.4	2989.2	3176.1	3362.9	3549.7
2000	3736.5	3923.4	4110.2	4297.0	4483.8	4670.7	4857.5	5044.3	5231.2	5418.0
3000	5604.8	5791.6	5978.5	6165.3	6352.1	6538.9	6725.8	6912.6	7099.4	7286.2
4000	7473.1	7659.9	7846.7	8033.6	8220.4	8407.2	8594.0	8780.9	8967.7	9154.5
5000	9341.3	9528.2	9715.0	9901.8	10089.	10275.	10462.	10649.	10836.	11023.
6000	11210.	11396.	11583.	11770.	11957.	12144.	12331.	12517.	12704.	12891.
7000	13078.	13265.	13452.	13638.	13825.	14012.	14199.	14386.	14572.	14759.
8000	14946.	15133.	15320.	15507.	15693.	15880.	16067.	16254.	16441.	16628.
9000	16814.	17001.	17188.	17375.	17562.	17749.	17935.	18122.	18309.	18496.

Pounds weight/square inch (lb/sq.in) ** – Technical atmospheres (at)

	0	100	200	300	400	500	600	700	800	900
0	0.0000	7.0307	14.061	21.092	28.123	35.153	42.184	49.215	56.246	63.276
1000	70.307	77.338	84.368	91.399	98.430	105.46	112.49	119.52	126.55	133.58
2000	140.61	147.64	154.68	161.71	168.74	175.77	182.80	189.83	196.86	203.89
3000	210.92	217.95	224.98	232.01	239.04	246.07	253.11	260.14	267.17	274.20
4000	281.23	288.26	295.29	302.32	309.35	316.38	323.41	330.44	337.47	344.50
5000	351.53	358.57	365.60	372.63	379.66	386.69	393.72	400.75	407.78	414.81
6000	421.84	428.87	435.90	442.93	449.96	457.00	464.03	471.06	478.09	485.12
7000	492.15	499.18	506.21	513.24	520.27	527.30	534.33	541.36	548.39	555.42
8000	562.46	569.49	576.52	583.55	590.58	597.61	604.64	611.67	618.70	625.73
9000	632.76	639.79	646.82	653.85	660.89	667.92	674.95	681.98	689.01	696.04

Millibars (mb) – Millimeters of water (mm H_2O)

	0	1	2	3	4	5	6	7	8	9
0	00.000	10.197	20.395	30.592	40.790	50.987	61.185	71.382	81.580	91.777
10	101.97	112.17	122.37	132.57	142.76	152.96	163.16	173.36	183.55	193.75
20	203.95	214.15	224.34	234.54	244.74	254.94	265.13	275.33	285.53	295.73
30	305.92	316.12	326.32	336.52	346.71	356.91	367.11	377.31	387.50	397.70
40	407.90	418.10	428.29	438.49	448.69	458.89	469.08	479.28	489.48	499.67
50	509.87	520.07	530.27	540.46	550.66	560.86	571.06	581.25	591.45	601.65
60	611.85	622.04	632.24	642.44	652.64	662.83	673.03	683.23	693.43	703.62
70	713.82	724.02	734.22	744.41	754.61	764.81	775.01	785.20	795.40	805.60
80	815.80	825.99	836.19	846.39	856.59	866.78	876.98	887.18	897.38	907.57
90	917.77	927.97	938.17	948.36	958.56	968.76	978.95	989.15	999.35	1009.5

Millimeters of mercury (mm Hg) – Millimeters of water (mm H_2O)

	0	1	2	3	4	5	6	7	8	9
0	00.000	13.595	27.191	40.786	54.382	67.977	81.573	95.168	108.76	122.36
10	135.95	149.55	163.15	176.74	190.34	203.93	217.53	231.12	244.72	258.31
20	271.91	285.51	299.10	312.70	326.29	339.89	353.48	367.08	380.67	394.27
30	407.86	421.46	435.06	448.65	462.25	475.84	489.44	503.03	516.63	530.22
40	543.82	557.41	571.01	584.61	598.20	611.80	625.39	638.99	652.58	666.18
50	679.77	693.37	706.96	720.56	734.16	747.75	761.35	774.94	788.54	802.13
60	815.73	829.32	842.92	856.52	870.11	883.71	897.30	910.90	924.49	938.09
70	951.68	965.28	978.87	992.47	1006.1	1019.7	1033.3	1046.9	1060.4	1074.0
80	1087.6	1101.2	1114.8	1128.4	1142.0	1155.6	1169.2	1182.8	1196.4	1210.0
90	1223.6	1237.2	1250.8	1264.4	1278.0	1291.6	1305.2	1318.8	1332.4	1346.0

Bars (b) – Physical atmospheres (atm)

	0	1	2	3	4	5	6	7	8	9
0	0.0000	0.9869	1.9738	2.9608	3.9477	4.9346	5.9215	6.9085	7.8954	8.8823
10	9.8692	10.856	11.843	12.830	13.817	14.804	15.791	16.778	17.765	18.752
20	19.738	20.725	21.712	22.699	23.686	24.673	25.660	26.647	27.634	28.621
30	29.608	30.595	31.582	32.568	33.555	34.542	35.529	36.516	37.503	38.490
40	39.477	40.464	41.451	42.438	43.425	44.412	45.398	46.385	47.372	48.359
50	49.346	50.333	51.320	52.307	53.294	54.281	55.268	56.255	57.242	58.228
60	59.215	60.202	61.189	62.176	63.163	64.150	65.137	66.124	67.111	68.098
70	69.085	70.072	71.058	72.045	73.032	74.019	75.006	75.993	76.980	77.967
80	78.954	79.941	80.928	81.915	82.902	83.888	84.875	85.862	86.849	87.836
90	88.823	89,810	90.797	91.784	92.771	93.758	94.745	95.732	96.718	97.705

Physical atmospheres (atm) – Millimeters of mercury (mm Hg)

	0	1	2	3	4	5	6	7	8	9
0	000.00	760.00	1520.0	2280.0	3040.0	3800.0	4560.0	5320.0	6080.0	6840.0
10	7600.0	8360.0	9120.0	9880.0	10640.	11400.	12160.	12920.	13680.	14440.
20	15200.	15960.	16720.	17480.	18240.	19000.	19760.	20520.	21280.	22040.
30	22800.	23560.	24320.	25080.	25840.	26600.	27360.	28120.	28880.	29640.
40	30400.	31160.	31920.	32680.	33440.	34200.	34960.	35720.	36480.	37240.
50	38000.	38760.	39520.	40280.	41040.	41800.	42560.	43320.	44080.	44840.
60	45600.	46360.	47120.	47880.	48640.	49400.	50160.	50920.	51680.	52440.
70	53200.	53960.	54720.	55480.	56240.	57000.	57760.	58520.	59280.	60040.
80	60800.	61560.	62320.	63080.	63840.	64600.	65360.	66120.	66880.	67640.
90	68400.	69160.	69920.	70680.	71440.	72200.	72960.	73720.	74480.	75240.

Technical atmospheres (at) – Physical atmospheres (atm)

	0	1	2	3	4	5	6	7	8	9
0	0.0000	0.9678	1.9357	2.9035	3.8714	4.8392	5.8070	6.7749	7.7427	8.7106
10	9.6784	10.646	11.614	12.582	13.550	14.518	15.485	16.453	17.421	18.389
20	19.357	20.325	21.293	22.260	23.228	24.196	25.164	26.132	27.100	28.067
30	29.035	30.003	30.971	31.939	32.907	33.874	34.842	35.810	36.778	37.746
40	38.714	39.681	40.649	41.617	42.585	43.553	44.521	45.489	46.456	47.424
50	48.392	49.360	50.328	51.296	52.263	53.231	54.199	55.167	56.135	57.103
60	58.070	59.038	60.006	60.974	61.942	62.910	63.878	64.845	65.813	66.781
70	67.749	68.717	69.685	70.652	71.620	72.588	73.556	74.524	75.492	76.459
80	77.427	78.395	79.363	80.331	81.299	82.266	83.234	84.202	85.170	86.138
90	87.106	88.074	89.041	90.009	90.977	91.945	92.913	93.881	94.848	95.816

Technical atmospheres (at) – Millimeters of mercury (mm Hg)

	0	1	2	3	4	5	6	7	8	9
0	000.00	735.78	1471.6	2207.3	2943.1	3678.9	4414.7	5150.5	5886.3	6622.0
10	7357.8	8093.6	8829.4	9565.2	10301.	11037.	11773.	12508.	13244.	13980.
20	14716.	15451.	16187.	16923.	17659.	18395.	19130.	19866.	20602.	21338.
30	22073.	22809.	23545.	24281.	25017.	25752.	26488.	27224.	27960.	28696.
40	29431.	30167.	30903.	31639.	32374.	33110.	33846.	34582.	35318.	36053.
50	36789.	37525.	38261.	38996.	39732.	40468.	41204.	41940.	42675.	43411.
60	44147.	44883.	45618.	46354.	47090.	47826.	48562.	49297.	50033.	50769.
70	51505.	52241.	52976.	53712.	54448.	55184.	55919.	56655.	57391.	58127.
80	58863.	59598.	60334.	61070.	61806.	62541.	63277.	64013.	64749.	65485.
90	66220.	66956.	67692.	68428.	69164.	69899.	70635.	71371.	72107.	72842.

Millimeters of mercury (mm Hg) – Inches of water at 3.96° C (in. H_2O)

	0	1	2	3	4	5	6	7	8	9
0	0.0000	0.5353	1.0705	1.6058	2.1410	2.6763	3.2115	3.7468	4.2820	4.8173
10	5.3526	5.8878	6.4231	6.9583	7.4936	8.0288	8.5641	9.0993	9.6346	10.170
20	10.705	11.240	11.776	12.311	12.846	13.381	13.917	14.452	14.987	15.522
30	16.058	16.593	17.128	17.663	18.199	18.734	19.269	19.804	20.340	20.875
40	21.410	21.945	22.481	23.016	23.551	24.086	24.622	25.157	25.692	26.227
50	26.763	27.298	27.833	28.369	28.904	29.439	29.974	30.510	31.045	31.580
60	32.115	32.651	33.186	33.721	34.256	34.792	35.327	35.862	36.397	36.933
70	37.468	38.003	38.538	39.074	39.609	40.144	40.679	41.215	41.750	42.285
80	42.820	43.356	43.891	44.426	44.961	45.497	46.032	46.567	47.102	47.638
90	48.173	48.708	49.243	49.779	50.314	50.849	51.384	51.920	52.455	52.990

Technical atmospheres (at) – Pounds weight/square inch (lb/sq.in) **

	0	1	2	3	4	5	6	7	8	9
0	00.000	14.223	28.447	42.670	56.893	71.117	85.340	99.563	113.79	128.01
10	142.23	156.46	170.68	184.90	199.13	213.35	227.57	241.80	256.02	270.24
20	284.47	298.69	312.91	327.14	341.36	355.58	369.81	384.03	398.25	412.48
30	426.70	440.92	455.15	469.37	483.59	497.82	512.04	526.26	540.49	554.71
40	568.93	583.16	597.38	611.60	625.83	640.05	654.27	668.50	682.72	696.94
50	711.17	725.39	739.61	753.84	768.06	782.28	796.51	810.73	824.95	839.18
60	853.40	867.62	881.85	896.07	910.29	924.52	938.74	952.96	967.19	981.41
70	995.63	1009.9	1024.1	1038.3	1052.5	1066.8	1081.0	1095.2	1109.4	1123.6
80	1137.9	1152.1	1166.3	1180.5	1194.8	1209.0	1223.2	1237.4	1251.7	1265.9
90	1280.1	1294.3	1308.5	1322.8	1337.0	1351.2	1365.4	1379.7	1393.9	1408.1

 ** Technical pressure unit.

Examples: 656 cal_{15} (0.656 $kcal_{15}$) = 2745.7 J; 65.6 cal_{15} = 274.57 J

15° calories (cal_{15}) – Joules (J)

cal_{15}	0	1	2	3	4	5	6	7	8	9
100	418.55	422.74	426.92	431.11	435.29	439.48	443.66	447.85	452.03	456.22
110	460.41	464.59	468.78	472.96	477.15	481.33	485.52	489.70	493.89	498.07
120	502.26	506.45	510.63	514.82	519.00	523.19	527.37	531.56	535.74	539.93
130	544.12	548.30	552.49	556.67	560.86	565.04	569.23	573.41	577.60	581.78
140	585.97	590.16	594.34	598.53	602.71	606.90	611.08	615.27	619.45	623.64
150	627.83	632.01	636.20	640.38	644.57	648.75	652.94	657.12	661.31	665.49
160	669.68	673.87	678.05	682.24	686.42	690.61	694.79	698.98	703.16	707.35
170	711.54	715.72	719.91	724.09	728.28	732.46	736.65	740.83	745.02	749.20
180	753.39	757.58	761.76	765.95	770.13	774.32	778.50	782.69	786.87	791.06
190	795.25	799.43	803.62	807.80	811.99	816.17	820.36	824.54	828.73	832.91
200	837.10	841.29	845.47	849.66	853.84	858.03	862.21	866.40	870.58	874.77
210	878.96	883.14	887.33	891.51	895.70	899.88	904.07	908.25	912.44	916.62
220	920.81	925.00	929.18	933.37	937.55	941.74	945.92	950.11	954.29	958.48
230	962.67	966.85	971.04	975.22	979.41	983.59	987.78	991.96	996.15	1000.3
240	1004.5	1008.7	1012.9	1017.1	1021.3	1025.4	1029.6	1033.8	1038.0	1042.2
250	1046.4	1050.6	1054.7	1058.9	1063.1	1067.3	1071.5	1075.7	1079.9	1084.0
260	1088.2	1092.4	1096.6	1100.8	1105.0	1109.2	1113.3	1117.5	1121.7	1125.9
270	1130.1	1134.3	1138.5	1142.6	1146.8	1151.0	1155.2	1159.4	1163.6	1167.8
280	1171.9	1176.1	1180.3	1184.5	1188.7	1192.9	1197.1	1201.2	1205.4	1209.6
290	1213.8	1218.0	1222.2	1226.4	1230.5	1234.7	1238.9	1243.1	1247.3	1251.5
300	1255.7	1259.8	1264.0	1268.2	1272.4	1276.6	1280.8	1284.9	1289.1	1293.3
310	1297.5	1301.7	1305.9	1310.1	1314.2	1318.4	1322.6	1326.8	1331.0	1335.2
320	1339.4	1343.5	1347.7	1351.9	1356.1	1360.3	1364.5	1368.7	1372.8	1377.0
330	1381.2	1385.4	1389.6	1393.8	1398.0	1402.1	1406.3	1410.5	1414.7	1418.9
340	1423.1	1427.3	1431.4	1435.6	1439.8	1444.0	1448.2	1452.4	1456.6	1460.7
350	1464.9	1469.1	1473.3	1477.5	1481.7	1485.9	1490.0	1494.2	1498.4	1502.6
360	1506.8	1511.0	1515.2	1519.3	1523.5	1527.7	1531.9	1536.1	1540.3	1544.4
370	1548.6	1552.8	1557.0	1561.2	1565.4	1569.6	1573.7	1577.9	1582.1	1586.3
380	1590.5	1594.7	1598.9	1603.0	1607.2	1611.4	1615.6	1619.8	1624.0	1628.2
390	1632.3	1636.5	1640.7	1644.9	1649.1	1653.3	1657.5	1661.6	1665.8	1670.0
400	1674.2	1678.4	1682.6	1686.8	1690.9	1695.1	1699.3	1703.5	1707.7	1711.9
410	1716.1	1720.2	1724.4	1728.6	1732.8	1737.0	1741.2	1745.4	1749.5	1753.7
420	1757.9	1762.1	1766.3	1770.5	1774.7	1778.8	1783.0	1787.2	1791.4	1795.6
430	1799.8	1804.0	1808.1	1812.3	1816.5	1820.7	1824.9	1829.1	1833.2	1837.4
440	1841.6	1845.8	1850.0	1854.2	1858.4	1862.5	1866.7	1870.9	1875.1	1879.3
450	1883.5	1887.7	1891.8	1896.0	1900.2	1904.4	1908.6	1912.8	1917.0	1921.1
460	1925.3	1929.5	1933.7	1937.9	1942.1	1946.3	1950.4	1954.6	1958.8	1963.0
470	1967.2	1971.4	1975.6	1979.7	1983.9	1988.1	1992.3	1996.5	2000.7	2004.9
480	2009.0	2013.2	2017.4	2021.6	2025.8	2030.0	2034.2	2038.3	2042.5	2046.7
490	2050.9	2055.1	2059.3	2063.5	2067.6	2071.8	2076.0	2080.2	2084.4	2088.6
500	2092.8	2096.9	2101.1	2105.3	2109.5	2113.7	2117.9	2122.0	2126.2	2130.4
510	2134.6	2138.8	2143.0	2147.2	2151.3	2155.5	2159.7	2163.9	2168.1	2172.3
520	2176.5	2180.6	2184.8	2189.0	2193.2	2197.4	2201.6	2205.8	2209.9	2214.1
530	2218.3	2222.5	2226.7	2230.9	2235.1	2239.2	2243.4	2247.6	2251.8	2256.0
540	2260.2	2264.4	2268.5	2272.7	2276.9	2281.1	2285.3	2289.5	2293.7	2297.8
550	2302.0	2306.2	2310.4	2314.6	2318.8	2323.0	2327.1	2331.3	2335.5	2339.7
560	2343.9	2348.1	2352.3	2356.4	2360.6	2364.8	2369.0	2373.2	2377.4	2381.5
570	2385.7	2389.9	2394.1	2398.3	2402.5	2406.7	2410.8	2415.0	2419.2	2423.4
580	2427.6	2431.8	2436.0	2440.1	2444.3	2448.5	2452.7	2456.9	2461.1	2465.3
590	2469.4	2473.6	2477.8	2482.0	2486.2	2490.4	2494.6	2498.7	2502.9	2507.1
600	2511.3	2515.5	2519.7	2523.9	2528.0	2532.2	2536.4	2540.6	2544.8	2549.0
610	2553.2	2557.3	2561.5	2565.7	2569.9	2574.1	2578.3	2582.5	2586.6	2590.8
620	2595.0	2599.2	2603.4	2607.6	2611.8	2615.9	2620.1	2624.3	2628.5	2632.7
630	2636.9	2641.1	2645.2	2649.4	2653.6	2657.8	2662.0	2666.2	2670.3	2674.5
640	2678.7	2682.9	2687.1	2691.3	2695.5	2699.6	2703.8	2708.0	2712.2	2716.4
650	2720.6	2724.8	2728.9	2733.1	2737.3	2741.5	2745.7	2749.9	2754.1	2758.2
660	2762.4	2766.6	2770.8	2775.0	2779.2	2783.4	2787.5	2791.7	2795.9	2800.1
670	2804.3	2808.5	2812.7	2816.8	2821.0	2825.2	2829.4	2833.6	2837.8	2842.0
680	2846.1	2850.3	2854.5	2858.7	2862.9	2867.1	2871.3	2875.4	2879.6	2883.8
690	2888.0	2892.2	2896.4	2900.6	2904.7	2908.9	2913.1	2917.3	2921.5	2925.7
700	2929.9	2934.0	2938.2	2942.4	2946.6	2950.8	2955.0	2959.1	2963.3	2967.5
710	2971.7	2975.9	2980.1	2984.3	2988.4	2992.6	2996.8	3001.0	3005.2	3009.4
720	3013.6	3017.7	3021.9	3026.1	3030.3	3034.5	3038.7	3042.9	3047.0	3051.2
730	3055.4	3059.6	3063.8	3068.0	3072.2	3076.3	3080.5	3084.7	3088.9	3093.1
740	3097.3	3101.5	3105.6	3109.8	3114.0	3118.2	3122.4	3126.6	3130.8	3134.9
750	3139.1	3143.3	3147.5	3151.7	3155.9	3160.1	3164.2	3168.4	3172.6	3176.8
760	3181.0	3185.2	3189.4	3193.5	3197.7	3201.9	3206.1	3210.3	3214.5	3218.6
770	3222.8	3227.0	3231.2	3235.4	3239.6	3243.8	3247.9	3252.1	3256.3	3260.5
780	3264.7	3268.9	3273.1	3277.2	3281.4	3285.6	3289.8	3294.0	3298.2	3302.4
790	3306.5	3310.7	3314.9	3319.1	3323.3	3327.5	3331.7	3335.8	3340.0	3344.2
800	3348.4	3352.6	3356.8	3361.0	3365.1	3369.3	3373.5	3377.7	3381.9	3386.1
810	3390.3	3394.4	3398.6	3402.8	3407.0	3411.2	3415.4	3419.6	3423.7	3427.9
820	3432.1	3436.3	3440.5	3444.7	3448.9	3453.0	3457.2	3461.4	3465.6	3469.8
830	3474.0	3478.2	3482.3	3486.5	3490.7	3494.9	3499.1	3503.3	3507.4	3511.6
840	3515.8	3520.0	3524.2	3528.4	3532.6	3536.7	3540.9	3545.1	3549.3	3553.5
850	3557.7	3561.9	3566.0	3570.2	3574.4	3578.6	3582.8	3587.0	3591.2	3595.3
860	3599.5	3603.7	3607.9	3612.1	3616.3	3620.5	3624.6	3628.8	3633.0	3637.2
870	3641.4	3645.6	3649.8	3653.9	3658.1	3662.3	3666.5	3670.7	3674.9	3679.1
880	3683.2	3687.4	3691.6	3695.8	3700.0	3704.2	3708.4	3712.5	3716.7	3720.9
890	3725.1	3729.3	3733.5	3737.7	3741.8	3746.0	3750.2	3754.4	3758.6	3762.8
900	3767.0	3771.1	3775.3	3779.5	3783.7	3787.9	3792.1	3796.2	3800.4	3804.6
910	3808.8	3813.0	3817.2	3821.4	3825.5	3829.7	3833.9	3838.1	3842.3	3846.5
920	3850.7	3854.8	3859.0	3863.2	3867.4	3871.6	3875.8	3880.0	3884.1	3888.3
930	3892.5	3896.7	3900.9	3905.1	3909.3	3913.4	3917.6	3921.8	3926.0	3930.2
940	3934.4	3938.6	3942.7	3946.9	3951.1	3955.3	3959.5	3963.7	3967.9	3972.0
950	3976.2	3980.4	3984.6	3988.8	3993.0	3997.2	4001.3	4005.5	4009.7	4013.9
960	4018.1	4022.3	4026.5	4030.6	4034.8	4039.0	4043.2	4047.4	4051.6	4055.7
970	4059.9	4064.1	4068.3	4072.5	4076.7	4080.9	4085.0	4089.2	4093.4	4097.6
980	4101.8	4106.0	4110.2	4114.3	4118.5	4122.7	4126.9	4131.1	4135.3	4139.5
990	4143.6	4147.8	4152.0	4156.2	4160.4	4164.6	4168.8	4172.9	4177.1	4181.3

Joules (J) – 15° calories (cal_{15})

J	0	1	2	3	4	5	6	7	8	9
100	23.892	24.131	24.370	24.609	24.848	25.087	25.326	25.564	25.803	26.042
110	26.281	26.520	26.759	26.998	27.237	27.476	27.715	27.954	28.193	28.431
120	28.670	28.909	29.148	29.387	29.626	29.865	30.104	30.343	30.582	30.821
130	31.060	31.299	31.537	31.776	32.015	32.254	32.493	32.732	32.971	33.210
140	33.449	33.688	33.927	34.166	34.404	34.643	34.882	35.121	35.360	35.599
150	35.838	36.077	36.316	36.555	36.794	37.033	37.272	37.510	37.749	37.988
160	38.227	38.466	38.705	38.944	39.183	39.422	39.661	39.900	40.139	40.377
170	40.616	40.855	41.094	41.333	41.572	41.811	42.050	42.289	42.528	42.767
180	43.006	43.245	43.483	43.722	43.961	44.200	44.439	44.678	44.917	45.156
190	45.395	45.634	45.873	46.112	46.350	46.589	46.828	47.067	47.306	47.545
200	47.784	48.023	48.262	48.501	48.740	48.979	49.218	49.456	49.695	49.934
210	50.173	50.412	50.651	50.890	51.129	51.368	51.607	51.846	52.085	52.323
220	52.562	52.801	53.040	53.279	53.518	53.757	53.996	54.235	54.474	54.713
230	54.952	55.191	55.429	55.668	55.907	56.146	56.385	56.624	56.863	57.102
240	57.341	57.580	57.819	58.058	58.296	58.535	58.774	59.013	59.252	59.491
250	59.730	59.969	60.208	60.447	60.686	60.925	61.164	61.402	61.641	61.880
260	62.119	62.358	62.597	62.836	63.075	63.314	63.553	63.792	64.031	64.269
270	64.508	64.747	64.986	65.225	65.464	65.703	65.942	66.181	66.420	66.659
280	66.898	67.137	67.375	67.614	67.853	68.092	68.331	68.570	68.809	69.048
290	69.287	69.526	69.765	70.004	70.242	70.481	70.720	70.959	71.198	71.437
300	71.676	71.915	72.154	72.393	72.632	72.871	73.110	73.348	73.587	73.826
310	74.065	74.304	74.543	74.782	75.021	75.260	75.499	75.738	75.977	76.215
320	76.454	76.693	76.932	77.171	77.410	77.649	77.888	78.127	78.366	78.605
330	78.844	79.083	79.321	79.560	79.799	80.038	80.277	80.516	80.755	80.994
340	81.233	81.472	81.711	81.950	82.188	82.427	82.666	82.905	83.144	83.383
350	83.622	83.861	84.100	84.339	84.578	84.817	85.056	85.294	85.533	85.772
360	86.011	86.250	86.489	86.728	86.967	87.206	87.445	87.684	87.923	88.161
370	88.400	88.639	88.878	89.117	89.356	89.595	89.834	90.073	90.312	90.551
380	90.790	91.029	91.267	91.506	91.745	91.984	92.223	92.462	92.701	92.940
390	93.179	93.418	93.657	93.896	94.134	94.373	94.612	94.851	95.090	95.329
400	95.568	95.807	96.046	96.285	96.524	96.763	97.002	97.240	97.479	97.718
410	97.957	98.196	98.435	98.674	98.913	99.152	99.391	99.630	99.869	100.11
420	100.35	100.59	100.82	101.06	101.30	101.54	101.78	102.02	102.26	102.50
430	102.74	102.97	103.21	103.45	103.69	103.93	104.17	104.41	104.65	104.89
440	105.12	105.36	105.60	105.84	106.08	106.32	106.56	106.80	107.04	107.28
450	107.51	107.75	107.99	108.23	108.47	108.71	108.95	109.19	109.43	109.66
460	109.90	110.14	110.38	110.62	110.86	111.10	111.34	111.58	111.81	112.05
470	112.29	112.53	112.77	113.01	113.25	113.49	113.73	113.96	114.20	114.44
480	114.68	114.92	115.16	115.40	115.64	115.88	116.12	116.35	116.59	116.83
490	117.07	117.31	117.55	117.79	118.03	118.27	118.50	118.74	118.98	119.22
500	119.46	119.70	119.94	120.18	120.42	120.65	120.89	121.13	121.37	121.61
510	121.85	122.09	122.33	122.57	122.80	123.04	123.28	123.52	123.76	124.00
520	124.24	124.48	124.72	124.96	125.19	125.43	125.67	125.91	126.15	126.39
530	126.63	126.87	127.11	127.34	127.58	127.82	128.06	128.30	128.54	128.78
540	129.02	129.26	129.49	129.73	129.97	130.21	130.45	130.69	130.93	131.17
550	131.41	131.64	131.88	132.12	132.36	132.60	132.84	133.08	133.32	133.56
560	133.80	134.03	134.27	134.51	134.75	134.99	135.23	135.47	135.71	135.95
570	136.18	136.42	136.66	136.90	137.14	137.38	137.62	137.86	138.10	138.33
580	138.57	138.81	139.05	139.29	139.53	139.77	140.01	140.25	140.48	140.72
590	140.96	141.20	141.44	141.68	141.92	142.16	142.40	142.64	142.87	143.11
600	143.35	143.59	143.83	144.07	144.31	144.55	144.79	145.02	145.26	145.50
610	145.74	145.98	146.22	146.46	146.70	146.94	147.17	147.41	147.65	147.89
620	148.13	148.37	148.61	148.85	149.09	149.33	149.56	149.80	150.04	150.28
630	150.52	150.76	151.00	151.24	151.48	151.71	151.95	152.19	152.43	152.67
640	152.91	153.15	153.39	153.63	153.86	154.10	154.34	154.58	154.82	155.06
650	155.30	155.54	155.78	156.01	156.25	156.49	156.73	156.97	157.21	157.45
660	157.69	157.93	158.17	158.40	158.64	158.88	159.12	159.36	159.60	159.84
670	160.08	160.32	160.55	160.79	161.03	161.27	161.51	161.75	161.99	162.23
680	162.47	162.70	162.94	163.18	163.42	163.66	163.90	164.14	164.38	164.62
690	164.85	165.09	165.33	165.57	165.81	166.05	166.29	166.53	166.77	167.01
700	167.24	167.48	167.72	167.96	168.20	168.44	168.68	168.92	169.16	169.39
710	169.63	169.87	170.11	170.35	170.59	170.83	171.07	171.31	171.54	171.78
720	172.02	172.26	172.50	172.74	172.98	173.22	173.46	173.69	173.93	174.17
730	174.41	174.65	174.89	175.13	175.37	175.61	175.85	176.08	176.32	176.56
740	176.80	177.04	177.28	177.52	177.76	178.00	178.23	178.47	178.71	178.95
750	179.19	179.43	179.67	179.91	180.15	180.38	180.62	180.86	181.10	181.34
760	181.58	181.82	182.06	182.30	182.53	182.77	183.01	183.25	183.49	183.73
770	183.97	184.21	184.45	184.69	184.92	185.16	185.40	185.64	185.88	186.12
780	186.36	186.60	186.84	187.07	187.31	187.55	187.79	188.03	188.27	188.51
790	188.75	188.99	189.22	189.46	189.70	189.94	190.18	190.42	190.66	190.90
800	191.14	191.37	191.61	191.85	192.09	192.33	192.57	192.81	193.05	193.29
810	193.53	193.76	194.00	194.24	194.48	194.72	194.96	195.20	195.44	195.68
820	195.91	196.15	196.39	196.63	196.87	197.11	197.35	197.59	197.83	198.06
830	198.30	198.54	198.78	199.02	199.26	199.50	199.74	199.98	200.21	200.45
840	200.69	200.93	201.17	201.41	201.65	201.89	202.13	202.37	202.60	202.84
850	203.08	203.32	203.56	203.80	204.04	204.28	204.52	204.75	204.99	205.23
860	205.47	205.71	205.95	206.19	206.43	206.67	206.90	207.14	207.38	207.62
870	207.86	208.10	208.34	208.58	208.82	209.06	209.29	209.53	209.77	210.01
880	210.25	210.49	210.73	210.97	211.21	211.44	211.68	211.92	212.16	212.40
890	212.64	212.88	213.12	213.36	213.59	213.83	214.07	214.31	214.55	214.79
900	215.03	215.27	215.51	215.74	215.98	216.22	216.46	216.70	216.94	217.18
910	217.42	217.66	217.90	218.13	218.37	218.61	218.85	219.09	219.33	219.57
920	219.81	220.05	220.28	220.52	220.76	221.00	221.24	221.48	221.72	221.96
930	222.20	222.43	222.67	222.91	223.15	223.39	223.63	223.87	224.11	224.35
940	224.58	224.82	225.06	225.30	225.54	225.78	226.02	226.26	226.50	226.74
950	226.97	227.21	227.45	227.69	227.93	228.17	228.41	228.65	228.89	229.12
960	229.36	229.60	229.84	230.08	230.32	230.56	230.80	231.04	231.27	231.51
970	231.75	231.99	232.23	232.47	232.71	232.95	233.19	233.42	233.66	233.90
980	234.14	234.38	234.62	234.86	235.10	235.34	235.58	235.81	236.05	236.29
990	236.53	236.77	237.01	237.25	237.49	237.73	237.96	238.20	238.44	238.68

The systems of electrical measurement may be divided into two groups: systems based on a representation of electricity and magnetism which is defined by a three-dimensional theory of action at a distance, and systems based on a representation defined by four-dimensional field theory.

The definition of electrical properties by a theory of action at a distance with the three dimensions length, mass and time (LMT) originates from the period when only mechanical methods of measurement were available to the experimenter in electricity and magnetism. Definition by field theory came more and more into use with the development of specifically electrical methods of measurement and of the field theory of electrodynamics. It is characterized by being based on four fundamental measurements (and thus on four fundamental properties, see page 199) of which at least one is specifically electrical, for example a measurement of resistance or of charge. The properties defined by the field theory may accordingly be reduced to four basic dimensions of which at least one is specifically electrical, e.g. to the dimensions LMTR (R = electrical resistance) or LMTμ_0 (μ_0 = absolute permeability) or LMTε_0 (ε_0 = absolute permittivity), etc. In practice, in conformity with OHM's Law, a combination of two methods of electrical measurement is usually used (potential combined with current or resistance) leading to the choice of two fundamental electrical units, volt and ampere, for the *absolute electrical system of measurement* (dimensions LTUI = length, time, potential, current; basic units m-s-V-A = meter, second, volt, ampere). This system, internationally recognized since 1948, is based on the MKSΩ-system originally proposed by GIORGI, which in turn is based on the MKS-system. Its fourth dimension, the absolute ohm, is defined by fixing a numerical value for the absolute permeability μ_0, measured in meters, seconds and ohms, so that

$$\mu_0 = 10^{-7}\, 4\pi\, \Omega\, s\, m^{-1}$$

The absolute ohm unit can thus be embodied in a resistance coil of suitable form and determined by an induction measurement. Conversion from the GIORGI m-kg-s-Ω-system to the absolute m-s-V-A-system is carried out by means of the following relations:

$$J\,(\text{joule}) = m^2\,kg\,s^{-2} \qquad \Omega = VA^{-1}$$

$$V = \sqrt{\frac{J\,\Omega}{s}} \qquad A = \sqrt{\frac{J}{\Omega\, s}}$$

$$\text{whence } V = m\,kg^{1/2}\,s^{-3/2}\,\Omega^{1/2} \qquad A = m\,kg^{1/2}\,s^{-3/2}\,\Omega^{-1/2}$$

The energy unit J (joule) and thus the units of force N (newton) and of power W (watt) of the absolute m-s-V-A-system are accordingly identical with the corresponding units of the MKS-system. The remaining units therefore also correspond, and these two systems are steadily displacing other systems in science and technology.

Up to now, the systems of measurement defined by a theory of action at a distance with the three dimensions LMT and the basic units cm, g, s (the *electromagnetic and electrostatic* CGS-*systems*) have been much employed in physics on account of their correspondence with the CGS-system of mechanics. The units of these systems are obtained *formally* by setting the absolute permeability μ_0 or the absolute permittivity ε_0 equal to unity in the LMTμ_0- or LMTε_0-systems and representing the dimensions LMT by the corresponding units cm, g, s. The LMTμ_0-system thus leads to the electromagnetic and the LMTε_0-system to the electrostatic CGS-system. Since $\varepsilon_0 \mu_0 c_0^2 = 1$ (c_0 = velocity of light, abbreviated to c in the following table), $\varepsilon_0 = 1/c_0^2$ when $\mu_0 = 1$, and $\mu_0 = 1/c_0^2$ when $\varepsilon_0 = 1$. The constant c_0 therefore appears as a factor in the interconversion of these systems.

The dimensions of the systems of electrical measurement described only partially correspond, i.e. the systems are unlike systems based on fundamentally different definitions (theory of action at a distance and field theory). The units of the various systems for one and the same property, for example electric field strength, cannot therefore be equated since although they are numerically equal they have different dimensions. This circumstance is not of practical importance since it is primarily the numerical values which are of interest when comparing measurements based on the various systems. It is accorded recognition in the following table by the use of the symbol ≙ for *numerically equal but dimensionally unequal* equivalents. The units of the CGS systems of electrical measurement are given the following symbols: emu = electromagnetic CGS-unit, esu = electrostatic CGS-unit.

Electrical or Magnetic Property *(Symbol)* Dimensional system System of measurement	Dimensions Unit	Symbol or abbreviation	Equivalents ≙ indicates numerical but not dimensional equivalence c = velocity of light in vacuum in centimeters per second = 2.99793×10^{10}
Absolute Permittivity (ε_0) (electric field constant, permittivity of vacuum)			
Dimensional system LTUI Absolute system m-s-V-A	$L^{-1}TU^{-1}I$ farad/meter	$F\,m^{-1}$	≙ $4\pi\,10^{-11}$ emu (= 1.2566×10^{-10} emu) ≙ $4\pi\,10^{-11} c^2$ [esu] (= 1.1294×10^{11} [esu])
Dimensional system LMTμ_0 Electromagnetic CGS-system	$L^{-2}T^2\mu_0^{-1}$ $cm^{-2}s^2$	emu	≙ $10^{11}/4\pi\,F\,m^{-1}$ (= $7.9577 \times 10^9\,F\,m^{-1}$) ≙ c^2 [esu] (= 8.9876×10^{20} [esu])
Dimensional system LMTε_0 Electrostatic CGS-system	ε_0 1	1 [esu]	≙ $10^{11}/4\pi c^2\,F\,m^{-1}$ (= $8.8542 \times 10^{-12}\,F\,m^{-1}$) ≙ $1/c^2$ emu (= 1.1126×10^{-21} emu)
Electric Potential (U) (electromotive force)			
Dimensional system LTUI Absolute system m-s-V-A	U volt	V	≙ 10^8 emu ≙ $10^8/c$ esu (= 3.3356×10^{-3} esu)
Dimensional system LMTμ_0 Electromagnetic CGS-system	$L^{3/2}M^{1/2}T^{-2}\mu_0^{1/2}$ $cm^{3/2}g^{1/2}s^{-2}$	emu	≙ 10^{-8} V ≙ $1/c$ esu (= 3.3356×10^{-11} esu)
Dimensional system LMTε_0 Electrostatic CGS-system	$L^{1/2}M^{1/2}T^{-1}\varepsilon_0^{-1/2}$ $cm^{1/2}g^{1/2}s^{-1}$	esu	≙ $10^{-8} c$ V (= 2.9979×10^2 V) ≙ c emu (= 2.9979×10^{10} emu)

Electrical or Magnetic Property (*Symbol*) Dimensional system System of measurement	Dimensions Unit	Symbol or abbre-viation	Equivalents $\triangleq$ indicates numerical but not dimensional equivalence c = velocity of light in vacuum in centimeters per second = 2.99793×10^{10}
Electric Current Strength (I)			
Dimensional system LTUI Absolute system m-s-V-A	I ampere	A	$\triangleq 10^{-1}$ emu $\triangleq 10^{-1} c$ esu $(= 2.9979 \times 10^{9}$ esu)
Dimensional system LMTμ_0 Electromagnetic CGS-system	$L^{1/2} M^{1/2} T^{-1} \mu_0^{-1/2}$ $cm^{1/2} g^{1/2} s^{-1}$	emu	$\triangleq 10$ A $\triangleq c$ esu $(= 2.9979 \times 10^{10}$ esu)
Dimensional system LMTε_0 Electrostatic CGS-system	$L^{3/2} M^{1/2} T^{-2} \varepsilon_0^{1/2}$ $cm^{3/2} g^{1/2} s^{-2}$	esu	$\triangleq 10/c$ A $(= 3.3356 \times 10^{-10}$ A) $\triangleq 1/c$ emu $(= 3.3356 \times 10^{-11}$ emu)
Electric Current Density (G)			
Dimensional system LTUI Absolute system m-s-V-A	$L^{-2} I$ ampere/square meter	A m^{-2}	$\triangleq 10^{-5}$ emu $\triangleq 10^{-5} c$ esu $(= 2.9979 \times 10^{5}$ esu)
Dimensional system LMTμ_0 Electromagnetic CGS-system	$L^{-3/2} M^{1/2} T^{-1} \mu_0^{1/2}$ $cm^{-3/2} g^{1/2} s^{-1}$	emu	$\triangleq 10^{5}$ A m^{-2} $\triangleq c$ esu $(= 2.9979 \times 10^{10}$ esu)
Dimensional system LMTε_0 Electrostatic CGS-system	$L^{-1/2} M^{1/2} T^{-2} \varepsilon_0^{1/2}$ $cm^{-1/2} g^{1/2} s^{-2}$	esu	$\triangleq 10^{5}/c$ A m^{-2} $(= 3.3356 \times 10^{-6}$ A m^{-2}) $\triangleq 1/c$ emu $(= 3.3356 \times 10^{-11}$ emu)
Electric Field Strength (E)			
Dimensional system LTUI Absolute system m-s-V-A	$L^{-1} U$ volt/meter	V m^{-1}	$\triangleq 10^{6}$ emu $\triangleq 10^{6}/c$ esu $(= 3.3356 \times 10^{-5}$ esu)
Dimensional system LMTμ_0 Electromagnetic CGS-system	$L^{1/2} M^{1/2} T^{-2} \mu_0^{1/2}$ $cm^{1/2} g^{1/2} s^{-2}$	emu	$\triangleq 10^{-6}$ V m^{-1} $\triangleq 1/c$ esu $(= 3.3356 \times 10^{-11}$ esu)
Dimensional system LMTε_0 Electrostatic CGS-system	$L^{-1/2} M^{1/2} T^{-1} \varepsilon_0^{-1/2}$ $cm^{-1/2} g^{1/2} s^{-1}$	esu	$\triangleq 10^{-6} c$ V m^{-1} $(= 2.9979 \times 10^{4}$ V m^{-1}) $\triangleq c$ emu $(= 2.9979 \times 10^{10}$ emu)
Electric Displacement (D)			
Dimensional system LTUI Absolute system m-s-V-A	$L^{-2} TI$ coulomb/square meter	C m^{-2}	$\triangleq 4\pi\, 10^{-5}$ emu $(= 1.2566 \times 10^{-4}$ emu) $\triangleq 4\pi\, 10^{-5} c$ esu $(= 3.7672 \times 10^{6}$ esu)
Dimensional system LMTμ_0 Electromagnetic CGS-system	$L^{-3/2} M^{1/2} \mu_0^{-1/2}$ $cm^{-3/2} g^{1/2}$	emu	$10^{5}/4\pi$ C m^{-2} $(= 7.9577 \times 10^{3}$ C m^{-2}) $\triangleq c$ esu $(= 2.9979 \times 10^{10}$ esu)
Dimensional system LMTε_0 Electrostatic CGS-system	$L^{-1/2} M^{1/2} T^{-1} \varepsilon_0^{1/2}$ $cm^{-1/2} g^{1/2} s^{-1}$	esu	$10^{5}/4\pi c$ C m^{-2} $(= 2.6544 \times 10^{-7}$ C m^{-2}) $\triangleq 1/c$ emu $(= 3.3356 \times 10^{-11}$ emu)
Electric Displacement Flux (Ψ)			
Dimensional system LTUI Absolute system m-s-V-A	TI coulomb (= A s)	C	$\triangleq 4\pi\, 10^{-1}$ emu $(= 1.2566$ emu) $\triangleq 4\pi\, 10^{-1} c$ esu $(= 3.7673 \times 10^{10}$ esu)
Dimensional system LMTμ_0 Electromagnetic CGS-system	$L^{1/2} M^{1/2} \mu_0^{-1/2}$ $cm^{1/2} g^{1/2}$	emu	$\triangleq 10/4\pi$ C $(= 7.9577 \times 10^{-1}$ C) $= c$ esu $(= 2.9979 \times 10^{10}$ esu)
Dimensional system LMTε_0 Electrostatic CGS-system	$L^{3/2} M^{1/2} T^{-1} \varepsilon_0^{1/2}$ $cm^{3/2} g^{1/2} s^{-1}$	esu	$\triangleq 10/4\pi c$ C $(= 2.6544 \times 10^{-11}$ C) $= 1/c$ emu $(= 3.3356 \times 10^{-11}$ emu)
Electric Polarization (P)			
Dimensional system LTUI Absolute system m-s-V-A	$L^{-2} TI$ coulomb/square meter	C m^{-2}	$\triangleq 10^{-5}$ emu $\triangleq 10^{-5} c$ esu $(= 2.9979 \times 10^{5}$ esu)
Dimensional system LMTμ_0 Electromagnetic CGS-system	$L^{-3/2} M^{1/2} \mu_0^{-1/2}$ $cm^{-3/2} g^{1/2}$	emu	$\triangleq 10^{5}$ C m^{-2} $\triangleq c$ esu $(= 2.9979 \times 10^{10}$ esu)
Dimensional system LMTε_0 Electrostatic CGS-system	$L^{-1/2} M^{1/2} T^{-1} \varepsilon_0^{1/2}$ $cm^{-1/2} g^{1/2} s^{-1}$	esu	$\triangleq 10^{5}/c$ C m^{-2} $(= 3.3356 \times 10^{-6}$ C m^{-2}) $\triangleq 1/c$ emu $(= 3.3356 \times 10^{-11}$ emu)

Electrical or Magnetic Property (*Symbol*) Dimensional system / System of measurement	Dimensions / Unit	Symbol or abbreviation	Equivalents ($\triangle$ indicates numerical but not dimensional equivalence; c = velocity of light in vacuum in centimeters per second = 2.99793×10^{10})
Electric Moment (p)			
Dimensional system LTUI / Absolute system m-s-V-A	LTI / coulomb × meter	C m	$\triangle$ 10 emu $\triangle$ 10 c esu (= 2.9979×10^{11} esu)
Dimensional system LMTμ_0 / Electromagnetic CGS-system	$L^{3/2} M^{1/2} \mu_0^{-1/2}$ / $cm^{3/2} g^{1/2}$	emu	$\triangle$ 10^{-1} C m $\triangle$ c esu (= 2.9979×10^{10} esu)
Dimensional system LMTε_0 / Electrostatic CGS-system	$L^{5/2} M^{1/2} T^{-1} \varepsilon_0^{1/2}$ / $cm^{5/2} g^{1/2} s^{-1}$	esu	$\triangle$ $10^{-1}/c$ C m (= 3.3356×10^{-12} C m) $\triangle$ $1/c$ emu (= 3.3356×10^{-11} emu)
Electric Susceptibility (χ)			
Dimensional system LTUI / Absolute system m-s-V-A	1 / 1	1 [abs]	$\triangle$ $1/4\pi$ [emu] (= 7.9577×10^{-2} [emu]) $\triangle$ $1/4\pi$ [esu]
Dimensional system LMTμ_0 / Electromagnetic CGS-system	1 / 1	1 [emu]	$\triangle$ 4π [abs] (= 1.2566×10 [abs]) $\triangle$ 1 [esu]
Dimensional system LMTε_0 / Electrostatic CGS-system	1 / 1	1 [esu]	$\triangle$ 4π [abs] (= 1.2566×10 [abs]) $\triangle$ 1 [emu]
Electric Charge (Q)			
Dimensional system LTUI / Absolute system m-s-V-A	TI / coulomb (= A s)	C	$\triangle$ 10^{-1} emu $\triangle$ $10^{-1} c$ esu (= 2.9979×10^{9} esu)
Dimensional system LMTμ_0 / Electromagnetic CGS-system	$L^{1/2} M^{1/2} \mu_0^{-1/2}$ / $cm^{1/2} g^{1/2}$	emu	$\triangle$ 10 C $\triangle$ c esu (= 2.9979×10^{10} esu)
Dimensional system LMTε_0 / Electrostatic CGS-system	$L^{3/2} M^{1/2} T^{-1} \varepsilon_0^{1/2}$ / $cm^{3/2} g^{1/2} s^{-1}$	esu	$\triangle$ $10/c$ C (= 3.3356×10^{-10} C) $\triangle$ $1/c$ emu (= 3.3356×10^{-11} emu)
Electric Space Charge (η)			
Dimensional system LTUI / Absolute system m-s-V-A	L^{-3} TI / coulomb/cubic meter	C m^{-3}	$\triangle$ 10^{-7} emu $\triangle$ $10^{-7} c$ esu (= 2.9979×10^{3} esu)
Dimensional system LMTμ_0 / Electromagnetic CGS-system	$L^{-5/2} M^{1/2} \mu_0^{-1/2}$ / $cm^{-5/2} g^{1/2}$	emu	$\triangle$ 10^{7} C m^{-3} $\triangle$ c esu (= 2.9979×10^{10} esu)
Dimensional system LMTε_0 / Electrostatic CGS-system	$L^{-3/2} M^{1/2} T^{-1} \varepsilon_0^{1/2}$ / $cm^{-3/2} g^{1/2} s^{-1}$	esu	$\triangle$ $10^{7}/c$ C m^{-3} (= 3.3356×10^{4} C m^{-3}) $\triangle$ $1/c$ emu (= 3.3356×10^{-11} emu)
Electric Capacitance (C)			
Dimensional system LTUI / Absolute system m-s-V-A	TU^{-1} I / farad (= A s/V)	F	$\triangle$ 10^{-9} emu $\triangle$ $10^{-9} c^2$ esu (= 8.9876×10^{11} esu)
Dimensional system LMTμ_0 / Electromagnetic CGS-system	$L^{-1} T^{2} \mu_0^{-1}$ / $cm^{-1} s^{2}$	emu	$\triangle$ 10^{9} F $\triangle$ c^2 esu (= 8.9876×10^{20} esu)
Dimensional system LMTε_0 / Electrostatic CGS-system	L ε_0 / cm	cm (esu)	$\triangle$ $10^{9}/c^2$ F (= 1.1126×10^{-12} F) $\triangle$ $1/c^2$ emu (= 1.1126×10^{-21} emu)
Electric Resistance (R)			
Dimensional system LTUI / Absolute system m-s-V-A	UI^{-1} / ohm (= VA^{-1}) (1 megohm = 10^{6} ohms)	Ω	$\triangle$ 10^{9} emu $\triangle$ $10^{9}/c^2$ esu (= 1.1126×10^{-12} esu)
Dimensional system LMTμ_0 / Electromagnetic CGS-system	$LT^{-1} \mu_0$ / cm s^{-1}	emu	$\triangle$ 10^{-9} Ω $\triangle$ $1/c^2$ esu (= 1.1126×10^{-21} esu)
Dimensional system LMTε_0 / Electrostatic CGS-system	$L^{-1} T \varepsilon_0^{-1}$ / cm^{-1} s	esu	$\triangle$ $10^{-9} c^2$ Ω (= 8.9876×10^{11} Ω) $\triangle$ c^2 emu (= 8.9876×10^{20} emu)

Electrical or Magnetic Property *(Symbol)* Dimensional system / System of measurement	Dimensions / Unit	Symbol or abbreviation	Equivalents: △ indicates numerical but not dimensional equivalence; c = velocity of light in vacuum in centimeters per second = 2.99793×10^{10}
Specific Electric Resistance (ρ)			
Dimensional system LTUI Absolute system m-s-V-A	$L\,U\,I^{-1}$ ohm × meter	Ω m	△ 10^{11} emu △ $10^{11}/c^2$ esu (= 1.1126×10^{10} esu)
Dimensional system LMTμ_0 Electromagnetic CGS-system	$L^2\,T^{-1}\,\mu_0$ $cm^2\,s^{-1}$	emu	△ 10^{-11} Ω m △ $1/c^2$ esu (= 1.1126×10^{-21} esu)
Dimensional system LMTε_0 Electrostatic CGS-system	$T\,\varepsilon_0^{-1}$ s	s (esu)	△ $10^{-11} c^2$ Ω m (= 8.9876×10^9 Ω m) △ c^2 emu (= 8.9876×10^{20} emu)
Electric Conductivity (σ)			
Dimensional system LTUI Absolute system m-s-V-A	$L^{-1}\,U^{-1}\,I$ mho*/meter	$\Omega^{-1} m^{-1}$	△ 10^{-11} emu △ $10^{-11} c^2$ esu (= 8.9876×10^9 esu)
Dimensional system LMTμ_0 Electromagnetic CGS-system	$L^{-2}\,T\,\mu_0^{-1}$ $cm^{-2}\,s$	emu	△ 10^{11} S m^{-1} △ c^2 esu (= 8.9876×10^{20} esu)
Dimensional system LMTε_0 Electrostatic CGS-system	$T^{-1}\,\varepsilon_0$ s^{-1}	esu	△ $10^{11}/c^2$ S m^{-1} (= 1.1126×10^{-10} S m^{-1}) △ $1/c^2$ emu (= 1.1126×10^{-21} emu)
Electric Inductance (e_L)			
Dimensional system LTUI Absolute system m-s-V-A	$T\,U\,I^{-1}$ henry = V s A^{-1}	H	△ 10^9 emu △ $10^9/c^2$ esu (= 1.1126×10^{-12} esu)
Dimensional system LMTμ_0 Electromagnetic CGS-system	$L\,\mu_0$ cm	cm (emu)	△ 10^{-9} H △ $1/c^2$ esu (= 1.1126×10^{-21} esu)
Dimensional system LMTε_0 Electrostatic CGS-system	$L^{-1}\,T^2\,\varepsilon_0^{-1}$ $cm^{-1}\,s^2$	esu	△ $10^{-9} c^2$ H (= 8.9876×10^{11} H) △ c^2 emu (= 8.9876×10^{20} emu)
Absolute Permeability (μ_0) (magnetic field constant, permeability of vacuum)			
Dimensional system LTUI Absolute system m-s-V-A	$L^{-1}\,T\,U\,I^{-1}$ henry/meter	H m^{-1}	△ $10^7/4\pi$ [emu] (= 7.9577×10^5 [emu]) △ $10^7/4\pi\, c^2$ esu (= 8.8542×10^{-16} esu)
Dimensional system LMTμ_0 Electromagnetic CGS-system	μ_0 1	1 [emu]	△ $4\pi\, 10^{-7}$ H m^{-1} (= 1.2566×10^{-6} H m^{-1}) △ $1/c^2$ esu (= 1.1126×10^{-21} esu)
Dimensional system LMTε_0 Electrostatic CGS-system	$L^{-2}\,T^2\,\varepsilon_0^{-1}$ $cm^{-2}\,s^2$	esu	△ $4\pi\, 10^{-7} c^2$ H m^{-1} (= 1.1294×10^{15} H m^{-1}) △ c^2 [emu] (= 8.9876×10^{20} [emu])
Magnetic Potential (V) (magnetomotive force)			
Dimensional system LTUI Absolute system m-s-V-A	I ampere	A	△ $4\pi\, 10^{-1}$ Gb (= 1.2566 Gb) △ $4\pi\, 10^{-1} c$ esu (= 3.7673×10^{10} esu)
Dimensional system LMTμ_0 Electromagnetic CGS-system	$L^{1/2}\,M^{1/2}\,T^{-1}\,\mu_0^{-1/2}$ gilbert = $cm^{1/2}\,g^{1/2}\,s^{-1}$	Gb	△ $10/4\pi$ A (= 7.9577×10^{-1} A) △ c esu (= 2.9979×10^{10} esu)
Dimensional system LMTε_0 Electrostatic CGS-system	$L^{3/2}\,M^{1/2}\,T^{-2}\,\varepsilon_0^{1/2}$ $cm^{3/2}\,g^{1/2}\,s^{-2}$	esu	△ $10/4\pi c$ A (= 2.6544×10^{-11} A) △ $1/c$ emu (= 3.3356×10^{-11} emu)

* Reciprocal ohm. In German-speaking countries the name 'Siemens' (S) is used.

Electrical or Magnetic Property *(Symbol)* Dimensional system / System of measurement	Dimensions / Unit	Symbol or abbreviation	Equivalents: $\triangle$ indicates numerical but not dimensional equivalence; c = velocity of light in vacuum in centimeters per second $= 2.99793 \times 10^{10}$
Magnetic Field Strength (***H***)			
Dimensional system LTUI / Absolute system m-s-V-A	$L^{-1}I$ / ampere/meter	$A\,m^{-1}$	$\triangle\, 4\pi\, 10^{-3}\, Oe (= 1.2566 \times 10^{-2}\, Oe)\ \triangle\, 4\pi\, 10^{-3} c\, esu\ (= 3.7673 \times 10^{8}\, esu)$
Dimensional system $LMT\mu_0$ / Electromagnetic CGS-system	$L^{-1/2} M^{1/2} T^{-1} \mu_0^{-1/2}$ / oersted* $= cm^{-1/2} g^{1/2} s^{-1}$	Oe	$\triangle\, 1\, Gb\, cm^{-1}\ \triangle\, 10^{3}/4\pi\, A\, m^{-1} (= 7.9577 \times 10\, A\, m^{-1})$; $\triangle$ 1 line of force per square centimeter; $\triangle\, c\, esu (= 2.9979 \times 10^{10}\, esu)$
Dimensional system $LMT\varepsilon_0$ / Electrostatic CGS-system	$L^{1/2} M^{1/2} T^{-2} \varepsilon_0^{1/2}$ / $cm^{1/2} g^{1/2} s^{-2}$	esu	$\triangle\, 10^{3}/4\pi\, c\, A\, m^{-1} (= 2.6544 \times 10^{-9}\, A\, m^{-1})$; $\triangle\, 1/c\, Oe\, (= 3.3356 \times 10^{-11}\, Oe)$
Magnetic Vector Potential (***A***)			
Dimensional system LTUI / Absolute system m-s-V-A	$L^{-1}TU$ / weber/meter	$Wb\, m^{-1}$	$\triangle\, 10^{6}\, emu\ \triangle\, 10^{6}/c\, esu (= 3.3356 \times 10^{-5}\, esu)$
Dimensional system $LMT\mu_0$ / Electromagnetic CGS-system	$L^{1/2} M^{1/2} T^{-1} \mu_0^{1/2}$ / $cm^{1/2} g^{1/2} s^{-1}$	emu $(= G\, cm)$	$\triangle\, 10^{-6}\, Wb\, m^{-1}\ \triangle\, 1/c\, esu (= 3.3356 \times 10^{-11}\, esu)$
Dimensional system $LMT\varepsilon_0$ / Electrostatic CGS-system	$L^{-1/2} M^{1/2} \varepsilon_0^{-1/2}$ / $cm^{-1/2} g^{1/2}$	esu	$\triangle\, 10^{-6} c\, Wb\, m^{-1} (= 2.9979 \times 10^{4}\, Wb\, m^{-1})\ \triangle\, c\, emu\ (= 2.9979 \times 10^{10}\, emu)$
Magnetic Induction (***B***) (magnetic flux density)			
Dimensional system LTUI / Absolute system m-s-V-A	$L^{-2}TU$ / weber/square meter	$Wb\, m^{-2}$	$\triangle\, 10^{4}\, gauss\ \triangle\, 10^{4}/c\, esu (= 3.3356 \times 10^{-7}\, esu)$
Dimensional system $LMT\mu_0$ / Electromagnetic CGS-system	$L^{-1/2} M^{1/2} T^{-1} \mu_0^{1/2}$ / gauss* $= cm^{-1/2} g^{1/2} s^{-1}$	G	$= 1$ maxwell per $cm^2\ \triangle\, 10^{-4}\, Wb\, m^{-2}$; $\triangle\, 1/c\, esu\, (= 3.3356 \times 10^{-11}\, esu)$
Dimensional system $LMT\varepsilon_0$ / Electrostatic CGS-system	$L^{-3/2} M^{1/2} \varepsilon_0^{-1/2}$ / $cm^{-3/2} g^{1/2}$	esu	$\triangle\, 10^{-4} c\, Wb\, m^{-2} (= 2.9979 \times 10^{6}\, Wb\, m^{-2})$; $\triangle\, c\, G\, (= 2.9979 \times 10^{10}\, G)$
Magnetic Flux (Φ)			
Dimensional system LTUI / Absolute system m-s-V-A	TU / weber $(= V\, s)$	Wb	$\triangle\, 10^{8}\, Mx\ \triangle\, 10^{8}/c\, esu (= 3.3356 \times 10^{-3}\, esu)$
Dimensional system $LMT\mu_0$ / Electromagnetic CGS-system	$L^{3/2} M^{1/2} T^{-1} \mu_0^{1/2}$ / maxwell $= cm^{3/2} g^{1/2} s^{-1}$	Mx	$\triangle\, 10^{-8}\, Wb\ \triangle\, 1/c\, esu (= 3.3356 \times 10^{-11}\, esu)$
Dimensional system $LMT\varepsilon_0$ / Electrostatic CGS-system	$L^{1/2} M^{1/2} \varepsilon_0^{-1/2}$ / $cm^{1/2} g^{1/2}$	esu	$\triangle\, 10^{-8} c\, Wb (= 2.9979 \times 10^{2}\, Wb) = c\, Mx (= 2.9979 \times 10^{10}\, Mx)$
Magnetic Polarization (***J***) (intensity of magnetization, intrinsic induction)			
Dimensional system LTUI / Absolute system m-s-V-A	$L^{-2}TU$ / weber/square meter	$Wb\, m^{-2}$	$\triangle\, 10^{4}/4\pi\, G (= 7.9577 \times 10^{2}\, G)$; $\triangle\, 10^{4}/4\pi\, c\, esu\, (= 2.6544 \times 10^{-8}\, esu)$
Dimensional system $LMT\mu_0$ / Electromagnetic CGS-system	$L^{-1/2} M^{1/2} T^{-1} \mu_0^{1/2}$ / gauss* $= cm^{-1/2} g^{1/2} s^{-1}$	G	$\triangle\, 4\pi\, 10^{-4}\, Wb\, m^{-2} (= 1.2566 \times 10^{-3}\, Wb\, m^{-2})$; $\triangle\, 1/c\, esu\, (= 3.3357 \times 10^{-11}\, esu)$
Dimensional system $LMT\varepsilon_0$ / Electrostatic CGS-system	$L^{-3/2} M^{1/2} \varepsilon_0^{-1/2}$ / $cm^{-3/2} g^{1/2}$	esu	$\triangle\, 4\pi\, 10^{-4} c\, Wb\, m^{-2} (= 3.7673 \times 10^{7}\, Wb\, m^{-2})$; $\triangle\, c\, G\, (= 2.9979 \times 10^{10}\, G)$

* The name 'gauss' instead of 'oersted' is often used for the CGS-unit of magnetic field strength, and the name 'oersted' instead of 'gauss' for the CGS-unit of magnetic induction.

Electrical or Magnetic Property *(Symbol)* Dimensional system / System of measurement	Dimensions / Unit	Symbol of abbreviation	Equivalents: $\triangleq$ indicates numerical but not dimensional equivalence; c = velocity of light in vacuum in centimeters per second = 2.99793×10^{10}
Magnetic Moment (Coulomb's) (m_H)			
Dimensional system LTUI / Absolute system m-s-V-A	LTU / weber × meter	Wb m	$\triangleq 10^{10}/4\pi$ emu $(= 7.9577 \times 10^{8}$ emu) $\triangleq 10^{10}/4\pi c$ esu $(= 2.6544 \times 10^{-2}$ esu)
Dimensional system $LMT\mu_0$ / Electromagnetic CGS-system	$L^{5/2} M^{1/2} T^{-1} \mu_0^{1/2}$ / $cm^{5/2} g^{1/2} s^{-1}$	emu	$\triangleq 4\pi 10^{-10}$ Wb m $(= 1.2566 \times 10^{-9}$ Wb m) $\triangleq 1/c$ esu $(= 3.3356 \times 10^{-11}$ esu)
Dimensional system $LMT\varepsilon_0$ / Electrostatic CGS-system	$L^{3/2} M^{1/2} \varepsilon_0^{-1/2}$ / $cm^{3/2} g^{1/2}$	esu	$\triangleq 4\pi 10^{-10} c$ Wb m $(= 3.7673 \times 10$ Wb m) $\triangleq c$ emu $(= 2.9979 \times 10^{10}$ emu)
Magnetic Pole Strength (Coulomb's) (p)			
Dimensional system LTUI / Absolute system m-s-V-A	TU / weber	Wb	$\triangleq 10^{8}/4\pi$ emu $(= 7.9577 \times 10^{6}$ emu) $\triangleq 10^{8}/4\pi c$ esu $(= 2.6544 \times 10^{-4}$ esu)
Dimensional system $LMT\mu_0$ / Electromagnetic CGS-system	$L^{3/2} M^{1/2} T^{-1} \mu_0^{1/2}$ / $cm^{3/2} g^{1/2} s^{-1}$	emu	$\triangleq 4\pi 10^{-8}$ Wb $(= 1.2566 \times 10^{-7}$ Wb) $\triangleq 1/c$ esu $(= 3.3356 \times 10^{-11}$ esu)
Dimensional system $LMT\varepsilon_0$ / Electrostatic CGS-system	$L^{1/2} M^{1/2} \varepsilon_0^{-1/2}$ / $cm^{1/2} g^{1/2}$	esu	$\triangleq 4\pi 10^{-8} c$ Wb $(= 3.7673 \times 10^{-3}$ Wb) $\triangleq c$ emu $(= 2.9979 \times 10^{10}$ emu)
Magnetization (M)			
Dimensional system LTUI / Absolute system m-s-V-A	$L^{-1} I$ / ampere/meter	$A\ m^{-1}$	$\triangleq 10^{-3}$ emu $\triangleq 10^{-3} c$ esu $(= 2.9979 \times 10^{7}$ esu)
Dimensional system $LMT\mu_0$ / Electromagnetic CGS-system	$L^{-1/2} M^{1/2} T^{-1} \mu_0^{-1/2}$ / $cm^{-1/2} g^{1/2} s^{-1}$	emu	$\triangleq 10^{3}\ A\ m^{-1} \triangleq c$ esu $(= 2.9979 \times 10^{10}$ esu)
Dimensional system $LMT\varepsilon_0$ / Electrostatic CGS-system	$L^{1/2} M^{1/2} T^{-2} \varepsilon_0^{1/2}$ / $cm^{1/2} g^{1/2} s^{-2}$	esu	$\triangleq 10^{3}/c\ A\ m^{-1} (= 3.3356 \times 10^{-8}\ A\ m^{-1}) \triangleq 1/c$ emu $(= 3.3356 \times 10^{-11}$ emu)
Magnetic Moment (Ampère's) (m_B)			
Dimensional system LTUI / Absolute system m-s-V-A	$L^{2} I$ / ampere × square meter	$A\ m^{2}$	$\triangleq 10^{3}$ emu $\triangleq 10^{3} c$ esu $(= 2.9979 \times 10^{13}$ esu)
Dimensional system $LMT\mu_0$ / Electromagnetic CGS-system	$L^{5/2} M^{1/2} T^{-1} \mu_0^{-1/2}$ / $cm^{5/2} g^{1/2} s^{-1}$	emu	$\triangleq 10^{-3}\ A\ m^{2} \triangleq c$ esu $(= 2.9979 \times 10^{10}$ esu)
Dimensional system $LMT\varepsilon_0$ / Electrostatic CGS-system	$L^{7/2} M^{1/2} T^{-2} \varepsilon_0^{1/2}$ / $cm^{7/2} g^{1/2} s^{-2}$	esu	$\triangleq 10^{-3}/c\ A\ m^{2} (= 3.3356 \times 10^{-14}\ A\ m^{2}) \triangleq 1/c$ emu $(= 3.3356 \times 10^{-11}$ emu)
Magnetic Pole Strength (Ampère's) (m)			
Dimensional system LTUI / Absolute system m-s-V-A	LI / ampere × meter	A m	$\triangleq 10$ emu $\triangleq 10 c$ esu $(= 2.9979 \times 10^{11}$ esu)
Dimensional system $LMT\mu_0$ / Electromagnetic CGS-system	$L^{3/2} M^{1/2} T^{-1} \mu_0^{-1/2}$ / $cm^{3/2} g^{1/2} s^{-1}$	emu	$\triangleq 10^{-1}$ A m $\triangleq c$ esu $(= 2.9979 \times 10^{10}$ esu)
Dimensional system $LMT\varepsilon_0$ / Electrostatic CGS-system	$L^{5/2} M^{1/2} T^{-2} \varepsilon_0^{1/2}$ / $cm^{5/2} g^{1/2} s^{-2}$	esu	$\triangleq 10^{-1}/c$ A m $(= 3.3356 \times 10^{-12}$ A m) $\triangleq 1/c$ esu $(= 3.3356 \times 10^{-11}$ emu)
Magnetic Susceptibility $(\varkappa)$			
Dimensional system LTUI / Absolute system m-s-V-A	1 / 1	1 [abs]	$\triangleq 1/4\pi$ [emu] $(= 7.9577 \times 10^{-2}$ [emu]) $\triangleq 1/4\pi$ [esu]
Dimensional system $LMT\mu_0$ / Electromagnetic CGS-system	1 / 1	1 [emu]	$\triangleq 4\pi$ [abs] $(= 1.2566 \times 10$ [abs]) $\triangleq$ [esu]
Dimensional system $LMT\varepsilon_0$ / Electrostatic CGS-system	1 / 1	1 (esu)	$\triangleq 4\pi$ [abs] $(= 1.2566 \times 10$ [abs]) $\triangleq$ [emu]

Electrical or Magnetic Property *(Symbol)* — Dimensional system / System of measurement	Dimensions / Unit	Symbol or abbreviation	Equivalents — △ indicates numerical but not dimensional equivalence; c = velocity of light in vacuum in centimeters per second $= 2.99793 \times 10^{10}$
Magnetic Permeance (Λ)			
Dimensional system LTUI Absolute system m-s-V-A	TUI^{-1} henry $= V\,s\,A^{-1}$	H	△ $10^9/4\pi$ emu ($= 7.9577 \times 10^7$ emu) △ $10^9/4\pi c^2$ esu ($= 8.8542 \times 10^{-14}$ esu)
Dimensional system LMTμ_0 Electromagnetic CGS-system	$L\,\mu_0$ cm	cm (emu)	△ $4\pi\,10^{-9}$ H ($= 1.2566 \times 10^{-8}$ H) △ $1/c^2$ esu ($= 1.1126 \times 10^{-21}$ esu)
Dimensional system LMTε_0 Electrostatic CGS-system	$L^{-1}T^2\varepsilon_0^{-1}$ $cm^{-1}s^2$	esu	△ $4\pi\,10^{-9}c^2$ H ($= 1.1294 \times 10^{13}$ H) △ c^2 emu ($= 8.9876 \times 10^{20}$ emu)
Electromagnetic Induction (m_L) (self-inductance)			
Dimensional system LTUI Absolute system m-s-V-A	TUI^{-1} henry $= V\,s\,A^{-1}$	H	△ 10^9 emu (cm) △ $10^9/c^2$ esu ($= 1.1126 \times 10^{-12}$ esu)
Dimensional system LMTμ_0 Electromagnetic CGS-system	$L\,\mu_0$ cm	cm (emu)	△ 10^{-9} H △ $1/c^2$ esu ($= 1.1126 \times 10^{-21}$ esu)
Dimensional system LMTε_0 Electrostatic CGS-system	$L^{-1}T^2\varepsilon_0^{-1}$ $cm^{-1}s^2$	esu	△ $10^{-9}c^2$ H ($= 8.9876 \times 10^{11}$ H) △ c^2 emu ($= 8.9876 \times 10^{20}$ emu)
Electric or Magnetic Force (F)			
Dimensional system LTUI Absolute system m-s-V-A	$L^{-1}TUI$ newton	N	$\equiv 10^5$ dyn — For other equivalents see Force units, page 214
Dimensional system LMTμ_0 Dimensional system LMTε_0	LMT^{-2}		
Electromagnetic CGS-system Electrostatic CGS-system	dyne $\equiv cm\,g\,s^{-2}$	dyn	$\equiv 10^{-5}$ N
Electric or Magnetic Energy (W) (work)			
Dimensional system LTUI Absolute system m-s-V-A	TUI joule $\equiv W\,s$ $\equiv A\,V\,s \equiv N\,m$ $\equiv m^2\,kg\,s^{-2}$	J	$\equiv 10^7$ erg — For other equivalents see Energy units, page 216
Dimensional system LMTμ_0 Dimensional system LMTε_0	L^2MT^{-2}		
Electromagnetic CGS-system Electrostatic CGS-system	erg $\equiv cm^2\,g\,s^{-2}$	erg	$\equiv 10^{-7}$ J
Electric or Magnetic Power (P)			
Dimensional system LTUI Absolute system m-s-V-A	UI watt ($=$ V A)	W	$\equiv 10^7\,erg\,s^{-1}$ — For other equivalents see Power units, page 216
Dimensional system LMTμ_0 Dimensional system LMTε_0	L^2MT^{-3}		
Electromagnetic CGS-system Electrostatic CGS-system	erg/second ($\equiv cm^2\,g\,s^{-3}$)	$erg\,s^{-1}$	$\equiv 10^{-7}$ W
Energy of Electromagnetic Radiation (S) (POYNTING vector)			
Dimensional system LTUI Absolute system m-s-V-A	$L^{-2}UI$ watt/square meter	$W\,m^{-2}$	$= 10^3\,g\,s^{-3}$
Dimensional system LMTμ_0 Dimensional system LMTε_0	MT^{-3}		
Electromagnetic CGS-system Electrostatic CGS-system	$g\,s^{-3} \equiv erg\,s^{-1}\,cm^{-2}$	$g\,s^{-3}$	$= 10^{-3}\,W\,m^{-2}$

Radioactive decay

The *international unit of radioactive decay* is the curie (c). It is defined[1] as *that quantity of a radioactive nuclide which has an activity of* 3.700×10^{10} *disintegrations per second.*

A *nuclide* consists of atoms having the same nuclear charge and the same mass number. It has become customary to express quantities of radioactive nuclides in curies, for example "1 curie of cesium-137" instead of "an amount of cesium-137 having an activity of 1 curie".

The curie is subdivided as follows:

1 curie $= 10^3$ millicuries (mc)
$= 10^6$ microcuries (μc)
$= 10^9$ nanocuries (nc)

1 millicurie $= 3.7 \times 10^7$ disintegrations per second
1 microcurie $= 3.7 \times 10^4$ disintegrations per second
1 nanocurie $= 3.7 \times 10$ disintegrations per second

Specific activity

Since the isotopes used in radiotherapy and tracer techniques are rarely pure radioisotopes the concept of specific activity has been introduced. This expression is used to indicate both the proportion of radioactive atoms in an isotope preparation to the total number of atoms present, and the actual activity (in curies) contained in 1 gram of the preparation. The specific activity (curies per gram) of a pure nuclide (100% radioactive atoms) is calculated as follows:

$$\text{Rate of disintegration per gram of pure nuclide} = \frac{0.693 \times N}{T \times A}$$

where N = AVOGADRO's number (6.025×10^{23} mol^{-1}; cf. page 243), T = half-life of the nuclide in seconds, A = mass number of the nuclide. This is converted into specific activity by dividing by the disintegration rate of one curie (3.7×10^{10}):

$$\text{Specific activity of pure nuclide} = \frac{0.693 \times N}{T \times A \times 3.7 \times 10^{10}} = \frac{1.1287 \times 10^{13}}{T \times A}$$

The percentage of radioactive isotope in an isotope preparation is then

$$\frac{\text{Specific activity (c/g) of preparation} \times 100}{\text{Specific activity (c/g) of pure nuclide}}\ \%$$

Older units

The *old curie* was defined as that quantity of radium emanation (radon) in equilibrium with 1 g of radium. This definition was later extended[2] so that the curie became the equilibrium quantity of any decay product in the radium series, i.e. that quantity of such a product which in a certain time exhibits the same number of disintegrations as 1 g of radium in the same time.

In balneology the unit *eman* is still in use to express the concentration of radioactivity in natural waters, natural gases and the like:

1 eman $= 10^{-10}$ old curies per liter

The *Mache unit* (ME), also a unit of concentration, is that quantity of radon per liter of water or gas which without decay products and with complete utilization of the α-particles can maintain by its ionization of air a saturation current of 10^{-3} esu $\triangleq 3.3356 \times 10^{-13}$ ampere. For 1 old curie this saturation current has been measured[3,4] at 2.75×10^6 esu $\triangleq$ 0.92 A, whence

1 Mache unit $= 3.64 \times 10^{-10}$ old curies per liter $= 3.64$ eman

The activity unit "Mache unit × liters" is also known as the millistat (mst)[5]:

1 millistat per liter = 1 Mache unit

1) International Union of Pure and Applied Physics, *Rep. 7th Gen. Ass. I.U.P.A.P.*, Copenhagen, 1951. *2)* International Radium Standard Commission, *J. Amer. chem. Soc.*, **53**, 2437 (1931). *3)* FLAMM and MACHE, *S.-B. Akad. Wiss. Wien*, Abt. IIa, **121**, 227 (1912). *4)* FLAMM and MACHE, *S.-B. Akad. Wiss. Wien*, Abt. IIa, **122**, 535 (1913). *5)* MEYER, S., *S.-B. Akad. Wiss. Wien*, Abt. IIa, **138**, 557 (1929).

Radiological dose units

The whole field of radiation dosimetry is still the subject of international discussion and it is fairly certain that changes will be made during the next few years, particularly in respect of an extended definition of the roentgen and a new, mass-specific ionization unit. The following description of the radiological dose units has been abstracted from the 1956 Report of the International Commission on Radiological Units and Measurements (ICRU), published as *Handbook 62* of the National Bureau of Standards, Washington, 1957.

The difference between the dose of a drug administered and the amount (dose) of it which is absorbed in the organism, as well as the difficulty of determining the latter, is well known to the physician. He is also aware that different drugs which act in the same way often require different dosages in order to produce the same effect. This situation has its counterpart in radiation dosimetry and has resulted in the following distinctions being made:

(*a*) The "administered" dose is designated *exposure dose*. The unit is the roentgen.

(*b*) The unit of the *absorbed dose* is the rad (from "radiation absorbed dose").

(*c*) The *relative biological effectiveness* (RBE) of a radiation is a factor expressing its effectiveness (per unit of absorbed dose) relative to other radiations. The *RBE dose* (RBE × absorbed dose in rad) is the absorbed dose having regard to the biological activity of the radiation concerned. The unit of RBE dose is the rem.

The roentgen and rad are internationally accepted units. The RBE factor and unit rem are "recognized" by the ICRU. The use of the rem should be restricted to statements relating to radiation protection (permissible RBE doses). See also remarks on page 238.

1. Exposure dose

Definition: *the exposure dose of* X- *or* γ*-radiation at a certain place is a measure of the radiation that is based upon its ability to produce ionization.*

The international unit of exposure dose is the roentgen (r), defined as *an exposure dose of* X- *or* γ*-radiation such that the associated corpuscular emission per 0.001 293 g of air produces, in air, ions carrying 1 electrostatic unit of quantity of electricity of either sign**.

0.001 293 g of air is the mass of 1 cm³ of dry atmospheric air under normal conditions (0° C, 760 mm Hg). A quantity of 1 electrostatic unit of electricity is usually called an electrostatic unit of charge (esu_{charge}) and corresponds to 3.3356×10^{-10} coulomb (C). Cf. also pages 229 and 230.

In practice, accurate measurements in roentgens can only be made under conditions of electronic equilibrium. Either the ionization chamber used must be so constructed that the air contained in it is in electronic equilibrium, or it must be suitably calibrated (for example, a thimble ionization chamber). With increasing energy of the radiation it becomes increasingly difficult to maintain electronic equilibrium, so that 3 Mev is arbitrarily regarded as the upper limit for which the roentgen should be used.

Under conditions of electronic equilibrium the roentgen can be considered to be a unit of (ionic) charge in relation to a mass of air:

$$1\ \text{r} = \frac{1\ \text{esu}}{0.001\,293\ \text{g air}} = \frac{773.40\ \text{esu}}{1\ \text{g air}} \triangleq \frac{2.5798 \times 10^{-4}\ \text{C}}{1\ \text{kg air}} \quad \textbf{(1)}$$

(with electronic equilibrium)

2. Exposure dose rate

Definition: *the exposure dose rate is the exposure dose per unit time.*

The unit of exposure dose rate is the roentgen per unit time. The units of time used are the second, minute, hour and also day, week, etc. (for conversion factors see Table 1 opposite).

Under conditions of electronic equilibrium the roentgen dose rate per second is obtained from formula (**1**):

$$1\ \frac{\text{r}}{\text{s}} \triangleq \frac{2.5798 \times 10^{-4}\ \text{C/s}}{1\ \text{kg air}} = \frac{2.5798 \times 10^{-4}\ \text{A}}{1\ \text{kg air}} \quad \textbf{(2)}$$

This current strength corresponds to an ionization current which can be maintained by 1 r/s per kg of air in electronic equilibrium.

* In vacuum this conception of radiation dose ceases to have any meaning. In this case only the radiation flux or intensity (in the strictly physical sense) can be measured.

Table 1 Conversion of roentgen dose rates

To convert from a unit under **A** into any unit under **B**, multiply by the factor given in the appropriate column under **B**.

A	B				
	mr/h	μr/s	r/h	r/min	r/s
mr/h	1×1	$2.\dot{7}\times 10^{-1}$	1×10^{-3}	$1.\dot{6}\times 10^{-5}$	$2.\dot{7}\times 10^{-7}$
μr/s	3.6×1	1×1	3.6×10^{-3}	6×10^{-5}	1×10^{-6}
r/h	1×10^{3}	$2.\dot{7}\times 10^{2}$	1×1	$1.\dot{6}\times 10^{-2}$	$2.\dot{7}\times 10^{-4}$
r/min	6×10^{4}	$1.\dot{6}\times 10^{4}$	6×10	1×1	$1.\dot{6}\times 10^{-2}$
r/s	3.6×10^{6}	1×10^{6}	3.6×10^{3}	6×10	1×1

3. Specific γ-ray emission (*k*-factor)

Definition: *the specific γ-ray emission of a radioactive nuclide is the exposure dose rate produced by the unfiltered γ-rays from a point source of a defined quantity of that nuclide at a defined distance.*

The unit of specific γ-ray emission is the roentgen per millicurie hour (r/mch) at 1 cm.

Table 2 *k*-Factors in roentgens per millicurie and hour at a distance of 1 cm

Nuclide	Half-life T	Energy of γ-radiation MeV	k r/mch at 1 cm	References
^{22}Na	2.6 y	1.28	11.6	*1, 2*
^{24}Na	15 h	1.37; 2.76	18.7	*3*
^{42}K	12.5 h	1.53	1.5*	*5*
^{51}Cr	27.8 d	0.323	1.8	*6*
^{52}Mn	5.7 d	0.7; 0.9; 1.5	19.5	*6*
^{54}Mn	291 d	0.84	4.7	*1, 2*
^{56}Mn	2.58 h	2.06; 1.77; 0.822	9.4	*4*
^{59}Fe	45 d	1.3; 1.1; 0.19	6.2	*1, 2*
^{60}Co	5.25 y	1.33; 1.17	12.8 ± 0.1 13.0 13.5 ± 0.3	*3, 7* *1, 2* *7*
^{65}Zn	245 d	1.11	2.8	*1, 2*
^{74}As	17.5 d	0.635; 0.596; 0.511	5.1	*6*
^{76}As	26.8 h	1.70; 1.2; 0.55	2.3	*1, 2*
^{82}Br	36 h	0.55–1.48	14.6	*1, 2*
^{124}Sb	60 d	0.21–2.04	8.9	*1*
^{131}I	8.04 d	0.08 (0.3%); 0.284 (3%) 0.364 (79%); 0.368 (12.5%); 0.72 (5.2%)	2.2	*1, 2*
^{132}I	2.4 h	0.69; 1.41; 2.0	11.9	*1*
^{137}Cs	30 y	0.661	3.1	*1, 2*
^{170}Tm	129 d	0.084	0.4*	*1, 2*
^{182}Ta	112 d	0.066–1.223 (eff. 1.13)	6.1	*4*
^{192}Ir	74.4 d	0.136–0.613 (eff. 0.6)	5.0	*3*
^{198}Au	2.69 d	0.41; 0.67; 1.1	2.35	*6*
^{203}Hg	47.9 d	0.279	1.6	*6*
^{226}Ra	1600 y	13 lines from 0.184 to 2.45	8.25 ± 0.08** 7.60 ± 0.05***	*8* *9*

References: *1)* Calculated from the decay scheme and quoted by FAIRES and PARKS, *Radioisotope Laboratory Techniques*, London, 1958, page 40. *2)* Calculated from the decay scheme and quoted by PRICE et al., *Radiation Shielding*, London, 1957, page 305. *3)* Experimental value of the National Physical Laboratory Standards Committee (London). Cf. PERRY, W. E., *Acta radiol. (Stockh.)*, Suppl. 117, 105 (1954). *4)* RAJEWSKY, B., *Strahlendosis und Strahlenwirkung*, 2nd ed., Stuttgart, 1956, pages N 13–N 21. *5)* Calculated from the decay scheme and quoted by SINCLAIR, W. K., in HINE and BROWNELL (Eds.), *Radiation Dosimetry*, New York, 1956, page 518. *6)* Calculated from the decay scheme and quoted by HINE, G. J., in HINE and BROWNELL, *loc. cit.*, pages 899 and 903. *7)* ROBINSON, B. W., *Acta radiol. (Stockh.)*, Suppl. 117, 71 (1954). *8)* Experimental value of GARRETT, C., *Canad. J. Phys.*, **36**, 149 (1958). *9)* LÜTHY, H., personal communication.

* In practice probably much higher since bremsstrahlung (from the β-radiation) has been ignored.

** With 0.5 mm platinum filtering.

*** With 1.0 mm platinum filtering.

The specific γ-ray emission of a nuclide is a material constant and has therefore also been given the name dose constant. From it the roentgen emission of the γ-rays of a quantity M of a radioactive nuclide at a distance p can be calculated as follows:

$$\frac{\mathrm{r}}{\mathrm{h}} = k\,\frac{M}{p^2} \quad (M \text{ in millicuries}, p \text{ in centimeters})$$

4. β-Ray emission

In analogy with γ-ray emission, the dose rate from β-emitting isotopes can be calculated from a dose factor k_β. This factor is dependent on the energy of the β-radiation:

Table 3 Dose factor k_β in roentgens per millicurie per hour at a distance of 1 cm as a function of energy of β-radiation (From MAYNEORD and SINCLAIR, *Advanc. biol. med. Phys.*, 3, 1 [1953])

Energy of β-radiation MeV	k_β r/mch	Energy of β-radiation MeV	k_β r/mch
0.3	616	1.0	355
0.5	477	2.0	318
0.7	420	10.0	372

5. Absorbed dose

Definition: *the absorbed dose of any ionizing radiation is the energy imparted to matter by ionizing particles per unit mass of irradiated material at the place of interest.*

The unit of absorbed dose is the rad, defined as

$$1 \text{ rad} = \frac{100 \text{ ergs}}{1 \text{ g}} = \frac{0.01 \text{ J}}{1 \text{ kg}} \tag{3}$$

Because the rad does not specify the medium, the latter should be stated unless it is clearly implied, for example "rads (tissue)", "rads (air)".

The absorbed dose rate is the absorbed dose per unit time, the unit being rad per unit time (time units and conversion factors are the same as for the roentgen in Table 1):

$$1\,\frac{\text{rad}}{\text{s}} = \frac{100 \text{ ergs/s}}{1 \text{ g}} = \frac{0.01 \text{ W}}{1 \text{ kg}} \tag{4}$$

6. Integral absorbed dose

Definition: *the integral absorbed dose in a certain region is the energy imparted to matter by ionizing particles in that region.*

The unit of integral absorbed dose is the gram rad (g rad):

$$1 \text{ g rad} = 100 \text{ ergs} = 10^{-5} \text{ J}$$

7. Relationship between absorbed dose and exposure dose of X- or γ-radiation

The direct calorimetric measurement of absorbed dose is extremely difficult, and for this reason it has always been calculated from ionization measurements in air. This is still the commonest indirect method but it is likely that others (for example, radiochemical methods) will find increasing use in the future because of their advantages in the higher quantum-energy ranges.

(*a*) *Calculation of absorbed dose D when the exposure dose can be measured in roentgens (electronic equilibrium):*

$$D_m = f_m \times R \text{ (in rads)}$$

where m = medium concerned

R = exposure dose in roentgens

f = absorbed dose in rads per roentgen of exposure dose

(*b*) *Calculation of absorbed dose D when the exposure dose cannot be measured in roentgens (electronic equilibrium conditions not satisfied):*

In this case the ionization is measured at the place of interest in a very small air-filled ionization chamber having walls* that are

* Preferably matching the surrounding medium fairly closely in composition.

very thin compared with the range of the secondary electrons (BRAGG-GRAY principle[1]):

$D_m = f'_m \times Q$ (in rads)

where m = medium concerned

Q = charge in esu per 0.001 293 g air

f' = absorbed dose in rads per 1 esu

Table 4 Values of the factor f (absorbed dose in rad per roentgen) for monochromatic photon beams
(From ICRU Report 1956[2])

Photon energy MeV	Factor f for			
	Air*	Water	Muscle	Bone
0.010	0.87_7	0.92_0	0.93_3	3.58
0.015	0.87_7	0.89_7	0.92_5	4.00
0.020	0.87_7	0.88_7	0.92_5	4.27
0.030	0.87_7	0.87_7	0.91_9	4.43
0.040	0.87_7	0.88_7	0.92_8	4.18
0.050	0.87_7	0.90_0	0.93_4	3.61
0.060	0.87_7	0.91_3	0.93_7	2.94
0.080	0.87_7	0.94_0	0.94_8	1.93
0.10	0.87_7	0.95_7	0.95_7	1.47
0.15	0.87_7	0.97_1	0.96_4	1.06
0.20	0.87_7	0.98_2	0.97_2	0.98_8
0.30	0.87_7	0.97_7	0.96_5	0.94_7
0.40	0.87_7	0.97_5	0.96_3	0.93_6
0.50	0.87_7	0.97_4	0.96_6	0.93_3
0.60	0.87_7	0.97_5	0.96_6	0.93_3
0.80	0.87_7	0.97_4	0.96_5	0.92_9
1.0	0.87_7	0.97_4	0.96_5	0.92_7
1.5	0.87_7	0.97_3	0.96_6	0.92_9
2.0	0.87_7	0.97_4	0.96_3	0.92_9
3.0	0.87_7	0.97_1	0.96_3	0.93_7

* The factor 0.87_7 is calculated from the roentgen as follows: 1 ion pair carries an electric charge of 4.80273×10^{-10} esu (see Physical Constants, page 247). 1 r therefore produces 2.08215×10^9 ion pairs in 0.001 293 g air, or 1.61032×10^{12} ion pairs in 1 g air. The energy required for the production of one ion pair in air by electrons for radiations above 20 keV is 34 eV $= 5.4469 \times 10^{-11}$ erg (ICRU Report 1956[2]). The production of 1.61032×10^{12} ion pairs in 1 g air therefore requires 87.712, or roughly 88 ergs. This energy is absorbed from the radiation by the air and is the so-called energy equivalent of the roentgen. From the definition of the rad it is equal to 0.87_7 rad (air).

Table 5 Values of the factor f (average absorbed dose in rad per roentgen) for various primary X-ray spectra
(From ICRU Report 1956[2])

Radiation				Factor f for			
Tube potential kV	Filter mm	Half-value layer mm	Spectrum	Air*	Water	Muscle	Bone
100	0.18 Cu	0.25 Cu or 5.5 Al	measured	0.87_7	0.91	0.94	3.10
100	as above	as above	calculated[3]	0.87_7	0.91	0.94	3.13
150	0.075 Cu	0.2 Cu	calculated[3]	0.87_7	0.92	0.94	2.69
200	0.20 Cu	0.5 Cu	calculated[3]	0.87_7	0.94	0.95	2.05
250	0.17 Cu + 3.0 Al	1.0 Cu	calculated[3]	0.87_7	0.95	0.95	1.76
250	0.9 Cu + 3.0 Al	2.0 Cu	calculated[3]	0.87_7	0.96	0.96	1.42
280	...	1.7 Cu	measured	0.87_7	0.96	0.96	1.44
280	...	2.5 Cu	measured	0.87_7	0.97	0.96	1.22
280	...	3.1 Cu	measured	0.87_7	0.97	0.96_5	1.13
400	...	4.16 Cu	measured	0.87_7	0.97	0.97	1.11

* See the footnote to Table 4.

Table 6 Values of the factor f' (absorbed dose in rad per 1 esu)
(From *Röntgen- und Gammastrahlen in Medizin und Biologie: Regeln für die Dosimetrie,* DIN 6809 [Vornorm], Berlin, 1958)

Radiation		Factor f' for		
Tube potential kV	Half-value layer mm Cu	Air*	Water	Soft tissues**
150	0.2	0.87_7	1.03	1.02
200	0.5	0.87_7	1.03	1.02
250	1.0	0.87_7	1.03	1.01
280	1.7	0.87_7	1.03	1.01
400	4.2	0.87_7	1.02	1.01
15 000	...	0.87_7	0.98	0.96
Isotope	Quantum energy MeV			
^{137}Cs	0.67	0.87_7	1.02	1.00
^{60}Co	1.25	0.87_7	1.01	1.00

* See the footnote to Table 4.

** Values of f' for soft tissues are also valid for bone embedded in soft tissue since the effect of the bone substance has already been taken into account in measuring the charge Q with the thin-walled chamber.

8. Relative biological effectiveness (RBE)

(*a*) The factor RBE, commonly represented by the symbol η, is used to compare the biological effectiveness of absorbed doses of radiation of the same magnitude delivered in different ways. It signifies that m rads delivered by a particular irradiation procedure produces a biological response identical with that produced by $m\eta$ rads delivered by a different procedure. The statement that "the RBE of α-radiation relative to γ-radiation is 10" signifies that m rads of α-radiation produces a particular biological response in the same degree as $10\,m$ rads of γ-radiation.

The concept of relative biological effectiveness has a limited usefulness because the biological effectiveness of any radiation depends on many factors. Thus the RBE of two radiations cannot in general be expressed by a single factor but varies with many subsidiary factors, such as the type and degree of biological damage (and hence with the absorbed dose), the absorbed dose rate, the fractionation, the oxygen tension, the pH, and the temperature.

(*b*) The RBE dose is equal numerically to the product of the dose in rads and an agreed conventional value of the RBE with respect to a particular form of radiation effect. The standard of comparison is X- or γ-radiation having a linear energy transfer (LET) in water of 3 keV/μm delivered at a rate of about 10 rad/min.

The unit of RBE dose is the rem. It has the same inherent looseness as the RBE and in addition assumes conventional and not necessarily measured values of RBE. It is therefore recommended that the use of the rem be restricted to statements relating to radiation protection, for example "the permissible weekly whole body RBE dose is 0.3 rem regardless of the type of radiation to which a person is exposed".

In the case of mixed radiations the RBE dose is assumed to be equal to the sum of the products of the absorbed dose of each radiation and its RBE:

$$\text{RBE dose in rems} = \Sigma\,[(\text{absorbed dose in rads}) \times \text{RBE}]$$

For purposes of radiation protection the following RBE values are recommended by RAJEWSKY, B., *Strahlendosis und Strahlenwirkung*, 2nd ed., Stuttgart, 1956:

Radiation	RBE
X-, γ- and β-Rays up to 3 MeV	1
α-Rays	20
Protons and deuterons	10
Fast neutrons	5
Heavy recoil nuclei	20

In any given circumstances ultra-hard X- and γ-rays over 1 MeV appear to be 15–30% less effective than X-rays of 200 kV.

1) Cf. SPIERS, F. W., in HINE and BROWNELL (Eds.), *Radiation Dosimetry*, New York, 1956, page 23. 2) *Handbook 62*, National Bureau of Standards, Washington, 1957. 3) KRAMERS, H. A., *Phil. Mag.*, **46**, 836 (1923).

Property and definition	Unit	Symbol or abbreviation
The **luminous flux** Φ is the total visible energy emitted by a source of light. The bases for its evaluation are the *relative spectral sensitivity* V_λ* of the eye adapted to bright light and the mechanical equivalent of light M**.	lumen	lm
The **quantity of light** Q is the product of the luminous flux and its duration.	lumen second lumen hour	lms lmh
The **luminous intensity** I in a given direction is the relation between the luminous flux radiated in that direction and the area upon which it falls, i.e. luminous flux per unit area. The unit is the *candela* or international candle***. A source of light having a luminous intensity of one candela in all directions produces a luminous flux of 4π lumen.	candela	cd
The **luminance (brightness)** L of a surface in a given direction is the ratio of the luminous intensity in that direction to the orthogonal projection of the radiating surface in that direction.	stilb $\equiv$ cd/cm² apostilb $\equiv$ sb/$10^4\pi$ lambert $\equiv$ sb/$\pi \equiv 10^4$asb	sb asb La
The unit of **brightness for scotopic vision,** in contrast to the preceding units, is related to the eye adapted to vision in the dark (rod vision). The conversion factor between this and the luminance L depends on the composition of the light. The unit is used only up to 10 skot.	skot $= 10^{-3}$ asb for radiation with a color temperature of 2360° K	sk
The **specific luminous radiation** H of a surface is the ratio of the radiated luminous flux to the area of the surface.	phot† $\equiv$ lm/cm²	ph
The **intensity of illumination** E is the ratio of the luminous flux incident upon a surface to the area A of the surface ($E = \Phi/A$) and therefore corresponds to the specific radiation with respect to that part of the radiation reaching the surface illuminated. 1 lumen uniformly distributed over 1 square meter of surface produces an intensity of 1 lux.	lux $\equiv$ lm/m²	lx
The unit of **intensity of illumination for scotopic vision** is analogous to that of brightness for scotopic vision, and relates to the eye adapted to vision in the dark.	nox $= 10^{-3}$ lx for radiation with a color temperature of 2360° K	nx
The **quantity of illumination** is the product of the intensity of illumination and its duration.	lux second	lxs
The **luminous efficiency** of a source of light is the ratio of the total luminous flux emitted to the power absorbed.	lumen/watt	lm/W

* For the relative spectral sensitivity V_λ of the eye the following internationally recognized values are used (λ = wave-length of light in nanometers [millimicrons]):

λ	V_λ	λ	V_λ	λ	V_λ	λ	V_λ	λ	V_λ	λ	V_λ	λ	V_λ	λ	V_λ	λ	V_λ	λ	V_λ
400	0.0004	440	0.023	480	0.139	520	0.710	555	1.000	590	0.757	630	0.265	670	0.032	710	0.0021	750	0.00012
410	0.0012	450	0.038	490	0.208	530	0.862	560	0.995	600	0.631	640	0.175	680	0.017	720	0.00105	760	0.00006
420	0.0040	460	0.060	500	0.323	540	0.954	570	0.952	610	0.503	650	0.107	690	0.0082	730	0.00052		
430	0.0116	470	0.091	510	0.503	550	0.995	580	0.870	620	0.381	660	0.061	700	0.0041	740	0.00025		

** The mechanical or electrical equivalent of light M is calculated for the lumen based on the candela as $M = (1.46_7 \pm 0.010) \times 10^{-3}\ \mathrm{J} \times (\mathrm{s} \times \mathrm{lm})^{-1} = (1.46_7 \pm 0.010) \times 10^{-3}$ W/lm, or $1/M = (680 \pm 5)$ lm/W. The new lumen therefore corresponds to a radiation of 0.001 46 watt.

*** The candela is defined by the condition that the luminance L of a black-body radiator amounts to 60 candela per square centimeter at the temperature of solidifying platinum.

† The phot, which by definition is the unit of specific radiation, is frequently used as a unit of illumination. In this case 1 phot = 10^4 lux.

Acoustic Units

Property and definition	Dimensions	Unit MKS-equivalent	Unit CGS-equivalent
Sound Pressure The instantaneous sound pressure at a point is the incremental change in the static atmospheric pressure at a given instant caused by the presence of a sound wave. Values not otherwise specified are root mean square values.	$L^{-1}MT^{-2}$	$N\ m^{-2}$	$dyn\ cm^{-2}$ ($\equiv \mu b$)
Particle Velocity The instantaneous particle velocity at a point is the velocity, due to a sound wave only, of a given particle of the medium at a given instant. Values not otherwise specified are root mean square values.	LM^{-1}	$m\ s^{-1}$	$cm\ s^{-1}$
Sound Pressure Level The sound pressure level in decibels (db), is 20 times the logarithm to the base 10 of the ratio of the measured pressure p of the sound to the reference sound pressure $p_0 = 2 \times 10^{-4}\ \mu b$[1].	1	db	db
Sound Energy Sound energy is mechanical energy radiated as sound.	L^2MT^{-2}	Ws	erg
Sound Power The sound power is the sound energy per second.	L^2MT^{-3}	W	$erg\ s^{-1}$
Sound Intensity The sound intensity measured in a specified direction at a point is the average rate at which sound energy is transmitted through a unit area perpendicular to the specified direction at the point considered.	MT^{-3}	$W\ m^{-2}$	$erg\ s^{-1}\ cm^{-2}$
Velocity of Sound The velocity of sound is the velocity of propagation of a sound wave. As a constant of the transmitting medium it is normally independent of the frequency and intensity of the sound wave. In air the velocity of sound depends mainly on the temperature and is given approximately by the following formula: $331.4 + (0.607 \times t)\ m\ s^{-1}$, where t is the ambient temperature in degrees Centigrade. Note: At very high intensities (for example, sound waves from explosions) the velocity can reach higher values.	LT^{-1}	$m\ s^{-1}$	$cm\ s^{-1}$
Frequency (Voice frequency) Frequency is the number of cycles per second of a periodical process.	T^{-1}	cps*	
Standard Tuning Frequency (Standard Musical Pitch) The standard tuning frequency is the frequency of the note A in the treble stave and is equal to 440 cps[2]. See under Tone Scales on page 242.			
Loudness Level[1] The phon is a dimensionless unit used to express the loudness level of a given sound or noise. The loudness level of a sound is expressed as n phons when it is judged by normal observers to be equal in loudness to a pure tone of frequency 1000 cps and consisting of a plane progressive sound wave, coming from directly in front of the observer, the sound pressure level of which is n decibels above the standard reference pressure of $2 \times 10^{-4}\ \mu b$. Fundamentally, loudness levels in phons can therefore be measured solely by means of subjective hearing comparisons; objective methods of measurement give only approximations.	1	phon	
The loudness level of a sound may be expressed uniquely in phons in accordance with the procedure defining the phon scale (see above). Owing to the arbitrary definition of this scale, however, loudness level values in phons *(continued opposite)*	1	sone	

* Known as the Hertz (Hz) in German-speaking countries.

1) International Organization for Standardization (ISO), *Recommendation R 131, Expression of the physical and subjective magnitudes of sound or noise*, 1st ed., 1959 (obtainable from the American Standards Association, New York, N.Y., or other national standards organizations).

2) International Organization for Standardization (ISO), *Recommendation R 16, Standard tuning frequency (standard musical pitch)*, 1st ed., 1955 (obtainable from the American Standards Association, New York, N.Y., or other national standards organizations).

Property and definition	Dimensions	Unit	
		MKS-equivalent	CGS-equivalent
do not immediately convey the magnitude of the loudness sensation but must be interpreted by the user on the basis of his experience of sounds previously heard to which phon values have been attached. A loudness scale in sones has therefore been established to provide a numerical designation of loudness levels which is proportional to the subjective magnitude as estimated by normal observers as follows: The relation between the loudness level of any sound in sones, S, and phons, P, is given by the following relation, known as the loudness function: $S = 2^{(P-40)/10}$ or $\log_{10} S \approx 0.03\,(P-40)$.	1	sone	

Values of S and P are given in the table below. It should be noted that

1. A loudness of 1 sone (unit of loudness) corresponds by definition to a loudness level of 40 phon.
2. The unit sone cannot be measured directly, but must be calculated from the loudness level in phons.
3. A twofold change in loudness corresponds to an interval of 10 phon.
4. Experimental confirmation of this relation exists over the range 20–120 phon and its use outside this range is an extrapolation.

phon	sone	phon	sone
20	0.25	75	11.3
25	0.35	80	16.0
30	0.50	85	22.6
35	0.70	90	32.0
40	*1.00*	95	45.3
45	1.41	100	64.0
50	2.00	105	90.5
55	2.83	110	128
60	4.00	115	181
65	5.66	120	256
70	8.00		

Sound Level Meters[1]

In view of the difficulty of establishing subjective hearing comparisons as required for the measurement of loudness levels in phons and of the complexity of the human ear, sound level meters have been standardized which measure certain weighted sound pressure levels. The weighting applied to each sinusoidal component of the sound pressure is given as a function of frequency by three standard reference curves (A, B and C). The varying sensitivity of the ear is taken into account by using curve A for low sound levels, curve B for moderate sound levels, and curve C for high sound levels. The weighted sound levels are expressed in decibels. The curve used must be indicated by placing the appropriate letter after the decibel value, as in the following table showing the approximate loudness levels of some everyday noises measured in this way.

Noise	Sound Level
Propeller transport airplane at 5 m	130 db (C)
Pneumatic hammer at 1 m	120 db (C)
Brass foundry	110 db (C)
Automobile horn at 5 m	100 db (C)
Haulage truck at 5 m	90 db (C)
Loud radio music	80 db (B)
Normal conversation at 1 m	70 db (B)
Automobile at 10 m	60 db (B)
Quiet stream or river	50 db (A)
Residential district without traffic	40 db (A)
Quiet garden	30 db (A)
Ticking of a watch	20 db (A)
Limit of audible noise	10 db (A)
Absolute silence	0 db (A)

Tone Scales

The tone scales are built up on the basis of definite frequency ratios between the tones in accordance with the musical sensitivity of the human ear. The most important tone intervals are arranged according to consonance and dissonance:

Consonant tone interval	Frequency ratio
Twelfth	3:1
Octave	2:1
Major sixth	5:3
Fifth	3:2
Fourth	4:3
Major third	5:4
Minor third	6:5
Unison	1:1

Dissonant tone interval	Frequency ratio
Major seventh	15:8
Minor seventh	9:5
Minor sixth	8:5
Major whole tone	9:8
Minor whole tone	10:9
Major semitone	16:15
Minor semitone	25:24

1) International Electrotechnical Commission, *Recommendations for sound level meters* (Publication 123), 1st ed., Geneva, 1961.

Diatonic major scale

Tone interval	Note symbol	Frequency ratio
First	C	1
Second	D	10:9
Major third	E	5:4
Fourth	F	4:3
Fifth	G	3:2
Major sixth	A	5:3
Major seventh	B	15:8
Octave	C′	2

Diatonic minor scale

Tone interval	Note symbol	Frequency ratio
First	C	1
Second	D	10:9
Minor third	E flat	6:5
Fourth	F	4:3
Fifth	G	3:2
Minor sixth	A flat	8:5
Minor seventh	B	9:5
Octave	C′	2

The borderline between consonance and dissonance is fluid and shows a tendency to shift in favor of those intervals which were formerly felt to be dissonant, such as the minor sixth and minor seventh.

The *diatonic* and *chromatic* tone scales differ in the manner in which they are built up. In the case of the diatonic major and minor scales, 7 notes are distributed unequally over the octave.

In the case of the chromatic scale, 12 semitones are distributed equally (equal temperament) over the octave, each semitone having $\sqrt[12]{2}$ times the frequency of the previous one.

Chromatic scale

Note symbol	Frequency ratio
C	1
C sharp = D flat	$2^{1/12}$
D	$2^{2/12}$
D sharp = E flat	$2^{3/12}$
E = F flat	$2^{4/12}$
F = E sharp	$2^{5/12}$
F sharp = G flat	$2^{6/12}$
G	$2^{7/12}$
A flat = G sharp	$2^{8/12}$
A	$2^{9/12}$
B flat = A sharp	$2^{10/12}$
B = C′ flat	$2^{11/12}$
C′ = B sharp	$2^{12/12}$

These divisions of the tone scale hold good for any octave range whatever and are independent of the absolute value of the basic note of the scale. The pitch of the tone scale is fixed by the frequency of the note C = $2^4 \times 16$ cps = 256 cps.

The 12-interval chromatic scale is fixed by the pitch of the note A in the treble stave. From 1859 to 1939 the French concert-pitch a′ = 435 cps (agreed upon at the Vienna tuning pitch conference in 1891) was accepted as the "international pitch". In 1939 the conference of the International Federation of National Standards Associations (ISA) in London fixed the standard pitch at 440 cps, and this pitch was subsequently endorsed by the ISA's successor, the International Organization for Standardization (ISO) in 1953[1]. The frequencies of the 12-interval chromatic scale, which is today internationally accepted, are given in the table below.

1) See footnote *2)* on page 240. A musical tone of this standard pitch is broadcast almost continuously day and night by two National Bureau of Standards shortwave stations for the benefit of scientists, electronics engineers and musical instrument makers. Cf. *Tech. News Bull. Nat. Bur. Stand.*, **41**, 120 (1957).

Vibration frequencies of the 12-interval chromatic scale, A = 440.0 cps

		c^{-3}	c^{-2}	c^{-1}	c^0	c^1	c^2	c^3	c^4	Ratios
C		16.35	32.70	65.41	130.81	261.63	523.25	1046.50	2093.00	1.000 00
C♯	D♭	17.32	34.65	69.30	138.59	277.18	554.37	1108.73	2217.46	$\sqrt[12]{2}$ = 1.059 46
D		18.35	36.71	73.42	146.83	293.66	587.33	1174.66	2349.32	$\sqrt[12]{2^2}$ = 1.122 46
D♯	E♭	19.45	38.89	77.78	155.56	311.13	622.25	1244.51	2489.02	$\sqrt[12]{2^3}$ = 1.189 21
E		20.60	41.20	82.41	164.81	329.63	659.26	1318.51	2637.02	$\sqrt[12]{2^4}$ = 1.259 92
F		21.83	43.65	87.31	174.61	349.23	689.46	1396.91	2793.83	$\sqrt[12]{2^5}$ = 1.334 84
F♯	G♭	23.12	46.25	92.50	185.00	369.99	739.99	1479.98	2959.96	$\sqrt[12]{2^6}$ = 1.414 21
G		24.50	49.00	98.00	196.00	392.00	783.99	1567.98	3135.96	$\sqrt[12]{2^7}$ = 1.498 31
G♯	A♭	25.96	51.91	103.83	207.65	415.30	830.61	1661.22	3322.44	$\sqrt[12]{2^8}$ = 1.587 40
A		27.50	55.00	110.00	220.00	440.00	880.00	1760.00	3520.00	$\sqrt[12]{2^9}$ = 1.681 79
A♯	B♭	29.14	58.27	116.54	233.08	466.16	932.33	1864.66	3729.31	$\sqrt[12]{2^{10}}$ = 1.781 80
B		30.87	61.74	123.47	246.94	493.88	987.77	1975.53	3951.07	$\sqrt[12]{2^{11}}$ = 1.887 75
										($\log_{10} \sqrt[12]{2}$ = 0.025 085 832 972)

$c^{-3} = C_2$ = subcontra-octave; $c^{-2} = C_1$ = contra-octave; c^{-1} = C = great octave; c^0 = c = small octave; c^1 = c′ = one-line octave; c^2 = c″ = two-line octave; etc. Only the pipe organ can cover the whole range c^{-3} to c^5 (c^5 = frequency of 4186.0 cps).

Individual Chemical Mass Units

Mass* of N molecules or atoms of a chemically homogeneous substance

This is equal to the molecular or atomic weight of the substance multiplied by the unit of mass.

Dimension in the LMT-systems of measurement = M

Units in the related systems:

CGS-system**: mole (mol) ≡ (molecular or atomic weight of the substance) × gram
MKS-system**: kilomole (kmol) ≡ (molecular or atomic weight of the substance) × kilogram

AVOGADRO's number N*** is the number of molecules or atoms contained in one mole of a substance.

To convert from a unit under **A** into any unit under **B**, multiply by the appropriate factor under **B**

A		B			
Name	Abbreviation	μmol	mmol	mol	kmol
Micromole	μmol	1	10^{-3}	10^{-6}	10^{-9}
Millimole	mmol	10^{3}	1	10^{-3}	10^{-6}
Mole	mol	10^{6}	10^{3}	1	10^{-3}
Kilomole	kmol	10^{9}	10^{6}	10^{3}	1

Unit	Number of molecules or atoms	
	Chemical scale	Physical scale
Micromole	6.0234×10^{17}	6.0250×10^{17}
Millimole	6.0234×10^{20}	6.0250×10^{20}
Mole	6.0234×10^{23}	6.0250×10^{23}
Kilomole	6.0234×10^{26}	6.0250×10^{26}

Mass* of N/z ions of a chemically homogeneous substance

This is equal to the molecular or atomic weight of the ions divided by their valency and multiplied by the unit of mass.

Dimension in the LMT-systems of measurement = M

Units in the related systems:

CGS-system: gram equivalent or equivalent (Eq or equiv. or g.equiv.)†
≡ (molecular or atomic weight of the ions/valency) × gram ≡ mole/valency

MKS-system: kilogram equivalent (kEq or kg.equiv.)† ≡ (molecular or atomic weight of the ions/valency) × kilogram
≡ kilomole/valency

N = AVOGADRO's number***

To convert from a unit under **A** into any unit under **B**, multiply by the appropriate factor under **B**

A		B			
Name	Abbreviation	μEq	mEq	Eq	kEq
Microequivalent	μEq	1	10^{-3}	10^{-6}	10^{-9}
Milliequivalent	mEq	10^{3}	1	10^{-3}	10^{-6}
Equivalent	Eq	10^{6}	10^{3}	1	10^{-3}
Kiloequivalent	kEq	10^{9}	10^{6}	10^{3}	1

Unit	Electric charge carried††			
	Chemical scale		Physical scale	
	C	esu	C	esu
Microequivalent	9.6495×10^{-2}	2.8929×10^{8}	9.6522×10^{-2}	2.8937×10^{8}
Milliequivalent	9.6495×10	2.8929×10^{11}	9.6522×10	2.8937×10^{11}
Equivalent	9.6495×10^{4}	2.8929×10^{14}	9.6522×10^{4}	2.8937×10^{14}
Kiloequivalent	9.6495×10^{7}	2.8929×10^{17}	9.6522×10^{7}	2.8937×10^{17}

* In physical chemistry, quantities of substances are often expressed in moles or equivalents.

** The names 'gram mole' and 'kilogram mole' are also used. For elements the corresponding expressions are 'gram atom' and 'kilogram atom'.

*** AVOGADRO's number N is the numerical value of AVOGADRO's constant N_0. In German-speaking countries it is known as 'LOSCHMIDT's number' (L_0), and the name 'AVOGADRO's number' is used to denote the number of molecules contained in one cubic centimeter of an ideal gas at NTP. Cf. also page 247.

† In German-speaking countries the names 'val' and 'kiloval' are used.

†† For the unit 'equivalent' this charge is known as the FARADAY constant (see page 247).

Concentration units

Designation	Symbol	Definition
Mass/Mass		
Mass per cent	% (weight %)	Grams of the substance contained in 100 grams of total mass
Milligrams per cent	mg %*	Milligrams of the substance contained in 100 grams of total mass
Molar fraction	mol/total mol	Moles of the substance as fraction of total moles of all components
Moles per cent	mol%	Molar fraction × 100, or moles of the substance per 100 moles of the mixture
Solutions (liquid)		
Mass per cent	% (weight %)	Grams of solute contained in 100 grams of solution
	g/100 g solvent	Grams of solute contained in 100 grams of solvent
	mg %*	Milligrams of solute contained in 100 grams of solution
	mol/100 g solution g. atom/100 g solution Eq/100 g solution, etc.	Moles, gram atoms or equivalents, etc., of solute in 100 grams of solution, etc.
	mol/100 g solvent g. atom/100 g solvent Eq/100 g solvent, etc.	Moles, gram atoms or equivalents, etc., of solute in 100 grams of solvent, etc.
Molecular or molar ratio	mol%	Moles of solute in 100 moles of solution
	mol‰	Millimoles of solute in 1 mole of solution or moles of solute in 1000 moles of solution
	mol/100 mol solvent	Moles of solute in 100 moles of solvent
	mol/1000 mol solvent	Moles of solute in 1000 moles of solvent
Dilution	g solvent/1 g solute	Grams of solvent per gram of solute
	mol solvent/1 mol solute	Moles of solvent per mole of solute
Molality	mol/1000 g solvent g. atom/1000 g solvent	Moles Gram atoms } of solute in 1000 grams of solvent
Mass/Volume**		
Solutions (liquid)		
	g/100 ml solution	Grams of solute in 100 ml of solution
	mg %*	Milligrams of solute in 100 ml of solution
	g/l	Grams of solute in 1 liter of solution
	g/100 ml	Grams of solute in 100 ml of solution
	g/100 ml solvent	Grams of solute in 100 ml of solvent
Molarity	mol/l g. atom/l	Moles Gram atoms } of the substance in 1 liter of solution (0.1-M, 0.01-M, etc.
Normality	N Eq/l	Equivalents of the solute in 1 liter of solution (0.1-N, 0.01-N, etc.)
Volume/Volume		
Volume per cent	vol %	Milliliters of solute in 100 ml of solution or milliliters of gas in 100 ml of solution or milliliters of gas in 100 ml of gas mixture

* The expression mg% is an unfortunate one in that the units concerned are rarely specified. In medical literature it is used to mean both mg/100 g and mg/100 ml, particularly with reference to blood, urine, etc. For this reason its use has been avoided in these *Scientific Tables*.

** Dependent upon temperature.

For bibliographical references see page 248

I. Standard substances

A. Mercury

Normal density (0° C, 760 mm Hg)[1] .... ρ_n(Hg) = (13.595 05 ± 0.000 14) g/cm³

Assumed normal density of the International Temperature Scales 1927 and 1948 (0°C, 760 mm Hg)[1,28] .... ρ_n(Hg) = 13.595**1** g/cm³

Density relative to water (specific gravity)[1] .... δ_n(Hg) = 13.595 43 ± 0.000 10

B. Water

Maximum density (4° C, 760 mm Hg, free of air)[2] .... $\rho_m(H_2O)$ = **1** g/ml = (0.999 972 ± 0.000 003) g/cm³

Density between 0 and 40° C (760 mm Hg, free of air)[3]:

°C	g/ml	°C	g/ml	°C	g/ml	°C	g/ml
0	0.999 8676	4	**1.0**	8	0.999 8765	12	0.999 5261
1	0.999 9265	5	0.999 9919	9	0.999 8092	13	0.999 4059
2	0.999 9678	6	0.999 9683	10	0.999 7281	14	0.999 2732
3	0.999 9922	7	0.999 9297	11	0.999 6336		

°C	0.0	0.1	0.2	0.3	0.4
15	0.999 1286	0.999 1134	0.999 0982	0.999 0828	0.999 0674
16	0.998 9721	0.998 9558	0.998 9394	0.998 9229	0.998 9062
17	0.998 8041	0.998 7867	0.998 7691	0.998 7515	0.998 7337
18	0.998 6248	0.998 6063	0.998 5877	0.998 5689	0.998 5501
19	0.998 4346	0.998 4150	0.998 3953	0.998 3754	0.998 3555
20	0.998 2336	0.998 2130	0.998 1922	0.998 1713	0.998 1503
21	0.998 0221	0.998 0004	0.997 9786	0.997 9567	0.997 9346
22	0.997 8003	0.997 7776	0.997 7547	0.997 7318	0.997 7088
23	0.997 5684	0.997 5447	0.997 5208	0.997 4969	0.997 4729
24	0.997 3266	0.997 3019	0.997 2771	0.997 2522	0.997 2272
25	0.997 0751	0.997 0494	0.997 0237	0.996 9978	0.996 9718

°C	0.5	0.6	0.7	0.8	0.9
15	0.999 0518	0.999 0360	0.999 0202	0.999 0043	0.998 9882
16	0.998 8895	0.998 8726	0.998 8557	0.998 8386	0.998 8214
17	0.998 7158	0.998 6979	0.998 6798	0.998 6616	0.998 6433
18	0.998 5311	0.998 5120	0.998 4928	0.998 4735	0.998 4541
19	0.998 3355	0.998 3153	0.998 2950	0.998 2747	0.998 2542
20	0.998 1292	0.998 1080	0.998 0867	0.998 0653	0.998 0438
21	0.997 9125	0.997 8903	0.997 8679	0.997 8455	0.997 8230
22	0.997 6856	0.997 6624	0.997 6390	0.997 6156	0.997 5921
23	0.997 4487	0.997 4245	0.997 4002	0.997 3758	0.997 3512
24	0.997 2021	0.997 1769	0.997 1516	0.997 1262	0.997 1007
25	0.996 9458	0.996 9196	0.996 8934	0.996 8671	0.996 8406

°C	g/ml	°C	g/ml	°C	g/ml	°C	g/ml
26	0.996 8141	30	0.995 6783	34	0.994 4030	38	0.992 9970
27	0.996 5437	31	0.995 3722	35	0.994 0635	39	0.992 6260
28	0.996 2642	32	0.995 0575	36	0.993 7159	40	0.992 2473
29	0.995 9757	33	0.994 7344	37	0.993 3604		

Density of heavy water (100% D_2O, 760 mm Hg, free of air):

°C	g/ml	References	°C	g/ml	References
3.8	1.105 33	*3*	20	1.105 27	*3*
5	1.105 49	*3*	25	1.104 37	*5*
10	1.105 88	*3*	30	1.103 15	*5*
11.23	1.105 96*	*4*	35	1.101 67	*5*
15	1.105 77	*3*	40	1.099 89	*5*

* maximum density

Specific heat of water between 0 and 100° C (at 760 mm Hg)[6]:

J g⁻¹ degree⁻¹

°C	0	1	2	3	4	5	6	7	8	9
	4.	4.	4.	4.	4.	4.	4.	4.	4.	4.
0	2174	2138	2104	2074	2048	2019	1996	1974	1954	1936
10	1919	1904	1890	1877	1866	1855	1846	1837	1829	1822
20	1816	1810	1805	1801	1797	1793	1790	1787	1785	1783
30	1782	1781	1780	1780	1779	1779	1780	1780	1781	1782
40	1783	1784	1786	1788	1789	1792	1794	1796	1799	1801
50	1804	1807	1811	1814	1817	1821	1825	1829	1833	1837
60	1841	1846	1850	1855	1860	1865	1871	1876	1882	1887
70	1893	1899	1905	1912	1918	1925	1932	1939	1946	1954
80	1961	1969	1977	1985	1994	2002	2011	2020	2029	2039
90	2048	2058	2068	2078	2089	2100	2111	2122	2133	2145
100	2156									

cal_{15} g⁻¹ degree⁻¹ (calculated by the editors from data in the literature[6])

°C	0	1	2	3	4	5	6	7	8	9
	1. *0.*	1. *0.*	1. *0.*	1. *0.*	1. *0.*	1. *0.*	1. *0.*	1. *0.*	1. *0.*	1. *0.*
0	00762	00676	00595	00523	00454	00392	00337	00284	00237	00194
10	00153	00117	00084	00053	00026	00000	*99978*	*99957*	*99938*	*99921*
20	*99907*	*99892*	*99881*	*99871*	*99861*	*99852*	*99845*	*99838*	*99833*	*99828*
30	*99826*	*99823*	*99821*	*99821*	*99818*	*99818*	*99821*	*99821*	*99823*	*99826*
40	*99828*	*99830*	*99835*	*99840*	*99842*	*99849*	*99854*	*99859*	*99866*	*99871*
50	*99878*	*99885*	*99895*	*99902*	*99909*	*99919*	*99928*	*99938*	*99947*	*99957*
60	*99967*	*99978*	*99988*	00000	00012	00024	00038	00050	00065	00076
70	00091	00105	00119	00136	00151	00167	00184	00201	00217	00237
80	00253	00272	00291	00311	00332	00351	00373	00394	00416	00440
90	00461	00485	00509	00533	00559	00585	00612	00638	00664	00693
100	00719									

For the ice, triple and steam points see page 211. For pressure of saturated water vapor see pages 296-298.

C. Air

Normal density of dry air containing 0.04% carbon dioxide (0°C, 760 mm Hg)[7] .... ρ_n(air) = 1.293 0₇ g/l

"Normal" air in spectroscopy: 760 mm Hg, 15° C, 0.03% CO_2, dry.

ICAO Standard Atmosphere (–1 to 20 km). See pages 292–294.

COSPAR International Reference Atmosphere, 1961 (average values)[8]

Altitude km	Pressure mm Hg	Temperature °K	Altitude km	Pressure mm Hg	Temperature °K
26	1.65×10	223.59	96	4.20×10^{-4}	195.81
30	9.05×10	228.28	100	2.19×10^{-4}	212.10
36	3.79×10	238.38	110	5.46×10^{-5}	265.02
40	2.17×10	247.86	120	1.83×10^{-5}	342.96
46	9.84×10^{-1}	262.95	130	8.70×10^{-6}	569.44
52	4.63×10^{-1}	270.72	140	5.42×10^{-6}	799.13
56	2.81×10^{-1}	267.73	150	3.81×10^{-6}	1014.53
60	1.69×10^{-1}	257.82	160	2.86×10^{-6}	1155.26
66	7.47×10^{-2}	234.32	180	1.69×10^{-6}	1193.17
70	4.13×10^{-2}	217.04	200	1.02×10^{-6}	1226.77
76	1.56×10^{-2}	194.79	300	1.19×10^{-7}	1358.51
80	7.70×10^{-3}	184.60	400	2.28×10^{-8}	1436.16
86	2.55×10^{-3}	178.47	600	2.02×10^{-9}	1474.15
90	1.22×10^{-3}	181.14	800	3.04×10^{-10}	1474.15

II. Terrestrial constants

A. Acceleration of gravity

Normal acceleration of gravity[9] . g_n = 980 66**5** gal (cm s⁻²)

International gravity formula[10–14] (in accordance with the international terrestrial geoid) ... $\gamma_0 = (980.632272 - 2.586145 \cos 2B + 0.002878 \cos 4B - 0.000004 \cos 6B)$ gal

where γ_0 = acceleration of gravity at sea level, B = latitude. This formula yields the following values for different degrees of latitude (calculated by the editors):

Latitude °	γ_0 gal	γ_0/g_n	g_n/γ_0	Latitude °	γ_0 gal	γ_0/g_n	g_n/γ_0
0	978.0490	0.997332	1.002675	45	980.6294	0.999964	1.000036
5	0881	372	635	46	7196	1.000056	0.999944
10	2043	491	516	47	8098	148	852
15	3940	684	321	48	8998	239	761
20	6517	947	057	49	9894	331	669
25	9694	0.998271	1.001732	50	981.0787	1.000422	0.999578
30	979.3378	0.998647	1.001355	51	1673	512	488
31	4165	727	275	52	2554	602	398
32	4968	809	193	53	3427	691	309
33	5785	892	109	54	4291	779	221
34	6614	977	025	55	981.5146	1.000866	0.999134
35	979.7456	0.999062	1.000938	56	5990	952	048
36	8308	149	851	57	6822	1.001037	0.998964
37	9170	237	763	58	7642	121	880
38	980.0041	326	674	59	8448	203	798
39	0920	416	585	60	981.9239	1.001284	0.998718
40	980.1805	0.999506	1.000494	65	982.2941	661	342
41	2696	597	403	70	6139	987	017
42	3591	688	312	75	8734	1.002252	0.997753
43	4490	780	220	80	983.0647	447	559
44	5391	872	128	85	1818	566	440
				90	2213	607	400

The true acceleration of gravity is probably 10–20 mgal less than the value calculated from the international gravity formula[15,16].

For bibliographical references see page 248

B. Other physical constants

Constants of the international terrestrial geoid (after HAYFORD[12, 17]):

Semi-major axis	$a_{\oplus}$	$6.378\,388 \times 10^6$ m
Flattening	$\alpha_{\oplus}$	1/297
Semi-minor axis	$b_{\oplus}$	$6.356\,912 \times 10^6$ m
Numerical eccentricity	ε	0.081 991 89
Equatorial quadrant	Q^{Ae}	$1.001\,9148 \times 10^7$ m
Meridian quadrant	Q^{Me}	$1.000\,2288 \times 10^7$ m

Mass constants[18]

Total mass	M	$(5.9765 \pm 0.0050) \times 10^{24}$ kg
Surface density	ρ_s	$(2.60 \pm 0.05) \times 10^3$ kg m^{-3}
Density at the center	ρ_c	$(1.126 \pm 0.025) \times 10^4$ kg m^{-3}
Mean density	ρ	$(5.517 \pm 0.006) \times 10^3$ kg m^{-3}

III. Cosmic constants

A. Sun

Mean distance from the earth[19]	1.495×10^{11} m = 498.7 light seconds
Radius[20]	6.965×10^8 m ~ 109 × earth's radius
Mass[20]	1.987×10^{30} kg
Mean density[20]	1.41×10^3 kg m^{-3}
Accel. of gravity at surface[19] ..	2.74×10^2 m s^{-2}
Total radiation[19]	3.72×10^{26} W
Effective temperature[19]	5714° K
Luminous intensity[19]	2.8×10^{27} cd

B. Moon

Mean distance from the earth[20]	3.844×10^8 m ~ 60.27 × earth's radius
Radius[19]	1.738×10^6 m ~ 0.272 × earth's radius
Mass[20]	7.343×10^{22} kg
Mean density[19]	3.342×10^3 kg m^{-3}
Sidereal period of revolution[19]	27.321 661 days
Synodical period of revolution[19]	29.530 588 days

C. Planets

	Sidereal period of revolution	Mean distance from the sun (earth = 1)	Diameter m	Mass (earth = 1)	Mean density kg m^{-3}
Mercury	$0^a\ 87^d97$	0.387 099	4.8000×10^6	0.055	5.72×10^3
Venus	0 224.70	0.723 332	1.2200×10^7	0.814	5.12×10^3
Earth	1 0.01	1	1.2757×10^7	1	5.51×10^3
Mars	1 321.74	1.523 688	6.8000×10^6	0.107	3.90×10^3
Jupiter	11 314.92	5.202 561	1.4270×10^8	316.9	1.25×10^3
Saturn	29 167.21	9.554 747	1.2080×10^8	94.8	6.1×10^2
Uranus	84 8.11	19.218 14	4.9700×10^7	14.51	1.35×10^3
Neptune	164 281.6	30.109 57	5.3000×10^7	17.19	1.32×10^3
Pluto	248 157	39.517 74	$\sim 1.0000 \times 10^7$	~0.9	$\sim 1 \times 10^3$

IV. General physical constants

A. International standard values (*agreed* values)

Constant	Symbol and formula	Numerical value	CGS-unit (and factor)	MKS-unit (and factor)	Nonintegrated units	References
Standard acceleration of gravity	g_n	9.806 65	10^2 gal (= cm s^{-2})	m s^{-2}		9
Standard pressure	p_0	1.013 25 1 7.6	10^6 dyn cm^{-2}	10^5 N m^{-2}	atm 10^2 mm Hg	21, 22
Standard temperature (thermodynamic and international scales) = ice point of water	T_0 t_0	2.7315 0	10^2 °K °C	10^2 °K °C		22, 23
Liter volume	l	1.000 028	10^3 cm^3	10^{-3} m^3		24, 25
Lattice constant of calcite (definition of SIEGBAHN X-unit)	$d_{\infty}^{18°C}$ ($CaCO_3$)	3.029 45 1.002 030 ($\pm 20 \times 10^{-6}$)	10^{-8} cm	10^{-10} m	10^3 X.U.	1 32
Wave length of red cadmium line $6\,{}^1D_2 - 6\,{}^1P_1$ in spectroscopically normal air (definition of ångström)	λn_{Cd}	6.438 4696 $6.438\,469_6$ ($\pm 3 \times 10^{-6}$)	10^{-5} cm	10^{-7} m	10^3 Å	26 1
Definition of the meter based on the wave length of the orange-red line of the krypton-86 atom (1 Å = 1 × 10^{-10} m)	m	1.650 763 73			$10^7 \lambda_{0_{Kr\text{-}86}}$	35
Vacuum wave length of the orange-red line $2\,p_{10} - 5\,d_5$ of the krypton-86 atom	$\lambda_{0_{Kr\text{-}86}}$	6.057 802 1	10^{-5} cm	10^{-7} m		*
Atomic weight of the isotope oxygen-16 on the physical scale (reference weight of this scale)	$M_{O\text{-}16}$	16				
Atomic weight of the "natural" isotopic oxygen mixture on the chemical scale (reference weight of this scale)	A_O	16				
Conversion factor chemical/physical atomic weights (SMYTHE factor)	A/M	1.000 275**				27
Normal density of mercury (international temperature scales)	ρ_n (Hg)	1.359 51	10 g cm^{-3}	10^4 kg m^{-3}		1, 28
Second PLANCK radiation constant (International Temperature Scale 1948)	c_2 (int. 1948)	1.438	cm degree	10^{-2} m degree		22, 23
Standard values of the international terrestrial geoid:						
Semi-major axis (equatorial radius)	$a_{\oplus}$	6.378 388	10^8 cm	10^6 m		12
Flattening	$\alpha_{\oplus}$	1/297				12
Solar parallax	$\pi_{\odot}$	8.8	seconds of arc	seconds of arc		29

B. Gravitational constant

Constant	Symbol	Numerical value	CGS-unit	MKS-unit	Nonintegrated units	References
Gravitational constant	G	6.670 ± 0.007	10^{-8} cm^3 g^{-1}s^{-2}	10^{-11} m^3 kg^{-1} s^{-2}		30, 31

* Calculated by the editors from the formulas given. ** Used by Commission on Atomic Weights, International Union of Pure and Applied Chemistry.

For bibliographical references see page 248

C. Electromagnetic field constants (see also pages 229–235)

Constant	Symbol and formula	Numerical value	CGS-unit (and factor)	MKS-unit (and factor)	Nonintegrated units	References
Velocity of light in vacuum	c	2.997 9250	10^{10} cm s^{-1}	10^{8} m s^{-1}		*33*
	$1/c$	3.335 6405	10^{-11} cm^{-1}s	10^{-9} m^{-1}s		*
	c^2	8.987 5543	10^{20} cm^2 s^{-2}	10^{16} m^2 s^{-2}		*
	$1/c^2$	1.112 6497	10^{-21} cm^{-2}s^2	10^{-17} m^{-2}s^2		*
Magnetic field constant	$\mu_0 = 10^{-7}\,4\pi$ H m^{-1}	1.256 637 062		10^{-6} H m^{-1}		*
Electric field constant	$\varepsilon_0 = 10^7/4\pi c^2$ F m^{-1}	8.854 1853		10^{-12} F m^{-1}		*
Impedance of vacuum	$\Gamma_0 = \mu_0 c$	3.767 3037		10^{2} Ω		*

D. Thermodynamic constants

Constant	Symbol and formula	Numerical value	CGS-unit (and factor)	MKS-unit (and factor)	Nonintegrated units	References
Normal specific volume of an ideal gas						
physical scale	v_0	2.242 07	10^4 cm^3 mol$^{-1}_{\rm Ph}$	10 m^3 kmol$^{-1}_{\rm Ph}$		*27*
chemical scale		2.241 45	10^4 cm^3 mol$^{-1}_{\rm Ch}$	10 m^3 kmol$^{-1}_{\rm Ch}$		
Universal gas constant physical scale	$R_0 = p_0 v_0/T_0$	8.316 96	10^7 erg mol$^{-1}_{\rm Ph}$degree^{-1}	10^3 J kmol$^{-1}_{\rm Ph}$degree^{-1}		*
		8.207 97			10^{-2} latm mol$^{-1}_{\rm Ph}$ degree^{-1}	*
		1.9871			cal$_{15}$ mol$^{-1}_{\rm Ph}$degree^{-1}	*
chemical scale		8.314 67	10^7 erg mol$^{-1}_{\rm Ch}$degree^{-1}	10^3 J kmol$^{-1}_{\rm Ch}$degree^{-1}		*
		8.205 71			10^{-2} latm mol$^{-1}_{\rm Ch}$degree^{-1}	*
		1.9865			cal$_{15}$ mol$^{-1}_{\rm Ch}$ degree^{-1}	*
Boltzmann entropy constant	$k = R_0/N_0$	1.380 40	10^{-16} erg degree^{-1}	10^{-23} J degree^{-1}		*
		1.362 31			10^{-25} latm degree^{-1}	*
		3.2981			10^{-24} cal$_{15}$ degree^{-1}	*
		8.616 65			10^{-5} eV degree^{-1}	*

E. Atomic constants

Constant	Symbol and formula	Numerical value	CGS-unit (and factor)	MKS-unit (and factor)	Nonintegrated units	References
Avogadro's constant**						
physical scale	N_0	6.025 02	10^{23} mol$^{-1}_{\rm Ph}$	10^{26} kmol$^{-1}_{\rm Ph}$		*16*
chemical scale		6.023 36	10^{23} mol$^{-1}_{\rm Ch}$	10^{26} kmol$^{-1}_{\rm Ch}$		*
Loschmidt's number***	$L_0 = N_0/v_0$	2.687 26	10^{19} cm^{-3}	10^{25} m^{-3}		*
Faraday constant (specific ionic charge)						
physical scale	$F = N_0 e$	2.893 65	10^{14} esu Eq$^{-1}_{\rm Ph}$			*
	$F' = N_0 e'$; $F'' = N_0 e''$	9.652 19	10^3 emu Eq$^{-1}_{\rm Ph}$	10^7 C kEq$^{-1}_{\rm Ph}$		*
chemical scale	$F' = N_0 e'$; $F'' = N_0 e''$	9.649 54	10^3 emu Eq$^{-1}_{\rm Ch}$	10^7 C kEq$^{-1}_{\rm Ch}$		*
Elementary electric charge (charge of the electron)	e	4.802 73	10^{-10} esu			*16*
	$e' = e/c$; $e'' = 10\,e'$	1.602 02	10^{-20} emu	10^{-19} C		*
Planck's constant (energy quantum)	$h = 2\pi e^2/\alpha c$	6.624 91	10^{-27} erg s	10^{-34} J s		*
	h/e	1.379 40	10^{-17} erg s esu^{-1}			*
	h/e'; h/e''	4.135 35	10^{-7} erg s emu^{-1}	10^{-15} Wb		*
Quantum-mechanical unit of angular momentum	$\hbar = h/2\pi$	1.054 39	10^{-27} erg s	10^{-34} J s		*
Sommerfeld fine-structure constant	$1/\alpha$	1.370 39 × 10^2				*16*
	α	7.297 19 × 10^{-3}				*16*
1st Planck radiation constant	$c_1 = hc^2$	5.954 17	10^{-6} erg s^{-1}cm^2	10^{-17} W m^2		*
2nd Planck radiation constant	$c_2 = hc/k$	1.438 78	cm degree	10^{-2} m degree		*
Constant of specific atomic heat	c_2/c	4.799 26	10^{-11} s degree	10^{-11} s degree		*
Constant of Wien's displacement law	c_2/x; $x = 5\,(1-e^x)$	2.897 78	10^{-1} cm degree	10^{-3} m degree		* (c_2), *30* (x)
Stefan-Boltzmann radiation constant	$\sigma = 2\pi^5 k^4/15 h^3 c^2$	5.6693	10^{-5} erg s^{-1}cm^{-2} degree^{-4}	10^{-8} W m^{-2} degree^{-4}		*
Bohr radius (lowest energy orbit)	$a_0 = \alpha/4\pi R_\infty$	5.291 65	10^{-9} cm	10^{-11} m		*
Classical electron radius	$r_0 = \alpha^3/4\pi R_\infty$	2.817 75	10^{-13} cm	10^{-15} m		*
Thomson cross section	$(8/3)\,\pi r_0^2$	6.651 55	10^{-25} cm^2	10^{-29} m^2	10^{-1} barn (1 barn = 10^{-24} cm^2)	*
Compton wave lengths						
Electron	$\lambda_{Ce} = h/m_e c$	2.426 20	10^{-10} cm	10^{-12} m		*
	$\lambda_{Ce} = \hbar/m_e c$	3.861 42	10^{-11} cm	10^{-13} m		*
Proton	$\lambda_{Cp} = h/m_p c$	1.321 39	10^{-13} cm	10^{-15} m		*
	$\lambda_{Cp} = \hbar/m_p c$	2.103 06	10^{-14} cm	10^{-16} m		*
Neutron	$\lambda_{Cn} = h/m_n c$	1.319 58	10^{-13} cm	10^{-15} m		*
	$\lambda_{Cn} = \hbar/m_n c$	2.100 17	10^{-14} cm	10^{-16} m		*
Rydberg constant for a nucleus of infinite mass	R_∞	1.097 373 28	10^5 cm^{-1}	10^7 m^{-1}		*16*
Rydberg constant for the hydrogen-1 atom	$R_H = R_\infty/(1+m_e/m_p)$	1.096 775 94	10^5 cm^{-1}	10^7 m^{-1}		*
Rydberg fundamental frequency for hydrogen-1 atom	$R'_H = c\,R_H$	3.288 052 01	10^{15} s^{-1}	10^{15} s^{-1}		*

* Calculated by the editors from the formulas given.

** Number of molecules in 1 mole of an ideal gas. Known as Loschmidt's constant in German-speaking countries. Cf. page 243.

*** Number of molecules in 1 cm³ of an ideal gas at NTP. Known as Avogadro's number in German-speaking countries. Cf. page 243.

E. Atomic constants (continued)

Constant	Symbol and formula	Numerical value	CGS-unit (and factor)	MKS-unit (and factor)	Nonintegrated units	References
Specific charge of electron	e/m_e	5.272 97	10^{17} esu g^{-1}			*
	e'/m_e; e''/m_e	1.758 87	10^{7} emu g^{-1}	10^{11} C kg^{-1}		*
Specific charge of proton	e/m_p	2.871 85	10^{14} esu g^{-1}			*
	e'/m_p; e''/m_p	9.579 45	10^{3} emu g^{-1}	10^{7} C kg^{-1}		*
Gyromagnetic ratio of the proton	γ'_p	2.675 13	10^{4} rad s^{-1} $oersted^{-1}$			*34*
	$\gamma''_p \triangle 10^{-3} 4\pi\gamma'_p$	3.361 68		10^{2} m C^{-1}		*
Magnetic moments						
Bohr's magneton	$\mu'_B = he'/4\pi m_e$	9.272 67	10^{-21} erg $oersted^{-1}$			*
	$\mu''_B = he''/m_e$	1.165 24		10^{-29} Wb m		*
Nuclear magneton	$\mu'_K = he'/4\pi m_p$	5.050 23	10^{-24} erg $oersted^{-1}$			*
	$\mu''_K = he''/m_p$	6.346 30		10^{-33} Wb m		*
Electron	$\mu'_e = \mu'_B \times (\mu_e/\mu_B)$	9.283 43	10^{-21} erg $oersted^{-1}$			*
	$\mu''_e = \mu''_B \times (\mu_e/\mu_B)$	1.166 59		10^{-29} Wb m		*
	$\mu_e/\mu_B = 1 + \alpha/2\pi - 0.328\,\alpha^2/\pi^2$	1.001 1596				*16*
Proton	$\mu'_p = \gamma'_p h/4\pi$	1.410 31	10^{-23} erg $oersted^{-1}$			*
	$\mu''_p = \gamma''_p h/4\pi$	1.772 25		10^{-32} Wb m		*
	μ_p/μ_K	2.792 57				*
Zeeman displacement	μ_B/hc	4.668 79	10^{-5} cm^{-1} $oersted^{-1}$			*
	μ''_B/hc	5.866 97		10^{-5} A^{-1}		*
Mass values						
Mass unit	$MU = 1/N_0$	1.659 75	10^{-24} g	10^{-27} kg		*
Electron	$m_e = 4\pi e^2 R_\infty/\alpha^3 c^2$	9.108 20	10^{-28} g	10^{-31} kg		*
Proton	$m_p = m_H - m_e$	1.672 35	10^{-24} g	10^{-27} kg		*
	m_p/m_e	$1.836\,09 \times 10^{3}$				*
Neutron	$m_n = M_n/N_0$	1.674 65	10^{-24} g	10^{-27} kg		*
Hydrogen-1 atom	$m_H = M_H/N_0$	1.673 26	10^{-24} g	10^{-27} kg		*
Reduced mass of electron in the hydrogen atom	$\mu = m_e m_p/m_H$	9.103 24	10^{-28} g	10^{-31} kg		*
Atomic weights (physical scale)						
Electron	$M_e = Nm_e$	$5.487\,71 \times 10^{-4}$				*
Proton	$M_p = Nm_p$	1.007 593				*
Neutron	M_n	1.008 982				*27*
Hydrogen-1 atom	M_H	1.008 142				*27*
Energy conversion factors **						
Electron volt	$eV = e''V$	1.602 02	10^{-12} erg	10^{-19} J		*16*
	erg/eV; J/eV	6.242 13	10^{11}	10^{18}		*
Rydberg	$Ry = hR'_H$	2.178 30	10^{-11} erg	10^{-18} J		*
		1.359 73			10 eV	*
$Second^{-1}$	$E_{s^{-1}} = h/s$	6.624 91	10^{-27} erg	10^{-34} J		*
		4.135 35			10^{-15} eV	*
$Centimeter^{-1}$	$E_{cm^{-1}} = hc/cm$	1.986 10	10^{-16} erg	10^{-23} J		*
		1.239 74			10^{-4} eV	*
Degree Kelvin	$E_{°K} = k/degree$	1.380 40	10^{-16} erg	10^{-23} J		*
		8.616 65			10^{-5} eV	*
Gram	$E_g = c^2 g$	8.987 554	10^{20} erg	10^{13} J		*
		5.610 15			10^{32} eV	*
Mass unit	$E_{MU} = c^2\,MU$	1.491 71	10^{-3} erg	10^{-10} J		*
		9.311 41			10^{8} eV	*
Mass of the electron	$E_{m_e} = c^2 m_e$	8.186 04	10^{-7} erg	10^{-14} J		*
		5.109 83			10^{5} eV	*
Mass of the proton	$E_{m_p} = c^2 m_p$	1.503 03	10^{-3} erg	10^{-10} J		*
		9.382 12			10^{8} eV	*
Mass of the neutron	$E_{m_n} = c^2 m_n$	1.505 10	10^{-3} erg	10^{-10} J		*
		9.395 05			10^{8} eV	*

* Calculated by the editors from the formulas given.
** See also page 216.

References: *1)* Stille, U., *Messen und Rechnen in der Physik*, Braunschweig, 1955. *2)* Comité international des Poids et Mesures, *P. V. Com. int. Poids Mes.*, **22**, 77 and 94 (1950). *3)* Chang and Chien, *J. Amer. chem. Soc.*, **63**, 1709 (1941). *4)* Stokland et al., *Trans. Faraday Soc.*, **35**, 312 (1939). *5)* Schrader and Wirtz, *Z. Naturf.*, **6a**, 220 (1951). *6)* Comité international des Poids et Mesures, *P. V. Com. int. Poids Mes.*, **22**, 79 (1950). *7)* Roth, W.A., in Roth and Scheel (Eds.), *Landolt-Börnstein Physikalisch-Chemische Tabellen*, 5th ed., vol. I, Berlin, 1923, page 43. *8)* From Committee on Space Research, *CIRA 1961*, Amsterdam, 1961. *9) Comptes rendus de la 3e Conférence générale des Poids et Mesures*, Paris, 1901, page 68. *10)* Union géodésique et géophysique internationale, *Bull. géod. int.*, No. 27, 238 (1930). *11)* Heiskanen, W., *Gerlands Beitr. Geophys.*, **19**, 356 (1928). *12)* Cassinis, G., *Bull. géod. int.*, No. 26, 40 (1930). *13)* Cassinis, G., *Bull. géod. int.*, No. 32, 313 (1931). *14)* Cassinis et al., *R. Comm. geod. ital.* (new series), No. 13 (1937). *15)* Stille, U., *Messen und Rechnen in der Physik*, Braunschweig, 1955, page 318. *16)* DuMond, J. W. M., *Ann. Phys. (N. Y.)*, **7**, 365 (1959). *17)* Hayford, J. F., *Supplementary Investigation in 1909 of the Figure of the Earth and Isostacy*, U. S. Coast and Geodetic Survey, Washington, 1910. *18)* Berroth, A., *Z. Geophys.*, **18**, 42 (1943). *19)* Westphal, W. H., *Physikalisches Wörterbuch*, Berlin, 1952. *20)* Smithsonian Institution, *Physical Tables*, 9th ed., Washington, 1954. *21)* Comité international des Poids et Mesures, *P. V. Com. int. Poids Mes.*, **21**, 71 (1948), *22) Comptes rendus de la 10e Conférence générale des Poids et Mesures*, Paris, 1955. *23)* Comité international des Poids et Mesures, *P. V. Com. int. Poids Mes.*, **21**, 69, Tables 18 and 30 (1948). *24)* Guillaume, C. H., *Comptes rendus de la 4e Conférence générale des Poids et Mesures*, Paris, 1907, page 50. *25)* Comité international des Poids et Mesures, *P. V. Com. int. Poids Mes.*, **22**, 94 (1950). *26)* The International Union for Co-operation in Solar Research, *Trans. int. Un. sol. Res.*, **2**, 20 (1908). *27)* Cohen and DuMond, in Flügge, S., *Handbuch der Physik*, vol. 35, Berlin, 1957. *28) Comptes rendus de la 7e Conférence générale des Poids et Mesures*, Paris, 1927. *29)* Cf. Stille, U., *Messen und Rechnen in der Physik*, Braunschweig, 1955, page 84. *30)* Heyl, P. R., *Proc. nat. Acad. Sci. (Wash.)*, **13**, 601 (1927). *31)* Heyl, P. R., *J. Res. nat. Bur. Stand.*, **5**, 1243 (1930). *32)* Birge, R. T., *Amer. J. Phys.*, **13**, 69 (1945); on this subject see also *16)*. *33)* Froome, K. D., *Proc. roy. Soc. A.*, **247**, 109 (1958). This value ($\pm$ 4 × 10^{3} cm s^{-1}) has been accepted by the International Scientific Radio Union and the International Union of Geodesy and Geophysics. *34)* Driscoll and Bender, *Phys. Rev. Letters*, **1**, 413 (1958). *35)* Barrell, H., *Nature*, **180**, 1387 (1957); Editorial, *Science*, **132**, 1384 (1960).

Periodic System of the Elements

Adapted from VON ANGERER et al., in EUCKEN, A. (Ed.), *Landolt-Börnstein Zahlenwerte und Funktionen*, 6th ed., vol. I, Part 1, Berlin, 1950, page 11

The following data are given for each element: Atomic number (in *italics*), symbol, atomic weight[1]

Period	Group I a	Group I b	Group II a	Group II b	Group III a	Group III b	Group IV a	Group IV b	Group V a	Group V b	Group VI a	Group VI b	Group VII a	Group VII b	Group VIII a	Group VIII b[2]
1	*1.* H 1.0080						*0.n*([3]) 1.008986		*e*([4]) 5.485×10^{-4}							*2.* He 4.003
2	*3.* Li 6.940		*4.* Be 9.013			*5.* B 10.82		*6.* C 12.011		*7.* N 14.008		*8.* O 16[5]		*9.* F 19.00		*10.* Ne 20.183
3	*11.* Na 22.991		*12.* Mg 24.32			*13.* Al 26.98		*14.* Si 28.09		*15.* P 30.975		*16.* S[6] 32.066		*17.* Cl 35.457		*18.* Ar 39.944
4	*19.* K 39.100		*20.* Ca 40.08		*21.* Sc 44.96		*22.* Ti 47.90		*23.* V 50.95		*24.* Cr 52.01		*25.* Mn 54.94		*26.* Fe; *27.* Co; *28.* Ni 55.85 58.94 58.71	
(3 d)		*29.* Cu 63.54		*30.* Zn 65.38		*31.* Ga 69.72		*32.* Ge 72.60		*33.* As 74.91		*34.* Se 78.96		*35.* Br 79.916		*36.* Kr 83.80
5	*37.* Rb 85.48		*38.* Sr 87.63		*39.* Y 88.92		*40.* Zr 91.22		*41.* Nb 92.91		*42.* Mo 95.95		*43.* Tc (97)		*44.* Ru; *45.* Rh; *46.* Pd 101.1 102.91 106.4	
(4 d)		*47.* Ag 107.880		*48.* Cd 112.41		*49.* In 114.82		*50.* Sn 118.70		*51.* Sb 121.76		*52.* Te 127.61		*53.* I 126.91		*54.* Xe 131.30
6	*55.* Cs 132.91		*56.* Ba 137.36		*57.* La 138.92 4f		*72.* Hf 178.50		*73.* Ta 180.95		*74.* W 183.86		*75.* Re 186.22		*76.* Os; *77.* Ir; *78.* Pt 190.2 192.2 195.09	
(5 d) (4 f)		*79.* Au 197.0		*80.* Hg 200.61		*81.* Tl 204.39		*82.* Pb 207.21		*83.* Bi 209.00		*84.* Po (210)*		*85.* At (210)		*86.* Rn (222)
7 (6 d) (5 f)	*87.* Fr (223)		*88.* Ra (226)		*89.* Ac (227) 5f											

Lanthanides (rare-earth elements)

4f	*58.* Ce 140.13	*59.* Pr 140.92	*60.* Nd 144.27	*61.* Pm (147)*	*62.* Sm 150.35	*63.* Eu 152.0	*64.* Gd 157.26	*65.* Tb 158.93	*66.* Dy 162.51	*67.* Ho 164.94	*68.* Er 167.27	*69.* Tm 168.94	*70.* Yb 173.04	*71.* Lu 174.99

Actinides

5f	*90.* Th (232)	*91.* Pa (231)	*92.* U (238)	*93.* Np (237)	*94.* Pu (242)	*95.* Am (243)	*96.* Cm (247)	*97.* Bk (247)	*98.* Cf (249)	*99.* Es (254)	*100.* Fm (253)	*101.* Md (256)	*102.* No (253?)[7]	*103.* Lw (257?)

1) International Atomic Weights 1959 (Commission on Atomic Weights, *Proceedings of the 20th Conference of the International Union of Pure and Applied Chemistry*, London, 1960, page 202). A value in parentheses indicates the mass number of the most stable known isotope or, in the case of those marked with an asterisk, of the best known one.

2) Also known as Group 0.

3) Neutron.

4) Electron.

5) A defined value and hence an exact number.

6) Because of natural variations in the relative abundance of the isotopes of sulfur the atomic weight of this element has a range of ± 0.003.

7) Cf. MILSTED, J., *Nature*, **180**, 1012 (1957).

Alphabetical Table of the Names of the Elements

Name	Symbol	Atomic number	Atomic weight[1]
Actinium	Ac	89	(227)
Aluminum	Al	13	26.98
Americium	Am	95	(243)
Antimony	Sb	51	121.76
Argon	Ar	18	39.944
Arsenic	As	33	74.91
Astatine	At	85	(210)
Barium	Ba	56	137.36
Berkelium	Bk	97	(247)
Beryllium	Be	4	9.013
Bismuth	Bi	83	209.00
Boron	B	5	10.82
Bromine	Br	35	79.916
Cadmium	Cd	48	112.41
Calcium	Ca	20	40.08
Californium	Cf	98	(249)
Carbon	C	6	12.011
Cassiopeium	Cp	See Lutetium	
Cerium	Ce	58	140.13
Cesium	Cs	55	132.91
Chlorine	Cl	17	35.457
Chromium	Cr	24	52.01
Cobalt	Co	27	58.94
Columbium	Cb	See Niobium	
Copper	Cu	29	63.54
Curium	Cm	96	(247)
Dysprosium	Dy	66	162.51
Einsteinium	Es	99	(254)
Emanation	Em	See Radon	
Erbium	Er	68	167.27
Europium	Eu	63	152.0
Fermium	Fm	100	(253)
Fluorine	F	9	19.00
Francium	Fr	87	(223)
Gadolinium	Gd	64	157.26
Gallium	Ga	31	69.72
Germanium	Ge	32	72.60
Glucinium	Gl	See Beryllium	
Gold	Au	79	197.0
Hafnium	Hf	72	178.50
Helium	He	2	4.003
Holmium	Ho	67	164.94
Hydrogen	H	1	1.0080
Illinium	Il	See Promethium	
Indium	In	49	114.82
Iodine	I	53	126.91
Iridium	Ir	77	192.2
Iron	Fe	26	55.85
Krypton	Kr	36	83.80
Lanthanum	La	57	138.92
Lawrencium	Lw	103	(257 ?)
Lead	Pb	82	207.21
Lithium	Li	3	6.940
Lutetium	Lu	71	174.99
Magnesium	Mg	12	24.32
Manganese	Mn	25	54.94
Mendelevium	Md	101	(256)
Mercury	Hg	80	200.61
Molybdenum	Mo	42	95.95
Neodymium	Nd	60	144.27
Neon	Ne	10	20.183
Neptunium	Np	93	(237)
Nickel	Ni	28	58.71
Niobium	Nb	41	92.91
Niton	Nt	See Radon	
Nitrogen	N	7	14.008
Nobelium	No	102	(253?)[4]
Osmium	Os	76	190.2
Oxygen	O	8	**16**[2]
Palladium	Pd	46	106.4
Phosphorus	P	15	30.975
Platinum	Pt	78	195.09
Plutonium	Pu	94	(242)
Polonium	Po	84	(210)*
Potassium	K	19	39.100
Praseodymium	Pr	59	140.92
Promethium	Pm	61	(147)*
Protactinium	Pa	91	(231)
Radium	Ra	88	(226)
Radon	Rn	86	(222)
Rhenium	Re	75	186.22
Rhodium	Rh	45	102.91
Rubidium	Rb	37	85.48
Ruthenium	Ru	44	101.1
Samarium	Sm	62	150.35
Scandium	Sc	21	44.96
Selenium	Se	34	78.96
Silicon	Si	14	28.09
Silver	Ag	47	107.880
Sodium	Na	11	22.991
Strontium	Sr	38	87.63
Sulfur	S	16	32.066[3]
Tantalum	Ta	73	180.95
Technetium	Tc	43	(97)
Tellurium	Te	52	127.61
Terbium	Tb	65	158.93
Thallium	Tl	81	204.39
Thorium	Th	90	(232)
Thulium	Tm	69	168.94
Tin	Sn	50	118.70
Titanium	Ti	22	47.90
Tungsten	W	74	183.86
Uranium	U	92	(238)
Vanadium	V	23	50.95
Wolfram	W	See Tungsten	
Xenon	Xe	54	131.30
Ytterbium	Yb	70	173.04
Yttrium	Y	39	88.92
Zinc	Zn	30	65.38
Zirconium	Zr	40	91.22

1) International Atomic Weights 1959 (Commission on Atomic Weights, *Proceedings of the 20th Conference of the International Union of Pure and Applied Chemistry*, London, 1960, page 202). A value in parentheses indicates the mass number of the most stable known isotope or, in the case of those marked with an asterisk, of the best known one.

2) A defined value and hence an exact number.

3) Because of natural variations in the relative abundance of the isotopes of sulfur the atomic weight of this element has a range of ± 0.003.

4) Cf. MILSTED, J., *Nature*, **180**, 1012 (1957).

Alphabetical Table of the Symbols of the Elements

Symbol	Name	Atomic number	Atomic weight[1]
Ac	Actinium	89	(227)
Ag	Silver	47	107.880
Al	Aluminum	13	26.98
Am	Americium	95	(243)
Ar	Argon	18	39.944
As	Arsenic	33	74.91
At	Astatine	85	(210)
Au	Gold	79	197.0
B	Boron	5	10.82
Ba	Barium	56	137.36
Be	Beryllium	4	9.013
Bi	Bismuth	83	209.00
Bk	Berkelium	97	(247)
Br	Bromine	35	79.916
C	Carbon	6	12.011
Ca	Calcium	20	40.08
Cb	Columbium	See Nb	
Cd	Cadmium	48	112.41
Ce	Cerium	58	140.13
Cf	Californium	98	(249)
Cl	Chlorine	17	35.457
Cm	Curium	96	(247)
Co	Cobalt	27	58.94
Cp	Cassiopeium	See Lu	
Cr	Chromium	24	52.01
Cs	Cesium	55	132.91
Cu	Copper	29	63.54
Dy	Dysprosium	66	162.51
Em	Emanation	See Rn	
Er	Erbium	68	167.27
Es	Einsteinium	99	(254)
Eu	Europium	63	152.0
F	Fluorine	9	19.00
Fe	Iron	26	55.85
Fm	Fermium	100	(253)
Fr	Francium	87	(223)
Ga	Gallium	31	69.72
Gd	Gadolinium	64	157.26
Ge	Germanium	32	72.60
Gl	Glucinium	See Be	
H	Hydrogen	1	1.0080
He	Helium	2	4.003
Hf	Hafnium	72	178.50
Hg	Mercury	80	200.61
Ho	Holmium	67	164.94
I	Iodine	53	126.91
Il	Illinium	See Pm	
In	Indium	49	114.82
Ir	Iridium	77	192.2
K	Potassium	19	39.100
Kr	Krypton	36	83.80
La	Lanthanum	57	138.92
Li	Lithium	3	6.940
Lu	Lutetium	71	174.99
Lw	Lawrencium	103	(257?)
Md	Mendelevium	101	(256)
Mg	Magnesium	12	24.32
Mn	Manganese	25	54.94
Mo	Molybdenum	42	95.95
N	Nitrogen	7	14.008
Na	Sodium	11	22.991
Nb	Niobium	41	92.91
Nd	Neodymium	60	144.27
Ne	Neon	10	20.183
Ni	Nickel	28	58.71
No	Nobelium	102	(253?)[4]
Np	Neptunium	93	(237)
Nt	Niton	See Rn	
O	Oxygen	8	**16**[2]
Os	Osmium	76	190.2
P	Phosphorus	15	30.975
Pa	Protactinium	91	(231)
Pb	Lead	82	207.21
Pd	Palladium	46	106.4
Pm	Promethium	61	(147)*
Po	Polonium	84	(210)*
Pr	Praseodymium	59	140.92
Pt	Platinum	78	195.09
Pu	Plutonium	94	(242)
Ra	Radium	88	(226)
Rb	Rubidium	37	85.48
Re	Rhenium	75	186.22
Rh	Rhodium	45	102.91
Rn	Radon	86	(222)
Ru	Ruthenium	44	101.1
S	Sulfur	16	32.066[3]
Sb	Antimony	51	121.76
Sc	Scandium	21	44.96
Se	Selenium	34	78.96
Si	Silicon	14	28.09
Sm	Samarium	62	150.35
Sn	Tin	50	118.70
Sr	Strontium	38	87.63
Ta	Tantalum	73	180.95
Tb	Terbium	65	158.93
Tc	Technetium	43	(97)
Te	Tellurium	52	127.61
Th	Thorium	90	(232)
Ti	Titanium	22	47.90
Tl	Thallium	81	204.39
Tm	Thulium	69	168.94
Tu	Tungsten	See W	
U	Uranium	92	(238)
V	Vanadium	23	50.95
W	Tungsten	74	183.86
Xe	Xenon	54	131.30
Y	Yttrium	39	88.92
Yb	Ytterbium	70	173.04
Zn	Zinc	30	65.38
Zr	Zirconium	40	91.22

1) International Atomic Weights 1959 (Commission on Atomic Weights, *Proceedings of the 20th Conference of the International Union of Pure and Applied Chemistry*, London 1960, page 202). A value in parentheses indicates the mass number of the most stable known isotope or, in the case of those marked with an asterisk, of the best known one.

2) A defined value and hence an exact number.

3) Because of natural variations in the relative abundance of the isotopes of sulfur the atomic weight of this element has a range of ± 0.003.

4) Cf. Milsted, J., *Nature*, **180**, 1012 (1957).

Atomic number Z	Symbol	Element English French German (Latin)	Atomic weight 1959[1] or [mol.wt.] (chemical scale)	Valency	Melting point at 760 mm Hg (unless otherwise stated) °C	Boiling point at 760 mm Hg (unless otherwise stated) °C	Density Gases: g/liter at 760 mm Hg and 0° C; Others: g/cm³ or specific gravity 20°/4° C (unless otherwise stated)		Natural abundance: in the earth's crust, etc.[3] %	in the atmosphere (troposphere)	in the universe (atoms per 10^6 Si atoms)[4]	in the human body %	Natural isotopes[2]: Isotope (mass number A)	Relative abundance %	Atomic weight (physical scale)[1]	Mode of decay[5]	Energy in MeV	Half-life[6]
1	H $[H_2]$	**Hydrogen**[7] Hydrogène Wasserstoff	1.0080 [2.016]	1	−259.20	−252.77[7]	gas liquid solid	0.08987 0.0709/−252.7° 0.0808/−262°	0.88	0.00005 vol% 0.0007%	4.00×10^{10}	10.0	^{1}H(H) ^{2}H(D) ^{3}H(T)	99.985 0.015 see[8,16]	1.008145 2.014740 3.01700_5	β− no γ	0.0180	12.26 y
2	He	**Helium** Hélium Helium	4.003	0	−269.7	−268.944	gas liquid	0.1785 0.147/−270.8° 0.126/−268.9°	4.2×10^{-7}	0.000524 vol% 0.000065%	3.08×10^{9}		^{3}He ^{4}He	~1.3×10^{-4} (atmosphere) ~100	3.01698_6 4.00387_4			
3	Li	**Lithium** Lithium Lithium	6.940	1	180	1326	solid liquid	0.534 0.507/200°	0.005		100	trace	^{6}Li ^{7}Li	7.5 92.5	6.01703_4 7.01823_2			
4	Be	**Beryllium** Glucinium Beryllium	9.013	2	1283	2970	solid	1.85	5×10^{-4}		20	trace	^{9}Be	100	9.01504_6			
5	B	**Boron** Bore Bor	10.82	3	2040	~2550	crystalline amorphous	2.54 2.45	0.0014		24	trace	^{10}B ^{11}B	18.7 81.3	10.01611_9 11.01279_5			
6	C	**Carbon** Carbone Kohlenstoff	12.011	2,4	3550 (subl. > 3500)	4200	amorphous graphite diamond	1.8–2.1 2.25 3.51	0.087	CO_2 0.03 vol% 0.05%	3.5×10^{6}	18.0	^{12}C ^{13}C ^{14}C	98.89 1.11 see[16]	12.00380_3 13.00747_8 14.007687	β− no γ	0.1561	5.76×10^{3} y
7	N $[N_2]$	**Nitrogen** Azote Stickstoff	14.008 [28.016]	3,5	−210.01/ 94 mm Hg	−195.82	gas liquid solid	1.25060 0.808/−195.8° 1.026/−252.5°	0.030	78.09 vol% 75.50%	6.6×10^{6}	3.0	^{14}N ^{15}N	99.635 0.365	14.00752_0 15.00486_2			
8	O $[O_2]$	**Oxygen** Oxygène Sauerstoff	**16** [32]	2	−218.76	−182.970[10]	gas liquid solid	1.4290 1.14/−183° 1.426/−252.5°	49.4	20.95 vol% 23.15%	2.15×10^{7}	65.0	^{16}O ^{17}O ^{18}O	99.75_9 0.037 0.204	**16** 17.00453_4 18.00485_5			
9	F $[F_2]$	**Fluorine** Fluor Fluor	19.00 [38.00]	1	−217.96	−187.92	gas liquid solid	1.695 1.108/−187° 1.3/−223°	0.027		1600	~0.009	^{19}F	100	19.00444_8			
10	Ne	**Neon** Néon Neon	20.183	0	−248.59/ 324 mm Hg	−245.9	gas liquid solid	0.9002 1.204/−245.9° (1.0)	5×10^{-7}	0.0018 vol% 0.0014%	8.6×10^{6}		^{20}Ne ^{21}Ne ^{22}Ne	90.9_2 0.257 8.8_2	19.99876_9 21.00049_9 21.99835_4			
11	Na	**Sodium** Sodium Natrium	22.991	1	98	889	liquid solid	0.928/100° 0.97	2.64		4.38×10^{4}	0.109	^{23}Na	100	22.99705_3			
12	Mg	**Magnesium** Magnésium Magnesium	24.32	2	650	1107	liquid solid	1.72/651° 1.74	1.94		9.12×10^{5}	0.036	^{24}Mg ^{25}Mg ^{26}Mg	78.6_0 10.1_1 11.2_9	23.99264_0 24.99375_2 25.99080			

13	Al	**Aluminum** or **Aluminium** Aluminium Aluminium	26.98	3	660.1[11] (freezing point)	2450	liquid solid	2.380/660° 2.702	7.51		9.48×10^4	~0.001	^{27}Al	100	26.99008$_1$				
14	Si	**Silicon** Silicium Silizium	28.09	4	1410	(2600)	adamantine amorphous graphitoidal	2.42 2.0 ca. 2.4	25.75		10^6	~0.002	^{28}Si ^{29}Si ^{30}Si	92.18 4.71 3.12	27.98577$_5$ 28.98566 29.98325$_2$				
15	P	**Phosphorus** Phosphore Phosphor	30.975	3,5	yellow 44.2 (ignites at 34°) red 590/43 at violet 593	280	yellow: solid red: liquid red: solid violet: solid black	1.82 1.745/44.5° 2.20 2.36 2.7	0.12		1×10^4	1.16	^{31}P	100	30.98356				
16	S	**Sulfur** or **Sulphur** Soufre Schwefel	32.066[9]	2,4, 6	rhomb. 112.8 monocl. 119.0	444.600[11]	liquid rhomb.: solid monocl.: solid	1.808/115° 2.07 1.957	0.048		3.75×10^5	0.196	^{32}S ^{33}S ^{34}S ^{36}S	95.018 0.750 4.215 0.017	31.98220 32.98189 33.9786$_4$ 35.9784$_4$				
17	Cl [Cl_2]	**Chlorine** Chlore Chlor	35.457 [70.914]	1,3, 5,7	−101	−34.06	gas liquid solid	3.214 1.557/−33.6° (1.9)	0.19		8850	0.156	^{35}Cl ^{37}Cl	75.53 24.47	34.97990 36.97754				
18	Ar	**Argon** Argon Argon	39.944	0	−189.2	−185.87	gas liquid solid	1.7824 1.402/−185.7° 1.65/−223°	3.6×10^{-4}	0.93 vol% 1.292%	1.5×10^5		^{36}Ar ^{38}Ar ^{40}Ar	0.34 0.06 99.60	35.97892 37.9747$_9$ 39.9750$_5$				
19	K	**Potassium** Potassium Kalium	39.100	1	63.4	757	liquid solid	0.819/100° 0.86	2.40		3160	0.2	^{39}K ^{40}K ^{41}K	93.08 0.0119 6.91	38.9760$_4$ 39.9766$_5$ 40.9747$_6$	 β^-,γ K	 1.35 1.46		 1.3×10^9y
20	Ca	**Calcium** Calcium Kalzium	40.08	2	850	1200 ± 30	solid	1.55	3.39		4.90×10^4	2.01	^{40}Ca ^{42}Ca ^{43}Ca ^{44}Ca ^{46}Ca ^{48}Ca	96.96 0.64 0.14$_5$ 2.07 0.0033 0.18$_5$	39.9752$_3$ 41.9718$_9$ 42.9723$_5$ 43.9693$_4$ 47.9677				 $>2\times10^{16}$y
21	Sc	**Scandium** Scandium Scandium	44.96	3	1400	3900	solid	3.02/10°	6×10^{-4}		28		^{45}Sc	100	44.9700$_7$				
22	Ti	**Titanium** Titane Titan	47.90	2,3, 4	1812	(> 3000)	solid	4.50	0.58		2440		^{46}Ti ^{47}Ti ^{48}Ti ^{49}Ti ^{50}Ti	7.99 7.32 73.9$_9$ 5.46 5.25	45.9669$_5$ 46.9665$_0$ 47.9631$_2$ 48.9633$_9$ 49.9605$_8$				
23	V	**Vanadium** Vanadium Vanadium	50.95	2,3, 4,5	1730	(3000)	solid	5.96	0.016		220		^{50}V ^{51}V	0.24 99.76	49.9631$_2$ 50.9600$_4$				$>10^{14}$y
24	Cr	**Chromium** Chrome Chrom	52.01	2,3, 6	1903±10	(2200)	solid	7.1	0.033		7800		^{50}Cr ^{52}Cr ^{53}Cr ^{54}Cr	4.31 83.7$_6$ 9.5$_5$ 2.38	49.9616$_4$ 51.9569$_9$ 52.9574$_6$ 53.9560$_2$				

For footnotes see page 262.

Atomic number Z	Symbol	Element: English, French, German, (Latin)	Atomic weight 1959[1] (chemical scale)	Valency	Melting point at 760 mm Hg (unless otherwise stated) °C	Boiling point at 760 mm Hg (unless otherwise stated) °C	Density: Gases: g/liter at 760 mm Hg and 0°C; Others: g/cm³ or specific gravity 20°/4°C (unless otherwise stated)	Natural abundance: in the earth's crust, etc.[3] %	Natural abundance: in the atmosphere (troposphere)	Natural abundance: in the universe (atoms per 10⁶ Si atoms)[4]	Natural abundance: in the human body %	Natural isotopes[2]: Isotope (mass number A)	Relative abundance %	Atomic weight (physical scale)[1]	Mode of decay[5]	Energy in MeV	Half-life[6]
25	Mn	**Manganese** Manganèse Mangan	54.94	2,3, 4,6, 7	1244	2087	solid 7.20	0.085		6850	~0.001	^{55}Mn	100	54.9554_0			
26	Fe	**Iron** Fer Eisen (Ferrum)	55.85	2,3, 6	1535	2800	liquid 6.9/1530° solid 7.86	4.7		6.00×10^5	0.010	^{54}Fe ^{56}Fe ^{57}Fe ^{58}Fe	5.8_4 91.6_8 2.17 0.31	53.9566_4 55.9526_4 56.9534_2 57.9514_7			
27	Co	**Cobalt** Cobalt Kobalt	58.94	2,3	1492[11] (freezing point)	3100	solid 8.9	0.0018		1800	~0.001	^{59}Co	100	58.9519			
28	Ni	**Nickel** Nickel Nickel	58.71	2,3	1453[11] (freezing point)	2800	solid 8.90	0.018		2.74×10^4	~0.001	^{58}Ni ^{60}Ni ^{61}Ni ^{62}Ni ^{64}Ni	67.8 26.2 1.25 3.66 1.1_6	57.9538 59.9499 60.9497 61.9476 63.9481			
29	Cu	**Copper** Cuivre Kupfer (Cuprum)	63.54	1,2	1083[11] (freezing point	2582	liquid 8.3/1083° solid 8.92	0.010		212	~0.002	^{63}Cu ^{65}Cu	69.1 30.9	62.9494 64.9484			
30	Zn	**Zinc** Zinc Zink	65.38	2	419.5[11] (freezing point)	907	liquid 6.92/419.5° solid 7.133	0.02		486	~0.002	^{64}Zn ^{66}Zn ^{67}Zn ^{68}Zn ^{70}Zn	48.8_9 27.8_1 4.1_1 18.5_6 0.62	63.9493 65.9469 66.9485 67.9465 69.9474			
31	Ga	**Gallium** Gallium Gallium	69.72	2,3	29.78	(1983)	liquid 6.095/29.8° solid 5.91	5×10^{-4}		11.4		^{69}Ga ^{71}Ga	60.2 39.8	68.9476 70.9474			
32	Ge	**Germanium** Germanium Germanium	72.60	2,4	937.6 ± 0.5	(2700)	solid 5.36	1×10^{-4}		50.5		^{70}Ge ^{72}Ge ^{73}Ge ^{74}Ge ^{76}Ge	20.5_5 27.3_7 7.6_7 36.7_4 7.6_7	69.9464 71.9446 72.9464_5 73.9445_9 75.9453_3			
33	As	**Arsenic** Arsenic Arsen	74.91	3,5	crystalline 817/35.8 at (subl. 615)		crystalline 5.727/14° amorphous 4.7 yellow: solid 2.0	5.5×10^{-4}		4.0		^{75}As	100	74.9454_0			
34	Se	**Selenium** Sélénium Selen	78.96	2,4, 6	grey 217.4 /0.0043 mm Hg red 144	736	grey 4.80/25° red 4.50/25°	8×10^{-5}		67.6		^{74}Se ^{76}Se ^{77}Se ^{78}Se ^{80}Se ^{82}Se	0.87 9.0_2 7.5_8 23.5_2 49.8_2 9.1_9	73.9458_9 75.9433_4 76.9443_6 77.9420_9 79.9420 81.9426_1			

35	Br	**Bromine** Brome Brom	79.916	1,3, 5,7	−7.3	58.78	gas liquid solid	7.59 3.119 (3.14)	6×10^{-4}		13.4	~0.002	^{79}Br	50.54	78.94341			
													^{81}Br	49.46	80.9421			
36	Kr	**Krypton** Krypton Krypton	83.80	0	−157.21/ 549 mm Hg	−153.23	gas liquid solid	3.708 2.6/−146° (2)	1.9×10^{-8}	0.0001 vol% 0.0003%	51.3							
													^{78}Kr	0.35_4	77.9448_9			
													^{80}Kr	2.2_7	79.9419			
													^{82}Kr	11.5_6	81.9394			
													^{83}Kr	11.5_5	82.9403			
													^{84}Kr	57.9_0	83.9381			
													^{86}Kr	17.3_7	85.9382			
37	Rb	**Rubidium** Rubidium Rubidium	85.48	1	38.8	679	liquid solid	1.475/39.0° 1.53	0.0034		6.5		^{85}Rb	72.1_5	84.9389			
													^{87}Rb	27.8_5	86.9368_7	β− no γ	0.27_5	5×10^{10} y
38	Sr	**Strontium** Strontium Strontium	87.63	2	770	1384	solid	2.6	0.017		18.9							
													^{84}Sr	0.5_6	83.9399			
													^{86}Sr	9.87	85.9366			
													^{87}Sr	7.0_2	86.9365_8			
													^{88}Sr	82.5_6	87.9338			
39	Y	**Yttrium** Yttrium Yttrium	88.92	3	(1500)	(4100)	solid	(5.51)	0.005		8.9		^{89}Y	100	88.9341			
40	Zr	**Zirconium** Zirconium Zirkon	91.22	2,4	1852 ± 10	(> 2900)	solid	6.4	0.023		54.5							
													^{90}Zr	51.4_6	89.9328			
													^{91}Zr	11.2_3	90.9341			
													^{92}Zr	17.1_1	91.9338			
													^{94}Zr	17.4_0	93.9358			
													^{96}Zr	2.80	95.938_5			
41	Nb (Cb)	**Niobium** (Columbium) Niobium Niob	92.91	3,5	2487 (ignites at 1950°)	(> 3300)	solid	8.55	4×10^{-5}		1.00		^{93}Nb	100	92.9353			$>2\times10^{16}$y
42	Mo	**Molybdenum** Molybdène Molybdän	95.95	2,3, 4,5, 6	2610	(3700)	solid	10.2	7.2×10^{-4}		2.42	trace						
													^{92}Mo	15.8_6	91.9352			
													^{94}Mo	9.1_2	93.9343			
													^{95}Mo	15.7_0	94.9357			
													^{96}Mo	16.5_0	95.9349			
													^{97}Mo	9.4_5	96.936_5			
													^{98}Mo	23.7_5	97.936_6			
													^{100}Mo	9.6_2	99.938_3			
43	Tc	**Technetium** Technétium Technetium	97[12]	6,7	2200 ± 50		solid	11.50	0				$^{92-102}Tc$ $^{104,105}Tc$ and ^{107}Tc	artificial element: all very unstable, except ^{97}Tc, ^{98}Tc, ^{99}Tc (half-lives 2.6×10^6 y, ca. 10^5 y, $2.1_2\times10^5$ y)				
44	Ru	**Ruthenium** Ruthénium Ruthenium	101.1	3,4, 6,8	2500	4110	solid	12.2	5×10^{-6}		1.49							
													^{96}Ru	5.5	95.937_9			
													^{98}Ru	1.9	97.937_1			
													^{99}Ru	12.7	98.938_2			
													^{100}Ru	12.7				
													^{101}Ru	17.0				
													^{102}Ru	31.5	101.936_4			
													^{104}Ru	18.7	103.937_8			
45	Rh	**Rhodium** Rhodium Rhodium	102.91	1,2, 3,4	1960[11] (freezing point)	3960	solid	12.5	1×10^{-6}		0.214		^{103}Rh	100	102.937_9			

For footnotes see page 262.

Atomic number Z	Symbol	Element: English, French, German, (Latin)	Atomic weight 1959[1] (chemical scale)	Valency	Melting point at 760 mm Hg (unless otherwise stated) °C	Boiling point at 760 mm Hg (unless otherwise stated) °C	Density: Gases: g/liter at 760 mm Hg and 0° C; Others: g/cm³ or specific gravity 20°/4° C (unless otherwise stated)		Natural abundance: in the earth's crust, etc.[3] %	Natural abundance: in the atmosphere (troposphere)	Natural abundance: in the universe (atoms per 10^6 Si atoms)[4]	Natural abundance: in the human body %	Natural isotopes[2]: Isotope (mass number A)	Relative abundance %	Atomic weight (physical scale)[1]	Mode of decay[5]	Energy in MeV	Half-life[6]
46	Pd	**Palladium**	106.4	2,4	1552[11] (freezing point)	3560	liquid	11/1550°	5×10^{-6}		0.675		^{102}Pd	0.96	101.937_5			
		Palladium					solid	11.97					^{104}Pd	10.9_7	103.936_9			
		Palladium											^{105}Pd	22.2_3	104.938_1			
													^{106}Pd	27.3_3	105.936_4			
													^{108}Pd	26.7_1	107.9378			
													^{110}Pd	11.8_1	109.939_6			
47	Ag	**Silver**	107.880	1	960.8[10] (freezing point)	2193	liquid	9.3/960.5°	4×10^{-6}		0.26		^{107}Ag	51.3_5	106.9389			
		Argent					solid	10.5					^{109}Ag	48.6_5	108.9393			
		Silber																
		(Argentum)																
48	Cd	**Cadmium**	112.41	2	320.9[11] (freezing point)	767	liquid	8.01/330°	1.1×10^{-5}		0.89		^{106}Cd	1.21	105.939_5			
		Cadmium					solid	8.65					^{108}Cd	0.88	107.9382			
		Cadmium											^{110}Cd	12.3_9	109.9383			
													^{111}Cd	12.7_5	110.939_4			
													^{112}Cd	24.0_7	111.938_2			
													^{113}Cd	12.2_6	112.940_3			
													^{114}Cd	28.8_6	113.939_6			
													^{116}Cd	7.5_8	115.941_8			
49	In	**Indium**	114.82	1,3	156.4	(2087)	solid	7.30	1×10^{-5}		0.11		^{113}In	4.23	112.940_1			
		Indium											^{115}In	95.77	114.940_5	β−	(0.50)	6×10^{14} y
		Indium																
50	Sn	**Tin**	118.70	2,4	231.9[11] (freezing point)	2337	liquid	6.98/232°	6×10^{-4}		1.33	trace	^{112}Sn	0.95	111.940_3			
		Etain					cub.(α): solid	5.750					^{114}Sn	0.65	113.939_5			
		Zinn					tetr. (β-): solid	7.31					^{115}Sn	0.34	114.940_0			
		(Stannum)					rhomb. (γ-): solid	6.52–6.56					^{116}Sn	14.24	115.939_0			
													^{117}Sn	7.57	116.940_2			
													^{118}Sn	24.0_1	117.939_3			
													^{119}Sn	8.58	118.941_0			
													^{120}Sn	32.9_7	119.9401			
													^{122}Sn	4.71	121.942_1			
													^{124}Sn	5.98	123.9445			
51	Sb	**Antimony**	121.76	3,5	630.5[11] (freezing point)	1440	liquid	6.55/631°	2.3×10^{-5}		0.246		^{121}Sb	57.2_5	120.942_0			
		Antimoine					solid	6.691					^{123}Sb	42.7_5	122.943_1			
		Antimon																
		(Stibium)																
52	Te	**Tellurium**	127.61	2,4,6	450/0.18 mm Hg	1087	rhomb.	6.24	1×10^{-6}		4.67		^{120}Te	0.089	119.942_5			
		Tellure					amorphous	6.00					^{122}Te	2.46	121.941_6			
		Tellur											^{123}Te	0.87	122.943_3			$>10^{13}$ y
													^{124}Te	4.61	123.942_1			
													^{125}Te	6.99	124.944_1			
													^{126}Te	18.7_1	125.943_6			
													^{128}Te	31.7_9	127.946_1			
													^{130}Te	32.4_9	129.947_8			$>10^{21}$ y

53	I	**Iodine** Iode Jod	126.91	1,3, 5,7	113.6	184.35	gas liquid solid	11.27 4.00/107° 4.93	6×10^{-6}		0.80	0.016	^{127}I	100	126.944_8			
54	Xe	**Xenon** Xénon Xenon	131.30	0	−111.9/611 mm Hg	−108.1	gas liquid solid	5.851 3.06/−109° 2.7/−140°	2.4×10^{-9}	8×10^{-6}vol% 4×10^{-5}%	4.0		^{124}Xe	0.096	123.945_4			
													^{126}Xe	0.090	125.944_5			
													^{128}Xe	1.91_9	127.944_5			
													^{129}Xe	26.4_4	128.945_6			
													^{130}Xe	4.08	129.944_6			
													^{131}Xe	21.1_8	130.946_6			
													^{132}Xe	26.8_9	131.946_0			
													^{134}Xe	10.44	133.947_6			
													^{136}Xe	8.87	135.950_0			
55	Cs	**Cesium** or **Caesium** Césium Caesium	132.91	1	28.7	690	liquid solid	1.84/28° 1.9	7×10^{-5}		0.456		^{133}Cs	100	132.947_2			
56	Ba	**Barium** Baryum Barium	137.36	2	704	1638	solid	3.5	0.047		3.66		^{130}Ba	0.101	129.947_4			
													^{132}Ba	0.097				
													^{134}Ba	2.42	133.946_8			
													^{135}Ba	6.59				
													^{136}Ba	7.81				
													^{137}Ba	11.3_2	136.949_6			
													^{138}Ba	71.6_6	137.948_7			
57	La	**Lanthanum** Lanthane Lanthan	138.92	3	880	(1800)	solid	6.15	5×10^{-4}		2.00		^{138}La	0.089	137.950_1	β^- γ K	1.0 1.43/0.80/0.5	1.1×10^{11} y
													^{139}La	99.911	138.949_5			
58	Ce	**Cerium** Cérium Cer	140.13	3,4	775	(1400)	cubic hexagonal	6.90 6.7	0.0022		2.26		^{136}Ce	0.19_3				
													^{138}Ce	0.25_0	137.949_0			
													^{140}Ce	88.4_8	139.948_9			
													^{142}Ce	11.0_7	141.953_0			
59	Pr	**Praseo- dymium** Praséodyme Praseodym	140.92	3,4, 5	932		solid	6.5	3.5×10^{-4}		0.40		^{141}Pr	100	140.951_1			
60	Nd	**Neodymium** Néodyme Neodym	144.27	3	1024		solid	6.9	0.0012		1.44		^{142}Nd	27.0_9	141.951_5			
													^{143}Nd	12.14	142.954_1			
													^{144}Nd	23.8_3	143.954_9	α	1.9	~2×10^{15}y
													^{145}Nd	8.29				
													^{146}Nd	17.26	145.958_7			
													^{148}Nd	5.74	147.964_0			
													^{150}Nd	5.63	149.967_9			>10^{16} y
61	Pm	**Promethium** Prométhéum Promethium	147[13]	3									^{141}Pm and $^{143-151}$Pm	all radioactive; natural occurrence uncertain				
62	Sm	**Samarium** Samarium Samarium	150.35	2,3	1052		solid	(6.93)	5×10^{-4}		0.664		^{144}Sm	3.1_6	143.956_0			
													^{147}Sm	15.0_7	146.960_3	α	2.18	1.3×10^{11} y
													^{148}Sm	11.2_7	147.961_3			
													^{149}Sm	13.8_4	148.963_5			
													^{150}Sm	7.4_7	149.963_4			
													^{152}Sm	26.6_3	151.967_3			
													^{154}Sm	22.5_3	153.970_5			

For footnotes see page 262.

Atomic number Z	Symbol	Element English French German (Latin)	Atomic weight 1959[1] (chemical scale)	Valency	Melting point at 760 mm Hg (unless otherwise stated) °C	Boiling point at 760 mm Hg (unless otherwise stated) °C	Density Gases: g/liter at 760 mm Hg and 0° C Others: g/cm³ or specific gravity 20°/4° C (unless otherwise stated)		Natural abundance: in the earth's crust, etc.[3] %	in the atmosphere (troposphere)	in the universe (atoms per 10^6 Si atoms)[4]	in the human body %	Natural isotopes[2]: Isotope (mass number A)	Relative abundance %	Atomic weight (physical scale)[1]	Mode of decay[5]	Energy in MeV	Half-life[6]
63	Eu	**Europium** Europium Europium	152.0	2,3	(1150 ± 50)		solid	(5.22)	1.4×10^{-4}		0.187		^{151}Eu	47.7_7				
													^{153}Eu	52.23				
64	Gd	**Gadolinium** Gadolinium Gadolinium	157.26	3	(1350)		solid	(7.94)	5×10^{-4}		0.684		^{152}Gd	0.20				
													^{154}Gd	2.15	153.969_7			
													^{155}Gd	14.7_3	154.970_9			
													^{156}Gd	20.4_7	155.971_5			
													^{157}Gd	15.6_8	156.971_2			
													^{158}Gd	24.8_7	157.973_4			
													^{160}Gd	21.9_0	159.977_8			
65	Tb	**Terbium** Terbium Terbium	158.93	3	(1450 ± 50)		solid	(8.33)	7×10^{-5}		0.0956		^{159}Tb	100				
66	Dy	**Dysprosium** Dysprosium Dysprosium	162.51	3	(1500)		solid	(8.56)	5×10^{-4}		0.556		^{156}Dy	0.052				
													^{158}Dy	0.090				
													^{160}Dy	2.29	159.976			
													^{161}Dy	18.8_8				
													^{162}Dy	25.5_3	161.977			
													^{163}Dy	24.9_7				
													^{164}Dy	28.1_8	163.980			
67	Ho	**Holmium** Holmium Holmium	164.94	3	(1500)		solid	(8.76)	7×10^{-5}		0.118		^{165}Ho	100	164.981			
68	Er	**Erbium** Erbium Erbium	167.27	3	(1525 ± 25)		solid	(9.16)	4×10^{-4}		0.316		^{162}Er	0.13_6				
													^{164}Er	1.5_6	163.981_7			
													^{166}Er	33.4				
													^{167}Er	22.9				
													^{168}Er	27.1	167.983_9			
													^{170}Er	14.9	169.989			
69	Tm	**Thulium** Thulium Thulium	168.94	3	(1600 ± 50)		solid	(9.34)	7×10^{-5}		0.0318		^{169}Tm	100				
70	Yb	**Ytterbium** Ytterbium Ytterbium	173.04	3	ca. 1800		solid	(7.01)	5×10^{-4}		0.220		^{168}Yb	0.14				
													^{170}Yb	3.0_3				
													^{171}Yb	14.3_1				
													^{172}Yb	21.8_2	171.984			
													^{173}Yb	16.1_3				
													^{174}Yb	31.8_4	173.981			
													^{176}Yb	12.7_3				

71	Lu	**Lutetium** (Cassiopeium) Lutécium Lutetium or Lutecium	174.99	3	(1700 ± 50)		solid	(9.7)	1×10^{-5}	0.050	^{175}Lu	97.4				
											^{176}Lu	2.6	175.997	β^- γ K	0.43 0.20/0.31/0.09	3×10^{10}y
72	Hf	**Hafnium** Hafnium Hafnium	178.50	4	2227	(> 3200)	solid	(13.3)	0.0025	0.438	^{174}Hf	0.19				
											^{176}Hf	5.19	175.996			
											^{177}Hf	18.4$_7$				
											^{178}Hf	27.1$_5$	178.000			
											^{179}Hf	13.75				
											^{180}Hf	35.2$_5$				
73	Ta	**Tantalum** Tantale Tantal	180.95	3,5	2977	(> 4100)	solid	16.6	1.2×10^{-5}	0.065	^{180}Ta	0.012	180.002			> 10^7 y
											^{181}Ta	99.988				
74	W	**Tungsten** Tungstène Wolfram	183.86	2,4, 5,6	3380[11]	(5900)	solid	19.3	0.0055	0.49	^{180}W	0.13$_5$	180.001	α	3.2	~3×10^{14}y
											^{182}W	26.4	182.004			
											^{183}W	14.4	183.005			
											^{184}W	30.6	184.006			
											^{186}W	28.4	186.010			
75	Re	**Rhenium** Rhénium Rhenium	186.22	3,4, 5,6, 7	3147		solid	21.40	1×10^{-7}	0.135	^{185}Re	37.0$_7$				
											^{187}Re	62.9$_3$	187.011	β^-	< 0.008	5×10^{10}y
76	Os	**Osmium** Osmium Osmium	190.2	2,3, 4,6, 8	2700	4400	solid (heaviest element)	22.48	5×10^{-6}	1.00	^{184}Os	0.018				
											^{186}Os	1.59	186.010			
											^{187}Os	1.64	187.011			
											^{188}Os	13.3	188.014			
											^{189}Os	16.1	189.018			
											^{190}Os	26.4	190.017			
											^{192}Os	41.0	192.022			
77	Ir	**Iridium** Iridium Iridium	192.2[14]	3,4	2443[11] (freezing point)	4350	solid	22.4	1×10^{-6}	0.821	^{191}Ir	38.5	191.021			
											^{193}Ir	61.5	193.025			
78	Pt	**Platinum** Platine Platin	195.09	2,4	1769[11] (freezing point)	4010	liquid solid	19/1755° 21.45	2×10^{-5}	1.625	^{190}Pt	0.012		α	3.3	~1×10^{12}y
											^{192}Pt	0.78	192.023			
											^{194}Pt	32.8	194.024			
											^{195}Pt	33.7	195.026$_4$			
											^{196}Pt	25.4	196.026$_9$			
											^{198}Pt	7.2	198.029			
79	Au	**Gold** Or Gold (Aurum)	197.0	1,3	1063.0[10] (freezing point)	2660	liquid solid	17.0/1300° 19.3	5×10^{-7}	0.145	^{197}Au	100	197.028			
80	Hg	**Mercury** Mercure Quecksilber (Hydrar- gyrum)	200.61	1,2	−38.87[11] (freezing point)	356.58[11]		14.43/−38.87° 13.595/0° 13.546/20°[15]	2.7×10^{-6}	0.284	^{196}Hg	0.14$_6$	196.027			
											^{198}Hg	10.0$_2$	198.029			
											^{199}Hg	16.84	199.031			
											^{200}Hg	23.1$_3$	200.032			
											^{201}Hg	13.2$_2$	201.034			
											^{202}Hg	29.8$_0$	(202.035$_4$)			
											^{204}Hg	6.85	204.0373			

For footnotes see page 262.

Atomic number Z	Symbol	Element English French German (Latin)	Atomic weight 1959[1] (chemical scale)	Valency	Melting point at 760 mm Hg (unless otherwise stated) °C	Boiling point at 760 mm Hg (unless otherwise stated) °C	Density Gases: g/liter at 760 mm Hg and 0° C Others: g/cm³ or specific gravity 20°/4° C (unless otherwise stated)		Natural abundance in the earth's crust, etc.[3] %	in the atmosphere (troposphere)	in the universe (atoms per 10⁶ Si atoms)[4]	in the human body %	Natural isotopes[2] Isotope (mass number A)	Relative abundance %	Atomic weight (physical scale)[1]	Mode of decay[5]	Energy in MeV	Half-life[6]
81	Tl	**Thallium** Thallium Thallium	204.39	1,3	303.6	1457	solid	11.85	1×10^{-5}		0.108		^{203}Tl	29.5_0	203.0360			
													^{205}Tl	70.5_0	205.0384_8			
													^{206}Tl (Radium-E″)		206.04045	β⁻ no γ	1.51	4.20 m
													^{207}Tl (Actinium-C″)		207.04214	β⁻ γ	1.47 0.87	4.78 m
													^{208}Tl (Thorium-C″)		208.04701	β⁻ γ	1.80/1.29/1.52/2.38 0.583/2.615/ 0.511/0.86	3.1 m
													^{210}Tl (Radium-C″)		210.05562	β⁻	1.8	1.32 m
82	Pb	**Lead** Plomb Blei (Plumbum)	207.21	2,4	327.3[11] (freezing point)	1750	liquid solid	10.51/400° 11.34	0.002		0.47		^{204}Pb	1.5	204.0368_6			
													^{206}Pb (Radium-G)	23.6	206.03883			
													^{207}Pb	22.6	207.04058			
													^{208}Pb	52.3	208.04164			
													^{210}Pb (Radium-D)		210.04983	β⁻ γ	0.017 0.0467	19.4 y
													^{211}Pb (Actinium-B)		211.0547_5	β⁻ γ	~1.4/0.5 0.82_9 $0.065–0.76_4$	36.1 m
													^{212}Pb (Thorium-B)		212.05817	β⁻ γ	0.35/0.59 $0.2386_0/0.299$ 0.115–0.249	10.64 h
													^{214}Pb (Radium-B)		214.0665_8	β⁻ γ	0.65 $0.3519_9/0.2952_2$ $0.05323_6–0.2578$	26.8 m
83	Bi	**Bismuth** Bismuth Wismut	209.00	3,5	271.0	1420	solid	9.8	3.4×10^{-6}		0.144		^{209}Bi	100	209.0457_9	α	~3	~2×10^{17}y
													^{210}Bi (Radium-E)		210.04976	α β⁻ no γ	4.77 1.17_0	5.00 d
													^{211}Bi (Actinium-C)		211.0532_6	α β⁻ γ	$6.61_9/6.27_3$ 0.35_0	2.16 m
													^{212}Bi (Thorium-C)		212.05754	α β⁻ γ	6.047/6.086 $2.25_3/2.1_5$ 0.040–2.2	60.5 m
													^{214}Bi (Radium-C)		214.06552	α β⁻ γ	5.505/5.444 1.65/3.17 1.76/0.45–2.43	19.7 m
													^{215}Bi		(215.0689)	β⁻		8 m

84	Po	**Polonium** Polonium Polonium	210[13]	(2, 3, 4)	254	962	solid	α-form 9.32 β-form 9.51	1.5×10^{-15}			^{210}Po (Radium-F)	210.04850	α γ	5.298 0.80_2	138.40 d
												^{211}Po (Actinium-C′)	211.05261	α γ	7.43_4/6.56/ 6.88 0.88/0.56	0.52 s
												^{212}Po (Thorium-C′)	212.05512_9	α	8.77_6	0.304 μs
												^{214}Po (Radium-C′)	214.06211	α	7.68_0	164 μs
												^{215}Po (Actinium-A)	215.0667_1	α β−	7.36_5	1.83×10^{-3} s
												^{216}Po (Thorium-A)	216.06946	α	6.77_4	0.158 s
												^{218}Po (Radium-A)	218.0770_2	α β−	5.998	3.05 m
85	At	**Astatine** Astatine or Astate Astatin	210[12]	(1, 3,5, 7)					4×10^{-23}			^{215}At	215.0658_9	α	8.00	~10^{-4} s
												^{216}At	216.0699_5	α	7.7_9	3×10^{-4} s
												^{218}At	218.0766	α β−	6.6_3	~2 s
												^{219}At		α β−	6.27	0.9 m
86	Rn	**Radon** (Emanation, Niton) Radon Radon	222[12]	0	−71	−61.8	gas liquid solid	9.73 4.4/−62° (4)	6×10^{-18}			^{219}Rn (Actinon)	219.0780_4	α γ	$6.82_4/6.55_9/6.43_4$ 0.198/0.067-0.589	3.92 s
												^{220}Rn (Thoron)	220.08021	α γ	6.27_8 0.54_2	52 s
												^{222}Rn (Radon)	222.0869_0	α γ	5.48_6 0.51_0	3.825 d
87	Fr	**Francium** Francium Francium	223[12]	1					7×10^{-23}			^{223}Fr (Actinium-K)	223.0896_0	α β− γ	5.3_4 1.1_5/1.3 0.050–0.31	21 m
88	Ra	**Radium** Radium Radium	226[12]	2	700	(1140)	solid	(5)	7×10^{-12}		$<1\times10^{-12}$	^{223}Ra (Actinium-X)	223.0883_2	α γ	$5.71_9/5.43_3$–5.75_0 0.026–0.44	11.68 d
												^{224}Ra (Thorium-X)	224.09030	α γ	5.681/ $5.44_8/5.19_4$ 0.241	3.64 d
												^{226}Ra	226.0960_0	α γ	4.777/4.591 0.186/0.6_6	1622 y
												^{228}Ra (Mesothorium-I)	228.1025_6	β− no γ	< 0.01	6.7 y
89	Ac	**Actinium** Actinium Actinium	227[12]	3	1050 ± 50				3×10^{-15}			^{227}Ac	227.0988_8	α β−	4.94 0.045_5	21.8 y
												^{228}Ac (Mesothorium-II)	228.1025_1	β− γ	1.11/0.45–2.18 0.057/0.098/ 0.127/1.59 0.08–1.64	6.13 h
90	Th	**Thorium** Thorium Thorium	232[12]	4	1750	(> 3000)	solid	11.7	0.0025			^{227}Th (Radioactinium)	227.0987_9	α γ	$5.97_2/5.70_4$–6.03_0 0.050/0.113/ 0.23_6/0.335/0.03-0.64	18.4 d
												^{228}Th (Radiothorium)	228.1001_1	α γ	$5.42_1/5.33_8$/ $5.20_8/5.17_3$ 0.084_5/0.212/ 0.137/0.169	1.91 y

For footnotes see page 262.

Atomic number Z	Symbol	Element: **English**, French, German, (Latin)	Atomic weight 1959[1] (chemical scale)	Valency	Melting point at 760 mm Hg (unless otherwise stated) °C	Boiling point at 760 mm Hg (unless otherwise stated) °C	Density: Gases: g/liter at 760 mm Hg and 0° C; Others: g/cm³ or specific gravity 20°/4° C (unless otherwise stated)		Natural abundance: in the earth's crust, etc.[3] %	in the atmosphere (troposphere)	in the universe (atoms per 10^6 Si atoms)[4]	in the human body %	Natural isotopes[2]: Isotope (mass number A)	Relative abundance %	Atomic weight (physical scale)[1]	Mode of decay[5]	Energy in MeV	Half-life[6]
90	Th	**Thorium** (continued) Thorium Thorium	232.05	4	1750	(> 3000)	solid	11.7	0.0025				^{230}Th (Ionium)		230.1050_0	α γ	$4.68_5/4.61_8$ 0.068/ 0.14–0.26	8×10^4 y
													^{231}Th (Uranium-Y)		231.1086_1	β⁻ γ	0.094/0.302/ 0.21_6 0.022/0.085/ 0.061	25.64 h
													^{232}Th	100	232.1108_0	α γ	3.98/3.93 0.055	1.39×10^{10} y
													^{234}Th (Uranium-X_1)		234.1167_8	β⁻ γ	0.193/0.103 0.092/0.063/ 0.029	24.10 d
91	Pa	**Protactinium** Protactinium Protactinium	231[12]	5	(< 1873)		solid	15.37	6×10^{-12}				^{231}Pa		231.1082_7	α γ	5.00_6/5.020/5.049 0.331/0.027/ 0.102	3.43×10^4 y
													^{234}Pa (Uranium-X_2)			β⁻ γ IT	2.31 1.0/0.76	1.175 m
													^{234}Pa (Uranium-Z)		234.1166	β⁻ γ	0.5 0.04–1.7	6.66 h
92	U	**Uranium** Uranium Uran	238[12]	3,4, 6	1131 ± 1	3818	solid	19.04/25°	2×10^{-5}				^{234}U (Uranium-II)	0.0058	234.1140_8	α γ	$4.76_3/4.70_7/4.59_3$ 0.018/0.053/ 0.12/0.09	2.48×10^5 y
													^{235}U (Actinium-U)	0.720	235.1175_0	α γ	4.39/4.57/4.18 0.18/0.37	7.13×10^8 y
													^{238}U (Uranium-I)	99.274	238.1252_2	α γ	4.18_0 0.045	4.51×10^9 y

Footnotes (pages 252–262)

1) Cf. Commission on Atomic Weights, *Proceedings of the 20th Conference of the International Union of Pure and Applied Chemistry*, London, 1960, page 202.

2) After SULLIVAN, W. H., *Trilinear Chart of Nuclides*, Washington (United States Atomic Energy Commission), 1957, with additional energy data from STEHN and CLANCY, in LANGE, N.A. (Ed.), *Handbook of Chemistry*, 10th ed., Sandusky, 1961, pages 114-147. Only the naturally occurring isotopes are listed.

3) Values are total percentages in the lithosphere (outer 10 miles), hydrosphere and atmosphere (after REMY, H., *Lehrbuch der anorganischen Chemie*, 7th edition, vol. II, Leipzig, 1954, page 542).

4) After SUESS and UREY, *Rev. mod. Phys.*, **28**, 53 (1956).

5) α = alpha particle (helium nucleus = 2 protons + 2 neutrons), β⁻ = beta particle (electron), γ = gamma ray, e⁻ = internal electron conversion, K = orbital electron capture, IT = isomeric transition.

6) y = year, d = day, h = hour, m = minute, s = second.

7) Normal molecular hydrogen is a mixture of *ortho-* and *para*-hydrogen (molecules in which the two nuclei have respectively parallel and antiparallel spins) in the proportions 3:1. Pure *ortho*-hydrogen has b.p. – 272.71° C. Cf. WOOLLEY et al., *J. Res. nat. Bur. Stand.*, **41**, 379 (1948).

8) The ratio of ^{1}H to ^{3}H atoms in atmospheric hydrogen is of the order of 10^{14}. Cf. GROSSE et al., *Phys. Rev.*, **93**, 250 (1954).

9) Because of natural variations in the relative abundances of the isotopes of sulfur the atomic weight of this element has a range of ± 0.003.

10) Primary fixed point of the International Temperature Scale 1948. Cf. STIMSON, H. F., *J. Res. nat. Bur. Stand.*, **42**, 209 (1949).

11) Secondary fixed point of the International Temperature Scale 1948. Cf. STIMSON, H. F., *J. Res. nat. Bur. Stand.*, **42**, 209 (1949).

12) Mass number of the most stable known isotope.

13) Mass number of the best known isotope.

14) The atomic weight of iridium was determined by analysis. It has not yet been possible to obtain this element sufficiently pure for the experimental atomic weight to agree with that calculated from the isotopic constitution.

15) For internationally accepted density values for mercury at different temperatures see GRAY, D. E. (Ed.), *American Institute of Physics Handbook*, New York, 1957, pages 2–140; KAYE and LABY, *Tables of Physical and Chemical Constants and Some Mathematical Functions*, 11th ed., London, 1956, page 31.

16) Strictly speaking, not a natural isotope since it is a disintegration product of ^{14}N in the atmosphere due to cosmic rays.

Atomic number Z	Symbol	Transuranic element[1]	Atomic weight[2]	Valency	Melting point °C	Boiling point °C	Density g/cm³	Isotope (mass number A)[3]	Atomic weight (physical scale)	Mode of decay[4]	Energy in MeV	Half-life[5]
93	Np	**Neptunium**	237	3, 4, 5, 6	640 ± 1		solid: α-form 20.2/20° β-form 19.36/313°	^{231}Np	231.1105$_8$	α	6.28	50 m
								^{232}Np	(232.1126$_4$)	γ, K		~13 m
								^{233}Np	233.1135$_2$	α K	5.53	35 m
								^{234}Np	(234.1164)	α β+ γ K, L	 ~0.8 0.44$_5$–1.57	4.40 d
								^{235}Np	235.1176$_7$	α no γ K, L	5.06	1.12 y
								^{236}Np	236.1205$_0$	β− γ e− K	0.51$_8$/0.47$_5$ 0.044$_6$/0.045$_2$	22 h
								^{236}Np		β−		>5000 y
								^{237}Np	237.1222$_0$	α γ	4.78$_7$/4.52–4.87 0.087/0.02–0.20	2.20×10^6 y
								^{238}Np	238.1253$_6$	β− γ	1.26/0.26 0.044/0.102–1.03	2.10 d
								^{239}Np	239.1277$_7$	β− γ	0.32$_9$–0.72 0.061/0.105/0.277/0.045-0.49	2.33 d
								^{240}Np	240.1314$_2$	β− γ	2.16/1.59 0.040–1.50	7.3 m
								^{240}Np		β− γ	0.9 0.97/0.88/1.14/0.16–1.16	60 m
								^{241}Np(?)		β−		16 m
94	Pu	**Plutonium**	242	3, 4, 5, 6	639.5		solid: α-form 19.74/25° β-form 17.65/150° liquid 16.5 ± 0.08/665°	^{232}Pu	232.1137$_0$	α (K)	6.58	36 m
								^{233}Pu	(233.1158$_5$)	α K	6.3	20 m
								^{234}Pu	234.1166$_0$	α no γ K	6.19	9 h
								^{235}Pu	235.1189$_0$	α K, L	5.85	26 m
								^{236}Pu	236.1199$_6$	α γ	5.75 ~0.045	2.7 y
								^{237}Pu	(237.1224$_3$)	γ K	~0.064	40 d
								^{238}Pu	238.1239$_6$	α γ	5.49$_5$/5.45$_3$/5.35$_2$ 0.044/0.100/0.15	89.6 y
								^{239}Pu	239.1270$_0$	α γ	5.15$_0$/5.13$_7$/5.09$_9$ 0.053/0.039	2.44×10^4 y

For footnotes see page 266.

Atomic number Z	Symbol	Transuranic element[1]	Atomic weight[2]	Valency	Melting point °C	Boiling point °C	Density g/cm³	Isotopes[3]: Isotope (mass number A)	Atomic weight (physical scale)	Mode of decay[4]	Energy in MeV	Half-life[5]
94	Pu	**Plutonium** (continued)	242	3, 4, 5, 6	639.5		solid: α-form 19.74/25° β-form 17.65/150° liquid 16.5 ± 0.08/665°	^{240}Pu	240.1291_0	α γ	$5.16_2/5.11_8$ 0.050	6600 y
								^{241}Pu	241.1321_5	α β− γ	4.91 0.020 0.100/0.145	13.2 y
								^{242}Pu	242.1344_5	α	4.89_8	3.8×10^5 y
								^{243}Pu	243.1380_9	β− γ	0.57/0.47/0.37 0.085/0.12	4.98 h
								^{244}Pu	(244.1406)	α	(4.8)	7×10^7 y
								^{245}Pu	(245.144_1)	β− γ		11 h
								^{246}Pu	(246.1471)	β− γ	0.15 $0.103/0.22/0.043/0.17_5$	11 d
95	Am	**Americium**	243	3, 4, 5, 6	> 1100	1200	solid 11.7 ± 0.3	^{237}Am	237.1239_6	α K	6.01	~1.3 h
								^{238}Am	(238.1266)	no α γ K, e−	 $0.58/0.98/0.10_2$	1.86 h
								^{239}Am	239.1278_4	α γ K, e−	5.75 0.286/0.048/0.3	12 h
								^{240}Am	(240.1305_6)	γ K, e−	1.02/1.40/0.92	50 h
								^{241}Am	241.1321_3	α γ	$5.47_6/5.43_3/5.38–5.54$ 0.0596/0.026–0.37	462 y
								^{242}Am		β− γ K	0.625 0.0422/0.045	16.0 h
								^{242}Am	242.1351_9	α β− γ K	5.5 0.585 0.042	100 y
								^{243}Am	243.1374_8	α γ	5.267/5.224/5.17–5.34 0.075	7950 y
								^{244}Am	244.1409_2	β− K	1.50	26 m
								^{245}Am	(245.1428_3)	β− γ	0.9_0 $0.036/0.25_5/0.06–0.23_2$	2.0 h
								^{246}Am	(246.1468)	β− γ	1.2 $1.07/0.80/0.10_3/0.019$	25 m
96	Cm	**Curium**	247	3			solid (7)	^{238}Cm	238.1275_7	α K	6.5_0	2.5 h
								^{239}Cm	(239.1298)	K		~3 h
								^{240}Cm	240.1306_6	α	6.25	26.8 d

					^{241}Cm	(241.1331)	α	5.90	35 d
							γ	$0.47_2/0.59$	
							K		
					^{242}Cm	242.1345_1	α	6.110/6.066/5.96	162.5 d
							γ	$0.044/0.100/0.15_7$	
					^{243}Cm	243.1374_8	α	5.777/5.732/5.985	~35 y
							γ	0.334/0.278/0.21/0.23/0.045	
					^{244}Cm	244.1393_1	α	$5.79_8/5.75_5/5.65_5$	18.4 y
							γ	0.043/0.100/0.150	
					^{245}Cm	(245.1428_3)	α	5.3_6	2×10^4 y
							γ	0.10/0.17	
					^{246}Cm	(246.1441_3)	α	5.37_3	6.6×10^3 y
					^{247}Cm	(247.1475_0)			$>4\times10^7$ y
					^{248}Cm	(248.1501)	α	5.05_4	4.2×10^5 y
					^{249}Cm	(249.153_6)	β⁻		short
97	Bk	**Berkelium**	247	3, 4					
					^{243}Bk	243.1390_5	α	6.55/6.72/6.20	4.5 h
							γ	0.15–0.96	
					^{244}Bk	(244.1415)	α	6.66	4.4 h
							γ	0.90–1.7	
							K		
					^{245}Bk	245.1429_2	α	6.17/5.89/6.37	5.0 d
							γ	0.165/0.205/0.48	
							K		
					^{246}Bk	(246.1457)	γ	0.145–1.13	1.9 d
							K		
					^{247}Bk	(247.1476)	α	5.67/5.50/5.30	~10^4 y
							γ	$0.085/0.26_5/0.42?$	
					^{248}Bk	248.1507	β⁻	0.67	18 h
					^{249}Bk	(249.1526_1)	α	$5.4_0/5.0_8$	290 d
							β⁻	0.10	
							γ	0.32	
					^{250}Bk	(250.1566_4)	β⁻	0.9/1.9	3.1 h
							γ	0.9	
98	Cf	**Californium**	249	(3)					
					^{244}Cf	244.1423_5	α	7.17	25 m
							(K)		
					^{245}Cf	(245.1446)	α	7.11	44 m
					^{246}Cf	246.1457_5	α	$6.75_3/6.71_1$	35.7 h
							γ	$0.044/0.097/0.14_9$	
					^{247}Cf	(247.1485)	γ	$0.28_5/0.49$	2.4 h
							K		
					^{248}Cf	248.1500_2	α	6.26	250 d
					^{249}Cf	(249.1525)	α	5.82/5.91/6.19	360 y
							γ	0.40/0.34	
					^{250}Cf	250.1546_0	α	6.02/5.98	10 y
							γ	0.042_8	
					^{251}Cf	(251.1580)	γ	0.18	~700 y
					^{252}Cf	(252.1607)	α	$6.11_2/6.07$	2.2 y
							γ	0.043/0.10	
					^{253}Cf	(253.163_9)	β⁻		18 d
					^{254}Cf	(254.1668)			60 d

For footnotes see page 266.

Atomic number Z	Symbol	Transuranic element[1]	Atomic weight[2]	Valency	Melting point °C	Boiling point °C	Density g/cm³	Isotopes[3]				
								Isotope (mass number A)	Atomic weight (physical scale)	Mode of decay[4]	Energy in MeV	Half-life[5]
99	Es	**Einsteinium**[6]	254	(3)				^{246}Es	(246.150_2)	K		short
								^{247}Es	247.1509	α	7.35	7.3 m
										(K)		
								^{248}Es	(248.1531)	α	6.8_7	25 m
								^{249}Es	(249.1542)	α	6.76	2 h
								^{250}Es	(250.156_7)	α?		8 h
								^{251}Es	(251.158_8)	α	6.48	1.5 d
								^{252}Es	(252.1617)	α	6.64	~140 d
								^{253}Es	(253.1637)	α	6.63/6.60/6.55	20 d
										γ	0.042–0.39	
								^{254}Es	(254.167_5)	β⁻	1.0_4	38 h
										γ	0.68	
										K		
								^{254}Es	254.167_3	α	6.44	~320 d
								^{255}Es	(255.169_8)	β⁻		30 d
								^{256}Es	(256.174_2)	β⁻		short
100	Fm	**Fermium**[6]	253	(3)				^{250}Fm	250.1577	α	7.4	30 m
								^{251}Fm	(251.160_0)	α	6.9	7.5 h
								^{252}Fm	252.1616	α	7.0_4	36 h
								^{253}Fm	(253.1642)	α	6.8_5	3 d
								^{254}Fm	(254.1663)	α	7.22/7.18	3.38 h
										γ	0.042/0.094	
								^{255}Fm	(255.1696)	α	7.08	21.5 h
								^{256}Fm	(256.172_1)			3.1 h
101	Md	**Mendelevium**	256	(3)				^{256}Md	(256.173_8)	K		~1.5 h
102	No	**Nobelium**	253 (?)[7]					(^{253}No)		α	8.5	~10 m
103	Lw	**Lawrencium**	(257?)									

Footnotes (pages 263–266)

1) The transuranic elements have become known as artificially produced elements. However, since they have in the past occurred naturally (or are still, like plutonium-239, identifiable in very small amounts in nature) they can be regarded also as naturally occurring elements. In a sense they are elements which as a result of their short half-lives have become extinct.

2) Mass number of the most stable known isotope. Cf. Commission on AtomicWeights, *Proceedings of the 20th Conference of the International Union of Pure and Applied Chemistry*, London, 1960, page 202.

3) After SULLIVAN, W. H., *Trilinear Chart of Nuclides*, Washington (United States Atomic Energy Commission), 1957, with additional energy data from STEIN and CLANCY, in LANGE, N.A. (Ed.), *Handbook of Chemistry*, 9th ed., Sandusky, 1956, pages 147–149.

4) α = alpha particle (helium nucleus = 2 protons + 2 neutrons), β⁻ = beta particle (electron), β⁺ = positron, γ = gamma ray, e⁻ = internal electron conversion, K, L = orbital electron capture, IT = isomeric transition.

5) y = year, d = day, h = hour, m = minute, s = second.

6) Originally discovered in the debris of the first hydrogen bomb explosion at Eniwetok in 1952.

7) Cf. MILSTED, J., *Nature*, **180**, 1012 (1957).

Electronic Configurations of the Elements[1]

E_r = resonance energy (eV); E_i = ionization energy (eV); E_{i_1} = resonance energy of singly-ionized atom (eV)

Atomic number	Symbol	E_r	E_i	E_{i_1}	K	L		M			N				O				P			Q
					1s	2s	2p	3s	3p	3d	4s	4p	4d	4f	5s	5p	5d	5f	6s	6p	6d	7s
1	H	10.19	13.60		1																	
2	He	21.20	24.58	40.8	2																	
3	Li	1.85	5.39	62.2	2	1																
4	Be	5.28	9.32	3.96	2	2																
5	B	4.96	8.30	9.10	2	2	1															
6	C	7.48	11.26	9.29	2	2	2															
7	N	10.3	14.54	11.4	2	2	3															
8	O	9.52	13.61	14.8	2	2	4															
9	F	12.98	17.42	20.42	2	2	5															
10	Ne	16.84	21.56	26.89	2	2	6															
11	Na	2.10	5.14	33.3	2	2	6	1														
12	Mg	4.34	7.64	4.42	2	2	6	2														
13	Al	3.14	5.98	7.42	2	2	6	2	1													
14	Si	4.92	8.15	6.86	2	2	6	2	2													
15	P	6.94	10.95	8.09	2	2	6	2	3													
16	S	6.86	10.36	9.84	2	2	6	2	4													
17	Cl	9.21	13.01	11.56	2	2	6	2	5													
18	Ar	11.53	15.75	13.47	2	2	6	2	6													
19	K	1.61	4.34	20.6	2	2	6	2	6		1											
20	Ca	2.93	6.11	3.12	2	2	6	2	6		2											
21	Sc	2.32	6.56	3.40	2	2	6	2	6	1	2											
22	Ti	1.97	6.83	3.66	2	2	6	2	6	2	2											
23	V	2.24	6.74	4.40	2	2	6	2	6	3	2											
24	Cr	2.89	6.76	6.00	2	2	6	2	6	5	1											
25	Mn	3.07	7.43	4.76	2	2	6	2	6	5	2											
26	Fe	3.21	7.90	5.20	2	2	6	2	6	6	2											
27	Co	3.57	7.86	5.83	2	2	6	2	6	7	2											
28	Ni	3.54	7.63	6.39	2	2	6	2	6	8	2											
29	Cu	3.79	7.72	8.26	2	2	6	2	6	10	1											
30	Zn	4.03	9.39	5.91	2	2	6	2	6	10	2											
31	Ga	3.07	6.00	8.78	2	2	6	2	6	10	2	1										
32	Ge	4.64	8.13	8.06	2	2	6	2	6	10	2	2										
33	As	6.28	9.81	9.14	2	2	6	2	6	10	2	3										
34	Se	6.32	9.75	10.39	2	2	6	2	6	10	2	4										
35	Br	8.32	11.84	12.21	2	2	6	2	6	10	2	5										
36	Kr	10.03	13.99	15.82	2	2	6	2	6	10	2	6										
37	Rb	1.59	4.17	17.8	2	2	6	2	6	10	2	6			1							
38	Sr	2.69	5.69	2.94	2	2	6	2	6	10	2	6			2							
39	Y	1.99	6.57	2.91	2	2	6	2	6	10	2	6	1		2							
40	Zr	2.02	6.95	3.47	2	2	6	2	6	10	2	6	2		2							
41	Nb	2.97	6.77	4.13	2	2	6	2	6	10	2	6	4		1							
42	Mo	3.18	7.18	6.08	2	2	6	2	6	10	2	6	5		1							
43	Tc	2.88	7.45	4.68	2	2	6	2	6	10	2	6	(5)		(2)							
44	Ru	3.26	7.5	6.29	2	2	6	2	6	10	2	6	7		1							
45	Rh	3.35	7.7	4.97	2	2	6	2	6	10	2	6	8		1							
46	Pd	4.22	8.33	8.12	2	2	6	2	6	10	2	6	10									
47	Ag	3.66	7.58	11.1	2	2	6	2	6	10	2	6	10		1							
48	Cd	3.80	8.99	5.47	2	2	6	2	6	10	2	6	10		2							
49	In	3.02	5.78	7.82	2	2	6	2	6	10	2	6	10		2	1						
50	Sn	4.30	7.33	7.30	2	2	6	2	6	10	2	6	10		2	2						
51	Sb	5.36	8.64	9.56	2	2	6	2	6	10	2	6	10		2	3						
52	Te	5.78	9.01	8.82	2	2	6	2	6	10	2	6	10		2	4						
53	I	7.67	10.44	10.04	2	2	6	2	6	10	2	6	10		2	5						
54	Xe	8.44	12.13	11.27	2	2	6	2	6	10	2	6	10		2	6						
55	Cs	1.38	3.89	15.2	2	2	6	2	6	10	2	6	10		2	6			1			
56	Ba	2.24	5.21	2.51	2	2	6	2	6	10	2	6	10		2	6			2			
57	La	1.64	5.61	1.75	2	2	6	2	6	10	2	6	10		2	6	1		2			
58	Ce		6.91	2.72	2	2	6	2	6	10	2	6	10	2	2	6			2?			
59	Pr		5.76	2.81	2	2	6	2	6	10	2	6	10	3	2	6			2?			
60	Nd		6.31	2.63	2	2	6	2	6	10	2	6	10	4	2	6			2?			
61	Pm				2	2	6	2	6	10	2	6	10	5	2	6			2?			
62	Sm	1.71	5.6	2.63	2	2	6	2	6	10	2	6	10	6	2	6			2			
63	Eu	1.74	5.67	2.95	2	2	6	2	6	10	2	6	10	7	2	6			2			
64	Gd	1.665	6.16	3.18	2	2	6	2	6	10	2	6	10	7	2	6	1		2			
65	Tb		6.74		2	2	6	2	6	10	2	6	10	8	2	6	1		2?			
66	Dy		6.82		2	2	6	2	6	10	2	6	10	9	2	6	1		2?			
67	Ho				2	2	6	2	6	10	2	6	10	10	2	6	1		2?			
68	Er				2	2	6	2	6	10	2	6	10	11	2	6	1		2?			
69	Tm	2.62 ?		2.68	2	2	6	2	6	10	2	6	10	13	2	6			2			
70	Yb	2.23	6.2	3.35	2	2	6	2	6	10	2	6	10	14	2	6			2			
71	Lu	2.16 ?	5.0	3.38	2	2	6	2	6	10	2	6	10	14	2	6	1		2			
72	Hf	2.19	5.5	3.43	2	2	6	2	6	10	2	6	10	14	2	6	2		2			
73	Ta	2.44	6	3.63	2	2	6	2	6	10	2	6	10	14	2	6	3		2			
74	W	2.49	7.98	4.48	2	2	6	2	6	10	2	6	10	14	2	6	4		2			
75	Re	3.57	7.88		2	2	6	2	6	10	2	6	10	14	2	6	5		2			
76	Os	2.80	8.7		2	2	6	2	6	10	2	6	10	14	2	6	6		2			
77	Ir	4.65	9.2		2	2	6	2	6	10	2	6	10	14	2	6	7		2			
78	Pt	4.04	8.97	6.38	2	2	6	2	6	10	2	6	10	14	2	6	9		1			
79	Au	4.63	9.22	7.81	2	2	6	2	6	10	2	6	10	14	2	6	10		1			
80	Hg	4.89	10.43	6.38	2	2	6	2	6	10	2	6	10	14	2	6	10		2			
81	Tl	3.28	6.11	9.38	2	2	6	2	6	10	2	6	10	14	2	6	10		2	1		
82	Pb	4.33	7.42	7.35	2	2	6	2	6	10	2	6	10	14	2	6	10		2	2		
83	Bi	4.04	8.0	8.63	2	2	6	2	6	10	2	6	10	14	2	6	10		2	3		
84	Po		7.25		2	2	6	2	6	10	2	6	10	14	2	6	10		2	4		
85	At				2	2	6	2	6	10	2	6	10	14	2	6	10		2	5		
86	Rn	6.78	10.75		2	2	6	2	6	10	2	6	10	14	2	6	10		2	6		
87	Fr				2	2	6	2	6	10	2	6	10	14	2	6	10		2	6		1
88	Ra	2.57	5.28	2.65	2	2	6	2	6	10	2	6	10	14	2	6	10		2	6		2
89	Ac				2	2	6	2	6	10	2	6	10	14	2	6	10		2	6	1	2 ?
90	Th			2.12	2	2	6	2	6	10	2	6	10	14	2	6	10		2	6	2	2 ?
91	Pa				2	2	6	2	6	10	2	6	10	14	2	6	10	2	2	6	1	2 ?
92	U	1.44	~4	3.21	2	2	6	2	6	10	2	6	10	14	2	6	10	3	2	6	1	2 ?
93	Np				2	2	6	2	6	10	2	6	10	14	2	6	10	4	2	6	1	2 ?
94	Pu				2	2	6	2	6	10	2	6	10	14	2	6	10	5	2	6	1	2 ?
95	Am				2	2	6	2	6	10	2	6	10	14	2	6	10	7	2	6		2 ?
96	Cm				2	2	6	2	6	10	2	6	10	14	2	6	10	7	2	6	1	2 ?
97	Bk				2	2	6	2	6	10	2	6	10	14	2	6	10	8	2	6	1	2 ?
98	Cf				2	2	6	2	6	10	2	6	10	14	2	6	10	10	2	6		2 ?
99	Es				2	2	6	2	6	10	2	6	10	14	2	6	10	11	2	6		2 ?
100	Fm				2	2	6	2	6	10	2	6	10	14	2	6	10	12	2	6		2 ?
101	Md				2	2	6	2	6	10	2	6	10	14	2	6	10	13	2	6		2 ?

1) From Mavrodineanu and Boiteux, *L'analyse spectrale quantitative par la flamme*, Masson, Paris, 1954. Reproduced by kind permission of the authors and publishers. Additional data have been included from Hodgman et al. (Eds.), *Handbook of Chemistry and Physics*, 42nd ed., Cleveland, 1960.

Flame Emission Spectra[1]

This table lists the lines and band heads, in order of wave length in ångströms, recorded in air/acetylene and oxygen/acetylene flames, together with the atom, ion or molecule responsible. Wave lengths have been rounded off to the first decimal place. The various symbols have the following meanings:

Column 1: "R" or "V" following the wave length indicates that it is a band head, with the band fading in the direction of longer or shorter wave length respectively.

Column 2: "*F*" indicates that the band is due to the flame itself, and is followed by the ion responsible.

Column 3: "A" indicates that the line or band appears in the air/acetylene flame, "O" that it appears in the oxygen/acetylene flame. "K" indicates that the line appears only in the inner cone of the flame; "Res" indicates a resonance line.

Wave length Å	Due to	Remarks (see above)	Wave length Å	Due to	Remarks (see above)	Wave length Å	Due to	Remarks (see above)	Wave length Å	Due to	Remarks (see above)
2428.0	Au	A, Res	3039.4	In	A	3391.1	Ni	A	3510.3	Ni	A
47.9	Pd	O	44.0	Co	A	93.0	Ni	A	12.6	Co	A
76.4	Pd	O	47.6	Fe	A	95.4	Co	A	12.9 R	SnO	A
78.6	C	O, K	50.8	Ni	O	96.9	Rh	A, Res	13.5	Co	A
83.3	Fe	O	57.6	Ni	O	3404,6	Pd	A, Res	15.1	Ni	A, Res
88.1	Fe	O	59.1	Fe	A	05.1	Co	A	16.9	Pd	A
90.6	Fe	O	64 R	(*F*, OH)	A, O	06.9 R	SnO	A	19.2	Tl	A
2522.8	Fe	O	64.6	Ni	O	09.2	Co	A	20.1	Co	A
27.4	Fe	O	64.7	Pt	A, Res	12.3	Co	A	21.3	Fe	A
36.5	Hg	A, Res	75.9	Zn	A, K, Res	12.6	Co	A	21.6	Co	O
2609 R	(*F*, OH)	O, K	3122 R	(*F*, OH)	A, O	14.8	Ni	A, Res	23.4	Co	O
13.7	Pb	O	32.6	Mo	A, K	15.8 R	SnO	A	24.5	Ni	A, Res
14.2	Pb	O	34.1	Ni	O	17.2	Co	A	26.8	Co	O
59.4	Pt	O	44	(*F*, CH)	A, O	21.2	Pd	A, Res	28.0	Rh	A
61.2	Sn	A, K	58.2	Mo	A, K	23.7	Ni	A	29.0	Co	O
76.0	Au	A, Res	70.3	Mo	A, K	28 R	(*F*, OH)	O	29.4	Tl	A
77 R	(*F*, OH)	O, K	75.0	Sn	A, K, Res	28.3	Ru	A	29.8	Co	A
2706.5	Sn	A, K, Res	85 R	(*F*, OH)	A, O	31.6	Co	A	33.4	Co	A
53 R	(*F*, OH)	O, K	94.0	Mo	A, K	33.0	Co	A	38.1	Rh	O
61.8	Sn	A, K	3205.8 R	SnO	A	33.4	Pd	O	42.4 R	SnO	A
63.1	Pd	O	08.8	Mo	A, K	33.6	Ni	A	43.9	Rh	O
67.9	Tl	A	32.6	Li	A	34.9	Rh	A	49.5	Rh	O
76.7	Mg	A, K	33.0	Ni	O	36.7	Ru	A	50.6	Co	A
78.3	Mg	A, K	42.7	Pd	A	37.3	Ni	A	53.1	Pd	A
79.8	Mg	A, K	43.1	Ni	O	40.6	Fe	A	65.4	Fe	A
79.8	Sn	A, K	47.5	Cu	A, Res	41.0	Fe	A	66.2 V	LaO	A
81.4	Mg	A, K	51.4 R	SnO	A	41.4	Pd	O	66.4	Ni	A
83.0	Mg	A, K	54 R	(*F*, OH)	O	43.6	Co	A	69.4	Co	A
85.0	Sn	A, K	56.1	In	A	44.6 R	SnO	A	70.1	Fe	A
94.8	Mn	A	58.6	In	A	46.3	Ni	A	70.2	Rh	A
95.5	Mg II	A	61.1	Cd	A, Res	46.4	K	A	71.2	Pd	O
98.3	Mn	A	62.3	Sn	A, K	47.4	K	A	71.9	Ni	A
2801.1	Mn	A	62.4	SnO	A	49.2	Co	A	75.0	Co	A
02.7	Mg II	A	74.0	Cu	A, Res	49.4	Co	A	75.4	Co	A
11 R	(*F*, OH)	A, K; O	80.7	Ag	A, Res	52.9	Ni	A	78.7	Cr	A
13.6	Sn	A, K	82.3	Zn	A, K	53.5	Co	A	81.2	Fe	A
33.1	Pb	A, Res	91.8 R	SnO	A	55.2	Co	A	83.1	Rh	A
40.0	Sn	A, K, Res	3302.1	Pd	A	55.2	Rh	O	83.9	(*F*, CN)	A, K
50.6	Sn	A, K	02.3	Na	A	58.5	Ni	A	85.4 R	SnO	A
52.1	Mg	A, Res	03.0	Na	A	60.8	Pd	A	85.9	(*F*, CN)	A, K
63.3	Sn	A, K, Res	15.7	Ni	O	61.7	Ni	A	87.1	Rb	A
74.2	Ga	O	23.1	Rh	O	62.0	Rh	O	87.2	Co	A
75 R	(*F*, OH)	O	23.4 R	SnO	A	62.8	Co	A	89.2	Ru	A
2943.6	Ga	O	29.9	Mg	A, K	65.8	Co	A	90.4	(*F*, CN)	A, K
44.2	Ga	O	30.6	Sn	A, K	65.9	Fe	A	91.6	Rb	A
45 R	(*F*, OH)	O	32.2	Mg	A, K	72.5	Ni	A	93.0	Ru	A
66.9	Fe	A	34.1	Co	A	74.0	Co	A, Res	93.5	Cr	A
73.1	Fe	A	36.7	Mg	A, K	75.4	Fe	A	94.9	Co	A
73.2	Fe	A	45.0	Zn	A, K	81.2	Pd	A	96.2	Rh	O
83.6	Fe	A	45.6	Zn	A, K	83.4	Co	A	96.2	Ru	O
94.4	Fe	A	45.9	Zn	A, K	83.8	Ni	A	97.1	Rh	O
			54.4	Co	A	84.5 R	SnO	A	97.7	Ni	A
3000.9	Fe	A	60	(*F*, NH)	A, K; O	85 R	(*F*, OH)	O	3602.1	Co	A
02.5	Ni	O	67.1	Co	A	90.6	Fe	A	04.6 V	LaO	A
03.6	Ni	O	69.6	Ni	A	93.0	Ni	A, Res	05.3	Cr	A
08.1	Fe	A	73.0	Pd	A	95.7	Co	A	08.1 V	LaO	A
09.1	Sn	A, K, Res	80.6	Ni	A	98.7	Rh	O	08.9	Fe	A
12.0	Ni	O	80.9	Ni	O	98.9	Ru	A	09.5	Pd	A
20.5	Fe	A	81.7 R	SnO	A	3502.3	Co	A	10.5	Ni	A
20.6	Fe	A	82.9	Ag	A, Res	02.5	Rh	A	11.5 V	LaO	A
34.1	Sn	A, K, Res	85.2	Co	A	06.3	Co	A	12.5	Rh	O
37.4	Fe	A	88.2	Co	A	07.3	Rh	O	12.7	Ni	A
37.9	Ni	O	88.3 R	SnO	A	09.8	Co	A	14.7 R	SnO	A

1) Modified from MAVRODINEANU and BOITEUX, *L'analyse spectrale quantitative par la flamme*, Masson, Paris, 1954. Reproduced by kind permission of the authors and publishers. Additional data have been included from HODGMAN et al. (Eds.), *Handbook of Chemistry and Physics*, 42nd ed., Cleveland, 1960.

Wave length Å	Due to	Remarks (see opposite page)
3614.9 V	LaO	A
18.8	Fe	A
19.4	Ni	A
26.6	Rh	O
27.8	Co	A
31.5	Fe	A
34.7	Pd	A, Res
34.9	Ru	O
39.6	Pb	A, Res
42.7	MgO	A
47.7	Co	A
47.8	Fe	O
47.9	Fe	A
48.6	MgO	A
52.5	Co	A
58.0	Rh	A
61.4	Ru	A
66.2	Rh	O
74.8	MgO	A
79.9	Fe	A
81.6	MgO	A
83.0	Fe	A
83.5	Pb	A, Res
90.3	Pd	O
90.7	Rh	A
91.4 R	SnO	A
92.4	Rh	A
3700.9	Rh	A
05.6	Fe	A
09.6 V	LaO	A
13.0	Rh	O
18.9	Pd	O
20.0	Fe	A
20.7	MgO	A
21.0	MgO	A
21.2 R	SnO	A
22.6	Fe	A
24.4	MgO	A
24.8	MgO	A
25.9	MgO	A
26.9	Ru	A, Res
28.0	Ru	A, Res
30.4	Ru	O
33.3	Fe	O
34.9	Fe	A
37.1	Fe	A
42.3	Ru	A
45.6	Fe	A
48.2	Rh	O
48.3	Fe	O
49.5	Fe	A
52.3 R	SnO	A
55.9	Ru	O
58.2	Fe	A
63.8	Fe	A
65.1	Rh	O
66.5	MgO	A
67.2	Fe	A
72.2	MgO	A
75.7	Tl	A, Res.
78.2	MgO	A
86.1	Ru	O
87.9	Fe	A
88.5	Rh	O
90.5	Ru	A
93.2	Rh	O
98.1	Ru	A
98.3	Mo	A, K, Res
98.9	Ru	A
99.1	MgO	A
99.2	Pd	O
99.3	Ru	A
99.3	Rh	O
3801.0	Sn	A, K
02.7 R	SnO	A

Wave length Å	Due to	Remarks (see opposite page)
3805.0	MgO	A
06.8	Rh	O
07.1	Ni	A
11.3	MgO	A
18.2	Rh	O
20.4	Fe	A
22.3	Rh	O
23.3	Mg	A, K
25.9	Fe	O
27.8	Fe	O
28.5	Rh	O
29.4	Mg	A, K
32.3	Mg	A, K
32.3	Pd	O
33.2 R	SnO	A
33.9	Rh	O
34.2	Fe	A
38.3	Mg	A, K
40.4	Fe	A
42.1	Co	A
48.5	MgO	A
49.8	MgO	A
54.7	(*F*, CN)	A, K
56.4	Fe	A, Res
56.5	Rh	O
58.3	Ni	A
59.9	Fe	A, Res
61.9	(*F*, CN)	A, K
64.1	Mo	A, K, Res
71.4	(*F*, CN)	A, K
72 R	(*F*, CH)	A, K
73.1	Co	A
74.0	Co	A
76.4	Cs	A
78.6	Fe	A, Res
81.9	Co	A
84.3	(*F*, CH)	A, K
86.3	Fe	A, Res
88.7	Cs	A
94.1	Co	A
94.2	Pd	O
95.7	Fe	A, Res
99.3 R	SnO	A
99.7	Fe	A, Res
3902.9	Fe	A
03.0	Mo	A, K, Res
05.1	MgO	A
10.9	MgO	A
20.3	Fe	A, Res
22.9	Fe	A, Res
25.9	Ru	A
27.9	Fe	A, Res
30.3	Fe	A, Res
31.8	Ru	A
33.7	Ca II	A
34.2	Rh	O
38.4	MgO	A
43.7	MgO	A
44.0	Al	A, Res
51.0 R	SnO	A
58.6	Pd	O
58.9	Rh	O
61.5	Al	A, Res
68.5	Ca II	A
83.9 R	SnO	A
95.3	Co	A
4030.8	Mn	A, Res
33.0	Ga	A, Res
33.1	Mn	A, Res
34.5	Mn	A, Res
44.2	K	A
45.8	Fe	O
47.2	K	A
57.8	Pb	A, Res

Wave length Å	Due to	Remarks (see opposite page)
4071.7	Fe	O
77.7	Sr II	A
80.6	Ru	A
82.8	Rh	O
4101.8	In	A, Res
08.9 R	SnO	A
12.7	Ru	O
18.8	Co	A
21.3	Co	A
28.9	Rh	O
35.3	Rh	O
44.4 R	SnO	A
72.1	Ga	A, Res
96.5	Rh	O
98.9	Ru	O
4201.9	Rb	A
06.0	Ru	O
11.1	Rh	O
12.1	Ru	O
13.0	Pd	O
15.5	Sr II	A
15.6	Rb	A
26.7	Ca	A, Res
40.3 R	SnO	A
54.3	Cr	A, Res
71.8	Fe	O
74.8	Cr	A, Res
89.7	Cr	A, Res
4307.9	Fe	O
12.5 V	(*F*, CH)	A, K
24	(*F*, CH)	A, K
25.8	Fe	O
52.6 R	AlO	A
65.2 V	(*F*, C_2)	A, K
71.4 V	(*F*, C_2)	A, K
72.0 R	LaO	A
73.7 R	AlO	A
74.8	Rh	O
75.8 R	LaO	A
79.7 R	LaO	A
82.5 V	(*F*, C_2)	A, K
83.5	Fe	O
83.5 R	LaO	A
87.6 R	LaO	A
91.6 R	LaO	A
93.8 R	AlO	A
95.7 R	LaO	A
4404.7	Fe	O
18.2 R	LaO	A
23.2 R	LaO	A
28.1 R	LaO	A
33.0 R	LaO	A
38.0 R	LaO	A
43.0 R	LaO	A
48.0 R	LaO	A
70.5 R	AlO	A
94.0 R	AlO	A
4511.3	In	A, Res
16.4 R	AlO	A
24.0 R	BaO	A
24.7	Sn	A, K
28.7	Rh	O
37.6 R	AlO	A
37.8 R	BaO	A
54.0	Ba II	A
54.5	Ru	O
55.4	Cs	A
57.6 R	AlO	A
76.3 R	AlO	A
79.4 R	BaO	A
84.4	Ru	O
93.2	Cs	A
4607.3	Sr	A
21.1 R	BaO	A
36.8 R	BaO	A

Wave length Å	Due to	Remarks (see opposite page)
4648.2 R	AlO	A
63.5 R	BaO	A
72.0 R	AlO	A
78.6 V	(*F*, C_2)	A, K
80.3 R	BaO	A
84.8 V	(*F*, C_2)	A, K
94.6 R	AlO	A
97.6 V	(*F*, C_2)	A, K
4715.2 V	(*F*, C_2)	A, K
15.5 R	AlO	A
22.2	Zn	A, K
22.7 R	BaO	A
35.8 R	AlO	A
37.1 V	(*F*, C_2)	A, K
41.0 R	BaO	A
70.1 R	(*F*, C_2)	O, K
84.1 R	BaO	A
4810.5	Zn	A, K
30.0 R	BaO	A
36.1 R	(*F*, C_2)	O, K
42.3 R	AlO	A
50.6 R	BaO	A
66.4 R	AlO	A
73.8 R	BaO	A
96.5 R	BaO	A
4911.0 R	(*F*, C_2)	O, K
34.1	Ba II	A
41.7 R	BaO	A
65.4 R	BaO	A
96.7 R	(*F*, C_2)	O, K
5012.4 R	BaO	A
86.7 R	BaO	A
97.7 V	(*F*, C_2)	A,K; O,K
5129.3 V	(*F*, C_2)	A,K; O,K
37	Ba	
58	$MnCl_2$	
65.2 V	(*F*, C_2)	A,K; O,K
93	B	
93	$MnCl_2$	
5204.5	Cr	A
06.0	Cr	A
08.4	Cr	A
14.7 R	BaO	A
30	$MnCl_2$	
81.2 R	CaO	A
5346.0 R	CaO	A
47	Ba	
49.7 R	BaO	A
50.5	Tl	A, Res
56.4 R	CrO	A
59.4 R	MnO	A
60	$MnCl_2$	
66.7 R	BaO	A
82.5 R	LaO	A
89.4 R	MnO	A
92	$MnCl_2$	
94.7	Mn	A
5402.7 R	BaO	A
07.7 R	LaO	A
16.5 R	CrO	A
19.8 R	BaO	A
23.8 R	MnO	A
24	$MnCl_2$	
32.5	Mn	A
33.1 R	LaO	A
40	B	
54.6 R	BaO	A
58.7 R	LaO	A
70.3 V	(*F*, C_2)	A,K; O,K
75.0 R	CaO	A
79.2 R	CrO	A
81	B	
92.7 R	BaO	A
5501.9 V	(*F*, C_2)	A,K; O,K

Wave length Å	Due to	Remarks (see page 268)
5506.5 R	CaO	A
09.7 R	BaO	A
27.9 R	FeO	A
35.6	Ba	A, Res
40.7 V	(F, C_2)	A,K; O,K
43.2 R	FeO	A
43.7 R	CrO	A
44	Ca	
47.8 R	BaO	A
64.1 R	CrO	A
82.5 R	FeO	A
85.5 V	(F, C_2)	A,K; O,K
86.4 R	MnO	A
92	$MnCl_2$	
5602.4 R	LaO	A
02.4 R	BaO	A
09.5 R	MnO	A
13.9 R	FeO	A
23.3 R	CrO	A
28.6 R	LaO	A
35.5 V	(F, C_2)	A,K; O,K
38.9 R	MnO	A
44.1 R	BaO	A
54.8 R	LaO	A
59.0 R	BaO	A
72.9 R	BaO	A
81.1 R	LaO	A
85.1 R	CrO	A
99.0	Ru	A
5710.0 R	BaO	A
13.7 R	BaO	A
19.3 R	CaO	A
48.7 R	CrO	A
58.4 R	BaO	A
70.1 R	BaO	A
89.6 R	FeO	A
94.4 R	CrO	A
5805.1 R	BaO	A
05.6 R	FeO	A
12.2 R	CaO	A
17.6 R	BaO	A
18.4 R	FeO	A
29.2 R	BaO	A
52.1 R	CrO	A
59.6 R	MnO	A
64.5 R	BaO	A
67.6 R	FeO	A
69.5 R	LaO	A
75.3 R	BaO	A
80.3 R	MnO	A
86.9 R	BaO	A
90.0	Na	A, Res
95.9	Na	A, Res
96.7 R	LaO	A
5902.6 R	FeO	A
09.1 R	MnO	A
13.1 R	CrO	A
23.4 V	(F, C_2)	A,K; O,K
24.0 R	LaO	A
25.1 R	BaO	A
51.3 R	LaO	A
58.7 V	(F, C_2)	A,K; O,K
75 R	NdO	A
75.9 R	CrO	A
76.3 R	BaO	A
78.8 R	LaO	A
84.9 R	BaO	A

Wave length Å	Due to	Remarks (see page 268)
6002.2 V	CaO	A
03 V	NdO	A
04.9 V	(F, C_2)	A,K; O,K
39.6 R	BaO	A
42.8 R	CrO	A
51.6 R	CrO	A
59.7 V	(F, C_2)	A,K; O,K
60	Sr	
85.1 V	SrO	A
90.2 V	SrO	A
94.8 R	FeO	A
96.5 V	SrO	A
6101.3 V	SrO	A
02.3 R	BaO	A
03.6	Li	A
07.5 V	SrO	A
08.0 R	CrO	A
09.3 R	FeO	A
09.9 V	SrO	A
11.0 R	BaO	A
11.9 V	SrO	A
16.2 V	SrO	A
16.2 R	BaO	A
22.1 V	(F, C_2)	A,K; O,K
54.9 R	MnO	A
65.1 R	BaO	A
67.3 R	CrO	A
69.6 R	BaO	A
75.9 R	MnO	A
80.7 R	FeO	A
82	Ca	
91.2 V	(F, C_2)	A,K; O,K
6203	Ca	
03.2 R	MnO	A
13	Cs	
18.3 R	FeO	A
24.7 R	BaO	A
29.1 R	CrO	A
69.0 V	CaO	A
91.0 R	BaO	A
94.1 R	CrO	A
6358.0 R	BaO	A
63.7 R	CrO	A
94.3 R	CrO	A
6411 R	NdO	A
23.1 R	BaO	A
25 R	NdO	A
40 R	NdO	A
42.3 V	(F, C_2)	O,K
51.5 R	CrO	A
80.5 V	(F, C_2)	O,K
93.1 R	BaO	A
6500 V	CaO	A
11 R	SmO	A
11.8 R	CrO	A
33 R	SmO	A
33.7 V	(F, C_2)	O,K
57 R	SmO	A
63.2 R	BaO	A
70 R	SmO	A
75.1 R	CrO	A
80 R	NdO	A
99.2 V	(F, C_2)	O,K
6600 R	NdO	A
20 R	NdO	A
28	Sr	
34.5 R	BaO	A

Wave length Å	Due to	Remarks (see page 268)
6643.6 R	CrO	A
50 R	NdO	A
77.3 V	(F, C_2)	O,K
6700 R	FeO	A
04.5 R	BaO	A
07.9	Li	A, Res
15.1 R	CrO	A
23.3	Cs	
47	Sr	
50 V	CaO	A
63.2 V	(F, C_2)	O,K
71.8 R	CrO	A
82.8 R	BaO	A
6829.2 R	CrO	A
57.2 R	BaO	A
58.8 V	(F, C_2)	O,K
61.4 V	SrO	A
67.9 V	SrO	A
75.6 V	SrO	A
84.5 V	SrO	A
91.5 R	CrO	A
6931.4 R	BaO	A
39.0	K	A
57.2 R	CrO	A
64.7	K	A
73.3	Cs	
7007.1 R	BaO	A
11.2 R	LaO	A
22 R	FeO	A
27.5 R	CrO	A
40.8 R	LaO	A
70.8 R	LaO	A
97.4 R	BaO	A
7101.0 R	LaO	A
31.6 R	LaO	A
62.6 R	LaO	A
76.6 R	BaO	A
87.1 R	CrO	A
93.7 R	LaO	A
7208.0 V	SrO	A
49.1 R	CrO	A
54.3 R	BaO	A
64.5 V	SrO	A
86.0 V	SrO	A
7308.3 R	CaO	A
13.8 R	CrO	A
18.5 R	CaO	A
26 R	CaO	A
36.9 R	BaO	A
75.3 R	CrO	A
7403.5 R	LaO	A
28 R	FeO	A
34.3 R	LaO	A
36 V	SrO	A
39.5 R	CrO	A
40.4 R	BaO	A
65.2 R	LaO	A
89.7 V	SrO	A
96.5 R	LaO	A
7500.6 R	SrO	A
22.8 R	SrO	A
23.5 R	BaO	A
27 R	FeO	A
28.2 R	LaO	A
41.6 R	SrO	A
60.0 R	LaO	A
92.3 R	LaO	A

Wave length Å	Due to	Remarks (see page 268)
7610.1 R	BaO	A
18.9	Rb	A
25.0 R	LaO	A
57.8 R	LaO	A
64.9	K	A, Res
87.8 R	CaO	A
90 R	FeO	A
91.1 R	LaO	A
99.0	K	A, Res
7712.2 R	CaO	A
13.9 R	CrO	A
15.5 R	CaO	A
21.1 R	CaO	A
25.0 R	LaO	A
57.7	Rb	A
75 R	FeO	A
78.1 R	CrO	A
7800.3	Rb	A, Res
15.2 R	BaO	A
42.8 R	CrO	A
52.8 R	SrO	A
82.3 R	SrO	A
7902.0 R	SrO	A
05.1 R	BaO	A
08.0 R	CrO	A
10.5 R	LaO	A
44.9 R	LaO	A
47.6	Rb	A, Res
79.7 R	LaO	A
8014.8 R	LaO	A
15.7	Cs	A
50.2 R	LaO	A
78.9	Cs	A
79.0	Cs	A
86.1 R	LaO	A
8112 R	FeO	A
22.2 R	LaO	A
53.1 R	CaO	A
59.0 R	LaO	A
64.7 R	CaO	A
67.3 R	CaO	A
83.3	Na	A
94.8	Na	A
96.1 R	LaO	A
8230 R	FeO	A
33.1 R	LaO	A
57.8 R	SrO	A
70.7 R	LaO	A
72.2 R	SrO	A
8302 R	FeO	A
60.3 R	CrO	A
8453.5 R	LaO	A
90.0 R	LaO	A
8521.1	Cs	A, Res
26.6 R	LaO	A
63.5 R	LaO	A
78 R	FeO	A
8600.8 R	LaO	A
38.5 R	LaO	A
52.2 R	CaO	A
76.6 R	LaO	A
8700.0 R	SrO	A
22.5 R	SrO	A
61.4	Cs	A
90 R	FeO	A
8943.5	Cs	A, Res

Application of Artificial Radioisotopes in Medicine and Biology*

By Hilde Levi, Ph.D.
Zoophysiological Laboratory A, University of Copenhagen

In recent years, artificial radioisotopes have been produced in the United States, in Britain and – although to a somewhat lesser extent – on the continent of Europe in such quantities that their application in medicine and biology has made a multitude of new investigations possible.

Following the release for research and therapy of radioactive material produced in the atomic piles, the tracer method developed by G. Hevesy has become an important tool, indispensable in any research laboratory or hospital. Innumerable designs of measuring equipment are commercially available, and these instruments have been built for a variety of special purposes. Just as is the case with any other method, it is a prerequisite for the successful application of radioactive tracers that we master the measuring technique and, moreover, are able properly to interpret the results of the measurements. Investigations performed by means of isotopic tracers remain meaningless unless they are based on a thorough knowledge of the biological processes involved and of the basic principles of physics and chemistry.

The following tables provide a survey of the isotopes used in biological and medical research together with the nuclear data needed for the evaluation of the applicability and the radiobiological effect of these substances. In compiling the tables a limited choice has had to be made among the hundreds of artificial radioisotopes now available. The tables contain only those isotopes which have been or could be applied in biological and medical research. This, in turn, depends on whether the element plays a part, if only a minor one, in the organism, and whether the physical properties of its radioactive isotope make its application feasible. Some radioactive isotopes which are interesting from a biological point of view decay so rapidly, that is to say, in the course of seconds or minutes, that their short half-lives make them unsuited for biological experiments. Such isotopes have been omitted from the tables.

Furthermore, isotopes which have been used only as "trace elements" are not included. The possibility of detecting radioisotopes in extremely low concentration (or high dilution) enables us to apply non-toxic quantities of these elements. In experiments on animals, numerous radioisotopes of trace elements have been administered, their distribution in the organism and their excretion have been measured; however, no particularly striking conclusions have been drawn from these experiments.

Table 1 **Nuclear data of the most important artificial radioisotopes in medicine and biology**

Isotope	Half-life[1]	Mode of decay	Maximum energy of β-radiation[1] MeV	Mean energy of β-radiation MeV	Maximum range of β-radiation in H_2O mm	Energy of γ-radiation[1] MeV	Fraction disintegrating per day (cf. Table 2, col. 3)
^{3}H	12.26 y	β−	0.018	0.006	0.003		2×10^{-4}
^{11}C	20 m	β+	0.98	0.38	4		1.0
^{14}C	5760 y[2]	β−	0.155	0.05	0.3		4×10^{-7}
^{13}N	10 m	β+	1.25	0.48	5.6		1.0
^{18}F	1.87 h	β+	0.65	0.25	2.5		1.0
^{22}Na	2.6 y	β+; γ	0.54	0.2	2	1.28	7×10^{-4}
^{24}Na	15.0 h	β−; γ	1.39	0.54	6	1.37; 2.76	0.68
^{31}Si	2.62 h	β−; γ	1.47	0.6	7	1.26	0.998
^{32}P	14.2 d	β−	1.71	0.68	8		0.05
^{35}S	87 d	β−	0.167	0.05	0.3		0.008
^{36}Cl	3.1×10^{5} y	β−	0.714	0.24	2.5		5×10^{-9}
^{38}Cl	37.3 m	β−; γ	4.8; 2.8; 1.1	1.39	27	1.6; 2.15	1.0
^{42}K	12.5 h	β−; γ	3.6; 2.0	1.4	19	1.53	0.74
^{45}Ca	153 d	β−	0.25	0.09	0.6		0.004
^{51}Cr	27.8 d	γ; K		0.01		0.323	0.025
^{52}Mn	5.7 d	β+; γ; K	0.58	0.2	2.2	0.7; 0.9; 1.5	0.10
^{54}Mn	291 d	γ; K		0.005		0.84	0.002
^{55}Fe	2.94 y	K		0.006			6×10^{-4}
^{59}Fe	45 d	β−; γ	0.46; 0.27; 1.56	0.12	1.6	1.1; 1.3; 0.19	0.015
^{60}Co	5.25 y	β−; γ	0.306	0.1	0.8	1.17; 1.33	4×10^{-3}
^{63}Zn	38 m	β+; γ; K	2.36; 1.4	0.96	11	1.0; 1.9; 2.6	1.0
^{65}Zn	245 d	β+; γ; K	0.325	0.1	0.8	1.11	0.003
^{82}Br	36 h	β−; γ	0.44	0.15	1.4	0.55–1.48	0.40
^{85}Kr	10.6 y	β−; γ	0.67	0.2	2.5	0.52	2×10^{-4}
^{89}Sr	51 d	β−; γ	1.46	0.55	7	0.91	0.013
^{131}I	8 d	β−; γ	0.61; 0.81	0.2	2	0.36; 0.6–0.72	0.08
^{198}Au	2.69 d	β−; γ	0.96; 0.29; 1.37	0.34	3.8	0.41; 0.67; 1.1	0.26

1) The data are from the *Table of Isotopes* of Strominger et al., *Rev. mod. Phys.*, **30**, 585 (1958), and the *International Directory of Radioisotopes*, vol. I, International Atomic Energy Agency, Vienna, 1959.

2) Redetermined value of National Bureau of Standards, *Nat. Bur. Stand. techn. News Bull.*, **45**, 21 (1961).

* Definitions of units: erg (erg) and electron volt (eV), see page 216; millicurie (mc), microcurie (μc) and roentgen (r), see page 236; rad, see page 237.

Column six of Table 1 gives the maximum range of the β-component in water. This value is of interest when determining the amount of tissue irradiated after the radioisotope is applied locally. The density of fresh tissue is simply set equal to that of water, i.e. equal to unity. If, for example, a given amount of phosphorus-32 is introduced as a point source into some soft tissue (in this connection we have in mind an insoluble, non-metabolized compound), the surrounding tissue is irradiated to a distance of 8 mm from the point of application. Furthermore, the maximum range indicates the shielding required for complete absorption of the β-radiation. The last column lists the fraction of the isotope which decays per day. This value enters the dosage calculation and is therefore repeated in Table 2.

It must be stressed here that half-lives and maximum energies of some isotopes are not yet finally determined. More exact and more recent measurements have yielded results which deviate from those obtained earlier.

Table 2 **Dosimetry of some artificial radioisotopes***

(1) Isotope	(2) Half-life T	(3) Fraction disintegrating per day f_d	(4) Mean energy of β-radiation $\bar{E}_\beta$ (MeV)	(5) Dose factor K_β (rad)	(6) Maximum permissible concentration S_β (μc/kg)	(7) Critical organ[1]	(8) Weight of critical organ[1] (g)	(9) Maximum permissible concentration in the total body[1] (μc)
^{3}H	12.26 y	2×10^{-4}	0.006	2000	125	total body	7×10^4	10^3
^{11}C	20 m	1.0	0.38	0.4	125	–	–	–
^{14}C	5760 y	4×10^{-7}	0.05	8×10^6	16	fat; total body	10^4; 7×10^4	300; 400
^{13}N	10 m	1.0	0.48	0.25	200	–	–	–
^{18}F	1.87 h	1.0	0.25	1.5	33	–	–	–
^{22}Na	2.6 y	7×10^{-4}	0.2	1.5×10^4	5	total body	7×10^4	10
^{24}Na	15.0 h	0.68	0.54	24	3	total body	7×10^4	7
^{31}Si	2.62 h	0.998	0.6	5	10	total body	7×10^4	30
^{32}P	14.2 d	0.05	0.68	720	1	bone	7×10^3	6
^{35}S	87 d	0.008	0.05	320	20	skin; testis	2×10^3; 40	100
^{36}Cl	3.1×10^5 y	5×10^{-9}	0.24	3.10^9	3	total body	7×10^4	80
^{38}Cl	37.3 m	1.0	1.39	2.7	19	–	–	–
^{42}K	12.5 h	0.74	1.4	60	1	muscle	3×10^4	20
^{45}Ca	153 d	0.004	0.09	1000	12	bone	7×10^3	30
^{51}Cr	27.8 d	0.025	0.01	17	300	total body	7×10^4	800
^{52}Mn	5.7 d	0.10	0.2	8	60	total body	7×10^4	9
^{54}Mn	291 d	0.002	0.005	115	220	liver	1.7×10^3	20
^{55}Fe	2.94 y	6×10^{-4}	0.006	480	170	spleen; blood	150; 5×10^3	1000
^{59}Fe	45 d	0.015	0.12	400	8	spleen; blood	150; 5×10^3	20
^{60}Co	5.25 y	4×10^{-3}	0.1	1.4×10^4	9	total body	7×10^4	10
^{63}Zn	38 m	1.0	0.96	2	25	–	–	–
^{65}Zn	245 d	0.003	0.1	185	90	total body	7×10^4	60
^{82}Br	36 h	0.40	0.15	17	7	total body	7×10^4	10
^{85}Kr	10.6 y	2×10^{-4}	0.2	5×10^4	5	–	–	–
^{89}Sr	51 d	0.013	0.55	2200	2	bone	7×10^3	4
^{131}I	8 d	0.08	0.2	120	5	thyroid	20	0.7
^{198}Au	2.69 d	0.26	0.34	67	3	kidney	3×10^3	20

Column 3: Fraction of isotope disintegrating in 24 hours: $f_d = (1 - e^{-0.693/T})$, where T = half-life in days (see also pages 277–291).

4: In the case of ^{51}Cr, ^{54}Mn and ^{55}Fe, which have no β-radiation, the data are for the γ-radiation following K-electron capture.

5: $K_\beta = 74 \cdot \bar{E}_\beta \cdot T$ = dose in rad for one microcurie completely disintegrated per gram of tissue. The values are based on the physical data given in the table.

6: The maximum permissible concentration in microcuries per gram of tissue which delivers the maximum permissible dose of 0.05 rad/day is $S_\beta = \dfrac{0.05 \times 1000}{K_\beta \times f_d}$. In calculating the concentrations for simultaneous β- and γ-emitters, only the β-component has been taken into consideration*. The values are based on the physical data given in the table.

* Dose rates for a number of γ-emitting isotopes are given in Table 3.

1) The data in columns 7–9 are from National Bureau of Standards Handbook No. 52, *Maximum Permissible Amounts of Radioisotopes in the Human Body and Maximum Permissible Concentrations in Air and Water*, Washington, 1953, pages 15–16, and from *Recommendations of the International Commission on Radiological Protection*, Pergamon Press, London and New York, 1959, as amended by *ICRP Publication* 2 (Report of Committee II on permissible dose from internal radiation, 1959), Pergamon Press, London and New York, 1960.

Table 2 gives the data necessary for dosage calculations, the maximum permissible concentration in microcuries per kilogram of tissue, and the maximum permissible concentrations of some radioisotopes in the human body for continuous radiation. Since a more detailed discussion of maximum permissible levels would fall beyond the scope of the present survey, it suffices to mention briefly that the maximum permissible dose of 0.3 r (or 0.3 rad) per working week (generally 40 hours) forms the basis for the calculations. This value for the maximum permissible dose has been recognized in recent years in most countries but it is not final.

Table 3 **Dose rates from a 1 mc point source of some γ-emitting isotopes***

Isotope	Half-life (approx.)	γ-energy in MeV (approx.)	Dose rate**	
			in mr/h from 1 mc at 1 m	in r/h from 1 mc at 1 cm
^{22}Na	2.6 y	1.3	1.16	11.6
^{24}Na	15.0 h	1.4; 2.8	1.87	18.7
^{38}Cl	37 m	1.6; 2.2	0.76	7.6
^{42}K	12.5 h	1.5	0.15	1.5
^{51}Cr	27.8 d	0.3	0.18	1.8
^{52}Mn	5.7 d	0.7; 0.9; 1.5	1.95	19.5
^{56}Mn	2.6 h	0.8; 1.8; 2.1	0.94	9.4
^{59}Fe	45 d	1.1; 1.3; 0.2	0.62	6.2
^{60}Co	5.3 y	1.2; 1.3	1.31	13.1
^{63}Zn	38 m	1.0; 1.9; 2.6	0.69	6.9
^{65}Zn	245 d	1.1	0.28	2.8
^{82}Br	36 h	0.5–1.5	1.46	14.6
^{131}I	8 d	0.4; 0.6–0.7	0.22	2.2
^{137}Cs	30 y	0.7	0.31	3.1
^{182}Ta	112 d	effective 1.1	0.61	6.1
^{192}Ir	74.4 d	effective 0.6	0.50	5.0
^{198}Au	2.7 d	0.4; 0.7; 1.1	0.24	2.35

* For further information see under Radiological Dose Units, page 237.

** For the sources of these data see the table of dose rates (*k*-factors) on page 237.

Columns 1, 2 and 3 of Table 2 give the half-lives, the fractions decaying per day, and the mean energies of the β-radiation. The dosage factor K_β is calculated according to the equation $K_\beta = 74 \cdot \bar{E}_\beta \cdot T$, where $\bar{E}_\beta$ is the mean energy of the β-radiation, T the half-life in days; the factor 74 accounts, inter alia, for the conversion of MeV into the energy unit erg. The dose factor thus gives the dosage in rad for one microcurie completely disintegrated per gram of tissue (column 5). The maximum permissible concentration is listed in column 6. Assuming that the isotopes listed in column 1 are distributed uniformly in a kilogram of tissue, it has been calculated which concentration of the respective isotopes will deliver to this tissue mass the maximum permissible dose of 0.05 rad per day. (The value of 0.05 rad = $^1/_6$ of the weekly dose is, like the latter, a rough approximation.) It is obvious that the values for S_β can only serve as a guide, particularly as very few substances are distributed uniformly in the tissue. For some elements, for example iodine and calcium, the tissue mass in which the isotope is preferentially accumulated is known; it therefore becomes possible to estimate how many microcuries can be introduced into the body without exceeding the permissible level in the respective tissue. For some important isotopes which are both β- and γ-emitters, Table 3 gives the dose rates for the γ-component due to a source of the isotope with a strength of 1 millicurie at distances of 1 meter and 1 centimeter. (For dose rates of other γ-emitting isotopes used in radiotherapy see page 237.)

Permissible tracer levels

On the basis of the above considerations, tables have been presented in the literature which contain values for the permissible tracer level. This term refers to the quantity of a given isotope in microcuries which can be introduced into the human organism without at any time and in any tissue exceeding the permissible concentration. A reliable calculation of such "permissible" tracer concentrations requires, however, that numerous biological and physico-chemical factors are taken into account (absorption, retention and rate of excretion, "biological half-life", distribution, etc.). In the author's view, a publication of this kind from a really competent team of scientists is not yet available.

Valuable information and guidance through these complex problems can be obtained from the recommendations of the International Commission on Radiological Protection (ICRP). These are published regularly in various scientific journals[1] and are also contained in the Handbooks of the National Bureau of Standards, Washington[2]. It must be kept in mind, however, that from the start the ICRP discussed occupational exposure only, i.e. external irradiation with X- or γ-radiation. In recent years, Subcommittee II of the ICRP has compiled information on and made calculations of the maximum permissible concentrations of radionuclides in air and water, and has sought to evaluate the maximum body burdens of these substances for continuous uptake. Handbook No. 52 of the National Bureau of Standards[2] contains these values, which constitute useful data for persons responsible for tracer experiments as well as for those concerned with diagnostic and therapeutic applications of radioactive isotopes in man.

The latest recommendations of the ICRP (1958[3] and 1959[4]) are more extensive than any previous ones in that they include a

1) In the following journals: *British Journal of Radiology* (especially Supplement No. 6, 1955); *American Journal of Roentgenology*; *Nucleonics*; *Fortschritte der Röntgenstrahlung.*

2) National Bureau of Standards Handbook No. 47, *Recommendations of the International Commission on Radiological Protection and of the International Commission on Radiological Units*, Washington, 1950; National Bureau of Standards Handbook No. 52, *Maximum Permissible Amounts of Radioisotopes in the Human Body and Maximum Permissible Concentrations in Air and Water*, Washington, 1953.

3) *Recommendations of the International Commission on Radiological Protection, 1958*, Pergamon Press, London and New York, 1959.

4) *ICRP Publication 2* (Report of Committee II on Permissible Dose for Internal Radiation, 1959), Pergamon Press, London and New York, 1960 (also in *Brit. J. Radiol.*, **33**, 189 [1960]).

Table 4 **Weight distribution in the standard man[1] (total body weight 70 kg)**

Organ	Weight in grams	Organ	Weight in grams
Fat	10,000	Lymphoid tissue	700
Muscles	30,000	Brain	1500
Skeleton:		Spinal cord	30
Bones (without marrow)	7000	Bladder	150
Red marrow	1500	Salivary glands	50
Yellow marrow	1500	Eyes	30
Blood	5400	Teeth	20
Gastrointestinal tract (without contents)	2000	Prostate	20
Lungs	1000	Adrenals	20
Liver	1700	Thymus	10
Kidneys	300	Skin	2100
Spleen	150	Connective tissue	4100
Pancreas	70	Testes	40
Thyroid	20	Heart	300

1) From Recommendations of the International Commission on Radiological Protection, *Brit. J. Radiol.*, Suppl. No. 6 (1955).

Table 5 **Other data pertaining to the standard man (total body weight 70 kg)**

Chemical composition of the body[1]			Water balance[1]	
Element	Percentage of total body weight	Total weight g		Milliliters per day
Oxygen	65.0	45,500	Daily water intake:	
Carbon	18.0	12,600	In food (including 300 ml water of oxidation)	1000
Hydrogen	10.0	7000	As fluids	1500
Nitrogen	3.0	2100	Total water intake	2500
Calcium	1.5	1050		
Phosphorus	1.0	700	Daily water excretion:	
Sulfur	0.25	175	Sweat	500
Potassium	0.2	140	From lungs	400
Sodium	0.15	105	In feces	100
Chlorine	0.15	105	In urine	1500
Magnesium	0.05	35	Total	2500
Iron	0.006	4	Air inhaled per day:	
Copper	0.0002	0.1	8 hours at work	10×10^6
Manganese	0.000 03	0.02	16 hours not at work	10×10^6
Iodine	0.000 04	0.03	Total	20×10^6

1) From Recommendations of the International Commission on Radiological Protection, *Brit. J. Radiol.*, Suppl. No. 6 (1955).

critical evaluation of the concept "maximum permissible dose" for individuals and groups other than those subject to occupational exposure. The general philosophy underlying the recommendations is made clear in the 1958 publication[1]. As regards occupational exposure, the following passage may be quoted: "The maximum permissible total dose accumulated in the gonads, the blood-forming organs and the lenses of the eyes at any age over 18 years shall be governed by the relation $D = 5\,(N - 18)$ where D is the tissue dose rate in rems and N is the age in years. For a person who is occupationally exposed at a constant rate from age 18 years, the formula implies a maximum weekly dose of 0.1 rem. It is recommended that this value be used for purposes of planning and design."

The 1958 "*Recommendations*" go on to state that "for exposure that is essentially restricted to portions or single organs of the body, with the exception of the gonads, the blood-forming organs and the lenses of the eyes, a higher dose than the one derived from the above formula is permitted". The following maximum doses are recommended: *A maximum dose of 8 rems/13 weeks for the skin and thyroid; a maximum dose of 20 rems/13 weeks for the hands and forearms, feet and ankles; a maximum dose of 4 rems/13 weeks for limited exposure of internal organs other than the thyroid, the gonads and the blood-forming organs.*

The maximum permissible internal exposure of individuals due to the intake of radioactive isotopes is not discussed explicitly in the ICRP recommendations, but the 1958–59 revision of the figures for maximum permissible body burdens for continuous exposure, in conjunction with the recommendations concerning the exposure of individuals, can serve as a basis for an estimate of permissible tracer levels in man.

The problem of genetic damage to the population at large from external and internal radiation has little bearing on the present discussion of the application of radioactive tracers in medical research or therapy. The reader interested in this aspect is likewise referred to the 1958 recommendations[1] (pages 14–16).

In order to facilitate the estimation of permissible concentrations, Tables 4 and 5 give some data for the "standard man" on which the calculations of the International Radiological Commissions have been based.

Table 6 presents a survey of the radioisotopes used in medicine and biology. Under medical applications, therapy and diagnosis are listed separately, while medico-physiological tracer investigations are given under biological applications. The literature available in this field is so extensive that any attempt at referring to the original papers would inevitably lead to an incomplete and therefore biased picture of the investigations which have been carried out.

1) *Recommendations of the International Commission on Radiological Protection, 1958*, Pergamon Press, London and New York, 1959.

Table 6 **Applications of radioisotopes**

Application in medicine	Isotope	Application in biological and physiological research
	Hydrogen ^{3}H	Body water content.
	Carbon ^{11}C ^{14}C	CO_2 metabolism. Application of ^{14}C labeled compounds to metabolic studies (localization, reaction mechanism, retention or lifetime, metabolic pool of a substance by means of the isotope dilution method). Carbohydrate, fat, albumin, amino acid metabolism.
	Nitrogen ^{13}N	Respiratory gas exchange.
	Fluorine ^{18}F	Physiology and chemistry of bones and teeth.

Table 6 **Applications of radioisotopes (continued)**

Application in medicine	Isotope	Application in biological and physiological research
Therapy: Whole body irradiation, erythropoiesis, polyglobuly. Diagnosis: Circulation measurements with ^{24}Na labeled plasma. Determination of the extravascular space by the dilution method. Blood circulation in extremities and organs. Cardiac failure.	Sodium ^{24}Na	(Also ^{22}Na.) Excretion, absorption; permeability of capillaries, gastric mucosa, intestinal walls, placenta, organ cell walls. Distribution between plasma and tissue. Ion transport.
Therapy: Surface therapy of deformities and malformations, skin lesions, eczema. Chronic leukemia and polycythemia. Selective irradiation with colloids containing ^{32}P. Diagnosis: Blood volume determinations and circulation time with ^{32}P labeled erythrocytes.	Phosphorus ^{32}P	Mineral metabolism, intermediary metabolism.
Therapy: Selective irradiation of the joints. Diagnosis: Sulfur accumulation in tumors.	Sulfur ^{35}S	Permeability studies. Intermediary metabolism. Metabolism of sulfur-containing amino acids and peptides, ^{35}S labeled pharmaceuticals. Mineral metabolism.
	Chlorine ^{36}Cl ^{38}Cl	Mineral metabolism, permeability, ion transport through membranes.
	Potassium ^{42}K	Mineral metabolism, adrenal physiology.
	Calcium ^{45}Ca	Mineral metabolism, incorporation of calcium in the bones of rachitic and vitamin D treated animals. Bone healing.
Diagnosis: Blood volume and circulation studies with ^{51}Cr labeled erythrocytes.	Chromium ^{51}Cr	Plasma albumin studies with labeled chromic chloride.
Therapy: Local irradiation of lymph nodes. Distribution of colloidal manganese dioxide in the reticuloendothelial system.	Manganese ^{52}Mn ^{54}Mn	Mineral metabolism.
Diagnosis: Blood volume; lifetime of erythrocytes.	Iron ^{55}Fe ^{59}Fe	Mineral metabolism, blood physiology, absorption by gastric and intestinal mucosa. Distribution of iron in the organism. Blood preservation.
Therapy: Telecurie therapy, external (high depth doses). Cobalt wire for local application. Intracavitary cobalt chloride solution in rubber bags as cavity applicator (bladder).	Cobalt ^{60}Co	Mineral metabolism.
Therapy: Intratumoral therapy. ^{63}Zn as insoluble sulfide and as sol; intraperitoneal and intrapleural application. ^{63}Zn in coarse-disperse sulfide form is selectively fixed in the lungs.	Zinc ^{63}Zn ^{65}Zn	Mineral metabolism. Lifetime of leukocytes.
	Bromine ^{82}Br	Electrolyte exchange. Thyroid physiology, distribution of brominated dyes.
Diagnosis: Minute-volume determination.	Krypton ^{85}K	Respiratory gas exchange.
Therapy of bone sarcoma.	Strontium ^{89}Sr	Absorption, distribution, excretion. Bone physiology.
Therapy: Selective irradiation of the thyroid. Treatment of hyperthyroidism, thyroid carcinoma, diffuse and nodular goiter. Diagnosis: Thyroidal dysfunction. Localization of tumors by means of ^{131}I-diiodofluorescein.	Iodine ^{131}I	Iodine metabolism. Thyroid physiology.
Telecurie therapy.	Cesium ^{137}Cs	
Therapy: Surface irradiation with applicators; threads.	Tantalum ^{182}Ta	
Therapy: Interstitial application.	Iridium ^{192}Ir	
Therapy: In soluble form (pectin sol) for intracavitary treatment (bladder). Carcinomatosis of peritoneum and pleura, intratumoral therapy.	Gold ^{198}Au	Absorption, distribution, excretion; distribution in arthritis.

Principles of Radiotherapy with Artificial Isotopes[1]

By Dr. H. Lüthy, Isotope Laboratory, Civic Hospital, Basle, Switzerland

In contrast to the natural radioactive isotopes, which on account of their gaseous fission products can only be used for therapeutic purposes when enclosed in a gastight container (needles, tubes or plaques of platinum, gold or monel metal), the artificial isotopes can mostly be used without enclosure and in either the solid or liquid form. The basic principle of radiotherapy is the localization of the radioisotope in the circumscribed focus of disease with maximum possible protection of the surrounding healthy tissue. Various methods are used to achieve this.

1. Teletherapy (γ-emitting isotopes)

Isotope (usual): Cobalt-60. Sources with a specific activity of 20–100 curies per gram are used, usually as cylinders 10×10 mm up to 25×25 mm. Equipments with charges ranging from 20 to 2000 curies are available. The source as purchased is fully shielded in a tungsten or lead container, the emergent radiation being controlled by an adjustable or exchangeable tungsten diaphragm. Exposure time is adjusted by a remote-controlled tungsten shutter. Irradiation distance: 20–100 cm according to the activity. Field size: somewhat smaller than in deep X-ray therapy. Cross-fire technique, rotation therapy or arc therapy. Advantages over 200 kv X-ray therapy are: higher relative depth dose; sharper lateral limitation of the field; absorption in bone practically the same as in soft tissues (less injury to the bones); maximum dose 4–5 mm *beneath* the skin (dose on skin surface 25–30% of maximum, with correspondingly milder skin reaction). The biological effectiveness of the radiation from cobalt-60 is about 80% of that of 200 kv X-rays, so that the dosages given are usually somewhat higher.

Isotope: Cesium-137. Sources may be contaminated with the shorter-lived isotope Cs-134 (half-life 2.3 y compared with 30 y for Cs-137), in which case there is a more rapid loss of activity. The advantage of this isotope lies in its longer half-life than Co-60; its disadvantages are its much lower specific activity, necessitating larger sources and therefore larger penumbra, and its lower γ-energy, resulting in more injury to the skin and bones.

2. Contact therapy (β- and γ-emitting isotopes)

Pure β-emitters are used for the irradiation of surface foci of infection in dermatology and ophthalmology and are applied directly to the lesion in suitable forms.

Isotope: Phosphorus-32. Maximum depth of penetration 5–8 mm, effective range ca. 3 mm. Commercially available in the form of flexible plastic foils containing 20% red phosphorus which have been activated in a reactor.

Isotope: Strontium-90/Yttrium-90. Available in metal capsules with a silver foil filter over the exit surface. Activity is due to the β-radiation of the daughter isotope yttrium-90 ($\bar{E}_\beta$ 2.3 Mev). Ophthalmological applicators shaped to fit the corneal curvature are available.

A greater depth effect is obtained with γ-emitters applied to the surface to be treated. Commercially available is *cobalt-60* granulate in a soft plastic mass (Plastobalt) or as plastic spheres enclosed in 6-mm gold foil. These provide optimal adaptation to surfaces of complex shape. *Tantalum-182* is available in the form of wire in a plastic tube and is particularly suitable for ring sources for epibulbar irradiation. The dose of γ-emitters decreases sharply with increasing depth since the intensity is inversely proportional to the square of the distance.

3. Interstitial irradiation

(*a*) *Needles: Cobalt-60* is supplied as wire of the ductile alloy "Cobanic" (55% nickel + 45% cobalt) in steel needles or nylon tubes. These "threads" are sewn into the lesion and have marked advantages over rigid carriers.

Tantalum-182 wire (0.4 mm diameter with platinum envelope 0.1 mm thick) is formed into hairpin-shaped loops which are inserted into tumor tissue, particularly in the wall of the bladder. *Iridium-192* is also very suitable for interstitial application in this way. The threads are withdrawn from the tissues at the end of the irradiation period.

For tumors which are accessible for only a short time, "seeds" of *radiogold* (*Au-198*) ca. 2.5 mm long and 0.8 mm in diameter are used, the β-radiation being filtered out by means of an inactive gold or platinum coating. Such seeds can be quickly and accurately placed in the tissue with the aid of a "pistol" for which filled "magazines" with 15 seeds are available. The magazines must be sterilized before placing in the pistol. Another equipment allows pieces of any desired length to be cut under shielding from radiogold wire coated with inactive gold. The pieces are then inserted into the tissue through a special tube. Radiogold seeds have important advantages over radon seeds.

(*b*) *Infiltration methods:* The radioactive substance is injected directly into the tumor tissue in the form of a stabilized colloidal solution. The irradiation can be assumed to be practically homogeneous when the individual depots are not more than 3 mm apart. β-Emitters are particularly suitable for this type of application, for example colloidal *radiogold* (*Au-198*) or *phosphorus-32* in the form of colloidal chromium phosphate or magnesium ammonium phosphate. There is some loss of activity via the lymph ducts with concentration in the neighboring lymph nodes.

The dose is calculated as follows (assuming homogeneous distribution of the isotope):

C = specific activity of isotope in mc/g (see page 236)
$\bar{E}_\beta$ = mean β-ray energy ($\cong E_{max}/3$)
T_{eff} = effective half-life (≅ physical half-life) in days
g = mean geometric factor for spheres[2] (when $R < 10$ cm $\cong 3\pi R$)
k = dose factor in r/mch for γ-radiation (see page 237)

For β-radiation:

Total dose D_β $= 73.8 \times C \times \bar{E}_\beta \times T_{eff}$ [rads]
Dose $D_{\beta t}$ after time $t = D_\beta \times (1 - e^{\lambda t})$ [rads]
where $\lambda = 0.693/T_{eff}$

For γ-radiation:

Mean absorbed dose after complete disintegration
$D_{\gamma(\infty)} = 0.0322 \times C \times g \times k \times T_{eff}$ [rads]

4. Intracavitary irradiation

(*a*) Colloidal suspensions of *radiogold* (*Au-198*) are used for intraperitoneal and intrapleural infusion in superficial or disseminated carcinomatosis. Individual doses of 100–150 mc are given, repeated if necessary after several months up to a total dose of 500 mc. The main activity is due to the β-radiation, with a small depth effect up to ca. 3 mm. This technique has recently been used for irradiation of the inner wall of the bladder, using 300 mc of *radiogold* for a 4-hour period (for nomogram for dosage calculation see Ellis and Oliver[3]).

(*b*) Solid applicators in the form of plastic masses containing *cobalt-60* grains of diameter ca. 1 mm are used principally for irradiation of tumors of the mouth, nose and pharyngeal cavities. Beads of *cobalt-60* of diameter 6 mm are strung together for insertion into the esophagus, or can be packed into natural or surgically opened body cavities. Dosages must be determined experimentally from isodose curves obtained with small ionization chambers.

5. Enteral and intravenous applications

A therapeutic effect from intravenous or peroral administration of isotopes is only obtainable when the isotope can be concentrated sufficiently in the tissue to be treated. The only successful application so far is that of *radioiodine* (*I-131*), 30–50% of the amount administered being stored in the thyroid. In some cases of primary tumors or metastases (at the most 10% of all thyroid gland tumors) sufficient of the isotope has been concentrated in the lesion to provide an adequate radiation dose. The usual dose is 100–150 mc peroral.

Hyperthyroidism is treated by administration of peroral doses of 4–10 mc of *radioiodine*, repeated if necessary under regular clinical control. The dose achieved depends on the percentage uptake (determined by tracer test), the effective half-life of the isotope and the size of the thyroid. The concentration of the isotope may vary a hundredfold within the gland so that theoretical calculations are useless and dosage must be estimated on an empirical clinical basis.

In the treatment of blood diseases (erythremia, leukosis), *phosphorus-32* is the isotope of choice. Assuming 20–40% excretion in urine after intravenous injection, the total radiation to which a 70-kg man is exposed per millicurie of the isotope corresponds to 10 r. The dosage is adjusted in accordance with the changes in the blood picture observed. The isotope is administered as a phosphate in isotonic solution.

---

1) For further details see Hine and Brownell (Eds.), *Radiation Dosimetry*, New York, 1956; Beierwaltes et al., *Clinical Use of Radioisotopes*, Philadelphia, 1957; Hahn, P. F. (Ed.), *Therapeutic Use of Artificial Radioisotopes*, New York, 1956; Fields and Seed (Eds.), *Clinical Use of Radioisotopes*, Chicago, 1957; Veall and Vetter, *Radioisotope Techniques in Clinical Research and Diagnosis*, London, 1958; Schwiegk, H., *Künstliche radioaktive Isotope in Physiologie, Diagnostik und Therapie*, Berlin, 1953. 2) For cylinders see Loevinger et al., in Hine and Brownell (Eds.), *loc. cit.*, page 801. 3) Ellis and Oliver, *Brit. med. J.*, 1, 136 (1955).

Explanation of the tables (pages 277–291)*

Columns 1–3: t = elapsed time ($t - t_0$) in days (d), hours (h) and minutes (min).

Column 4: N_t = amount of isotope not disintegrated at time t expressed as percentage of N_0 (the values apply equally to the activities A_t and A_0).

Columns 5 and 6: factors and their logarithms for calculating N_0 (or A_0) from N_t (or A_t):

$$N_0 = \frac{N_0}{N_t} N_t \quad \text{or} \quad A_0 = \frac{A_0}{A_t} A_t$$

The half-lives T have been taken from Knolls Atomic Power Laboratory *Chart of the Nuclides*, 5th ed., General Electric Company, New York, 1956. Note that there are slight differences in some cases between these values and those in the *International Directory of Radioisotopes*, vol. I, International Atomic Energy Agency, Vienna, 1959, which are given in the tables on pages 271 and 272. These differences have a negligible effect, however, on the data given here.

The data in the tables have been calculated (by electronic computer) on the basis of the following relationships:

Column 4: $$\ln \frac{N_t}{N_0} = \frac{-\ln 2}{T_t}\, t$$

Columns 5 and 6: $$\ln \frac{N_0}{N_t} = \frac{\ln 2}{T_t}\, t$$

$$\left(\text{Disintegration constant } \lambda_t = \frac{\ln 2}{T_t}\right)$$

Sodium-24
Half-life 15.0 h

d	h	min	N_t	N_0/N_t	$\log_{10} N_0/N_t$
		00	100.00	1.000	0.00000
		10	99.23	1.007	0.00335
		20	98.47	1.015	0.00669
		30	97.72	1.023	0.01003
		40	96.97	1.031	0.01338
		50	96.22	1.039	0.01672
	1	00	95.48	1.047	0.02007
		10	94.75	1.055	0.02341
		20	94.02	1.063	0.02676
		30	93.30	1.071	0.03010
		40	92.59	1.080	0.03345
		50	91.88	1.088	0.03679
	2	00	91.17	1.096	0.04014
		10	90.47	1.105	0.04348
		20	89.78	1.113	0.04683
		30	89.09	1.122	0.05017
		40	88.41	1.131	0.05352
		50	87.73	1.139	0.05686
	3	00	87.06	1.148	0.06021
		10	86.39	1.157	0.06355
		20	85.72	1.166	0.06690
		30	85.07	1.175	0.07024
		40	84.41	1.184	0.07359
		50	83.77	1.193	0.07693
	4	00	83.12	1.203	0.08028
		10	82.49	1.212	0.08362
		20	81.85	1.221	0.08696
		30	81.23	1.231	0.09031
		40	80.60	1.240	0.09365
		50	79.98	1.250	0.09700
	5	00	79.37	1.259	0.10034
		10	78.76	1.269	0.10369
		20	78.16	1.279	0.10703
		30	77.56	1.289	0.11038
		40	76.96	1.299	0.11372
		50	76.37	1.309	0.11707
	6	00	75.79	1.319	0.12041
		10	75.20	1.329	0.12376
		20	74.63	1.339	0.12710
		30	74.05	1.350	0.13045
		40	73.49	1.360	0.13379
		50	72.92	1.371	0.13714
	7	00	72.36	1.381	0.14048
		10	71.81	1.392	0.14383
		20	71.26	1.403	0.14717
		30	70.71	1.414	0.15052
		40	70.17	1.425	0.15386
		50	69.63	1.436	0.15720
	8	00	69.10	1.447	0.16055
		10	68.57	1.458	0.16389
		20	68.04	1.469	0.16724
		30	67.52	1.481	0.17058
		40	67.00	1.492	0.17393
		50	66.49	1.504	0.17727
	9	00	65.98	1.515	0.18062
		10	65.47	1.527	0.18396
		20	64.97	1.539	0.18731
		30	64.47	1.551	0.19065
		40	63.97	1.563	0.19400
		50	63.48	1.575	0.19734
	10	00	63.00	1.587	0.20069
		10	62.51	1.599	0.20403
		20	62.03	1.612	0.20738
		30	61.56	1.624	0.21072
		40	61.08	1.637	0.21407
		50	60.62	1.649	0.21741
	11	00	60.15	1.662	0.22076
		10	59.69	1.675	0.22410
		20	59.23	1.688	0.22745
		30	58.78	1.701	0.23079
		40	58.33	1.714	0.23413
		50	57.88	1.727	0.23748
	12	00	57.43	1.741	0.24082
		10	56.99	1.754	0.24417
		20	56.56	1.768	0.24751
		30	56.12	1.781	0.25086
		40	55.69	1.795	0.25420
		50	55.27	1.809	0.25755
	13	00	54.84	1.823	0.26089
		10	54.42	1.837	0.26424
		20	54.00	1.851	0.26758
		30	53.59	1.866	0.27093
		40	53.18	1.880	0.27427
		50	52.77	1.895	0.27762
	14	00	52.36	1.909	0.28096
		10	51.96	1.924	0.28431
		20	51.56	1.939	0.28765
		30	51.17	1.954	0.29100
		40	50.78	1.969	0.29434
		50	50.39	1.984	0.29769
	15	00	50.00	2.000	0.30103
		10	49.62	2.015	0.30438
		20	49.24	2.031	0.30772
		30	48.86	2.046	0.31106
		40	48.48	2.062	0.31441
		50	48.11	2.078	0.31775
	16	00	47.74	2.094	0.32110
		10	47.38	2.110	0.32444
		20	47.01	2.127	0.32779
		30	46.65	2.143	0.33113
		40	46.29	2.160	0.33448
		50	45.94	2.176	0.33782
	17	00	45.59	2.193	0.34117
		10	45.24	2.210	0.34451
		20	44.89	2.227	0.34786
		30	44.54	2.244	0.35120
		40	44.20	2.262	0.35455
		50	43.86	2.279	0.35789
	18	00	43.53	2.297	0.36124
		10	43.19	2.315	0.36458
		20	42.86	2.333	0.36793
		30	42.53	2.351	0.37127
		40	42.21	2.369	0.37462
		50	41.88	2.387	0.37796
	19	00	41.56	2.406	0.38131
		10	41.24	2.424	0.38465
		20	40.93	2.443	0.38799
		30	40.61	2.462	0.39134
		40	40.30	2.481	0.39468
		50	39.99	2.500	0.39803
	20	00	39.69	2.519	0.40137
		10	39.38	2.539	0.40472
		20	39.08	2.558	0.40806
		30	38.78	2.578	0.41141
		40	38.48	2.598	0.41475
		50	38.19	2.618	0.41810
	21	00	37.89	2.639	0.42144
		10	37.60	2.659	0.42479
		20	37.31	2.679	0.42813
		30	37.03	2.700	0.43148
		40	36.74	2.721	0.43482
		50	36.46	2.742	0.43817
	22	00	36.18	2.763	0.44151
		10	35.90	2.785	0.44486
		20	35.63	2.806	0.44820
		30	35.36	2.828	0.45155
		40	35.08	2.850	0.45489
		50	34.81	2.872	0.45823
	23	00	34.55	2.894	0.46158
		10	34.28	2.916	0.46492
		20	34.02	2.939	0.46827
		30	33.76	2.962	0.47161
		40	33.50	2.985	0.47496
		50	33.24	3.008	0.47830
1	00		32.99	3.031	0.48165
	01		31.50	3.174	0.50172
	02		30.08	3.324	0.52179
	03		28.72	3.482	0.54185
	04		27.42	3.646	0.56192
	05		26.18	3.819	0.58199
	06		25.00	3.999	0.60206
	07		23.87	4.189	0.62213
	08		22.79	4.387	0.64220
	09		21.76	4.594	0.66227
	10		20.78	4.812	0.68233
	11		19.84	5.039	0.70240
	12		18.95	5.278	0.72247
	13		18.09	5.527	0.74254
	14		17.27	5.789	0.76261
	15		16.49	6.062	0.78268
	16		15.75	6.349	0.80274
	17		15.04	6.649	0.82281
	18		14.36	6.964	0.84288
	19		13.71	7.293	0.86295
	20		13.09	7.638	0.88302
	21		12.50	7.999	0.90308
	22		11.94	8.378	0.92315
	23		11.40	8.774	0.94322
2	00		10.88	9.189	0.96329
	01		10.39	9.623	0.98335
	02		9.92	10.079	1.00343
	03		9.47	10.556	1.02350
	04		9.05	11.055	1.04357
	05		8.64	11.578	1.06364
	06		8.25	12.125	1.08371
	07		7.87	12.699	1.10378
	08		7.52	13.299	1.12385
	09		7.18	13.928	1.14391
	10		6.86	14.587	1.16398
	11		6.55	15.277	1.18405
	12		6.25	16.000	1.20412
	13		5.97	16.756	1.22419
	14		5.70	17.549	1.24426
	15		5.44	18.379	1.26433
	16		5.20	19.248	1.28439
	17		4.96	20.158	1.30446
	18		4.74	21.112	1.32453
	19		4.52	22.110	1.34460
	20		4.32	23.156	1.36467
	21		4.12	24.251	1.38474
	22		3.94	25.398	1.40481
	23		3.76	26.599	1.42488
3	00		3.59	27.857	1.44494
	01		3.43	29.175	1.46501
	02		3.27	30.554	1.48508
	03		3.13	32.000	1.50515
	04		2.98	33.513	1.52522
	05		2.85	35.098	1.54529
	06		2.72	36.758	1.56536
	07		2.60	38.496	1.58542
	08		2.48	40.317	1.60549
	09		2.37	42.224	1.62556
	10		2.26	44.221	1.64563
	11		2.16	46.312	1.66570
	12		2.06	48.502	1.68577
	13		1.97	50.796	1.70584
	14		1.88	53.199	1.72590
	15		1.79	55.714	1.74597
	16		1.71	58.349	1.76604
	17		1.64	61.109	1.78611
	18		1.56	63.999	1.80618
	19		1.49	67.026	1.82625
	20		1.42	70.196	1.84631
	21		1.36	73.515	1.86638
	22		1.30	76.992	1.88645
	23		1.24	80.634	1.90652
4	00		1.18	84.447	1.92659
	01		1.13	88.440	1.94665
	02		1.08	92.623	1.96672
	03		1.03	97.003	1.98679
	04		0.98	101.594	2.00687
	05		0.94	106.398	2.02694
	06		0.90	111.430	2.04700
	07		0.86	116.701	2.06708
	08		0.82	122.219	2.08714
	09		0.78	128.000	2.10721
	10		0.75	134.053	2.12728
	11		0.71	140.394	2.14735
	12		0.68	147.032	2.16741
	13		0.65	153.988	2.18749
	14		0.62	161.269	2.20755
	15		0.59	168.896	2.22762
	16		0.57	176.884	2.24769
	17		0.54	185.250	2.26776
	18		0.52	194.012	2.28783
	19		0.49	203.185	2.30789
	20		0.47	212.797	2.32797
	21		0.45	222.861	2.34803
	22		0.43	233.399	2.36810
	23		0.41	244.439	2.38817

Magnesium-28
Half-life 21.3 h

d	h	min	N_t	N_0/N_t	$\log_{10} N_0/N_t$
		00	100.00	1.000	0.00000
		10	99.46	1.005	0.00236
		20	98.92	1.010	0.00471
		30	98.39	1.016	0.00707
		40	97.85	1.021	0.00942
		50	97.32	1.027	0.01178
	1	00	96.80	1.033	0.01413
		10	96.27	1.038	0.01649
		20	95.75	1.044	0.01884
		30	95.24	1.050	0.02120
		40	94.72	1.055	0.02356
		50	94.21	1.061	0.02591
	2	00	93.70	1.067	0.02827
		10	93.19	1.073	0.03062
		20	92.69	1.078	0.03298
		30	92.19	1.084	0.03533
		40	91.69	1.090	0.03769
		50	91.19	1.096	0.04004
	3	00	90.70	1.102	0.04240
		10	90.21	1.108	0.04475
		20	89.72	1.114	0.04711
		30	89.23	1.120	0.04947
		40	88.75	1.126	0.05182
		50	88.27	1.132	0.05418
	4	00	87.79	1.139	0.05653
		10	87.32	1.145	0.05889
		20	86.85	1.151	0.06124
		30	86.38	1.157	0.06360
		40	85.91	1.164	0.06595
		50	85.45	1.170	0.06831
	5	00	84.98	1.176	0.07066
		10	84.52	1.183	0.07302
		20	84.07	1.189	0.07538
		30	83.61	1.195	0.07773
		40	83.16	1.202	0.08009
		50	82.71	1.209	0.08244
	6	00	82.26	1.215	0.08480
		10	81.82	1.222	0.08715
		20	81.38	1.228	0.08951

* Reproduction of pages 277–291 only by permission of the publishers of these *Scientific Tables*.

t d	t h	t min	N_t	N_0/N_t	$\log_{10} N_0/N_t$
		30	80.94	1.235	0.09186
		40	80.50	1.242	0.09422
		50	80.06	1.249	0.09658
	7	00	79.63	1.255	0.09893
		10	79.20	1.262	0.10129
		20	78.77	1.269	0.10364
		30	78.34	1.276	0.10600
		40	77.92	1.283	0.10835
		50	77.50	1.290	0.11071
	8	00	77.08	1.297	0.11306
		10	76.66	1.304	0.11542
		20	76.25	1.311	0.11777
		30	75.84	1.318	0.12013
		40	75.42	1.325	0.12249
		50	75.02	1.333	0.12484
	9	00	74.61	1.340	0.12720
		10	74.21	1.347	0.12955
		20	73.81	1.354	0.13191
		30	73.41	1.362	0.13426
		40	73.01	1.369	0.13662
		50	72.62	1.377	0.13897
	10	00	72.22	1.384	0.14133
		10	71.83	1.392	0.14368
		20	71.44	1.399	0.14604
		30	71.06	1.407	0.14840
		40	70.67	1.414	0.15075
		50	70.29	1.422	0.15311
	11	00	69.91	1.430	0.15546
		10	69.53	1.438	0.15782
		20	69.16	1.446	0.16017
		30	68.78	1.453	0.16253
		40	68.41	1.461	0.16488
		50	68.04	1.469	0.16724
	12	00	67.67	1.477	0.16959
		10	67.31	1.485	0.17195
		20	66.94	1.493	0.17431
		30	66.58	1.501	0.17666
		40	66.22	1.510	0.17902
		50	65.86	1.518	0.18137
	13	00	65.50	1.526	0.18373
		10	65.15	1.534	0.18608
		20	64.80	1.543	0.18844
		30	64.45	1.551	0.19079
		40	64.10	1.560	0.19315
		50	63.75	1.568	0.19550
	14	00	63.41	1.577	0.19786
		10	63.06	1.585	0.20022
		20	62.72	1.594	0.20257
		30	62.38	1.602	0.20493
		40	62.05	1.611	0.20728
		50	61.71	1.620	0.20964
	15	00	61.38	1.629	0.21199
		10	61.05	1.638	0.21435
		20	60.72	1.647	0.21670
		30	60.39	1.655	0.21906
		40	60.06	1.665	0.22142
		50	59.74	1.674	0.22377
	16	00	59.41	1.683	0.22613
		10	59.09	1.692	0.22848
		20	58.77	1.701	0.23084
		30	58.45	1.710	0.23319
		40	58.14	1.720	0.23555
		50	57.82	1.729	0.23790
	17	00	57.51	1.738	0.24026
		10	57.20	1.748	0.24261
		20	56.89	1.757	0.24497
		30	56.58	1.767	0.24733
		40	56.28	1.776	0.24968
		50	55.97	1.786	0.25204
	18	00	55.67	1.796	0.25439
		10	55.37	1.806	0.25675
		20	55.07	1.815	0.25910
		30	54.77	1.825	0.26146
		40	54.47	1.835	0.26381
		50	54.18	1.845	0.26617
	19	00	53.89	1.855	0.26852
		10	53.59	1.865	0.27088
		20	53.30	1.876	0.27324
		30	53.02	1.886	0.27559
		40	52.73	1.896	0.27795
		50	52.44	1.906	0.28030
	20	00	52.16	1.917	0.28266
		10	51.88	1.927	0.28501
		20	51.60	1.938	0.28737
		30	51.32	1.948	0.28972
		40	51.04	1.959	0.29208
		50	50.77	1.969	0.29444
	21	00	50.49	1.980	0.29679
		10	50.22	1.991	0.29915
		20	49.95	2.002	0.30150
		30	49.68	2.013	0.30386
		40	49.41	2.024	0.30621
		50	49.14	2.035	0.30857
	22	00	48.87	2.046	0.31092
		10	48.61	2.057	0.31328
		20	48.35	2.068	0.31563
		30	48.09	2.079	0.31799
		40	47.83	2.090	0.32035
		50	47.57	2.102	0.32270
	23	00	47.31	2.113	0.32506

t d	t h	t min	N_t	N_0/N_t	$\log_{10} N_0/N_t$
		10	47.05	2.125	0.32741
		20	46.80	2.136	0.32977
		30	46.55	2.148	0.33212
		40	46.29	2.160	0.33448
		50	46.04	2.171	0.33683
1	00		45.79	2.183	0.33919
	01		44.33	2.255	0.35332
	02		42.91	2.330	0.36745
	03		41.53	2.407	0.38159
	04		40.20	2.487	0.39572
	05		38.92	2.569	0.40985
	06		37.67	2.654	0.42399
	07		36.47	2.742	0.43812
	08		35.30	2.833	0.45225
	09		34.17	2.926	0.46638
	10		33.07	3.023	0.48052
	11		32.01	3.123	0.49465
	12		30.99	3.226	0.50878
	13		30.00	3.333	0.52292
	14		29.04	3.443	0.53705
	15		28.11	3.557	0.55118
	16		27.21	3.675	0.56532
	17		26.34	3.797	0.57945
	18		25.49	3.922	0.59358
	19		24.68	4.052	0.60771
	20		23.89	4.186	0.62185
	21		23.12	4.324	0.63598
	22		22.38	4.467	0.65011
	23		21.66	4.615	0.66424
2	00		20.97	4.768	0.67838
	01		20.30	4.926	0.69251
	02		19.65	5.089	0.70664
	03		19.02	5.257	0.72078
	04		18.41	5.431	0.73491
	05		17.82	5.611	0.74904
	06		17.25	5.796	0.76317
	07		16.70	5.988	0.77731
	08		16.16	6.186	0.79144
	09		15.65	6.391	0.80557
	10		15.15	6.602	0.81970
	11		14.66	6.820	0.83384
	12		14.19	7.046	0.84797
	13		13.74	7.279	0.86210
	14		13.30	7.520	0.87623
	15		12.87	7.769	0.89037
	16		12.46	8.025	0.90450
	17		12.06	8.291	0.91863
	18		11.67	8.565	0.93276
	19		11.30	8.848	0.94689
	20		10.94	9.141	0.96103
	21		10.59	9.444	0.97516
	22		10.25	9.756	0.98929
	23		9.92	10.079	1.00343
3	00		9.60	10.412	1.01757
	01		9.30	10.757	1.03170
	02		9.00	11.113	1.04583
	03		8.71	11.480	1.05997
	04		8.43	11.860	1.07410
	05		8.16	12.252	1.08823
	06		7.90	12.657	1.10236
	07		7.65	13.076	1.11650
	08		7.40	13.509	1.13063
	09		7.17	13.956	1.14476
	10		6.94	14.417	1.15890
	11		6.71	14.894	1.17303
	12		6.50	15.387	1.18716
	13		6.29	15.896	1.20129
	14		6.09	16.422	1.21543
	15		5.89	16.965	1.22956
	16		5.71	17.526	1.24369
	17		5.52	18.106	1.25783
	18		5.35	18.705	1.27196
	19		5.17	19.323	1.28609
	20		5.01	19.962	1.30022
	21		4.85	20.623	1.31436
	22		4.69	21.305	1.32849
	23		4.54	22.010	1.34262
4	00		4.40	22.738	1.35676
	01		4.26	23.490	1.37089
	02		4.12	24.267	1.38502
	03		3.99	25.069	1.39915
	04		3.86	25.899	1.41329
	05		3.74	26.755	1.42742
	06		3.62	27.640	1.44155
	07		3.50	28.555	1.45569
	08		3.39	29.499	1.46982
	09		3.28	30.475	1.48395
	10		3.18	31.483	1.49808
	11		3.07	32.524	1.51222
	12		2.98	33.600	1.52635
	13		2.88	34.712	1.54048
	14		2.79	35.860	1.55462
	15		2.70	37.046	1.56875
	16		2.61	38.271	1.58288
	17		2.53	39.537	1.59701
	18		2.45	40.845	1.61115
	19		2.37	42.196	1.62528
	20		2.29	43.592	1.63941
	21		2.22	45.034	1.65355

t d	t h	t min	N_t	N_0/N_t	$\log_{10} N_0/N_t$
	22		2.15	46.523	1.66768
	23		2.08	48.062	1.68181
5	00		2.01	49.652	1.69594
	06		1.66	60.358	1.78074
	12		1.36	73.372	1.86553
	18		1.12	89.192	1.95033
6	00		0.92	108.425	2.03513
	06		0.76	131.804	2.11993
	12		0.62	160.223	2.20473
	18		0.51	194.772	2.28953
7	00		0.42	236.764	2.37432
	06		0.35	287.819	2.45912
	12		0.29	349.882	2.54392
	18		0.24	425.314	2.62871
8	00		0.19	517.009	2.71350
	06		0.16	628.496	2.79830
	12		0.13	764.000	2.88309
	18		0.11	928.763	2.96791

Phosphorus-32

Half-life 14.5 d

t d	t h	t min	N_t	N_0/N_t	$\log_{10} N_0/N_t$
	0	00	100.00	1.000	0.00000
	6		98.81	1.012	0.00519
	12		97.64	1.024	0.01038
	18		96.48	1.036	0.01557
1	00		95.33	1.048	0.02076
	06		94.20	1.061	0.02595
	12		93.08	1.074	0.03114
	18		91.97	1.087	0.03633
2	00		90.88	1.100	0.04152
	06		89.80	1.113	0.04671
	12		88.74	1.126	0.05190
	18		87.68	1.140	0.05709
3	00		86.64	1.154	0.06228
	06		85.61	1.168	0.06747
	12		84.59	1.182	0.07266
	18		83.59	1.196	0.07785
4	00		82.60	1.210	0.08304
	06		81.61	1.225	0.08823
	12		80.64	1.240	0.09342
	18		79.69	1.254	0.09861
5	00		78.74	1.269	0.10380
	06		77.80	1.285	0.10899
	12		76.88	1.300	0.11418
	18		75.97	1.316	0.11937
6	00		75.06	1.332	0.12456
	06		74.17	1.348	0.12975
	12		73.29	1.364	0.13494
	18		72.42	1.380	0.14014
7	00		71.56	1.397	0.14533
	06		70.71	1.414	0.15052
	12		69.87	1.431	0.15571
	18		69.04	1.448	0.16090
8	00		68.22	1.465	0.16609
	06		67.41	1.483	0.17128
	12		66.61	1.501	0.17647
	18		65.82	1.519	0.18166
9	00		65.04	1.537	0.18685
	06		64.26	1.556	0.19204
	12		63.50	1.574	0.19723
	18		62.75	1.593	0.20242
10	00		62.00	1.612	0.20761
	06		61.26	1.632	0.21280
	12		60.54	1.651	0.21799
	18		59.82	1.671	0.22318
11	00		59.11	1.691	0.22837
	06		58.40	1.712	0.23356
	12		57.71	1.732	0.23875
	18		57.02	1.753	0.24394
12	00		56.35	1.774	0.24913
	06		55.68	1.796	0.25432
	12		55.02	1.817	0.25951
	18		54.36	1.839	0.26470
13	00		53.72	1.861	0.26989
	06		53.08	1.883	0.27508
	12		52.45	1.906	0.28027
	18		51.83	1.929	0.28546
14	00		51.21	1.952	0.29065
	06		50.60	1.976	0.29584
	12		50.00	2.000	0.30103
	18		49.41	2.024	0.30622
15	00		48.82	2.048	0.31141
	06		48.24	2.073	0.31660
	12		47.67	2.097	0.32179
	18		47.10	2.123	0.32698
16	00		46.54	2.148	0.33217
	06		45.99	2.174	0.33736
	12		45.44	2.200	0.34255
	18		44.90	2.227	0.34774
17	00		44.37	2.253	0.35293
	06		43.84	2.280	0.35812
	12		43.32	2.308	0.36331
	18		42.81	2.336	0.36850
18	00		42.30	2.364	0.37369
	06		41.79	2.392	0.37888

t d	t h	t min	N_t	N_0/N_t	$\log_{10} N_0/N_t$
	12		41.30	2.421	0.38407
	18		40.81	2.450	0.38926
19	00		40.32	2.480	0.39445
	06		39.84	2.509	0.39964
	12		39.37	2.539	0.40483
	18		38.90	2.570	0.41002
20	00		38.44	2.601	0.41521
	06		37.98	2.632	0.42040
	12		37.53	2.664	0.42559
	18		37.09	2.696	0.43078
21	00		36.65	2.728	0.43597
	06		36.21	2.761	0.44117
	12		35.78	2.794	0.44636
	18		35.36	2.828	0.45155
22	00		34.94	2.862	0.45674
	06		34.52	2.896	0.46193
	12		34.11	2.931	0.46712
	18		33.71	2.966	0.47231
23	00		33.30	3.002	0.47750
	06		32.91	3.038	0.48269
	12		32.52	3.075	0.48788
	18		32.13	3.112	0.49307
24	00		31.75	3.149	0.49826
	06		31.37	3.187	0.50345
	12		31.00	3.225	0.50864
	18		30.63	3.264	0.51383
25	00		30.27	3.303	0.51902
	06		29.91	3.343	0.52421
	12		29.55	3.383	0.52940
	18		29.20	3.424	0.53459
26	00		28.86	3.465	0.53978
	06		28.51	3.507	0.54497
	12		28.17	3.549	0.55016
	18		27.84	3.592	0.55535
27	00		27.51	3.635	0.56054
	06		27.18	3.678	0.56573
	12		26.86	3.723	0.57092
	18		26.54	3.767	0.57611
28	00		26.22	3.813	0.58130
	06		25.91	3.859	0.58649
	12		25.60	3.905	0.59168
	18		25.30	3.952	0.59687
29	00		25.00	3.999	0.60206
	06		24.70	4.048	0.60725
	12		24.41	4.096	0.61244
	18		24.12	4.146	0.61763
30	00		23.83	4.195	0.62282
	06		23.55	4.246	0.62801
	12		23.27	4.297	0.63320
	18		22.99	4.349	0.63839
31	00		22.72	4.401	0.64358
	06		22.45	4.454	0.64877
	12		22.18	4.507	0.65396
	18		21.92	4.561	0.65915
32	00		21.66	4.616	0.66434
	06		21.40	4.672	0.66953
	12		21.15	4.728	0.67472
	18		20.90	4.785	0.67991
33	00		20.65	4.842	0.68510
	06		20.40	4.901	0.69029
	12		20.16	4.960	0.69548
	18		19.92	5.019	0.70067
34	00		19.69	5.079	0.70586
	06		19.45	5.141	0.71105
	12		19.22	5.202	0.71624
	18		18.99	5.265	0.72143
35	00		18.77	5.328	0.72662
	06		18.54	5.392	0.73181
	12		18.32	5.457	0.73700
	18		18.11	5.523	0.74219
36	00		17.89	5.589	0.74738
	06		17.68	5.656	0.75257
	12		17.47	5.724	0.75776
	18		17.26	5.793	0.76295
37	00		17.06	5.863	0.76814
	06		16.85	5.933	0.77333
	12		16.65	6.005	0.77852
	18		16.45	6.077	0.78371
38	00		16.26	6.150	0.78890
	06		16.07	6.224	0.79409
	12		15.88	6.299	0.79928
	18		15.69	6.374	0.80447
39	00		15.50	6.451	0.80967
	06		15.32	6.529	0.81485
	12		15.13	6.607	0.82005
	18		14.95	6.687	0.82524
40	00		14.78	6.767	0.83043
	12		14.43	6.931	0.84081
41	00		14.09	7.098	0.85119
	12		13.75	7.270	0.86157
42	00		13.43	7.446	0.87195
	12		13.11	7.626	0.88233
43	00		12.80	7.810	0.89270
	12		12.50	7.999	0.90308
44	00		12.20	8.193	0.91346
	12		11.92	8.391	0.92384

t (d)	t (h)	t (min)	N_t	N_0/N_t	$\log_{10} N_0/N_t$
45	00		11.64	8.594	0.93422
	12		11.36	8.802	0.94460
46	00		11.09	9.015	0.95498
	12		10.83	9.233	0.96536
47	00		10.57	9.456	0.97574
	12		10.32	9.685	0.98612
48	00		10.08	9.919	0.99650
	12		9.84	10.159	1.00689
49	00		9.61	10.405	1.01727
	12		9.38	10.657	1.02765
50	00		9.16	10.915	1.03803
	12		8.95	11.179	1.04842
51	00		8.73	11.449	1.05880
	12		8.53	11.726	1.06918
52	00		8.33	12.010	1.07956
	12		8.13	12.300	1.08994
53	00		7.94	12.598	1.10032
	12		7.75	12.903	1.11070
54	00		7.57	13.215	1.12108
	12		7.39	13.534	1.13146
55	00		7.21	13.862	1.14184
	12		7.04	14.197	1.15222
56	00		6.88	14.541	1.16260
	12		6.71	14.892	1.17298
57	00		6.56	15.253	1.18336
	12		6.40	15.622	1.19374
58	00		6.25	16.000	1.20412
	12		6.10	16.387	1.21450
59	00		5.96	16.783	1.22488
	12		5.82	17.189	1.23526
60			5.68	17.605	1.24564
61			5.41	18.467	1.26640
62			5.16	19.371	1.28716
63			4.92	20.319	1.30792
64			4.69	21.314	1.32868
65			4.47	22.358	1.34945
66			4.26	23.453	1.37021
67			4.06	24.601	1.39097
68			3.88	25.806	1.41173
69			3.69	27.069	1.43249
70			3.52	28.395	1.45325
71			3.36	29.785	1.47401
72			3.20	31.244	1.49477
73			3.05	32.774	1.51553
74			2.91	34.378	1.53629
75			2.77	36.062	1.55705
76			2.64	37.827	1.57781
77			2.52	39.680	1.59857
78			2.40	41.622	1.61933
79			2.29	43.661	1.64009
80			2.18	45.798	1.66086
81			2.08	48.041	1.68162
82			1.98	50.393	1.70238
83			1.89	52.861	1.72314
84			1.80	55.449	1.74390
85			1.72	58.164	1.76466
86			1.64	61.012	1.78542
87			1.56	63.999	1.80618
88			1.49	67.133	1.82694
89			1.42	70.420	1.84770
90			1.35	73.868	1.86846
91			1.29	77.485	1.88922
92			1.23	81.279	1.90998
93			1.17	85.258	1.93074
94			1.12	89.432	1.95150
95			1.07	93.811	1.97226
96			1.02	98.404	1.99302
97			0.97	103.225	2.01379
98			0.92	108.280	2.03455
99			0.88	113.582	2.05531
100			0.84	119.142	2.07607
120			0.32	309.942	2.49128
140			0.12	806.321	2.90651
160			0.05	2097.76	3.32176
180			0.02	5455.54	3.73684

Phosphorus-33

Half-life 25 d

t (d)	t (h)	t (min)	N_t	N_0/N_t	$\log_{10} N_0/N_t$
	0		100.00	1.000	0.00000
	6		99.31	1.006	0.00301
	12		98.62	1.013	0.00602
	18		97.94	1.021	0.00903
1	00		97.27	1.028	0.01204
	06		96.59	1.035	0.01505
	12		95.93	1.042	0.01806
	18		95.26	1.049	0.02107
2	00		94.61	1.057	0.02408
	06		93.95	1.064	0.02709
	12		93.30	1.071	0.03010
	18		92.66	1.079	0.03311
3	00		92.02	1.086	0.03612
	06		91.38	1.094	0.03913
	12		90.75	1.101	0.04214
	18		90.13	1.109	0.04515
4	00		89.50	1.117	0.04817
	06		88.88	1.125	0.05118
	12		88.27	1.132	0.05419
	18		87.66	1.140	0.05720
5	00		87.06	1.148	0.06021
	06		86.45	1.156	0.06322
	12		85.86	1.164	0.06623
	18		85.26	1.172	0.06924
6	00		84.67	1.180	0.07225
	06		84.09	1.189	0.07526
	12		83.51	1.197	0.07827
	18		82.93	1.205	0.08128
7	00		82.36	1.214	0.08429
	06		81.79	1.222	0.08730
	12		81.23	1.231	0.09031
	18		80.66	1.239	0.09332
8	00		80.11	1.248	0.09633
	06		79.55	1.257	0.09934
	12		79.00	1.265	0.10235
	18		78.46	1.274	0.10536
9	00		77.92	1.283	0.10837
	06		77.38	1.292	0.11138
	12		76.84	1.301	0.11439
	18		76.31	1.310	0.11740
10	00		75.79	1.319	0.12041
	06		75.26	1.328	0.12342
	12		74.74	1.337	0.12643
	18		74.23	1.347	0.12944
11	00		73.71	1.356	0.13245
	06		73.20	1.366	0.13546
	12		72.70	1.375	0.13847
	18		72.20	1.385	0.14148
12	00		71.70	1.394	0.14449
	06		71.20	1.404	0.14751
	12		70.71	1.414	0.15052
	18		70.22	1.424	0.15353
13	00		69.74	1.433	0.15654
	06		69.26	1.443	0.15955
	12		68.78	1.453	0.16256
	18		68.30	1.464	0.16557
14	00		67.83	1.474	0.16858
	06		67.36	1.484	0.17159
	12		66.90	1.494	0.17460
	18		66.43	1.505	0.17761
15	00		65.98	1.515	0.18062
	06		65.52	1.526	0.18363
	12		65.07	1.536	0.18664
	18		64.62	1.547	0.18965
16	00		64.17	1.558	0.19266
	06		63.73	1.569	0.19567
	12		63.29	1.580	0.19868
	18		62.85	1.591	0.20169
17	00		62.42	1.602	0.20470
	06		61.99	1.613	0.20771
	12		61.56	1.624	0.21072
	18		61.13	1.635	0.21373
18	00		60.71	1.647	0.21674
	06		60.29	1.658	0.21975
	12		59.87	1.670	0.22276
	18		59.46	1.681	0.22577
19	00		59.05	1.693	0.22878
	06		58.64	1.705	0.23179
	12		58.24	1.717	0.23480
	18		57.83	1.729	0.23781
20	00		57.43	1.741	0.24082
	06		57.04	1.753	0.24383
	12		56.64	1.765	0.24685
	18		56.25	1.777	0.24986
21	00		55.86	1.790	0.25287
	06		55.48	1.802	0.25588
	12		55.10	1.815	0.25889
	18		54.71	1.827	0.26190
22	00		54.34	1.840	0.26491
	06		53.96	1.853	0.26792
	12		53.59	1.866	0.27093
	18		53.22	1.879	0.27394
23	00		52.85	1.892	0.27695
	06		52.49	1.905	0.27996
	12		52.12	1.918	0.28297
	18		51.76	1.931	0.28598
24	00		51.41	1.945	0.28899
	06		51.05	1.958	0.29200
	12		50.70	1.972	0.29501
	18		50.35	1.986	0.29802
25	00		50.00	2.000	0.30103
	06		49.65	2.013	0.30404
	12		49.31	2.027	0.30705
	18		48.97	2.042	0.31006
26	00		48.63	2.056	0.31307
	06		48.30	2.070	0.31608
	12		47.96	2.084	0.31909
	18		47.63	2.099	0.32210
27	00		47.30	2.114	0.32511
	06		46.98	2.128	0.32812
	12		46.65	2.143	0.33113
	18		46.33	2.158	0.33414
28	00		46.01	2.173	0.33715
	06		45.69	2.188	0.34016
	12		45.38	2.203	0.34317
	18		45.06	2.219	0.34619
29	00		44.75	2.234	0.34920
	06		44.44	2.250	0.35221
	12		44.14	2.265	0.35522
	18		43.83	2.281	0.35823
30	00		43.53	2.297	0.36124
	06		43.23	2.313	0.36425
	12		42.93	2.329	0.36726
	18		42.63	2.345	0.37027
31	00		42.34	2.361	0.37328
	06		42.04	2.378	0.37629
	12		41.75	2.394	0.37930
	18		41.47	2.411	0.38231
32	00		41.18	2.428	0.38532
	06		40.90	2.445	0.38833
	12		40.61	2.462	0.39134
	18		40.33	2.479	0.39435
33	00		40.05	2.496	0.39736
	06		39.78	2.514	0.40037
	12		39.50	2.531	0.40338
	18		39.23	2.549	0.40639
34	00		38.96	2.566	0.40940
	06		38.69	2.584	0.41241
	12		38.42	2.602	0.41542
	18		38.16	2.620	0.41843
35	00		37.89	2.639	0.42144
	06		37.63	2.657	0.42445
	12		37.37	2.675	0.42746
	18		37.11	2.694	0.43047
36	00		36.86	2.713	0.43348
	06		36.60	2.732	0.43649
	12		36.35	2.751	0.43950
	18		36.10	2.770	0.44251
37	00		35.85	2.789	0.44552
	06		35.60	2.808	0.44854
	12		35.36	2.828	0.45155
	18		35.11	2.848	0.45456
38	00		34.87	2.867	0.45757
	06		34.63	2.887	0.46058
	12		34.39	2.907	0.46359
	18		34.15	2.928	0.46660
39	00		33.92	2.948	0.46961
	06		33.68	2.969	0.47262
	12		33.45	2.989	0.47563
	18		33.22	3.010	0.47864
40	00		32.99	3.031	0.48165
	12		32.53	3.073	0.48767
41	00		32.09	3.116	0.49369
	12		31.64	3.160	0.49971
42	00		31.21	3.204	0.50573
	12		30.78	3.249	0.51175
43	00		30.35	3.294	0.51777
	12		29.94	3.340	0.52379
44	00		29.52	3.386	0.52981
	12		29.12	3.434	0.53583
45	00		28.72	3.482	0.54185
	12		28.32	3.530	0.54788
46	00		27.93	3.580	0.55390
	12		27.55	3.630	0.55992
47	00		27.17	3.680	0.56594
	12		26.79	3.732	0.57196
48	00		26.43	3.784	0.57798
	12		26.06	3.837	0.58400
49	00		25.70	3.890	0.59002
	12		25.35	3.944	0.59604
50	00		25.00	3.999	0.60206
	12		24.66	4.055	0.60808
51	00		24.32	4.112	0.61410
	12		23.98	4.169	0.62012
52	00		23.65	4.228	0.62614
	12		23.33	4.287	0.63216
53	00		23.00	4.346	0.63818
	12		22.69	4.407	0.64420
54	00		22.38	4.469	0.65022
	12		22.07	4.531	0.65625
55	00		21.76	4.594	0.66227
	12		21.46	4.658	0.66829
56	00		21.17	4.723	0.67431
	12		20.88	4.789	0.68033
57	00		20.59	4.856	0.68635
	12		20.31	4.924	0.69237
58	00		20.03	4.993	0.69839
	12		19.75	5.063	0.70441
59	00		19.48	5.133	0.71043
	12		19.21	5.205	0.71645
60	00		18.95	5.278	0.72247
	12		18.69	5.351	0.72849
61	00		18.43	5.426	0.73451
	12		18.17	5.502	0.74053
62	00		17.92	5.578	0.74655
	12		17.68	5.656	0.75257
63	00		17.43	5.735	0.75859
	12		17.19	5.815	0.76462

t (d)	t (h)	t (min)	N_t	N_0/N_t	$\log_{10} N_0/N_t$
64	00		16.96	5.897	0.77064
	12		16.72	5.979	0.77666
65	00		16.49	6.062	0.78268
	12		16.27	6.147	0.78870
66	00		16.04	6.233	0.79472
	12		15.82	6.320	0.80074
67	00		15.60	6.408	0.80676
	12		15.39	6.497	0.81278
68	00		15.18	6.588	0.81880
	12		14.97	6.680	0.82482
69	00		14.76	6.773	0.83084
	12		14.56	6.868	0.83686
70			14.36	6.964	0.84288
71			13.97	7.160	0.85492
72			13.58	7.361	0.86696
73			13.21	7.568	0.87900
74			12.85	7.781	0.89104
75			12.50	7.999	0.90308
76			12.16	8.224	0.91513
77			11.83	8.456	0.92717
78			11.50	8.693	0.93921
79			11.19	8.938	0.95125
80			10.88	9.189	0.96329
81			10.58	9.447	0.97533
82			10.30	9.713	0.98737
83			10.01	9.986	0.99941
84			9.74	10.267	1.01146
85			9.47	10.556	1.02350
86			9.21	10.852	1.03554
87			8.96	11.157	1.04758
88			8.72	11.471	1.05963
89			8.48	11.794	1.07167
90			8.25	12.125	1.08371
91			8.02	12.466	1.09575
92			7.80	12.817	1.10779
93			7.59	13.177	1.11983
94			7.38	13.547	1.13187
95			7.18	13.928	1.14391
96			6.98	14.320	1.15596
97			6.79	14.723	1.16800
98			6.61	15.136	1.18004
99			6.43	15.562	1.19208
100			6.25	16.000	1.20412
105			5.44	18.379	1.26433
110			4.74	21.112	1.32453
115			4.12	24.251	1.38474
120			3.59	27.857	1.44494
125			3.13	32.000	1.50515
130			2.72	36.758	1.56536
135			2.37	42.224	1.62556
140			2.06	48.502	1.68577
145			1.79	55.714	1.74597
150			1.56	63.999	1.80618
155			1.36	73.515	1.86638
160			1.18	84.447	1.92659
165			1.03	97.003	1.98679
170			0.90	111.430	2.04700
175			0.78	128.000	2.10721
180			0.68	147.032	2.16741
185			0.59	168.896	2.22762
190			0.52	194.012	2.28783
195			0.45	222.861	2.34803
200			0.39	255.996	2.40823
205			0.34	294.065	2.46844
210			0.30	337.792	2.52865
215			0.26	388.018	2.58885
220			0.22	445.712	2.64906
225			0.20	512.006	2.70928
230			0.17	588.131	2.76947
235			0.15	675.584	2.82968

Sulfur-35

Half-life 87 d

t (d)	t (h)	t (min)	N_t	N_0/N_t	$\log_{10} N_0/N_t$
0			100.00	1.000	0.00000
1			99.21	1.007	0.00346
2			98.42	1.016	0.00692
3			97.64	1.024	0.01038
4			96.86	1.032	0.01384
5			96.09	1.040	0.01730
6			95.33	1.048	0.02076
7			94.58	1.057	0.02422
8			93.83	1.065	0.02768
9			93.08	1.074	0.03114
10			92.34	1.082	0.03460
11			91.61	1.091	0.03806
12			90.88	1.100	0.04152
13			90.16	1.109	0.04498
14			89.45	1.117	0.04844
15			88.74	1.126	0.05190
16			88.03	1.135	0.05536
17			87.33	1.145	0.05882
18			86.64	1.154	0.06228
19			85.95	1.163	0.06574
20			85.27	1.172	0.06920

t d	t h	t min	N_t	N_0/N_t	$\log_{10} N_0/N_t$
21			84.59	1.182	0.07266
22			83.92	1.191	0.07612
23			83.26	1.201	0.07958
24			82.60	1.210	0.08304
25			81.94	1.220	0.08650
26			81.29	1.230	0.08996
27			80.64	1.240	0.09342
28			80.00	1.249	0.09688
29			79.37	1.259	0.10034
30			78.74	1.269	0.10380
31			78.12	1.280	0.10726
32			77.50	1.290	0.11072
33			76.88	1.300	0.11418
34			76.27	1.311	0.11764
35			75.67	1.321	0.12110
36			75.06	1.332	0.12456
37			74.47	1.342	0.12802
38			73.88	1.353	0.13148
39			73.29	1.364	0.13494
40			72.71	1.375	0.13841
41			72.13	1.386	0.14187
42			71.56	1.397	0.14533
43			70.99	1.408	0.14879
44			70.43	1.419	0.15225
45			69.87	1.431	0.15571
46			69.32	1.442	0.15917
47			68.77	1.454	0.16263
48			68.22	1.465	0.16609
49			67.68	1.477	0.16955
50			67.14	1.489	0.17301
51			66.61	1.501	0.17647
52			66.08	1.513	0.17993
53			65.56	1.525	0.18339
54			65.04	1.537	0.18685
55			64.52	1.549	0.19031
56			64.01	1.562	0.19377
57			63.50	1.574	0.19723
58			63.00	1.587	0.20069
59			62.50	1.600	0.20415
60			62.00	1.612	0.20761
61			61.51	1.625	0.21107
62			61.02	1.638	0.21453
63			60.54	1.651	0.21799
64			60.06	1.665	0.22145
65			59.58	1.678	0.22491
66			59.11	1.691	0.22837
67			58.64	1.705	0.23183
68			58.17	1.719	0.23529
69			57.71	1.732	0.23875
70			57.25	1.746	0.24221
71			56.80	1.760	0.24567
72			56.35	1.774	0.24913
73			55.90	1.788	0.25259
74			55.46	1.803	0.25605
75			55.02	1.817	0.25951
76			54.58	1.832	0.26297
77			54.15	1.846	0.26643
78			53.72	1.861	0.26989
79			53.29	1.876	0.27335
80			52.87	1.891	0.27681
81			52.45	1.906	0.28027
82			52.03	1.921	0.28373
83			51.62	1.937	0.28719
84			51.21	1.952	0.29065
85			50.80	1.968	0.29411
86			50.40	1.984	0.29757
87			50.00	2.000	0.30103
88			49.60	2.015	0.30449
89			49.21	2.032	0.30795
90			48.82	2.048	0.31141
91			48.43	2.064	0.31487
92			48.05	2.081	0.31833
93			47.67	2.097	0.32179
94			47.29	2.114	0.32525
95			46.91	2.131	0.32871
96			46.54	2.148	0.33217
97			46.17	2.165	0.33563
98			45.80	2.183	0.33909
99			45.44	2.200	0.34255
100			45.08	2.218	0.34601
102			44.37	2.253	0.35293
104			43.67	2.290	0.35985
106			42.98	2.326	0.36677
108			42.30	2.364	0.37369
110			41.63	2.402	0.38061
112			40.97	2.440	0.38753
114			40.32	2.480	0.39445
116			39.69	2.519	0.40137
118			39.06	2.560	0.40829
120			38.44	2.601	0.41521
122			37.83	2.643	0.42213
124			37.23	2.685	0.42905
126			36.65	2.728	0.43597
128			36.07	2.772	0.44290
130			35.50	2.817	0.44982
132			34.94	2.862	0.45674
134			34.38	2.908	0.46366
136			33.84	2.955	0.47058

t d	t h	t min	N_t	N_0/N_t	$\log_{10} N_0/N_t$
138			33.30	3.002	0.47750
140			32.78	3.050	0.48442
142			32.26	3.099	0.49134
144			31.75	3.149	0.49826
146			31.25	3.200	0.50518
148			30.75	3.251	0.51210
150			30.27	3.303	0.51902
152			29.79	3.356	0.52594
154			29.32	3.410	0.53286
156			28.86	3.465	0.53978
158			28.40	3.521	0.54670
160			27.95	3.577	0.55362
162			27.51	3.635	0.56054
164			27.07	3.693	0.56746
166			26.65	3.753	0.57438
168			26.22	3.813	0.58130
170			25.81	3.874	0.58822
172			25.40	3.936	0.59514
174			25.00	3.999	0.60206
176			24.60	4.064	0.60898
178			24.22	4.129	0.61590
180			23.83	4.195	0.62282
182			23.46	4.263	0.62974
184			23.09	4.331	0.63666
186			22.72	4.401	0.64358
188			22.36	4.471	0.65050
190			22.01	4.543	0.65742
192			21.66	4.616	0.66434
194			21.32	4.690	0.67126
196			20.98	4.766	0.67818
198			20.65	4.842	0.68510
200			20.32	4.920	0.69202
202			20.00	4.999	0.69894
204			19.69	5.079	0.70586
206			19.37	5.161	0.71278
208			19.07	5.244	0.71970
210			18.77	5.328	0.72662
212			18.47	5.414	0.73354
214			18.18	5.501	0.74046
216			17.89	5.589	0.74738
218			17.61	5.679	0.75430
220			17.33	5.770	0.76122
222			17.06	5.863	0.76814
224			16.79	5.957	0.77506
226			16.52	6.053	0.78198
228			16.26	6.150	0.78890
230			16.00	6.249	0.79582
232			15.75	6.349	0.80274
234			15.50	6.451	0.80967
236			15.26	6.555	0.81659
238			15.01	6.660	0.82351
240			14.78	6.767	0.83043
242			14.54	6.876	0.83735
244			14.31	6.986	0.84427
246			14.09	7.098	0.85119
248			13.86	7.212	0.85811
250			13.65	7.328	0.86503
255			13.11	7.626	0.88233
260			12.60	7.936	0.89962
265			12.11	8.258	0.91692
270			11.64	8.594	0.93422
275			11.18	8.943	0.95152
280			10.74	9.307	0.96882
285			10.32	9.685	0.98612
290			9.92	10.079	1.00343
295			9.53	10.488	1.02073
300			9.16	10.915	1.03803
305			8.80	11.358	1.05534
310			8.46	11.820	1.07264
315			8.13	12.300	1.08994
320			7.81	12.800	1.10724
325			7.51	13.321	1.12454
330			7.21	13.862	1.14184
335			6.93	14.425	1.15914
340			6.66	15.012	1.17644
345			6.40	15.622	1.19374
350			6.15	16.256	1.21104
360			5.68	17.605	1.24564
370			5.25	19.065	1.28024
380			4.84	20.646	1.31484
390			4.47	22.358	1.34945
400			4.13	24.212	1.38405
410			3.81	26.220	1.41865
420			3.52	28.395	1.45325
430			3.25	30.750	1.48785
440			3.00	33.300	1.52245
450			2.77	36.062	1.55705
460			2.56	39.052	1.59165
470			2.36	42.291	1.62625
480			2.18	45.798	1.66086
490			2.02	49.597	1.69546
500			1.86	53.710	1.73006
600			0.84	119.142	2.07607
700			0.38	264.291	2.42208
800			0.17	586.269	2.76810
900			0.08	1300.56	3.11413

Potassium-42

Half-life 12.5 h

t d	t h	t min	N_t	N_0/N_t	$\log_{10} N_0/N_t$
		00	100.00	1.000	0.00000
		10	99.08	1.009	0.00401
		20	98.17	1.018	0.00803
		30	97.27	1.028	0.01204
		40	96.37	1.037	0.01606
		50	95.48	1.047	0.02007
	1	00	94.61	1.057	0.02408
		10	93.74	1.066	0.02810
		20	92.87	1.076	0.03211
		30	92.02	1.086	0.03612
		40	91.17	1.096	0.04014
		50	90.33	1.107	0.04415
	2	00	89.50	1.117	0.04817
		10	88.68	1.127	0.05218
		20	87.86	1.138	0.05619
		30	87.06	1.148	0.06021
		40	86.25	1.159	0.06422
		50	85.46	1.170	0.06823
	3	00	84.67	1.180	0.07225
		10	83.90	1.191	0.07626
		20	83.12	1.203	0.08028
		30	82.36	1.214	0.08429
		40	81.60	1.225	0.08830
		50	80.85	1.236	0.09232
	4	00	80.11	1.248	0.09633
		10	79.37	1.259	0.10034
		20	78.64	1.271	0.10436
		30	77.92	1.283	0.10837
		40	77.20	1.295	0.11239
		50	76.49	1.307	0.11640
	5	00	75.79	1.319	0.12041
		10	75.09	1.331	0.12443
		20	74.40	1.344	0.12844
		30	73.71	1.356	0.13245
		40	73.04	1.369	0.13647
		50	72.36	1.381	0.14048
	6	00	71.70	1.394	0.14449
		10	71.04	1.407	0.14851
		20	70.38	1.420	0.15252
		30	69.74	1.433	0.15654
		40	69.10	1.447	0.16055
		50	68.46	1.460	0.16456
	7	00	67.83	1.474	0.16858
		10	67.21	1.487	0.17259
		20	66.59	1.501	0.17660
		30	65.98	1.515	0.18062
		40	65.37	1.529	0.18463
		50	64.77	1.543	0.18865
	8	00	64.17	1.558	0.19266
		10	63.58	1.572	0.19667
		20	63.00	1.587	0.20069
		30	62.42	1.602	0.20470
		40	61.84	1.617	0.20871
		50	61.27	1.632	0.21273
	9	00	60.71	1.647	0.21674
		10	60.15	1.662	0.22076
		20	59.60	1.677	0.22477
		30	59.05	1.693	0.22878
		40	58.51	1.709	0.23280
		50	57.97	1.725	0.23681
	10	00	57.43	1.741	0.24082
		10	56.91	1.757	0.24484
		20	56.38	1.773	0.24885
		30	55.86	1.790	0.25287
		40	55.35	1.806	0.25688
		50	54.84	1.823	0.26089
	11	00	54.34	1.840	0.26491
		10	53.84	1.857	0.26892
		20	53.34	1.874	0.27293
		30	52.85	1.892	0.27695
		40	52.36	1.909	0.28096
		50	51.88	1.927	0.28498
	12	00	51.41	1.945	0.28899
		10	50.93	1.963	0.29300
		20	50.46	1.981	0.29702
		30	50.00	2.000	0.30103
		40	49.54	2.018	0.30504
		50	49.08	2.037	0.30906
	13	00	48.63	2.056	0.31307
		10	48.19	2.075	0.31709
		20	47.74	2.094	0.32110
		30	47.30	2.114	0.32511
		40	46.87	2.133	0.32913
		50	46.44	2.153	0.33314
	14	00	46.01	2.173	0.33715
		10	45.59	2.193	0.34117
		20	45.17	2.214	0.34518
		30	44.75	2.234	0.34920
		40	44.34	2.255	0.35321
		50	43.93	2.276	0.35722
	15	00	43.53	2.297	0.36124
		10	43.13	2.318	0.36525
		20	42.73	2.340	0.36926
		30	42.34	2.361	0.37328

t d	t h	t min	N_t	N_0/N_t	$\log_{10} N_0/N_t$
		40	41.95	2.383	0.37729
		50	41.56	2.406	0.38131
	16	00	41.18	2.428	0.38532
		10	40.80	2.450	0.38933
		20	40.43	2.473	0.39335
		30	40.05	2.496	0.39736
		40	39.69	2.519	0.40137
		50	39.32	2.543	0.40539
	17	00	38.96	2.566	0.40940
		10	38.60	2.590	0.41341
		20	38.24	2.614	0.41743
		30	37.89	2.639	0.42144
		40	37.54	2.663	0.42546
		50	37.20	2.688	0.42947
	18	00	36.86	2.713	0.43348
		10	36.52	2.738	0.43750
		20	36.18	2.763	0.44151
		30	35.85	2.789	0.44552
		40	35.52	2.815	0.44954
		50	35.19	2.841	0.45355
	19	00	34.87	2.867	0.45757
		10	34.55	2.894	0.46158
		20	34.23	2.921	0.46559
		30	33.92	2.948	0.46961
		40	33.60	2.975	0.47362
		50	33.29	3.003	0.47763
	20	00	32.99	3.031	0.48165
		10	32.68	3.059	0.48566
		20	32.38	3.087	0.48968
		30	32.09	3.116	0.49369
		40	31.79	3.145	0.49770
		50	31.50	3.174	0.50172
	21	00	31.21	3.204	0.50573
		10	30.92	3.234	0.50974
		20	30.64	3.264	0.51376
		30	30.35	3.294	0.51777
		40	30.08	3.324	0.52179
		50	29.80	3.355	0.52580
	22	00	29.52	3.386	0.52981
		10	29.25	3.418	0.53383
		20	28.98	3.450	0.53784
		30	28.72	3.482	0.54185
		40	28.45	3.514	0.54587
		50	28.19	3.547	0.54988
	23	00	27.93	3.580	0.55390
		10	27.68	3.613	0.55791
		20	27.42	3.646	0.56192
		30	27.17	3.680	0.56594
		40	26.92	3.714	0.56995
		50	26.67	3.749	0.57396
1	00		26.43	3.784	0.57798
	01		25.00	3.999	0.60206
	02		23.65	4.228	0.62614
	03		22.38	4.469	0.65022
	04		21.17	4.723	0.67431
	05		20.03	4.993	0.69839
	06		18.95	5.278	0.72247
	07		17.92	5.578	0.74655
	08		16.96	5.897	0.77064
	09		16.04	6.233	0.79472
	10		15.18	6.588	0.81880
	11		14.36	6.964	0.84288
	12		13.58	7.361	0.86696
	13		12.85	7.781	0.89104
	14		12.16	8.224	0.91513
	15		11.50	8.693	0.93921
	16		10.88	9.189	0.96329
	17		10.30	9.713	0.98737
	18		9.74	10.267	1.01146
	19		9.21	10.852	1.03554
	20		8.72	11.471	1.05963
	21		8.25	12.125	1.08371
	22		7.80	12.817	1.10779
	23		7.38	13.547	1.13187
2	00		6.98	14.320	1.15596
	01		6.61	15.136	1.18004
	02		6.25	16.000	1.20412
	03		5.91	16.912	1.22820
	04		5.59	17.876	1.25229
	05		5.29	18.895	1.27637
	06		5.01	19.973	1.30045
	07		4.74	21.112	1.32453
	08		4.48	22.315	1.34861
	09		4.24	23.588	1.37270
	10		4.01	24.933	1.39678
	11		3.79	26.354	1.42086
	12		3.59	27.857	1.44494
	13		3.40	29.445	1.46903
	14		3.21	31.124	1.49311
	15		3.04	32.899	1.51719
	16		2.88	34.775	1.54127
	17		2.72	36.758	1.56536
	18		2.57	38.854	1.58944
	19		2.43	41.069	1.61352
	20		2.30	43.411	1.63760
	21		2.18	45.886	1.66169
	22		2.06	48.502	1.68577
	23		1.95	51.268	1.70985

t d	t h	t min	N_t	N_0/N_t	$\log_{10} N_0/N_t$
3	00		1.85	54.191	1.73393
	01		1.75	57.281	1.75801
	02		1.65	60.547	1.78210
	03		1.56	63.999	1.80618
	04		1.48	67.648	1.83026
	05		1.40	71.505	1.85434
	06		1.32	75.582	1.87842
	07		1.25	79.891	1.90250
	08		1.18	84.447	1.92659
	09		1.12	89.261	1.95067
	10		1.06	94.351	1.97475
	11		1.00	99.730	1.99883
	12		0.95	105.419	2.02292
	13		0.90	111.430	2.04700
	14		0.85	117.784	2.07109
	15		0.80	124.500	2.09517
	16		0.76	131.597	2.11925
	17		0.72	139.101	2.14333
	18		0.68	147.032	2.16741
	19		0.64	155.417	2.19150
	20		0.61	164.279	2.21558
	21		0.58	173.644	2.23966
	22		0.54	183.546	2.26375
	23		0.52	194.012	2.28783
4	00		0.49	205.073	2.31191
	01		0.46	216.764	2.33599
	02		0.44	229.126	2.36008
	03		0.41	242.189	2.38416
	04		0.39	255.996	2.40823
	05		0.37	270.599	2.43233
	06		0.35	286.024	2.45640
	07		0.33	302.334	2.48049
	08		0.31	319.570	2.50457
	09		0.30	337.792	2.52865
	10		0.28	357.053	2.55273
	11		0.26	377.415	2.57682
	12		0.25	398.930	2.60090
	13		0.24	421.674	2.62498
	14		0.22	445.712	2.64906
	15		0.21	471.142	2.67315
	16		0.20	498.007	2.69724
	17		0.19	526.398	2.72132

Calcium-45

Half-life 160 d

t d	t h	t min	N_t	N_0/N_t	$\log_{10} N_0/N_t$
0			100.00	1.000	0.00000
1			99.57	1.004	0.00188
2			99.14	1.008	0.00376
3			98.71	1.013	0.00564
4			98.28	1.017	0.00753
5			97.86	1.021	0.00941
6			97.43	1.026	0.01129
7			97.01	1.030	0.01317
8			96.59	1.035	0.01505
9			96.18	1.039	0.01693
10			95.76	1.044	0.01881
11			95.35	1.048	0.02070
12			94.93	1.053	0.02258
13			94.52	1.057	0.02446
14			94.12	1.062	0.02634
15			93.71	1.067	0.02822
16			93.30	1.071	0.03010
17			92.90	1.076	0.03198
18			92.50	1.081	0.03387
19			92.10	1.085	0.03575
20			91.70	1.090	0.03763
21			91.30	1.095	0.03951
22			90.91	1.099	0.04139
23			90.52	1.104	0.04327
24			90.13	1.109	0.04515
25			89.74	1.114	0.04704
26			89.35	1.119	0.04892
27			88.96	1.124	0.05080
28			88.58	1.128	0.05268
29			88.19	1.133	0.05456
30			87.81	1.138	0.05644
31			87.43	1.143	0.05833
32			87.06	1.148	0.06021
33			86.68	1.153	0.06209
34			86.30	1.158	0.06397
35			85.93	1.163	0.06585
36			85.56	1.168	0.06773
37			85.19	1.173	0.06961
38			84.82	1.178	0.07150
39			84.45	1.184	0.07338
40			84.09	1.189	0.07526
41			83.73	1.194	0.07714
42			83.36	1.199	0.07902
43			83.00	1.204	0.08090
44			82.65	1.209	0.08278
45			82.29	1.215	0.08467
46			81.93	1.220	0.08655
47			81.58	1.225	0.08843
48			81.23	1.231	0.09031
49			80.87	1.236	0.09219
50			80.52	1.241	0.09407
51			80.18	1.247	0.09595
52			79.83	1.252	0.09784
53			79.48	1.258	0.09972
54			79.14	1.263	0.10160
55			78.80	1.269	0.10348
56			78.46	1.274	0.10536
57			78.12	1.280	0.10724
58			77.78	1.285	0.10912
59			77.45	1.291	0.11101
60			77.11	1.296	0.11289
61			76.78	1.302	0.11477
62			76.45	1.308	0.11665
63			76.11	1.313	0.11853
64			75.79	1.319	0.12041
65			75.46	1.325	0.12229
66			75.13	1.330	0.12418
67			74.81	1.336	0.12606
68			74.48	1.342	0.12794
69			74.16	1.348	0.12982
70			73.84	1.354	0.13170
71			73.52	1.360	0.13358
72			73.20	1.366	0.13546
73			72.89	1.371	0.13735
74			72.57	1.377	0.13923
75			72.26	1.383	0.14111
76			71.95	1.389	0.14299
77			71.64	1.395	0.14487
78			71.33	1.402	0.14675
79			71.02	1.408	0.14863
80			70.71	1.414	0.15052
81			70.41	1.420	0.15240
82			70.10	1.426	0.15428
83			69.80	1.432	0.15616
84			69.50	1.438	0.15804
85			69.20	1.445	0.15992
86			68.90	1.451	0.16180
87			68.60	1.457	0.16369
88			68.30	1.464	0.16557
89			68.01	1.470	0.16745
90			67.71	1.476	0.16933
91			67.42	1.483	0.17121
92			67.13	1.489	0.17309
93			66.84	1.496	0.17497
94			66.55	1.502	0.17686
95			66.26	1.509	0.17874
96			65.98	1.515	0.18062
97			65.69	1.522	0.18250
98			65.41	1.528	0.18438
99			65.12	1.535	0.18626
100			64.84	1.542	0.18814
105			63.45	1.575	0.19755
110			62.09	1.610	0.20696
115			60.76	1.645	0.21637
120			59.46	1.681	0.22577
125			58.19	1.718	0.23518
130			56.94	1.756	0.24459
135			55.72	1.794	0.25399
140			54.53	1.834	0.26340
145			53.36	1.874	0.27281
150			52.21	1.915	0.28222
155			51.09	1.957	0.29162
160			50.00	2.000	0.30103
165			48.93	2.043	0.31044
170			47.88	2.088	0.31985
175			46.85	2.134	0.32925
180			45.85	2.181	0.33866
185			44.87	2.228	0.34807
190			43.91	2.277	0.35747
195			42.97	2.327	0.36688
200			42.04	2.378	0.37629
205			41.14	2.430	0.38570
210			40.26	2.483	0.39510
215			39.40	2.538	0.40451
220			38.56	2.593	0.41392
225			37.73	2.650	0.42332
230			36.92	2.708	0.43273
235			36.13	2.767	0.44214
240			35.36	2.828	0.45155
245			34.60	2.890	0.46095
250			33.86	2.953	0.47036
255			33.13	3.018	0.47977
260			32.42	3.084	0.48917
265			31.73	3.151	0.49858
270			31.05	3.220	0.50799
275			30.38	3.291	0.51740
280			29.73	3.363	0.52680
285			29.09	3.437	0.53621
290			28.47	3.512	0.54562
295			27.86	3.589	0.55502
300			27.26	3.668	0.56443
305			26.68	3.748	0.57384
310			26.11	3.830	0.58325
315			25.55	3.914	0.59265
320			25.00	3.999	0.60206
325			24.46	4.087	0.61147
330			23.94	4.177	0.62087
335			23.43	4.268	0.63028
340			22.93	4.362	0.63969
345			22.43	4.457	0.64910
350			21.95	4.555	0.65850
355			21.48	4.654	0.66791
360			21.02	4.756	0.67732
365			20.57	4.860	0.68672
370			20.13	4.967	0.69613
375			19.70	5.076	0.70554
380			19.28	5.187	0.71495
385			18.86	5.300	0.72435
390			18.46	5.417	0.73376
395			18.06	5.535	0.74317
400			17.68	5.656	0.75257
405			17.30	5.780	0.76198
410			16.93	5.907	0.77139
415			16.57	6.036	0.78080
420			16.21	6.168	0.79020
425			15.86	6.303	0.79961
430			15.52	6.441	0.80902
435			15.19	6.582	0.81842
440			14.87	6.727	0.82783
445			14.55	6.874	0.83724
450			14.23	7.024	0.84664
455			13.93	7.178	0.85605
460			13.63	7.335	0.86546
465			13.34	7.496	0.87486
470			13.05	7.660	0.88427
475			12.77	7.828	0.89368
480			12.50	7.999	0.90308
485			12.23	8.175	0.91249
490			11.97	8.354	0.92190
495			11.71	8.536	0.93130
500			11.46	8.723	0.94071
520			10.51	9.513	0.97834
540			9.64	10.374	1.01598
560			8.84	11.313	1.05361
580			8.11	12.337	1.09123
600			7.43	13.454	1.12886
620			6.82	14.672	1.16649
640			6.25	16.000	1.20412
660			5.73	17.448	1.24175
680			5.26	19.027	1.27938
700			4.82	20.749	1.31701
720			4.42	22.627	1.35464
740			4.05	24.675	1.39226
760			3.72	26.908	1.42989
780			3.41	29.344	1.46752
800			3.13	32.000	1.50515
820			2.87	34.896	1.54278
840			2.63	38.054	1.58041
860			2.41	41.498	1.61804
880			2.21	45.254	1.65567
900			2.03	49.350	1.69329
920			1.86	53.817	1.73092
940			1.70	58.688	1.76855
960			1.56	63.999	1.80618
980			1.43	69.791	1.84381
1000			1.31	76.108	1.88143
1020			1.20	82.996	1.91906
1040			1.10	90.507	1.95669
1060			1.01	98.699	1.99431
1080			0.93	107.634	2.03195
1100			0.85	117.376	2.06958
1120			0.78	128.000	2.10721
1140			0.72	139.584	2.14484
1160			0.66	152.218	2.18247
1180			0.60	165.994	2.22009
1200			0.55	181.018	2.25772
1220			0.51	197.402	2.29535
1240			0.46	215.271	2.33299
1260			0.43	234.752	2.37061
1280			0.39	255.996	2.40823
1300			0.36	279.173	2.44587
1320			0.33	304.432	2.48349
1340			0.30	331.994	2.52113
1360			0.28	362.043	2.55876
1380			0.25	394.804	2.59638
1400			0.23	430.533	2.63401
1420			0.21	469.505	2.67164
1440			0.20	512.006	2.70928
1460			0.18	558.347	2.74690
1480			0.16	608.865	2.78452

Chromium-51

Half-life 27 d

t d	t h	t min	N_t	N_0/N_t	$\log_{10} N_0/N_t$
	0		100.00	1.000	0.00000
	6		99.36	1.006	0.00279
	12		98.72	1.012	0.00558
	18		98.09	1.019	0.00836
1	00		97.47	1.026	0.01115
	06		96.84	1.032	0.01394
	12		96.22	1.039	0.01672
	18		95.61	1.045	0.01951
2	00		95.00	1.052	0.02230
	06		94.39	1.059	0.02509
	12		93.78	1.066	0.02787
	18		93.18	1.073	0.03066
3	00		92.59	1.080	0.03345
	06		92.00	1.087	0.03624
	12		91.41	1.094	0.03902
	18		90.82	1.101	0.04181
4	00		90.24	1.108	0.04460
	06		89.66	1.115	0.04738
	12		89.09	1.122	0.05017
	18		88.52	1.129	0.05296
5	00		87.95	1.136	0.05575
	06		87.39	1.144	0.05853
	12		86.83	1.151	0.06132
	18		86.28	1.159	0.06411
6	00		85.72	1.166	0.06690
	06		85.18	1.174	0.06968
	12		84.63	1.181	0.07247
	18		84.09	1.189	0.07526
7	00		83.55	1.196	0.07805
	06		83.02	1.204	0.08083
	12		82.49	1.212	0.08362
	18		81.96	1.220	0.08641
8	00		81.43	1.227	0.08919
	06		80.91	1.235	0.09198
	12		80.40	1.243	0.09477
	18		79.88	1.251	0.09756
9	00		79.37	1.259	0.10034
	06		78.86	1.268	0.10313
	12		78.36	1.276	0.10592
	18		77.86	1.284	0.10871
10	00		77.36	1.292	0.11149
	06		76.86	1.301	0.11428
	12		76.37	1.309	0.11707
	18		75.88	1.317	0.11986
11	00		75.40	1.326	0.12264
	06		74.92	1.334	0.12543
	12		74.44	1.343	0.12822
	18		73.96	1.352	0.13100
12	00		73.49	1.360	0.13379
	06		73.02	1.369	0.13658
	12		72.55	1.378	0.13937
	18		72.09	1.387	0.14215
13	00		71.62	1.396	0.14494
	06		71.17	1.405	0.14773
	12		70.71	1.414	0.15052
	18		70.26	1.423	0.15330
14	00		69.81	1.432	0.15609
	06		69.36	1.441	0.15888
	12		68.92	1.450	0.16166
	18		68.48	1.460	0.16445
15	00		68.04	1.469	0.16724
	06		67.60	1.479	0.17003
	12		67.17	1.488	0.17281
	18		66.74	1.498	0.17560
16	00		66.32	1.507	0.17839
	06		65.89	1.517	0.18118
	12		65.47	1.527	0.18396
	18		65.05	1.537	0.18675
17	00		64.63	1.547	0.18954
	06		64.22	1.557	0.19233
	12		63.81	1.567	0.19511
	18		63.40	1.577	0.19790
18	00		63.00	1.587	0.20069
	06		62.59	1.597	0.20347
	12		62.19	1.607	0.20626
	18		61.79	1.618	0.20905
19	00		61.40	1.628	0.21184
	06		61.01	1.639	0.21462
	12		60.62	1.649	0.21741
	18		60.23	1.660	0.22020
20	00		59.84	1.671	0.22299
	06		59.46	1.681	0.22577
	12		59.08	1.692	0.22856
	18		58.70	1.703	0.23135
21	00		58.33	1.714	0.23413
	06		57.95	1.725	0.23692
	12		57.58	1.736	0.23971
	18		57.21	1.747	0.24250
22	00		56.85	1.759	0.24528
	06		56.48	1.770	0.24807
	12		56.12	1.781	0.25086
	18		55.76	1.793	0.25365
23	00		55.41	1.804	0.25643
	06		55.05	1.816	0.25922
	12		54.70	1.828	0.26201
	18		54.35	1.839	0.26480
24	00		54.00	1.851	0.26758
	06		53.66	1.863	0.27037
	12		53.31	1.875	0.27316
	18		52.97	1.887	0.27594
25	00		52.63	1.899	0.27873
	06		52.30	1.912	0.28152
	12		51.96	1.924	0.28431
	18		51.63	1.936	0.28709
26	00		51.30	1.949	0.28988
	06		50.97	1.961	0.29267
	12		50.65	1.974	0.29546
	18		50.32	1.987	0.29824
27	00		50.00	2.000	0.30103

t d	t h	t min	N_t	N_0/N_t	$\log_{10} N_0/N_t$
	06		49.68	2.012	0.30382
	12		49.36	2.025	0.30661
	18		49.05	2.038	0.30939
28	00		48.73	2.052	0.31218
	06		48.42	2.065	0.31497
	12		48.11	2.078	0.31775
	18		47.80	2.091	0.32054
29	00		47.50	2.105	0.32333
	06		47.19	2.118	0.32612
	12		46.89	2.132	0.32890
	18		46.59	2.146	0.33169
30	00		46.29	2.160	0.33448
	06		46.00	2.174	0.33727
	12		45.70	2.188	0.34005
	18		45.41	2.202	0.34284
31	00		45.12	2.216	0.34563
	06		44.83	2.230	0.34841
	12		44.54	2.244	0.35120
	18		44.26	2.259	0.35399
32	00		43.98	2.273	0.35678
	06		43.70	2.288	0.35956
	12		43.42	2.303	0.36235
	18		43.14	2.318	0.36514
33	00		42.86	2.333	0.36793
	06		42.59	2.348	0.37071
	12		42.32	2.363	0.37350
	18		42.04	2.378	0.37629
34	00		41.78	2.393	0.37908
	06		41.51	2.409	0.38186
	12		41.24	2.424	0.38465
	18		40.98	2.440	0.38744
35	00		40.72	2.455	0.39022
	06		40.46	2.471	0.39301
	12		40.20	2.487	0.39580
	18		39.94	2.503	0.39859
36	00		39.69	2.519	0.40137
	06		39.43	2.536	0.40416
	12		39.18	2.552	0.40695
	18		38.93	2.568	0.40974
37	00		38.68	2.585	0.41252
	06		38.43	2.602	0.41531
	12		38.19	2.618	0.41810
	18		37.94	2.635	0.42088
38	00		37.70	2.652	0.42367
	06		37.46	2.669	0.42646
	12		37.22	2.686	0.42925
	18		36.98	2.704	0.43203
39	00		36.74	2.721	0.43482
	06		36.51	2.739	0.43761
	12		36.27	2.756	0.44040
	18		36.04	2.774	0.44318
40	00		35.81	2.792	0.44597
	06		35.58	2.810	0.44876
	12		35.36	2.828	0.45155
	18		35.13	2.846	0.45433
41	00		34.90	2.864	0.45712
	06		34.68	2.883	0.45991
	12		34.46	2.901	0.46269
	18		34.24	2.920	0.46548
42	00		34.02	2.939	0.46827
	06		33.80	2.958	0.47106
	12		33.59	2.977	0.47384
	18		33.37	2.996	0.47663
43	00		33.16	3.015	0.47942
	06		32.95	3.035	0.48221
	12		32.73	3.054	0.48499
	18		32.53	3.074	0.48778
44	00		32.32	3.094	0.49057
	06		32.11	3.114	0.49336
	12		31.90	3.134	0.49614
	18		31.70	3.154	0.49893
45	00		31.50	3.174	0.50172
	06		31.30	3.195	0.50450
	12		31.10	3.215	0.50729
	18		30.90	3.236	0.51008
46	00		30.70	3.257	0.51287
	06		30.50	3.278	0.51565
	12		30.31	3.299	0.51844
	18		30.11	3.320	0.52123
47	00		29.92	3.342	0.52402
	06		29.73	3.363	0.52680
	12		29.54	3.385	0.52959
	18		29.35	3.407	0.53238
48	00		29.16	3.428	0.53516
	06		28.98	3.451	0.53795
	12		28.79	3.473	0.54074
	18		28.61	3.495	0.54353
49	00		28.42	3.518	0.54631
	06		28.24	3.540	0.54910
	12		28.06	3.563	0.55189
	18		27.88	3.586	0.55468
50	00		27.70	3.609	0.55746
	12		27.35	3.656	0.56304
51	00		27.00	3.703	0.56861
	12		26.66	3.751	0.57419
52	00		26.32	3.799	0.57976

t d	t h	t min	N_t	N_0/N_t	$\log_{10} N_0/N_t$
	12		25.98	3.848	0.58534
53	00		25.65	3.898	0.59091
	12		25.32	3.948	0.59649
54	00		25.00	3.999	0.60206
	12		24.68	4.051	0.60763
55	00		24.37	4.104	0.61321
	12		24.06	4.157	0.61878
56	00		23.75	4.210	0.62436
	12		23.45	4.265	0.62993
57	00		23.15	4.320	0.63551
	12		22.85	4.376	0.64108
58	00		22.56	4.432	0.64666
	12		22.27	4.489	0.65223
59	00		21.99	4.547	0.65781
	12		21.71	4.606	0.66338
60	00		21.43	4.666	0.66896
	12		21.16	4.726	0.67453
61	00		20.89	4.787	0.68010
	12		20.62	4.849	0.68568
62	00		20.36	4.911	0.69125
	12		20.10	4.975	0.69683
63	00		19.84	5.039	0.70240
	12		19.59	5.104	0.70798
64	00		19.34	5.170	0.71355
	12		19.09	5.237	0.71913
65	00		18.85	5.305	0.72470
	12		18.61	5.373	0.73028
66	00		18.37	5.443	0.73585
	12		18.14	5.513	0.74142
67	00		17.91	5.584	0.74700
	12		17.68	5.656	0.75257
68	00		17.45	5.729	0.75815
	12		17.23	5.803	0.76372
69	00		17.01	5.878	0.76930
	12		16.79	5.954	0.77487
70			16.58	6.031	0.78045
71			16.16	6.188	0.79160
72			15.75	6.349	0.80274
73			15.35	6.514	0.81389
74			14.96	6.684	0.82504
75			14.58	6.857	0.83619
76			14.21	7.036	0.84734
77			13.85	7.219	0.85849
78			13.50	7.406	0.86964
79			13.16	7.599	0.88079
80			12.83	7.797	0.89194
81			12.50	7.999	0.90308
82			12.18	8.207	0.91423
83			11.87	8.421	0.92538
84			11.57	8.640	0.93653
85			11.28	8.865	0.94768
86			10.99	9.095	0.95883
87			10.72	9.332	0.96998
88			10.44	9.574	0.98113
89			10.18	9.823	0.99227
90			9.92	10.079	1.00343
91			9.67	10.341	1.01458
92			9.42	10.610	1.02573
93			9.19	10.886	1.03688
94			8.95	11.169	1.04803
95			8.73	11.459	1.05918
96			8.50	11.757	1.07033
97			8.29	12.063	1.08148
98			8.08	12.377	1.09263
99			7.87	12.699	1.10378
100			7.67	13.029	1.11493
105			6.75	14.814	1.17067
110			5.94	16.842	1.22642
115			5.22	19.149	1.28217
120			4.59	21.772	1.33791
125			4.04	24.754	1.39366
130			3.55	28.145	1.44940
135			3.13	32.000	1.50515
140			2.75	36.382	1.56090
145			2.42	41.365	1.61664
150			2.13	47.031	1.67239
155			1.87	53.473	1.72814
160			1.64	60.796	1.78388
165			1.45	69.123	1.83963
170			1.27	78.590	1.89537
175			1.12	89.353	1.95111
180			0.98	101.594	2.00687
185			0.87	115.508	2.06261
190			0.76	131.328	2.11836
195			0.67	149.316	2.17411
200			0.59	169.767	2.22986
205			0.52	193.016	2.28560
210			0.46	219.452	2.34134
215			0.40	249.513	2.39709
220			0.35	283.687	2.45284
225			0.31	322.539	2.50858
230			0.27	366.716	2.56433
235			0.24	416.944	2.62008
240			0.21	474.045	2.67582
245			0.19	538.967	2.73156
250			0.16	612.782	2.78731
255			0.14	696.718	2.84306

Manganese-52

Half-life 5.7 d

t d	t h	t min	N_t	N_0/N_t	$\log_{10} N_0/N_t$
	0		100.00	1.000	0.00000
	1		99.49	1.005	0.00220
	2		98.99	1.010	0.00440
	3		98.49	1.015	0.00660
	4		97.99	1.020	0.00880
	5		97.50	1.025	0.01100
	6		97.01	1.030	0.01320
	7		96.52	1.036	0.01540
	8		96.03	1.041	0.01760
	9		95.54	1.046	0.01980
	10		95.06	1.051	0.02201
	11		94.58	1.057	0.02421
	12		94.10	1.062	0.02641
	13		93.63	1.068	0.02861
	14		93.15	1.073	0.03081
	15		92.68	1.078	0.03301
	16		92.21	1.084	0.03521
	17		91.75	1.089	0.03741
	18		91.28	1.095	0.03961
	19		90.82	1.101	0.04181
	20		90.36	1.106	0.04401
	21		89.91	1.112	0.04621
	22		89.45	1.117	0.04841
	23		89.00	1.123	0.05061
1	**00**		88.55	1.129	0.05281
	01		88.10	1.135	0.05501
	02		87.66	1.140	0.05721
	03		87.21	1.146	0.05941
	04		86.77	1.152	0.06161
	05		86.33	1.158	0.06382
	06		85.90	1.164	0.06602
	07		85.46	1.170	0.06822
	08		85.03	1.176	0.07042
	09		84.60	1.181	0.07262
	10		84.17	1.188	0.07482
	11		83.75	1.194	0.07702
	12		83.33	1.200	0.07922
	13		82.91	1.206	0.08142
	14		82.49	1.212	0.08362
	15		82.07	1.218	0.08582
	16		81.65	1.224	0.08802
	17		81.24	1.230	0.09022
	18		80.83	1.237	0.09242
	19		80.42	1.243	0.09462
	20		80.02	1.249	0.09682
	21		79.61	1.256	0.09902
	22		79.21	1.262	0.10122
	23		78.81	1.268	0.10342
2	**00**		78.41	1.275	0.10563
	01		78.01	1.281	0.10783
	02		77.62	1.288	0.11003
	03		77.23	1.294	0.11223
	04		76.84	1.301	0.11443
	05		76.45	1.308	0.11663
	06		76.05	1.314	0.11883
	07		75.68	1.321	0.12103
	08		75.30	1.328	0.12323
	09		74.92	1.334	0.12543
	10		74.54	1.341	0.12763
	11		74.16	1.348	0.12983
	12		73.79	1.355	0.13203
	13		73.41	1.362	0.13423
	14		73.04	1.369	0.13643
	15		72.67	1.376	0.13863
	16		72.30	1.383	0.14083
	17		71.94	1.390	0.14303
	18		71.58	1.397	0.14523
	19		71.21	1.404	0.14743
	20		70.85	1.411	0.14964
	21		70.50	1.418	0.15184
	22		70.14	1.425	0.15404
	23		69.79	1.432	0.15624
3	**00**		69.43	1.440	0.15844
	01		69.08	1.447	0.16064
	02		68.73	1.454	0.16284
	03		68.39	1.462	0.16504
	04		68.04	1.469	0.16724
	05		67.70	1.477	0.16944
	06		67.35	1.484	0.17164
	07		67.01	1.492	0.17384
	08		66.67	1.499	0.17604
	09		66.34	1.507	0.17824
	10		66.00	1.515	0.18044
	11		65.67	1.522	0.18264
	12		65.34	1.530	0.18484
	13		65.01	1.538	0.18704
	14		64.68	1.546	0.18924
	15		64.35	1.553	0.19144
	16		64.03	1.561	0.19365
	17		63.70	1.569	0.19585
	18		63.38	1.577	0.19805
	19		63.06	1.585	0.20025
	20		62.74	1.593	0.20245
	21		62.42	1.601	0.20465
	22		62.11	1.610	0.20685
	23		61.79	1.618	0.20905

t d	t h	t min	N_t	N_0/N_t	$\log_{10} N_0/N_t$
4	**00**		61.48	1.626	0.21125
	01		61.17	1.634	0.21345
	02		60.86	1.643	0.21565
	03		60.55	1.651	0.21785
	04		60.25	1.659	0.22005
	05		59.94	1.668	0.22225
	06		59.64	1.676	0.22445
	07		59.34	1.685	0.22665
	08		59.04	1.693	0.22885
	09		58.74	1.702	0.23105
	10		58.44	1.711	0.23325
	11		58.15	1.719	0.23546
	12		57.86	1.728	0.23766
	13		57.56	1.737	0.23986
	14		57.27	1.746	0.24206
	15		56.98	1.754	0.24426
	16		56.69	1.763	0.24646
	17		56.41	1.772	0.24866
	18		56.12	1.781	0.25086
	19		55.84	1.790	0.25306
	20		55.56	1.799	0.25526
	21		55.28	1.809	0.25746
	22		55.00	1.818	0.25966
	23		54.72	1.827	0.26186
5	**00**		54.44	1.836	0.26406
	06		52.81	1.893	0.27727
	12		51.23	1.951	0.29047
	18		49.70	2.012	0.30367
6	**00**		48.21	2.074	0.31687
	06		46.77	2.138	0.33008
	12		45.36	2.204	0.34328
	18		44.01	2.272	0.35648
7	**00**		42.69	2.342	0.36969
	06		41.41	2.414	0.38289
	12		40.17	2.489	0.39609
	18		38.97	2.566	0.40930
8	**00**		37.80	2.645	0.42250
	06		36.67	2.727	0.43570
	12		35.57	2.811	0.44890
	18		34.51	2.898	0.46211
9	**00**		33.47	2.987	0.47531
	06		32.47	3.079	0.48851
	12		31.50	3.174	0.50172
	18		30.55	3.272	0.51492
10	**00**		29.64	3.373	0.52812
	06		28.75	3.477	0.54133
	12		27.89	3.585	0.55453
	18		27.06	3.695	0.56773
11	**00**		26.25	3.810	0.58094
	06		25.46	3.927	0.59414
	12		24.70	4.048	0.60734
	18		23.96	4.173	0.62054
12	**00**		23.24	4.302	0.63375
	06		22.54	4.435	0.64695
	12		21.87	4.572	0.66015
	18		21.22	4.713	0.67336
13	**00**		20.58	4.859	0.68656
	06		19.96	5.009	0.69976
	12		19.37	5.163	0.71297
	18		18.79	5.323	0.72617
14	**00**		18.22	5.487	0.73937
	06		17.68	5.656	0.75257
	12		17.15	5.831	0.76578
	18		16.63	6.011	0.77898
15	**00**		16.14	6.197	0.79218
	06		15.65	6.388	0.80539
	12		15.18	6.585	0.81859
	18		14.73	6.788	0.83179
16	**00**		14.29	6.998	0.84499
	06		13.86	7.214	0.85820
	12		13.45	7.437	0.87140
	18		13.04	7.666	0.88460
17	**00**		12.65	7.903	0.89780
	06		12.27	8.147	0.91101
	12		11.91	8.398	0.92421
	18		11.55	8.657	0.93741
18	**00**		11.20	8.925	0.95061
	06		10.87	9.200	0.96382
	12		10.54	9.484	0.97702
	18		10.23	9.777	0.99022
19	**00**		9.92	10.079	1.00343
	06		9.62	10.390	1.01664
	12		9.34	10.711	1.02984
	18		9.06	11.041	1.04304
20			8.79	11.382	1.05625
21			7.78	12.854	1.10906
22			6.89	14.516	1.16187
23			6.10	16.393	1.21468
24			5.40	18.513	1.26750
25			4.78	20.907	1.32031
26			4.24	23.611	1.37312
27			3.75	26.664	1.42593
28			3.32	30.112	1.47874
29			2.94	34.006	1.53156

t: d	h	min	N_t	N_0/N_t	$\log_{10} N_0/N_t$
30			2.60	38.403	1.58437
31			2.31	43.369	1.63718
32			2.04	48.977	1.68999
33			1.81	55.310	1.74280
34			1.60	62.461	1.79561
35			1.42	70.538	1.84843
36			1.26	79.659	1.90124
37			1.11	89.959	1.95405
38			0.98	101.594	2.00687
39			0.87	114.730	2.05968
40			0.77	129.565	2.11249
41			0.68	146.320	2.16531
42			0.61	165.240	2.21812
43			0.54	186.605	2.27092
44			0.47	210.734	2.32374
45			0.42	237.987	2.37655
46			0.37	268.759	2.42936
47			0.33	303.508	2.48217
48			0.29	342.759	2.53499
49			0.26	387.086	2.58781
50			0.23	437.139	2.64062
51			0.20	493.656	2.69343
52			0.18	557.475	2.74623
53			0.16	629.564	2.79904
54			0.14	710.984	2.85186

Manganese-54

Half-life 300 d

t: d	h	min	N_t	N_0/N_t	$\log_{10} N_0/N_t$
0			100.00	1.000	0.00000
5			98.85	1.011	0.00502
10			97.72	1.023	0.01003
15			96.59	1.035	0.01505
20			95.48	1.047	0.02007
25			94.39	1.059	0.02509
30			93.30	1.071	0.03010
35			92.23	1.084	0.03512
40			91.17	1.096	0.04014
45			90.13	1.109	0.04515
50			89.09	1.122	0.05017
55			88.07	1.135	0.05519
60			87.06	1.148	0.06021
65			86.06	1.162	0.06522
70			85.07	1.175	0.07024
75			84.09	1.189	0.07526
80			83.12	1.203	0.08028
85			82.17	1.217	0.08529
90			81.23	1.231	0.09031
95			80.29	1.245	0.09533
100			79.37	1.259	0.10034
105			78.46	1.274	0.10536
110			77.56	1.289	0.11038
115			76.67	1.304	0.11540
120			75.79	1.319	0.12041
125			74.92	1.334	0.12543
130			74.05	1.350	0.13045
135			73.20	1.366	0.13546
140			72.36	1.381	0.14048
145			71.53	1.397	0.14550
150			70.71	1.414	0.15052
155			69.90	1.430	0.15553
160			69.10	1.447	0.16055
165			68.30	1.464	0.16557
170			67.52	1.481	0.17058
175			66.74	1.498	0.17560
180			65.98	1.515	0.18062
185			65.22	1.533	0.18564
190			64.47	1.551	0.19065
195			63.73	1.569	0.19567
200			63.00	1.587	0.20069
205			62.27	1.605	0.20570
210			61.56	1.624	0.21072
215			60.85	1.643	0.21574
220			60.15	1.662	0.22076
225			59.46	1.681	0.22577
230			58.78	1.701	0.23079
235			58.10	1.721	0.23581
240			57.43	1.741	0.24082
245			56.78	1.761	0.24584
250			56.12	1.781	0.25086
255			55.48	1.802	0.25588
260			54.84	1.823	0.26089
265			54.21	1.844	0.26591
270			53.59	1.866	0.27093
275			52.97	1.887	0.27594
280			52.36	1.909	0.28096
285			51.76	1.931	0.28598
290			51.17	1.954	0.29100
295			50.58	1.977	0.29601
300			50.00	2.000	0.30103
305			49.43	2.023	0.30605
310			48.86	2.046	0.31106
315			48.30	2.070	0.31608
320			47.74	2.094	0.32110
325			47.19	2.118	0.32612
330			46.65	2.143	0.33113
335			46.12	2.168	0.33615
340			45.59	2.193	0.34117
345			45.06	2.219	0.34619
350			44.54	2.244	0.35120
355			44.03	2.271	0.35622
360			43.53	2.297	0.36124
365			43.03	2.324	0.36625
370			42.53	2.351	0.37127
375			42.04	2.378	0.37629
380			41.56	2.406	0.38131
385			41.08	2.434	0.38632
390			40.61	2.462	0.39134
395			40.15	2.490	0.39636
400			39.69	2.519	0.40137
405			39.23	2.549	0.40639
410			38.78	2.578	0.41141
415			38.33	2.608	0.41643
420			37.89	2.639	0.42144
425			37.46	2.669	0.42646
430			37.03	2.700	0.43148
435			36.60	2.732	0.43649
440			36.18	2.763	0.44151
445			35.77	2.795	0.44653
450			35.36	2.828	0.45155
455			34.95	2.861	0.45656
460			34.55	2.894	0.46158
465			34.15	2.928	0.46660
470			33.76	2.962	0.47161
475			33.37	2.996	0.47663
480			32.99	3.031	0.48165
485			32.61	3.066	0.48667
490			32.23	3.102	0.49168
495			31.86	3.138	0.49670
500			31.50	3.174	0.50172
510			30.78	3.249	0.51175
520			30.08	3.324	0.52179
530			29.39	3.402	0.53182
540			28.72	3.482	0.54185
550			28.06	3.563	0.55189
560			27.42	3.646	0.56192
570			26.79	3.732	0.57196
580			26.18	3.819	0.58199
590			25.58	3.908	0.59203
600			25.00	3.999	0.60206
610			24.43	4.093	0.61209
620			23.87	4.189	0.62213
630			23.33	4.287	0.63216
640			22.79	4.387	0.64220
650			22.27	4.489	0.65223
660			21.76	4.594	0.66227
670			21.27	4.702	0.67230
680			20.78	4.812	0.68233
690			20.31	4.924	0.69237
700			19.84	5.039	0.70240
710			19.39	5.157	0.71244
720			18.95	5.278	0.72247
730			18.51	5.401	0.73251
740			18.09	5.527	0.74254
750			17.68	5.656	0.75257
760			17.27	5.789	0.76261
770			16.88	5.924	0.77264
780			16.49	6.062	0.78268
790			16.12	6.204	0.79271
800			15.75	6.349	0.80274
810			15.39	6.497	0.81278
820			15.04	6.649	0.82281
830			14.69	6.805	0.83285
840			14.36	6.964	0.84288
850			14.03	7.127	0.85292
860			13.71	7.293	0.86295
870			13.40	7.464	0.87298
880			13.09	7.638	0.88302
890			12.79	7.817	0.89305
900			12.50	7.999	0.90308
910			12.21	8.186	0.91312
920			11.94	8.378	0.92315
930			11.66	8.574	0.93319
940			11.40	8.774	0.94322
950			11.14	8.979	0.95325
960			10.88	9.189	0.96329
970			10.63	9.404	0.97332
980			10.39	9.623	0.98335
990			10.15	9.848	0.99339
1000			9.92	10.079	1.00343
1020			9.47	10.556	1.02350
1040			9.05	11.055	1.04357
1060			8.64	11.578	1.06364
1080			8.25	12.125	1.08371
1100			7.87	12.699	1.10378
1120			7.52	13.299	1.12385
1140			7.18	13.928	1.14391
1160			6.86	14.587	1.16398
1180			6.55	15.277	1.18405
1200			6.25	16.000	1.20412
1220			5.97	16.756	1.22419
1240			5.70	17.549	1.24426
1260			5.44	18.379	1.26433
1280			5.20	19.248	1.28439
1300			4.96	20.158	1.30446
1320			4.74	21.112	1.32453
1340			4.52	22.110	1.34460
1360			4.32	23.156	1.36467
1380			4.12	24.251	1.38474
1400			3.94	25.398	1.40481
1450			3.51	28.508	1.45498
1500			3.13	32.000	1.50515
1550			2.78	35.918	1.55532
1600			2.48	40.317	1.60549
1650			2.21	45.254	1.65567
1700			1.97	50.796	1.70584
1750			1.75	57.017	1.75601
1800			1.56	63.999	1.80618
1850			1.39	71.837	1.85635
1900			1.24	80.634	1.90652
1950			1.10	90.507	1.95669
2000			0.98	101.594	2.00687
2500			0.31	322.539	2.50858
3000			0.10	1023.96	3.01028
3500			0.03	3250.98	3.51201
4000			0.01	10319.9	4.01368

Iron-59

Half-life 45 d

t: d	h	min	N_t	N_0/N_t	$\log_{10} N_0/N_t$
	0		100.00	1.000	0.00000
	6		99.62	1.003	0.00167
	12		99.23	1.007	0.00335
	18		98.85	1.011	0.00502
1	**00**		98.47	1.015	0.00669
	06		98.09	1.019	0.00836
	12		97.72	1.023	0.01003
	18		97.34	1.027	0.01171
2	**00**		96.97	1.031	0.01338
	06		96.59	1.035	0.01505
	12		96.22	1.039	0.01672
	18		95.85	1.043	0.01840
3	**00**		95.48	1.047	0.02007
	06		95.12	1.051	0.02174
	12		94.75	1.055	0.02341
	18		94.39	1.059	0.02509
4	**00**		94.02	1.063	0.02676
	06		93.66	1.067	0.02843
	12		93.30	1.071	0.03010
	18		92.94	1.075	0.03178
5	**00**		92.59	1.080	0.03345
	06		92.23	1.084	0.03512
	12		91.88	1.088	0.03679
	18		91.52	1.092	0.03847
6	**00**		91.17	1.096	0.04014
	06		90.82	1.101	0.04181
	12		90.47	1.105	0.04348
	18		90.13	1.109	0.04515
7	**00**		89.78	1.113	0.04683
	06		89.43	1.118	0.04850
	12		89.09	1.122	0.05017
	18		88.75	1.126	0.05184
8	**00**		88.41	1.131	0.05352
	06		88.07	1.135	0.05519
	12		87.73	1.139	0.05686
	18		87.39	1.144	0.05853
9	**00**		87.06	1.148	0.06021
	06		86.72	1.153	0.06188
	12		86.39	1.157	0.06355
	18		86.06	1.162	0.06522
10	**00**		85.72	1.166	0.06690
	06		85.39	1.171	0.06857
	12		85.07	1.175	0.07024
	18		84.74	1.180	0.07191
11	**00**		84.41	1.184	0.07359
	06		84.09	1.189	0.07526
	12		83.77	1.193	0.07693
	18		83.44	1.198	0.07860
12	**00**		83.12	1.203	0.08028
	06		82.80	1.207	0.08195
	12		82.49	1.212	0.08362
	18		82.17	1.217	0.08529
13	**00**		81.85	1.221	0.08696
	06		81.54	1.226	0.08864
	12		81.23	1.231	0.09031
	18		80.91	1.235	0.09198
14	**00**		80.60	1.240	0.09365
	06		80.29	1.245	0.09533
	12		79.98	1.250	0.09700
	18		79.68	1.255	0.09867
15	**00**		79.37	1.259	0.10034
	06		79.07	1.264	0.10202
	12		78.76	1.269	0.10369
	18		78.46	1.274	0.10536
16	**00**		78.16	1.279	0.10703
	06		77.86	1.284	0.10871
	12		77.56	1.289	0.11038
	18		77.26	1.294	0.11205
17	**00**		76.96	1.299	0.11372
	06		76.67	1.304	0.11540
	12		76.37	1.309	0.11707
	18		76.08	1.314	0.11874
18	**00**		75.79	1.319	0.12041
	06		75.49	1.324	0.12208
	12		75.20	1.329	0.12376
	18		74.92	1.334	0.12543
19	**00**		74.63	1.339	0.12710
	06		74.34	1.345	0.12877
	12		74.05	1.350	0.13045
	18		73.77	1.355	0.13212
20			73.49	1.360	0.13379
21			72.36	1.381	0.14048
22			71.26	1.403	0.14717
23			70.17	1.425	0.15386
24			69.10	1.447	0.16055
25			68.04	1.469	0.16724
26			67.00	1.492	0.17393
27			65.98	1.515	0.18062
28			64.97	1.539	0.18731
29			63.97	1.563	0.19400
30			63.00	1.587	0.20069
31			62.03	1.612	0.20738
32			61.08	1.637	0.21407
33			60.15	1.662	0.22076
34			59.23	1.688	0.22745
35			58.33	1.714	0.23413
36			57.43	1.741	0.24082
37			56.56	1.768	0.24751
38			55.69	1.795	0.25420
39			54.84	1.823	0.26089
40			54.00	1.851	0.26758
41			53.18	1.880	0.27427
42			52.36	1.909	0.28096
43			51.56	1.939	0.28765
44			50.78	1.969	0.29434
45			50.00	2.000	0.30103
46			49.24	2.031	0.30772
47			48.48	2.062	0.31441
48			47.74	2.094	0.32110
49			47.01	2.127	0.32779
50			46.29	2.160	0.33448
51			45.59	2.193	0.34117
52			44.89	2.227	0.34786
53			44.20	2.262	0.35455
54			43.53	2.297	0.36124
55			42.86	2.333	0.36793
56			42.21	2.369	0.37462
57			41.56	2.406	0.38131
58			40.93	2.443	0.38799
59			40.30	2.481	0.39468
60			39.69	2.519	0.40137
61			39.08	2.558	0.40806
62			38.48	2.598	0.41475
63			37.89	2.639	0.42144
64			37.31	2.679	0.42813
65			36.74	2.721	0.43482
66			36.18	2.763	0.44151
67			35.63	2.806	0.44820
68			35.08	2.850	0.45489
69			34.55	2.894	0.46158
70			34.02	2.939	0.46827
71			33.50	2.985	0.47496
72			32.99	3.031	0.48165
73			32.48	3.078	0.48834
74			31.99	3.126	0.49503
75			31.50	3.174	0.50172
76			31.02	3.224	0.50841
77			30.54	3.274	0.51510
78			30.08	3.324	0.52179
79			29.62	3.376	0.52848
80			29.16	3.428	0.53516
81			28.72	3.482	0.54185
82			28.28	3.536	0.54854
83			27.85	3.591	0.55523
84			27.42	3.646	0.56192
85			27.00	3.703	0.56861
86			26.59	3.760	0.57530
87			26.18	3.819	0.58199
88			25.78	3.878	0.58868
89			25.39	3.938	0.59537
90			25.00	3.999	0.60206
91			24.62	4.062	0.60875
92			24.24	4.125	0.61544
93			23.87	4.189	0.62213
94			23.51	4.254	0.62882
95			23.15	4.320	0.63551
96			22.79	4.387	0.64220
97			22.44	4.455	0.64889
98			22.10	4.524	0.65558
99			21.76	4.594	0.66227
100			21.43	4.666	0.66896
101			21.10	4.738	0.67564
102			20.78	4.812	0.68233
103			20.46	4.886	0.68902
104			20.15	4.962	0.69571

t (d)	N_t	N_0/N_t	$\log_{10} N_0/N_t$
105	19.84	5.039	0.70240
106	19.54	5.117	0.70909
107	19.24	5.197	0.71578
108	18.95	5.278	0.72247
109	18.66	5.359	0.72916
110	18.37	5.443	0.73585
111	18.09	5.527	0.74254
112	17.81	5.613	0.74923
113	17.54	5.700	0.75592
114	17.27	5.789	0.76261
115	17.01	5.878	0.76930
116	16.75	5.970	0.77599
117	16.49	6.062	0.78268
118	16.24	6.156	0.78937
119	15.99	6.252	0.79606
120	15.75	6.349	0.80274
121	15.51	6.448	0.80943
122	15.27	6.548	0.81612
123	15.04	6.649	0.82281
124	14.81	6.753	0.82950
125	14.58	6.857	0.83619
126	14.36	6.964	0.84288
127	14.14	7.072	0.84957
128	13.92	7.182	0.85626
129	13.71	7.293	0.86295
130	13.50	7.406	0.86964
131	13.29	7.521	0.87633
132	13.09	7.638	0.88302
133	12.89	7.757	0.88971
134	12.69	7.877	0.89640
135	12.50	7.999	0.90308
136	12.31	8.124	0.90977
137	12.12	8.250	0.91646
138	11.94	8.378	0.92315
139	11.75	8.508	0.92984
140	11.57	8.640	0.93653
141	11.40	8.774	0.94322
142	11.22	8.910	0.94991
143	11.05	9.048	0.95660
144	10.88	9.189	0.96329
145	10.72	9.332	0.96998
146	10.55	9.476	0.97667
147	10.39	9.623	0.98335
148	10.23	9.773	0.99004
149	10.08	9.925	0.99673
150	9.92	10.079	1.00343
152	9.62	10.394	1.01681
154	9.33	10.719	1.03019
156	9.05	11.055	1.04357
158	8.77	11.401	1.05695
160	8.50	11.757	1.07033
162	8.25	12.125	1.08371
164	8.00	12.505	1.09709
166	7.75	12.896	1.11047
168	7.52	13.299	1.12385
170	7.29	13.715	1.13722
172	7.07	14.145	1.15060
174	6.86	14.587	1.16398
176	6.65	15.043	1.17736
178	6.45	15.514	1.19074
180	6.25	16.000	1.20412
182	6.06	16.500	1.21750
184	5.88	17.016	1.23088
186	5.70	17.549	1.24426
188	5.53	18.098	1.25764
190	5.36	18.664	1.27102
192	5.20	19.248	1.28439
194	5.04	19.850	1.29777
196	4.88	20.471	1.31115
198	4.74	21.112	1.32453
200	4.59	21.772	1.33791
205	4.25	23.515	1.37136
210	3.94	25.398	1.40481
215	3.65	27.431	1.43826
220	3.38	29.627	1.47170
225	3.13	32.000	1.50515
230	2.89	34.561	1.53860
235	2.68	37.328	1.57205
240	2.48	40.317	1.60549
245	2.30	43.545	1.63894
250	2.13	47.031	1.67239
255	1.97	50.796	1.70584
260	1.82	54.863	1.73928
265	1.69	59.255	1.77273
270	1.56	63.999	1.80618
275	1.45	69.123	1.83963
280	1.34	74.656	1.87307
285	1.24	80.634	1.90652
290	1.15	87.089	1.93996
295	1.06	94.060	1.97341
300	0.98	101.594	2.00687
320	0.72	138.247	2.14066
340	0.53	188.125	2.27445
360	0.39	255.996	2.40823
380	0.29	348.359	2.54203
400	0.21	474.045	2.67582

Zinc-65

Half-life 245 d

t (d)	N_t	N_0/N_t	$\log_{10} N_0/N_t$
0	100.00	1.000	0.00000
5	98.60	1.014	0.00614
10	97.21	1.028	0.01229
15	95.85	1.043	0.01843
20	94.50	1.058	0.02457
25	93.17	1.073	0.03072
30	91.86	1.088	0.03686
35	90.57	1.104	0.04300
40	89.30	1.119	0.04915
45	88.05	1.135	0.05529
50	86.81	1.151	0.06144
55	85.59	1.168	0.06758
60	84.39	1.185	0.07372
65	83.20	1.201	0.07987
70	82.03	1.219	0.08601
75	80.88	1.236	0.09215
80	79.75	1.253	0.09830
85	78.63	1.271	0.10444
90	77.52	1.289	0.11058
95	76.43	1.308	0.11673
100	75.36	1.326	0.12287
105	74.30	1.345	0.12901
110	73.26	1.365	0.13516
115	72.23	1.384	0.14130
120	71.21	1.404	0.14744
125	70.21	1.424	0.15359
130	69.23	1.444	0.15973
135	68.25	1.465	0.16587
140	67.30	1.485	0.17202
145	66.35	1.507	0.17816
150	65.42	1.528	0.18430
155	64.50	1.550	0.19045
160	63.59	1.572	0.19659
165	62.70	1.594	0.20273
170	61.82	1.617	0.20888
175	60.95	1.640	0.21502
180	60.09	1.664	0.22117
185	59.25	1.687	0.22731
190	58.42	1.711	0.23345
195	57.60	1.736	0.23960
200	56.79	1.760	0.24574
205	55.99	1.786	0.25188
210	55.20	1.811	0.25803
215	54.43	1.837	0.26417
220	53.66	1.863	0.27031
225	52.91	1.889	0.27646
230	52.17	1.916	0.28260
235	51.43	1.944	0.28874
240	50.71	1.971	0.29489
245	50.00	2.000	0.30103
250	49.30	2.028	0.30717
255	48.61	2.057	0.31332
260	47.92	2.086	0.31946
265	47.25	2.116	0.32560
270	46.59	2.146	0.33175
275	45.93	2.177	0.33789
280	45.29	2.208	0.34403
285	44.65	2.239	0.35018
290	44.02	2.271	0.35632
295	43.40	2.303	0.36247
300	42.79	2.336	0.36861
305	42.19	2.370	0.37475
310	41.60	2.403	0.38090
315	41.02	2.438	0.38704
320	40.44	2.472	0.39318
325	39.87	2.507	0.39933
330	39.31	2.543	0.40547
335	38.76	2.579	0.41161
340	38.22	2.616	0.41776
345	37.68	2.653	0.42390
350	37.15	2.691	0.43004
355	36.63	2.730	0.43619
360	36.11	2.769	0.44233
365	35.61	2.808	0.44847
370	35.11	2.848	0.45462
375	34.61	2.889	0.46076
380	34.13	2.930	0.46690
385	33.65	2.971	0.47305
390	33.17	3.014	0.47919
395	32.71	3.057	0.48533
400	32.25	3.100	0.49148
405	31.80	3.145	0.49762
410	31.35	3.189	0.50376
415	30.91	3.235	0.50991
420	30.48	3.281	0.51605
425	30.05	3.328	0.52220
430	29.63	3.375	0.52834
435	29.21	3.423	0.53448
440	28.80	3.472	0.54063
445	28.39	3.521	0.54677
450	28.00	3.572	0.55291
455	27.60	3.622	0.55906
460	27.21	3.674	0.56520
465	26.83	3.726	0.57134
470	26.46	3.779	0.57749
475	26.08	3.833	0.58363
480	25.72	3.888	0.58977
485	25.36	3.943	0.59592
490	25.00	3.999	0.60206
495	24.65	4.056	0.60820
500	24.30	4.114	0.61435
505	23.96	4.173	0.62049
510	23.62	4.232	0.62663
515	23.29	4.293	0.63278
520	22.97	4.354	0.63892
525	22.64	4.416	0.64506
530	22.33	4.479	0.65121
535	22.01	4.543	0.65735
540	21.70	4.607	0.66349
545	21.40	4.673	0.66964
550	21.10	4.740	0.67578
555	20.80	4.807	0.68192
560	20.51	4.876	0.68807
565	20.22	4.945	0.69421
570	19.94	5.015	0.70035
575	19.66	5.087	0.70650
580	19.38	5.159	0.71264
585	19.11	5.233	0.71879
590	18.84	5.307	0.72493
595	18.57	5.383	0.73107
600	18.31	5.460	0.73722
605	18.06	5.538	0.74336
610	17.80	5.616	0.74950
615	17.55	5.696	0.75565
620	17.31	5.778	0.76179
625	17.06	5.860	0.76793
630	16.82	5.943	0.77408
635	16.59	6.028	0.78022
640	16.35	6.114	0.78636
645	16.12	6.201	0.79251
650	15.90	6.289	0.79865
655	15.68	6.379	0.80479
660	15.45	6.470	0.81094
665	15.24	6.562	0.81708
670	15.02	6.656	0.82322
675	14.81	6.750	0.82937
680	14.60	6.847	0.83551
685	14.40	6.944	0.84165
690	14.20	7.043	0.84780
695	14.00	7.143	0.85394
700	13.80	7.245	0.86008
710	13.42	7.453	0.87237
720	13.04	7.667	0.88466
730	12.68	7.887	0.89694
740	12.32	8.113	0.90923
750	11.98	8.346	0.92151
760	11.65	8.586	0.93380
770	11.32	8.832	0.94609
780	11.01	9.085	0.95837
790	10.70	9.346	0.97066
800	10.40	9.614	0.98295
810	10.11	9.890	0.99523
820	9.83	10.174	1.00753
830	9.55	10.466	1.01982
840	9.29	10.767	1.03210
850	9.03	11.076	1.04439
860	8.78	11.394	1.05668
870	8.53	11.720	1.06896
880	8.29	12.057	1.08125
890	8.06	12.403	1.09354
900	7.84	12.759	1.10583
910	7.62	13.125	1.11811
920	7.41	13.502	1.13040
930	7.20	13.889	1.14269
940	7.00	14.288	1.15497
950	6.80	14.698	1.16726
960	6.61	15.119	1.17955
970	6.43	15.553	1.19183
980	6.25	16.000	1.20412
990	6.08	16.459	1.21641
1000	5.91	16.931	1.22869
1020	5.58	17.917	1.25327
1040	5.27	18.960	1.27784
1060	4.98	20.063	1.30242
1080	4.71	21.231	1.32699
1100	4.45	22.467	1.35156
1120	4.21	23.775	1.37614
1140	3.97	25.160	1.40071
1160	3.76	26.624	1.42529
1180	3.55	28.174	1.44986
1200	3.35	29.814	1.47443
1220	3.17	31.550	1.49901
1240	3.00	33.387	1.52358
1260	2.83	35.330	1.54815
1280	2.67	37.387	1.57273
1300	2.53	39.564	1.59730
1320	2.39	41.867	1.62188
1340	2.26	44.304	1.64645
1360	2.13	46.883	1.67102
1380	2.02	49.613	1.69560
1400	1.90	52.501	1.72017
1450	1.65	60.478	1.78160
1500	1.44	69.668	1.84304
1550	1.25	80.254	1.90447
1600	1.08	92.448	1.96590
1650	0.94	106.498	2.02734
1700	0.82	122.681	2.08878
1750	0.71	141.322	2.15021
1800	0.61	162.797	2.21165
1850	0.53	187.536	2.27309
1900	0.46	216.034	2.33452
1950	0.40	248.861	2.39596

Bromine-82

Half-life 35.9 h

t (h)	t (min)	N_t	N_0/N_t	$\log_{10} N_0/N_t$
	00	100.00	1.000	0.00000
	10	99.68	1.003	0.00140
	20	99.36	1.006	0.00280
	30	99.04	1.009	0.00419
	40	98.72	1.012	0.00559
	50	98.40	1.016	0.00699
1	**00**	98.09	1.019	0.00839
	10	97.77	1.022	0.00978
	20	97.46	1.026	0.01118
	30	97.15	1.029	0.01258
	40	96.83	1.032	0.01398
	50	96.52	1.036	0.01537
2	**00**	96.21	1.039	0.01677
	10	95.90	1.042	0.01817
	20	95.59	1.046	0.01957
	30	95.29	1.049	0.02096
	40	94.98	1.052	0.02236
	50	94.68	1.056	0.02376
3	**00**	94.37	1.059	0.02516
	10	94.07	1.063	0.02655
	20	93.77	1.066	0.02795
	30	93.47	1.069	0.02935
	40	93.17	1.073	0.03075
	50	92.87	1.076	0.03214
4	**00**	92.57	1.080	0.03354
	10	92.27	1.083	0.03494
	20	91.97	1.087	0.03634
	30	91.68	1.090	0.03773
	40	91.38	1.094	0.03913
	50	91.09	1.097	0.04053
5	**00**	90.80	1.101	0.04193
	10	90.51	1.104	0.04332
	20	90.22	1.108	0.04472
	30	89.93	1.112	0.04612
	40	89.64	1.115	0.04752
	50	89.35	1.119	0.04891
6	**00**	89.06	1.122	0.05031
	10	88.78	1.126	0.05171
	20	88.49	1.130	0.05311
	30	88.21	1.133	0.05450
	40	87.92	1.137	0.05590
	50	87.64	1.141	0.05730
7	**00**	87.36	1.144	0.05870
	10	87.08	1.148	0.06009
	20	86.80	1.152	0.06149
	30	86.52	1.155	0.06289
	40	86.24	1.159	0.06429
	50	85.96	1.163	0.06568
8	**00**	85.69	1.167	0.06708
	10	85.41	1.170	0.06848
	20	85.14	1.174	0.06988
	30	84.86	1.178	0.07128
	40	84.59	1.182	0.07267
	50	84.32	1.185	0.07407
9	**00**	84.05	1.189	0.07547
	10	83.78	1.193	0.07687
	20	83.51	1.197	0.07826
	30	83.24	1.201	0.07966
	40	82.97	1.205	0.08106
	50	82.71	1.209	0.08246
10	**00**	82.44	1.212	0.08385
	20	81.91	1.220	0.08665
	40	81.39	1.228	0.08944
11	**00**	80.87	1.236	0.09224
	20	80.35	1.244	0.09503
	40	79.83	1.252	0.09783
12	**00**	79.32	1.260	0.10062
	20	78.81	1.268	0.10342
	40	78.30	1.277	0.10621
13	**00**	77.80	1.285	0.10901
	20	77.30	1.293	0.11180
	40	76.81	1.301	0.11460
14	**00**	76.31	1.310	0.11739
	20	75.82	1.318	0.12019
	40	75.34	1.327	0.12298
15	**00**	74.86	1.335	0.12578
	20	74.37	1.344	0.12857
	40	73.90	1.353	0.13137
16	**00**	73.42	1.361	0.13416

t: d	h	min	N_t	N_0/N_t	$\log_{10} N_0/N_t$
		20	72.95	1.370	0.13696
		40	72.48	1.379	0.13975
	17	00	72.02	1.388	0.14255
		20	71.56	1.397	0.14534
		40	71.10	1.406	0.14814
	18	00	70.64	1.415	0.15093
		20	70.19	1.424	0.15373
		40	69.74	1.433	0.15652
	19	00	69.29	1.443	0.15932
		20	68.85	1.452	0.16212
		40	68.41	1.461	0.16491
	20	00	67.97	1.471	0.16771
		20	67.53	1.480	0.17050
		40	67.10	1.490	0.17330
	21	00	66.67	1.499	0.17609
		20	66.24	1.509	0.17889
		40	65.81	1.519	0.18168
	22	00	65.39	1.529	0.18448
		20	64.97	1.539	0.18727
		40	64.56	1.549	0.19007
	23	00	64.14	1.559	0.19286
		20	63.73	1.569	0.19566
		40	63.32	1.579	0.19845
1	00		62.92	1.589	0.20125
	01		61.71	1.620	0.20963
	02		60.53	1.652	0.21802
	03		59.37	1.684	0.22640
	04		58.24	1.717	0.23479
	05		57.13	1.750	0.24317
	06		56.03	1.784	0.25156
	07		54.96	1.819	0.25994
	08		53.91	1.854	0.26833
	09		52.88	1.891	0.27671
	10		51.87	1.927	0.28510
	11		50.88	1.965	0.29348
	12		49.90	2.003	0.30187
	13		48.95	2.042	0.31025
	14		48.01	2.082	0.31864
	15		47.10	2.123	0.32702
	16		46.19	2.164	0.33541
	17		45.31	2.206	0.34380
	18		44.44	2.249	0.35218
	19		43.59	2.293	0.36057
	20		42.76	2.338	0.36895
	21		41.94	2.384	0.37734
	22		41.14	2.430	0.38572
	23		40.35	2.478	0.39411
2	00		39.58	2.526	0.40249
	01		38.83	2.575	0.41088
	02		38.08	2.625	0.41926
	03		37.36	2.676	0.42765
	04		36.64	2.729	0.43603
	05		35.94	2.782	0.44442
	06		35.25	2.836	0.45280
	07		34.58	2.891	0.46119
	08		33.92	2.948	0.46957
	09		33.27	3.005	0.47796
	10		32.63	3.064	0.48634
	11		32.01	3.124	0.49473
	12		31.40	3.185	0.50311
	13		30.80	3.247	0.51150
	14		30.21	3.310	0.51989
	15		29.63	3.374	0.52827
	16		29.06	3.440	0.53666
	17		28.51	3.507	0.54504
	18		27.96	3.576	0.55343
	19		27.43	3.645	0.56181
	20		26.90	3.717	0.57020
	21		26.39	3.789	0.57858
	22		25.88	3.863	0.58697
	23		25.39	3.938	0.59535
3	00		24.90	4.015	0.60374
	01		24.43	4.093	0.61212
	02		23.96	4.173	0.62051
	03		23.50	4.254	0.62889
	04		23.05	4.337	0.63728
	05		22.61	4.422	0.64566
	06		22.18	4.508	0.65405
	07		21.76	4.596	0.66243
	08		21.34	4.686	0.67082
	09		20.93	4.777	0.67920
	10		20.53	4.870	0.68759
	11		20.14	4.965	0.69597
	12		19.75	5.062	0.70436
	13		19.38	5.161	0.71274
	14		19.01	5.261	0.72113
	15		18.64	5.364	0.72951
	16		18.29	5.468	0.73790
	17		17.94	5.575	0.74629
	18		17.59	5.684	0.75467
	19		17.26	5.795	0.76306
	20		16.93	5.907	0.77144
	21		16.60	6.023	0.77983
	22		16.29	6.140	0.78821
	23		15.97	6.260	0.79660
4	00		15.67	6.382	0.80498
	01		15.37	6.506	0.81337
	02		15.07	6.633	0.82175
	03		14.79	6.762	0.83014
	04		14.50	6.894	0.83852
	05		14.23	7.029	0.84691
	06		13.95	7.166	0.85529
	07		13.69	7.305	0.86368
	08		13.43	7.448	0.87206
	09		13.17	7.593	0.88045
	10		12.92	7.741	0.88883
	11		12.67	7.892	0.89722
	12		12.43	8.046	0.90560
	13		12.19	8.203	0.91398
	14		11.96	8.363	0.92237
	15		11.73	8.526	0.93075
	16		11.50	8.692	0.93914
	17		11.28	8.861	0.94752
	18		11.07	9.034	0.95591
	19		10.86	9.210	0.96429
	20		10.65	9.390	0.97268
	21		10.45	9.573	0.98106
	22		10.25	9.759	0.98945
	23		10.05	9.950	0.99783
5	00		9.86	10.144	1.00623
	06		8.78	11.390	1.05654
	12		7.82	12.789	1.10685
	18		6.96	14.360	1.15716
6	00		6.20	16.124	1.20747
	06		5.52	18.104	1.25779
	12		4.92	20.328	1.30810
	18		4.38	22.824	1.35841
7	00		3.90	25.628	1.40872
	06		3.48	28.776	1.45903
	12		3.09	32.310	1.50934
	18		2.76	36.278	1.55966
8	00		2.45	40.734	1.60996
	06		2.19	45.737	1.66028
	12		1.95	51.355	1.71059
	18		1.73	57.663	1.76090
9	00		1.54	64.745	1.81121
	06		1.38	72.697	1.86152
	12		1.23	81.625	1.91183
	18		1.09	91.650	1.96214
10	00		0.97	102.910	2.01246
	06		0.87	115.549	2.06277
	12		0.77	129.742	2.11308
	18		0.69	145.677	2.16339
11	00		0.61	163.569	2.21370
	06		0.54	183.658	2.26401
	12		0.48	206.215	2.31432
	18		0.43	231.545	2.36464
12	00		0.38	259.983	2.41495
	06		0.34	291.919	2.46526
	12		0.31	327.772	2.51557
	18		0.27	368.025	2.56588
13	00		0.24	413.223	2.61619
	06		0.22	463.994	2.66651
	12		0.19	520.969	2.71681
	18		0.17	584.966	2.76713

Strontium-89

Half-life 54 d

t: d	h	min	N_t	N_0/N_t	$\log_{10} N_0/N_t$
	0		100.00	1.000	0.00000
	6		99.68	1.003	0.00139
	12		99.36	1.006	0.00279
	18		99.04	1.009	0.00418
1			98.72	1.012	0.00558
2			97.47	1.026	0.01115
3			96.22	1.039	0.01672
4			95.00	1.052	0.02230
5			93.78	1.066	0.02787
6			92.59	1.080	0.03345
7			91.41	1.094	0.03902
8			90.24	1.108	0.04460
9			89.09	1.122	0.05017
10			87.95	1.136	0.05575
11			86.83	1.151	0.06132
12			85.72	1.166	0.06690
13			84.63	1.181	0.07247
14			83.55	1.196	0.07805
15			82.49	1.212	0.08362
16			81.43	1.227	0.08919
17			80.40	1.243	0.09477
18			79.37	1.259	0.10034
19			78.36	1.276	0.10592
20			77.36	1.292	0.11149
21			76.37	1.309	0.11707
22			75.40	1.326	0.12264
23			74.44	1.343	0.12822
24			73.49	1.360	0.13379
25			72.55	1.378	0.13937
26			71.62	1.396	0.14494
27			70.71	1.414	0.15052
28			69.81	1.432	0.15609
29			68.92	1.450	0.16166
30			68.04	1.469	0.16724
31			67.17	1.488	0.17281
32			66.32	1.507	0.17839
33			65.47	1.527	0.18396

t: d	h	min	N_t	N_0/N_t	$\log_{10} N_0/N_t$
34			64.63	1.547	0.18954
35			63.81	1.567	0.19511
36			63.00	1.587	0.20069
37			62.19	1.607	0.20626
38			61.40	1.628	0.21184
39			60.62	1.649	0.21741
40			59.84	1.671	0.22299
41			59.08	1.692	0.22856
42			58.33	1.714	0.23413
43			57.58	1.736	0.23971
44			56.85	1.759	0.24528
45			56.12	1.781	0.25086
46			55.41	1.804	0.25643
47			54.70	1.828	0.26201
48			54.00	1.851	0.26758
49			53.31	1.875	0.27316
50			52.63	1.899	0.27873
51			51.96	1.924	0.28431
52			51.30	1.949	0.28988
53			50.65	1.974	0.29546
54			50.00	2.000	0.30103
55			49.36	2.025	0.30661
56			48.73	2.052	0.31218
57			48.11	2.078	0.31775
58			47.50	2.105	0.32333
59			46.89	2.132	0.32890
60			46.29	2.160	0.33448
61			45.70	2.188	0.34005
62			45.12	2.216	0.34563
63			44.54	2.244	0.35120
64			43.98	2.273	0.35678
65			43.42	2.303	0.36235
66			42.86	2.333	0.36793
67			42.32	2.363	0.37350
68			41.78	2.393	0.37908
69			41.24	2.424	0.38465
70			40.72	2.455	0.39022
71			40.20	2.487	0.39580
72			39.69	2.519	0.40137
73			39.18	2.552	0.40695
74			38.68	2.585	0.41252
75			38.19	2.618	0.41810
76			37.70	2.652	0.42367
77			37.22	2.686	0.42925
78			36.74	2.721	0.43482
79			36.27	2.756	0.44040
80			35.81	2.792	0.44597
81			35.36	2.828	0.45155
82			34.90	2.864	0.45712
83			34.46	2.901	0.46269
84			34.02	2.939	0.46827
85			33.59	2.977	0.47384
86			33.16	3.015	0.47942
87			32.73	3.054	0.48499
88			32.32	3.094	0.49057
89			31.90	3.134	0.49614
90			31.50	3.174	0.50172
91			31.10	3.215	0.50729
92			30.70	3.257	0.51287
93			30.31	3.299	0.51844
94			29.92	3.342	0.52402
95			29.54	3.385	0.52959
96			29.16	3.428	0.53516
97			28.79	3.473	0.54074
98			28.42	3.518	0.54631
99			28.06	3.563	0.55189
100			27.70	3.609	0.55746
101			27.35	3.656	0.56304
102			27.00	3.703	0.56861
103			26.66	3.751	0.57419
104			26.32	3.799	0.57976
105			25.98	3.848	0.58534
106			25.65	3.898	0.59091
107			25.32	3.948	0.59649
108			25.00	3.999	0.60206
109			24.68	4.051	0.60763
110			24.37	4.104	0.61321
111			24.06	4.157	0.61878
112			23.75	4.210	0.62436
113			23.45	4.265	0.62993
114			23.15	4.320	0.63551
115			22.85	4.376	0.64108
116			22.56	4.432	0.64666
117			22.27	4.489	0.65223
118			21.99	4.547	0.65781
119			21.71	4.606	0.66338
120			21.43	4.666	0.66896
121			21.16	4.726	0.67453
122			20.89	4.787	0.68010
123			20.62	4.849	0.68568
124			20.36	4.911	0.69125
125			20.10	4.975	0.69683
126			19.84	5.039	0.70240
127			19.59	5.104	0.70798
128			19.34	5.170	0.71355
129			19.09	5.237	0.71913
130			18.85	5.305	0.72470
131			18.61	5.373	0.73028

t: d	h	min	N_t	N_0/N_t	$\log_{10} N_0/N_t$
132			18.37	5.443	0.73585
133			18.14	5.513	0.74142
134			17.91	5.584	0.74700
135			17.68	5.656	0.75257
136			17.45	5.729	0.75815
137			17.23	5.803	0.76372
138			17.01	5.878	0.76930
139			16.79	5.954	0.77487
140			16.58	6.031	0.78045
141			16.37	6.109	0.78602
142			16.16	6.188	0.79160
143			15.95	6.268	0.79717
144			15.75	6.349	0.80274
145			15.55	6.431	0.80832
146			15.35	6.514	0.81389
147			15.15	6.598	0.81947
148			14.96	6.684	0.82504
149			14.77	6.770	0.83062
150			14.58	6.857	0.83619
151			14.40	6.946	0.84177
152			14.21	7.036	0.84734
153			14.03	7.127	0.85292
154			13.85	7.219	0.85849
155			13.68	7.312	0.86406
156			13.50	7.406	0.86964
157			13.33	7.502	0.87521
158			13.16	7.599	0.88079
159			12.99	7.697	0.88636
160			12.83	7.797	0.89194
162			12.50	7.999	0.90308
164			12.18	8.207	0.91423
166			11.87	8.421	0.92538
168			11.57	8.640	0.93653
170			11.28	8.865	0.94768
172			10.99	9.095	0.95883
174			10.72	9.332	0.96998
176			10.44	9.574	0.98113
178			10.18	9.823	0.99227
180			9.92	10.079	1.00343
182			9.67	10.341	1.01458
184			9.42	10.610	1.02573
186			9.19	10.886	1.03688
188			8.95	11.169	1.04803
190			8.73	11.459	1.05918
192			8.50	11.757	1.07033
194			8.29	12.063	1.08148
196			8.08	12.377	1.09263
198			7.87	12.699	1.10378
200			7.67	13.029	1.11493
202			7.48	13.368	1.12608
204			7.29	13.715	1.13722
206			7.11	14.072	1.14837
208			6.93	14.438	1.15952
210			6.75	14.814	1.17067
212			6.58	15.199	1.18182
214			6.41	15.594	1.19297
216			6.25	16.000	1.20412
218			6.09	16.416	1.21527
220			5.94	16.842	1.22642
222			5.79	17.280	1.23757
224			5.64	17.730	1.24872
226			5.50	18.191	1.25987
228			5.36	18.664	1.27102
230			5.22	19.149	1.28217
232			5.09	19.647	1.29331
234			4.96	20.158	1.30446
236			4.83	20.682	1.31561
238			4.71	21.220	1.32676
240			4.59	21.772	1.33791
242			4.48	22.338	1.34906
244			4.36	22.919	1.36021
246			4.25	23.515	1.37136
248			4.14	24.127	1.38251
250			4.04	24.754	1.39366
252			3.94	25.398	1.40481
254			3.84	26.058	1.41596
256			3.74	26.736	1.42711
258			3.65	27.431	1.43826
260			3.55	28.145	1.44940
262			3.46	28.877	1.46055
264			3.38	29.627	1.47170
266			3.29	30.398	1.48285
268			3.21	31.188	1.49400
270			3.13	32.000	1.50515
280			2.75	36.382	1.56090
290			2.42	41.365	1.61664
300			2.13	47.031	1.67239
310			1.87	53.473	1.72814
320			1.64	60.796	1.78388
330			1.45	69.123	1.83963
340			1.27	78.590	1.89537
350			1.12	89.353	1.95111
360			0.98	101.594	2.00687
370			0.87	115.508	2.06261
380			0.76	131.328	2.11836
390			0.67	149.316	2.17411
400			0.59	169.767	2.22986

t: d	t: h	t: min	N_t	N_0/N_t	$\log_{10} N_0/N_t$
410			0.52	193.016	2.28560
420			0.46	219.452	2.34134
430			0.40	249.513	2.39709
440			0.35	283.687	2.45284
450			0.31	322.539	2.50858
460			0.27	366.716	2.56433
470			0.24	416.944	2.62008
480			0.21	474.045	2.67582
490			0.19	538.967	2.73156

Iodine-131

Half-life 8.05 d

t: d	t: h	t: min	N_t	N_0/N_t	$\log_{10} N_0/N_t$
	0		100.00	1.000	0.00000
	1		99.64	1.003	0.00156
	2		99.29	1.007	0.00312
	3		98.93	1.010	0.00467
	4		98.58	1.014	0.00623
	5		98.22	1.018	0.00779
	6		97.87	1.021	0.00935
	7		97.52	1.025	0.01091
	8		97.17	1.029	0.01247
	9		96.82	1.032	0.01402
	10		96.48	1.036	0.01558
	11		96.13	1.040	0.01714
	12		95.79	1.043	0.01870
	13		95.44	1.047	0.02026
	14		95.10	1.051	0.02181
	15		94.76	1.055	0.02337
	16		94.42	1.059	0.02493
	17		94.08	1.062	0.02649
	18		93.75	1.066	0.02805
	19		93.41	1.070	0.02960
	20		93.08	1.074	0.03116
	21		92.74	1.078	0.03272
	22		92.41	1.082	0.03428
	23		92.08	1.086	0.03584
1	00		91.75	1.089	0.03740
	01		91.42	1.093	0.03895
	02		91.09	1.097	0.04051
	03		90.77	1.101	0.04207
	04		90.44	1.105	0.04363
	05		90.12	1.109	0.04519
	06		89.80	1.113	0.04674
	07		89.47	1.117	0.04830
	08		89.15	1.121	0.04986
	09		88.83	1.125	0.05142
	10		88.52	1.129	0.05298
	11		88.20	1.133	0.05453
	12		87.88	1.137	0.05609
	13		87.57	1.141	0.05765
	14		87.26	1.146	0.05921
	15		86.94	1.150	0.06077
	16		86.63	1.154	0.06233
	17		86.32	1.158	0.06388
	18		86.01	1.162	0.06544
	19		85.70	1.166	0.06700
	20		85.40	1.171	0.06856
	21		85.09	1.175	0.07012
	22		84.79	1.179	0.07167
	23		84.48	1.183	0.07323
2	00		84.18	1.187	0.07479
	01		83.88	1.192	0.07635
	02		83.58	1.196	0.07791
	03		83.28	1.200	0.07947
	04		82.98	1.205	0.08102
	05		82.68	1.209	0.08258
	06		82.39	1.213	0.08414
	07		82.09	1.218	0.08570
	08		81.80	1.222	0.08726
	09		81.51	1.226	0.08881
	10		81.21	1.231	0.09037
	11		80.92	1.235	0.09193
	12		80.63	1.240	0.09349
	13		80.34	1.244	0.09505
	14		80.06	1.249	0.09660
	15		79.77	1.253	0.09816
	16		79.48	1.258	0.09972
	17		79.20	1.262	0.10128
	18		78.92	1.267	0.10284
	19		78.63	1.271	0.10440
	20		78.35	1.276	0.10595
	21		78.07	1.280	0.10751
	22		77.79	1.285	0.10907
	23		77.51	1.290	0.11063
3	00		77.24	1.294	0.11219
	01		76.96	1.299	0.11374
	02		76.68	1.304	0.11530
	03		76.41	1.308	0.11686
	04		76.13	1.313	0.11842
	05		75.86	1.318	0.11998
	06		75.59	1.322	0.12153
	07		75.32	1.327	0.12309
	08		75.05	1.332	0.12465
	09		74.78	1.337	0.12621
	10		74.51	1.342	0.12777
	11		74.25	1.346	0.12933
	12		73.98	1.351	0.13088
	13		73.72	1.356	0.13244
	14		73.45	1.361	0.13400
	15		73.19	1.366	0.13556
	16		72.93	1.371	0.13712
	17		72.67	1.376	0.13867
	18		72.41	1.381	0.14023
	19		72.15	1.386	0.14179
	20		71.89	1.391	0.14335
	21		71.63	1.396	0.14491
	22		71.37	1.401	0.14646
	23		71.12	1.406	0.14802
4	00		70.86	1.411	0.14958
	01		70.61	1.416	0.15114
	02		70.36	1.421	0.15270
	03		70.10	1.426	0.15425
	04		69.85	1.431	0.15581
	05		69.60	1.436	0.15737
	06		69.35	1.441	0.15893
	07		69.11	1.447	0.16049
	08		68.86	1.452	0.16205
	09		68.61	1.457	0.16360
	10		68.37	1.462	0.16516
	11		68.12	1.467	0.16672
	12		67.88	1.473	0.16828
	13		67.63	1.478	0.16984
	14		67.39	1.483	0.17139
	15		67.15	1.489	0.17295
	16		66.91	1.494	0.17451
	17		66.67	1.499	0.17607
	18		66.43	1.505	0.17763
	19		66.19	1.510	0.17918
	20		65.96	1.516	0.18074
	21		65.72	1.521	0.18230
	22		65.48	1.527	0.18386
	23		65.25	1.532	0.18542
5	00		65.02	1.538	0.18698
	06		63.63	1.571	0.19632
	12		62.28	1.605	0.20567
	18		60.95	1.640	0.21502
6	00		59.65	1.676	0.22437
	06		58.38	1.712	0.23372
	12		57.14	1.750	0.24307
	18		55.92	1.788	0.25242
7	00		54.73	1.827	0.26177
	06		53.57	1.866	0.27111
	12		52.42	1.907	0.28046
	18		51.31	1.948	0.28981
8	00		50.22	1.991	0.29916
	06		49.15	2.034	0.30851
	12		48.10	2.079	0.31786
	18		47.08	2.124	0.32721
9	00		46.07	2.170	0.33656
	06		45.09	2.217	0.34590
	12		44.13	2.265	0.35525
	18		43.19	2.315	0.36460
10	00		42.27	2.365	0.37395
	06		41.37	2.417	0.38330
	12		40.49	2.469	0.39265
	18		39.63	2.523	0.40200
11	00		38.78	2.578	0.41135
	06		37.96	2.634	0.42069
	12		37.15	2.691	0.43004
	18		36.36	2.750	0.43939
12	00		35.58	2.810	0.44874
	06		34.83	2.871	0.45809
	12		34.08	2.933	0.46744
	18		33.36	2.997	0.47679
13	00		32.65	3.062	0.48614
	06		31.95	3.129	0.49548
	12		31.27	3.197	0.50483
	18		30.61	3.267	0.51418
14	00		29.96	3.338	0.52353
	06		29.32	3.410	0.53288
	12		28.69	3.485	0.54223
	18		28.08	3.561	0.55158
15	00		27.48	3.638	0.56093
	06		26.90	3.717	0.57027
	12		26.33	3.798	0.57962
	18		25.76	3.881	0.58897
16	00		25.22	3.965	0.59832
	06		24.68	4.051	0.60767
	12		24.15	4.140	0.61702
	18		23.64	4.230	0.62637
17	00		23.14	4.322	0.63572
	06		22.64	4.416	0.64506
	12		22.16	4.512	0.65441
	18		21.69	4.610	0.66376
18	00		21.23	4.710	0.67311
	06		20.78	4.813	0.68246
	12		20.33	4.918	0.69181
	18		19.90	5.025	0.70116
19	00		19.48	5.134	0.71051
	06		19.06	5.246	0.71985
	12		18.66	5.360	0.72920
	18		18.26	5.477	0.73855
20	00		17.87	5.596	0.74790
	06		17.49	5.718	0.75725
	12		17.12	5.842	0.76660
	18		16.75	5.969	0.77595
21	00		16.39	6.099	0.78529
	06		16.05	6.232	0.79464
	12		15.70	6.367	0.80399
	18		15.37	6.506	0.81334
22	00		15.04	6.647	0.82269
	06		14.72	6.792	0.83204
	12		14.41	6.940	0.84139
	18		14.10	7.091	0.85073
23	00		13.80	7.245	0.86008
	06		13.51	7.403	0.86943
	12		13.22	7.564	0.87878
	18		12.94	7.729	0.88813
24	00		12.66	7.897	0.89748
	06		12.39	8.069	0.90682
	12		12.13	8.244	0.91617
	18		11.87	8.424	0.92552
25	00		11.62	8.607	0.93487
	06		11.37	8.794	0.94422
	12		11.13	8.985	0.95357
	18		10.89	9.181	0.96291
26	00		10.66	9.381	0.97226
	06		10.43	9.585	0.98161
	12		10.21	9.793	0.99096
	18		9.99	10.007	1.00032
27	00		9.78	10.225	1.00967
	06		9.57	10.447	1.01901
	12		9.37	10.674	1.02836
	18		9.17	10.907	1.03771
28	00		8.97	11.144	1.04706
	06		8.78	11.387	1.05641
	12		8.59	11.634	1.06576
	18		8.41	11.887	1.07511
29	00		8.23	12.146	1.08446
	06		8.06	12.410	1.09381
	12		7.89	12.680	1.10315
	18		7.72	12.956	1.11250
30	00		7.55	13.238	1.12185
	06		7.39	13.526	1.13120
	12		7.24	13.821	1.14055
	18		7.08	14.122	1.14990
31	00		6.93	14.429	1.15925
	06		6.78	14.743	1.16860
	12		6.64	15.064	1.17794
	18		6.50	15.391	1.18729
32	00		6.36	15.726	1.19664
	06		6.22	16.069	1.20599
	12		6.09	16.418	1.21534
	18		5.96	16.775	1.22469
33	00		5.83	17.140	1.23404
	06		5.71	17.513	1.24338
	12		5.59	17.895	1.25273
	18		5.47	18.284	1.26208
34	00		5.35	18.682	1.27143
	06		5.24	19.088	1.28078
	12		5.13	19.504	1.29013
	18		5.02	19.928	1.29948
35	00		4.91	20.362	1.30883
	06		4.81	20.805	1.31818
	12		4.70	21.258	1.32752
	18		4.60	21.720	1.33687
36	00		4.51	22.193	1.34622
	06		4.41	22.676	1.35557
	12		4.32	23.169	1.36492
	18		4.22	23.673	1.37427
37	00		4.13	24.188	1.38362
	06		4.05	24.715	1.39296
	12		3.96	25.253	1.40231
	18		3.88	25.802	1.41166
38	00		3.79	26.364	1.42101
	06		3.71	26.937	1.43036
	12		3.63	27.523	1.43971
	18		3.56	28.122	1.44906
39	00		3.48	28.734	1.45841
	06		3.41	29.359	1.46776
	12		3.33	29.998	1.47710
	18		3.26	30.651	1.48645
40	00		3.19	31.318	1.49580
	06		3.13	32.000	1.50515
	12		3.06	32.696	1.51450
	18		2.99	33.407	1.52385
41	00		2.93	34.134	1.53320
	06		2.87	34.877	1.54255
	12		2.81	35.636	1.55189
	18		2.75	36.411	1.56124
42	00		2.69	37.204	1.57059
	06		2.63	38.013	1.57994
	12		2.57	38.840	1.58929
	18		2.52	39.686	1.59864
43	00		2.47	40.549	1.60799
	06		2.41	41.431	1.61734
	12		2.36	42.333	1.62668
	18		2.31	43.254	1.63603
44	00		2.26	44.195	1.64538
	06		2.21	45.157	1.65473
	12		2.17	46.140	1.66408
	18		2.12	47.144	1.67343
45	00		2.08	48.169	1.68278
	06		2.03	49.217	1.69212
	12		1.99	50.288	1.70147
	18		1.95	51.383	1.71082
46	00		1.90	52.501	1.72017
	06		1.86	53.643	1.72952
	12		1.82	54.811	1.73887
	18		1.79	56.003	1.74822
47	00		1.75	57.222	1.75757
	06		1.71	58.467	1.76691
	12		1.67	59.739	1.77626
	18		1.64	61.039	1.78561
48	00		1.60	62.367	1.79496
	06		1.57	63.724	1.80431
	12		1.54	65.111	1.81366
	18		1.50	66.528	1.82301
49	00		1.47	67.975	1.83236
	06		1.44	69.454	1.84170
	12		1.41	70.965	1.85105
	18		1.38	72.510	1.86040
50			1.35	74.087	1.86975
51			1.24	80.749	1.90714
52			1.14	88.010	1.94453
53			1.04	95.924	1.98193
54			0.96	104.552	2.01933
55			0.88	113.953	2.05673
56			0.81	124.200	2.09412
57			0.74	135.367	2.13151
58			0.68	147.540	2.16891
59			0.62	160.807	2.20631
60			0.57	175.266	2.24370
61			0.52	191.029	2.28110
62			0.48	208.203	2.31849
63			0.44	226.927	2.35589
64			0.40	247.334	2.39329
65			0.37	269.570	2.43067
66			0.34	293.815	2.46807
67			0.31	320.235	2.50547
68			0.29	349.027	2.54286
69			0.26	380.416	2.58026
70			0.24	414.628	2.61766
71			0.22	451.895	2.65504
72			0.20	492.538	2.69244

Iodine-133

Half-life 21 h

t: d	t: h	t: min	N_t	N_0/N_t	$\log_{10} N_0/N_t$
		00	100.00	1.000	0.00000
		10	99.45	1.005	0.00239
		20	98.91	1.011	0.00478
		30	98.36	1.016	0.00717
		40	97.82	1.022	0.00956
		50	97.29	1.027	0.01195
	1	00	96.75	1.033	0.01434
		10	96.22	1.039	0.01672
		20	95.69	1.044	0.01911
		30	95.17	1.050	0.02150
		40	94.65	1.056	0.02389
		50	94.13	1.062	0.02628
	2	00	93.61	1.068	0.02867
		10	93.10	1.074	0.03106
		20	92.59	1.080	0.03345
		30	92.08	1.086	0.03584
		40	91.57	1.092	0.03823
		50	91.07	1.098	0.04062
	3	00	90.57	1.104	0.04300
		10	90.08	1.110	0.04539
		20	89.58	1.116	0.04778
		30	89.09	1.122	0.05017
		40	88.60	1.128	0.05256
		50	88.12	1.134	0.05495
	4	00	87.63	1.141	0.05734
		10	87.15	1.147	0.05973
		20	86.67	1.153	0.06212
		30	86.20	1.160	0.06451
		40	85.72	1.166	0.06690
		50	85.25	1.172	0.06929
	5	00	84.79	1.179	0.07167
		10	84.32	1.185	0.07406
		20	83.86	1.192	0.07645
		30	83.40	1.199	0.07884
		40	82.94	1.205	0.08123
		50	82.49	1.212	0.08362
	6	00	82.03	1.219	0.08601
		10	81.58	1.225	0.08840
		20	81.14	1.232	0.09079
		30	80.69	1.239	0.09318
		40	80.25	1.246	0.09557
		50	79.81	1.253	0.09795
	7	00	79.37	1.259	0.10034
		10	78.93	1.266	0.10273
		20	78.50	1.273	0.10512
		30	78.07	1.280	0.10751
		40	77.64	1.287	0.10990
		50	77.22	1.295	0.11229
	8	00	76.79	1.302	0.11468
		10	76.37	1.309	0.11707
		20	75.95	1.316	0.11946

t: d	t: h	t: min	N_t	N_0/N_t	$\log_{10} N_0/N_t$
		30	75.54	1.323	0.12185
		40	75.12	1.331	0.12424
		50	74.71	1.338	0.12662
	9	00	74.30	1.345	0.12901
		10	73.89	1.353	0.13140
		20	73.49	1.360	0.13379
		30	73.08	1.368	0.13618
		40	72.68	1.375	0.13857
		50	72.28	1.383	0.14096
	10	00	71.89	1.391	0.14335
		10	71.49	1.398	0.14574
		20	71.10	1.406	0.14813
		30	70.71	1.414	0.15052
		40	70.32	1.422	0.15290
		50	69.94	1.429	0.15529
	11	00	69.55	1.437	0.15768
		10	69.17	1.445	0.16007
		20	68.79	1.453	0.16246
		30	68.41	1.461	0.16485
		40	68.04	1.469	0.16724
		50	67.67	1.477	0.16963
	12	00	67.30	1.485	0.17202
		10	66.93	1.494	0.17441
		20	66.56	1.502	0.17680
		30	66.19	1.510	0.17918
		40	65.83	1.519	0.18157
		50	65.47	1.527	0.18396
	13	00	65.11	1.535	0.18635
		10	64.75	1.544	0.18874
		20	64.40	1.552	0.19113
		30	64.04	1.561	0.19352
		40	63.69	1.570	0.19591
		50	63.34	1.578	0.19830
	14	00	63.00	1.587	0.20069
		10	62.65	1.596	0.20308
		20	62.31	1.604	0.20547
		30	61.96	1.613	0.20785
		40	61.62	1.622	0.21024
		50	61.29	1.631	0.21263
	15	00	60.95	1.640	0.21502
		10	60.62	1.649	0.21741
		20	60.28	1.658	0.21980
		30	59.95	1.667	0.22219
		40	59.62	1.677	0.22458
		50	59.30	1.686	0.22697
	16	00	58.97	1.695	0.22936
		10	58.65	1.705	0.23175
		20	58.33	1.714	0.23413
		30	58.01	1.723	0.23652
		40	57.69	1.733	0.23891
		50	57.37	1.743	0.24130
	17	00	57.06	1.752	0.24369
		10	56.74	1.762	0.24608
		20	56.43	1.772	0.24847
		30	56.12	1.781	0.25086
		40	55.82	1.791	0.25325
		50	55.51	1.801	0.25564
	18	00	55.20	1.811	0.25803
		10	54.90	1.821	0.26042
		20	54.60	1.831	0.26280
		30	54.30	1.841	0.26519
		40	54.00	1.851	0.26758
		50	53.71	1.861	0.26997
	19	00	53.41	1.872	0.27236
		10	53.12	1.882	0.27475
		20	52.83	1.892	0.27714
		30	52.54	1.903	0.27953
		40	52.25	1.913	0.28192
		50	51.96	1.924	0.28431
	20	00	51.68	1.935	0.28670
		10	51.39	1.945	0.28908
		20	51.11	1.956	0.29147
		30	50.83	1.967	0.29386
		40	50.55	1.978	0.29625
		50	50.28	1.989	0.29864
	21	00	50.00	2.000	0.30103
		10	49.73	2.011	0.30342
		20	49.45	2.022	0.30581
		30	49.18	2.033	0.30820
		40	48.91	2.044	0.31059
		50	48.64	2.055	0.31298
	22	00	48.38	2.067	0.31537
		10	48.11	2.078	0.31775
		20	47.85	2.089	0.32014
		30	47.58	2.101	0.32253
		40	47.32	2.113	0.32492
		50	47.06	2.124	0.32731
	23	00	46.81	2.136	0.32970
		10	46.55	2.148	0.33209
		20	46.29	2.160	0.33448
		30	46.04	2.172	0.33687
		40	45.79	2.184	0.33926
		50	45.54	2.196	0.34165
1	00		45.29	2.208	0.34403
	01		43.82	2.282	0.35837
	02		42.39	2.358	0.37270
	03		41.02	2.438	0.38704
	04		39.69	2.519	0.40137
	05		38.40	2.604	0.41571

t: d	t: h	t: min	N_t	N_0/N_t	$\log_{10} N_0/N_t$
	06		37.15	2.691	0.43004
	07		35.94	2.782	0.44438
	08		34.78	2.875	0.45871
	09		33.65	2.971	0.47305
	10		32.56	3.071	0.48738
	11		31.50	3.174	0.50172
	12		30.48	3.281	0.51605
	13		29.49	3.391	0.53039
	14		28.53	3.505	0.54472
	15		27.60	3.622	0.55906
	16		26.71	3.744	0.57339
	17		25.84	3.870	0.58773
	18		25.00	3.999	0.60206
	19		24.19	4.134	0.61640
	20		23.40	4.272	0.63073
	21		22.64	4.416	0.64506
	22		21.91	4.564	0.65940
	23		21.20	4.717	0.67373
2	00		20.51	4.876	0.68807
	01		19.84	5.039	0.70240
	02		19.20	5.208	0.71674
	03		18.57	5.383	0.73107
	04		17.97	5.564	0.74541
	05		17.39	5.750	0.75974
	06		16.82	5.943	0.77408
	07		16.28	6.143	0.78841
	08		15.75	6.349	0.80274
	09		15.24	6.562	0.81708
	10		14.74	6.782	0.83141
	11		14.26	7.010	0.84575
	12		13.80	7.245	0.86008
	13		13.35	7.488	0.87442
	14		12.92	7.740	0.88875
	15		12.50	7.999	0.90308
	16		12.09	8.268	0.91742
	17		11.70	8.545	0.93175
	18		11.32	8.832	0.94609
	19		10.95	9.128	0.96042
	20		10.60	9.435	0.97475
	21		10.25	9.751	0.98909
	22		9.92	10.079	1.00343
	23		9.60	10.417	1.01777
3	00		9.29	10.767	1.03210
	01		8.99	11.128	1.04644
	02		8.69	11.501	1.06077
	03		8.41	11.887	1.07511
	04		8.14	12.286	1.08944
	05		7.87	12.699	1.10378
	06		7.62	13.125	1.11811
	07		7.37	13.565	1.13245
	08		7.13	14.021	1.14678
	09		6.90	14.491	1.16112
	10		6.68	14.977	1.17545
	11		6.46	15.480	1.18979
	12		6.25	16.000	1.20412
	13		6.05	16.536	1.21846
	14		5.85	17.091	1.23279
	15		5.66	17.665	1.24712
	16		5.48	18.258	1.26146
	17		5.30	18.870	1.27579
	18		5.13	19.504	1.29013
	19		4.96	20.158	1.30446
	20		4.80	20.835	1.31880
	21		4.64	21.534	1.33313
	22		4.49	22.257	1.34747
	23		4.35	23.003	1.36180
4	00		4.21	23.775	1.37614
	01		4.07	24.573	1.39047
	02		3.94	25.398	1.40481
	03		3.81	26.250	1.41914
	04		3.69	27.131	1.43348
	05		3.57	28.042	1.44781
	06		3.45	28.983	1.46215
	07		3.34	29.955	1.47648
	08		3.23	30.960	1.49082
	09		3.13	32.000	1.50515
	10		3.02	33.073	1.51948
	11		2.93	34.183	1.53382
	12		2.83	35.330	1.54815
	13		2.74	36.516	1.56249
	14		2.65	37.741	1.57682
	15		2.56	39.008	1.59116
	16		2.48	40.317	1.60549
	17		2.40	41.670	1.61983
	18		2.32	43.068	1.63416
	19		2.25	44.514	1.64850
	20		2.17	46.007	1.66283
	21		2.10	47.551	1.67717
	22		2.03	49.147	1.69150
	23		1.97	50.796	1.70584
5	00		1.90	52.501	1.72017
	06		1.56	63.999	1.80618
	12		1.28	78.015	1.89218
	18		1.05	95.101	1.97819
6	00		0.86	115.932	2.06421
	06		0.71	141.322	2.15021
	12		0.58	172.274	2.23622
	18		0.48	210.004	2.32223
7	00		0.39	255.996	2.40823
	06		0.32	312.070	2.49425
	12		0.26	380.416	2.58026
	18		0.22	463.735	2.66627
8	00		0.18	565.291	2.75227
	06		0.15	689.084	2.83827
	12		0.12	839.983	2.92427
	18		0.10	1023.960	3.01028

Gold-198

Half-life 2.70 d

t: d	t: h	N_t	N_0/N_t	$\log_{10} N_0/N_t$
	0	100.00	1.000	0.00000
	1	98.94	1.010	0.00465
	2	97.88	1.021	0.00929
	3	96.84	1.032	0.01394
	4	95.81	1.043	0.01858
	5	94.79	1.054	0.02323
	6	93.78	1.066	0.02787
	7	92.79	1.077	0.03252
	8	91.80	1.089	0.03716
	9	90.82	1.101	0.04181
	10	89.86	1.112	0.04646
	11	88.90	1.124	0.05110
	12	87.95	1.136	0.05575
	13	87.02	1.149	0.06039
	14	86.09	1.161	0.06504
	15	85.18	1.174	0.06968
	16	84.27	1.186	0.07433
	17	83.37	1.199	0.07897
	18	82.49	1.212	0.08362
	19	81.61	1.225	0.08827
	20	80.74	1.238	0.09291
	21	79.88	1.251	0.09756
	22	79.03	1.265	0.10220
	23	78.19	1.278	0.10685
1	00	77.36	1.292	0.11149
	01	76.54	1.306	0.11614
	02	75.72	1.320	0.12078
	03	74.92	1.334	0.12543
	04	74.12	1.349	0.13008
	05	73.33	1.363	0.13472
	06	72.55	1.378	0.13937
	07	71.78	1.393	0.14401
	08	71.01	1.408	0.14866
	09	70.26	1.423	0.15330
	10	69.51	1.438	0.15795
	11	68.77	1.454	0.16259
	12	68.04	1.469	0.16724
	13	67.32	1.485	0.17188
	14	66.60	1.501	0.17653
	15	65.89	1.517	0.18118
	16	65.19	1.533	0.18582
	17	64.50	1.550	0.19047
	18	63.81	1.567	0.19511
	19	63.13	1.584	0.19976
	20	62.46	1.601	0.20440
	21	61.79	1.618	0.20905
	22	61.14	1.635	0.21369
	23	60.49	1.653	0.21834
2	00	59.84	1.671	0.22299
	01	59.21	1.689	0.22763
	02	58.58	1.707	0.23228
	03	57.95	1.725	0.23692
	04	57.34	1.744	0.24157
	05	56.73	1.762	0.24621
	06	56.12	1.781	0.25086
	07	55.53	1.800	0.25550
	08	54.94	1.820	0.26015
	09	54.35	1.839	0.26480
	10	53.77	1.859	0.26944
	11	53.20	1.879	0.27409
	12	52.63	1.899	0.27873
	13	52.07	1.920	0.28338
	14	51.52	1.940	0.28802
	15	50.97	1.961	0.29267
	16	50.43	1.982	0.29731
	17	49.89	2.004	0.30196
	18	49.36	2.025	0.30661
	19	48.84	2.047	0.31125
	20	48.32	2.069	0.31590
	21	47.80	2.091	0.32054
	22	47.29	2.114	0.32519
	23	46.79	2.137	0.32983
3	00	46.29	2.160	0.33448
	01	45.80	2.183	0.33912
	02	45.31	2.206	0.34377
	03	44.83	2.230	0.34841
	04	44.35	2.254	0.35306
	05	43.88	2.278	0.35771
	06	43.42	2.303	0.36235
	07	42.95	2.328	0.36700
	08	42.50	2.353	0.37164
	09	42.04	2.378	0.37629
	10	41.60	2.403	0.38093
	11	41.15	2.429	0.38558
	12	40.72	2.455	0.39022
	13	40.28	2.482	0.39487
	14	39.86	2.509	0.39952

t: d	t: h	t: min	N_t	N_0/N_t	$\log_{10} N_0/N_t$
	15		39.43	2.536	0.40416
	16		39.01	2.563	0.40881
	17		38.60	2.590	0.41345
	18		38.19	2.618	0.41810
	19		37.78	2.646	0.42274
	20		37.38	2.675	0.42739
	21		36.98	2.704	0.43203
	22		36.59	2.733	0.43668
	23		36.20	2.762	0.44133
4	00		35.81	2.792	0.44597
	01		35.43	2.822	0.45062
	02		35.05	2.852	0.45526
	03		34.68	2.883	0.45991
	04		34.31	2.914	0.46455
	05		33.95	2.945	0.46920
	06		33.59	2.977	0.47384
	07		33.23	3.009	0.47849
	08		32.87	3.041	0.48313
	09		32.53	3.074	0.48778
	10		32.18	3.107	0.49243
	11		31.84	3.141	0.49707
	12		31.50	3.174	0.50172
	13		31.16	3.208	0.50636
	14		30.83	3.243	0.51101
	15		30.50	3.278	0.51565
	16		30.18	3.313	0.52030
	17		29.86	3.349	0.52494
	18		29.54	3.385	0.52959
	19		29.23	3.421	0.53424
	20		28.91	3.458	0.53888
	21		28.61	3.495	0.54353
	22		28.30	3.533	0.54817
	23		28.00	3.571	0.55282
5	00		27.70	3.609	0.55746
	06		25.98	3.848	0.58534
	12		24.37	4.104	0.61321
	18		22.85	4.376	0.64108
6	00		21.43	4.666	0.66896
	06		20.10	4.975	0.69683
	12		18.85	5.305	0.72470
	18		17.68	5.656	0.75257
7	00		16.58	6.031	0.78045
	06		15.55	6.431	0.80832
	12		14.58	6.857	0.83619
	18		13.68	7.312	0.86406
8	00		12.83	7.797	0.89194
	06		12.03	8.313	0.91981
	12		11.28	8.865	0.94768
	18		10.58	9.452	0.97555
9	00		9.92	10.079	1.00343
	06		9.30	10.747	1.03131
	12		8.73	11.459	1.05918
	18		8.18	12.219	1.08705
10	00		7.67	13.029	1.11493
	06		7.20	13.893	1.14280
	12		6.75	14.814	1.17067
	18		6.33	15.795	1.19855
11	00		5.94	16.842	1.22642
	06		5.57	17.959	1.25429
	12		5.22	19.149	1.28217
	18		4.90	20.419	1.31004
12	00		4.59	21.772	1.33791
	06		4.31	23.215	1.36578
	12		4.04	24.754	1.39366
	18		3.79	26.395	1.42153
13	00		3.55	28.145	1.44940
	06		3.33	30.010	1.47728
	12		3.13	32.000	1.50515
	18		2.93	34.121	1.53302
14	00		2.75	36.382	1.56090
	06		2.58	38.794	1.58877
	12		2.42	41.365	1.61664
	18		2.27	44.107	1.64452
15	00		2.13	47.031	1.67239
	06		1.99	50.148	1.70026
	12		1.87	53.473	1.72814
	18		1.75	57.017	1.75601
16	00		1.64	60.796	1.78388
	06		1.54	64.826	1.81175
	12		1.45	69.123	1.83963
	18		1.36	73.705	1.86750
17	00		1.27	78.590	1.89537
	06		1.19	83.799	1.92324
	12		1.12	89.353	1.95111
	18		1.05	95.276	1.97899
18	00		0.98	101.594	2.00687
	06		0.92	108.328	2.03474
	12		0.87	115.508	2.06261
	18		0.81	123.164	2.09049
19	00		0.76	131.328	2.11836
	06		0.71	140.034	2.14624
	12		0.67	149.316	2.17411
	18		0.63	159.212	2.20198
20			0.59	169.767	2.22986
25			0.16	612.782	2.78731
30			0.05	2211.900	3.34477
35			0.01	7987.220	3.90240

Isotope Decay Tables – Cobalt-60

Half-life 5.2 y

d →	0			10			20			30			40		
↓	N_t	N_0/N_t	$\log_{10} N_0/N_t$	N_t	N_0/N_t	$\log_{10} N_0/N_t$	N_t	N_0/N_t	$\log_{10} N_0/N_t$	N_t	N_0/N_t	$\log_{10} N_0/N_t$	N_t	N_0/N_t	$\log_{10} N_0/N_t$
0	100.00	1.000	0.00000	99.64	1.003	0.00159	99.27	1.007	0.00317	98.91	1.011	0.00476	98.55	1.014	0.00634
100	96.42	1.037	0.01585	96.06	1.040	0.01744	95.72	1.044	0.01902	95.37	1.048	0.02061	95.02	1.052	0.02219
200	92.96	1.075	0.03170	92.62	1.079	0.03329	92.28	1.083	0.03487	91.95	1.087	0.03646	91.61	1.091	0.03804
300	89.63	1.115	0.04755	89.30	1.119	0.04914	88.98	1.123	0.05072	88.65	1.127	0.05231	88.33	1.132	0.05389
400	86.42	1.157	0.06340	86.10	1.161	0.06499	85.79	1.165	0.06657	85.48	1.169	0.06816	85.16	1.174	0.06974
500	83.32	1.200	0.07925	83.02	1.204	0.08084	82.71	1.208	0.08242	82.41	1.213	0.08401	82.11	1.217	0.08559
600	80.33	1.244	0.09510	80.04	1.249	0.09669	79.75	1.253	0.09827	79.46	1.258	0.09986	79.17	1.263	0.10144
700	77.46	1.291	0.11095	77.17	1.295	0.11254	76.89	1.300	0.11412	76.61	1.305	0.11571	76.33	1.310	0.11729
800	74.68	1.339	0.12680	74.41	1.343	0.12839	74.14	1.348	0.12997	73.87	1.353	0.13155	73.60	1.358	0.13314
900	72.00	1.388	0.14265	71.74	1.393	0.14423	71.48	1.399	0.14582	71.22	1.404	0.14740	70.96	1.409	0.14899
1000	69.42	1.440	0.15850	69.17	1.445	0.16008	68.92	1.451	0.16167	68.67	1.456	0.16325	68.42	1.461	0.16484
1100	66.93	1.493	0.17435	66.69	1.499	0.17593	66.45	1.504	0.17752	66.21	1.510	0.17910	65.96	1.515	0.18069
1200	64.54	1.549	0.19020	64.30	1.555	0.19178	64.07	1.560	0.19337	63.83	1.566	0.19495	63.60	1.572	0.19654
1300	62.22	1.607	0.20605	62.00	1.612	0.20763	61.77	1.618	0.20922	61.55	1.624	0.21080	61.32	1.630	0.21239
1400	59.99	1.666	0.22190	59.77	1.672	0.22348	59.56	1.679	0.22507	59.34	1.685	0.22665	59.12	1.691	0.22824
1500	57.84	1.728	0.23775	57.63	1.735	0.23933	57.42	1.741	0.24092	57.21	1.747	0.24250	57.00	1.754	0.24409
1600	55.77	1.793	0.25360	55.57	1.799	0.25518	55.36	1.806	0.25677	55.16	1.812	0.25835	54.96	1.819	0.25994
1700	53.77	1.859	0.26945	53.58	1.866	0.27103	53.38	1.873	0.27262	53.19	1.880	0.27420	52.99	1.887	0.27579
1800	51.84	1.928	0.28530	51.66	1.935	0.28688	51.47	1.942	0.28847	51.28	1.950	0.29005	51.09	1.957	0.29164
1900	49.99	2.000	0.30115	49.80	2.007	0.30273	49.62	2.015	0.30432	49.44	2.022	0.30590	49.26	2.029	0.30749
2000	48.19	2.074	0.31700	48.02	2.082	0.31858	47.84	2.090	0.32017	47.67	2.097	0.32175	47.50	2.105	0.32334
2100	46.47	2.152	0.33285	46.30	2.159	0.33443	46.13	2.167	0.33602	45.96	2.175	0.33760	45.79	2.183	0.33919
2200	44.80	2.232	0.34870	44.64	2.240	0.35028	44.48	2.248	0.35187	44.31	2.256	0.35345	44.15	2.264	0.35504
2300	43.20	2.314	0.36455	43.04	2.323	0.36613	42.88	2.331	0.36772	42.73	2.340	0.36930	42.57	2.349	0.37089
2400	41.65	2.401	0.38040	41.50	2.409	0.38198	41.35	2.418	0.38357	41.20	2.427	0.38515	41.05	2.436	0.38674
2500	40.16	2.490	0.39625	40.01	2.499	0.39783	39.86	2.508	0.39942	39.72	2.517	0.40100	39.57	2.526	0.40259
2600	38.72	2.582	0.41210	38.58	2.592	0.41368	38.44	2.601	0.41527	38.30	2.611	0.41685	38.16	2.620	0.41844
2700	37.33	2.678	0.42795	37.19	2.688	0.42953	37.06	2.698	0.43112	36.92	2.708	0.43270	36.79	2.718	0.43429
2800	35.99	2.778	0.44380	35.86	2.788	0.44538	35.73	2.798	0.44697	35.60	2.809	0.44855	35.47	2.819	0.45014
2900	34.70	2.881	0.45965	34.58	2.892	0.46123	34.45	2.902	0.46282	34.32	2.913	0.46440	34.20	2.924	0.46599
3000	33.46	2.988	0.47550	33.34	2.999	0.47708	33.21	3.010	0.47867	33.09	3.021	0.48025	32.97	3.032	0.48184
3100	32.26	3.099	0.49135	32.14	3.111	0.49293	32.02	3.122	0.49452	31.91	3.134	0.49610	31.79	3.145	0.49769
3200	31.10	3.215	0.50720	30.99	3.226	0.50878	30.88	3.238	0.51037	30.76	3.250	0.51195	30.65	3.262	0.51354
3300	29.99	3.334	0.52305	29.88	3.346	0.52463	29.77	3.359	0.52622	29.66	3.371	0.52780	29.55	3.383	0.52939
3400	28.91	3.458	0.53890	28.81	3.471	0.54048	28.70	3.483	0.54207	28.60	3.496	0.54365	28.49	3.509	0.54524
3500	27.88	3.587	0.55475	27.78	3.600	0.55633	27.67	3.613	0.55792	27.57	3.626	0.55950	27.47	3.639	0.56109
3600	26.88	3.720	0.57060	26.78	3.734	0.57218	26.68	3.747	0.57377	26.59	3.761	0.57535	26.49	3.775	0.57694
3700	25.92	3.858	0.58645	25.82	3.872	0.58803	25.73	3.887	0.58962	25.63	3.901	0.59120	25.54	3.915	0.59279
3800	24.99	4.002	0.60230	24.90	4.016	0.60388	24.80	4.031	0.60547	24.71	4.046	0.60705	24.62	4.061	0.60864
3900	24.09	4.150	0.61815	24.00	4.166	0.61973	23.92	4.181	0.62132	23.83	4.196	0.62290	23.74	4.211	0.62449
4000	23.23	4.305	0.63400	23.14	4.320	0.63558	23.06	4.336	0.63717	22.97	4.352	0.63875	22.89	4.368	0.64034
4100	22.40	4.465	0.64985	22.31	4.481	0.65143	22.23	4.497	0.65302	22.15	4.514	0.65460	22.07	4.530	0.65619
4200	21.59	4.631	0.66570	21.51	4.648	0.66728	21.44	4.665	0.66887	21.36	4.682	0.67045	21.28	4.699	0.67204
4300	20.82	4.803	0.68155	20.74	4.820	0.68313	20.67	4.838	0.68472	20.59	4.856	0.68630	20.52	4.874	0.68789
4400	20.07	4.981	0.69740	20.00	5.000	0.69898	19.93	5.018	0.70057	19.85	5.036	0.70215	19.78	5.055	0.70374
4500	19.35	5.167	0.71325	19.28	5.185	0.71483	19.21	5.204	0.71642	19.14	5.223	0.71800	19.07	5.243	0.71959
4600	18.66	5.359	0.72910	18.59	5.378	0.73068	18.52	5.398	0.73227	18.46	5.418	0.73385	18.39	5.437	0.73544
4700	17.99	5.558	0.74495	17.93	5.578	0.74653	17.86	5.599	0.74812	17.80	5.619	0.74970	17.73	5.640	0.75129
4800	17.35	5.764	0.76080	17.28	5.786	0.76238	17.22	5.807	0.76397	17.16	5.828	0.76555	17.09	5.849	0.76714
4900	16.72	5.979	0.77665	16.66	6.001	0.77823	16.60	6.023	0.77982	16.54	6.045	0.78140	16.48	6.067	0.78299
5000	16.13	6.201	0.79250	16.07	6.224	0.79408	16.01	6.246	0.79567	15.95	6.269	0.79725	15.89	6.292	0.79884
5100	15.55	6.431	0.80835	15.49	6.455	0.80993	15.43	6.479	0.81152	15.38	6.502	0.81310	15.32	6.526	0.81468
5200	14.99	6.671	0.82419	14.94	6.695	0.82578	14.88	6.719	0.82736	14.83	6.744	0.82895	14.77	6.769	0.83053
5300	14.45	6.919	0.84004	14.40	6.944	0.84163	14.35	6.969	0.84321	14.30	6.995	0.84480	14.24	7.020	0.84638
5400	13.94	7.176	0.85589	13.88	7.202	0.85748	13.83	7.228	0.85906	13.78	7.255	0.86065	13.73	7.281	0.86223
5500	13.44	7.442	0.87174	13.39	7.470	0.87333	13.34	7.497	0.87491	13.29	7.524	0.87650	13.24	7.552	0.87808
5600	12.95	7.719	0.88759	12.91	7.747	0.88918	12.86	7.776	0.89076	12.81	7.804	0.89235	12.77	7.833	0.89393
5700	12.49	8.006	0.90344	12.44	8.035	0.90503	12.40	8.065	0.90661	12.35	8.094	0.90820	12.31	8.124	0.90978
5800	12.04	8.304	0.91929	12.00	8.334	0.92088	11.95	8.364	0.92246	11.91	8.395	0.92405	11.87	8.426	0.92563
5900	11.61	8.612	0.93514	11.57	8.644	0.93672	11.53	8.675	0.93831	11.48	8.707	0.93989	11.44	8.739	0.94148
6000	11.19	8.932	0.95099	11.15	8.965	0.95257	11.11	8.998	0.95416	11.07	9.031	0.95574	11.03	9.064	0.95733
6100	10.79	9.264	0.96684	10.75	9.298	0.96842	10.72	9.332	0.97001	10.68	9.366	0.97159	10.64	9.401	0.97318
6200	10.41	9.609	0.98269	10.37	9.644	0.98427	10.33	9.679	0.98586	10.29	9.714	0.98744	10.26	9.750	0.98903
6300	10.03	9.966	0.99853	10.00	10.003	1.00013	9.96	10.039	1.00172	9.92	10.076	1.00330	9.89	10.113	1.00489
6400	9.67	10.337	1.01440	9.64	10.374	1.01598	9.60	10.412	1.01757	9.57	10.450	1.01915	9.53	10.489	1.02074
6500	9.33	10.721	1.03025	9.29	10.760	1.03183	9.26	10.799	1.03342	9.23	10.839	1.03500	9.19	10.878	1.03659
6600	8.99	11.119	1.04610	8.96	11.160	1.04768	8.93	11.201	1.04927	8.90	11.242	1.05085	8.86	11.283	1.05244
6700	8.67	11.533	1.06195	8.64	11.575	1.06353	8.61	11.617	1.06512	8.58	11.660	1.06670	8.55	11.702	1.06829
6800	8.36	11.961	1.07780	8.33	12.005	1.07938	8.30	12.049	1.08097	8.27	12.093	1.08255	8.24	12.137	1.08414
6900	8.06	12.406	1.09365	8.03	12.451	1.09523	8.00	12.497	1.09682	7.97	12.542	1.09840	7.94	12.588	1.09999
7000	7.77	12.867	1.10950	7.74	12.914	1.11108	7.71	12.961	1.11267	7.69	13.009	1.11425	7.66	13.056	1.11584
7100	7.49	13.345	1.12535	7.47	13.394	1.12693	7.44	13.443	1.12852	7.41	13.492	1.13010	7.38	13.542	1.13169
7200	7.22	13.841	1.14120	7.20	13.892	1.14278	7.17	13.943	1.14437	7.15	13.994	1.14595	7.12	14.045	1.14754
7300	6.97	14.356	1.15705	6.94	14.408	1.15863	6.91	14.461	1.16022	6.89	14.514	1.16180	6.86	14.567	1.16339
7400	6.72	14.890	1.17290	6.69	14.944	1.17448	6.67	14.999	1.17607	6.64	15.053	1.17765	6.62	15.109	1.17924
7500	6.48	15.443	1.18875	6.45	15.499	1.19033	6.43	15.556	1.19192	6.40	15.613	1.19350	6.38	15.670	1.19509
7600	6.24	16.017	1.20460	6.22	16.076	1.20618	6.20	16.134	1.20777	6.18	16.193	1.20935	6.15	16.253	1.21094
7700	6.02	16.612	1.22045	6.00	16.673	1.22203	5.98	16.734	1.22362	5.95	16.795	1.22520	5.93	16.857	1.22679
7800	5.80	17.230	1.23630	5.78	17.293	1.23788	5.76	17.356	1.23947	5.74	17.420	1.24105	5.72	17.483	1.24264
7900	5.60	17.870	1.25215	5.58	17.936	1.25373	5.56	18.001	1.25532	5.53	18.067	1.25690	5.51	18.133	1.25849
8000	5.40	18.535	1.26800	5.38	18.602	1.26958	5.36	18.670	1.27117	5.34	18.739	1.27275	5.32	18.807	1.27434
8100	5.20	19.224	1.28385	5.18	19.294	1.28543	5.16	19.364	1.28702	5.15	19.435	1.28860	5.13	19.506	1.29019
8200	5.02	19.938	1.29970	5.00	20.011	1.30128	4.98	20.084	1.30287	4.96	20.158	1.30445	4.94	20.231	1.30604
8300	4.84	20.679	1.31555	4.82	20.755	1.31713	4.80	20.831	1.31872	4.78	20.907	1.32030	4.77	20.983	1.32189
8400	4.66	21.448	1.33140	4.65	21.526	1.33298	4.63	21.605	1.33457	4.61	21.684	1.33615	4.59	21.763	1.33774
8500	4.50	22.245	1.34725	4.48	22.326	1.34883	4.46	22.408	1.35042	4.45	22.490	1.35200	4.43	22.572	1.35359
8600	4.33	23.072	1.36310	4.32	23.156	1.36468	4.30	23.241	1.36627	4.29	23.326	1.36785	4.27	23.411	1.36944
8700	4.18	23.930	1.37895	4.16	24.017	1.38053	4.15	24.105	1.38212	4.13	24.193	1.38370	4.12	24.282	1.38529
8800	4.03	24.819	1.39480	4.01	24.910	1.39638	4.00	25.001	1.39797	3.99	25.092	1.39955	3.97	25.184	1.40114
8900	3.88	25.742	1.41065	3.87	25.836	1.41223	3.86	25.930	1.41381	3.84	26.025	1.41540	3.83	26.120	1.41699
9000	3.75	26.698	1.42650	3.73	26.796	1.42808	3.72	26.894	1.42967	3.70	26.992	1.43125	3.69	27.091	1.43284
9100	3.61	27.691	1.44235	3.60	27.792	1.44393	3.58	27.894	1.44551	3.57	27.996	1.44710	3.56	28.098	1.44868
9200	3.48	28.720	1.45820	3.47	28.825	1.45978	3.46	28.931	1.46137	3.44	29.036	1.46295	3.43	29.143	1.46454
9300	3.36	29.788	1.47405	3.34	29.897	1.47563	3.33	30.006	1.47721	3.32	30.116	1.47880	3.31	30.226	1.48039
9400	3.24	30.895	1.48990	3.22	31.008	1.49148	3.21	31.121	1.49307	3.20	31.235	1.49465	3.19	31.349	1.49623
9500	3.12	32.043	1.50574	3.11	32.160	1.50733	3.10	32.278	1.50891	3.09	32.396	1.51050	3.08	32.515	1.51208
9600	3.01	33.234	1.52159	3.00	33.356	1.52318	2.99	33.478	1.52477	2.98	33.600	1.52635	2.97	33.723	1.52793
9700	2.90	34.470	1.53745	2.89	34.596	1.53903	2.88	34.722	1.54061	2.87	34.849	1.54220	2.86	34.977	1.54378
9800	2.80	35.751	1.55329	2.79	35.882	1.55488	2.78	36.013	1.55646	2.77	36.145	1.55805	2.76	36.277	1.55963
9900	2.70	37.080	1.56914	2.69	37.215	1.57073	2.68	37.352	1.57231	2.67	37.488	1.57390	2.66	37.625	1.57548
10000	2.60	38.458	1.58499												

Half-life 5.2 y

d → ↓	50			60			70			80			90		
	N_t	N_0/N_t	$\log_{10} N_0/N_t$	N_t	N_0/N_t	$\log_{10} N_0/N_t$	N_t	N_0/N_t	$\log_{10} N_0/N_t$	N_t	N_0/N_t	$\log_{10} N_0/N_t$	N_t	N_0/N_t	$\log_{10} N_0/N_t$
0	98.19	1.018	0.00793	97.83	1.022	0.00951	97.48	1.025	0.01110	97.12	1.029	0.01268	96.77	1.033	0.01427
100	94.67	1.056	0.02378	94.33	1.060	0.02536	93.98	1.064	0.02695	93.64	1.067	0.02853	93.30	1.071	0.03012
200	91.28	1.095	0.03963	90.95	1.099	0.04121	90.62	1.103	0.04280	90.29	1.107	0.04438	89.96	1.111	0.04597
300	88.01	1.136	0.05548	87.69	1.140	0.05706	87.37	1.144	0.05865	87.05	1.148	0.06023	86.73	1.152	0.06182
400	84.85	1.178	0.07133	84.55	1.182	0.07291	84.24	1.187	0.07450	83.93	1.191	0.07608	83.62	1.195	0.07767
500	81.81	1.222	0.08718	81.52	1.226	0.08876	81.22	1.231	0.09035	80.92	1.235	0.09193	80.63	1.240	0.09352
600	78.88	1.267	0.10303	78.59	1.272	0.10461	78.31	1.277	0.10620	78.02	1.281	0.10778	77.74	1.286	0.10937
700	76.05	1.314	0.11888	75.78	1.319	0.12046	75.50	1.324	0.12205	75.23	1.329	0.12363	74.95	1.334	0.12522
800	73.33	1.363	0.13472	73.06	1.368	0.13631	72.80	1.373	0.13789	72.53	1.378	0.13948	72.27	1.383	0.14106
900	70.70	1.414	0.15057	70.44	1.419	0.15216	70.19	1.424	0.15374	69.93	1.429	0.15533	69.68	1.435	0.15691
1000	68.17	1.466	0.16642	67.92	1.472	0.16801	67.67	1.477	0.16959	67.42	1.483	0.17118	67.18	1.488	0.17276
1100	65.72	1.521	0.18227	65.48	1.527	0.18386	65.25	1.532	0.18544	65.01	1.538	0.18703	64.77	1.543	0.18861
1200	63.37	1.578	0.19812	63.14	1.583	0.19971	62.91	1.589	0.20129	62.68	1.595	0.20288	62.45	1.601	0.20446
1300	61.10	1.636	0.21397	60.88	1.642	0.21556	60.65	1.648	0.21714	60.43	1.654	0.21873	60.21	1.660	0.22031
1400	58.91	1.697	0.22982	58.69	1.703	0.23141	58.48	1.709	0.23299	58.27	1.716	0.23458	58.05	1.722	0.23616
1500	56.80	1.760	0.24567	56.59	1.767	0.24726	56.38	1.773	0.24884	56.18	1.780	0.25043	55.97	1.786	0.25201
1600	54.76	1.826	0.26152	54.56	1.832	0.26311	54.36	1.839	0.26469	54.17	1.846	0.26628	53.97	1.852	0.26786
1700	52.80	1.893	0.27737	52.61	1.900	0.27896	52.42	1.907	0.28054	52.22	1.914	0.28213	52.03	1.921	0.28371
1800	50.91	1.964	0.29322	50.72	1.971	0.29481	50.54	1.978	0.29639	50.35	1.985	0.29798	50.17	1.993	0.29956
1900	49.08	2.037	0.30907	48.90	2.044	0.31066	48.73	2.052	0.31224	48.55	2.059	0.31383	48.37	2.067	0.31541
2000	47.32	2.113	0.32492	47.15	2.120	0.32651	46.98	2.128	0.32809	46.81	2.136	0.32968	46.64	2.144	0.33126
2100	45.63	2.191	0.34077	45.46	2.199	0.34236	45.30	2.207	0.34394	45.13	2.215	0.34553	44.97	2.223	0.34711
2200	43.99	2.273	0.35662	43.83	2.281	0.35821	43.67	2.289	0.35979	43.51	2.298	0.36138	43.35	2.306	0.36296
2300	42.42	2.357	0.37247	42.26	2.366	0.37406	42.11	2.374	0.37564	41.95	2.383	0.37723	41.80	2.392	0.37881
2400	40.90	2.445	0.38832	40.75	2.454	0.38991	40.60	2.463	0.39149	40.45	2.472	0.39308	40.30	2.481	0.39466
2500	39.43	2.536	0.40417	39.29	2.545	0.40576	39.14	2.554	0.40734	39.00	2.564	0.40893	38.86	2.573	0.41051
2600	38.02	2.630	0.42002	37.88	2.640	0.42161	37.74	2.649	0.42319	37.60	2.659	0.42478	37.47	2.669	0.42636
2700	36.65	2.728	0.43587	36.52	2.738	0.43746	36.39	2.748	0.43904	36.26	2.758	0.44063	36.12	2.768	0.44221
2800	35.34	2.829	0.45172	35.21	2.839	0.45331	35.08	2.850	0.45489	34.96	2.860	0.45648	34.83	2.871	0.45806
2900	34.07	2.934	0.46757	33.95	2.945	0.46916	33.83	2.956	0.47074	33.70	2.967	0.47233	33.58	2.977	0.47391
3000	32.85	3.043	0.48342	32.73	3.054	0.48501	32.61	3.066	0.48659	32.50	3.077	0.48818	32.38	3.088	0.48976
3100	31.68	3.156	0.49927	31.56	3.168	0.50086	31.45	3.180	0.50244	31.33	3.191	0.50403	31.22	3.203	0.50561
3200	30.54	3.274	0.51512	30.43	3.286	0.51671	30.32	3.298	0.51829	30.21	3.310	0.51988	30.10	3.322	0.52146
3300	29.45	3.396	0.53097	29.34	3.408	0.53256	29.23	3.420	0.53414	29.13	3.433	0.53573	29.02	3.445	0.53731
3400	28.39	3.522	0.54682	28.29	3.535	0.54841	28.18	3.548	0.54999	28.08	3.561	0.55158	27.98	3.574	0.55316
3500	27.37	3.653	0.56267	27.27	3.666	0.56426	27.17	3.679	0.56584	27.08	3.693	0.56743	26.98	3.706	0.56901
3600	26.39	3.788	0.57852	26.30	3.802	0.58011	26.20	3.816	0.58169	26.10	3.830	0.58328	26.01	3.844	0.58486
3700	25.45	3.929	0.59437	25.35	3.944	0.59596	25.26	3.958	0.59754	25.17	3.973	0.59913	25.08	3.987	0.60071
3800	24.53	4.075	0.61022	24.45	4.090	0.61181	24.36	4.105	0.61339	24.27	4.120	0.61498	24.18	4.135	0.61656
3900	23.66	4.227	0.62607	23.57	4.242	0.62766	23.48	4.258	0.62924	23.40	4.273	0.63083	23.31	4.289	0.63241
4000	22.81	4.384	0.64192	22.72	4.400	0.64351	22.64	4.416	0.64509	22.56	4.432	0.64668	22.48	4.448	0.64826
4100	21.99	4.547	0.65777	21.91	4.564	0.65936	21.83	4.580	0.66094	21.75	4.597	0.66253	21.67	4.614	0.66411
4200	21.20	4.716	0.67362	21.12	4.733	0.67521	21.05	4.751	0.67679	20.97	4.768	0.67838	20.89	4.785	0.67996
4300	20.44	4.891	0.68947	20.37	4.909	0.69106	20.29	4.927	0.69264	20.22	4.945	0.69423	20.15	4.963	0.69581
4400	19.71	5.073	0.70532	19.64	5.092	0.70691	19.57	5.110	0.70849	19.50	5.129	0.71008	19.42	5.148	0.71166
4500	19.00	5.262	0.72117	18.93	5.281	0.72276	18.87	5.300	0.72434	18.80	5.320	0.72593	18.73	5.339	0.72751
4600	18.32	5.457	0.73702	18.26	5.477	0.73861	18.19	5.497	0.74019	18.12	5.517	0.74178	18.06	5.538	0.74336
4700	17.67	5.660	0.75287	17.60	5.681	0.75446	17.54	5.702	0.75604	17.47	5.723	0.75763	17.41	5.743	0.75921
4800	17.03	5.871	0.76872	16.97	5.892	0.77031	16.91	5.914	0.77189	16.85	5.935	0.77348	16.79	5.957	0.77506
4900	16.42	6.089	0.78457	16.36	6.111	0.78616	16.30	6.133	0.78774	16.24	6.156	0.78933	16.18	6.178	0.79091
5000	15.83	6.315	0.80042	15.78	6.338	0.80201	15.72	6.361	0.80359	15.66	6.385	0.80518	15.60	6.408	0.80676
5100	15.27	6.550	0.81627	15.21	6.574	0.81785	15.16	6.598	0.81944	15.10	6.622	0.82102	15.04	6.646	0.82261
5200	14.72	6.793	0.83212	14.67	6.818	0.83370	14.61	6.843	0.83529	14.56	6.868	0.83687	14.51	6.893	0.83846
5300	14.19	7.046	0.84797	14.14	7.072	0.84955	14.09	7.098	0.85114	14.04	7.123	0.85272	13.99	7.150	0.85431
5400	13.68	7.308	0.86382	13.63	7.335	0.86540	13.58	7.361	0.86699	13.53	7.388	0.86857	13.48	7.415	0.87016
5500	13.19	7.579	0.87967	13.14	7.607	0.88125	13.10	7.635	0.88284	13.05	7.663	0.88442	13.00	7.691	0.88601
5600	12.72	7.861	0.89552	12.67	7.890	0.89710	12.63	7.919	0.89869	12.58	7.948	0.90027	12.54	7.977	0.90186
5700	12.26	8.153	0.91137	12.22	8.183	0.91295	12.17	8.213	0.91454	12.13	8.243	0.91612	12.09	8.273	0.91771
5800	11.82	8.456	0.92722	11.78	8.487	0.92880	11.74	8.518	0.93038	11.70	8.550	0.93197	11.65	8.581	0.93355
5900	11.40	8.771	0.94306	11.36	8.803	0.94465	11.32	8.835	0.94623	11.28	8.867	0.94782	11.24	8.900	0.94940
6000	10.99	9.097	0.95891	10.95	9.130	0.96050	10.91	9.163	0.96208	10.87	9.197	0.96367	10.83	9.231	0.96525
6100	10.60	9.435	0.97476	10.56	9.469	0.97635	10.52	9.504	0.97793	10.48	9.539	0.97952	10.44	9.574	0.98110
6200	10.22	9.786	0.99061	10.18	9.821	0.99220	10.14	9.857	0.99378	10.11	9.893	0.99537	10.07	9.930	0.99695
6300	9.85	10.150	1.00647	9.82	10.187	1.00806	9.78	10.224	1.00964	9.74	10.261	1.01123	9.71	10.299	1.01281
6400	9.50	10.527	1.02232	9.46	10.565	1.02391	9.43	10.604	1.02549	9.40	10.643	1.02708	9.36	10.682	1.02866
6500	9.16	10.918	1.03817	9.13	10.958	1.03976	9.09	10.998	1.04134	9.06	11.038	1.04293	9.03	11.079	1.04451
6600	8.83	11.324	1.05402	8.80	11.365	1.05561	8.77	11.407	1.05719	8.73	11.449	1.05878	8.70	11.491	1.06036
6700	8.51	11.745	1.06987	8.48	11.788	1.07146	8.45	11.831	1.07304	8.42	11.874	1.07463	8.39	11.918	1.07621
6800	8.21	12.182	1.08572	8.18	12.226	1.08731	8.15	12.271	1.08889	8.12	12.316	1.09048	8.09	12.361	1.09206
6900	7.91	12.634	1.10157	7.89	12.681	1.10316	7.86	12.727	1.10474	7.83	12.773	1.10633	7.80	12.820	1.10791
7000	7.63	13.104	1.11742	7.60	13.152	1.11901	7.58	13.200	1.12059	7.55	13.248	1.12218	7.52	13.297	1.12376
7100	7.36	13.591	1.13327	7.33	13.641	1.13486	7.30	13.691	1.13644	7.28	13.741	1.13803	7.25	13.791	1.13961
7200	7.09	14.096	1.14912	7.07	14.148	1.15071	7.04	14.200	1.15229	7.02	14.251	1.15388	6.99	14.304	1.15546
7300	6.84	14.620	1.16497	6.81	14.674	1.16656	6.79	14.727	1.16814	6.77	14.781	1.16973	6.74	14.835	1.17131
7400	6.59	15.164	1.18082	6.57	15.219	1.18241	6.55	15.275	1.18399	6.52	15.331	1.18558	6.50	15.387	1.18716
7500	6.36	15.727	1.19667	6.33	15.785	1.19826	6.31	15.843	1.19984	6.29	15.901	1.20143	6.27	15.959	1.20301
7600	6.13	16.312	1.21252	6.11	16.372	1.21411	6.09	16.431	1.21569	6.06	16.492	1.21728	6.04	16.552	1.21886
7700	5.91	16.918	1.22837	5.89	16.980	1.22996	5.87	17.042	1.23154	5.85	17.105	1.23313	5.82	17.167	1.23471
7800	5.70	17.547	1.24422	5.68	17.611	1.24581	5.66	17.676	1.24739	5.64	17.740	1.24898	5.62	17.805	1.25056
7900	5.49	18.199	1.26007	5.47	18.266	1.26166	5.45	18.333	1.26324	5.43	18.400	1.26483	5.41	18.467	1.26641
8000	5.30	18.876	1.27592	5.28	18.945	1.27751	5.26	19.014	1.27909	5.24	19.084	1.28068	5.22	19.154	1.28226
8100	5.11	19.578	1.29177	5.09	19.649	1.29336	5.07	19.721	1.29494	5.05	19.793	1.29653	5.03	19.865	1.29811
8200	4.92	20.305	1.30762	4.91	20.380	1.30921	4.89	20.454	1.31079	4.87	20.529	1.31238	4.85	20.604	1.31396
8300	4.75	21.060	1.32347	4.73	21.137	1.32506	4.71	21.214	1.32664	4.70	21.292	1.32823	4.68	21.370	1.32981
8400	4.58	21.843	1.33932	4.56	21.923	1.34091	4.54	22.003	1.34249	4.53	22.083	1.34408	4.51	22.164	1.34566
8500	4.41	22.655	1.35517	4.40	22.738	1.35676	4.38	22.821	1.35834	4.37	22.904	1.35993	4.35	22.988	1.36151
8600	4.26	23.497	1.37102	4.24	23.583	1.37260	4.22	23.669	1.37419	4.21	23.756	1.37578	4.19	23.842	1.37736
8700	4.10	24.370	1.38687	4.09	24.459	1.38846	4.07	24.549	1.39004	4.06	24.639	1.39163	4.04	24.729	1.39321
8800	3.96	25.276	1.40272	3.94	25.369	1.40430	3.93	25.461	1.40589	3.91	25.554	1.40748	3.90	25.648	1.40906
8900	3.81	26.216	1.41857	3.80	26.312	1.42016	3.79	26.408	1.42174	3.77	26.504	1.42333	3.76	26.601	1.42491
9000	3.68	27.190	1.43442	3.66	27.290	1.43600	3.65	27.389	1.43759	3.64	27.489	1.43917	3.62	27.590	1.44076
9100	3.55	28.201	1.45027	3.53	28.304	1.45185	3.52	28.407	1.45344	3.51	28.511	1.45502	3.49	28.616	1.45661
9200	3.42	29.249	1.46612	3.41	29.356	1.46770	3.39	29.463	1.46929	3.38	29.571	1.47087	3.37	29.679	1.47246
9300	3.30	30.336	1.48197	3.28	30.447	1.48355	3.27	30.558	1.48514	3.26	30.670	1.48672	3.25	30.782	1.48831
9400	3.18	31.464	1.49782	3.17	31.579	1.49940	3.16	31.694	1.50099	3.14	31.810	1.50257	3.13	31.927	1.50416
9500	3.06	32.633	1.51367	3.05	32.753	1.51526	3.04	32.873	1.51684	3.03	32.993	1.51842	3.02	33.113	1.52001
9600	2.95	33.846	1.52952	2.94	33.970	1.53110	2.93	34.094	1.53269	2.92	34.219	1.53427	2.91	34.344	1.53586
9700	2.85	35.104	1.54537	2.84	35.233	1.54695	2.83	35.362	1.54854	2.82	35.491	1.55012	2.81	35.621	1.55171
9800	2.75	36.409	1.56122	2.74	36.543	1.56281	2.73	36.676	1.56439	2.72	36.810	1.56597	2.71	36.945	1.56756
9900	2.65	37.763	1.57707	2.64	37.901	1.57866	2.63	38.039	1.58024	2.62	38.178	1.58182	2.61	38.318	1.58341

Isotope Decay Tables – Cesium-137

Half-life 30 y

d →	0			100			200			300			400		
↓	N_t	N_0/N_t	$\log_{10} N_0/N_t$	N_t	N_0/N_t	$\log_{10} N_0/N_t$	N_t	N_0/N_t	$\log_{10} N_0/N_t$	N_t	N_0/N_t	$\log_{10} N_0/N_t$	N_t	N_0/N_t	$\log_{10} N_0/N_t$
0	100.00	1.000	0.00000	99.37	1.006	0.00275	98.74	1.012	0.00550	98.12	1.019	0.00824	97.50	1.025	0.01099
1000	93.87	1.065	0.02747	93.28	1.072	0.03022	92.69	1.078	0.03297	92.11	1.085	0.03572	91.52	1.092	0.03846
2000	88.12	1.134	0.05495	87.56	1.142	0.05769	87.01	1.149	0.06044	86.46	1.156	0.06319	85.91	1.163	0.06594
3000	82.71	1.208	0.08242	82.19	1.216	0.08517	81.67	1.224	0.08792	81.16	1.232	0.09066	80.65	1.239	0.09341
4000	77.64	1.287	0.10989	77.15	1.296	0.11264	76.67	1.304	0.11539	76.18	1.312	0.11814	75.70	1.320	0.12088
5000	72.88	1.372	0.13737	72.42	1.380	0.14011	71.97	1.389	0.14286	71.51	1.398	0.14561	71.06	1.407	0.14836
6000	68.42	1.461	0.16484	67.99	1.470	0.16759	67.56	1.480	0.17033	67.13	1.489	0.17308	66.71	1.499	0.17583
7000	64.22	1.557	0.19231	63.82	1.566	0.19506	63.42	1.576	0.19781	63.02	1.586	0.20056	62.62	1.596	0.20330
8000	60.29	1.658	0.21979	59.91	1.669	0.22253	59.53	1.679	0.22528	59.15	1.690	0.22803	58.78	1.701	0.23078
9000	56.59	1.767	0.24726	56.23	1.778	0.25001	55.88	1.789	0.25275	55.53	1.800	0.25550	55.18	1.812	0.25825
10000	53.12	1.882	0.27473	52.79	1.894	0.27748	52.45	1.906	0.28023	52.12	1.918	0.28298	51.79	1.930	0.28572
11000	49.86	2.005	0.30221	49.55	2.018	0.30495	49.24	2.030	0.30770	48.93	2.043	0.31045	48.62	2.056	0.31320
12000	46.81	2.136	0.32968	46.51	2.149	0.33243	46.22	2.163	0.33517	45.93	2.177	0.33792	45.64	2.191	0.34067
13000	43.94	2.275	0.35715	43.66	2.290	0.35990	43.39	2.304	0.36265	43.11	2.319	0.36539	42.84	2.334	0.36814
14000	41.25	2.424	0.38463	40.99	2.439	0.38737	40.73	2.455	0.39012	40.47	2.470	0.39287	40.21	2.486	0.39562
15000	38.72	2.582	0.41210	38.47	2.599	0.41485	38.23	2.615	0.41759	37.99	2.632	0.42034	37.75	2.649	0.42309
16000	36.34	2.751	0.43957	36.11	2.768	0.44232	35.89	2.786	0.44507	35.66	2.804	0.44781	35.44	2.822	0.45056
17000	34.12	2.931	0.46705	33.90	2.949	0.46979	33.69	2.968	0.47254	33.47	2.987	0.47529	33.26	3.006	0.47804
18000	32.02	3.122	0.49452	31.82	3.142	0.49727	31.62	3.162	0.50001	31.42	3.182	0.50276	31.22	3.202	0.50551
19000	30.06	3.326	0.52199	29.87	3.347	0.52474	29.68	3.368	0.52749	29.50	3.390	0.53023	29.31	3.411	0.53298
20000	28.22	3.543	0.54947	28.04	3.566	0.55221	27.86	3.588	0.55496	27.69	3.611	0.55771	27.51	3.634	0.56045
21000	26.49	3.775	0.57694	26.32	3.799	0.57969	26.16	3.823	0.58243	25.99	3.847	0.58518	25.83	3.871	0.58793
22000	24.87	4.021	0.60441	24.71	4.047	0.60716	24.55	4.072	0.60991	24.40	4.098	0.61265	24.24	4.124	0.61540
23000	23.34	4.284	0.63189	23.19	4.311	0.63463	23.05	4.338	0.63738	22.90	4.366	0.64013	22.76	4.394	0.64287
24000	21.91	4.564	0.65936	21.77	4.593	0.66211	21.63	4.622	0.66485	21.50	4.651	0.66760	21.36	4.681	0.67035
25000	20.57	4.862	0.68683	20.44	4.893	0 68958	20.31	4.924	0.69233	20.18	4.955	0.69507	20.05	4.986	0.69782
26000	19.31	5.179	0.71430	19.18	5.212	0.71705	19.06	5.245	0.71980	18.94	5.278	0.72255	18.82	5.312	0.72529
27000	18.12	5.517	0.74178	18.01	5.552	0.74452	17.89	5.588	0.74727	17.78	5.623	0.75002	17.67	5.659	0.75277
28000	17.01	5.878	0.76925	16.90	5.915	0.77200	16.80	5.953	0.77474	16.69	5.990	0.77749	16.59	6.028	0.78024
29000	15.97	6.262	0.79672	15.87	6.301	0.79947	15.77	6.341	0.80222	15.67	6.382	0.80496	15.57	6.422	0.80771
30000	14.99	6.671	0.82420	14.90	6.713	0.82694	14.80	6.755	0.82969	14.71	6.798	0.83244	14.62	6.842	0.83518
31000	14.07	7.106	0.85167	13.98	7.151	0.85442	13.89	7.197	0.85716	13.81	7.242	0.85991	13.72	7.288	0.86266
32000	13.21	7.570	0.87914	13.13	7.618	0.88189	13.04	7.667	0.88463	12.96	7.715	0.88738	12.88	7.764	0.89013
33000	12.40	8.065	0.90661	12.32	8.116	0.90936	12.24	8.167	0.91211	12.17	8.219	0.91485	12.09	8.271	0.91760
34000	11.64	8.591	0.93408	11.57	8.646	0.93683	11.49	8.701	0.93958	11.42	8.756	0.94233	11.35	8.811	0.94507
35000	10.93	9.152	0.96156	10.86	9.210	0.96430	10.79	9.269	0.96705	10.72	9.328	0.96980	10.65	9.387	0.97254
36000	10.26	9.750	0.98903	10.19	9.812	0.99177	10.13	9.874	0.99452	10.06	9.937	0.99727	10.00	10.000	1.00003
37000	9.63	10.387	1.01651	9.57	10.453	1.01926	9.51	10.519	1.02201	9.45	10.586	1.02475	9.39	10.653	1.02750
38000	9.04	11.065	1.04398	8.98	11.136	1.04673	8.92	11.206	1.04948	8.87	11.277	1.05223	8.81	11.349	1.05497
39000	8.48	11.788	1.07146	8.43	11.863	1.07420	8.38	11.938	1.07695	8.32	12.014	1.07970	8.27	12.090	1.08245
40000	7.96	12.558	1.09893	7.91	12.637	1.10168	7.86	12.718	1.10443	7.81	12.798	1.10717	7.76	12.880	1.10992
41000	7.47	13.378	1.12640	7.43	13.463	1.12915	7.38	13.548	1.13190	7.33	13.634	1.13465	7.29	13.721	1.13739
42000	7.02	14.252	1.15388	6.97	14.342	1.15662	6.93	14.433	1.15937	6.88	14.525	1.16212	6.84	14.617	1.16487
43000	6.59	15.182	1.18135	6.54	15.279	1.18410	6.50	15.376	1.18685	6.46	15.473	1.18959	6.42	15.571	1.19234
44000	6.18	16.174	1.20882	6.14	16.276	1.21157	6.10	16.380	1.21432	6.07	16.484	1.21707	6.03	16.588	1.21981
45000	5.80	17.230	1.23630	5.77	17.339	1.23904	5.73	17.449	1.24179	5.69	17.560	1.24454	5.66	17.671	1.24729
46000	5.45	18.355	1.26377	5.41	18.472	1.26652	5.38	18.589	1.26927	5.35	18.707	1.27201	5.31	18.826	1.27476
47000	5.11	19.554	1.29124	5.08	19.678	1.29399	5.05	19.803	1.29674	5.02	19.928	1.29949	4.99	20.055	1.30223
48000	4.80	20.831	1.31872	4.77	20.963	1.32146	4.74	21.096	1.32421	4.71	21.230	1.32696	4.68	21.365	1.32971
49000	4.51	22.191	1.34619	4.48	22.332	1.34894	4.45	22.474	1.35168	4.42	22.616	1.35443	4.39	22.760	1.35718
50000	4.23	23.640	1.37366	4.20	23.790	1.37641	4.18	23.941	1.37916	4.15	24.093	1.38191	4.12	24.246	1.38465
51000	3.97	25.184	1.40114	3.95	25.344	1.40388	3.92	25.505	1.40663	3.90	25.667	1.40938	3.87	25.830	1.41213
52000	3.73	26.829	1.42861	3.70	26.999	1.43136	3.68	27.170	1.43410	3.66	27.343	1.43685	3.63	27.516	1.43960
53000	3.50	28.581	1.45608	3.48	28.762	1.45883	3.45	28.945	1.46158	3.43	29.128	1.46433	3.41	29.313	1.46707
54000	3.28	30.447	1.48356	3.26	30.641	1.48630	3.24	30.835	1.48905	3.22	31.031	1.49180	3.20	31.228	1.49455
55000	3.08	32.436	1.51103	3.06	32.641	1.51378	3.04	32.849	1.51652	3.03	33.057	1.51927	3.01	33.267	1.52202
56000	2.89	34.554	1.53850	2.88	34.773	1.54125	2.86	34.994	1.54400	2.84	35.216	1.54674	2.82	35.439	1.54949
57000	2.72	36.810	1.56598	2.70	37.044	1.56872	2.68	37.279	1.57147	2.67	37.516	1.57422	2.65	37.754	1.57697
58000	2.55	39.214	1.59345	2.53	39.463	1.59620	2.52	39.713	1.59894	2.50	39.965	1.60169	2.49	40.219	1.60444
59000	2.39	41.775	1.62092	2.38	42.040	1.62367	2.36	42.307	1.62642	2.35	42.575	1.62916	2.33	42.846	1.63191
60000	2.25	44.503	1.64840	2.23	44.786	1.65114	2.22	45.070	1.65389	2.20	45.356	1.65664	2.19	45.643	1.65938
61000	2.11	47.409	1.67587	2.10	47.710	1.67862	2.08	48.013	1.68136	2.07	48.318	1.68411	2.06	48.624	1.68686
62000	1.98	50.505	1.70334	1.97	50.826	1.70609	1.96	51.148	1.70884	1.94	51.473	1.71158	1.93	51.800	1.71433
63000	1.86	53.803	1.73081	1.85	54.145	1.73356	1.84	54.489	1.73631	1.82	54.834	1.73906	1.81	55.182	1.74180
64000	1.74	57.317	1.75829	1.73	57.681	1.76103	1.72	58.047	1.76378	1.71	58.415	1.76653	1.70	58.786	1.76928
65000	1.64	61.060	1.78576	1.63	61.448	1.78851	1.62	61.837	1.79126	1.61	62.230	1.79400	1.60	62.625	1.79675
66000	1.54	65.047	1.81323	1.53	65.460	1.81598	1.52	65.876	1.81873	1.51	66.294	1.82148	1.50	66.714	1.82422
67000	1.44	69.295	1.84071	1.43	69.735	1.84345	1.42	70.177	1.84620	1.42	70.622	1.84895	1.41	71.071	1.85169
68000	1.35	73.820	1.86818	1.35	74.289	1.87093	1.34	74.760	1.87367	1.33	75.234	1.87642	1.32	75.712	1.87917
69000	1.27	78.641	1.89565	1.26	79.140	1.89840	1.26	79.642	1.90115	1.25	80.147	1.90389	1.24	80.656	1.90664
70000	1.19	83.776	1.92312	1.19	84.307	1.92587	1.18	84.842	1.92862	1.17	85.381	1.93136	1.16	85.923	1.93411
71000	1.12	89.246	1.95059	1.11	89.813	1.95334	1.11	90.383	1.95609	1.10	90.957	1.95884	1.09	91.534	1.96158
72000	1.05	95.074	1.97806	1.05	95.678	1.98081	1.04	96.285	1.98356	1.03	96.896	1.98631	1.03	97.510	1.98905
73000	0.99	101.285	2.00555	0.98	101.928	2.00830	0.97	102.575	2.01104	0.97	103.225	2.01379	0.96	103.880	2.01654
74000	0.93	107.900	2.03302	0.92	108.584	2.03577	0.92	109.274	2.03852	0.91	109.967	2.04126	0.90	110.664	2.04401
75000	0.87	114.946	2.06050	0.86	115.675	2.06324	0.86	116.409	2.06599	0.85	117.148	2.06874	0.85	117.891	2.07148
76000	0.82	122.452	2.08797	0.81	123.230	2.09072	0.81	124.011	2.09346	0.80	124.798	2.09621	0.80	125.590	2.09896
77000	0.77	130.449	2.11544	0.76	131.276	2.11819	0.76	132.109	2.12093	0.75	132.948	2.12368	0.75	133.791	2.12643
78000	0.72	138.968	2.14292	0.72	139.850	2.14566	0.71	140.738	2.14841	0.71	141.631	2.15116	0.70	142.529	2.15390
79000	0.68	148.042	2.17039	0.67	148.982	2.17314	0.67	149.927	2.17588	0.66	150.879	2.17863	0.66	151.837	2.18138
80000	0.63	157.711	2.19786	0.63	158.712	2.20061	0.63	159.718	2.20336	0.62	160.732	2.20611	0.62	161.752	2.20885
81000	0.60	168.010	2.22534	0.59	169.075	2.22808	0.59	170.149	2.23083	0.58	171.227	2.23357	0.58	172.315	2.23633
82000	0.56	178.980	2.25281	0.56	180.118	2.25556	0.55	181.261	2.25831	0.55	182.411	2.26105	0.54	183.567	2.26380
83000	0.52	190.668	2.28028	0.52	191.879	2.28303	0.52	193.098	2.28578	0.51	194.321	2.28852	0.51	195.556	2.29127
84000	0.49	203.119	2.30775	0.49	204.411	2.31051	0.49	205.706	2.31325	0.48	207.013	2.31600	0.48	208.324	2.31874
85000	0.46	216.384	2.33523	0.46	217.755	2.33797	0.46	219.139	2.34072	0.45	220.531	2.34347	0.45	221.931	2.34622
86000	0.43	230.515	2.36270	0.43	231.980	2.36545	0.43	233.448	2.36819	0.43	234.929	2.37094	0.42	236.423	2.37369
87000	0.41	245.567	2.39017	0.40	247.127	2.39292	0.40	248.694	2.39567	0.40	250.275	2.39842	0.40	251.863	2.40117
88000	0.38	261.602	2.41764	0.38	263.268	2.42040	0.38	264.935	2.42314	0.38	266.616	2.42589	0.37	268.312	2.42864
89000	0.36	278.691	2.44512	0.36	280.457	2.44787	0.35	282.238	2.45062	0.35	284.026	2.45336	0.35	285.828	2.45611
90000	0.34	296.885	2.47259	0.33	298.775	2.47534	0.33	300.670	2.47809	0.33	302.581	2.48084	0.33	304.497	2.48358
91000	0.32	316.275	2.50007	0.31	318.278	2.50281	0.31	320.307	2.50557	0.31	322.331	2.50830	0.31	324.380	2.51106
92000	0.30	336.927	2.52754	0.29	339.063	2.53028	0.29	341.215	2.53303	0.29	343.383	2.53578	0.29	345.566	2.53853
93000	0.28	358.937	2.55502	0.28	361.206	2.55776	0.28	363.504	2.56051	0.27	365.804	2.56325	0.27	368.134	2.56601
94000	0.26	382.365	2.58248	0.26	384.792	2.58523	0.26	387.236	2.58798	0.26	389.696	2.59073	0.25	392.172	2.59348
95000	0.25	407.348	2.60997	0.24	409.920	2.61270	0.24	412.524	2.61545	0.24	415.144	2.61820	0.24	417.780	2.62095
96000	0.23	433.933	2.63742	0.23	436.700	2.64018	0.23	439.463	2.64292	0.23	442.262	2.64568	0.22	445.057	2.64842
97000	0.22	462.278	2.66490	0.21	465.224	2.66766	0.21	468.164	2.67040	0.21	471.142	2.67315	0.21	474.135	2.67590
98000	0.20	492.465	2.69238	0.20	495.589	2.69512	0.20	498.728	2.69786	0.20	501.907	2.70062	0.20	505.101	2.70338
99000	0.19	524.631	2.71985	0.19	527.955	2.72260	0.19	531.321	2.72536	0.19	534.673	2.72809	0.19	538.068	2.73084
100000	0.18	558.877	2.74732												

Half-life 30 y

d → ↓	500			600			700			800			900		
	N_t	N_0/N_t	$\log_{10} N_0/N_t$	N_t	N_0/N_t	$\log_{10} N_0/N_t$	N_t	N_0/N_t	$\log_{10} N_0/N_t$	N_t	N_0/N_t	$\log_{10} N_0/N_t$	N_t	N_0/N_t	$\log_{10} N_0/N_t$
0	96.89	1.032	0.01374	96.28	1.038	0.01648	95.67	1.045	0.01923	95.07	1.051	0.02198	94.47	1.058	0.02473
1000	90.95	1.099	0.04121	90.37	1.106	0.04396	89.80	1.113	0.04670	89.24	1.120	0.04945	88.67	1.127	0.05220
2000	85.37	1.171	0.06868	84.83	1.178	0.07143	84.30	1.186	0.07418	83.77	1.193	0.07693	83.24	1.201	0.07967
3000	80.14	1.247	0.09616	79.63	1.255	0.09890	79.13	1.263	0.10165	78.63	1.271	0.10440	78.14	1.279	0.10715
4000	75.23	1.329	0.12363	74.75	1.337	0.12638	74.28	1.346	0.12912	73.81	1.354	0.13187	73.35	1.363	0.13462
5000	70.62	1.416	0.15110	70.17	1.425	0.15385	69.73	1.434	0.15660	69.29	1.443	0.15935	68.85	1.452	0.16209
6000	66.29	1.508	0.17858	65.87	1.518	0.18132	65.45	1.527	0.18407	65.04	1.537	0.18682	64.63	1.547	0.18957
7000	62.22	1.607	0.20605	61.83	1.617	0.20880	61.44	1.627	0.21154	61.05	1.637	0.21429	60.67	1.648	0.21704
8000	58.41	1.712	0.23352	58.04	1.722	0.23627	57.67	1.733	0.23902	57.31	1.744	0.24177	56.95	1.755	0.24451
9000	54.83	1.823	0.26100	54.48	1.835	0.26374	54.14	1.847	0.26649	53.80	1.858	0.26924	53.46	1.870	0.27199
10000	51.47	1.942	0.28847	51.14	1.955	0.29122	50.82	1.967	0.29396	50.50	1.980	0.29671	50.18	1.992	0.29946
11000	48.31	2.069	0.31594	48.01	2.083	0.31869	47.70	2.096	0.32144	47.40	2.109	0.32419	47.11	2.122	0.32693
12000	45.35	2.205	0.34342	45.06	2.219	0.34616	44.78	2.233	0.34891	44.50	2.247	0.35166	44.22	2.261	0.35441
13000	42.57	2.349	0.37089	42.30	2.363	0.37364	42.04	2.378	0.37638	41.77	2.394	0.37913	41.51	2.409	0.38188
14000	39.96	2.502	0.39836	39.71	2.518	0.40111	39.46	2.534	0.40386	39.21	2.550	0.40660	38.96	2.566	0.40935
15000	37.51	2.665	0.42584	37.27	2.682	0.42858	37.04	2.699	0.43133	36.81	2.716	0.43408	36.57	2.734	0.43683
16000	35.21	2.839	0.45331	34.99	2.857	0.45606	34.77	2.876	0.45880	34.55	2.894	0.46155	34.33	2.912	0.46430
17000	33.05	3.025	0.48078	32.85	3.044	0.48353	32.64	3.063	0.48628	32.43	3.083	0.48902	32.23	3.102	0.49177
18000	31.03	3.222	0.50826	30.83	3.243	0.51100	30.64	3.263	0.51375	30.44	3.284	0.51650	30.25	3.305	0.51925
19000	29.13	3.433	0.53573	28.94	3.455	0.53848	28.76	3.477	0.54122	28.58	3.499	0.54397	28.40	3.521	0.54672
20000	27.34	3.657	0.56320	27.17	3.680	0.56595	27.00	3.704	0.56870	26.83	3.727	0.57144	26.66	3.751	0.57419
21000	25.66	3.896	0.59068	25.50	3.921	0.59342	25.34	3.946	0.59617	25.18	3.971	0.59892	25.02	3.996	0.60166
22000	24.09	4.150	0.61815	23.94	4.177	0.62090	23.79	4.203	0.62364	23.64	4.230	0.62639	23.49	4.257	0.62914
23000	22.61	4.422	0.64562	22.47	4.450	0.64837	22.33	4.478	0.65112	22.19	4.506	0.65386	22.05	4.535	0.65661
24000	21.23	4.710	0.67309	21.09	4.740	0.67584	20.96	4.770	0.67859	20.83	4.801	0.68134	20.70	4.831	0.68408
25000	19.93	5.018	0.70057	19.80	5.050	0.70332	19.68	5.082	0.70606	19.55	5.114	0.70881	19.43	5.147	0.71156
26000	18.71	5.346	0.72804	18.59	5.380	0.73079	18.47	5.414	0.73354	18.35	5.448	0.73628	18.24	5.483	0.73903
27000	17.56	5.695	0.75551	17.45	5.731	0.75826	17.34	5.767	0.76101	17.23	5.804	0.76376	17.12	5.841	0.76650
28000	16.48	6.067	0.78299	16.38	6.105	0.78573	16.27	6.144	0.78848	16.17	6.183	0.79123	16.07	6.222	0.79398
29000	15.47	6.463	0.81046	15.37	6.504	0.81321	15.28	6.545	0.81595	15.18	6.587	0.81870	15.09	6.628	0.82145
30000	14.52	6.885	0.83793	14.43	6.929	0.84068	14.34	6.973	0.84343	14.25	7.017	0.84617	14.16	7.061	0.84892
31000	13.63	7.335	0.86540	13.55	7.381	0.86815	13.46	7.428	0.87090	13.38	7.475	0.87365	13.29	7.523	0.87639
32000	12.80	7.814	0.89288	12.72	7.863	0.89562	12.64	7.913	0.89837	12.56	7.963	0.90112	12.48	8.014	0.90387
33000	12.01	8.324	0.92035	11.94	8.377	0.92310	11.86	8.430	0.92584	11.79	8.483	0.92859	11.71	8.537	0.93134
34000	11.28	8.867	0.94782	11.21	8.924	0.95057	11.13	8.980	0.95331	11.06	9.037	0.95606	10.99	9.095	0.95881
35000	10.59	9.446	0.97529	10.52	9.506	0.97804	10.45	9.567	0.98079	10.39	9.627	0.98353	10.32	9.689	0.98628
36000	9.94	10.064	1.00277	9.87	10.127	1.00552	9.81	10.192	1.00827	9.75	10.256	1.01102	9.69	10.321	1.01376
37000	9.33	10.721	1.03025	9.27	10.789	1.03300	9.21	10.857	1.03574	9.15	10.926	1.03849	9.09	10.996	1.04124
38000	8.76	11.421	1.05772	8.70	11.493	1.06047	8.65	11.566	1.06322	8.59	11.640	1.06596	8.54	11.714	1.06871
39000	8.22	12.167	1.08519	8.17	12.244	1.08794	8.12	12.322	1.09069	8.06	12.400	1.09344	8.01	12.479	1.09618
40000	7.71	12.961	1.11267	7.67	13.044	1.11541	7.62	13.126	1.11816	7.57	13.210	1.12091	7.52	13.294	1.12366
41000	7.24	13.808	1.14014	7.20	13.895	1.14289	7.15	13.984	1.14564	7.11	14.072	1.14838	7.06	14.162	1.15113
42000	6.80	14.710	1.16761	6.76	14.803	1.17036	6.71	14.897	1.17311	6.67	14.991	1.17586	6.63	15.087	1.17860
43000	6.38	15.670	1.19509	6.34	15.770	1.19783	6.30	15.870	1.20058	6.26	15.970	1.20333	6.22	16.072	1.20608
44000	5.99	16.693	1.22256	5.95	16.799	1.22531	5.91	16.906	1.22806	5.88	17.013	1.23080	5.84	17.121	1.23355
45000	5.62	17.784	1.25003	5.59	17.897	1.25278	5.55	18.010	1.25553	5.52	18.124	1.25828	5.48	18.239	1.26102
46000	5.28	18.945	1.27751	5.25	19.065	1.28025	5.21	19.186	1.28300	5.18	19.308	1.28575	5.15	19.431	1.28850
47000	4.95	20.182	1.30498	4.92	20.310	1.30773	4.89	20.439	1.31048	4.86	20.569	1.31322	4.83	20.699	1.31597
48000	4.65	21.500	1.33245	4.62	21.637	1.33520	4.59	21.774	1.33795	4.56	21.912	1.34070	4.53	22.051	1.34344
49000	4.37	22.904	1.35993	4.34	23.050	1.36267	4.31	23.196	1.36542	4.28	23.343	1.36817	4.26	23.491	1.37092
50000	4.10	24.400	1.38740	4.07	24.555	1.39015	4.05	24.711	1.39290	4.02	24.868	1.39564	4.00	25.025	1.39839
51000	3.85	25.994	1.41487	3.82	26.158	1.41762	3.80	26.324	1.42037	3.77	26.492	1.42312	3.75	26.660	1.42586
52000	3.61	27.691	1.44235	3.59	27.867	1.44509	3.57	28.044	1.44784	3.54	28.222	1.45059	3.52	28.401	1.45334
53000	3.39	29.499	1.46982	3.37	29.686	1.47257	3.35	29.875	1.47531	3.33	30.064	1.47806	3.31	30.255	1.48081
54000	3.18	31.426	1.49729	3.16	31.625	1.50004	3.14	31.826	1.50279	3.12	32.028	1.50554	3.10	32.231	1.50828
55000	2.99	33.478	1.52477	2.97	33.690	1.52751	2.95	33.904	1.53026	2.93	34.119	1.53301	2.91	34.336	1.53576
56000	2.80	35.664	1.55224	2.79	35.891	1.55499	2.77	36.118	1.55773	2.75	36.348	1.56048	2.73	36.578	1.56323
57000	2.63	37.993	1.57971	2.62	38.234	1.58246	2.60	38.477	1.58521	2.58	38.721	1.58796	2.57	38.967	1.59070
58000	2.47	40.474	1.60719	2.46	40.731	1.60993	2.44	40.990	1.61268	2.42	41.250	1.61543	2.41	41.512	1.61817
59000	2.32	43.117	1.63466	2.30	43.391	1.63741	2.29	43.666	1.64015	2.28	43.944	1.64290	2.26	44.222	1.64565
60000	2.18	45.933	1.66213	2.16	46.225	1.66488	2.15	46.518	1.66763	2.14	46.813	1.67037	2.12	47.110	1.67312
61000	2.04	48.933	1.68960	2.03	49.243	1.69235	2.02	49.556	1.69510	2.01	49.870	1.69785	1.99	50.187	1.70059
62000	1.92	52.128	1.71708	1.91	52.459	1.71983	1.89	52.792	1.72257	1.88	53.127	1.72532	1.87	53.464	1.72807
63000	1.80	55.533	1.74455	1.79	55.885	1.74730	1.78	56.240	1.75005	1.77	56.596	1.75279	1.76	56.956	1.75554
64000	1.69	59.159	1.77202	1.68	59.534	1.77477	1.67	59.912	1.77752	1.66	60.292	1.78027	1.65	60.675	1.78301
65000	1.59	63.022	1.79950	1.58	63.422	1.80224	1.57	63.825	1.80499	1.56	64.230	1.80774	1.55	64.637	1.81049
66000	1.49	67.137	1.82697	1.48	67.563	1.82972	1.47	67.992	1.83246	1.46	68.424	1.83521	1.45	68.858	1.83796
67000	1.40	71.522	1.85444	1.39	71.976	1.85719	1.38	72.432	1.85994	1.37	72.892	1.86268	1.36	73.355	1.86543
68000	1.31	76.192	1.88191	1.30	76.675	1.88466	1.30	77.162	1.88741	1.29	77.652	1.89016	1.28	78.145	1.89290
69000	1.23	81.168	1.90939	1.22	81.683	1.91213	1.22	82.201	1.91488	1.21	82.723	1.91763	1.20	83.248	1.92037
70000	1.16	86.468	1.93686	1.15	87.017	1.93960	1.14	87.569	1.94235	1.13	88.125	1.94510	1.13	88.683	1.94785
71000	1.09	92.114	1.96433	1.08	92.699	1.96708	1.07	93.287	1.96982	1.07	93.879	1.97257	1.06	94.475	1.97532
72000	1.02	98.129	1.99180	1.01	98.752	1.99455	1.01	99.378	1.99729	1.00	100.012	2.00005	0.99	100.647	2.00280
73000	0.96	104.540	2.01928	0.95	105.203	2.02203	0.94	105.871	2.02478	0.94	106.543	2.02753	0.93	107.219	2.03027
74000	0.90	111.367	2.04676	0.89	112.073	2.04950	0.89	112.785	2.05225	0.88	113.500	2.05500	0.88	114.221	2.05775
75000	0.84	118.639	2.07423	0.84	119.393	2.07698	0.83	120.150	2.07973	0.83	120.913	2.08247	0.82	121.679	2.08522
76000	0.79	126.387	2.10170	0.79	127.189	2.10445	0.78	127.996	2.10720	0.78	128.809	2.10995	0.77	129.626	2.11269
77000	0.74	134.640	2.12918	0.74	135.495	2.13193	0.73	136.354	2.13467	0.73	137.221	2.13742	0.72	138.091	2.14017
78000	0.70	143.432	2.15665	0.69	144.343	2.15940	0.69	145.260	2.16215	0.68	146.181	2.16489	0.68	147.108	2.16764
79000	0.65	152.800	2.18412	0.65	153.770	2.18687	0.65	154.746	2.18962	0.64	155.726	2.19236	0.64	156.715	2.19511
80000	0.61	162.778	2.21160	0.61	163.810	2.21434	0.61	164.850	2.21709	0.60	165.898	2.21984	0.60	166.950	2.22259
81000	0.58	173.409	2.23907	0.57	174.507	2.24182	0.57	175.617	2.24457	0.57	176.731	2.24731	0.56	177.853	2.25006
82000	0.54	184.733	2.26655	0.54	185.904	2.26929	0.53	187.083	2.27204	0.53	188.270	2.27478	0.53	189.465	2.27753
83000	0.51	196.796	2.29402	0.50	198.043	2.29676	0.50	199.302	2.29951	0.50	200.565	2.30226	0.50	201.840	2.30501
84000	0.48	209.648	2.32149	0.47	210.979	2.32424	0.47	212.318	2.32699	0.47	213.666	2.32974	0.47	215.021	2.33248
85000	0.45	223.338	2.34896	0.44	224.754	2.35171	0.44	226.182	2.35446	0.44	227.619	2.35721	0.44	229.063	2.35996
86000	0.42	237.925	2.37644	0.42	239.434	2.37919	0.42	240.952	2.38193	0.41	242.483	2.38468	0.41	244.021	2.38743
87000	0.39	253.459	2.40391	0.39	255.069	2.40666	0.39	256.686	2.40940	0.39	258.317	2.41215	0.38	259.956	2.41490
88000	0.37	270.014	2.43139	0.37	271.724	2.43413	0.37	273.448	2.43688	0.36	275.186	2.43963	0.36	276.931	2.44237
89000	0.35	287.645	2.45886	0.35	289.469	2.46160	0.34	291.307	2.46435	0.34	293.151	2.46709	0.34	295.020	2.46985
90000	0.33	306.428	2.48633	0.32	308.375	2.48908	0.32	310.327	2.49182	0.32	312.295	2.49457	0.32	314.277	2.49731
91000	0.31	326.434	2.51380	0.30	328.515	2.51656	0.30	330.600	2.51930	0.30	332.690	2.52204	0.30	334.806	2.52479
92000	0.29	347.753	2.54127	0.29	349.968	2.54403	0.28	352.187	2.54677	0.28	354.421	2.54952	0.28	356.671	2.55227
93000	0.27	370.466	2.56875	0.27	372.814	2.57149	0.27	375.178	2.57424	0.26	377.557	2.57698	0.26	379.953	2.57973
94000	0.25	394.664	2.59623	0.25	397.156	2.59896	0.25	399.680	2.60171	0.25	402.220	2.60446	0.25	404.776	2.60722
95000	0.24	420.433	2.62370	0.24	423.101	2.62644	0.23	425.785	2.62919	0.23	428.485	2.63194	0.23	431.201	2.63468
96000	0.22	447.888	2.65117	0.22	450.734	2.65392	0.22	453.597	2.65667	0.22	456.475	2.65942	0.22	459.368	2.66216
97000	0.21	477.144	2.67865	0.21	480.169	2.68139	0.21	483.208	2.68413	0.21	486.286	2.68689	0.20	489.356	2.68963
98000	0.20	508.285	2.70611	0.20	511.508	2.70885	0.19	514.774	2.71162	0.19	518.027	2.71435	0.19	521.322	2.71711
99000	0.18	541.477	2.73358	0.18	544.929	2.73634	0.18	548.395	2.73909	0.18	551.876	2.74184	0.18	555.370	2.74458

ICAO Standard Atmosphere[1]

The ICAO Standard Atmosphere is based on the following agreed data:

1. The *measure of altitude* is the geopotential meter (symbol m′), in MKS units equivalent to 9.80665 $m^2\ s^{-2}$. An increase in altitude of 1 meter at a place with the standard acceleration of gravity 9.80665 $m\ s^{-2}$ equals 1 geopotential meter. Since the acceleration of gravity changes only by a few parts per 100 in the altitude range given in the table below, the geopotential meter can in practice be regarded as equal to the meter. Zero altitude is the sea level of the international terrestrial geoid.
2. *Composition of the terrestrial atmosphere.* This is assumed to be dry and to have the following composition:

		Mol.wt.*	Vol. %
Nitrogen	(N_2)	28.016	78.09
Oxygen	(O_2)	32.000	20.95
Argon	(A)	39.944	0.93
Carbon dioxide	(CO_2)	44.010	0.03
Neon	(Ne)	20.183	1.8×10^{-3}
Helium	(He)	4.003	5.24×10^{-4}
Krypton	(Kr)	83.7	1.0×10^{-4}
Hydrogen	(H_2)	2.016	5.0×10^{-5}
Xenon	(Xe)	131.3	8.0×10^{-6}
Ozone	(O_3)	48.000	1.0×10^{-6}
Radon	(Rn)	222	6.0×10^{-18}

The resulting equivalent molecular weight of atmospheric air (M) is 28.966.

3. *Zero values at sea level*
Pressure $p_0 = 1.013\,250\times10^5\ N\ m^{-2}$ (= 760 mm Hg)
Temperature $T_0 = 288.16°K\ (= t_0 = 15°C)$
Velocity of sound $c_0 = 331.45\ m\ s^{-1}$
4. *Constants*
Universal gas constant $R = 8.31436\times10^3\ J\ kmol^{-1} grad^{-1}$
Dynamic viscosity at 23°C $\mu = 1.8325\times10^{-5}\ m^{-1} kg\ s^{-1}$
Sutherland constant $S = 120°K$
5. *Derived zero values at sea level*
Density $\rho_0 = \dfrac{p_0 M}{R\,T_0} = 1.2250\ m^{-3} kg$ (M in kg kmol⁻¹)
Dynamic viscosity $\mu_0 = \mu \left(\dfrac{T_0}{T_\mu}\right)^{3/2} \left(\dfrac{T_\mu + S}{T_0 + S}\right) = 1.7932\times10^{-5} m^{-1} kg\ s^{-1}$
($T_\mu = [23 + 273.16]°K$)
6. For calculation of altitude gradients see original publication[1]

Altitude (or depth) m′	Temperature °C	Atmospheric pressure p mb	mm Hg	p/p_0 (sea level)	Boiling point of water** °C	Density $m^{-3}kg$	Dynamic viscosity $m^{-1}kg\,s^{-1}$ ($\times 10^6$)	Velocity of sound $m\,s^{-1}$	Altitude (or depth) feet
−1000	21.500	1139.29	854.54	1.12439	103.32	1.3470	18.252	344.247	−3280.8
950	21.175	1132.70	849.60	1.11789	103.15	1.3407	18.236	344.057	3116.8
900	20.850	1126.14	844.68	1.11142	102.99	1.3344	18.220	343.867	2952.8
850	20.525	1119.62	839.78	1.10498	102.82	1.3282	18.204	343.677	2788.7
800	20.200	1113.12	834.91	1.09856	102.65	1.3219	18.188	343.487	2624.7
750	19.875	1106.65	830.06	1.09218	102.49	1.3157	18.172	343.297	2460.6
700	19.550	1100.22	825.23	1.08583	102.32	1.3095	18.156	343.106	2296.6
650	19.225	1093.81	820.43	1.07951	102.16	1.3033	18.140	342.915	2132.5
600	18.900	1087.44	815.64	1.07322	101.99	1.2972	18.124	342.725	1968.5
550	18.575	1081.09	810.89	1.06695	101.83	1.2910	18.108	342.534	1804.5
500	18.250	1074.78	806.15	1.06072	101.66	1.2849	18.092	342.343	1640.4
450	17.925	1068.49	801.43	1.05452	101.49	1.2788	18.076	342.152	1476.4
400	17.600	1062.23	796.74	1.04834	101.33	1.2728	18.060	341.961	1312.3
350	17.275	1056.01	792.07	1.04220	101.16	1.2667	18.044	341.770	1148.3
300	16.950	1049.81	787.42	1.03608	101.00	1.2607	18.028	341.579	984.3
250	16.625	1043.65	782.80	1.03000	100.83	1.2547	18.012	341.387	820.2
200	16.300	1037.51	778.20	1.02394	100.67	1.2487	17.996	341.196	656.2
150	15.975	1031.40	773.61	1.01791	100.50	1.2428	17.980	341.004	492.1
100	15.650	1025.32	769.05	1.01191	100.33	1.2368	17.964	340.812	328.1
50	15.325	1019.27	764.52	1.00594	100.17	1.2309	17.948	340.621	164.0
0	15.000	1013.25	760.00	1.00000	100.00	1.2250	17.932	340.429	**0**
+ 50	14.675	1007.26	755.51	0.994086	99.84	1.2191	17.916	340.237	+ 164.0
100	14.350	1001.29	751.03	0.988201	99.67	1.2133	17.900	340.045	328.1
150	14.025	995.36	746.58	0.982343	99.50	1.2075	17.884	339.852	492.1
200	13.700	989.45	742.15	0.976514	99.34	1.2017	17.868	339.660	656.2
250	13.375	983.58	737.74	0.970713	99.17	1.1959	17.852	339.468	820.2
300	13.050	977.73	733.35	0.964940	99.01	1.1901	17.836	339.275	984.3
350	12.725	971.90	728.99	0.959195	98.84	1.1844	17.820	339.082	1148.3
400	12.400	966.11	724.64	0.953477	98.67	1.1787	17.804	338.890	1312.3
450	12.075	960.35	720.32	0.947787	98.51	1.1730	17.787	338.697	1476.4
500	11.750	954.61	716.01	0.942125	98.34	1.1673	17.771	338.504	1640.4
550	11.425	948.90	711.73	0.936490	98.17	1.1616	17.755	338.310	1804.5
600	11.100	943.22	707.47	0.930882	98.01	1.1560	17.739	338.117	1968.5
650	10.775	937.56	703.23	0.925302	97.84	1.1504	17.723	337.924	2132.5
700	10.450	931.94	699.01	0.919748	97.67	1.1448	17.707	337.730	2296.6
750	10.125	926.34	694.81	0.914222	97.51	1.1392	17.690	337.537	2460.6
800	9.800	920.76	690.63	0.908723	97.34	1.1337	17.674	337.343	2624.7
850	9.475	915.22	686.47	0.903250	97.18	1.1281	17.658	337.149	2788.7
900	9.150	909.70	682.33	0.897804	97.01	1.1226	17.642	336.956	2952.8
950	8.825	904.21	678.21	0.892385	96.84	1.1171	17.626	336.761	3116.8
1000	8.500	898.74	674.11	0.886992	96.68	1.1117	17.609	336.567	3280.8
1050	8.175	893.31	670.04	0.881626	96.51	1.1062	17.593	336.373	3444.9
1100	7.850	887.90	665.98	0.876286	96.34	1.1008	17.577	336.179	3608.9
1150	7.525	882.51	661.94	0.870972	96.18	1.0954	17.561	335.984	3773.0
1200	7.200	877.15	657.92	0.865685	96.01	1.0900	17.544	335.790	3937.0
1250	6.875	871.82	653.92	0.860423	95.84	1.0846	17.528	335.595	4101.0
1300	6.550	866.52	649.94	0.855187	95.68	1.0793	17.512	335.400	4265.1
1350	6.225	861.24	645.98	0.849977	95.51	1.0739	17.496	335.205	4429.1
1400	5.900	855.99	642.04	0.844793	95.34	1.0686	17.479	335.010	4593.2
1450	5.575	850.76	638.12	0.839635	95.18	1.0633	17.463	334.815	4757.2
1500	5.250	845.56	634.22	0.834502	95.01	1.0581	17.447	334.620	4921.3
1550	4.925	840.38	630.34	0.829394	94.85	1.0528	17.430	334.425	5085.3
1600	4.600	835.23	626.48	0.824312	94.68	1.0476	17.414	334.229	5249.3
1650	4.275	830.11	622.63	0.819255	94.51	1.0424	17.398	334.034	5413.4
1700	3.950	825.01	618.81	0.814223	94.34	1.0372	17.381	333.838	5577.4
1750	3.625	819.94	615.00	0.809217	94.18	1.0320	17.365	333.642	5741.5
1800	3.300	814.89	611.22	0.804235	94.01	1.0269	17.349	333.446	5905.5
1850	2.975	809.87	607.45	0.799278	93.85	1.0218	17.332	333.250	6069.6
1900	2.650	804.87	603.70	0.794346	93.68	1.0167	17.316	333.054	6233.6
1950	2.325	799.90	599.97	0.789438	93.51	1.0116	17.299	332.858	6397.6
2000	2.000	794.95	596.26	0.784555	93.34	1.0065	17.283	332.661	6561.7
2050	1.675	790.03	592.57	0.779697	93.18	1.0015	17.267	332.465	6725.7
2100	1.350	785.13	588.90	0.774863	93.01	0.99642	17.250	332.268	6889.8
2150	1.025	780.26	585.24	0.770053	92.84	0.99141	17.234	332.071	7053.8
2200	0.700	775.41	581.60	0.765268	92.68	0.98642	17.217	331.874	7217.8
2250	0.375	770.58	577.98	0.760506	92.51	0.98145	17.201	331.677	7381.9
2300	0.050	765.78	574.38	0.755769	92.34	0.97649	17.184	331.480	7545.9
2350	− 0.275	761.01	570.80	0.751056	92.18	0.97156	17.168	331.283	7710.0
2400	− 0.600	756.26	567.24	0.746366	92.01	0.96664	17.151	331.086	7874.0
2450	− 0.925	751.53	563.69	0.741700	91.84	0.96175	17.135	330.888	8038.1
2500	− 1.250	746.82	560.16	0.737058	91.68	0.95687	17.119	330.691	8202.1
2550	− 1.575	742.14	556.65	0.732439	91.51	0.95201	17.102	330.493	8366.1
2600	− 1.900	737.49	553.16	0.727844	91.34	0.94717	17.086	330.295	8530.2
2650	− 2.225	732.86	549.69	0.723272	91.17	0.94235	17.069	330.097	8694.2
2700	− 2.550	728.25	546.23	0.718723	91.01	0.93755	17.052	329.899	8858.3
2750	− 2.875	723.66	542.79	0.714198	90.84	0.93277	17.036	329.701	9022.3
2800	− 3.200	719.10	539.37	0.709696	90.67	0.92800	17.019	329.503	9186.4
2850	− 3.525	714.56	535.96	0.705216	90.50	0.92326	17.003	329.304	9350.4
2900	− 3.850	710.05	532.58	0.700760	90.34	0.91853	16.986	329.106	9514.4
2950	− 4.175	705.55	529.21	0.696327	90.17	0.91382	16.970	328.907	9678.5

1) Values from *Manuel de l'atmosphère type OACI*, Montreal, 1954. Reproduced by kind permission of the International Civil Aviation Organization, Montreal, Canada.

* International Atomic Weights 1947.
** Interpolated from the table on page 297.

Altitude m′	Temperature °C	Atmospheric pressure p mb	mm Hg	p/p_0 (sea level)	Boiling point of water °C	Density m^{-3} kg	Dynamic viscosity m^{-1} kg s^{-1} ($\times 10^6$)	Velocity of sound m s^{-1}	Altitude feet
3000	− 4.500	701.08	525.86	0.691916	90.00	0.90913	16.953	328.709	9842.5
3050	− 4.825	696.64	522.52	0.687528	89.84	0.90446	16.937	328.510	10006.6
3100	− 5.150	692.21	519.20	0.683162	89.67	0.89981	16.920	328.311	10170.6
3150	− 5.475	687.81	515.90	0.678819	89.50	0.89517	16.903	328.112	10334.6
3200	− 5.800	683.44	512.62	0.674498	89.33	0.89055	16.887	327.912	10498.7
3250	− 6.125	679.08	509.35	0.670200	89.17	0.88596	16.870	327.713	10662.7
3300	− 6.450	674.75	506.10	0.665924	89.00	0.88138	16.853	327.513	10826.8
3350	− 6.775	670.44	502.87	0.661670	88.83	0.87681	16.837	327.314	10990.8
3400	− 7.100	666.15	499.65	0.657438	88.66	0.87227	16.820	327.114	11154.9
3450	− 7.425	661.88	496.45	0.653227	88.50	0.86774	16.803	326.914	11318.9
3500	− 7.750	657.64	493.27	0.649039	88.33	0.86324	16.787	326.714	11482.9
3550	− 8.075	653.42	490.10	0.644873	88.16	0.85875	16.770	326.514	11647.0
3600	− 8.400	649.22	486.95	0.640728	87.99	0.85427	16.753	326.314	11811.0
3650	− 8.725	645.04	483.82	0.636605	87.83	0.84982	16.737	326.114	11975.1
3700	− 9.050	640.88	480.70	0.632503	87.66	0.84538	16.720	325.913	12139.1
3750	− 9.375	636.75	477.60	0.628423	87.49	0.84097	16.703	325.713	12303.1
3800	− 9.700	632.64	474.52	0.624364	87.32	0.83656	16.687	325.512	12467.2
3850	− 10.025	628.55	471.45	0.620326	87.15	0.83218	16.670	325.311	12631.2
3900	− 10.350	624.48	468.40	0.616310	86.99	0.82782	16.653	325.110	12795.3
3950	− 10.675	620.43	465.36	0.612314	86.82	0.82347	16.636	324.909	12959.3
4000	− 11.000	616.40	462.34	0.608340	86.65	0.81914	16.620	324.708	13123.4
4050	− 11.325	612.39	459.33	0.604386	86.48	0.81482	16.603	324.506	13287.4
4100	− 11.650	608.41	456.34	0.600454	86.31	0.81053	16.586	324.305	13451.4
4150	− 11.975	604.45	453.37	0.596542	86.15	0.80625	16.569	324.103	13615.5
4200	− 12.300	600.50	450.41	0.592651	85.98	0.80199	16.552	323.902	13779.5
4250	− 12.625	596.58	447.47	0.588780	85.81	0.79774	16.536	323.700	13943.6
4300	− 12.950	592.68	444.55	0.584930	85.64	0.79352	16.519	323.498	14107.6
4350	− 13.275	588.80	441.64	0.581100	85.48	0.78931	16.502	323.296	14271.7
4400	− 13.600	584.94	438.74	0.577291	85.31	0.78511	16.485	323.094	14435.7
4450	− 13.925	581.10	435.86	0.573501	85.14	0.78094	16.468	322.891	14599.7
4500	− 14.250	577.28	433.00	0.569732	84.97	0.77678	16.451	322.689	14763.8
4550	− 14.575	573.48	430.15	0.565983	84.80	0.77264	16.434	322.486	14927.8
4600	− 14.900	569.70	427.31	0.562254	84.63	0.76851	16.418	322.283	15091.9
4650	− 15.225	565.95	424.49	0.558545	84.47	0.76441	16.401	322.081	15255.9
4700	− 15.550	562.21	421.69	0.554856	84.30	0.76032	16.384	321.878	15419.9
4750	− 15.875	558.49	418.90	0.551187	84.13	0.75624	16.367	321.675	15584.0
4800	− 16.200	554.79	416.13	0.547537	83.96	0.75218	16.350	321.471	15748.0
4850	− 16.525	551.11	413.37	0.543907	83.79	0.74814	16.333	321.268	15912.1
4900	− 16.850	547.46	410.63	0.540296	83.63	0.74412	16.316	321.064	16076.1
4950	− 17.175	543.82	407.90	0.536705	83.46	0.74011	16.299	320.861	16240.2
5000	− 17.500	540.20	405.18	0.533133	83.29	0.73612	16.282	320.657	16404.2
5050	− 17.825	536.60	402.48	0.529581	83.12	0.73215	16.265	320.453	16568.2
5100	− 18.150	533.02	399.80	0.526047	82.95	0.72819	16.248	320.249	16732.3
5150	− 18.475	529.46	397.13	0.522533	82.78	0.72425	16.231	320.045	16896.3
5200	− 18.800	525.91	394.47	0.519038	82.61	0.72032	16.214	319.841	17060.4
5250	− 19.125	522.39	391.83	0.515561	82.45	0.71641	16.197	319.636	17224.4
5300	− 19.450	518.89	389.20	0.512104	82.28	0.71252	16.180	319.432	17388.5
5350	− 19.775	515.41	386.59	0.508665	82.11	0.70864	16.163	319.227	17552.5
5400	− 20.100	511.94	383.99	0.505245	81.94	0.70478	16.146	319.022	17716.5
5450	− 20.425	508.49	381.40	0.501844	81.77	0.70094	16.129	318.817	17880.6
5500	− 20.750	505.07	378.83	0.498461	81.60	0.69711	16.112	318.612	18044.6
5550	− 21.075	501.66	376.27	0.495097	81.43	0.69330	16.095	318.407	18208.7
5600	− 21.400	498.27	373.73	0.491751	81.26	0.68950	16.078	318.202	18372.7
5650	− 21.725	494.90	371.20	0.488424	81.09	0.68572	16.061	317.996	18536.7
5700	− 22.050	491.54	368.69	0.485115	80.93	0.68196	16.044	317.791	18700.8
5750	− 22.375	488.21	366.19	0.481824	80.76	0.67821	16.027	317.585	18864.8
5800	− 22.700	484.89	363.70	0.478551	80.59	0.67448	16.010	317.379	19028.9
5850	− 23.025	481.59	361.22	0.475296	80.42	0.67076	15.992	317.173	19192.9
5900	− 23.350	478.31	358.76	0.472059	80.25	0.66706	15.975	316.967	19357.0
5950	− 23.675	475.05	356.32	0.468840	80.08	0.66337	15.958	316.761	19521.0
6000	− 24.000	471.81	353.89	0.465639	79.91	0.65970	15.941	316.555	19685.0
6050	− 24.325	468.58	351.47	0.462455	79.74	0.65605	15.924	316.348	19849.1
6100	− 24.650	465.37	349.06	0.459289	79.57	0.65241	15.907	316.141	20013.1
6150	− 24.975	462.18	346.67	0.456141	79.41	0.64878	15.890	315.935	20177.2
6200	− 25.300	459.01	344.29	0.453010	79.23	0.64517	15.872	315.728	20341.2
6250	− 25.625	455.86	341.92	0.449897	79.07	0.64158	15.855	315.521	20505.2
6300	− 25.950	452.72	339.57	0.446801	78.90	0.63800	15.838	315.313	20669.3
6350	− 26.275	449.60	337.23	0.443722	78.73	0.63444	15.821	315.106	20833.3
6400	− 26.600	446.50	334.90	0.440660	78.56	0.63090	15.804	314.899	20997.4
6450	− 26.925	443.41	332.59	0.437616	78.39	0.62736	15.786	314.691	21161.4
6500	− 27.250	440.35	330.29	0.434588	78.22	0.62385	15.769	314.483	21325.5
6550	− 27.575	437.30	328.00	0.431578	78.05	0.62035	15.752	314.275	21489.5
6600	− 27.900	434.26	325.72	0.428584	77.88	0.61686	15.734	314.067	21653.5
6650	− 28.225	431.25	323.46	0.425608	77.71	0.61339	15.717	313.859	21817.6
6700	− 28.550	428.25	321.21	0.422648	77.54	0.60993	15.700	313.651	21981.6
6750	− 28.875	425.27	318.98	0.419705	77.37	0.60649	15.683	313.442	22145.7
6800	− 29.200	422.30	316.75	0.416778	77.20	0.60306	15.665	313.234	22309.7
6850	− 29.525	419.35	314.54	0.413868	77.03	0.59965	15.648	313.025	22473.8
6900	− 29.850	416.42	312.34	0.410974	76.86	0.59625	15.631	312.816	22637.8
6950	− 30.175	413.50	310.15	0.408097	76.69	0.59287	15.613	312.607	22801.8
7000	− 30.500	410.61	307.98	0.405236	76.52	0.58950	15.596	312.398	22965.9
7050	− 30.825	407.72	305.82	0.402392	76.35	0.58615	15.579	312.189	23129.9
7100	− 31.150	404.86	303.67	0.399563	76.18	0.58281	15.561	311.980	23294.0
7150	− 31.475	402.01	301.53	0.396751	76.01	0.57949	15.544	311.770	23458.0
7200	− 31.800	399.17	299.41	0.393955	75.84	0.57618	15.526	311.560	23622.0
7250	− 32.125	396.36	297.29	0.391175	75.67	0.57288	15.509	311.350	23786.1
7300	− 32.450	393.56	295.19	0.388410	75.50	0.56960	15.492	311.140	23950.1
7350	− 32.775	390.77	293.10	0.385662	75.33	0.56634	15.474	310.930	24114.2
7400	− 33.100	388.00	291.03	0.382929	75.16	0.56309	15.457	310.720	24278.2
7450	− 33.425	385.25	288.96	0.380212	74.99	0.55985	15.439	310.510	24442.3
7500	− 33.750	382.51	286.91	0.377511	74.82	0.55663	15.422	310.299	24606.3
7550	− 34.075	379.79	284.87	0.374825	74.65	0.55342	15.404	310.088	24770.3
7600	− 34.400	377.09	282.84	0.372154	74.48	0.55022	15.387	309.878	24934.4
7650	− 34.725	374.40	280.82	0.369499	74.31	0.54704	15.369	309.667	25098.4
7700	− 35.050	371.72	278.81	0.366860	74.14	0.54387	15.352	309.456	25262.5
7750	− 35.375	369.06	276.82	0.364236	73.97	0.54072	15.334	309.244	25426.5
7800	− 35.700	366.42	274.84	0.361627	73.80	0.53758	15.317	309.033	25590.6
7850	− 36.025	363.79	272.86	0.359033	73.63	0.53446	15.299	308.821	25754.6
7900	− 36.350	361.18	270.90	0.356454	73.46	0.53135	15.282	308.610	25918.6
7950	− 36.675	358.58	268.96	0.353890	73.29	0.52825	15.264	308.398	26082.7

ICAO Standard Atmosphere (concluded)

Altitude m′	Temperature °C	Atmospheric pressure p mb	mm Hg	p/p_0 (sealevel)	Boiling point of water °C	Density m^{-3} kg	Dynamic viscosity m^{-1} kg s^{-1} ($\times 10^6$)	Velocity of sound m s^{-1}	Altitude feet
8000	− 37.000	356.00	267.02	0.351341	73.12	0.52517	15.247	308.186	26246.7
8050	− 37.325	353.43	265.09	0.348807	72.95	0.52210	15.229	307.974	26410.8
8100	− 37.650	350.88	263.18	0.346288	72.78	0.51904	15.212	307.761	26574.8
8150	− 37.975	348.34	261.28	0.343784	72.61	0.51600	15.194	307.549	26738.8
8200	− 38.300	345.82	259.38	0.341294	72.43	0.51297	15.176	307.336	26902.9
8250	− 38.625	343.31	257.50	0.338819	72.26	0.50996	15.159	307.124	27066.9
8300	− 38.950	340.82	255.63	0.336359	72.09	0.50696	15.141	306.911	27231.0
8350	− 39.275	338.34	253.77	0.333913	71.92	0.50397	15.124	306.698	27395.0
8400	− 39.600	335.87	251.93	0.331481	71.75	0.50100	15.106	306.485	27559.1
8450	− 39.925	333.42	250.09	0.329064	71.58	0.49804	15.088	306.271	27723.1
8500	− 40.250	330.99	248.26	0.326661	71.41	0.49509	15.071	306.058	27887.1
8550	− 40.575	328.57	246.45	0.324272	71.24	0.49216	15.053	305.844	28051.2
8600	− 40.900	326.16	244.64	0.321897	71.07	0.48924	15.035	305.630	28215.2
8650	− 41.225	323.77	242.85	0.319537	70.90	0.48633	15.018	305.417	28379.3
8700	− 41.550	321.39	241.06	0.317191	70.72	0.48344	15.000	305.203	28543.3
8750	− 41.875	319.03	239.29	0.314858	70.55	0.48056	14.982	304.988	28707.3
8800	− 42.200	316.68	237.53	0.312540	70.38	0.47769	14.965	304.774	28871.4
8850	− 42.525	314.35	235.78	0.310235	70.21	0.47483	14.947	304.559	29035.4
8900	− 42.850	312.02	234.04	0.307944	70.04	0.47199	14.929	304.345	29199.5
8950	− 43.175	309.72	232.31	0.305667	69.87	0.46916	14.911	304.130	29363.5
9000	− 43.500	307.42	230.59	0.303403	69.69	0.46635	14.893	303.915	29527.6
9050	− 43.825	305.14	228.88	0.301153	69.52	0.46355	14.876	303.700	29691.6
9100	− 44.150	302.88	227.18	0.298917	69.35	0.46076	14.858	303.485	29855.6
9150	− 44.475	300.62	225.49	0.296694	69.18	0.45798	14.840	303.269	30019.7
9200	− 44.800	298.39	223.81	0.294484	69.01	0.45522	14.822	303.054	30183.7
9250	− 45.125	296.16	222.14	0.292288	68.84	0.45247	14.805	302.838	30347.8
9300	− 45.450	293.95	220.48	0.290105	68.66	0.44973	14.787	302.622	30511.8
9350	− 45.775	291.75	218.83	0.287935	68.49	0.44700	14.769	302.406	30675.9
9400	− 46.100	289.57	217.19	0.285779	68.32	0.44429	14.751	302.190	30839.9
9450	− 46.425	287.39	215.56	0.283635	68.15	0.44159	14.733	301.973	31003.9
9500	− 46.750	285.23	213.94	0.281505	67.98	0.43890	14.715	301.757	31168.0
9550	− 47.075	283.09	212.33	0.279388	67.80	0.43623	14.697	301.540	31332.0
9600	− 47.400	280.96	210.74	0.277283	67.63	0.43356	14.679	301.323	31496.1
9650	− 47.725	278.84	209.15	0.275191	67.46	0.43091	14.662	301.106	31660.1
9700	− 48.050	276.73	207.57	0.273113	67.29	0.42828	14.644	300.889	31824.1
9750	− 48.375	274.64	206.00	0.271046	67.12	0.42565	14.626	300.672	31988.2
9800	− 48.700	272.56	204.43	0.268993	66.94	0.42304	14.608	300.455	32152.2
9850	− 49.025	270.49	202.88	0.266952	66.77	0.42044	14.590	300.237	32316.3
9900	− 49.350	268.43	201.34	0.264924	66.60	0.41785	14.572	300.019	32480.3
9950	− 49.675	266.39	199.81	0.262908	66.43	0.41527	14.554	299.801	32644.4
10000	− 50.000	264.36	198.29	0.260905	66.25	0.41271	14.536	299.583	32808.4
10050	− 50.325	262.34	196.77	0.258914	66.08	0.41015	14.518	299.365	32972.4
10100	− 50.650	260.34	195.27	0.256934	65.91	0.40761	14.500	299.147	33136.5
10150	− 50.975	258.35	193.78	0.254969	65.74	0.40509	14.482	298.928	33300.5
10200	− 51.300	256.37	192.29	0.253014	65.56	0.40257	14.464	298.709	33464.6
10250	− 51.625	254.40	190.81	0.251072	65.39	0.40007	14.446	298.491	33628.6
10300	− 51.950	252.44	189.35	0.249142	65.22	0.39757	14.428	298.272	33792.7
10350	− 52.275	250.50	187.89	0.247224	65.04	0.39509	14.410	298.052	33956.7
10400	− 52.600	248.57	186.44	0.245318	64.87	0.39263	14.392	297.833	34120.7
10450	− 52.925	246.65	185.00	0.243424	64.70	0.39017	14.374	297.614	34284.8
10500	− 53.250	244.74	183.57	0.241542	64.53	0.38773	14.355	297.394	34448.8
10550	− 53.575	242.85	182.15	0.239672	64.35	0.38529	14.337	297.174	34612.9
10600	− 53.900	240.96	180.74	0.237813	64.18	0.38287	14.319	296.954	34776.9
10650	− 54.225	239.09	179.33	0.235966	64.01	0.38046	14.301	296.734	34940.9
10700	− 54.550	237.23	177.94	0.234131	63.83	0.37806	14.283	296.513	35105.0
10750	− 54.875	235.39	176.55	0.232307	63.66	0.37568	14.265	296.293	35269.0
10800	− 55.200	233.55	175.18	0.230495	63.49	0.37330	14.247	296.072	35433.1
10850	− 55.525	231.72	173.81	0.228694	63.31	0.37094	14.229	295.852	35597.1
10900	− 55.850	229.91	172.45	0.226905	63.14	0.36859	14.210	295.631	35761.2
10950	− 56.175	228.11	171.10	0.225127	62.97	0.36625	14.192	295.409	35925.2
11000	− 56.500	226.32	169.75	0.223360	62.79	0.36392	14.174	295.188	36089.2
11100	− 56.500	222.78	167.10	0.219866	62.45	0.35822	14.174	295.188	36417.3
11200	− 56.500	219.29	164.48	0.216426	62.10	0.35262	14.174	295.188	36745.4
11300	− 56.500	215.86	161.91	0.213040	61.75	0.34710	14.174	295.188	37073.5
11400	− 56.500	212.49	159.38	0.209707	61.41	0.34167	14.174	295.188	37401.6
11500	− 56.500	209.16	156.88	0.206426	61.07	0.33633	14.174	295.188	37729.7
11600	− 56.500	205.89	154.43	0.203196	60.72	0.33107	14.174	295.188	38057.7
11700	− 56.500	202.67	152.01	0.200017	60.38	0.32589	14.174	295.188	38385.8
11800	− 56.500	199.50	149.63	0.196888	60.04	0.32079	14.174	295.188	38713.9
11900	− 56.500	196.38	147.29	0.193808	59.70	0.31577	14.174	295.188	39042.0
12000	− 56.500	193.30	144.99	0.190776	59.36	0.31083	14.174	295.188	39370.1
12100	− 56.500	190.28	142.72	0.187791	59.02	0.30597	14.174	295.188	39698.2
12200	− 56.500	187.30	140.49	0.184853	58.68	0.30118	14.174	295.188	40026.2
12300	− 56.500	184.37	138.29	0.181961	58.35	0.29647	14.174	295.188	40354.3
12400	− 56.500	181.49	136.13	0.179114	58.01	0.29183	14.174	295.188	40682.4
12500	− 56.500	178.65	134.00	0.176312	57.68	0.28726	14.174	295.188	41010.5
12600	− 56.500	175.85	131.90	0.173553	57.34	0.28277	14.174	295.188	41338.6
12700	− 56.500	173.10	129.84	0.170838	57.01	0.27834	14.174	295.188	41666.7
12800	− 56.500	170.39	127.81	0.168165	56.67	0.27399	14.174	295.188	41994.8
12900	− 56.500	167.73	125.81	0.165534	56.34	0.26970	14.174	295.188	42322.8
13000	− 56.500	165.10	123.84	0.162944	56.01	0.26548	14.174	295.188	42650.9
13100	− 56.500	162.52	121.90	0.160395	55.68	0.26133	14.174	295.188	42979.0
13200	− 56.500	159.98	119.99	0.157886	55.35	0.25724	14.174	295.188	43307.1
13300	− 56.500	157.47	118.12	0.155416	55.02	0.25322	14.174	295.188	43635.2
13400	− 56.500	155.01	116.27	0.152984	54.69	0.24925	14.174	295.188	43963.3
13500	− 56.500	152.59	114.45	0.150591	54.36	0.24536	14.174	295.188	44291.3
13600	− 56.500	150.20	112.66	0.148235	54.03	0.24152	14.174	295.188	44619.4
13700	− 56.500	147.85	110.90	0.145915	53.71	0.23774	14.174	295.188	44947.5
13800	− 56.500	145.54	109.16	0.143633	53.38	0.23402	14.174	295.188	45275.6
13900	− 56.500	143.26	107.45	0.141385	53.06	0.23036	14.174	295.188	45603.7
14000	− 56.500	141.02	105.77	0.139173	52.73	0.22675	14.174	295.188	45931.8
14500	− 56.500	130.33	97.753	0.128622	51.12	0.20956	14.174	295.188	47572.2
15000	− 56.500	120.45	90.341	0.118870	49.53	0.19367	14.174	295.188	49212.6
15500	− 56.500	111.31	83.492	0.109858	47.96	0.17899	14.174	295.188	50853.0
16000	− 56.500	102.87	77.162	0.101529	46.40	0.16542	14.174	295.188	52493.4
16500	− 56.500	95.075	71.312	0.093832	44.86	0.15288	14.174	295.188	54133.9
17000	− 56.500	87.867	65.905	0.086718	43.34	0.14129	14.174	295.188	55774.3
18000	− 56.500	75.048	56.291	0.074067	40.34	0.12068	14.174	295.188	59055.1
19000	− 56.500	64.100	48.079	0.063262	37.40	0.10307	14.174	295.188	62336.0
20000	− 56.500	54.749	41.065	0.054033	34.53	0.08804	14.174	295.188	65616.8

Subtract from the barometer reading the amount $\Delta\beta_t$ corresponding to the actual temperature t, *or* multiply the barometer reading by the correction factor f_t. The vapor pressure correction for air fully saturated with water vapor is already included in the conversion tables for gas volumes on pages 300–309 and can be ignored.

The correction factor f_t is calculated from the formula $f_t = 1 - \frac{(\beta - \alpha)\,t}{1+\beta t}$,

where

$\beta = 1.818 \times 10^{-4}\,°C^{-1} \approx$ volume expansion coefficient of mercury,

$\alpha = 1.84 \times 10^{-5}\,°C^{-1} \approx$ linear expansion coefficient of brass, or

$\alpha = 8.5 \times 10^{-6}\,°C^{-1} \approx$ linear expansion coefficient of glass.

Brass Scale

Barometer reading β_t in millimeters. Amount $\Delta\beta_t$ in millimeters to be subtracted.

Barometer temperature t = °C	600	610	620	630	640	650	660	670	680	690	700	710	720	730	740	750	760	770	780	790	Correction factor f_t
1	0.10	0.10	0.10	0.10	0.10	0.11	0.11	0.11	0.11	0.11	0.11	0.12	0.12	0.12	0.12	0.12	0.12	0.13	0.13	0.13	0.999 837
2	0.20	0.20	0.20	0.21	0.21	0.21	0.22	0.22	0.22	0.23	0.23	0.23	0.24	0.24	0.24	0.25	0.25	0.25	0.26	0.26	999 673
3	0.29	0.29	0.30	0.30	0.31	0.31	0.32	0.32	0.33	0.33	0.34	0.34	0.35	0.35	0.36	0.36	0.36	0.37	0.37	0.38	999 520
4	0.39	0.40	0.41	0.41	0.42	0.43	0.43	0.44	0.44	0.45	0.46	0.46	0.47	0.48	0.48	0.49	0.50	0.50	0.51	0.52	999 346
5	0.49	0.50	0.51	0.51	0.52	0.53	0.54	0.55	0.55	0.56	0.57	0.58	0.59	0.60	0.60	0.61	0.62	0.63	0.64	0.64	0.999 184
6	0.59	0.60	0.61	0.62	0.63	0.64	0.65	0.66	0.67	0.68	0.69	0.70	0.70	0.71	0.72	0.73	0.74	0.75	0.76	0.77	999 021
7	0.69	0.70	0.71	0.72	0.73	0.74	0.75	0.77	0.78	0.79	0.80	0.81	0.82	0.83	0.85	0.86	0.87	0.88	0.89	0.90	998 858
8	0.78	0.80	0.81	0.82	0.84	0.85	0.86	0.87	0.89	0.90	0.91	0.93	0.94	0.95	0.97	0.98	0.99	1.00	1.02	1.03	998 695
9	0.88	0.90	0.91	0.92	0.94	0.95	0.97	0.98	1.00	1.01	1.03	1.04	1.06	1.07	1.09	1.10	1.12	1.13	1.15	1.16	998 532
10	0.98	0.99	1.01	1.03	1.04	1.06	1.08	1.09	1.11	1.13	1.14	1.16	1.17	1.19	1.21	1.22	1.24	1.26	1.27	1.29	0.998 369
11	1.08	1.09	1.11	1.13	1.15	1.17	1.18	1.20	1.22	1.24	1.26	1.27	1.29	1.31	1.33	1.35	1.36	1.38	1.40	1.42	998 206
12	1.17	1.19	1.21	1.23	1.25	1.27	1.29	1.31	1.33	1.35	1.37	1.39	1.41	1.43	1.45	1.47	1.49	1.51	1.53	1.55	998 044
13	1.27	1.29	1.31	1.33	1.36	1.38	1.40	1.42	1.44	1.46	1.48	1.50	1.53	1.55	1.57	1.59	1.61	1.63	1.65	1.67	997 881
14	1.37	1.39	1.41	1.44	1.46	1.48	1.51	1.53	1.55	1.57	1.60	1.62	1.64	1.67	1.69	1.71	1.73	1.76	1.78	1.80	997 718
15	1.47	1.49	1.52	1.54	1.56	1.59	1.61	1.64	1.66	1.69	1.71	1.74	1.76	1.78	1.81	1.83	1.86	1.88	1.91	1.93	0.997 556
16	1.56	1.59	1.62	1.64	1.67	1.69	1.72	1.75	1.77	1.80	1.82	1.85	1.88	1.90	1.93	1.96	1.98	2.01	2.03	2.06	997 393
17	1.66	1.69	1.72	1.74	1.77	1.80	1.83	1.86	1.88	1.91	1.94	1.97	1.99	2.02	2.05	2.08	2.10	2.13	2.16	2.19	997 231
18	1.76	1.79	1.82	1.85	1.88	1.91	1.94	1.96	1.99	2.02	2.05	2.08	2.11	2.14	2.17	2.20	2.23	2.26	2.29	2.32	997 068
19	1.86	1.89	1.92	1.95	1.98	2.01	2.04	2.07	2.10	2.13	2.17	2.20	2.23	2.26	2.29	2.32	2.35	2.38	2.41	2.44	996 906
20	1.95	1.99	2.02	2.05	2.08	2.12	2.15	2.18	2.21	2.25	2.28	2.31	2.34	2.38	2.41	2.44	2.47	2.51	2.54	2.57	0.996 744
21	2.05	2.08	2.12	2.15	2.19	2.22	2.26	2.29	2.32	2.36	2.39	2.43	2.46	2.50	2.53	2.56	2.60	2.63	2.67	2.70	996 582
22	2.15	2.18	2.22	2.26	2.29	2.33	2.36	2.40	2.43	2.47	2.51	2.54	2.58	2.61	2.65	2.69	2.72	2.76	2.79	2.83	996 420
23	2.25	2.28	2.32	2.36	2.39	2.43	2.47	2.51	2.54	2.58	2.62	2.66	2.69	2.73	2.77	2.81	2.84	2.88	2.92	2.96	996 258
24	2.34	2.38	2.42	2.46	2.50	2.54	2.58	2.62	2.66	2.69	2.73	2.77	2.81	2.85	2.89	2.93	2.97	3.01	3.05	3.08	996 095
25	2.44	2.48	2.52	2.56	2.60	2.64	2.68	2.72	2.76	2.81	2.85	2.89	2.93	2.97	3.01	3.05	3.09	3.13	3.17	3.21	0.995 934
26	2.54	2.58	2.62	2.66	2.71	2.75	2.79	2.83	2.88	2.92	2.96	3.00	3.04	3.09	3.13	3.17	3.21	3.26	3.30	3.34	995 772
27	2.63	2.68	2.72	2.77	2.81	2.85	2.90	2.94	2.99	3.03	3.07	3.12	3.16	3.20	3.25	3.29	3.34	3.38	3.42	3.47	995 610
28	2.73	2.78	2.82	2.87	2.91	2.96	3.00	3.05	3.10	3.14	3.19	3.23	3.28	3.32	3.37	3.41	3.46	3.51	3.55	3.60	995 448
29	2.83	2.88	2.92	2.97	3.02	3.06	3.11	3.16	3.21	3.25	3.30	3.35	3.39	3.44	3.49	3.54	3.58	3.63	3.68	3.72	995 286
30	2.93	2.97	3.02	3.07	3.12	3.17	3.22	3.27	3.32	3.36	3.41	3.46	3.51	3.56	3.61	3.66	3.71	3.75	3.80	3.85	0.995 125
31	3.02	3.07	3.12	3.17	3.22	3.27	3.32	3.37	3.43	3.48	3.53	3.58	3.63	3.68	3.73	3.78	3.83	3.88	3.93	3.98	994 963
32	3.12	3.17	3.22	3.28	3.33	3.38	3.43	3.48	3.54	3.59	3.64	3.69	3.74	3.80	3.85	3.90	3.95	4.00	4.06	4.11	994 801
33	3.22	3.27	3.32	3.38	3.43	3.48	3.54	3.59	3.64	3.70	3.75	3.81	3.86	3.91	3.97	4.02	4.07	4.13	4.18	4.23	994 640
34	3.31	3.37	3.42	3.48	3.53	3.59	3.64	3.70	3.75	3.81	3.86	3.92	3.98	4.03	4.09	4.14	4.20	4.25	4.31	4.36	994 479
35	3.41	3.47	3.52	3.58	3.64	3.69	3.75	3.81	3.86	3.92	3.98	4.03	4.09	4.15	4.21	4.26	4.32	4.38	4.43	4.49	0.994 317
36	3.51	3.56	3.62	3.68	3.74	3.80	3.86	3.92	3.97	4.03	4.09	4.15	4.21	4.27	4.32	4.38	4.44	4.50	4.56	4.62	994 156
37	3.60	3.66	3.72	3.78	3.84	3.90	3.96	4.02	4.08	4.14	4.20	4.26	4.32	4.38	4.44	4.50	4.56	4.62	4.68	4.74	993 995
38	3.70	3.76	3.82	3.89	3.95	4.01	4.07	4.13	4.19	4.26	4.32	4.38	4.44	4.50	4.56	4.63	4.69	4.75	4.81	4.87	993 833
39	3.80	3.86	3.92	3.99	4.05	4.11	4.18	4.24	4.30	4.37	4.43	4.49	4.56	4.62	4.68	4.75	4.81	4.87	4.94	5.00	993 672
40	3.89	3.96	4.02	4.09	4.15	4.22	4.28	4.35	4.41	4.48	4.54	4.61	4.67	4.74	4.80	4.87	4.93	5.00	5.06	5.13	0.993 511

Glass Scale

Barometer temperature t = °C	600	610	620	630	640	650	660	670	680	690	700	710	720	730	740	750	760	770	780	790	Correction factor f_t
1	0.10	0.11	0.11	0.11	0.11	0.11	0.11	0.12	0.12	0.12	0.12	0.12	0.12	0.13	0.13	0.13	0.13	0.13	0.13	0.14	0.999 827
2	0.21	0.21	0.21	0.22	0.22	0.22	0.23	0.23	0.24	0.24	0.24	0.25	0.25	0.25	0.26	0.26	0.26	0.27	0.27	0.27	999 654
3	0.31	0.32	0.32	0.33	0.33	0.34	0.34	0.35	0.35	0.36	0.36	0.37	0.37	0.38	0.38	0.39	0.40	0.40	0.41	0.41	999 480
4	0.42	0.42	0.43	0.44	0.44	0.45	0.46	0.46	0.47	0.48	0.49	0.49	0.50	0.51	0.51	0.52	0.53	0.53	0.54	0.55	999 307
5	0.52	0.53	0.54	0.55	0.55	0.56	0.57	0.58	0.59	0.60	0.61	0.61	0.62	0.63	0.64	0.65	0.66	0.67	0.68	0.68	0.999 134
6	0.62	0.63	0.64	0.65	0.66	0.68	0.69	0.70	0.71	0.72	0.73	0.74	0.75	0.76	0.77	0.78	0.79	0.80	0.81	0.82	998 961
7	0.73	0.74	0.75	0.76	0.78	0.79	0.80	0.81	0.82	0.84	0.85	0.86	0.87	0.88	0.90	0.91	0.92	0.93	0.95	0.96	998 788
8	0.83	0.84	0.86	0.87	0.89	0.90	0.91	0.93	0.94	0.95	0.97	0.98	1.00	1.01	1.02	1.04	1.05	1.07	1.08	1.09	998 616
9	0.93	0.95	0.97	0.98	1.00	1.01	1.03	1.04	1.06	1.07	1.09	1.11	1.12	1.14	1.15	1.17	1.18	1.20	1.21	1.23	998 443
10	1.04	1.06	1.07	1.09	1.11	1.12	1.14	1.16	1.18	1.19	1.21	1.23	1.25	1.26	1.28	1.30	1.31	1.33	1.35	1.37	0.998 270
11	1.14	1.16	1.18	1.20	1.22	1.24	1.26	1.27	1.29	1.31	1.33	1.35	1.37	1.39	1.41	1.43	1.45	1.46	1.48	1.50	998 098
12	1.25	1.27	1.29	1.31	1.33	1.35	1.37	1.39	1.41	1.43	1.45	1.47	1.49	1.51	1.54	1.56	1.58	1.60	1.62	1.64	997 925
13	1.35	1.37	1.39	1.42	1.44	1.46	1.48	1.51	1.53	1.55	1.57	1.60	1.62	1.64	1.66	1.69	1.71	1.73	1.75	1.78	997 752
14	1.45	1.48	1.50	1.52	1.55	1.57	1.60	1.62	1.65	1.67	1.69	1.72	1.74	1.77	1.79	1.82	1.84	1.86	1.89	1.91	997 580
15	1.56	1.58	1.61	1.63	1.66	1.68	1.71	1.74	1.76	1.79	1.81	1.84	1.87	1.89	1.92	1.94	1.97	2.00	2.02	2.05	0.997 408
16	1.66	1.69	1.71	1.74	1.77	1.80	1.82	1.85	1.88	1.91	1.94	1.96	1.99	2.02	2.05	2.07	2.10	2.13	2.16	2.18	997 235
17	1.76	1.79	1.82	1.85	1.88	1.91	1.94	1.97	2.00	2.03	2.06	2.09	2.11	2.14	2.17	2.20	2.23	2.26	2.29	2.32	997 063
18	1.87	1.90	1.93	1.96	1.99	2.02	2.05	2.08	2.11	2.15	2.18	2.21	2.24	2.27	2.30	2.33	2.36	2.39	2.43	2.46	996 891
19	1.97	2.00	2.03	2.07	2.10	2.13	2.17	2.20	2.23	2.26	2.30	2.33	2.36	2.40	2.43	2.46	2.49	2.53	2.56	2.59	996 719
20	2.07	2.11	2.14	2.18	2.21	2.24	2.28	2.31	2.35	2.38	2.42	2.45	2.49	2.52	2.56	2.59	2.62	2.66	2.69	2.73	0.996 547
21	2.18	2.21	2.25	2.28	2.32	2.36	2.39	2.43	2.47	2.50	2.54	2.57	2.61	2.65	2.68	2.72	2.76	2.79	2.83	2.86	996 375
22	2.28	2.32	2.35	2.39	2.43	2.47	2.51	2.54	2.58	2.62	2.66	2.70	2.73	2.77	2.81	2.85	2.89	2.92	2.96	3.00	996 203
23	2.38	2.42	2.46	2.50	2.54	2.58	2.62	2.66	2.70	2.74	2.78	2.82	2.86	2.90	2.94	2.98	3.02	3.06	3.10	3.14	996 031
24	2.48	2.53	2.57	2.61	2.65	2.69	2.73	2.77	2.82	2.86	2.90	2.94	2.98	3.02	3.06	3.11	3.15	3.19	3.23	3.27	995 859
25	2.59	2.63	2.67	2.72	2.76	2.80	2.85	2.89	2.93	2.98	3.02	3.06	3.11	3.15	3.19	3.23	3.28	3.32	3.36	3.41	0.995 687
26	2.69	2.74	2.78	2.83	2.87	2.92	2.96	3.00	3.05	3.09	3.14	3.18	3.23	3.27	3.32	3.36	3.41	3.45	3.50	3.54	995 515
27	2.79	2.84	2.89	2.93	2.98	3.03	3.07	3.12	3.17	3.21	3.26	3.31	3.35	3.40	3.45	3.49	3.54	3.59	3.63	3.68	995 344
28	2.90	2.95	2.99	3.04	3.09	3.14	3.19	3.24	3.28	3.33	3.38	3.43	3.48	3.53	3.57	3.62	3.67	3.72	3.77	3.82	995 170
29	3.00	3.05	3.10	3.15	3.20	3.25	3.30	3.35	3.40	3.45	3.50	3.55	3.60	3.65	3.70	3.75	3.80	3.85	3.90	3.95	995 001
30	3.10	3.15	3.21	3.26	3.31	3.36	3.41	3.46	3.52	3.57	3.62	3.67	3.72	3.77	3.83	3.88	3.93	3.98	4.03	4.09	0.994 829
31	3.21	3.26	3.31	3.37	3.42	3.47	3.53	3.58	3.63	3.69	3.74	3.79	3.85	3.90	3.95	4.01	4.06	4.11	4.17	4.22	994 658
32	3.31	3.36	3.42	3.47	3.53	3.58	3.64	3.69	3.75	3.80	3.86	3.91	3.97	4.02	4.08	4.13	4.19	4.25	4.30	4.36	994 487
33	3.41	3.47	3.52	3.58	3.64	3.70	3.75	3.81	3.87	3.92	3.98	4.04	4.09	4.15	4.21	4.26	4.32	4.38	4.43	4.49	994 315
34	3.51	3.57	3.63	3.69	3.75	3.81	3.86	3.92	3.98	4.04	4.10	4.16	4.22	4.27	4.33	4.39	4.45	4.51	4.57	4.63	994 144
35	3.62	3.68	3.74	3.80	3.86	3.92	3.98	4.04	4.10	4.16	4.22	4.28	4.34	4.40	4.46	4.52	4.58	4.64	4.70	4.76	0.993 974
36	3.72	3.78	3.84	3.90	3.97	4.03	4.09	4.15	4.21	4.28	4.34	4.40	4.46	4.52	4.59	4.65	4.71	4.77	4.83	4.90	993 802
37	3.82	3.89	3.95	4.01	4.08	4.14	4.20	4.27	4.33	4.39	4.46	4.52	4.59	4.65	4.71	4.78	4.84	4.90	4.97	5.03	993 631
38	3.92	3.99	4.05	4.12	4.19	4.25	4.32	4.38	4.45	4.51	4.58	4.64	4.71	4.77	4.84	4.91	4.97	5.04	5.10	5.17	993 460
39	4.03	4.09	4.16	4.23	4.30	4.36	4.43	4.50	4.56	4.63	4.70	4.76	4.83	4.90	4.97	5.03	5.10	5.17	5.23	5.30	993 289
40	4.13	4.20	4.27	4.34	4.40	4.47	4.54	4.61	4.68	4.75	4.82	4.89	4.96	5.02	5.09	5.16	5.23	5.30	5.37	5.44	0.993 118

Saturation pressure of water vapor below 0° C over ice[1]

in microbars (μb)

°C	0	−1	−2	−3	−4	−5	−6	−7	−8	−9
−90	0.09_3	0.07_7	0.06_4	0.05_3	0.04_4	0.03_6	0.02_9	0.02_4	0.02_0	0.01_6
−80	0.53	0.45	0.39	0.32	0.27	0.23	0.19	0.16	0.13	0.11_2
−70	2.59	2.23	1.91	1.64	1.40	1.20	1.03	0.88	0.75	0.63
−60	10.7_7	9.3_7	8.1_9	7.1_2	6.1_9	5.3_7	4.6_5	4.0_3	3.4_8	3.0_0
−50	39.4_0	34.8	30.7	27.1	23.7	20.9	18.4	16.1	14.1	12.3_3
−40	128.8	114.9	102.4	91.2	81.2	72.1	64.1	56.8	50.4	44.5
−30	381.2	343.3	309.0	277.8	249.7	224.1	200.9	180.1	161.2	144.1

in 0.001 mm Hg

°C	0	−1	−2	−3	−4	−5	−6	−7	−8	−9
−90	0.07_0	0.05_8	0.04_8	0.04_0	0.03_3	0.02_7	0.02_2	0.01_8	0.01_5	0.01_2
−80	0.40	0.34	0.29	0.24	0.20	0.17	0.14	0.12	0.10	0.08_4
−70	1.94	1.67	1.43	1.23	1.05	0.90	0.77	0.66	0.56	0.47
−60	8.0_8	7.0_3	6.1_4	5.3_4	4.6_4	4.0_3	3.4_9	3.0_2	2.6_1	2.2_5
−50	29.5_5	26.1	23.0	20.3	17.8	15.7	13.8	12.1	10.6	9.2_5
−40	96.6	86.2	76.8	68.4	60.9	54.1	48.1	42.6	37.8	33.4
−30	285.9	257.5	231.8	208.4	187.3	168.1	150.7	135.1	120.9	108.1

in millibars (mb)

°C	0	−0.1	−0.2	−0.3	−0.4	−0.5	−0.6	−0.7	−0.8	−0.9
−29	0.423	0.419	0.415	0.409	0.405	0.401	0.397	0.393	0.389	0.385
−28	0.468	0.464	0.459	0.455	0.449	0.445	0.440	0.436	0.432	0.427
−27	0.519	0.513	0.508	0.503	0.499	0.493	0.488	0.483	0.479	0.473
−26	0.573	0.568	0.563	0.557	0.552	0.545	0.540	0.535	0.529	0.524
−25	0.635	0.628	0.623	0.616	0.609	0.604	0.597	0.592	0.585	0.580
−24	0.701	0.693	0.687	0.680	0.673	0.667	0.660	0.653	0.648	0.641
−23	0.773	0.765	0.759	0.751	0.744	0.736	0.729	0.721	0.715	0.708
−22	0.853	0.844	0.836	0.828	0.820	0.812	0.804	0.796	0.789	0.781
−21	0.940	0.931	0.921	0.913	0.904	0.896	0.887	0.879	0.869	0.861
−20	1.035	1.025	1.015	1.005	0.996	0.987	0.977	0.968	0.959	0.949
−19	1.139	1.128	1.117	1.107	1.096	1.085	1.075	1.065	1.055	1.044
−18	1.252	1.240	1.228	1.216	1.205	1.193	1.183	1.172	1.160	1.149
−17	1.375	1.361	1.349	1.336	1.324	1.312	1.300	1.288	1.275	1.263
−16	1.509	1.495	1.481	1.468	1.455	1.440	1.427	1.413	1.401	1.388
−15	1.655	1.640	1.625	1.611	1.595	1.581	1.567	1.552	1.537	1.523
−14	1.815	1.797	1.781	1.765	1.749	1.733	1.717	1.701	1.685	1.671
−13	1.986	1.969	1.952	1.933	1.916	1.899	1.881	1.865	1.848	1.831
−12	2.176	2.156	2.136	2.117	2.098	2.078	2.061	2.042	2.024	2.005
−11	2.380	2.358	2.337	2.316	2.296	2.276	2.254	2.234	2.214	2.194
−10	2.600	2.578	2.554	2.532	2.510	2.488	2.465	2.444	2.422	2.400
− 9	2.841	2.816	2.790	2.766	2.742	2.718	2.694	2.670	2.646	2.624
− 8	3.101	3.074	3.046	3.021	2.994	2.968	2.942	2.916	2.890	2.865
− 7	3.382	3.353	3.324	3.296	3.266	3.238	3.210	3.182	3.156	3.128
− 6	3.686	3.656	3.624	3.593	3.562	3.532	3.501	3.470	3.441	3.412
− 5	4.017	3.982	3.949	3.916	3.882	3.849	3.816	3.784	3.750	3.720
− 4	4.373	4.336	4.300	4.264	4.228	4.192	4.156	4.121	4.086	4.052
− 3	4.757	4.718	4.678	4.640	4.601	4.562	4.524	4.485	4.448	4.410
− 2	5.173	5.130	5.088	5.046	5.004	4.962	4.921	4.880	4.840	4.798
− 1	5.622	5.576	5.529	5.484	5.438	5.393	5.349	5.305	5.261	5.217
0	6.105	6.055	6.005	5.955	5.907	5.860	5.812	5.764	5.716	5.669

in mm Hg

°C	0	−0.1	−0.2	−0.3	−0.4	−0.5	−0.6	−0.7	−0.8	−0.9
−29	0.317	0.314	0.311	0.307	0.304	0.301	0.298	0.295	0.292	0.289
−28	0.351	0.348	0.344	0.341	0.337	0.334	0.330	0.327	0.324	0.320
−27	0.389	0.385	0.381	0.377	0.374	0.370	0.366	0.362	0.359	0.355
−26	0.430	0.426	0.422	0.418	0.414	0.409	0.405	0.401	0.397	0.393
−25	0.476	0.471	0.467	0.462	0.457	0.453	0.448	0.444	0.439	0.435
−24	0.526	0.520	0.515	0.510	0.505	0.500	0.495	0.490	0.486	0.481
−23	0.580	0.574	0.569	0.563	0.558	0.552	0.547	0.541	0.536	0.531
−22	0.640	0.633	0.627	0.621	0.615	0.609	0.603	0.597	0.592	0.586
−21	0.705	0.698	0.691	0.685	0.678	0.672	0.665	0.659	0.652	0.646
−20	0.776	0.769	0.761	0.754	0.747	0.740	0.733	0.726	0.719	0.712
−19	0.854	0.846	0.838	0.830	0.822	0.814	0.806	0.799	0.791	0.783
−18	0.939	0.930	0.921	0.912	0.904	0.895	0.887	0.879	0.870	0.862
−17	1.031	1.021	1.012	1.002	0.993	0.984	0.975	0.966	0.956	0.947
−16	1.132	1.121	1.111	1.101	1.091	1.080	1.070	1.060	1.051	1.041
−15	1.241	1.230	1.219	1.208	1.196	1.186	1.175	1.164	1.153	1.142
−14	1.361	1.348	1.336	1.324	1.312	1.300	1.288	1.276	1.264	1.253
−13	1.490	1.477	1.464	1.450	1.437	1.424	1.411	1.399	1.386	1.373
−12	1.632	1.617	1.602	1.588	1.574	1.559	1.546	1.532	1.518	1.504
−11	1.785	1.769	1.753	1.737	1.722	1.707	1.691	1.676	1.661	1.646
−10	1.950	1.934	1.916	1.899	1.883	1.866	1.849	1.833	1.817	1.800
− 9	2.131	2.112	2.093	2.075	2.057	2.039	2.021	2.003	1.985	1.968
− 8	2.326	2.306	2.285	2.266	2.246	2.226	2.207	2.187	2.168	2.149
− 7	2.537	2.515	2.493	2.472	2.450	2.429	2.408	2.387	2.367	2.346
− 6	2.765	2.742	2.718	2.695	2.672	2.649	2.626	2.603	2.581	2.559
− 5	3.013	2.987	2.962	2.937	2.912	2.887	2.862	2.838	2.813	2.790
− 4	3.280	3.252	3.225	3.198	3.171	3.144	3.117	3.091	3.065	3.039
− 3	3.568	3.539	3.509	3.480	3.451	3.422	3.393	3.364	3.336	3.308
− 2	3.880	3.848	3.816	3.785	3.753	3.722	3.691	3.660	3.630	3.599
− 1	4.217	4.182	4.147	4.113	4.079	4.045	4.012	3.979	3.946	3.913
0	4.579	4.542	4.504	4.467	4.431	4.395	4.359	4.323	4.287	4.252

Saturation pressure of water vapor below 0° C over water[1]

in millibars (mb)

°C	0	−0.1	−0.2	−0.3	−0.4	−0.5	−0.6	−0.7	−0.8	−0.9
−14	2.080	2.062	2.045	2.029	2.014	1.996	1.980	1.962	1.947	1.932
−13	2.254	2.237	2.220	2.201	2.182	2.165	2.148	2.132	2.113	2.096
−12	2.445	2.425	2.405	2.386	2.368	2.348	2.330	2.312	2.293	2.273
−11	2.649	2.628	2.606	2.585	2.565	2.545	2.524	2.504	2.484	2.464
−10	2.865	2.845	2.821	2.798	2.778	2.756	2.733	2.712	2.690	2.668
− 9	3.101	3.076	3.052	3.028	3.005	2.981	2.958	2.934	2.912	2.889
− 8	3.352	3.326	3.300	3.274	3.249	3.224	3.198	3.173	3.149	3.124
− 7	3.620	3.593	3.565	3.538	3.510	3.484	3.457	3.429	3.404	3.377
− 6	3.908	3.878	3.849	3.821	3.790	3.762	3.733	3.704	3.676	3.648
− 5	4.217	4.185	4.153	4.122	4.092	4.061	4.029	4.000	3.968	3.940
− 4	4.546	4.512	4.478	4.445	4.412	4.378	4.345	4.313	4.281	4.249
− 3	4.897	4.862	4.826	4.790	4.756	4.720	4.685	4.649	4.614	4.581
− 2	5.274	5.236	5.197	5.161	5.121	5.084	5.046	5.009	4.973	4.936
− 1	5.677	5.636	5.594	5.553	5.513	5.473	5.433	5.393	5.354	5.314
0	6.105	6.061	6.017	5.973	5.930	5.887	5.846	5.804	5.760	5.718

in mm Hg

°C	0	−0.1	−0.2	−0.3	−0.4	−0.5	−0.6	−0.7	−0.8	−0.9
−14	1.560	1.547	1.534	1.522	1.511	1.497	1.485	1.472	1.460	1.449
−13	1.691	1.678	1.665	1.651	1.637	1.624	1.611	1.599	1.585	1.572
−12	1.834	1.819	1.804	1.790	1.776	1.761	1.748	1.734	1.720	1.705
−11	1.987	1.971	1.955	1.939	1.924	1.909	1.893	1.878	1.863	1.848
−10	2.149	2.134	2.116	2.099	2.084	2.067	2.050	2.034	2.018	2.001
− 9	2.326	2.307	2.289	2.271	2.254	2.236	2.219	2.201	2.184	2.167
− 8	2.514	2.495	2.475	2.456	2.437	2.418	2.399	2.380	2.362	2.343
− 7	2.715	2.695	2.674	2.654	2.633	2.613	2.593	2.572	2.553	2.533
− 6	2.931	2.909	2.887	2.866	2.843	2.822	2.800	2.778	2.757	2.736
− 5	3.163	3.139	3.115	3.092	3.069	3.046	3.022	3.000	2.976	2.955
− 4	3.410	3.384	3.359	3.334	3.309	3.284	3.259	3.235	3.211	3.187
− 3	3.673	3.647	3.620	3.593	3.567	3.540	3.514	3.487	3.461	3.436
− 2	3.956	3.927	3.898	3.871	3.841	3.813	3.785	3.757	3.730	3.702
− 1	4.258	4.227	4.196	4.165	4.135	4.105	4.075	4.045	4.016	3.986
0	4.579	4.546	4.513	4.480	4.448	4.416	4.385	4.353	4.320	4.289

Saturation pressure of water vapor above 100° C[2]

in bars (b)

°C	0	1	2	3	4	5	6	7	8	9
100	1.0133	1.0499	1.0877	1.1267	1.1667	1.2080	1.2505	1.2940	1.3391	1.3851
110	1.4326	1.4815	1.5315	1.5831	1.6362	1.6905	1.7464	1.8038	1.8628	1.9234
120	1.9854	2.0489	2.1146	2.1816	2.2502	2.3211	2.3933	2.4676	2.5436	2.6216
130	2.7013	2.7830	2.8670	2.9526	3.0408	3.1294	3.2215	3.3173	3.4139	3.5128
140	3.614	3.718	3.823	3.931	4.042	4.155	4.271	4.389	4.510	4.635
150	4.760	4.889	5.022	5.155	5.293	5.434	5.578	5.724	5.873	6.026
160	6.181	6.340	6.502	6.666	6.835	7.008	7.182	7.361	7.544	7.730
170	7.921	8.113	8.311	8.510	8.717	8.925	9.136	9.353	9.573	9.798
180	10.026	10.258	10.495	10.736	10.982	11.231	11.487	11.746	12.009	12.277
190	12.550	12.826	13.107	13.395	13.686	13.984	14.286	14.592	14.905	15.222
200	15.544	15.873	16.206	16.543	16.887	17.237	17.595	17.956	18.322	18.695
210	19.072	19.458	19.850	20.245	20.649	21.055	21.471	21.892	22.321	22.755
220	23.192	23.640	24.095	24.555	25.020	25.495	25.975	26.463	26.958	27.460
230	27.969	28.484	29.007	29.536	30.075	30.621	31.175	31.734	32.303	32.879
240	33.465	34.055	34.656	35.263	35.880	36.505	37.138	37.778	38.429	39.086
250	39.754	40.429	41.114	41.806	42.510	43.220	43.940	44.670	45.409	46.155
260	46.913	47.678	48.454	49.239	50.035	50.840	51.652	52.478	53.311	54.155
270	55.010	55.876	56.750	57.635	58.531	59.436	60.354	61.280	62.221	63.171
280	64.134	65.106	66.088	67.083	68.091	69.112	70.143	71.188	72.244	73.313
290	74.39	75.48	76.59	77.71	78.84	79.99	81.14	82.32	83.49	84.70
300	85.90	87.13	88.37	89.61	90.87	92.14	93.42	94.73	96.06	97.36
310	98.69	100.05	101.43	102.81	104.21	105.63	107.05	108.49	109.95	111.42
320	112.91	114.42	115.94	117.48	119.03	120.59	122.17	123.76	125.38	127.02
330	128.67	130.33	132.02	133.72	135.43	137.16	138.92	140.69	142.48	144.29
340	146.11	147.94	149.80	151.65	153.56	155.47	157.42	159.36	161.34	163.33
350	165.32	167.35	169.39	171.45	173.53	175.63	177.75	179.91	182.09	184.29
360	186.51	188.75	191.02	193.31	195.63	198.01	200.41	202.82	205.26	207.74
370	210.24	212.76	215.33	217.94	220.60	← critical temperature				

in atmospheres (atm)

°C	0	1	2	3	4	5	6	7	8	9
100	1.0000	1.0362	1.0735	1.1120	1.1514	1.1922	1.2341	1.2771	1.3216	1.3670
110	1.4139	1.4621	1.5115	1.5624	1.6148	1.6684	1.7236	1.7802	1.8384	1.8982
120	1.9594	2.0221	2.0869	2.1531	2.2208	2.2907	2.3620	2.4353	2.5103	2.5873
130	2.6660	2.7466	2.8295	2.9140	3.0010	3.0885	3.1794	3.2739	3.3693	3.4669
140	3.567	3.669	3.773	3.880	3.989	4.101	4.215	4.332	4.451	4.574
150	4.698	4.825	4.956	5.088	5.224	5.363	5.505	5.649	5.796	5.947
160	6.100	6.257	6.417	6.579	6.746	6.916	7.088	7.265	7.445	7.629
170	7.817	8.007	8.202	8.399	8.603	8.808	9.017	9.231	9.448	9.670
180	9.895	10.124	10.358	10.596	10.838	11.084	11.337	11.592	11.852	12.116
190	12.386	12.658	12.936	13.220	13.507	13.801	14.099	14.401	14.710	15.023
200	15.341	15.665	15.994	16.327	16.666	17.012	17.365	17.721	18.082	18.451
210	18.823	19.204	19.590	19.980	20.379	20.780	21.190	21.606	22.029	22.457
220	22.889	23.331	23.780	24.234	24.693	25.162	25.635	26.117	26.605	27.101
230	27.603	28.112	28.628	29.150	29.682	30.221	30.767	31.319	31.881	32.449
240	33.027	33.610	34.203	34.802	35.411	36.028	36.652	37.284	37.926	38.575
250	39.234	39.900	40.576	41.259	41.954	42.655	43.365	44.086	44.815	45.551
260	46.300	47.055	47.820	48.595	49.381	50.175	50.977	51.792	52.614	53.447
270	54.291	55.145	56.008	56.881	57.766	58.659	59.565	60.479	61.407	62.345
280	63.295	64.255	65.224	66.206	67.201	68.208	69.226	70.257	71.299	72.354
290	73.42	74.49	75.59	76.69	77.81	78.94	80.08	81.24	82.40	83.59
300	84.78	85.99	87.21	88.44	89.68	90.94	92.20	93.49	94.80	96.09
310	97.40	98.74	100.10	101.47	102.85	104.25	105.65	107.07	108.51	109.96
320	111.43	112.92	114.42	115.94	117.47	119.01	120.57	122.14	123.74	125.36
330	126.99	128.63	130.29	131.97	133.66	135.37	137.10	138.85	140.62	142.40
340	144.20	146.01	147.84	149.67	151.55	153.44	155.36	157.28	159.23	161.19
350	163.16	165.16	167.17	169.21	171.26	173.33	175.43	177.56	179.71	181.88
360	184.07	186.28	188.52	190.78	193.07	195.42	197.79	200.17	202.58	205.02
370	207.49	209.98	212.51	215.09	217.72	← critical temperature				

1) Values in mm Hg are from Washburn, E.W., *Monthly Weath. Rev.*, **52**, 488 (1924), and Washburn, E.W., in Washburn, E.W. (Ed.), *International Critical Tables*, 1st ed., vol. III, New York, 1928, page 210. *2)* Values in atm are from Keyes, F.G., in Washburn, E.W. (Ed.), *loc. cit.*, page 233. Values in other units have been calculated by the editors.

Saturation pressure in mm Hg

°C	0.0	0.1	0.2	0.3	0.4	0.5	0.6	0.7	0.8	0.9
0	4.577	4.610	4.644	4.678	4.712	4.746	4.781	4.815	4.850	4.885
1	4.921	4.956	4.992	5.028	5.064	5.101	5.138	5.174	5.212	5.249
2	5.287	5.325	5.363	5.401	5.440	5.479	5.518	5.557	5.597	5.637
3	5.677	5.717	5.758	5.799	5.840	5.881	5.923	5.965	6.007	6.049
4	6.092	6.135	6.178	6.222	6.266	6.310	6.354	6.399	6.444	6.489
5	6.534	6.580	6.626	6.672	6.719	6.766	6.813	6.860	6.908	6.956
6	7.004	7.053	7.102	7.151	7.201	7.250	7.300	7.351	7.402	7.452
7	7.504	7.556	7.608	7.660	7.713	7.766	7.819	7.872	7.926	7.980
8	8.035	8.090	8.145	8.201	8.257	8.312	8.369	8.426	8.483	8.541
9	8.599	8.657	8.715	8.774	8.833	8.893	8.953	9.013	9.075	9.135
10	9.197	9.259	9.321	9.383	9.446	9.509	9.573	9.637	9.701	9.766
11	9.832	9.897	9.963	10.029	10.096	10.163	10.231	10.299	10.367	10.435
12	10.504	10.574	10.644	10.714	10.785	10.856	10.928	11.000	11.072	11.145
13	11.218	11.292	11.365	11.440	11.515	11.590	11.666	11.742	11.819	11.895
14	11.973	12.051	12.130	12.208	12.287	12.367	12.447	12.528	12.609	12.691
15	12.773	12.855	12.938	13.021	13.105	13.190	13.275	13.360	13.446	13.532
16	13.619	13.707	13.794	13.882	13.971	14.060	14.150	14.241	14.331	14.422
17	14.514	14.606	14.699	14.793	14.886	14.980	15.075	15.171	15.267	15.363
18	15.460	15.558	15.656	15.754	15.853	15.953	16.053	16.154	16.256	16.358
19	16.460	16.563	16.667	16.771	16.875	16.981	17.086	17.193	17.300	17.408
20	17.515	17.625	17.734	17.844	17.955	18.066	18.177	18.290	18.403	18.517
21	18.631	18.746	18.860	18.976	19.093	19.210	19.328	19.447	19.567	19.687
22	19.807	19.928	20.049	20.171	20.296	20.419	20.543	20.669	20.794	20.921
23	21.047	21.175	21.304	21.432	21.562	21.693	21.824	21.956	22.089	22.221
24	22.356	22.490	22.625	22.761	22.898	23.036	23.174	23.313	23.453	23.593
25	23.734	23.876	24.019	24.162	24.306	24.450	24.595	24.743	24.890	25.037
26	25.185	25.336	25.485	25.636	25.788	25.940	26.094	26.247	26.403	26.558
27	26.715	26.871	27.030	27.189	27.348	27.509	27.671	27.833	27.995	28.159
28	28.324	28.489	28.656	28.823	28.991	29.160	29.330	29.500	29.672	29.844
29	30.017	30.190	30.365	30.540	30.719	30.896	31.073	31.254	31.434	31.614
30	31.797	31.980	32.163	32.349	32.533	32.721	32.907	33.097	33.287	33.476
31	33.668	33.861	34.053	34.248	34.443	34.640	34.835	35.034	35.233	35.433
32	35.634	35.837	36.040	36.244	36.449	36.654	36.861	37.069	37.278	37.487
33	37.698	37.912	38.125	38.338	38.553	38.771	38.987	39.205	39.426	39.645
34	39.868	40.090	40.315	40.538	40.765	40.991	41.220	41.448	41.679	41.911
35	42.142	42.376	42.612	42.848	43.083	43.321	43.561	43.802	44.044	44.287
36	44.531	44.776	45.022	45.270	45.518	45.767	46.018	46.270	46.523	46.776
37	47.035	47.291	47.548	47.807	48.070	48.330	48.592	48.859	49.123	49.388
38	49.658	49.926	50.198	50.468	50.742	51.018	51.292	51.570	51.846	52.127
39	52.409	52.688	52.972	53.258	53.545	53.833	54.118	54.409	54.701	54.994
40	55.288	55.584	55.881	56.179	56.478	56.779	57.081	57.384	57.689	57.999
41	58.306	58.614	58.924	59.235	59.552	59.865	60.180	60.501	60.819	61.138
42	61.463	61.784	62.112	62.436	62.767	63.094	63.427	63.757	64.093	64.430
43	64.764	65.104	65.446	65.784	66.128	66.474	66.821	67.170	67.516	67.867
44	68.220	68.575	68.931	69.288	69.647	70.008	70.370	70.733	71.098	71.464
45	71.832	72.207	72.578	72.950	73.325	73.700	74.082	74.461	74.841	75.228
46	75.612	75.996	76.388	76.776	77.171	77.563	77.961	78.355	78.757	79.154
47	79.559	79.960	80.368	80.777	81.183	81.596	82.011	82.421	82.839	83.259
48	83.680	84.104	84.522	84.949	85.377	85.807	86.238	86.672	87.107	87.544
49	87.983	88.423	88.865	89.309	89.761	90.208	90.657	91.108	91.561	92.015
50	92.478	92.936	93.396	93.864	94.328	94.793	95.267	95.736	96.214	96.686
51	97.161	97.644	98.129	98.610	99.098	99.582	100.076	100.564	101.061	101.559
52	102.052	102.555	103.059	103.566	104.067	104.577	105.090	105.604	106.120	106.638
53	107.159	107.681	108.198	108.724	109.252	109.782	110.323	110.857	111.394	111.932
54	112.473	113.015	113.560	114.107	114.665	115.215	115.768	116.324	116.889	117.449
55	118.010	118.582	119.148	119.716	120.295	120.867	121.450	122.026	122.613	123.194
56	123.786	124.371	124.968	125.566	126.158	126.761	127.366	127.965	128.575	129.187
57	129.792	130.409	131.028	131.649	132.273	132.899	133.517	134.148	134.781	134.525
58	136.054	136.694	137.336	137.981	138.628	139.278	139.930	140.594	141.251	141.910
59	142.572	143.235	143.901	144.581	145.252	145.926	146.602	147.291	147.972	148.656
60	149.352	150.041	150.743	151.436	152.133	152.842	153.543	154.258	154.964	155.684
61	156.406	157.120	157.848	158.567	159.300	160.035	160.762	161.503	162.247	162.993
62	163.730	164.481	165.236	165.993	166.753	167.515	168.268	169.036	169.806	170.580
63	171.356	172.135	172.916	173.700	174.488	175.278	176.070	176.866	177.677	178.478
64	179.282	180.089	180.899	181.724	182.540	183.358	184.178	185.016	185.842	186.672
65	187.518	188.354	189.193	190.047	190.892	191.752	192.602	193.470	194.325	195.199
66	196.060	196.940	197.807	198.693	199.581	200.458	201.352	202.250	203.136	204.039
67	204.947	205.857	206.755	207.671	208.590	209.513	210.439	211.368	212.284	213.219
68	214.158	215.099	216.044	216.992	217.943	218.898	219.855	220.817	221.781	222.748
69	223.736	224.710	225.687	226.668	227.651	228.638	229.646	230.640	231.637	232.638
70	233.659	234.666	235.676	236.708	237.725	238.764	239.788	240.815	241.864	242.899
71	243.955	244.997	246.059	247.107	248.177	249.250	250.309	251.390	252.455	253.543
72	254.634	255.710	256.809	257.911	259.017	260.107	261.220	262.337	263.458	264.582
73	265.690	266.822	267.958	269.096	270.239	271.385	272.535	273.689	274.847	276.008
74	277.173	278.342	279.516	280.691	281.872	283.056	284.244	285.457	286.653	287.852
75	289.055	290.263	291.496	292.710	293.930	295.152	296.401	297.632	298.866	300.128
76	301.369	302.638	303.889	305.143	306.423	307.686	308.976	310.247	311.544	312.822
77	314.128	315.439	316.728	318.047	319.345	320.672	322.003	323.314	324.653	325.997
78	327.320	328.671	330.028	331.389	332.754	334.131	335.471	336.849	338.231	339.617
79	341.008	342.403	343.802	345.206	346.587	348.001	349.416	350.837	352.290	353.720
80	355.154	356.594	358.037	359.485	360.937	362.392	363.855	365.347	366.818	368.293
81	369.771	371.283	372.772	374.264	375.761	377.292	378.798	380.309	381.854	383.374
82	384.928	386.458	388.022	389.560	391.103	392.681	394.235	395.822	397.414	398.981
83	400.582	402.160	403.771	405.356	406.978	408.604	410.204	411.841	413.481	415.129
84	416.746	418.402	420.064	421.730	423.368	425.043	426.724	428.411	430.101	431.798
85	433.499	435.170	436.882	438.598	440.319	442.045	443.776	445.513	447.255	449.002
86	450.753	452.545	454.308	456.075	457.847	459.626	461.409	463.198	465.028	466.826
87	468.630	470.438	472.291	474.111	475.934	477.765	479.638	481.480	483.325	485.214
88	487.073	488.972	490.840	492.713	494.630	496.513	498.442	500.337	502.276	504.182
89	506.133	508.049	510.010	511.978	513.912	515.891	517.834	519.823	521.821	523.781
90	525.788	527.801	529.820	531.804	533.833	535.870	537.912	539.916	541.971	544.029
91	546.095	548.166	550.243	552.326	554.414	556.464	558.566	560.673	562.785	564.904
92	567.026	569.157	571.294	573.434	575.630	577.784	579.943	582.110	584.280	586.460
93	588.643	590.835	593.077	595.280	597.489	599.703	601.975	604.199	606.432	608.672
94	610.966	613.217	615.476	617.789	620.060	622.335	624.668	626.957	629.302	631.604
95	633.962	636.275	638.649	640.973	643.358	645.697	648.095	650.448	652.858	655.223
96	657.647	660.077	662.462	664.905	667.355	669.759	672.222	674.694	677.115	679.599
97	682.090	684.587	687.090	689.547	692.063	694.589	697.118	699.656	702.201	704.694
98	707.254	709.819	712.389	714.969	717.555	720.149	722.747	725.353	727.968	730.586
99	733.217	735.850	738.489	741.140	743.853	746.516	749.185	751.860	754.545	757.234
100	760.000									

Boiling point in degrees Centigrade

mm Hg	0	1	2	3	4	5	6	7	8	9
0		−17.28	−9.69	−5.03	−1.63	+1.22	3.78	5.99	7.93	9.67
10	11.25	12.70	14.03	15.27	16.43	17.52	18.54	19.51	20.44	21.32
20	22.15	22.96	23.73	24.47	25.18	25.87	26.53	27.18	27.80	28.40
30	28.99	29.55	30.11	30.64	31.17	31.68	32.18	32.66	33.14	33.60
40	34.05	34.50	34.93	35.36	35.78	36.19	36.59	36.98	37.37	37.75
50	38.12	38.49	38.85	39.20	39.55	39.90	40.23	40.57	40.90	41.22
60	41.54	41.85	42.16	42.47	42.77	43.06	43.36	43.65	43.93	44.21
70	44.49	44.77	45.04	45.31	45.57	45.84	46.10	46.35	46.60	46.86
80	47.10	47.35	47.59	47.83	48.07	48.31	48.54	48.77	49.00	49.23
90	49.45	49.67	49.89	50.11	50.32	50.54	50.75	50.96	51.17	51.37
100	51.58	51.78	51.98	52.18	52.38	52.58	52.77	52.96	53.16	53.35
110	53.54	53.72	53.91	54.09	54.28	54.46	54.64	54.81	54.99	55.17
120	55.34	55.52	55.69	55.86	56.03	56.20	56.37	56.53	56.70	56.86
130	57.03	57.19	57.35	57.51	57.67	57.93	57.99	58.14	58.30	58.45
140	58.61	58.76	58.91	59.06	59.21	59.36	59.51	59.65	59.80	59.94
150	60.09	60.23	60.38	60.52	60.66	60.80	60.94	61.08	61.22	61.35
160	61.49	61.63	61.76	61.90	62.03	62.16	62.30	62.43	62.56	62.69
170	62.82	62.95	63.08	63.21	63.33	63.46	63.59	63.71	63.84	63.96
180	64.08	64.21	64.33	64.45	64.57	64.69	64.81	64.93	65.05	65.17
190	65.29	65.41	65.52	65.64	65.76	65.87	65.99	66.10	66.22	66.33
200	66.44	66.56	66.67	66.78	66.89	67.00	67.11	67.22	67.33	67.44
210	67.55	67.66	67.76	67.87	67.98	68.08	68.19	68.30	68.40	68.51
220	68.61	68.71	68.82	68.92	69.02	69.12	69.23	69.33	69.43	69.53
230	69.63	69.73	69.83	69.93	70.03	70.13	70.23	70.32	70.42	70.52
240	70.62	70.71	70.81	70.90	71.00	71.10	71.19	71.28	71.38	71.47
250	71.57	71.66	71.75	71.85	71.94	72.03	72.12	72.21	72.30	72.39
260	72.49	72.58	72.66	72.75	72.84	72.93	73.02	73.11	73.20	73.29
270	73.37	73.46	73.55	73.64	73.72	73.81	73.89	73.98	74.07	74.15
280	74.24	74.32	74.41	74.49	74.57	74.66	74.74	74.82	74.91	74.99
290	75.07	75.15	75.24	75.32	75.40	75.48	75.56	75.64	75.72	75.81
300	75.88	75.97	76.04	76.12	76.20	76.28	76.36	76.44	76.52	76.60
310	76.68	76.75	76.83	76.91	76.99	77.06	77.14	77.22	77.29	77.37
320	77.44	77.52	77.59	77.67	77.75	77.82	77.90	77.97	78.05	78.12
330	78.19	78.27	78.34	78.41	78.49	78.56	78.63	78.71	78.78	78.85
340	78.92	78.99	79.07	79.14	79.21	79.28	79.35	79.42	79.49	79.57
350	79.64	79.71	79.78	79.84	79.91	79.98	80.05	80.12	80.19	80.26
360	80.33	80.40	80.47	80.54	80.60	80.67	80.74	80.81	80.88	80.94
370	81.01	81.08	81.14	81.21	81.28	81.34	81.41	81.48	81.54	81.61
380	81.67	81.74	81.80	81.87	81.94	82.00	82.07	82.13	82.19	82.26
390	82.32	82.39	82.45	82.52	82.58	82.64	82.71	82.77	82.83	82.90
400	82.96	83.02	83.08	83.15	83.21	83.27	83.33	83.40	83.46	83.52
410	83.58	83.64	83.70	83.77	83.83	83.89	83.95	84.01	84.07	84.13
420	84.19	84.25	84.31	84.37	84.43	84.49	84.55	84.61	84.67	84.73
430	84.79	84.85	84.91	84.97	85.02	85.08	85.14	85.20	85.26	85.32
440	85.38	85.43	85.49	85.55	85.61	85.67	85.72	85.78	85.84	85.89
450	85.95	86.01	86.06	86.12	86.18	86.23	86.29	86.35	86.40	86.46
460	86.52	86.57	86.63	86.68	86.74	86.79	86.85	86.90	86.96	87.02
470	87.07	87.13	87.18	87.23	87.29	87.34	87.40	87.45	87.51	87.56
480	87.61	87.67	87.72	87.78	87.83	87.88	87.94	87.99	88.04	88.10
490	88.15	88.20	88.26	88.31	88.36	88.41	88.47	88.52	88.57	88.62
500	88.68	88.73	88.78	88.83	88.89	88.94	88.99	89.04	89.09	89.14
510	89.19	89.25	89.30	89.35	89.40	89.45	89.50	89.55	89.60	89.65
520	89.70	89.75	89.80	89.86	89.91	89.96	90.01	90.06	90.10	90.15
530	90.20	90.25	90.30	90.35	90.40	90.45	90.50	90.55	90.60	90.65
540	90.70	90.75	90.80	90.85	90.89	90.94	90.99	91.04	91.09	91.14
550	91.18	91.23	91.28	91.33	91.38	91.42	91.47	91.52	91.57	91.62
560	91.66	91.71	91.76	91.81	91.85	91.90	91.95	91.99	92.04	92.09
570	92.13	92.18	92.23	92.27	92.32	92.37	92.41	92.46	92.51	92.55
580	92.60	92.64	92.69	92.74	92.78	92.83	92.87	92.92	92.97	93.01
590	93.06	93.10	93.15	93.19	93.24	93.28	93.33	93.37	93.42	93.46
600	93.51	93.55	93.60	93.64	93.69	93.73	93.78	93.82	93.87	93.91
610	93.95	94.00	94.04	94.09	94.13	94.17	94.22	94.26	94.30	94.35
620	94.39	94.44	94.48	94.52	94.57	94.61	94.65	94.70	94.74	94.78
630	94.83	94.87	94.91	94.95	95.00	95.04	95.08	95.13	95.17	95.21
640	95.25	95.30	95.34	95.38	95.42	95.47	95.51	95.55	95.59	95.63
650	95.68	95.72	95.76	95.80	95.84	95.89	95.93	95.97	96.01	96.05
660	96.09	96.13	96.18	96.22	96.26	96.30	96.34	96.38	96.42	96.46
670	96.50	96.55	96.59	96.63	96.67	96.71	96.75	96.79	96.83	96.87
680	96.91	96.95	96.99	97.03	97.07	97.11	97.15	97.19	97.23	97.27
690	97.31	97.35	97.39	97.43	97.47	97.51	97.55	97.59	97.63	97.67
700	97.71	97.75	97.79	97.83	97.87	97.91	97.95	97.99	98.02	98.06
710	98.10	98.14	98.18	98.22	98.26	98.30	98.33	98.37	98.41	98.45
720	98.49	98.53	98.57	98.60	98.64	98.68	98.72	98.76	98.80	98.83
730	98.87	98.91	98.95	98.99	99.02	99.06	99.10	99.14	99.18	99.21
740	99.25	99.29	99.33	99.36	99.40	99.44	99.48	99.51	99.55	99.59
750	99.63	99.66	99.70	99.74	99.77	99.81	99.85	99.89	99.92	99.96
760	100.00	100.03	100.07	100.11	100.14	100.18	100.22	100.25	100.29	100.33
770	100.36	100.40	100.44	100.47	100.51	100.54	100.58	100.62	100.65	100.69
780	100.73	100.76	100.80	100.83	100.87	100.91	100.94	100.98	101.01	101.05
790	101.08	101.12	101.16	101.19	101.23	101.26	101.30	101.33	101.37	101.40
800	101.44	101.47	101.51	101.55	101.58	101.62	101.65	101.69	101.72	101.76
810	101.79	101.83	101.86	101.90	101.93	101.96	102.00	102.03	102.07	102.10
820	102.14	102.17	102.21	102.24	102.28	102.31	102.35	102.38	102.41	102.45
830	102.48	102.52	102.55	102.58	102.62	102.65	102.69	102.72	102.76	102.79
840	102.82	102.86	102.89	102.92	102.96	102.99	103.02	103.06	103.09	103.13
850	103.16	103.19	103.23	103.26	103.29	103.33	103.36	103.40	103.43	103.46
860	103.50	103.53	103.56	103.60	103.63	103.66	103.70	103.73	103.76	103.80
870	103.83	103.86	103.89	103.93	103.96	103.99	104.03	104.06	104.09	104.12
880	104.16	104.19	104.22	104.25	104.29	104.32	104.35	104.38	104.42	104.45
890	104.48	104.51	104.54	104.58	104.61	104.64	104.67	104.70	104.74	104.77
900	104.80	104.83	104.86	104.90	104.93	104.96	104.99	105.02	105.06	105.09
910	105.12	105.15	105.18	105.21	105.25	105.28	105.31	105.34	105.37	105.40
920	105.44	105.47	105.50	105.53	105.56	105.59	105.62	105.66	105.69	105.72
930	105.75	105.78	105.81	105.84	105.87	105.90	105.94	105.97	106.00	106.03
940	106.06	106.09	106.12	106.15	106.18	106.21	106.24	106.28	106.31	106.34
950	106.37	106.40	106.43	106.46	106.49	106.52	106.55	106.58	106.61	106.64
960	106.67	106.70	106.73	106.77	106.80	106.83	106.86	106.89	106.92	106.95
970	106.98	107.01	107.04	107.07	107.10	107.13	107.16	107.19	107.22	107.25
980	107.28	107.31	107.34	107.37	107.40	107.43	107.46	107.49	107.52	107.55
990	107.58	107.61	107.63	107.66	107.69	107.72	107.75	107.78	107.81	107.84
1000	107.87									

* Reproduction only by permission of the publishers of these *Scientific Tables*.

Saturation pressure in millibars

°C	0.0	0.1	0.2	0.3	0.4	0.5	0.6	0.7	0.8	0.9
0	6.102	6.147	6.192	6.237	6.282	6.328	6.374	6.420	6.466	6.513
1	6.560	6.608	6.656	6.704	6.752	6.801	6.850	6.899	6.949	6.998
2	7.048	7.099	7.150	7.201	7.253	7.304	7.357	7.409	7.462	7.515
3	7.569	7.622	7.676	7.731	7.786	7.841	7.897	7.952	8.009	8.065
4	8.123	8.180	8.237	8.295	8.354	8.412	8.472	8.531	8.591	8.651
5	8.712	8.772	8.834	8.896	8.958	9.020	9.083	9.146	9.210	9.274
6	9.338	9.403	9.468	9.534	9.600	9.666	9.733	9.801	9.868	9.936
7	10.005	10.073	10.143	10.212	10.283	10.354	10.424	10.496	10.568	10.640
8	10.712	10.786	10.859	10.934	11.008	11.082	11.158	11.233	11.310	11.387
9	11.464	11.542	11.620	11.698	11.777	11.857	11.937	12.017	12.099	12.180
10	12.262	12.344	12.427	12.510	12.595	12.678	12.764	12.849	12.934	13.021
11	13.108	13.196	13.284	13.371	13.460	13.550	13.640	13.730	13.821	13.913
12	14.005	14.097	14.191	14.285	14.379	14.473	14.569	14.665	14.761	14.859
13	14.956	15.055	15.153	15.252	15.352	15.453	15.553	15.655	15.757	15.859
14	15.963	16.067	16.172	16.276	16.382	16.488	16.595	16.703	16.811	16.920
15	17.029	17.139	17.250	17.361	17.472	17.586	17.698	17.812	17.926	18.042
16	18.157	18.274	18.391	18.508	18.627	18.745	18.865	18.986	19.106	19.228
17	19.350	19.473	19.597	19.722	19.846	19.972	20.099	20.226	20.354	20.483
18	20.612	20.742	20.873	21.004	21.136	21.269	21.403	21.537	21.673	21.809
19	21.945	22.082	22.221	22.359	22.498	22.639	22.780	22.923	23.065	23.209
20	23.352	23.498	23.644	23.790	23.938	24.086	24.234	24.384	24.535	24.687
21	24.839	24.993	25.145	25.300	25.455	25.612	25.769	25.927	26.087	26.247
22	26.407	26.568	26.730	26.893	27.059	27.223	27.388	27.556	27.723	27.893
23	28.061	28.231	28.403	28.574	28.748	28.922	29.097	29.273	29.450	29.626
24	29.805	29.985	30.164	30.346	30.529	30.712	30.897	31.082	31.268	31.455
25	31.643	31.832	32.022	32.213	32.405	32.598	32.791	32.988	33.184	33.380
26	33.578	33.778	33.978	34.178	34.382	34.584	34.790	34.994	35.202	35.408
27	35.617	35.826	36.037	36.250	36.461	36.676	36.892	37.108	37.324	37.542
28	37.762	37.983	38.205	38.428	38.652	38.877	39.104	39.331	39.559	39.789
29	40.019	40.251	40.484	40.717	40.955	41.191	41.428	41.669	41.909	42.149
30	42.394	42.636	42.880	43.128	43.374	43.625	43.873	44.126	44.380	44.631
31	44.888	45.145	45.400	45.660	45.921	46.183	46.443	46.708	46.974	47.241
32	47.509	47.779	48.049	48.321	48.595	48.869	49.145	49.422	49.700	49.980
33	50.260	50.546	50.829	51.114	51.400	51.691	51.979	52.269	52.564	52.856
34	53.154	53.449	53.749	54.047	54.350	54.650	54.956	55.259	55.568	55.877
35	56.185	56.497	56.811	57.127	57.440	57.758	58.077	58.398	58.721	59.045
36	59.370	59.697	60.025	60.355	60.686	61.019	61.353	61.688	62.025	62.364
37	62.708	63.050	63.393	63.738	64.088	64.436	64.785	65.140	65.492	65.846
38	66.206	66.563	66.925	67.286	67.652	68.019	68.384	68.755	69.123	69.497
39	69.873	70.246	70.625	71.005	71.388	71.772	72.153	72.540	72.929	73.320
40	73.712	74.106	74.502	74.899	75.298	75.699	76.102	76.506	76.912	77.326
41	77.735	78.146	78.559	78.974	79.396	79.814	80.234	80.662	81.086	81.511
42	81.944	82.373	82.809	83.242	83.682	84.119	84.563	85.002	85.450	85.900
43	86.345	86.799	87.254	87.705	88.164	88.625	89.088	89.553	90.014	90.482
44	90.953	91.426	91.900	92.377	92.856	93.336	93.819	94.303	94.790	95.278
45	95.769	96.268	96.763	97.259	97.758	98.259	98.769	99.274	99.780	100.297
46	100.808	101.322	101.844	102.361	102.888	103.410	103.940	104.466	105.002	105.531
47	106.071	106.606	107.150	107.696	108.237	108.788	109.340	109.888	110.445	111.005
48	111.566	112.131	112.689	113.258	113.828	114.402	114.977	115.555	116.135	116.718
49	117.302	117.889	118.479	119.071	119.673	120.270	120.868	121.469	122.073	122.679
50	123.296	123.907	124.520	125.144	125.762	126.383	127.015	127.640	128.277	128.907
51	129.539	130.184	130.831	131.471	132.123	132.768	133.425	134.075	134.738	135.402
52	136.060	136.730	137.402	138.078	138.746	139.426	140.109	140.795	141.483	142.174
53	142.868	143.564	144.253	144.954	145.659	146.366	147.087	147.799	148.514	149.232
54	149.953	150.676	151.403	152.131	152.875	153.609	154.346	155.087	155.841	156.587
55	157.335	158.098	158.852	159.609	160.381	161.144	161.921	162.690	163.473	164.247
56	165.036	165.816	166.612	167.409	168.198	169.003	169.810	170.608	171.421	172.236
57	173.044	173.866	174.691	175.519	176.351	177.185	178.010	178.851	179.695	179.354
58	181.392	182.245	183.102	183.962	184.824	185.690	186.559	187.445	188.321	189.199
59	190.082	190.966	191.855	192.760	193.655	194.553	195.455	196.374	197.282	198.193
60	199.122	200.040	200.976	201.900	202.829	203.774	204.710	205.662	206.604	207.564
61	208.526	209.478	210.448	211.407	212.385	213.365	214.334	215.321	216.314	217.308
62	218.290	219.293	220.298	221.307	222.321	223.337	224.341	225.365	226.392	227.423
63	228.458	229.496	230.538	231.584	232.633	233.687	234.743	235.804	236.885	237.953
64	239.025	240.101	241.180	242.281	243.368	244.459	245.553	246.670	247.772	248.878
65	250.006	251.120	252.238	253.378	254.504	255.651	256.784	257.941	259.081	260.246
66	261.395	262.567	263.724	264.904	266.088	267.258	268.450	269.647	270.828	272.033
67	273.242	274.456	275.653	276.874	278.099	279.330	280.565	281.803	283.024	284.271
68	285.523	286.778	288.037	289.302	290.569	291.843	293.119	294.401	295.686	296.976
69	298.293	299.591	300.894	302.202	303.513	304.829	306.172	307.498	308.827	310.161
70	311.522	312.866	314.212	315.588	316.944	318.328	319.694	321.064	322.462	323.841
71	325.249	326.637	328.054	329.452	330.878	332.309	333.721	335.162	336.582	338.033
72	339.488	340.922	342.387	343.856	345.331	346.784	348.268	349.757	351.251	352.751
73	354.227	355.737	357.251	358.768	360.292	361.820	363.354	364.892	366.436	367.984
74	369.537	371.096	372.660	374.228	375.802	377.380	378.964	380.582	382.176	383.775
75	385.379	386.988	388.633	390.252	391.878	393.507	395.173	396.813	398.458	400.141
76	401.796	403.488	405.156	406.827	408.535	410.218	411.938	413.632	415.361	417.065
77	418.807	420.554	422.273	424.032	425.762	427.531	429.306	431.054	432.839	434.631
78	436.395	438.197	440.005	441.819	443.639	445.431	447.262	449.099	450.941	452.789
79	454.644	456.504	458.368	460.241	462.082	463.967	465.854	467.749	469.686	471.592
80	473.504	475.424	477.348	479.278	481.213	483.154	485.104	487.094	489.055	491.020
81	492.992	495.007	496.992	498.982	500.978	503.019	505.027	507.042	509.102	511.128
82	513.200	515.239	517.324	519.374	521.432	523.536	525.607	527.724	529.846	531.935
83	534.070	536.174	538.321	540.435	542.597	544.765	546.898	549.081	551.268	553.464
84	555.621	557.828	560.044	562.265	564.449	566.682	568.923	571.173	573.426	575.688
85	577.955	580.183	582.466	584.754	587.049	589.350	591.657	593.974	596.295	598.625
86	600.959	603.348	605.699	608.055	610.418	612.789	615.166	617.551	619.991	622.388
87	624.793	627.204	629.674	632.100	634.531	636.973	639.470	641.926	644.386	646.904
88	649.381	651.913	654.404	656.901	659.458	661.968	664.539	667.066	669.651	672.193
89	674.793	677.348	679.962	682.586	685.164	687.802	690.393	693.045	695.709	698.322
90	700.998	703.682	706.374	709.018	711.724	714.439	717.162	719.834	722.574	725.318
91	728.072	730.833	733.602	736.379	739.163	741.896	744.698	747.507	750.323	753.148
92	755.978	758.819	761.667	764.520	767.448	770.320	773.198	776.088	778.981	781.887
93	784.798	787.720	790.709	793.646	796.592	799.543	802.572	805.537	808.514	811.500
94	814.559	817.560	820.572	823.655	826.684	829.716	832.826	835.879	839.005	842.074
95	845.217	848.302	851.466	854.565	857.745	860.863	864.061	867.198	870.410	873.563
96	876.795	880.035	883.214	886.472	889.737	892.943	896.227	899.522	902.751	906.062
97	909.383	912.712	916.049	919.324	922.679	926.046	929.419	932.802	936.195	939.519
98	942.932	946.351	949.778	953.218	956.666	960.124	963.587	967.061	970.548	974.038
99	977.545	981.056	984.575	988.109	991.726	995.276	998.835	1002.411	1005.991	1009.576
100	1013.253									

Boiling point in degrees Centigrade

mb	0	1	2	3	4	5	6	7	8	9
0		-16.52	-12.90	-8.35	-5.02	-2.40	-0.21	+1.90	3.78	5.46
10	6.99	8.38	9.67	10.87	11.99	13.04	14.03	14.97	15.86	16.71
20	17.52	18.29	19.04	19.75	20.44	21.10	21.74	22.36	22.96	23.54
30	24.10	24.65	25.18	25.70	26.21	26.70	27.18	27.65	28.10	28.55
40	28.99	29.41	29.83	30.24	30.65	31.04	31.43	31.80	32.18	32.54
50	32.90	33.26	33.60	33.94	34.28	34.61	34.93	35.25	35.57	35.88
60	36.19	36.49	36.79	37.08	37.37	37.66	37.94	38.22	38.49	38.76
70	39.03	39.29	39.55	39.81	40.07	40.32	40.57	40.82	41.06	41.30
80	41.54	41.77	42.01	42.24	42.47	42.69	42.92	43.14	43.36	43.58
90	43.79	44.00	44.22	44.43	44.63	44.84	45.04	45.24	45.44	45.64
100	45.84	46.03	46.23	46.42	46.61	46.79	46.98	47.17	47.35	47.53
110	47.72	47.89	48.07	48.25	48.42	48.60	48.77	48.94	49.11	49.28
120	49.45	49.62	49.78	49.95	50.11	50.27	50.43	50.59	50.75	50.91
130	51.07	51.22	51.38	51.53	51.68	51.83	51.99	52.14	52.28	52.43
140	52.58	52.72	52.87	53.01	53.16	53.30	53.44	53.58	53.72	53.86
150	54.00	54.14	54.28	54.41	54.55	54.68	54.82	54.95	55.08	55.21
160	55.35	55.48	55.61	55.73	55.86	55.99	56.12	56.24	56.37	56.49
170	56.62	56.74	56.87	56.99	57.11	57.23	57.35	57.47	57.59	57.71
180	57.93	57.98	58.07	58.18	58.30	58.42	58.53	58.64	58.76	58.87
190	58.99	59.10	59.21	59.32	59.43	59.54	59.65	59.76	59.87	59.98
200	60.09	60.20	60.31	60.41	60.52	60.63	60.73	60.84	60.94	61.04
210	61.15	61.25	61.36	61.46	61.56	61.66	61.76	61.86	61.97	62.07
220	62.17	62.26	62.36	62.46	62.56	62.66	62.76	62.85	62.95	63.05
230	63.14	63.24	63.33	63.43	63.52	63.62	63.71	63.81	63.90	63.99
240	64.09	64.18	64.27	64.36	64.45	64.54	64.64	64.72	64.82	64.91
250	64.99	65.08	65.17	65.26	65.35	65.44	65.53	65.61	65.70	65.79
260	65.87	65.96	66.05	66.13	66.22	66.30	66.39	66.47	66.56	66.64
270	66.72	66.81	66.89	66.97	67.06	67.14	67.22	67.31	67.39	67.47
280	67.55	67.63	67.71	67.79	67.87	67.95	68.03	68.11	68.19	68.27
290	68.35	68.43	68.51	68.59	68.66	68.74	68.82	68.90	68.97	69.05
300	69.13	69.20	69.28	69.36	69.43	69.51	69.58	69.66	69.73	69.81
310	69.88	69.96	70.03	70.10	70.18	70.25	70.33	70.40	70.47	70.54
320	70.62	70.69	70.76	70.83	70.91	70.98	71.05	71.12	71.19	71.26
330	71.33	71.40	71.47	71.54	71.61	71.68	71.75	71.82	71.89	71.96
340	72.03	72.10	72.17	72.24	72.30	72.37	72.44	72.51	72.58	72.64
350	72.71	72.78	72.84	72.91	72.98	73.05	73.11	73.18	73.24	73.31
360	73.38	73.44	73.51	73.57	73.64	73.70	73.77	73.83	73.90	73.96
370	74.02	74.09	74.15	74.22	74.28	74.34	74.41	74.47	74.53	74.60
380	74.66	74.72	74.78	74.85	74.91	74.97	75.03	75.10	75.16	75.22
390	75.28	75.34	75.40	75.46	75.52	75.58	75.65	75.71	75.77	75.83
400	75.89	75.95	76.01	76.07	76.13	76.19	76.25	76.31	76.36	76.42
410	76.48	76.54	76.60	76.66	76.72	76.77	76.83	76.89	76.95	77.01
420	77.06	77.12	77.18	77.24	77.29	77.35	77.41	77.46	77.52	77.58
430	77.63	77.69	77.75	77.80	77.86	77.92	77.97	78.03	78.08	78.14
440	78.19	78.25	78.30	78.36	78.42	78.47	78.53	78.58	78.64	78.69
450	78.74	78.80	78.85	78.91	78.96	79.01	79.07	79.12	79.18	79.23
460	79.28	79.34	79.39	79.44	79.50	79.55	79.60	79.66	79.71	79.76
470	79.81	79.86	79.92	79.97	80.02	80.07	80.12	80.18	80.23	80.28
480	80.33	80.38	80.44	80.49	80.54	80.59	80.64	80.69	80.74	80.79
490	80.84	80.89	80.94	81.00	81.05	81.09	81.15	81.20	81.25	81.30
500	81.35	81.40	81.45	81.49	81.54	81.59	81.64	81.69	81.74	81.79
510	81.84	81.89	81.94	81.99	82.03	82.08	82.13	82.18	82.23	82.28
520	82.33	82.37	82.42	82.47	82.52	82.57	82.61	82.66	82.71	82.76
530	82.80	82.85	82.90	82.94	82.99	83.04	83.09	83.13	83.18	83.23
540	83.27	83.32	83.37	83.41	83.46	83.51	83.55	83.60	83.65	83.69
550	83.74	83.78	83.83	83.87	83.92	83.97	84.01	84.06	84.10	84.15
560	84.19	84.24	84.28	84.33	84.37	84.42	84.46	84.51	84.55	84.60
570	84.64	84.69	84.73	84.78	84.82	84.86	84.91	84.95	85.00	85.04
580	85.09	85.13	85.17	85.22	85.26	85.31	85.35	85.39	85.44	85.48
590	85.52	85.57	85.61	85.65	85.70	85.74	85.78	85.83	85.87	85.91
600	85.95	86.00	86.04	86.08	86.12	86.17	86.21	86.25	86.29	86.33
610	86.38	86.42	86.46	86.50	86.55	86.59	86.63	86.67	86.71	86.75
620	86.80	86.84	86.88	86.92	86.96	87.00	87.05	87.09	87.13	87.17
630	87.21	87.25	87.29	87.33	87.37	87.41	87.46	87.50	87.54	87.58
640	87.62	87.66	87.70	87.74	87.78	87.82	87.86	87.90	87.94	87.98
650	88.02	88.06	88.10	88.14	88.18	88.22	88.26	88.30	88.34	88.38
660	88.42	88.46	88.50	88.54	88.57	88.61	88.65	88.69	88.73	88.77
670	88.81	88.85	88.89	88.93	88.96	89.00	89.04	89.08	89.12	89.16
680	89.20	89.23	89.27	89.31	89.35	89.39	89.43	89.46	89.50	89.54
690	89.58	89.62	89.66	89.69	89.73	89.77	89.81	89.84	89.88	89.92
700	89.96	90.00	90.03	90.07	90.11	90.14	90.18	90.22	90.26	90.29
710	90.33	90.37	90.41	90.44	90.48	90.52	90.55	90.59	90.63	90.66
720	90.70	90.74	90.77	90.81	90.85	90.88	90.92	90.96	90.99	91.03
730	91.06	91.10	91.14	91.17	91.21	91.25	91.28	91.32	91.35	91.39
740	91.43	91.46	91.50	91.53	91.57	91.61	91.64	91.68	91.71	91.75
750	91.78	91.82	91.85	91.89	91.93	91.96	92.00	92.03	92.07	92.10
760	92.14	92.17	92.21	92.24	92.28	92.31	92.35	92.38	92.41	92.45
770	92.48	92.52	92.55	92.59	92.62	92.66	92.69	92.73	92.76	92.80
780	92.83	92.86	92.90	92.93	92.97	93.00	93.04	93.07	93.10	93.14
790	93.17	93.20	93.24	93.27	93.31	93.34	93.37	93.41	93.44	93.48
800	93.51	93.54	93.58	93.61	93.64	93.68	93.71	93.74	93.78	93.81
810	93.84	93.88	93.91	93.94	93.98	94.01	94.04	94.08	94.11	94.14
820	94.18	94.21	94.24	94.27	94.31	94.34	94.37	94.41	94.44	94.47
830	94.50	94.54	94.57	94.60	94.63	94.67	94.70	94.73	94.76	94.79
840	94.83	94.86	94.89	94.92	94.96	94.99	95.02	95.05	95.09	95.12
850	95.15	95.18	95.21	95.24	95.28	95.31	95.34	95.37	95.40	95.44
860	95.47	95.50	95.53	95.56	95.59	95.62	95.66	95.69	95.72	95.75
870	95.78	95.81	95.85	95.88	95.91	95.94	95.97	96.00	96.03	96.06
880	96.09	96.13	96.16	96.19	96.22	96.25	96.28	96.31	96.34	96.37
890	96.40	96.43	96.47	96.50	96.53	96.56	96.59	96.62	96.65	96.68
900	96.71	96.74	96.77	96.80	96.83	96.86	96.89	96.92	96.95	96.98
910	97.01	97.04	97.07	97.10	97.13	97.16	97.19	97.22	97.25	97.29
920	97.32	97.34	97.37	97.40	97.43	97.46	97.49	97.52	97.55	97.58
930	97.61	97.64	97.67	97.70	97.73	97.76	97.79	97.82	97.85	97.88
940	97.91	97.94	97.97	98.00	98.03	98.06	98.08	98.11	98.14	98.17
950	98.20	98.23	98.26	98.29	98.32	98.35	98.38	98.40	98.43	98.46
960	98.49	98.52	98.55	98.58	98.61	98.64	98.66	98.69	98.72	98.75
970	98.78	98.81	98.84	98.87	98.89	98.92	98.95	98.98	99.01	99.04
980	99.06	99.09	99.12	99.15	99.18	99.21	99.24	99.26	99.29	99.32
990	99.35	99.37	99.40	99.43	99.46	99.49	99.52	99.54	99.57	99.60
1000	99.63									

The table gives factors for conversion of spirometer values to lung values calculated from the formula

$$f = \frac{(p - p_{t\,H_2O})(1 + 37\alpha)}{(p - p_{37°\,H_2O})(1 + \alpha t)}$$

where

p = measured pressure of the spirometer volume

$p_{t\,H_2O}$ and $p_{37°\,H_2O}$ = pressure of water vapor at the measured temperature of the spirometer volume and at 37°C in the lungs respectively

α = volume coefficient of expansion of air per °C (cf. page 300)

°C = temperature, mm Hg = pressure of spirometer gas volume

mm Hg / °C	490	500	510	520	530	540	550	560	570	580	590	600	610	620	630
0	1.2447	1.2423	1.2400	1.2378	1.2357	1.2337	1.2317	1.2299	1.2281	1.2263	1.2247	1.2231	1.2215	1.2200	1.2186
1	2393	2369	2347	2325	2304	2284	2265	2246	2228	2211	2195	2179	2164	2149	2134
2	2339	2315	2293	2271	2250	2231	2212	2193	2176	2159	2143	2127	2112	2097	2083
3	2284	2261	2239	2217	2197	2177	2159	2141	2123	2107	2091	2075	2060	2046	2032
4	2229	2206	2184	2163	2143	2124	2105	2088	2071	2054	2038	2023	2008	1994	1980
5	1.2174	1.2151	1.2130	1.2109	1.2089	1.2070	1.2052	1.2034	1.2018	1.2001	1.1986	1.1971	1.1956	1.1942	1.1929
6	2118	2096	2075	2054	2035	2016	1998	1981	1964	1948	1933	1918	1904	1890	1877
7	2062	2041	2020	2000	1980	1962	1944	1927	1911	1895	1880	1866	1852	1838	1825
8	2006	1985	1964	1944	1926	1907	1890	1873	1857	1842	1827	1813	1799	1786	1773
9	1949	1928	1908	1889	1870	1853	1836	1819	1803	1788	1774	1760	1746	1733	1720
10	1.1892	1.1872	1.1852	1.1833	1.1815	1.1797	1.1781	1.1764	1.1749	1.1734	1.1720	1.1706	1.1693	1.1680	1.1667
11	1835	1814	1795	1776	1759	1742	1725	1709	1694	1680	1666	1652	1639	1627	1614
12	1777	1757	1738	1720	1702	1685	1669	1654	1639	1625	1611	1598	1585	1573	1561
13	1718	1698	1680	1662	1645	1629	1613	1598	1584	1570	1556	1543	1531	1519	1507
14	1658	1640	1622	1604	1588	1572	1556	1542	1528	1514	1501	1488	1476	1464	1453
15	1.1598	1.1580	1.1562	1.1546	1.1529	1.1514	1.1499	1.1485	1.1471	1.1458	1.1445	1.1433	1.1421	1.1409	1.1398
16	1538	1520	1503	1486	1471	1456	1441	1427	1414	1401	1389	1377	1365	1354	1343
17	1476	1459	1442	1426	1411	1397	1383	1369	1356	1344	1332	1320	1309	1298	1288
18	1414	1397	1381	1366	1351	1337	1323	1310	1298	1286	1274	1263	1252	1242	1232
19	1351	1335	1319	1304	1290	1276	1263	1251	1239	1227	1216	1205	1195	1184	1175
20	1.1287	1.1271	1.1256	1.1242	1.1228	1.1215	1.1203	1.1191	1.1179	1.1168	1.1157	1.1146	1.1136	1.1127	1.1117
21	1221	1207	1193	1179	1166	1153	1141	1129	1118	1108	1097	1087	1078	1068	1059
22	1156	1141	1128	1115	1102	1090	1079	1068	1057	1047	1037	1027	1018	1009	1001
23	1089	1075	1062	1050	1038	1026	1015	1005	0995	0985	0975	0966	0958	0949	0941
24	1020	1008	0995	0983	0972	0961	0951	0941	0931	0922	0913	0905	0896	0888	0881
25	1.0951	1.0939	1.0927	1.0916	1.0906	1.0895	1.0886	1.0876	1.0867	1.0859	1.0850	1.0842	1.0834	1.0827	1.0819
26	0880	0869	0858	0848	0838	0828	0819	0810	0802	0794	0786	0778	0771	0764	0757
27	0808	0798	0788	0778	0769	0760	0752	0744	0736	0728	0721	0714	0707	0701	0694
28	0735	0725	0716	0707	0699	0691	0683	0675	0668	0661	0655	0648	0642	0636	0630
29	0660	0651	0643	0635	0627	0620	0613	0606	0600	0593	0587	0581	0576	0570	0565
30	1.0584	1.0576	1.0568	1.0561	1.0554	1.0548	1.0542	1.0536	1.0530	1.0524	1.0519	1.0514	1.0509	1.0504	1.0499
31	0506	0499	0492	0486	0480	0474	0469	0464	0459	0454	0449	0444	0440	0436	0432
32	0426	0420	0415	0409	0404	0399	0395	0390	0386	0382	0378	0374	0370	0367	0363
33	0345	0340	0335	0331	0327	0323	0319	0315	0312	0309	0304	0302	0299	0296	0293
34	0261	0258	0254	0251	0248	0245	0242	0239	0236	0234	0231	0229	0227	0224	0222
35	1.0176	1.0174	1.0171	1.0169	1.0167	1.0165	1.0163	1.0161	1.0159	1.0157	1.0156	1.0154	1.0153	1.0151	1.0150
36	0089	0088	0087	0086	0084	0083	0082	0081	0081	0080	0079	0078	0077	0076	0076

mm Hg / °C	640	650	660	670	680	690	700	710	720	730	740	750	760	770	780
0	1.2172	1.2158	1.2145	1.2133	1.2120	1.2109	1.2097	1.2086	1.2075	1.2065	1.2054	1.2045	1.2035	1.2025	1.2016
1	2121	2107	2094	2082	2070	2058	2047	2036	2025	2015	2005	1995	1985	1976	1967
2	2070	2056	2044	2031	2019	2008	1997	1986	1975	1965	1955	1945	1936	1927	1918
3	2018	2005	1993	1981	1969	1957	1946	1936	1925	1915	1905	1896	1886	1877	1869
4	1967	1954	1942	1930	1918	1907	1896	1885	1875	1865	1855	1846	1837	1828	1819
5	1.1916	1.1903	1.1891	1.1879	1.1867	1.1856	1.1846	1.1835	1.1825	1.1815	1.1806	1.1796	1.1787	1.1778	1.1770
6	1864	1852	1840	1828	1817	1806	1795	1785	1775	1765	1756	1746	1738	1729	1721
7	1812	1800	1788	1777	1765	1755	1744	1734	1724	1715	1706	1697	1688	1679	1671
8	1760	1748	1736	1725	1714	1704	1693	1683	1674	1664	1655	1647	1638	1630	1621
9	1708	1696	1685	1674	1663	1652	1642	1633	1623	1614	1605	1596	1588	1580	1572
10	1.1655	1.1644	1.1633	1.1622	1.1611	1.1601	1.1591	1.1582	1.1572	1.1563	1.1554	1.1546	1.1538	1.1530	1.1522
11	1603	1591	1580	1570	1559	1549	1540	1530	1521	1512	1504	1495	1487	1479	1472
12	1549	1538	1528	1517	1507	1497	1488	1479	1470	1461	1453	1444	1437	1429	1421
13	1496	1485	1475	1464	1455	1445	1436	1427	1418	1410	1401	1393	1386	1378	1371
14	1442	1431	1421	1411	1402	1392	1383	1375	1366	1358	1350	1342	1334	1327	1320
15	1.1388	1.1377	1.1367	1.1358	1.1348	1.1339	1.1331	1.1322	1.1314	1.1306	1.1298	1.1290	1.1283	1.1276	1.1269
16	1333	1323	1313	1304	1295	1286	1277	1269	1261	1253	1246	1238	1231	1224	1217
17	1278	1268	1258	1249	1241	1232	1224	1216	1208	1200	1193	1186	1179	1172	1166
18	1222	1212	1203	1194	1186	1178	1170	1162	1154	1147	1140	1133	1126	1120	1113
19	1165	1156	1147	1139	1131	1123	1115	1108	1100	1093	1086	1080	1073	1067	1061
20	1.1108	1.1100	1.1091	1.1083	1.1075	1.1067	1.1060	1.1053	1.1046	1.1039	1.1032	1.1026	1.1020	1.1014	1.1008
21	1051	1042	1034	1026	1019	1011	1004	0997	0991	0984	0978	0972	0966	0960	0954
22	0992	0984	0976	0969	0962	0955	0948	0941	0935	0929	0923	0917	0911	0905	0900
23	0933	0926	0918	0911	0904	0897	0891	0885	0879	0873	0867	0861	0856	0851	0845
24	0873	0866	0859	0852	0846	0839	0833	0827	0822	0816	0810	0805	0800	0795	0790
25	1.0812	1.0806	1.0799	1.0793	1.0787	1.0781	1.0775	1.0769	1.0764	1.0759	1.0753	1.0748	1.0744	1.0739	1.0734
26	0751	0744	0738	0732	0727	0721	0716	0710	0705	0700	0696	0691	0686	0682	0678
27	0688	0682	0677	0671	0666	0661	0656	0651	0646	0642	0637	0633	0629	0625	0621
28	0625	0619	0614	0609	0604	0599	0595	0590	0586	0582	0578	0574	0570	0566	0563
29	0560	0555	0551	0546	0542	0537	0533	0529	0525	0521	0518	0514	0511	0507	0504
30	1.0495	1.0490	1.0486	1.0482	1.0478	1.0474	1.0470	1.0467	1.0463	1.0460	1.0457	1.0453	1.0450	1.0447	1.0444
31	0428	0424	0420	0417	0413	0410	0407	0403	0400	0397	0395	0392	0389	0386	0384
32	0360	0357	0353	0350	0347	0345	0342	0339	0337	0334	0332	0329	0327	0325	0322
33	0291	0288	0285	0283	0280	0278	0276	0274	0272	0270	0268	0266	0264	0262	0260
34	0220	0218	0216	0214	0212	0211	0209	0207	0206	0204	0202	0201	0199	0198	0197
35	1.0148	1.0147	1.0145	1.0144	1.0143	1.0142	1.0141	1.0139	1.0138	1.0137	1.0136	1.0135	1.0134	1.0133	1.0132
36	0075	0074	0073	0073	0072	0072	0071	0070	0070	0069	0069	0068	0068	0067	0067

The remarks which follow are applicable to any other gas in place of air without appreciable error (see under Basis of calculation, below).

Explanation of the tables

mm Hg = values in the uppermost line of each table = observed pressure of the measured gas volume. Under many conditions of measurement this will be the same as the ambient (atmospheric) pressure, i.e. the observed barometric pressure after correction for temperature. Correction for pressure of water vapor under conditions of saturation is also provided for in the table (see under "*sat.*" below). For conversion of mm Hg into millibars and vice versa see page 226.

°C = values in the extreme left-hand column = observed temperature of the measured gas volume.

"dry" = factors for the reduction of measured volumes of *dry* gases to *normal conditions* (0° C, 760 mm Hg, dry). Normal gas volumes are indicated by the abbreviation NTP (normal temperature and pressure). Since this abbreviation does not indicate the state of humidity and does not correspond to a *physiologically* normal condition, some lung specialists have introduced the abbreviation STPD (standard temperature and pressure, dry). However, the use of different expressions in physics and physiology is better avoided.

"*sat.*" = factors for the reduction of measured volumes of gases *saturated with water vapor* to normal conditions (0° C, 760 mm Hg, dry). Gases may be assumed to be saturated with water vapor if they are in contact with water. This applies to the air in the lungs and to exhaled air, as also to spirometer air (if not dried). For the pressure of saturated water vapor at various temperatures see pages 296–298.

Use of the tables

A. Reduction of measured gas volumes to normal conditions (NTP)

The measured volume is multiplied by the factor appropriate to the conditions of measurement (temperature, pressure, dry or saturated).

Examples: 1. What is the volume at NTP of 1.6 liters of dry gas measured at 25°C and 712 mm Hg? Required volume at NTP = 1.6×0.8581 = 1.3730 liters (NTP).

2. What is the volume at NTP of 1.6 liters of gas saturated with water vapor measured at 25°C and 712 mm Hg? Required volume at NTP = 1.6×0.8295 = 1.3272 liters (NTP). This is the type of calculation required to convert spirometer values to NTP.

B. Conversion of measured volumes to other conditions

The measured volume is multiplied by the appropriate conversion factor to NTP and the resulting value divided by the conversion factor corresponding to the required conditions (temperature, pressure, dry or moist).

Examples: 1. What will be the volume occupied by 1.6 liters of gas measured at 25°C and 730 mm Hg in contact with water when warmed at constant pressure to 37°C? Required volume = 1.6×0.8512/0.7912 = 1.7213 liters. This is the type of calculation required to convert spirometer values to lung values. The expression BTPS (body temperature and pressure, saturated) is frequently used to indicate gas volumes under lung conditions, i.e. 37° C, atmospheric pressure, saturated with water vapor. For direct conversion factors for spirometer to lung values see page 299.

2. What will be the volume occupied by 1.6 liters of dry gas measured at 0° C and 600 mm Hg after saturation with water vapor, warming to 25° C and compression to 760 mm Hg? Required volume = 1.6×0.7895/0.8873 = 1.4236 liters.

Basis of calculation

The conversion factors have been calculated on the basis of the following formulas:

Conversion factor for reduction of *dry* gas volumes to standard $= \frac{p}{760(1+\alpha t)}$, Conversion factor for reduction of *saturated* gas volumes to standard $= \frac{p - p_{H_2O}}{760(1+\alpha t)}$, where

p, t = pressure in mm Hg and temperature in °C of the measured gas volume.

p_{H_2O} = pressure of saturated water vapor at the temperature t (see pages 296–298).

α = volume coefficient of thermal expansion of the gas between 0 and 100° C at a constant pressure of 760 mm Hg. In these tables the value for air, 0.003 670 per °C (Regnault, 1842), has been used. Under the same conditions the value for an ideal gas is 0.003 661 (=1/273.15), for nitrogen 0.003 671, for carbon monoxide 0.003 669, for carbon dioxide 0.003 723, for acetylene 0.003 739. The conversion factors are therefore clearly applicable without sensible error to other gases in addition to air.

Note that in calculating the factors the 4th decimal place has been obtained by rounding off the 5th decimal place upwards or downwards. Any discrepancies with factors given in other tables (e.g. those in the *Handbook of Chemistry and Physics*) are due to the use of other values for the expansion coefficient or of other methods of rounding off.

P	600		601		602		603		604	
°C	dry	*sat.*	dry	*sat.*	dry	*sat.*	dry	*sat.*	dry	*sat.*
0	0.7895	*0.7834*	0.7908	*0.7848*	0.7921	*0.7861*	0.7934	*0.7874*	0.7947	*0.7887*
1	7866	*7801*	7879	*7814*	7892	*7828*	7905	*7841*	7918	*7854*
2	7837	*7768*	7850	*7781*	7863	*7794*	7876	*7807*	7889	*7820*
3	7809	*7735*	7822	*7748*	7835	*7761*	7848	*7774*	7861	*7787*
4	7781	*7701*	7793	*7714*	7806	*7727*	7819	*7740*	7832	*7753*
5	0.7752	*0.7668*	0.7765	*0.7681*	0.7778	*0.7694*	0.7791	*0.7707*	0.7804	*0.7720*
6	7725	*7634*	7738	*7647*	7750	*7660*	7763	*7673*	7776	*7686*
7	7697	*7601*	7710	*7613*	7723	*7626*	7735	*7639*	7748	*7652*
8	7670	*7567*	7682	*7580*	7695	*7592*	7708	*7605*	7721	*7618*
9	7642	*7533*	7655	*7545*	7668	*7558*	7681	*7571*	7693	*7584*
10	0.7615	*0.7498*	0.7628	*0.7511*	0.7641	*0.7524*	0.7653	*0.7536*	0.7666	*0.7549*
11	7588	*7464*	7601	*7477*	7614	*7489*	7626	*7502*	7639	*7514*
12	7562	*7429*	7574	*7442*	7587	*7454*	7600	*7467*	7612	*7480*
13	7535	*7394*	7548	*7407*	7560	*7419*	7573	*7432*	7585	*7444*
14	7509	*7359*	7521	*7371*	7534	*7384*	7546	*7396*	7559	*7409*
15	0.7483	*0.7323*	0.7495	*0.7336*	0.7508	*0.7348*	0.7520	*0.7361*	0.7533	*0.7373*
16	7457	*7287*	7469	*7300*	7482	*7312*	7494	*7325*	7507	*7337*
17	7431	*7251*	7443	*7264*	7456	*7276*	7468	*7288*	7481	*7301*
18	7406	*7215*	7418	*7227*	7430	*7239*	7443	*7252*	7455	*7264*
19	7380	*7177*	7392	*7190*	7405	*7202*	7417	*7214*	7429	*7227*
20	0.7355	*0.7140*	0.7367	*0.7152*	0.7379	*0.7164*	0.7392	*0.7177*	0.7404	*0.7189*
21	7330	*7102*	7342	*7114*	7354	*7126*	7366	*7139*	7379	*7151*
22	7305	*7064*	7317	*7076*	7329	*7088*	7341	*7100*	7354	*7112*
23	7280	*7025*	7292	*7037*	7304	*7049*	7317	*7061*	7329	*7073*
24	7256	*6985*	7268	*6997*	7280	*7009*	7292	*7021*	7304	*7033*
25	0.7231	*0.6945*	0.7243	*0.6957*	0.7255	*0.6969*	0.7267	*0.6981*	0.7279	*0.6993*
26	7207	*6904*	7219	*6916*	7231	*6928*	7243	*6940*	7255	*6952*
27	7183	*6863*	7195	*6875*	7207	*6887*	7219	*6899*	7231	*6911*
28	7159	*6821*	7171	*6833*	7183	*6845*	7195	*6857*	7207	*6869*
29	7135	*6778*	7147	*6790*	7159	*6802*	7171	*6814*	7183	*6826*
30	0.7112	*0.6735*	0.7124	*0.6746*	0.7135	*0.6758*	0.7147	*0.6770*	0.7159	*0.6782*
31	7088	*6690*	7100	*6702*	7112	*6714*	7124	*6726*	7136	*6737*
32	7065	*6645*	7077	*6657*	7089	*6669*	7100	*6680*	7112	*6692*
33	7042	*6599*	7054	*6611*	7065	*6623*	7077	*6634*	7089	*6646*
34	7019	*6552*	7031	*6564*	7042	*6576*	7054	*6587*	7066	*6599*
35	0.6996	*0.6504*	0.7008	*0.6516*	0.7019	*0.6528*	0.7031	*0.6539*	0.7043	*0.6551*
36	6973	*6455*	6985	*6467*	6997	*6479*	7008	*6490*	7020	*6502*
37	6951	*6406*	6962	*6417*	6974	*6429*	6986	*6440*	6997	*6452*
38	6928	*6355*	6940	*6366*	6952	*6378*	6963	*6389*	6975	*6401*
39	6906	*6303*	6918	*6314*	6929	*6326*	6941	*6337*	6952	*6349*
40	0.6884	*0.6249*	0.6896	*0.6261*	0.6907	*0.6272*	0.6919	*0.6284*	0.6930	*0.6295*
41	6862	*6195*	6874	*6206*	6885	*6218*	6896	*6229*	6908	*6241*
42	6840	*6139*	6852	*6151*	6863	*6162*	6875	*6173*	6886	*6185*

P	605		606		607		608		609	
°C	dry	*sat.*	dry	*sat.*	dry	*sat.*	dry	*sat.*	dry	*sat.*
0	0.7961	*0.7900*	0.7974	*0.7913*	0.7987	*0.7927*	0.8000	*0.7940*	0.8013	*0.7953*
1	7931	*7867*	7945	*7880*	7958	*7893*	7971	*7906*	7984	*7919*
2	7903	*7833*	7916	*7846*	7929	*7859*	7942	*7873*	7955	*7886*
3	7874	*7800*	7887	*7813*	7900	*7826*	7913	*7839*	7926	*7852*
4	7845	*7766*	7858	*7779*	7871	*7792*	7884	*7805*	7897	*7818*
5	0.7817	*0.7733*	0.7830	*0.7745*	0.7843	*0.7758*	0.7856	*0.7771*	0.7869	*0.7784*
6	7789	*7699*	7802	*7712*	7815	*7724*	7828	*7737*	7841	*7750*
7	7761	*7665*	7774	*7678*	7787	*7690*	7800	*7703*	7812	*7716*
8	7733	*7631*	7746	*7643*	7759	*7656*	7772	*7669*	7785	*7682*
9	7706	*7596*	7719	*7609*	7731	*7622*	7744	*7635*	7757	*7647*
10	0.7679	*0.7562*	0.7691	*0.7575*	0.7704	*0.7587*	0.7717	*0.7600*	0.7729	*0.7613*
11	7652	*7527*	7664	*7540*	7677	*7552*	7690	*7565*	7702	*7578*
12	7625	*7492*	7637	*7505*	7650	*7517*	7663	*7530*	7675	*7543*
13	7598	*7457*	7611	*7470*	7623	*7482*	7636	*7495*	7648	*7507*
14	7572	*7421*	7584	*7434*	7597	*7447*	7609	*7459*	7622	*7472*
15	0.7545	*0.7386*	0.7558	*0.7398*	0.7570	*0.7411*	0.7583	*0.7423*	0.7595	*0.7436*
16	7519	*7350*	7531	*7362*	7544	*7374*	7556	*7387*	7569	*7399*
17	7493	*7313*	7505	*7325*	7518	*7338*	7530	*7350*	7543	*7363*
18	7467	*7276*	7480	*7289*	7492	*7301*	7504	*7313*	7517	*7326*
19	7442	*7239*	7454	*7251*	7466	*7264*	7479	*7276*	7491	*7288*
20	0.7416	*0.7201*	0.7428	*0.7213*	0.7441	*0.7226*	0.7453	*0.7238*	0.7465	*0.7250*
21	7391	*7163*	7403	*7175*	7415	*7188*	7428	*7200*	7440	*7212*
22	7366	*7124*	7378	*7137*	7390	*7149*	7402	*7161*	7415	*7173*
23	7341	*7085*	7353	*7097*	7365	*7110*	7377	*7122*	7389	*7134*
24	7316	*7046*	7328	*7058*	7340	*7070*	7352	*7082*	7364	*7094*
25	0.7292	*0.7005*	0.7304	*0.7017*	0.7316	*0.7029*	0.7328	*0.7041*	0.7340	*0.7053*
26	7267	*6964*	7279	*6976*	7291	*6988*	7303	*7000*	7315	*7012*
27	7243	*6923*	7255	*6935*	7267	*6947*	7279	*6959*	7291	*6971*
28	7219	*6880*	7231	*6892*	7243	*6904*	7255	*6916*	7266	*6928*
29	7195	*6838*	7207	*6849*	7219	*6861*	7230	*6873*	7242	*6885*
30	0.7171	*0.6794*	0.7183	*0.6806*	0.7195	*0.6817*	0.7207	*0.6829*	0.7218	*0.6841*
31	7147	*6749*	7159	*6761*	7171	*6773*	7183	*6785*	7195	*6797*
32	7124	*6704*	7136	*6716*	7147	*6728*	7159	*6739*	7171	*6751*
33	7101	*6658*	7112	*6670*	7124	*6681*	7136	*6693*	7148	*6705*
34	7077	*6611*	7089	*6622*	7101	*6634*	7113	*6646*	7124	*6657*
35	0.7054	*0.6563*	0.7066	*0.6574*	0.7078	*0.6586*	0.7089	*0.6598*	0.7101	*0.6609*
36	7032	*6514*	7043	*6525*	7055	*6537*	7066	*6548*	7078	*6560*
37	7009	*6464*	7020	*6475*	7032	*6487*	7044	*6498*	7055	*6510*
38	6986	*6412*	6998	*6424*	7009	*6436*	7021	*6447*	7032	*6459*
39	6964	*6360*	6975	*6372*	6987	*6383*	6998	*6395*	7010	*6406*
40	0.6942	*0.6307*	0.6953	*0.6318*	0.6964	*0.6330*	0.6976	*0.6341*	0.6987	*0.6353*
41	6919	*6252*	6931	*6264*	6942	*6275*	6954	*6286*	6965	*6298*
42	6897	*6196*	6909	*6208*	6920	*6219*	6932	*6230*	6943	*6242*

P / °C	610 dry	610 sat.	611 dry	611 sat.	612 dry	612 sat.	613 dry	613 sat.	614 dry	614 sat.	615 dry	615 sat.	616 dry	616 sat.	617 dry	617 sat.	618 dry	618 sat.	619 dry	619 sat.
0	0.8026	0.7966	0.8039	0.7979	0.8053	0.7992	0.8066	0.8006	0.8079	0.8019	0.8092	0.8032	0.8105	0.8045	0.8118	0.8058	0.8132	0.8071	0.8145	0.8084
1	7997	7932	8010	7945	8023	7959	8036	7972	8049	7985	8063	7998	8076	8011	8089	8024	8102	8037	8115	8050
2	7968	7899	7981	7912	7994	7925	8007	7938	8020	7951	8033	7964	8046	7977	8059	7990	8072	8003	8085	8016
3	7939	7865	7952	7878	7965	7891	7978	7904	7991	7917	8004	7930	8017	7943	8030	7956	8043	7969	8056	7982
4	7910	7831	7923	7844	7936	7857	7949	7870	7962	7883	7975	7896	7988	7909	8001	7922	8014	7935	8027	7948
5	0.7882	0.7797	0.7895	0.7810	0.7908	0.7823	0.7920	0.7836	0.7933	0.7849	0.7946	0.7862	0.7959	0.7875	0.7972	0.7888	0.7985	0.7901	0.7998	0.7913
6	7853	7763	7866	7776	7879	7789	7892	7802	7905	7815	7918	7827	7931	7840	7944	7853	7956	7866	7969	7879
7	7825	7729	7838	7742	7851	7755	7864	7767	7877	7780	7889	7793	7902	7806	7915	7819	7928	7832	7941	7844
8	7797	7695	7810	7707	7823	7720	7836	7733	7849	7746	7861	7758	7874	7771	7887	7784	7900	7797	7912	7810
9	7770	7660	7782	7673	7795	7686	7808	7698	7821	7711	7833	7724	7846	7736	7859	7749	7872	7762	7884	7775
10	0.7742	0.7625	0.7755	0.7638	0.7768	0.7651	0.7780	0.7663	0.7793	0.7676	0.7806	0.7689	0.7818	0.7701	0.7831	0.7714	0.7844	0.7727	0.7856	0.7740
11	7715	7590	7728	7603	7740	7616	7753	7628	7765	7641	7778	7654	7791	7666	7803	7679	7816	7692	7829	7704
12	7688	7555	7700	7568	7713	7580	7726	7593	7738	7606	7751	7618	7763	7631	7776	7643	7789	7656	7801	7669
13	7661	7520	7673	7532	7686	7545	7698	7557	7711	7570	7724	7583	7736	7595	7749	7608	7761	7620	7774	7633
14	7634	7484	7647	7497	7659	7509	7672	7522	7684	7534	7697	7547	7709	7559	7722	7572	7734	7584	7747	7597
15	0.7608	0.7448	0.7620	0.7461	0.7632	0.7473	0.7645	0.7485	0.7657	0.7498	0.7670	0.7510	0.7682	0.7523	0.7695	0.7535	0.7707	0.7548	0.7720	0.7560
16	7581	7412	7594	7424	7606	7437	7618	7449	7631	7461	7643	7474	7656	7486	7668	7499	7681	7511	7693	7524
17	7555	7375	7567	7387	7580	7400	7592	7412	7605	7425	7617	7437	7629	7449	7642	7462	7654	7474	7666	7486
18	7529	7338	7541	7350	7554	7363	7566	7375	7578	7387	7591	7400	7603	7412	7615	7424	7628	7437	7640	7449
19	7503	7300	7515	7313	7528	7325	7540	7337	7552	7350	7565	7362	7577	7374	7589	7387	7602	7399	7614	7411
20	0.7477	0.7263	0.7490	0.7275	0.7502	0.7287	0.7514	0.7299	0.7527	0.7312	0.7539	0.7324	0.7551	0.7336	0.7563	0.7348	0.7576	0.7361	0.7588	0.7373
21	7452	7224	7464	7236	7476	7249	7489	7261	7501	7273	7513	7285	7525	7297	7538	7310	7550	7322	7562	7334
22	7427	7185	7439	7197	7451	7210	7463	7222	7475	7234	7488	7246	7500	7258	7512	7271	7524	7283	7536	7295
23	7402	7146	7414	7158	7426	7170	7438	7182	7450	7194	7462	7207	7474	7219	7486	7231	7499	7243	7511	7255
24	7377	7106	7389	7118	7401	7130	7413	7142	7425	7154	7437	7166	7449	7179	7461	7191	7473	7203	7485	7215
25	0.7352	0.7065	0.7364	0.7078	0.7376	0.7090	0.7388	0.7102	0.7400	0.7114	0.7412	0.7126	0.7424	0.7138	0.7436	0.7150	0.7448	0.7162	0.7460	0.7174
26	7327	7024	7339	7036	7351	7048	7363	7060	7375	7072	7387	7084	7399	7096	7411	7108	7423	7120	7435	7132
27	7303	6983	7315	6995	7327	7007	7339	7018	7351	7030	7363	7042	7375	7054	7386	7066	7398	7078	7410	7090
28	7278	6940	7290	6952	7302	6964	7314	6976	7326	6988	7338	7000	7350	7012	7362	7024	7374	7036	7386	7048
29	7254	6897	7266	6909	7278	6921	7290	6933	7302	6945	7314	6956	7326	6968	7337	6980	7349	6992	7361	7004
30	0.7230	0.6853	0.7242	0.6865	0.7254	0.6877	0.7266	0.6889	0.7278	0.6900	0.7290	0.6912	0.7301	0.6924	0.7313	0.6936	0.7325	0.6948	0.7337	0.6960
31	7206	6808	7218	6820	7230	6832	7242	6844	7254	6856	7266	6867	7277	6879	7289	6891	7301	6903	7313	6915
32	7183	6763	7195	6775	7206	6786	7218	6798	7230	6810	7242	6822	7253	6833	7265	6845	7277	6857	7289	6869
33	7159	6716	7171	6728	7183	6740	7194	6752	7206	6763	7218	6775	7230	6787	7241	6799	7253	6810	7265	6822
34	7136	6669	7148	6681	7159	6693	7171	6704	7183	6716	7194	6728	7206	6739	7218	6751	7229	6763	7241	6774
35	0.7113	0.6621	0.7124	0.6633	0.7136	0.6644	0.7148	0.6656	0.7159	0.6668	0.7171	0.6679	0.7183	0.6691	0.7194	0.6703	0.7206	0.6714	0.7218	0.6726
36	7090	6572	7101	6583	7113	6595	7125	6607	7136	6618	7148	6630	7159	6641	7171	6653	7183	6665	7194	6676
37	7067	6521	7078	6533	7090	6545	7101	6556	7113	6568	7125	6579	7136	6591	7148	6603	7159	6614	7171	6626
38	7044	6470	7056	6482	7067	6493	7079	6505	7090	6516	7102	6528	7113	6539	7125	6551	7136	6563	7148	6574
39	7021	6418	7033	6429	7044	6441	7056	6452	7067	6464	7079	6475	7090	6487	7102	6498	7113	6510	7125	6521
40	0.6999	0.6364	0.7010	0.6376	0.7022	0.6387	0.7033	0.6399	0.7045	0.6410	0.7056	0.6421	0.7068	0.6433	0.7079	0.6444	0.7091	0.6456	0.7102	0.6467
41	6977	6309	6988	6321	6999	6332	7011	6344	7022	6355	7034	6367	7045	6378	7057	6389	7068	6401	7079	6412
42	6954	6253	6966	6265	6977	6276	6989	6287	7000	6299	7011	6310	7023	6322	7034	6333	7046	6344	7057	6356

P / °C	620 dry	620 sat.	621 dry	621 sat.	622 dry	622 sat.	623 dry	623 sat.	624 dry	624 sat.	625 dry	625 sat.	626 dry	626 sat.	627 dry	627 sat.	628 dry	628 sat.	629 dry	629 sat.
0	0.8158	0.8098	0.8171	0.8111	0.8184	0.8124	0.8197	0.8137	0.8211	0.8150	0.8224	0.8163	0.8237	0.8177	0.8250	0.8190	0.8263	0.8203	0.8276	0.8216
1	8128	8063	8141	8077	8154	8090	8167	8103	8181	8116	8194	8129	8207	8142	8220	8155	8233	8168	8246	8181
2	8098	8029	8112	8042	8125	8055	8138	8068	8151	8082	8164	8095	8177	8108	8190	8121	8203	8134	8216	8147
3	8069	7995	8082	8008	8095	8021	8108	8034	8121	8047	8134	8060	8147	8073	8160	8086	8173	8099	8186	8112
4	8040	7961	8053	7974	8066	7987	8079	8000	8092	8013	8105	8026	8118	8039	8131	8052	8144	8064	8157	8077
5	0.8011	0.7926	0.8024	0.7939	0.8037	0.7952	0.8050	0.7965	0.8063	0.7978	0.8075	0.7991	0.8088	0.8004	0.8101	0.8017	0.8114	0.8030	0.8127	0.8043
6	7982	7892	7995	7905	8008	7918	8021	7930	8034	7943	8047	7956	8059	7969	8072	7982	8085	7995	8098	8008
7	7954	7857	7966	7870	7979	7883	7992	7896	8005	7909	8018	7921	8031	7934	8043	7947	8056	7960	8069	7973
8	7925	7822	7938	7835	7951	7848	7964	7861	7976	7874	7989	7886	8002	7899	8015	7912	8027	7925	8040	7937
9	7897	7787	7910	7800	7923	7813	7935	7826	7948	7838	7961	7851	7973	7864	7986	7877	7999	7889	8012	7902
10	0.7869	0.7752	0.7882	0.7765	0.7894	0.7778	0.7907	0.7790	0.7920	0.7803	0.7933	0.7816	0.7945	0.7828	0.7958	0.7841	0.7971	0.7854	0.7983	0.7866
11	7841	7717	7854	7729	7867	7742	7879	7755	7892	7767	7905	7780	7917	7793	7930	7805	7943	7818	7955	7831
12	7814	7681	7826	7694	7839	7706	7852	7719	7864	7732	7877	7744	7889	7757	7902	7769	7915	7782	7927	7795
13	7786	7645	7799	7658	7812	7670	7824	7683	7837	7696	7849	7708	7862	7721	7874	7733	7887	7746	7899	7758
14	7759	7609	7772	7622	7784	7634	7797	7647	7809	7659	7822	7672	7834	7684	7847	7697	7859	7709	7872	7722
15	0.7732	0.7573	0.7745	0.7585	0.7757	0.7598	0.7770	0.7610	0.7782	0.7623	0.7795	0.7635	0.7807	0.7648	0.7820	0.7660	0.7832	0.7673	0.7844	0.7685
16	7705	7536	7718	7548	7730	7561	7743	7573	7755	7586	7768	7598	7780	7611	7792	7623	7805	7635	7817	7648
17	7679	7499	7691	7511	7704	7524	7716	7536	7728	7548	7741	7561	7753	7573	7766	7586	7778	7598	7790	7610
18	7652	7461	7665	7474	7677	7486	7689	7498	7702	7511	7714	7523	7726	7535	7739	7548	7751	7560	7763	7572
19	7626	7423	7638	7436	7651	7448	7663	7460	7675	7473	7688	7485	7700	7497	7712	7510	7725	7522	7737	7534
20	0.7600	0.7385	0.7612	0.7397	0.7625	0.7410	0.7637	0.7422	0.7649	0.7434	0.7661	0.7446	0.7674	0.7459	0.7686	0.7471	0.7698	0.7483	0.7710	0.7495
21	7574	7346	7586	7359	7599	7371	7611	7383	7623	7395	7635	7407	7647	7420	7660	7432	7672	7444	7684	7456
22	7548	7307	7561	7319	7573	7331	7585	7344	7597	7356	7609	7368	7621	7380	7634	7392	7646	7404	7658	7417
23	7523	7267	7535	7279	7547	7292	7559	7304	7571	7316	7584	7328	7596	7340	7608	7352	7620	7364	7632	7376
24	7498	7227	7510	7239	7522	7251	7534	7263	7546	7275	7558	7287	7570	7299	7582	7312	7594	7324	7606	7336
25	0.7472	0.7186	0.7484	0.7198	0.7496	0.7210	0.7508	0.7222	0.7521	0.7234	0.7533	0.7246	0.7545	0.7258	0.7557	0.7270	0.7569	0.7282	0.7581	0.7294
26	7447	7144	7459	7156	7471	7168	7483	7181	7495	7193	7507	7205	7519	7217	7531	7229	7543	7241	7555	7253
27	7422	7102	7434	7114	7446	7126	7458	7138	7470	7150	7482	7162	7494	7174	7506	7186	7518	7198	7530	7210
28	7398	7059	7410	7071	7422	7083	7434	7095	7445	7107	7457	7119	7469	7131	7481	7143	7493	7155	7505	7167
29	7373	7016	7385	7028	7397	7040	7409	7052	7421	7063	7433	7075	7445	7087	7456	7099	7468	7111	7480	7123
30	0.7349	0.6972	0.7361	0.6983	0.7372	0.6995	0.7384	0.7007	0.7396	0.7019	0.7408	0.7031	0.7420	0.7043	0.7432	0.7055	0.7444	0.7066	0.7455	0.7078
31	7325	6927	7336	6938	7348	6950	7360	6962	7372	6974	7384	6986	7395	6997	7407	7009	7419	7021	7431	7033
32	7301	6881	7312	6892	7324	6904	7336	6916	7348	6928	7359	6939	7371	6951	7383	6963	7395	6975	7406	6987
33	7277	6834	7288	6846	7300	6857	7312	6869	7324	6881	7335	6892	7347	6904	7359	6916	7371	6928	7382	6939
34	7253	6786	7265	6798	7276	6810	7288	6821	7300	6833	7311	6845	7323	6856	7335	6868	7346	6880	7358	6891
35	0.7229	0.6738	0.7241	0.6749	0.7253	0.6761	0.7264	0.6773	0.7276	0.6784	0.7288	0.6796	0.7299	0.6807	0.7311	0.6819	0.7323	0.6831	0.7334	0.6842
36	7206	6688	7217	6700	7229	6711	7241	6723	7252	6734	7264	6746	7276	6758	7287	6769	7299	6781	7310	6793
37	7183	6637	7194	6649	7206	6660	7217	6672	7229	6684	7240	6695	7252	6707	7264	6718	7275	6730	7287	6742
38	7159	6586	7171	6597	7183	6609	7194	6620	7206	6632	7217	6643	7229	6655	7240	6666	7252	6678	7263	6690
39	7136	6533	7148	6544	7159	6556	7171	6567	7182	6579	7194	6590	7206	6602	7217	6613	7229	6625	7240	6636
40	0.7114	0.6479	0.7125	0.6490	0.7137	0.6502	0.7148	0.6513	0.7160	0.6525	0.7171	0.6536	0.7182	0.6548	0.7194	0.6559	0.7205	0.6571	0.7217	0.6582
41	7091	6424	7102	6435	7114	6447	7125	6458	7137	6469	7148	6481	7160	6492	7171	6504	7182	6515	7194	6527
42	7068	6367	7080	6379	7091	6390	7103	6401	7114	6413	7125	6424	7137	6436	7148	6447	7160	6458	7171	6470

P	630		631		632		633		634		635		636		637		638		639	
°C	dry	sat.	dry	sat.	dry	sat.	dry	sat.	dry	sat.	dry	sat.	dry	sat.	dry	sat.	dry	sat.	dry	sat.
0	0.8289	0.8229	0.8303	0.8242	0.8316	0.8256	0.8329	0.8269	0.8342	0.8282	0.8355	0.8295	0.8368	0.8308	0.8382	0.8321	0.8395	0.8334	0.8408	0.8348
1	8259	8195	8272	8208	8285	8221	8298	8234	8312	8247	8325	8260	8338	8273	8351	8286	8364	8299	8377	8313
2	8229	8160	8242	8173	8255	8186	8268	8199	8281	8212	8294	8225	8307	8238	8321	8251	8334	8264	8347	8277
3	8199	8125	8212	8138	8225	8151	8238	8164	8251	8177	8264	8190	8277	8203	8290	8216	8303	8229	8316	8242
4	8170	8090	8183	8103	8195	8116	8208	8129	8221	8142	8234	8155	8247	8168	8260	8181	8273	8194	8286	8207
5	0.8140	0.8056	0.8153	0.8068	0.8166	0.8081	0.8179	0.8094	0.8192	0.8107	0.8205	0.8120	0.8218	0.8133	0.8231	0.8146	0.8243	0.8159	0.8256	0.8172
6	8111	8021	8124	8033	8137	8046	8149	8059	8162	8072	8175	8085	8188	8098	8201	8111	8214	8124	8227	8136
7	8082	7985	8095	7998	8108	8011	8120	8024	8133	8037	8146	8050	8159	8062	8172	8075	8184	8088	8197	8101
8	8053	7950	8066	7963	8079	7976	8091	7989	8104	8001	8117	8014	8130	8027	8143	8040	8155	8052	8168	8065
9	8024	7915	8037	7928	8050	7940	8063	7953	8075	7966	8088	7978	8101	7991	8114	8004	8126	8017	8139	8029
10	0.7996	0.7879	0.8009	0.7892	0.8021	0.7905	0.8034	0.7917	0.8047	0.7930	0.8059	0.7943	0.8072	0.7955	0.8085	0.7968	0.8098	0.7981	0.8110	0.7993
11	7968	7843	7980	7856	7993	7869	8006	7881	8018	7894	8031	7907	8044	7919	8056	7932	8069	7944	8082	7957
12	7940	7807	7952	7820	7965	7832	7978	7845	7990	7858	8003	7870	8015	7883	8028	7895	8041	7908	8053	7921
13	7912	7771	7925	7784	7937	7796	7950	7809	7962	7821	7975	7834	7987	7846	8000	7859	8012	7871	8025	7884
14	7884	7734	7897	7747	7909	7759	7922	7772	7934	7784	7947	7797	7959	7809	7972	7822	7984	7834	7997	7847
15	0.7857	0.7697	0.7869	0.7710	0.7882	0.7722	0.7894	0.7735	0.7907	0.7747	0.7919	0.7760	0.7932	0.7772	0.7944	0.7785	0.7957	0.7797	0.7969	0.7810
16	7830	7660	7842	7673	7855	7685	7867	7698	7879	7710	7892	7722	7904	7735	7917	7747	7929	7760	7942	7772
17	7803	7623	7815	7635	7827	7647	7840	7660	7852	7672	7865	7685	7877	7697	7889	7709	7902	7722	7914	7734
18	7776	7585	7788	7597	7800	7609	7813	7622	7825	7634	7838	7646	7850	7659	7862	7671	7875	7684	7887	7696
19	7749	7546	7761	7559	7774	7571	7786	7583	7798	7596	7811	7608	7823	7620	7835	7633	7848	7645	7860	7657
20	0.7723	0.7508	0.7735	0.7520	0.7747	0.7532	0.7759	0.7544	0.7772	0.7557	0.7784	0.7569	0.7796	0.7581	0.7808	0.7593	0.7821	0.7606	0.7833	0.7618
21	7696	7468	7709	7481	7721	7493	7733	7505	7745	7517	7757	7530	7770	7542	7782	7554	7794	7566	7806	7578
22	7670	7429	7682	7441	7695	7453	7707	7465	7719	7477	7731	7490	7743	7502	7755	7514	7768	7526	7780	7538
23	7644	7389	7656	7401	7668	7413	7681	7425	7693	7437	7705	7449	7717	7461	7729	7474	7741	7486	7753	7498
24	7618	7348	7631	7360	7643	7372	7655	7384	7667	7396	7679	7408	7691	7420	7703	7432	7715	7445	7727	7457
25	0.7593	0.7307	0.7605	0.7319	0.7617	0.7331	0.7629	0.7343	0.7641	0.7355	0.7653	0.7367	0.7665	0.7379	0.7677	0.7391	0.7689	0.7403	0.7701	0.7415
26	7567	7265	7579	7277	7591	7289	7603	7301	7615	7313	7627	7325	7639	7337	7651	7349	7663	7361	7675	7373
27	7542	7222	7554	7234	7566	7246	7578	7258	7590	7270	7602	7282	7614	7294	7626	7306	7638	7318	7650	7330
28	7517	7179	7529	7191	7541	7203	7553	7215	7565	7226	7577	7238	7589	7250	7601	7262	7612	7274	7624	7286
29	7492	7135	7504	7147	7516	7159	7528	7170	7540	7182	7552	7194	7563	7206	7575	7218	7587	7230	7599	7242
30	0.7467	0.7090	0.7479	0.7102	0.7491	0.7114	0.7503	0.7126	0.7515	0.7138	0.7527	0.7149	0.7538	0.7161	0.7550	0.7173	0.7562	0.7185	0.7574	0.7197
31	7443	7045	7455	7056	7466	7068	7478	7080	7490	7092	7502	7104	7514	7116	7525	7127	7537	7139	7549	7151
32	7418	6998	7430	7010	7442	7022	7454	7034	7465	7045	7477	7057	7489	7069	7501	7081	7512	7093	7524	7104
33	7394	6951	7406	6963	7417	6975	7429	6986	7441	6998	7453	7010	7464	7022	7476	7033	7488	7045	7500	7057
34	7370	6903	7382	6915	7393	6927	7405	6938	7417	6950	7428	6962	7440	6973	7452	6985	7463	6997	7475	7008
35	0.7346	0.6854	0.7358	0.6866	0.7369	0.6877	0.7381	0.6889	0.7393	0.6901	0.7404	0.6912	0.7416	0.6924	0.7428	0.6936	0.7439	0.6947	0.7451	0.6959
36	7322	6804	7334	6816	7345	6827	7357	6839	7369	6851	7380	6862	7392	6874	7403	6886	7415	6897	7427	6909
37	7298	6753	7310	6765	7322	6776	7333	6788	7345	6799	7356	6811	7368	6823	7380	6834	7391	6846	7403	6857
38	7275	6701	7286	6713	7298	6724	7310	6736	7321	6747	7333	6759	7344	6770	7356	6782	7367	6793	7379	6805
39	7252	6648	7263	6659	7275	6671	7286	6682	7298	6694	7309	6705	7321	6717	7332	6729	7344	6740	7355	6752
40	0.7228	0.6594	0.7240	0.6605	0.7251	0.6617	0.7263	0.6628	0.7274	0.6639	0.7286	0.6651	0.7297	0.6662	0.7309	0.6674	0.7320	0.6685	0.7332	0.6697
41	7205	6538	7217	6549	7228	6561	7240	6572	7251	6584	7262	6595	7274	6607	7285	6618	7297	6630	7308	6641
42	7182	6481	7194	6493	7205	6504	7217	6515	7228	6527	7239	6538	7251	6550	7262	6561	7274	6572	7285	6584

P	640		641		642		643		644		645		646		647		648		649	
°C	dry	sat.	dry	sat.	dry	sat.	dry	sat.	dry	sat.	dry	sat.	dry	sat.	dry	sat.	dry	sat.	dry	sat.
0	0.8421	0.8361	0.8434	0.8374	0.8447	0.8387	0.8461	0.8400	0.8474	0.8413	0.8487	0.8427	0.8500	0.8440	0.8513	0.8453	0.8526	0.8466	0.8539	0.8479
1	8390	8326	8403	8339	8416	8352	8430	8365	8443	8378	8456	8391	8469	8404	8482	8417	8495	8431	8508	8444
2	8360	8291	8373	8304	8386	8317	8399	8330	8412	8343	8425	8356	8438	8369	8451	8382	8464	8395	8477	8408
3	8329	8255	8342	8268	8355	8281	8368	8294	8381	8307	8394	8320	8407	8333	8420	8346	8433	8359	8446	8372
4	8299	8220	8312	8233	8325	8246	8338	8259	8351	8272	8364	8285	8377	8298	8390	8311	8403	8324	8416	8337
5	0.8269	0.8185	0.8282	0.8198	0.8295	0.8211	0.8308	0.8224	0.8321	0.8236	0.8334	0.8249	0.8347	0.8262	0.8360	0.8275	0.8373	0.8288	0.8386	0.8301
6	8240	8149	8252	8162	8265	8175	8278	8188	8291	8201	8304	8214	8317	8227	8330	8239	8343	8252	8355	8265
7	8210	8114	8223	8127	8236	8139	8249	8152	8261	8165	8274	8178	8287	8191	8300	8204	8313	8216	8326	8229
8	8181	8078	8194	8091	8206	8104	8219	8116	8232	8129	8245	8142	8258	8155	8270	8168	8283	8180	8296	8193
9	8152	8042	8165	8055	8177	8068	8190	8080	8203	8093	8215	8106	8228	8119	8241	8131	8254	8144	8266	8157
10	0.8123	0.8006	0.8136	0.8019	0.8148	0.8031	0.8161	0.8044	0.8174	0.8057	0.8186	0.8070	0.8199	0.8082	0.8212	0.8095	0.8224	0.8108	0.8237	0.8120
11	8094	7970	8107	7982	8120	7995	8132	8008	8145	8020	8158	8033	8170	8046	8183	8058	8195	8071	8208	8084
12	8066	7933	8078	7946	8091	7958	8104	7971	8116	7984	8129	7996	8141	8009	8154	8021	8167	8034	8179	8047
13	8038	7897	8050	7909	8063	7922	8075	7934	8088	7947	8100	7959	8113	7972	8125	7984	8138	7997	8151	8010
14	8010	7860	8022	7872	8035	7885	8047	7897	8060	7910	8072	7922	8085	7935	8097	7947	8110	7960	8122	7972
15	0.7982	0.7822	0.7994	0.7835	0.8007	0.7847	0.8019	0.7860	0.8032	0.7872	0.8044	0.7885	0.8056	0.7897	0.8069	0.7909	0.8081	0.7922	0.8094	0.7934
16	7954	7785	7966	7797	7979	7809	7991	7822	8004	7834	8016	7847	8029	7859	8041	7872	8053	7884	8066	7896
17	7927	7747	7939	7759	7951	7771	7964	7784	7976	7796	7988	7808	8001	7821	8013	7833	8026	7846	8038	7858
18	7899	7708	7912	7721	7924	7733	7936	7745	7949	7758	7961	7770	7973	7782	7986	7795	7998	7807	8010	7819
19	7872	7669	7884	7682	7897	7694	7909	7706	7921	7719	7934	7731	7946	7743	7958	7756	7971	7768	7983	7780
20	0.7845	0.7630	0.7857	0.7643	0.7870	0.7655	0.7882	0.7667	0.7894	0.7679	0.7907	0.7692	0.7919	0.7704	0.7931	0.7716	0.7943	0.7728	0.7956	0.7741
21	7818	7591	7831	7603	7843	7615	7855	7627	7867	7640	7880	7652	7892	7664	7904	7676	7916	7688	7928	7701
22	7792	7551	7804	7563	7816	7575	7828	7587	7841	7599	7853	7611	7865	7624	7877	7636	7889	7648	7902	7660
23	7766	7510	7778	7522	7790	7534	7802	7546	7814	7558	7826	7571	7838	7583	7850	7595	7863	7607	7875	7619
24	7739	7469	7751	7481	7764	7493	7776	7505	7788	7517	7800	7529	7812	7541	7824	7553	7836	7566	7848	7578
25	0.7713	0.7427	0.7725	0.7439	0.7737	0.7451	0.7750	0.7463	0.7762	0.7475	0.7774	0.7487	0.7786	0.7499	0.7798	0.7511	0.7810	0.7523	0.7822	0.7536
26	7688	7385	7700	7397	7712	7409	7724	7421	7736	7433	7748	7445	7760	7457	7772	7469	7784	7481	7796	7493
27	7662	7342	7674	7354	7686	7366	7698	7378	7710	7390	7722	7402	7734	7414	7746	7426	7758	7438	7770	7449
28	7636	7298	7648	7310	7660	7322	7672	7334	7684	7346	7696	7358	7708	7370	7720	7382	7732	7394	7744	7405
29	7611	7254	7623	7266	7635	7278	7647	7289	7659	7301	7670	7313	7682	7325	7694	7337	7706	7349	7718	7361
30	0.7586	0.7209	0.7598	0.7220	0.7610	0.7232	0.7621	0.7244	0.7633	0.7256	0.7645	0.7268	0.7657	0.7280	0.7669	0.7292	0.7681	0.7303	0.7693	0.7315
31	7561	7163	7573	7175	7584	7186	7596	7198	7608	7210	7620	7222	7632	7234	7644	7245	7655	7257	7667	7269
32	7536	7116	7548	7128	7560	7140	7571	7151	7583	7163	7595	7175	7607	7187	7618	7199	7630	7210	7642	7222
33	7511	7069	7523	7080	7535	7092	7547	7104	7558	7115	7570	7127	7582	7139	7594	7151	7605	7162	7617	7174
34	7487	7020	7499	7032	7510	7044	7522	7055	7534	7067	7545	7079	7557	7090	7569	7102	7580	7114	7592	7125
35	0.7462	0.6971	0.7474	0.6982	0.7486	0.6994	0.7497	0.7006	0.7509	0.7017	0.7521	0.7029	0.7532	0.7041	0.7544	0.7052	0.7556	0.7064	0.7567	0.7076
36	7438	6920	7450	6932	7462	6944	7473	6955	7485	6967	7496	6978	7508	6990	7520	7002	7531	7013	7543	7025
37	7414	6869	7426	6881	7437	6892	7449	6904	7461	6915	7472	6927	7484	6939	7495	6950	7507	6962	7519	6973
38	7390	6817	7402	6828	7413	6840	7425	6851	7437	6863	7448	6874	7460	6886	7471	6897	7483	6909	7494	6920
39	7367	6763	7378	6775	7390	6786	7401	6798	7413	6809	7424	6821	7436	6832	7447	6844	7459	6855	7470	6867
40	0.7343	0.6708	0.7355	0.6720	0.7366	0.6731	0.7378	0.6743	0.7389	0.6754	0.7400	0.6766	0.7412	0.6777	0.7423	0.6789	0.7435	0.6800	0.7446	0.6812
41	7320	6652	7331	6664	7343	6675	7354	6687	7365	6698	7377	6710	7388	6721	7400	6732	7411	6744	7423	6755
42	7296	6595	7308	6607	7319	6618	7331	6629	7342	6641	7353	6652	7365	6664	7376	6675	7388	6686	7399	6698

P	650		651		652		653		654		655		656		657		658		659	
°C	dry	*sat.*	dry	*sat.*	dry	*sat.*	dry	*sat.*	dry	*sat.*	dry	*sat.*	dry	*sat.*	dry	*sat.*	dry	*sat.*	dry	*sat.*
0	0.8553	*0.8492*	0.8566	*0.8506*	0.8579	*0.8519*	0.8592	*0.8532*	0.8605	*0.8545*	0.8618	*0.8558*	0.8632	*0.8571*	0.8645	*0.8584*	0.8658	*0.8598*	0.8671	*0.8611*
1	8521	*8457*	8534	*8470*	8548	*8483*	8561	*8496*	8574	*8509*	8587	*8522*	8600	*8535*	8613	*8549*	8626	*8562*	8639	*8575*
2	8490	*8421*	8503	*8434*	8516	*8447*	8529	*8460*	8543	*8473*	8556	*8486*	8569	*8500*	8582	*8513*	8595	*8526*	8608	*8539*
3	8459	*8386*	8473	*8399*	8486	*8412*	8499	*8425*	8512	*8438*	8525	*8451*	8538	*8464*	8551	*8477*	8564	*8490*	8577	*8503*
4	8429	*8350*	8442	*8363*	8455	*8376*	8468	*8389*	8481	*8402*	8494	*8415*	8507	*8428*	8520	*8441*	8533	*8454*	8546	*8466*
5	0.8399	*0.8314*	0.8411	*0.8327*	0.8424	*0.8340*	0.8437	*0.8353*	0.8450	*0.8366*	0.8463	*0.8379*	0.8476	*0.8392*	0.8489	*0.8404*	0.8502	*0.8417*	0.8515	*0.8430*
6	8368	*8278*	8381	*8291*	8394	*8304*	8407	*8317*	8420	*8330*	8433	*8342*	8446	*8355*	8458	*8368*	8471	*8381*	8484	*8394*
7	8338	*8242*	8351	*8255*	8364	*8268*	8377	*8281*	8390	*8293*	8403	*8306*	8415	*8319*	8428	*8332*	8441	*8345*	8454	*8357*
8	8309	*8206*	8321	*8219*	8334	*8231*	8347	*8244*	8360	*8257*	8373	*8270*	8385	*8283*	8398	*8295*	8411	*8308*	8424	*8321*
9	8279	*8170*	8292	*8182*	8305	*8195*	8317	*8208*	8330	*8220*	8343	*8233*	8356	*8246*	8368	*8259*	8381	*8271*	8394	*8284*
10	0.8250	*0.8133*	0.8263	*0.8146*	0.8275	*0.8158*	0.8288	*0.8171*	0.8301	*0.8184*	0.8313	*0.8196*	0.8326	*0.8209*	0.8339	*0.8222*	0.8351	*0.8235*	0.8364	*0.8247*
11	8221	*8096*	8233	*8109*	8246	*8122*	8259	*8134*	8271	*8147*	8284	*8159*	8297	*8172*	8309	*8185*	8322	*8197*	8335	*8210*
12	8192	*8059*	8204	*8072*	8217	*8085*	8230	*8097*	8242	*8110*	8255	*8122*	8267	*8135*	8280	*8148*	8293	*8160*	8305	*8173*
13	8163	*8022*	8176	*8035*	8188	*8047*	8201	*8060*	8213	*8072*	8226	*8085*	8239	*8097*	8251	*8110*	8264	*8123*	8276	*8135*
14	8135	*7985*	8147	*7997*	8160	*8010*	8172	*8022*	8185	*8035*	8197	*8047*	8210	*8060*	8222	*8072*	8235	*8085*	8247	*8097*
15	0.8106	*0.7947*	0.8119	*0.7959*	0.8131	*0.7972*	0.8144	*0.7984*	0.8156	*0.7997*	0.8169	*0.8009*	0.8181	*0.8022*	0.8194	*0.8034*	0.8206	*0.8047*	0.8219	*0.8059*
16	8078	*7909*	8091	*7921*	8103	*7934*	8116	*7946*	8128	*7959*	8140	*7971*	8153	*7983*	8165	*7996*	8178	*8008*	8190	*8021*
17	8050	*7870*	8063	*7883*	8075	*7895*	8088	*7908*	8100	*7920*	8112	*7932*	8125	*7945*	8137	*7957*	8149	*7969*	8162	*7982*
18	8023	*7832*	8035	*7844*	8047	*7856*	8060	*7869*	8072	*7881*	8084	*7893*	8097	*7906*	8109	*7918*	8121	*7930*	8134	*7943*
19	7995	*7792*	8007	*7805*	8020	*7817*	8032	*7829*	8044	*7842*	8057	*7854*	8069	*7866*	8081	*7879*	8094	*7891*	8106	*7903*
20	0.7968	*0.7753*	0.7980	*0.7765*	0.7992	*0.7777*	0.8005	*0.7790*	0.8017	*0.7802*	0.8029	*0.7814*	0.8041	*0.7826*	0.8054	*0.7839*	0.8066	*0.7851*	0.8078	*0.7863*
21	7941	*7713*	7953	*7725*	7965	*7737*	7977	*7749*	7990	*7762*	8002	*7774*	8014	*7786*	8026	*7798*	8038	*7811*	8051	*7823*
22	7914	*7672*	7926	*7684*	7938	*7697*	7950	*7709*	7962	*7721*	7975	*7733*	7987	*7745*	7999	*7758*	8011	*7770*	8023	*7782*
23	7887	*7631*	7899	*7643*	7911	*7656*	7923	*7668*	7935	*7680*	7948	*7692*	7960	*7704*	7972	*7716*	7984	*7728*	7996	*7740*
24	7860	*7590*	7872	*7602*	7884	*7614*	7897	*7626*	7909	*7638*	7921	*7650*	7933	*7662*	7945	*7674*	7957	*7686*	7969	*7699*
25	0.7834	*0.7548*	0.7846	*0.7560*	0.7858	*0.7572*	0.7870	*0.7584*	0.7882	*0.7596*	0.7894	*0.7608*	0.7906	*0.7620*	0.7918	*0.7632*	0.7930	*0.7644*	0.7942	*0.7656*
26	7808	*7505*	7820	*7517*	7832	*7529*	7844	*7541*	7856	*7553*	7868	*7565*	7880	*7577*	7892	*7589*	7904	*7601*	7916	*7613*
27	7782	*7461*	7794	*7473*	7806	*7485*	7817	*7497*	7829	*7509*	7841	*7521*	7853	*7533*	7865	*7545*	7877	*7557*	7889	*7569*
28	7756	*7417*	7768	*7429*	7780	*7441*	7791	*7453*	7803	*7465*	7815	*7477*	7827	*7489*	7839	*7501*	7851	*7513*	7863	*7525*
29	7730	*7373*	7742	*7385*	7754	*7396*	7766	*7408*	7778	*7420*	7789	*7432*	7801	*7444*	7813	*7456*	7825	*7468*	7837	*7480*
30	0.7704	*0.7327*	0.7716	*0.7339*	0.7728	*0.7351*	0.7740	*0.7363*	0.7752	*0.7375*	0.7764	*0.7386*	0.7775	*0.7398*	0.7787	*0.7410*	0.7799	*0.7422*	0.7811	*0.7434*
31	7679	*7281*	7691	*7293*	7703	*7305*	7714	*7316*	7726	*7328*	7738	*7340*	7750	*7352*	7762	*7364*	7774	*7375*	7785	*7387*
32	7654	*7234*	7666	*7246*	7677	*7257*	7689	*7269*	7701	*7281*	7713	*7293*	7724	*7304*	7736	*7316*	7748	*7328*	7760	*7340*
33	7629	*7186*	7640	*7198*	7652	*7209*	7664	*7221*	7676	*7233*	7687	*7245*	7699	*7256*	7711	*7268*	7723	*7280*	7734	*7292*
34	7604	*7137*	7616	*7149*	7627	*7160*	7639	*7172*	7651	*7184*	7662	*7196*	7674	*7207*	7686	*7219*	7697	*7231*	7709	*7242*
35	0.7579	*0.7087*	0.7591	*0.7099*	0.7602	*0.7111*	0.7614	*0.7122*	0.7626	*0.7134*	0.7637	*0.7146*	0.7649	*0.7157*	0.7661	*0.7169*	0.7672	*0.7181*	0.7684	*0.7192*
36	7555	*7037*	7566	*7048*	7578	*7060*	7589	*7071*	7601	*7083*	7613	*7095*	7624	*7106*	7636	*7118*	7648	*7130*	7659	*7141*
37	7530	*6985*	7542	*6996*	7553	*7008*	7565	*7020*	7576	*7031*	7588	*7043*	7600	*7054*	7611	*7066*	7623	*7078*	7634	*7089*
38	7506	*6932*	7517	*6944*	7529	*6955*	7541	*6967*	7552	*6978*	7564	*6990*	7575	*7001*	7587	*7013*	7598	*7024*	7610	*7036*
39	7482	*6878*	7493	*6890*	7505	*6901*	7516	*6913*	7528	*6924*	7539	*6936*	7551	*6947*	7562	*6959*	7574	*6970*	7585	*6982*
40	0.7458	*0.6823*	0.7469	*0.6835*	0.7481	*0.6846*	0.7492	*0.6857*	0.7504	*0.6869*	0.7515	*0.6880*	0.7527	*0.6892*	0.7538	*0.6903*	0.7550	*0.6915*	0.7561	*0.6926*
41	7434	*6767*	7445	*6778*	7457	*6790*	7468	*6801*	7480	*6813*	7491	*6824*	7503	*6835*	7514	*6847*	7526	*6858*	7537	*6870*
42	7410	*6709*	7422	*6721*	7433	*6732*	7445	*6743*	7456	*6755*	7467	*6766*	7479	*6778*	7490	*6789*	7502	*6800*	7513	*6812*

P	660		661		662		663		664		665		666		667		668		669	
0	0.8684	*0.8624*	0.8697	*0.8637*	0.8711	*0.8650*	0.8724	*0.8663*	0.8737	*0.8677*	0.8750	*0.8690*	0.8763	*0.8703*	0.8776	*0.8716*	0.8789	*0.8729*	0.8803	*0.8742*
1	8652	*8588*	8666	*8601*	8679	*8614*	8692	*8627*	8705	*8640*	8718	*8653*	8731	*8667*	8744	*8680*	8757	*8693*	8770	*8706*
2	8621	*8552*	8634	*8565*	8647	*8578*	8660	*8591*	8673	*8604*	8686	*8617*	8699	*8630*	8712	*8643*	8725	*8656*	8738	*8669*
3	8590	*8516*	8603	*8529*	8616	*8542*	8629	*8555*	8642	*8568*	8655	*8581*	8668	*8594*	8681	*8607*	8694	*8620*	8707	*8633*
4	8559	*8479*	8572	*8492*	8585	*8505*	8597	*8518*	8610	*8531*	8623	*8544*	8636	*8557*	8649	*8570*	8662	*8583*	8675	*8596*
5	0.8528	*0.8443*	0.8541	*0.8056*	0.8554	*0.8469*	0.8566	*0.8482*	0.8579	*0.8495*	0.8592	*0.8508*	0.8605	*0.8521*	0.8618	*0.8534*	0.8631	*0.8547*	0.8644	*0.8559*
6	8497	*8407*	8510	*8420*	8523	*8433*	8536	*8445*	8549	*8458*	8561	*8471*	8574	*8484*	8587	*8497*	8600	*8510*	8613	*8523*
7	8467	*8370*	8480	*8383*	8492	*8396*	8505	*8409*	8518	*8422*	8531	*8434*	8544	*8447*	8556	*8460*	8569	*8473*	8582	*8486*
8	8437	*8334*	8449	*8346*	8462	*8359*	8475	*8372*	8488	*8385*	8500	*8398*	8513	*8410*	8526	*8423*	8539	*8436*	8552	*8449*
9	8407	*8297*	8419	*8310*	8432	*8322*	8445	*8335*	8457	*8348*	8470	*8361*	8483	*8373*	8496	*8386*	8508	*8399*	8521	*8412*
10	0.8377	*0.8260*	0.8389	*0.8273*	0.8402	*0.8285*	0.8415	*0.8298*	0.8428	*0.8311*	0.8440	*0.8323*	0.8453	*0.8336*	0.8466	*0.8349*	0.8478	*0.8361*	0.8491	*0.8374*
11	8347	*8223*	8360	*8235*	8373	*8248*	8385	*8261*	8398	*8273*	8410	*8286*	8423	*8299*	8436	*8311*	8448	*8324*	8461	*8337*
12	8318	*8185*	8330	*8198*	8343	*8211*	8356	*8223*	8368	*8236*	8381	*8248*	8394	*8261*	8406	*8274*	8419	*8286*	8431	*8299*
13	8289	*8148*	8301	*8160*	8314	*8173*	8326	*8185*	8339	*8198*	8352	*8211*	8364	*8223*	8377	*8236*	8389	*8248*	8402	*8261*
14	8260	*8110*	8272	*8122*	8285	*8135*	8297	*8147*	8310	*8160*	8322	*8172*	8335	*8185*	8347	*8197*	8360	*8210*	8372	*8222*
15	0.8231	*0.8072*	0.8244	*0.8084*	0.8256	*0.8097*	0.8269	*0.8109*	0.8281	*0.8121*	0.8293	*0.8134*	0.8306	*0.8146*	0.8318	*0.8159*	0.8331	*0.8171*	0.8343	*0.8184*
16	8203	*8033*	8215	*8046*	8227	*8058*	8240	*8070*	8252	*8083*	8265	*8095*	8277	*8108*	8290	*8120*	8302	*8133*	8314	*8145*
17	8174	*7994*	8187	*8007*	8199	*8019*	8211	*8031*	8224	*8044*	8236	*8056*	8249	*8069*	8261	*8081*	8273	*8093*	8286	*8106*
18	8146	*7955*	8158	*7967*	8171	*7980*	8183	*7992*	8195	*8004*	8208	*8017*	8220	*8029*	8232	*8041*	8245	*8054*	8257	*8066*
19	8118	*7915*	8130	*7928*	8143	*7940*	8155	*7952*	8167	*7965*	8180	*7977*	8192	*7989*	8204	*8002*	8217	*8014*	8229	*8026*
20	0.8090	*0.7875*	0.8103	*0.7888*	0.8115	*0.7900*	0.8127	*0.7912*	0.8139	*0.7924*	0.8152	*0.7937*	0.8164	*0.7949*	0.8176	*0.7961*	0.8188	*0.7973*	0.8201	*0.7986*
21	8063	*7835*	8075	*7847*	8087	*7859*	8099	*7872*	8112	*7884*	8124	*7896*	8136	*7908*	8148	*7920*	8161	*7933*	8173	*7945*
22	8035	*7794*	8048	*7806*	8060	*7818*	8072	*7831*	8084	*7843*	8096	*7855*	8108	*7867*	8121	*7879*	8133	*7891*	8145	*7904*
23	8008	*7753*	8020	*7765*	8033	*7777*	8045	*7789*	8057	*7801*	8069	*7813*	8081	*7825*	8093	*7838*	8105	*7850*	8117	*7862*
24	7981	*7711*	7993	*7723*	8005	*7735*	8018	*7747*	8030	*7759*	8042	*7771*	8054	*7783*	8066	*7795*	8078	*7807*	8090	*7819*
25	0.7954	*0.7668*	0.7966	*0.7680*	0.7978	*0.7692*	0.7991	*0.7704*	0.8003	*0.7716*	0.8015	*0.7728*	0.8027	*0.7740*	0.8039	*0.7752*	0.8051	*0.7765*	0.8063	*0.7777*
26	7928	*7625*	7940	*7637*	7952	*7649*	7964	*7661*	7976	*7673*	7988	*7685*	8000	*7697*	8012	*7709*	8024	*7721*	8036	*7733*
27	7901	*7581*	7913	*7593*	7925	*7605*	7937	*7617*	7949	*7629*	7961	*7641*	7973	*7653*	7985	*7665*	7997	*7677*	8009	*7689*
28	7875	*7537*	7887	*7549*	7899	*7561*	7911	*7573*	7923	*7584*	7935	*7596*	7947	*7608*	7959	*7620*	7970	*7632*	7982	*7644*
29	7849	*7492*	7861	*7503*	7873	*7515*	7885	*7527*	7896	*7539*	7908	*7551*	7920	*7563*	7932	*7575*	7944	*7587*	7956	*7599*
30	0.7823	*0.7446*	0.7835	*0.7458*	0.7847	*0.7469*	0.7858	*0.7481*	0.7870	*0.7493*	0.7882	*0.7505*	0.7894	*0.7517*	0.7906	*0.7529*	0.7918	*0.7541*	0.7930	*0.7552*
31	7797	*7399*	7809	*7411*	7821	*7423*	7833	*7435*	7844	*7446*	7856	*7458*	7868	*7470*	7880	*7482*	7892	*7494*	7903	*7505*
32	7772	*7352*	7783	*7363*	7795	*7375*	7807	*7387*	7819	*7399*	7830	*7410*	7842	*7422*	7854	*7434*	7866	*7446*	7877	*7458*
33	7746	*7303*	7758	*7315*	7770	*7327*	7781	*7338*	7793	*7350*	7805	*7362*	7817	*7374*	7828	*7385*	7840	*7397*	7852	*7409*
34	7721	*7254*	7733	*7266*	7744	*7277*	7756	*7289*	7768	*7301*	7779	*7313*	7791	*7324*	7803	*7336*	7814	*7348*	7826	*7359*
35	0.7696	*0.7204*	0.7707	*0.7216*	0.7719	*0.7227*	0.7731	*0.7239*	0.7742	*0.7251*	0.7754	*0.7262*	0.7766	*0.7274*	0.7777	*0.7286*	0.7789	*0.7297*	0.7801	*0.7309*
36	7671	*7153*	7682	*7164*	7694	*7176*	7706	*7188*	7717	*7199*	7729	*7211*	7740	*7223*	7752	*7234*	7764	*7246*	7775	*7257*
37	7646	*7101*	7658	*7112*	7669	*7124*	7681	*7135*	7692	*7147*	7704	*7159*	7715	*7170*	7727	*7182*	7739	*7193*	7750	*7205*
38	7621	*7048*	7633	*7059*	7644	*7071*	7656	*7082*	7668	*7094*	7679	*7105*	7691	*7117*	7702	*7128*	7714	*7140*	7725	*7151*
39	7597	*6993*	7608	*7005*	7620	*7016*	7631	*7028*	7643	*7039*	7654	*7051*	7666	*7062*	7677	*7074*	7689	*7085*	7700	*7097*
40	0.7573	*0.6938*	0.7584	*0.6949*	0.7596	*0.6961*	0.7607	*0.6972*	0.7618	*0.6984*	0.7630	*0.6995*	0.7641	*0.7007*	0.7653	*0.7018*	0.7664	*0.7030*	0.7676	*0.0741*
41	7548	*6881*	7560	*6893*	7571	*6904*	7583	*6915*	7594	*6927*	7606	*6938*	7617	*6950*	7628	*6961*	7640	*6973*	7651	*6984*
42	7524	*6823*	7536	*6835*	7547	*6846*	7559	*6857*	7570	*6869*	7581	*6880*	7593	*6892*	7604	*6903*	7616	*6914*	7627	*6926*

P	670		671		672		673		674		675		676		677		678		679	
°C	dry	sat.	dry	sat.	dry	sat.	dry	sat.	dry	sat.	dry	sat.	dry	sat.	dry	sat.	dry	sat.	dry	sat.
0	0.8816	0.8756	0.8829	0.8769	0.8842	0.8782	0.8855	0.8795	0.8868	0.8808	0.8882	0.8821	0.8895	0.8834	0.8908	0.8848	0.8921	0.8861	0.8934	0.8874
1	8784	8719	8797	8732	8810	8745	8823	8758	8836	8771	8849	8785	8862	8798	8875	8811	8888	8824	8902	8837
2	8752	8682	8765	8695	8778	8709	8791	8722	8804	8735	8817	8748	8830	8761	8843	8774	8856	8787	8869	8800
3	8720	8646	8733	8659	8746	8672	8759	8685	8772	8698	8785	8711	8798	8724	8811	8737	8824	8750	8837	8763
4	8688	8609	8701	8622	8714	8635	8727	8648	8740	8661	8753	8674	8766	8687	8779	8700	8792	8713	8805	8726
5	0.8657	0.8572	0.8670	0.8585	0.8683	0.8598	0.8696	0.8611	0.8709	0.8624	0.8722	0.8637	0.8734	0.8650	0.8747	0.8663	0.8760	0.8676	0.8773	0.8689
6	8626	8536	8639	8548	8652	8561	8664	8574	8677	8587	8690	8600	8703	8613	8716	8626	8729	8639	8742	8651
7	8595	8499	8608	8511	8621	8524	8633	8537	8646	8550	8659	8563	8672	8576	8685	8588	8698	8601	8710	8614
8	8564	8462	8577	8474	8590	8487	8603	8500	8615	8513	8628	8525	8641	8538	8654	8551	8667	8564	8679	8577
9	8534	8424	8547	8437	8559	8450	8572	8462	8585	8475	8598	8488	8610	8501	8623	8513	8636	8526	8649	8539
10	0.8504	0.8387	0.8516	0.8400	0.8529	0.8412	0.8542	0.8425	0.8554	0.8438	0.8567	0.8450	0.8580	0.8463	0.8593	0.8476	0.8605	0.8488	0.8618	0.8501
11	8474	8349	8486	8362	8499	8375	8512	8387	8524	8400	8537	8412	8550	8425	8562	8438	8575	8450	8588	8463
12	8444	8311	8457	8324	8469	8337	8482	8349	8494	8362	8507	8374	8520	8387	8532	8400	8545	8412	8557	8425
13	8414	8273	8427	8286	8439	8298	8452	8311	8465	8324	8477	8336	8490	8349	8502	8361	8515	8374	8527	8386
14	8385	8235	8397	8247	8410	8260	8423	8272	8435	8285	8448	8298	8460	8310	8473	8323	8485	8335	8498	8348
15	0.8356	0.8196	0.8368	0.8209	0.8381	0.8221	0.8393	0.8234	0.8406	0.8246	0.8418	0.8259	0.8431	0.8271	0.8443	0.8284	0.8456	0.8296	0.8468	0.8309
16	8327	8157	8339	8170	8352	8182	8364	8195	8377	8207	8389	8220	8401	8232	8414	8244	8426	8257	8439	8269
17	8298	8118	8310	8131	8323	8143	8335	8155	8348	8168	8360	8180	8372	8192	8385	8205	8397	8217	8410	8230
18	8270	8078	8282	8091	8294	8103	8307	8116	8319	8128	8331	8140	8344	8153	8356	8165	8368	8177	8381	8190
19	8241	8038	8253	8051	8266	8063	8278	8075	8290	8088	8303	8100	8315	8112	8327	8125	8340	8137	8352	8149
20	0.8213	0.7998	0.8225	0.8010	0.8237	0.8023	0.8250	0.8035	0.8262	0.8047	0.8274	0.8059	0.8287	0.8072	0.8299	0.8084	0.8311	0.8096	0.8323	0.8108
21	8185	7957	8197	7969	8209	7982	8222	7994	8234	8006	8246	8018	8258	8030	8270	8043	8283	8055	8295	8067
22	8157	7916	8169	7928	8182	7940	8194	7952	8206	7964	8218	7977	8230	7989	8242	8001	8255	8013	8267	8025
23	8130	7874	8142	7886	8154	7898	8166	7910	8178	7922	8190	7935	8202	7947	8215	7959	8227	7971	8239	7983
24	8102	7832	8114	7844	8126	7856	8138	7868	8151	7880	8163	7892	8175	7904	8187	7916	8199	7928	8211	7940
25	0.8075	0.7789	0.8087	0.7801	0.8099	0.7813	0.8111	0.7825	0.8123	0.7837	0.8135	0.7849	0.8147	0.7861	0.8159	0.7873	0.8171	0.7885	0.8183	0.7897
26	8048	7745	8060	7757	8072	7769	8084	7781	8096	7793	8108	7805	8120	7817	8132	7829	8144	7841	8156	7853
27	8021	7701	8033	7713	8045	7725	8057	7737	8069	7749	8081	7761	8093	7773	8105	7785	8117	7797	8129	7809
28	7994	7656	8006	7668	8018	7680	8030	7692	8042	7704	8054	7716	8066	7728	8078	7740	8090	7751	8102	7763
29	7968	7611	7980	7622	7992	7634	8003	7646	8015	7658	8027	7670	8039	7682	8051	7694	8063	7706	8075	7718
30	0.7941	0.7564	0.7953	0.7576	0.7965	0.7588	0.7977	0.7600	0.7989	0.7612	0.8001	0.7623	0.8013	0.7635	0.8024	0.7647	0.8036	0.7659	0.8048	0.7671
31	7915	7517	7927	7529	7939	7541	7951	7553	7963	7564	7974	7576	7986	7588	7998	7600	8010	7612	8022	7624
32	7889	7469	7901	7481	7913	7493	7925	7505	7936	7516	7948	7528	7960	7540	7972	7552	7983	7564	7995	7575
33	7863	7421	7875	7432	7887	7444	7899	7456	7910	7468	7922	7479	7934	7491	7946	7503	7957	7515	7969	7526
34	7838	7371	7849	7383	7861	7394	7873	7406	7885	7418	7896	7430	7908	7441	7920	7453	7931	7465	7943	7476
35	0.7812	0.7321	0.7824	0.7332	0.7836	0.7344	0.7847	0.7356	0.7859	0.7367	0.7871	0.7379	0.7882	0.7390	0.7894	0.7402	0.7906	0.7414	0.7917	0.7425
36	7787	7269	7799	7281	7810	7292	7822	7304	7833	7316	7845	7327	7857	7339	7868	7350	7880	7362	7892	7374
37	7762	7217	7773	7228	7785	7240	7797	7251	7808	7263	7820	7274	7831	7286	7843	7298	7854	7309	7866	7321
38	7737	7163	7748	7175	7760	7186	7771	7198	7783	7209	7795	7221	7806	7232	7818	7244	7829	7255	7841	7267
39	7712	7108	7723	7120	7735	7131	7747	7143	7758	7154	7770	7166	7781	7177	7793	7189	7804	7200	7816	7212
40	0.7687	0.7053	0.7699	0.7064	0.7710	0.7075	0.7722	0.7087	0.7733	0.7098	0.7745	0.7110	0.7756	0.7121	0.7768	0.7133	0.7779	0.7144	0.7791	0.7156
41	7663	6996	7674	7007	7686	7018	7697	7030	7709	7041	7720	7053	7731	7064	7743	7076	7754	7087	7766	7098
42	7638	6937	7650	6949	7661	6960	7673	6971	7684	6983	7695	6994	7707	7006	7718	7017	7730	7028	7741	7040

P	680		681		682		683		684		685		686		687		688		689	
°C	dry	sat.	dry	sat.	dry	sat.	dry	sat.	dry	sat.	dry	sat.	dry	sat.	dry	sat.	dry	sat.	dry	sat.
0	0.8947	0.8887	0.8961	0.8900	0.8974	0.8913	0.8987	0.8927	0.9000	0.8940	0.9013	0.8953	0.9026	0.8966	0.9039	0.8979	0.9053	0.8992	0.9066	0.9006
1	8915	8850	8928	8863	8941	8876	8954	8889	8967	8903	8980	8916	8993	8929	9006	8942	9020	8955	9033	8968
2	8882	8813	8895	8826	8908	8839	8921	8852	8934	8865	8947	8878	8961	8891	8974	8904	8987	8918	9000	8931
3	8850	8776	8863	8789	8876	8802	8889	8815	8902	8828	8915	8841	8928	8854	8941	8867	8954	8880	8967	8893
4	8818	8739	8831	8752	8844	8765	8857	8778	8870	8791	8883	8804	8896	8817	8909	8830	8922	8843	8935	8856
5	0.8786	0.8702	0.8799	0.8715	0.8812	0.8727	0.8825	0.8740	0.8838	0.8753	0.8851	0.8766	0.8864	0.8779	0.8877	0.8792	0.8890	0.8805	0.8902	0.8818
6	8755	8664	8767	8677	8780	8690	8793	8703	8806	8716	8819	8729	8832	8742	8845	8754	8858	8767	8870	8780
7	8723	8627	8736	8640	8749	8653	8762	8665	8775	8678	8787	8691	8800	8704	8813	8717	8826	8730	8839	8742
8	8692	8589	8705	8602	8718	8615	8731	8628	8743	8640	8756	8653	8769	8666	8782	8679	8794	8692	8807	8704
9	8661	8552	8674	8564	8687	8577	8699	8590	8712	8603	8725	8615	8738	8628	8750	8641	8763	8654	8776	8666
10	0.8631	0.8514	0.8643	0.8526	0.8656	0.8539	0.8669	0.8552	0.8681	0.8565	0.8694	0.8577	0.8707	0.8590	0.8719	0.8603	0.8732	0.8615	0.8745	0.8628
11	8600	8476	8613	8488	8625	8501	8638	8514	8651	8526	8663	8539	8676	8552	8689	8564	8701	8577	8714	8590
12	8570	8437	8583	8450	8595	8463	8608	8475	8620	8488	8633	8500	8646	8513	8658	8526	8671	8538	8683	8551
13	8540	8399	8552	8411	8565	8424	8578	8437	8590	8449	8603	8462	8615	8474	8628	8487	8640	8499	8653	8512
14	8510	8360	8523	8373	8535	8385	8548	8398	8560	8410	8573	8423	8585	8435	8598	8448	8610	8460	8623	8473
15	0.8481	0.8321	0.8493	0.8334	0.8505	0.8346	0.8518	0.8358	0.8530	0.8371	0.8543	0.8383	0.8555	0.8396	0.8568	0.8408	0.8580	0.8421	0.8593	0.8433
16	8451	8282	8464	8294	8476	8307	8488	8319	8501	8331	8513	8344	8526	8356	8538	8369	8551	8381	8563	8394
17	8422	8242	8434	8254	8447	8267	8459	8279	8471	8292	8484	8304	8496	8316	8509	8329	8521	8341	8533	8353
18	8393	8202	8405	8214	8418	8227	8430	8239	8442	8251	8455	8264	8467	8276	8479	8288	8492	8301	8504	8313
19	8364	8161	8376	8174	8389	8186	8401	8198	8413	8211	8426	8223	8438	8235	8450	8248	8463	8260	8475	8272
20	0.8336	0.8121	0.8348	0.8133	0.8360	0.8145	0.8372	0.8157	0.8385	0.8170	0.8397	0.8182	0.8409	0.8194	0.8421	0.8206	0.8434	0.8219	0.8446	0.8231
21	8307	8079	8319	8092	8332	8104	8344	8116	8356	8128	8368	8140	8380	8153	8393	8165	8405	8177	8417	8189
22	8279	8038	8291	8050	8303	8062	8315	8074	8328	8086	8340	8098	8352	8111	8364	8123	8376	8135	8389	8147
23	8251	7995	8263	8007	8275	8020	8287	8032	8299	8044	8312	8056	8324	8068	8336	8080	8348	8092	8360	8104
24	8223	7952	8235	7965	8247	7977	8259	7989	8271	8001	8284	8013	8296	8025	8308	8037	8320	8049	8332	8061
25	0.8195	0.7909	0.8207	0.7921	0.8220	0.7933	0.8232	0.7945	0.8244	0.7957	0.8256	0.7969	0.8268	0.7981	0.8280	0.7993	0.8292	0.8006	0.8304	0.8018
26	8168	7865	8180	7877	8192	7889	8204	7901	8216	7913	8228	7925	8240	7937	8252	7949	8264	7961	8276	7973
27	8141	7821	8153	7833	8165	7845	8177	7857	8189	7868	8201	7880	8213	7892	8225	7904	8236	7916	8248	7928
28	8114	7775	8126	7787	8137	7799	8149	7811	8161	7823	8173	7835	8185	7847	8197	7859	8209	7871	8221	7883
29	8087	7729	8099	7741	8110	7753	8122	7765	8134	7777	8146	7789	8158	7801	8170	7813	8182	7825	8194	7836
30	0.8060	0.7683	0.8072	0.7695	0.8084	0.7706	0.8096	0.7718	0.8107	0.7730	0.8119	0.7742	0.8131	0.7754	0.8143	0.7766	0.8155	0.7778	0.8167	0.7789
31	8033	7635	8045	7647	8057	7659	8069	7671	8081	7683	8092	7694	8104	7706	8116	7718	8128	7730	8140	7742
32	8007	7587	8019	7599	8031	7611	8042	7622	8054	7634	8066	7646	8078	7658	8089	7670	8101	7681	8113	7693
33	7981	7538	7993	7550	8004	7561	8016	7573	8028	7585	8039	7597	8051	7608	8063	7620	8075	7632	8086	7644
34	7955	7488	7966	7500	7978	7511	7990	7523	8002	7535	8013	7547	8025	7558	8037	7570	8048	7582	8060	7593
35	0.7929	0.7437	0.7941	0.7449	0.7952	0.7460	0.7964	0.7472	0.7976	0.7484	0.7987	0.7495	0.7999	0.7507	0.8011	0.7519	0.8022	0.7530	0.8034	0.7542
36	7903	7385	7915	7397	7926	7409	7938	7420	7950	7432	7961	7443	7973	7455	7985	7467	7996	7478	8008	7490
37	7878	7332	7889	7344	7901	7356	7912	7367	7924	7379	7936	7390	7947	7402	7959	7413	7970	7425	7982	7437
38	7852	7278	7864	7290	7875	7302	7887	7313	7898	7325	7910	7336	7922	7348	7933	7359	7945	7371	7956	7382
39	7827	7223	7839	7235	7850	7246	7862	7258	7873	7269	7885	7281	7896	7293	7908	7304	7919	7316	7931	7327
40	0.7802	0.7167	0.7814	0.7179	0.7825	0.7190	0.7836	0.7202	0.7848	0.7213	0.7859	0.7225	0.7871	0.7236	0.7882	0.7248	0.7894	0.7259	0.7905	0.7271
41	7777	7110	7789	7121	7800	7133	7811	7144	7823	7156	7834	7167	7846	7179	7857	7190	7869	7201	7880	7213
42	7752	7051	7764	7063	7775	7074	7787	7085	7798	7097	7809	7108	7821	7120	7832	7131	7844	7142	7855	7154

Reduction of Gas Volumes (continued)

P / °C	690 dry	690 sat.	691 dry	691 sat.	692 dry	692 sat.	693 dry	693 sat.	694 dry	694 sat.	695 dry	695 sat.	696 dry	696 sat.	697 dry	697 sat.	698 dry	698 sat.	699 dry	699 sat.
0	0.9079	0.9019	0.9092	0.9032	0.9105	0.9045	0.9118	0.9058	0.9132	0.9071	0.9145	0.9084	0.9158	0.9098	0.9171	0.9111	0.9184	0.9124	0.9197	0.9137
1	9046	8981	9059	8994	9072	9007	9085	9020	9098	9034	9111	9047	9124	9060	9138	9073	9151	9086	9164	9099
2	9013	8944	9026	8957	9039	8970	9052	8983	9065	8996	9078	9009	9091	9022	9104	9035	9117	9048	9130	9061
3	8980	8906	8993	8919	9006	8932	9019	8945	9032	8958	9045	8971	9058	8984	9071	8997	9084	9010	9097	9023
4	8948	8868	8961	8881	8974	8894	8986	8907	8999	8920	9012	8933	9025	8946	9038	8959	9051	8972	9064	8985
5	0.8915	0.8831	0.8928	0.8844	0.8941	0.8857	0.8954	0.8870	0.8967	0.8882	0.8980	0.8895	0.8993	0.8908	0.9006	0.8921	0.9019	0.8934	0.9032	0.8947
6	8883	8793	8896	8806	8909	8819	8922	8832	8935	8845	8948	8857	8961	8870	8973	8883	8986	8896	8999	8909
7	8852	8755	8864	8768	8877	8781	8890	8794	8903	8806	8916	8819	8929	8832	8941	8845	8954	8858	8967	8871
8	8820	8717	8833	8730	8846	8743	8858	8756	8871	8768	8884	8781	8897	8794	8909	8807	8922	8819	8935	8832
9	8789	8679	8801	8692	8814	8704	8827	8717	8840	8730	8852	8743	8865	8755	8878	8768	8891	8781	8903	8794
10	0.8758	0.8641	0.8770	0.8653	0.8783	0.8666	0.8796	0.8679	0.8808	0.8691	0.8821	0.8704	0.8834	0.8717	0.8846	0.8730	0.8859	0.8742	0.8872	0.8755
11	8727	8602	8739	8615	8752	8627	8765	8640	8777	8653	8790	8665	8803	8678	8815	8691	8828	8703	8840	8716
12	8696	8563	8709	8576	8721	8589	8734	8601	8746	8614	8759	8626	8772	8639	8784	8652	8797	8664	8809	8677
13	8666	8524	8678	8537	8691	8550	8703	8562	8716	8575	8728	8587	8741	8600	8753	8612	8766	8625	8779	8637
14	8635	8485	8648	8498	8660	8510	8673	8523	8685	8535	8698	8548	8710	8560	8723	8573	8735	8585	8748	8598
15	0.8605	0.8446	0.8618	0.8458	0.8630	0.8471	0.8643	0.8483	0.8655	0.8496	0.8668	0.8508	0.8680	0.8521	0.8693	0.8533	0.8705	0.8546	0.8717	0.8558
16	8575	8406	8588	8418	8600	8431	8613	8443	8625	8456	8638	8468	8650	8481	8662	8493	8675	8505	8687	8518
17	8546	8366	8558	8378	8571	8391	8583	8403	8595	8415	8608	8428	8620	8440	8632	8453	8645	8465	8657	8477
18	8516	8325	8529	8338	8541	8350	8553	8362	8566	8375	8578	8387	8590	8399	8603	8412	8615	8424	8627	8436
19	8487	8284	8499	8297	8512	8309	8524	8321	8536	8334	8549	8346	8561	8358	8573	8371	8586	8383	8598	8395
20	0.8458	0.8243	0.8470	0.8255	0.8483	0.8268	0.8495	0.8280	0.8507	0.8292	0.8519	0.8304	0.8532	0.8317	0.8544	0.8329	0.8556	0.8341	0.8568	0.8353
21	8429	8201	8442	8214	8454	8226	8466	8238	8478	8250	8490	8263	8503	8275	8515	8287	8527	8299	8539	8311
22	8401	8159	8413	8171	8425	8184	8437	8196	8449	8208	8462	8220	8474	8232	8486	8245	8498	8257	8510	8269
23	8372	8117	8384	8129	8397	8141	8409	8153	8421	8165	8433	8177	8445	8189	8457	8202	8469	8214	8481	8226
24	8344	8073	8356	8086	8368	8098	8380	8110	8392	8122	8404	8134	8417	8146	8429	8158	8441	8170	8453	8182
25	0.8316	0.8030	0.8328	0.8042	0.8340	0.8054	0.8352	0.8066	0.8364	0.8078	0.8376	0.8090	0.8388	0.8102	0.8400	0.8114	0.8412	0.8126	0.8424	0.8138
26	8288	7985	8300	7997	8312	8009	8324	8021	8336	8033	8348	8045	8360	8057	8372	8069	8384	8081	8396	8093
27	8260	7940	8272	7952	8284	7964	8296	7976	8308	7988	8320	8000	8332	8012	8344	8024	8356	8036	8368	8048
28	8233	7895	8245	7907	8257	7919	8269	7930	8281	7942	8293	7954	8305	7966	8316	7978	8328	7990	8340	8002
29	8206	7848	8218	7860	8229	7872	8241	7884	8253	7896	8265	7908	8277	7920	8289	7932	8301	7943	8313	7955
30	0.8178	0.7801	0.8190	0.7813	0.8202	0.7825	0.8214	0.7837	0.8226	0.7849	0.8238	0.7861	0.8250	0.7872	0.8261	0.7884	0.8273	0.7896	0.8285	0.7908
31	8152	7753	8163	7765	8175	7777	8187	7789	8199	7801	8211	7813	8222	7824	8234	7836	8246	7848	8258	7860
32	8125	7705	8137	7717	8148	7728	8160	7740	8172	7752	8184	7764	8195	7775	8207	7787	8219	7799	8231	7811
33	8098	7655	8110	7667	8122	7679	8133	7691	8145	7702	8157	7714	8169	7726	8180	7738	8192	7749	8204	7761
34	8072	7605	8083	7617	8095	7628	8107	7640	8119	7652	8130	7664	8142	7675	8154	7687	8165	7699	8177	7710
35	0.8046	0.7554	0.8057	0.7565	0.8069	0.7577	0.8080	0.7589	0.8092	0.7600	0.8104	0.7612	0.8115	0.7624	0.8127	0.7635	0.8139	0.7647	0.8150	0.7659
36	8019	7501	8031	7513	8043	7525	8054	7536	8066	7548	8078	7560	8089	7571	8101	7583	8112	7594	8124	7606
37	7994	7448	8005	7460	8017	7471	8028	7483	8040	7495	8051	7506	8063	7518	8075	7529	8086	7541	8098	7553
38	7968	7394	7979	7405	7991	7417	8002	7429	8014	7440	8026	7452	8037	7463	8049	7475	8060	7486	8072	7498
39	7942	7339	7954	7350	7965	7362	7977	7373	7988	7385	8000	7396	8011	7408	8023	7419	8034	7431	8046	7442
40	0.7917	0.7282	0.7928	0.7293	0.7940	0.7305	0.7951	0.7316	0.7963	0.7328	0.7974	0.7339	0.7986	0.7351	0.7997	0.7362	0.8009	0.7374	0.8020	0.7385
41	7892	7224	7903	7236	7914	7247	7926	7259	7937	7270	7949	7281	7960	7293	7972	7304	7983	7316	7994	7327
42	7866	7165	7878	7177	7889	7188	7901	7199	7912	7211	7923	7222	7935	7234	7946	7245	7958	7256	7969	7268

P / °C	700 dry	700 sat.	701 dry	701 sat.	702 dry	702 sat.	703 dry	703 sat.	704 dry	704 sat.	705 dry	705 sat.	706 dry	706 sat.	707 dry	707 sat.	708 dry	708 sat.	709 dry	709 sat.
0	0.9211	0.9150	0.9224	0.9163	0.9237	0.9177	0.9250	0.9190	0.9263	0.9203	0.9276	0.9216	0.9289	0.9229	0.9303	0.9242	0.9316	0.9256	0.9329	0.9269
1	9177	9112	9190	9125	9203	9138	9216	9152	9229	9165	9242	9178	9256	9191	9269	9204	9282	9217	9295	9230
2	9143	9074	9156	9087	9170	9100	9183	9113	9196	9127	9209	9140	9222	9153	9235	9166	9248	9179	9261	9192
3	9110	9036	9123	9049	9136	9062	9149	9075	9162	9088	9175	9101	9188	9114	9201	9127	9214	9140	9227	9153
4	9077	8998	9090	9011	9103	9024	9116	9037	9129	9050	9142	9063	9155	9076	9168	9089	9181	9102	9194	9115
5	0.9045	0.8960	0.9057	0.8973	0.9070	0.8986	0.9083	0.8999	0.9096	0.9012	0.9109	0.9025	0.9122	0.9038	0.9135	0.9050	0.9148	0.9063	0.9161	0.9076
6	9012	8922	9025	8935	9038	8948	9051	8960	9064	8973	9076	8986	9089	8999	9102	9012	9115	9025	9128	9038
7	8980	8883	8993	8896	9005	8909	9018	8922	9031	8935	9044	8948	9057	8960	9070	8973	9082	8986	9095	8999
8	8948	8845	8961	8858	8973	8871	8986	8883	8999	8896	9012	8909	9025	8922	9037	8934	9050	8947	9063	8960
9	8916	8806	8929	8819	8942	8832	8954	8845	8967	8857	8980	8870	8992	8883	9005	8896	9018	8908	9031	8921
10	0.8884	0.8768	0.8897	0.8780	0.8910	0.8793	0.8923	0.8806	0.8935	0.8818	0.8948	0.8831	0.8961	0.8844	0.8973	0.8856	0.8986	0.8869	0.8999	0.8882
11	8853	8729	8866	8741	8878	8754	8891	8767	8904	8779	8916	8792	8929	8805	8942	8817	8954	8830	8967	8842
12	8822	8689	8835	8702	8847	8715	8860	8727	8872	8740	8885	8752	8898	8765	8910	8778	8923	8790	8935	8803
13	8791	8650	8804	8663	8816	8675	8829	8688	8841	8700	8854	8713	8866	8725	8879	8738	8892	8751	8904	8763
14	8760	8610	8773	8623	8785	8635	8798	8648	8810	8660	8823	8673	8836	8685	8848	8698	8861	8711	8873	8723
15	0.8730	0.8570	0.8742	0.8583	0.8755	0.8595	0.8767	0.8608	0.8780	0.8620	0.8792	0.8633	0.8805	0.8645	0.8817	0.8658	0.8830	0.8670	0.8842	0.8683
16	8700	8530	8712	8543	8725	8555	8737	8568	8749	8580	8762	8592	8774	8605	8787	8617	8799	8630	8812	8642
17	8670	8490	8682	8502	8694	8514	8707	8527	8719	8539	8732	8552	8744	8564	8756	8576	8769	8589	8781	8601
18	8640	8449	8652	8461	8664	8473	8677	8486	8689	8498	8701	8510	8714	8523	8726	8535	8739	8547	8751	8560
19	8610	8407	8622	8420	8635	8432	8647	8444	8659	8457	8672	8469	8684	8481	8696	8494	8709	8506	8721	8518
20	0.8581	0.8366	0.8593	0.8378	0.8605	0.8390	0.8617	0.8403	0.8630	0.8415	0.8642	0.8427	0.8654	0.8439	0.8667	0.8452	0.8679	0.8464	0.8691	0.8476
21	8551	8324	8564	8336	8576	8348	8588	8360	8600	8372	8613	8385	8625	8397	8637	8409	8649	8421	8661	8434
22	8522	8281	8535	8293	8547	8305	8559	8318	8571	8330	8583	8342	8595	8354	8608	8366	8620	8378	8632	8391
23	8494	8238	8506	8250	8518	8262	8530	8274	8542	8286	8554	8299	8566	8311	8579	8323	8591	8335	8603	8347
24	8465	8194	8477	8206	8489	8219	8501	8231	8513	8243	8525	8255	8537	8267	8550	8279	8562	8291	8574	8303
25	0.8436	0.8150	0.8449	0.8162	0.8461	0.8174	0.8473	0.8186	0.8485	0.8198	0.8497	0.8210	0.8509	0.8222	0.8521	0.8235	0.8533	0.8247	0.8545	0.8259
26	8408	8105	8420	8117	8432	8129	8444	8141	8456	8153	8468	8165	8480	8178	8492	8189	8504	8202	8516	8214
27	8380	8060	8392	8072	8404	8084	8416	8096	8428	8108	8440	8120	8452	8132	8464	8144	8476	8156	8488	8168
28	8352	8014	8364	8026	8376	8038	8388	8050	8400	8062	8412	8074	8424	8086	8436	8098	8448	8109	8460	8121
29	8325	7967	8336	7979	8348	7991	8360	8003	8372	8015	8384	8027	8396	8039	8408	8051	8420	8062	8432	8074
30	0.8297	0.7920	0.8309	0.7932	0.8321	0.7944	0.8333	0.7955	0.8344	0.7967	0.8356	0.7979	0.8368	0.7991	0.8380	0.8003	0.8392	0.8015	0.8404	0.8026
31	8270	7872	8281	7883	8293	7895	8305	7907	8317	7919	8329	7931	8341	7943	8352	7954	8364	7966	8376	7978
32	8243	7823	8254	7834	8266	7846	8278	7858	8290	7870	8301	7881	8313	7893	8325	7905	8337	7917	8348	7929
33	8216	7773	8227	7784	8239	7796	8251	7808	8262	7820	8274	7831	8286	7843	8298	7855	8309	7867	8321	7878
34	8189	7722	8200	7734	8212	7745	8224	7757	8236	7769	8247	7780	8259	7792	8271	7804	8282	7816	8294	7827
35	0.8162	0.7670	0.8174	0.7682	0.8185	0.7694	0.8197	0.7705	0.8209	0.7717	0.8220	0.7729	0.8232	0.7740	0.8244	0.7752	0.8255	0.7764	0.8267	0.7775
36	8136	7618	8147	7629	8159	7641	8171	7653	8182	7664	8194	7676	8205	7687	8217	7699	8229	7711	8240	7722
37	8109	7564	8121	7576	8133	7587	8144	7599	8156	7610	8167	7622	8179	7634	8190	7645	8202	7657	8214	7668
38	8083	7509	8095	7521	8106	7533	8118	7544	8129	7556	8141	7567	8153	7579	8164	7590	8176	7602	8187	7613
39	8057	7454	8069	7465	8080	7477	8092	7488	8103	7500	8115	7511	8126	7523	8138	7534	8149	7546	8161	7557
40	0.8032	0.7397	0.8043	0.7408	0.8054	0.7420	0.8066	0.7431	0.8077	0.7443	0.8089	0.7454	0.8100	0.7466	0.8112	0.7477	0.8123	0.7489	0.8135	0.7500
41	8006	7339	8017	7350	8029	7362	8040	7373	8052	7384	8063	7396	8075	7407	8086	7419	8097	7430	8109	7442
42	7980	7279	7992	7291	8003	7302	8015	7313	8026	7325	8037	7336	8049	7348	8060	7359	8072	7370	8083	7382

P °C	710 dry	710 sat.	711 dry	711 sat.	712 dry	712 sat.	713 dry	713 sat.	714 dry	714 sat.	715 dry	715 sat.	716 dry	716 sat.	717 dry	717 sat.	718 dry	718 sat.	719 dry	719 sat.
0	0.9342	0.9282	0.9355	0.9295	0.9368	0.9308	0.9382	0.9321	0.9395	0.9334	0.9408	0.9348	0.9421	0.9361	0.9434	0.9374	0.9447	0.9387	0.9461	0.9400
1	9308	9243	9321	9256	9334	9270	9347	9283	9360	9296	9373	9309	9387	9322	9400	9335	9413	9348	9426	9361
2	9274	9205	9287	9218	9300	9231	9313	9244	9326	9257	9339	9270	9352	9283	9365	9296	9379	9309	9392	9322
3	9240	9166	9253	9179	9266	9192	9279	9205	9292	9218	9305	9231	9318	9244	9331	9257	9344	9270	9358	9284
4	9207	9128	9220	9141	9233	9154	9246	9167	9259	9180	9272	9193	9285	9206	9298	9219	9311	9232	9324	9245
5	0.9174	0.9089	0.9187	0.9102	0.9200	0.9115	0.9213	0.9128	0.9225	0.9141	0.9238	0.9154	0.9251	0.9167	0.9264	0.9180	0.9277	0.9193	0.9290	0.9206
6	9141	9051	9154	9063	9167	9076	9179	9089	9192	9102	9205	9115	9218	9128	9231	9141	9244	9154	9257	9166
7	9108	9012	9121	9025	9134	9037	9147	9050	9159	9063	9172	9076	9185	9089	9198	9102	9211	9114	9224	9127
8	9076	8973	9088	8986	9101	8998	9114	9011	9127	9024	9140	9037	9152	9050	9165	9062	9178	9075	9191	9088
9	9043	8934	9056	8946	9069	8959	9082	8972	9094	8985	9107	8997	9120	9010	9133	9023	9145	9036	9158	9048
10	0.9011	0.8895	0.9024	0.8907	0.9037	0.8920	0.9049	0.8933	0.9062	0.8945	0.9075	0.8958	0.9088	0.8971	0.9100	0.8983	0.9113	0.8996	0.9126	0.9009
11	8980	8855	8992	8868	9005	8880	9018	8893	9030	8906	9043	8918	9055	8931	9068	8944	9081	8956	9093	8969
12	8948	8815	8961	8828	8973	8841	8986	8853	8998	8866	9011	8878	9024	8891	9036	8904	9049	8916	9061	8929
13	8917	8776	8929	8788	8942	8801	8954	8813	8967	8826	8979	8838	8992	8851	9005	8864	9017	8876	9030	8889
14	8886	8736	8898	8748	8911	8761	8923	8773	8936	8786	8948	8798	8961	8811	8973	8823	8986	8836	8998	8848
15	0.8855	0.8695	0.8867	0.8708	0.8880	0.8720	0.8892	0.8733	0.8905	0.8745	0.8917	0.8758	0.8929	0.8770	0.8942	0.8782	0.8954	0.8795	0.8967	0.8807
16	8824	8655	8836	8667	8849	8679	8861	8692	8874	8704	8886	8717	8899	8729	8911	8742	8923	8754	8936	8766
17	8793	8614	8806	8626	8818	8638	8831	8651	8843	8663	8855	8675	8868	8688	8880	8700	8893	8713	8905	8725
18	8763	8572	8776	8585	8788	8597	8800	8609	8813	8622	8825	8634	8837	8646	8850	8659	8862	8671	8874	8683
19	8733	8530	8745	8543	8758	8555	8770	8567	8782	8580	8795	8592	8807	8604	8819	8617	8832	8629	8844	8641
20	0.8703	0.8488	0.8716	0.8501	0.8728	0.8513	0.8740	0.8525	0.8752	0.8537	0.8765	0.8550	0.8777	0.8562	0.8789	0.8574	0.8801	0.8586	0.8814	0.8599
21	8674	8446	8686	8458	8698	8470	8710	8482	8722	8495	8735	8507	8747	8519	8759	8531	8771	8544	8784	8556
22	8644	8403	8656	8415	8669	8427	8681	8439	8693	8451	8705	8464	8717	8476	8729	8488	8742	8500	8754	8512
23	8615	8359	8627	8371	8639	8384	8651	8396	8663	8408	8676	8420	8688	8432	8700	8444	8712	8456	8724	8468
24	8586	8315	8598	8327	8610	8339	8622	8352	8634	8364	8646	8376	8658	8388	8671	8400	8683	8412	8695	8424
25	0.8557	0.8271	0.8569	0.8283	0.8581	0.8295	0.8593	0.8307	0.8605	0.8319	0.8617	0.8331	0.8629	0.8343	0.8641	0.8355	0.8653	0.8367	0.8665	0.8379
26	8528	8226	8540	8238	8552	8250	8564	8262	8576	8274	8588	8286	8600	8298	8612	8310	8624	8322	8636	8334
27	8500	8180	8512	8192	8524	8204	8536	8216	8548	8228	8560	8240	8572	8252	8584	8264	8596	8276	8608	8287
28	8472	8133	8483	8145	8495	8157	8507	8169	8519	8181	8531	8193	8543	8205	8555	8217	8567	8229	8579	8241
29	8443	8086	8455	8098	8467	8110	8479	8122	8491	8134	8503	8146	8515	8158	8527	8169	8539	8181	8550	8193
30	0.8416	0.8038	0.8427	0.8050	0.8439	0.8062	0.8451	0.8074	0.8463	0.8086	0.8475	0.8098	0.8487	0.8109	0.8499	0.8121	0.8510	0.8133	0.8522	0.8145
31	8388	7990	8400	8002	8411	8013	8423	8025	8435	8037	8447	8049	8459	8061	8471	8072	8482	8084	8494	8096
32	8360	7940	8372	7952	8384	7964	8396	7976	8407	7987	8419	7999	8431	8011	8443	8023	8454	8035	8466	8046
33	8333	7890	8345	7902	8356	7914	8368	7925	8380	7937	8392	7949	8403	7961	8415	7972	8427	7984	8439	7996
34	8306	7839	8317	7851	8329	7862	8341	7874	8353	7886	8364	7897	8376	7909	8388	7921	8399	7933	8411	7944
35	0.8279	0.7787	0.8290	0.7799	0.8302	0.7810	0.8314	0.7822	0.8325	0.7834	0.8337	0.7845	0.8349	0.7857	0.8360	0.7869	0.8372	0.7880	0.8384	0.7892
36	8252	7734	8263	7746	8275	7757	8287	7769	8298	7780	8310	7792	8322	7804	8333	7815	8345	7827	8356	7839
37	8225	7680	8237	7692	8248	7703	8260	7715	8272	7726	8283	7738	8295	7749	8306	7761	8318	7773	8329	7784
38	8199	7625	8210	7636	8222	7648	8233	7660	8245	7671	8256	7683	8268	7694	8280	7706	8291	7717	8303	7729
39	8172	7569	8184	7580	8195	7592	8207	7603	8218	7615	8230	7626	8241	7638	8253	7649	8264	7661	8276	7672
40	0.8146	0.7511	0.8158	0.7523	0.8169	0.7534	0.8181	0.7546	0.8192	0.7557	0.8204	0.7569	0.8215	0.7580	0.8227	0.7592	0.8238	0.7603	0.8249	0.7615
41	8120	7453	8132	7464	8143	7476	8155	7487	8166	7499	8177	7510	8189	7522	8200	7533	8212	7545	8223	7556
42	8094	7393	8106	7405	8117	7416	8129	7427	8140	7439	8151	7450	8163	7462	8174	7473	8186	7484	8197	7496

P °C	720 dry	720 sat.	721 dry	721 sat.	722 dry	722 sat.	723 dry	723 sat.	724 dry	724 sat.	725 dry	725 sat.	726 dry	726 sat.	727 dry	727 sat.	728 dry	728 sat.	729 dry	729 sat.
0	0.9474	0.9413	0.9487	0.9427	0.9500	0.9440	0.9513	0.9453	0.9526	0.9466	0.9539	0.9479	0.9553	0.9492	0.9566	0.9506	0.9579	0.9519	0.9592	0.9532
1	9439	9374	9452	9388	9465	9401	9478	9414	9491	9427	9505	9440	9518	9453	9531	9466	9544	9479	9557	9492
2	9405	9336	9418	9349	9431	9362	9444	9375	9457	9388	9470	9401	9483	9414	9496	9427	9509	9440	9522	9453
3	9371	9297	9384	9310	9397	9323	9410	9336	9423	9349	9436	9362	9449	9375	9462	9388	9475	9401	9488	9414
4	9337	9258	9350	9270	9363	9283	9376	9296	9388	9309	9401	9322	9414	9335	9427	9348	9440	9361	9453	9374
5	0.9303	0.9218	0.9316	0.9231	0.9329	0.9244	0.9342	0.9257	0.9355	0.9270	0.9368	0.9283	0.9380	0.9296	0.9393	0.9309	0.9406	0.9322	0.9419	0.9335
6	9270	9179	9282	9192	9295	9205	9308	9218	9321	9231	9334	9244	9347	9257	9360	9269	9373	9282	9385	9295
7	9236	9140	9249	9153	9262	9166	9275	9179	9288	9191	9301	9204	9313	9217	9326	9230	9339	9243	9352	9255
8	9203	9101	9216	9113	9229	9126	9242	9139	9255	9152	9267	9165	9280	9177	9293	9190	9306	9203	9319	9216
9	9171	9061	9184	9074	9196	9087	9209	9099	9222	9112	9234	9125	9247	9138	9260	9150	9273	9163	9285	9176
10	0.9138	0.9021	0.9151	0.9034	0.9164	0.9047	0.9176	0.9060	0.9189	0.9072	0.9202	0.9085	0.9214	0.9098	0.9227	0.9110	0.9240	0.9123	0.9253	0.9136
11	9106	8982	9119	8994	9131	9007	9144	9020	9157	9032	9169	9045	9182	9057	9195	9070	9207	9083	9220	9095
12	9074	8942	9087	8954	9099	8967	9112	8979	9124	8992	9137	9005	9150	9017	9162	9030	9175	9042	9187	9055
13	9042	8901	9055	8914	9067	8926	9080	8939	9093	8951	9105	8964	9118	8977	9130	8989	9143	9002	9155	9014
14	9011	8861	9023	8873	9036	8886	9048	8898	9061	8911	9073	8923	9086	8936	9098	8948	9111	8961	9123	8973
15	0.8979	0.8820	0.8992	0.8832	0.9004	0.8845	0.9017	0.8857	0.9029	0.8870	0.9042	0.8882	0.9054	0.8895	0.9067	0.8907	0.9079	0.8920	0.9092	0.8932
16	8948	8779	8961	8791	8973	8804	8986	8816	8998	8829	9010	8841	9023	8853	9035	8866	9048	8878	9060	8891
17	8917	8737	8930	8750	8942	8762	8954	8775	8967	8787	8979	8799	8992	8812	9004	8824	9016	8836	9029	8849
18	8887	8696	8899	8708	8911	8720	8924	8733	8936	8745	8948	8757	8961	8770	8973	8782	8985	8794	8998	8807
19	8856	8653	8868	8666	8881	8678	8893	8690	8905	8703	8918	8715	8930	8727	8942	8740	8955	8752	8967	8764
20	0.8826	0.8611	0.8838	0.8623	0.8850	0.8635	0.8863	0.8648	0.8875	0.8660	0.8887	0.8672	0.8899	0.8684	0.8912	0.8697	0.8924	0.8709	0.8936	0.8721
21	8796	8568	8808	8580	8820	8592	8832	8605	8845	8617	8857	8629	8869	8641	8881	8653	8894	8666	8906	8678
22	8766	8525	8778	8537	8790	8549	8802	8561	8815	8573	8827	8585	8839	8598	8851	8610	8863	8622	8875	8634
23	8736	8481	8748	8493	8761	8505	8773	8517	8785	8529	8797	8541	8809	8553	8821	8566	8833	8578	8845	8590
24	8707	8436	8719	8448	8731	8460	8743	8472	8755	8485	8767	8497	8779	8509	8791	8521	8804	8533	8816	8545
25	0.8678	0.8391	0.8690	0.8403	0.8702	0.8415	0.8714	0.8427	0.8726	0.8439	0.8738	0.8451	0.8750	0.8464	0.8762	0.8476	0.8774	0.8488	0.8786	0.8500
26	8648	8346	8660	8358	8672	8370	8684	8382	8696	8394	8709	8406	8721	8418	8733	8430	8745	8442	8757	8454
27	8620	8299	8632	8311	8644	8323	8655	8335	8667	8347	8679	8359	8691	8371	8703	8383	8715	8395	8727	8407
28	8591	8253	8603	8265	8615	8276	8627	8288	8639	8300	8651	8312	8662	8324	8674	8336	8686	8348	8698	8360
29	8562	8205	8574	8217	8586	8229	8598	8241	8610	8253	8622	8265	8634	8276	8646	8288	8658	8300	8669	8312
30	0.8534	0.8157	0.8546	0.8169	0.8558	0.8181	0.8570	0.8192	0.8581	0.8204	0.8593	0.8216	0.8605	0.8228	0.8617	0.8240	0.8629	0.8252	0.8641	0.8264
31	8506	8108	8518	8120	8530	8132	8541	8143	8553	8155	8565	8167	8577	8179	8589	8191	8600	8202	8612	8214
32	8478	8058	8490	8070	8502	8082	8513	8093	8525	8105	8537	8117	8549	8129	8560	8141	8572	8152	8584	8164
33	8450	8007	8462	8019	8474	8031	8485	8043	8497	8054	8509	8066	8521	8078	8532	8090	8544	8101	8556	8113
34	8423	7956	8434	7968	8446	7979	8458	7991	8469	8003	8481	8014	8493	8026	8505	8038	8516	8050	8528	8061
35	0.8395	0.7904	0.8407	0.7915	0.8419	0.7927	0.8430	0.7939	0.8442	0.7950	0.8454	0.7962	0.8465	0.7974	0.8477	0.7985	0.8489	0.7997	0.8500	0.8008
36	8368	7850	8380	7862	8391	7873	8403	7885	8415	7897	8426	7908	8438	7920	8449	7932	8461	7943	8473	7955
37	8341	7796	8353	7807	8364	7819	8376	7831	8387	7842	8399	7854	8411	7865	8422	7877	8434	7888	8445	7900
38	8314	7740	8326	7752	8337	7763	8349	7775	8360	7787	8372	7798	8383	7810	8395	7821	8407	7833	8418	7844
39	8287	7684	8299	7695	8311	7707	8322	7718	8334	7730	8345	7741	8357	7753	8368	7764	8380	7776	8391	7787
40	0.8261	0.7626	0.8272	0.7638	0.8284	0.7649	0.8295	0.7661	0.8307	0.7672	0.8318	0.7684	0.8330	0.7695	0.8341	0.7707	0.8353	0.7718	0.8364	0.7729
41	8235	7567	8246	7579	8257	7590	8269	7602	8280	7613	8292	7625	8303	7636	8315	7647	8326	7659	8338	7670
42	8208	7507	8220	7519	8231	7530	8243	7542	8254	7553	8265	7564	8277	7576	8288	7587	8300	7599	8311	7610

P / °C	730 dry	730 sat.	731 dry	731 sat.	732 dry	732 sat.	733 dry	733 sat.	734 dry	734 sat.	735 dry	735 sat.	736 dry	736 sat.	737 dry	737 sat.	738 dry	738 sat.	739 dry	739 sat.
0	0.9605	*0.9545*	0.9618	*0.9558*	0.9632	*0.9571*	0.9645	*0.9584*	0.9658	*0.9598*	0.9671	*0.9611*	0.9684	*0.9624*	0.9697	*0.9637*	0.9711	*0.9650*	0.9724	*0.9663*
1	9570	*9506*	9583	*9519*	9596	*9532*	9609	*9545*	9623	*9558*	9636	*9571*	9649	*9584*	9662	*9597*	9675	*9610*	9688	*9624*
2	9535	*9466*	9548	*9479*	9561	*9492*	9574	*9505*	9588	*9518*	9601	*9531*	9614	*9544*	9627	*9558*	9640	*9571*	9653	*9584*
3	9501	*9427*	9514	*9440*	9527	*9453*	9540	*9466*	9553	*9479*	9566	*9492*	9579	*9505*	9592	*9518*	9605	*9531*	9618	*9544*
4	9466	*9387*	9479	*9400*	9492	*9413*	9505	*9426*	9518	*9439*	9531	*9452*	9544	*9465*	9557	*9478*	9570	*9491*	9583	*9504*
5	0.9432	*0.9348*	0.9445	*0.9361*	0.9458	*0.9373*	0.9471	*0.9386*	0.9484	*0.9399*	0.9497	*0.9412*	0.9510	*0.9425*	0.9523	*0.9438*	0.9536	*0.9451*	0.9548	*0.9464*
6	9398	*9308*	9411	*9321*	9424	*9334*	9437	*9347*	9450	*9360*	9463	*9372*	9476	*9385*	9488	*9398*	9501	*9411*	9514	*9424*
7	9365	*9268*	9378	*9281*	9390	*9294*	9403	*9307*	9416	*9320*	9429	*9332*	9442	*9345*	9454	*9358*	9467	*9371*	9480	*9384*
8	9331	*9228*	9344	*9241*	9357	*9254*	9370	*9267*	9382	*9280*	9395	*9292*	9408	*9305*	9421	*9318*	9434	*9331*	9446	*9344*
9	9298	*9188*	9311	*9201*	9324	*9214*	9336	*9227*	9349	*9239*	9362	*9252*	9375	*9265*	9387	*9278*	9400	*9290*	9413	*9303*
10	0.9265	*0.9148*	0.9278	*0.9161*	0.9291	*0.9174*	0.9303	*0.9186*	0.9316	*0.9199*	0.9329	*0.9212*	0.9341	*0.9225*	0.9354	*0.9237*	0.9367	*0.9250*	0.9379	*0.9263*
11	9233	*9108*	9245	*9121*	9258	*9133*	9270	*9146*	9283	*9159*	9296	*9171*	9308	*9184*	9321	*9197*	9334	*9209*	9346	*9222*
12	9200	*9068*	9213	*9080*	9225	*9093*	9238	*9105*	9251	*9118*	9263	*9131*	9276	*9143*	9288	*9156*	9301	*9168*	9314	*9181*
13	9168	*9027*	9180	*9039*	9193	*9052*	9206	*9064*	9218	*9077*	9231	*9090*	9243	*9102*	9256	*9115*	9268	*9127*	9281	*9140*
14	9136	*8986*	9148	*8998*	9161	*9011*	9173	*9023*	9186	*9036*	9198	*9048*	9211	*9061*	9223	*9073*	9236	*9086*	9248	*9098*
15	0.9104	*0.8945*	0.9117	*0.8957*	0.9129	*0.8970*	0.9141	*0.8982*	0.9154	*0.8994*	0.9166	*0.9007*	0.9179	*0.9019*	0.9191	*0.9032*	0.9204	*0.9044*	0.9216	*0.9057*
16	9073	*8903*	9085	*8916*	9097	*8928*	9110	*8940*	9122	*8953*	9135	*8965*	9147	*8978*	9160	*8990*	9172	*9003*	9184	*9015*
17	9041	*8861*	9054	*8874*	9066	*8886*	9078	*8898*	9091	*8911*	9103	*8923*	9115	*8936*	9128	*8948*	9140	*8960*	9153	*8973*
18	9010	*8819*	9022	*8831*	9035	*8844*	9047	*8856*	9059	*8868*	9072	*8881*	9084	*8893*	9096	*8905*	9109	*8918*	9121	*8930*
19	8979	*8776*	8991	*8789*	9004	*8801*	9016	*8813*	9028	*8826*	9041	*8838*	9053	*8850*	9065	*8863*	9078	*8875*	9090	*8887*
20	0.8948	*0.8734*	0.8961	*0.8746*	0.8973	*0.8758*	0.8985	*0.8770*	0.8997	*0.8783*	0.9010	*0.8795*	0.9022	*0.8807*	0.9034	*0.8819*	0.9047	*0.8832*	0.9059	*0.8844*
21	8918	*8690*	8930	*8702*	8942	*8715*	8955	*8727*	8967	*8739*	8979	*8751*	8991	*8763*	9003	*8776*	9016	*8788*	9028	*8800*
22	8888	*8646*	8900	*8658*	8912	*8671*	8924	*8683*	8936	*8695*	8949	*8707*	8961	*8719*	8973	*8732*	8985	*8744*	8997	*8756*
23	8858	*8602*	8870	*8614*	8882	*8626*	8894	*8638*	8906	*8650*	8918	*8663*	8930	*8675*	8943	*8687*	8955	*8699*	8967	*8711*
24	8828	*8557*	8840	*8569*	8852	*8581*	8864	*8593*	8876	*8605*	8888	*8618*	8900	*8630*	8912	*8642*	8924	*8654*	8937	*8666*
25	0.8798	*0.8512*	0.8810	*0.8524*	0.8822	*0.8536*	0.8834	*0.8548*	0.8846	*0.8560*	0.8858	*0.8572*	0.8870	*0.8584*	0.8882	*0.8596*	0.8894	*0.8608*	0.8907	*0.8620*
26	8769	*8466*	8781	*8478*	8793	*8490*	8805	*8502*	8817	*8514*	8829	*8526*	8841	*8538*	8853	*8550*	8865	*8562*	8877	*8574*
27	8739	*8419*	8751	*8431*	8763	*8443*	8775	*8455*	8787	*8467*	8799	*8479*	8811	*8491*	8823	*8503*	8835	*8515*	8847	*8527*
28	8710	*8372*	8722	*8384*	8734	*8396*	8746	*8408*	8758	*8420*	8770	*8432*	8782	*8444*	8794	*8455*	8806	*8467*	8818	*8479*
29	8681	*8324*	8693	*8336*	8705	*8348*	8717	*8360*	8729	*8372*	8741	*8383*	8753	*8395*	8765	*8407*	8776	*8419*	8788	*8431*
30	0.8653	*0.8275*	0.8664	*0.8287*	0.8676	*0.8299*	0.8688	*0.8311*	0.8700	*0.8323*	0.8712	*0.8335*	0.8724	*0.8347*	0.8736	*0.8358*	0.8747	*0.8370*	0.8759	*0.8382*
31	8624	*8226*	8636	*8238*	8648	*8250*	8660	*8261*	8671	*8273*	8683	*8285*	8695	*8297*	8707	*8309*	8719	*8321*	8730	*8332*
32	8596	*8176*	8608	*8188*	8619	*8199*	8631	*8211*	8643	*8223*	8655	*8235*	8666	*8246*	8678	*8258*	8690	*8270*	8702	*8282*
33	8568	*8125*	8579	*8137*	8591	*8148*	8603	*8160*	8615	*8172*	8626	*8184*	8638	*8195*	8650	*8207*	8662	*8219*	8673	*8230*
34	8540	*8073*	8551	*8085*	8563	*8096*	8575	*8108*	8586	*8120*	8598	*8131*	8610	*8143*	8622	*8155*	8633	*8167*	8645	*8178*
35	0.8512	*0.8020*	0.8524	*0.8032*	0.8535	*0.8043*	0.8547	*0.8055*	0.8559	*0.8067*	0.8570	*0.8078*	0.8582	*0.8090*	0.8594	*0.8102*	0.8605	*0.8113*	0.8617	*0.8125*
36	8484	*7966*	8496	*7978*	8508	*7990*	8519	*8001*	8531	*8013*	8542	*8025*	8554	*8036*	8566	*8048*	8577	*8059*	8589	*8071*
37	8457	*7912*	8468	*7923*	8480	*7935*	8492	*7946*	8503	*7958*	8515	*7970*	8526	*7981*	8538	*7993*	8550	*8004*	8561	*8016*
38	8430	*7856*	8441	*7867*	8453	*7879*	8464	*7890*	8476	*7902*	8487	*7914*	8499	*7925*	8510	*7937*	8522	*7948*	8534	*7960*
39	8403	*7799*	8414	*7810*	8426	*7822*	8437	*7834*	8449	*7845*	8460	*7857*	8472	*7868*	8483	*7880*	8495	*7891*	8506	*7903*
40	0.8376	*0.7741*	0.8387	*0.7752*	0.8399	*0.7764*	0.8410	*0.7775*	0.8422	*0.7787*	0.8433	*0.7798*	0.8445	*0.7810*	0.8456	*0.7821*	0.8467	*0.7833*	0.8479	*0.7844*
41	8349	*7682*	8360	*7693*	8372	*7705*	8383	*7716*	8395	*7728*	8406	*7739*	8418	*7750*	8429	*7762*	8440	*7773*	8452	*7785*
42	8322	*7621*	8334	*7633*	8345	*7644*	8357	*7656*	8368	*7667*	8379	*7678*	8391	*7690*	8402	*7701*	8414	*7713*	8425	*7724*

P / °C	740 dry	740 sat.	741 dry	741 sat.	742 dry	742 sat.	743 dry	743 sat.	744 dry	744 sat.	745 dry	745 sat.	746 dry	746 sat.	747 dry	747 sat.	748 dry	748 sat.	749 dry	749 sat.
0	0.9737	*0.9677*	0.9750	*0.9690*	0.9763	*0.9703*	0.9776	*0.9716*	0.9789	*0.9729*	0.9803	*0.9742*	0.9816	*0.9756*	0.9829	*0.9769*	0.9842	*0.9782*	0.9855	*0.9795*
1	9701	*9637*	9714	*9650*	9727	*9663*	9741	*9676*	9754	*9689*	9767	*9702*	9780	*9715*	9793	*9728*	9806	*9742*	9819	*9755*
2	9666	*9597*	9679	*9610*	9692	*9623*	9705	*9636*	9718	*9649*	9731	*9662*	9744	*9675*	9757	*9688*	9770	*9701*	9783	*9714*
3	9631	*9557*	9644	*9570*	9657	*9583*	9670	*9596*	9683	*9609*	9696	*9622*	9709	*9635*	9722	*9648*	9735	*9661*	9748	*9674*
4	9596	*9517*	9609	*9530*	9622	*9543*	9635	*9556*	9648	*9569*	9661	*9582*	9674	*9595*	9687	*9608*	9700	*9621*	9713	*9634*
5	0.9561	*0.9477*	0.9574	*0.9490*	0.9587	*0.9503*	0.9600	*0.9516*	0.9613	*0.9529*	0.9626	*0.9541*	0.9639	*0.9554*	0.9652	*0.9567*	0.9665	*0.9580*	0.9678	*0.9593*
6	9527	*9437*	9540	*9450*	9553	*9463*	9566	*9475*	9579	*9488*	9591	*9501*	9604	*9514*	9617	*9527*	9630	*9540*	9643	*9553*
7	9493	*9397*	9506	*9409*	9519	*9422*	9531	*9435*	9544	*9448*	9557	*9461*	9570	*9474*	9583	*9486*	9596	*9499*	9608	*9512*
8	9459	*9356*	9472	*9369*	9485	*9382*	9497	*9395*	9510	*9407*	9523	*9420*	9536	*9433*	9549	*9446*	9561	*9459*	9574	*9471*
9	9426	*9316*	9438	*9329*	9451	*9341*	9464	*9354*	9476	*9367*	9489	*9380*	9502	*9392*	9515	*9405*	9527	*9418*	9540	*9430*
10	0.9392	*0.9275*	0.9405	*0.9288*	0.9418	*0.9301*	0.9430	*0.9313*	0.9443	*0.9326*	0.9456	*0.9339*	0.9468	*0.9351*	0.9481	*0.9364*	0.9494	*0.9377*	0.9506	*0.9389*
11	9359	*9235*	9372	*9247*	9384	*9260*	9397	*9272*	9410	*9285*	9422	*9298*	9435	*9310*	9448	*9323*	9460	*9336*	9473	*9348*
12	9326	*9194*	9339	*9206*	9351	*9219*	9364	*9231*	9377	*9244*	9389	*9257*	9402	*9269*	9414	*9282*	9427	*9294*	9440	*9307*
13	9293	*9152*	9306	*9165*	9319	*9178*	9331	*9190*	9344	*9203*	9356	*9215*	9369	*9228*	9381	*9240*	9394	*9253*	9406	*9265*
14	9261	*9111*	9274	*9124*	9286	*9136*	9299	*9149*	9311	*9161*	9324	*9174*	9336	*9186*	9349	*9199*	9361	*9211*	9374	*9224*
15	0.9229	*0.9069*	0.9241	*0.9082*	0.9254	*0.9094*	0.9266	*0.9107*	0.9279	*0.9119*	0.9291	*0.9132*	0.9304	*0.9144*	0.9316	*0.9157*	0.9329	*0.9169*	0.9341	*0.9182*
16	9197	*9027*	9209	*9040*	9222	*9052*	9234	*9065*	9247	*9077*	9259	*9090*	9271	*9102*	9284	*9114*	9296	*9127*	9309	*9139*
17	9165	*8985*	9177	*8997*	9190	*9010*	9202	*9022*	9215	*9035*	9227	*9047*	9239	*9059*	9252	*9072*	9264	*9084*	9277	*9097*
18	9133	*8942*	9146	*8955*	9158	*8967*	9171	*8979*	9183	*8992*	9195	*9004*	9208	*9017*	9220	*9029*	9232	*9041*	9245	*9054*
19	9102	*8899*	9114	*8912*	9127	*8924*	9139	*8936*	9151	*8949*	9164	*8961*	9176	*8973*	9188	*8986*	9201	*8998*	9213	*9010*
20	0.9071	*0.8856*	0.9083	*0.8868*	0.9096	*0.8881*	0.9108	*0.8893*	0.9120	*0.8905*	0.9132	*0.8917*	0.9145	*0.8930*	0.9157	*0.8942*	0.9169	*0.8954*	0.9181	*0.8966*
21	9040	*8812*	9052	*8825*	9065	*8837*	9077	*8849*	9089	*8861*	9101	*8873*	9113	*8886*	9126	*8898*	9138	*8910*	9150	*8922*
22	9009	*8768*	9022	*8780*	9034	*8792*	9046	*8805*	9058	*8817*	9070	*8829*	9082	*8841*	9095	*8853*	9107	*8865*	9119	*8878*
23	8979	*8723*	8991	*8735*	9003	*8748*	9015	*8760*	9027	*8772*	9040	*8784*	9052	*8796*	9064	*8808*	9076	*8820*	9088	*8833*
24	8949	*8678*	8961	*8690*	8973	*8702*	8985	*8714*	8997	*8726*	9009	*8739*	9021	*8751*	9033	*8763*	9045	*8775*	9057	*8787*
25	0.8919	*0.8632*	0.8931	*0.8644*	0.8943	*0.8656*	0.8955	*0.8668*	0.8967	*0.8680*	0.8979	*0.8693*	0.8991	*0.8705*	0.9003	*0.8717*	0.9015	*0.8729*	0.9027	*0.8741*
26	8889	*8586*	8901	*8598*	8913	*8610*	8925	*8622*	8937	*8634*	8949	*8646*	8961	*8658*	8973	*8670*	8985	*8682*	8997	*8694*
27	8859	*8539*	8871	*8551*	8883	*8563*	8895	*8575*	8907	*8587*	8919	*8599*	8931	*8611*	8943	*8623*	8955	*8635*	8967	*8647*
28	8830	*8491*	8841	*8503*	8853	*8515*	8865	*8527*	8877	*8539*	8889	*8551*	8901	*8563*	8913	*8575*	8925	*8587*	8937	*8599*
29	8800	*8443*	8812	*8455*	8824	*8467*	8836	*8479*	8848	*8491*	8860	*8502*	8872	*8514*	8883	*8526*	8895	*8538*	8907	*8550*
30	0.8771	*0.8394*	0.8783	*0.8406*	0.8795	*0.8418*	0.8807	*0.8429*	0.8819	*0.8441*	0.8830	*0.8453*	0.8842	*0.8465*	0.8854	*0.8477*	0.8866	*0.8489*	0.8878	*0.8501*
31	8742	*8344*	8754	*8356*	8766	*8368*	8778	*8380*	8789	*8391*	8801	*8403*	8813	*8415*	8825	*8427*	8837	*8439*	8849	*8450*
32	8714	*8294*	8725	*8305*	8737	*8317*	8749	*8329*	8761	*8341*	8772	*8352*	8784	*8364*	8796	*8376*	8808	*8388*	8820	*8400*
33	8685	*8242*	8697	*8254*	8708	*8266*	8720	*8277*	8732	*8289*	8744	*8301*	8755	*8313*	8767	*8324*	8779	*8336*	8791	*8348*
34	8657	*8190*	8668	*8202*	8680	*8213*	8692	*8225*	8703	*8237*	8715	*8248*	8727	*8260*	8739	*8272*	8750	*8284*	8762	*8295*
35	0.8629	*0.8137*	0.8640	*0.8148*	0.8652	*0.8160*	0.8663	*0.8172*	0.8675	*0.8183*	0.8687	*0.8195*	0.8698	*0.8207*	0.8710	*0.8218*	0.8722	*0.8230*	0.8733	*0.8242*
36	8601	*8083*	8612	*8094*	8624	*8106*	8635	*8117*	8647	*8129*	8659	*8141*	8670	*8152*	8682	*8164*	8694	*8176*	8705	*8187*
37	8573	*8027*	8584	*8039*	8596	*8051*	8608	*8062*	8619	*8074*	8631	*8085*	8642	*8097*	8654	*8109*	8665	*8120*	8677	*8132*
38	8545	*7971*	8557	*7983*	8568	*7994*	8580	*8006*	8591	*8018*	8603	*8029*	8614	*8041*	8626	*8052*	8638	*8064*	8649	*8075*
39	8518	*7914*	8529	*7926*	8541	*7937*	8552	*7949*	8564	*7960*	8575	*7972*	8587	*7983*	8598	*7995*	8610	*8006*	8621	*8018*
40	0.8490	*0.7856*	0.8502	*0.7867*	0.8513	*0.7879*	0.8525	*0.7890*	0.8536	*0.7902*	0.8548	*0.7913*	0.8559	*0.7925*	0.8571	*0.7936*	0.8582	*0.7947*	0.8594	*0.7959*
41	8463	*7796*	8475	*7808*	8486	*7819*	8498	*7830*	8509	*7842*	8521	*7853*	8532	*7865*	8543	*7876*	8555	*7888*	8566	*7899*
42	8436	*7735*	8448	*7747*	8459	*7758*	8471	*7770*	8482	*7781*	8493	*7792*	8505	*7804*	8516	*7815*	8528	*7827*	8539	*7838*

P	750		751		752		753		754		755		756		757		758		759	
°C	dry	sat.	dry	sat.	dry	sat.	dry	sat.	dry	sat.	dry	sat.	dry	sat.	dry	sat.	dry	sat.	dry	sat.
0	0.9868	0.9808	0.9882	0.9821	0.9895	0.9834	0.9908	0.9848	0.9921	0.9861	0.9934	0.9874	0.9947	0.9887	0.9961	0.9900	0.9974	0.9913	0.9987	0.9927
1	9832	9768	9845	9781	9859	9794	9872	9807	9885	9820	9898	9833	9911	9846	9924	9860	9937	9873	9950	9886
2	9797	9727	9810	9740	9823	9753	9836	9767	9849	9780	9862	9793	9875	9806	9888	9819	9901	9832	9914	9845
3	9761	9687	9774	9700	9787	9713	9800	9726	9813	9739	9826	9752	9839	9765	9852	9778	9865	9791	9878	9804
4	9726	9647	9739	9660	9752	9672	9765	9685	9778	9698	9790	9711	9803	9724	9816	9737	9829	9750	9842	9763
5	0.9691	0.9606	0.9704	0.9619	0.9716	0.9632	0.9729	0.9645	0.9742	0.9658	0.9755	0.9671	0.9768	0.9684	0.9781	0.9697	0.9794	0.9709	0.9807	0.9722
6	9656	9566	9669	9578	9682	9591	9694	9604	9707	9617	9720	9630	9733	9643	9746	9656	9759	9669	9772	9681
7	9621	9525	9634	9538	9647	9551	9660	9563	9673	9576	9685	9589	9698	9602	9711	9615	9724	9627	9737	9640
8	9587	9484	9600	9497	9613	9510	9625	9522	9638	9535	9651	9548	9664	9561	9676	9574	9689	9586	9702	9599
9	9553	9443	9566	9456	9578	9469	9591	9481	9604	9494	9617	9507	9629	9520	9642	9532	9655	9545	9668	9558
10	0.9519	0.9402	0.9532	0.9415	0.9544	0.9428	0.9557	0.9440	0.9570	0.9453	0.9583	0.9466	0.9595	0.9478	0.9608	0.9491	0.9621	0.9504	0.9633	0.9516
11	9485	9361	9498	9374	9511	9386	9523	9399	9536	9412	9549	9424	9561	9437	9574	9450	9587	9462	9599	9475
12	9452	9320	9465	9332	9477	9345	9490	9357	9503	9370	9515	9383	9528	9395	9540	9408	9553	9420	9566	9433
13	9419	9278	9432	9291	9444	9303	9457	9316	9469	9328	9482	9341	9494	9353	9507	9366	9520	9378	9532	9391
14	9386	9236	9399	9249	9411	9261	9424	9274	9436	9286	9449	9299	9461	9311	9474	9324	9486	9336	9499	9349
15	0.9354	0.9194	0.9366	0.9206	0.9378	0.9219	0.9391	0.9231	0.9403	0.9244	0.9416	0.9256	0.9428	0.9269	0.9441	0.9281	0.9453	0.9294	0.9466	0.9306
16	9321	9152	9334	9164	9346	9176	9358	9189	9371	9201	9383	9214	9396	9226	9408	9239	9421	9251	9433	9263
17	9289	9109	9301	9121	9314	9134	9326	9146	9338	9158	9351	9171	9363	9183	9376	9196	9388	9208	9400	9220
18	9257	9066	9269	9078	9282	9091	9294	9103	9306	9115	9319	9128	9331	9140	9343	9152	9356	9165	9368	9177
19	9225	9022	9237	9035	9250	9047	9262	9059	9274	9072	9287	9084	9299	9096	9311	9109	9324	9121	9336	9133
20	0.9194	0.8979	0.9206	0.8991	0.9218	0.9003	0.9230	0.9015	0.9243	0.9028	0.9255	0.9040	0.9267	0.9052	0.9279	0.9064	0.9292	0.9077	0.9304	0.9089
21	9162	8934	9175	8947	9187	8959	9199	8971	9211	8983	9223	8996	9236	9008	9248	9020	9260	9032	9272	9044
22	9131	8890	9143	8902	9156	8914	9168	8926	9180	8938	9192	8951	9204	8963	9216	8975	9229	8987	9241	8999
23	9100	8845	9112	8857	9125	8869	9137	8881	9149	8893	9161	8905	9173	8917	9185	8930	9197	8942	9209	8954
24	9070	8799	9082	8811	9094	8823	9106	8835	9118	8847	9130	8859	9142	8872	9154	8884	9166	8896	9178	8908
25	0.9039	0.8753	0.9051	0.8765	0.9063	0.8777	0.9075	0.8789	0.9087	0.8801	0.9099	0.8813	0.9111	0.8825	0.9123	0.8837	0.9136	0.8849	0.9148	0.8861
26	9009	8706	9021	8718	9033	8730	9045	8742	9057	8754	9069	8766	9081	8778	9093	8790	9105	8802	9117	8814
27	8979	8659	8991	8671	9003	8683	9015	8695	9027	8706	9039	8718	9051	8730	9063	8742	9074	8754	9086	8766
28	8949	8611	8961	8623	8973	8634	8985	8646	8997	8658	9008	8670	9020	8682	9032	8694	9044	8706	9056	8718
29	8919	8562	8931	8574	8943	8586	8955	8598	8967	8609	8979	8621	8991	8633	9002	8645	9014	8657	9026	8669
30	0.8890	0.8512	0.8902	0.8524	0.8913	0.8536	0.8925	0.8548	0.8937	0.8560	0.8949	0.8572	0.8961	0.8584	0.8973	0.8595	0.8984	0.8607	0.8996	0.8619
31	8860	8462	8872	8474	8884	8486	8896	8498	8908	8510	8919	8521	8931	8533	8943	8545	8955	8557	8967	8569
32	8831	8411	8843	8423	8855	8435	8867	8447	8878	8458	8890	8470	8902	8482	8914	8494	8925	8506	8937	8517
33	8802	8360	8814	8371	8826	8383	8838	8395	8849	8407	8861	8418	8873	8430	8885	8442	8896	8453	8908	8465
34	8774	8307	8785	8319	8797	8330	8809	8342	8820	8354	8832	8365	8844	8377	8856	8389	8867	8400	8879	8412
35	0.8745	0.8253	0.8757	0.8265	0.8768	0.8277	0.8780	0.8288	0.8792	0.8300	0.8803	0.8312	0.8815	0.8323	0.8827	0.8335	0.8838	0.8347	0.8850	0.8358
36	8717	8199	8728	8210	8740	8222	8752	8234	8763	8245	8775	8257	8786	8269	8798	8280	8810	8292	8821	8303
37	8689	8143	8700	8155	8712	8167	8723	8178	8735	8190	8747	8201	8758	8213	8770	8224	8781	8236	8793	8248
38	8661	8087	8672	8098	8684	8110	8695	8121	8707	8133	8718	8145	8730	8156	8741	8168	8753	8179	8765	8191
39	8633	8029	8644	8041	8656	8052	8667	8064	8679	8075	8690	8087	8702	8098	8713	8110	8725	8121	8736	8133
40	0.8605	0.7970	0.8617	0.7982	0.8628	0.7993	0.8640	0.8005	0.8651	0.8016	0.8663	0.8028	0.8674	0.8039	0.8685	0.8051	0.8697	0.8062	0.8708	0.8074
41	8578	7910	8589	7922	8601	7933	8612	7945	8623	7956	8635	7968	8646	7979	8658	7991	8669	8002	8681	8013
42	8550	7849	8562	7861	8573	7872	8585	7884	8596	7895	8607	7906	8619	7918	8630	7929	8642	7941	8653	7952

	760		761		762		763		764		765		766		767		768		769	
0	1.0000	0.9940	1.0013	0.9953	1.0026	0.9966	1.0039	0.9979	1.0053	0.9992	1.0066	1.0006	1.0079	1.0019	1.0092	1.0032	1.0105	1.0045	1.0118	1.0058
1	0.9963	9899	0.9977	9912	0.9990	9925	0003	9938	0016	9951	0029	0.9964	0042	0.9978	0055	0.9991	0068	0004	0081	0017
2	9927	9858	9940	9871	9953	9884	0.9966	9897	0.9979	9910	0.9992	9923	0006	9936	0019	9949	0032	0.9962	0045	0.9976
3	9891	9817	9904	9830	9917	9843	9930	9856	9943	9869	9956	9882	0.9969	9895	0.9982	9908	0.9995	9921	0008	9934
4	9855	9776	9868	9789	9881	9802	9894	9815	9907	9828	9920	9841	9933	9854	9946	9867	9959	9880	0.9972	9893
5	0.9820	0.9735	0.9833	0.9748	0.9846	0.9761	0.9859	0.9774	0.9871	0.9787	0.9884	0.9800	0.9897	0.9813	0.9910	0.9826	0.9923	0.9839	0.9936	0.9852
6	9785	9694	9797	9707	9810	9720	9823	9733	9836	9746	9849	9759	9862	9772	9875	9784	9888	9797	9900	9810
7	9750	9653	9762	9666	9775	9679	9788	9692	9801	9704	9814	9717	9827	9730	9839	9743	9852	9756	9865	9769
8	9715	9612	9728	9625	9740	9638	9753	9650	9766	9663	9779	9676	9791	9689	9804	9701	9817	9714	9830	9727
9	9680	9571	9693	9583	9706	9596	9718	9609	9731	9622	9744	9634	9757	9647	9769	9660	9782	9673	9795	9685
10	0.9646	0.9529	0.9659	0.9542	0.9671	0.9554	0.9684	0.9567	0.9697	0.9580	0.9709	0.9593	0.9722	0.9605	0.9735	0.9618	0.9748	0.9631	0.9760	0.9643
11	9612	9487	9625	9500	9637	9513	9650	9525	9663	9538	9675	9551	9688	9563	9700	9576	9713	9589	9726	9601
12	9578	9446	9591	9458	9603	9471	9616	9483	9629	9496	9641	9509	9654	9521	9666	9534	9679	9546	9692	9559
13	9545	9404	9557	9416	9570	9429	9582	9441	9595	9454	9607	9466	9620	9479	9633	9491	9645	9504	9658	9517
14	9511	9361	9524	9374	9536	9386	9549	9399	9561	9411	9574	9424	9586	9436	9599	9449	9611	9461	9624	9474
15	0.9478	0.9319	0.9491	0.9331	0.9503	0.9344	0.9516	0.9356	0.9528	0.9369	0.9541	0.9381	0.9553	0.9394	0.9566	0.9406	0.9578	0.9419	0.9590	0.9431
16	9445	9276	9458	9288	9470	9301	9483	9313	9495	9326	9508	9338	9520	9350	9532	9363	9545	9375	9557	9388
17	9413	9233	9425	9245	9438	9258	9450	9270	9462	9282	9475	9295	9487	9307	9499	9319	9512	9332	9524	9344
18	9380	9189	9393	9202	9405	9214	9417	9226	9430	9239	9442	9251	9454	9263	9467	9276	9479	9288	9491	9300
19	9348	9145	9360	9158	9373	9170	9385	9182	9397	9195	9410	9207	9422	9219	9434	9232	9447	9244	9459	9256
20	0.9316	0.9101	0.9328	0.9114	0.9341	0.9126	0.9353	0.9138	0.9365	0.9150	0.9377	0.9163	0.9390	0.9175	0.9402	0.9187	0.9414	0.9199	0.9427	0.9212
21	9284	9057	9297	9069	9309	9081	9321	9093	9333	9105	9346	9118	9358	9130	9370	9142	9382	9154	9394	9167
22	9253	9012	9265	9024	9277	9036	9289	9048	9302	9060	9314	9072	9326	9085	9338	9097	9350	9109	9362	9121
23	9222	8966	9234	8978	9246	8990	9258	9002	9270	9015	9282	9027	9294	9039	9307	9051	9319	9063	9331	9075
24	9191	8920	9203	8932	9215	8944	9227	8956	9239	8968	9251	8980	9263	8992	9275	9005	9287	9017	9299	9029
25	0.9160	0.8873	0.9172	0.8885	0.9184	0.8897	0.9196	0.8909	0.9208	0.8922	0.9220	0.8934	0.9232	0.8946	0.9244	0.8958	0.9256	0.8970	0.9268	0.8982
26	9129	8826	9141	8838	9153	8850	9165	8862	9177	8874	9189	8886	9201	8898	9213	8910	9225	8922	9237	8934
27	9098	8778	9110	8790	9122	8802	9134	8814	9146	8826	9158	8838	9170	8850	9182	8862	9194	8874	9206	8886
28	9068	8730	9080	8742	9092	8754	9104	8766	9116	8778	9128	8790	9140	8801	9152	8813	9164	8825	9176	8837
29	9038	8681	9050	8693	9062	8705	9074	8716	9086	8728	9098	8740	9109	8752	9121	8764	9133	8776	9145	8788
30	0.9008	0.8631	0.9020	0.8643	0.9032	0.8655	0.9044	0.8667	0.9056	0.8678	0.9067	0.8690	0.9079	0.8702	0.9091	0.8714	0.9103	0.8726	0.9115	0.8738
31	8979	8580	8990	8592	9002	8604	9014	8616	9026	8628	9038	8640	9049	8651	9061	8663	9073	8675	9085	8687
32	8949	8529	8961	8541	8973	8553	8984	8564	8996	8576	9008	8588	9020	8600	9031	8612	9043	8623	9055	8635
33	8920	8477	8931	8489	8943	8500	8955	8512	8967	8524	8978	8536	8990	8547	9002	8559	9014	8571	9025	8583
34	8891	8424	8902	8436	8914	8447	8926	8459	8937	8471	8949	8482	8961	8494	8973	8506	8984	8517	8996	8529
35	0.8862	0.8370	0.8873	0.8382	0.8885	0.8393	0.8897	0.8405	0.8908	0.8417	0.8920	0.8428	0.8932	0.8440	0.8943	0.8452	0.8955	0.8463	0.8967	0.8475
36	8833	8315	8845	8327	8856	8338	8868	8350	8879	8362	8891	8373	8903	8385	8914	8396	8926	8408	8938	8420
37	8804	8259	8816	8271	8828	8282	8839	8294	8851	8306	8862	8317	8874	8329	8886	8340	8897	8352	8909	8363
38	8776	8202	8788	8214	8799	8225	8811	8237	8822	8248	8834	8260	8845	8272	8857	8283	8868	8295	8880	8306
39	8748	8144	8759	8156	8771	8167	8782	8179	8794	8190	8805	8202	8817	8213	8828	8225	8840	8236	8852	8248
40	0.8720	0.8085	0.8731	0.8097	0.8743	0.8108	0.8754	0.8120	0.8766	0.8131	0.8777	0.8143	0.8789	0.8154	0.8800	0.8165	0.8812	0.8177	0.8823	0.8188
41	8692	8025	8704	8036	8715	8048	8726	8059	8738	8071	8749	8082	8761	8093	8772	8105	8784	8116	8795	8128
42	8664	7963	8676	7975	8687	7986	8699	7998	8710	8009	8721	8020	8733	8032	8744	8043	8756	8055	8767	8066

P / °C	770		771		772		773		774		775		776		777		778		779	
	dry	sat.	dry	sat.	dry	sat.	dry	sat.	dry	sat.	dry	sat.	dry	sat.	dry	sat.	dry	sat.	dry	sat.
0	1.0132	1.0071	1.0145	1.0084	1.0158	1.0098	1.0171	1.0111	1.0184	1.0124	1.0197	1.0137	1.0211	1.0150	1.0224	1.0163	1.0237	1.0177	1.0250	1.0190
1	0095	0030	0108	0043	0121	0056	0134	0069	0147	0082	0160	0096	0173	0109	0186	0122	0199	0135	0213	0148
2	0058	0.9989	0071	0002	0084	0015	0097	0028	0110	0041	0123	0054	0136	0067	0149	0080	0162	0093	0175	0106
3	0021	9947	0034	0.9960	0047	0.9973	0060	0.9986	0073	0.9999	0086	0012	0099	0025	0112	0038	0125	0051	0138	0064
4	0.9985	9906	0.9998	9919	0011	9932	0024	9945	0037	9958	0050	0.9971	0063	0.9984	0076	0.9997	0089	0010	0102	0023
5	0.9949	0.9864	0.9962	0.9877	0.9975	0.9890	0.9988	0.9903	1.0001	0.9916	1.0014	0.9929	1.0027	0.9942	1.0039	0.9955	1.0052	0.9968	1.0065	0.9981
6	9913	9823	9926	9836	9939	9849	9952	9862	0.9965	9874	0.9978	9887	0.9991	9900	0003	9913	0016	9926	0029	9939
7	9878	9781	9891	9794	9903	9807	9916	9820	9929	9833	9942	9846	9955	9858	0.9968	9871	0.9980	9884	0.9993	9897
8	9843	9740	9855	9753	9868	9765	9881	9778	9894	9791	9907	9804	9919	9816	9932	9829	9945	9842	9958	9855
9	9808	9698	9820	9711	9833	9723	9846	9736	9859	9749	9871	9762	9884	9774	9897	9787	9910	9800	9922	9813
10	0.9773	0.9656	0.9786	0.9669	0.9798	0.9681	0.9811	0.9694	0.9824	0.9707	0.9836	0.9719	0.9849	0.9732	0.9862	0.9745	0.9874	0.9758	0.9887	0.9770
11	9738	9614	9751	9627	9764	9639	9776	9652	9789	9665	9802	9677	9814	9690	9827	9702	9840	9715	9852	9728
12	9704	9572	9717	9584	9729	9597	9742	9609	9755	9622	9767	9635	9780	9647	9792	9660	9805	9672	9818	9685
13	9670	9529	9683	9542	9695	9554	9708	9567	9720	9579	9733	9592	9746	9605	9758	9617	9771	9630	9783	9642
14	9636	9486	9649	9499	9661	9511	9674	9524	9687	9537	9699	9549	9712	9562	9724	9574	9737	9587	9749	9599
15	0.9603	0.9443	0.9615	0.9456	0.9628	0.9468	0.9640	0.9481	0.9653	0.9493	0.9665	0.9506	0.9678	0.9518	0.9690	0.9531	0.9703	0.9543	0.9715	0.9556
16	9570	9400	9582	9413	9595	9425	9607	9437	9619	9450	9632	9462	9644	9475	9657	9487	9669	9500	9682	9512
17	9537	9357	9549	9369	9561	9381	9574	9394	9586	9406	9599	9419	9611	9431	9623	9443	9636	9456	9648	9468
18	9504	9313	9516	9325	9528	9337	9541	9350	9553	9362	9565	9374	9578	9387	9590	9399	9603	9411	9615	9424
19	9471	9268	9483	9281	9496	9293	9508	9305	9520	9318	9533	9330	9545	9342	9557	9355	9570	9367	9582	9379
20	0.9439	0.9224	0.9451	0.9236	0.9463	0.9248	0.9476	0.9261	0.9488	0.9273	0.9500	0.9285	0.9512	0.9297	0.9525	0.9310	0.9537	0.9322	0.9549	0.9334
21	9407	9179	9419	9191	9431	9203	9443	9215	9455	9228	9468	9240	9480	9252	9492	9264	9504	9277	9517	9289
22	9375	9133	9387	9145	9399	9158	9411	9170	9423	9182	9436	9194	9448	9206	9460	9219	9472	9231	9484	9243
23	9343	9087	9355	9099	9367	9112	9379	9124	9391	9136	9404	9148	9416	9160	9428	9172	9440	9184	9452	9197
24	9311	9041	9324	9053	9336	9065	9348	9077	9360	9089	9372	9101	9384	9113	9396	9125	9408	9138	9420	9150
25	0.9280	0.8994	0.9292	0.9006	0.9304	0.9018	0.9316	0.9030	0.9328	0.9042	0.9340	0.9054	0.9352	0.9066	0.9364	0.9078	0.9377	0.9090	0.9389	0.9102
26	9249	8946	9261	8958	9273	8970	9285	8982	9297	8994	9309	9006	9321	9018	9333	9030	9345	9042	9357	9054
27	9218	8898	9230	8910	9242	8922	9254	8934	9266	8946	9278	8958	9290	8970	9302	8982	9314	8994	9326	9006
28	9187	8849	9199	8861	9211	8873	9223	8885	9235	8897	9247	8909	9259	8921	9271	8933	9283	8945	9295	8957
29	9157	8800	9169	8812	9181	8824	9193	8835	9205	8847	9216	8859	9228	8871	9240	8883	9252	8895	9264	8907
30	0.9127	0.8750	0.9139	0.8761	0.9150	0.8773	0.9162	0.8785	0.9174	0.8797	0.9186	0.8809	0.9198	0.8821	0.9210	0.8832	0.9222	0.8844	0.9233	0.8856
31	9097	8699	9108	8710	9120	8722	9132	8734	9144	8746	9156	8758	9168	8769	9179	8781	9191	8793	9203	8805
32	9067	8647	9079	8659	9090	8670	9102	8682	9114	8694	9126	8706	9137	8717	9149	8729	9161	8741	9173	8753
33	9037	8594	9049	8606	9061	8618	9072	8629	9084	8641	9096	8653	9108	8665	9119	8676	9131	8688	9143	8700
34	9008	8541	9019	8553	9031	8564	9043	8576	9054	8588	9066	8599	9078	8611	9089	8623	9101	8634	9113	8646
35	0.8978	0.8487	0.8990	0.8498	0.9002	0.8510	0.9013	0.8522	0.9025	0.8533	0.9037	0.8545	0.9048	0.8557	0.9060	0.8568	0.9072	0.8580	0.9083	0.8591
36	8949	8431	8961	8443	8972	8455	8984	8466	8996	8478	9007	8489	9019	8501	9031	8513	9042	8524	9054	8536
37	8920	8375	8932	8387	8943	8398	8955	8410	8967	8421	8978	8433	8990	8445	9001	8456	9013	8468	9025	8479
38	8892	8318	8903	8329	8915	8341	8926	8352	8938	8364	8949	8375	8961	8387	8972	8399	8984	8410	8995	8422
39	8863	8259	8875	8271	8886	8282	8898	8294	8909	8305	8921	8317	8932	8328	8944	8340	8955	8351	8967	8363
40	0.8835	0.8200	0.8846	0.8211	0.8858	0.8223	0.8869	0.8234	0.8881	0.8246	0.8892	0.8257	0.8903	0.8269	0.8915	0.8280	0.8926	0.8292	0.8938	0.8303
41	8806	8139	8818	8151	8829	8162	8841	8174	8852	8185	8864	8196	8875	8208	8887	8219	8898	8231	8909	8242
42	8778	8077	8790	8089	8801	8100	8813	8112	8824	8123	8835	8134	8847	8146	8858	8157	8870	8169	8881	8180

P / °C	780		781		782		783		784		785		786		787		788		789	
	dry	sat.	dry	sat.	dry	sat.	dry	sat.	dry	sat.	dry	sat.	dry	sat.	dry	sat.	dry	sat.	dry	sat.
0	1.0263	1.0203	1.0276	1.0216	1.0289	1.0229	1.0303	1.0242	1.0316	1.0256	1.0329	1.0269	1.0342	1.0282	1.0355	1.0295	1.0368	1.0308	1.0382	1.0321
1	0226	0161	0239	0174	0252	0187	0265	0200	0278	0213	0291	0227	0304	0240	0317	0253	0331	0266	0344	0279
2	0188	0119	0201	0132	0214	0145	0228	0158	0241	0171	0254	0185	0267	0198	0280	0211	0293	0224	0306	0237
3	0151	0077	0164	0090	0177	0103	0190	0116	0203	0129	0216	0142	0229	0155	0242	0169	0256	0182	0269	0195
4	0115	0036	0128	0049	0141	0061	0154	0074	0167	0087	0180	0100	0192	0113	0205	0126	0218	0139	0231	0152
5	1.0078	0.9994	1.0091	1.0007	1.0104	1.0020	1.0117	1.0032	1.0130	1.0045	1.0143	1.0058	1.0156	1.0071	1.0169	1.0084	1.0182	1.0097	1.0195	1.0110
6	0042	9952	0055	0.9965	0068	0.9977	0081	0.9990	0094	0003	0106	0016	0119	0029	0132	0042	0145	0055	0158	0068
7	0006	9910	0019	9923	0032	9935	0045	9948	0057	0.9961	0070	0.9974	0083	0.9987	0096	0000	0109	0012	0122	0025
8	0.9970	9868	0.9983	9880	0.9996	9893	0009	9906	0022	9919	0034	9932	0047	9944	0060	0.9957	0073	0.9970	0085	0.9983
9	9935	9825	9948	9838	9960	9851	0.9973	9864	0.9986	9876	0.9999	9889	0011	9902	0024	9915	0037	9927	0050	9940
10	0.9900	0.9783	0.9913	0.9796	0.9925	0.9808	0.9938	0.9821	0.9951	0.9834	0.9963	0.9846	0.9976	0.9859	0.9989	0.9872	1.0001	0.9884	1.0014	0.9897
11	9865	9740	9878	9753	9890	9766	9903	9778	9916	9791	9928	9804	9941	9816	9953	9829	0.9966	9842	0.9979	9854
12	9830	9698	9843	9710	9855	9723	9868	9735	9881	9748	9893	9761	9906	9773	9918	9786	9931	9799	9944	9811
13	9796	9655	9808	9667	9821	9680	9833	9692	9846	9705	9859	9718	9871	9730	9884	9743	9896	9755	9909	9768
14	9762	9612	9774	9624	9787	9637	9799	9649	9812	9662	9824	9674	9837	9687	9849	9699	9862	9712	9874	9724
15	0.9728	0.9568	0.9740	0.9581	0.9753	0.9593	0.9765	0.9606	0.9778	0.9618	0.9790	0.9631	0.9802	0.9643	0.9815	0.9655	0.9827	0.9668	0.9840	0.9680
16	9694	9524	9706	9537	9719	9549	9731	9562	9744	9574	9756	9587	9768	9599	9781	9611	9793	9624	9806	9636
17	9660	9480	9673	9493	9685	9505	9698	9518	9710	9530	9722	9542	9735	9555	9747	9567	9760	9580	9772	9592
18	9627	9436	9640	9449	9652	9461	9664	9473	9677	9486	9689	9498	9701	9510	9714	9523	9726	9535	9738	9547
19	9594	9391	9606	9404	9619	9416	9631	9428	9643	9441	9656	9453	9668	9465	9680	9478	9693	9490	9705	9502
20	0.9561	0.9346	0.9574	0.9359	0.9586	0.9371	0.9598	0.9383	0.9610	0.9395	0.9623	0.9408	0.9635	0.9420	0.9647	0.9432	0.9659	0.9444	0.9672	0.9457
21	9529	9301	9541	9313	9553	9325	9565	9338	9578	9350	9590	9362	9602	9374	9614	9386	9627	9399	9639	9411
22	9496	9255	9509	9267	9521	9279	9533	9292	9545	9304	9557	9316	9569	9328	9582	9340	9594	9352	9606	9365
23	9464	9209	9476	9221	9489	9233	9501	9245	9513	9257	9525	9269	9537	9281	9549	9294	9561	9306	9573	9318
24	9432	9162	9444	9174	9457	9186	9469	9198	9481	9210	9493	9222	9505	9234	9517	9246	9529	9258	9541	9271
25	0.9401	0.9114	0.9413	0.9126	0.9425	0.9138	0.9437	0.9150	0.9449	0.9163	0.9461	0.9175	0.9473	0.9187	0.9485	0.9199	0.9497	0.9211	0.9509	0.9223
26	9369	9066	9381	9078	9393	9090	9405	9102	9417	9114	9429	9126	9441	9138	9453	9150	9465	9162	9477	9174
27	9338	9018	9350	9030	9362	9042	9374	9054	9386	9066	9398	9078	9410	9090	9422	9102	9434	9114	9446	9126
28	9307	8969	9319	8980	9331	8992	9343	9004	9355	9016	9366	9028	9378	9040	9390	9052	9402	9064	9414	9076
29	9276	8919	9288	8931	9300	8942	9312	8954	9323	8966	9335	8978	9347	8990	9359	9002	9371	9014	9383	9026
30	0.9245	0.8868	0.9257	0.8880	0.9269	0.8892	0.9281	0.8904	0.9293	0.8915	0.9305	0.8927	0.9316	0.8939	0.9328	0.8951	0.9340	0.8963	0.9352	0.8975
31	9215	8817	9227	8829	9238	8840	9250	8852	9262	8864	9274	8876	9286	8888	9297	8899	9309	8911	9321	8923
32	9185	8765	9196	8776	9208	8788	9220	8800	9232	8812	9243	8823	9255	8835	9267	8847	9279	8859	9291	8871
33	9154	8712	9166	8723	9178	8735	9190	8747	9201	8759	9213	8770	9225	8782	9237	8794	9248	8806	9260	8817
34	9125	8658	9136	8670	9148	8681	9160	8693	9171	8705	9183	8716	9195	8728	9206	8740	9218	8751	9230	8763
35	0.9095	0.8603	0.9107	0.8615	0.9118	0.8626	0.9130	0.8638	0.9142	0.8650	0.9153	0.8661	0.9165	0.8673	0.9177	0.8685	0.9188	0.8696	0.9200	0.8708
36	9065	8548	9077	8559	9089	8571	9100	8582	9112	8594	9124	8606	9135	8617	9147	8629	9158	8640	9170	8652
37	9036	8491	9048	8502	9059	8514	9071	8526	9082	8537	9094	8549	9106	8560	9117	8572	9129	8584	9140	8595
38	9007	8433	9019	8445	9030	8456	9042	8468	9053	8479	9065	8491	9076	8503	9088	8514	9099	8526	9111	8537
39	8978	8374	8990	8386	9001	8398	9013	8409	9024	8421	9036	8432	9047	8444	9059	8455	9070	8467	9082	8478
40	0.8949	0.8315	0.8961	0.8326	0.8972	0.8338	0.8984	0.8349	0.8995	0.8361	0.9007	0.8372	0.9018	0.8383	0.9030	0.8395	0.9041	0.8406	0.9053	0.8418
41	8921	8254	8932	8265	8944	8276	8955	8288	8967	8299	8978	8311	8989	8322	9001	8334	9012	8345	9024	8357
42	8892	8191	8904	8203	8915	8214	8927	8226	8938	8237	8949	8248	8961	8260	8972	8271	8984	8283	8995	8294

Multiples of Atomic Weights

This table is based on the International Atomic Weights 1957. Note that in calculating the multiples these atomic weights have been treated as exact numbers.

Atomic Number Z			Factors	0	1	2	3	4	5	6	7	8	9
1	H	Hydrogen	0	0.000	1.008	2.016	3.024	4.032	5.040	6.048	7.056	8.064	9.072
			10	10.080	11.088	12.096	13.104	14.112	15.120	16.128	17.136	18.144	19.152
			20	20.160	21.168	22.176	23.184	24.192	25.200	26.208	27.216	28.224	29.232
			30	30.240	31.248	32.256	33.264	34.272	35.280	36.288	37.296	38.304	39.312
			40	40.320	41.328	42.336	43.344	44.352	45.360	46.368	47.376	48.384	49.392
			50	50.400	51.408	52.416	53.424	54.432	55.440	56.448	57.456	58.464	59.472
			60	60.480	61.488	62.496	63.504	64.512	65.520	66.528	67.536	68.544	69.552
			70	70.560	71.568	72.576	73.584	74.592	75.600	76.608	77.616	78.624	79.632
			80	80.640	81.648	82.656	83.664	84.672	85.680	86.688	87.696	88.704	89.712
			90	90.720	91.728	92.736	93.744	94.752	95.760	96.768	97.776	98.784	99.792
			100	100.800	101.808	102.816	103.824	104.832	105.840	106.848	107.856	108.864	109.872
			110	110.880	111.888	112.896	113.904	114.912	115.920	116.928	117.936	118.944	119.952
			120	120.960	121.968	122.976	123.984	124.992	126.000	127.008	128.016	129.024	130.032
			130	131.040	132.048	133.056	134.064	135.072	136.080	137.088	138.096	139.104	140.112
			140	141.120	142.128	143.136	144.144	145.152	146.160	147.168	148.176	149.184	150.192
			150	151.200	152.208	153.216	154.224	155.232	156.240	157.248	158.256	159.264	160.272
			160	161.280	162.288	163.296	164.304	165.312	166.320	167.328	168.336	169.344	170.352
			170	171.360	172.368	173.376	174.384	175.392	176.400	177.408	178.416	179.424	180.432
			180	181.440	182.448	183.456	184.464	185.472	186.480	187.488	188.496	189.504	190.512
			190	191.520	192.528	193.536	194.544	195.552	196.560	197.568	198.576	199.584	200.592
6	C	Carbon	0	00.000	12.011	24.022	36.033	48.044	60.055	72.066	84.077	96.088	108.099
			10	120.110	132.121	144.132	156.143	168.154	180.165	192.176	204.187	216.198	228.209
			20	240.220	252.231	264.242	276.253	288.264	300.275	312.286	324.297	336.308	348.319
			30	360.330	372.341	384.352	396.363	408.374	420.385	432.396	444.407	456.418	468.429
			40	480.440	492.451	504.462	516.473	528.484	540.495	552.506	564.517	576.528	588.539
			50	600.550	612.561	624.572	636.583	648.594	660.605	672.616	684.627	696.638	708.649
			60	720.660	732.671	744.682	756.693	768.704	780.715	792.726	804.737	816.748	828.759
			70	840.770	852.781	864.792	876.803	888.814	900.825	912.836	924.847	936.858	948.869
			80	960.880	972.891	984.902	996.913	1008.924	1020.935	1032.946	1044.957	1056.968	1068.979
			90	1080.990	1093.001	1105.012	1117.023	1129.034	1141.045	1153.056	1165.067	1177.078	1189.089
7	N	Nitrogen	0	00.000	14.008	28.016	42.024	56.032	70.040	84.048	98.056	112.064	126.072
			10	140.080	154.088	168.096	182.104	196.112	210.120	224.128	238.136	252.144	266.152
			20	280.160	294.168	308.176	322.184	336.192	350.200	364.208	378.216	392.224	406.232
			30	420.240	434.248	448.256	462.264	476.272	490.280	504.288	518.296	532.304	546.312
			40	560.320	574.328	588.336	602.344	616.352	630.360	644.368	658.376	672.384	686.392
8	O	Oxygen	0	00.0	16.0	32.0	48.0	64.0	80.0	96.0	112.0	128.0	144.0
			10	160.0	176.0	192.0	208.0	224.0	240.0	256.0	272.0	288.0	304.0
			20	320.0	336.0	352.0	368.0	384.0	400.0	416.0	432.0	448.0	464.0
			30	480.0	496.0	512.0	528.0	544.0	560.0	576.0	592.0	608.0	624.0
			40	640.0	656.0	672.0	688.0	704.0	720.0	736.0	752.0	768.0	784.0
9	F	Fluorine	0	00.00	19.00	38.00	57.00	76.00	95.00	114.00	133.00	152.00	171.00
11	Na	Sodium	0	00.000	22.991	45.982	68.973	91.964	114.955	137.946	160.937	183.928	206.919
12	Mg	Magnesium	0	00.00	24.32	48.64	72.96	97.28	121.60	145.92	170.24	194.56	218.88
13	Al	Aluminum	0	00.00	26.98	53.96	80.94	107.92	134.90	161.88	188.86	215.84	242.82
14	Si	Silicon	0	00.00	28.09	56.18	84.27	112.36	140.45	168.54	196.63	224.72	252.81
15	P	Phosphorus	0	00.000	30.975	61.950	92.925	123.900	154.875	185.850	216.825	247.800	278.775
			10	309.750	340.725	371.700	402.675	433.650	464.625	495.600	526.575	557.550	588.525
16	S	Sulfur	0	00.000	32.066	64.132	96.198	128.264	160.330	192.396	224.462	256.528	288.594
			10	320.660	352.726	384.792	416.858	448.924	480.990	513.056	545.122	577.188	609.254
17	Cl	Chlorine	0	00.000	35.457	70.914	106.371	141.828	177.285	212.742	248.199	283.656	319.113
19	K	Potassium	0	00.000	39.100	78.200	117.300	156.400	195.500	234.600	273.700	312.800	351.900
20	Ca	Calcium	0	00.00	40.08	80.16	120.24	160.32	200.40	240.48	280.56	320.64	360.72
25	Mn	Manganese	0	00.00	54.94	109.88	164.82	219.76	274.70	329.64	384.58	439.52	494.46
26	Fe	Iron	0	00.00	55.85	111.70	167.55	223.40	279.25	335.10	390.95	446.80	502.65
27	Co	Cobalt	0	00.00	58.94	117.88	176.82	235.76	294.70	353.64	412.58	471.52	530.46
29	Cu	Copper	0	00.00	63.54	127.08	190.62	254.16	317.70	381.24	444.78	508.32	571.86
30	Zn	Zinc	0	00.00	65.38	130.76	196.14	261.52	326.90	392.28	457.66	523.04	588.42
33	As	Arsenic	0	00.00	74.91	149.82	224.73	299.64	374.55	449.46	524.37	599.28	674.19
35	Br	Bromine	0	00.000	79.916	159.832	239.748	319.664	399.580	479.496	559.412	639.328	719.244
53	I	Iodine	0	000.00	126.91	253.82	380.73	507.64	634.55	761.46	888.37	1015.28	1142.19
56	Ba	Barium	0	000.00	137.36	274.72	412.08	549.44	686.80	824.16	961.52	1098.88	1236.24
80	Hg	Mercury	0	000.00	200.61	401.22	601.83	802.44	1003.05	1203.66	1404.27	1604.88	1805.49
	H_2O	Water ($\frac{1}{2}H_2O$ = 9.008)	0	00.000	18.016	36.032	54.048	72.064	90.080	108.096	126.112	144.128	162.144
			10	180.160	198.176	216.192	234.208	252.224	270.240	288.256	306.272	324.288	342.304
	CH_2	Methylene	0	00.000	14.027	28.054	42.081	56.108	70.135	84.162	98.189	112.216	126.243
			10	140.270	154.297	168.324	182.351	196.378	210.405	224.432	238.459	252.486	266.513
			20	280.540	294.567	308.594	322.621	336.648	350.675	364.702	378.729	392.756	406.783
			30	420.810	434.837	448.864	462.891	476.918	490.945	504.972	518.999	533.026	547.053
			40	561.080	575.107	589.134	603.161	617.188	631.215	645.242	659.269	673.296	687.323
	CH_3	Methyl	0	00.000	15.035	30.070	45.105	60.140	75.175	90.210	105.245	120.280	135.315
			10	150.350	165.385	180.420	195.455	210.490	225.525	240.560	255.595	270.630	285.665
			20	300.700	315.735	330.770	345.805	360.840	375.875	390.910	405.945	420.980	436.015

Compound	Formula	Mol. wt.
Acetanilide	$C_6H_5NHCOCH_3$	135.17
Acetophenetidine	$C_6H_4(NHCOCH_3)(OC_2H_5)$-1,4	179.22
Acetylcholine chloride	$[CH_3COOCH_2CH_2N(CH_3)_3]Cl$	181.67
Acetylsalicylic acid	$C_6H_4(COOH)(OCOCH_3)$-1,2	180.16
Aconitine	$C_{34}H_{49}O_{11}N$	647.77
Adrenaline	See Epinephrine	
Allyl isothiocyanate	$CH_2{:}CHCH_2NCS$	99.16
Amidopyrine	See Aminopyrine	
Aminophylline	$[N(CH_3)CON(CH_3)C{:}CCO\ N{:}CHNH]_2 \cdot NH_2CH_2CH_2NH_2 + 2H_2O$	456.48
Aminopyrine (Dimethyl-aminoantipyrine)	$N(C_6H_5)N(CH_3)C(CH_3){:}C[N(CH_3)_2]CO$	231.30
Amphetamine	$C_6H_5CH_2CH(NH_2)CH_3$	135.21
Amyl nitrite	$(CH_3)_2CHCH_2CH_2ONO$	117.15
Antimony potassium tartrate (Tartar emetic)	$[KOOC(CHOH)_2COOSbO] + \frac{1}{2}H_2O$	333.94
Antipyrine	$N(C_6H_5)N(CH_3)C(CH_3){:}CHCO$	188.23
Apomorphine hydrochloride	$[C_{17}H_{17}O_2N \cdot HCl] + \frac{1}{2}H_2O$	312.80
Atropine	$C_{17}H_{23}O_3N$	289.38
Barbital (Barbitone)	$NHCONHCOC(C_2H_5)_2CO$	184.20
Barbital sodium	$NHC(ONa){:}NCOC(C_2H_5)_2CO$	206.18
Bromoform	$CHBr_3$	252.77
Butacaine sulfate	$[H_2NC_6H_4COO(CH_2)_3N(C_4H_9)_2\text{-}1,4]_2 \cdot H_2SO_4$	710.99
Caffeine	$[N(CH_3)CON(CH_3)C{:}CCO\ N{:}CHN(CH_3)] + H_2O$	212.22
Calcium gluconate	$[[CH_2OH(CHOH)_4COO]_2Ca] + H_2O$	448.40
– glycerophosphate	$[C_3H_5(OH)_2OPO_3Ca] + H_2O$	228.16
– lactate	$[[CH_3CH(OH)COO]_2Ca] + 5H_2O$	308.31
– mandelate	$[C_6H_5CH(OH)COO]_2Ca$	342.37
Camphor	$C(CH_3)CH_2CH_2CHC(CH_3)_2\ CH_2CO$	152.24
N-Carbamyl-arsanilic acid	$C_6H_4[AsO(OH)_2][NHCONH_2]$-1,4	260.08
Carbromal	$(C_2H_5)_2CBrCONHCONH_2$	237.11
Chloral hydrate	$CCl_3CH(OH)_2$	165.42
Chloramphenicol	$CH(OH)(C_6H_4\text{-}p\text{-}NO_2) \cdot CH(NHCOCHCl_2) \cdot CH_2OH$	323.15
Chloroform	$CHCl_3$	119.39
Chloroquine	$C_9H_5N[Cl][NHCH(CH_3)\cdot(CH_2)_3\cdot N(C_2H_5)_2]$-7,4	319.89
Cholesterol	$C_{27}H_{45}OH$	386.67
Cinchophen	$CH{:}CH\cdot CH{:}CH\cdot C{:}C\cdot C(COOH){:}CH\cdot C(C_6H_5){:}N$	249.27
Cocaine	$C_{17}H_{21}O_4N$	303.36
Codeine	$[C_{18}H_{21}O_3N]+H_2O$	317.39
Colchicine	$C_{22}H_{25}O_6N$	399.45
Coumarin	$CH{:}CHCH{:}CHC{:}C\cdot O\cdot CO\cdot CH{:}CH$	146.15
Creatinine	$CH_3NC({:}NH)NHCOCH_2$	113.12
Cresol	$CH_3C_6H_4OH$	108.14
Cyclopropane	$CH_2CH_2CH_2$	42.08
Dextrose (D-Glucose)	$[CH_2(OH)\cdot CH(OH)\cdot CH(OH)\cdot (HO)CH\cdot CH(OH)\cdot CHO]+H_2O$	198.18
Diethylbarbituric acid	See Barbital	
Diethylstilbestrol	See Stilbestrol	
Digitonin	$C_{55}H_{90}O_{29}$	1215.33
Digitoxin	$C_{41}H_{64}O_{13}$	764.96
Dihydromorphinone	$C_{17}H_{19}O_3N$	285.35
Dihydrostreptomycin hydrochloride	$C_{21}H_{41}O_{12}N_7.3HCl$	693.01
– sulfate	$(C_{21}H_{41}O_{12}N_7)_2.3H_2SO_4$	1461.48
Diiodohydroxyquinoline	$CI{:}CHCI{:}C(OH)C{:}CCH{:}CHCH{:}N$	396.97
Dimercaprol (BAL)	$CH_2(SH)CH(SH)CH_2OH$	124.23
m-Dinitrobenzene	$C_6H_4(NO_2)_2$-1,3	168.11
Dioxan	$OCH_2CH_2OCH_2CH_2$	88.11
Diphenylhydantoin	See Phenytoin	
Emetine hydrochloride	$C_{29}H_{40}O_4N_2.2HCl$	553.59
Ephedrine hydrochloride	$C_6H_5CH(OH)CH(NHCH_3)CH_3.HCl$	201.70
Epinephrine hydrochloride	$C_6H_3[CH(OH)CH_2NHCH_3][OH]_2.HCl$-1,3,4	219.68
Ergonovine (Ergometrine)	$C_{19}H_{23}O_2N_3$	325.42
Ergotamine	$C_{33}H_{35}N_5O_5$	581.68
– tartrate	$(C_{33}H_{35}N_5O_5)_2.H_2C_4H_4O_6$	1313.46
Ergotoxine	$C_{35}H_{41}O_6N_5$	627.75
Ethanol (Ethyl alcohol)	C_2H_5OH	46.07
Ether	$(C_2H_5)_2O$	74.12
Ethylmorphine hydrochloride	$[C_{19}H_{23}O_3N]\cdot HCl+2H_2O$	385.90
N-Ethylpiperidine	$CH_2CH_2CH_2CH_2CH_2NC_2H_5$	113.21
Eucalyptol	$(CH_3)_2CCHCH_2CH_2C(O)(CH_3)\cdot CH_2CH_2$	154.25
Eucatropine	$C_6H_5CH(OH)COOCHCH_2C(CH_3)_2N(CH_3)CH(CH_3)CH_2$	291.40
Formaldehyde	HCHO	30.03
GIRARD's reagent	$[(CH_3)_3NCH_2CONHNH_2]Cl$	167.65
Glycerol	$HOCH_2CH(OH)CH_2OH$	92.10
Histamine	$N{:}CHNHCH{:}CCH_2CH_2NH_2$	111.15
Homatropine	$C_{16}H_{21}O_3N$	275.35
Hyoscine	See Scopolamine	
Hyoscyamine	$C_{17}H_{23}O_3N$	289.38
Iodoform	CHI_3	393.75
Lactic acid	$CH_3CH(OH)COOH$	90.08
Lanatoside C	$C_{49}H_{76}O_{20}$	985.15
Mandelic acid	$C_6H_5CH(OH)COOH$	152.15
Menthol	$(CH_3)_2CHCHCH(OH)CH_2CH(CH_3)CH_2CH_2$	156.27
Mepacrine	See Quinacrine	
Meperidine	$C_6H_5\cdot C(COOC_2H_5)\cdot CH_2CH_2N(CH_3)CH_2CH_2$	247.34
Methanol (Methyl alcohol)	CH_3OH	32.04
Methylene blue	$[C_{16}H_{18}ClN_3S]+3H_2O$	373.92
Morphine	$[C_{17}H_{19}O_3N]+H_2O$	303.36
Neostigmine bromide	$C_6H_4[N(CH_3)_3Br][OCON(CH_3)_2]$-1,3	303.22
Nikethamide	$CH{:}CHCH{:}NCH{:}CCON(C_2H_5)_2$	178.24
Nitrogen mustard	See Allyl isothiocyanate	
Ouabain (Strophanthin-G)	$[C_{29}H_{44}O_{12}]+8H_2O$	728.80
Papaverine	$C_{20}H_{21}O_4N$	339.40
Penicillin-G sodium	$C_{16}H_{17}N_2NaO_4S$	356.39
Pentobarbital	$NHCONHCOC[CH(CH_3)C_3H_7][C_2H_5]CO$	226.28
Phenacetin	See Acetophenetidine	
Phenazone	See Antipyrine	
Phenobarbital	$NHCONHCOC(C_6H_5)(C_2H_5)CO$	232.24
– sodium	$NHC(ONa){:}NCOC(C_6H_5)(C_2H_5)CO$	254.23
Phenytoin	$(C_6H_5)_2CNHCONHCO$	252.28
Physostigmine	$C_{15}H_{21}O_2N_3$	275.36
Picrotoxin	$C_{30}H_{34}O_{13}$	602.60
Pilocarpine	$C_{11}H_{16}O_2N_2$	208.27
Piperocaine	$C_6H_5COO(CH_2)_3N\cdot(CH_2)_4\cdot CH(CH_3)$	261.37
Procaine hydrochloride	$C_6H_4[COOCH_2CH_2N(C_2H_5)_2][NH_2].HCl$-1,4	272.78
Quinacrine	$C_{23}H_{30}ClON_3$	399.97
Quinidine	$C_{20}H_{24}O_2N_2$	324.43
Quinine	$[C_{20}H_{24}O_2N_2]+3H_2O$	378.48
Resorcinol	$C_6H_4(OH)_2$-1,3	110.11
Rochelle salt (Potassium sodium tartrate)	$[CH(OH)(COOK)\cdot CH(OH)(COONa)]+4H_2O$	282.23
Rutin	$[C_{27}H_{30}O_{16}]+3H_2O$	664.59
Salicylic acid	$C_6H_4(COOH)(OH)$-1,2	138.13
Santonin	$CH{:}CH\cdot CO\cdot C(CH_3){:}C\cdot C(CH_3)\cdot CH_2\cdot CH_2\cdot CH\cdot CH\cdot O\cdot CO\cdot CH\cdot CH_3$	246.31
Scopolamine (Hyoscine)	$C_{17}H_{21}O_4N$	303.36
Sodium lactate	$CH_3CH(OH)COONa$	112.06
Stilbestrol	$p\text{-}HOC_6H_4(C_2H_5)C{:}C(C_2H_5)C_6H_4OH\text{-}p'$	268.36
Streptomycin hydrochloride	$C_{21}H_{39}O_{12}N_7.3HCl$	690.99
– sulfate	$(C_{21}H_{39}O_{12}N_7)_2.3H_2SO_4$	1457.44
Strophanthin-G	See Ouabain	
Strychnine	$C_{21}H_{22}O_2N_2$	334.42
Sulfadiazine	$p\text{-}NH_2\cdot C_6H_4\cdot SO_2NHC{:}N\cdot CH{:}CH\cdot CH{:}N$	250.29
Sulfamerazine	$p\text{-}NH_2\cdot C_6H_4\cdot SO_2NHC{:}N\cdot CH{:}CH\cdot C(CH_3){:}N$	264.32
Sulfanilamide	$p\text{-}NH_2\cdot C_6H_4\cdot SO_2NH_2$	172.21
Sulfapyridine	$p\text{-}NH_2\cdot C_6H_4\cdot SO_2NHC{:}N\cdot CH{:}CH\cdot CH{:}CH$	249.30
Sulfathiazole	$p\text{-}NH_2\cdot C_6H_4\cdot SO_2NHC{:}N\cdot CH{:}CH\cdot S$	255.33
Theobromine	$NH\cdot CO\cdot N(CH_3)\cdot C{:}C\cdot CO\ N{:}CH\cdot NCH_3$	180.17
Theophylline	$N(CH_3)\cdot CO\cdot N(CH_3)\cdot C{:}C\cdot CO\ N{:}CH\cdot NH\cdot H_2O$	198.19
Tryparsamide	$[p\text{-}NH_2COCH_2NH\cdot C_6H_4AsO(OH)ONa]+\frac{1}{2}H_2O$	305.09
Tubocurarine chloride	$[C_{33}H_{44}O_6N_2]Cl_2+5H_2O$	785.78
Undecylenic acid	$CH_2{:}CH\cdot (CH_2)_8\cdot COOH$	184.28
Urea (Carbamide)	$CO(NH_2)_2$	60.06
Urethane	$H_2NCOOC_2H_5$	89.10
Uric acid	$NH\cdot CO\cdot NH\cdot C{:}C\cdot CO\ NH\cdot CO\cdot NH$	168.12

Chemical Conversion Factors

For conversion factors for electrolytes see also pages 328–330

1. Conversion factors for compounds

For converting		Factor	$\log_{10}$	For converting		Factor	$\log_{10}$
Acetone	into acetoacetic acid	1.758	0.245 50	Acetoacetic acid.....	into acetone......	0.5689	0.7550−1
Acetone	into β-hydroxybutyric acid	1.792	0.2533	β-Hydroxybutyric acid	into acetone	0.5579	0.7466−1
Ca	into CaO............	1.399	0.1458	CaO..............	into Ca	0.7147	0.8548−1
Cl...........	into NaCl	1.649	0.2172	NaCl	into Cl	0.6066	0.7829−1
K...........	into K_2O............	1.205	0.0810	K_2O............	into K..........	0.8301	0.9191−1
Mg	into MgO............	1.658	0.2196	MgO	into Mg	0.6032	0.7805−1
Na..........	into NaCl	2.542	0.4052	NaCl	into Na..........	0.3934	0.5948−1
Na	into Na_2O............	1.348	0.1297	Na_2O............	into Na..........	0.7419	0.8704−1
P	into P_2O_5	2.291	0.3600	P_2O_5	into P	0.4365	0.6400−1
P	into H_3PO_4	3.164	0.4997	H_3PO_4	into P	0.3161	0.4998−1
S	into SO_3	2.497	0.4065	SO_3	into S	0.4005	0.6026−1
S	into H_2SO_4	3.059	0.4857	H_2SO_4............	into S	0.3269	0.5144−1
Nitrogen							
Protein-N....	into protein	6.25	0.7959	Protein	into protein-N....	0.16	0.2041−1
Ammonia-N .	into ammonia	1.216	0.0849	Ammonia	into ammonia-N ..	0.8225	0.9151−1
Creatine-N ...	into creatine	3.120	0.4942	Creatine	into creatine-N ...	0.3205	0.5058−1
Creatinine-N .	into creatinine	2.692	0.4301	Creatinine	into creatinine-N..	0.3715	0.5700−1
Urea-N	into urea	2.144	0.3312	Urea...............	into urea-N	0.4665	0.6689−1
Uric acid-N ..	into uric acid	3.000	0.4771	Uric acid	into uric acid-N...	0.3333	0.5228−1
Lipids*							
Lipid-P	into phosphatides	23.5	1.3711				
Lipid-P......	into lecithin	25	1.3979	Lecithin	into lipid-P.......	0.04	0.0021−2

* Lipids = phospholipids (phosphatides) + steroids. Cf. pages 385-389.

2. Conversion of mg/100 ml into millimoles per liter and vice versa

$$\text{mmol/l} = \frac{10 \times \text{mg/100 ml}}{\text{molecular weight}} = \frac{10{,}000 \times \text{g/100 ml}}{\text{molecular weight}}$$

$$\text{mg/100 ml} = \frac{\text{mmol} \times \text{molecular weight}}{10}$$

3. Conversion of ml of gas/100 ml into millimoles per liter and vice versa

$$\text{mmol/l} = \frac{\text{ml/100 ml}}{2.24} \quad (2.24 = \text{millimolar volume})$$

$$\text{ml/100 ml} = 2.24 \times \text{mmol/l}$$

4. Conversion of mg/100 ml into milliequivalents per liter and vice versa

$$\text{mEq/l} = \frac{10 \times \text{mg/100 ml} \times \text{valency}}{\text{molecular weight}}$$

$$\text{mg/100 ml} = \frac{\text{mEq/l} \times \text{molecular weight}}{10 \times \text{valency}}$$

5. Conversion of normality into milliequivalents per liter

$$\text{N/1000} = 0.001\text{-N} = 1 \text{ ml N/10 per 100 ml} = 1 \text{ ml N per liter} = 1 \text{ mEq per liter}$$
$$= 1 \text{ mmol per liter/valency} = \text{equivalent weight (in mg) per liter}$$

	Molecular weight	Hydrogen equivalent	1 ml of 0.1-N solution contains (gram)	Mantissa of $\log_{10}$ of equivalent weight
Acetic acid	60.05	CH_3COOH	0.006005	7786
Ammonia	17.03	NH_3	0.001703	2311
Ammonium chloride	53.50	NH_4Cl	0.005350	7284
Ammonium hydroxide	35.05	NH_4OH	0.003505	5447
Ammonium nitrate	80.05	NH_4NO_3	0.008005	9034
Ammonium sulfate	132.15	$\frac{1}{2}(NH_4)_2SO_4$	0.006607	8200
Ammonium thiocyanate	76.13	NH_4CNS	0.007613	8816
Barium carbonate	197.37	$\frac{1}{2}BaCO_3$	0.009869	9943
Barium chloride	244.31	$\frac{1}{2}[BaCl_2+2H_2O]$	0.012215	0869
Barium hydroxide	315.50	$\frac{1}{2}[Ba(OH)_2+8H_2O]$	0.015775	1980
Barium oxide	153.36	$\frac{1}{2}BaO$	0.007668	8847
Borax. See Sodium tetraborate decahydrate				
Boric acid	61.84	$\frac{1}{3}H_3BO_3$	0.002061	3141
Bromine	159.83	$\frac{1}{2}Br_2$	0.007992	9026
Calcium carbonate	100.09	$\frac{1}{2}CaCO_3$	0.005005	6994
Calcium chloride	110.99	$\frac{1}{2}CaCl_2$	0.005550	7443
Calcium chloride hexahydrate	219.09	$\frac{1}{2}[CaCl_2+6H_2O]$	0.010955	0396
Calcium hydroxide	74.10	$\frac{1}{2}Ca(OH)_2$	0.003705	5688
Calcium oxide	56.08	$\frac{1}{2}CaO$	0.002804	4478
Carbon dioxide	44.01	$\frac{1}{2}CO_2$	0.002201	3426
Chlorine	70.91	$\frac{1}{2}Cl_2$	0.003546	5497
Citric acid	210.15	$\frac{1}{3}[C_6H_8O_7+H_2O]$	0.007005	8454
Copper oxide	79.54	$\frac{1}{2}CuO$	0.003977	5996
Copper sulfate	249.69	$\frac{1}{2}[CuSO_4+5H_2O]$	0.012484	0964
Hydriodic acid	127.92	HI	0.012792	1070
Hydrobromic acid	80.92	HBr	0.008092	9080
Hydrochloric acid	36.47	HCl	0.003647	5619
Hydrocyanic acid	27.03	HCN	0.002703	4319
Iodine	253.82	$\frac{1}{2}I_2$	0.012691	1035
Lactic acid	90.08	$CH_3{\cdot}CHOH{\cdot}COOH$	0.009008	9546
Lead carbonate	267.22	$\frac{1}{2}PbCO_3$	0.013361	1258
Lead oxide	223.21	$\frac{1}{2}PbO$	0.011161	0477
Magnesium carbonate	84.33	$\frac{1}{2}MgCO_3$	0.004217	6250
Magnesium chloride	95.23	$\frac{1}{2}MgCl_2$	0.004762	6778
Magnesium chloride hexahydrate	203.33	$\frac{1}{2}[MgCl_2+6H_2O]$	0.010167	0071_{928}
Magnesium oxide	40.32	$\frac{1}{2}MgO$	0.002016	3045
Malic acid	134.09	$\frac{1}{2}C_4H_6O_5$	0.006705	8264
Manganese sulfate	151.01	$\frac{1}{2}MnSO_4$	0.007550	8779
Mercuric chloride (Corrosive sublimate)	271.52	$\frac{1}{2}HgCl_2$	0.013576	1328
Nitric acid	63.02	HNO_3	0.006302	7994
Nitrous acid	47.02	HNO_2	0.004702	6723
Oxalic acid	90.04	$\frac{1}{2}HOOC{\cdot}COOH$	0.004502	6534
Oxalic acid dihydrate	126.07	$\frac{1}{2}[HOOC{\cdot}COOH+2H_2O]$	0.006304	7996
Phosphoric acid	98.00	$\frac{1}{3}H_3PO_4$	0.003267	5141
Potassium bicarbonate	100.12	$KHCO_3$	0.010012	0005_{208}
Potassium bitartrate	188.18	$C_4H_5O_6K$	0.018818	2746
Potassium carbonate	138.21	$\frac{1}{2}K_2CO_3$	0.006911	8396
Potassium chloride	74.56	KCl	0.007456	8726
Potassium cyanide	65.12	KCN	0.006512	8137
Potassium dichromate	294.22	$\frac{1}{6}K_2Cr_2O_7$	0.004904	6906
Potassium hydroxide	56.11	KOH	0.005611	7491
Potassium oxide	94.20	$\frac{1}{2}K_2O$	0.004710	6730
Potassium permanganate for CO determination	158.04	$\frac{1}{5}KMnO_4$	0.003161	4998
Potassium permanganate for Mn determination	158.04	$\frac{1}{3}KMnO_4$	0.005268	7217
Potassium tartrate	226.28	$\frac{1}{2}C_4H_4O_6K_2$	0.011314	0536
Potassium tetroxalate	254.20	$\frac{1}{3}[KH_3(C_2O_4)_2+2H_2O]$	0.008473	9281
Silver nitrate	169.89	$AgNO_3$	0.016989	2302
Sodium bicarbonate	84.01	$NaHCO_3$	0.008401	9244
Sodium carbonate	105.99	$\frac{1}{2}Na_2CO_3$	0.005300	7243
Sodium chloride	58.45	$NaCl$	0.005845	7668
Sodium hydroxide	40.00	$NaOH$	0.004000	6021
Sodium oxide	61.98	$\frac{1}{2}Na_2O$	0.003099	4913
Sodium phosphate (Disodium phosphate)	178.00	$\frac{1}{2}[Na_2HPO_4+2H_2O]$	0.008900	9494
Sodium phosphate (Trisodium phosphate)	380.14	$\frac{1}{3}[Na_3PO_4+12H_2O]$	0.012671	1028
Sodium sulfide	78.05	$\frac{1}{2}Na_2S$	0.003902	5913
Sodium tetraborate	201.26	$\frac{1}{2}Na_2B_4O_7$	0.010063	0027_{275}
Sodium tetraborate decahydrate (Borax)	381.42	$\frac{1}{2}[Na_2B_4O_7+10H_2O]$	0.019071	2804
Succinic acid	118.09	$\frac{1}{2}C_4H_6O_4$	0.005905	7713
Sulfuric acid	98.08	$\frac{1}{2}H_2SO_4$	0.004904	6906
Sulfur trioxide	80.07	$\frac{1}{2}SO_3$	0.004003	6024
Tartaric acid	150.09	$\frac{1}{2}C_4H_6O_6$	0.007505	8754
Zinc sulfate	287.56	$\frac{1}{2}[ZnSO_4+7H_2O]$	0.014378	1577

Unless otherwise stated, stock solutions and buffers should be prepared and made up with distilled water free from carbon dioxide. Standard reagents should be used. The strength of solutions made up with reagents of doubtful purity or degree of hydration must be checked by titration. The amounts x and y of the stock solutions required to yield a desired pH value are given in the table on the opposite page. In the table below, the buffers are arranged in the alphabetical order of their chemical names.

No.	Buffer	pH range	Stock solutions A	Stock solutions B	Composition of the buffer
1	WALPOLE's acetate[1,2]	3.6–5.6	0.2 molar acetic acid (12.0 g/l)	0.2 molar sodium acetate (16.4 g $C_2H_3O_2Na$ or 27.2 g $C_2H_3O_2Na{\cdot}3H_2O$ per liter)	x ml A + y ml B made up to 100 ml
2	GOMORI's aconitate[2]	2.5–5.7	0.5 molar aconitic acid (87.1 g/l)	0.2-N NaOH	10 ml A + x ml B made up to 100 ml
3	MICHAELIS's barbital sodium[3]	6.8–9.6	0.1 molar barbital sodium (20.6 g/l)	0.1-N HCl	x ml A + (100–x) ml B
4	MICHAELIS's barbital sodium–acetate[4]	2.6–9.4	$^1/_7$ molar sodium acetate in $^1/_7$ molar barbital sodium (19.43 g $C_2H_3O_2{\cdot}3H_2O$ + 29.43 g barbital sodium in 1 liter)	0.1-N HCl	50 ml A + x ml B + 20 ml 8.5% NaCl solution made up to 250 ml
5	CLARK and LUBS's borate[5]	7.8–10.0	0.1 molar boric acid in 0.1 molar KCl (6.2 g H_3BO_3 + 7.46 g KCl per liter)	0.1-N NaOH	50 ml A + x ml B made up to 100 ml
6	KOLTHOFF's borax–phosphate[6,7]	5.8–9.2	0.05 molar borax (19.1 g/l)	0.1 molar monopotassium phosphate (13.6 g KH_2PO_4 per liter)	x ml A + (100–x) ml B
7	KOLTHOFF's borax–succinic acid[7]	3.0–5.8	0.05 molar borax (19.1 g/l)	0.05 molar succinic acid (5.9 g/l)	x ml A + (100–x) ml B
8	PLUMEL's cacodylate[2,8]	5.0–7.4	0.2 molar sodium cacodylate (42.8 g $Na[CH_3]_2AsO_2{\cdot}3H_2O$ per liter)	0.2-N HCl	25 ml A + x ml B made up to 100 ml
9	DELORY and KING's carbonate–bicarbonate[2,9]	9.2–10.7	0.2 molar anhydrous sodium carbonate (21.2 g/l)	0.2 molar sodium bicarbonate (16.8 g/l)	x ml A + y ml B made up to 100 ml
10	SØRENSEN's citrate I[10,11]	2.2–4.8	0.1 molar disodium citrate (21.0 g citric acid [$1H_2O$] diss. in 200 ml 1-N NaOH and made up to 1 liter)	0.1-N HCl	x ml A + (100–x) ml B
11	SØRENSEN's citrate II[10,11]	5.0–6.8	As No. 10	0.1-N NaOH	x ml A + (100–x) ml B
12	TEORELL and STENHAGEN's citrate–phosphate–borate[12]	2.0–12.0	To citric acid and phosphoric acid solutions (ca. 100 ml), each corr. to 100 ml 1-N NaOH, add 3.54 g cryst. orthoboric acid and 343 ml 1-N NaOH, and make up the mixture to 1 liter	0.1-N HCl	20 ml A + x ml B made up to 100 ml
13	McILVAINE's citric acid–phosphate[13]	2.2–8.0	0.1 molar citric acid (21.0 g $C_6H_8O_7{\cdot}1H_2O$ per liter)	0.2 molar disodium phosphate (35.6 g $Na_2HPO_4{\cdot}2H_2O$ per liter)	x ml A + (100–x) ml B
14	STAFFORD, WATSON and RAND's dimethylglutarate[14]	3.2–7.6	0.1 molar ββ-dimethylglutaric acid (16.02 g/l)	0.2-N NaOH	(*a*) 100 ml A + x ml B made up to 1000 ml (*b*) 100 ml A + x ml B + 5.845 g NaCl made up to 1000 ml (≙ 0.1 molar NaCl)
15	SØRENSEN's glycine I[10,11]	1.2–3.6	0.1 molar glycine in 0.1-N NaCl (7.5 g glycine + 5.85 g NaCl in 1 liter)	0.1-N HCl	x ml A + (100–x) ml B
16	SØRENSEN's glycine II[10,11]	8.4–13.0	As No. 15	0.1-N NaOH	x ml A + (100–x) ml B
17	SØRENSEN's phosphate[11,15]	5.0–8.2	$^1/_{15}$ molar monopotassium phosphate (9.08 g KH_2PO_4 per liter)	$^1/_{15}$ molar disodium phosphate (11.88 g $Na_2HPO_4{\cdot}2H_2O$ per liter)	x ml A + (100–x) ml B
18	CLARK and LUBS's phthalate I[5]	2.2–3.8	0.1 molar potassium biphthalate (20.4 g $KHC_8H_4O_4$ per liter)	0.1-N HCl	50 ml A + x ml B made up to 100 ml
19	CLARK and LUBS's phthalate II[5]	4.0–6.2	As No. 18	0.1-N NaOH	50 ml A + x ml B made up to 100 ml
20	SMITH and SMITH's piperazine[16]	4.8–7.0 8.8–11.0	Molar piperazine dihydrochloride (159.1 g/l)	1-N NaOH	1000 ml A + x ml B
21	SMITH and SMITH's piperazine (sea-water)[16]	5.4–9.8	0.01 molar piperazine dihydrochloride in filtered sea water (pH 8.0) (1.591 g/l)	1-N NaOH	1000 ml A + x ml B
22	SMITH and SMITH's piperazine–glycylglycine[16]	4.4–10.8	0.01 molar piperazine dihydrochloride in 0.01 molar glycylglycine (1.591 g piperazine·2HCl + 1.321 g glycylglycine in 1 liter)	1-N NaOH	1000 ml A + x ml B
23	CLARK and LUB's potassium chloride–hydrochloric acid[5]	1.0–2.2	0.2-N KCl (14.9 g/l)	0.2-N HCl	25 ml A + x ml B made up to 100 ml
24	GOMORI's succinate[2]	3.8–6.0	0.2 molar succinic acid (23.62 g/l)	0.2-N NaOH	25 ml A + x ml B made up to 100 ml
25	GOMORI's tris[2,17]	7.2–9.0	0.2 molar tris (24.2 g tris[hydroxymethyl]aminomethane per liter)	0.2-N HCl	25 ml A + x ml B made up to 100 ml
26	GOMORI's tris–maleate[2,17]	5.2–8.6	0.2 molar tris acid maleate (24.2 g tris-[hydroxymethyl]aminomethane + 23.2 g maleic acid or 19.6 g maleic anhydride in 1 liter)	0.2-N NaOH	25 ml A + x ml B made up to 100 ml

1) WALPOLE, G. S., *J. chem. Soc.*, **105**, 2501 (1914). *2)* GOMORI, G., in COLOWICK and KAPLAN (Eds.), *Methods in Enzymology*, vol. I, New York, 1955, page 138. *3)* MICHAELIS, L., *J. biol. Chem.*, **87**, 33 (1930). *4)* MICHAELIS, L., *Biochem. Z.*, **234**, 139 (1931). *5)* CLARK and LUBS, *J. Bact.*, **2**, 1 (1917). *6)* KOLTHOFF, I. M., *Säure-Basen-Indicatoren*, Berlin, 1932, page 257. *7)* KOLTHOFF, I. M., *J. biol. Chem.*, **63**, 135 (1925). *8)* PLUMEL, M., *Bull. Soc. chim. biol. (Paris)*, **30**, 129 (1948). *9)* DELORY and KING, *Biochem. J.*, **39**, 245 (1945). *10)* SØRENSEN, S. P. L., *Biochem. Z.*, **21**, 131 (1909). *11)* SØRENSEN, S. P. L., *Ergebn. Physiol.*, **12**, 393 (1912). *12)* TEORELL and STENHAGEN, *Biochem. Z.*, **299**, 416 (1938). *13)* McILVAINE, T. C., *J. biol. Chem.*, **49**, 183 (1921). *14)* STAFFORD et al., *Biochim. biophys. Acta*, **18**, 319 (1955); KREBS and HEMS, personal communication (1957). *15)* SØRENSEN, S. P. L., *Biochem. Z.*, **22**, 352 (1909). *16)* SMITH and SMITH, *Biol. Bull.*, **96**, 233 (1949). *17)* GOMORI, G., *Proc. Soc. exp. Biol. (N. Y.)*, **68**, 354 (1948).

This table gives the quantities (*x* or *x*, *y*) of stock solutions required to make up any of the numbered buffers listed on the page opposite to a desired pH value at the temperature given.

pH	**1** (23°C)		**2** (23°C)	**4** (23°C)	**5** (20°C)	**6** (18°C)	**7** (18°C)	**8** (23°C)		**10** (*)	**11** (18°C)	**12** (20°C)	**13** (21°C)	**14a** (21°C)	**14b** (21°C)	**15** (18°C)	**17** (18°C)	**18** (20°C)	**19** (20°C)	**20** (25°C)	**21** (25°C)	**22** (25°C)	**23** (20°C)	**25** (23°C)	**26** (23°C)	pH
	x	*y*	*x*	*x*	*x*	*x*	*x*	*x*		*x*	*x*	*x*	*x*	*x*	*x*	*x*	*x*	*x*	*x*	*x*	*x*	*x*	*x*	*x*	*x*	
1.0	—		—	—	—	—	—	—		—	—	—	—	—	—	—	—	—	—	—	—	—	48.50	—	—	1.0
2	—		—	—	—	—	—	—		—	—	—	—	—	—	15.0	—	—	—	—	—	—	32.25	—	—	2
4	—		—	—	—	—	—	—		—	—	—	—	—	—	28.7	—	—	—	—	—	—	20.75	—	—	4
6	—		—	—	—	—	—	—		—	—	—	—	—	—	38.2	—	—	—	—	—	—	13.15	—	—	6
8	—		—	—	—	—	—	—		—	—	—	—	—	—	45.7	—	—	—	—	—	—	8.40	—	—	8
2.0	—		—	—	—	—	—	—		—	—	73.30	—	—	—	52.3	—	—	—	—	—	—	5.30	—	—	2.0
2	—		—	—	—	—	—	—		33.0	—	67.85	98.00	—	—	58.3	—	46.70	—	—	—	—	3.35	—	—	2
4	—		—	—	—	—	—	—		34.6	—	63.85	93.80	—	—	64.5	—	39.60	—	—	—	—	—	—	—	4
6	—		9.0	160.5	—	—	—	—		36.4	—	60.80	89.10	—	—	70.2	—	32.95	—	—	—	—	—	—	—	6
8	—		12.3	157.5	—	—	—	—		38.4	—	58.45	84.15	—	—	75.6	—	26.42	—	—	—	—		—	—	8
3.0	—		16.0	154.0	—	—	1.4	—		40.5	—	56.50	79.45	—	—	80.8	—	20.32	—	—	—	—	**24** (23°C)	—	—	3.0
2	—		20.0	150.0	—	—	3.5	—		42.8	—	54.95	75.30	8.3	15.7	85.6	—	14.70	—	—	—	—		—	—	2
4	—		24.0	146.0	—	—	6.0	—		46.0	—	53.70	71.50	14.7	22.1	90.3	—	9.90	—	—	—	—		—	—	4
6	46.3	3.7	28.0	140.0	—	—	9.5	—		48.5	—	52.65	67.80	22.0	27.9	94.5	—	5.97	—	—	—	—	—	—	—	6
8	44.0	6.0	32.0	133.5	—	—	13.7	—		52.0	—	51.55	64.50	27.4	33.3	—	—	2.63	—	—	—	—	7.5	—	—	8
4.0	41.0	9.0	36.0	125.5	—	—	17.8	—		55.8	—	50.50	61.45	33.3	37.4	—	—	—	0.40	—	—	—	10.0	—	—	4.0
2	36.8	13.2	39.8	117.5	—	—	22.2	—		61.2	—	49.45	58.60	36.8	40.9	—	—	—	3.70	—	—	—	13.3	—	—	2
4	30.5	19.5	43.3	109.5	—	—	26.2	—		67.8	—	48.35	55.90	39.8	43.6	—	—	—	7.50	—	—	0.07	16.7	—	—	4
6	25.5	24.5	46.8	101.5	—	—	30.0	—		76.6	—	47.26	53.25	41.7	46.2	—	—	—	12.15	—	—	0.54	20.0	—	—	6
8	20.0	30.0	50.0	94.5	—	—	33.5	—		88.2	—	46.22	50.70	43.9	48.9	—	—	—	17.70	70.0	—	1.20	23.5	—	—	8
5.0	14.8	35.2	52.8	88.0	—	—	36.8	23.5		—	96.3	45.18	48.50	46.2	52.0	—	98.8	—	23.85	111.0	—	2.20	26.7	—	—	5.0
2	10.5	39.5	55.3	82.5	—	—	39.5	22.5		—	85.0	44.05	46.40	49.0	54.3	—	98.0	—	29.95	174.0	—	3.20	30.3	—	3.5	2
4	8.8	41.2	58.0	78.0	—	—	42.1	21.5		—	76.5	42.94	44.25	52.0	59.2	—	96.7	—	35.45	258.0	0.88	4.19	34.2	—	5.4	4
6	4.8	45.2	61.3	75.0	—	—	44.3	19.6		—	69.3	41.80	42.00	55.8	64.6	—	94.8	—	39.85	355.0	2.00	5.38	37.5	—	7.8	6
8	—		—	72.5	—	7.9	46.0	17.4		—	63.3	40.61	39.55	59.7	69.7	—	91.9	—	43.00	466.0	3.53	6.51	40.7	—	10.3	8
6.0	—			71.0	—	12.3	—	14.8		—	59.5	39.42	36.85	65.0	74.6	—	87.7	—	45.45	581.0	4.93	7.45	43.5	—	13.0	6.0
2	—		**3** (23°C)	69.5	—	17.0	—	11.9		—	56.7	38.09	33.90	70.5	79.5	—	81.5	—	47.00	690.0	6.15	8.27	—	—	15.8	2
4	—			68.5	—	23.0	—	9.2		—	54.5	36.74	30.75	75.5	84.2	—	73.2	—	—	780.0	7.18	8.99	—	—	18.5	4
6	—			66.5	—	28.8	—	6.7		—	53.0	35.36	27.25	84.7	88.1	—	62.7	—	—	850.0	7.97	9.53	—	—	21.3	6
8	—		52.2	64.0	—	34.2	—	4.7		—	51.8	33.92	22.75	88.0	91.5	—	50.8	—	—	900.0	8.54	9.99	—	—	22.5	8
7.0	—		53.6	60.5	—	39.0	—	3.2		—	—	32.65	18.15	90.4	93.6	—	39.2	—	—	936.0	8.95	10.45	—	—	24.0	7.0
2	—		55.4	56.5	—	43.4	—	2.1		—	—	31.45	13.05	92.1	95.1	—	28.5	—	—	936.0	9.23	10.91	—	22.1	25.5	2
4	—		58.1	50.5	—	46.4	—	1.4		—	—	30.35	9.15	93.2	96.0	—	19.6	—	—	936.0	9.47	11.52	—	20.7	27.0	4
6	—		61.5	43.0	—	49.2	—	—		—	—	29.43	6.35	94.0	97.0		13.2	—	—	936.0	9.65	12.31	—	19.2	29.0	6
8	—		66.2	34.5	2.61	52.0	—	—		—	—	28.68	4.30	—	—	**16** (18°C)	8.6	—	—	936.0	9.83	13.29	—	16.3	31.8	8
8.0	—		71.6	26.0	3.97	55.0	—	—		—	—	28.02	2.75	—	—		5.5	—	—	936.0	10.01	14.45	—	13.4	34.5	8.0
2	—		76.9	18.5	5.90	57.6	—			—	—	27.45	—	—	—		3.3	—	—	936.0	10.27	15.71	—	11.0	37.5	2
4	—		82.3	13.0	8.50	62.0	—	**9** (23°C)		—	—	26.90	—	—	—	96.5	—	—	—	936.0	10.65	16.97	—	8.3	40.5	4
6	—		87.1	9.0	12.00	68.0	—			—	—	26.10	—	—	—	94.8	—	—	—	936.0	11.13	18.25	—	6.1	43.3	6
8	—		90.8	6.0	16.30	75.2	—			—	—	24.90	—	—	—	92.1	—	—	—	1079.0	11.76	19.50	—	4.1	—	8
9.0	—		93.6	4.0	21.30	86.8	—	*x*	*y*	—	—	23.75	—	—	—	88.5	—	—	—	1121.0	12.62	20.64	—	2.5	—	9.0
2	—		95.2	2.0	26.70	100.0	—	2.0	23.0	—	—	22.38	—	—	—	84.2	—	—	—	1179.0	13.62	21.85	—	—	—	2
4	—		97.4	1.0	32.00	—	—	4.8	20.3	—	—	21.12	—	—	—	79.0	—	—	—	1252.0	14.88	23.13	—	—	—	4
6	—		98.5	—	36.85	—	—	8.0	17.0	—	—	19.94	—	—	—	73.2	—	—	—	1346.0	16.42	24.51	—	—	—	6
8	—		—	—	40.80	—	—	11.0	14.0	—	—	18.81	—	—	—	67.7	—	—	—	1456.0	18.65	25.87	—	—	—	8
10.0	—		—	—	43.90	—	—	13.8	11.3	—	—	17.92	—	—	—	63.0	—	—	—	1566.0	—	27.17	—	—	—	10.0
2	—		—	—	—	—	—	16.5	8.5	—	—	16.97	—	—	—	59.0	—	—	—	1666.0	—	28.32	—	—	—	2
4	—		—	—	—	—	—	19.3	5.8	—	—	16.36	—	—	—	56.1	—	—	—	1762.0	—	29.37	—	—	—	4
6	—		—	—	—	—	—	21.3	3.8	—	—	15.95	—	—	—	53.7	—	—	—	1844.0	—	30.42	—	—	—	6
8	—		—	—	—	—	—	—		—	—	15.40	—	—	—	52.2	—	—	—	1905.0	—	31.53	—	—	—	8
11.0	—		—	—	—	—	—	—		—	—	14.52	—	—	—	51.0	—	—	—	1952.0	—	—	—	—	—	11.0
2	—		—	—	—	—	—	—		—	—	13.20	—	—	—	50.3	—	—	—	—	—	—	—	—	—	2
4	—		—	—	—	—	—	—		—	—	11.23	—	—	—	49.7	—	—	—	—	—	—	—	—	—	4
6	—		—	—	—	—	—	—		—	—	8.40	—	—	—	48.8	—	—	—	—	—	—	—	—	—	6
8	—		—	—	—	—	—	—		—	—	4.70	—	—	—	47.8	—	—	—	—	—	—	—	—	—	8
12.0	—		—	—	—	—	—	—		—	—	0.40	—	—	—	46.2	—	—	—	—	—	—	—	—	—	12.0
2	—		—	—	—	—	—	—		—	—	—	—	—	—	43.6	—	—	—	—	—	—	—	—	—	2
4	—		—	—	—	—	—	—		—	—	—	—	—	—	40.0	—	—	—	—	—	—	—	—	—	4
6	—		—	—	—	—	—	—		—	—	—	—	—	—	33.4	—	—	—	—	—	—	—	—	—	6
8	—		—	—	—	—	—	—		—	—	—	—	—	—	24.2	—	—	—	—	—	—	—	—	—	8
13.0	—		—											—	—	7.5	—	—	—	—	—	—	—	—	—	13.0

* pH variation negligible over the normal working temperature range.

pH Ranges of Indicators *

Based on data of the Federal Materials Testing and Research Institute, St.Gall, Switzerland

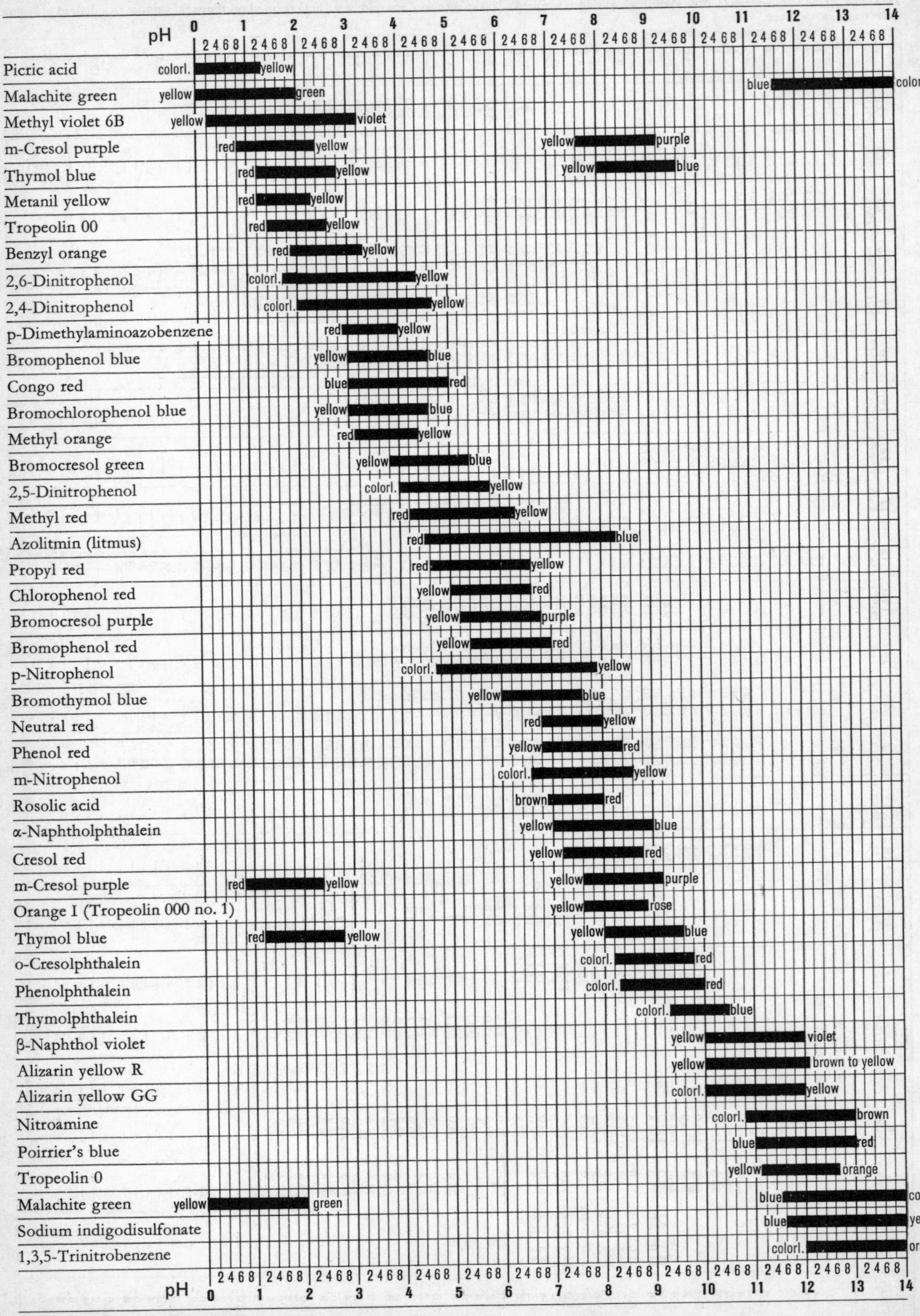

* With acknowledgments to Distillation Products Industries, Rochester, N.Y.

Nitric acid

Spec. grav.	° Baumé (NBS scale)	Grams per liter	% HNO_3	N
1.0036	0.5	10.04	1	0.159
1.0091	1.3	20.18	2	0.320
1.0146	2.1	30.44	3	0.483
1.0201	2.9	40.80	4	0.647
1.0256	3.6	51.28	5	0.814
1.0312	4.4	61.87	6	0.982
1.0369	5.2	72.58	7	1.15
1.0427	5.9	83.42	8	1.32
1.0485	6.7	94.37	9	1.50
1.0543	7.5	105.4	10	1.67
1.0602	8.2	116.6	11	1.85
1.0661	9.0	127.9	12	2.03
1.0721	9.8	139.4	13	2.21
1.0781	10.5	150.9	14	2.39
1.0842	11.3	162.6	15	2.58
1.0903	12.0	174.4	16	2.77
1.0964	12.8	186.4	17	2.96
1.1026	13.5	198.5	18	3.15
1.1088	14.2	210.7	19	3.34
1.1150	15.0	223.0	20	3.54
1.1213	15.7	235.5	21	3.74
1.1276	16.4	248.1	22	3.94
1.1340	17.1	260.8	23	4.13
1.1404	17.9	273.7	24	4.34
1.1469	18.6	286.7	25	4.55
1.1534	19.4	299.9	26	4.76
1.1600	20.0	313.2	27	4.97
1.1666	20.7	326.6	28	5.18
1.1733	21.4	340.3	29	5.40
1.1800	22.1	354.0	30	5.62
1.1867	22.8	367.9	31	5.84
1.1934	23.5	381.9	32	6.06
1.2002	24.2	396.1	33	6.29
1.2071	24.9	410.4	34	6.51
1.2140	25.6	424.9	35	6.74

Spec. grav.	° Baumé (NBS scale)	Grams per liter	% HNO_3	N
1.2205	26.2	439.4	36	6.97
1.2270	26.8	454.0	37	7.20
1.2335	27.5	468.7	38	7.44
1.2399	28.1	483.6	39	7.67
1.2463	28.7	498.5	40	7.91
1.2527	29.3	513.6	41	8.15
1.2591	29.8	528.8	42	8.39
1.2655	30.4	544.2	43	8.64
1.2719	31.0	559.6	44	8.88
1.2783	31.6	575.2	45	9.13
1.2847	32.1	591.0	46	9.38
1.2911	32.7	606.8	47	9.63
1.2975	33.2	622.8	48	9.88
1.3040	33.8	639.0	49	10.1
1.3100	34.3	655.0	50	10.4
1.3160	34.8	671.2	51	10.7
1.3219	35.3	687.4	52	10.9
1.3278	35.8	703.7	53	11.1
1.3336	36.3	720.1	54	11.4
1.3393	36.7	736.6	55	11.7
1.3449	37.2	753.1	56	12.0
1.3505	37.6	769.8	57	12.2
1.3560	38.1	786.5	58	12.5
1.3614	38.5	803.2	59	12.7
1.3667	38.9	820.0	60	13.0
1.3719	39.3	836.9	61	13.3
1.3769	39.7	853.7	62	13.5
1.3818	40.1	870.5	63	13.8
1.3866	40.4	887.4	64	14.1
1.3913	40.8	904.3	65	14.4
1.3959	41.1	921.3	66	14.6
1.4004	41.5	938.3	67	14.9
1.4048	41.8	955.3	68	15.2
1.4091	42.1	972.3	69	15.4
1.4134	42.4	989.4	70	15.7

Spez. grav.	° Baumé (NBS scale)	Grams per liter	% HNO_3	N
1.4176	42.7	1006	71	16.0
1.4218	43.0	1024	72	16.3
1.4258	43.3	1041	73	16.5
1.4298	43.6	1058	74	16.8
1.4337	43.9	1075	75	17.1
1.4375	44.1	1093	76	17.3
1.4413	44.4	1110	77	17.6
1.4450	44.7	1127	78	17.9
1.4486	44.9	1144	79	18.2
1.4521	45.1	1162	80	18.4
1.4555	45.4	1179	81	18.7
1.4589	45.6	1196	82	19.0
1.4622	45.8	1214	83	19.3
1.4655	46.1	1231	84	19.5
1.4686	46.3	1248	85	19.8
1.4716	46.5	1266	86	20.1
1.4745	46.7	1283	87	20.4
1.4773	46.8	1300	88	20.6
1.4800	47.0	1317	89	20.9
1.4826	47.2	1334	90	21.2
1.4850	47.4	1351	91	21.4
1.4873	47.5	1368	92	21.7
1.4892	47.6	1385	93	22.0
1.4912	47.8	1402	94	22.3
1.4932	47.9	1419	95	22.5
1.4952	48.0	1435	96	22.8
1.4974	48.2	1452	97	23.0
1.5008	48.4	1471	98	23.3
1.5056	48.7	1491	99	23.7
1.5129	49.2	1513	100	24.0

Sulfuric acid

Spec. grav.	° Baumé (NBS scale)	Grams per liter	% H_2SO_4	N
1.0051	0.7	10.05	1	0.205
1.0118	1.7	20.24	2	0.413
1.0184	2.6	30.55	3	0.623
1.0250	3.5	41.00	4	0.836
1.0317	4.5	51.59	5	1.05
1.0385	5.4	62.31	6	1.27
1.0453	6.3	73.17	7	1.49
1.0522	7.2	84.18	8	1.72
1.0591	8.1	95.32	9	1.94
1.0661	9.0	106.6	10	2.17
1.0731	9.9	118.0	11	2.41
1.0802	10.8	129.6	12	2.64
1.0874	11.7	141.4	13	2.88
1.0947	12.5	153.3	14	3.13
1.1020	13.4	165.3	15	3.37
1.1094	14.3	177.5	16	3.62
1.1168	15.2	189.9	17	3.87
1.1243	16.0	202.4	18	4.13
1.1318	16.9	215.0	19	4.38
1.1394	17.7	227.9	20	4.65
1.1471	18.6	240.9	21	4.91
1.1548	19.4	254.1	22	5.18
1.1626	20.3	267.4	23	5.45
1.1704	21.1	280.9	24	5.73
1.1783	21.9	294.6	25	6.01
1.1862	22.8	308.4	26	6.29
1.1942	23.6	322.4	27	6.57
1.2023	24.4	336.6	28	6.86
1.2104	25.2	351.0	29	7.16
1.2185	26.0	365.6	30	7.46
1.2267	26.8	380.3	31	7.76
1.2349	27.6	395.2	32	8.06
1.2432	28.4	410.3	33	8.37
1.2515	29.1	425.5	34	8.68
1.2599	29.9	441.0	35	8.99

Spec. grav.	° Baumé (NBS scale)	Grams per liter	% H_2SO_4	N
1.2684	30.7	456.6	36	9.31
1.2769	31.4	472.5	37	9.64
1.2855	32.2	488.5	38	9.96
1.2941	33.0	504.7	39	10.3
1.3028	33.7	521.1	40	10.6
1.3116	34.5	537.8	41	11.0
1.3205	35.2	554.6	42	11.3
1.3294	35.9	571.6	43	11.7
1.3384	36.7	588.9	44	12.0
1.3476	37.4	606.4	45	12.4
1.3569	38.1	624.2	46	12.7
1.3663	38.9	642.2	47	13.1
1.3758	39.6	660.4	48	13.5
1.3854	40.3	678.8	49	13.8
1.3951	41.1	697.6	50	14.2
1.4049	41.8	716.5	51	14.6
1.4148	42.5	735.7	52	15.0
1.4248	43.2	755.1	53	15.4
1.4350	44.0	774.9	54	15.8
1.4453	44.7	794.9	55	16.2
1.4557	45.4	815.2	56	16.6
1.4662	46.1	835.7	57	17.0
1.4768	46.8	856.5	58	17.5
1.4875	47.5	877.6	59	17.9
1.4983	48.2	899.0	60	18.3
1.5091	48.9	920.6	61	18.8
1.5200	49.6	942.4	62	19.2
1.5310	50.3	964.5	63	19.7
1.5421	51.0	986.9	64	20.1
1.5533	51.7	1010	65	20.6
1.5646	52.3	1033	66	21.1
1.5760	53.0	1056	67	21.5
1.5874	53.7	1079	68	22.0
1.5989	54.3	1103	69	22.5
1.6105	55.0	1127	70	23.0

Spec. grav.	° Baumé (NBS scale)	Grams per liter	% H_2SO_4	N
1.6221	55.6	1152	71	23.5
1.6338	56.3	1176	72	24.0
1.6456	56.9	1201	73	24.5
1.6574	57.5	1226	74	25.0
1.6692	58.1	1252	75	25.5
1.6810	58.7	1278	76	26.1
1.6927	59.3	1303	77	26.6
1.7043	59.9	1329	78	27.1
1.7158	60.5	1355	79	27.6
1.7272	61.1	1382	80	28.2
1.7383	61.6	1408	81	28.7
1.7491	62.1	1434	82	29.2
1.7594	62.6	1460	83	29.8
1.7693	63.0	1486	84	30.3
1.7786	63.5	1512	85	30.8
1.7872	63.9	1537	86	31.3
1.7951	64.2	1562	87	31.9
1.8022	64.5	1586	88	32.3
1.8087	64.8	1610	89	32.8
1.8144	65.1	1633	90	33.3
1.8195	65.3	1656	91	33.8
1.8240	65.5	1678	92	34.2
1.8279	65.7	1700	93	34.7
1.8312	65.8	1721	94	35.1
1.8337	65.9	1742	95	35.5
1.8355	66.0	1762	96	35.9
1.8364	66.0	1781	97	36.3
1.8361	66.0	1799	98	36.7
1.8342	65.9	1816	99	37.0
1.8305	65.8	1831	100	37.3

1) Values from LANGE and FORKER (Eds.), *Handbook of Chemistry*, 9th ed., Sandusky, 1956; and HODGMAN et al. (Eds.), *Handbook of Chemistry and Physics*, 42nd ed., Cleveland, 1960.

Acetic acid

Spec. grav.	° Baumé (NBS scale)	Grams per liter	% $C_2H_4O_2$	Spec. grav.	° Baumé (NBS scale)	Grams per liter	% $C_2H_4O_2$
0.9982	...	....	0	1.0575	7.9	528.8	50
0.9996	...	9.996	1	1.0582	8.0	539.7	51
1.0012	0.2	20.02	2	1.0590	8.1	550.7	52
1.0025	0.4	30.08	3	1.0597	8.2	561.6	53
1.0040	0.6	40.16	4	1.0604	8.3	572.6	54
1.0055	0.8	50.28	5	1.0611	8.4	583.6	55
1.0069	1.0	60.41	6	1.0618	8.4	594.6	56
1.0083	1.2	70.58	7	1.0624	8.5	605.6	57
1.0097	1.4	80.78	8	1.0631	8.6	616.6	58
1.0111	1.6	91.00	9	1.0637	8.7	627.6	59
1.0125	1.8	101.3	10	1.0642	8.8	638.5	60
1.0139	2.0	111.5	11	1.0648	8.8	649.5	61
1.0154	2.2	121.8	12	1.0653	8.9	660.5	62
1.0168	2.4	132.2	13	1.0658	9.0	671.5	63
1.0182	2.6	142.5	14	1.0662	9.0	682.4	64
1.0195	2.8	152.9	15	1.0666	9.1	693.3	65
1.0209	3.0	163.3	16	1.0671	9.1	704.3	66
1.0223	3.2	173.8	17	1.0675	9.2	715.2	67
1.0236	3.3	184.2	18	1.0678	9.2	726.1	68
1.0250	3.5	194.8	19	1.0682	9.3	737.1	69
1.0263	3.7	205.3	20	1.0685	9.3	748.0	70
1.0276	3.9	215.8	21	1.0687	9.3	758.8	71
1.0288	4.1	226.3	22	1.0690	9.4	769.7	72
1.0301	4.2	236.9	23	1.0693	9.4	780.6	73
1.0313	4.4	247.5	24	1.0694	9.4	791.4	74
1.0326	4.6	258.2	25	1.0696	9.4	802.2	75
1.0338	4.7	268.8	26	1.0698	9.5	813.0	76
1.0349	4.9	279.4	27	1.0699	9.5	823.8	77
1.0361	5.1	290.1	28	1.0700	9.5	834.6	78
1.0372	5.2	300.8	29	1.0700	9.5	845.3	79
1.0384	5.4	311.5	30	1.0700	9.5	856.0	80
1.0395	5.5	322.2	31	1.0699	9.5	866.6	81
1.0406	5.7	333.0	32	1.0698	9.5	877.2	82
1.0417	5.8	343.8	33	1.0696	9.4	887.8	83
1.0428	6.0	354.6	34	1.0693	9.4	898.2	84
1.0438	6.1	365.3	35	1.0689	9.4	908.6	85
1.0449	6.2	376.2	36	1.0685	9.3	918.9	86
1.0459	6.4	387.0	37	1.0680	9.2	929.2	87
1.0469	6.5	397.8	38	1.0675	9.2	939.4	88
1.0479	6.6	408.7	39	1.0668	9.1	949.5	89
1.0488	6.8	419.5	40	1.0661	9.0	959.5	90
1.0498	6.9	430.4	41	1.0652	8.9	969.3	91
1.0507	7.0	441.3	42	1.0643	8.8	979.2	92
1.0516	7.1	452.2	43	1.0632	8.6	988.8	93
1.0525	7.2	463.1	44	1.0619	8.5	998.2	94
1.0534	7.4	474.0	45	1.0605	8.3	1007	95
1.0542	7.5	484.9	46	1.0588	8.1	1016	96
1.0551	7.6	495.9	47	1.0570	7.8	1025	97
1.0559	7.7	506.8	48	1.0549	7.6	1034	98
1.0567	7.8	517.8	49	1.0524	7.2	1042	99
				1.0498	6.9	1050	100

Hydrochloric acid

Spec. grav.	° Baumé (NBS scale)	Grams per liter	% HCl	N
1.0032	0.5	10.03	1	0.275
1.0082	1.2	20.16	2	0.553
1.0181	2.6	40.72	4	1.12
1.0279	3.9	61.67	6	1.69
1.0376	5.3	83.01	8	2.28
1.0474	6.6	104.7	10	2.87
1.0574	7.9	126.9	12	3.48
1.0675	9.2	149.5	14	4.10
1.0776	10.4	172.4	16	4.73
1.0878	11.7	195.8	18	5.37
1.0980	12.9	219.6	20	6.02
1.1083	14.2	243.8	22	6.69
1.1187	15.4	268.5	24	7.36
1.1290	16.6	293.5	26	8.05
1.1392	17.7	319.0	28	8.75
1.1493	18.8	344.8	30	9.46
1.1593	19.9	371.0	32	10.2
1.1691	21.0	397.5	34	10.9
1.1789	22.0	424.4	36	11.6
1.1885	23.0	451.6	38	12.4
1.1980	24.0	479.2	40	13.1

Phosphoric acid

Spec. grav.	° Baumé (NBS scale)	Grams per liter	% H_3PO_4	Grams per liter	% P_2O_5
1.0038	0.6	10.04	1	7.271	0.7244
1.0092	1.3	20.18	2	14.62	1.449
1.0200	2.8	40.80	4	29.56	2.898
1.0309	4.3	61.85	6	44.81	4.346
1.0420	5.8	83.36	8	60.39	5.795
1.0532	7.3	105.3	10	76.29	7.244
1.0647	8.8	127.8	12	92.55	8.693
1.0764	10.3	150.7	14	109.2	10.14
1.0884	11.8	174.1	16	126.1	11.59
1.1008	13.3	198.1	18	143.5	13.04
1.1134	14.8	222.7	20	161.3	14.49
1.1263	16.3	247.8	22	179.5	15.94
1.1395	17.8	273.5	24	198.1	17.39
1.1529	19.2	299.8	26	217.1	18.83
1.1665	20.7	326.6	28	236.6	20.28
1.1805	22.2	354.2	30	256.5	21.73
1.216	25.8	425.6	35	308.3	25.35
1.254	29.4	501.6	40	363.4	28.98
1.293	32.9	581.9	45	421.5	32.60
1.335	36.4	667.5	50	483.5	36.22
1.379	39.9	758.5	55	549.4	39.84
1.426	43.3	855.6	60	619.8	43.46
1.475	46.7	958.8	65	694.5	47.09
1.526	50.0	1068	70	773.8	50.71
1.579	53.2	1184	75	857.9	54.33
1.633	56.2	1306	80	946.4	57.95
1.689	59.2	1436	85	1040	61.57
1.746	62.0	1571	90	1138	65.20
1.770	63.1	1628	92	1180	66.64
1.794	64.2	1686	94	1222	68.09
1.819	65.3	1746	96	1265	69.54
1.844	66.4	1807	98	1309	70.99
1.870	67.5	1870	100	1355	72.44

Sodium thiosulfate

Spec. grav.	° Baumé (NBS scale)	Grams per liter	% $Na_2S_2O_3$	Grams per liter	% $Na_2S_2O_3 + 5H_2O$
1.0065	0.9	10.07	1	15.80	1.570
1.0148	2.1	20.30	2	31.86	3.139
1.0315	4.4	41.26	4	64.77	6.279
1.0483	6.7	62.90	6	98.73	9.418
1.0654	8.9	85.23	8	133.8	12.56
1.0827	11.1	108.3	10	170.0	15.70
1.1003	13.2	132.0	12	207.3	18.84
1.1182	15.3	156.5	14	245.7	21.98
1.1365	17.4	181.8	16	285.4	25.12
1.1551	19.5	207.9	18	326.4	28.25
1.1740	21.5	234.8	20	368.6	31.39
1.1932	23.5	262.5	22	412.1	34.53
1.2128	25.4	291.1	24	456.9	37.67
1.2328	27.4	320.5	26	503.1	40.81
1.2532	29.3	350.9	28	550.8	43.95
1.2739	31.2	382.2	30	599.9	47.09
1.3273	35.8	464.6	35	729.2	54.94
1.3827	40.1	553.1	40	868.2	62.79

Ferric chloride

Spec. grav.	° Baumé (NBS scale)	Grams per liter	% $FeCl_3$
1.007	1.0	10.07	1
1.015	2.1	20.30	2
1.032	4.5	41.28	4
1.049	6.8	62.94	6
1.067	9.1	85.36	8
1.085	11.4	108.5	10
1.104	13.7	132.5	12
1.123	15.9	157.2	14
1.142	18.0	182.7	16
1.162	20.2	209.2	18
1.182	22.3	236.4	20
1.234	27.5	308.5	25
1.291	32.7	387.3	30
1.353	37.8	473.6	35
1.418	42.7	567.2	40
1.485	47.4	668.3	45
1.551	51.5	775.5	50

1) Values from LANGE and FORKER (Eds.), *Handbook of Chemistry*, 9th ed., Sandusky, 1956; and HODGMAN et al. (Eds.), *Handbook of Chemistry and Physics*, 42nd ed., Cleveland, 1960.

Barium chloride

Spec. grav.	° Baumé (NBS scale)	Grams per liter	% $BaCl_2$	Grams per liter	% $BaCl_2.2H_2O$
1.0159	2.3	20.32	2	23.83	2.346
1.0341	4.8	41.36	4	48.52	4.692
1.0528	7.3	63.17	6	74.10	7.038
1.0721	9.8	85.77	8	100.6	9.384
1.0921	12.2	109.2	10	128.1	11.73
1.1128	14.7	133.5	12	156.6	14.08
1.1342	17.2	158.8	14	186.3	16.42
1.1564	19.6	185.0	16	217.0	18.77
1.1793	22.0	212.3	18	249.0	21.11
1.2031	24.5	240.6	20	282.2	23.46
1.2277	26.9	270.1	22	316.8	25.81
1.2531	29.3	300.7	24	352.8	28.15
1.2793	31.7	332.6	26	390.2	30.50

Calcium chloride

Spec. grav.	° Baumé (NBS scale)	Grams per liter	% $CaCl_2$	Grams per liter	% $CaCl_2.6H_2O$
1.0148	2.1	20.30	2	40.06	3.948
1.0316	4.4	41.26	4	81.46	7.896
1.0486	6.7	62.92	6	124.2	11.84
1.0659	9.0	85.27	8	168.3	15.79
1.0835	11.2	108.4	10	213.9	19.74
1.1015	13.4	132.2	12	260.9	23.69
1.1198	15.5	156.8	14	309.5	27.64
1.1386	17.7	182.2	16	359.6	31.58
1.1578	19.8	208.4	18	411.4	35.53
1.1775	21.9	235.5	20	465.9	39.48
1.2284	27.0	307.1	25	606.2	49.35
1.2816	31.9	384.5	30	759.0	59.22
1.3373	36.6	468.1	35	923.9	69.09
1.3957	41.1	558.3	40	1102.0	78.96

Sodium chloride

Spec. grav.	° Baumé (NBS scale)	Grams per liter	% NaCl
1.0053	0.8	10.05	1
1.0125	1.8	20.25	2
1.0268	3.8	41.07	4
1.0413	5.8	62.48	6
1.0559	7.7	84.47	8
1.0707	9.6	107.1	10
1.0857	11.5	130.3	12
1.1009	13.3	154.1	14
1.1162	15.1	178.6	16
1.1319	16.9	203.7	18
1.1478	18.7	229.6	20
1.1640	20.4	256.1	22
1.1804	22.2	283.3	24
1.1972	23.9	311.3	26

Sodium sulfate

Spec. grav.	° Baumé (NBS scale)	Grams per liter	% Na_2SO_4	Grams per liter	% $Na_2SO_4.10H_2O$
1.0073	1.1	10.07	1	22.85	2.268
1.0164	2.3	20.33	2	46.11	4.536
1.0348	4.9	41.39	4	93.88	9.073
1.0535	7.4	63.21	6	143.4	13.61
1.0724	9.8	85.79	8	194.6	18.15
1.0915	12.2	109.2	10	247.6	22.68
1.1109	14.5	133.3	12	302.4	27.22
1.1306	16.8	158.3	14	359.0	31.75
1.1506	19.0	184.1	16	417.6	36.29
1.1709	21.2	210.8	18	478.1	40.83
1.1915	23.3	238.3	20	540.5	45.36
1.2124	25.4	266.7	22	605.0	49.90
1.2336	27.5	296.1	24	671.5	54.44

Conversion of Hydrometer Scales[1]

m = value of 1 degree on the scale
ρ = density
T = standard temperature of the scale

Scale	T °C	$\rho > 1$	$\rho < 1$
Balling	17.5	$\rho = \frac{200}{200-m}$	$\rho = \frac{200}{200+m}$
Baumé (rational) (Germany)	15	$\rho = \frac{144.3}{144.3-m}$	$\rho = \frac{144.3}{144.3+m}$
Baumé (National Bureau of Standards, U.S.A.)*	15.56 (60°F)	$\rho = \frac{145}{145-m}$	$\rho = \frac{140}{130+m}$
Baumé (Holland)	12.5	$\rho = \frac{144}{144-m}$	$\rho = \frac{144}{145+m}$
Baumé (Gerlach)	17.5	$\rho = \frac{146.3}{146.3-m}$	$\rho = \frac{146.3}{146.3+m}$
Beck	12.5	$\rho = \frac{170}{170-m}$	$\rho = \frac{170}{170+m}$
Brix	15.625	$\rho = \frac{400}{400-m}$	$\rho = \frac{400}{400+m}$
Cartier	12.5	$\rho = \frac{136.8}{126.1-m}$	$\rho = \frac{136.8}{126.1+m}$
Stoppani	15.625	$\rho = \frac{166}{166-m}$	$\rho = \frac{166}{166+m}$
Twaddell (U.K.)*	15.56 (60°F)	$\rho = 1 + \frac{m}{200}$	not used

Density greater than 1

Density	° Baumé (NBS scale)	Twaddell	Density	° Baumé (NBS scale)	Twaddell	Density	° Baumé (NBS scale)	Twaddell
1.00	0.00	0	1.35	37.59	70	1.70	59.71	140
1.01	1.44	2	1.36	38.38	72	1.71	60.20	142
1.02	2.84	4	1.37	39.16	74	1.72	60.70	144
1.03	4.22	6	1.38	39.93	76	1.73	61.18	146
1.04	5.58	8	1.39	40.68	78	1.74	61.67	148
1.05	6.91	10	1.40	41.43	80	1.75	62.14	150
1.06	8.21	12	1.41	42.16	82	1.76	62.61	152
1.07	9.49	14	1.42	42.89	84	1.77	63.08	154
1.08	10.74	16	1.43	43.60	86	1.78	63.54	156
1.09	11.97	18	1.44	44.31	88	1.79	63.99	158
1.10	13.18	20	1.45	45.00	90	1.80	64.44	160
1.11	14.37	22	1.46	45.68	92	1.81	64.89	162
1.12	15.54	24	1.47	46.36	94	1.82	65.31	164
1.13	16.68	26	1.48	47.03	96	1.83	65.77	166
1.14	17.81	28	1.49	47.68	98	1.84	66.20	168
1.15	18.91	30	1.50	48.33	100	1.85	66.62	170
1.16	20.00	32	1.51	48.97	102	1.86	67.04	172
1.17	21.07	34	1.52	49.60	104	1.87	67.46	174
1.18	22.12	36	1.53	50.23	106	1.88	67.87	176
1.19	23.15	38	1.54	50.84	108	1.89	68.28	178
1.20	24.17	40	1.55	51.45	110	1.90	68.68	180
1.21	25.16	42	1.56	52.05	112	1.91	69.08	182
1.22	26.15	44	1.57	52.64	114	1.92	69.48	184
1.23	27.11	46	1.58	53.23	116	1.93	69.87	186
1.24	28.06	48	1.59	53.80	118	1.94	70.26	188
1.25	29.00	50	1.60	54.38	120	1.95	70.64	190
1.26	29.92	52	1.61	54.94	122	1.96	71.02	192
1.27	30.83	54	1.62	55.49	124	1.97	71.40	194
1.28	31.72	56	1.63	56.04	126	1.98	71.77	196
1.29	32.60	58	1.64	56.58	128	1.99	72.14	198
1.30	33.46	60	1.65	57.12	130	2.00	72.50	200
1.31	34.31	62	1.66	57.65	132			
1.32	35.15	64	1.67	58.17	134			
1.33	35.98	66	1.68	58.69	136			
1.34	36.79	68	1.69	59.20	138			

1) Values from LANGE and FORKER (Eds.), *Handbook of Chemistry*, 9th ed., Sandusky, 1956; and HODGMAN et al. (Eds.), *Handbook of Chemistry and Physics*, 42nd ed., Cleveland, 1960. * See adjacent table.

Sodium hydroxide $\left(\frac{20°}{4°}\ C\right)$

Spec. grav.	° Baumé (NBS scale)	Grams per liter	% NaOH	Spec. grav.	° Baumé (NBS scale)	Grams per liter	% NaOH
1.0095	1.4	10.10	1	1.2411	28.2	273.0	22
1.0207	2.9	20.41	2	1.2629	30.2	303.1	24
1.0318	4.5	30.95	3	1.2848	32.1	334.0	26
1.0428	6.0	41.71	4	1.3064	34.0	365.8	28
1.0538	7.4	52.69	5	1.3279	35.8	398.4	30
1.0648	8.8	63.89	6	1.3490	37.5	431.7	32
1.0758	10.2	75.31	7	1.3696	39.1	465.7	34
1.0869	11.6	86.95	8	1.3900	40.7	500.4	36
1.0979	12.9	98.81	9	1.4101	42.2	535.8	38
1.1089	14.2	110.9	10	1.4300	43.6	572.0	40
1.1309	16.8	135.7	12	1.4494	45.0	608.7	42
1.1530	19.2	161.4	14	1.4685	46.3	646.1	44
1.1751	21.6	188.0	16	1.4873	47.5	684.2	46
1.1972	23.9	215.5	18	1.5065	48.8	723.1	48
1.2191	26.1	243.8	20	1.5253	49.9	762.7	50

Ammonia $\left(\frac{20°}{4°}\ C\right)$

Spec. grav.	° Baumé (NBS scale)	Grams per liter	% NH_3
0.9939	10.9	9.939	1
0.9895	11.5	19.79	2
0.9811	12.7	39.24	4
0.9730	13.9	58.38	6
0.9651	15.1	77.21	8
0.9575	16.2	95.75	10
0.9501	17.3	114.0	12
0.9430	18.5	132.0	14
0.9362	19.5	149.8	16
0.9295	20.6	167.3	18
0.9229	21.7	184.6	20
0.9164	22.8	201.6	22
0.9101	23.8	218.4	24
0.9040	24.9	235.0	26
0.8980	25.9	251.4	28
0.8920	27.0	267.6	30

Potassium hydroxide $\left(\frac{15°}{4°}\ C\right)$

Spec. grav.	° Baumé (NBS scale)	Grams per liter	% KOH	Spec. grav.	° Baumé (NBS scale)	Grams per liter	% KOH	Spec. grav.	° Baumé (NBS scale)	Grams per liter	% KOH
1.0083	1.2	10.08	1	1.1984	24.0	251.7	21	1.4103	42.2	578.2	41
1.0175	2.5	20.35	2	1.2083	25.0	265.8	22	1.4215	43.0	597.0	42
1.0267	3.8	30.80	3	1.2184	26.0	280.2	23	1.4329	43.8	616.1	43
1.0359	5.0	41.44	4	1.2285	27.0	294.8	24	1.4443	44.6	635.5	44
1.0452	6.3	52.26	5	1.2387	27.9	309.7	25	1.4558	45.4	655.1	45
1.0544	7.5	63.26	6	1.2489	28.9	324.7	26	1.4673	46.2	675.0	46
1.0637	8.7	74.46	7	1.2592	29.8	340.0	27	1.4790	47.0	695.1	47
1.0730	9.9	85.84	8	1.2695	30.8	355.5	28	1.4907	47.7	715.5	48
1.0824	11.0	97.42	9	1.2800	31.7	371.2	29	1.5025	48.5	736.2	49
1.0918	12.2	109.2	10	1.2905	32.6	387.2	30	1.5143	49.2	757.2	50
1.1013	13.3	121.1	11	1.3010	33.6	403.3	31	1.5262	50.0	778.4	51
1.1108	14.5	133.3	12	1.3117	34.5	419.7	32	1.5382	50.7	799.9	52
1.1203	15.6	145.6	13	1.3224	35.4	436.4	33				
1.1299	16.7	158.2	14	1.3331	36.2	453.3	34				
1.1396	17.8	170.9	15	1.3440	37.1	470.4	35				
1.1493	18.8	183.9	16	1.3549	38.0	487.8	36				
1.1590	19.9	197.0	17	1.3659	38.8	505.4	37				
1.1688	20.9	210.4	18	1.3769	39.7	523.2	38				
1.1786	22.0	223.9	19	1.3879	40.5	541.3	39				
1.1884	23.0	237.7	20	1.3991	41.4	559.6	40				

Sucrose $\left(\frac{20°}{4°}\ C\right)$

Spec. grav.	° Baumé (NBS scale)	Grams per liter	% $C_{12}H_{22}O_{11}$	Spec. grav.	° Baumé (NBS scale)	Grams per liter	% $C_{12}H_{22}O_{11}$	Spec. grav.	° Baumé (NBS scale)	Grams per liter	% $C_{12}H_{22}O_{11}$
0.9982	…	……	0	1.1270	16.3	338.1	30	1.2865	32.3	771.9	60
1.0021	0.3	10.02	1	1.1318	16.9	350.8	31	1.2924	32.8	788.3	61
1.0060	0.9	20.12	2	1.1366	17.5	363.7	32	1.2983	33.3	804.9	62
1.0099	1.4	30.30	3	1.1415	18.0	376.7	33	1.3043	33.8	821.7	63
1.0139	2.0	40.56	4	1.1463	18.6	389.8	34	1.3103	34.3	838.6	64
1.0179	2.5	50.89	5	1.1513	19.1	402.9	35	1.3163	34.8	855.6	65
1.0219	3.1	61.31	6	1.1562	19.6	416.2	36	1.3224	35.4	872.8	66
1.0259	3.6	71.81	7	1.1612	20.1	429.7	37	1.3286	35.9	890.1	67
1.0299	4.1	82.40	8	1.1663	20.7	443.2	38	1.3347	36.4	907.6	68
1.0340	4.7	93.06	9	1.1713	21.2	456.8	39	1.3409	36.9	925.2	69
1.0381	5.3	103.8	10	1.1764	21.7	470.6	40	1.3472	37.4	943.0	70
1.0423	5.8	114.7	11	1.1816	22.3	484.5	41	1.3535	37.9	961.0	71
1.0465	6.4	125.6	12	1.1868	22.8	498.4	42	1.3598	38.4	979.0	72
1.0507	7.0	136.6	13	1.1920	23.3	512.6	43	1.3661	38.9	997.3	73
1.0549	7.5	147.7	14	1.1972	23.9	526.8	44	1.3725	39.4	1016	74
1.0592	8.1	158.9	15	1.2025	24.4	541.1	45	1.3790	39.9	1034	75
1.0635	8.7	170.2	16	1.2079	25.0	555.6	46	1.3854	40.4	1053	76
1.0678	9.2	181.5	17	1.2132	25.5	570.2	47	1.3920	40.9	1072	77
1.0721	9.8	193.0	18	1.2186	26.0	584.9	48	1.3985	41.4	1091	78
1.0765	10.3	204.5	19	1.2241	26.5	599.8	49	1.4051	41.8	1110	79
1.0810	10.8	216.2	20	1.2296	27.1	614.8	50	1.4117	42.2	1129	80
1.0854	11.4	227.9	21	1.2351	27.6	629.9	51	1.4184	42.7	1149	81
1.0899	12.0	239.8	22	1.2406	28.1	645.1	52	1.4251	43.2	1169	82
1.0944	12.5	251.7	23	1.2462	28.7	660.5	53	1.4318	43.7	1188	83
1.0990	13.1	263.8	24	1.2519	29.2	676.0	54	1.4386	44.2	1208	84
1.1036	13.6	275.9	25	1.2575	29.7	691.6	55	1.4454	44.7	1229	85
1.1082	14.2	288.1	26	1.2632	30.3	707.4	56	1.4522	45.2	1249	86
1.1128	14.7	300.5	27	1.2690	30.8	723.3	57	1.4591	45.6	1269	87
1.1175	15.3	312.9	28	1.2748	31.3	739.4	58	1.4660	46.1	1290	88
1.1222	15.8	325.4	29	1.2806	31.8	755.6	59	1.4730	46.6	1311	89

1) Values from LANGE and FORKER (Eds.), *Handbook of Chemistry*, 9th ed., Sandusky, 1956; and HODGMAN et al. (Eds.), *Handbook of Chemistry and Physics*, 42nd ed., Cleveland, 1960.

Glycerol $\left(\frac{20°}{4°}\text{C}\right)$

Spec. grav.	°Baumé (NBS scale)	Grams per liter	% $C_3H_8O_3$
1.00060	0.1	10.01	1
1.00300	0.4	20.06	2
1.00540	0.8	30.16	3
1.00780	1.1	40.31	4
1.01015	1.5	50.51	5
1.01255	1.8	60.75	6
1.01495	2.1	71.04	7
1.01730	2.5	81.38	8
1.01970	2.8	91.77	9
1.02210	3.1	102.2	10
1.02455	3.5	112.7	11
1.02705	3.8	123.3	12
1.02955	4.1	133.8	13
1.03200	4.5	144.5	14
1.03450	4.8	155.2	15
1.03695	5.2	165.9	16
1.03945	5.5	176.7	17
1.04195	5.8	187.6	18
1.04440	6.2	198.5	19
1.04690	6.5	209.4	20
1.04950	6.8	220.4	21
1.05205	7.2	231.4	22
1.05465	7.5	242.5	23
1.05720	7.8	253.7	24
1.05980	8.2	264.9	25
1.06240	8.5	276.2	26
1.06495	8.8	287.5	27
1.06755	9.2	298.9	28
1.07010	9.5	310.3	29
1.07270	9.8	321.8	30
1.07535	10.2	333.3	31
1.07800	10.5	345.0	32
1.08070	10.8	356.6	33
1.08335	11.2	368.3	34
1.08600	11.5	380.1	35
1.08865	11.8	391.9	36
1.09135	12.1	403.8	37
1.09400	12.5	415.8	38
1.09665	12.8	427.8	39
1.09930	13.1	439.8	40
1.10200	13.4	451.9	41
1.10470	13.8	464.1	42
1.10740	14.1	476.2	43
1.11010	14.4	488.5	44
1.11280	14.7	500.8	45
1.11550	15.0	513.1	46
1.11820	15.3	525.6	47
1.12090	15.6	538.0	48
1.12360	16.0	550.6	49
1.12630	16.3	563.2	50
1.12905	16.6	575.8	51
1.13180	16.9	588.5	52
1.13455	17.2	601.2	53
1.13730	17.5	614.0	54
1.14005	17.8	626.9	55
1.14280	18.1	639.8	56
1.14555	18.4	652.8	57
1.14830	18.7	665.8	58
1.15105	19.0	678.9	59
1.15380	19.3	692.0	60
1.15655	19.6	705.2	61
1.15930	19.9	718.4	62
1.16205	20.2	731.7	63
1.16475	20.5	745.1	64
1.16750	20.8	758.6	65
1.17025	21.0	772.0	66
1.17300	21.3	785.5	67
1.17575	21.6	799.1	68
1.17850	21.9	812.8	69
1.18125	22.2	826.6	70
1.18395	22.5	840.4	71
1.18670	22.8	854.1	72
1.18940	23.1	868.0	73
1.19215	23.3	881.9	74
1.19485	23.6	895.8	75
1.19760	23.9	909.8	76
1.20030	24.2	923.8	77
1.20305	24.4	938.0	78
1.20575	24.7	952.1	79
1.20850	25.0	966.3	80
1.21115	25.2	980.6	81
1.21380	25.5	994.9	82
1.21650	25.8	1009	83
1.21915	26.0	1024	84
1.22180	26.3	1038	85
1.22445	26.5	1053	86
1.22710	26.8	1067	87
1.22975	27.1	1082	88
1.23245	27.3	1096	89
1.23510	27.6	1111	90
1.23770	27.8	1126	91
1.24035	28.1	1141	92
1.24300	28.3	1156	93
1.24560	28.6	1171	94
1.24825	28.8	1186	95
1.25080	29.1	1201	96
1.25335	29.3	1216	97
1.25590	29.5	1231	98
1.25850	29.8	1246	99
1.26108	30.0	1261	100

Ethanol $\left(\frac{15.56°}{15.56°}\text{C}\right)$

Spec. grav.	Vol%	Wt.%	g/100 ml
1.00000	0.00	0.00	0.00
0.99984	0.10	0.08	0.08
0.99968	0.20	0.16	0.16
0.99953	0.30	0.24	0.24
0.99937	0.40	0.32	0.32
0.99923	0.50	0.40	0.40
0.99907	0.60	0.48	0.48
0.99892	0.70	0.56	0.56
0.99877	0.80	0.64	0.64
0.99861	0.90	0.71	0.71
0.99849	1.00	0.79	0.79
0.99834	1.10	0.87	0.87
0.99819	1.20	0.95	0.95
0.99805	1.30	1.03	1.03
0.99790	1.40	1.11	1.11
0.99775	1.50	1.19	1.19
0.99760	1.60	1.27	1.27
0.99745	1.70	1.35	1.35
0.99731	1.80	1.43	1.43
0.99716	1.90	1.51	1.51
0.99701	2.00	1.59	1.59
0.99687	2.10	1.67	1.66
0.99672	2.20	1.75	1.74
0.99658	2.30	1.83	1.82
0.99643	2.40	1.91	1.90
0.99629	2.50	1.99	1.98
0.99615	2.60	2.07	2.06
0.99600	2.70	2.15	2.14
0.99586	2.80	2.23	2.22
0.99571	2.90	2.31	2.30
0.99557	3.00	2.39	2.38
0.99543	3.10	2.47	2.46
0.99529	3.20	2.55	2.54
0.99515	3.30	2.64	2.62
0.99501	3.40	2.72	2.70
0.99487	3.50	2.80	2.78
0.99473	3.60	2.88	2.86
0.99459	3.70	2.96	2.94
0.99445	3.80	3.04	3.02
0.99431	3.90	3.12	3.10
0.99417	4.00	3.20	3.18
0.99403	4.10	3.28	3.26
0.99390	4.20	3.36	3.34
0.99376	4.30	3.44	3.42
0.99363	4.40	3.52	3.50
0.99349	4.50	3.60	3.58
0.99335	4.60	3.68	3.66
0.99322	4.70	3.76	3.74
0.99308	4.80	3.84	3.81
0.99295	4.90	3.92	3.89
0.99281	5.00	4.00	3.97
0.99268	5.10	4.08	4.05
0.99255	5.20	4.16	4.13
0.99241	5.30	4.24	4.21
0.99228	5.40	4.32	4.29
0.99215	5.50	4.40	4.37
0.99202	5.60	4.48	4.44
0.99189	5.70	4.56	4.52
0.99175	5.80	4.64	4.60
0.99162	5.90	4.72	4.68
0.99149	6.00	4.80	4.76
0.99136	6.10	4.88	4.84
0.99123	6.20	4.96	4.92
0.99111	6.30	5.05	5.00
0.99098	6.40	5.13	5.08
0.99085	6.50	5.21	5.16
0.99072	6.60	5.29	5.24
0.99059	6.70	5.37	5.32
0.99047	6.80	5.45	5.40
0.99034	6.90	5.53	5.48
0.99021	7.00	5.61	5.56
0.99009	7.10	5.69	5.64
0.98996	7.20	5.77	5.72
0.98984	7.30	5.86	5.80
0.98971	7.40	5.94	5.88
0.98959	7.50	6.02	5.96
0.98947	7.60	6.10	6.04
0.98934	7.70	6.18	6.11
0.98922	7.80	6.26	6.19
0.98909	7.90	6.34	6.27
0.98897	8.00	6.42	6.35
0.98885	8.10	6.50	6.43
0.98873	8.20	6.58	6.51
0.98861	8.30	6.67	6.59
0.98849	8.40	6.75	6.67
0.98837	8.50	6.83	6.75
0.98825	8.60	6.91	6.83
0.98813	8.70	6.99	6.91
0.98801	8.80	7.07	6.99
0.98789	8.90	7.15	7.07
0.98777	9.00	7.23	7.14
0.98765	9.10	7.31	7.22
0.98754	9.20	7.39	7.30
0.98742	9.30	7.48	7.38
0.98730	9.40	7.56	7.46
0.98719	9.50	7.64	7.54
0.98707	9.60	7.72	7.62
0.98695	9.70	7.80	7.70
0.98683	9.80	7.88	7.78
0.98672	9.90	7.96	7.85
0.98660	10.00	8.04	7.93
0.98649	10.10	8.12	8.01
0.98637	10.20	8.20	8.09
0.98626	10.30	8.29	8.17
0.98614	10.40	8.37	8.25

1) Values from LANGE and FORKER (Eds.), *Handbook of Chemistry*, 9th ed., Sandusky, 1956; and HODGMAN et al. (Eds.), *Handbook of Chemistry and Physics*, 42nd ed., Cleveland, 1960.

Ethanol $\left(\frac{15.56°}{15.56°}\,C\right)$ (continued)

Spec. grav.	Vol%	Wt.%	g/100 ml	Spec. grav.	Vol%	Wt.%	g/100 ml	Spec. grav.	Vol%	Wt.%	g/100 ml
0.98603	10.50	8.45	8.33	0.97808	18.00	14.60	14.28	0.97044	25.50	20.85	20.24
0.98592	10.60	8.53	8.41	0.97798	18.10	14.68	14.36	0.97033	25.60	20.93	20.32
0.98580	10.70	8.61	8.49	0.97788	18.20	14.77	14.44	0.97023	25.70	21.02	20.40
0.98569	10.80	8.70	8.57	0.97778	18.30	14.85	14.52	0.97012	25.80	21.10	20.47
0.98557	10.90	8.78	8.65	0.97768	18.40	14.94	14.60	0.97001	25.90	21.19	20.55
0.98546	11.00	8.86	8.73	0.97758	18.50	15.02	14.68	0.96991	26.00	21.27	20.63
0.98535	11.10	8.94	8.81	0.97748	18.60	15.10	14.76	0.96980	26.10	21.35	20.71
0.98524	11.20	9.02	8.89	0.97738	18.70	15.18	14.84	0.96969	26.20	21.44	20.79
0.98513	11.30	9.11	8.97	0.97728	18.80	15.27	14.92	0.96959	26.30	21.52	20.87
0.98502	11.40	9.19	9.05	0.97718	18.90	15.38	15.00	0.96949	26.40	21.61	20.95
0.98491	11.50	9.27	9.13	0.97708	19.00	15.43	15.08	0.96937	26.50	21.69	21.03
0.98479	11.60	9.35	9.21	0.97698	19.10	15.51	15.15	0.96926	26.60	21.77	21.11
0.98468	11.70	9.43	9.29	0.97688	19.20	15.59	15.23	0.96915	26.70	21.86	21.19
0.98457	11.80	9.51	9.36	0.97678	19.30	15.68	15.31	0.96905	26.80	21.94	21.27
0.98446	11.90	9.59	9.44	0.97668	19.40	15.76	15.39	0.96894	26.90	22.03	21.35
0.98435	12.00	9.67	9.52	0.97658	19.50	15.84	15.47	0.96883	27.00	22.11	21.43
0.98424	12.10	9.75	9.60	0.97648	19.60	15.93	15.55	0.96872	27.10	22.20	21.51
0.98413	12.20	9.83	9.68	0.97638	19.70	16.01	15.63	0.96861	27.20	22.28	21.59
0.98402	12.30	9.92	9.76	0.97628	19.80	16.09	15.71	0.96850	27.30	22.37	21.67
0.98391	12.40	10.00	9.84	0.97618	19.90	16.18	15.79	0.96839	27.40	22.45	21.75
0.98381	12.50	10.08	9.92	0.97608	20.00	16.26	15.87	0.96828	27.50	22.54	21.83
0.98370	12.60	10.16	10.00	0.97598	20.10	16.34	15.95	0.96816	27.60	22.62	21.90
0.98359	12.70	10.24	10.07	0.97588	20.20	16.42	16.03	0.96805	27.70	22.71	21.98
0.98348	12.80	10.33	10.15	0.97578	20.30	16.51	16.10	0.96794	27.80	22.79	22.06
0.98337	12.90	10.41	10.23	0.97568	20.40	16.59	16.18	0.96783	27.90	22.88	22.14
0.98326	13.00	10.49	10.31	0.97558	20.50	16.67	16.26	0.96772	28.00	22.96	22.22
0.98315	13.10	10.57	10.39	0.97547	20.60	16.75	16.34	0.96761	28.10	23.04	22.30
0.98305	13.20	10.65	10.47	0.97537	20.70	16.84	16.42	0.96749	28.20	23.13	22.38
0.98294	13.30	10.74	10.55	0.97527	20.80	16.92	16.50	0.96738	28.30	23.21	22.45
0.98283	13.40	10.82	10.63	0.97517	20.90	17.01	16.58	0.96726	28.40	23.30	22.53
0.98273	13.50	10.90	10.71	0.97507	21.00	17.09	16.66	0.96715	28.50	23.38	22.61
0.98262	13.60	10.98	10.79	0.97497	21.10	17.17	16.74	0.96704	28.60	23.47	22.69
0.98251	13.70	11.06	10.87	0.97487	21.20	17.26	16.82	0.96692	28.70	23.55	22.77
0.98240	13.80	11.15	10.95	0.97477	21.30	17.34	16.90	0.96681	28.80	23.64	22.85
0.98230	13.90	11.23	11.03	0.97467	21.40	17.43	16.98	0.96669	28.90	23.72	22.93
0.98219	14.00	11.31	11.11	0.97457	21.50	17.51	17.06	0.96658	29.00	23.81	23.01
0.98209	14.10	11.39	11.19	0.97446	21.60	17.59	17.14	0.96646	29.10	23.89	23.09
0.98198	14.20	11.47	11.27	0.97436	21.70	17.67	17.22	0.96635	29.20	23.98	23.17
0.98188	14.30	11.56	11.35	0.97426	21.80	17.76	17.30	0.96623	29.30	24.06	23.25
0.98177	14.40	11.64	11.43	0.97416	21.90	17.84	17.38	0.96611	29.40	24.15	23.33
0.98167	14.50	11.72	11.51	0.97406	22.00	17.92	17.46	0.96600	29.50	24.23	23.41
0.98156	14.60	11.80	11.59	0.97396	22.10	18.00	17.54	0.96587	29.60	24.32	23.49
0.98146	14.70	11.88	11.67	0.97386	22.20	18.09	17.62	0.96576	29.70	24.40	23.57
0.98135	14.80	11.97	11.75	0.97375	22.30	18.17	17.70	0.96564	29.80	24.49	23.65
0.98125	14.90	12.05	11.82	0.97365	22.40	18.26	17.78	0.96553	29.90	24.57	23.73
0.98114	15.00	12.13	11.90	0.97355	22.50	18.34	17.86	0.96541	30.00	24.66	23.81
0.98104	15.10	12.21	11.98	0.97345	22.60	18.42	17.94	0.96529	30.10	24.74	23.89
0.98093	15.20	12.29	12.06	0.97335	22.70	18.51	18.02	0.96517	30.20	24.83	23.97
0.98083	15.30	12.38	12.14	0.97324	22.80	18.59	18.10	0.96505	30.30	24.91	24.04
0.98073	15.40	12.46	12.22	0.97314	22.90	18.68	18.18	0.96493	30.40	25.00	24.12
0.98063	15.50	12.54	12.30	0.97304	23.00	18.76	18.26	0.96481	30.50	25.08	24.20
0.98052	15.60	12.62	12.37	0.97294	23.10	18.84	18.33	0.96469	30.60	25.17	24.28
0.98042	15.70	12.70	12.45	0.97283	23.20	18.92	18.41	0.96457	30.70	25.25	24.36
0.98032	15.80	12.79	12.53	0.97273	23.30	19.01	18.49	0.96445	30.80	25.34	24.44
0.98021	15.90	12.87	12.61	0.97263	23.40	19.09	18.57	0.96433	30.90	25.42	24.52
0.98011	16.00	12.95	12.69	0.97253	23.50	19.17	18.65	0.96421	31.00	25.51	24.60
0.98001	16.10	13.03	12.77	0.97242	23.60	19.25	18.73	0.96409	31.10	25.60	24.68
0.97991	16.20	13.12	12.85	0.97232	23.70	19.34	18.81	0.96396	31.20	25.68	24.76
0.97980	16.30	13.20	12.93	0.97222	23.80	19.42	18.88	0.96384	31.30	25.77	24.84
0.97970	16.40	13.29	13.01	0.97211	23.90	19.51	18.96	0.96372	31.40	25.85	24.92
0.97960	16.50	13.37	13.09	0.97201	24.00	19.59	19.04	0.96360	31.50	25.94	25.00
0.97950	16.60	13.45	13.17	0.97191	24.10	19.67	19.12	0.96347	31.60	26.03	25.08
0.97940	16.70	13.53	13.25	0.97180	24.20	19.76	19.20	0.96335	31.70	26.11	25.16
0.97929	16.80	13.62	13.33	0.97170	24.30	19.84	19.28	0.96323	31.80	26.20	25.24
0.97917	16.90	13.70	13.41	0.97159	24.40	19.93	19.36	0.96310	31.90	26.28	25.32
0.97909	17.00	13.78	13.49	0.97149	24.50	20.01	19.44	0.96298	32.00	26.37	25.40
0.97899	17.10	13.86	13.57	0.97139	24.60	20.09	19.52	0.96285	32.10	26.46	25.48
0.97889	17.20	13.94	13.65	0.97128	24.70	20.18	19.60	0.96273	32.20	26.54	25.56
0.97879	17.30	14.03	13.73	0.97118	24.80	20.26	19.68	0.96260	32.30	26.63	25.64
0.97869	17.40	14.11	13.81	0.97107	24.90	20.35	19.76	0.96248	32.40	26.71	25.71
0.97859	17.50	14.19	13.89	0.97097	25.00	20.43	19.84	0.96235	32.50	26.80	25.79
0.97848	17.60	14.27	13.96	0.97086	25.10	20.51	19.92	0.96222	32.60	26.89	25.87
0.97838	17.70	14.35	14.04	0.97076	25.20	20.60	20.00	0.96210	32.70	26.97	25.95
0.97828	17.80	14.44	14.12	0.97065	25.30	20.68	20.08	0.96197	32.80	27.06	26.03
0.97818	17.90	14.52	14.20	0.97055	25.40	20.77	20.16	0.96185	32.90	27.14	26.11

1) Values from LANGE and FORKER (Eds.), *Handbook of Chemistry*, 9th ed., Sandusky, 1956; and HODGMAN et al. (Eds.), *Handbook of Chemistry and Physics*, 42nd ed., Cleveland, 1960.

Ethanol $\left(\frac{15.56°}{15.56°}\ C\right)$ (concluded)

Spec. grav.	Vol%	Wt.%	g/100 ml
0.96172	33.00	27.23	26.19
0.96159	33.10	27.32	26.27
0.96146	33.20	27.40	26.35
0.96133	33.30	27.49	26.43
0.96120	33.40	27.57	26.51
0.96108	33.50	27.66	26.59
0.96095	33.60	27.75	26.67
0.96082	33.70	27.83	26.75
0.96069	33.80	27.92	26.82
0.96056	33.90	28.00	26.90
0.96043	34.00	28.09	26.98
0.96030	34.10	28.18	27.06
0.96016	34.20	28.26	27.14
0.96003	34.30	28.35	27.22
0.95990	34.40	28.43	27.30
0.95977	34.50	28.52	27.38
0.95963	34.60	28.61	27.46
0.95950	34.70	28.70	27.54
0.95937	34.80	28.78	27.62
0.95923	34.90	28.87	27.70
0.95910	35.00	28.96	27.78
0.95896	35.10	29.05	27.86
0.95883	35.20	29.13	27.94
0.95869	35.30	29.22	28.02
0.95855	35.40	29.30	28.09
0.95842	35.50	29.38	28.17
0.95828	35.60	29.48	28.25
0.95814	35.70	29.57	28.33
0.95800	35.80	29.65	28.41
0.95787	35.90	29.74	28.49
0.95773	36.00	29.83	28.57
0.95759	36.10	29.92	28.65
0.95745	36.20	30.00	28.73
0.95731	36.30	30.09	28.81
0.95717	36.40	30.17	28.88
0.95703	36.50	30.26	28.96
0.95688	36.60	30.35	29.04
0.95674	36.70	30.44	29.12
0.95660	36.80	30.52	29.20
0.95646	36.90	30.61	29.29
0.95632	37.00	30.70	29.36
0.95618	37.10	30.79	29.44
0.95603	37.20	30.88	29.52
0.95589	37.30	30.96	29.60
0.95574	37.40	31.05	29.68
0.95560	37.50	31.14	29.76
0.95545	37.60	31.23	29.84
0.95531	37.70	31.32	29.92
0.95516	37.80	31.40	30.00
0.95502	37.90	31.49	30.08
0.95487	38.00	31.58	30.16
0.95472	38.10	31.67	30.24
0.95457	38.20	31.76	30.32
0.95442	38.30	31.85	30.40
0.95427	38.40	31.94	30.48
0.95413	38.50	32.03	30.56
0.95398	38.60	32.12	30.64
0.95383	38.70	32.20	30.72
0.95368	38.80	32.29	30.79
0.95353	38.90	32.37	30.87
0.95338	39.00	32.46	30.95
0.95323	39.10	32.55	31.03
0.95307	39.20	32.64	31.11
0.95292	39.30	32.72	31.18
0.95277	39.40	32.81	31.26
0.95262	39.50	32.90	31.34
0.95246	39.60	32.99	31.42
0.95231	39.70	33.08	31.50
0.95216	39.80	33.17	31.58
0.95200	39.90	33.27	31.66
0.95185	40.00	33.35	31.74
0.95169	40.10	33.44	31.82
0.95154	40.20	33.53	31.90
0.95138	40.30	33.61	31.98
0.95122	40.40	33.70	32.06

Spec. grav.	Vol%	Wt.%	g/100 ml
0.95107	40.50	33.79	32.14
0.95091	40.60	33.88	32.22
0.95075	40.70	33.97	32.30
0.95059	40.80	34.06	32.38
0.95044	40.90	34.15	32.46
0.95028	41.00	34.24	32.54
0.95012	41.10	34.33	32.62
0.94996	41.20	34.42	32.70
0.94980	41.30	34.50	32.78
0.94964	41.40	34.59	32.86
0.94948	41.50	34.68	32.93
0.94932	41.60	34.77	33.01
0.94916	41.70	34.86	33.09
0.94900	41.80	34.95	33.17
0.94884	41.90	35.04	33.25
0.94868	42.00	35.13	33.33
0.94852	42.10	35.22	33.41
0.94835	42.20	35.31	33.49
0.94810	42.30	35.40	33.57
0.94802	42.40	35.49	33.65
0.94786	42.50	35.58	33.73
0.94770	42.60	35.67	33.81
0.94753	42.70	35.76	33.89
0.94737	42.80	35.85	33.97
0.94720	42.90	35.94	34.04
0.94704	43.00	36.03	34.12
0.94687	43.10	36.12	34.20
0.94670	43.20	36.21	34.28
0.94654	43.30	36.30	34.36
0.94637	43.40	36.39	34.44
0.94620	43.50	36.48	34.52
0.94603	43.60	36.57	34.60
0.94586	43.70	36.66	34.68
0.94570	43.80	36.75	34.76
0.94553	43.90	36.84	34.84
0.94536	44.00	36.93	34.91
0.94519	44.10	37.02	34.99
0.94502	44.20	37.11	35.07
0.94484	44.30	37.21	35.15
0.94467	44.40	37.30	35.23
0.94450	44.50	37.39	35.31
0.94433	44.60	37.48	35.39
0.94416	44.70	37.57	35.47
0.94398	44.80	37.66	35.55
0.94381	44.90	37.76	35.63
0.94364	45.00	37.84	35.71
0.94346	45.10	37.93	35.79
0.94329	45.20	38.02	35.87
0.94311	45.30	38.12	35.95
0.94294	45.40	38.21	36.03
0.94276	45.50	38.30	36.11
0.94258	45.60	38.39	36.19
0.94241	45.70	38.48	36.26
0.94223	45.80	38.57	36.34
0.94206	45.90	38.66	36.42
0.94188	46.00	38.75	36.50
0.94170	46.10	38.84	36.58
0.94152	46.20	38.93	36.66
0.94134	46.30	39.03	36.74
0.94116	46.40	39.12	36.82
0.94098	46.50	39.21	36.90
0.94080	46.60	39.30	36.98
0.94062	46.70	39.39	37.06
0.94044	46.80	39.49	37.13
0.94026	46.90	39.58	37.21
0.94008	47.00	39.67	37.29
0.93990	47.10	39.76	37.37
0.93971	47.20	39.85	37.45
0.93953	47.30	39.95	37.53
0.93934	47.40	40.04	37.61
0.93916	47.50	40.13	37.69
0.93898	47.60	40.22	37.77
0.93879	47.70	40.32	37.85
0.93861	47.80	40.41	37.93
0.93842	47.90	40.51	38.01

Spec. grav.	Vol%	Wt.%	g/100 ml
0.93824	48.00	40.60	38.09
0.93805	48.10	40.69	38.17
0.93786	48.20	40.78	38.25
0.93768	48.30	40.88	38.33
0.93749	48.40	40.97	38.41
0.93730	48.50	41.06	38.49
0.93711	48.60	41.15	38.57
0.93692	48.70	41.24	38.65
0.93679	48.80	41.34	38.72
0.93655	48.90	41.43	38.80
0.93636	49.00	41.52	38.88
0.93617	49.10	41.61	38.96
0.93598	49.20	41.71	39.04
0.93578	49.30	41.80	39.12
0.93559	49.40	41.90	39.20
0.93540	49.50	41.99	39.28
0.93521	49.60	42.08	39.36
0.93502	49.70	42.18	39.44
0.93482	49.80	42.27	39.52
0.93463	49.90	42.37	39.60
0.9344	50.00	42.47	39.69
0.9325	51.00	43.41	40.48
0.9305	52.00	44.35	41.27
0.9285	53.00	45.31	42.07
0.9264	54.00	46.27	42.86
0.9244	55.00	47.23	43.66
0.9222	56.00	48.20	44.45
0.9201	57.00	49.18	45.23
0.9180	58.00	50.16	46.04
0.9158	59.00	51.15	46.83
0.9136	60.00	52.16	47.63
0.9113	61.00	53.15	48.41
0.9091	62.00	54.16	49.21
0.9068	63.00	55.16	50.00
0.9044	64.00	56.18	50.80
0.9021	65.00	57.21	51.59
0.8997	66.00	58.24	52.39
0.8974	67.00	59.28	53.19
0.8949	68.00	60.33	53.98
0.8925	69.00	61.39	54.77
0.8900	70.00	62.45	55.56
0.8876	71.00	63.51	56.36
0.8850	72.00	64.59	57.16
0.8825	73.00	65.67	57.95
0.8799	74.00	66.76	58.74
0.8773	75.00	67.84	59.53
0.8747	76.00	68.99	60.33
0.8721	77.00	70.10	61.12
0.8694	78.00	71.25	61.91
0.8667	79.00	72.38	62.71
0.8639	80.00	73.54	63.51
0.8611	81.00	74.68	64.30
0.8583	82.00	75.82	65.09
0.8554	83.00	77.00	65.89
0.8525	84.00	78.18	66.68
0.8496	85.00	79.40	67.47
0.8465	86.00	80.62	68.27
0.8435	87.00	81.85	69.06
0.8404	88.00	83.11	69.86
0.8372	89.00	84.38	70.65
0.8339	90.00	85.66	71.44
0.8306	91.00	86.97	72.23
0.8272	92.00	88.29	73.03
0.8236	93.00	89.61	73.82
0.8199	94.00	91.00	74.62
0.8161	95.00	92.41	75.41
0.8121	96.00	93.82	76.21
0.8079	97.00	95.29	77.01
0.8035	98.00	96.78	77.79
0.7989	99.00	98.37	78.59
0.7939	100.00	100.00	79.39

1) Values from LANGE and FORKER (Eds.), *Handbook of Chemistry*, 9th ed., Sandusky, 1956; and HODGMAN et al. (Eds.), *Handbook of Chemistry and Physics*, 42nd ed., Cleveland, 1960.

The vital functions of highly developed organisms are closely dependent on the internal aqueous medium and on the maintenance in it of extreme constancy of chemical and physical properties. For the physician a knowledge of some of the properties of aqueous solutions is therefore essential to an understanding of water and electrolyte balance and how it may be modified clinically in disease.

In spite of the advances made in physical chemistry there remain considerable gaps in our knowledge of aqueous solutions. The properties of solutions with concentrations up to 0.01 mol/kg can now be calculated with great accuracy, but for solutions of higher concentration it is necessary to introduce empirical correction factors in order to reconcile measured with theoretical values. In biology and medicine, however, this is of little importance since the approximate formulas derived from theory are sufficiently accurate for most practical purposes.

This section should be read in conjunction with the tables on pages 326–330, 333 and 334 and with the chapter Water and Electrolyte Balance (pages 538–545).

Definition of the molecule

The concept of the molecule and the chemical units of measurement derived from it occupy an important place in the study of the properties of aqueous solutions.

A molecule (Latin *molecula*, a small mass) is the smallest part of a chemically homogeneous substance which possesses all the properties of that substance and which can exist in the free state in some phase of the substance concerned (gas, solid, liquid, in solution). This definition clearly distinguishes the molecule from the atom, which is the smallest quantity of an element which is capable of entering into chemical combination.

The concept of the molecule thus embraces not only compounds and the polyatomic molecules of elements but also the individual atoms of the elements which do not enter into chemical combination (the inert gases). The ions of dissolved salts, whether monatomic or polyatomic, can also be considered as molecules since in this phase they have a largely independent existence. There are thus monatomic and polyatomic molecules as well as "molecular" and "non-molecular" atoms.

Units of measurement

Mole. The unit of measurement for molecules is the mole (international symbol: mol) and is defined as follows: 1 mole of an atomic or molecular substance is the *mass* of 6.023×10^{23} atoms or molecules*. The mole is also often used to denote simply the *number* 6.023×10^{23} molecules. The present tendency in physical chemistry is to follow the practice in physics and use the mole as a unit of mass; in this case the number of moles is known as *molar number n*, e.g. 1 mole, 2 moles, 3 moles, etc., $n = 1, 2, 3$, etc.

The connection between the individual** chemical mass unit *mole* and the general physical mass unit *gram* is the molecular weight in the case of polyatomic molecules and the atomic weight in the case of monatomic molecules:

$$1 \text{ mol} = \text{molecular weight (atomic weight)} \times \text{gram} \quad (1)$$

The molecular weight is obtained from the empirical formula by adding together the atomic weights (for atomic weights see pages 250, 251 and 310). The molecular weights of some medically important substances are given on pages 311 and 328.

Gram atom. For monatomic elements and ions the expression gram atom (symbol: g.atom) is also in use. It is identical with the mole but applies only to monatomic molecules. Since monatomic and polyatomic molecules usually occur together in physiological solutions it is preferable to use the expression mole for all the components.

Osmole. The osmole (symbol: osm) is a unit frequently used in biology and medicine but unknown in physical chemistry. It is not internationally recognized since it can be freely replaced by the mole. It represents the mass of 6.023×10^{23} osmotically active particles in an aqueous solution and is therefore merely a mole related to the solution phase It differs from the mole only when it relates to the undissociated solute. The degree of dissociation is dependent on many factors and is not a constant. In defining the osmole in relation to the undissociated solute it is therefore necessary to assume complete dissociation. It is defined by

$$1 \text{ osm}_{(\text{undiss. solute})} = 1 \text{ mol}_{(\text{undiss. solute})}/\nu \quad (2)$$

where ν is the number of ions into which the undissociated solute breaks down on complete dissociation.

Since dissociation is never complete the osmolar concentration of a solute never corresponds exactly to the right-hand side of equation (**2**). The osmole related to the undissociated solute is therefore only suitable for rough calculations, while the osmolar concentration of a solution can be perfectly well expressed in moles.

Gram equivalent. While the mole is the mass of 6.023×10^{23} molecules, the gram equivalent (symbol: Eq or equiv.) represents the mass of the quantity of ions with a total of 6.023×10^{23} **valencies.** It is defined (see page 243) by

$$1 \text{ gram equivalent} = 1 \text{ mole/valency} = \frac{\text{molecular weight}}{\text{(atomic weight)}} \times \text{gram/valency} \quad (3)$$

Since the valency of polyvalent ions varies according to the reaction in which they are participating, the gram equivalent for such ions also varies according to the reaction. Should there be any doubt in such cases the reaction for which the gram equivalents have been calculated should be stated. In the case of substances which dissociate in stages it is necessary to base the gram equivalent calculations on an "average valency" (for example, see phosphorus and serum proteins, page 330, right-hand column).

The use of the gram equivalent is indispensable in all cases in which acid-base relationships are under investigation.

Measures of concentration

Normality (symbol: N) is the concentration in gram equivalents per liter of *solution:*

$$\text{Normality } N = n\frac{1000}{V} \quad (4)$$

where n = number of gram equivalents in the solution
V = volume of the solution in milliliters

With polyvalent ions the normality also varies according to the reaction (see under gram equivalent above). Titration data for 0.1-normal solutions of a number of substances are given on page 313.

Molarity, molality. By the molarity and molality of a solution are meant the concentrations in moles per liter of solution and in moles per 1000 g water respectively:

$$\text{Molarity (per unit volume) } c = n\frac{1000}{V} \quad (5)$$

$$\text{Molality (per unit weight) } m = n\frac{1000}{n_0 M_0} \quad (6)$$

where n = molar number of the dissolved (undissociated) substance (in mixed solutions to be replaced by $\Sigma n = n_1 + n_2 + n_3 + \cdots$, and m and c to be designated Σm and Σc), V = volume of the solution in ml, n_0 and M_0 = molar number and molecular weight of water ($n_0 M_0$ = weight of water).

In very dilute solutions, molarity and molality are practically equal; at higher concentrations the difference between them is significant and increases as the specific volume of the dissolved solute or solutes increases. Thus the molarity of serum differs from its molality owing to the high specific volume of proteins. In order to calculate the molality of any particular serum component, its concentration, e.g. in mg/100 ml serum, must be converted into its concentration in the serum water.

This conversion can be made by means of either the specific gravity or the protein content of serum. The former method is the more accurate and the appropriate factors are given on page 547. On the basis of protein content the conversion is made by means of the following formula[1]:

Water content of serum in g/100 ml serum
= 98.40 minus (0.718 × protein content) (in g/100 ml serum) (7)

(The figure of 98.40 instead of 100 represents a correction for the volume occupied by inorganic and other constituents.)

The molality is more appropriate than the molarity for the calculation of osmotic relationships since to a first approximation it is only the ratio of molecules of solute to molecules of water which is important. If, for example, the molar concentration of the osmotically active particles of a moderately concentrated solution is determined by means of the freezing-point depression, the result obtained is for practical purposes identical with the molality.

* 6.023×10^{23} is AVOGADRO's number (LOSCHMIDT's number in German-speaking countries) and varies slightly according to whether the mole is measured on the chemical or physical scale of atomic weights (see pages 243 and 246).

** "Individual", since the mass of a mole, which varies from substance to substance, is "individual".

1) PETERS, J. P., *Water Balance in Health and Disease*, in DUNCAN, G. G. (Ed.), *Diseases of Metabolism*, 3rd ed., Philadelphia, 1953, page 315.

Example: The freezing-point depression of serum is 0.56°C, corresponding to a molality of 300 mmol (300 mmol/1000 g water). The molarity of a normal serum is accordingly 300×0.940 = 282 mmol/l serum (table on page 547, factor in column 4 divided by 1000, spec. gravity 1.026).

In the following only the molality will be used. It should be noted that molality and molarity are sometimes confused even by reputable authors, so that it is advisable always to examine carefully what is meant by the expression "molarity" in any particular case.

In order to avoid this confusion the molarity and molality should always be related to the *undissociated* solute; otherwise they should be clearly specified, e.g. "the molality of all osmotically active particles", etc.

Osmolarity, osmolality. These two expressions are used to indicate the molar concentrations of all the osmotically active particles in a solution (see remarks under Osmole, above):

$$\text{Osmolarity (per unit volume)} = n\,\frac{1000}{V} \qquad \textbf{(8)}$$

$$\text{Osmolality (per unit weight)} = n\,\frac{1000}{n_0\,M_0} \qquad \textbf{(9)}$$

where n = number of osmoles of the solute in the solution = number of moles of osmotically active particles of the solute in solution (in mixed solutions to be replaced by $\Sigma\, n = n_1+n_2+n_3+\cdots$), n_0 and M_0 = molar number and molecular weight of water.

In order to avoid confusion in the following text, the osmotically active concentration of a solute or mixture of solutes which is to be expected on the basis of the structural formula and assumed complete dissociation will be designated the *ideal* osmolarity or osmolality. It is expressed by the product $n\times\nu$, where ν = the number of individual particles into which a molecule of the undissociated solute breaks down on complete dissociation, and n = the molar (not osmolar) number of the undissociated solute. In mixtures $\nu\, n$ is to be replaced by $\Sigma \nu n = \nu_1 n_1+\nu_2 n_2+\nu_3 n_3+\cdots$.

Conversions. In order to avoid mistakes in decimal places, calculations should always be made using units which correspond:

mol → Eq → g → °C → atm, etc.
or mmol → mEq → mg → m°C → matm, etc.

In the formulas below, n_{mol}, n_{Eq}, n_{osm} and n_g are the numbers of moles, gram equivalents, osmoles and grams, the osmole unit being that related to the undissociated solute; ν = the number of particles into which a molecule breaks down on complete dissociation, z = ionic valency, M = molecular weight.

Required	Given	Conversion	
n_{mol}	n_g	$n_{mol} = n_g/M$	**(10)**
	n_{osm}	$= n_{osm}/\nu$	**(11)**
	n_{Eq}	$= n_{Eq}/z$	**(12)**
n_{Eq}	n_g	$n_{Eq} = n_g\times z/M$	**(13)**
	n_{mol}	$= n_{mol}\times z$	**(14)**
	n_{osm}	$= n_{osm}\times z/\nu$	**(15)**
n_{osm}	n_g	$n_{osm} = n_g/\nu\times M$	**(16)**
	n_{mol}	$= n_{mol}\times\nu$	**(17)**
	n_{Eq}	$= n_{Eq}\times\nu/z$	**(18)**
n_g	n_{mol}	$n_g = n_{mol}\times M$	**(19)**
	n_{Eq}	$= n_{Eq}\times M/z$	**(20)**
	n_{osm}	$= n_{osm}\times\nu\times M$	**(21)**

These conversion formulas are also valid for concentrations, provided that a uniform definition of concentration is used throughout the calculation.

Electrolytes

An electrolyte is a substance (usually a salt, acid or base) which in solution dissociates wholly or partly into electrically charged particles known as ions (the term is also used to denote the solution itself, which has a higher electrical conductivity than the pure solvent). The positively charged ions, the cations, which migrate to the cathode in an electric field, are usually indicated by plus signs against the symbol (the number indicating the valency) and the negatively charged anions, which migrate to the anode, by minus signs. Examples: magnesium ion = Mg^{++}, sulfate ion = SO_4^{--}.

Two kinds of electrolytes are distinguished, strong and weak. The former are dissociated up to 50% in concentrated solution and practically completely in dilute solution; weak electrolytes never dissociate completely even in the most dilute solutions. Among strong electrolytes are most neutral salts and strong acids such as hydrochloric, nitric and sulfuric acids. Most organic acids and bases (and carbonic acid) are weak electrolytes.

The dissociation of electrolytes is very markedly dependent on concentration; it increases with increasing dilution of the solution. Since the ions can be regarded as molecules, the molecular concentration of an electrolyte is greater than its molar content of undissociated solute. On the assumption of complete dissociation the (ideal) concentration of all osmotically active particles is $\nu\, n$ (ν = number of particles into which a molecule breaks down on complete dissociation, n = molar number of the undissociated solute). In reality the osmotic concentration is smaller by a factor g, so that:

$$\text{real}\ \frac{\text{osmolarity}}{\text{osmolality}} = g\times\text{ideal}\ \frac{\text{osmolarity}}{\text{osmolality}}$$

The factor g, known as the *osmotic coefficient*, can be calculated for very dilute solutions from the Debye-Hückel theory but is usually an empirically determined magnitude (see below). It is dependent not only on the concentration but also on the type of ions present, and increases with increasing valency of the ions.

For biological electrolytes these complicated relationships can with advantage be simplified as follows:

(*a*) by ignoring the factor g and assuming complete dissociation. In the case of strong electrolytes this does not give rise to any considerable error; calculations are made using the ideal osmolarity or osmolality;
(*b*) if the factor for the required concentration is known, by assuming that it is unaffected by the presence in a mixed solution of other kinds of ions; or
(*c*) by determining the osmotically active concentration empirically.

Ideal and real solutions

The thermodynamic treatment of aqueous solutions is based on the concept of the ideal solution. For reasons of space it is impossible here to discuss this concept in detail, suffice it to say that real solutions only approximate to ideal solutions at very low concentrations. To a first approximation the properties of an ideal solution (at constant temperature and pressure) change in proportion to the molecular concentration. It follows that the various properties also change in proportion to one another. In practice this circumstance is utilized in that the osmotic pressure, which is only measurable with difficulty, is calculated from the easily measurable freezing-point depression. The osmotically active concentration therefore influences not only the osmotic pressure but also the freezing-point depression, the boiling-point elevation, and so on.

The osmotic pressure and freezing-point depression of ideal solutions are calculated as follows:

Osmotic pressure (ideal) = $P_{ideal} = 0.08205\times T\times\nu\times m$ **(22)***
in atm

Freezing-point depression (ideal) = ΔT_{ideal}
in °C $= 1.858\times\nu\times m$ **(23)***

where $0.08205 = R$ = the gas constant in liter atmospheres; T = absolute temperature in °K = °C + 273.16; 1.858 = cryoscopic constant = molal freezing-point depression of water; ν = number of particles into which a molecule breaks down on complete dissociation; m = molality = moles of undissociated substance per 1000 g water*. For conversion factors for pressure units see page 215; for osmotic pressure and freezing-point depression for osmotic concentrations from 10–740 mmol/1000 g water, see page 326.

From **(22)** and **(23)** it follows that

$$P_{(atm)} = 0.0442\times T\times\Delta T_{(°C)}\quad [T \text{ as in } \textbf{(22)}] \qquad \textbf{(24)}$$

$$\text{or}\quad P_{(atm,\ at\ 0°C)} = 12.06\times\Delta T_{(°C)} \qquad \textbf{(25)}$$

In contrast to **(22)** and **(23)**, equations **(24)** and **(25)** are valid for a wide range of concentrations. P and ΔT have therefore been written in place of P_{ideal} and ΔT_{ideal}.

Real solutions. As already stated, the link between ideal and real solutions is the osmotic coefficient g. This can now be determined by means of equation **(23)**:

Osmotic coefficient

$$g = \frac{\Delta T}{\Delta T_{ideal}} = \frac{\Delta T}{1.858\,\nu\, m} = \frac{\Delta T/n}{1.858\,\nu} \qquad \textbf{(26)}$$

where ΔT = actual freezing-point depression;
n = molar number of the weighed or analytically determined solute (undissociated) in 1000 g water;
T/n = so-called molecular freezing-point depression of the solute concerned (i.e., "molecular" related to the undissociated solute) (physicochemical tables, e.g.

* In solutions containing more than one solute, νm is to be replaced by $\Sigma\,\nu m = \Sigma\,\nu n\,\frac{1000}{n_0\,M_0}\,(\Sigma\,\nu\, n = \nu_1 n_1+\nu_2 n_2+\nu_3 n_3+\cdots)$.

Calculation of Freezing-point Depression and Osmotic Pressure

International Critical Tables, Handbook of Chemistry and Physics, Landolt-Börnstein, mostly give this molecular freezing-point depression, which requires only to be divided by $1.858 \times \nu$ to give g);

ν = number of particles into which a molecule of the solute concerned breaks down on complete dissociation.

The osmotic coefficient g of one component of a mixed solution cannot be determined. In order to calculate the osmotic concentration of such a component it is assumed that g possesses the same magnitude as in a simple solution with the same osmolality as the solution in question.

The real osmolality is obtained from the real freezing-point depression according to equation (**23**) for the ideal freezing-point depression:

$$\text{real osmolality} = \Delta T/1.858 \qquad \textbf{(27)}$$

The ideal osmolality is obtained from the real osmolality by using the osmotic coefficient g:

$$\text{ideal osmolality} = \text{real osmolality}/g \qquad \textbf{(28)}$$

This last equation is only required when it is desired to find the weight of a substance necessary to produce any given real osmolality. In other cases, when the weight is given, the ideal osmolality can always be calculated stoichiometrically ($\nu \times m$).

Applications

Calculation of the osmolality of blood serum from the freezing-point depression (0.56° C). According to equation (**27**) the real osmolality of serum = 0.56/1.858 = 301.4 mmol (can be approximated to 300 mmol without sensible error).

For the calculation of freezing-point depression and osmotic pressure from the tonicity and vice versa, see the adjacent table.

Calculation of NaCl and glucose solutions (see table on page 327).

(*a*) The **weights** of NaCl and glucose (or fructose) **corresponding to given ideal osmolalities** are obtained from columns 1/2 and 1/6. Column 7 gives the corresponding calorific values for glucose and fructose.

(*b*) The **ideal osmolalities corresponding to given weights** of NaCl and glucose (or fructose) are obtained from columns 11/12 and 11/13. The corresponding calorific values for glucose and fructose are given in column 14.

(*c*) The **osmotic coefficients** g (or $1/g$) are obtained for NaCl from columns 1/4 (or 1/5) and for glucose from columns 1/9 (or 1/10), the values in column 1 corresponding to real osmolalities.

Example 1. Required is the weight of NaCl necessary to yield a solution with a real osmolality of 500 mmol. From equation (**28**) the ideal osmolality = real osmolality/g = 500/0.9170 = 500 × 1.0905 = 545.25 mmol. The corresponding weight of NaCl from (*a*) above lies between 15.783 and 16.075 at ca. 15.9 g. This is therefore the quantity of NaCl which must be dissolved in 1000 g water in order to yield an osmolality of 500 mmol.

The inconvenience of first calculating the ideal osmolality can be avoided by calculating the required weight direct from column 2 (for NaCl) or column 6 (for glucose). To do this, the weight given in column 2 against the figure for the real osmolality in column 1 is multiplied by the corresponding value for $1/g$. The above example, with a real osmolality of 500 mmol, thus gives the result: 14.613 × 1.0905 = 15.935 g NaCl.

Example 2. It is required to increase to 500 mmol the osmolality of a solution of 400 mmol by addition of NaCl. Here the calculation is simplified by assuming that the factor g does not change when the solution becomes a mixed solution. $1/g$ for NaCl for 500 mmol/1000 g water is 1.0905. Since 100 mmol are to be added by means of NaCl, the required weight (see paragraph 2 of example 1) is 2.923 × 1.0905 = 3.188 g NaCl.

(*d*) **Exact calculation of isotonic solutions.** These can be calculated by the methods given in examples 1 and 2, or more simply from columns 1/3 (NaCl) and 1/8 (glucose).

Example 1. In order to obtain an isotonic NaCl or glucose solution (osmolality 300 mmol), 9.448 g NaCl or 53.399 g glucose must be dissolved in 1000 g water.

Example 2. It is required to render a solution of osmolality 200 mmol isotonic with serum by addition of NaCl, i.e. to increase the osmolality to 300 mmol. Since the additional osmolality is 100 mmol (column 1) the necessary weight of NaCl is 3.150 g (column 3). The figure for glucose can be calculated in a similar manner.

The conversion tables on pages 328–330 are self-explanatory. For explanation of the tables on pages 333 and 334 see pages 331–333.

Calculation of freezing-point depression and osmotic pressure (see pages 324–326)

Real osmolality in mmol/1000 g water	Freezing-point depression Δ T° C	Osmotic pressure at 0° C atm	Osmotic pressure at 38° C* atm	Freezing-point depression Δ T° C	Real osmolality in mmol/1000 g water	Osmotic pressure at 0° C atm	Osmotic pressure at 38° C* atm
10	0.01858	0.22	0.26	0.01	5.38	0.12	0.14
20	03716	0.45	0.51	02	10.76	0.24	0.28
30	05574	0.67	0.78	03	16.15	0.36	0.41
40	07432	0.90	1.02	04	21.53	0.48	0.55
50	0.09290	1.12	1.28	0.05	26.91	0.60	0.69
60	11148	1.35	1.53	06	32.29	0.72	0.83
70	13006	1.57	1.79	07	37.68	0.84	0.96
80	14864	1.79	2.04	08	43.01	0.97	1.10
90	16722	2.02	2.30	09	48.44	1.09	1.24
100	0.18580	2.24	2.56	**0.10**	53.82	1.21	1.38
10	20438	2.47	2.81	11	59.20	1.33	1.51
20	22296	2.69	3.07	12	64.59	1.45	1.65
30	24154	2.91	3.32	13	69.97	1.57	1.79
40	26012	3.14	3.58	14	75.35	1.69	1.93
50	0.27870	3.36	3.83	0.15	80.73	1.81	2.06
60	29728	3.59	4.09	16	86.11	1.93	2.20
70	31586	3.81	4.34	17	91.50	2.05	2.34
80	33444	4.03	4.60	18	96.88	2.17	2.48
90	35302	4.26	4.86	19	102.26	2.29	2.61
200	0.37160	4.48	5.11	**0.20**	107.64	2.41	2.75
10	39018	4.71	5.37	21	113.02	2.53	2.89
20	40876	4.93	5.62	22	118.41	2.65	3.03
30	42734	5.16	5.88	23	123.79	2.77	3.16
40	44592	5.38	6.13	24	129.17	2.89	3.30
50	0.46450	5.60	6.39	0.25	134.55	3.02	3.44
60	48308	5.83	6.64	26	139.94	3.14	3.58
70	50166	6.05	6.90	27	145.32	3.26	3.71
80	52024	6.28	7.15	28	150.70	3.38	3.85
90	53882	6.50	7.41	29	156.08	3.50	3.99
300	**0.55740**	**6.72**	**7.67**	**0.30**	161.46	3.62	4.13
10	57598	6.95	7.92	31	166.85	3.74	4.26
20	59456	7.17	8.18	32	172.23	3.86	4.40
30	61314	7.40	8.43	33	177.61	3.98	4.54
40	63172	7.62	8.69	34	182.99	4.10	4.68
50	0.65030	7.84	8.94	0.35	188.38	4.22	4.81
60	66888	8.07	9.20	36	193.76	4.34	4.95
70	68746	8.29	9.45	37	199.14	4.46	5.09
80	70604	8.52	9.71	38	204.52	4.58	5.23
90	72462	8.74	9.97	39	209.90	4.70	5.36
400	0.74320	8.97	10.22	**0.40**	215.28	4.83	5.50
10	76178	9.19	10.47	41	220.67	4.95	5.64
20	78036	9.41	10.73	42	226.04	5.07	5.78
30	79894	9.64	10.99	43	231.43	5.19	5.91
40	81752	9.86	11.24	44	236.81	5.31	6.05
50	0.83610	10.09	11.50	0.45	242.20	5.43	6.19
60	85468	10.31	11.75	46	247.58	5.55	6.33
70	87326	10.53	12.01	47	252.96	5.67	6.46
80	89184	10.76	12.26	48	258.34	5.79	6.60
90	91042	10.98	12.52	49	263.72	5.91	6.74
500	0.92900	11.21	12.78	**0.50**	269.11	6.03	6.88
10	94758	11.43	13.03	51	274.49	6.15	7.01
20	96616	11.66	13.29	52	279.88	6.27	7.15
30	98474	11.88	13.54	53	285.25	6.39	7.29
40	1.00332	12.10	13.80	54	290.63	6.51	7.43
50	1.02190	12.33	14.05	0.55	296.02	6.63	7.57
60	04048	12.55	14.31	**56**	**301.40**	**6.76**	**7.70**
70	05906	12.78	14.57	57	306.78	6.88	7.84
80	07764	13.00	14.82	58	312.16	7.00	7.98
90	09622	13.22	15.08	59	317.55	7.12	8.11
600	1.11480	13.45	15.33	**0.60**	322.93	7.24	8.25
10	13338	13.67	15.59	61	328.31	7.36	8.39
20	15196	13.90	15.84	62	333.69	7.48	8.53
30	17054	14.12	16.10	63	339.07	7.60	8.66
40	18912	14.34	16.35	64	344.46	7.72	8.80
50	1.20770	14.57	16.61	0.65	349.84	7.84	8.94
60	22628	14.79	16.87	66	355.22	7.96	9.08
70	24486	15.02	17.12	67	360.60	8.08	9.21
80	26344	15.24	17.38	68	365.98	8.20	9.35
90	28202	15.47	17.63	69	371.37	8.32	9.49
700	1.30060	15.69	17.89	**0.70**	376.75	8.44	9.63
10	31918	15.91	18.14	71	382.13	8.56	9.76
20	33776	16.14	18.40	72	387.51	8.68	9.90
30	35634	16.36	18.65	73	392.90	8.81	10.04
40	37492	16.59	18.91	74	398.28	8.92	10.18

* Normal blood temperature = ca. 38° C = 311.16° K.

Values in columns 3–5 and 8–10 relate to the real osmotic concentrations in millimoles or grams per 1000 grams water (see pages 324–326). Values of the osmotic coefficient *g* are calculated from the data of GARNER, W.E., in WASHBURN et al. (Eds.), *International Critical Tables*, 1st ed., vol. IV, New York, 1928, page 429.

Osmolality (ideal)	Common salt, NaCl, mol.wt. 58.448				D-Glucose*, $C_6H_{12}O_6$, mol.wt. 180.16						Common salt NaCl	D-Glucose* $C_6H_{12}O_6$	
	corresponds to a weight of	at a freezing-point depression of 0.56°C (osmolality = 300 mmol) corresponds to a weight of	Osmotic coefficient for a real osmolality corresponding to the ideal value given in column 1		corresponds to a weight of	corresponds to a calorific value of	at a freezing-point depression of 0.56°C (osmolality = 300 mmol) corresponds to a weight of	Osmotic coefficient for a real osmolality corresponding to the ideal value given in column 1			corresponds to an ideal osmolality of	corresponds to an ideal osmolality of	corresponds to a calorific value of
mmol	grams	grams	*g*	1/*g*	grams	calories**	grams	*g*	1/*g*	grams	mmol	mmol	calories**
10	0.292	0.315	0.9780	1.0225	1.802	7.53	1.780	1.0011	0.9989	1	34.22	5.55	4.18
20	0.585	0.630	9699	0310	3.603	15.07	3.560	0011	9989	2	68.43	11.10	8.36
30	0.877	0.945	9649	0364	5.405	22.60	5.340	0011	9989	3	102.65	16.65	12.55
40	1.169	1.260	9607	0409	7.206	30.14	7.120	0011	9989	4	136.86	22.20	16.73
50	1.461	1.574	0.9574	1.0445	9.008	37.67	8.900	1.0011	0.9989	5	171.08	27.75	20.91
60	1.754	1.890	9546	0476	10.810	45.21	10.680	0011	9989	6	205.29	33.30	25.09
70	2.046	2.205	9522	0502	12.611	52.74	12.460	0011	9989	7	239.51	38.85	29.27
80	2.338	2.519	9500	0526	14.413	60.27	14.240	0011	9989	8	273.72	44.41	33.46
90	2.630	2.834	9480	0549	16.214	67.81	16.020	0011	9989	9	307.93	49.96	37.64
100	2.923	3.150	0.9462	1.0569	18.016	75.34	17.800	1.0011	0.9989	**10**	342.15	55.51	41.82
10	3.215	3.464	9447	0585	19.818	82.88	19.580	0016	9984	11	376.36	61.06	46.00
20	3.507	3.779	9434	0600	21.619	90.41	21.360	0021	9979	12	410.58	66.61	50.18
30	3.800	4.095	9423	0612	23.421	97.95	23.140	0027	9973	13	444.79	72.16	54.37
40	4.092	4.410	9413	0624	25.222	105.48	24.920	0032	9968	14	479.01	77.71	58.55
50	4.384	4.724	0.9404	1.0634	27.024	113.01	26.700	1.0037	0.9963	15	513.22	83.26	62.73
60	4.676	5.039	9395	0644	28.826	120.55	28.480	0042	9958	16	547.44	88.81	66.91
70	4.969	5.355	9386	0654	30.627	128.08	30.260	0048	9952	17	581.65	94.36	71.09
80	5.261	5.669	9377	0664	32.429	135.62	32.040	0054	9946	18	615.87	99.91	75.28
90	5.553	5.984	9368	0675	34.230	143.15	33.820	0059	9941	19	650.08	105.46	79.46
200	5.845	6.299	0.9360	1.0684	36.032	150.68	35.600	1.0065	0.9935	**20**	684.30	111.01	83.64
10	6.138	6.614	9351	0694	37.834	158.22	37.380	0071	9930	21	718.51	116.56	87.82
20	6.430	6.929	9342	0704	39.635	165.75	39.120	0077	9924	22	752.73	122.11	92.00
30	6.722	7.244	9334	0714	41.437	173.29	40.940	0083	9918	23	786.94	127.66	96.19
40	7.015	7.559	9326	0723	43.238	180.82	42.720	0089	9912	24	821.16	133.22	100.37
50	7.307	7.874	0.9318	1.0732	45.040	188.36	44.500	1.0095	0.9906	25	855.37	138.77	104.55
60	7.599	8.189	9310	0741	46.842	195.89	46.280	0101	9900	26	889.59	144.32	108.73
70	7.891	8.503	9302	0750	48.643	203.43	48.060	0106	9895	27	923.80	149.87	112.91
80	8.184	8.819	9295	0759	50.445	210.96	49.840	0112	9889	28	958.02	155.42	117.10
90	8.476	9.124	9287	0768	52.246	218.49	51.619	0117	9884	29	992.45	160.97	121.28
300	8.768	**9.448**	**0.9280**	**1.0776**	54.048	226.03	**53.399**	**1.0122**	**0.9880**	**30**	1026.45	166.52	125.46
10	9.060		9273	0784	55.850	233.56		0126	9876	31	1060.66	172.06	129.64
20	9.353		9266	0792	57.651	241.10		0132	9870	32	1094.88	177.62	133.82
30	9.645		9259	0800	59.453	248.63		0138	9864	33	1129.09	183.17	138.01
40	9.937		9252	0808	61.254	256.17		0143	9859	34	1163.31	188.72	142.19
50	10.230		0.9245	1.0816	63.056	263.70		1.0148	0.9854	35	1197.52	194.27	146.37
60	10.522		9238	0824	64.858	271.23		0153	9849	36	1231.74	199.82	150.55
70	10.814		9232	0832	66.659	278.77		0158	9845	37	1265.95	205.37	154.73
80	11.106		9226	0839	68.461	286.30		0163	9840	38	1300.17	210.92	158.92
90	11.399		9220	0846	70.262	293.84		0167	9836	39	1334.38	216.47	163.10
400	11.691		0.9214	1.0853	72.064	301.37		1.0172	0.9831	**40**	1368.60	222.03	167.28
10	11.983		9209	0859	73.866	308.91		0176	9827	41	1402.81	227.58	171.46
20	12.275		9204	0865	75.667	316.44		0180	9823	42	1437.03	233.13	175.64
30	12.568		9199	0871	77.469	323.98		0184	9819	43	1471.24	238.68	179.82
40	12.860		9194	0877	79.270	331.51		0187	9816	44	1505.46	244.23	184.00
50	13.152		0.9190	1.0881	81.072	339.04		1.0191	0.9813	45	1539.67	249.78	188.19
60	13.444		9186	0886	82.874	346.58		0194	9810	46	1573.89	255.33	192.37
70	13.737		9182	0891	84.675	354.11		0197	9807	47	1608.10	260.88	196.55
80	14.029		9178	0896	86.477	361.64		0200	9804	48	1642.32	266.43	200.74
90	14.321		9174	0900	88.278	369.18		0203	9801	49	1676.53	271.98	204.92
500	14.613		0.9170	1.0905	90.080	376.72		1.0207	0.9797	**50**	1710.74	277.53	209.10
10	14.906		9167	0909	91.882	384.25		0210	9794	51	1744.96	283.08	213.28
20	15.198		9164	0912	93.683	391.78		0213	9791	52	1779.18	288.63	217.46
30	15.490		9161	0916	95.485	399.32		0216	9789	53	1813.39	294.18	221.65
40	15.783		9158	0919	97.286	406.85		0219	9786	54	1847.61	299.73	225.82
50	16.075		0.9155	1.0923	99.088	414.39		1.0222	0.9783	55	1881.82	305.28	230.01
60	16.367		9152	0927	100.890	421.92		0225	9780	56	1916.03	310.84	234.19
70	16.659		9149	0930	102.691	429.45		0228	9777	57	1950.25	316.39	238.37
80	16.952		9146	0934	104.493	436.98		0231	9774	58	1984.47	321.94	242.56
90	17.244		9143	0937	106.294	444.52		0233	9772	59	2018.68	327.49	246.73
600	17.536		0.9140	1.0941	108.096	452.06		1.0236	0.9769	**60**	2052.90	333.04	250.92
10	17.829		9137	0945	109.898	459.59		0238	9767	61	2087.11	338.59	255.10
20	18.121		9134	0948	111.699	467.13		0241	9765	62	2121.33	344.14	259.28
30	18.413		9131	0952	113.501	474.66		0243	9763	63	2155.54	349.69	263.47
40	18.705		9128	0955	115.302	482.19		0246	9760	64	2189.76	355.24	267.65
50	18.998		0.9126	1.0958	117.104	489.73		1.0248	0.9758	65	2223.97	360.79	271.83
60	19.290		9123	0961	118.906	497.26		0250	9756	66	2258.19	366.34	276.01
70	19.582		9121	0964	120.707	504.80		0252	9754	67	2292.40	371.89	280.19
80	19.874		9119	0966	122.509	512.33		0255	9751	68	2326.62	377.44	284.38
90	20.167		9117	0969	124.310	519.87		0257	9749	69	2360.83	382.99	288.56
700	20.459		0.9115	1.0971	126.112	527.40		1.0259	0.9748	**70**	2395.05	388.55	292.74
10	20.751		9113	0973	127.914	534.93		0261	9746	71	2429.26	394.09	296.92
20	21.043		9111	0976	129.715	542.47		0264	9743	72	2463.48	399.65	301.10
30	21.336		9109	0978	131.517	550.00		0266	9741	73	2497.69	405.20	305.29
40	21.628		9107	0981	133.318	557.54		0268	9738	74	2531.91	410.75	309.47

(Column 3, from 310 mmol on:) These values are obtained by dividing those in column 2 by 0.9280, or multiplying them by 1.0776 (*g* or 1/*g* for NaCl at an osmolality of 300 mmol or mosm).

(Column 8, from 310 mmol on:) These values are obtained by dividing those in column 6 by 1.0122, or multiplying them by 0.9880 (*g* or 1/*g* for glucose at an osmolality of 300 mmol or mosm).

* (*a*) Since the elementary composition of fructose is the same as that of glucose, columns 6, 7, 13 and 14 can also be used for fructose. Note that the osmotic coefficient *g* for fructose is not the same as that for glucose.
(*b*) Since the molecular weight of water is almost exactly one-tenth of that of glucose, columns 6 and 13 can also be used for water by moving the decimal point one place to the left in column 6 and one place to the right in column 13.

** LOEWY's value for the calorific equivalent of carbohydrates (4.182 calories per gram) has been used.

This table gives (*a*) the molecular weight and solubilities (in hot and cold water) of the electrolytes; (*b*) for a given weight of electrolyte, the millimoles of undissociated solute, the milligram equivalents (mEq) and weights of the cation and anion, and the milliosmoles of solute on the assumption of complete dissociation.

	Electrolyte (data for 1 gram unless otherwise stated)		Molecular weight	Undiss. solute	Solubility[1] g per 1000 g water		Cation			Anion			Milli-osmoles*
				mmol	cold	hot	mEq	mg		mEq	mg		
	Calcium, Ca												
1	acetate	$Ca(C_2H_3O_2)_2 + H_2O$	176.19	5.68	436^{20}	343^{100}	11.35	228	Ca^{++}	11.35	670	$C_2H_3O_2^-$	17.03
2		$Ca(C_2H_3O_2)_2 + 2H_2O$	194.20	5.15	347^{0}	335^{50}	10.30	206	Ca^{++}	10.30	608	$C_2H_3O_2^-$	15.45
3	chloride	$CaCl_2 + 2H_2O$	147.03	6.80	977^{0}	3260^{60}	13.60	273	Ca^{++}	13.60	482	Cl^-	20.40
4		$CaCl_2 + 6H_2O$	219.09	4.56	2790^{0}	5360^{20}	9.13	183	Ca^{++}	9.13	324	Cl^-	13.69
5	citrate	$Ca_3(C_6H_5O_7)_2 + 4H_2O$	570.52	1.75	8.5^{18}	9.6^{23}	10.52	211	Ca^{++}	10.52	663	$C_6H_5O_7^{---}$	8.76
6	D-gluconate	$Ca(C_6H_{11}O_7)_2 + H_2O$	448.40	2.23	33^{15}		4.46	89	Ca^{++}	4.46	870	$C_6H_{11}O_7^-$	6.69
7	lactate	$Ca(C_3H_5O_3)_2 + 5H_2O$	308.31	3.24	31^{0}	79^{30}	6.49	130	Ca^{++}	6.49	578	$C_3H_5O_3^-$	9.73
8	levulinate	$Ca(C_5H_7O_3)_2 + 2H_2O$	306.33	3.27	400		6.53	131	Ca^{++}	6.53	752	$C_5H_7O_3^-$	9.79
9	oxide (lime)**	CaO	56.08	17.83	1.31^{10}d	0.7^{80}d	35.66	715	Ca^{++}				
10	phosphate, dibasic	$CaHPO_4 + 2H_2O$	172.10	5.81	0.2^{25}	0.75^{100}	11.62	233	Ca^{++}	11.62	558/180	HPO_4^{--}/P	11.62
11	thiosulfate	$CaS_2O_3 + 6H_2O$	260.31	3.84	1000^{3}	d	7.68	154	Ca^{++}	7.68	431/246	$S_2O_3^{--}$/S	7.68
	Chlorine, Cl												
12	Ammonium chloride	NH_4Cl	53.50	18.69	297^{0}	758^{100}	18.69	337	NH_4^+	18.69	663	Cl^-	37.38
13	Hydrochloric acid (10% solution)												
	1 gram	(0.1 g HCl)	36.465	2.74	823^{0}	561^{60}	2.74	2.8	H^+	2.74	97.2	Cl^-	5.48
	1 milliliter	(0.1047 g HCl)	36.465	2.87			2.87	2.9	H^+	2.87	101.8	Cl^-	5.74
	See also Calcium (3,4), Magnesium (14,15), Potassium (22) and Sodium (35)												
	Magnesium, Mg												
14	chloride	$MgCl_2$	95.23	10.50	542.5^{20}	727^{100}	21.00	255	Mg^{++}	21.0	745	Cl^-	31.50
15		$MgCl_2 + 6H_2O$	203.33	4.92	1670	3670	9.84	120	Mg^{++}	9.84	349	Cl^-	14.75
16	hydroxide	$Mg(OH)_2$	58.34	17.14	0.009^{18}	0.04^{100}	34.28	417	Mg^{++}				
17	oxide (magnesia)**	MgO	40.32	24.80	0.0062	0.086^{30}	49.60	603	Mg^{++}				
18	sulfate (Epsom salts)	$MgSO_4 + 7H_2O$	246.50	4.06	710^{20}	910^{40}	8.11	98.7	Mg^{++}	8.11	390/130	SO_4^{--}/S	8.11
	Phosphorus, P												
	See Calcium (10), Potassium (26, 27) and Sodium (30, 31, 40–42)												
	Potassium, K												
19	acetate	$K(C_2H_3O_2)$	98.15	10.19	2530^{20}	4920^{62}	10.19	398	K^+	10.19	602	$C_2H_3O_2^-$	20.38
20	bicarbonate	$KHCO_3$	100.12	9.99	224	600^{60}	9.99	391	K^+	9.99	610	HCO_3^-	19.98
21	bromide	KBr	119.02	8.40	534.8^{0}	1020^{100}	8.40	329	K^+	8.40	672	Br^-	16.81
22	chloride	KCl	74.56	13.41	347^{20}	567^{100}	13.41	525	K^+	13.41	476	Cl^-	26.83
23	citrate	$K_3(C_6H_5O_7) + H_2O$	324.42	3.08	1670^{15}	1997^{31}	9.25	362	K^+	9.25	583	$C_6H_5O_7^{---}$	12.33
24	D-gluconate	$K(C_6H_{11}O_7)$	234.25	4.27			4.27	167	K^+	4.27	833	$C_6H_{11}O_7^-$	8.54
25	oxide**	K_2O	94.20	10.62	d	d	21.23	830					
26	phosphate, monobasic	KH_2PO_4	136.09	7.35	330^{25}	v.s.	7.35 7.35	287 7.4	K^+ H^+	14.70	705/228	HPO_4^{--}/P	22.04
27	phosphate, dibasic	K_2HPO_4	174.18	5.74	1670^{20}	v.s.	11.48	449	K^+	11.48	551/178	HPO_4^{--}/P	17.22
	Sodium, Na												
28	acetate	$Na(C_2H_3O_2) + 3H_2O$	136.09	7.35	762^{0}	1388^{50}	7.35	169	Na^+	7.35	434	$C_2H_3O_2^-$	14.70
29	acid citrate	$Na_2H(C_6H_5O_7) + 1\frac{1}{2}H_2O$	263.12	3.80	v.s.	v.s.	7.60	175	Na^+	7.60	723	$H(C_6H_5O_7)^{--}$	11.40
							7.60 3.80	175 3.83	Na^+ H^+	11.4	719	$C_6H_5O_7^{---}$	15.20
30	acid phosphate	$NaH_2PO_4 + H_2O$	138.00	7.25	599^{0}	427^{100}	7.25 7.25	167 7.3	Na^+ H^+	14.49	696/224	HPO_4^{--}/P	21.74
31		$NaH_2PO_4 + 2H_2O$	156.01	6.41	710^{0}	3900^{83}	6.41 6.41	147 6.5	Na^+ H^+	12.82	615/199	HPO_4^{--}/P	19.23
32	aminosalicylate	$Na(C_7H_6O_3N) + 2H_2O$	211.16	4.74			4.74	109	Na^+	4.74	720	$C_7H_6O_3N^-$	9.47
33	bicarbonate***	$NaHCO_3$	84.01	11.90	69^{0}	164^{60}	11.90	274	Na^+	11.90	726	HCO_3^-	23.80
34	bromide	$NaBr$	102.91	9.72	795^{0}	1210^{100}	9.72	224	Na^+	9.72	777	Br^-	19.43
35	chloride (common salt)	$NaCl$	58.45	17.11	357^{0}	391^{100}	17.11	393	Na^+	17.11	607	Cl^-	34.22
36	citrate	$Na_3(C_6H_5O_7) + 2H_2O$	294.11	3.40	720^{25}	1670^{100}	10.19	235	Na^+	10.19	643	$C_6H_5O_7^{---}$	13.60
37		$Na_3(C_6H_5O_7) + 5\frac{1}{2}H_2O$	357.17	2.80	926^{25}	2500^{100}	8.40	193	Na^+	8.40	529	$C_6H_5O_7^{---}$	11.20
38	lactate***	$Na(C_3H_5O_3)$	112.06	8.92	v.s.		8.92	205	Na^+	8.92	795	$C_3H_5O_3^-$	17.85
39	oxide**	Na_2O	61.98	16.13	d	d	32.26	742	Na^+				
40	phosphate	Na_2HPO_4	141.97	7.04			14.08	324	Na^+	14.08	676/218	HPO_4^{--}/P	21.13
41		$Na_2HPO_4 + 2H_2O$	178.00	5.62	1000^{50}	1170^{80}	11.24	258	Na^+	11.24	539/174	HPO_4^{--}/P	16.85
42		$Na_2HPO_4 + 12H_2O$	358.16	2.79	41.5	874^{34}	5.58	128	Na^+	5.58	268/86.5	HPO_4^{--}/P	8.38
43	salicylate	$Na(C_7H_5O_3)$	160.11	6.25	1110^{15}	1250^{25}	6.25	144	Na^+	6.25	856	$C_7H_5O_3^-$	12.49
44	sulfate (anhydrous)	Na_2SO_4	142.05	7.04	47.6^{0}	427^{100}	14.08	324	Na^+	14.08	676/226	SO_4^{--}/S	21.12
45	sulfate (Glauber's salt)	$Na_2SO_4 + 10H_2O$	322.21	3.10	110^{0}	927^{30}	6.21	143	Na^+	6.21	298/100	SO_4^{--}/S	9.31
46	thiosulfate	$Na_2S_2O_3$	158.11	6.32	500	2310^{100}	12.65	291	Na^+	12.65	709/406	$S_2O_3^{--}$/S	18.97
	Sulfur, S												
	See Calcium (11), Magnesium (18) and Sodium (44–46)												

* On the assumption of complete dissociation.

** The oxides have been included in view of the continuing use of the older nutritional tables.

*** The sodium content of 1 gram sodium bicarbonate corresponds to that of 1.33 grams sodium lactate. The sodium content of 1 gram sodium lactate corresponds to that of 0.75 gram sodium bicarbonate.

1) Data from HODGMAN et al. (Eds.), *Handbook of Chemistry and Physics*, 42nd ed., Cleveland, 1960. The index figures are the temperatures in °C; v.s. = very soluble; d = decomposes.

For a given number of milliosmoles of solute on the assumption of complete dissociation, this table gives the corresponding weight and number of millimoles (mmol) of the undissociated solute and the corresponding milligram equivalents (mEq) and weights of the cation and anion.

	Electrolyte (data for 10 milliosmoles of solute unless otherwise stated)		Undissociated solute		Cation			Anion		
			g	mmol	mEq	mg		mEq	mg	
	Calcium, Ca									
1	acetate	$Ca(C_2H_3O_2)_2+H_2O$	0.587	$3\frac{1}{3}$	$6\frac{2}{3}$	134	Ca^{++}	$6\frac{2}{3}$	394	$C_2H_3O_2^-$
2		$Ca(C_2H_3O_2)_2+2H_2O$	0.647	$3\frac{1}{3}$	$6\frac{2}{3}$	134	Ca^{++}	$6\frac{2}{3}$	394	$C_2H_3O_2^-$
3	chloride	$CaCl_2+2H_2O$	0.490	$3\frac{1}{3}$	$6\frac{2}{3}$	134	Ca^{++}	$6\frac{2}{3}$	236	Cl^-
4		$CaCl_2+6H_2O$	0.730	$3\frac{1}{3}$	$6\frac{2}{3}$	134	Ca^{++}	$6\frac{2}{3}$	236	Cl^-
5	citrate	$Ca_3(C_6H_5O_7)_2+4H_2O$	1.141	2	12	241	Ca^{++}	12	756	$C_6H_5O_7^{---}$
6	D-gluconate	$Ca(C_6H_{11}O_7)_2+H_2O$	1.495	$3\frac{1}{3}$	$6\frac{2}{3}$	134	Ca^{++}	$6\frac{2}{3}$	1301	$C_6H_{11}O_7^-$
7	lactate	$Ca(C_3H_5O_3)_2+5H_2O$	1.028	$3\frac{1}{3}$	$6\frac{2}{3}$	134	Ca^{++}	$6\frac{2}{3}$	594	$C_3H_5O_3^-$
8	levulinate	$Ca(C_5H_7O_3)_2+2H_2O$	1.021	$3\frac{1}{3}$	$6\frac{2}{3}$	134	Ca^{++}	$6\frac{2}{3}$	767	$C_5H_7O_3^-$
10	phosphate, dibasic	$CaHPO_4+2H_2O$	0.861	5	10	200	Ca^{++}	10	480	HPO_4^{--}
									155	P
11	thiosulfate	$CaS_2O_3+6H_2O$	1.302	5	10	200	Ca^{++}	10	561	$S_2O_3^{--}$
									321	S
	Chlorine, Cl									
12	Ammonium chloride	NH_4Cl	0.268	5	5	90	NH_4^+	5	177	Cl^-
13	Hydrochloric acid (10% solution)									
	1 gram	(0.1 g HCl/g)	1.823	5	5	5	H^+	5	177	Cl^-
	1 milliliter	(0.1047 g HCl/ml)	1.741	5	5	5	H^+	5	177	Cl^-
	See also Calcium (3,4), Magnesium (14,15), Potassium (22) and Sodium (35)									
	Magnesium, Mg									
14	chloride	$MgCl_2$	0.317	$3\frac{1}{3}$	$6\frac{2}{3}$	81	Mg^{++}	$6\frac{2}{3}$	236	Cl^-
15		$MgCl_2+6H_2O$	0.678	$3\frac{1}{3}$	$6\frac{2}{3}$	81	Mg^{++}	$6\frac{2}{3}$	236	Cl^-
18	sulfate	$MgSO_4+7H_2O$	1.233	5	10	122	Mg^{++}	10	480	SO_4^{--}
									160	S
	Phosphorus, P									
	See Calcium (10), Potassium (26, 27) and Sodium (30, 31, 40–42)									
	Potassium, K									
19	acetate	$K(C_2H_3O_2)$	0.491	5	5	196	K^+	5	295	$C_2H_3O_2^-$
20	bicarbonate	$KHCO_3$	0.501	5	5	196	K^+	5	305	HCO_3^-
21	bromide	KBr	0.595	5	5	196	K^+	5	400	Br^-
22	chloride	KCl	0.373	5	5	196	K^+	5	177	Cl^-
23	citrate	$K_3(C_6H_5O_7)+H_2O$	0.811	$2\frac{1}{2}$	$7\frac{1}{2}$	293	K^+	$7\frac{1}{2}$	473	$C_6H_5O_7^{---}$
24	D-gluconate	$K(C_6H_{11}O_7)$	1.171	5	5	196	K^+	5	976	$C_6H_{11}O_7^-$
26	phosphate, monobasic	KH_2PO_4	0.454	$3\frac{1}{3}$	$3\frac{1}{3}$	130	K^+	$6\frac{2}{3}$	320	HPO_4^{--}
									103	P
27	phosphate, dibasic	K_2HPO_4	0.581	$3\frac{1}{3}$	$6\frac{2}{3}$	261	K^+	$6\frac{2}{3}$	320	HPO_4^{--}
									103	P
	Sodium, Na									
28	acetate	$Na(C_2H_3O_2)+3H_2O$	0.681	5	5	115	Na^+	5	295	$C_2H_3O_2^-$
29	acid citrate	$Na_2H(C_6H_5O_7)+1\frac{1}{2}H_2O$	0.658	$2\frac{1}{2}$	5	115	Na^+	$7\frac{1}{2}$	473	$C_6H_5O_7^{---}$
30	acid phosphate	$NaH_2PO_4+H_2O$	0.460	$3\frac{1}{3}$	$3\frac{1}{3}$	77	Na^+	$6\frac{2}{3}$	320	HPO_4^{--}
31		$NaH_2PO_4+2H_2O$	0.520	$3\frac{1}{3}$	$3\frac{1}{3}$	77	Na^+	$6\frac{2}{3}$	320	HPO_4^{--}
									103	P
32	aminosalicylate	$Na(C_7H_6O_3N)+2H_2O$	1.056	5	5	115	Na^+	5	761	$C_7H_6O_3N^-$
33	bicarbonate	$NaHCO_3$	0.420	5	5	115	Na^+	5	305	HCO_3^-
34	bromide	NaBr	0.515	5	5	115	Na^+	5	400	Br^-
35	chloride	NaCl	0.292	5	5	115	Na^+	5	177	Cl^-
36	citrate	$Na_3(C_6H_5O_7)+2H_2O$	0.735	$2\frac{1}{2}$	$7\frac{1}{2}$	173	Na^+	$7\frac{1}{2}$	473	$C_6H_5O_7^{---}$
37		$Na_3(C_6H_5O_7)+5\frac{1}{2}H_2O$	0.893	$2\frac{1}{2}$	$7\frac{1}{2}$	173	Na^+	$7\frac{1}{2}$	473	$C_6H_5O_7^{---}$
38	lactate	$Na(C_3H_5O_3)$	0.560	5	5	115	Na^+	5	445	$C_3H_5O_3^-$
40	phosphate	Na_2HPO_4	0.473	$3\frac{1}{3}$	$6\frac{2}{3}$	153	Na^+	$6\frac{2}{3}$	320	HPO_4^{--}
									103	P
41		$Na_2HPO_4+2H_2O$	0.593	$3\frac{1}{3}$	$6\frac{2}{3}$	153	Na^+	$6\frac{2}{3}$	320	HPO_4^{--}
									103	P
42		$Na_2HPO_4+12H_2O$	1.194	$3\frac{1}{3}$	$6\frac{2}{3}$	153	Na^+	$6\frac{2}{3}$	320	HPO_4^{--}
									103	P
43	salicylate	$Na(C_7H_5O_3)$	0.801	5	5	115	Na^+	5	686	$C_7H_5O_3^-$
44	sulfate (anhydrous)	Na_2SO_4	0.474	$3\frac{1}{3}$	$6\frac{2}{3}$	153	Na^+	$6\frac{2}{3}$	320	SO_4^{--}
									107	S
45	sulfate	$Na_2SO_4+10H_2O$	1.074	$3\frac{1}{3}$	$6\frac{2}{3}$	153	Na^+	$6\frac{2}{3}$	320	SO_4^{--}
									107	S
46	thiosulfate	$Na_2S_2O_3$	0.527	$3\frac{1}{3}$	$6\frac{2}{3}$	153	Na^+	$6\frac{2}{3}$	374	$S_2O_3^{--}$
									214	S
	Sulfur, S									
	See Calcium (11), Magnesium (18) and Sodium (44–46)									

The table below has been compiled in collaboration with A. F. Essellier and P. Jeanneret, University Medical Clinic, Zurich (Prof. W. Löffler)

Inorganic ions

Left-hand column: **Given:** weight of the inorganic ions. **Required:** corresponding weight of the salt.
Right-hand column: **Given:** milliequivalents of the ions. **Required:** corresponding weight of the salt.

No.						
1	**1 gram = 49.90 mEq Calcium (Ca^{++}) corresponds to:**			**1 mEq = 20.04 mg Calcium (Ca^{++}) corresponds to:**		
2	4.396 g	Calcium acetate	$Ca(C_2H_3O_2)_2+H_2O$	88.10 mg	Calcium acetate	$Ca(C_2H_3O_2)_2+H_2O$
3	4.845 g	dihydrate	$Ca(C_2H_3O_2)_2+2H_2O$	97.10 mg	dihydrate	$Ca(C_2H_3O_2)_2+2H_2O$
4	3.668 g	Calcium chloride	$CaCl_2+2H_2O$	73.51 mg	Calcium chloride	$CaCl_2+2H_2O$
5	5.466 g	hexahydrate	$CaCl_2+6H_2O$	109.54 mg	hexahydrate	$CaCl_2+6H_2O$
6	4.745 g	Calcium citrate	$Ca_3(C_6H_5O_7)_2+4H_2O$	95.08 mg	Calcium citrate	$Ca_3(C_6H_5O_7)_2+4H_2O$
7	11.188 g	Calcium D-gluconate	$Ca(C_6H_{11}O_7)_2+H_2O$	224.20 mg	Calcium D-gluconate	$Ca(C_6H_{11}O_7)_2+H_2O$
8	7.692 g	Calcium lactate	$Ca(C_3H_5O_3)_2+5H_2O$	154.15 mg	Calcium lactate	$Ca(C_3H_5O_3)_2+5H_2O$
9	7.643 g	Calcium levulinate	$Ca(C_5H_7O_3)_2+2H_2O$	153.16 mg	Calcium levulinate	$Ca(C_5H_7O_3)_2+2H_2O$
11	4.294 g	Calcium phosphate, dibasic	$CaHPO_4+2H_2O$	86.05 mg	Calcium phosphate, dibasic	$CaHPO_4+2H_2O$
12	6.495 g	Calcium thiosulfate	$CaS_2O_3+6H_2O$	130.15 mg	Calcium thiosulfate	$CaS_2O_3+6H_2O$
	1 gram Carbon dioxide, CO_2, corresponds to 1.387 g = 22.72 mEq bicarbonate ions (HCO_3^-) **1 vol% Carbon dioxide, CO_2,** at 0° C and 760 mm Hg corresponds to 27.40 mg/l = 0.449 mEq/l bicarbonate ions (HCO_3^-)*			**1 mEq = 61.02 mg Bicarbonate ions** (HCO_3^-) corresponds to 44.01 mg carbon dioxide (CO_2) **1 mEq/l = 61.02 mg/l Bicarbonate ions** (HCO_3^-) corresponds at 0° C and 760 mm Hg to 2.23 vol% carbon dioxide (CO_2)*		
13	**1 gram = 28.20 mEq Chloride (Cl^-) corresponds to:**			**1 mEq = 35.457 mg Chloride (Cl^-) corresponds to:**		
14	1.509 g	Ammonium chloride	NH_4Cl	53.50 mg	Ammonium chloride	NH_4Cl
4	2.073 g	Calcium chloride	$CaCl_2+2H_2O$	73.51 mg	Calcium chloride	$CaCl_2+2H_2O$
5	3.090 g	hexahydrate	$CaCl_2+6H_2O$	109.54 mg	hexahydrate	$CaCl_2+6H_2O$
15	10.28 g or 9.551 ml	Hydrochloric acid, 10%		364.7 mg or 348.28 μl	Hydrochloric acid, 10%	
17	1.343 g	Magnesium chloride	$MgCl_2$	47.62 mg	Magnesium chloride	$MgCl_2$
18	2.867 g	hexahydrate	$MgCl_2+6H_2O$	101.67 mg	hexahydrate	$MgCl_2+6H_2O$
27	2.103 g	Potassium chloride	KCl	74.56 mg	Potassium chloride	KCl
41	1.648 g	Sodium chloride	$NaCl$	58.45 mg	Sodium chloride	$NaCl$
16	**1 gram = 82.24 mEq Magnesium (Mg^{++}) corresponds to:**			**1 mEq = 12.16 mg Magnesium (Mg^{++}) corresponds to:**		
17	3.916 g	Magnesium chloride	$MgCl_2$	47.62 mg	Magnesium chloride	$MgCl_2$
18	8.361 g	hexahydrate	$MgCl_2+6H_2O$	101.67 mg	hexahydrate	$MgCl_2+6H_2O$
21	10.136 g	Magnesium sulfate	$MgSO_4+7H_2O$	123.25 mg	Magnesium sulfate	$MgSO_4+7H_2O$
22	**1 gram Phosphorus, P, corresponds to:**			At pH 4.3 **one gram Phosphorus (P)** corresponds to 32.28 mEq $H_2PO_4^-$ ions, and **1 mEq of $H_2PO_4^-$ ions** corresponds to 30.98 mg phosphorus (with only a small error these figures can be used for urine). At pH 9.6 **one gram Phosphorus (P)** corresponds to 64.56 mEq HPO_4^{--} ions, and **1 mEq of HPO_4^{--} ions** corresponds to 15.49 mg phosphorus. At pH 7.4 **1 gram Phosphorus** corresponds to 58.1 mEq of phosphate ions, and **1 mEq of Phosphate ions** corresponds to 17.21 mg phosphorus (ca. 20% $H_2PO_4^-$ ions and ca. 80% HPO_4^{--} ions).		
11	5.556 g	Calcium phosphate, dibasic	$CaHPO_4+2H_2O$			
31	4.394 g	Potassium phosphate, monobasic	KH_2PO_4			
32	5.623 g	Potassium phosphate, dibasic	K_2HPO_4			
36	4.455 g	Sodium acid phosphate	$NaH_2PO_4+H_2O$			
37	5.037 g	dihydrate	$NaH_2PO_4+2H_2O$			
46	4.583 g	Sodium phosphate	Na_2HPO_4			
47	5.747 g	dihydrate	$Na_2HPO_4+2H_2O$			
48	11.563 g	dodecahydrate	$Na_2HPO_4+12H_2O$			
23	**1 gram = 25.58 mEq Potassium (K^+) corresponds to:**			**1 mEq = 39.10 mg Potassium (K^+) corresponds to:**		
24	2.510 g	Potassium acetate	$K(C_2H_3O_2)$	98.15 mg	Potassium acetate	$K(C_2H_3O_2)$
25	2.561 g	Potassium bicarbonate	$KHCO_3$	100.12 mg	Potassium bicarbonate	$KHCO_3$
26	3.044 g	Potassium bromide	KBr	119.02 mg	Potassium bromide	KBr
27	1.907 g	Potassium chloride	KCl	74.56 mg	Potassium chloride	KCl
28	2.766 g	Potassium citrate	$K_3(C_6H_5O_7)+H_2O$	108.14 mg	Potassium citrate	$K_3(C_6H_5O_7)+H_2O$
29	5.991 g	Potassium D-gluconate	$K(C_6H_{11}O_7)$	234.25 mg	Potassium D-gluconate	$K(C_6H_{11}O_7)$
31	3.481 g	Potassium phosphate, monobasic	KH_2PO_4	136.09 mg	Potassium phosphate, monobasic	KH_2PO_4
32	2.227 g	Potassium phosphate, dibasic	K_2HPO_4	87.09 mg	Potassium phosphate, dibasic	K_2HPO_4
33	**1 gram = 43.48 mEq Sodium (Na^+) corresponds to:**			**1 mEq = 22.991 mg Sodium (Na^+) corresponds to:**		
34	5.919 g	Sodium acetate	$Na(C_2H_3O_2)+3H_2O$	136.09 mg	Sodium acetate	$Na(C_2H_3O_2)+3H_2O$
35	5.722 g	Sodium acid citrate	$Na_2H(C_6H_5O_7)+1\frac{1}{2}H_2O$	131.55 mg	Sodium acid citrate	$Na_2H(C_6H_5O_7)+1\frac{1}{2}H_2O$
36	6.002 g	Sodium acid phosphate	$NaH_2PO_4+H_2O$	138.00 mg	Sodium acid phosphate	$NaH_2PO_4+H_2O$
37	6.786 g	dihydrate	$NaH_2PO_4+2H_2O$	156.01 mg	dihydrate	$NaH_2PO_4+2H_2O$
38	9.184 g	Sodium aminosalicylate	$Na(C_7H_6O_3N)+2H_2O$	211.16 mg	Sodium aminosalicylate	$Na(C_7H_6O_3N)+2H_2O$
39	3.654 g	Sodium bicarbonate	$NaHCO_3$	84.01 mg	Sodium bicarbonate	$NaHCO_3$
41	2.542 g	Sodium chloride	$NaCl$	58.45 mg	Sodium chloride	$NaCl$
42	4.264 g	Sodium citrate	$Na_3(C_6H_5O_7)+2H_2O$	98.03 mg	Sodium citrate	$Na_3(C_6H_5O_7)+2H_2O$
43	5.178 g	Sodium citrate	$Na_3(C_6H_5O_7)+5\frac{1}{2}H_2O$	119.05 mg	Sodium citrate	$Na_3(C_6H_5O_7)+5\frac{1}{2}H_2O$
44	4.874 g	Sodium lactate	$Na(C_3H_5O_3)$	112.06 mg	Sodium lactate	$Na(C_3H_5O_3)$
46	3.088 g	Sodium phosphate	Na_2HPO_4	70.98 mg	Sodium phosphate	Na_2HPO_4
47	3.871 g	dihydrate	$Na_2HPO_4+2H_2O$	89.00 mg	dihydrate	$Na_2HPO_4+2H_2O$
48	7.789 g	dodecahydrate	$Na_2HPO_4+12H_2O$	179.08 mg	dodecahydrate	$Na_2HPO_4+12H_2O$
49	6.964 g	Sodium salicylate	$Na(C_7H_5O_3)$	160.11 mg	Sodium salicylate	$Na(C_7H_5O_3)$
50	3.089 g	Sodium sulfate (anhydrous)	Na_2SO_4	71.02 mg	Sodium sulfate (anhydrous)	Na_2SO_4
51	7.007 g	Sodium sulfate	$Na_2SO_4+10H_2O$	161.10 mg	Sodium sulfate	$Na_2SO_4+10H_2O$
52	3.439 g	Sodium thiosulfate	$Na_2S_2O_3$	79.05 mg	Sodium thiosulfate	$Na_2S_2O_3$
53	**1 gram Sulfur (S) corresponds to:**			**1 gram Sulfur (S)** corresponds to 62.37 mEq SO_4^{--} ions and **1 mEq** SO_4^{--} ions corresponds to 16.03 mg sulfur.		
12	4.059 g	Calcium thiosulfate	$CaS_2O_3+6H_2O$	At pH 7.4 and 38° C and with an albumin/globulin ratio of 1.8, **1 gram of serum proteins** corresponds to 0.241 basic mEq of ionized serum proteins, and **1 basic mEq** of ionized serum proteins corresponds to 4.15 grams of serum proteins[1].		
21	7.687 g	Magnesium sulfate	$MgSO_4+7H_2O$			
50	4.430 g	Sodium sulfate (anhydrous)	Na_2SO_4			
51	10.048 g	Sodium sulfate	$Na_2SO_4+10H_2O$			
52	2.465 g	Sodium thiosulfate	$Na_2S_2O_3$			

* The conversion factors (0.449 and 2.23) given here for vol% CO_2 into mmol CO_2/l and mEq CO_2/l (bicarbonate-CO_2) are derived from the molar volume of this gas (22.257 liters at 0° C and 760 mm Hg). The conversion factor 2.24 often used in medical literature is mistakenly based on the molar volume of ideal gases (22.412 liters). For practical purposes the difference between these two factors is negligible. The same factor, rounded off to 2.226, is used in the section on blood gases in Synopsis of Blood, page 571.

1) After Van Slyke et al., *J. biol. Chem.*, **79**, 768 (1928).

Aqueous Solutions – Parenteral Infusion Therapy

By A. F. ESSELLIER and P. JEANNERET, University Medical Clinic, Zurich (Prof. W. LÖFFLER)

(For bibliographical references see page 333)

In this chapter (pages 331–334) the composition and characteristics of the solutions in common use for parenteral replacement therapy of electrolytes are described. Commercial infusion fluids have not been included. Particular attention has been given to the administration of potassium, but that of magnesium, calcium and phosphate is not discussed since the importance of these ions in parenteral replacement therapy is still uncertain. The chapter concludes with a tabular summary (pages 333 and 334) of the ionic contents and osmolar concentrations of the important infusion solutions which will facilitate the comparison of solutions and the selection of those most suitable for the patient's needs. Parenteral infusion therapy should be based on a few carefully chosen solutions which can be suitably combined to meet the various indications, if necessary supplemented by high-dosage ampoules for calcium and potassium replacement.

When it is necessary to administer calories in the form of carbohydrates at the same time, glucose, fructose or invert sugar can be added to any of the infusion solutions listed up to a total concentration of 900–1200 mmol/l (100 g/l glucose or fructose = 550 mmol). For further details see page 327.

The following remarks apply to the table on pages 333 and 334.

A. "Physiological" solutions

Isotonicity. A "physiological" solution is one which is isotonic with respect to blood serum, i.e. of the same osmotic concentration (osmolarity)*. The extent to which the various solutions deviate from this condition is shown by the data in the extreme right-hand column of the table. Isotonicity is essential in physiological investigations involving the perfusion of isolated organs but it is not an indispensable condition in intravenous replacement therapy. Clinically, it is desirable for subcutaneous infusions in order to avoid irritation of the tissues. As a result, however, of the rapid dilution of the infusion fluid which takes place in intravenous administration, considerable deviations from isotonicity can be tolerated without irritation of the walls of the veins. For example, 20% invert sugar solutions (ca. 1110 mosm/l), 2–2.5% salt solutions (513–769 mosm/l), mixtures such as 10% glucose solution with 3 g potassium chloride and 4 g salt (772 mosm/l), are well tolerated.

According to definition an infusion solution is isotonic with serum if it shows the same freezing-point depression (ΔT = 0.56° C[1]). Isotonic osmotic concentrations for some electrolytes are as follows:

	Osmotic concentration*			
	in 1000 g water		in 1 liter of solution	
	mmol	grams	mmol	grams
Sodium chloride**	325	9.5	325	9.5 (0.95%)
Ammonium chloride ...	312	8.35	310	8.3 (0.83%)
Sodium bicarbonate....	336	1.41	333	14.0 (1.40%)
Glucose**	301	54.3	291	52.5 (5.25%)

In the table on pages 333 and 334, the values for the isotonic osmotic concentrations of sodium chloride (0.95%), sodium bicarbonate (1.40%) and glucose (5.25%) are from MICHAELS and MÜNZEL[1]. Those for sodium lactate (1.75%) and ammonium chloride (0.83 %) are from JEANNERET et al.[2]. The *Pharmacopoea Danica IX* gives 1.72% for isotonic sodium lactate solution[3].

If glucose is combined with electrolytes for the purpose of increasing the calorie intake, the osmolarity of the glucose must be added to that of the electrolytes. A 5.25% (isotonic) glucose solution contains 291 mmol/l, a 10% glucose solution 555 mmol/l.

Ionic composition. An isotonic solution is only truly "physiological" when it has the same composition as blood serum. From the table on pages 333 and 334 it will be seen that some of the solutions listed under A differ markedly in composition from blood serum (cf. Water and Electrolyte Balance, pages 538–545). This is immaterial when the kidneys are healthy since these organs eliminate the surplus ions and thus prevent changes in the ionic composition of the extracellular fluid. On the other hand, it is often necessary to infuse solutions of composition different from that of serum in order to raise the intake of some particular mineral component. However, in the experimental perfusion of isolated organs the proportions of the cations Na^+, K^+ and Ca^{++} are of importance.

* Osmotic concentration (ideal), on the assumption of complete electrolytic dissociation. Cf. pages 324–326. ** See also page 327.

1. The so-called physiological salt solution contains Na^+ and Cl^- ions in the proportion 1:1 while the proportion in serum water is 3:2 (cf. Water and Electrolyte Balance, page 542). Infusion of this solution in large quantities or with impaired kidney function thus has an acidifying effect[4].

2. The isotonic sodium lactate–salt solution (as modified by BUTLER and DARROW[5,6]) is "physiological" both as regards isotonicity and the ratio of the Na^+ and Cl^- ions.

If sodium lactate is not available or is contraindicated, a freshly prepared sodium bicarbonate solution can be used instead: 1 *dry* ampoule of 14 g sodium bicarbonate freshly dissolved in 1 liter of sterile distilled water yields an isotonic sodium bicarbonate solution (14 g sodium bicarbonate = 167 mEq Na, osmolarity 333 mmol/l) (see also remarks under B below). On the preparation of lactate solutions see WALDOE[8].

3. (*a*) This widely used glucose–salt solution can be employed to meet not only the requirement of sodium and chloride but also *to some extent* that of water, which can only be partly met by isotonic salt solution. Since the carbohydrate in glucose, fructose and invert sugar solutions is utilized metabolically, the water of the solution is available to meet the needs of water balance.

(*b*) This is an improved version of solution (*a*) with 1 volume of isotonic salt solution replaced by 1 volume of isotonic sodium lactate–salt solution (see solution 2 above).

If a greater calorie intake is desired, as is usually the case, the infusion solutions 3(*a*) and 3(*b*) can be made up with 10–20 % glucose, fructose or invert sugar solution instead of 5.25 %. These solutions are then hypertonic and cannot therefore be used subcutaneously. Glucose solution is being increasingly replaced by fructose solution because of the more efficient and rapid utilization of fructose compared to glucose, even by diabetics.

If administration of glucose is undesirable, the salt solution should be diluted with distilled water instead of glucose solution. The resulting solution is hypotonic and therefore also unsuitable for subcutaneous use.

4. In RINGER's solution the ratio of the Na^+ and Cl^- ions is the same as in physiological salt solution; the potassium content is too small to meet the daily potassium requirement, so that it cannot be used for potassium replacement. This and similar solutions such as TYRODE's and RINGER-LOCKE[1,7], and solutions with supplementary magnesium and phosphate[7–10], are used in experimental physiology (perfusion of isolated organs) and in cytological studies. The clinical value of this group of solutions resembling blood serum in composition is uncertain; the significance of calcium, magnesium and phosphate ions in parenteral replacement therapy with water and electrolytes is uncertain and their administration in infusion fluids still rests largely on theoretical considerations.

5. In RINGER's lactate solution[7] the ratio of the Na^+ and Cl^- ion concentrations is physiological. In extensive infusions it is therefore preferable to the usual RINGER's solution and to salt solution, particularly in cases of acidosis.

6. This solution contains sodium and chloride in the "physiological" ratio of 14:10 and calcium in the same concentration as in serum. The content of potassium and magnesium is double that in serum. When the solution is given parenterally the potassium concentration is barely sufficient to meet the normal potassium demand (see below). For clinical purposes this solution nevertheless represents an advance over RINGER's solution on account of its higher potassium content. Note that it contains no phosphate.

B. Solutions for the correction of acidosis and alkalosis

The acidifying or alkalizing action of a salt depends on the different metabolic utilization of its cations and anions. The lactate ion is mainly converted in the liver into glycogen, the ammonium ion into urea.

1. *Sodium lactate* solutions, which are stable and easily sterilized, are now often used in infusion fluids in place of sodium bicarbonate. *Sodium bicarbonate* solutions cannot be sterilized, so that the preparation of sterile solutions requires the use of dry sodium bicarbonate from ampoules. These are dissolved immediately before use by light agitation in the infusion fluid warmed to body temperature. 1 g sodium bicarbonate corresponds to 1.33 g sodium lactate, and 1 g sodium lactate corresponds to 0.75 g sodium bicarbonate. The bicarbonate or lactate solutions are usually administered diluted with glucose solution or distilled water. The

combination with glucose solution is indicated particularly in renal acidosis. The alkalizing action of sodium lactate is diminished in severe liver damage since its breakdown is retarded[11].

2. The treatment of alkalotic conditions by intravenous ammonium chloride has been described in detail[12]. In liver disease, ammonium chloride given intravenously can have a transient toxic effect owing to retarded breakdown of the ammonium ions[11]. In practice this occurs only in severe injury to the liver parenchyma since the conversion of ammonium salts into urea continues even in the perfused isolated liver[13].

Since neither sudden alkalization nor sudden acidification is desirable, these solutions are in practice never used alone but only in combination with others.

In practice the calculation of the quantity of an acidifying or alkalizing infusion solution required for adults[12,14] is based on an average value for the water content of the body of 50% by weight (see Water and Electrolyte Balance, page 538) and on a uniform intra- and extra-cellular distribution of bicarbonate ions[15]. This method naturally yields only rough figures, particularly since little is known of the intracellular concentration of bicarbonate[11,16] and in any case chloride ions are not distributed uniformly throughout all the body fluids[17]. The calculation can be simplified by reckoning in milliequivalents (see pages 324–326).

With an average water content of 50%, 0.5 mEq of alkalizing or acidifying ions per kilogram body weight raises or lowers the alkali reserve theoretically by 1 mEq/l = 2.23 vol%. Column 11 of the table gives for each solution the content of lactate, bicarbonate or ammonium ions, thus giving a rough idea of the amount of solution required to be infused in order to achieve the desired change in the alkali reserve. For example, in order to increase or decrease the alkali reserve in a patient weighing 70 kg by 6 mEq, a quantity of lactate, bicarbonate or ammonium ions of $70 \times 6 \times 0.5 = 210$ mEq must be administered. In order to avoid the danger of an acidosis becoming converted into an alkalosis it is advisable not to attempt a complete normalization of the alkali reserve by means of an alkalizing solution[16], and such solutions should never be administered without supplementary potassium.

In children a higher water content of 66% must be reckoned with, so that the calculation yields relatively high[18,19] infusion quantities. The differences between the calculated and observed effects of alkalizing and of acidifying compounds can be considerable since the above approximate calculation ignores a number of important factors[17–19].

In *diabetic acidosis* many authors[8,9,20,21] consider it is inadvisable to administer large quantities of sodium salts without potassium salts. On the other hand extremely good results have been reported in the intensive lactate treatment of diabetic coma[22]. There is no doubt that a moderate alkali therapy is indicated in diabetic ketosis with very much lowered alkali reserve, since it has been shown that insulin activity is inhibited by acidosis[23–25] and that acidosis increases the blood sugar[26].

C. Solutions for potassium replacement

Potassium intake and excretion. On a normal diet the average daily potassium intake and excretion amounts to 77–102 mEq (3–4 g), while on a potassium-rich diet it can reach more than double this amount. On a completely potassium-free diet the potassium content of urine in healthy adults can fall to 1.6 mEq (6.3 mg%)[27]. In severe illness, however, it is rare for the potassium content of the urine to fall below that of the serum[28]. It has been shown that the tubular reabsorption of potassium can be affected by metabolic disturbances, particularly acidosis and stress[27], which explains the frequent potassium deficiency often observed during infusion therapy without potassium when sufficient of the element is given orally[21]. Potassium deficiency also arises through loss of fluids from the digestive tract (drainage, diarrhea, vomiting). In the infusion treatment of diabetic coma considerable deficiencies may arise, amounting in adults to 300–400 mEq (12–16 g). Other important causes of potassium deficiency are the administration of alkalizing sodium salts and high-dosage adrenocortical hormone therapy (see under Adrenocortical Hormones, page 490).

Prophylaxis of potassium deficiency. When there is no other source of potassium, at least 30–40 mEq (1.2–1.6 g) potassium per day should be administered *intravenously*. This assumes that potassium is eliminated only in the urine and that no other loss of potassium, e.g. by vomiting, diarrhea, etc., is occurring and that no alkalizing sodium salts or adrenocortical hormones are being administered. When oral administration of potassium salts is impossible the potassium demand may be met simply by infusion of a solution of ca. 15–30 mEq (0.6–1.2 g) potassium ions per liter. One liter of this solution should be administered over 4 hours (83 drops per minute*). There is no danger in giving potassium at this rate and concentration[29].

Treatment of potassium deficiency. In treating an existing potassium deficiency it is essential to distinguish between *acute* and *chronic* conditions. It has been shown that an acute potassium deficiency is of the order of 1.5–5 g (38–130 mEq), a chronic deficiency of the order of 10–20 g (260–520 mEq)[30], in exceptional cases up to 39 g (1000 mEq)[31]. The correction of the deficit, however, requires large amounts of potassium since its continuous excretion must also be compensated for. With a maximum daily potassium intake of 8–10 g and normal diuresis, correction of the deficit always requires several days. In severe diabetic coma, 6–8 g (153–205 mEq) potassium should be administered during the first two days, initially intravenously, then as soon as possible orally[30]. In cases of marked potassium deficiency with normal diuresis, quantities of up to 3.7 mEq (145 mg) potassium per day per kilogram body weight have been recommended by Tarail and Elkinton[28] and of up to 3 mEq (117 mg) per day per kilogram by Darrow and Pratt[6].

Rate of infusion. When diuresis is normal and there is no adrenocortical insufficiency, any toxic effects observed will be due not to the total amount administered but to the rate of intravenous administration.

An infusion rate of 20 mEq (782 mg) potassium per hour at a concentration of 80 mEq (3.12 g) potassium per liter of infusion solution has been recommended in adults[28,31]. It has also been shown that up to 1 g (25.6 mEq) potassium per hour can be administered intravenously without any significant increase of the serum potassium level[32], and that a concentration of 40–90 mEq (1.6–3.5 g) potassium per liter of infusion fluid is permissible with slow administration[12]. Other authors[6] regard 36 mEq (1.4 g) potassium per liter of infusion fluid as a safe concentration and for children dilute their solutions to 12 mEq/l. Potassium administration is not indicated in the initial infusions in the treatment of diabetic coma[8,9,33], during the first postoperative days[34,35], in marked oliguria or anuria following traumatic shock, or after extensive muscular lesions[33].

For the routine treatment of potassium deficiency the administration of 30 mEq (ca. 1.2 g) per liter of infusion solution over 4 hours (83 drops per minute*) is recommended. This dosage lies well outside the limits of toxicity and in severe cases it may be doubled with impunity[29].

Choice of potassium salt. The only contraindication for potassium chloride, the commonest potassium salt, is renal hyperchloremic acidosis. Alkalizing potassium salts are the lactate[8], the acetate[36–38] and the gluconate[39].

Since intracellular loss of potassium is accompanied by loss of phosphates, use of a buffered potassium phosphate mixture with mono- and di-basic phosphate in the ratio of 1:4.5 has been recommended[31,40]. It is advisable to limit the administration of potassium phosphate solutions to not more than 1 mEq phosphate per 3 mEq potassium[41,42].

Theoretically, solutions with a high phosphate content are indicated for the treatment of marked potassium deficiencies only when the probability of intracellular loss of phosphates exists, but this has not been confirmed clinically.

1. and 5. In adults, Darrow's potassium solutions[6] are suitable for the potassium therapy described above without too high a fluid loading resulting.

2. (*a*) Butler's earlier pediatric solution[43] consisted of a hypertonic glucose solution (10%) with very low potassium, sodium and chloride content. This solution is contraindicated in diabetic coma so long as the blood sugar is not normalized. The solution contains so little potassium that it cannot meet the daily potassium demand in adults and is therefore useless for potassium replacement therapy; it contains 0.04 g phosphorus per liter as phosphate.

(*b*) Butler's new pediatric solution[9] is suitable also for the treatment of adults. Owing to its high magnesium, potassium and phosphate content it is contraindicated during the first hours of treatment of diabetic coma; in its place (for adults) the administration of about 1 liter of the lactate–salt solution (solution A 2)

---

* In order to calculate the number of normal drops per minute necessary to provide x liters of infusion solution in 24 hours, multiply x by 13.9. This factor is approximately valid for all simple electrolytes and glucose solutions up to 20%.

diluted to half the concentration is recommended. This solution contains 5.3 mEq magnesium and 0.21 g phosphorus per liter.

3. and 6. See the remarks above on phosphate administration. Both these solutions are to be found in the *Pharmacopoea Danica IX*[3,44].

4. and 7. These solutions contain much phosphate (1.03 g phosphorus per liter); in solution C 4 potassium is present exclusively as potassium phosphate, so that high potassium dosage results in excessive phosphate intake[41]. In solution C 7, of 82.1 mEq potassium 41.8 are present as phosphate. Since not more than 1 mEq in 3 of potassium should be administered as potassium phosphate[41], this solution should be used with caution. The potassium content of solution C 7 is the maximum permissible.

Ampoule solutions. Ampoule solutions of 30–40 mEq potassium per liter can be used prophylactically and in the treatment of potassium deficiency. One ampoule in one liter infused dropwise over 4 hours (83 drops per minute) is recommended as the normal dosage. For choice of potassium salt see above.

D. Electrolyte replacement in loss of digestive tract secretions

Solutions D 1 and D 2 have approximately the same potassium, sodium and chloride ion content as the average digestive tract secretions (see also Water and Electrolyte Balance, page 542). If a supplementary calorie intake is desired, the same amounts of electrolyte can be administered in 5–10% glucose solution.

Preserved blood and plasma: approximate sodium, potassium and chloride content

	Na^+		K^+		Cl^-	
	mEq	mg	mEq	mg	mEq	mg
Initial concentrations in plasma of *freshly preserved blood:*						
With anticoagulant solution consisting of sodium citrate [5½H_2O] 258.5 g, citric acid 76.1 g, glucose 333.3 g, distilled water to 10,000 ml:						
per 400 ml preserved whole blood	43	990	0.850	30	17.5	620
per liter preserved plasma	165	3800	3.300	130	67.5	2400
With anticoagulant solution consisting of sodium citrate [5½H_2O] 160 g, citric acid 47 g, glucose 250 g, distilled water to 10,000 ml:						
per 400 ml preserved whole blood	36	830	0.850	30	17.5	620
per liter preserved plasma	138	3180	3.30	130	67.5	2400
Concentrations in a quantity of dried plasma yielding ca. 250 ml reconstituted citrate plasma:						
in the dried plasma	34	780	0.9	40	18	640
in 1 liter of the reconstituted plasma	137	3150	3.5	140	72	2560

Both reconstituted dried plasma and the plasma of freshly preserved blood contain the donor's electrolytes, to which must be added the electrolyte of the anticoagulant solution. Since the electrolyte level and hematocrit value of the donor's blood are unknown, the electrolyte content of preserved blood and plasma can only be estimated approximately. The values in this table are based on the average normal values for sodium, potassium and chloride content of serum (see Water and Electrolyte Balance, page 542), on a hematocrit value of 45%, and on a mixture before drying consisting of ca. 310 ml of blood and ca. 90 ml of anticoagulant solution.

After 10 days' storage under normal conditions, or even earlier, the potassium content of the plasma of preserved blood can rise to double the original level owing to the liberation of cell potassium. After 20 days the level can reach four times the original or more[45,46].

The potassium content of the plasma is very variable even in freshly preserved blood. Tests have shown that in dissolved dried plasma, however, the potassium concentration is largely identical with that calculated from the original mixture of blood and anticoagulant; the reason for this is that dried plasma is usually prepared immediately after separation from the donor's blood, before liberation of cell potassium takes place.

References

1) Michaels and Münzel, *Pharm. Acta Helvet.*, **24**, 58, 199 (1949). *2*) Jeanneret et al., *Helv. med. Acta*, **21**, 191 (1954). *3*) Waldoe, M., *Svensk farm. T.*, **55**, 332 (1951), quoted by Lauber and Münzel, *Schweiz. ApothZtg*, **91**, 833 (1953). *4*) Black, D. A. K., *Lancet*, **1**, 353 (1953). *5*) Butler and Talbot, *New Engl. J. Med.*, **231**, 585, 621 (1944). *6*) Darrow and Pratt, *J. Amer. med. Ass.*, **143**, 365, 432 (1950). *7*) Hartmann, A. F., *J. Amer. med. Ass.*, **103**, 1349 (1934). *8*) Butler, A. M., *Acta paediat. (Uppsala)*, **38**, 59 (1949). *9*) Butler, A. M., *New Engl. J. Med.*, **243**, 648 (1950). *10*) Cooke and Crowley, *New Engl. J. Med.*, **246**, 637 (1952). *11*) Peters and Van Slyke, *Quantitative Clinical Chemistry*, vol. I, *Interpretations*, 2nd ed., Baltimore, 1946. *12*) Bodansky, O., *Amer. J. med. Sci.*, **218**, 567 (1949). *13*) Löffler, W., *Biochem. Z.*, **85**, 230 (1918). *14*) Maddock, W. G., *Ohio St. med. J.*, **45**, 462 (1949). *15*) Peters, J. P., *Body Water. The Exchange of Fluids in Man*, Springfield, 1935. *16*) Darrow and Pratt, *J. Pediat.*, **41**, 688 (1952). *17*) Goldfinch and Holt, *Lancet*, **2**, 801 (1953). *18*) Hartmann and Senn, *J. clin. Invest.*, **11**, 327 (1932). *19*) Hartmann et al., *J. Pediat.*, **13**, 692 (1938). *20*) Bland, J. H., *The Clinical Use of Fluid and Electrolyte*, Philadelphia, 1952. *21*) Joslin et al., *The Treatment of Diabetes Mellitus*, 9th ed., Philadelphia, 1952. *22*) Hartmann and Erganian, *J. Pediat.*, **31**, 274 (1947). *23*) Guest, G. M., *Amer. J. Med.*, **7**, 630 (1949). *24*) Guest et al., *Diabetes*, **1**, 276 (1952). *25*) François and Ruiton-Ugliengo, *Presse méd.*, **62**, 867 (1954). *26*) Markees and Menczer, *Schweiz. med. Wschr.*, **75**, 255 (1945). *27*) Fourman, P., *Lancet*, **1**, 1042 (1952). *28*) Tarail and Elkinton, *J. clin. Invest.*, **28**, 99 (1949). *29*) Lans et al., *Surg. Gynec. Obstet.*, **95**, 321 (1952). *30*) Martin et al., *J. Amer. med. Ass.*, **147**, 24 (1951). *31*) Elkinton and Tarail, *Amer. J. Med.*, **9**, 200 (1950). *32*) Kühlmayer, R., *Arch. klin. Chir. (Langenbecks)*, **271**, 475 (1952). *33*) Plattner, C. H., *Le métabolisme du potassium et ses perturbations*, Paris, 1954. *34*) Eliel et al., *New Engl. J. Med.*, **243**, 471 (1950). *35*) Randall et al., *Surgery*, **26**, 341 (1949). *36*) Mudge et al., *Proc. Soc. exp. Biol. (N. Y.)*, **71**, 136 (1949). *37*) Winfield et al., *Ann. Surg.*, **134**, 626 (1951). *38*) Fox et al., *J. Amer. med. Ass.*, **148**, 827 (1952). *39*) Bernard, A., *Science*, **113**, 751 (1951). *40*) Elman and Weichselbaum, *Ann. Surg.*, **135**, 164 (1952). *41*) Davidsen et al., *Lancet*, **1**, 375 (1951). *42*) Davidsen and Kjerulf-Jensen, *Lancet*, **2**, 17 (1951). *43*) Butler et al., *Amer. J. Dis. Child.*, **72**, 481 (1946). *44*) Koefoed, H., quoted by Münzel, K., *Schweiz. ApothZtg*, **92**, 93 (1954). *45*) Best and Taylor, *Physiological Basis of Medical Practice*, 6th ed., Baltimore, 1950. *46*) Weisberg, H. F., *Water, Electrolyte and Acid-Base Balance*, Baltimore, 1953.

Infusion solutions for water and electrolyte therapy

See remarks on pages 331–333. For bibliographical references see above.

Solution (% = g/100 ml of solution)	Na^+		K^+		Ca^{++}		Mg^{++}		Cl^-		Other ions*	Phosphorus	Osmolarity (ideal)
	mEq/l	mg/l	mEq/l	mg/l	mEq/l	mg/l	mEq/l	mg/l	mEq/l	mg/l	mEq/l	mg/l	mmol/l
A. "Physiological" solutions													
1. Isotonic salt solution (0.95%)	162.5	3733							162.5	5767			325
2. Isotonic sodium lactate**-salt solution: 1 vol. sodium lactate solution (1.75%)+2 vols. salt solution (0.95%) (sodium lactate 5.83 g, sodium chloride 6.33 g, aqua dest. to 1000 ml)	160.3	3683							108.3	3842	52.0		321

For footnotes see the following page.

Infusion solutions for water and electrolyte therapy (continued)

Solution (% = g/100 ml of solution)	Na^+		K^+		Ca^{++}		Mg^{++}		Cl^-		Other ions*	Phos-phorus	Osmolarity (ideal)
	mEq/l	mg/l	mEq/l	mg/l	mEq/l	mg/l	mEq/l	mg/l	mEq/l	mg/l	mEq/l	mg/l	mmol/l
3. (*a*) Glucose–salt solution: 2 vols. isotonic glucose solution (5.25%)+1 vol. isotonic salt solution (0.95%) (glucose 35.0 g, sodium chloride 3.16 g, aqua dest. to 1000 ml)	54.1	1242							54.1	1918			302
(*b*) Glucose–sodium lactate–salt solution: 2 vols. isotonic glucose solution (5.25%) + 1 vol. isotonic sodium lactate–salt solution (glucose 35.0 g, sodium lactate 1.94 g, sodium chloride 2.11 g, aqua dest. to 1000 ml)	53.4	1227							36.1	1290	17.3		301
4. RINGER's solution after BEST and TAYLOR[45] (sodium chloride 9.00 g, potassium chloride 0.40 g, calcium chloride [$6H_2O$] 0.25 g, sodium bicarbonate 0.20 g, aqua dest. to 1000 ml)	156.4	3592	5.4	210	2.3	46			161.7	5738	2.4		324
5. RINGER's lactate solution after HARTMANN[7] (sodium chloride 6.00 g, sodium lactate 3.05 g, potassium chloride 0.40 g, calcium chloride [$6H_2O$] 0.20 g, magnesium chloride [$6H_2O$] 0.20 g, aqua dest. to 1000 ml)	129.8	2983	5.4	210	1.8	37	2.0	24.0	111.8	3967	27.2		276
6. Solution of Fox et al.[37,38]. Total organic anions (lactate + acetate) 55 mEq/l	140	3220	10	390	5	100.2	3	36.5	103	3660	55		316
B. Solutions for correction of acidosis or alkalosis													
Treatment of acidosis													
1. Isotonic sodium lactate solution** (1.75%) (sodium lactate 17.5 g, aqua dest. to 1000 ml)	156.1	3587									156.1		312
Treatment of alkalosis													
2. Isotonic ammonium chloride solution (0.83%) (ammonium chloride 8.30 g, aqua dest. to 1000 ml)									155.1	5503	155.1		310
C. Solutions for potassium replacement													
For use in acidosis or when alkali reserve is normal													
1. DARROW's solution[6,12,31] (potassium chloride 2.70 g, sodium lactate** 5.80 g, sodium chloride 4.00 g, aqua dest. to 1000 ml)	120.2	2761	36.2	1417					104.7	3713	51.7		313
For infants DARROW recommends dilution of 1 vol. of this solution with 2 vols. isotonic glucose solution	40.7	920	12.1	472					34.9	1238	17.2		with 5.25% glucose: 299
2. (*a*) BUTLER's pediatric solution[43] (potassium chloride 0.89 g, potassium hydrogen phosphate 0.25 g, sodium lactate** 2.24 g, sodium chloride 0.58 g, 10% glucose solution to 1000 ml)	29.9	687	14.8	580					21.9	775	20.0	44.5	643
(*b*) BUTLER's new pediatric solution[9] (potassium chloride 1.0 g, potassium hydrogen phosphate 1.0 g, sodium lactate** 2.8 g, sodium chloride 1.8 g, sodium dihydrogen phosphate monohydrate 0.14 g, anhydrous magnesium chloride 0.25 g, 2–10% glucose solution to 1000 ml) (the magnesium chloride must be separately sterilized)	56.8	1304	24.9	974			5.3	63.8	49.5	1755	25.0	209.4	without glucose 167
3. Solution of DAVIDSEN and KJERULF-JENSEN[42] (potassium chloride 3.8 g, sodium dihydrogen phosphate dihydrate 0.3 g, sodium hydrogen phosphate dihydrate 1.2 g, sodium chloride 5.4 g, aqua dest. to 1000 ml)	107.8	2476	51.0	1995					143.4	5087		269	313
4. Solution of ELKINTON and TARAIL[31] (potassium hydrogen phosphate 4.5 g, potassium dihydrogen phosphate 1.0 g, sodium chloride 5.5 g, aqua dest. to 1000 ml)	94.1	2162	59.0	2307					94.1	3339		1029	288
For use in alkalosis or when alkali reserve is normal													
5. DARROW's solution[6] (potassium chloride 2.70 g, sodium chloride 6.00 g, aqua dest. to 1000 ml).	102.6	2358	36.2	1418					138.8	4927			278
For infants DARROW recommends dilution of 1 vol. of this solution with 2 vols. isotonic glucose solution	34.2	786	12.0	473					46.3	1642			with 5.25% glucose: 287
6. Solution of DAVIDSEN and KJERULF-JENSEN[42] (potassium chloride 3.8 g, sodium dihydrogen phosphate dihydrate 0.3 g, sodium hydrogen phosphate dihydrate 1.2 g, sodium lactate** 10.3 g, aqua dest. to 1000 ml)	107.3	2465	51.0	1995					51.0	1809	91.9	269	312
7. Solution of ELKINTON and TARAIL[31] (potassium chloride 3.0 g, sodium chloride 4.2 g, potassium hydrogen phosphate 3.2 g, potassium dihydrogen phosphate 0.7 g, aqua dest. to 1000 ml)	71.9	1651	82.1	3213					112.1	3977		729.2	295
D. Solutions for replacement of digestive tract secretions													
1. Solution for replacement of gastric juice[10] (sodium chloride 3.70 g, potassium chloride 1.30 g, ammonium chloride 3.74 g, aqua dest. to 1000 ml)	63.3	1454	17.4	683					150.6	5344	69.9		301
2. Solution for the replacement of alkaline secretions (bile and secretion of the pancreas and small intestine)[10] (sodium lactate** 5.60 g, sodium chloride 5.10 g, potassium chloride 0.90 g, aqua dest. to 1000 ml)	137.2	3152	12.1	473					99.4	3524	50.0		299

* Lactate (–), bicarbonate (–), or ammonium (+) ions (cf. composition of solution in column 1).
** May be replaced by bicarbonate (see remarks under A 2 on page 331).

Contents of Pages 336–448

This chapter, Constituents of Living Matter, has been written in consultation with Professor Sir H. A. Krebs, F.R.S., Dr. K. Burton, Dr. D. B. Keech, Dr. H. L. Kornberg, Dr. J. M. Lowenstein and Dr. J. R. Quayle, Department of Biochemistry, University of Oxford, England.

1. Carbohydrates[1]

Carbohydrates are carbon compounds which contain hydrogen and oxygen in the ratio 2:1, their general empirical formula being $C_x(H_2O)_y$*. The term is also extended, however, to oxidation and reduction products of carbohydrates proper, as well as to their simple derivatives such as amino and phosphorylated sugars.

Carbohydrates are frequently referred to as "sugars" (saccharides) because many of them possess a sweet taste** but actually the term "sugar" is only loosely defined and may denote a wide variety of carbohydrate compounds. To the carbohydrate chemist, however, it means a mono- or oligo-saccharide but *not* a polysaccharide (see below). Mono- and oligosaccharides are given names with the suffix "-ose", e.g. glucose, fructose, lactose.

Monosaccharides (see also pages 341–343)

Carbohydrates which cannot be split further by hydrolysis are called simple sugars or monosaccharides. Their general empirical formula is $[C(H_2O)]_n$ and they are classed as aldehydic alcohols (aldoses) or ketonic alcohols (ketoses).

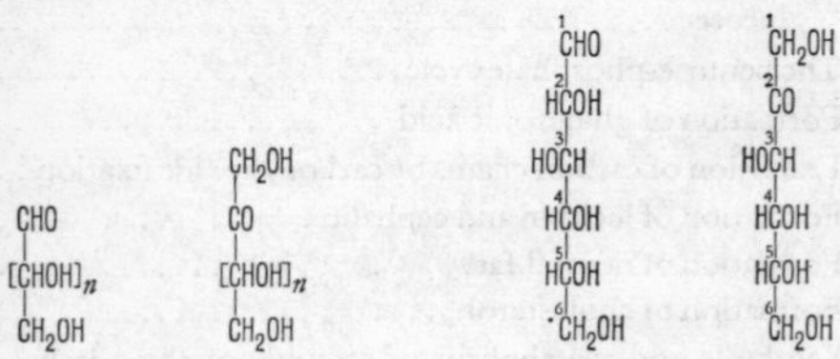

Aldose Ketose Glucose Fructose

Sugars with chain lengths of 3, 4, 5, 6, etc. carbon atoms are known as trioses, tetroses, pentoses, hexoses, etc.*** The numbering convention is shown above in the structures of glucose and fructose.

The open-chain form of sugars (aldehyde or ketone form) normally occurs only in aqueous solution, where it is a transitional form in equilibrium with the ring form. The latter is the rule with carbohydrates of longer chain length, and with few exceptions the ring is usually 5- or 6-membered. By analogy with the similar heterocyclic compounds† furan and pyran, these ring forms are known as *furanoses* and *pyranoses* respectively:

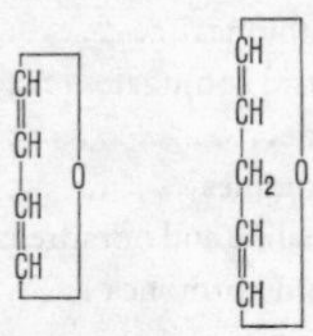

Furan Pyran

The ring forms are formed from chain forms by the reaction of the hydroxyl group in the 4 or 5 position with the carbonyl group. Carbon atom 4 is involved in the case of furanoses, carbon atom 5 in the case of pyranoses. This results in the formation of an oxygen bridge between the carbon atoms concerned and of a hydroxyl group on the carbon atom of the original carbonyl group:

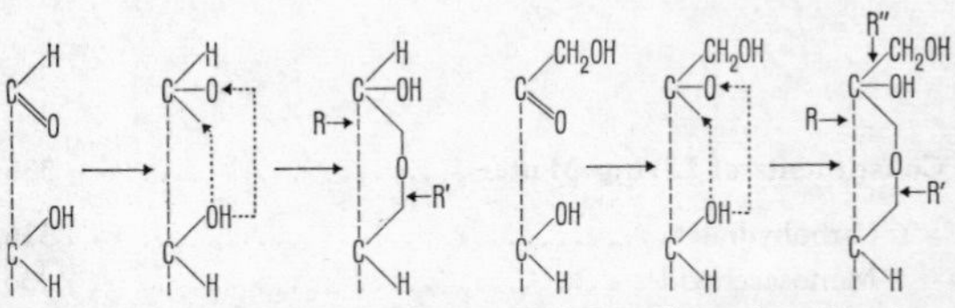

Chain form (aldoses) Ring form Chain form (ketoses) Ring form

The compound formed is an intramolecular hemiacetal (when derived from an aldose) or hemiketal (when derived from a ketose).

Acetal Hemiacetal Ketal Hemiketal

The hydroxyl group attached to the hemiacetal or hemiketal carbon atom (C-1 or C-2 respectively) is particularly reactive and is known as the glycosidic hydroxyl. It combines readily with the alcoholic or phenolic groups of other molecules, and when this reaction takes place with a compound which is not another sugar (an aglycon), the resulting compound is known as a *glycoside:*

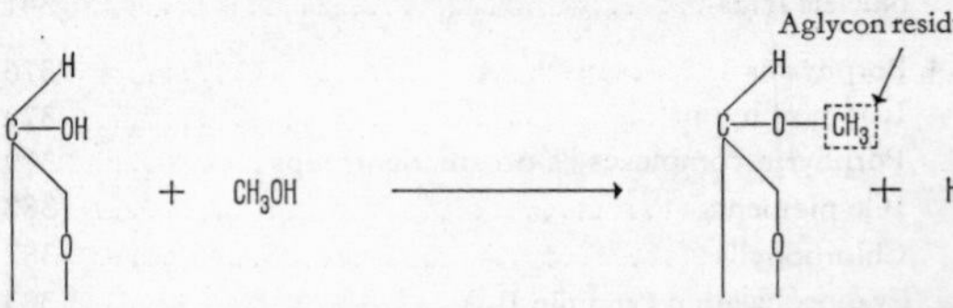

Sugar Aglycon (here methanol) Glycoside (methylglycoside)

When the reaction takes place with a molecule of another sugar the resulting compound is known not as a glycoside but as a disaccharide (cf. Oligo- and Poly-saccharides, page 340).

Stereochemistry of sugars

The stereoisomerism of sugars and related substances is of particular importance in biochemistry*, and for this reason it will be dealt with in some detail here. For a more thorough treatment of the subject see Honeyman[2]. A carbon atom with four different substituents, for example C-2 of glyceraldehyde, is known as an *asymmetric* carbon atom. This grouping cannot be superimposed on its mirror image and the resulting lack of symmetry gives rise to a type of isomerism which is associated with optical activity. The two possible spatial configurations of the substituents can be readily seen if one imagines the asymmetric C atom to be in the middle of a regular tetrahedron with the valencies pointing to the corners. The two possible configurations of glyceraldehyde which are shown as an example in Figure 1 cannot in any way be superimposed one upon the other. They are related to one another as an object to its mirror image, and are known as enantiomorphs. No such asymmetry exists with a carbon atom possessing at least two identical substituents.

Enantiomorphic isomers are optically active, i.e. in solution one of the isomers rotates the plane of polarized light to the right, the other an equal amount to the left. The degree of rotation depends on the length of the polarimeter tube, on the wave length of the polarized light, on the concentration, and on the solvent and its temperature**. The direction of rotation was originally indicated by

* There are, however, compounds with this empirical formula which do not fall into the category of carbohydrates such as, for example, acetic acid, lactic acid, phloroglucinol.

** The sweetest of the sugars is fructose. Polysaccharides have no taste.

*** According to Beilstein (1938) these names are derived from the number of oxygen atoms. In the case of "ordinary" monosaccharides $[C(H_2O)]_n$ both nomenclatures are identical. They are different in the case of substituted and desoxy sugars. In general the nomenclature which is based on the number of carbon atoms is the more commonly used and permits a better understanding of carbohydrate metabolism (anabolism of the carbon chain from small molecules and its subsequent catabolism).

† Heterocycles are ring molecules in which apart from carbon atoms the ring contains at least one atom of another element.

* Stereoisomerism is of importance in nature not only in the case of carbohydrates but for all compounds where stereoisomers are possible. This is because as a rule only specific stereoisomers are synthesized or degraded in naturally occurring reactions (this is a characteristic difference compared to laboratory synthesis). One reason is the stereospecificity of many enzymes, but the fundamental mechanism is unknown.

** The specific rotation [α] is defined as the rotation in degrees of 1 g of substance in 1 ml of solution in a tube with a length of 10 cm. The D-line of sodium is as a rule used as a source of light. The temperature, wave length of the incident light, nature of solvent and the concentration must also be included where these diverge from the definition, e.g. $[\alpha]_D^{25°}$, 20% (H_2O) = + 12°.

I, II, III

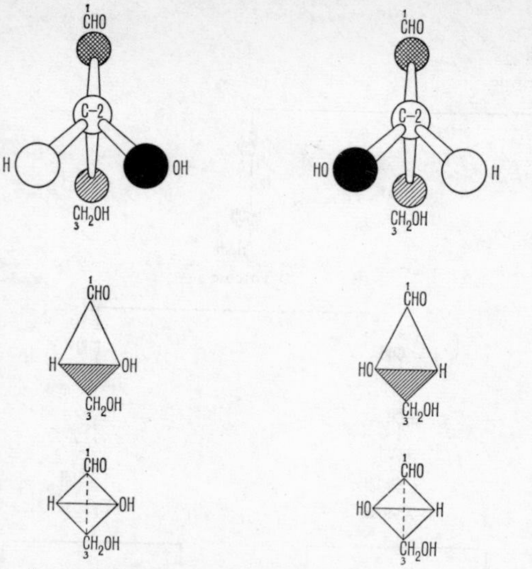

Fig. 1 Stereoisomerism of glyceraldehyde

I Atomic models.

II Tetrahedron representation of I. The edge of the tetrahedron joining C-1 and C-3 (imagined to be in or below the plane of the paper) is invisible, as is also the asymmetric carbon atom C-2 lying inside the tetrahedron.

III Conventional representation of the tetrahedra. The edge between C-1 and C-3 in the plane of the paper is indicated by a broken line, the other edges (all above the plane of the paper) by full lines.

prefixing the name of the isomer by *dextro-* (*d*-) and *levo-* (*l*-) respectively. The alternative symbols (+) and (−) are now more commonly used*.

In a mixture containing equal amounts of an enantiomorphic pair of isomers the rotations due to the isomers cancel each other out. An optically *inactive* substance of this kind is known as a *racemate* and is indicated by the prefix *dl-* or DL-*.

It must not be confused with an optically inactive *meso*-form. This may arise in the case of a molecule which possesses more than one asymmetric center where the configuration is such that there is a plane or center of symmetry in the molecule as a whole. The various directions of rotation then cancel each other out within the molecule (internal compensation). These racemic and meso-forms are illustrated by the cases of tartaric acid and hexahydro-hexahydroxybenzene:

Isomers of tartaric acid

Racemate

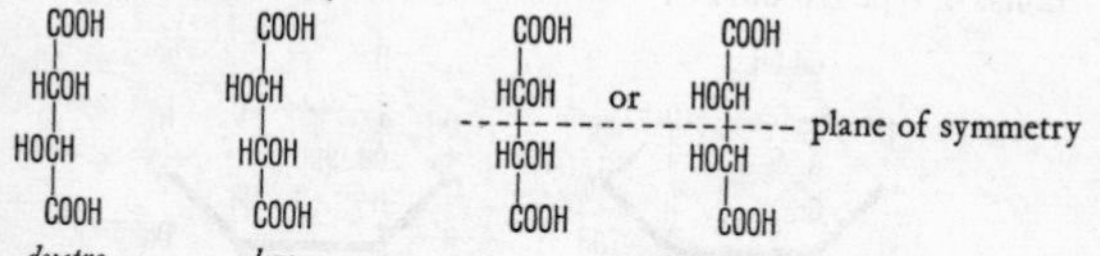

dextro *levo* *meso*

(mirror-image forms) (identical forms, as can be seen by turning one through 180° in the plane of the paper)

Isomers of hexahydrohexahydroxybenzene (inositol)

Racemate

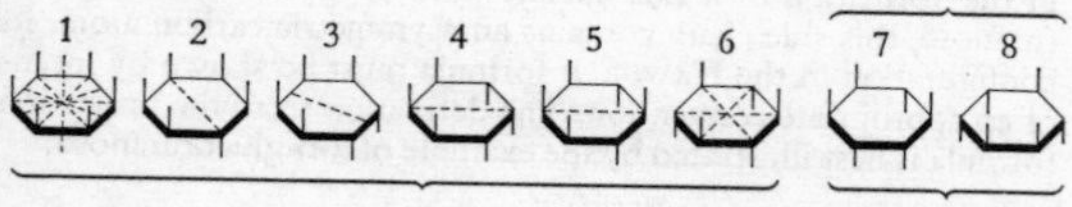

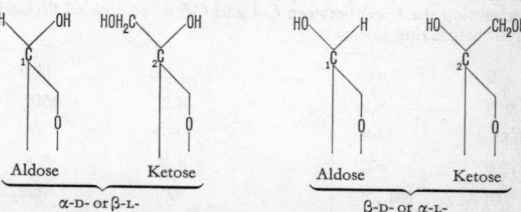

*meso*** optically active enantiomorphs

(The vertical lines indicate the positions of the OH groups, the broken lines the planes of symmetry)

* The use of the letters *d* and *l* to denote optical rotation is now discouraged in favor of *dextro* and *levo*, or better (+) and (−). DL- is likewise preferred for racemates.

** Although structures nos. 1–6 are all meso-forms and optically inactive, the name mesoinositol is confined to the compound of structure no. 5.

Meso-forms do not occur in the case of sugars since the carbonyl group on one side of the ring renders meso-symmetry impossible.

The classification of carbohydrate molecules is based on their relationship to the simplest optically active sugar, glyceraldehyde, to which ROSANOFF[3] arbitrarily assigned the following configurations:

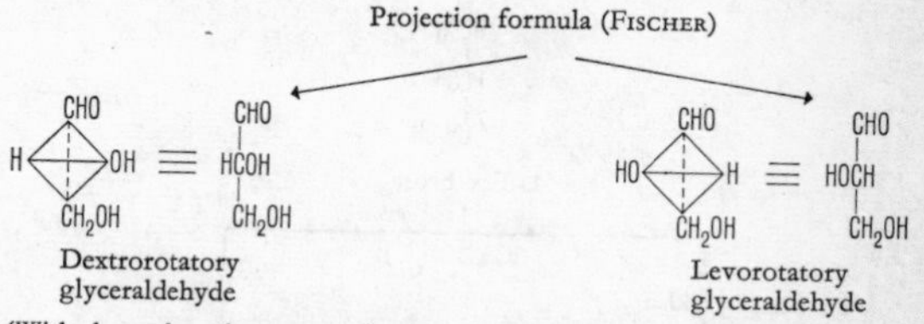

(With the carbonyl group at the top, the hydroxyl group is written on the right of the asymmetric carbon atom in the case of the dextrorotatory compound, and on the left in the case of the levorotatory compound)

Sugars with longer carbon chains can be considered to be derived from dextro- or levo-rotatory glyceraldehyde by the successive addition of secondary alcohol groups (–CHOH) to the carbonyl carbon. With each additional asymmetric center the number of possible isomers is increased, while the optical rotation relative to the parent substance can increase or decrease or even be reversed in sign. To designate the direction of rotation of a sugar as *d*- or *l*- therefore in no way indicates whether it is derived from dextro- or levo-rotatory glyceraldehyde. The designations D- and L-, introduced by ROSANOFF, make clear this genetic relationship. According to this usage, all sugars (and related substances such as tartaric acid) are assigned to the D-series, irrespective of their direction of rotation, if the secondary alcohol group which is furthest from the principal function (i.e. the aldehydo, keto, carbonyl group, etc.), possesses the same spatial configuration as that of dextrorotatory glyceraldehyde. They are assigned to the L-series if this group has the configuration of levorotatory glyceraldehyde. This arbitrary configuration has now been found to correspond absolutely with the true configuration in the case of tartaric acid, the absolute structure of which has been determined by BIJVOET[4] by physical methods.

With a few exceptions, all naturally occurring sugars belong to the D-series. The D-series of aldoses and ketoses with a carbon chain length up to 6 are shown in Figures 2 and 3.

The D- or L-designation thus gives no indication of the direction of rotation of a substance, and if it is desired to show this the appropriate prefix is added, e.g. D-(+)glyceraldehyde, D-(−)erythrose. In the case of tartaric acid, the dextrorotatory form belongs to the L-series, the levorotatory form to the D-series, so that they are designated L-(+)tartaric acid and D-(−)tartaric acid respectively. L-isomers are enantiomorphs of D-isomers, with opposite rotations, so that a DL-substance is a racemate.

On ring closure of a straight-chain carbohydrate molecule a secondary alcohol group is formed from the original carbonyl group, thus introducing an additional asymmetric center. The two stereoisomers of a cyclic sugar molecule which arise in this way are denoted by the symbols α and β (after HUDSON[5]), that isomer being designated α which in the D-series is more strongly *dextro*rotatory and in the L-series more strongly *levo*rotatory. In the FISCHER projection formula the OH group is again arbitrarily written on the right of the asymmetric carbon atom in the case of the more strongly dextrorotatory isomers (α-D- or β-L-configuration) and on the left in the case of the more strongly levorotatory isomers (β-D- or α-L-configuration):

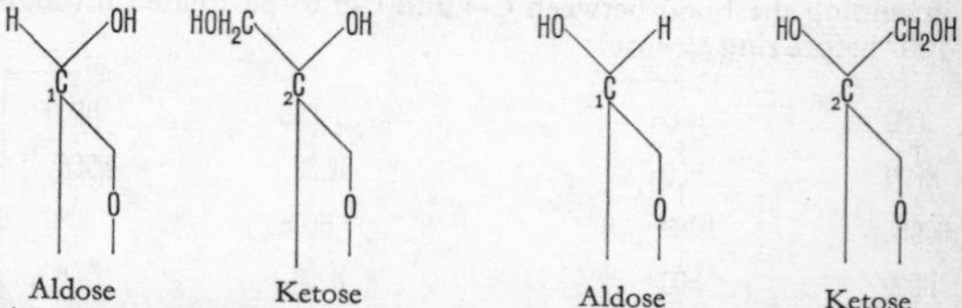

Aldose Ketose Aldose Ketose

α-D- or β-L- β-D- or α-L-

The α- and β-isomers yield corresponding α- and β-glycosides. This is of importance insofar as many glycosidases have been found to be α- or β-specific in their action.

Fig. 2 Configurational relationships of the D-aldo-sugars

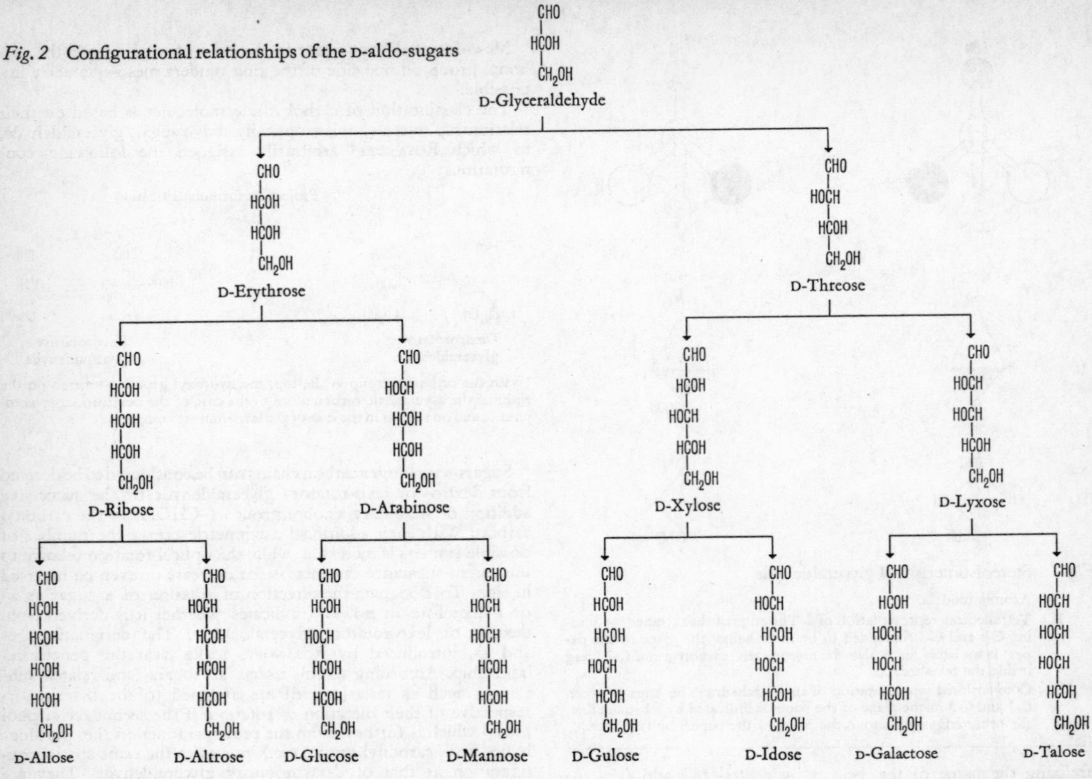

The representation of cyclic sugars by the FISCHER projection convention is best illustrated by the example of D-glucose:

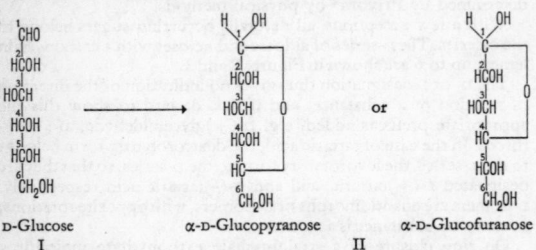

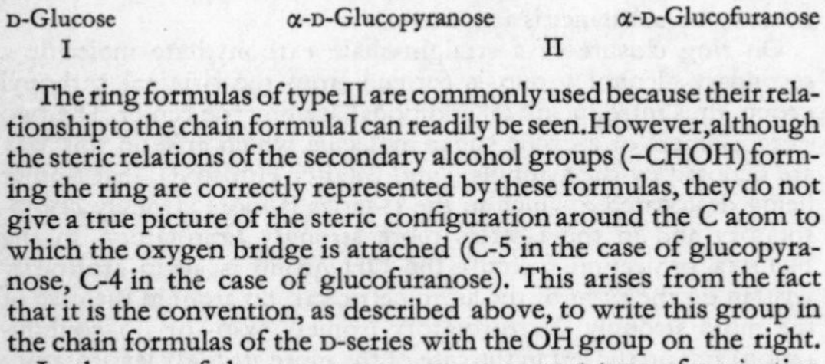

D-Glucose I — α-D-Glucopyranose II — α-D-Glucofuranose

The ring formulas of type II are commonly used because their relationship to the chain formula I can readily be seen. However, although the steric relations of the secondary alcohol groups (–CHOH) forming the ring are correctly represented by these formulas, they do not give a true picture of the steric configuration around the C atom to which the oxygen bridge is attached (C-5 in the case of glucopyranose, C-4 in the case of glucofuranose). This arises from the fact that it is the convention, as described above, to write this group in the chain formulas of the D-series with the OH group on the right.

In the case of the pyranoses, a more correct type of projection formula is that illustrated by III and IV for glucose (derived by imagining the bond between C-4 and C-5 to be rotated through 180° before ring closure):

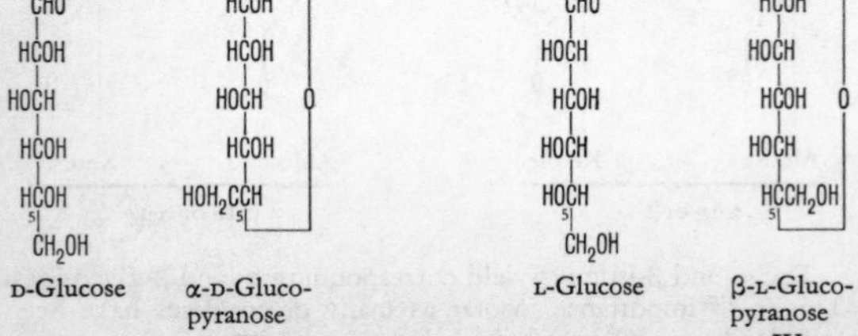

D-Glucose — α-D-Glucopyranose III — L-Glucose — β-L-Glucopyranose IV

In formulas III and IV, however, the D- and L-configurations respectively of the OH group attached to C-5 are no longer readily recognizable. These defects of the FISCHER projection formulas led HAWORTH to introduce a type of ring formula in which the steric relations of the groups are shown unequivocally. The ring is imagined as being looked at obliquely from above, the three thickened edges being those nearest to the observer:

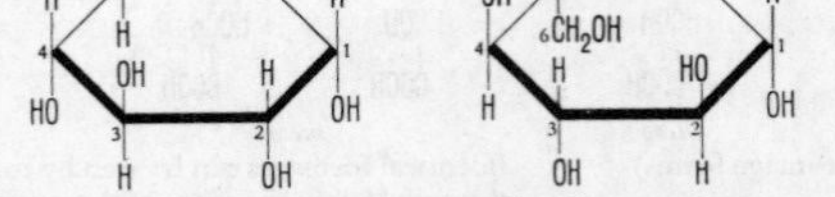

Furanose ring — Pyranose ring

The positions of the substituents correspond to those in formulas of type III and IV:

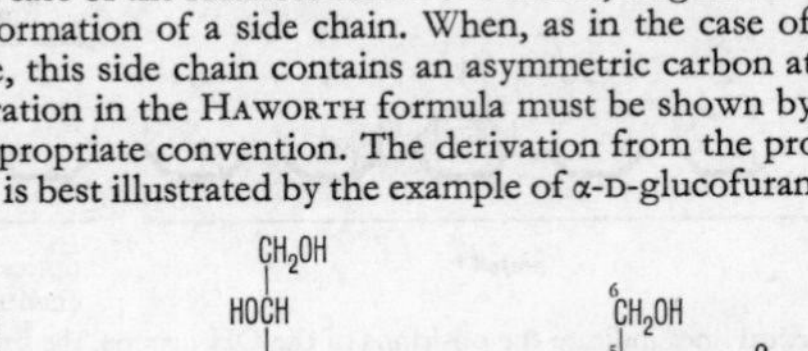

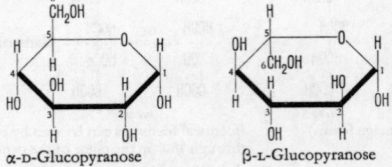

α-D-Glucopyranose — β-L-Glucopyranose

In the case of the furanose forms of hexoses, ring closure results in the formation of a side chain. When, as in the case of glucofuranose, this side chain contains an asymmetric carbon atom, its configuration in the HAWORTH formula must be shown by means of an appropriate convention. The derivation from the projection formula is best illustrated by the example of α-D-glucofuranose:

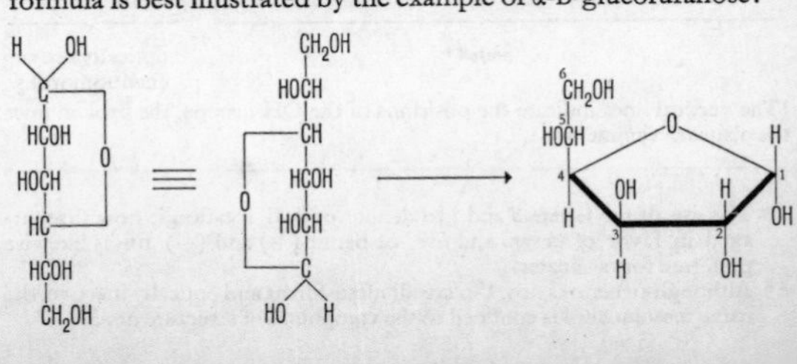

Fig. 3 Configurational relationships of the D-keto-sugars

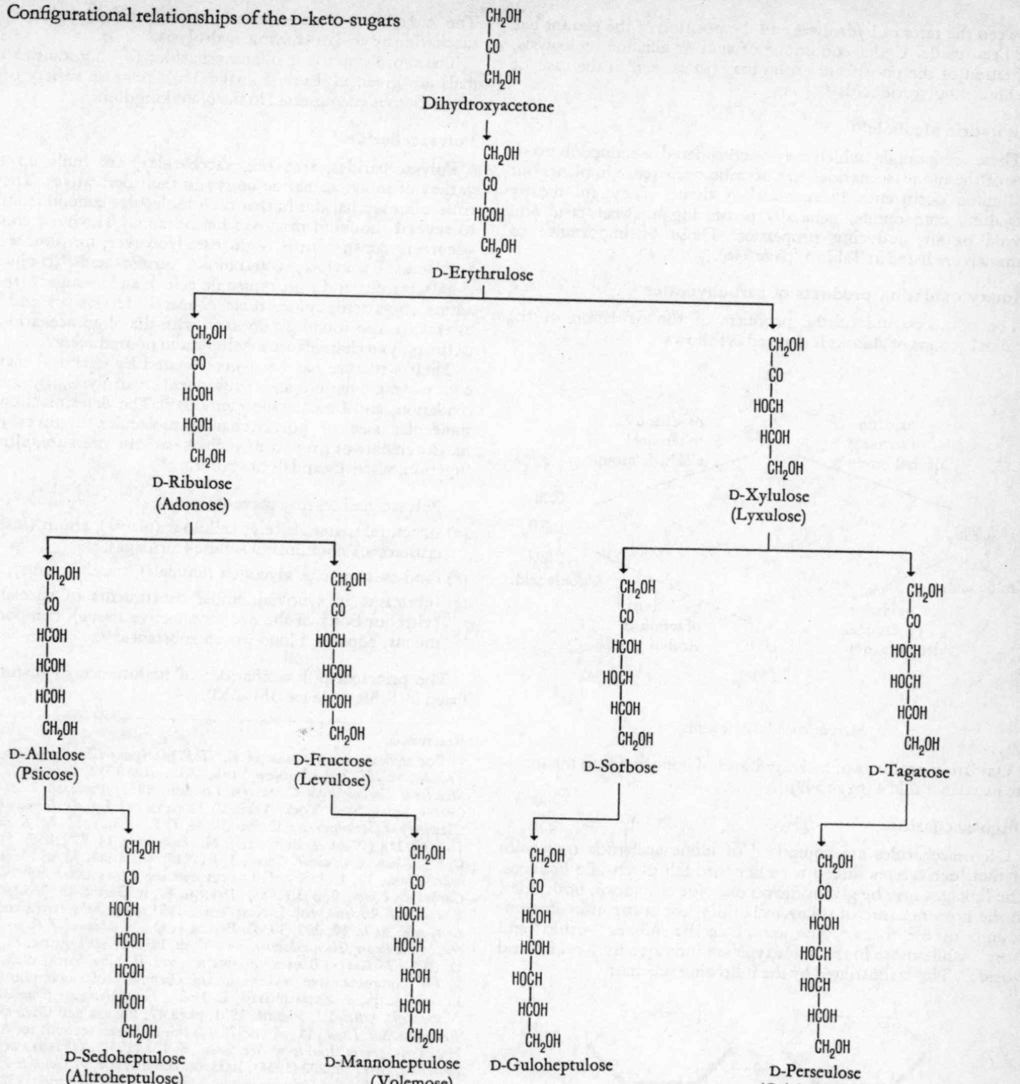

For convenience in writing the formulas of polysaccharides and other complex sugar compounds, the HAWORTH rings are sometimes written upside down or back to front with respect to the examples shown above, i.e. in the positions obtained by rotating the ring through 180° about two axes in the plane of the ring or about an axis passing vertically through the center of it. The alternative positions for α-D-glucopyranose are as follows:

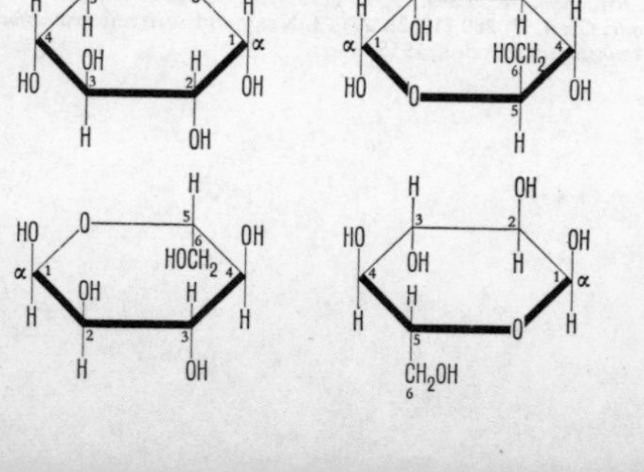

It is now known that the pyranose ring is not planar, and most of its properties can be explained on the assumption that it has the "chair" form. The furanose ring is usually planar. For further information see MILLS[6].

The monosaccharides of importance to mammals are listed in Table 1 (pages 341–343). The newer techniques of chromatography have found extensive application in the analysis of sugars[7], and many specific color reactions have been developed[8].

Sugar phosphates[9]

Phosphorylated sugars are intermediates in glycolysis; they are components of nucleic acids, nucleotides and polysaccharides[10] (see Table 2, pages 344–347).

The separation of sugar phosphates by paper chromatography[11], electrophoresis[12] and ion-exchange chromatography[13] has been extensively developed in recent years. The quantitative determination of phosphate is usually carried out by spectrophotometric measurement of molybdenum blue, an intensely-colored reduction product of phosphomolybdic acid. Methods have been devised for the specific production of this complex from various types of organic phosphate[14].

The stability of phosphate groups toward acid or alkaline hydrolysis varies over a wide range[15] and, as yet, detailed correlation between the rates of hydrolysis and the position of the groups has not been made. Under conditions of acid or alkaline hydrolysis, migration of the phosphate group may occur, e.g. in the case of the phosphoglyceric acids[16].

Polyhydric alcohols[17]

These compounds, which may be considered as reduction products of the monosaccharides, are of wide occurrence in plants but of limited occurrence in mammalian tissue. They are mostly crystalline compounds, generally possessing a sweet taste and devoid of any reducing properties. Those of importance to mammals are listed in Table 3 (page 348).

Primary oxidation products of carbohydrates

The nomenclature of the products of the oxidation of the terminal groups of aldoses is derived as follows:

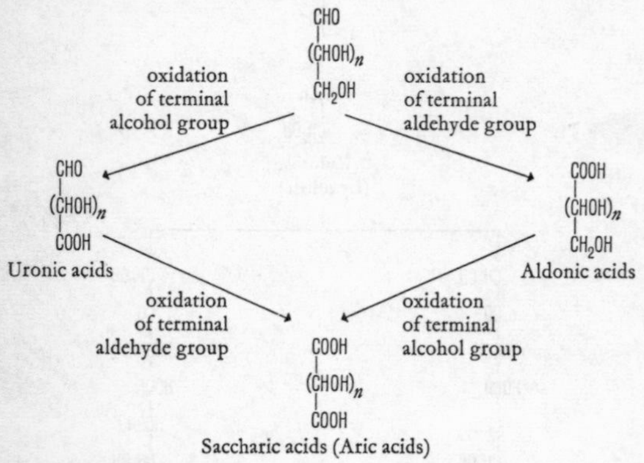

Oxidation products of carbohydrates of importance to mammals are listed in Table 4 (page 349).

Oligosaccharides

Oligosaccharides are composed of monosaccharide molecules or their derivatives linked together through glycosidic linkages. The linkages may be glycosidic on one side only or on both sides. In the nomenclature of oligosaccharides, the sugar units in compounds of the former type are given the suffixes "-osido" and "-ose", while those in the latter type are indicated by "-osido" and "-oside". This is illustrated by the following scheme:

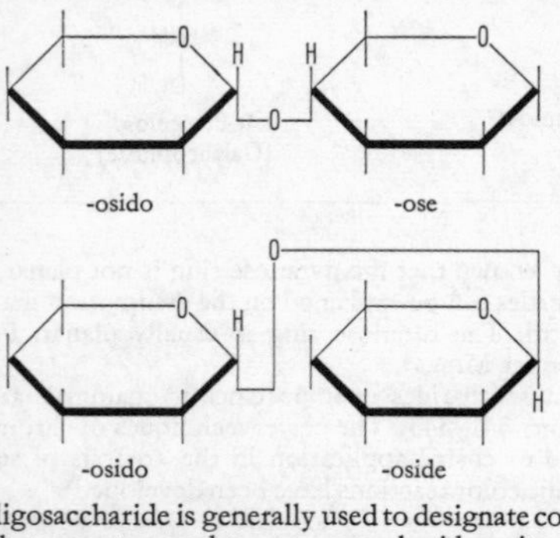

The term oligosaccharide is generally used to designate compounds containing between two and ten monosaccharide units per molecule. Oligosaccharides may be reducing or nonreducing, depending on the presence or absence of free hemiacetal hydroxyl groups. The constituent monosaccharides are set free from an oligosaccharide by acid or enzymic hydrolysis.

The more important oligosaccharides of importance to mammals are given in Table 5 (page 350). A great variety of oligosaccharides is encountered in the plant kingdom.

Polysaccharides[18]

Polysaccharides, like oligosaccharides, are built up from a variety of monosaccharide units and their derivatives. They differ from oligosaccharides in that their molecules contain from ten up to several thousand monosaccharide units. The most commonly occurring constituent is D-glucose. However, D-mannose, D- and L-galactose, D-xylose, L-arabinose, uronic acids (D-glucuronic, D-galacturonic and D-mannuronic acids), amino-sugars (D-glucosamine, D-galactosamine, their N-acetyl derivatives and sulfate esters) are also found. In contrast with the oligosaccharides many of the polysaccharides are insoluble and nonreducing.

Their structure has been investigated by chemical methods[18], e.g. by methylation and subsequent hydrolysis, by periodate oxidation, and by enzymic methods[19]. The determination of the molecular size of polysaccharide molecules involves physical measurements of properties such as osmotic pressure, ultracentrifugation, viscosity and light scattering[20].

Polysaccharides may serve as:

(*a*) structural materials, e.g. cellulose (plants), chitin (insects and crustaceae), chondroitin sulfate (cartilage),

(*b*) food storage, e.g. glycogen (animals), starch (plants),

(*c*) lubricants in synovial fluids, constituents of special tissues (vitreous body of the eye; connective tissue), components of mucus, heparin, blood group substances[21].

The principal polysaccharides of importance to mammals are listed in Table 6 (pages 351–353).

References

1) For reviews see GILMAN et al. (Eds.), *Organic Chemistry: An Advanced Treatise*, vol. II, 2nd ed., New York, 1943, page 1532; PERCIVAL, E. G. V., *Structural Carbohydrate Chemistry*, London, 1950; PIGMAN, W. (Ed.), *The Carbohydrates*, New York, 1957. *2)* HONEYMAN, J., *An Introduction to the Chemistry of Carbohydrates*, Oxford, 1948. *3)* ROSANOFF, M. A., *J. Amer. chem. Soc.*, **28**, 114 (1906). *4)* BIJVOET, J. M., *Endeavour*, **14**, 71 (1955). *5)* HUDSON, C. S., *Advanc. Carbohydr. Chem.*, **3**, 1 (1948). *6)* MILLS, J. A., *Advanc. Carbohydr. Chem.*, **10**, 1 (1955). *7)* For reviews see KOWKABANY, G. N., *Advanc. Carbohydr. Chem.*, **9**, 303 (1954); HOUGH, L., in GLICK, D. (Ed.), *Methods of Biochemical Analysis*, vol. I, New York, 1954, page 205; ISHERWOOD, F. A., *Brit. med. Bull.*, **10**, 202 (1954); BLOCK et al., *A Manual of Paper Chromatography and Paper Electrophoresis*, New York, 1955. *8)* See DISCHE, Z., in GLICK, D. (Ed.), *Methods of Biochemical Analysis*, vol. II, New York, 1955, page 313. *9)* For comprehensive reviews of the chemistry of sugar phosphates see LELOIR, L. F., in ZECHMEISTER, L. (Ed.), *Fortschritte der Chemie organischer Naturstoffe*, vol. VIII, Vienna, 1951, page 47; FOSTER and OVEREND, *Quart. Rev. chem. Soc. Lond.*, **11**, 61 (1957). *10)* For a general account see AVISON and HAWKINS, *Quart. Rev. chem. Soc. Lond.*, **5**, 171 (1951). *11)* ISHERWOOD, F. A., *Brit. med. Bull.*, **10**, 202 (1954); BALSTON and TALBOT, *A Guide to Filter Paper and Cellulose Powder Chromatography*, London and Maidstone, 1952, page 60; BLOCK et al., *A Manual of Paper Chromatography and Paper Electrophoresis*, New York, 1955, page 144. *12)* LEDERER, M., *An Introduction to Paper Electrophoresis and Related Methods*, New York, 1955; BLOCK et al., *A Manual of Paper Chromatography and Paper Electrophoresis*, New York, 1955, page 333. *13)* COHN, W. E., in CHARGAFF and DAVIDSON (Eds.), *The Nucleic Acids*, vol. I, New York, 1955, page 211. *14)* LINDBERG and ERNSTER, in GLICK, D. (Ed.), *Methods of Biochemical Analysis*, vol. III, New York, 1956, page 1. *15)* See LELOIR, L. F., in ZECHMEISTER, L. (Ed.), *Fortschritte der Chemie organischer Naturstoffe*, vol. VIII, Vienna, 1951, page 47. *16)* See BALLOU and FISCHER, *J. Amer. chem. Soc.*, **76**, 3188 (1954). *17)* For a review see LOHMAR, R. L., in PIGMAN, W. (Ed.), *The Carbohydrates*, New York, 1957, page 241. *18)* For reviews see WHISTLER and SMART, *Polysaccharide Chemistry*, New York, 1953; WHISTLER and MCGILVRAY, *Ann. Rev. Biochem.*, **23**, 79 (1954); ASPINALL and SCHWARZ, *Ann. Rep. Progr. Chem.*, **52**, 255 (1955). *19)* MANNERS, D. J., *Quart. Rev. chem. Soc. Lond.*, **9**, 73 (1955). *20)* GREENWOOD, C. T., *Advanc. Carbohydr. Chem.*, **7**, 289 (1952). *21)* Cf. KENT and WHITEHOUSE, *Biochemistry of the Aminosugars*, London, 1955.

Table 1 Monosaccharides of importance to mammals

Some of the more important sugars which are constituents of substances of medical interest are also included in this table

Name	Formula and mol. wt.	Structure	Specific rotation	Occurrence
		Trioses		
D-Glyceraldehyde (2,3-dihydroxy-propanal)	$C_3H_6O_3$ 90.08	CHO / HCOH / CH_2OH	$[\alpha]_D^{20} + 13.5°$	As phosphate ester (see Table 2, page 344)
s-Dihydroxyacetone (1,3-dihydroxy-propan-2-one, oxantin)	$C_3H_6O_3$ 90.08	CH_2OH / CO / CH_2OH or CH_2OH / C(OH) / CHOH	(inactive)	As phosphate ester (see Table 2, page 344)
		Tetroses		
D-Erythrose	$C_4H_8O_4$ 120.11	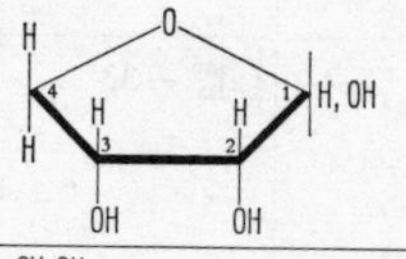	$[\alpha]_D^{20} - 14.8°$	As phosphate ester (see Table 2, page 344)
L-Erythrulose	$C_4H_8O_4$ 120.11	CH_2OH / CO / HOCH / CH_2OH	$[\alpha]_D^{20} + 12°$	As metabolically active phosphate ester (see Table 2, page 344)
2-Desoxy-D-ribose (2-desoxy-D-*erythro*-pentose, thyminose, desoxyarabinose)	$C_5H_{10}O_4$ 134.14	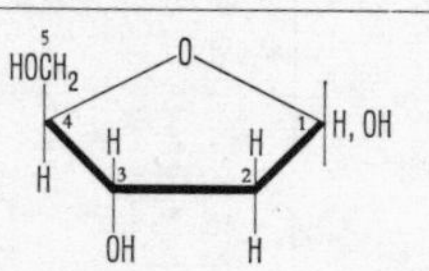	$[\alpha]_D^{25} - 50°$	Universal occurrence as constituent of nucleosides, nucleotides and nucleic acids. For phosphates see Table 2, page 345
D-Digitoxose (2-desoxy-D-*altro*-methylose)	$C_6H_{12}O_4$ 148.16	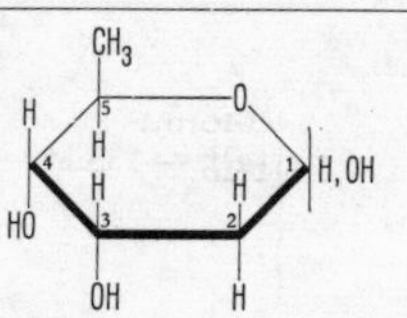	$[\alpha]_D^{20} + 46.5°$	Component of digitalis glycosides
		Pentoses		
β-D-Arabinose	$C_5H_{10}O_5$ 150.14	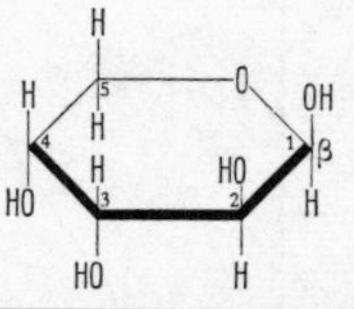	$[\alpha]_D^{20} - 105°$	In glycosides of aloe and tubercle bacilli
DL-Arabinose	$C_5H_{10}O_5$ 150.14	– (equimolecular mixture of D- and L-arabinoses)	(inactive)	Isolated from urine in pentosuria (rare case of metabolic formation of a racemate)
L-Fucose (6-desoxy-L-galactose)	$C_6H_{12}O_5$ 164.16	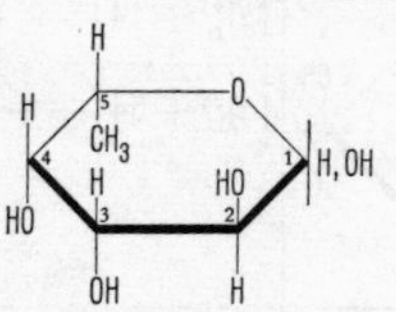	$[\alpha]_D^{20} - 153° \rightarrow + 76°$	Component of polysaccharides of human milk, blood-group substances, marine algae, gum tragacanth
L-Rhamnose (6-desoxy-L-mannose, *iso*dulcitol)	$C_6H_{12}O_5$ 164.16	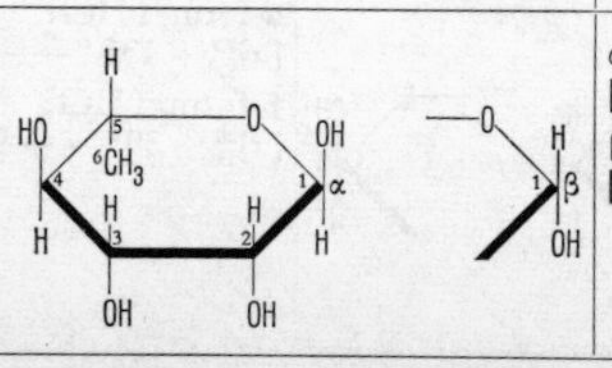	α-form, 1 H_2O: $[\alpha]_D^{20} - 9°$ β-form: $[\alpha]_D^{20} + 38°$	As glycoside in plant pigments, gums and mucilages. Common component of cardiac glycosides

Table 1 Monosaccharides of importance to mammals (*continued*)

Name	Formula and mol. wt.	Structure	Specific rotation	Occurrence
D-Ribose (D-ribofuranose)	$C_5H_{10}O_5$ 150.14	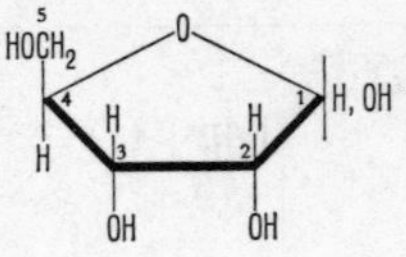	$[\alpha]_D^{20}$ − 23.7° (4% soln.)	Universal occurrence as constituent of nucleosides, nucleotides and nucleic acids. For phosphates see Table 2, pages 344 and 345
D-Ribulose (D-*erythro*-pentulose, D-adonose, D-arabulose)	$C_5H_{10}O_5$ 150.14	CH_2OH CO HCOH HCOH CH_2OH		As phosphate esters (see Table 2, page 345). Intermediary metabolite in glucose oxidation
D-Xylulose (D-*threo*-pentulose, D-xyloketose, D-lyxulose, D-lyxoketose)	$C_5H_{10}O_5$ 150.14	CH_2OH CO HOCH HCOH CH_2OH	$[\alpha]_D^{20}$ − 33°	As phosphate ester (see Table 2, page 345)
L-Xylulose (L-xyloketose, L-lyxulose, L-lyxoketose)	$C_5H_{10}O_5$ 150.14	CH_2OH CO HCOH HOCH CH_2OH	$[\alpha]_D^{20}$ + 33°	In urine in pentosuria
		Hexoses		
D-Fructose (2-keto-D-arabohexose, levulose, fruit sugar)	$C_6H_{12}O_6$ 180.16	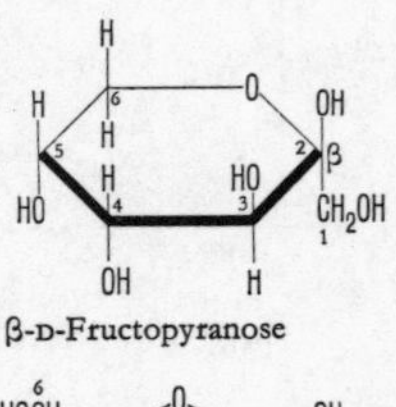 β-D-Fructopyranose 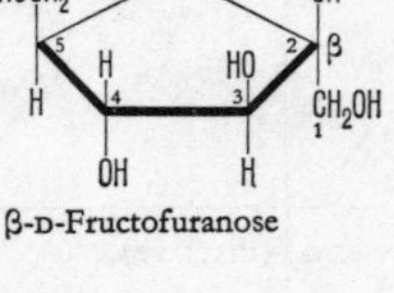 β-D-Fructofuranose	β-form: $[\alpha]_D^{20}$ − 133.5° → − 92°	As phosphate esters (see Table 2, page 345). Component of many polysaccharides (combined with glucose in sucrose). Has pyranose form when crystalline, but furanose form in all natural products. Sweetest of all known sugars
D-Galactose (cerebrose, brain sugar)	$C_6H_{12}O_6$ 180.16	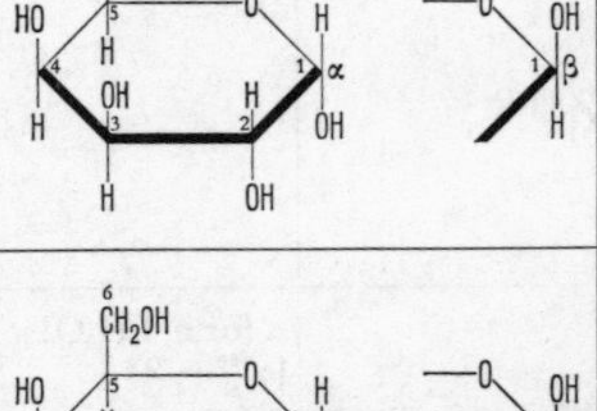	α-form: $[\alpha]_D^{20}$ + 144° → + 80.5° β-form: $[\alpha]_D^{20}$ + 54° → + 80.5°	Present in mammalian tissues as phosphate ester (see Table 2, page 346). Component of cerebrosides and gangliosides, and of polysaccharides both as sugar and derived amino sugar (e.g. lactose, raffinose, stachyose)
D-Galactosamine (D-chondrosamine, 2-amino-2-desoxy-D-galactose)	$C_6H_{13}O_5N$ 179.18	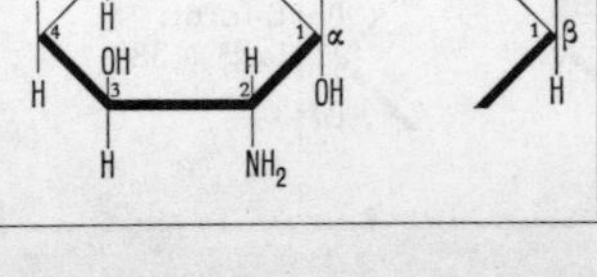	α-form, 1 HCl: $[\alpha]_D^{20}$ + 135 ° → + 93° β-form, 1 HCl: $[\alpha]_D^{20}$ + 39° → + 93°	Widely distributed in nature as component of mucopolysaccharides, cartilage, tendons (chondroitin), β-heparin, lipoids, cerebral gangliosides, blood-group substances

Table 1 Monosaccharides of importance to mammals (*concluded*)

Name	Formula and mol. wt.	Structure	Specific rotation	Occurrence
N-Acetyl-D-galactosamine	$C_8H_{15}O_6N$ 221.22	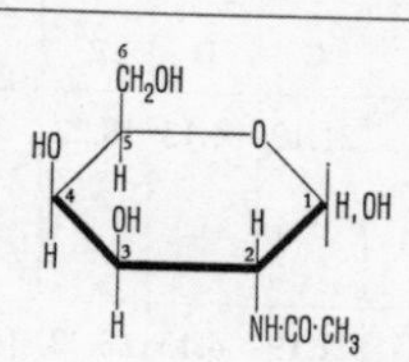	$[\alpha]^{20}_D + 115° \rightarrow + 80°$	Form in which D-galactosamine occurs as component of chondroitin, etc.
D-Glucose (dextrose, blood sugar, grape sugar, corn sugar)	$C_6H_{12}O_6$ 180.16	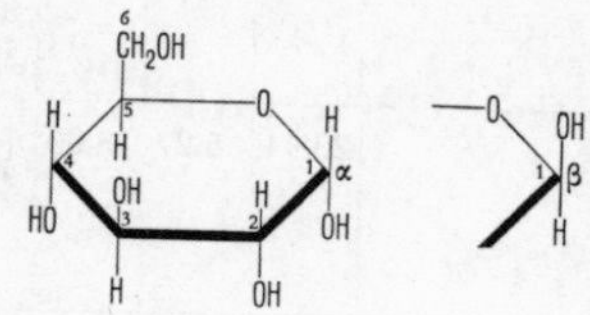	α-form: $[\alpha]^{20}_D + 113.4° \rightarrow + 52.5°$ β-form: $[\alpha]^{20}_D + 19.3° \rightarrow + 52.5°$	As phosphate esters (see Table 2, page 346). Most widely distributed of all sugars. Found free in many biological fluids, e.g. blood, lymph, cerebrospinal fluid. Component of polysaccharides both as sugar and amino sugar (see Glucosamine, below)
D-Glucosamine (chitosamine, 2-amino-2-desoxy-D-glucose)	$C_6H_{13}O_5N$ 179.18	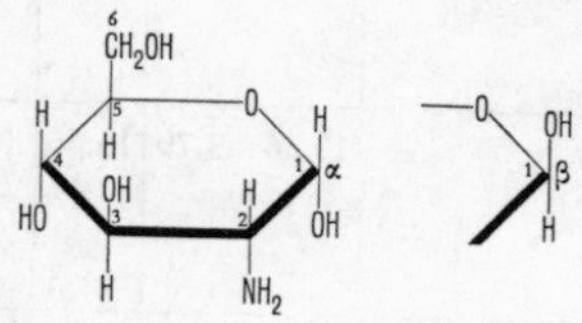	α-form: $[\alpha]^{20}_D + 100° \rightarrow + 47.5°$ β-form: $[\alpha]^{20}_D + 14° \rightarrow + 47.5°$	Component (as N-acetylglucosamine, see below) of chitin, heparin, hyaluronic acid, blood-group polysaccharides, oligosaccharides of human milk
N-Acetyl-D-glucosamine	$C_8H_{15}O_6N$ 221.22	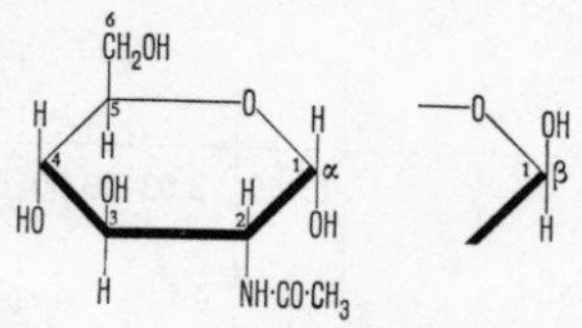		Sole component of chitin; component of heparin, hyaluronic acid, blood-group polysaccharides, oligosaccharides of human milk
N-Methyl-L-glucosamine	$C_7H_{15}O_5N$ 193.21	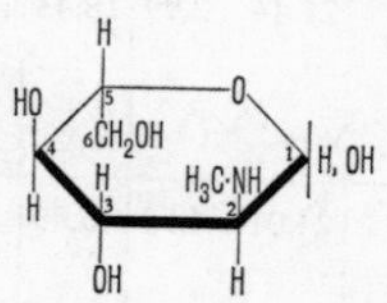		Component of streptomycin
D-Mannose (seminose)	$C_6H_{12}O_6$ 180.16	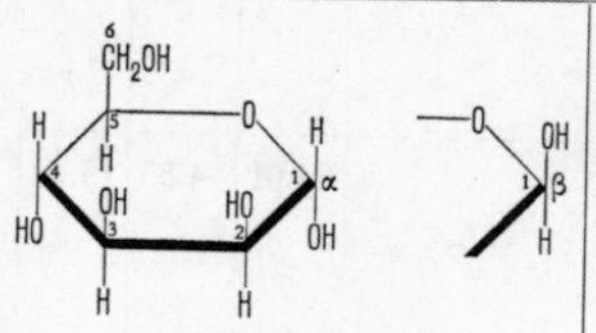	α-form: $[\alpha]^{20}_D + 29.9° \rightarrow + 14.5°$ β-form: $[\alpha]^{20}_D - 16.3° \rightarrow + 14.5°$	As phosphate ester (see Table 2, page 346). Widely distributed as component of mannans and hemicelluloses. Limited occurrence as component of glycoproteins.
		Heptose		
D-Sedoheptulose (D-*altro*-ketoheptose, D-*altro*-heptulose)	$C_7H_{14}O_7$ 210.19	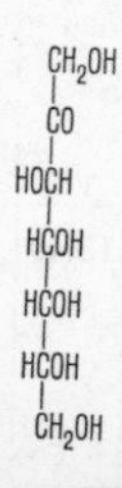	$[\alpha]^{20}_D + 2–3°$ Ba salt: $[\alpha]^{20}_{5461} + 8°$	As phosphate ester (see Table 2, page 347)

Table 2 Sugar phosphates of importance to mammals
(Not including nucleotides, for which see Tables 10c, 11 and 12, pages 367–375)

Name	Formula and mol. wt.	Structure	Elementary composition C	H	P	Specific rotation	Biological function	Reference*
Dihydroxyacetone phosphate	$C_3H_7O_6P$ 170.06	CH_2OH–CO–$CH_2OPO_3H_2$	21.19	4.15	18.22		Intermediate of glycolysis	*1*
D-Glyceraldehyde 3-phosphate ("FISCHER-BAER Ester")	$C_3H_7O_6P$ 170.06	CHO–HCOH–$CH_2OPO_3H_2$	21.19	4.15	18.22	$[\alpha]_D^{20}$ + 14°	Intermediate of glycolysis	*2*
L-Glycerol 1-phosphate	$C_3H_9O_6P$ 172.08	$CH_2OPO_3H_2$–HOCH–CH_2OH	20.94	5.27	18.00	$[\alpha]_D^{20}$ – 1.45° (Ba salt)	Intermediate of fat metabolism. Component of phospholipids	*3*
D-Glyceric acid 2-phosphate ("KIESSLING Ester")	$C_3H_7O_7P$ 186.06	COOH–$HCOPO_3H_2$–CH_2OH	19.36	3.79	16.65	$[\alpha]_D^{20}$ + 13° (N HCl)	Intermediate of glycolysis	*4*
D-Glyceric acid 3-phosphate	$C_3H_7O_7P$ 186.06	COOH–HCOH–$CH_2OPO_3H_2$	19.36	3.79	16.65	$[\alpha]_D^{20}$ – 14.5° (N HCl)	Intermediate of glycolysis	*5*
D-Glyceric acid 1,3-diphosphate	$C_3H_8O_{10}P_2$ 266.05	$COOPO_3H_2$–HCOH–$CH_2OPO_3H_2$	13.55	3.03	23.30	$[\alpha]_D^{20}$ – 2.3°	Intermediate of glycolysis	*6*
D-Glyceric acid 2,3-diphosphate	$C_3H_8O_{10}P_2$ 266.05	COOH–$HCOPO_3H_2$–$CH_2OPO_3H_2$	13.55	3.03	23.30	$[\alpha]_D^{20}$ – 2.3°	Intermediate of glycolysis	*7*
Pyruvic acid enol phosphate (phosphopyruvic acid)	$C_3H_5O_6P$ 168.05	COOH–$COPO_3H_2$=CH_2	21.44	2.99	18.43		Intermediate of glycolysis	*8*
D-Erythrose-4-phosphate	$C_4H_9O_7P$ 200.09	CHO–HCOH–HCOH–$CH_2OPO_3H_2$	24.01	4.53	15.49		Intermediate of pentose-phosphate cycle	*9*
L-Erythrulose-1-phosphate	$C_4H_9O_7P$ 200.09	$CH_2OPO_3H_2$–CO–HOCH–CH_2OH	24.01	4.53	15.49		Function not known	*10*
α-D-Ribose-1-phosphate (furanose form)	$C_5H_{11}O_8P$ 230.12	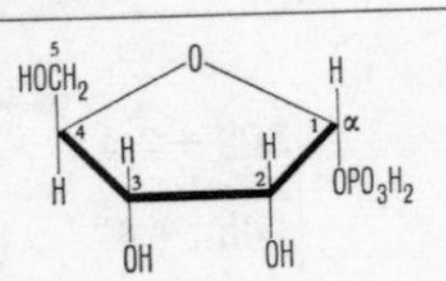	26.15	4.83	13.49		Intermediate of nucleotide metabolism	*11*
D-Ribose-5-phosphate (furanose form)	$C_5H_{11}O_8P$ 230.12	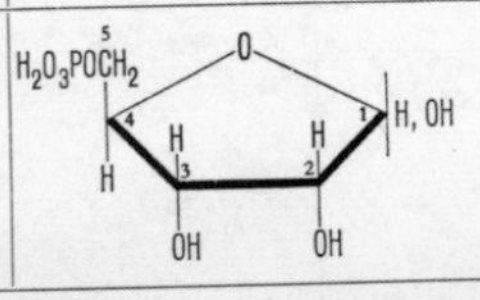	26.15	4.83	13.49	$[\alpha]_D^{20}$ + 16.5°	Intermediate of pentose-phosphate cycle and nucleotide synthesis	*12*

* See end of table, page 347.

Table 2 Sugar phosphates of importance to mammals (*continued*)

Name	Formula and mol. wt.	Structure	Elementary composition C	H	P	Specific rotation	Biological function	Reference*
D-Ribose-1,5-diphosphate (furanose form)	$C_5H_{12}O_{11}P_2$ 310.10	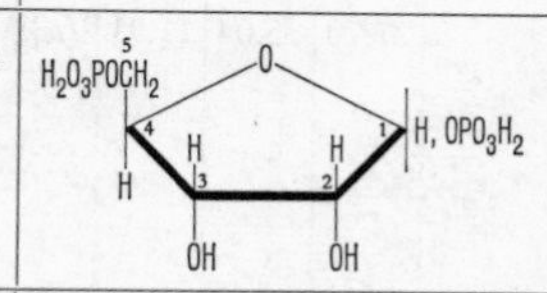	19.37	3.90	25.15		Intermediate of interconversion of ribose-1-phosphate and ribose-5-phosphate	*13*
D-Ribose-5-phosphate-1-pyrophosphate (5-phosphoribosyl-1-pyrophosphate)	$C_5H_{13}O_{14}P_3$ 390.08	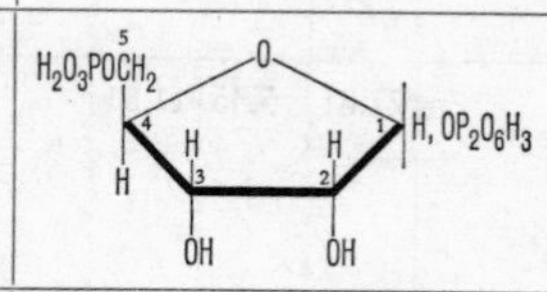	15.40	3.36	23.83		Intermediate of nucleotide synthesis	*14*
Desoxyribose-1-phosphate (furanose form)	$C_5H_{11}O_7P$ 214.12	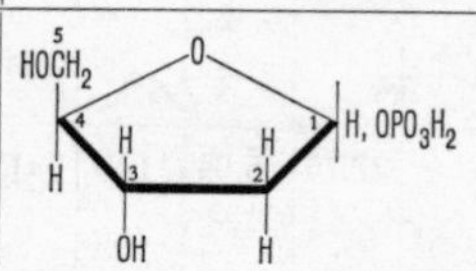	28.05	5.18	14.47		Product of nucleoside degradation	*15*
Desoxyribose-5-phosphate (furanose form)	$C_5H_{11}O_7P$ 214.12	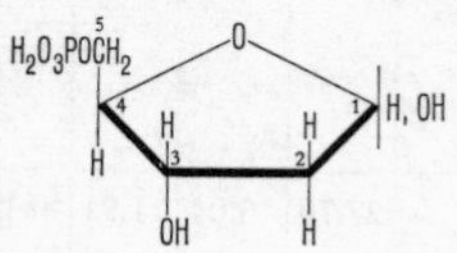	28.05	5.18	14.47		Component of desoxynucleic acids and desoxynucleotides	
D-Ribulose-5-phosphate	$C_5H_{11}O_8P$ 230.12	CH_2OH CO $HCOH$ $HCOH$ $CH_2OPO_3H_2$	26.15	4.83	13.49	$[\alpha]_D^{20}$ − 40°	Intermediate of pentose-phosphate cycle	*16*
D-Xylulose-5-phosphate	$C_5H_{11}O_8P$ 230.12	CH_2OH CO $HOCH$ $HCOH$ $CH_2OPO_3H_2$	26.15	4.83	13.49		Intermediate of pentose-phosphate cycle	*16*
D-Fructose-1-phosphate (pyranose form) ("Robison-Tanko Ester")	$C_6H_{13}O_9P$ 260.15	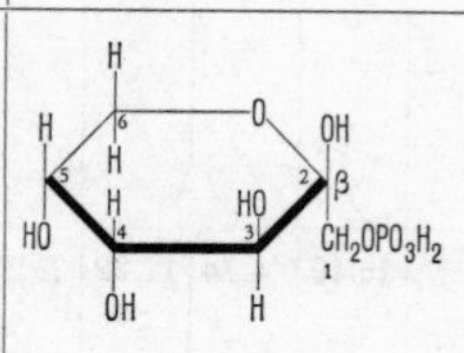	27.70	5.04	11.91	$[\alpha]_D^{20}$ − 56°	Intermediate of glycolysis	*17*
D-Fructose-6-phosphate (furanose form) ("Neuberg Ester")	$C_6H_{13}O_9P$ 260.15	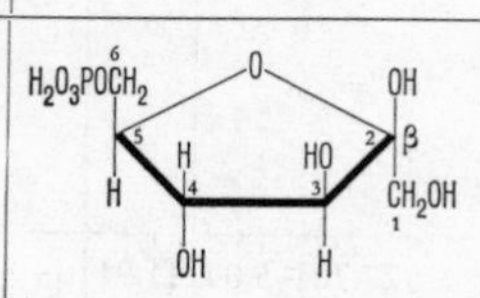	27.70	5.04	11.91	$[\alpha]_D^{19}$ + 3.58° (Ba salt)	Intermediate of glycolysis	*18*
D-Fructose-1,6-diphosphate (furanose form) ("Harden-Young Ester")	$C_6H_{14}O_{12}P_2$ 340.13	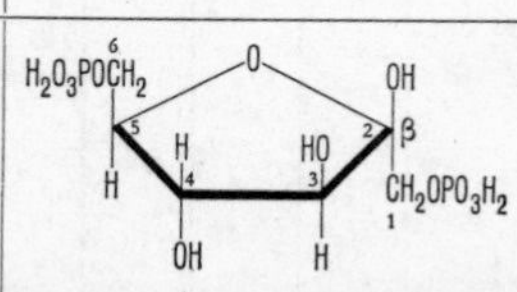	21.19	4.15	18.22	$[\alpha]_D^{17}$ + 4.1°	Intermediate of glycolysis	*18*

* See end of table, page 347.

Table 2 Sugar phosphates of importance to mammals (*continued*)

Name	Formula and mol. wt.	Structure	Elementary composition C	H	P	Specific rotation	Biological function	Reference*
α-D-Galactose-1-phosphate (pyranose form)	$C_6H_{13}O_9P$ 260.15	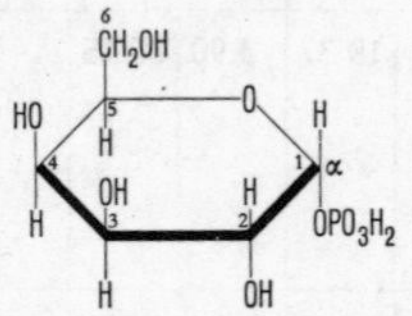	27.70	5.04	11.91	$[\alpha]_D^{18}$ + 148.5°	Intermediate of galactose metabolism	*19*
D-Galactosamine-1-phosphate	$C_6H_{14}O_8NP$ 259.16	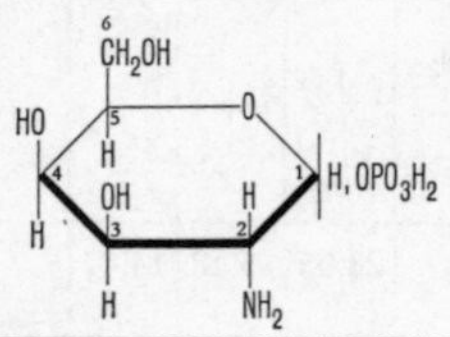	27.81	5.45	11.51		Formed from galactosamine in brain tissue extracts and *Saccharomyces fragilis*	*20*
α-D-Glucose-1-phosphate (pyranose form) ("Cori Ester")	$C_6H_{13}O_9P$ 260.15	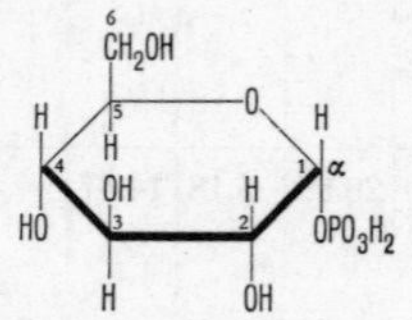	27.70	5.04	11.91	$[\alpha]_D^{25}$ + 120°	Intermediate of glucose–glycogen interconversion	*21*
D-Glucose-6-phosphate (pyranose form) ("Robison Ester")	$C_6H_{13}O_9P$ 260.15	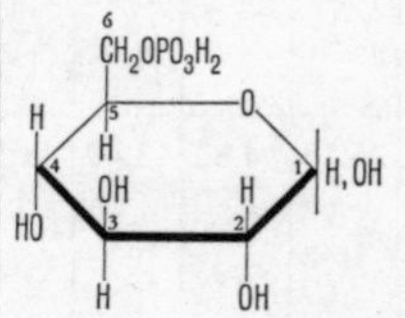	27.70	5.04	11.91	$[\alpha]_D^{25}$ + 34.2°	Intermediate of glycolysis	*22*
β-D-Glucose-1,6-diphosphate (pyranose form)	$C_6H_{14}O_{12}P_2$ 340.13	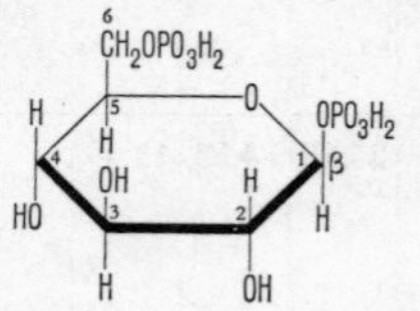	21.19	4.15	18.22	$[\alpha]_D^{20}$ − 19° (pH 8)	Intermediate of glucose–glycogen interconversion	*23*
D-Glucosamine-6-phosphate	$C_6H_{14}O_8NP$ 259.16	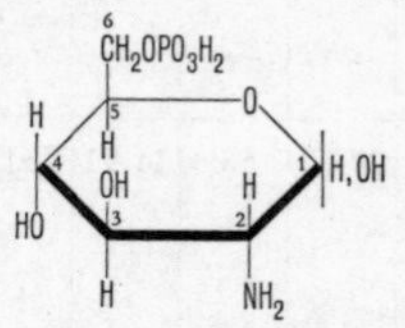	27.81	5.45	11.51	$[\alpha]_D^{20}$ + 48.5°	Formed from D-glucosamine by yeast enzyme preparations and by hexokinase	*24*
D-Gluconic acid 6-phosphate	$C_6H_{13}O_{10}P$ 276.15	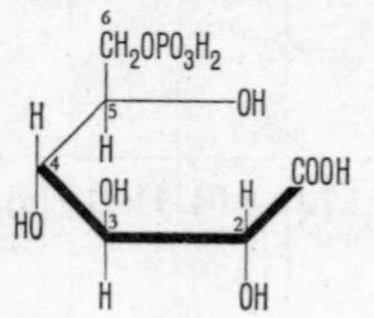	26.10	4.74	11.22	$[\alpha]_{5461}^{20}$ + 0.2°	Intermediate of pentose-phosphate cycle	*25*
D-Mannose-6-phosphate (pyranose form)	$C_6H_{13}O_9P$ 260.15	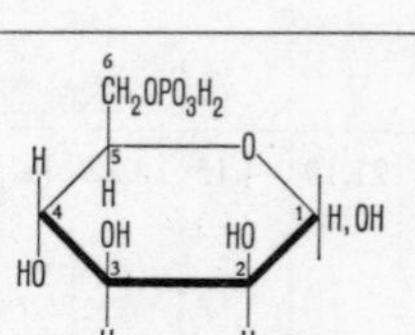	27.70	5.04	11.91	$[\alpha]_{5461}^{20}$ + 15.1°	Intermediate of mannose metabolism	*26*

* See end of table, page 347.

Table 2 Sugar phosphates of importance to mammals (*concluded*)

Name	Formula and mol. wt.	Structure	Elementary composition C	H	P	Specific rotation	Biological function	Reference (see below)
D-Sedoheptulose-7-phosphate	$C_7H_{15}O_{10}P$ 290.17	CH_2OH – CO – HOCH – HCOH – HCOH – HCOH – $CH_2OPO_3H_2$	28.97	5.21	10.68		Intermediate of pentose-phosphate cycle	*27*
D-Sedoheptulose-1,7-diphosphate	$C_7H_{16}O_{13}P_2$ 370.16	$CH_2OPO_3H_2$ – CO – HOCH – HCOH – HCOH – HCOH – $CH_2OPO_3H_2$	22.72	4.36	16.74		Intermediate of pentose-phosphate cycle	*28*
Lactose-phosphate	$C_{12}H_{23}O_{14}P$ 422.29	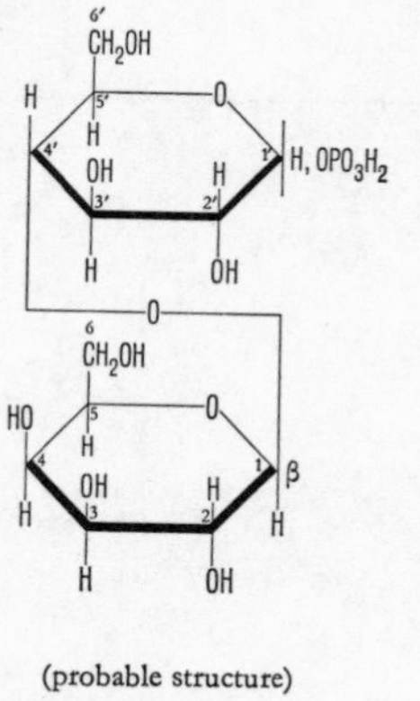 (probable structure)	34.13	5.49	7.34	$[\alpha]_D^{23}$ +99.5°	Possible intermediate in lactose synthesis	*29*

References

1) BALLOU and FISCHER, *J. Amer. chem. Soc.*, **78**, 1659 (1956). *2)* MEYERHOF, O., *Bull. Soc. Chim. biol. (Paris)*, **20**, 1033, 1345 (1938); BALLOU and FISCHER, *J. Amer. chem. Soc.*, **77**, 3329 (1955). *3)* BAER and FISCHER, *J. biol. Chem.*, **128**, 491 (1939); BAER and FISCHER, in BALL, E. G. (Ed.), *Biochemical Preparations*, vol. II, New York, 1952, page 31. *4)* KIESSLING, W., *Ber. dtsch. chem. Ges.*, **68**, 243 (1935); BALLOU and FISCHER, *J. Amer. chem. Soc.*, **76**, 3188 (1954). *5)* NEUBERG and LUSTIG, *Arch. Biochem.*, **1**, 311 (1942); BALLOU and FISCHER, *Abstr. Amer. chem. Soc. 126th Meeting*, 1954, page 7D. *6)* NEGELEIN and BRÖMEL, *Biochem. Z.*, **301**, 135 (1939). *7)* BAER, E., *J. biol. Chem.*, **185**, 763 (1950). *8)* LOHMANN and MEYERHOF, *Biochem. Z.*, **273**, 60 (1934); BAER and FISCHER, *J. biol. Chem.*, **180**, 145 (1949); BAER and FISCHER, in BALL, E. G. (Ed.), *Biochemical Preparations*, vol. II, New York, 1952, page 25. *9)* BALLOU et al., *J. Amer. chem. Soc.*, **77**, 2658 (1955). *10)* CHARALAMPOUS, F. C., *J. biol. Chem.*, **211**, 249 (1954). *11)* KALCKAR, H. M., *J. biol. Chem.*, **167**, 477 (1947); WRIGHT and KHORANA, *J. Amer. chem. Soc.*, **78**, 811 (1956). *12)* LELOIR, L. F., in ZECHMEISTER, L. (Ed.), *Fortschritte der Chemie organischer Naturstoffe*, vol. VIII, Vienna, 1951, page 70. *13)* KLENOW, H., *Arch. Biochem.*, **46**, 186 (1953). *14)* KORNBERG et al., *J. biol. Chem.*, **215**, 389 (1955). *15)* FRIEDKIN, M., *J. biol. Chem.*, **184**, 449 (1950). *16)* DICKENS and WILLIAMSON, *Nature*, **176**, 400 (1955). *17)* TANKO and ROBISON, *Biochem. J.*, **29**, 961 (1935); BRIGL and MÜLLER, *Ber. dtsch. chem. Ges.*, **72**, 2121 (1939). *18)* NEUBERG et al., *Arch. Biochem.*, **3**, 33 (1944); TANKO, B., *Abstracts of the Communications of the 1st International Congress of Biochemistry*, Cambridge, 1949, page 222. *19)* KOSTERLITZ, H. W., *Biochem. J.*, **37**, 318 (1943). *20)* CARDINI and LELOIR, *Arch. Biochem. Biophys.*, **45**, 55 (1953). *21)* CORI et al., *J. biol. Chem.*, **121**, 465 (1937); WOLFROM and PLETCHER, *J. Amer. chem. Soc.*, **63**, 1050 (1941); KRAHL and CORI, in CARTER, H. E. (Ed.), *Biochemical Preparations*, vol. I, New York, 1949, page 33. *22)* LELOIR, L. F., in ZECHMEISTER, L. (Ed.), *Fortschritte der Chemie organischer Naturstoffe*, vol. VIII, Vienna, 1951, page 76. *23)* CARDINI et al., *Arch. Biochem.*, **22**, 87 (1949); POSTERNAK, T., *J. biol. Chem.*, **180**, 1269 (1949). *24)* KENT and WHITEHOUSE, *Biochemistry of the Aminosugars*, London, 1955, page 31. *25)* ROBISON and KING, *Biochem. J.*, **25**, 323 (1931). *26)* ROBISON, R., *Biochem. J.*, **26**, 2191 (1932); SLEIN, M. W., *J. biol. Chem.*, **186**, 753 (1950). *27)* HORECKER and SMYRNIOTIS, *J. biol. Chem.*, **212**, 811 (1955). *28)* HORECKER et al., *J. biol. Chem.*, **212**, 827 (1955). *29)* MCGEOWN and MALPRESS, *Biochem. J.*, **52**, 606 (1952); GANDER et al., *Arch. Biochem. Biophys.*, **60**, 259 (1956).

Table 3 Polyhydric alcohols of importance to mammals

Name	Formula and mol. wt.	Structure	Specific rotation	Occurrence
Glycerol	$C_3H_8O_3$ 92.10	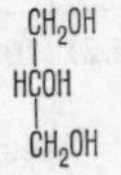		Wide occurrence in lipids of mammalian tissues. Sweet taste
Ribitol (adonitol)	$C_5H_{12}O_5$ 152.15	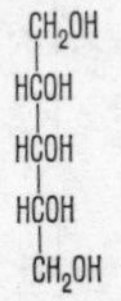		Component of riboflavin (vitamin B_2, see page 215). Also found in *Adonis vernalis*
myo-Inositol ("*meso*Inositol")	$C_6H_{12}O_6$ 180.16	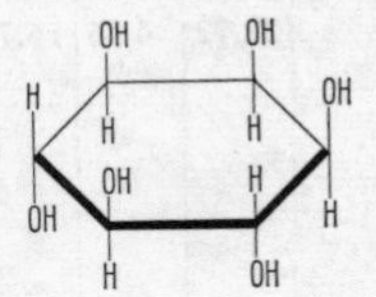	(inactive)	Widely distributed in plant and animal kingdoms. Found both free and combined in muscle, heart, liver and other tissues. Component of brain cephalin. The hexaphosphate (phytin) is the organic phosphorus reserve material of green plants. (See also page 470.)
Streptidine	$C_8H_{18}O_4N_6$ 262.28	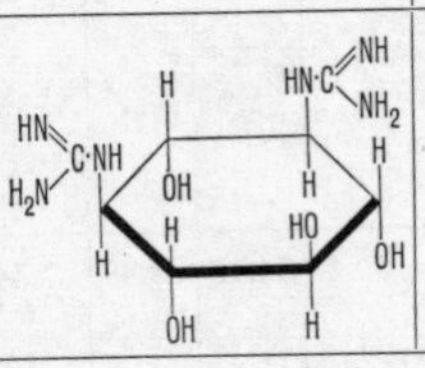		Component of streptomycin

Table 4 Oxidation products of carbohydrates

Name	Formula and mol. wt.	Structure	Specific rotation	Occurrence
		Aldonic acids		
D-Glyceric acid (D-α,β-dihydroxy-propionic acid)	$C_3H_6O_4$ 106.08	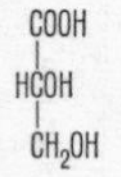		As phosphate esters (see Table 2, page 344) which are intermediates in glycolysis
L-Ascorbic acid (L-xyloascorbic acid, vitamin C)	$C_6H_8O_6$ 176.13	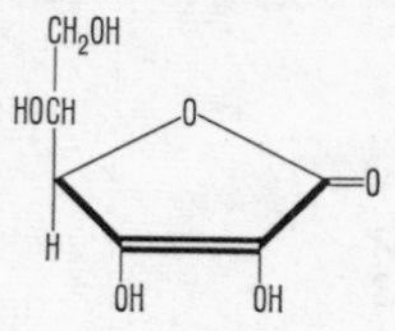	$[\alpha]_D^{20} + 49°$	See under Vitamins, page 467
D-Gluconic acid (dextronic acid)	$C_6H_{12}O_7$ 196.16	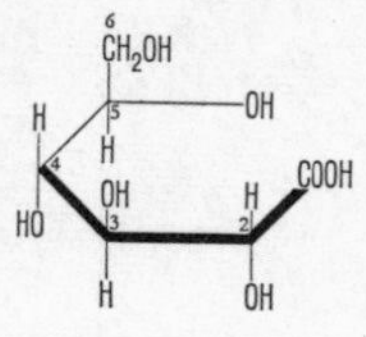	$[\alpha]_D^{20} - 6.7° \rightarrow + 17.5°$	As phosphate ester (see Table 2, page 346), intermediate in pentose-phosphate cycle (see page 428)
		Uronic acids		
α-D-Galacturonic acid	$C_6H_{12}O_7$ 196.16	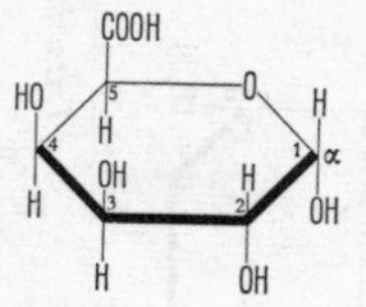	$[\alpha]_D^{21} + 100° \rightarrow + 68°$	Main component of pectins. Also occurs in some plant gums and mucilages and bacterial polysaccharides
β-D-Glucuronic acid	$C_6H_{12}O_7$ 196.16	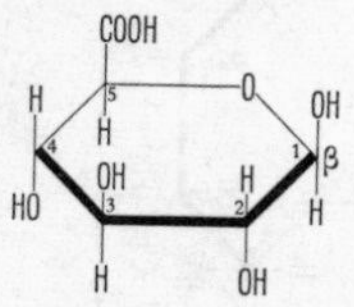	$[\alpha]_D^{20} + 12° \rightarrow + 36°$	Component of mucopolysaccharides[1]. Many aliphatic and aromatic hydroxy compounds and acids are excreted as glucuronides[2]. Has pyranose form in natural products (see also page 430)
D-Iduronic acid	$C_6H_{12}O_7$ 196.16	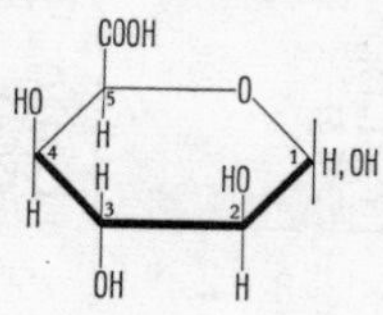		Component of chondroitin sulfate B[3]

References

1) Cf. KENT and WHITEHOUSE, *Biochemistry of the Aminosugars*, London, 1955. *2)* TEAGUE, R. S., *Advanc. Carbohydr. Chem.*, **9**, 185 (1954); WILLIAMS, R.T., *Detoxication Mechanisms*, 2nd ed., London, 1959. *3)* HOFFMAN et al., *Science*, **124**, 1252 (1956).

Table 5 Oligosaccharides of importance to mammals

Name	Formula and mol. wt.	Structure	Specific rotation	Remarks
		Disaccharides		
Cellobiose (4′-[β-D-gluco-pyranosido]-β-D-glucopyranose)	$C_{12}H_{22}O_{11}$ 342.31	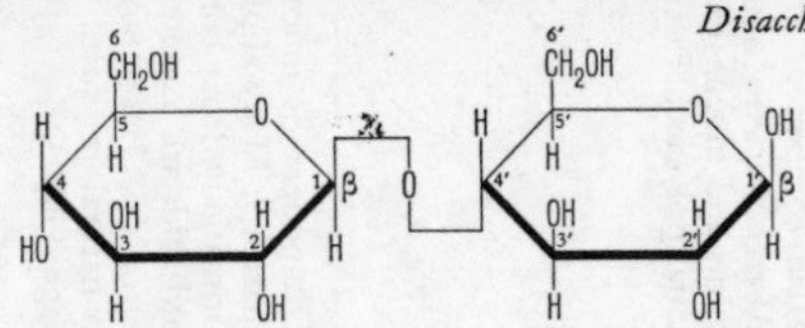	$[\alpha]_D^{20}$ + 14.2° → + 34.6°	Breakdown product of cellulose arising in herbivores in the course of digestion. Component also of lichenin
Lactose (4′-[β-D-galacto-pyranosido]-D-glucopyranose)	$C_{12}H_{22}O_{11}$ 342.31	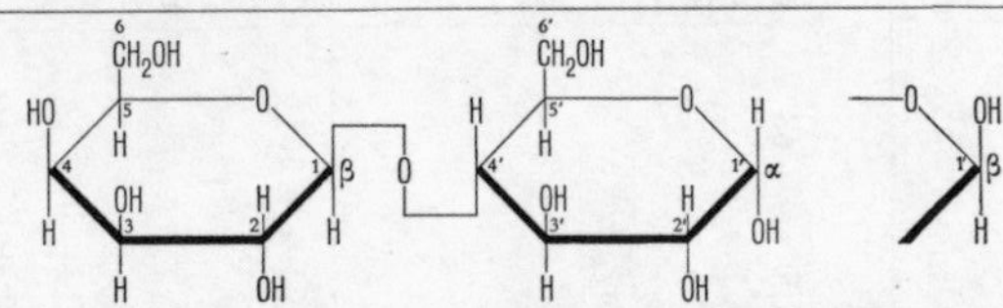	α-form, 1 H_2O: $[\alpha]_D^{20}$ + 85° → + 52.6° β-form: $[\alpha]_D^{20}$ + 34.9 → + 55.4°	Constituent of mammalian milk (4–8%)*. Only faintly sweet
Maltose (4′-[α-D-gluco-pyranosido]-β-D-glucopyranose)	$C_{12}H_{22}O_{11}$ 342.31	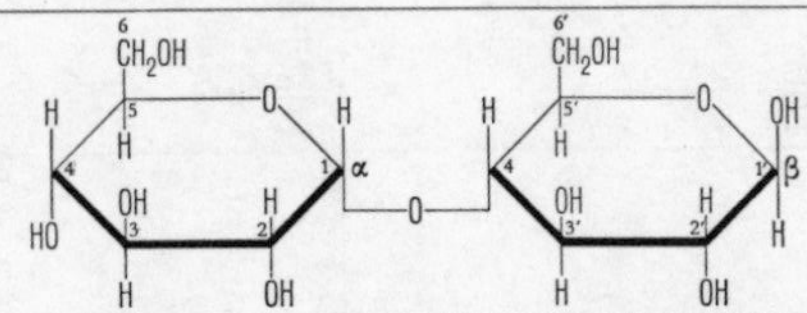	β-form, 1 H_2O: $[\alpha]_D^{20}$ + 111.7° → + 130.4°	Breakdown product of starch and glycogen, arising in the course of digestion. Found free in some plants (barley) and in honey
Sucrose (saccharose, canesugar, beet sugar, α-D-gluco-pyranosido-β-D-fructofuranoside)	$C_{12}H_{22}O_{11}$ 342.31	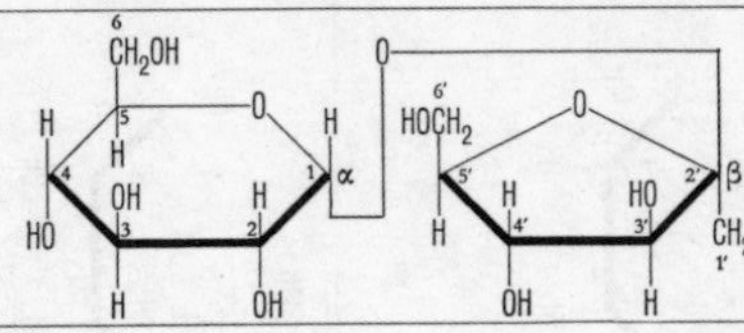	$[\alpha]_D^{20}$ + 66.53°	Almost universal occurrence in vegetable kingdom
		Trisaccharide		
Fucosidolactose (2-[α-L-fuco-pyranosido]lactose)	$C_{18}H_{30}O_{15}$ 486.44	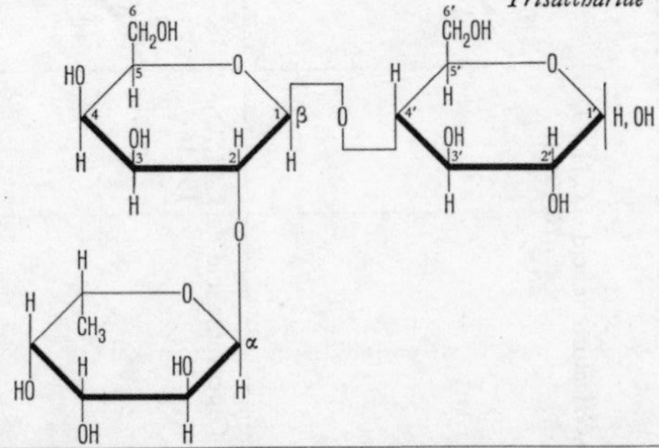		Occurs in traces in human milk*

* For other oligosaccharides isolated from human milk see BELL et al., *Ann. Rep. Progr. Chem.*, **52**, 333 (1955); KUHN, R., *Bull. Soc. Chim. biol. (Paris)*, **40**, 297 (1958).

Table 6 Polysaccharides of importance to mammals. (For references see page 353.)

Name	Mol. wt.	Structure	Specific rotation	Remarks
Amylopectin[1] (α-amylose, B-fraction of starch)	Up to 52×10^6 for potato amylopectin[2]	Highly-branched molecule composed of several hundred unit-chains, each of which comprises 20–26 α-1:4-linked glucose residues; the unit-chains are interlinked by glycosidic bonds from the reducing group to C-6 of a glucose residue in an adjacent chain: 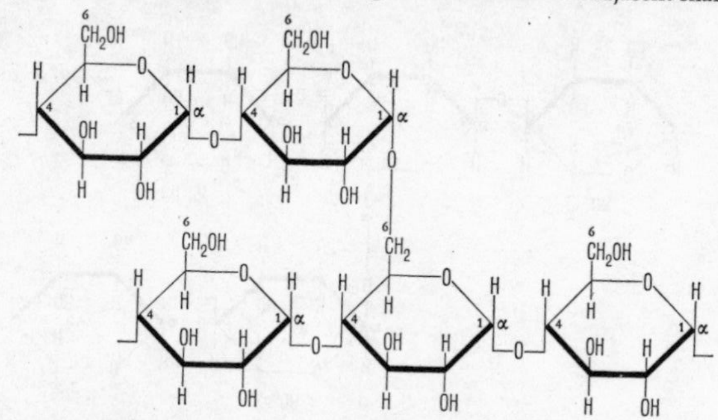	$[\alpha]_D^{20}$ + 150°	Main constituent of starches (usually ca. 80%). Has been synthesized by incubation of glucose-1-phosphate with Q-enzyme of potato juice in presence of potato phosphorylase[3]
Amylose[1] (β-amylose, A-fraction of starch)	$(323)_n$, up to 1×10^6	Essentially a linear chain of α-1:4-linked glucose residues: 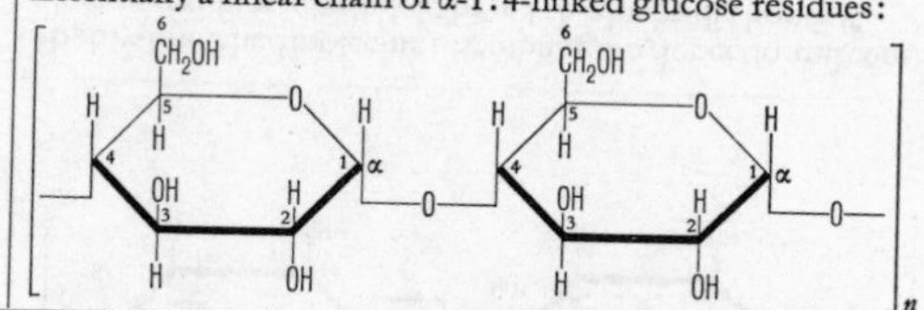	$[\alpha]_D^{20}$ + 220°	Constituent of starch (ca. 20%). Absent in some starches, e.g. that of "waxy" maize (corn). Has been synthesized by incubation of glucose-1-phosphate with potato phosphorylase[4]
Cellulose	$(323)_n$, up to 1.7×10^6	Linear chain of β-1:4-linked glucose residues: 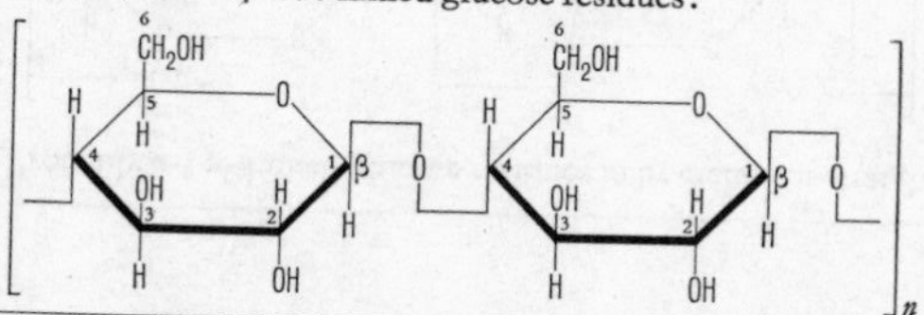		Chief structural polysaccharide of plants. Also found in algae, bacterial membranes, and as tunicin in some lower animals. Not digested by man
Chitin	$(203.19)_n$, ca. 4×10^5	Linear chain of β-1:4-linked N-acetyl-D-glucosamine residues: 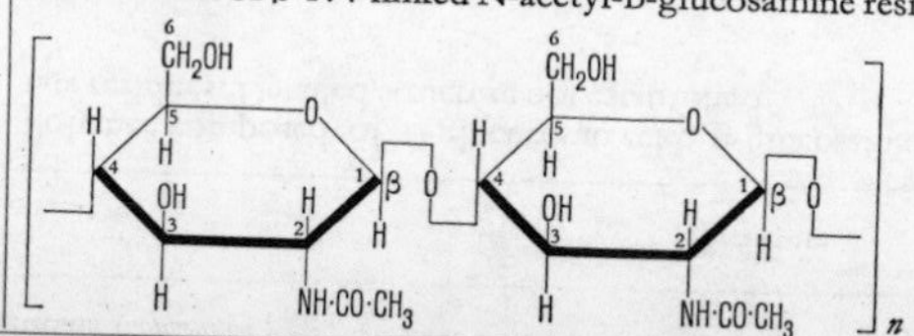	$[\alpha]_D^{20}$ − 14.7° (in HCl)	Skeletal substance of mollusks and insects. Also found in lower plants and fungi

Table 6 Polysaccharides of importance to mammals (*concluded*)

Name	Mol. wt.	Structure	Specific rotation	Remarks
Chondroitin sulfate	Highly polydisperse; minimum ca. 26,000[5]	Polymer composed of D-glucuronic acid, D-glucosamine, N-acetyl-D-galactosamine and sulfate residues. Detailed structure not established[6]		Present in most mammalian cartilaginous tissue
Dextrans[7]	$(323)_n$, ca. 4×10^6	Probably α-1:6-linked glucose residues in branched or straight chains, e.g. 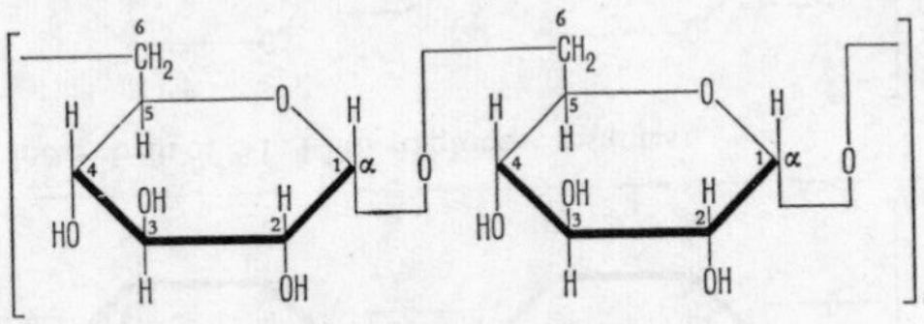		Produced extracellularly by bacteria, e.g. *Leuconostoc mesenteroides*. Partially degraded dextrans are used as blood-plasma substitutes[8]
Glycogen (liver starch)	Polydisperse; for most glycogens at least 2×10^6	Highly-branched molecule resembling amylopectin and consisting of unit chains of α-1:4-linked glucose residues interlinked by α-1:6-glucosidic bonds[10]: 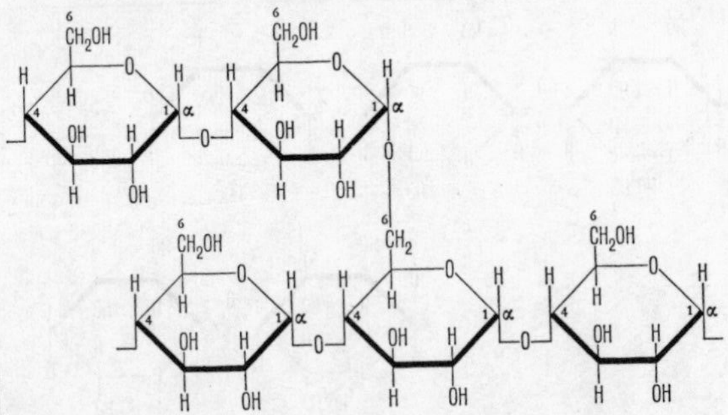	$[\alpha]_D^{20}$ + 191°	Reserve carbohydrate of animal tissues. Converted in muscle to lactic acid during glycolysis (see page 402). Also present in yeast. Has been synthesized by action of heart or liver phosphorylase on glucose-1-phosphate[9]
Heparin	ca. 17,000[11]	Polymer composed of D-glucosamine, D-glucuronic acid, acetate and sulfate residues. Detailed structure not established[6]		Occurs in animal tissue. Blood anticoagulant

Hyaluronic acid	ca. 1×10^6 [12]	Polymer composed of D-glucosamine, D-glucuronic acid, and acetate residues. Detailed structure not established[4]		Widely distributed in tissues and intercellular fluids
Inulin	$(162.14)_n$, ca. 5000	Linear chain of about 30 β-1:2-linked fructofuranose units: 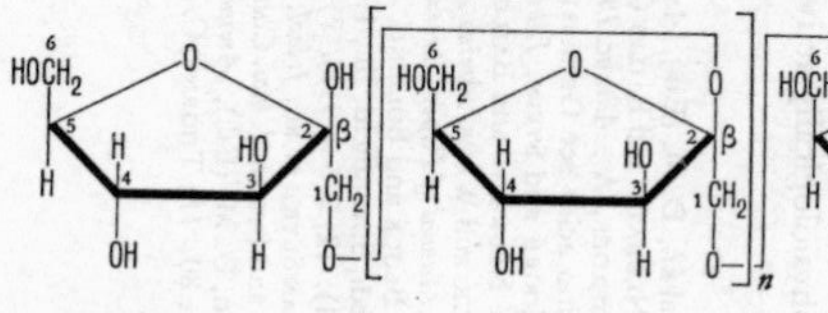	$[\alpha]_D^{20}$ − 40°	Reserve carbohydrate of many plants, alone or with starch
Pectic acid (pectins)	$(346)_n$, up to 5×10^4	Probably a linear chain of α-1:4-linked D-galacturonic acid residues[13]: 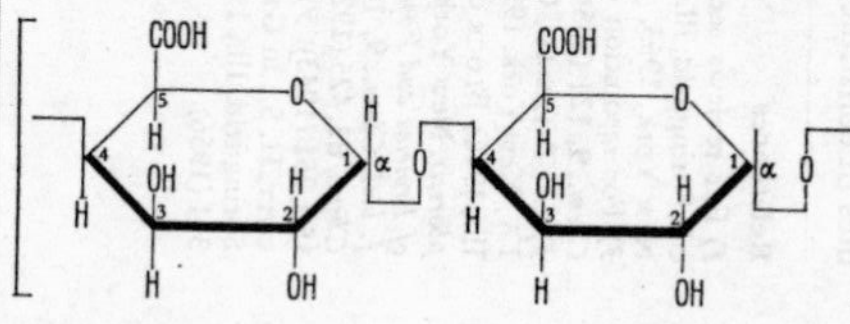	$[\alpha]_D^{20}$ ca. + 240°	Important cell-wall constituent of plants. Occurs as Ca salt or methyl ester
Pneumococcal polysaccharides Type 3	1.4×10^5	Alternating glucose and glucuronic acid residues, probably linked 1:3 and 1:4 respectively[14]: 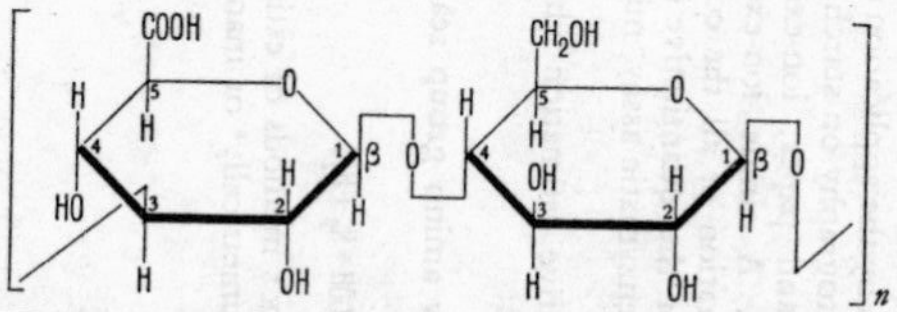		An example of the 40 odd pneumococcal polysaccharides known, many of unknown structure. Responsible for type specificity of pneumococci. Effective as antigen
Starches (amylum)	Highly polydisperse	Consist mainly of mixtures of amylose and amylopectin (see above in this Table) in proportion 20:80. Some starches contain no amylose		Reserve carbohydrates of many plants

References

1) For reviews of starch chemistry see BOURNE, E. J., *Chem. and Ind.*, **1951**, 1047; MEYER and GIBBONS, *Advanc. Enzymol.*, **12**, 341 (1951). *2)* WITNAUER et al., *J. chem. Phys.*, **20**, 1978 (1952). *3)* BOURNE and PEAT, *J. chem. Soc.*, **1945**, 877; BARKER et al., *ibid.*, **1949**, 1705, 1712. *4)* HANES, C. S., *Proc. roy. Soc. B*, **128**, 421 (1940); **129**, 174 (1940). *5)* BLIX and SNELLMAN, *Ark. Kemi Mineral. Geol.*, **19A**, No. 32 (1945). *6)* JEANLOZ, R. W., *Proceedings of the Third International Congress of Biochemistry, Brussels 1955*, New York, 1956, page 65. *7)* STACEY and RICKETTS, in ZECHMEISTER, L. (Ed.), *Fortschritte der Chemie organischer Naturstoffe*, vol. VIII, Vienna, 1951, page 28. *8)* MANNERS, D. J., *Quart. Rev. chem. Soc. Lond.*, **9**, 88 (1955). *9)* BEAR and CORI, *J. biol. Chem.*, **140**, 111 (1941). *10)* BELL and MANNERS, *J. chem. Soc.*, **1954**, 1891. *11)* JENSEN et al., *J. biol. Chem.*, **174**, 265 (1948). *12)* CHRISTIANSEN and JENSEN, *Acta chem. scand.*, **7**, 1247 (1953); LAURENT and GERGELY, *J. biol. Chem.*, **212**, 325 (1955). *13)* HIRST and JONES, *Advanc. Carbohydr. Chem.*, **2**, 235 (1946). *14)* REEVES and GOEBEL, *J. biol. Chem.*, **139**, 511 (1941).

2. Amino acids[1]

An amino acid is any compound which contains one or more amino groups and one or more carboxylic acid groups. Those of biological importance generally contain an amino group in the α-position to a carboxyl group, i.e. they are of the general structure:

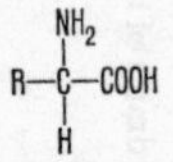

The asymmetry about the α-carbon atom renders the amino acids optically active, except when R = H, as in glycine. Their nomenclature is similar to that adopted for the carbohydrate series and involves the use of the small capital letters D and L to indicate their configuration about the α-carbon atom, sometimes followed by the sign of optical rotation in parentheses, e.g. L(+)-alanine. In the case of amino acids possessing two asymmetric centers, four stereoisomers are possible, and the isomer which has been found in proteins is referred to simply as the L-isomer. This is not, of course, a complete configurational description of this particular acid. (For the stereochemical configurations of amino acids see [2].) The value of the specific rotation for any particular amino acid varies with concentration, temperature and hydrogen-ion concentration. A precise control of the experimental conditions is thus necessary for indicating the identity and purity of an acid by means of specific rotation values[3].

The majority of amino acids are stable compounds and melt above 200° C with decomposition; they are insoluble in the common neutral solvents except water, and can usually be recrystallized from aqueous ethanol. Their salt-like behavior can be ascribed to their existence as internal salts, or "zwitterions", i.e.

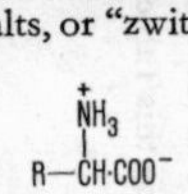

The amino acids behave as amphoteric compounds and possess characteristic isoelectric points; many of their physical properties exhibit maxima and minima at these points.

The separation and quantitative determination of amino acids have been revolutionized in recent years by the application of new procedures, such as adsorption chromatography on starch, partition chromatography on silica gel and paper, ion-exchange chromatography, and electrophoresis. A single ion-exchange column is now sufficient for the separation of all the common amino acids[4]. Many methods exist for the quantitative estimation of amino acids: isotope dilution, enzymatic assay, microbial assay and chemical methods[1, 5].

There are three methods of quantitative estimation which are applicable to the majority of amino acids:

(*a*) Amino acids containing a primary amino group react with nitrous acid to give nitrogen:

$$R\text{—}CH(NH_2)\cdot COOH + HNO_2 \longrightarrow R\text{—}CH(OH)\cdot COOH + N_2 + H_2O$$

This forms the basis of VAN SLYKE's methods of estimation, the nitrogen being measured volumetrically[6] or manometrically[7].

(*b*) Amino acids containing free carboxylic and primary α-amino groups are oxidized on heating with ninhydrin:

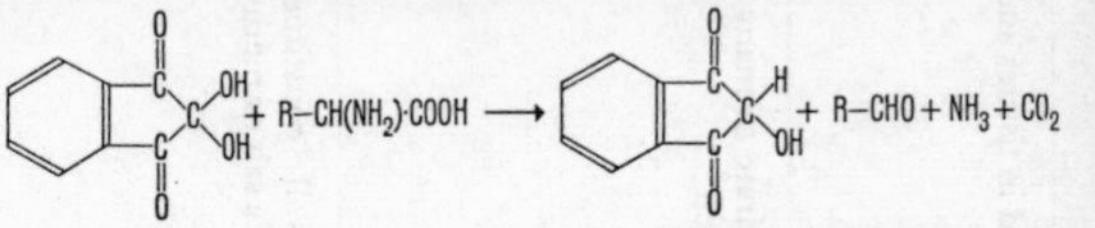

Ninhydrin (triketohydrindene hydrate) — Hydrindantin — Aldehyde

Either NH_3 or CO_2 can be quantitatively measured[8]. Alternatively, the blue color forming above pH 2 when the reaction mixture is heated, due to the following reaction, can be used for quantitative estimations[9]:

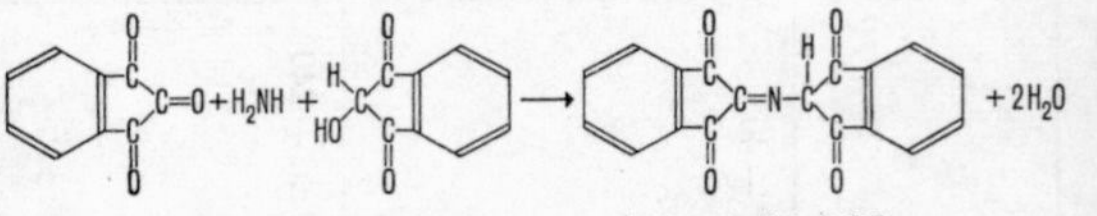

Triketohydrindene — Hydrindantin — Diketohydrindylidene-diketohydrindamine

(*c*) Formaldehyde reacts with the amino groups of an amino acid and thus reduces their basicity; this allows the acid to be directly titrated with alkali using phenolphthalein as indicator[10].

The amino acids are the structural units of protein molecules and just over twenty have been established in this role (Table 7, pages 355–358). These are all α-amino acids of the L-configuration and there is no conclusive evidence that any other type of amino acid is a protein constituent[2]. However, D-amino acids have been isolated from plants and microorganisms[11]. The latter frequently elaborate polypeptides (often possessing antibiotic properties) containing D-amino acids; and indeed, the capsules of certain bacilli, e.g. *Bacillus anthracis*, consist almost wholly of polypeptides of D-glutamic acid. The amino acids listed in Table 8, pages 359 and 360, are not found in proteins but occur as intermediary metabolites or constituents of physiologically active compounds.

References

1) For reviews see GREENBERG, D. M. (Ed.), *Amino Acids and Proteins*, 1st ed., Springfield, Ill., 1951; NEURATH and BAILEY (Eds.), *The Proteins*, vol. I A, New York, 1953. *2)* NEUBERGER, A., *Advanc. Protein Chem.*, **4**, 297 (1948). *3)* For resolution of α-amino acids see GREENSTEIN, J. P., *Advanc. Protein Chem.*, **9**, 121 (1954). *4)* MOORE and STEIN, *J. biol. Chem.*, **211**, 893 (1954). *5)* Cf. TRISTRAM, G. R., in NEURATH and BAILEY (Eds.), *The Proteins*, vol. I A, New York, 1953; BLOCK and WEISS, *Amino Acid Handbook*, Springfield, Ill., 1956; BLOCK et al., *A Manual of Paper Chromatography and Paper Electrophoresis*, New York, 1955; BLOCK and BOLLING, *The Amino Acid Composition of Proteins and Foods*, 2nd ed., Springfield, Ill., 1951. *6)* VAN SLYKE, D. D., *J. biol. Chem.*, **9**, 185 (1911); **12**, 275 (1912). *7)* VAN SLYKE, D. D., *J. biol. Chem.*, **83**, 425 (1929). *8)* VAN SLYKE et al., *J. biol. Chem.*, **141**, 627, 671 (1941); **150**, 251 (1943). *9)* MOORE and STEIN, *J. biol. Chem.*, **176**, 367 (1948). *10)* OLCOTT, H. S., in GREENBERG, D. M. (Ed.), *Amino Acids and Proteins*, 1st ed., Springfield, Ill., 1951, page 80. *11)* THORNE, C. B., *Ann. Rev. Microbiol.*, **10**, 331 (1956).

Table 7 Physical and chemical properties of amino acids occurring as protein constituents

Name	Abbreviation*	Formula and mol.wt.	Structure	Elementary composition (%) C	H	N	Solubility (grams per 100 g water at 25° C)	Specific rotation: Temperature (°C)	Concentration**	Solvent	$[\alpha]_D$	Special properties / *Organism for microbiological assay*	Special occurrence and biological function (*for references see page 358*)
α-Alanine (α-amino-propionic acid)	Ala.	$C_3H_7NO_2$ 89.10	$CH_3 \cdot CH(NH_2) \cdot COOH$	40.44	7.92	15.72	16.72	25 25 20	2.06 10.00 1.78	6-N HCl Water 3-N NaOH	+ 13.70 + 2.41 + 3.0	*Leuconostoc (Lactobacillus) citrovorum* 8081	
Arginine (α-amino-δ-guanido-*n*-valeric acid)	Arg.	$C_6H_{14}N_4O_2$ 174.21	$HN{=}C(H_2N) \cdot NH \cdot [CH_2]_3 \cdot CH(NH_2) \cdot COOH$	41.37	8.10	32.16	15	23.3 20 20	1.65 3.48 0.87	6-N HCl Water 0.5-N NaOH	+ 27.58 + 12.5 + 11.8	Basic. Gives SAKAGUCHI color reaction with α-naphthol and sodium hypohalite *Streptococcus faecalis* 9790; *Leuconostoc citrovorum*	Intermediate in ornithine cycle of urea synthesis (see page 445) and in creatine synthesis (see page 440)
Asparagine (aspartic acid β-monoamide; α-amino-β-carbamyl-propionic acid)	Asp-NH₂	$C_4H_8N_2O_3$ 132.12	$NH_2 \cdot CO \cdot CH_2 \cdot CH(NH_2) \cdot COOH$	36.37	6.11	21.21	2.46	20 20 20	2.24 1.41 11.23	3.4-N HCl Water 2.5-N NaOH	+ 34.26 − 5.30 − 6.35	Hydrolyzed by hot acid or specific enzymes to give NH_3 + aspartic acid	Found in free state in many plant tissues, especially etiolated seedlings
Aspartic acid (aminosuccinic acid)	Asp.	$C_4H_7NO_4$ 133.11	$HOOC \cdot CH_2 \cdot CH(NH_2) \cdot COOH$	36.09	5.30	10.52	0.50	24 18 18	2.02 1.33 1.33	6-N HCl Water 3-N NaOH	+ 24.6 + 4.7 − 1.7	Acidic. Yields 2 moles of CO_2 and 1 mole of NH_3 in ninhydrin reaction *Leuconostoc mesenteroides* P-60, 8042	Involved in transformation of citrulline to arginine (see page 445), and in biosynthesis of purines and pyrimidines (see pages 438 and 442)
Cysteine (α-amino-β-thiolpropionic acid)	CySH	$C_3H_7NO_2S$ 121.16	$HS \cdot CH_2 \cdot CH(NH_2) \cdot COOH$	29.73 Sulfur 26.46	5.82	11.56	very soluble	26	12.1	1-N HCl	+ 7.6	Readily autoxidized in neutral or basic solution to cystine	Interconvertible with cystine by oxido-reduction (see page 409). Component of glutathione (see page 441). Some aromatic compounds are excreted in urine as derivatives of N-acetylcysteine (mercapturic acids) (see pages 445 and 448)
Cystine (di-[α-amino-propionic]-β-disulfide)	Cys.	$C_6H_{12}N_2O_4S_2$ 240.31	$S \cdot CH_2 \cdot CH(NH_2) \cdot COOH$ $S \cdot CH_2 \cdot CH(NH_2) \cdot COOH$	29.99 Sulfur 26.68	5.03	11.66	0.011	24 18.5	1.0 0.4	1-N HCl 0.2-N NaOH	−214.4 − 70.0	Readily reduced to cysteine *Leuconostoc mesenteroides* P-60, 8042; *Lactobacillus arabinosus*	Occurs abundantly in hair, keratin and insulin. The disulfide bond links together different polypeptide chains or different parts of the same polypeptide chain within the protein molecule
3,5-Diiodo-tyrosine***		$C_9H_9NO_3I_2$ 433.00	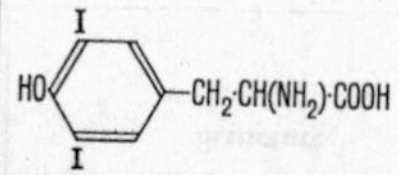	24.97 Iodine 58.62	2.10	3.23	0.062	20 20	5.08 4.41	1.1-N HCl 3.4-N NH_4OH	+ 2.89 + 2.27		Occurrence confined to protein of thyroid gland[3] (thyroid hormone; see pages 443 and 479)

* Used in the description of amino acid sequences in polypeptide and protein molecules[1].

** As grams per 100 ml solution, unless otherwise stated.

*** For chromatographic separation from other iodinated amino acids and estimation see BLOCK and WEISS[2].

Table 7 Physical and chemical properties of amino acids occurring as protein constituents (*continued*)

Name	Abbreviation*	Formula and mol.wt.	Structure	Elementary composition (%) C	H	N	Solubility (grams per 100 g water at 25°C)	Specific rotation: Temperature (°C)	Concentration**	Solvent	$[\alpha]_D$	Special properties / *Organism for microbiological assay*	Special occurrence and biological function (*for references see page 358*)
Glutamic acid (α-aminoglutaric acid)	Glu.	$C_5H_9NO_4$ 147.14	$HOOC·(CH_2)_2·CH(NH_2)·COOH$	40.81	6.17	9.52	0.843	22.4 18 18	1.00 1.47 1.47	6-N HCl Water 1-N NaOH	+ 31.2 + 11.5 + 10.96	Acidic. On boiling in solution over a wide pH range (4–10) is cyclized to pyrrolidone-carboxylic acid *Leuconostoc mesenteroides* P-60, 8042 ; *Lactobacillus arabinosus*	Component of glutathione (see page 441) and of the folic acid vitamins (see page 461). Present in high concentration in tissues. More readily dehydrogenated in animal tissue than any other amino acid, and also more reactive in enzymic transamination reactions
Glutamine (glutamic acid β-monoamide; α-amino-γ-carbamyl-butyric acid)	Glu-NH_2	$C_5H_{10}N_2O_3$ 146.15	$NH_2·CO·(CH_2)_2·CH(NH_2)·COOH$	41.09	6.90	19.17	3.6 (at 18°C)	22	3.6	Water	+ 5.0	On heating in solution to ca. 100°C at near neutrality cyclizes to ammonium salt of pyrrolidonecarboxylic acid. Amide group reacts with nitrous acid in presence of acetic acid to release N_2. Hydrolyzed by specific enzyme to ammonium glutamate	Occurs in the free state in animal tissues and many plants, e.g. sugar beet. Phenylacetic acid is excreted by man as phenacetylglutamine (see pages 445 and 448)
Glycine (aminoacetic acid)	Gly.	$C_2H_5NO_2$ 75.07	$NH_2·CH_2·COOH$	32.00	6.72	18.66	24.99					Optically inactive. Gives green color with *o*-phthalaldehyde *Leuconostoc mesenteroides* P-60, 8042	In many animals benzoic acid is excreted as benzoylglycine (hippuric acid) (see pages 445 and 448). Component of glutathione (see page 441). Metabolite in synthesis of creatine, porphyrins, purines, serine (see page 437)
Histidine (α-amino-β-[4-imidazole]-propionic acid)	His.	$C_6H_9N_3O_2$ 155.16	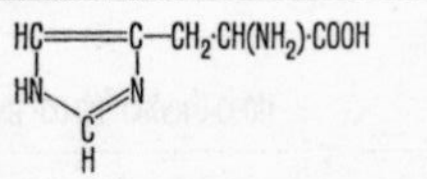	46.44	5.85	27.09	4.29	25 25 20	1.00–4.05 0.75–3.77 0.77	6.1-N HCl Water 0.5-N NaOH	+ 13.34 − 38.95 − 10.9	Basic. Gives biuret test; couples with diazotized sulfanilic acid to give intense red color (PAULY reaction) *Leuconostoc mesenteroides* P-60, 8042	Decarboxylated to histamine. Constituent of carnosine (β-alanylhistidine) found in muscle
δ-Hydroxylysine (α,ε-diamino-δ-hydroxy-*n*-caproic acid)		$C_6H_{14}N_2O_3$ 162.19	$NH_2·CH_2·CH(OH)·(CH_2)_2·CH(NH_2)·COOH$	44.43	8.70	17.28		25	2.0	6-N HCl	+ 14.5	Reacts with periodate to yield formaldehyde and ammonia	Has been found as protein constituent only in collagen and gelatin. Phosphate ester occurs naturally[d]
Hydroxyproline (γ-hydroxy-pyrrolidine-α-carboxylic acid)	Hypro.	$C_5H_9NO_3$ 131.14	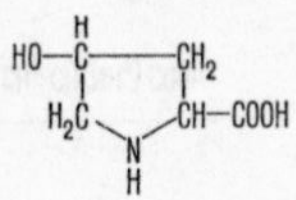	45.80	6.92	10.68	36.11	20 22.5 20	1.31 1.00 0.65	1-N HCl Water 0.5-N NaOH	− 47.3 − 75.2 − 70.6	Has no primary α-amino group and therefore differs in many respects from primary amino acids, e.g. with nitrous acid does not release nitrogen. Oxidized by hypochlorite to give hydroxypyrroline. Decarboxylated by ninhydrin to give reddish color below pH 4.4, yellowish color at higher pH. Forms bright blue condensation product with isatin	Present only in gelatin and collagen

Leucine (α-amino- *iso*caproic acid)	Leu.	$C_6H_{13}NO_2$ 131.18	$(CH_3)_2CH \cdot CH_2 \cdot CH(NH_2) \cdot COOH$	54.94	9.99	10.68	2.19	25 25 20	2.00 2.00 1.31	6-N HCl Water 3-N NaOH	+ 15.20 − 10.57 + 7.6	*Lactobacillus arabinosus* 17–5, 8014; *Lactobacillus helveticus; Streptococcus faecalis; Leuconostoc mesenteroides* P-60, 8042	
*iso*Leucine (α-amino- β-methyl- *n*-valeric acid)	Ileu.	$C_6H_{13}NO_2$ 131.18	$CH_3 \cdot CH_2 \cdot CH(CH_3) \cdot CH(NH_2) \cdot COOH$	54.94	9.99	10.68	2.93 (at 20°C)	20 20 20	5.09 3.10 3.34	6.1-N HCl Water 0.33-N NaOH	+ 40.61 + 11.29 + 11.09	*Lactobacillus arabinosus* 17–5, 8014; *Lactobacillus helveticus; Streptococcus faecalis; Leuconostoc mesenteroides* P-60, 8042	
Lysine (α,ε-diamino- *n*-caproic acid)	Lys.	$C_6H_{14}N_2O_2$ 146.19	$NH_2(CH_2)_4 \cdot CH(NH_2) \cdot COOH$	49.29	9.65	19.16	very soluble	23 20	2.00 6.50	6-N HCl Water	+ 25.9 + 14.6	Basic. Can be precipitated with phosphotungstic acid. Dry heating of proteins containing lysine causes an apparent loss of lysine *Streptococcus faecalis* 9790; *Leuconostoc mesenteroides* P-60, 8042	
Methionine (α-amino- γ-methylthiol- *n*-butyric acid)	Met.	$C_5H_{11}NO_2S$ 149.22	$CH_3 \cdot S \cdot CH_2 \cdot CH_2 \cdot CH(NH_2) \cdot COOH$	40.24	7.43 Sulfur 21.49	9.39	3.35 (for DL-acid)	20 25	5.00 0.80	3-N HCl Water	+ 23.40 − 8.11	*Leuconostoc mesenteroides* P-60, 8042; *Lactobacillus fermenti* 36 (for DL-acid)	Provides the sulfur atom for cysteine biosynthesis (see Cystathionine, Table 8, page 360). Carrier of "active" methyl groups
3-Monoiodo- tyrosine		$C_9H_{10}NO_3I$ 307.10	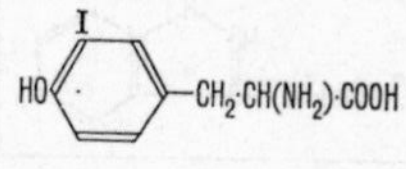	35.15	3.27 Iodine 41.2	4.57		20	5.0	1-N HCl	− 4.4		Occurrence confined to protein of thyroid gland[3] (thyroid hormone; see pages 443 and 479)
Norleucine (α-aminocaproic acid)		$C_6H_{13}NO_2$ 131.18	$CH_3(CH_2)_3 \cdot CH(NH_2) \cdot COOH$	54.94	9.99	10.68	1.15 (at 18°C)	20	4.3	6-N HCl	+ 21.3		Has not been proved to be a protein constituent[5]
Phenylalanine (α-amino-β-phenyl-propionic acid)	Phe.	$C_9H_{11}NO_2$ 165.20	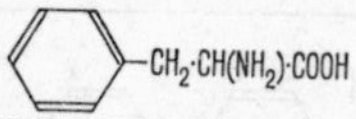	65.44	6.71	8.48	2.965	20	1.93	Water	− 35.14	*Leuconostoc mesenteroides* P-60, 8042	Can be converted to tyrosine in the human body (see page 410)
Proline (pyrrolidine- α-carboxylic acid)	Pro.	$C_5H_9NO_2$ 115.14	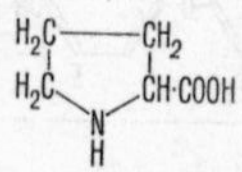	52.16	7.88	12.17	162.3	20 23.4 20	0.57 1.00 2.42	0.5-N HCl Water 0.6-N KOH	− 52.6 − 85.0 − 93.0	Neutral. Soluble in alcohol. Chemically very similar to hydroxyproline *Leuconostoc mesenteroides* P-60, 8042; *Lactobacillus brevis*	
Serine (α-amino- β-hydroxy- propionic acid)	Ser.	$C_3H_7NO_3$ 105.10	$HO \cdot CH_2 \cdot CH(NH_2) \cdot COOH$	34.28	6.71	13.33	5.023 (for DL-acid)	25 20	9.34 10.41	1-N HCl Water	+ 14.95 − 6.83	Split by periodate or lead tetra-acetate to formaldehyde and glyoxylic acid. Gives biuret test. Acid hydrolysis of protein leads to partial destruction *Leuconostoc mesenteroides* P-60, 8042; *Lactobacillus delbrueckii* LD 5; *Lactobacillus helveticus*	Most of the serine in phosphoproteins (vitellin, casein) occurs in form of phosphoserine.[6] Phosphatidylserine is a component of some phospholipids

* Used in the description of amino acid sequences in polypeptide and protein molecules[1]. ** As grams per 100 ml solution, unless otherwise stated.

Table 7 Physical and chemical properties of amino acids occurring as protein constituents (*continued*)

Name	Abbreviation*	Formula and mol.wt.	Structure	Elementary composition (%) C	H	N	Solubility (grams per 100 g water at 25° C)	Specific rotation: Temperature (°C)	Concentration**	Solvent	[α]D	Special properties / *Organism for microbiological assay*	Special occurrence and biological function (*for references see page 358*)
Threonine (β-methylserine; α-amino-β-hydroxy-butyric acid)	Thr.	$C_4H_9NO_3$ 119.12	$CH_3 \cdot CH(OH) \cdot CH(NH_2) \cdot COOH$	40.33	7.62	11.76		26	1.63 (g solute per 100 g solution)	Water	− 9.1	Some properties similar to those of serine. Oxidized by periodate to acetaldehyde and glyoxylic acid *Streptococcus faecalis* 9790; *Leuconostoc mesenteroides* P-60, 8042	Phosphothreonine has been found in casein hydrolysates[7]
Thyroxine (3,5,3′,5′-tetraiodo-thyronine)		$C_{15}H_{11}NO_4I_4$ 776.90	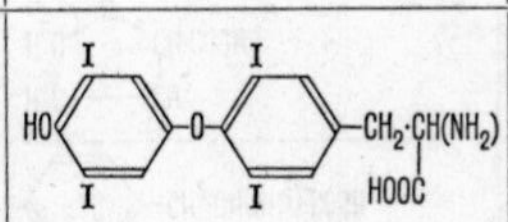	23.17 Iodine 65.35	1.43	1.80	0.001		3 (g solute per 100 g solution)	0.13-N NaOH in 70% ethanol	− 4.4		Occurrence confined to protein of thyroid gland[3] (thyroid hormone; see pages 443 and 479)
3,5,3′-Triiodo-thyronine		$C_{15}H_{12}NO_4I_3$ 651.00	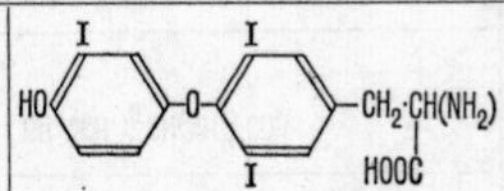	27.6 Iodine 58.5	1.8	2.2		29.5	4.75 (as hydro-chloride)	1-N HCl-ethanol (1:2)	+ 21.5		Occurrence confined to protein of thyroid gland[3] (thyroid hormone; see pages 443 and 479)
Tryptophan (α-amino-β-[3-indolyl]-propionic acid)	Try.	$C_{11}H_{12}N_2O_2$ 204.23	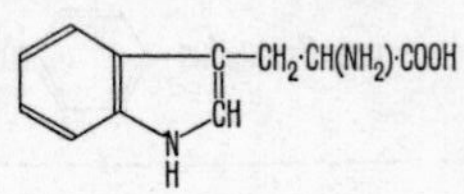	64.69	5.93	13.72	1.14	20 22.7 20	1.02 1.00 2.42	0.5-N HCl Water 0.5-N NaOH	+ 2.4 − 31.5 + 6.17	Destroyed on prolonged heating in hot acid. Gives MILLON reaction (see Tyrosine, below) and FOLIN test. Gives color reaction with *p*-dimethyl-aminobenzaldehyde and nitrous acid (EHRLICH test) *Lactobacillus arabinosus* 17–5, 8014; *Streptococcus faecalis*	
Tyrosine (α-amino-β-[*p*-hydroxyphenyl]-propionic acid)	Tyr.	$C_9H_{11}NO_3$ 181.20	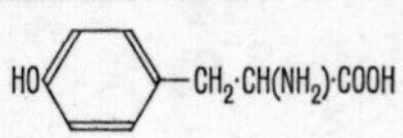	59.66	6.12	7.73	0.045	20 18	4.40 0.90	6.3-N HCl 3.0-N NaOH	− 8.64 − 13.2	Reacts with Hg salts and nitrous acid to give red color (MILLON reaction). Other less specific color tests are: reaction with α-nitroso-β-naphthol; reaction with FOLIN phenol reagent *Leuconostoc mesenteroides* P-60, 8042	Precursor of thyroxine[3] (see page 443), adrenaline (see page 442), melanin (see page 443)
Valine (α-amino-*iso*valeric acid)	Val.	$C_5H_{11}NO_2$ 117.15	$(CH_3)_2CH \cdot CH(NH_2) \cdot COOH$	51.26	9.46	11.96	8.85	20 20	3.4 3.58	6-N HCl Water	+ 28.8 + 6.42	*Lactobacillus arabinosus* 17–5, 8014; *Lactobacillus helveticus*; *Streptococcus faecalis*	

* Used in the description of amino acid sequences in polypeptide and protein molecules[1].
** As grams per 100 ml solution, unless otherwise stated.

References
1) BRAND and EDSALL, *Ann. Rev. Biochem.*, **16**, 223 (1947). 2) BLOCK and WEISS, *Amino Acid Handbook*, Springfield, Ill., 1956, page 37; ROCHE et al., in GLICK, D. (Ed.), *Methods of Biochemical Analysis*, vol. I, New York, 1954, page 243. 3) ROCHE and MICHEL, *Ann. Rev. Biochem.*, **23**, 481 (1954). 4) ASTRUP et al., *Acta physiol. scand.*, **24**, 202 (1952). 5) CONSDEN et al., *Biochem. J.*, **39**, 251 (1945). 6) ÅGREN et al., *Acta chem. scand.*, **5**, 324 (1951). 7) DE VERDIER, C.-H., *Nature*, **170**, 804 (1952).

Table 8 Physical and chemical properties of some amino acids not occurring in proteins but found in the free form

Name	Formula and mol. wt.	Structure	Elementary composition (%) C	H	N	Solubility (grams per 100 g water at 25° C)	Specific rotation: Temperature (°C)	Concentration (g per 100 ml solution)	Solvent	$[\alpha]_D$	Special properties	Occurrence and biological function (*for references see page 360*)
β-Alanine (β-amino-propionic acid)	$C_3H_7NO_2$ 89.10	$NH_2{\cdot}CH_2{\cdot}CH_2{\cdot}COOH$	40.44	7.92	15.72	very soluble						Breakdown product of pyrimidines (see page 413). Occurs as constituent of pantothenic acid, coenzyme A, carnosine and anserine
α-Aminoadipic acid	$C_6H_{11}NO_4$ 161.16	$HOOC{\cdot}(CH_2)_3{\cdot}CH(NH_2){\cdot}COOH$	44.71	6.88	8.69	0.22 (at 20°C)					Decomposes on heating to α-piperidone-α′-carboxylic acid	Intermediate in breakdown of lysine (see page 410)
α-Amino-*n*-butyric acid	$C_4H_9NO_2$ 103.12	$CH_3{\cdot}CH_2{\cdot}CH(NH_2){\cdot}COOH$	46.60	8.80	13.59	28 (for DL-acid)	20	5.46	Water	+ 7.86		Found in brain preparations[1]. Occurs as constituent of tripeptide ophthalmic acid in lens tissue[2]
γ-Amino-*n*-butyric acid	$C_4H_9NO_2$ 103.12	$NH_2{\cdot}(CH_2)_3{\cdot}COOH$	46.60	8.80	13.59							Found in brain[3], lung and heart[1] preparations
β-Amino*iso*butyric acid	$C_4H_9NO_2$ 103.12	$NH_2{\cdot}CH_2{\cdot}CH(CH_3){\cdot}COOH$	46.60	8.80	13.59							Breakdown product of thymine (see page 413)
δ-Aminolevulic acid (γ-keto-δ-amino-*n*-valeric acid)	$C_5H_9NO_3$ 131.14	$NH_2{\cdot}CH_2{\cdot}CO{\cdot}CH_2{\cdot}CH_2{\cdot}COOH$	45.82	6.90	10.71						Reduces BENEDICT's solution in the cold. Split by periodate to formaldehyde and succinic acid	Intermediate in porphyrin biosynthesis (see page 440)
Carbamylaspartic acid (ureidosuccinic acid)	$C_5H_8N_2O_5$ 176.14	$HOOC{\cdot}CH_2{\cdot}CH(COOH){\cdot}NH{\cdot}CO{\cdot}NH_2$	34.10	4.58	15.91	0.4 (at 20°C)	25		Water (Ba salt)	+ 24.1		Intermediate in biosynthesis of pyrimidines from aspartic acid in mammals and bacteria (see page 442)
Citrulline (α-amino-δ-ureido-*n*-valeric acid)	$C_6H_{13}N_3O_3$ 175.19	$NH_2{\cdot}CO{\cdot}NH{\cdot}(CH_2)_3{\cdot}CH(NH_2){\cdot}COOH$	41.13	7.47	23.98		21.23 21.23	5.00 5.00	0.3-N HCl Water	+ 17.9 + 3.5	Converted to ornithine by alkaline hydrolysis	Intermediate in ornithine cycle of urea synthesis (see 445 and 446)
Creatine (methyl-glycocyamine)	$C_4H_9N_3O_2$ 131.14	$(HN)(H_2N)C{\cdot}N(CH_3){\cdot}CH_2{\cdot}COOH$	36.64	6.92	32.05	1.35 (at 18°C)					Weakly basic. Gives creatinine on heating with dilute acids	Cell constituent. Creatine phosphate acts as store of "high energy" phosphate in vertebrate muscle (see page 440)
Creatinine (1-methylglyco-cyamidine)	$C_4H_7N_3O$ 113.12	$HN{=}C{\cdot}N(CH_3){\cdot}CH_2{\cdot}CO$ (ring closed through $N{-}H$)	42.48	6.24	37.15	8.7 (at 16°C)					Strongly basic	Present in urine

Table 8 Physical and chemical properties of some amino acids not occurring in proteins but found in the free form (*concluded*)

Name	Formula and mol. wt.	Structure	Elementary composition (%) C	H	N	Solubility (grams per 100 g water at 25° C	Specific rotation: Temperature (°C)	Concentration (g per 100 ml solution)	Solvent	[α]D	Special properties	Occurrence and biological function (*for references see page 360)*
Cystathionine	$C_7H_{14}N_2O_4S$ 222.27	HOOC·CH(NH$_2$)·CH$_2$·S·CH$_2$·CH$_2$·CH(NH$_2$)·COOH	37.82	6.35	12.60		22	1.0	1-N HCl	+ 23.7		Intermediate in transsulfuration of methionine with serine (see page 409)
			Sulfur 14.45									
Cysteic acid	$C_3H_7NO_5S$ 169.16	HO$_3$S·CH$_2$·CH(NH$_2$)·COOH	21.27	4.16	8.26		28	6.0	Water	+ 7.8		Intermediate in formation of taurine, a bile constituent, from cysteine
			Sulfur 18.90									
Ergothioneine (betaine of thiol-histidine)	$C_9H_{15}N_3O_2S$ 229.31	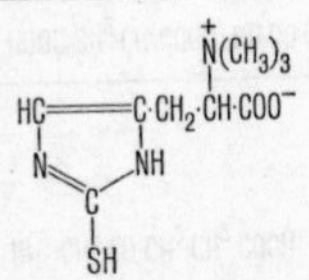	47.14	6.54	18.35		21	5.0	Water	+116.0	Basic. Stable to alkalis; thiol group is readily oxidized to sulfate under acid conditions. Gives reddish purple color with diazotized sulfanilic acid and alkali	Occurs in erythrocytes, liver, kidney, other tissues, and in urine and semen[4]. Constituent of ergot
			Sulfur 13.95									
Glycocyamine (guanidinoacetic acid)	$C_3H_7N_3O_2$ 117.11	HN=C(NH$_2$)·NH·CH$_2$·COOH	30.77	6.02	35.88	slightly soluble						In urine. Formed in kidney from arginine and glycine. Precursor of creatine and creatinine (see page 440)
Homoserine (α-amino-γ-hydroxy-*n*-butyric acid)	$C_4H_9NO_3$ 119.12	HO·CH$_2$·CH$_2$·CH(NH$_2$)·COOH	40.33	7.62	11.76		24–26	0.25	5-N HCl	+ 18.3		Intermediate in methionine metabolism (see page 409)
Ornithine (2,5-diamino-*n*-valeric acid)	$C_5H_{12}N_2O_2$ 132.17	NH$_2$·(CH$_2$)$_3$·CH(NH$_2$)·COOH	45.42	9.15	21.19	very soluble	20	0.84	0.45-N HCl	+ 14.1	Formed from arginine by alkaline hydrolysis	Intermediate in ornithine cycle of urea synthesis (see page 445). Benzoic acid is excreted by the fowl as N,N′-dibenzoylornithine
Taurine (2-aminoethane-sulfonic acid)	$C_2H_7NO_3S$ 125.15	NH$_2$·CH$_2$·CH$_2$·SO$_3$H	19.19	5.64	11.19	8.78 (at 20°C)						In muscle tissue of invertebrates. Formed in mammalian liver from cysteine (see page 441). Component of taurocholic acid (bile acid)
			Sulfur 25.62									

References

1) Walker, D. M., *Biochem. J.*, **52**, 679 (1952). *2)* Waley, S. G., *Biochem. J.*, **64**, 715 (1956). *3)* Udenfriend, S., *J. biol. Chem.*, **187**, 65 (1950).

4) For review of recent work see Bell, D. J., *Ann. Rep. Progr. Chem.*, **52**, 285 (1955).

3. Nucleotides and related substances

Nucleosides and nucleotides

A *nucleoside* is a sugar linked to a heterocyclic base. A *nucleotide* is a nucleoside in which the sugar is esterified with phosphoric acid.

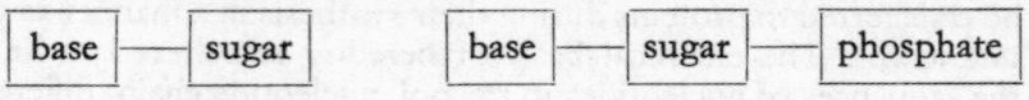

Nucleoside Nucleotide

The bases found in nucleosides and nucleotides are most commonly purines and pyrimidines. Others include pyridines and *iso*Alloxazines. The parent compounds of these bases are:

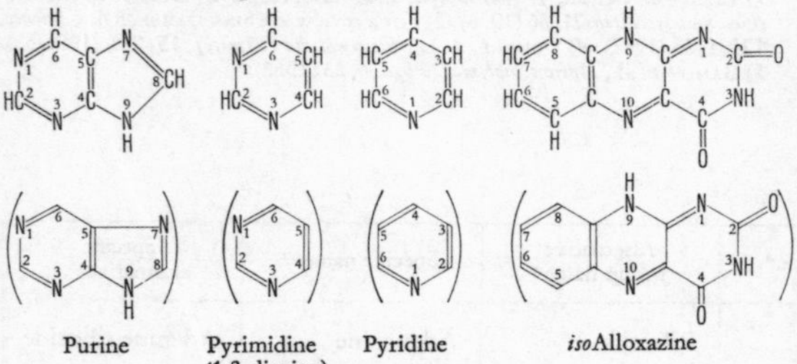

Purine Pyrimidine (1,3-diazine) Pyridine *iso*Alloxazine

The sugars found in nucleosides and nucleotides are most commonly either ribose or 2-desoxyribose:

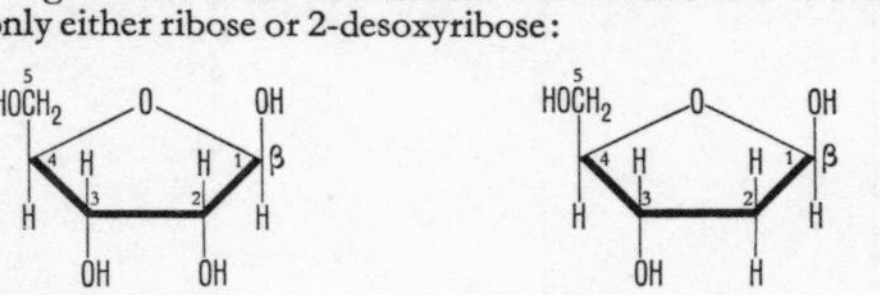

Ribose (β-D-ribofuranose) 2-Desoxyribose (β-D-2-desoxyribofuranose)

The base–glycoside linkage of nucleosides and nucleotides occupies the 9-position in the case of purines and the 3-position in the case of pyrimidines. Esterification of nucleosides is not confined to orthophosphoric acid. It occurs also with pyrophosphoric (diphosphoric) acid and triphosphoric acid.

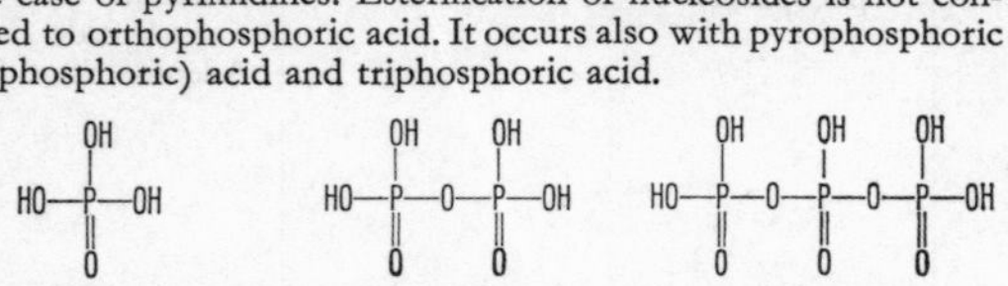

Orthophosphoric acid (monophosphoric acid) Pyrophosphoric acid (diphosphoric acid) Triphosphoric acid

The nomenclature of the nucleosides and nucleotides is demonstrated by the examples given in Table 9 on page 362.

The naturally-occurring nucleoside mono-, di- and tri-phosphates have the sugar–phosphate ester linkage in the 5′-position. Exceptions are the nucleoside 3′-monophosphates and the nucleoside 3′,5′-diphosphates formed during the enzymic digestion of ribonucleic acids (RNA). In the case of certain coenzymes, a nucleoside 2′,5′-diphosphate or nucleoside 3′,5′-diphosphate structure is also encountered (see Table 12, pages 369–375).

Nucleotides and polynucleotides (see under Nucleic acids, below) occur in all living cells. Certain naturally occurring bases, nucleosides and nucleotides have no known function apart from being intermediates in the synthesis or breakdown of other nucleotides (Tables 10a, b, c, pages 363–367).

Nucleoside di- or tri-phosphates are precursors of the nucleic acids. They act also as carriers of the free energy of pyrophosphate bonds. In this capacity, nucleotides may be regarded as coenzymes of the free-energy transfer which occurs in many synthetic and degradative reactions. Nucleoside diphosphates are formed from the corresponding monophosphates by nucleoside monophosphate kinase. This enzyme is analogous in action to adenylate kinase and catalyzes the general reaction[1,2]:

$$\text{nucleoside monophosphate} + \text{adenosine triphosphate} \rightleftharpoons \text{nucleoside diphosphate} + \text{adenosine diphosphate}$$

Nucleoside triphosphates are formed in turn from the corresponding diphosphates by nucleoside diphosphate kinase[1,2]:

$$\text{nucleoside diphosphate} + \text{adenosine triphosphate} \rightleftharpoons \text{nucleoside triphosphate} + \text{adenosine diphosphate}$$

A list of nucleoside mono-, di- and tri-phosphates and their functions is given in Table 11, page 368.

The nucleotide coenzymes act as carriers of hydrogen (codehydrogenases) and as carriers of the active forms of sugars, amino acids, fatty acids, dicarboxylic acids, carbon dioxide, and sulfate. The roles and modes of formation of nucleotide coenzymes are listed in Table 12, pages 369–375.

Nucleic acids

Nucleic acid is the generic name given to a group of substances which, chemically speaking, are *polynucleotides*. Two types of nucleic acid are known: the *ribonucleic acids* (RNA) which are found in the cytoplasm and in small amounts in the nucleus of the cell; and the *desoxyribonucleic acids* (DNA) which are found in the nucleus of the cell. Both types of compound generally occur conjugated with proteins. The polynucleotide structure of RNA and DNA is formed by the esterification of the phosphate group of 5′-nucleotides with the 3′-position of adjacent nucleotides. Four nucleotide units are found in RNA. They are adenylic acid, guanylic acid, cytidylic acid and uridylic acid. Four desoxyribonucleotide units are found in most types of DNA. They are desoxyadenylic acid, desoxyguanylic acid, desoxycytidylic acid and desoxythymidylic acid. The latter desoxyribonucleotide is usually referred to simply as "thymidylic acid" because no naturally occurring ribonucleotide containing the base thymine has so far been found. In certain types of DNA one of these nucleotide units is replaced partially or wholly by a different one. These exceptions are indicated in Table 11, page 368. Portions of RNA and DNA polynucleotides are shown in Figure 4 below.

The sequences in which nucleotides occur in different types of nucleic acid are not known at present. The nucleotide composition of DNA is species-specific. Although the nucleotide composition of RNA differs between viruses, yeasts and animals, it has not yet been decided whether it is species-specific in animals. No significant quantitative differences in the nucleotide composition of RNA and DNA from different organs of the same animals have been detected, but the nucleotide composition of RNA isolated from the cytoplasm differs from that isolated from the nucleus. DNA contains equal amounts of desoxyguanylic acid and desoxycytidylic acid and also of desoxyadenylic acid and desoxythymidylic acid, the second pair being present in somewhat larger amounts in animals than in other organisms.

The DNA molecule consists of a pair of polynucleotide chains which are aligned in the form of a double helix. The alignment is such that bases in one chain are linked to bases in the other chain

Fig. 4 Portions of RNA and DNA polynucleotides

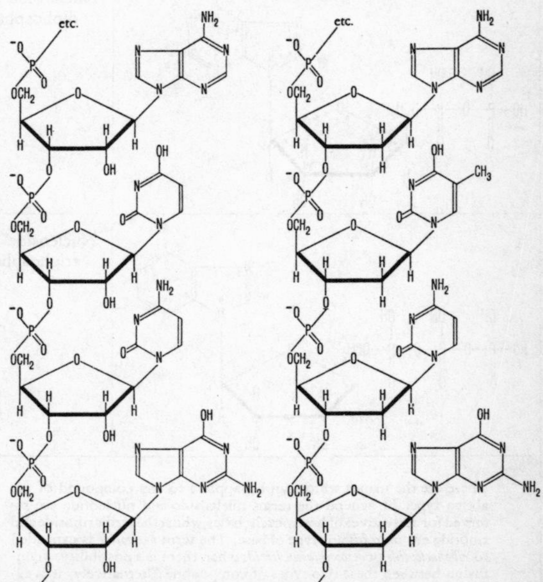

Portion of ribonucleic acid molecule

Portion of desoxyribonucleic acid molecule

by hydrogen bonds, adenine being linked to thymine and guanine to cytosine. The structure of RNA is less well understood, but it may be analogous to that of DNA.

The molecular weights of the nucleic acids vary considerably with their method of preparation, artefacts of aggregation or disaggregation being possible. Molecular weights obtained for RNA correspond to chain lengths of between 30 and 1000 mononucleotide units. Values obtained for DNA correspond to chain lengths of between 1500 and 15,000 mononucleotide units.

The functions of nucleic acids are not fully understood. RNA plays an as yet ill-defined role in protein synthesis. DNA combined with protein (desoxyribonucleoprotein) makes up part or all of the constituent material of the chromosomes and genes[3]. According to current theory it forms both the "card index" of heredity and the "master templates" of cell reproduction. It has been calculated that for a polynucleotide consisting of 300 mononucleotide units there can exist about 4×10^{87} different nucleic acids, assuming that there is complete freedom of choice in the arrangement of the four different mononucleotides[4]. The nucleic acids are thus capable of great specificity, and this specificity can be transferred to proteins during their synthesis in a manner as yet unknown[5]. The chemical basis of heredity is believed to lie in the sequences of nucleotides in the polynucleotide chain, different sequences of nucleotides reflecting specific types of information.

References
1) LIEBERMAN et al., *J. biol. Chem.*, **215**, 429 (1955). *2)* GIBSON et al., *Biochim. biophys. Acta*, **21**, 86 (1956). *3)* For a review see SINSHEIMER, R.L., *Science*, **125**, 1123 (1957). *4)* DOUNCE, A. L., *Enzymologia (Amst.)*, **15**, 251 (1951/53). *5)* GAMOW et al., *Advanc. biol. med. Phys.*, **4**, 23 (1956).

Table 9 Nomenclature of nucleosides and nucleotides

Structural formula	Group name*	Alternative group name*	Specific name**	Specific alternatives**
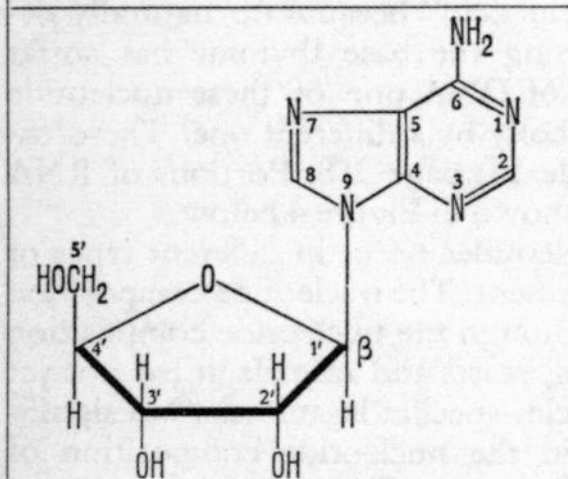	Nucleoside	Riboside	Adenosine	Adenine riboside
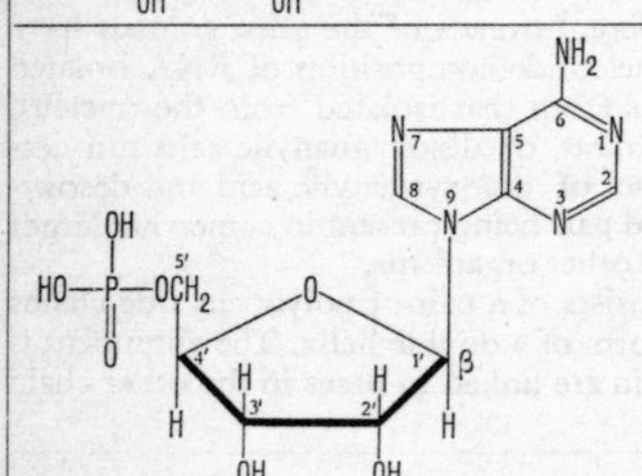	Nucleotide (Nucleoside mono-phosphate)	Ribotide (Riboside mono-phosphate)	5′-Adenylic acid (AMP)	Adenosine 5′-mono-phosphate Adenine nucleotide Adenine ribotide
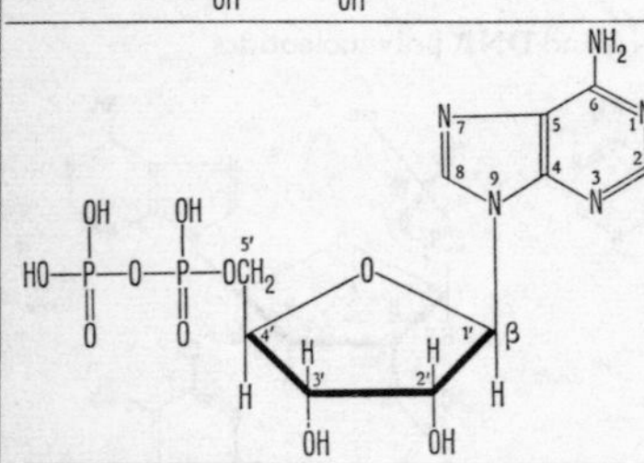	Nucleoside diphosphate	Riboside diphosphate	Adenosine diphosphate (ADP)	Adenosine 5′-pyro-phosphate
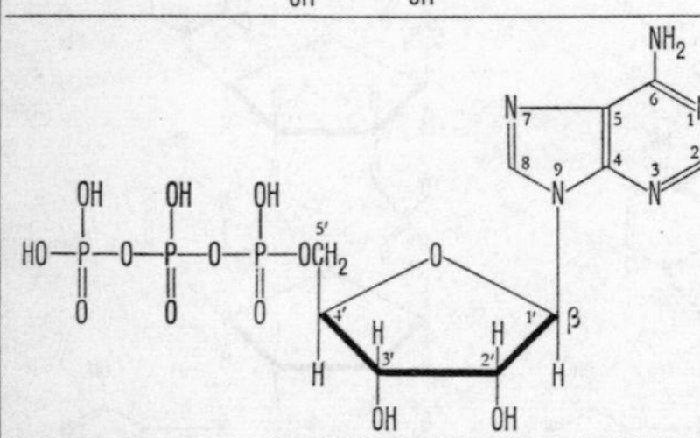	Nucleoside triphosphate	Riboside triphosphate	Adenosine triphosphate (ATP)	

* These are the names which can be applied to any compound of the above type. In general the terms nucleoside and nucleotide are reserved for derivatives of heterocyclic bases, whilst the terms riboside and ribotide are used for any type of base. The term *nucleotide* is expanded to *ribonucleotide* or *desoxyribonucleotide* when there is a possibility of confusion between these two types of compound. Alternatively, it is expanded to *mononucleotide* when it is necessary to distinguish between *mononucleotides* and *polynucleotides*. When necessary the position of the phosphate ester linkage may be indicated. For example, the nucleotide shown is a 5′-nucleotide or, more fully, a 5′-ribonucleotide. The use of the bracketed group names is confined to occasions when it is necessary to distinguish between *monophosphates* and *polyphosphates*.

** When the *nucleoside* or *nucleotide* under consideration contains desoxyribose in place of ribose, this is made clear by prefixing the syllable *desoxy* to the name of the compound, for example, *desoxyadenosine, desoxyadenylic acid.*

Table 10 a Compounds involved in the biosynthesis and breakdown of purine and pyrimidine nucleotides: Purines and pyrimidines

Name	Formula and mol.wt.	Structure	Properties	Occurrence	Function
Adenine (6-amino-purine)	$C_5H_5N_5$ 135.14	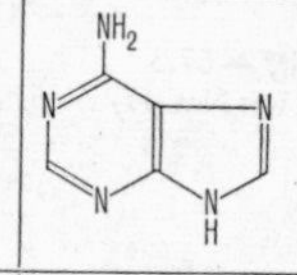	m.p. 365 °C (decomp.); picrate 298 °C	Occurs in tea, sugar beet, yeast, various animal organs	These bases are the products of the degradation of the corresponding nucleotides. They are further degraded by the pathways shown on pages 411–414. In mammals only adenine can be converted back to the corresponding nucleotide under normal conditions but the extent to which this occurs is uncertain
Guanine (2-amino-6-hydroxy-purine)	$C_5H_5ON_5$ 151.14	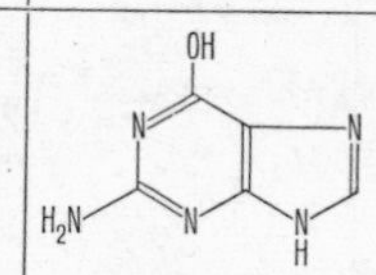	m.p. 365 °C (decomp.); picrate 258–260 °C	Occurs in scales and flesh of fish	
Uracil (2,6-dihydroxypyrimidine)	$C_4H_4O_2N_2$ 112.09	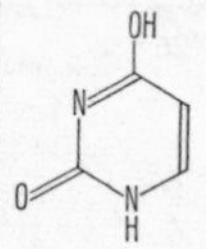	m.p. 338 °C (decomp.)		
Cytosine (6-amino-2-hydroxy-pyrimidine)	$C_4H_5ON_3$ 111.11	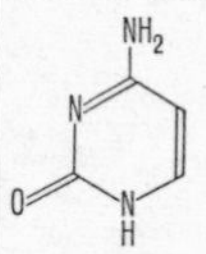	m.p. 320–325 °C (decomp.); picrate 333 °C		
Thymine (2,6-dihydroxy-5-methyl-pyrimidine)	$C_5H_6O_2N_2$ 126.12	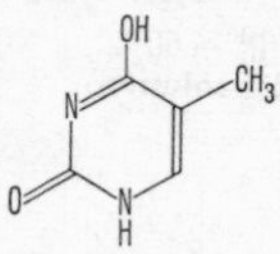	m.p. 321–325 °C		
5-Methyl-cytosine (5-methyl-6-amino-2-hydroxy-pyrimidine)	$C_5H_7ON_3$ 125.14	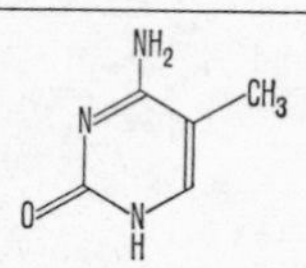	m.p. 270 °C (decomp.); picrate 290–291 °C	Occurs in calf thymus nucleic acid and wheat germ DNA	
Hypoxanthine (6-hydroxy-purine)	$C_5H_4ON_4$ 136.12	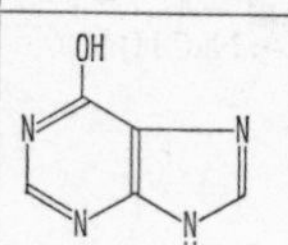	m.p. 150 °C (decomp.); picrate 246 °C	Occurs in muscle, meat extracts, blood, urine (the latter esp. in leukemia)	Product of deamination of adenine; precursor of xanthine
Xanthine (2,6-dihy-droxypurine)	$C_5H_4O_2N_4$ 152.12	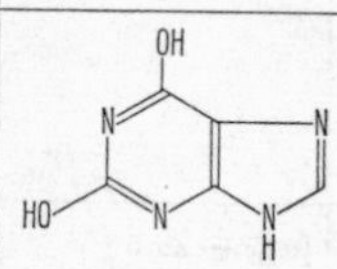	m.p. 262–264 °C (perchlorate)	Occurs in small quantities in plants, blood, liver, urine, yeast. Component of butterfly pigments and rare urinary calculi	Formed by oxidation of hypoxanthine, or by deamination of guanine; precursor of uric acid
Uric acid (2,6,8-tri-hydroxy-purine)	$C_5H_4O_3N_4$ 168.12	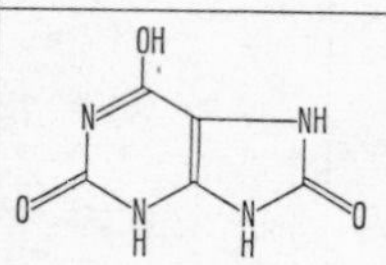	m.p. > 400 °C (decomp.) d^{25} 1.836	Occurs in urine and renal and urinary calculi (increased in urine and blood in gout, leukemia, nephritis, pneumonia). Also in feces of birds and reptiles	Formed by oxidation of xanthine. Chief product of nitrogen excretion in reptiles and birds. In mammals other than primates further degraded to allantoin (see page 412)
Orotic acid (2,6-dihy-droxypyrimi-dine-4-carb-oxylic acid)	$C_5H_4O_4N_2$ 156.10	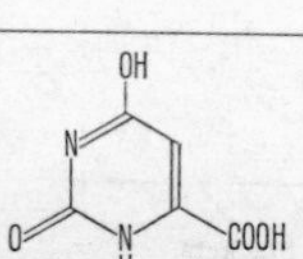	m.p. 345–347 °C (decomp.); ethyl ester 200 °C	Occurs in milk	Precursor of orotidylic acid (see page 442)

Table 10 b Compounds involved in the biosynthesis and breakdown of purine and pyrimidine nucleotides: Nucleosides

The purine nucleosides listed in this table all contain 9-N-β-riboside or -desoxyriboside linkages, the pyrimidine nucleosides 3-N-β-riboside or -desoxyriboside linkages. For explanation of the nomenclature see Table 9, page 362

Name*	Formula and mol.wt.	Structure	Specific rotation	Function in mammalian tissue
Adenosine (adenine riboside)	$C_{10}H_{13}O_4N_5$ 267.25	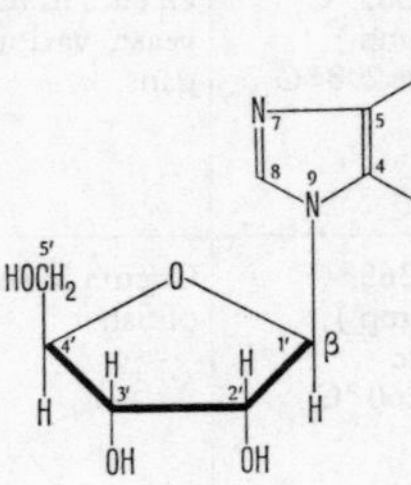	$[\alpha]_D^{20}$ −67.3° (0.1-N NaOH)	These nucleosides are products of the enzymic hydrolysis of the corresponding 3′- and 5′-nucleotides. The nucleosides in turn are broken down further by phosphorolysis to yield ribose-1-phosphate or desoxyribose-1-phosphate and the corresponding base. Nucleoside kinases which form 5′-nucleotides from nucleosides plus ATP are known to occur in yeast and in some animal tissues. Their importance in mammals has not at present been assessed
Desoxyadenosine (adenine desoxyriboside)	$C_{10}H_{13}O_3N_5$ 251.25	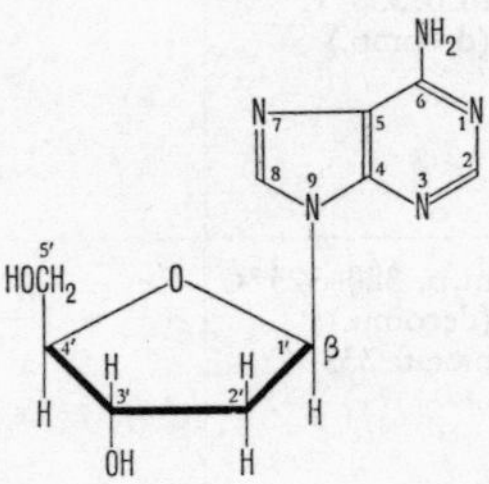	$[\alpha]_D^{21}$ −26°	
Guanosine (guanine riboside)	$C_{10}H_{13}O_5N_5$ 283.25	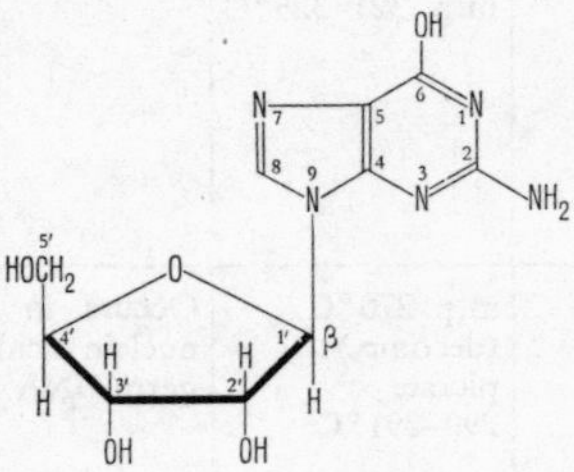	$[\alpha]_D^{20}$ −60° (2% solution)	
Desoxyguanosine (guanine desoxyriboside)	$C_{10}H_{13}O_4N_5$ 267.25	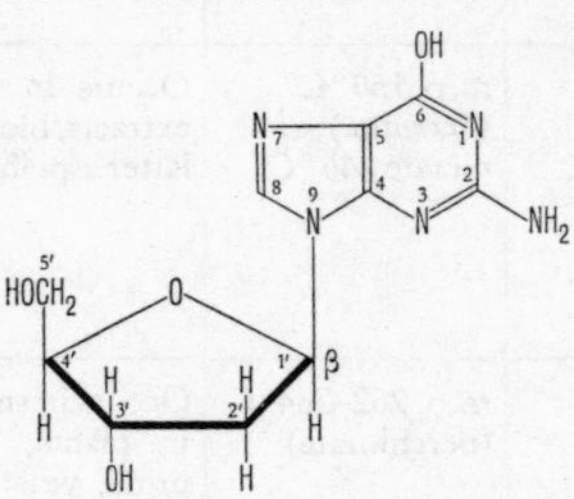	$[\alpha]_D^{19}$ −47.7° (1-N NaOH)	
Cytidine (cytosine riboside)	$C_9H_{13}O_5N_3$ 243.23	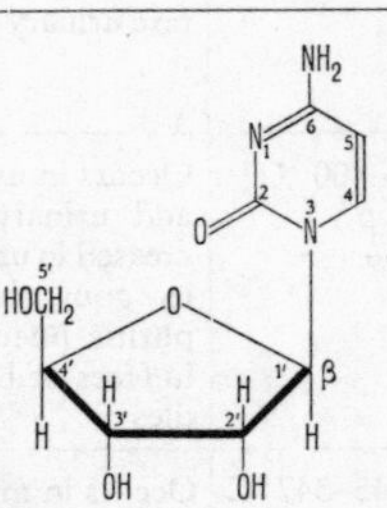	$[\alpha]_D^{20}$ +29.6°	

* The alternative name in "base riboside or desoxyriboside" nomenclature is given in brackets.

Table 10 b Compounds involved in the biosynthesis and breakdown of purine and pyrimidine nucleotides: Nucleosides (*continued*)

Name*	Formula and mol.wt.	Structure	Specific rotation	Function in mammalian tissue
Desoxycytidine (cytosine desoxyriboside)	$C_9H_{13}O_4N_3$ 227.23	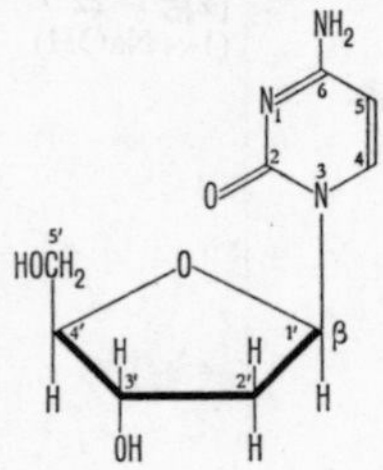	$[\alpha]_D^{25}$ +40 °	These nucleosides are products of the enzymic hydrolysis of the corresponding 3'- and 5'-nucleotides. The nucleosides in turn are broken down further by phosphorolysis to yield ribose-1-phosphate or desoxyribose-1-phosphate and the corresponding base. Nucleoside kinases which form 5'-nucleotides from nucleosides plus ATP are known to occur in yeast and in some animal tissues. Their importance in mammals has not at present been assessed
Uridine (uracil riboside)	$C_9H_{12}O_6N_2$ 244.21	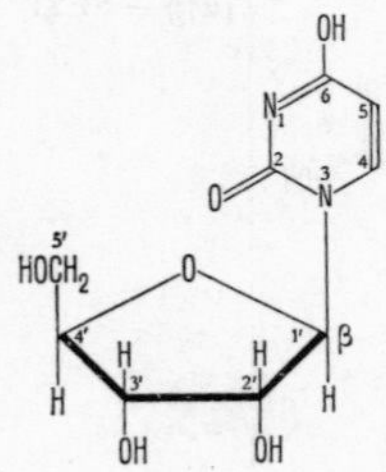	$[\alpha]_D^{16}$ +9.6 °	
(Desoxy)thymidine (thymine desoxyriboside)	$C_{10}H_{14}O_5N_2$ 242.24	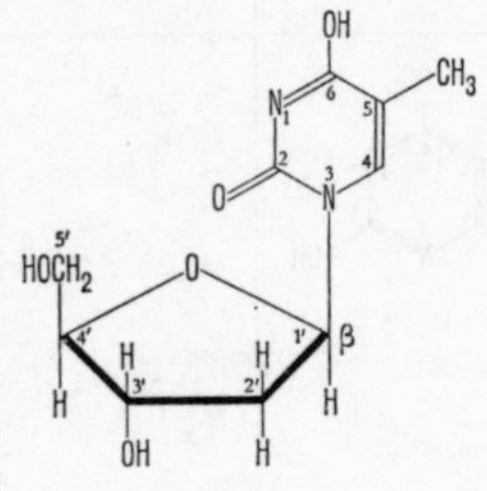	$[\alpha]_D^{16}$ +32.50 ° (1-N NaOH)	
Inosine (hypoxanthine riboside)	$C_{10}H_{12}O_5N_4$ 268.24	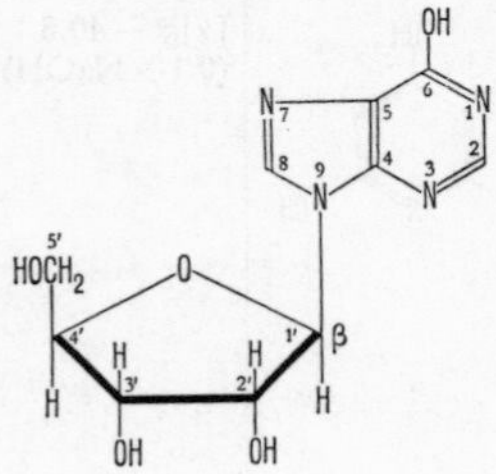	$[\alpha]_D^{18}$ −72.45 ° (0.1-N NaOH)	This nucleoside has no known function other than its role as intermediate in the synthesis or breakdown of nucleotides (see page 412)

* The alternative name in "base riboside or desoxyriboside" nomenclature is given in brackets.

Table 10 b Compounds involved in the biosynthesis and breakdown of purine and pyrimidine nucleotides: Nucleosides (*concluded*)

Name*	Formula and mol.wt.	Structure	Specific rotation	Function in mammalian tissue
Desoxyinosine (hypoxanthine desoxyriboside)	$C_{10}H_{12}O_4N_4$ 252.24	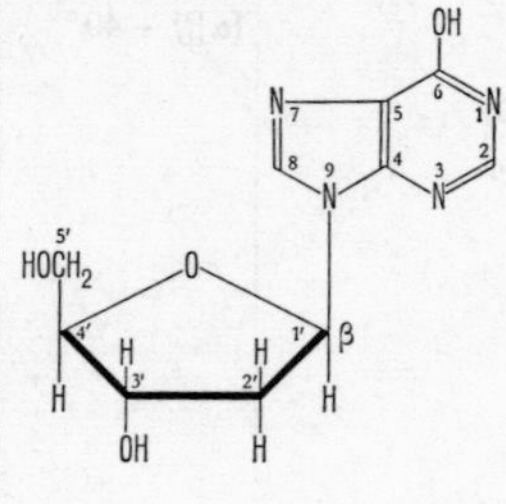	$[\alpha]_D^{19}$ − 22.9° (1-N NaOH)	
Xanthosine (xanthine riboside)	$C_{10}H_{12}O_6N_4$ 284.24	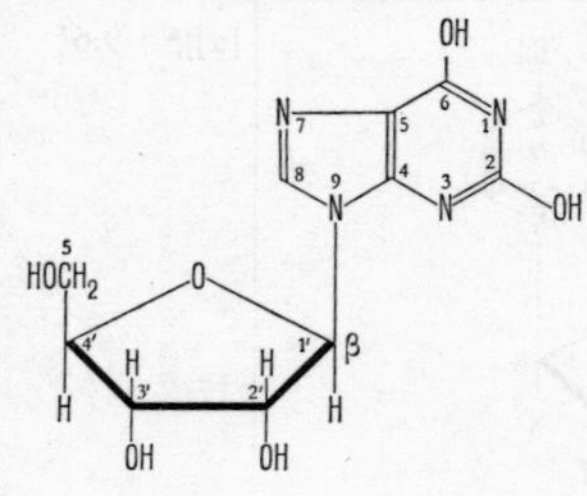	$[\alpha]_D^{30}$ − 51.21°	These nucleosides have no known function other than their role as intermediates in the synthesis or breakdown of nucleotides (see page 412)
Desoxyxanthosine (xanthine desoxyriboside)	$C_{10}H_{12}O_5N_4$ 268.24	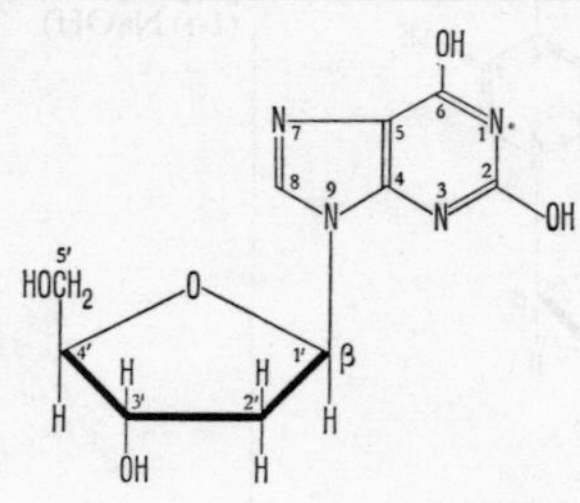		
Uric acid riboside	$C_{10}H_{12}O_7N_4$ 300.24	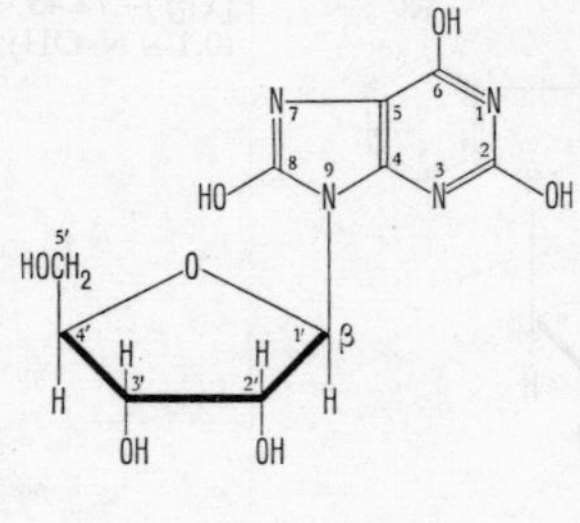	$[\alpha]_D^{20}$ − 40.8° (0.1-N NaOH)	

* The alternative name in "base riboside or desoxyriboside" nomenclature is given in brackets.

Table 10 c Compounds involved in the biosynthesis and breakdown of purine and pyrimidine nucleotides: Nucleotides

With the exception of inosinic acid, the compounds listed here have no known coenzyme activity

Name	Formula and mol.wt.	Structure*	Function
Orotidylic acid (OMP) (orotic acid ribotide)	$C_{10}H_{13}O_{11}N_2P$ 368.21	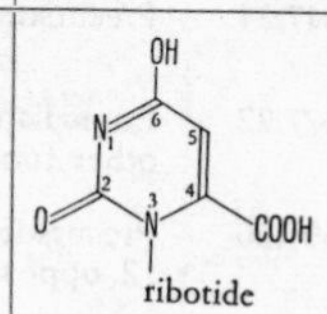	Intermediate in biosynthesis of pyrimidine nucleotides. Formed from orotic acid (see page 442)
5-Phosphoribosylamine (D-ribosylamine 5-phosphate)	$C_5H_{12}O_7NP$ 229.13	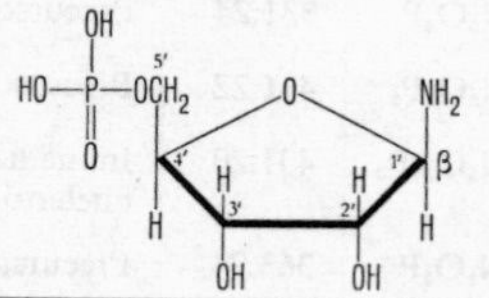	Intermediates in biosynthesis of inosinic acid (see pages 438 and 439)
Glycinamide ribotide	$C_7H_{15}O_8N_2P$ 286.19	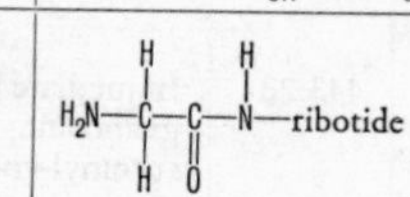	
Formylglycinamide ribotide	$C_8H_{15}O_9N_2P$ 314.20	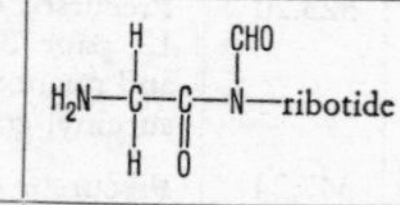	
Formylglycinamidine ribotide	$C_8H_{16}O_8N_3P$ 313.22	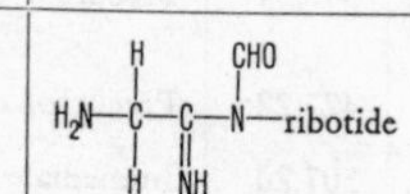	
5-Aminoimidazole ribotide	$C_8H_{14}O_7N_3P$ 295.20	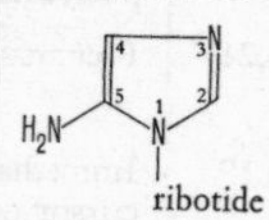	
5-Aminoimidazole-4-carboxamide ribotide	$C_9H_{15}O_8N_4P$ 338.23	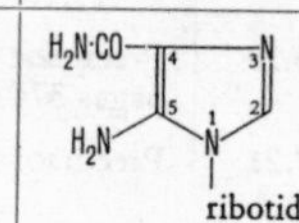	
Inosinic acid (IMP) (inosine 5′-phosphate)	$C_{10}H_{13}O_8N_4P$ 348.22	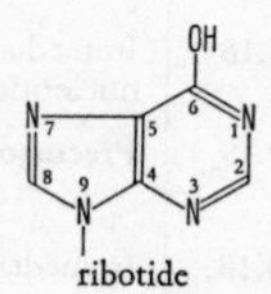	Precursor of adenosine 5′-phosphate (AMP) and guanosine 5′-phosphate (GMP) (see Table 11, page 368). Can partially replace certain coenzyme functions of other nucleotides
Succinyladenylic acid (succinyladenosine 5′-phosphate)	$C_{14}H_{18}O_{11}N_5P$ 463.31	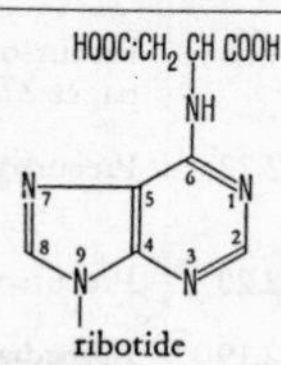	Intermediate in synthesis of adenosine 5′-phosphate (AMP) from inosinic acid (see page 439)
Xanthidylic acid (XMP) (xanthosine 5′-phosphate)	$C_{10}H_{13}O_9N_4P$ 364.22	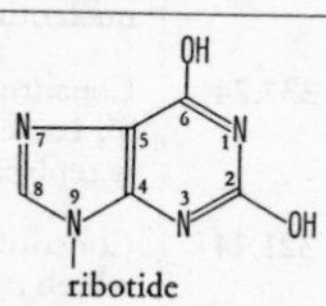	Intermediate in synthesis of guanosine 5′-phosphate (GMP) from inosinic acid (see page 440)

* For structure of the "ribotide" portion of the molecule, see Table 9, page 362.

Table 11 Nucleoside mono-, di- and tri-phosphates (nucleotides)

Name	Abbreviation	Formula	Mol.wt.	Function
Adenosine 5′-monophosphate (adenylic acid)	AMP	$C_{10}H_{14}N_5O_7P$	347.24	Precursor of ADP. Activates phosphorylase b
Adenosine diphosphate	ADP	$C_{10}H_{15}N_5O_{10}P_2$	427.22	Immediate precursor of polynucleotides. For other functions see page 415
Adenosine triphosphate	ATP	$C_{10}H_{16}N_5O_{13}P_3$	507.20	Precursor of adenosine coenzymes (see Table 12, opposite). For other functions see page 415
Desoxyadenosine monophosphate	DAMP	$C_{10}H_{14}N_5O_6P$	331.24	Precursor of desoxyadenosine diphosphate
Desoxyadenosine diphosphate	DADP	$C_{10}H_{15}N_5O_9P_2$	411.22	Precursor of desoxyadenosine triphosphate
Desoxyadenosine triphosphate	DATP	$C_{10}H_{16}N_5O_{12}P_3$	491.20	Immediate precursor of desoxyribosepolynucleotides
Guanosine monophosphate (guanylic acid)	GMP	$C_{10}H_{14}N_5O_8P$	363.24	Precursor of guanosine diphosphate
Guanosine diphosphate	GDP	$C_{10}H_{15}N_5O_{11}P_2$	443.22	Immediate precursor of polynucleotides. Yields guanosine triphosphate during cleavage of succinyl-coenzyme A
Guanosine triphosphate	GTP	$C_{10}H_{16}N_5O_{14}P_3$	523.20	Precursor of guanosine coenzymes (see Table 12, page 372). Formed from orthophosphate and guanosine diphosphate during cleavage of succinyl-coenzyme A
Desoxyguanosine monophosphate (desoxyguanylic acid)	DGMP	$C_{10}H_{14}N_5O_7P$	347.24	Precursor of desoxyguanosine diphosphate
Desoxyguanosine diphosphate	DGDP	$C_{10}H_{15}N_5O_{10}P_2$	427.22	Precursor of desoxyguanosine triphosphate
Desoxyguanosine triphosphate	DGTP	$C_{10}H_{16}N_5O_{13}P_3$	507.20	Immediate precursor of desoxyribosepolynucleotides
Cytidine monophosphate (cytidylic acid)	CMP	$C_9H_{14}N_3O_8P$	323.21	Precursor of cytidine diphosphate
Cytidine diphosphate	CDP	$C_9H_{15}N_3O_{11}P_2$	403.19	Immediate precursor of polynucleotides. Precursor of cytidine triphosphate
Cytidine triphosphate	CTP	$C_9H_{16}N_3O_{14}P_3$	483.18	Precursor of cytidine coenzymes (see Table 12, pages 374 and 375)
Desoxycytidine monophosphate (desoxycytidylic acid)	DCMP	$C_9H_{14}N_3O_7P$	307.21	Precursor of desoxycytidine diphosphate
Desoxycytidine diphosphate	DCDP	$C_9H_{15}N_3O_{10}P_2$	387.19	Precursor of desoxycytidine triphosphate
Desoxycytidine triphosphate	DCTP	$C_9H_{16}N_3O_{13}P_3$	467.18	Immediate precursor of desoxyribosepolynucleotides
Uridine monophosphate* (uridylic acid)	UMP	$C_9H_{13}N_2O_9P$	324.19	Precursor of uridine diphosphate
Uridine diphosphate*	UDP	$C_9H_{14}N_2O_{12}P_2$	404.18	Immediate precursor of polynucleotides. Precursor of uridine triphosphate
Uridine triphosphate*	UTP	$C_9H_{15}N_2O_{15}P_3$	484.16	Precursor of uridine coenzymes (see Table 12, pages 372–374)
(Desoxy)thymidine monophosphate** (thymidylic acid)	(D)TMP	$C_{10}H_{15}N_2O_8P$	322.22	Precursor of desoxythymidine diphosphate
(Desoxy)thymidinediphosphate**	(D)TDP	$C_{10}H_{16}N_2O_{11}P_2$	402.20	Precursor of desoxythymidine triphosphate
(Desoxy)thymidine triphosphate**	(D)TTP	$C_{10}H_{17}N_2O_{14}P_3$	482.19	Immediate precursor of desoxyribosepolynucleotides
(Desoxy)-5-hydroxymethylcytidine monophosphate**	(D)HMCMP	$C_{10}H_{16}N_3O_8P$	337.24	Constituent nucleotide of the DNA of T_2, T_4 and T_6 bacteriophages of *Escherichia coli*, in which it replaces desoxycytidine monophosphate
(Desoxy)-5-methylcytidine monophosphate	(D)MCMP	$C_{10}H_{16}N_3O_7P$	321.24	Constituent of the DNA of wheat germ, in which it partially replaces desoxycytidine monophosphate

* The corresponding desoxyribose compounds are not known. ** The corresponding ribose compounds are not known.

Table 12 Nucleotides with coenzyme functions

Name	Formula and mol.wt.	Structure	Functions	Reference*
Nicotinamide mononucleotide (NMN)	$C_{11}H_{15}O_8N_2P$ 334.23	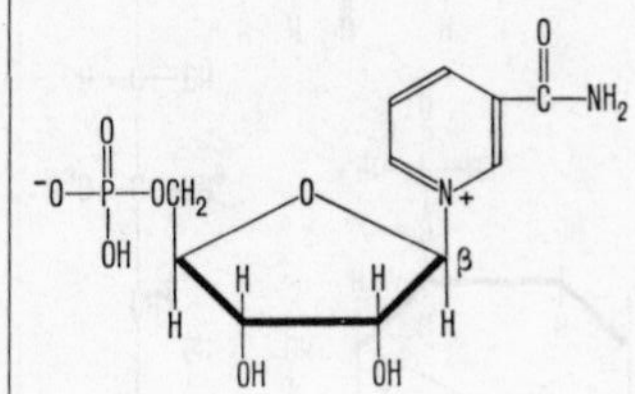	Constituent of di- and tri-phosphopyridine nucleotides (DPN and TPN)	*1*
Diphosphopyridine nucleotide (DPN) (adenosine diphospho-nicotinamide riboside; codehydrogen-ase I; coenzyme I [Co I]; cozymase; nicotinamide-adenine dinucleo-tide [NAD]**)	$C_{21}H_{27}O_{14}N_7P_2$ 663.45	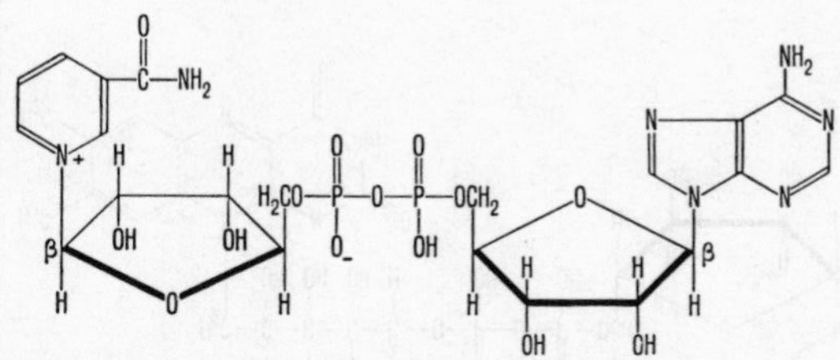	Formed by the reaction: nicotinamide mononucleotide + ATP → DPN + pyrophosphate. Coenzyme of many dehydrogenases, in which function the pyridine ring of the molecule is reduced reversibly as follows: 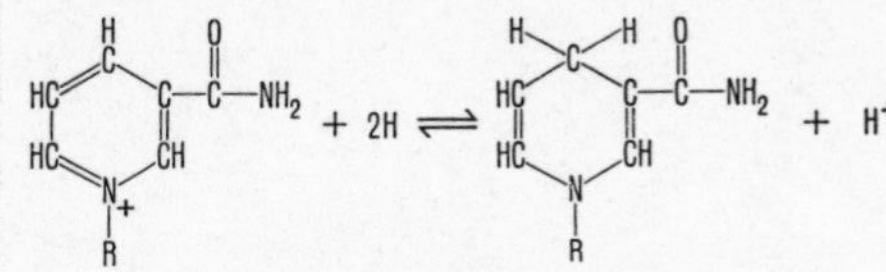	*1*
Triphosphopyridine nucleotide (TPN) (codehydrogenase II; coenzyme II [Co II]; nicotin-amide-adenine dinucleotide phosphate [NADP]**: 2′-phosphoadeno-sine diphospho-nicotinamide riboside; phos-pho-cozymase)	$C_{21}H_{28}O_{17}N_7P_3$ 743.44	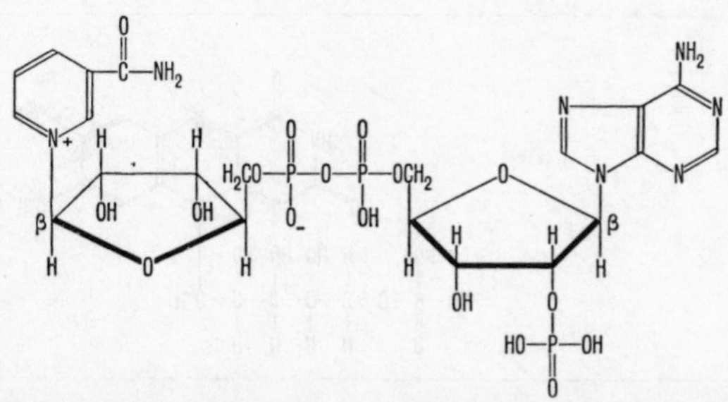	Formed by the reaction: DPN + ATP → TPN + ADP. Coenzyme of many dehydrogenases, in which function the pyridine ring of the molecule is reduced reversibly as shown above	*1*

* For references see page 375.

** New nomenclature recommended by the International Union of Pure and Applied Chemistry and the International Union of Biochemistry. Cf. Dixon, M., *Science*, **132**, 1548 (1960).

Table 12 Nucleotides with coenzyme functions (*continued*)

Name	Formula and mol.wt.	Structure	Functions	Reference*
Flavin mononucleotide (FMN) (flavin ribityl phosphate)	$C_{17}H_{21}O_9N_4P$ 456.36	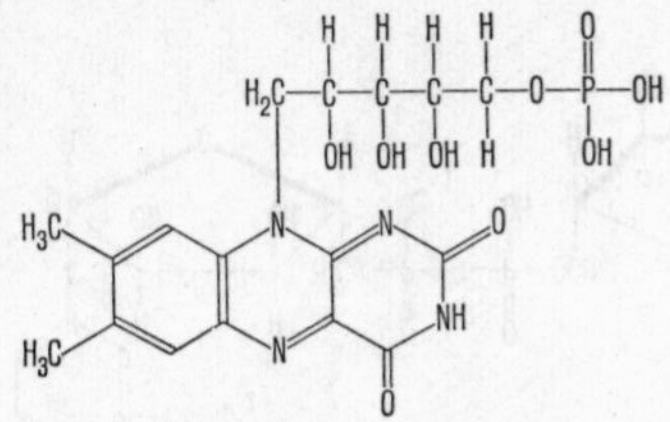	Constituent of flavin adenine dinucleotide (see below)	2
Flavin adenine dinucleotide (FAD) (adenosine diphosphoflavin ribitol)	$C_{27}H_{33}O_{15}N_9P_2$ 785.58	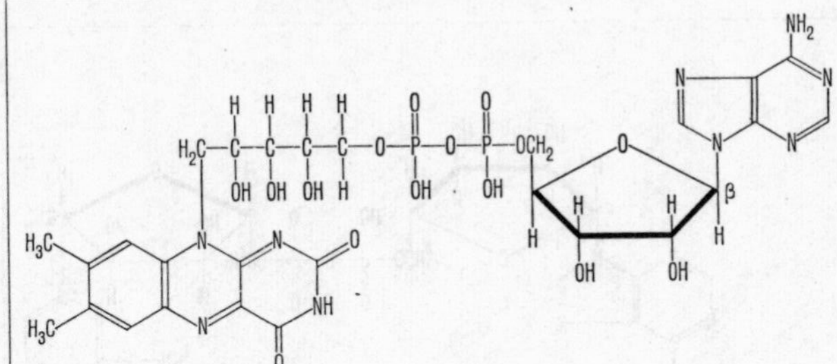	Formed by the reaction: flavin mononucleotide + ATP → flavin adenine dinucleotide + pyrophosphate. Prosthetic group of flavin enzymes (e.g. DPN- and TPN-cytochrome reductases, D-amino acid oxidase, succinic dehydrogenase, xanthine oxidase)	2
Coenzyme A (CoA)	$C_{21}H_{36}O_{16}N_7P_3S$ 767.57	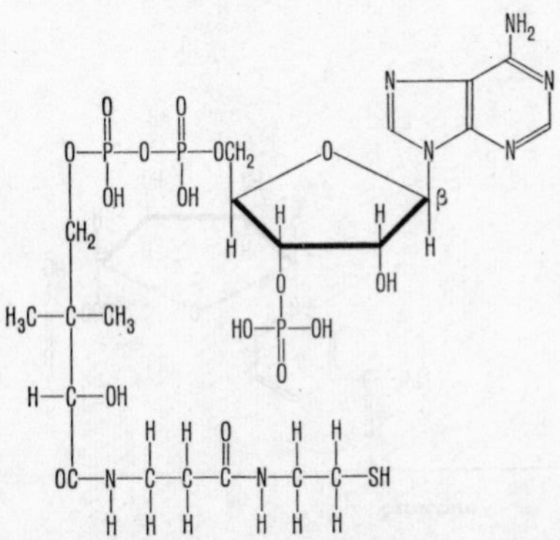	Coenzyme of acyl-group transfer. Formed from pantothenic acid, cysteine and ATP. Acyl groups combine with the sulfhydryl group of CoA to form thiol esters, e.g. $AMP - CO \cdot CH_3 + R \cdot SH \rightarrow AMP + R \cdot S \cdot CO \cdot CH_3$ CoA is involved in the following reactions: formation of citrate from oxaloacetate and acetate (page 402), oxidation of pyruvate (page 403), oxidation of α-ketoglutarate (page 402), oxidation and synthesis of fatty acids (page 403), synthesis of neutral fat (page 431) and phospholipids (page 431), and in the acetylation of amines (page 447), choline (page 437) and glucosamine	3

Acyl adenosine monophosphates	–	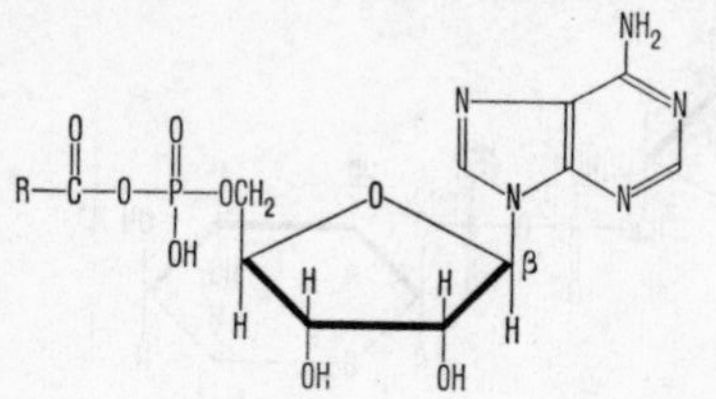 where R = $CH_3 \cdot (CH_2)_n$–	Formed by the reaction: fatty acid + ATP → acyl adenosine monophosphate + pyrophosphate. Intermediate in activation of acetic acid and other fatty acids (page 403)	4
Aminoacyl adenosine monophosphates	–	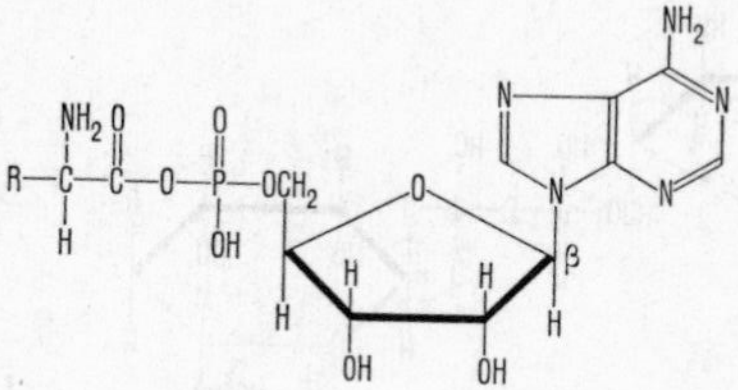 where R = amino-acid residue	Intermediate in activation of amino acids for protein synthesis	5
Adenosine diphosphate aspartic acid	$C_{14}H_{20}O_{11}N_6P_2$ 510.31	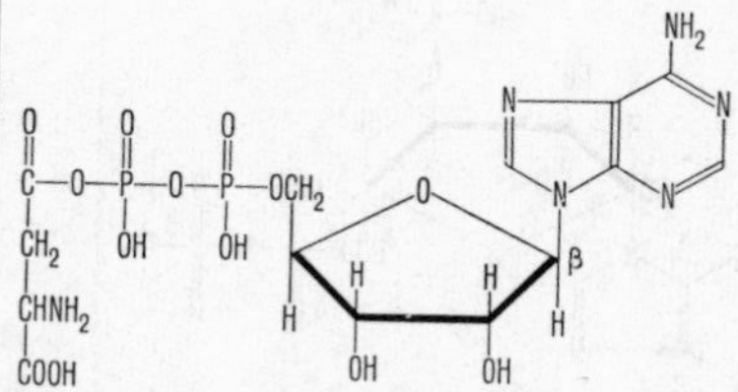	Function unknown. Possibly intermediate in formation of asparagine. The β-carboxyl linkage is not established with certainty	6
Adenosine diphosphate glutamic acid	$C_{15}H_{22}O_{13}N_6P_2$ 556.34	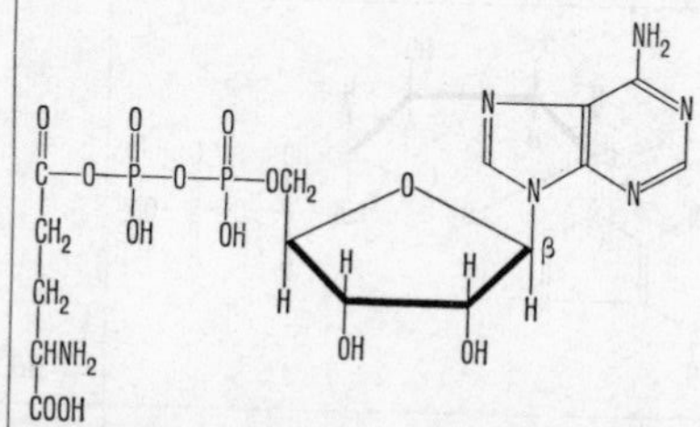	Function unknown. Possibly intermediate in formation of glutamine and γ-glutamyl peptides. The γ-carboxyl linkage is not established with certainty	6

* For references see page 375.

Table 12 Nucleotides with coenzyme functions (*continued*)

Name	Formula and mol.wt.	Structure	Functions	Reference*
Adenosine 5′-phosphosulfate	$C_{10}H_{14}O_{10}N_5PS$ 427.30	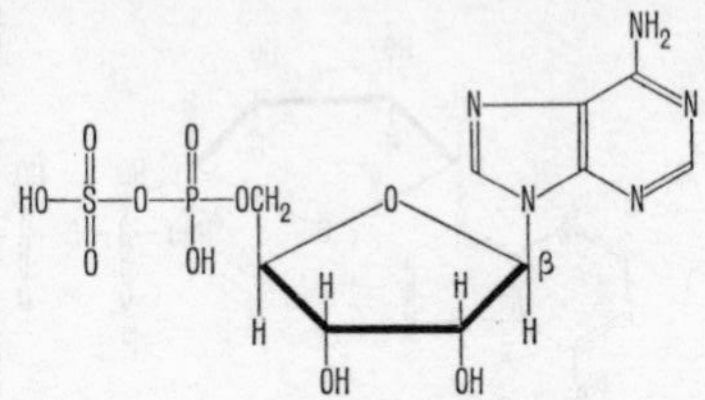	Formed from ATP and inorganic sulfate. Intermediate in sulfate ester synthesis (see page 448)	*7*
Adenosine 3′-phosphate 5′-phosphosulfate	$C_{10}H_{15}O_{13}N_5P_2S$ 507.29	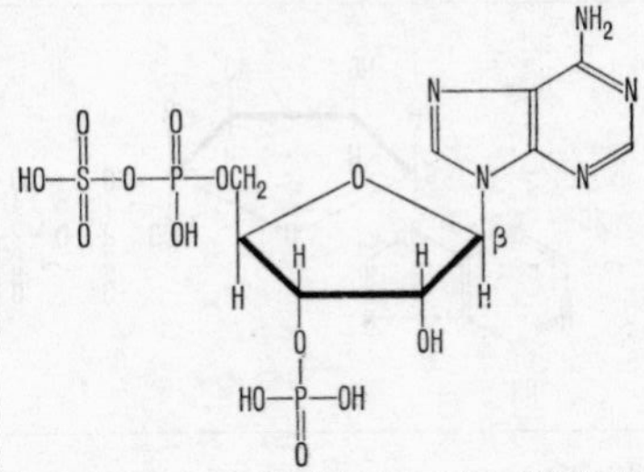	Formed from adenosine 5′-phosphosulfate and ATP. Donor of sulfate group in formation of esters of sulfuric acid (see page 448)	*7*
Guanosine diphosphate mannose	$C_{16}H_{25}O_{15}N_5P_2$ 604.38	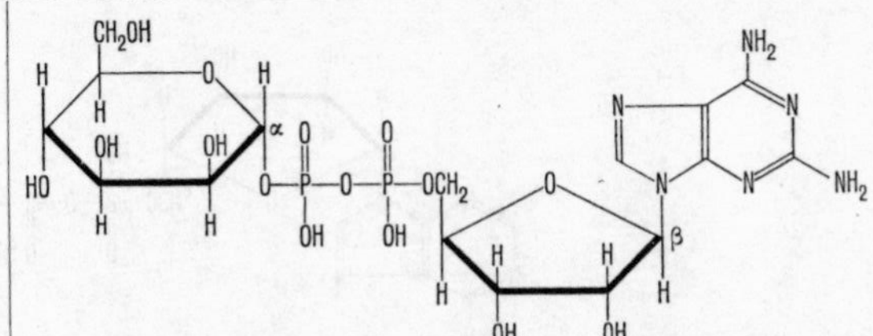	Probably intermediate in interconversions involving mannose. Formed from mannose-1-phosphate and guanosine triphosphate	*8*
Uridine diphosphate glucose	$C_{15}H_{24}O_{17}N_2P_2$ 566.32	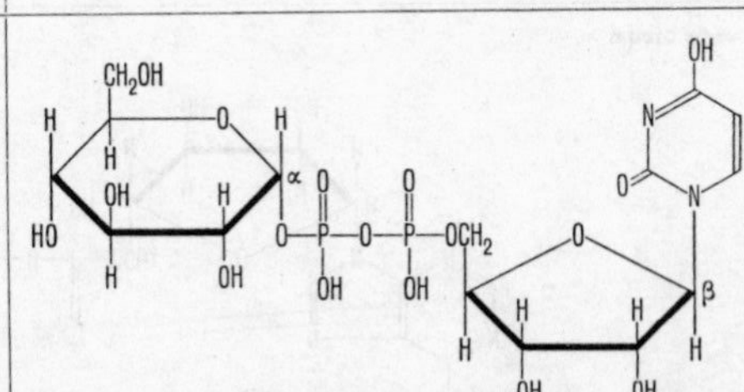	Formed by the reaction: glucose-1-phosphate + UTP → uridine diphosphate glucose + pyrophosphate. Precursor of uridine diphosphate glucuronic acid (see below). Intermediate in interconversion of glucose and galactose: uridine diphosphate glucose $\overset{DPN}{\rightleftharpoons}$ uridine diphosphate galactose. In this reaction DPN is required for the consecutive oxidation and reduction of the 4-position of the hexose ring: 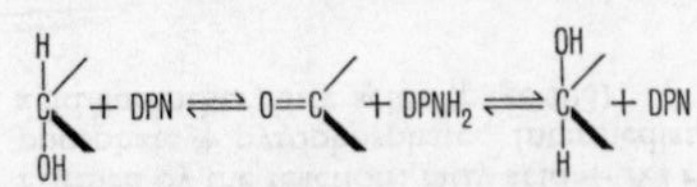	*9*

Uridine diphosphate galactose	$C_{15}H_{24}O_{17}N_2P_2$ 566.32	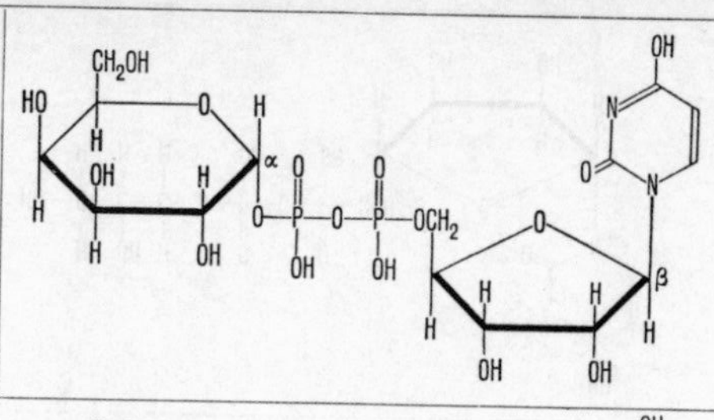	Intermediate in interconversion of galactose and glucose (see above). Probably intermediate in formation of lactose	*9*
Uridine diphosphate glucosamine	$C_{15}H_{25}O_{16}N_3P_2$ 565.34	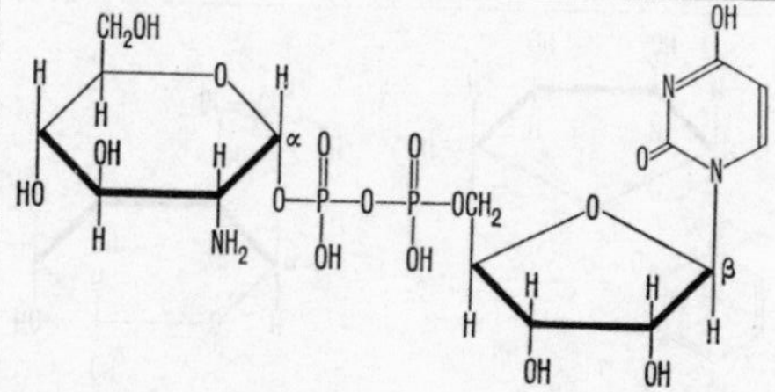	Intermediate in synthesis of mucopolysaccharides. Formed from uridine triphosphate and glucosamine-1-phosphate	*10*
Uridine diphosphate N-acetyl-glucosamine	$C_{17}H_{27}O_{17}N_3P_2$ 607.38	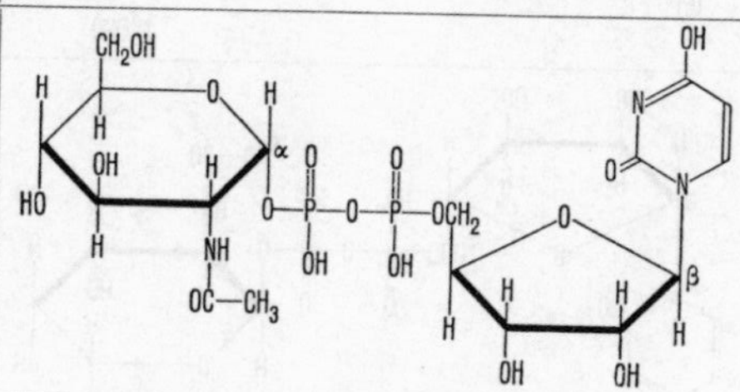	Intermediate in synthesis of mucopolysaccharides and glycoproteins	*11*
Uridine diphosphate acetylglucosamine phosphate	$C_{17}H_{28}O_{20}N_3P_3$ 687.36	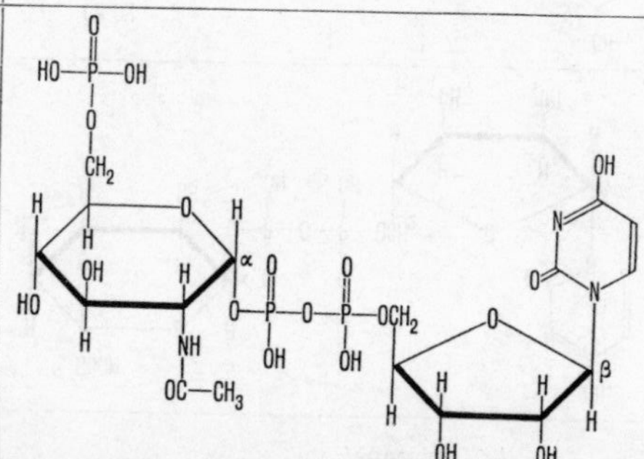	Intermediate in synthesis of mucopolysaccharides and glycoproteins	*12*

* For references see page 375.

Table 12 Nucleotides with coenzyme functions (*concluded*)

Name	Formula and mol.wt.	Structure	Functions	Reference
Uridine diphosphate glucuronic acid	$C_{15}H_{22}O_{18}N_2P_2$ 580.31	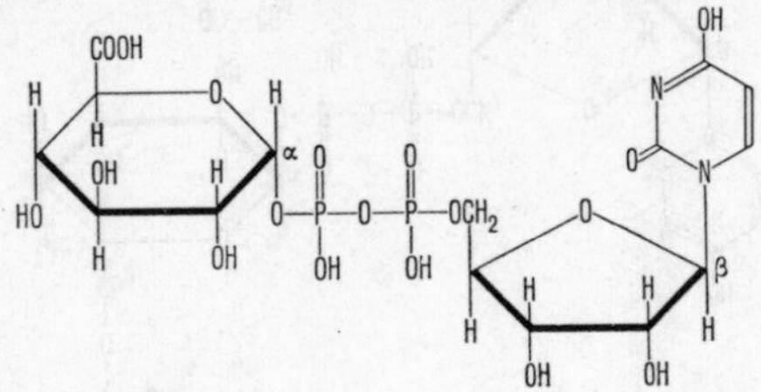	Formed from uridine diphosphate glucose by DPN-dependent oxidation. Donor of glucuronic acid in formation of glucuronoside detoxication products, and probably also in formation of polysaccharides containing glucuronic acid (see also page 431)	*13*
Uridine diphosphate N-acetyl-galactosamine	$C_{17}H_{27}O_{17}N_3P_2$ 607.38	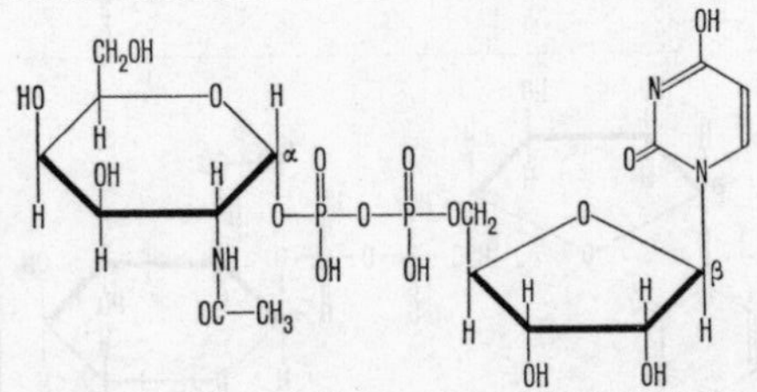	Probably intermediate in synthesis of mucopolysaccharides	*14*
Uridine diphosphate N-acetyl-galactosamine sulfate	$C_{17}H_{27}O_{20}N_3P_2S$ 687.44	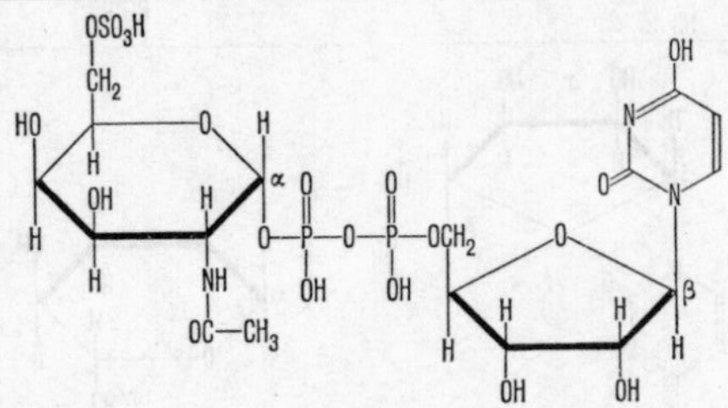	Intermediate in synthesis of mucopolysaccharides	*15*
Cytidine diphosphate glycerol	$C_{12}H_{21}O_{13}N_3P_2$ 477.27	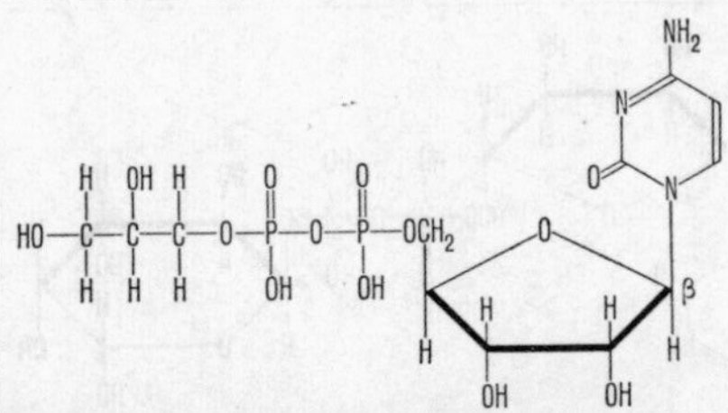	Function unknown	*16*

Cytidine diphosphate ribitol	$C_{14}H_{25}O_{15}N_3P_2$ 537.33	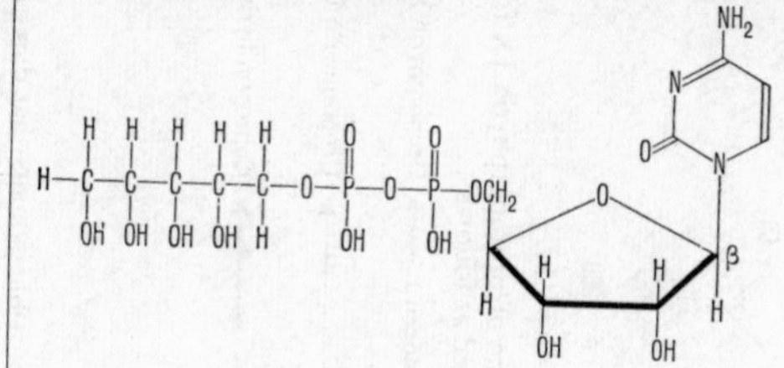	Function unknown	*16*
Cytidine diphosphate choline	$C_{14}H_{26}O_{11}N_4P_2$ 488.34	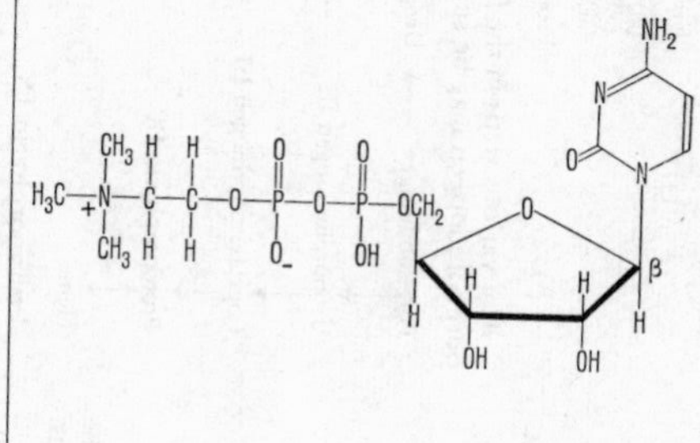	Formed from cytidine triphosphate and phosphorylcholine. Involved in formation of lecithin: cytidine diphosphate choline + α,β-diglyceride → lecithin + cytidine monophosphate (see also page 431)	*17*
Cytidine diphosphate ethanolamine	$C_{11}H_{20}O_{11}N_4P_2$ 446.26	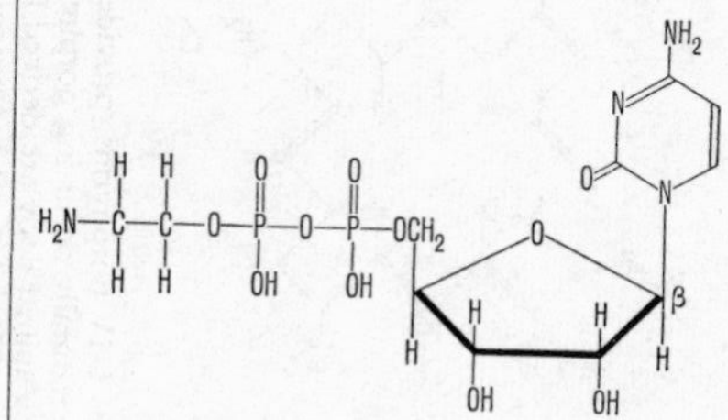	Formed from cytidine triphosphate and phosphorylethanolamine. Involved in formation of cephalin (phosphatidylethanolamine) (see also page 431)	*17*

References

1) Racker, E., *Physiol. Rev.*, **35**, 1 (1955). *2)* White et al., *Principles of Biochemistry*, London, 1954. *3)* Lipmann, F., *Bact. Rev.*, **17**, 1 (1953); Ward et al., *J. biol. Chem.*, **213**, 869 (1955); Hoagland and Novelli, *J. biol. Chem.*, **207**, 767 (1954). *4)* Berg, P., *J. biol. Chem.*, **222**, 991, 1015 (1956). *5)* Hoagland et al., *J. biol. Chem.*, **218**, 345 (1956); Keller and Zamecnik, *J. biol. Chem.*, **221**, 45 (1956); Berg, P., *J. biol. Chem.*, **222**, 1025 (1956). *6)* Hansen and Hageman, *Arch. Biochem. Biophys.*, **62**, 511 (1956). *7)* Robbins and Lipmann, *J. Amer. chem. Soc.*, **78**, 2652, 6409 (1956); Bandurski et al., *J. Amer. chem. Soc.*, **78**, 6408 (1956). *8)* Cabib and Leloir, *J. biol. Chem.*, **206**, 779 (1953); Strominger, J. L., *Fed. Proc.*, **13**, 307 (1954); Munch-Petersen, A., *Arch. Biochem. Biophys.*, **55**, 592 (1955). *9)* Caputto et al., *J. biol. Chem.*, **184**, 333 (1950); Maxwell, E. S., *J. Amer. chem. Soc.*, **78**, 1074 (1956); Park, J. T., *J. biol. Chem.*, **194**, 885 (1952); Gander et al., *Arch. Biochem. Biophys.*, **60**, 259 (1956). *10)* Maley et al., *J. Amer. chem. Soc.*, **78**, 5303 (1956). *11)* Cabib et al., *J. biol. Chem.*, **203**, 1055 (1953). *12)* Strominger, J. L., *Biochim. biophys. Acta*, **17**, 283 (1955). *13)* Storey and Dutton, *Biochem. J.*, **59**, 279 (1955); Smith and Mills, *Biochim. biophys. Acta*, **13**, 386 (1954); Strominger et al., *J. biol. Chem.*, **224**, 79 (1957). *14)* Pontis, H. G., *J. biol. Chem.*, **216**, 195 (1955). *15)* Strominger, J. L., *Biochim. biophys. Acta*, **17**, 283 (1955). *16)* Baddiley et al., *J. chem. Soc. Lond.*, **1956**, 4186, 4583; *Biochem. J.*, **63**, 15 P (1956). *17)* Kennedy, E. P., *J. biol. Chem.*, **222**, 185 (1956); Kennedy and Weiss, *J. biol. Chem.*, **222**, 193 (1956).

4. Porphyrins[1]

Porphyrins are tetrapyrrolic pigments which are sometimes found free in nature but more commonly occur as divalent metal-ion complexes, usually conjugated with proteins. Such proteins often function as enzymes.

The parent compound of the porphyrins is *porphin*, in the molecule of which four pyrrole rings are linked together through their α-carbon atoms by means of methene (=CH–) bridges:

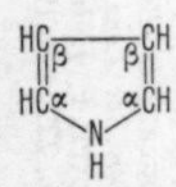

Pyrrole

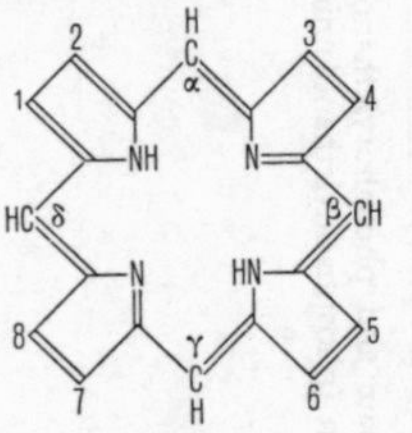

Porphin

The porphyrin molecule thus forms a closed ring of carbon and nitrogen atoms lying in one plane and containing a central sixteen-membered ring of twelve carbon and four nitrogen atoms.

The simplest of the porphyrins is etioporphyrin, which has four methyl and four ethyl groups in positions 1 to 8 of the porphin ring. Depending on the arrangement of the attached groups, four isomeric forms of etioporphyrin are possible[2]:

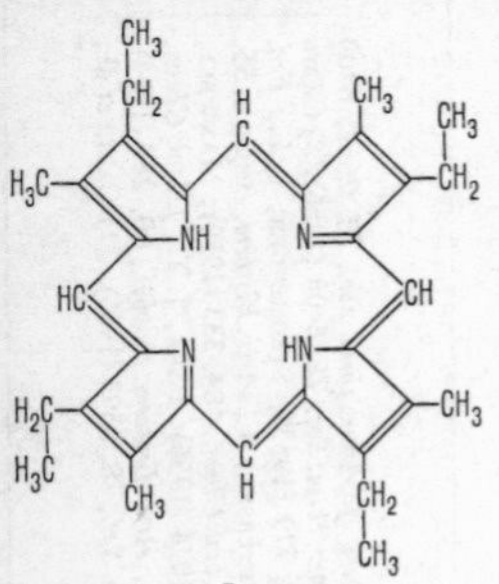

I

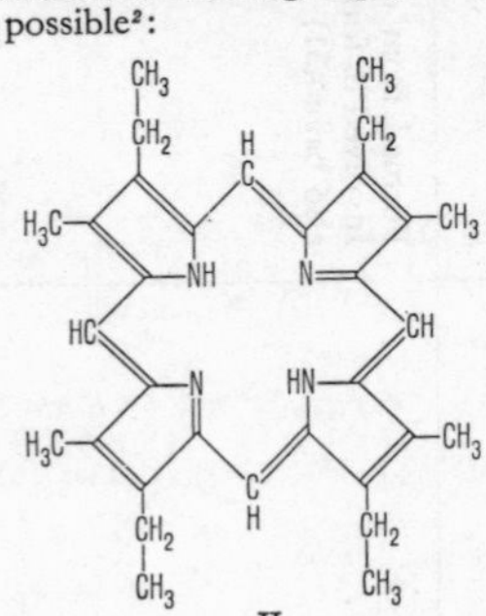

II

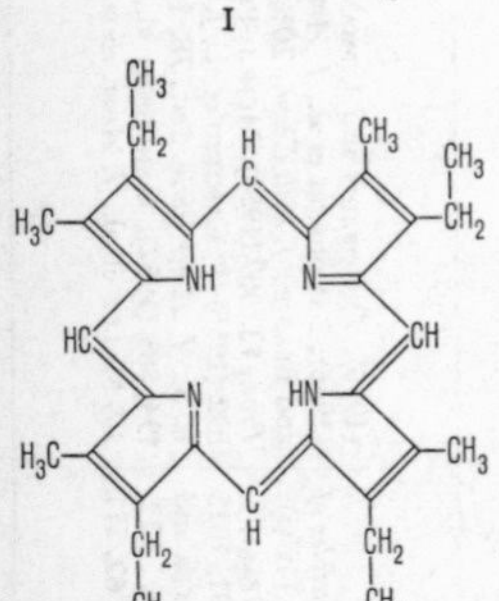

III

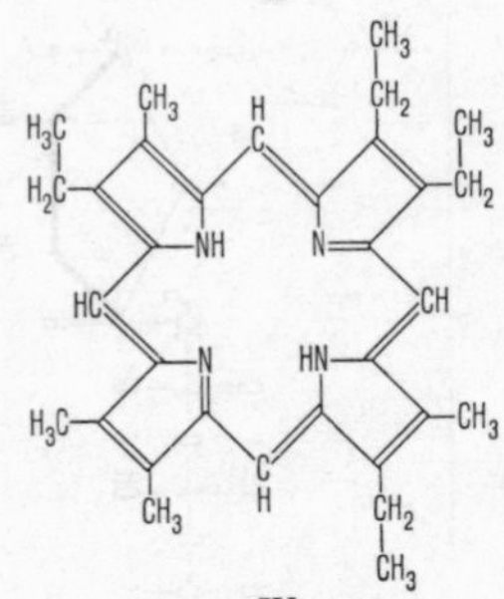

IV

These isomers, known as types I–IV porphyrins, provide the basis for the classification of the naturally occurring porphyrins.

All porphyrins occurring in the animal body are derived from porphobilinogen (see Table 13, page 377) and are related structurally

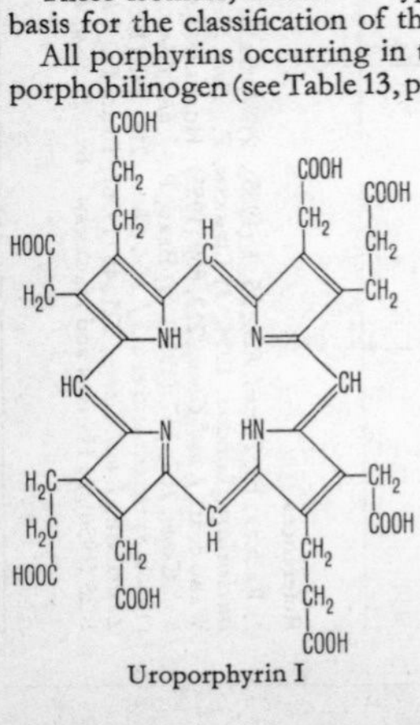

Uroporphyrin I

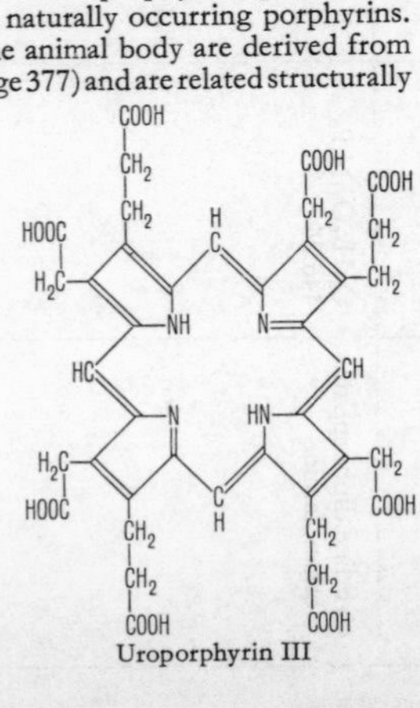

Uroporphyrin III

to *uroporphyrin I* or *uroporphyrin III*, compounds in which the eight β-hydrogen atoms of porphin are replaced by four acetic acid and four propionic acid groups.

Decarboxylation of the four acetic acid groups gives rise to the *coproporphyrins*, which contain four methyl and four propionic acid groups:

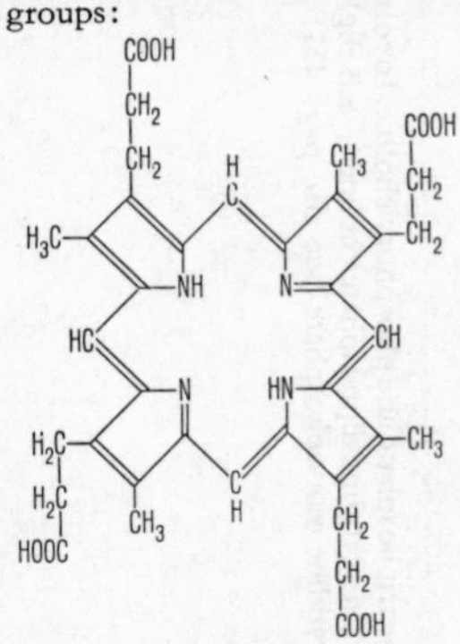

Coproporphyrin I

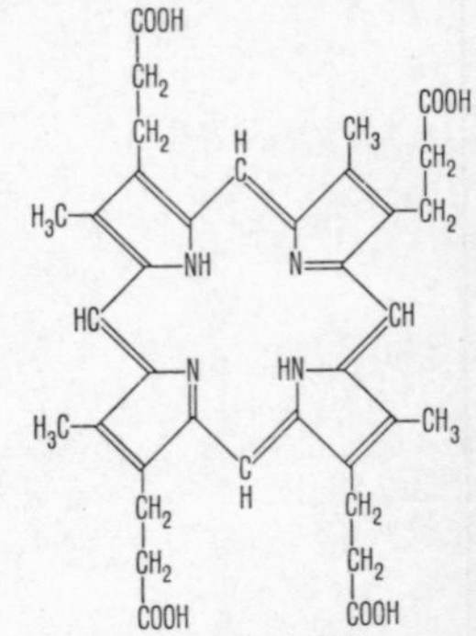

Coproporphyrin III

Decarboxylation and dehydrogenation of two of the propionic acid groups of coproporphyrin III yield *protoporphyrin IX*, which contains four methyl, two vinyl and two propionic acid groups:

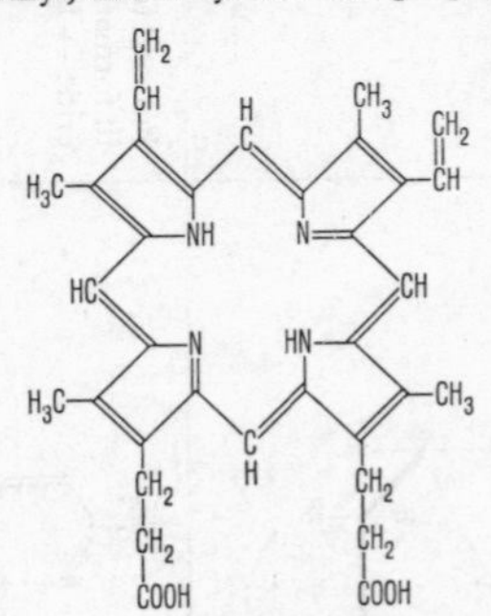

Protoporphyrin IX

The various steps in the formation of protoporphyrin IX from porphobilinogen may be summarized as follows[3]:

Porphobilinogen ⟶ Uroporphyrinogen I ⟶ Uroporphyrin I
↓
Uroporphyrinogen III ⟶ Uroporphyrin III
↓
Coproporphyrinogen III ⟶ Coproporphyrin III
↓
Protoporphyrin IX
↓ $+Fe^{++}$
Heme

Protoporphyrin IX, one of 15 possible isomers that differ only in the arrangement of the eight groups attached to the porphin ring, is the only protoporphyrin so far found in nature. In the form of its iron complex (heme) it constitutes the prosthetic group of hemoglobin and other biologically important proteins (see page 379).

Data on the naturally occurring porphyrins are summarized in Table 13 on pages 377–379. For biosynthesis of porphyrins see page 440.

Porphyrias[4,5]

Porphyrias comprise a small group of diseases associated with a primary abnormality of porphyrin synthesis. In congenital porphyria there is a genetically determined abnormality of the enzymic conversion of porphobilinogen to types I and III porphyrins in the bone marrow. Normally this enzymic conversion results in the formation primarily of type III porphyrins, which are involved in the synthesis of heme proteins, and the very small amounts of type I porphyrins synthesized are readily eliminated. In congenital porphyria the amount of type I porphyrins produced

(continued on page 379)

Table 13 Porphyrins of biological importance

Porphyrin	Structure	Occurrence
Porphobilinogen* $C_{10}H_{14}O_4N_2$	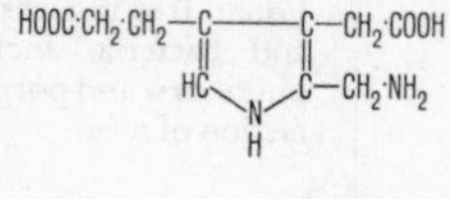	Obligatory precursor for biosynthesis of porphyrins and heme. Present in urine in hepatic porphyria, and in poisoning by lead and monoureide sedatives
Protoporphyrin IX $C_{34}H_{34}O_4N_4$	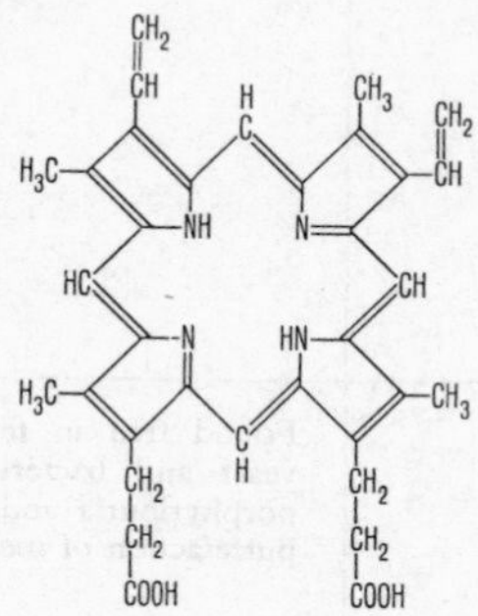	Found in bone marrow, erythrocytes and feces. The iron complexes form the prosthetic groups of hemoglobin, myoglobin, catalase, peroxidase, cytochrome b, cytochrome c and other important proteins. Also formed in the putrefaction of meat
Uroporphyrin I $C_{40}H_{38}O_{16}N_4$	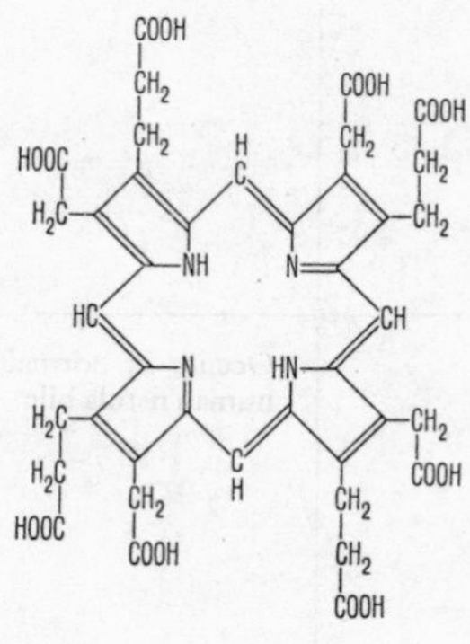	Found in very small amounts in human urine, in larger amounts in some forms of porphyria and lead poisoning
Uroporphyrin III $C_{40}H_{38}O_{16}N_4$	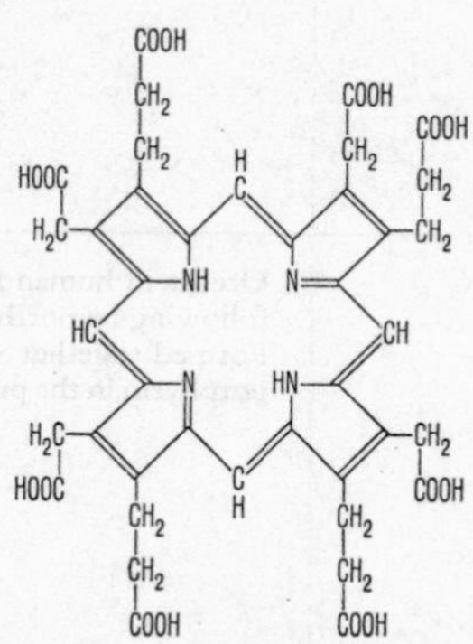	Found in very small amounts in human urine, in larger amounts in some forms of porphyria and lead poisoning

* Not a porphyrin but included on account of its importance in relation to the porphyrins.

Table 13 Porphyrins of biological importance *(continued)*

Porphyrin	Structure	Occurrence
Coproporphyrin I $C_{36}H_{38}O_8N_4$	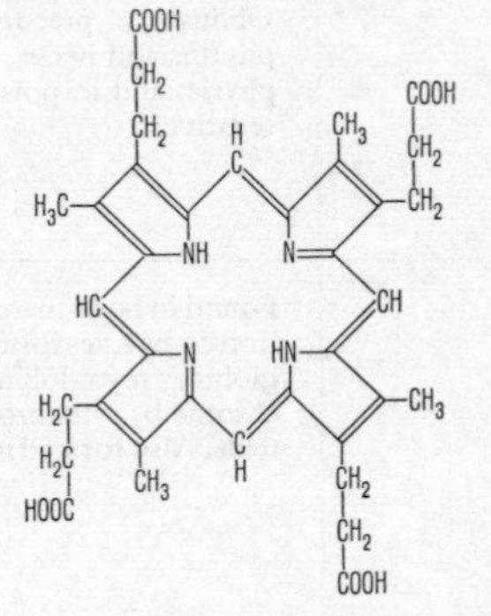	Found free in feces, urine, erythrocytes, bile, yeast and bacteria. Increased pathologically in porphyrinuria and porphyria. Also formed in the putrefaction of meat
Coproporphyrin III $C_{36}H_{38}O_8N_4$	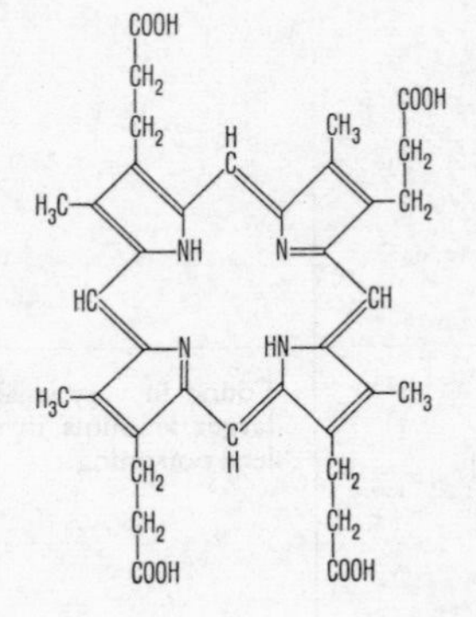	Found free in feces, urine, erythrocytes, bile, yeast and bacteria. Increased pathologically in porphyrinuria and porphyria. Also formed in the putrefaction of meat
Mesoporphyrin $C_{34}H_{38}O_4N_4$	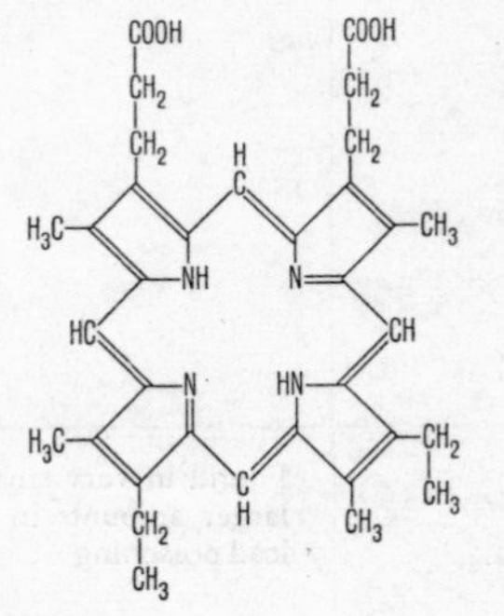	Occurs in normal human feces, possibly also in human fistula bile
Deuteroporphyrin $C_{30}H_{30}O_4N_4$	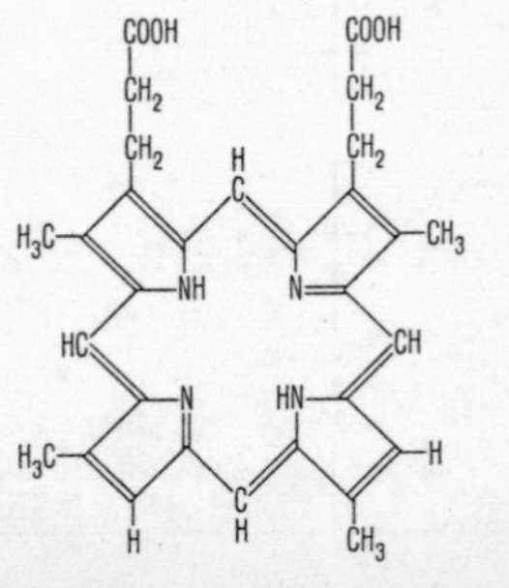	Occurs in human feces after ingestion of blood or following hemorrhages of the gastrointestinal tract. Formed together with protoporphyrin and coproporphyrin in the putrefaction of meat

Table 13 Porphyrins of biological importance *(concluded)*

Porphyrin	Structure	Occurrence
Hematoporphyrin $C_{34}H_{38}O_6N_4$	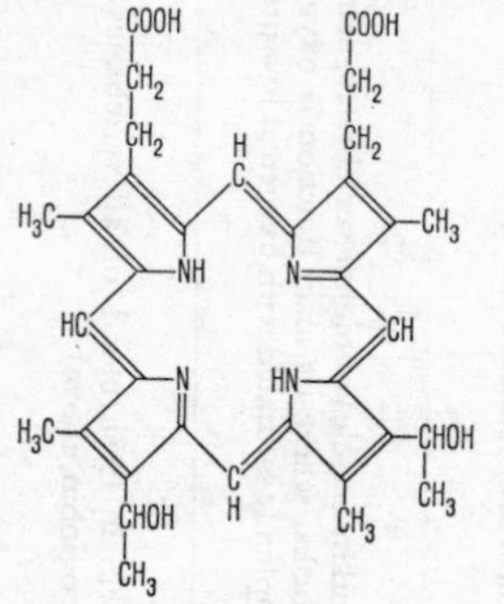	Probably not of biological importance. Natural occurrence not definitely established, but may be present in natural coproporphyrin and deuteroporphyrin fractions

(continued from page 376)

is very great. Type I porphyrins are useless as prosthetic groups and since they are not degraded to bile pigments (see page 382) they are either excreted or deposited in the tissues, causing the extreme sensitivity to light characteristic of the disease.

In acute porphyria, free porphyrins are present only in traces in the body. On the other hand, porphobilinogen is excreted in large quantities. This may be due either to a block in the conversion of porphobilinogen to porphyrins in the liver or to an excessive production of porphobilinogen by the body.

Iron porphyrins (heme derivatives)

The tendency of porphyrins to form complexes with divalent metal ions is one of their most characteristic properties. In the iron–porphyrin complexes, known collectively as *heme derivatives* or *hematin compounds* (see Tables 14 and 15), the two central hydrogen atoms of the porphyrin ring are replaced by an atom of iron, with various molecules or groups occupying the two coordination positions of the latter. The term *heme* itself is used to

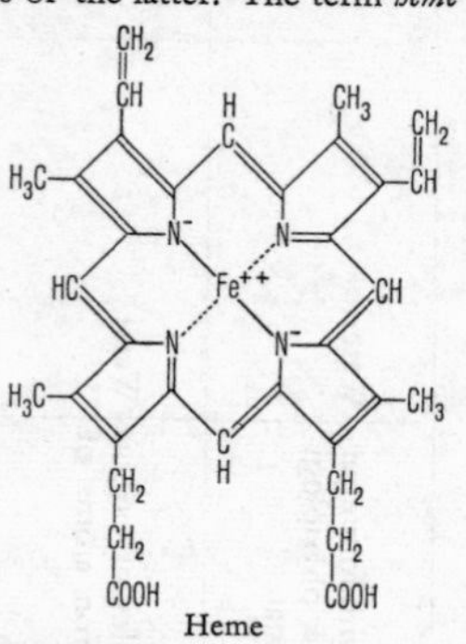

Heme

designate the complex of protoporphyrin IX with ferrous iron (Fe^{++}), where the two coordination positions are occupied by water molecules (not shown in the formula).

Heme (also known as protoheme and ferroheme) and other ferrous complexes of the porphyrins readily react with bases such as primary amines, pyridine, ammonia, imidazole compounds (e.g. histidine) and hydrazine, the resulting products being known as *hemochromes*.

The complex of protoporphyrin with ferric iron (Fe^{+++}) is known as *ferriheme*. It forms a hydroxide, *hematin*, and a chloride, *hemin:*

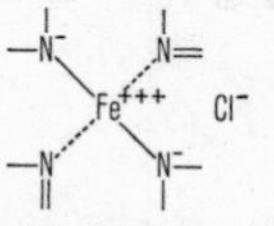

Hemin

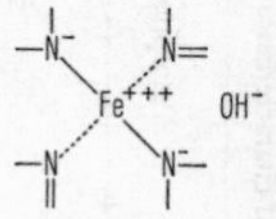

Hematin

Porphyrin complexes as prosthetic groups

Metal-ion complexes of the porphyrins form the prosthetic groups of many proteins and enzymes. For example, hemoglobin and myohemoglobin (myoglobin), which combine reversibly with molecular oxygen, consist of heme and the protein moiety globin. A series of pigments which act as enzymes in cellular metabolism (oxidases, catalase, peroxidases and cytochromes) also belong to this class of compound. In the case of catalase, the prosthetic group is the same as that of hemoglobin but the specific protein and its mode of linkage to heme are different.

The ferrous iron of the ferroheme proteins may be oxidized to the ferric state (in the combination of hemoglobin, etc. with molecular oxygen it remains in the ferrous state), the product in the case of hemoglobin being known as hemiglobin (methemoglobin). This oxidation is reversible. In the further biological oxidation of heme proteins, the porphin ring becomes disrupted

(continued on page 382)

Table 14 Nomenclature of iron porphyrins

Valency of iron atom	Coordination position occupied by (a)	(b)	Authors: Lemberg and Legge[1]	Pauling[6], Barron[7]	Anson[8], Keilin[9]
2	H_2O	H_2O	heme*	ferroheme	haem
3	OH	H_2O	hematin**	ferriheme hydroxide	haematin
3	Cl	—	hemin	ferriheme chloride	haemin
2	N-compound	N-compound	hemochrome	ferro-hemochromogen	haemochromogen
3	N-compound	N-compound	hemichrome	ferri-hemochromogen	parahaematin
2	globin	H_2O	hemoglobin	hemoglobin	haemoglobin
2	globin	O_2	oxyhemoglobin	oxyhemoglobin	oxyhaemoglobin
3	globin	H_2O	hemiglobin	ferrihemoglobin	acid methaemoglobin
3	globin	OH	hemiglobin hydroxide	ferrihemoglobin hydroxide	alkaline methaemoglobin
2	globin	CO	carboxyhemoglobin	carbon monoxy hemoglobin	

* Also referred to by some authors as ferroprotoporphyrin. ** Also referred to by some authors as ferriprotoporphyrin hydroxide.

Table 15 Iron porphyrins and heme proteins of biological importance

Substance	General nature	Spectral characteristics: Solvent	Spectral characteristics: Absorption maxima in mμ	Remarks
Heme $C_{34}H_{32}O_4N_4Fe$	Ferrous iron complex of protoporphyrin IX. Extremely unstable. Easily oxidized to hematin (see page 379)	Phosphate buffer pH 7.0	575 550 415	Prosthetic group of hemoglobin. Combines with many nitrogenous bases to form hemochromes
Hematin $C_{34}H_{35}O_7N_4Fe$	Ferric iron complex of protoporphyrin IX. Moderately stable (see page 379)	Acetic acid 10% NaOH Ether	630–635 540 510 400 580 650	Formed from hemoglobin in blood under many different conditions. The pigment of the malarial parasite *Plasmodium* has been shown to consist of hematin[10]
Hemoglobin	Four heme molecules combined with globin. Iron is in the ferrous state and readily oxidized	Water	560 430	Oxygen carrier in erythrocytes of all vertebrates. Combines reversibly with oxygen to form oxyhemoglobin, and with carbon monoxide to form carboxyhemoglobin (affinity for carbon monoxide over 100 times that for oxygen). Over 20 human hemoglobins differing in amino-acid composition and physicochemical properties are known[11]
Myohemoglobin (myoglobin)	As for hemoglobin	Water	555 435	Found in muscles of higher vertebrates, nematodes and mollusks, where its main function is oxygen storage. Completely saturated with oxygen at low pressures
Oxyhemoglobin	Compound of hemoglobin with four equivalents of oxygen available physiologically. Iron is in the ferrous state	Water	577 540 412	Present in fresh blood of all vertebrates (cf. under Hemoglobin, above)
Carboxyhemoglobin	Compound of four molecules of carbon monoxide with the four iron atoms of hemoglobin	Water	568–572 538 418	Rapidly formed in the body during exposure to carbon monoxide, resulting in failure of oxygen transport by hemoglobin (cf. under Hemoglobin, above)
Hemiglobin (methemoglobin)	Similar to hemoglobin except that iron is in the ferric state	Acid solution Alkaline solution	630 500 405 577 540 411	Formed reversibly from hemoglobin by oxidation (ferricyanide, nitrites, chlorates, etc.). Occurs in erythrocytes in larger amounts in some pathological conditions[12, 13]

Choleglobin (verdoglobin A, verdohemoglobin)	Native globin combined with a prosthetic group. Composition of this group not clarified, but formed by coupled oxidation of hemoglobin	Water	670 630	Normal hemoglobin degradation product and intermediary in bile pigment formation
Sulfhemoglobin (verdoglobin S)	Chemical structure not known	Water	620	Formed irreversibly from hemoglobin by action of hydrogen sulfide. Present in erythrocytes after ingestion of sulfur, sulfonamides, aromatic amines, occasionally trinitrotoluene; also in septicemia (especially *Clostridium perfringens* bacteremia) and severe constipation
Catalase	Prosthetic group same as in hemoglobin	Water	629 544 506 409 280	Decomposes hydrogen peroxide. Present in respiring cells; highly active in liver, erythrocytes, etc. Catalytic activity inhibited by cyanide, hydrogen sulfide, hydroxylamine, azides, aminophenols and 2,4-dichlorophenol
Cytochromes a, a_3, a_1, a_2	Nature of prosthetic group uncertain	Water	Reduced a_3 + a 605 445 Reduced a_1 590 434 Reduced a_2 635	Cytochrome a_3, and probably also a_1 and a_2, react with oxygen (oxidases) while cytochrome a is probably only an electron carrier; a_3 and a occur together in many animals, plants and some bacteria, a_1 and a_2 in other bacteria
Cytochromes c, c_1	Prosthetic group is related to protoporphyrin and is combined with cysteine groups of the protein by firm sulfur linkages	Water	Ferrocytochrome c 550 522 415 345 316 Ferricytochrome c 565 530 407 346	Occur in all animal and plant cells and in most microorganisms, and are specific electron carriers reacting with cytochrome a
Cytochromes b	Prosthetic group is heme (that of cytochrome b_2 is heme plus flavin)	Water	Reduced band in region 565–555 SORET band about 430	Essential electron carriers between flavoproteins and cytochrome c in the respiratory chain. Occur in living cells of all animals, plants and microorganisms except strict anaerobes
Peroxidases	Prosthetic groups: (1) horse-radish and cytochrome c peroxidases: hemin (2) lactic peroxidase: hemin analogue (3) myeloperoxidase: group similar to choleglobin	Weak acid Dithionite solution	(Horse-radish peroxidase) 645 583 548 498 558 594	Occur in plants and animals. Biological functions not well known

at one of the methene bridges with the formation of the compounds known from their appearance in the bile as bile pigments (see below). The oxidation of hemoglobin may give rise intermediately to choleglobin, in which a bile pigment and iron are linked to globin (see below and Table 15, page 381).

Three types of physiologically active heme proteins, depending on the valence state of the iron, can be visualized:

1. Fe remains divalent:	hemoglobin, myohemoglobin
2. Fe is reversibly oxidized and reduced:	cytochromes
3. Fe remains trivalent:	catalase and peroxidases

In all three types a similar iron porphyrin nucleus is involved as the prosthetic group and the essential biochemical reactions in which these conjugated proteins function center about the iron atom.

Nevertheless, the biological effect exerted by each type of heme protein is different. The distinctive nature of each reaction must be ascribed to the specific structure of the protein and to the mode of attachment of the protein to the prosthetic group. Physical and chemical data on biologically important heme proteins are summarized in Table 15 on pages 381 and 382.

Bile pigments[1, 14]

The metabolic breakdown of the hemoglobin released on the disintegration of erythrocytes results in the formation of bile pigments. The breakdown occurs by the oxidative cleavage of the porphyrin ring with the loss of a carbon atom to form open-chain tetrapyrroles. Bile pigments are generally represented as linear tetrapyrrolic chains with terminal hydroxyl groups:

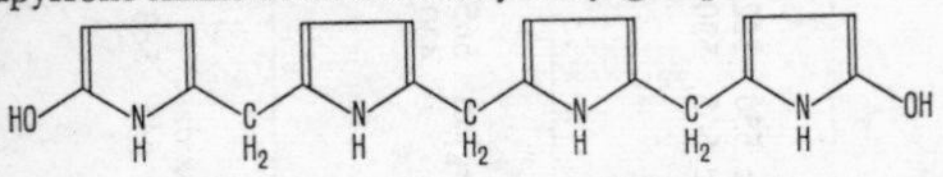

(*a*) Linear tetrapyrrolic structure of bile pigments

but their structure is more correctly represented by a tetrapyrrolic 'ring', closed by a hydrogen bond between oxygen atoms:

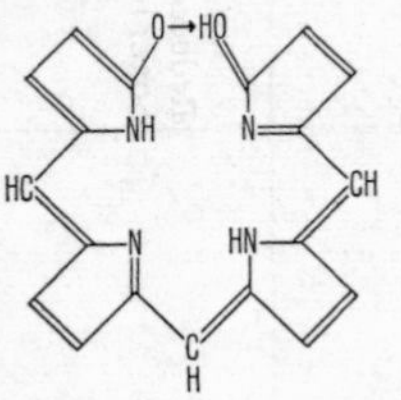

(*b*) 'Ring' structure of bile pigments

All naturally occurring bile pigments are derived from protoporphyrin IX by fission at the α-methene link. The possibility exists that the oxidative cleavage of the porphyrin ring occurs before the protoporphyrin is released from the globin, in which case choleglobin results[15]. The iron released by the catabolism of hemoglobin is largely retained in the body in the form of the protein ferritin, while the bile pigments are excreted. Current views about the formation in the organism of the various bile pigments (see also Table 16, pages 383 and 384) can be summarized as follows[16]:

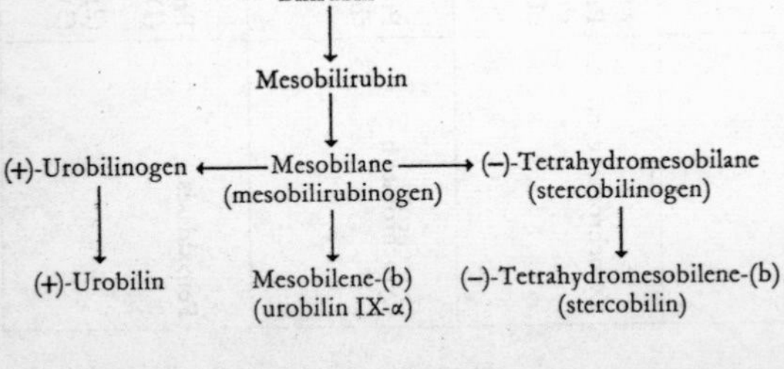

The principal sites of conversion of the heme portion of hemoglobin to bilirubin and mesobilane are believed to be the reticuloendothelial cells of the liver, spleen and bone marrow. The further degradation takes place mainly in the intestine.

The first bile pigment formed in the catabolism of hemoglobin is biliverdin. However, this compound is not found in normal human blood since the liver contains an enzyme which catalyzes its reduction to the pigment bilirubin, which is then excreted from the liver into the bile. Normal blood serum contains only traces of bilirubin (up to 1.1 mg/100 ml) but in the conditions known as jaundice it accumulates instead of being excreted in the bile, resulting in yellow pigmentation of the skin and mucous membranes.

Van den Bergh and Muller[17] were the first to observe that there is a difference between serum bilirubin and the bilirubin-like pigments excreted in bile in respect of their coupling with diazotized sulfanilic acid, the latter pigments reacting directly whereas serum bilirubin requires the presence of ethanol (direct and indirect Van den Bergh reactions respectively). Recently it has been shown[18,19] that bilirubin undergoes conjugation in the liver cells with glucuronic acid (and possibly other substances) and is excreted into the bile mainly as the diglucuronide and to a smaller extent as the monoglucuronide. This conjugated bilirubin is water-soluble, whereas bilirubin itself is soluble in lipids but insoluble in water. This difference in solubility explains not only the difference in the Van den Bergh reaction but also that in the physiological behavior of the two types of pigment. Thus it accounts for the fact that bile pigments are excreted in the urine in obstructive jaundice and hepatitis but not in hemolytic jaundice (see below). Since lipids have an affinity for brain tissue, it also explains why a great excess of bilirubin in the blood results in kernicterus.

Jaundice

Jaundice may broadly be classified into the hemolytic, obstructive and hepatogenous varieties. In hemolytic jaundice the excessive rate of breakdown of erythrocyte hemoglobin causes bilirubin to pass into the blood stream at a rate greater than that at which it can be conjugated and removed by the liver. Obstructive jaundice occurs when there is obstruction to the outflow of bile from the liver through the biliary ducts. In hepatogenous jaundice destruction of the normal architecture of the liver causes bile pigment to enter the blood stream. In both the latter cases the water-soluble bile pigment is excreted in the urine. For a more detailed discussion of jaundice see under Synopsis of Blood, page 559.

Bilirubinoids

The various intermediates (bilirubinoids) in the conversion of bilirubin to stercobilin by the reductive enzymes of the intestinal bacteria may be partly reabsorbed in the intestinal tract and either returned to the liver or excreted in the urine. Data on the most important of these compounds are summarized in Table 16, pages 383 and 384.

Chlorophylls

Other metallo-porphyrins which occur in nature include the magnesium porphyrin compounds which are components of the chlorophyll of green plants. The latter has been shown to consist mainly of a mixture of chlorophyll a and chlorophyll b, both of which contain a porphyrin esterified with the long-chain optically-active fatty alcohol phytol and magnesium. The porphyrins are characterized by the presence of an additional isocyclic ring.

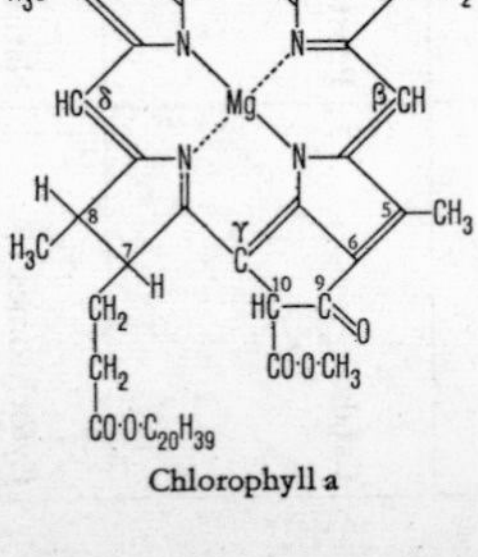

Chlorophyll a

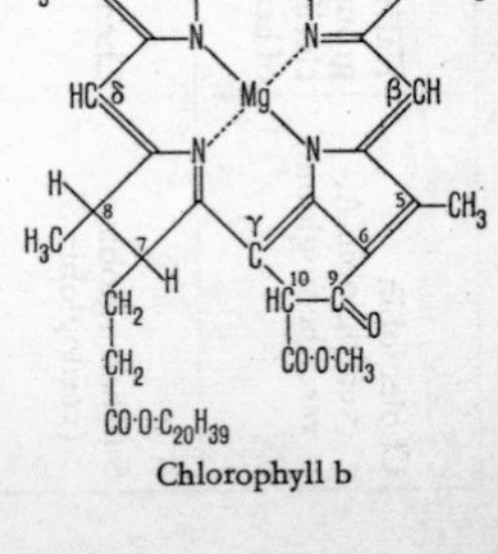

Chlorophyll b

Phytol is also a component of vitamin K_1 (see page 453). Spectral data have indicated the existence of two further chlorophylls, c and d. In leaf tissue, chlorophylls exist in the form of a protein complex, chloroplastin, which has been isolated[20].

The photosynthetic purple sulfur bacteria contain the pigment bacteriochlorophyll. This has been shown to differ from chlorophyll a only in the presence of an acetyl group in place of the vinyl group in position 2 and in the hydrogenation of the 3,4 double bond.

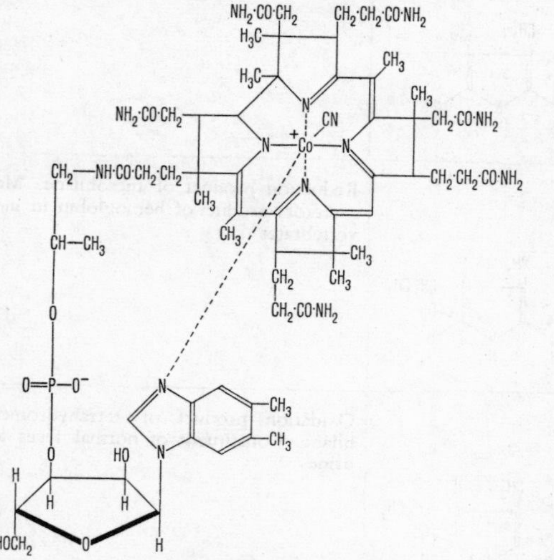

Cyanocobalamin (probable structure)

Cyanocobalamin (vitamin B_{12})

Cyanocobalamin, the cobalt-containing principle of liver extracts used in the treatment of pernicious anemia (see page 466) is a highly-substituted and partially-hydrogenated tetrapyrrole linked to the nucleotide 5,6-dimethyl-1-(α-ribofuranosyl)benzimidazole 3′-phosphate. The six coordinate valencies of the cobalt atom are satisfied by the four nitrogen atoms of the tetrapyrrole, a nitrogen atom of the nucleotide, and a cyanide ion[21–24].

References

1) For reviews see LEMBERG and LEGGE, *Hematin Compounds and Bile Pigments*, New York, 1949; WYMAN, J., *Advanc. Protein Chem.*, **4**, 407 (1948); THEORELL, H., *Advanc. Enzymol.*, **7**, 265 (1947); GRANICK and GILDER, *Advanc. Enzymol.*, **7**, 305 (1947). *2)* FISCHER and ORTH, *Chemie des Pyrrols*, vol. I/2, Leipzig, 1937, page 176. *3)* RIMINGTON, C., *Brit. med. Bull.*, **15**, 19 (1959). *4)* GOLDBERG, A., *Biochem. Soc. Symposia*, **12**, 27 (1954). *5)* GRAY, C. H., in THOMPSON and KING (Eds.), *Biochemical Disorders in Human Disease*, London, 1957, page 658. *6)* PAULING and CORYELL, *Proc. nat. Acad. Sci. (Wash.)*, **22**, 159 (1936). *7)* BARRON, E. S. G., *J. biol. Chem.*, **121**, 285 (1937). *8)* ANSON, M. L., *J. gen. Physiol.*, **23**, 239 (1939). *9)* KEILIN, D., *Proc. roy. Soc. B*, **100**, 129 (1926). *10)* RIMINGTON et al., *Biochem. J.*, **41**, 619 (1947). *11)* Annotations, *Brit. med. J.*, **1**, 1113, 1170, 1469 (1958). *12)* GIBSON and HARRISON, *Lancet*, **2**, 941 (1947). *13)* GIBSON, Q. H., *Biochem. J.*, **42**, 13 (1948). *14)* GRAY, C. H., *The Bile Pigments*, London, 1953. *15)* LEMBERG et al., *Biochem. J.*, **33**, 754 (1939). *16)* WATSON et al., *Proc. Soc. exp. Biol. (N. Y.)*, **49**, 647 (1942). *17)* HIJMANS VAN DEN BERGH and MULLER, *Biochem. Z.*, **77**, 90 (1916). *18)* BILLING et al., *Biochem. J.*, **65**, 774 (1957). *19)* SCHMIDT, R., *Helv. med. Acta*, **24**, 273 (1957); SCHMIDT et al., *Arch. Biochem.*, **70**, 285 (1957); TALAFANT, E., *Nature*, **178**, 312 (1956). *20)* STOLL and WIEDEMANN, *Fortschr. Chem. org. Naturstoffe*, **1**, 159 (1938); STOLL and WIEDEMANN, *Schweiz. med. Wschr.*, **77**, 664 (1947). *21)* ARMITAGE et al., *J. chem. Soc.*, **4**, 3849 (1953). *22)* BONNETT et al., *J. chem. Soc.*, **1**, 1158 (1957). *23)* BONNETT et al., *J. chem. Soc.*, **1**, 1168 (1957). *24)* HODGKIN et al., *Nature*, **176**, 325 (1955); **178**, 64 (1956). *25)* SCHWARTZ and WATSON, *Proc. Soc. exp. Biol. (N.Y.)*, **49**, 641 (1942); SCHWARTZ et al., *Proc. Soc. exp. Biol. (N. Y.)*, **49**, 643 (1942).

Table 16 Bilirubinoids and related compounds

Substance	Structure	Remarks
Bilirubin $C_{33}H_{36}O_6N_4$	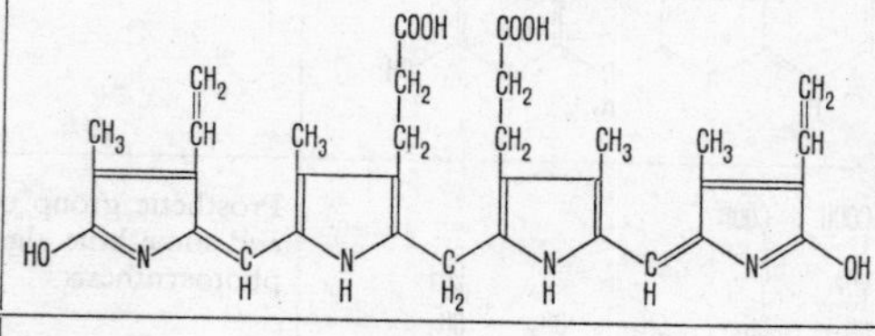	Breakdown product of hemoglobin and other heme compounds in reticuloendothelial system. Present in excess in serum and tissues in hemolytic jaundice. Also found in urine and feces of infants. Conjugated in liver cells with glucuronic acid to form bile pigment
Biliverdin $C_{33}H_{34}O_6N_4$	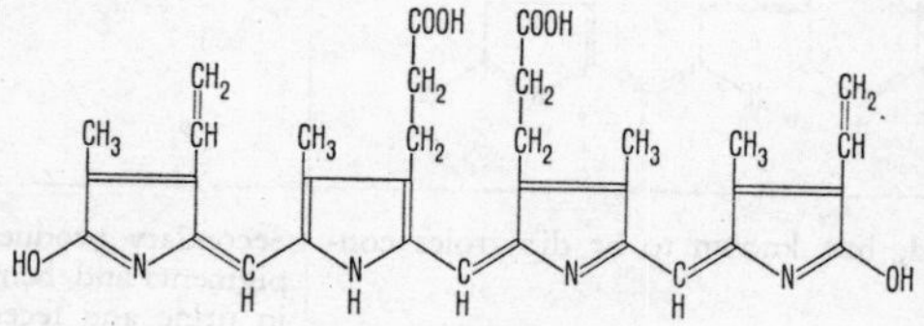	Breakdown product of hemoglobin, reduced enzymatically in liver to bilirubin. Not found in blood, but present in bile of some animals, in placenta of some mammals (uteroverdin) and in egg shells of many birds (oocyan). Also found in meconium of fetus and newborn and in bile after death. An iron complex may be the prosthetic group of inactive liver catalase
Mesobilirubin $C_{33}H_{40}O_6N_4$	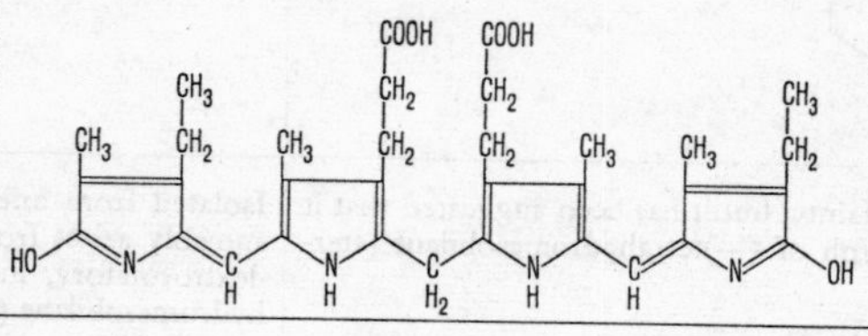	May be present in the small intestine as reduction product of bilirubin
Mesobilane (mesobilirubinogen, urobilinogen IX-α) $C_{33}H_{44}O_6N_4$	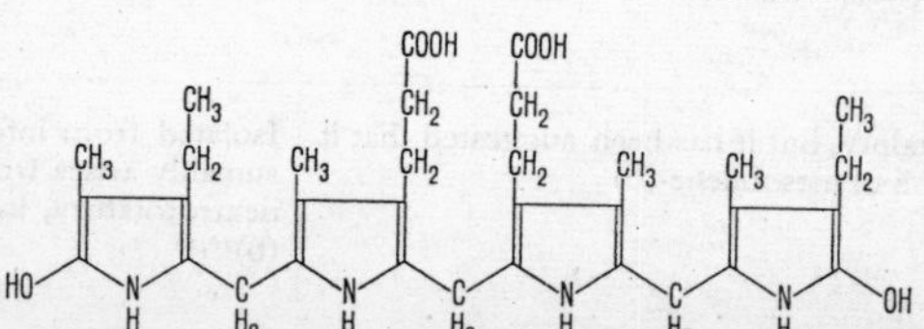	Degradation product of bilirubin in liver. Present in normal bile, urine and feces; increased in pathological conditions

Table 16 Bilirubinoids and related compounds *(continued)*

Substance	Structure	Remarks (for references see page 383)
Mesobilene-(b) (urobilin IX-α) $C_{33}H_{42}O_6N_4$	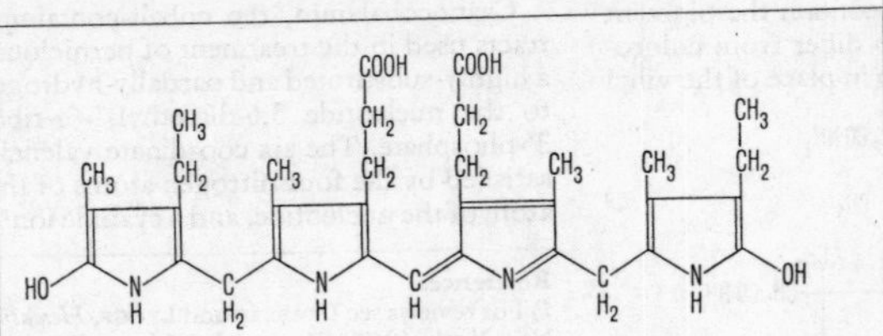	Oxidation product of mesobilane. Present in normal urine and feces
(−)-Tetrahydro-mesobilane (stercobilinogen) $C_{33}H_{48}O_6N_4$	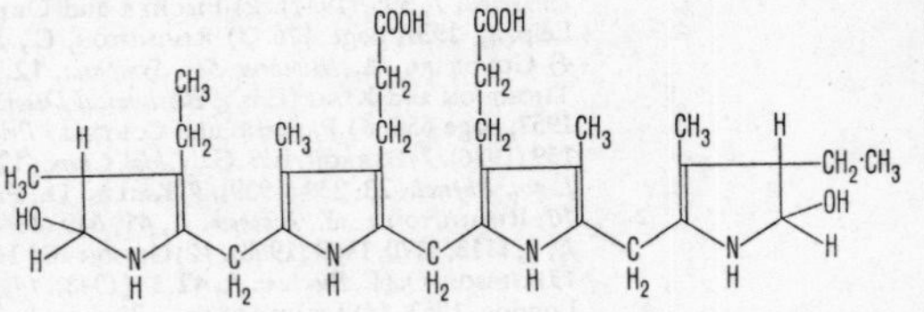	Reduction product of mesobilane. Main excretory product of hemoglobin in most vertebrates
(−)-Tetrahydro-mesobilene-(b) (stercobilin) $C_{33}H_{46}O_6N_4$	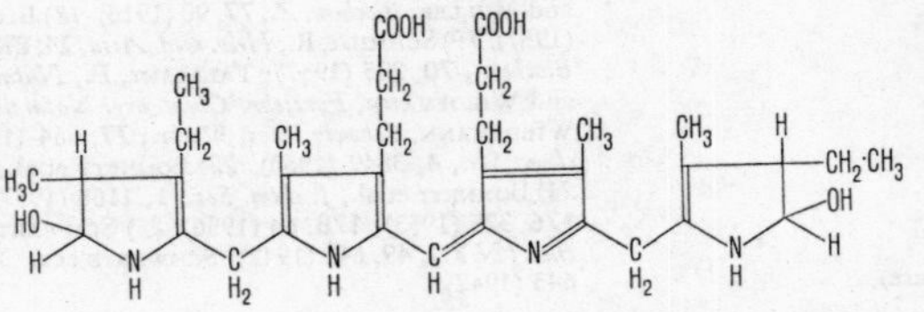	Oxidation product of tetrahydromesobilane. Constituent of normal feces and urine
Mesobiliviolin $C_{33}H_{40}O_6N_4$	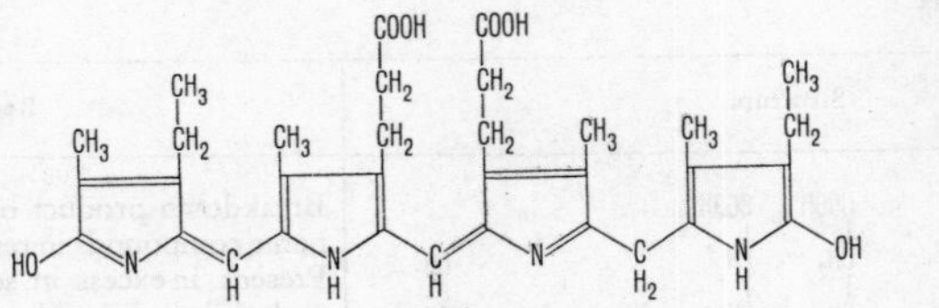	Found in human feces, probably derived from mesobilane. Forms prosthetic group of phycocyanins (chromoproteins of red and blue algae) which act as efficient photosensitizers in algal photosynthesis
Mesobilierythrin (mesobilirhodin) $C_{33}H_{40}O_6N_4$	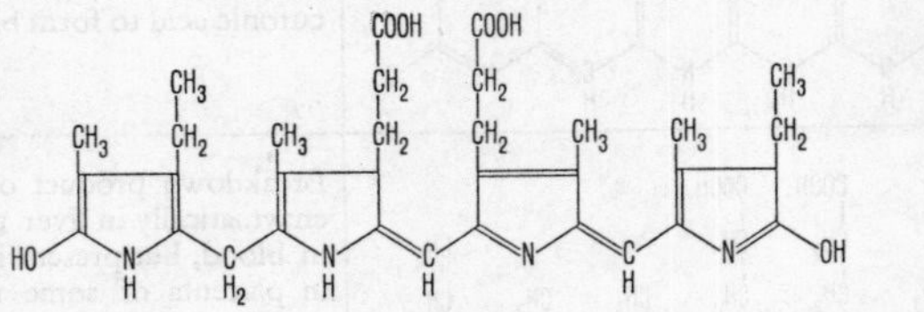	Prosthetic group of phycoerythrin of red and some blue algae. A sensitizer in algae photosynthesis
Probilifuscins Bilifuscins Propentdyopents $C_{16}H_{18-20}O_{4-5}N_2$	Not definitely established, but known to be dipyrroles containing the skeleton: 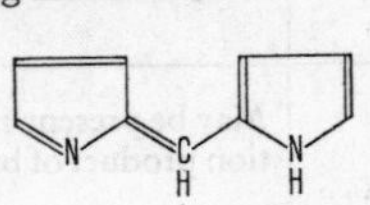	Secondary products of oxidation of bile pigments and heme compounds, excreted in urine and feces in jaundice and liver disease; present in gallstones
(+)-Urobilin $C_{33}H_{40}O_6N_4$	Not established with certainty, but it has been suggested that it is an optical enantiomorph of (−)tetrahydromesobilane (stercobilinogen)	Isolated from infected bile, where it presumably arises from mesobilane. Strongly dextrorotatory, in contrast to (−)-tetrahydromesobilane (stercobilinogen)[16,25]
(+)-Urobilinogen $C_{33}H_{42}O_6N_4$	Not established with certainty, but it has been suggested that it is an optical enantiomorph of mesobilene-(b)	Isolated from infected bile, where it presumably arises from mesobilane. Strongly dextrorotatory, in contrast to mesobilene-(b)[16,25]

5. Lipids[1]

Lipids (or lipoids) is the general term for a group of natural products of which fatty acids (see below) are essential components. In general they are saponifiable esters of fatty acids which are insoluble in water but soluble in the so-called fat solvents (ether, petroleum ether, acetone, hot alcohol, etc.) and utilizable by the animal organism, but this is not a rigorous definition. Saponification (alkaline hydrolysis) converts them into water-soluble substances. A classification of the saponifiable lipids, together with a summary of their structural components, is given in Table 17 below.

Table 17 Classification and structural components of saponifiable lipids

Classification of lipids*		Structural components (other than fatty acids)**		
		Alcohol	Nitrogenous base	Other
Triglycerides	(i) Fats	Glycerol	—	—
	(ii) Oils	Glycerol	—	(higher proportion of unsaturated fatty acids than in fats)
Glycerophosphatides	(i) Phosphatidic acids	Glycerol	—	Phosphoric acid
	(ii) Phosphatidyl esters (a) Phosphatidylcholines	Glycerol	Choline	Phosphoric acid
	(ii) Phosphatidyl esters (b) Phosphatidylethanolamines	Glycerol	Ethanolamine	Phosphoric acid
	(ii) Phosphatidyl esters (c) Phosphatidylserines	Glycerol	Serine	Phosphoric acid
	(iii) Lysophosphatides	Glycerol	Choline, Ethanolamine, Serine	Phosphoric acid
	(iv) Inositol phosphatides: mono-	Glycerol	—	Phosphoric acid, inositol
	(iv) Inositol phosphatides: di-	Glycerol	—	Phosphoric acid, inositol
	(v) Acetal phosphatides	Glycerol	(As for lysophosphatides)	Phosphoric acid, unknown long-chain alkyl group
Sphingolipids	(i) Sphingomyelins	Sphingosine	Choline	Phosphoric acid
	(ii) Cerebrosides	Sphingosine	—	Hexose, sulfate
	(iii) Gangliosides	Sphingosine	—	Hexose, neuraminic acid
Waxes	(i) True waxes	Long-chain aliphatic alcohols	—	—
	(ii) Steryl esters, Vitamin A and D_3 esters	Complex cyclic alcohols	—	—

* In Bloor's classification[3] the triglycerides (neutral fats) and waxes together constitute the "simple lipids", while the remaining classes listed here are collectively designated "compound lipids" (phospholipids, cerebrosides, gangliosides). The phospholipids or phosphatides comprise the glycerophosphatides and sphingomyelins, grouped together by virtue of their sole common component, the phosphate group. The classification of the sphingomyelins with the other sphingolipids (derivatives of sphingosine) is more rational.

** All compounds yield fatty acids on hydrolysis, with the possible exception of some acetal phosphatides.

Fatty acids

The different fatty acids (aliphatic monocarboxylic acids, R·COOH) present in animal and vegetable lipids are limited to some 50 in number. They include both the saturated and unsaturated, straight-chain and branched-chain types, although the great majority are of the straight-chain type. It is significant that the naturally occurring fatty acids are almost exclusively those containing an even number of carbon atoms, a circumstance which is in accordance with the concept that the biosynthesis of fatty acids takes place by the condensation of 2-carbon units (acetate) with other 2-carbon units or with larger units which were themselves built up from 2-carbon units[2]. The only important exception is isovaleric acid, which is a component of the depot fat of the dolphin and porpoise. Data on the principal fatty acid components of lipids are given in Table 18 on pages 390–395.

The naturally occurring unsaturated fatty acids are the *cis* geometrical isomers, although the *trans* forms of some have been detected in trace amounts, e.g. elaidic acid (*trans* isomer of oleic acid) and vaccenic acid (*trans*-11-octadecenoic acid). *Cis-trans* geometrical isomerism is illustrated by the case of oleic and elaidic acids:

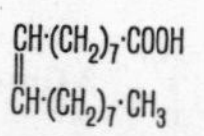

Oleic acid (*cis*)

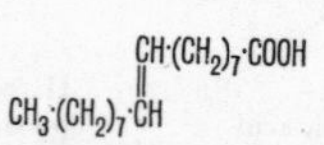

Elaidic acid (*trans*)

Unsaturated fatty acids with more than one double bond (polyolefinic or polyethenoid acids) play an important role in animal nutrition; some are apparently not synthesized in the organism at a rate sufficient to meet the requirements of growth and are therefore essential constituents of the diet. The most important of these are linoleic and arachidonic acids, the so-called "essential fatty acids", the ingestion of any of which is effective in preventing or curing the fat-deficiency syndrome due to a completely fat-free diet (see also page 471).

Fatty acids containing hydroxyl, keto or cyclic groups in the carbon chain, as well as a few with acetylenic linkings (ethynoic acids) have also been identified as components of lipids.

Fats (Triglycerides)[3]

By the term *fats* is understood those lipids which are glycerol tri-esters of fatty acids (triglycerides). At room temperature they may be either solid or liquid, and in the latter case are often referred to as (animal or vegetable) *oils*. Most natural fats contain at least 5 and up to 12 or more different fatty acids. Chemically they are complex mixtures of mixed triglycerides which may by represented by the general formula shown below and which on alkaline hydrolysis (saponification) yield the alkali salts of fatty acids (soaps) and glycerol:

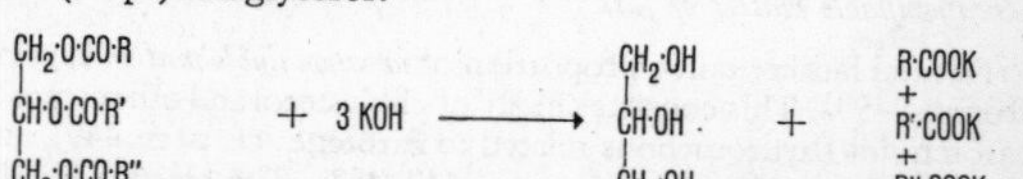

Mixed triglyceride — Glycerol — Salts of fatty acids

The tendency in all natural fats is towards maximum heterogeneity in the composition of the constituent triglycerides.

The fatty acids of most natural fats (and waxes) consist of mixtures of saturated and unsaturated acids. In general, the higher the proportion of saturated to unsaturated acids, the higher the melting point of the fat. The most important individual acids are the unsaturated acids oleic (C_{18}) and linoleic (C_{18}), and the saturated acids palmitic (C_{16}) and stearic (C_{18}). With the exception of stearic acid, these acids are very widely distributed in nature. The most abundant fatty acids are oleic and palmitic, present in practically every known natural fat.

From the standpoint of their fatty acid composition, the depot fats of land mammals are characterized by a preponderance of oleic acid, palmitic acid and in some important cases (e.g. ox, sheep) stearic acid. In the milk fat of land mammals this preponderance is diminished to an extent corresponding to the additional presence of the lower saturated fatty acids C_{12} down to C_4 (butyric acid). The fats of aquatic animals contain mainly the higher unsaturated acids C_{16} to C_{22} together with usually 10–18% of palmitic acid.

In any particular tissue in the same species of animal the composition of the fat shows variations, and it is known that this is due at least in part to dietary differences. An example is the "soft pork" produced from hogs fed on soybean oil.

Absorption and storage of fats

In the animal body, ingested fats are hydrolyzed in the intestine by the intestinal and pancreatic lipases, a process made possible by the emulsification of the fats by the bile acids. The resulting fatty acids and glycerol are absorbed into the intestinal mucosa where they are re-formed into triglycerides. About 60% of this re-formed fat passes via the lymph into the venous blood and is deposited in the various tissues (depot fats). The remainder is transported mainly to the liver, where it is metabolized (cf. Oxidative degradation of fat, page 403). Since the fat of a particular tissue normally exhibits a typical triglyceride composition, the fatty acids from ingested fats must undergo alteration before re-synthesis of triglycerides takes place. As indicated above, however, drastic changes in dietary fat may exceed the body's capacity to modify the acids with the result that a change in the composition of the depot fat occurs.

The principal locations of depot fats in the body are subcutaneous, intramuscular, in the omentum, and in association with various organs such as the heart, kidney, mesentery, ovaries, etc. Their main function is that of an energy reserve, for which purpose they are more efficient than carbohydrates or proteins. In warm-blooded animals, subcutaneous fat often provides insulation against heat loss which is essential for survival. Adipose tissue also affords some protection against mechanical injury to important organs. In certain species, notably some marine animals, triglycerides are almost entirely replaced as energy reserves by other lipids, for example waxes. In any particular animal the amount of depot fat laid down is dependent on the state of nutrition and other factors, and it is being continuously utilized and replaced.

In addition to dietary fat, triglycerides synthesized in the body itself are also stored, the fatty acids arising from carbohydrates and thus indirectly also from proteins, and the glycerol mainly from the splitting of blood glucose.

Blood fats. Fats are transported in the body by the blood stream in the form of fine droplets of 1 μm or less in diameter known as *chylomicrons*. They are surrounded by a stabilizing film of protein (α- and β-globulins) and may be separated by centrifuging. The level of fats (and of other lipids) in the blood (see page 561) rises after digestion of a meal containing fat. Hyperlipemia also occurs after several days' fasting, when it is due to increased metabolism of depot fat following the exhaustion of glycogen reserves. Ingestion of alcohol, as well as the administration of various narcotics, also cause a marked increase in blood fats. In general, the level of blood fats and other lipids is largely controlled by the thyroid. A high blood fat level is in rare cases congenital (idiopathic familial hyperlipemia) and is usually accompanied by enlargement of the liver and spleen and by xanthoma.

Unsaponifiable matter of fats

Natural fats contain a proportion of *unsaponifiable matter* varying from 0.1–5%. This consists chiefly of cholesterol and other sterols, carotenoids (hydrocarbons related to carotene; cf. page 449), and the fat-soluble vitamins (cf. pages 449–453). The reasons for the occurrence of these substances in natural fats are presumably their solubility in triglycerides and insolubility in water. Many fats contain steryl esters of fatty acids (see under Waxes, page 389) in addition to free sterols.

Squalene. An important unsaponifiable constituent of animal fats is the hydrocarbon squalene, $C_{30}H_{50}$:

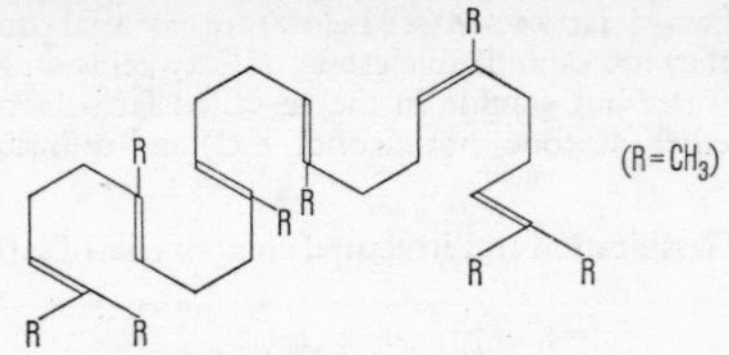

It occurs in the liver oils of many Elasmobranch fish, particularly sharks (up to 57% has been reported), also in yeast fat and human skin. Its role as a precursor of cholesterol in the animal liver has been demonstrated (see page 432).

Alkoxydiglycerides

The liver oils of Elasmobranch fish contain considerable proportions of compounds which differ from the triglycerides in containing an ether linkage. They are diglycerides in which the remaining hydroxyl group has formed an ether with a higher aliphatic alcohol (R·OH) and may therefore be designated either as alkoxydiglycerides or as fatty acid esters of glyceryl ethers:

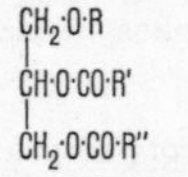

Alkoxydiglyceride

Ratfish liver oil consists almost exclusively of such compounds and contains practically no triglycerides.

Phospholipids (Phosphatides)

Broadly speaking, the phospholipids (phosphatides) are esters of fatty acids in which the alcohol component of the molecule contains a phosphate group as an integral part. They comprise principally the glycerophosphatides, containing glycerol, and the sphingomyelins containing choline. They are constituents of all organs, especially the more active tissues such as brain and nerve tissue, but are notably absent from depot fats. They are involved in a great many metabolic processes and may be regarded as a form in which fats undergo metabolic change or are transported in the body. Thus they have been shown to be involved in intestinal fat absorption, fatty acid transport and oxidation, and the development of fatty livers. They have also been implicated as structural components of organs and in the process of blood coagulation. Phospholipids are readily synthesized in the organism, mainly in the liver and small intestine.

Glycerophosphatides

The glycerophosphatides are of universal occurrence. Chemically, they consist of α-glycerophosphoric acid esterified with fatty acids and/or other constituents.

Both the α and β forms of glycerophosphoric acid are known, but contrary to the statements made in most reference books it is now considered doubtful whether β-glycerophosphoric acid or β-glycerophosphatides or other derivatives occur in nature. Thus it has been shown[4] that in the hydrolysis of lecithins (see below) there is a reversible migration of the phosphate group which results in the formation of mixtures of α- and β-glycerophosphoric acids. A similar change probably takes place during chemical isolation procedures. The migration of the phosphate group is thought to proceed as follows[5]:

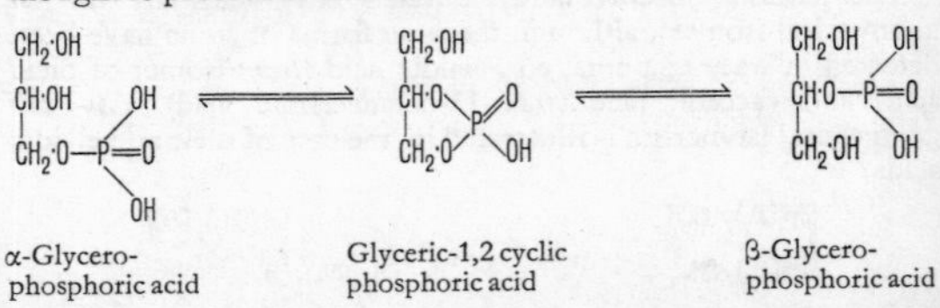

α-Glycerophosphoric acid — Glyceric-1,2 cyclic phosphoric acid — β-Glycerophosphoric acid

(*a*) *Phosphatidic acids.* Phosphatidic acids, the simplest of the glycerophosphatides and those most similar chemically to the triglycerides, are derived from α-glycerophosphoric acid by esterification of the two hydroxyl groups with fatty acids.

Alternatively, they may be envisaged as triglycerides in which one of the fatty acid residues has been replaced by a phosphoric acid residue:

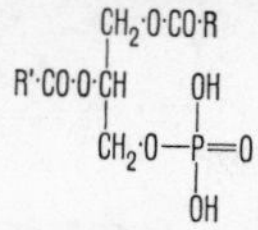

α-Phosphatidic acids
(where R·CO and R′·CO are fatty acid residues)

Phosphatidic acids have been isolated from a wide range of plant tissues and have been shown to occur in animal tissues[6]. Their biosynthesis from fatty acids, glycerol and adenosine triphosphate (ATP) has been demonstrated[7].

A phosphatidic acid derivative of importance is cardiolipin, which plays a role in the WASSERMANN reaction. This compound probably consists of a chain of two monoglycerides and two diglycerides linked through phosphoric acid residues[8]:

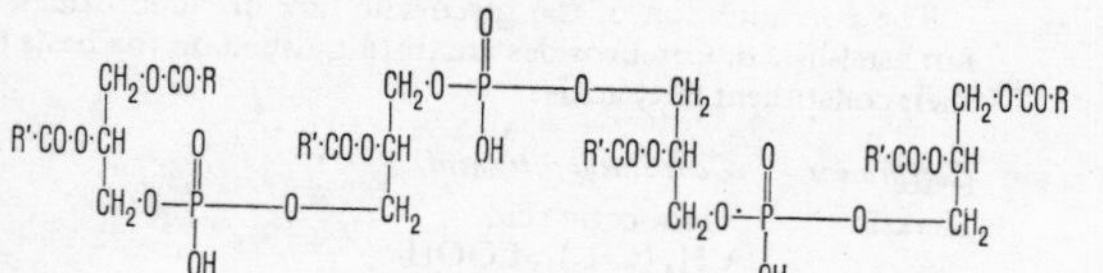

Cardiolipin

The fatty acids of cardiolipin consist almost entirely of oleic and linoleic acids in the ratio 1:5. Other derivatives of phosphatidic acids are cytidine diphosphate glycerol (see page 374) which occurs in *Lactobacillus arabinosus*[9] and α,α-diglycerophosphatidic acid, which has been isolated from algae[10]. This latter substance possesses two free hydroxyl groups:

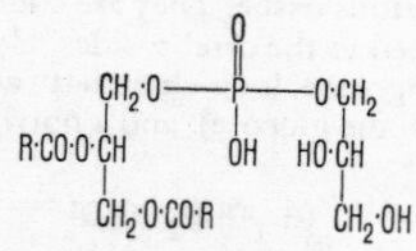

α,α-Diglycerophosphatidic acid

(*b*) *Phosphatidyl esters*. These substances are phosphatidic acids esterified with the hydroxyl groups of ethanolamine, choline or serine:

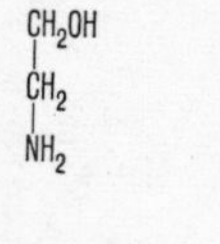

Ethanolamine

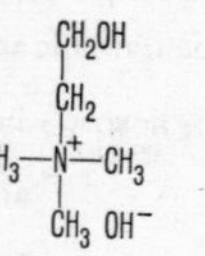

Choline

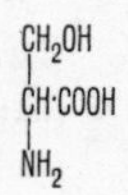

Serine

The resulting three types of phosphatidyl ester are:

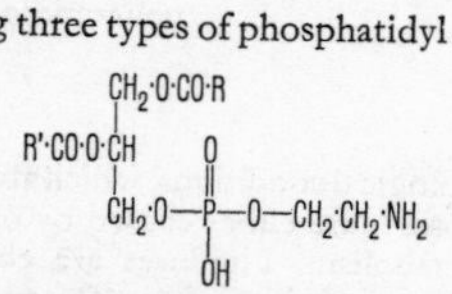

α-Phosphatidylethanolamines (cephalins)

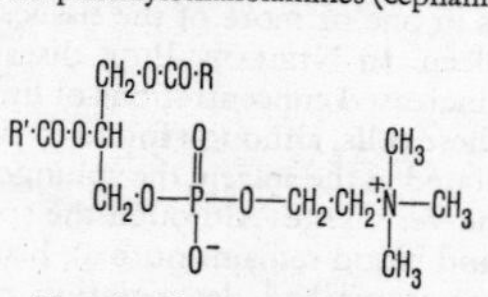

α-Phosphatidylcholines (lecithins)

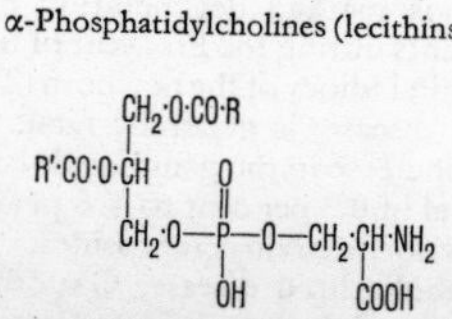

α-Phosphatidylserines

The term "cephalin" was originally given to an ethanol-insoluble lipid fraction isolated from brain and containing both α-phosphatidylethanolamines and α-phosphatidyl-L-serines. The fatty acid residues in the cephalins are predominantly those of oleic and stearic acids[11].

The lecithins obtained from many sources have all been shown to have the L-α-glyceryl-phosphoryl-choline skeleton given above[4], with the fatty acids as the only variant. The long-chain fatty acids (R·COOH and R′·COOH) are similar to those that predominate in triglycerides (oleic, palmitic, stearic and linoleic acids). The tetra-ethenoid fatty acid, arachidonic acid, is also found in some lecithins.

The lecithins of brain differ from those of other organs in their greater content of highly unsaturated fatty acids of chain length greater than C_{20}. Most lecithins contain both a saturated and an unsaturated fatty acid residue, but some[12,13] contain either two saturated or two unsaturated fatty acid residues.

(*c*) *Lysophosphatides*. The lysophosphatides consist of partially hydrolyzed glycerophosphatides (see page 426). Snake venoms contain an enzyme which splits one and only one of the two fatty acids from lecithins, yielding lysolecithins:

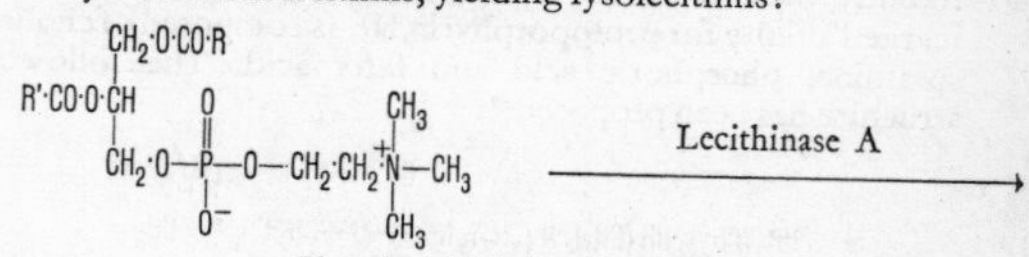

α-Phosphatidylcholine (lecithin)

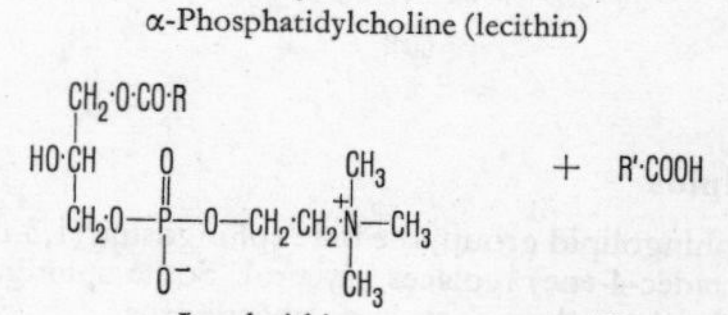

Lysolecithin Fatty acid

(*d*) α-*Glycerophosphoryl compounds* which lack both of the fatty acids present in phosphatidyl esters occur in mammalian tissues and fluids[14]. They are α-glycerophosphorylethanolamine and α-glycerophosphorylcholine:

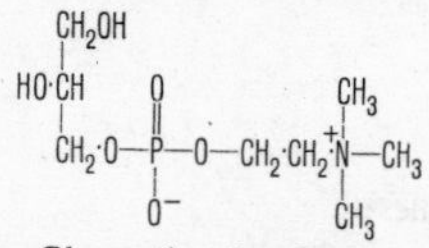

α-Glycerophosphorylcholine

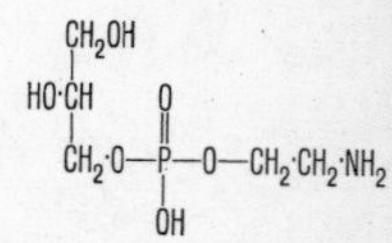

α-Glycerophosphorylethanolamine

(*e*) *Phosphatidylinositides*[15]. At least three distinct inositides have been described. These have been differentiated on the basis of the inositol derivatives obtained on hydrolysis. One type, the phosphatidylinositols[16], are analogous to the glycerophosphatides. They occur in liver, heart, wheat germ and soybean, and have the following structure:

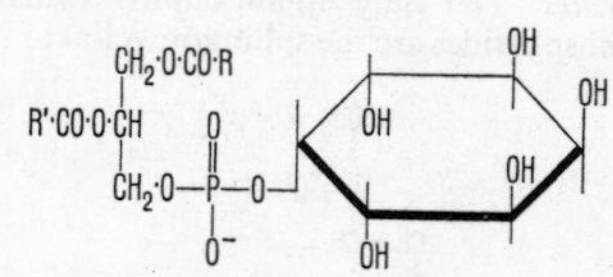

α-Phosphatidylinositols

A second type are the (di)-α-phosphatidylinositols, in which two phosphate groups are esterified in the inositol ring in the meta position[17]:

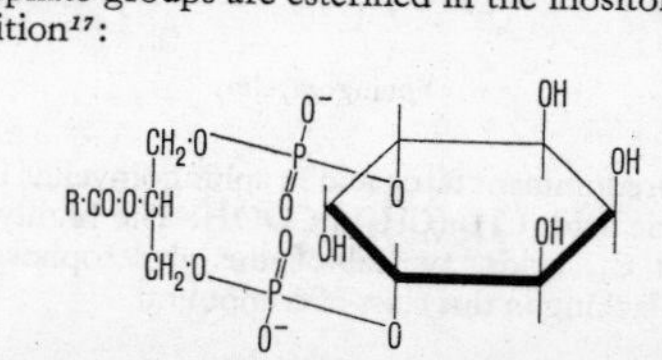

(Di)-α-phosphatidylinositols (tentative structure)

These compounds may exist as more complex copolymers.

(*f*) *Acetal phosphatides* (plasmalogens). These compounds are closely related to the phosphatidyl esters. Plasmalogens containing ethanolamine predominate in nature, but compounds in which ethanolamine is replaced by either serine or choline have also been reported.

Plasmalogens give a positive reaction for aldehydes, and the aldehydes corresponding to stearic and palmitic acids have been isolated from the crystalline acetal phosphatides of brain. They have been shown[18] to contain two long-chain alkyl groups, one of which is present in ester linkage and the other in an unsaturated vinyl ether linkage:

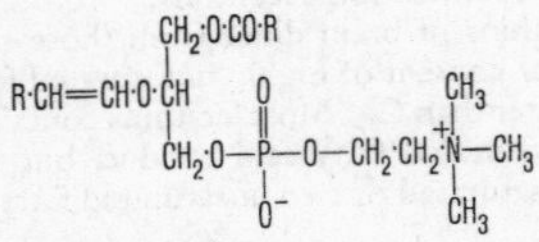

Acetal phosphatides (plasmalogens)

The existence of a phospholipid in malignant tumors has recently been reported. The compound, which possesses a marked affinity for protoporphyrin III, is composed of choline, spermine, phosphoric acid and fatty acid. The following structure has been proposed[19]:

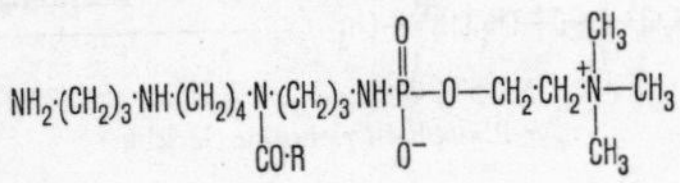

Sphingolipids

In the sphingolipid group, the base sphingosine (1,3-dihydroxy-2-aminooctadec-4-ene) replaces glycerol. Some sphingolipids are phosphatides, but others contain no phosphorus.

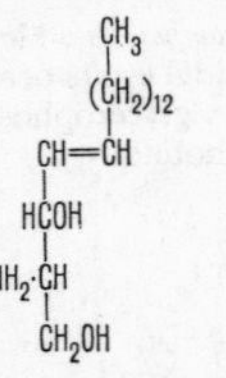

Sphingosine

In some minor members of the sphingolipid group, sphingosine is replaced by dihydrosphingosine (in which the double bond of sphingosine is saturated), or by the 4-hydroxy derivative of dihydrosphingosine (1,3,4-trihydroxy-2-aminooctadecane), phytosphingosine.

Nerve tissue is particularly rich in sphingolipids.

(*a*) *Sphingomyelins*. The only sphingolipids which resemble the glycerophosphatides are the sphingomyelins:

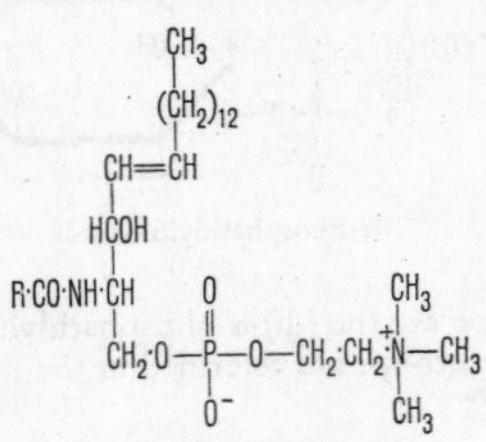

Sphingomyelins

The predominant fatty acid in sphingomyelins is the C_{24} acid lignoceric acid, $CH_3{\cdot}(CH_2)_{22}{\cdot}COOH$. The highly unsaturated C_{20} and C_{22} acids, typical of the glycerophosphatides, are entirely lacking in this class of compound.

(*b*) *Cerebrosides*. Cerebrosides are found chiefly in the brain. Although their concentration in other tissues is small, it becomes considerably elevated in GAUCHER's disease (see under Lipidoses, below. Most cerebrosides contain sphingosine (or dihydrosphingosine), a fatty acid and a hexose.

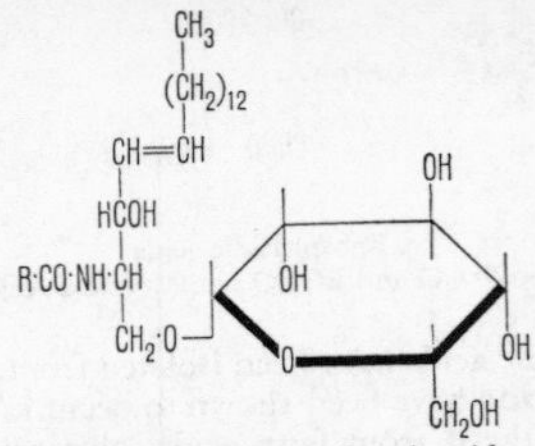

Probable structure of cerebrosides

The hexose is typically D-galactose but may sometimes be D-glucose. The cerebrosides do not contain phosphorus. A cerebroside isolated from brain contains sulfate esterified with the hydroxyl in the C-6 position of galactose.

The configuration of the glycosidic link of cerebrosides is not established. Cerebrosides are distinguished on the basis of their constituent fatty acids:

Cerebroside	*Constituent fatty acid*
Kerasin	Lignoceric acid $CH_3{\cdot}(CH_2)_{22}{\cdot}COOH$
Phrenosin	Cerebronic acid $CH_3{\cdot}(CH_2)_{21}{\cdot}CH(OH){\cdot}COOH$
Nervone	Nervonic acid $CH_3{\cdot}(CH_2)_7{\cdot}CH{=}CH{\cdot}(CH_2)_{13}{\cdot}COOH$
Hydroxy-nervone	Hydroxynervonic acid $CH_3{\cdot}(CH_2)_7{\cdot}CH{=}CH{\cdot}(CH_2)_{12}{\cdot}CH(OH){\cdot}COOH$

(*c*) *Gangliosides*. These compounds occur in nervous tissue and in most parenchymatous tissue. They are complex substances and appear to be related to the cerebrosides. Hydrolysis reveals the presence of sphingosine, long-chain fatty acids, hexoses (mainly galactose but some glucose), and a polyhydroxy amino acid, neuraminic acid[20]:

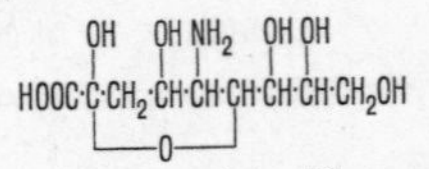

Neuraminic acid

A tentative structure for gangliosides is:

```
                            neuraminic acid
                                  |
sphingosine – hexose – hexose – hexose
                                  |
                             aminohexose
                                  |
          sphingosine – hexose – hexose
                                  |
                             neuraminic acid
```

Lipidoses[21]

A group of pathological conditions, which are generally grouped together as "lipidoses", are either caused by or result in a disturbance of lipid metabolism. Lipidoses are characterized by the accumulation of large quantities of some particular lipid. The accumulation occurs in one or more of the tissues, often selectively in the liver or spleen. In NIEMANN-PICK disease, large cells are found containing increased concentrations of lipid, predominantly sphingomyelin. These cells, although found in all body organs, are especially concentrated in the spleen, the sphingomyelin content of which may become very large. Although the sphingomyelin content of the brain and blood remains normal, histological evidence suggests that there is marked degeneration of the brain. The disease occurs in infants during the first year of life and is fatal.

Amaurotic congenital idiocy of the newborn (TAY-SACHS idiocy), like NIEMANN-PICK disease, is generally fatal. This condition is characterized by an increase in the ganglioside content of the brain from the normal level of 0.3 per cent to 4–8 per cent with a partial corresponding reduction in brain cerebrosides.

A non-fatal metabolic lipid disease, GAUCHER's disease, consists of a disturbance of the normal cerebroside metabolism in adults. Although the disturbance may be general, it is particularly noticeable in the spleen, which may become enormously enlarged owing to the accumulation of "GAUCHER cells". These are heavily laden with a peculiar type of cerebroside which contains only glucose, in contrast to the typical normal human spleen cerebrosides which contain predominantly galactose. In GAUCHER's disease the brain cerebrosides remain of the normal, exclusively galactose-containing type.

Waxes

The saponifiable waxes (as distinct from the hydrocarbon waxes) are conveniently divisible into the so-called *true waxes*, which are long-chain fatty acid esters of long-chain aliphatic alcohols, and the *steryl esters*, long-chain fatty acid esters of the complex cyclic alcohols, known as *sterols*. With the second group may be included the naturally occurring long-chain fatty acid esters of vitamin A (page 449) and vitamin D_3 (see page 450).

In general, the true waxes are products excreted by the epidermis of animals and plants for the purpose of providing a protective covering either to prevent water-loss or wetting. Examples of the former are the surface waxes of plants in arid climates, of the latter the lanolin present on the skin and fur of almost all fur-bearing animals and the surface wax of fruits in moist climates (e.g. apples). In certain animals, notably the sperm whale, waxes almost entirely replace triglycerides as the energy reserve material.

True waxes. These are mixtures of fatty acid esters of the higher aliphatic straight-chain monohydric alcohols, usually cetyl alcohol (hexadecanol, $CH_3\cdot[CH_2]_{14}\cdot CH_2OH$) and octadecyl alcohol (octadecanol, $CH_3\cdot[CH_2]_{16}\cdot CH_2OH$), but often including higher alcohols up to C_{36}. The fatty acids are usually of the saturated type, the commonest being cerotic acid (hexacosanoic acid, $CH_3\cdot(CH_2)_{24}\cdot COOH$), although acids containing a hydroxyl group are occasionally found. In many natural waxes the fatty acid and alcohol components have the same chain length.

Sterols. These substances, which also occur free as constituents of the unsaponifiable matter of fats, are alcohols belonging to the larger group known as *steroids*, compounds characterized by possession of the 17-carbon cyclopentanophenanthrene ring:

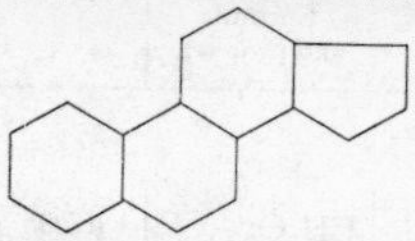

The steroids are very widely distributed in nature and include many important natural and synthetic hormones (cf. pages 486–497), as well as the bile acids.

The most important of the sterols is cholesterol, a cell constituent of most warm-blooded animals. It is present in relatively high concentration in the adrenal cortex, where it is a precursor of the adrenocortical hormones (see pages 487–492).

References

1) For detailed expositions see LOVERN, J. A., *The Chemistry of Lipids of Biochemical Significance*, London, 1955; DEUEL, H.J., *The Lipids*, vol. I, New York, 1951; HILDITCH, T. P., *The Chemical Constitution of Natural Fats*, 3rd ed., London, 1956; DAWSON, R. M. C., *Biol. Rev.*, **32**, 188 (1957). For recent reviews see SHORLAND, F. B., *Ann. Rev. Biochem.*, **25**, 101 (1956); KLENK and DEBUCH, *Ann. Rev. Biochem.*, **28**, 39 (1959). *2)* CHAIKOFF and BROWN, in GREENBERG, D.M. (Ed.), *Chemical Pathways of Metabolism*, vol. I, New York, 1954, page 324. *3)* BLOOR, W.R., *Chem. Rev.*, **2**, 243 (1925–26). *4)* BAER and KATES, *J. biol. Chem.*, **185**, 615 (1950); BAER et al., *J. Amer. chem. Soc.*, **78**, 232 (1956). *5)* BAILLY, M.-C., *C.R. Acad. Sci. (Paris)*, **206**, 1902 (1938); **208**, 443, 1820 (1939); CHARGAFF, E., *J. biol. Chem.*, **144**, 455 (1942); VERKADE et al., *Rec. Trav. chim. Pays-Bas*, **59**, 886 (1940). *6)* HOKIN and HOKIN, *J. biol. Chem.*, **233**, 800 (1958). *7)* BUBLITZ and KENNEDY, *J. biol. Chem.*, **211**, 951 (1954); KORNBERG and PRICER, *J. biol. Chem.*, **204**, 345 (1953). *8)* PANGBORN, M. C., *J. biol. Chem.*, **168**, 351 (1947). *9)* BADDILEY et al., *Biochem. J.*, **64**, 599 (1956). *10)* BENSON and MARUO, *Biochim. biophys. Acta*, **27**, 189 (1958). *11)* FOLCH, J., *J. biol. Chem.*, **174**, 439 (1948). *12)* HANAHAN, D. J., *J. biol. Chem.*, **211**, 313 (1954). *13)* HANAHAN and JAYKO, *J. Amer. chem. Soc.*, **74**, 5070 (1952). *14)* DAWSON, R. M. C., *Biochem. J.*, **65**, 627 (1957). *15)* FOLCH and LEBARON, *Canad. J. Biochem.*, **34**, 305 (1956). *16)* HAWTHORNE, J. N., *Biochem. J.*, **59**, ii (1955). *17)* FOLCH, J., *J. biol. Chem.*, **177**, 505 (1949). *18)* GRAY, G. M., *Biochem. J.*, **70**, 425 (1958). *19)* KOSAKI et al., *Science*, **127**, 1176 (1958). *20)* KLENK and DEBUCH, *Ann. Rev. Biochem.*, **28**, 57 (1959). *21)* THANNHAUSER, S. J., *Lipidoses – Diseases of the Cellular Lipid Metabolism*, 2nd ed., Oxford, 1950.

Table 18 Fatty acids

Name of acid	Formula and mol. wt.	Structure	Physical properties	Remarks
		Saturated straight-chain monocarboxylic acids		
Formic acid (methanoic acid)	CH_2O_2 46.03	H·COOH	m.p. 8.6° C b.p. 100.8° C d^{20} 1.220 n_D^{20} 1.3714	Occurs in human urine and many plant materials
Acetic acid (ethanoic acid)	$C_2H_4O_2$ 60.05	CH_3·COOH	m.p. 16.5° C b.p. 118.1° C d^{20} 1.0492 n_D^{25} 1.36976	Present in most biological materials. Formed from ethanol by many species of aerobic bacteria and from pentoses by some anaerobic species
Propionic acid (propanoic acid)	$C_3H_6O_2$ 74.08	CH_3·CH_2·COOH	m.p. – 22° C b.p. 140.9° C d^{20} 0.992 $n_D^{19.9}$ 1.38736	Formed by bacterial decomposition of carbohydrates
n-Butyric acid (butanoic acid)	$C_4H_8O_2$ 88.11	CH_3·$(CH_2)_2$·COOH	m.p. – 7.9° C b.p. 163° C d^{20} 0.9587 n_D^{20} 1.39906	Occurs in traces in many fats
n-Valeric acid (pentanoic acid)	$C_5H_{10}O_2$ 102.14	CH_3·$(CH_2)_3$·COOH	m.p. – 34.5° C b.p. 186.4° C d^{20} 0.9387 n_D^{20} 1.4086	
Caproic acid (hexoic acid, hexanoic acid)	$C_6H_{12}O_2$ 116.16	CH_3·$(CH_2)_4$·COOH	m.p. – 4° C b.p. 205° C d^{20} 0.929 n_D^{20} 1.41635	Occurs in traces in many fats
Enanthic acid (heptanoic acid)	$C_7H_{14}O_2$ 130.19	CH_3·$(CH_2)_5$·COOH	m.p. – 7.46° C b.p. 223° C d^{14} 0.9216 $n_D^{19.8}$ 1.42162	
Caprylic acid (octanoic acid)	$C_8H_{16}O_2$ 144.22	CH_3·$(CH_2)_6$·COOH	m.p. 16° C b.p. 239° C d^{20} 0.9088 n_D^{20} 1.4285	Constituent of many fats
Pelargonic acid (nonanoic acid)	$C_9H_{18}O_2$ 158.24	CH_3·$(CH_2)_7$·COOH	m.p. 12.3° C b.p. 254° C d^{20} 0.9055 n_D^{20} 1.4330	Occurs in oil of rue, Japan wax, fusel oils, leaves of *Pelargonium roseum*
Capric acid (decanoic acid)	$C_{10}H_{20}O_2$ 172.27	CH_3·$(CH_2)_8$·COOH	m.p. 31.3° C b.p. 269° C d^{40} 0.8858 n_D^{40} 1.42855	Component of many animal and vegetable fats
Undecylic acid (hendecanoic acid)	$C_{11}H_{22}O_2$ 186.30	CH_3·$(CH_2)_9$·COOH	m.p. 28.5° C b.p. 284° C d^{20} 0.8905 $n_D^{45.2}$ 1.4294	Found in *Pseudomonas*
Lauric acid (dodecanoic acid)	$C_{12}H_{24}O_2$ 200.32	CH_3·$(CH_2)_{10}$·COOH	m.p. 43.5° C b.p. 225° C/100 d^{20} 0.883 $n_D^{82.1}$ 1.4183	Major component of vegetable fats (esp. laurel). In smaller quantities in depot fat of animals, milk fat, fishliver oils
Tridecylic acid (tridecanoic acid)	$C_{13}H_{26}O_2$ 214.35	CH_3·$(CH_2)_{11}$·COOH	m.p. 51° C b.p. 312.4° C n_D^{70} 1.4249	Occurs in animal fats in very small traces
Myristic acid (tetradecanoic acid)	$C_{14}H_{28}O_2$ 228.38	CH_3·$(CH_2)_{12}$·COOH	m.p. 54.4° C b.p. 250.5° C/100 d^{54} 0.8622 n_D^{60} 1.4308	Component of almost all animal fats (1–5%) and vegetable fats, esp. milk fat, fish oils, palm oil, nutmegs

Table 18 Fatty acids *(continued)*

Name of acid	Formula and mol. wt.	Structure	Physical properties	Remarks
Pentadecylic acid (pentadecanoic acid)	$C_{15}H_{30}O_2$ 242.41	$CH_3 \cdot (CH_2)_{13} \cdot COOH$	m.p. 52.1° C b.p. 257° C/100 d^{80} 0.8423 n_D^{70} 1.4270	Occurs in traces in animal fats, esp. liver fats
Palmitic acid (hexadecanoic acid)	$C_{16}H_{32}O_2$ 256.43	$CH_3 \cdot (CH_2)_{14} \cdot COOH$	m.p. 62.85° C b.p. 268.5° C/100 d^{70} 0.8487 $n_D^{79.8}$ 1.4273	Widely distributed in nature. Present in almost all fats
Margaric acid (heptadecanoic acid)	$C_{17}H_{34}O_2$ 270.46	$CH_3 \cdot (CH_2)_{15} \cdot COOH$	m.p. 62° C b.p. 227° C/100 d^{60} 0.8579 n_D^{70} 1.4319	Occurs in traces in mutton fat
Stearic acid (octadecanoic acid)	$C_{18}H_{36}O_2$ 284.49	$CH_3 \cdot (CH_2)_{16} \cdot COOH$	m.p. 69.6° C b.p. 298° C/100 d^{20} 0.9408 $n_D^{80.2}$ 1.4299	Found abundantly in important edible fats. Also occurs in vegetable fats
Nondecylic acid (nonadecanoic acid)	$C_{19}H_{38}O_2$ 298.51	$CH_3 \cdot (CH_2)_{17} \cdot COOH$	m.p. 68–69° C b.p. 298° C/100	
Arachidic acid (eicosanoic acid)	$C_{20}H_{40}O_2$ 312.54	$CH_3 \cdot (CH_2)_{18} \cdot COOH$	m.p. 75.4° C b.p. 328° C d^{100} 0.824 n_D^{100} 1.4250	Occurs in traces in many seed and animal fats
Heneicosanoic acid	$C_{21}H_{42}O_2$ 326.57	$CH_3 \cdot (CH_2)_{19} \cdot COOH$	m.p. 75.1° C	
Behenic acid (docosanoic acid)	$C_{22}H_{44}O_2$ 340.59	$CH_3 \cdot (CH_2)_{20} \cdot COOH$	m.p. 80° C b.p. 306° C/60 d^{100} 0.8221 n_D^{100} 1.4270	Present in traces in animal fats and seed fats. Constitutes 50% of the spleen cerebrosides in GAUCHER's disease (see page 388)
Tricosanoic acid	$C_{23}H_{46}O_2$ 354.62	$CH_3 \cdot (CH_2)_{21} \cdot COOH$	m.p. 79.1° C	
Lignoceric acid (tetracosanoic acid)	$C_{24}H_{48}O_2$ 368.65	$CH_3 \cdot (CH_2)_{22} \cdot COOH$	m.p. 84.2° C d^{20} 0.8207 n_D^{100} 1.4287	Component of sphingomyelins and of kerasin (spleen cerebroside in GAUCHER's disease; see page 388). Also found in some vegetable fats and bacterial and insect waxes
Pentacosanoic acid	$C_{25}H_{50}O_2$ 382.68	$CH_3 \cdot (CH_2)_{23} \cdot COOH$	m.p. 83° C	
Cerotic acid (hexacosanoic acid)	$C_{26}H_{52}O_2$ 396.70	$CH_3 \cdot (CH_2)_{24} \cdot COOH$	m.p. 87.7° C d^{100} 0.8198 n_D^{100} 1.4301	Occurs free and combined. In Chinese wax (cetyl ester), beeswax, wool fat
Heptacosanoic acid	$C_{27}H_{54}O_2$ 410.73	$CH_3 \cdot (CH_2)_{25} \cdot COOH$	m.p. 87.6° C	
Montanic acid (octacosanoic acid)	$C_{28}H_{56}O_2$ 424.76	$CH_3 \cdot (CH_2)_{26} \cdot COOH$	m.p. 90.9° C d^{100} 0.8191 n_D^{100} 1.4313	Component of montan wax, beeswax, Chinese wax
Nonacosanoic acid	$C_{29}H_{58}O_2$ 438.78	$CH_3 \cdot (CH_2)_{27} \cdot COOH$	m.p. 90.3° C	
Melissic acid (triacontanoic acid)	$C_{30}H_{60}O_2$ 452.81	$CH_3 \cdot (CH_2)_{28} \cdot COOH$	m.p. 93.6° C n_D^{100} 1.4323	Occurs in beeswax

Table 18 Fatty acids *(continued)*

Name of acid	Formula and mol. wt.	Structure	Physical properties	Remarks
Lacceroic acid (dotriacontanoic acid)	$C_{32}H_{64}O_2$ 480.86	$CH_3 \cdot (CH_2)_{30} \cdot COOH$	m.p. 96.2° C	Occurs in stick-lac wax (from *Tachardia lacca)* and other natural waxes
Unsaturated (mono-olefinic) straight-chain monocarboxylic acids				
Acrylic acid (propenoic acid)	$C_3H_4O_2$ 72.07	$CH_2{=}CH \cdot COOH$	m.p. 13° C b.p. 141° C d^{16} 1.062 n_D^{20} 1.4224	
trans-(α-)Crotonic acid (*trans*-butenoic acid)	$C_4H_6O_2$ 86.09	$CH_3 \cdot CH \| HC \cdot COOH$	m.p. 72° C b.p. 189° C d^{72} 0.973 $n_D^{79.7}$ 1.4228	Constituent of croton oil (from *Croton tiglium* seeds)
iso-(β-)Crotonic acid (*cis*-butenoic acid)	$C_4H_6O_2$ 86.09	$HC \cdot CH_3 \| HC \cdot COOH$	m.p. 15.5° C b.p. 169° C d^{15} 1.0312 n_D^{20} 1.4457	Readily isomerizes to the *trans*-acid
Δ²-Hexenoic acid	$C_6H_{10}O_2$ 114.15	$CH_3 \cdot (CH_2)_2 \cdot CH{=}CH \cdot COOH$	m.p. 32° C b.p. 217° C d^{40} 0.9627 n_D^{40} 1.4601	Occurs in Japanese peppermint oil
Δ⁴-Decenoic acid (obtusilic acid)	$C_{10}H_{18}O_2$ 170.25	$CH_3 \cdot (CH_2)_4 \cdot CH{=}CH \cdot (CH_2)_2 \cdot COOH$	b.p. 148–150° C/13 d^{20} 0.9197 n_D^{20} 1.4497	Occurs in seed fat of *Lindera obtusiloba*
Δ⁹-Decenoic acid	$C_{10}H_{18}O_2$ 170.25	$CH_2{=}CH \cdot (CH_2)_7 \cdot COOH$	b.p. 143–148° C/15 d^{15} 0.9238 n_D^{20} 1.4488	Occurs in butter and milk fats and in sperm head oil
Δ⁴-Dodecenoic acid (linderic acid)	$C_{12}H_{22}O_2$ 198.31	$CH_3 \cdot (CH_2)_6 \cdot CH{=}CH \cdot (CH_2)_2 \cdot COOH$	m.p. 1–1.3° C b.p. 170–172° C/13 d^{20} 0.9081 n_D^{20} 1.4529	Occurs in various seed oils, e.g. *Lindera obtusiloba*
Δ⁵-Dodecenoic acid (lauroleic acid)	$C_{12}H_{22}O_2$ 198.31	$CH_3 \cdot (CH_2)_5 \cdot CH{=}CH \cdot (CH_2)_3 \cdot COOH$	d^{15} 0.9130 n_D^{15} 1.4535	Occurs in sperm blubber and head oil
Δ⁹-Dodecenoic acid	$C_{12}H_{22}O_2$ 198.31	$CH_3 \cdot CH_2 \cdot CH{=}CH \cdot (CH_2)_7 \cdot COOH$		Occurs in fat of cow's milk
Δ⁴-Tetradecenoic acid (tsuzuic acid)	$C_{14}H_{26}O_2$ 226.36	$CH_3 \cdot (CH_2)_8 \cdot CH{=}CH \cdot (CH_2)_2 \cdot COOH$	m.p. 18–18.5° C b.p. 185–188° C/13 d^{20} 0.9024 n_D^{20} 1.4557	Occurs in various tropical plant oils, esp. tsuzu oil
Δ⁵-Tetradecenoic acid (physeteric acid)	$C_{14}H_{26}O_2$ 226.36	$CH_3 \cdot (CH_2)_7 \cdot CH{=}CH \cdot (CH_2)_3 \cdot COOH$	d^{20} 0.9046 n_D^{20} 1.4552	Occurs in whale blubber and sardine oil
Δ⁹-Tetradecenoic acid (myristoleic acid)	$C_{14}H_{26}O_2$ 226.36	$CH_3 \cdot (CH_2)_3 \cdot CH{=}CH \cdot (CH_2)_7 \cdot COOH$	d^{20} 0.9018 n_D^{20} 1.4549	Occurs in milk fat and depot and liver fat of many animals
Δ⁹-Hexadecenoic acid (palmitoleic acid)	$C_{16}H_{30}O_2$ 254.42	$CH_3 \cdot (CH_2)_5 \cdot CH{=}CH \cdot (CH_2)_7 \cdot COOH$	m.p. 1° C b.p. 218–220° C d^{15} 0.9003	Widely distributed. In marine oils (15–20% of total fatty acids), in depot and milk fat of animals, vegetable oils and fats

Table 18 Fatty acids *(continued)*

Name of acid	Formula and mol. wt.	Structure	Physical properties	Remarks* (for references see page 395)
cis-Δ^6-Octadecenoic acid (petroselinic acid)	$C_{18}H_{34}O_2$ 282.47	$CH_3{\cdot}(CH_2)_{10}{\cdot}CH{=}CH{\cdot}(CH_2)_4{\cdot}COOH$	m.p. 32–33° C b.p. 208–210° C/10 d^{35} 0.8824 n_D^{47} 1.4535	Occurs in seeds of aromatic plants (parsley, celery, etc.) and in some umbellate fats
Oleic acid (*cis*-Δ^9-octadecenoic acid)	$C_{18}H_{34}O_2$ 282.47	$CH{\cdot}(CH_2)_7{\cdot}COOH$ ‖ $CH{\cdot}(CH_2)_7{\cdot}CH_3$	m.p. 13° C b.p. 286° C/100 d^{20} 0.895 n_D^{20} 1.45823	Most abundant of the unsaturated fatty acids. Present in nearly all natural fats (one-third of fatty acids of cow's milk; phosphatides). Occurs in traces in human urine
Elaidic acid (*trans*-Δ^9-octadecenoic acid)	$C_{18}H_{34}O_2$ 282.47	$CH_3{\cdot}(CH_2)_7{\cdot}CH$ ‖ $CH{\cdot}(CH_2)_7{\cdot}COOH$	m.p. 44–45° C b.p. 288° C/100 d^{79} 0.851 n_D^{70} 1.4405	Formed by isomerization of oleic acid
trans-Vaccenic acid (*trans*-Δ^{11}-octadecenoic acid)	$C_{18}H_{34}O_2$ 282.47	$CH_3{\cdot}(CH_2)_5{\cdot}CH$ ‖ $CH{\cdot}(CH_2)_9{\cdot}COOH$	m.p. 42.5° C d^{70} 0.8560 n_D^{60} 1.4439	Occurs in many animal fats and vegetable oils
cis-Vaccenic acid (*cis*-Δ^{11}-octadecenoic acid)	$C_{18}H_{34}O_2$ 282.47	$CH{\cdot}(CH_2)_9{\cdot}COOH$ ‖ $CH{\cdot}(CH_2)_5{\cdot}CH_3$	m.p. 12.4–13° C	Has been shown to be the hemolytic acid occurring in plasma and various animal tissues[1]. Also present in *Lactobacillus* species[2]
Δ^{12}-Octadecenoic acid	$C_{18}H_{34}O_2$ 282.47	$CH_3{\cdot}(CH_2)_4{\cdot}CH{=}CH{\cdot}(CH_2)_{10}{\cdot}COOH$		Occurs in partially hydrogenated peanut oil
Gadoleic acid (Δ^9-eicosenoic acid)	$C_{20}H_{38}O_2$ 310.52	$CH_3{\cdot}(CH_2)_9{\cdot}CH{=}CH{\cdot}(CH_2)_7{\cdot}COOH$	m.p. 24.5° C	*Cis*- and *trans*-forms. In many fish and marine animal oils, in vegetable oils, in brain phosphatides
Δ^{11}-Eicosenoic acid	$C_{20}H_{38}O_2$ 310.52	$CH_3{\cdot}(CH_2)_7{\cdot}CH{=}CH{\cdot}(CH_2)_9{\cdot}COOH$	m.p. *cis* 22° C *trans* 52–53° C	Principal acid of jojoba nuts ("goat nuts"), also in seed oil of *Conringia orientalis,* rape and mustard seed oils, fish oils
Cetoleic acid (Δ^{11}-docosenoic acid)	$C_{22}H_{42}O_2$ 338.58	$CH_3{\cdot}(CH_2)_9{\cdot}CH{=}CH{\cdot}(CH_2)_9{\cdot}COOH$	m.p. 32–33° C	Occurs in various marine oils
Erucic acid (*cis*-Δ^{13}-docosenoic acid)	$C_{22}H_{42}O_2$ 338.58	$CH{\cdot}(CH_2)_{11}{\cdot}COOH$ ‖ $CH{\cdot}(CH_2)_7{\cdot}CH_3$	m.p. 33.5° C b.p. 281° C/30 d^{55} 0.860 n_D^{64} 1.4480	Occurs in seed oils, esp. rapeseed oil
Brassidic acid (*trans*-Δ^{13}-docosenoic acid)	$C_{22}H_{42}O_2$ 338.58	$CH_3{\cdot}(CH_2)_7{\cdot}CH$ ‖ $CH{\cdot}(CH_2)_{11}{\cdot}COOH$	m.p. 61.5° C b.p. 282° C/30 d^{57} 0.8585 n_D^{100} 1.4347	Formed by isomerization of erucic acid
Selacholeic acid (nervonic acid, *cis*-Δ^{15}-tetracosenoic acid)	$C_{24}H_{46}O_2$ 366.63	$CH{\cdot}(CH_2)_{13}{\cdot}COOH$ ‖ $CH{\cdot}(CH_2)_7{\cdot}CH_3$	m.p. 40.5–41° C n_D^{46} 1.4535	Occurs in shark and ray liver oils, in brain cerebrosides (nervone) and sphingomyelins[3]
Ximenic acid (Δ^{17}-hexacosenoic acid)	$C_{26}H_{50}O_2$ 394.69	$CH_3{\cdot}(CH_2)_7{\cdot}CH{=}CH{\cdot}(CH_2)_{15}{\cdot}COOH$	m.p. 45° C	Occurs in *Ximenia americana* (tallow-wood). A hexacosenoic acid is found with nervonic acid in brain cerebrosides

Table 18 Fatty acids *(continued)*

Name of acid	Formula and mol. wt.	Structure	Physical properties	Remarks
		Unsaturated (polyolefinic) straight-chain monocarboxylic acids		
Sorbic acid ($\Delta^{2,4}$-hexadienoic acid)	$C_6H_8O_2$ 112.13	$CH_3\cdot CH{=}CH\cdot CH{=}CH\cdot COOH$	m.p. 134.5° C b.p. 228° C (decomp.)	Occurs as lactone in oil of unripe mountain ash berries
Linoleic acid (*cis-cis*-$\Delta^{9,12}$-octadecadienoic acid)	$C_{18}H_{32}O_2$ 280.45	$CH_3\cdot(CH_2)_4\cdot CH$ ‖ $CH\cdot CH_2\cdot CH$ ‖ $CH\cdot(CH_2)_7\cdot COOH$	m.p. −11(−5)° C b.p. 230° C/16 d^{20} 0.9025 n_D^{20} 1.4699	Widely distributed in plants, esp. in linseed, hemp and cottonseed oils. Also in depot fat of animals (component of phosphatides)
Hiragonic acid ($\Delta^{6,10,14}$-hexadecatrienoic acid)	$C_{16}H_{26}O_2$ 250.38	$CH\cdot(CH_2)_2\cdot CH{=}CH\cdot CH_3$ ‖ $CH\cdot(CH_2)_2\cdot CH{=}CH\cdot(CH_2)_4\cdot COOH$	d^{20} 0.9288 n_D^{20} 1.4855	Occurs in sardine oil
α-Eleostearic acid (*cis*-$\Delta^{9,11,13}$-octadecatrienoic acid)	$C_{18}H_{30}O_2$ 278.44	$CH_3\cdot(CH_2)_3\cdot(CH{=}CH)_3\cdot(CH_2)_7\cdot COOH$ (both α and β)	m.p. 48° C b.p. 235° C/12 d^{56} 0.8980 n_D^{56} 1.5080	Occurs in vegetable oils, esp. tung oil
β-Eleostearic acid (*trans*-$\Delta^{9,11,13}$-octadecatrienoic acid)	$C_{18}H_{30}O_2$ 278.44		m.p. 71° C d^{80} 0.8839 n_D^{74} 1.5000	Formed from α-eleostearic acid by action of light, heat and chemical reagents
Linolenic acid ($\Delta^{9,12,15}$-octadecatrienoic acid)	$C_{18}H_{30}O_2$ 278.44	$CH\cdot CH_2\cdot CH{=}CH\cdot CH_2\cdot CH_3$ ‖ $CH\cdot CH_2\cdot CH{=}CH\cdot(CH_2)_7\cdot COOH$	m.p. −11.2 to −11° C b.p. 230–232° C/17 d^{20} 0.9046 n_D^{20} 1.4780	Occurs in many vegetable oils, esp. drying oils such as linseed oil. Also in traces in animal fats (phosphatides)
Stearidonic acid (moroctic acid, $\Delta^{4,8,12,15}$-octadecatetraenoic acid)	$C_{18}H_{28}O_2$ 276.42	$CH_3\cdot CH_2\cdot CH{=}CH\cdot CH_2\cdot CH$ ‖ $CH\cdot(CH_2)_2\cdot CH{=}CH\cdot(CH_2)_2\cdot CH$ ‖ $CH\cdot(CH_2)_2\cdot COOH$	d^{20} 0.9297 n_D^{20} 1.4911	Occurs in fish oils. The position of the double bonds is not confirmed
Timnodonic acid ($\Delta^{4,8,12,15,18}$-eicosapentaenoic acid)	$C_{20}H_{30}O_2$ 302.46	$CH_3\cdot CH{=}CH\cdot CH_2\cdot CH{=}CH$ | $CH\cdot(CH_2)_2\cdot CH{=}CH\cdot CH_2$ ‖ $CH\cdot(CH_2)_2\cdot CH{=}CH\cdot(CH_2)_2\cdot COOH$		Occurs in sardine oil, cod-liver oil, pilot whale oil and oil from *Squalus suckleí* (spiny dog fish)
Arachidonic acid ($\Delta^{5,8,11,14}$-eicosatetraenoic acid)	$C_{20}H_{32}O_2$ 304.48	$CH_3\cdot(CH_2)_4\cdot CH{=}CH\cdot CH_2\cdot CH$ ‖ $CH\cdot CH_2\cdot CH{=}CH\cdot CH_2\cdot CH$ ‖ $CH\cdot(CH_2)_3\cdot COOH$	m.p. −49.5° C n_D^{20} 1.8482	Occurs in animal fats (liver, phosphatides) and in fish oils
Clupanodonic acid ($\Delta^{4,8,12,15,19}$-docosapentaenoic acid)	$C_{22}H_{34}O_2$ 330.51	$CH_3\cdot CH_2\cdot CH{=}CH\cdot(CH_2)_2\cdot CH$ ‖ $CH\cdot(CH_2)_2\cdot CH{=}CH\cdot CH_2\cdot CH$ ‖ $CH\cdot(CH_2)_2\cdot CH{=}CH\cdot(CH_2)_2\cdot COOH$	m.p. < −78° C b.p. 236° C/5 d^{20} 0.9290 n_D^{20} 1.4868	Occurs in fish oils
Nisinic acid ($\Delta^{4,8,12,15,18,21}$-tetracosahexaenoic acid)	$C_{24}H_{36}O_2$ 356.55	$CH_3\cdot CH_2\cdot CH{=}CH\cdot CH_2\cdot CH{=}CH\cdot CH_2$ | $CH\cdot(CH_2)_2\cdot CH{=}CH\cdot CH_2\cdot CH{=}CH$ ‖ $CH\cdot(CH_2)_2\cdot CH{=}CH\cdot(CH_2)_2\cdot COOH$		Occurs in tunny oil
Thynnic acid ($\Delta^?$-hexacosahexaenoic acid)	$C_{26}H_{40}O_2$ 384.61		d^{20} 0.9433 n_D^{20} 1.5022	Occurs in tunny oil

Table 18 Fatty acids *(concluded)*

Name of acid	Formula and mol. wt.	Structure	Physical properties	Remarks
		Unsaturated (acetylenic) straight-chain monocarboxylic acids		
Tariric acid (6-stearolic acid, 6-octadecynoic acid)	$C_{18}H_{32}O_2$ 280.45	$CH_3\cdot(CH_2)_{10}\cdot C{\equiv}C\cdot(CH_2)_4\cdot COOH$	m.p. 50.5° C	Occurs in fat of *Picramnia* spp. (tariri) (bitter-bush oil)
Stearolic acid (9-octadecynoic acid)	$C_{18}H_{32}O_2$ 280.45	$CH_3\cdot(CH_2)_7\cdot C{\equiv}C\cdot(CH_2)_7\cdot COOH$	m.p. 48.5° C b.p. 260° C	Formed by oxidation of oleic or elaidic acid
Behenolic acid (13-docosynoic acid)	$C_{22}H_{40}O_2$ 336.56	$CH_3\cdot(CH_2)_7\cdot C{\equiv}C\cdot(CH_2)_{11}\cdot COOH$	m.p. 57.5° C	Formed by oxidation of erucic or brassidic acid
		Branched-chain monocarboxylic acids		
*iso*Butyric acid (2-methyl-propanoic acid)	$C_4H_8O_2$ 88.11	CH_3 ⟩CH·COOH CH_3	m.p. −47° C b.p. 154.4° C d^{20} 0.949 n_D^{20} 1.393	Occurs free in carob beans *(Ceratonia siliqua)*, as ethyl ester in croton oil; also in feces and as product of enzymic breakdown of proteins. Intermediate in metabolism of valine (see page 408)
*iso*Valeric acid (3-methylbutanoic acid)	$C_5H_{10}O_2$ 102.14	CH_3 ⟩CH·CH_2·COOH CH_3	m.p. −51° C b.p. 176.7° C d^{15} 0.937 $n_D^{22.4}$ 1.40178	Occurs in root of valerian, tobacco leaves, volatile oils, depot fat of dolphins and porpoises, as glyceride in human feces. Formed from leucine in bacterial degradation of proteins. Intermediate in metabolism of leucine (see page 408)
Tiglic acid (*cis*-2-methyl-Δ^2-butenoic acid)	$C_5H_8O_2$ 100.12	$CH_3\cdot CH{=}C\cdot COOH$ | CH_3	m.p. 64.5° C b.p. 198.5° C d^{76} 0.964 n_D^{81} 1.4342	Occurs in croton oil (glyceride); in Roman cumin oil (esters), in geranium oils. Intermediate in metabolism of isoleucine (see page 408)
Tuberculostearic acid (D-(−)10-methyl-octadecanoic acid)	$C_{19}H_{38}O_2$ 298.51	$CH_3\cdot(CH_2)_7\cdot CH\cdot(CH_2)_8\cdot COOH$ | CH_3	m.p. 12.5–12.9 (23.5–25.8)° C b.p. 180° C/0.1 d^{24} 0.8771 n_D^{25} 1.4512 $[\alpha]_D^{19}$ −0.08°	Occurs free in lipids of tubercle bacilli and *Mycobacterium leprae*[4]
Mycolipenic acid ([+]-2,4,6-tri-methyltetracos-2-enoic acid)	$C_{27}H_{52}O_2$ 408.71	$CH_3\cdot(CH_2)_{17}\cdot CH\cdot CH_2\cdot CH\cdot CH{=}C\cdot COOH$ | | | CH_3 CH_3 CH_3		The so-called "phthioic acid" of tubercle bacilli has been shown to be a mixture of these acids and a third component[5]
Mycoceranic acid	$C_{32}H_{64}O_2$ 480.87	$CH_3\cdot(CH_2)_{22}\cdot CH\cdot CH_2\cdot CH\cdot CH_2\cdot CH\cdot COOH$ | | | CH_3 CH_3 CH_3		
		Hydroxy acids		
Ricinoleic acid (*cis*-12-hydroxy-Δ^9-octadecenoic acid)	$C_{18}H_{34}O_3$ 298.47	$CH\cdot CH_2\cdot CH(OH)\cdot(CH_2)_5\cdot CH_3$ ‖ $CH\cdot(CH_2)_7\cdot COOH$	m.p. 5; 7.7; 16° C (3 forms) b.p. 250° C/15 n_D^{20} 1.4711 $[\alpha]_D^{20}$ +7.8°	As glyceride, chief constituent of castor oil
Cerebronic acid (phrenosinic acid, 2-hydroxytetra-cosanoic acid)	$C_{24}H_{48}O_3$ 384.65	$CH_3\cdot(CH_2)_{21}\cdot CH(OH)\cdot COOH$	m.p. 90–93 (102)° C $[\alpha]_D^{22}$ +3.33°	Component of cerebroside phrenosin (cerebron). The natural product contains 15% of the corresponding hexacosanoic acid[6]
2-Hydroxynervonic acid (2-hydroxy-Δ^{15}-tetracosenoic acid)	$C_{24}H_{46}O_3$ 382.63	$CH_3\cdot(CH_2)_7\cdot CH{=}CH\cdot(CH_2)_{12}\cdot CH(OH)\cdot COOH$	m.p. 65° C $[\alpha]_D^{20}$ +2.87°	Component of cerebroside hydroxynervone, of which the isomeric Δ^{17}-acid is also a component

References

1) LASER, H., *J. Physiol. (Lond.)*, **110**, 338 (1949); MORTON and TODD, *Biochem. J.*, **47**, 327 (1950). *2)* BOUNDS et al., *J. chem. Soc.*, **1954**, 448. *3)* HOFMANN and SAX, *J. biol. Chem.*, **205**, 55 (1953). *4)* SCHMIDT and SHIRLEY, *J. Amer. chem. Soc.*, **71**, 3804 (1949); LINSTEAD et al., *J. chem. Soc.*, **1951**, 1130. *5)* POLGÁR, N., *J. chem. Soc.*, **1954**, 1008, 1011; ASSELINEAU et al., *Acta chem. scand.*, **11**, 196 (1957); LEDERER, E., *Angew. Chem.*, **72**, 372 (1960). *6)* CHIBNALL et al., *Biochem. J.*, **55**, 707 (1953); MISLOW and BLEICHER, *J. Amer. chem. Soc.*, **76**, 2825 (1954).

6. Enzymes

Enzymes are protein catalysts which range in molecular weight from about 13,000 (lysozyme, ribonuclease) up to as much as 840,000 (myosin). They are purified and isolated by the use of techniques for fractionating proteins[1]. Their general properties will be described in the section which follows. The specific enzymes responsible for digestion are dealt with on pages 416–427.

Nomenclature of enzymes

Enzymes are usually given names which indicate both the principal substrate and the reaction catalyzed (e.g. malic dehydrogenase). Many enzymes have, however, been given trivial names and these are often a cause of confusion.

The word "enzyme" usually denotes a catalytic protein plus any component that cannot be readily removed from the protein without denaturing it. The usage is not, however, very rigid for in some contexts "enzyme" is intended to include dissociable cofactors and in others to indicate the catalytic protein *per se*. If there is danger of ambiguity, the catalytic protein is denoted by the term "*apo-enzyme*" and the protein plus cofactors by "*holo-enzyme*".

Coenzymes or *prosthetic groups* are nonprotein organic compounds which, in combination with the apo-enzyme, play an intimate part in the catalysis by the enzyme. There is no generally-accepted distinction between coenzymes and prosthetic groups, but the latter name is usually reserved for groups that are bound relatively firmly by the protein. "*Activators*" are usually distinguished from coenzymes in being small ions that are required by some enzymes for full catalytic activity. Some enzymes do not appear to possess a prosthetic group or coenzyme nor do they require an activator.

Specificity of enzymes[2]

Although nearly all the individual reactions of intermediary metabolism are catalyzed by separate enzymes (see pages 401–415), few of these enzymes are absolutely specific to the structure of their substrates. Most enzymes can act on close structural analogues of their physiological substrates, although usually at much reduced rates, whilst a few enzymes can act on a relatively wide group of substrates. Like any other catalyst, an enzyme acts in both the forward and reverse reactions, but the extent of the reversibility is determined by the equilibrium of the reaction being catalyzed and the availability of the necessary reactants.

There are no completely general rules of enzyme specificity, for in different enzyme systems different parts of the substrate molecule appear to be important. Thus, the lipases require an ester bond in their substrates but there can be very considerable variation in the structures of the groups adjoining this susceptible bond. On the other hand, chymotrypsin and trypsin require certain configurations in the neighborhood of the susceptible bond, but the nature of the bond itself can vary. For example, these enzymes will hydrolyze peptide bonds in protein substrates but in certain artificial substrates (e.g. methyl cinnamate) ester bonds can be hydrolyzed.

An added complication is that those hydrolytic enzymes which can act on several substrates are usually capable of catalyzing a transferring reaction in which an alcohol or an amine replaces the water. Many of these transfer reactions are unlikely to be of physiological significance because of the prevalence of water molecules under physiological conditions.

Many enzymes show stereochemical specificity in being unable to attack geometrical or optical isomers of their substrates. Less specific enzymes such as the esterases can, however, attack stereochemical isomers although usually at reduced rates.

Mechanism of enzyme action

Enzymes combine with their substrates at three or more points[3]. An attractive hypothesis is that after the formation of this enzyme–substrate compound there is a simultaneous attack on the substrate by two groups of the enzyme, one withdrawing an electron and the other donating an electron to a different atom of the substrate and thus promoting the reaction of the substrate[4]. Such a bifunctional attack would be analogous to the catalytic hydrolysis of glycosides by 2-hydroxypyridine[5] and would explain why enzymes are much more effective catalysts than monofunctional catalysts such as acids or bases.

Some enzymes have been found to retain their activity after much selective chemical modification or enzymic degradation[6]. Only part of the enzyme protein is therefore essential for catalytic activity.

Equilibrium. Although an enzyme may induce a reaction that cannot be appreciably detected in its absence, the enzyme cannot affect the equilibrium position.

Enzyme kinetics[7]

When an enzyme is added to a suitable reaction mixture, there is first a very short lag before a steady rate of reaction is attained[8]. This lag is so short that it is not detectable when the rate is obtained from measurements made at intervals of one minute or longer. Once established, the rate remains constant for a period which may sometimes be as long as several hours, although in other cases it may be only a few minutes. The rate of reaction begins to fall after this period because of reduced substrate concentration and/or the accumulation of products. This decrease in reaction rate is not easily analyzed mathematically and it is therefore usual to study only the constant reaction rate. The following discussion is confined to this constant reaction rate.

If the enzyme is susceptible to inhibition by excess substrate (see below) the rate may at first increase as the inhibition is relieved by removal of the substrate.

Enzyme concentration. The reaction rate is usually proportional to the concentration of enzyme. Strict linearity may not always be achieved experimentally, for instance because the enzyme preparation may contain a dissociable activator or inhibitor or the enzyme may be unstable at low concentrations. Alternatively, the reaction may have proceeded so far that the rate has already commenced to fall off at the highest enzyme concentrations.

Hydrogen-ion concentration. Most enzymes possess well-defined pH optima with appreciable activity over a range of only 2–3 pH units. Some enzymes are inhibited by some of the buffers in common use. It is therefore often worthwhile to compare the results in one buffer with those obtained in another type of buffer solution of the same pH range.

The study of kinetic data obtained at different pH values with different substrates and different concentrations of a single substrate is of use in investigating the details of enzyme mechanisms[9,10]. For other purposes, the variations in the pH curve with different substrates and substrate concentrations are not usually important.

Temperature. The rate of an enzyme-catalyzed reaction increases by a factor which is usually 1.5–3 for every rise of 10°C. There is, however, an optimum temperature above which further increase reduces the amount of substrate reacting because the enzyme becomes inactivated. The optimum temperature for short-term experiments (e.g. of one hour duration) is often about 50°C. Most mammalian enzymes show little inactivation in the presence of their cofactors and substrates at 37°C so that this is usually a suitable temperature to study the reaction. It is not desirable to increase the temperature to the optimum because the rate of enzyme inactivation, and therefore the optimum temperature, is often greatly influenced by slight changes of the experimental conditions.

Substrate concentration. As the initial substrate concentration is increased, the rate of reaction is at first proportional to this concentration, but at higher values it usually becomes virtually independent of it. This relation can be justified theoretically by considering a mechanism such as

$$\mathrm{E} + \mathrm{S} \underset{k_2}{\overset{k_1}{\rightleftharpoons}} \mathrm{ES} \overset{k_3}{\rightarrow} \mathrm{E} + \mathrm{P} \qquad (1)$$

where E is the enzyme, S the substrate, ES the enzyme–substrate compound, P the products, and k_1, k_2 and k_3 the rate constants of the three reactions. The constant steady-state velocity v is given by

$$v = \frac{V[\mathrm{S}]}{K_s + [\mathrm{S}]} \qquad (2)$$

where V is the maximum velocity obtained at high substrate concentrations, [S] the concentration of substrate, and K_s a quantity which is termed the "MICHAELIS constant". [S] is strictly the concentration of substrate not combined with the enzyme, but the amount of enzyme is usually so low that there is virtually no difference between the concentrations of free and total substrate. Mathematically, V is given by k_3e where e is the total concentration of enzyme present. K_s is given by $(k_2 + k_3)/k_1$ and has the dimensions of concentration. Although K_s is independent of both [S] and e, it usually changes with pH, temperature, different substrates and the cofactor concentration. K_s may sometimes change with ionic strength or with different buffers and, like other characteristics of enzymes, it may differ for similar enzymes from different sources.

Fig. 5 Inhibition data plotted according to Table 19

Each line represents data for a series of substrate concentrations. One line of each graph is without inhibition and the other two are for two different concentrations of inhibitor

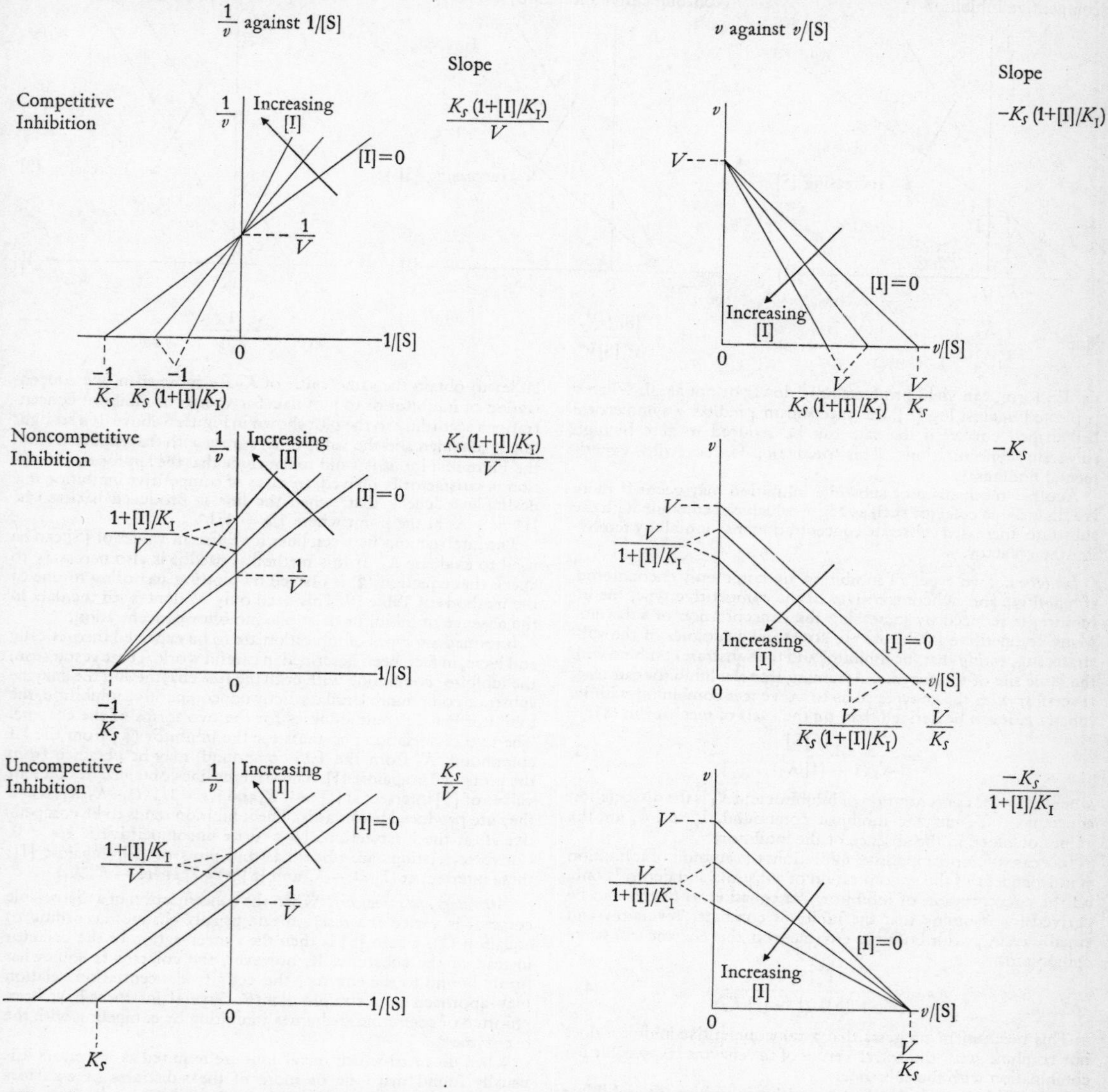

Equation (**2**) was first obtained theoretically by MICHAELIS and MENTEN[11] who assumed that the second reaction of mechanism (**1**) was the rate-limiting step. Under these conditions k_2 is much greater than k_3, and K_s becomes k_2/k_1, which is the dissociation constant of the enzyme–substrate compound. This assumption is known to be valid for some enzymes but not for others[4].

Evaluation of MICHAELIS *constant* K_s *and maximum velocity* V. K_s may be evaluated as being equal to the concentration of substrate at which the velocity is half the maximum. This may be done by plotting the curve of v against [S]. The experimental data can, however, be used more efficiently by plotting certain functions of v and [S] as shown in Table 19[12]. These plots give straight lines if equation (**2**) is obeyed. The plot of $1/v$ against $1/[S]$ has the advantage that the variables are separate and the calculations for plotting are thus quicker. Unfortunately the points are not evenly spread and the errors at low values of v are accentuated. This method gives accurate values for V but less accurate estimates for K_s. The second method (Table 19) is usually the most satisfactory for evaluating both K_s and V.

It is sometimes convenient, such as when comparing different substrates, to plot v against log [S]. This plot gives an S-shaped curve instead of a straight line; the inflection of this curve occurs at a value of log [S] equal to $\log K_s$.

Table 19 Linear plots for evaluating MICHAELIS constant K_s and maximum velocity V

The plot of v against $v/[S]$ is usually the most satisfactory

Plot		Slope	Intercept	
Ordinate	Abscissa		Ordinate	Abscissa
$1/v$	$1/[S]$	K_s/V	$1/V$	$-1/K_s$
v	$v/[S]$	$-K_s$	V	V/K_s
$[S]/v$	[S]	$1/V$	K_s/V	$-K_s$

Inhibition by excess substrate. This phenomenon occurs with some enzymes and is usually explained by postulating that the enzyme–substrate compound (ES) combines with a second molecule of S to form an inactive complex which, unless it reverts to the origi-

Fig. 6 Inhibition data: Plots of $1/v$ against [I][16]

Each line represents data for a series of inhibitor concentrations [I] but at different substrate concentrations [S]

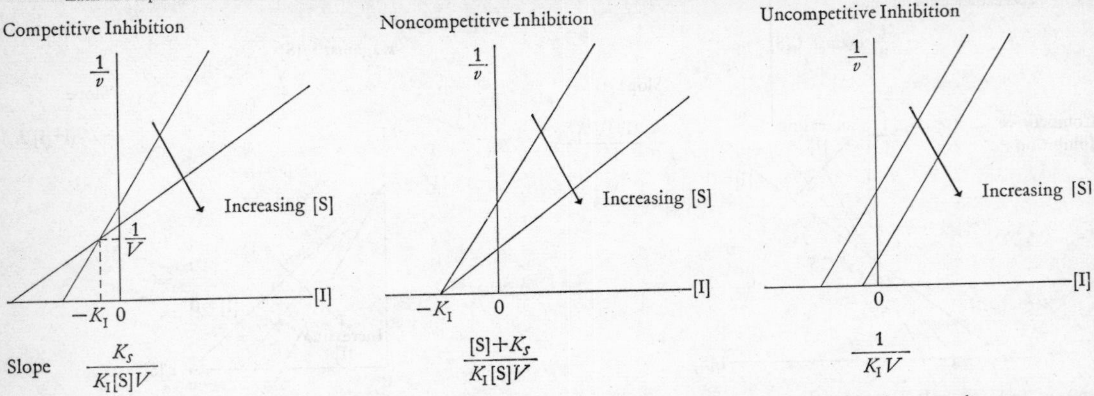

nal ES form, can yield products only slowly or not at all. When v is plotted against log [S], this mechanism predicts a symmetrical bell-shaped curve[13] if the rate can be reduced to zero by high substrate concentrations. This prediction agrees with experimental findings[14].

Another mechanism of substrate inhibition may occur if there is a dissociable cofactor such as Mg^{++} which can combine with the substrate. Increased substrate concentration may inhibit by removing the cofactor.

Inhibitors. Two types of inhibition are commonly encountered, competitive and noncompetitive. In the competitive type, the inhibition is reduced by increasing the concentration of substrate. Many competitive inhibitors are structural analogues of the substrate, suggesting that the inhibitor and the substrate combine with the same site of the enzyme. Assuming that the inhibitor can react reversibly with the enzyme so as to prevent it combining with its substrate, it can be derived that, on the basis of mechanism (**1**):

$$v = \frac{V[S]}{K_s(1 + [I]/K_I) + [S]} \qquad (3)$$

where [I] is the concentration of inhibitor and K_I is the dissociation constant of the enzyme–inhibitor compound. V and K_s are the values obtained in the absence of the inhibitor.

In a case of noncompetitive inhibition, the amount of inhibition is independent of the concentration of substrate and depends only on the concentration of inhibitor. An equation to fit this can be derived by assuming that the inhibitor combines reversibly and equally readily with both the enzyme and the enzyme–substrate compound:

$$v = \frac{V[S]}{(K_s + [S])\,(1 + [I]/K_I)} \qquad (4)$$

This mechanism suggests that a noncompetitive inhibitor does not combine with the active center of the enzyme responsible for combination with the substrate.

It should be noted that, in competitive inhibition, the inhibitor increases the apparent MICHAELIS constant without affecting the maximum velocity, whereas in noncompetitive inhibition the inhibitor decreases the maximum velocity without changing the MICHAELIS constant.

A third and less common type of inhibition is that in which both the maximum velocity and the MICHAELIS constant are reduced to a similar extent, so that there is no change in the ratio K_s/V as evaluated from the plots of Table 19. This type of inhibition has been termed uncompetitive and is illustrated by the action of azide on the oxidized form of cytochrome oxidase[15]. The appropriate equation is based on the assumption that the inhibitor combines only with the enzyme–substrate compound:

$$v = \frac{V[S]}{K_s + [S]\,(1 + [I]/K_I)} \qquad (5)$$

Plotting inhibition data. The different types of inhibition can be clearly differentiated by using any of the substrate plots of Table 19 and thus determining the effect of the inhibitor on the apparent K_s or V. Examples are shown in Figure 5 (page 397). K_I can be evaluated from the quantitative nature of this effect. To show that the appropriate equations are satisfactorily obeyed it is necessary either to obtain the same value of K_I for more than one concentration of inhibitor or to plot data for a series of inhibitor concentrations according to the plot shown in Figure 6 above. If a straight line is obtained and the value of K_I agrees with that expected from the Figure 5 plot, it is valid to conclude that the appropriate equation is satisfactorily obeyed. In cases of competitive inhibition it is desirable to check that, when the line is produced backwards, $[I] = -K_I$ at the point where $1/v = 1/V$.

The intersections between lines for different values of [S] can be used to evaluate K_I. If this method is used it is also necessary to check that equation (**2**) is obeyed by plotting according to one of the methods of Table 19. This need only be done with the data in the absence of inhibitor or at one inhibitor concentration.

Intermediate types of inhibition are to be expected theoretically and have, in fact, been described in careful work. These result from the inhibitor combining with both the free enzyme and the enzyme substrate compound. Unlike strictly noncompetitive inhibition, the inhibitor has different affinities for the two forms of the enzyme. The two dissociation constants for the inhibitor (K_I from the EI compound, K_I' from the EIS compound) may be obtained from the plots of $1/v$ against [I]. The straight lines obtained at different values of [S] intersect at $[I] = -K_I$ and $1/v = 1/V(1 - K_I/K_I')$ when they are produced backwards. The inhibition tends to be competitive if, at the intersection, $1/v > 0$, or uncompetitive if $1/v < 0$. Converse relations are obtained from plots of $[S]/v$ against [I]; these intersect at $[I] = -K_I'$ and $[S]/v = K_s/V(1 - K_I'/K_I)$.

Activators and coenzymes. When the concentration of a dissociable cofactor is varied the reaction rate usually changes according to equation (**2**), where [S] is then the concentration of the cofactor instead of the substrate. If, however, the cofactor is somewhat firmly bound to the enzyme, the activity–concentration relation may approach two straight lines[17]. Several instances have been reported of coenzyme analogues inhibiting by competing with the coenzyme[18].

When di- or tri-valent metal ions are required as activators it is usually found that one or more of the substrates or cofactors spontaneously combine with the activator. This can introduce serious complications into the kinetic relations.

References

1) SCHWIMMER and PARDEE, *Advanc. Enzymol.*, **14**, 375 (1953). *2)* For a review see HELFERICH, B., in SUMNER and MYRBÄCK (Eds.), *The Enzymes*, vol. I, part 1, New York 1950, page 79. *3)* OGSTON, A. G., *Nature*, **162**, 963 (1948). *4)* LAIDLER, K. J., *Disc. Faraday Soc.*, **20**, 83 (1955). *5)* SWAIN and BROWN, *J. Amer. chem. Soc.*, **74**, 2538 (1952). *6)* ROGERS and KALNITSKY, *Biochim. biophys. Acta*, **23**, 525 (1957). *7)* For more extensive treatments see WILSON, P. W., in LARDY, H. A. (Ed.), *Respiratory Enzymes*, Minneapolis, 1949; FRIEDENWALD and MAENGWYN-DAVIES, in MCELROY and GLASS (Eds.), *The Mechanism of Enzyme Action*, Baltimore, 1954, pages 154, 180, 191; ALBERTY, R. A., *Advanc. Enzymol.*, **17**, 1 (1956). *8)* GUTFREUND, H., *Disc. Faraday Soc.*, **20**, 167 (1955). *9)* ALBERTY, R. A., *Advanc. Enzymol.*, **17**, 1 (1956). *10)* LAIDLER, K. J., *Trans. Faraday Soc.*, **51**, 528, 540, 550 (1955). *11)* MICHAELIS and MENTEN, *Biochem. Z.*, **49**, 333 (1913); cf. HENRI, V., *C. R. Acad. Sci. (Paris)*, **135**, 916 (1902). *12)* HOFSTEE, B. H. J., *Enzymologia (Amst.)*, **17**, 273 (1956); HALDANE and STERN, *Allgemeine Chemie der Enzyme*, Dresden and Leipzig, 1932. *13)* FRIEDENWALD and MAENGWYN-DAVIES, in MCELROY and GLASS (Eds.), *The Mechanism of Enzyme Action*, Baltimore, 1954, page 180. *14)* For example see MARCUS and TALALAY, *Proc. roy. Soc. B*, **144**, 116 (1955). *15)* WINZLER, R. J., *J. cell. comp. Physiol.*, **21**, 229 (1943). *16)* DIXON, M., *Biochem. J.*, **55**, 170 (1953). *17)* THEORELL, H., *Biochem. Z.*, **278**, 263 (1935). *18)* For example see WALAAS and WALAAS. *Acta chem. scand.*, **10**, 122 (1956).

The following review of metabolism has been contributed by Professor Sir H. A. KREBS, F.R.S., Dr. R. B. CLAYTON, Dr. H. L. KORNBERG, Dr. J. M. LOWENSTEIN and Dr. J. R. QUAYLE, Department of Biochemistry, University of Oxford, England. The subject has been dealt with under the following broad headings:

This review should be read in conjunction with the preceding chapter, Constituents of Living Matter (pages 336–398).

General aspects of metabolism

Chemical changes taking place in living organisms are commonly referred to as *metabolism*. By far the greater part of metabolism arises directly or indirectly from the need of living cells for energy. A smaller proportion is due to the formation of new tissues in the growing organism; the synthesis of special substances such as hormones, antibodies, digestive enzymes, urea; the detoxication of drugs and other foreign substances; and the replacement of losses due to wear and tear of the body (for example of surface epithelia or of red and white blood cells).

Since all manifestations of life are accompanied by metabolic activities, the study of metabolism is a fundamental aspect of all branches of biology. It may be taken as axiomatic that all pathological events also involve metabolic changes, either qualitative or quantitative, and the study of the biochemistry of disease is therefore of the greatest importance to medicine. The concept that most diseases – those called organic – have an anatomical basis has long been established. Every anatomical change in turn has a material, that is chemical, basis and beyond the field covered by morbid anatomy there is therefore a "molecular pathology" which deals with pathological changes in terms of chemical substances and chemical reactions. A pathological tissue is liable to possess an abnormal chemical composition as well as abnormal chemical activities, and the study of these chemical abnormalities provides a closer insight into the nature of the disorder. It may also supply information about "functional" disorders where no morphological change is detectable, because not all chemical derangements are necessarily accompanied by morphological changes. In fact, at the molecular level the distinctions between organic and functional diseases are reduced to quantitative differences, organic diseases being those disorders where the molecular changes are large enough to come within the range of optical tools.

So far little more than a beginning has been made in the biochemical analysis of disease. The knowledge summarized in the following pages represents a foundation upon which molecular pathology will develop.

Energy metabolism

The need for energy springs from the fact that living matter is a thermodynamically unstable system which cannot be maintained unless energy is continuously added. Moreover, living matter is constantly engaged in performing various kinds of work, such as movement, chemical syntheses and transporting substances against concentration gradients. Activities of this kind cannot take place unless there is a supply of energy. Warm-blooded organisms need energy also to maintain the body temperature.

Energy is obtained by the degradation of foodstuffs. In higher organisms the overall effect of this degradation is essentially an oxidation of organic substances to carbon dioxide and water. This overall effect is the sum of many hundreds of separate chemical reactions many of which are now known in considerable detail.

Energy can also be obtained in the absence of air, i.e. anaerobically, by certain special degradation reactions of glucose and other hexoses. These are usually referred to as "fermentations" or "glycolysis". The only form of fermentation which occurs in animal tissues is the lactic acid fermentation, by which one molecule of glucose is split into two molecules of lactic acid:

$$C_6H_{12}O_6 \longrightarrow 2\ CH_3{\cdot}CH(OH){\cdot}COOH$$

Microorganisms possess many forms of fermentation, among which the most important is the alcoholic fermentation:

$$C_6H_{12}O_6 \longrightarrow 2\ CH_3{\cdot}CH_2OH + 2\ CO_2$$

The energy made available by fermentations is only a small fraction of that liberated by the oxidation of sugar. The complete oxidation of one mole of glucose yields about 686 kcal of free energy, whilst the fermentation of the same amount of glucose to lactic acid yields about 45 kcal. Thus to obtain the same amount of energy by fermentation about 15 times more glucose has to be decomposed.

Table 1 Rate of respiration (Q_{O_2}) of animal tissues*

Representative values, measured on isolated tissues, usually slices suspended in glucose–saline medium at 38–40° C. Unless otherwise stated the data refer to rat tissues. For further data see KREBS and JOHNSON[1]

Tissue	Q_{O_2}	*Tissue*	Q_{O_2}
Kidney cortex	−25	Rous sarcoma (chicken)	− 5
Kidney medulla (guinea pig)	− 8	FLEXNER's carcinoma	− 8
Liver	−13	Erythrocytes	− 0.6
Brain cortex	−12	Leukocytes	− 9
Brain, white matter	− 6	Thrombocytes	− 7
Retina	−30	Bone marrow, red	−10
Spleen	−12	Adipose tissue**	− 0.5
Lung	− 8	Connective tissue (renal capsule, goat)	− 1
Submaxillary gland	−12	Cartilage (costal)	− 0.5
Pancreas	− 4	Skin (newborn rat)	− 1
Intestinal mucosa	−12	Striated muscle:	
Colonic mucosa	−10	diaphragm	− 7
Adrenal gland	−10	– gastrocnemius	− 3
Pituitary gland	−12	– breast muscle (pigeon, minced)	−40
Thymus gland	− 5	Smooth muscle (gizzard, pigeon)	− 4
Thyroid (guinea pig)	− 8	Cardiac muscle (sheep, minced)	−18
Testis	−10		
JENSEN's sarcoma	−11		

* The magnitude of respiration and fermentation is commonly expressed by the "metabolic quotients" which are defined as follows:

$$Q_{O_2} = \frac{\text{microliters of } O_2 \text{ used}}{\text{milligrams dry weight} \times \text{hours}}$$

$$Q_{CO_2} = \frac{\text{microliters of } CO_2 \text{ used or produced}}{\text{milligrams dry weight} \times \text{hours}}$$

$$Q_{\text{lactic acid}} \text{ or } Q_L = \frac{\text{microliters of lactic acid formed}}{\text{milligrams dry weight} \times \text{hours}}$$

The disappearance of a substance is usually indicated by a negative sign, the formation by a positive sign. Anaerobic and aerobic conditions are denoted by the superscripts N_2 and O_2, e.g.: $Q_L^{N_2}$, $Q_L^{O_2}$

A nongaseous substance like lactic acid is treated as if it were a gas on the assumption that 1 millimole is equivalent to 22,400 µl of gas. The reasoning in favor of this somewhat unusual connotation is that many of the measurements have been made by gasometric methods even when a substance like lactic acid is not a gas. Lactic acid production is usually measured in the presence of bicarbonate and the formation of acid is therefore followed by the production of an equivalent amount of CO_2. Some authors prefer to express the amounts metabolized in micromoles. To convert micromoles into microliters, multiply micromoles by 22.4.

The following calculation translates the Q values into quantities which can be readily understood and which illustrate the high intensity of the metabolism of some cells. Since 1 milligram of lactic acid is equivalent to 250 µl of CO_2, a Q_L value of 25 means that the material produces 10% of its own dry weight of lactic acid per hour. Since 1 µl occupies roughly the space of 1 mg of tissue, and since the ratio of wet weight to dry weight is of the order of 5, a Q_{O_2} value of 5 means that the tissue uses about its own volume of oxygen per hour.

** Calculated for dry weight less ether-soluble matter.

References

1) KREBS and JOHNSON, *Tab. biol. (Amst.)*, **19**, 100 (1948), and ALBRITTON, E. C. (Ed.), *Standard Values in Nutrition and Metabolism*, Philadelphia, 1954.

Table 2 Rate of anaerobic lactic acid fermentation ($Q^{N_2}_{\text{lactic acid}}$) in animal tissues*

Representative values, measured on isolated tissues, usually slices suspended in glucose–saline medium at 38–40° C. Unless otherwise stated the data refer to rat tissues. For further data see [1]

Tissue	$Q^{N_2}_L$	*Tissue*	$Q^{N_2}_L$
Kidney cortex	3	Testis	8
Kidney medulla (guinea pig)	28	JENSEN's sarcoma	32
Liver	3	ROUS sarcoma (chicken)	30
Brain cortex	18	FLEXNER's carcinoma	30
Retina	88	Erythrocytes	0.35
Retina (pigeon)	180	Leukocytes (polymorphonuclear, rabbit)	22
Spleen	8	Leukocytes (mononuclear, rabbit)	22
Lung (rat embryo)	10	Thrombocytes	26
Submaxillary gland	5	Bone marrow, red	21
Pancreas (rabbit)	3.5	Adipose tissue**	0.7
Intestinal mucosa	14	Cartilage (costal)	1.5
Adrenal gland	4	Skin (newborn rat)	7
Pituitary gland	13	Embryo	12
Thymus gland	8		

* See footnote to Table 1, page 399.

** Calculated for dry weight less ether-soluble matter.

References

1) KREBS and JOHNSON, *Tab. biol. (Amst.)*, **19**, 100 (1948), and ALBRITTON, E.C. (Ed.), *Standard Values in Nutrition and Metabolism*, Philadelphia, 1954.

In most tissues of higher organisms, lactic acid fermentation is low in the presence of oxygen, but may be high in the absence of oxygen. The suppression of fermentation by oxygen, first observed by PASTEUR in yeast cells, is known as the PASTEUR effect.

Cell metabolism

The metabolism of the whole body is the result of the metabolic activities of the component tissues. Within the last 30 years methods have become available for the study of the metabolic activities of isolated tissues and organs. In particular, measurements have been made of the rate of respiration and lactic acid fermentation of many types of cells and tissues. A few representative figures for animal tissues are given in Tables 1 and 2.

There are wide variations in the metabolic activities of different materials. The highest rates of respiration and fermentation are found among microorganisms. *Azotobacter*, for example, at 38° C can give Q_{O_2} values of over 8000, and rates of 100–200 are common among bacteria. Anaerobic fermentation rates in microorganisms reach figures up to 400. The maximum rate of lactic acid production in muscle can probably reach $Q^{N_2}_L$ values of well over 100 for short periods. Avian retina gives the highest continuous rate of lactic acid production among animal tissues ($Q^{N_2}_L = 180$ in pigeon retina).

Low metabolic rates are generally found in tissues of relatively low physiological activity. This is true for resting glands or muscle and in particular for tissues whose function, like that of connective tissue or bone, is largely structural or, like that of adipose tissue, is concerned with the storage of metabolically inert material.

The rates of respiration and fermentation increase with temperature, like the majority of other chemical reactions. At a critical temperature – in the case of the warm-blooded animal at about 40° C, in the case of cold-blooded animals somewhat below this temperature – a further rise in temperature reduces metabolism. In exceptional cases, those of the thermophilic bacteria, the critical temperature may be as high as 80° C.

Among the factors which affect energy production in the intact warm-blooded animal, body size has long been recognized as being of major importance. The differences in the oxygen consumption of intact animals of different size are not exactly reflected in the rates of respiration of individual tissues. In general, the tissues of larger species have a somewhat lower metabolism than the tissues of smaller species, but the differences between the Q_{O_2} values of, for example, brain, kidney, liver, spleen and lung of different species are relatively small. The characteristic differences in the basal metabolic rate of animals of different size appear to be due mainly to differences in the resting metabolism of the musculature.

Energy-supplying reactions

The first stage in the utilization of foodstuffs either for the supply of energy or for other purposes consists of a hydrolytic breakdown of the large molecules of food to the small constituent units. Proteins are converted to amino acids, carbohydrates to hexoses, fats to glycerol and fatty acid, and nucleic acids to the constituent bases, pentoses and phosphate. This hydrolytic breakdown is commonly referred to as *digestion*. Biologically speaking, digestion results in the solubilization of the foodstuffs, a prerequisite to absorption from the intestine. Processes very similar to intestinal digestion also occur in most tissues when reserve materials are mobilized to serve as a source of energy, or when damaged tissues are "autolyzed".

Digestion is brought about by the combined action of many specific enzymes each dealing with the hydrolysis of one compound or of a series of closely related compounds. The basic properties of these enzymes are described on pages 416–427.

1. Intermediary stages of carbohydrate degradation

Hexoses formed by digestion in the intestinal tract are absorbed and reach the various tissues through the blood circulation. The main reaction by which hexoses are degraded is the anaerobic fermentation to lactic acid, followed by the oxidation of the products of fermentation. An alternative pathway of oxidation exists in which glucose is oxidized without first undergoing fission to a 3-carbon compound, but this pathway, the "pentose-phosphate cycle" (see page 428), is not a major source of energy in higher animals; it probably serves mainly to supply pentoses.

Table 3 Intermediary reactions of lactic acid fermentation (glycolysis) in animal tissues (for formulas of intermediates see Fig. 1)
These reactions occur in all animal tissues and in many microorganisms

No.	Intermediary reactions			Enzyme catalyzing the reaction
1	glucose + adenosine triphosphate (ATP)	→	glucose-6-phosphate + adenosine diphosphate (ADP)	Hexokinase
2	glucose-6-phosphate	→	fructose-6-phosphate	Hexose-phosphate isomerase
3	fructose-6-phosphate + ATP	→	fructose-1,6-diphosphate + ADP	Phosphofructokinase
4	fructose-1,6-diphosphate	→	dihydroxyacetone phosphate + 3-phosphoglyceraldehyde	Aldolase (zymohexase)
5	dihydroxyacetone phosphate	→	3-phosphoglyceraldehyde	Triose-phosphate isomerase
6	2 [3-phosphoglyceraldehyde + diphosphopyridine nucleotide (DPN) + phosphate	→	1,3-diphosphoglyceric acid + $DPNH_2$]	Triose-phosphate dehydrogenase
7	2 [1,3-diphosphoglyceric acid + ADP	→	3-phosphoglyceric acid + ATP]	Phosphoglycerokinase
8	2 [3-phosphoglyceric acid	→	2-phosphoglyceric acid]	Phosphoglyceromutase
9	2 [2-phosphoglyceric acid	→	phosphopyruvic acid + H_2O]	Enolase
10	2 [phosphopyruvic acid + ADP	→	pyruvic acid + ATP]	Pyruvate kinase
11	2 [pyruvic acid + $DPNH_2$	→	lactic acid + DPN]	Lactic dehydrogenase
	Balance: glucose + 2 ADP + 2 phosphate	→	2 lactic acid + 2 ATP + 2 H_2O	

Fig. 1 The intermediates of glycolysis formed from glucose

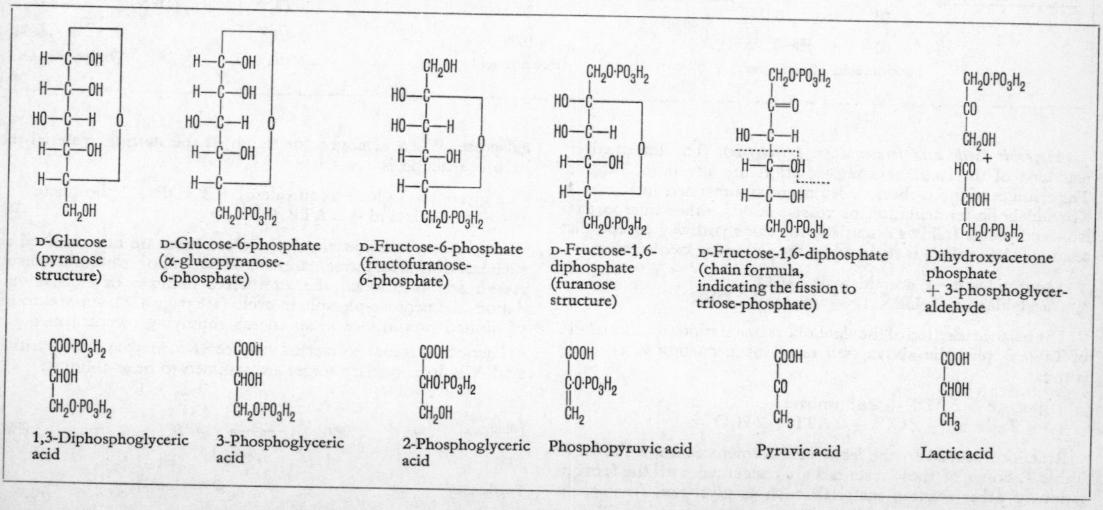

Table 4 Ancillary reactions of lactic acid fermentation in animal tissues

No.	Intermediary reactions			Enzyme catalyzing the reaction
1	glycogen + phosphate	⇌	glucose-1-phosphate	Phosphorylase
2	glucose-1-phosphate	⇌	glucose-6-phosphate	Phosphoglucomutase
3	fructose + ATP	→	fructose-6-phosphate + ADP	Hexokinase*
4	galactose + ATP	→	galactose-1-phosphate + ADP	Galactokinase[2]
5	galactose-1-phosphate + uridine diphosphoglucose	⇌	glucose-1-phosphate + uridine diphosphogalactose	Uridyl-transferase[3]
6	uridine diphosphogalactose	⇌	uridine diphosphoglucose	Galacto-waldenase[3]
7	uridine diphosphoglucose + pyrophosphate	⇌	uridine triphosphate (UTP) + glucose-1-phosphate	Pyrophosphorylase[4]
8	fructose + ATP	→	fructose-1-phosphate + ADP	Fructokinase (ketohexokinase)[5]
9	fructose-1-phosphate	⇌	dihydroxyacetone phosphate + glyceraldehyde	Aldolase[5]
10	glyceraldehyde + ATP	→	3-phosphoglyceraldehyde	Triokinase[5]

* Hexokinase reacts similarly with many other hexoses, e.g. mannose, 2-desoxyglucose[1].

References

1) Cf. SOLS and CRANE, *J. biol. Chem.*, **210**, 581 (1954). *2)* TRUCCO et al., *Arch. Biochem.*, **18**, 137 (1948). *3)* LELOIR, L. F., *Arch. Biochem. Biophys.*, **33**, 186 (1951); KALCKAR et al., *Nature*, **172**, 1038 (1953); KALCKAR and MAXWELL, *Biochim. biophys. Acta*, **22**, 588 (1956). *4)* MUNCH-PETERSEN et al., *Nature*, **172**, 1036 (1953). *5)* LEUTHARDT et al., *Helv. chim. Acta*, **36**, 227 (1953); HERS and KUSAKA, *Biochim. biophys. Acta*, **11**, 427 (1953).

Fig. 2 The individual stages of the tricarboxylic acid cycle

The names of the enzymes are given above the arrows, those of the coenzymes required below the arrows

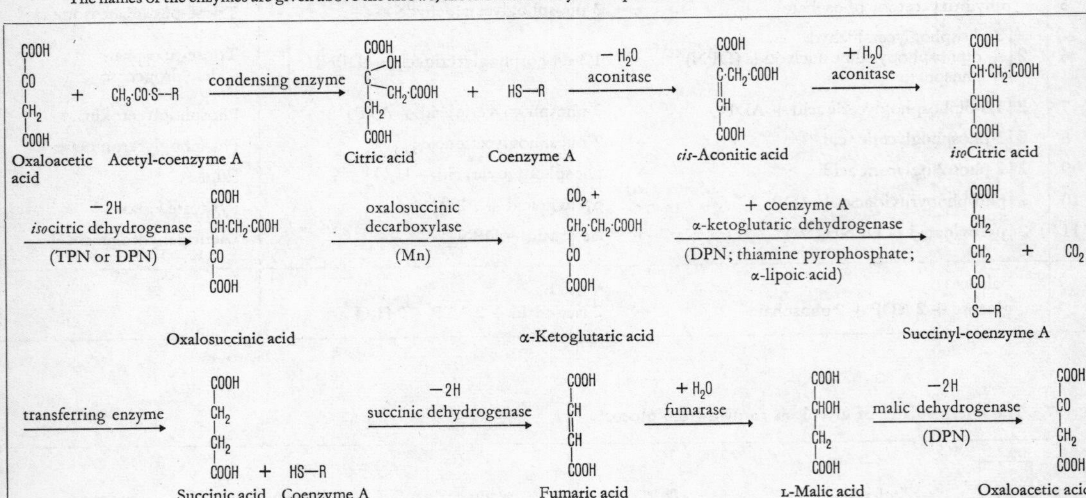

Anaerobic lactic acid fermentation (glycolysis). The intermediary reactions of the lactic acid fermentation are given in Table 3. The changes of the carbon skeleton are summarized in Figure 1. The alcoholic fermentation of yeasts, molds, other microorganisms and plants follows essentially the same pathway except that reaction 11 (Table 3) is replaced by the following two reactions:

pyruvic acid → acetaldehyde + CO_2
acetaldehyde + $DPNH_2$ → ethanol + DPN

The balance reaction of the alcoholic fermentation (reactions 1–10 of Table 3, plus the above two reactions occurring twice each) is thus:

glucose + 2 ADP + 2 phosphate
→ 2 ethanol + 2 CO_2 + 2 ATP + 2 H_2O

Reactions related to the lactic acid fermentation are shown in Table 4. Some of these reactions are concerned with the fermentation of other starting materials such as glycogen, fructose or galactose. When glycogen (or starch) is the starting material the balance reaction is

glycogen (1 glucose equivalent) + 3 ADP + 3 phosphate
→ 2 lactic acid + 3 ATP + 3 H_2O

Oxidation of carbohydrate. As a rule, sugars are not oxidized as such but only after fermentation to lactic acid or triose-phosphate. As already mentioned, the alternative pathway of glucose oxidation, the pentose-phosphate cycle (see page 428), appears to be of limited significance as an energy-supplying mechanism.

Lactic acid is first converted into acetyl-coenzyme A via pyruvic acid. The intermediary stages are assumed to be as follows:

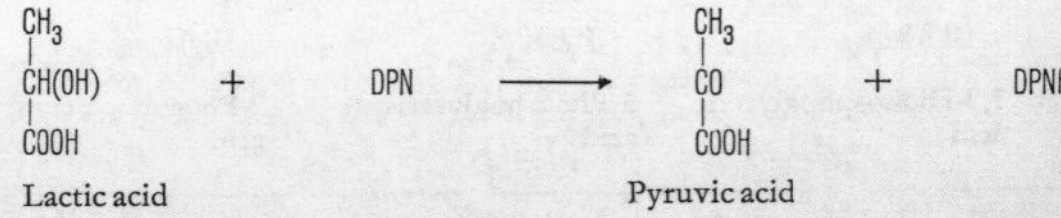

Lactic acid Pyruvic acid

The second step is assumed to be a reaction between pyruvate and thiamine pyrophosphate (TPP) in which an acetaldehyde-TPP complex is formed and CO_2 liberated:

Pyruvic acid — Thiamine pyrophosphate — Acetaldehyde-TPP complex

In the succeeding reaction the aldehyde-TPP complex reacts with the disulfide form of α-lipoic acid in such a manner that the aldehyde group of the complex is oxidized to a carboxyl group and the disulfide reduced to the dimercaptan; further the nascent carboxyl and one of the nascent thiol groups condense to form S-acetyl-α-lipoic acid:

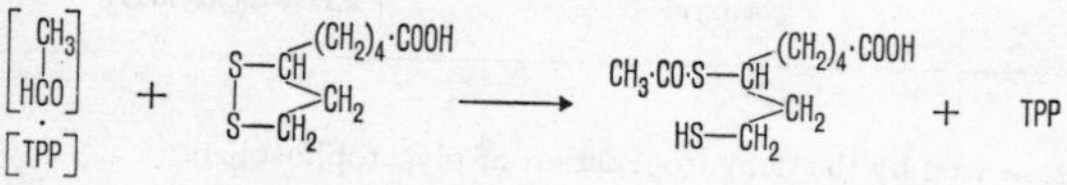

Acetaldehyde-TPP complex — Disulfide form of α-lipoic acid — S-acetyl-α-lipoic acid

In the next stage the acetyl group is transferred from α-lipoic acid to coenzyme A, with the formation of reduced lipoic acid and acetyl-coenzyme A. The reduced lipoic acid is reoxidized by interaction with DPN, catalyzed by lipoic acid dehydrogenase:

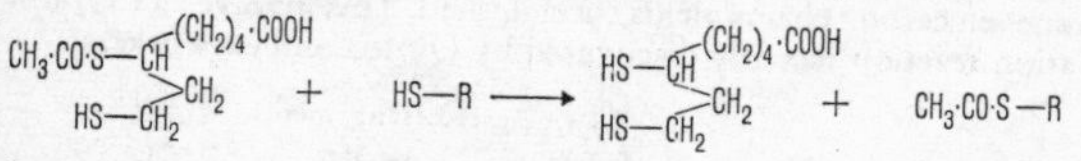

S-acetyl-α-lipoic acid + Coenzyme A — Reduced α-lipoic acid — Acetyl-coenzyme A

Reduced α-lipoic acid — Oxidized α-lipoic acid

The sum of the last four reactions is:

pyruvic acid + DPN + coenzyme A
→ acetyl-coenzyme A + $DPNH_2$ + CO_2

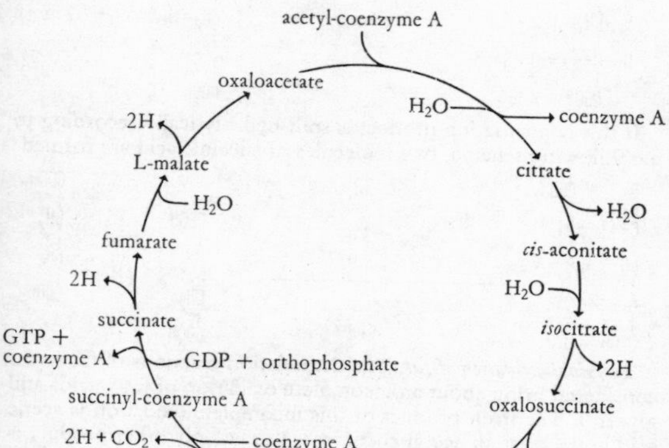

Fig. 3 The tricarboxylic acid cycle

Substances which enter the cycle (coenzyme A, H_2O) after the initial condensation of 1 molecule of acetyl-coenzyme A and 1 molecule of oxaloacetate are written inside the cycle; substances which arise are written outside. During one turn of the cycle, one acetic acid equivalent is completely oxidized. The four pairs of H atoms which arise react ultimately with O_2 to form water (for further details see KREBS, H. A., *Harvey Lect.*, **44**, 165 [1949-50], and KREBS, H. A., in GREENBERG, D. M. [Ed.], *Chemical Pathways of Metabolism*, vol. I, New York, 1954, page 109).

Analogous reactions probably occur whenever α-ketonic acids are oxidized. α-Ketonic acids arise in particular from α-amino acids; α-ketoglutarate is also formed during the tricarboxylic acid cycle.

Acetyl-coenzyme A is oxidized to completion by the tricarboxylic acid cycle (also referred to in the literature as the "citric acid cycle" or "KREBS cycle"). This cycle is initiated by a condensation of acetyl-coenzyme A and oxaloacetate leading to citrate. Citrate undergoes a series of reactions which, on balance, are oxidative and in which other tricarboxylic acids and dicarboxylic acids arise. They lead eventually to the regeneration of oxaloacetate which thus becomes available for another turn of the cycle. This means that oxaloacetate reacts after the manner of a catalyst. The hydrogen atoms arising in the course of the cycle react ultimately with molecular oxygen to form water, and the overall effect of one turn of the cycle is therefore:

$$CH_3\cdot COOH + 2\,O_2 \rightarrow 2\,CO_2 + 2\,H_2O$$

The component reactions of the cycle are given in Figure 2. The cycle itself is shown diagrammatically in Figure 3.

2. Oxidative degradation of fat[1]

Fats are not oxidized in the ester form in which they are deposited in tissues and present in foods. Prior to oxidation fat is hydrolyzed to free fatty acids and glycerol, a reaction catalyzed by lipases or esterases.

The oxidation of the free fatty acids is initiated by a reaction which results in the attachment of the fatty acid radical to the sulfur atom of coenzyme A. This reaction requires the participation of ATP and of specific enzyme systems now named "thiokinases". Two stages of the reaction have been identified. The first leads to the formation of an adenyl fatty acid (acyl-adenosine monophosphate)[2]:

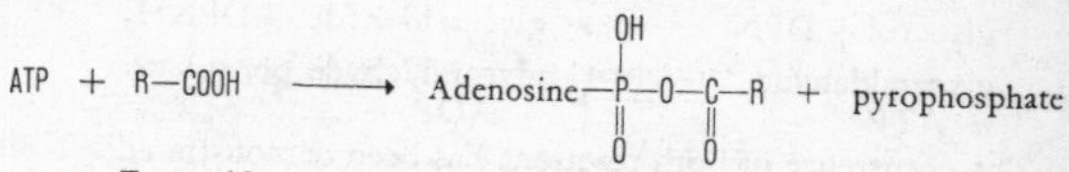

Fatty acid — Acyl-adenylate

The second is a transfer of the acyl group from adenylic acid to coenzyme A:

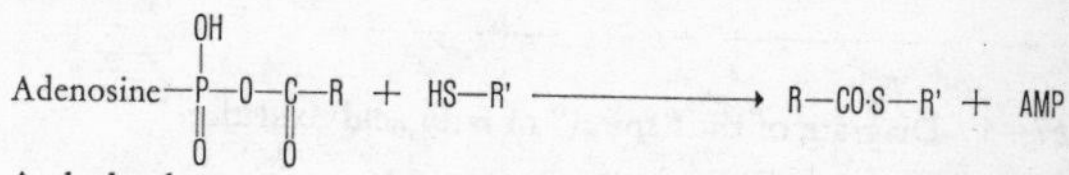

Acyl-adenylate — Coenzyme A — Acyl-coenzyme A

Several fatty acids, including acetic, propionic and higher fatty acids, have been shown to react in this way[3]. The acyl-coenzyme compounds thus formed represent the "active" forms of fatty acids which in the presence of further specific enzymes undergo a characteristic sequence of reactions, summarily referred to as β-oxidation, because the oxidation occurs at the β-carbon atom of the chain. It leads to the stepwise removal of acetic acid equivalents from the carbon chain. The intermediary enzymic reactions of this process are given in Figure 4. As shown in this scheme, β-oxidation involves four separate steps. The first is the dehydrogenation in the α-β position, the second the addition of water to the double bond and the formation of a β-hydroxy acid. The third is the dehydrogenation of the β-hydroxyl group to form a β-keto acid, the last is a "thiolysis", i.e. a fission of the carbon chain effected by the sulfhydryl group of coenzyme A. It results in the formation of one molecule of acetyl-coenzyme A and an acyl-coenzyme A derivative shorter than the original chain by two carbon atoms. The shortened chain repeatedly undergoes the same sequence of reactions until the whole fatty acid chain is reduced to a fragment of less than four carbon atoms. In the case of chains with even numbers of carbon atoms the last fragment is acetyl-coenzyme A, in the case of those with uneven numbers it is propionyl-coenzyme A.

The great majority of naturally-occurring fatty acids contain an even number of carbon atoms and therefore yield acetyl-coenzyme A as the only product. The propionyl-coenzyme A formed from uneven chains is known to enter a CO_2-fixation reaction leading to succinic acid (see page 404).

The sequence of reactions by which fatty acids are oxidized has been referred to as the "fatty acid cycle". It is not a cycle in the strict sense since the starting material is not regenerated by a full

Fig. 4 β-Oxidation of fatty acids

The nomenclature of the enzymes has been internationally proposed[4]. Acyl-dehydrogenase is a flavoprotein, β-hydroxyacyl-dehydrogenase requires DPN. All four reactions are reversible. The β-hydroxyacyl-coenzyme A compounds are optically active and belong to the D-series, in contrast to the free β-hydroxybutyrate in blood and urine which belong to the L-series. The latter arises by reduction of free acetoacetate[5]

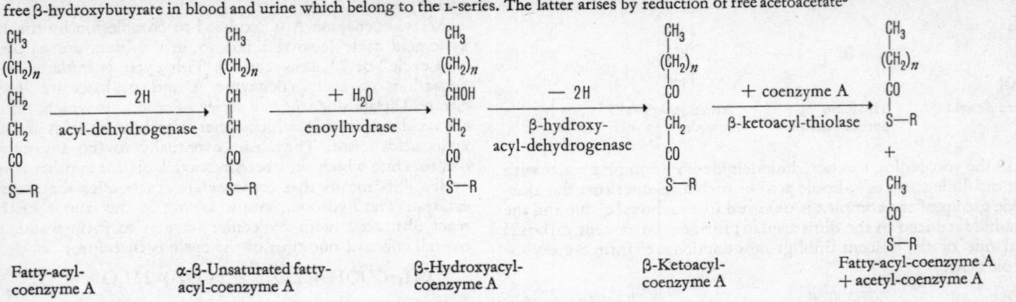

turn of the "cycle". What happens is a periodic repetition of the same *types* of reaction, but not of the same reactions. This is shown diagrammatically in Figure 5, from which it can be seen that the mechanism is a "spiral" rather than a "cycle".

The enzymic mechanism of the formation and degradation of unsaturated fatty acids is not yet known in any detail. It is possible that unsaturated fatty acids (among which oleic acid is the most common) are reduced to the saturated fatty acids before they are degraded.

Glycerol, the second constituent of neutral fats, is known to be convertible into carbohydrate in mammalian liver and the evidence suggests that this involves the formation of triosephosphate from glycerol[6]. Triosephosphate may be formed from glycerol by two pathways. The first consists of the following two reactions:

glycerol + DPN ⟶ glyceraldehyde + $DPNH_2$

glyceraldehyde + ATP ⟶("triokinase") glyceraldehyde phosphate + ADP

The occurrence of both reactions has been demonstrated[7].

Alternatively the primary step may be a phosphorylation of glycerol[8]:

glycerol + ATP → L-α-glycerophosphate + ADP

Fig. 5 Diagram of the "spiral" of fatty acid oxidation

Abbreviations:

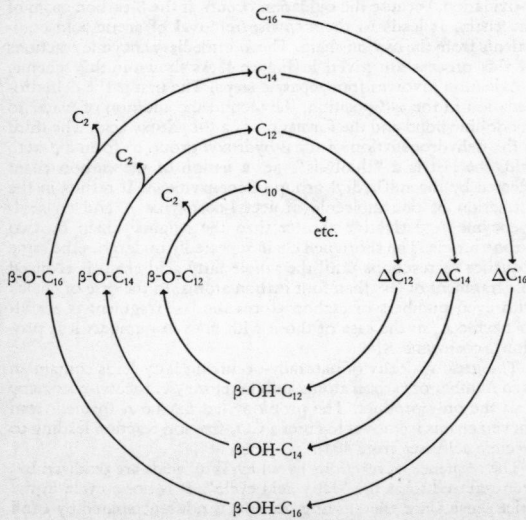

C_{16}, C_{14}, etc.	= fatty-acyl-coenzyme A
ΔC_{16}, ΔC_{14}, etc.	= unsaturated fatty-acyl-coenzyme A
β-OH-C_{16}, β-OH-C_{14}, etc.	= β-hydroxyacyl-coenzyme A
β-O-C_{16}, β-O-C_{14}, etc.	= β-ketoacyl-coenzyme A
C_2	= acetyl-coenzyme A

The subscripts indicate the length of the carbon chain

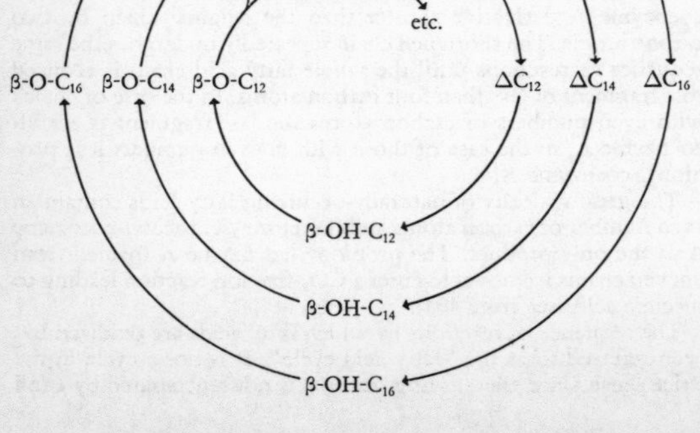

followed by the dehydrogenation of glycerophosphate:

L-α-glycerophosphate + DPN → dihydroxyacetone phosphate + $DPNH_2$

The triosephosphate formed from glycerol subsequently joins the reactions of triosephosphate arising from sugars.

Formation of succinic acid from propionyl-coenzyme A. As already mentioned, the propionyl-coenzyme A formed from fatty acids with uneven carbon chains yields succinic acid. This involves a CO_2-fixation reaction recently discovered by OCHOA and co-workers[9]:

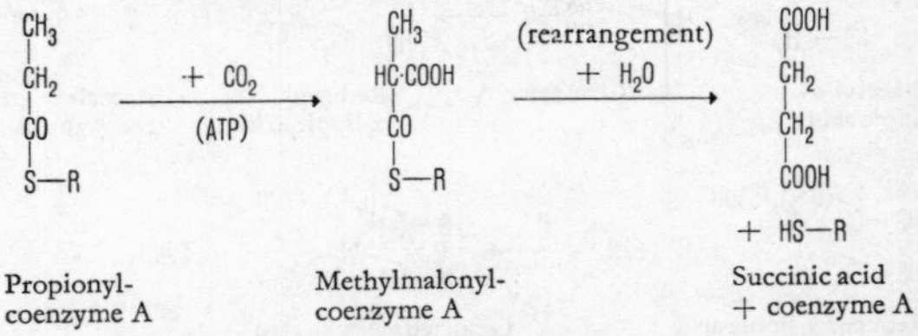

The conversion of methylmalonyl-coenzyme A to succinic acid by simple intramolecular rearrangement is difficult to visualize. FESSLER[10] has suggested that two molecules may react to form a condensation product, as follows:

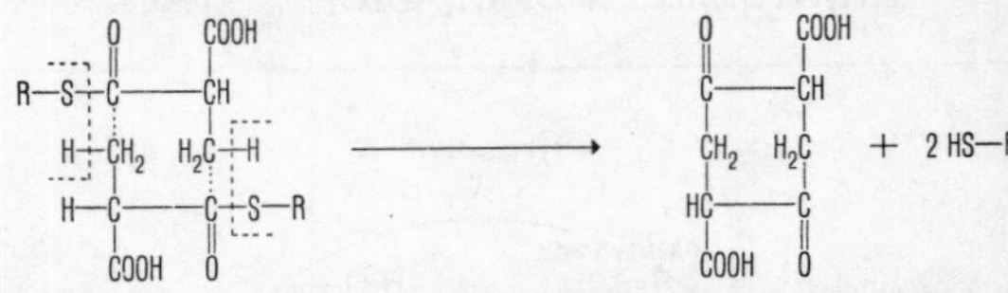

If this condensation product is split hydrolytically according to the following scheme, two molecules of succinic acid are formed:

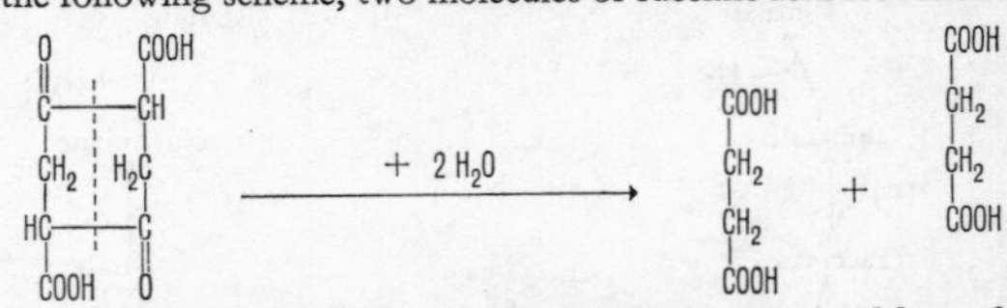

Terminal oxidation of fat. The degradation reactions of fat so far considered bring about an incomplete oxidation of fatty acids and glycerol. The main product of this incomplete oxidation is acetic acid in the form of acetyl-coenzyme A. The only other product is succinic acid, which arises from the three terminal carbon atoms of the fatty acid chain with uneven carbon numbers. Since fatty acids with uneven carbon numbers are uncommon in nature the total amount of succinate arising from fat is normally very small. Such fatty acids are uncommon because fatty acid chains are usually synthesized from 2-carbon units.

Acetyl-coenzyme A and succinate are oxidized to completion by the reactions of the tricarboxylic acid cycle described on pages 402 and 403.

Ketosis. In ketosis due to starvation or diabetes or other causes, the "ketone bodies", viz. acetoacetate ($CH_3 \cdot CO \cdot CH_2 \cdot COOH$), β-hydroxybutyrate ($CH_3 \cdot CHOH \cdot CH_2 \cdot COOH$) and acetone

($CH_3 \cdot CO \cdot CH_3$), accumulate in the tissues and body fluids. For reasons which are not yet fully understood more acetyl-coenzyme A is formed in ketosis, mainly from fatty acids, than can be oxidized through the tricarboxylic acid cycle. The surplus molecules of acetyl-coenzyme A condense in pairs to form acetoacetyl-coenzyme A which undergoes hydrolysis to free acetoacetate and coenzyme A (in liver free acetoacetate is not readily utilized):

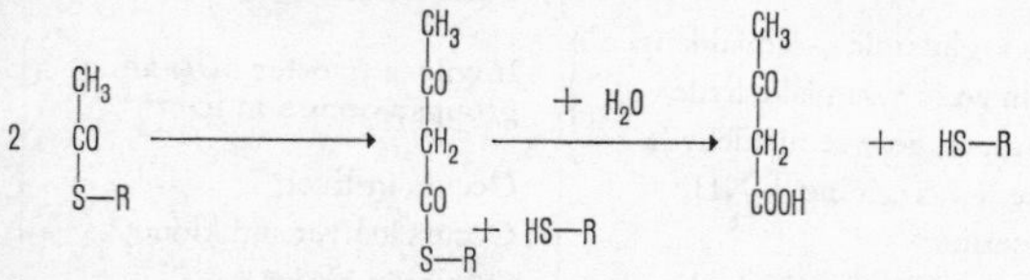

Acetyl-coenzyme A — Acetoacetyl-coenzyme A — Acetoacetic acid

Acetoacetate is the primary ketone body. β-Hydroxybutyrate is formed from it by reduction, acetone by decarboxylation. The latter reaction is mainly nonenzymic, and is due to the inherent instability of acetoacetate:

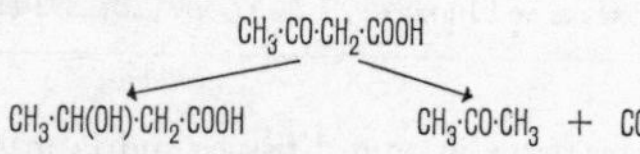

β-Hydroxybutyric acid — Acetone

The older view that acetoacetate arises directly from the four terminal carbon atoms of fatty acid chains is no longer tenable in view of isotope data which prove conclusively that *most* acetoacetate is formed by the condensation of two molecules of acetyl-coenzyme A.

It follows that all substances which can form acetyl-coenzyme A, including carbohydrate and many amino acids, can be parent substances of the ketone bodies. Why ketone bodies accumulate only when acetyl-coenzyme A is formed from fatty acids and the three ketogenic amino acids, and not when it is formed from carbohydrate and other amino acids, is not clear. Since the oxidation of acetyl-coenzyme A through the tricarboxylic acid cycle requires oxaloacetate it is likely that oxaloacetate is a key substance in the control of ketosis. It has been assumed that a sufficient level of oxaloacetate for the optimal operation of the tricarboxylic acid cycle cannot be maintained unless carbohydrate is oxidized, but why this should be the case is still a matter of conjecture.

Ancillary reactions of fatty acid degradation. Some ancillary degradation reactions of fatty acids are the following.

(*a*) Acetoacetyl-deacylase liberates free acetoacetate from the coenzyme A derivative:

acetoacetyl-coenzyme A + H_2O
→ acetoacetate + coenzyme A

This reaction is assumed to play a role in the appearance of the ketone bodies in blood and tissues in ketosis[11].

(*b*) β-Hydroxybutyric dehydrogenase catalyzes the reversible interconversion of acetoacetate and β-hydroxybutyrate:

β-hydroxybutyrate + DPN ⇌ acetoacetate + $DPNH_2$

and is responsible for the formation and removal of β-hydroxybutyrate.

(*c*) An enzyme transferring coenzyme A reversibly between acetoacetate and succinate ("thiopherase") may initiate the breakdown of free acetoacetate:

acetoacetate + succinyl-coenzyme A
⇌ acetoacetyl-coenzyme A + succinate[12]

(*d*) Acetoacetate breakdown can also be initiated by the reaction

acetoacetate + coenzyme A + ATP
→ acetoacetyl-coenzyme A + adenylic acid
+ pyrophosphate[13]

This is analogous to the reaction which initiates the degradation of fatty acids (page 403) and may involve the same type of intermediary stages, i.e. the formation of acetoacetyl-adenylate.

References

1) Cf. Lynen, F., *Harvey Lect.*, **48**, 210 (1952-53); Green, D. E., *Biol. Rev.*, **29**, 330 (1954); Popják and Le Breton (Eds.), *Biochemical Problems of Lipids*, London, 1956; Beinert et al., *Biochem. J.*, **64**, 782 (1956). *2)* Berg, P., *J. biol. Chem.*, **222**, 991, 1015, 1025 (1956). *3)* Peng, C. H. L., *Biochim. biophys. Acta*, **22**, 42 (1956); Jencks and Lipmann, *J. biol. Chem.*, **225**, 207 (1957); Whitehouse et al., *J. biol. Chem.*, **226**, 813 (1957). *4)* See *Biochem. J.*, **64**, 782 (1956). *5)* Lehninger and Greville, *Biochim. biophys. Acta*, **12**, 188 (1953). *6)* Ashmore et al., *J. biol. Chem.*, **215**, 153 (1955). *7)* Hers and Kusaka, *Biochim. biophys. Acta*, **11**, 427 (1953); Wolf and Leuthardt, *Helv. chim. Acta*, **36**, 1463 (1953). *8)* Bublitz and Kennedy, *J. biol. Chem.*, **211**, 951 (1954). *9)* Flavin et al., *Nature*, **176**, 823 (1955). *10)* Fessler, J. H. (1956), unpublished. *11)* Green, D. E., *Biol. Rev.*, **29**, 330 (1954). *12)* Stern et al., *J. Amer. chem. Soc.*, **75**, 1517 (1953). *13)* Stern and Ochoa, *J. biol. Chem.*, **191**, 161 (1951).

3. Intermediary stages of the degradation of amino acids

As in the case of carbohydrate and fat, the degradation of amino acids consists of two major stages. In the first stage the amino acids are converted into an intermediate which can be oxidized through the tricarboxylic acid cycle. The second or terminal stage is the tricarboxylic acid cycle. The following account is concerned with the first stage.

General degradation reactions. Some degradation reactions are common to all or several amino acids. These are (*a*) oxidative deamination, (*b*) transamination, (*c*) nonoxidative decarboxylation.

Oxidative deamination. The general reaction scheme of oxidative deamination is as follows:

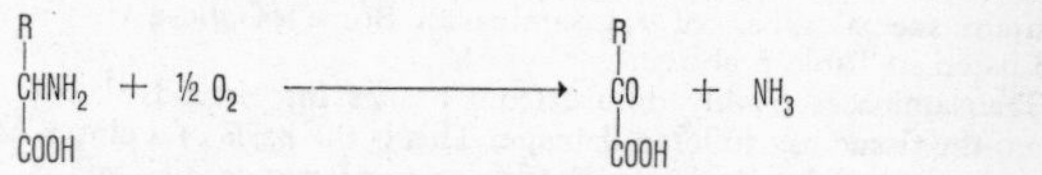

α-Amino acid — α-Ketonic acid

Liver and kidney contain enzymes which attack the majority of α-amino acids of both the D- and L-series in this way. In general the activity of the D-amino acid oxidases is greater than that of the L-amino acid oxidases, although D-amino acids occur very infrequently in natural products. One L-amino acid, however, reacts at a much greater rate than all other L-amino acids. This is glutamic acid, which is attacked by a specific L-glutamic acid dehydrogenase catalyzing the following reaction:

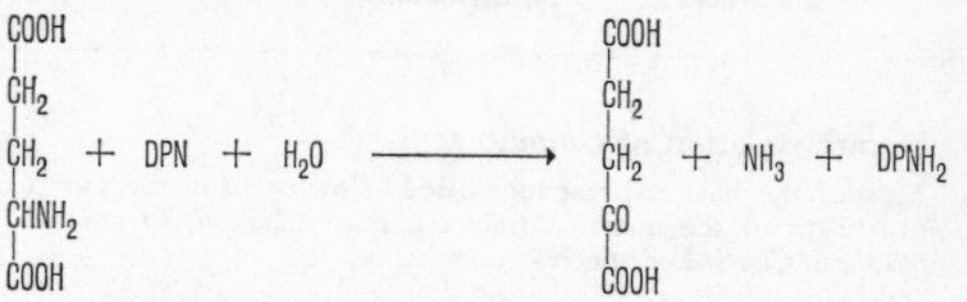

L-Glutamic acid — α-Ketoglutaric acid

This enzyme differs from all the other enzymes bringing about oxidative deamination in animal tissues in that it transfers hydrogen to diphosphopyridine nucleotide (DPN). In the case of oxidative deamination by the other enzymes, the primary acceptor is a flavoprotein. The L-amino acid oxidases of animal tissues are comparatively weak and it is probable that deamination is generally effected by transamination of α-amino acids with α-ketoglutarate (see below) followed by the dehydrogenation of glutamate according to the above reaction.

Transamination. Transamination is a reversible reaction between amino and α-ketonic acids leading to the exchange of the amino and ketonic groups. An example is the following:

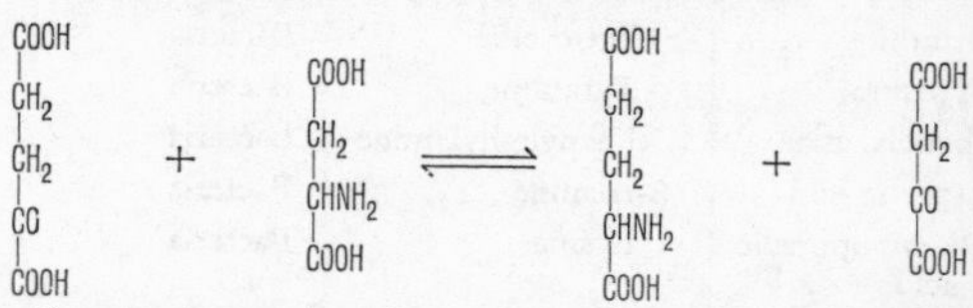

α-Ketoglutaric acid — L-Aspartic acid — L-Glutamic acid — Oxaloacetic acid

The majority of α-amino acids can replace aspartic acid in this type of reaction, according to the general scheme:

α-ketoglutarate + α-amino acid
⇌ L-glutamate + α-ketonic acid

Table 5 Some transamination reactions in animal tissues[1]

Reactions			Remarks
α-ketoglutarate + L-α-amino acid	⇌	L-glutamate + α-ketonic acid	Most α-amino acids can react in this way in liver and many other tissues
α-ketoglutarate + L-ornithine	⇌	L-glutamate + L-glutamic γ-semialdehyde	Involves transfer of ω-amino groups; occurs in liver[2,3]
glyoxylate + L-ornithine	⇌	glycine + L-glutamic γ-semialdehyde	
pyruvate + L-ornithine	⇌	L-alanine + L-glutamic γ-semialdehyde	
L-glutamine + α-keto-γ-guanidinovaleric acid	⇌	α-ketoglutarate + L-arginine + NH_3	Occurs in liver[2]
L-alanine + hydroxypyruvate	⇌	pyruvate + L-serine	Occurs in liver and kidney[4]
α-ketoglutarate + γ-aminobutyrate	⇌	L-glutamate + succinic semialdehyde	Occurs in brain[5]
α-ketoglutarate + β-alanine	⇌	L-glutamate + malonic semialdehyde	Occurs in brain[6]

References
1) For reviews see MEISTER, A., in MCELROY and GLASS (Eds.), *A Symposium on Amino Acid Metabolism*, Baltimore, 1955, page 3; MEISTER, A., *Advanc. Enzymol.*, **16**, 185 (1955). *2)* MEISTER, A., *J. biol. Chem.*, **206**, 587 (1954). *3)* QUASTEL and WITTY, *Nature*, **167**, 556 (1951). *4)* SALLACH H. J., in MCELROY and GLASS (Eds.), *A Symposium on Amino Acid Metabolism*, Baltimore, 1955, page 782. *5)* BESSMAN et al., *J. biol. Chem.*, **201**, 385 (1953). *6)* ROBERTS and BREGOFF, *J. biol. Chem.*, **201**, 393 (1953).

but the rate of reaction is by far the highest when aspartic acid is the amino-group donor. Transaminases occur in most animal tissues as well as in microorganisms and plants. Several tissues contain special types of transaminases. Some of these tissues are listed in Table 5 above.

Transaminases readily diffuse from tissues into blood plasma when the tissue has suffered damage. This is the basis of a clinical test, the rise of the plasma level of transaminase in cardiac infarction. Pyridoxal phosphate is a prosthetic group of transaminases.

Decarboxylation. Decarboxylation of amino acids proceeds according to the following general scheme:

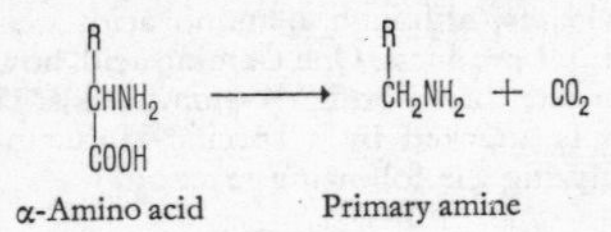

Table 6 Decarboxylation of L-amino acids[1]
Most of the bacterial reactions listed below occur in the microorganisms of the intestinal tract, e.g. *Escherichia coli*, *Streptococcus faecalis* or *Clostridium* species

Amino acid	Amine formed	Occurrence of enzyme
Histidine	Histamine	Animal tissues, bacteria
Cysteic acid	Taurine	Liver
Glutamic acid	γ-Aminobutyric acid	Brain, bacteria
5-Hydroxytryptophan	5-Hydroxytryptamine (serotonin)	Animal tissues
3,4-Dihydroxyphenylalanine	3,4-Dihydroxyphenylethylamine	Animal tissues
Serine	Ethanolamine	Animal tissues[2]
Lysine	Cadaverine	Bacteria
Ornithine	Putrescine	Bacteria
Tyrosine	Tyramine	Bacteria
Phenylalanine	Phenylethylamine	Bacteria
Aspartic acid	β-Alanine	Bacteria
α,ε-Diaminopimelic acid	Lysine	Bacteria[3]

References
1) BLASCHKO, H., *Advanc. Enzymol.*, **5**, 67 (1945); GALE, E. F., *Advanc. Enzymol.*, **6**, 1 (1946); SCHALES, O., in SUMNER and MYRBÄCK (Eds.), *The Enzymes*, vol. II, part 1, New York, 1951, page 216. *2)* ARNSTEIN, H.R.V., *Biochem. J.*, **48**, 27 (1951). *3)* DEWEY and WORK, *Nature*, **169**, 533 (1952).

Decarboxylases occur in animal tissues and in many microorganisms, but not every amino acid can undergo decarboxylation. Reactions which have been recorded are listed in Table 6. The significance of some of the decarboxylations which occur in animal tissues lies in the supply of essential metabolites, e.g. of taurine (required for the synthesis of bile acids), of histamine and serotonin (required for the functional activities of nervous tissue) or of ethanolamine (required for the synthesis of cephalins, choline and acetylcholine). Pyridoxal phosphate is a coenzyme also in most decarboxylation reactions. A notable exception is the decarboxylation of histidine.

4. Degradation of individual amino acids[1]

L-*Glutamic acid*, L-*aspartic acid*, L-*alanine*. On oxidative deamination or transamination these three amino acids yield α-ketonic acids which also occur as intermediates in the metabolism of carbohydrate; they are α-ketoglutarate, oxaloacetate and pyruvate respectively.

The degradation of the six amino acids L-*histidine*, L-*arginine*, L-*citrulline*, L-*ornithine*, L-*proline and* L-*hydroxyproline* leads in every case to glutamic acid and thence to α-ketoglutarate.

L-*Histidine* is converted to glutamic acid by an enzyme complex of liver tissue, formerly referred to as histidase. The overall result of the action of this complex is an hydrolysis according to the following scheme:

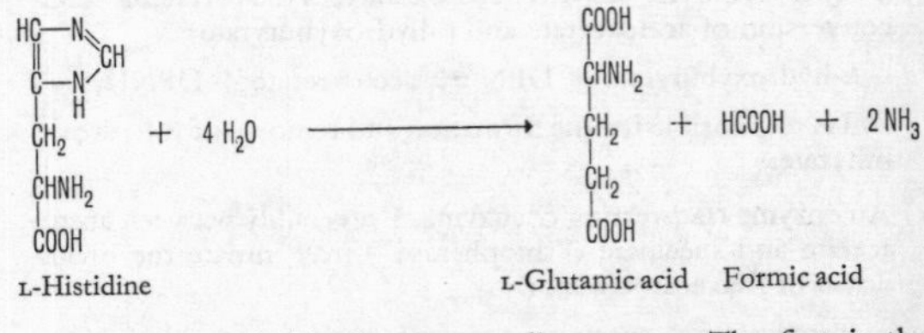

There are probably five intermediate stages. The first is the fission to ammonia and an unsaturated derivative of histidine. The other four are hydrolytic reactions, each accounting for the uptake of one molecule of water:

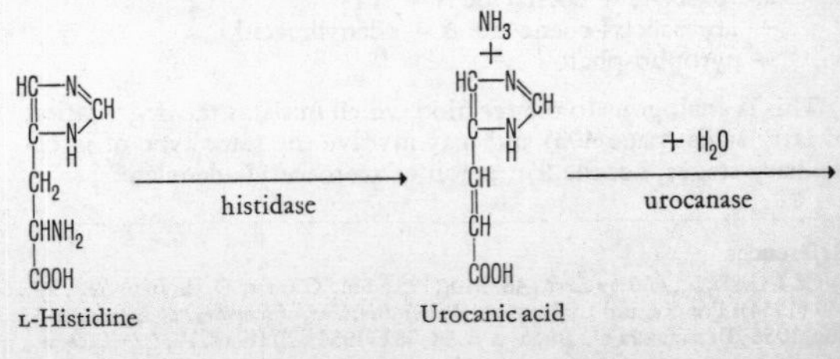

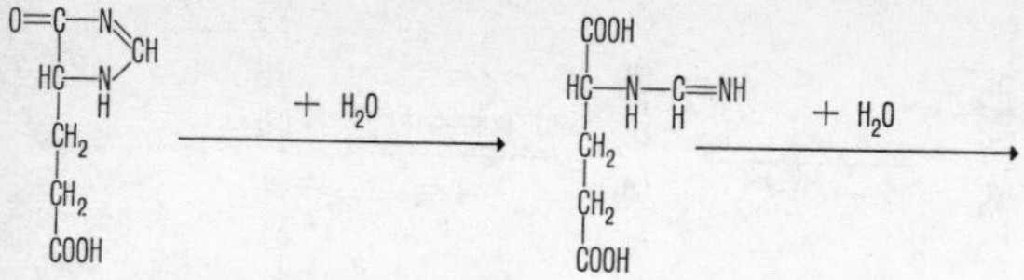

Imidazolonepropionic acid (hypothetical intermediate) — L-α-Formamidinoglutaric acid

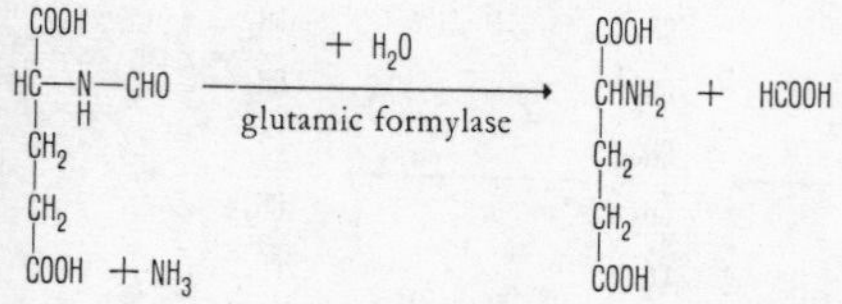

L-Formylglutamic acid — L-Glutamic acid — Formic acid

The stages up to L-α-formamidinoglutaric acid have also been verified in the bacteria *Pseudomonas fluorescens* and *Aerobacter aerogenes*.

L-*Citrulline* and L-*arginine* are converted in liver tissue into ornithine by the reactions of the ornithine cycle (see pages 445 and 446). L-*Ornithine* is known to yield glutamic γ-semialdehyde by transamination (see page 405) and the semialdehyde can form glutamic acid by dehydrogenation:

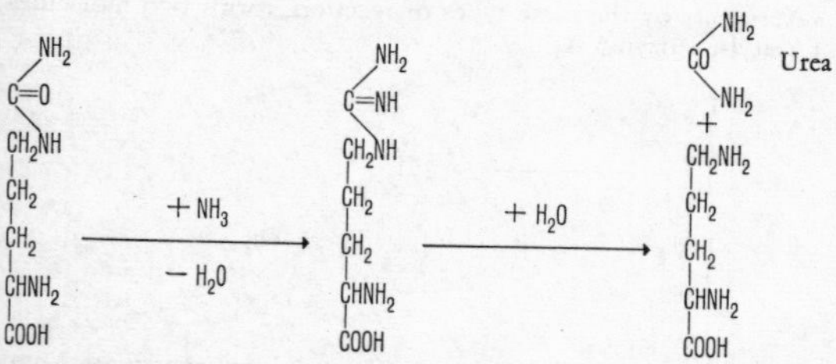

L-Citrulline — L-Arginine — L-Ornithine

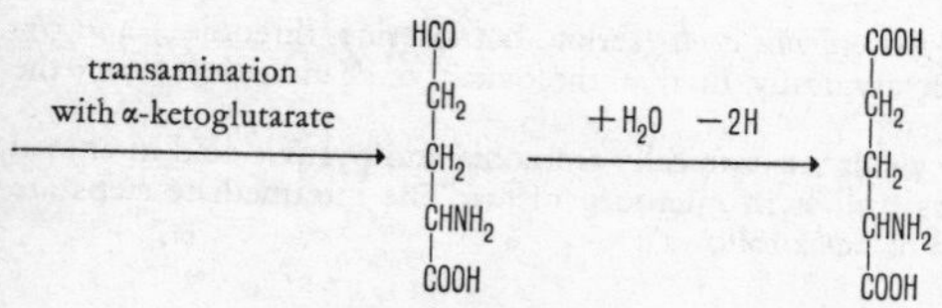

L-Glutamic γ-semialdehyde — L-Glutamic acid

D-*Ornithine*, under the influence of D-amino acid oxidase, follows a different route, the primary step being the removal of the α-amino group:

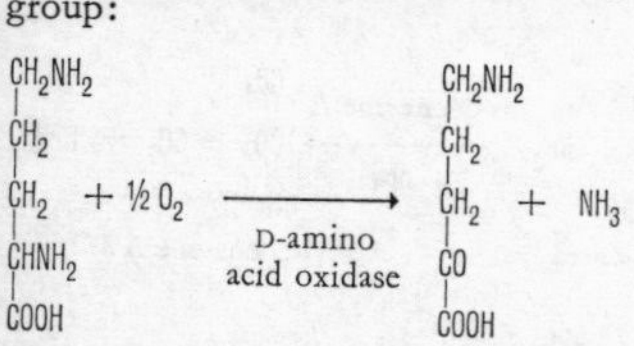

D-Ornithine — α-Keto-δ-aminovaleric acid

L-*Proline* forms glutamic acid by the following three steps[2], which include two dehydrogenations:

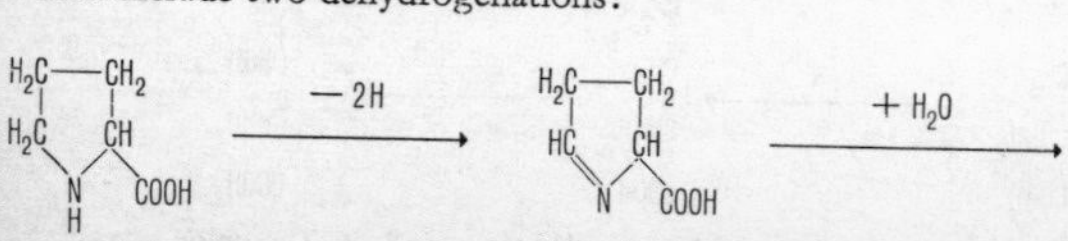

L-Proline — L-Δ^1-Pyrroline-5-carboxylic acid

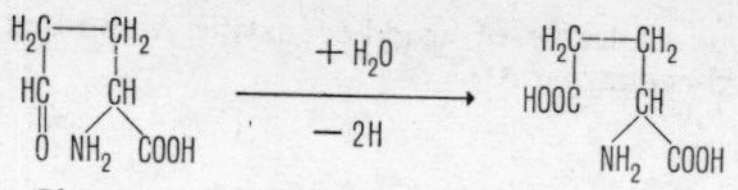

L-Glutamic γ-semialdehyde — L-Glutamic acid

These reactions have been shown to occur in both liver and bacteria.

D-*Proline* reacts differently in mammalian liver or kidney and gives the same α-ketonic acid as D-ornithine. This is to be expected as the point of attack of D-amino acid oxidase is always the α-carbon atom.

L-*Hydroxyproline* is known to form glutamic acid in liver and kidney but the intermediary stages of the conversion have not yet been established. It is possible that hydroxyproline is first converted into proline or a pyrrolinecarboxylic acid and shares the later stages of degradation with proline.

The degradation of the *leucines* and *valines* follows initially a common pattern. In every case transamination or oxidative deamination leads to the corresponding α-ketonic acid. This subsequently undergoes reactions analogous to those described for pyruvic acid (page 403), resulting in the formation of an acyl-coenzyme A derivative and CO_2. The acyl-coenzyme A derivative then reacts essentially in the same way as the acyl-coenzyme A derivative of long-chain fatty acids. Special reactions – CO_2-fixation and an aldol fission – follow in the case of leucine. The end-products are acetyl-coenzyme A and propionyl-coenzyme A, and in the case of valine probably methylmalonyl-coenzyme A. As already mentioned (page 404), both propionyl-coenzyme A and methylmalonyl-coenzyme A eventually yield succinate.

Leucine yields three molecules of acetyl-coenzyme A. The intermediate stages are as follows[3]:

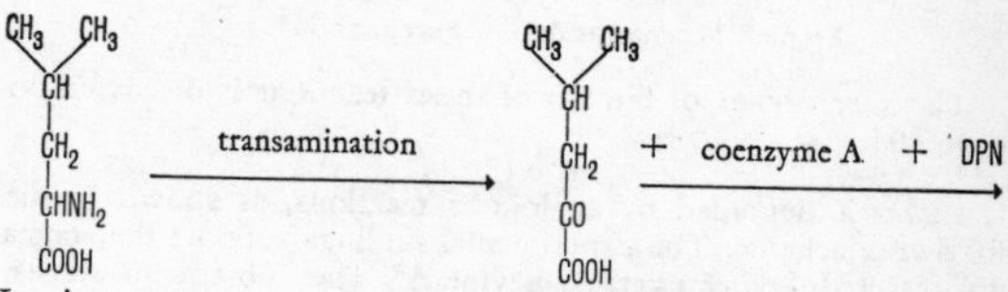

Leucine — α-Keto*iso*caproic acid

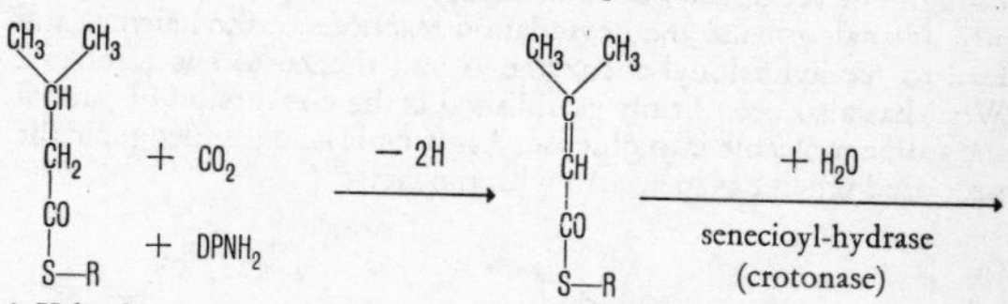

*iso*Valeryl-coenzyme A — Senecioyl-coenzyme A

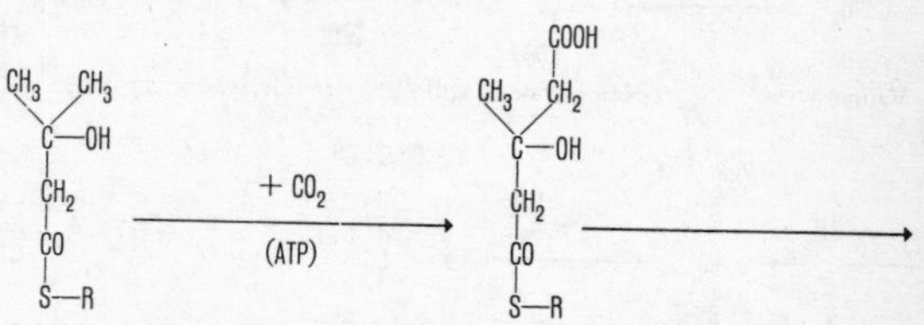

β-Hydroxy*iso*valeryl-coenzyme A — β-Hydroxy-β-methylglutaryl-coenzyme A

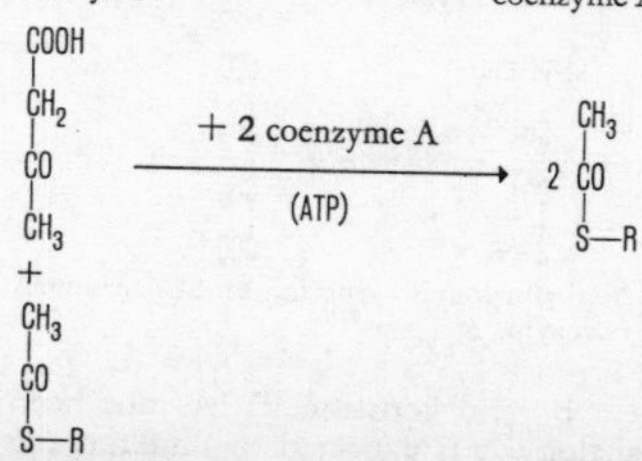

Acetoacetic acid + acetyl-coenzyme A — Acetyl-coenzyme A (2 molecules)

iso*Leucine* yields one molecule of acetyl-coenzyme A and one molecule of propionyl-coenzyme A[4]:

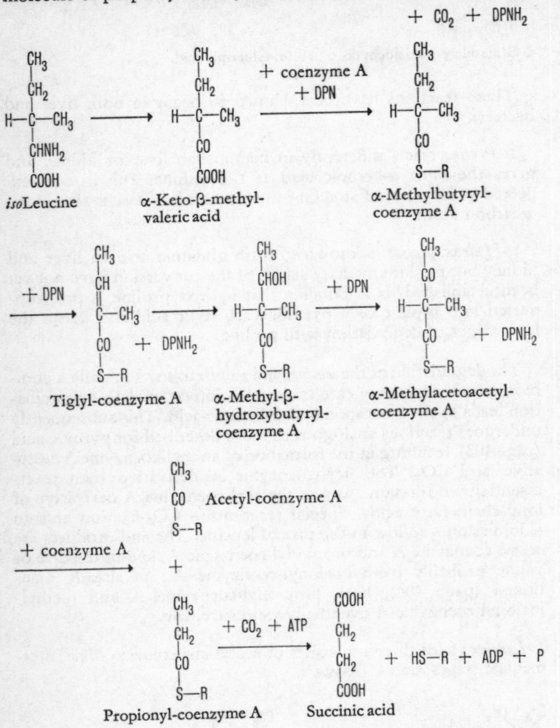

The mechanism of the last of these reactions is discussed on page 404.

Valine is degraded by analogous reactions, as shown in the following scheme. The experimental findings support the stages up to β-hydroxy*iso*butyryl-coenzyme A[5]. The subsequent stages, though not yet directly demonstrated, are very probable; they are strictly analogous to the degradation reactions of the leucines and lead to methylmalonyl-coenzyme A and thence to succinic acid. What has also been firmly established is the conversion of part of the valine molecule into glucose. As succinic acid is glucogenic the proposed scheme is in accord with the facts.

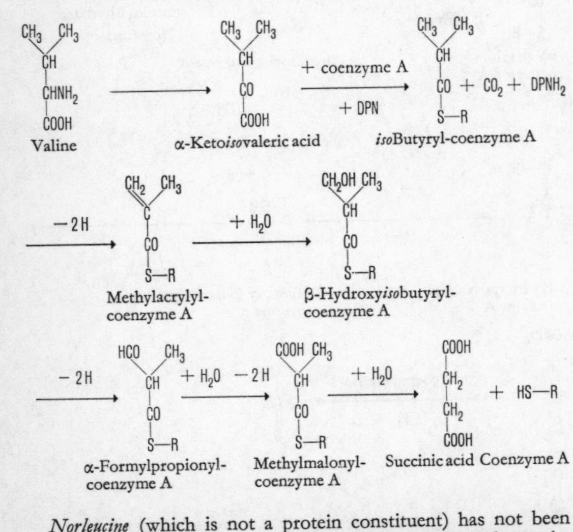

Norleucine (which is not a protein constituent) has not been studied in detail, but by analogy it is expected to undergo the following sequence of reactions leading to propionyl-coenzyme A and acetyl-coenzyme A:

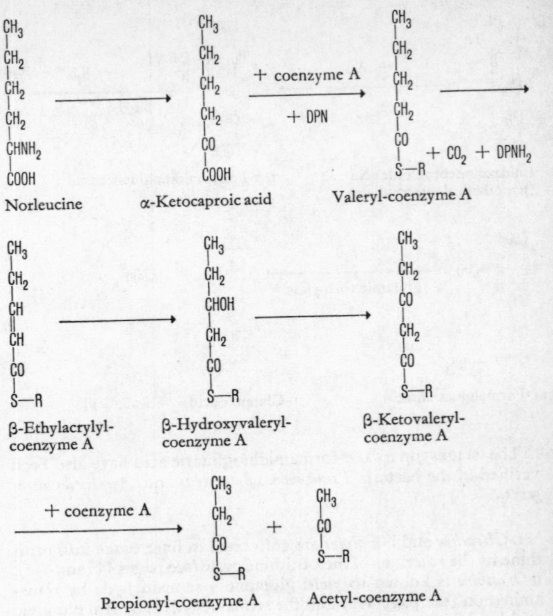

Norvaline, by the same types of reaction, forms two molecules of acetyl-coenzyme A:

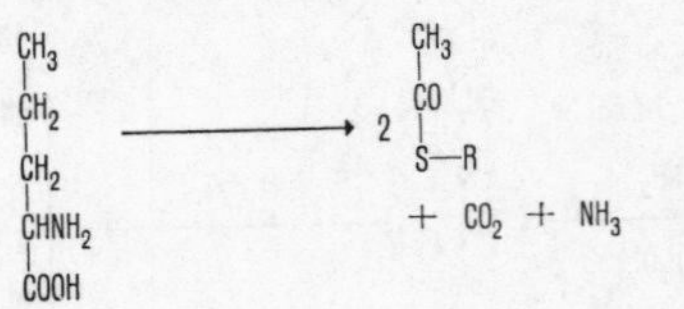

α-Aminobutyric acid by analogy forms propionyl-coenzyme A and thence succinate.

The *hydroxyamino acids* (serine, homoserine, threonine) and *glycine* react atypically in that the oxidative deamination is not the primary step.

Serine yields anaerobically ammonia and pyruvic acid in animal tissues as well as in microorganisms. The intermediate steps are assumed to be as follows[6]:

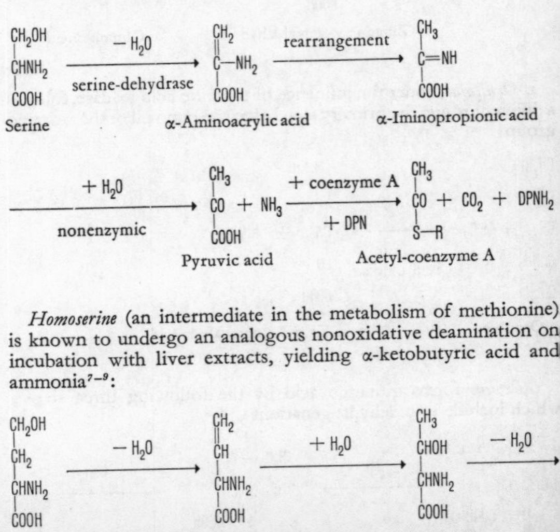

Homoserine (an intermediate in the metabolism of methionine) is known to undergo an analogous nonoxidative deamination on incubation with liver extracts, yielding α-ketobutyric acid and ammonia[7-9]:

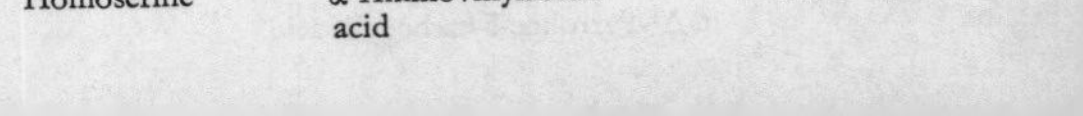

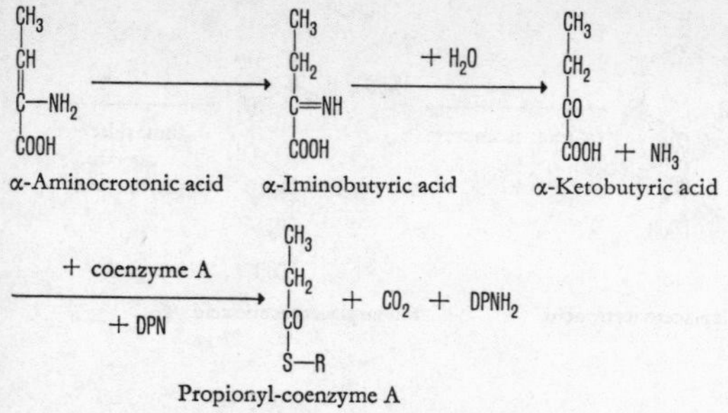

L-*Threonine* is degraded in animal tissues by an anaerobic fission catalyzed by an aldolase ("hydroxyamino acid aldolase")[10–12]:

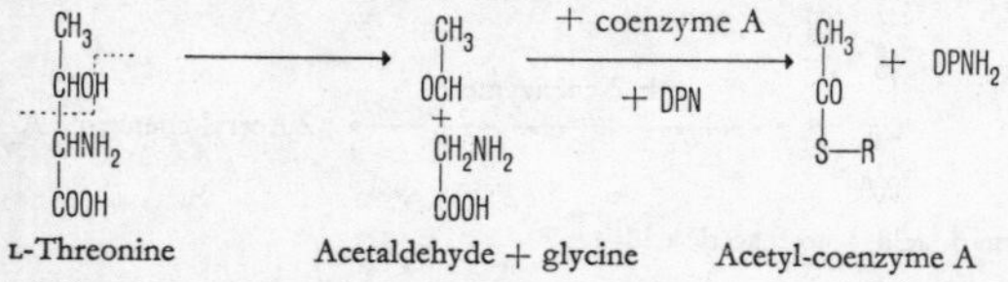

The acetaldehyde formed can be converted into acetyl-coenzyme A, whilst the glycine reacts as described later. Bacteria and molds possess enzymes which degrade threonine by reactions analogous to those of serine, yielding α-aminocrotonic acid, α-ketobutyric acid and propionic acid.

Glycine. The pathway of degradation of glycine is not yet fully clarified. One route is the conversion into serine by an aldol condensation with formaldehyde reacting in an "active form":

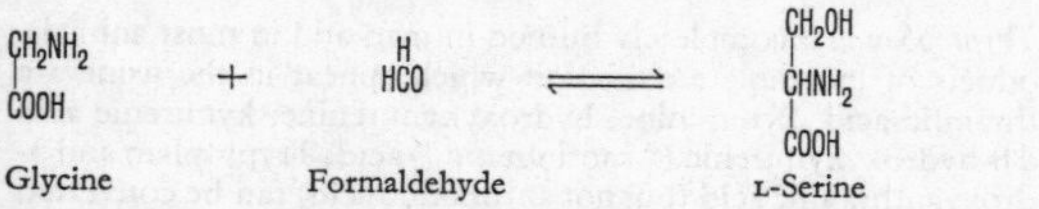

The ready interconversion of glycine and serine in animal tissues has been conclusively established. The cofactor requirement for the metabolism of "active" formaldehyde is complex[13]. It is possible that a major part of glycine shares the pathway of degradation with serine and thus yields acetyl-coenzyme A.

Another possible pathway of glycine degradation is initiated by the condensation with succinyl-coenzyme A[14,15]:

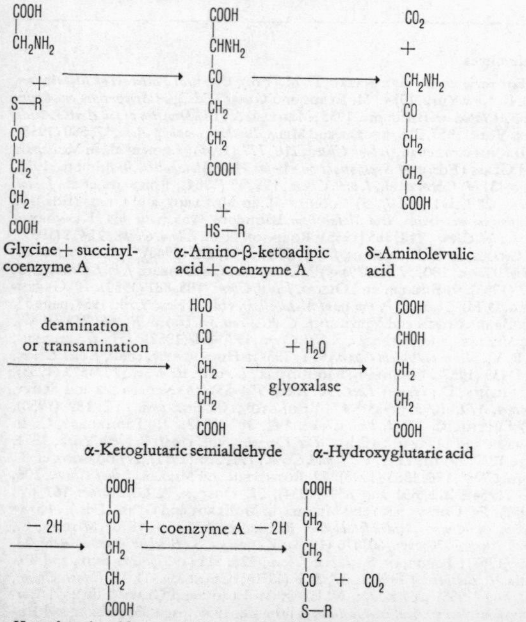

The reactions up to the stage of δ-aminolevulic acid have been firmly established[15–17] but the pathway beyond δ-aminolevulic acid leading eventually to succinyl coenzyme A is hypothetical and based on analogies.

L-*Cysteine* can be desulfurated, under the influence of the enzyme desulfurase, to yield pyruvate, NH_3 and H_2S[18,19]. The intermediate stages have been formulated as follows:

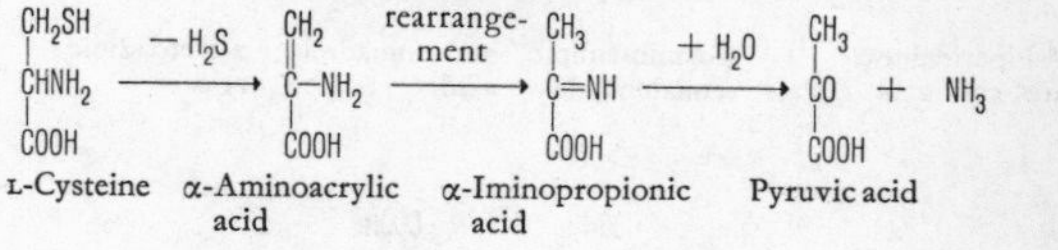

These reactions are closely analogous to those of serine (see the opposite page).

Cystine is converted in liver tissue into the same products as cysteine[18]; it is assumed that it undergoes reduction to cysteine before it is degraded.

L-*Homocysteine* also liberates H_2S in liver extracts, together with α-ketobutyrate and ammonia. There is no certainty about the intermediate stages. It is possible that desulfuration yields α-amino-α-vinylacetic acid, the fate of which is already described as a probable intermediate in the metabolism of homoserine (see above); it yields propionyl-coenzyme A. An alternative route is the transfer of the SH group to serine (transulfuration) with cystathionine as intermediate, in which case the end-product is likewise identical with that of homoserine:

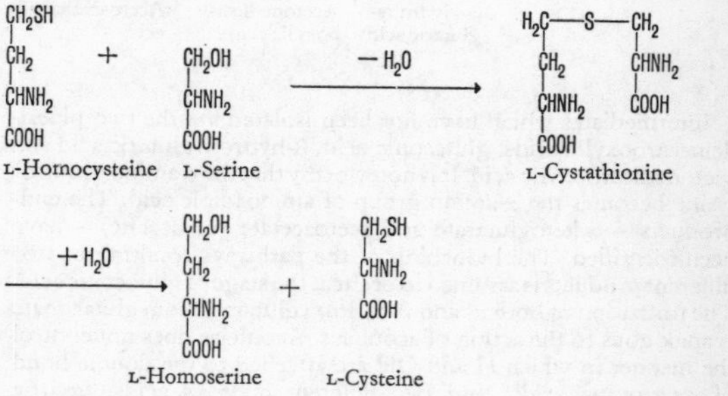

The evidence consists of the demonstration that homocysteine and serine form cystathionine in liver and that cystathionine, like homocysteine, is broken down to α-ketobutyrate and NH_3[7,20].

L-*Methionine*. The first stage in the degradation of L-methionine is the removal of the methyl group from the sulfur atom, which is effected by transfer to glycocyamine, ethanolamine, or other methyl acceptors. Demethylation results in the formation of homocysteine, the fate of which has already been discussed:

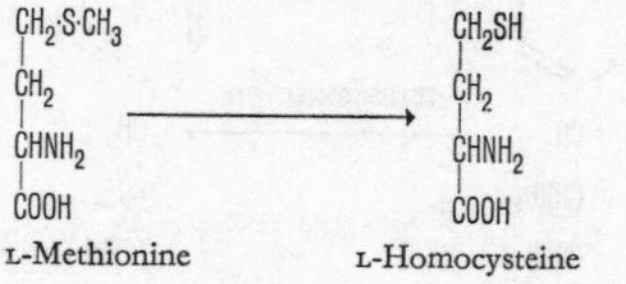

L-*Lysine*. The following pathway of the degradation of lysine is essentially based on isotopic evidence and the isolation of most of the intermediates[21,22]:

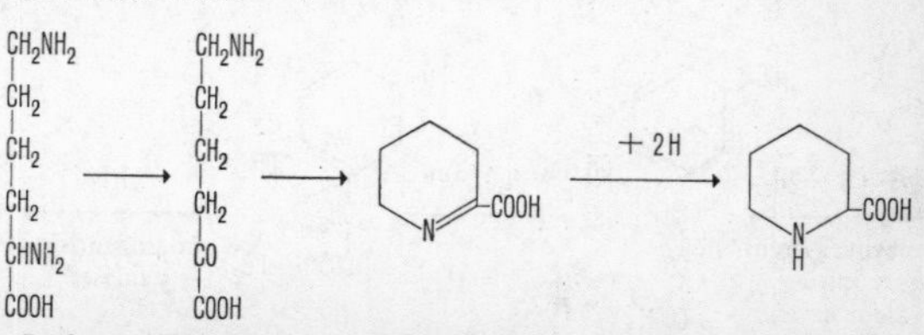

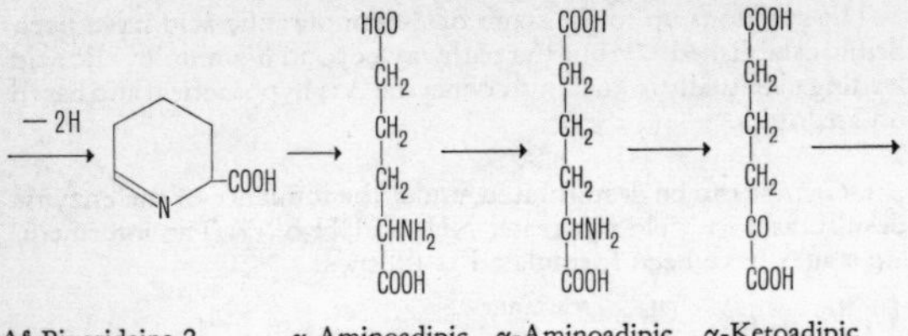

Δ⁶-Piperideine-2-carboxylic acid α-Aminoadipic semialdehyde α-Aminoadipic acid α-Ketoadipic acid

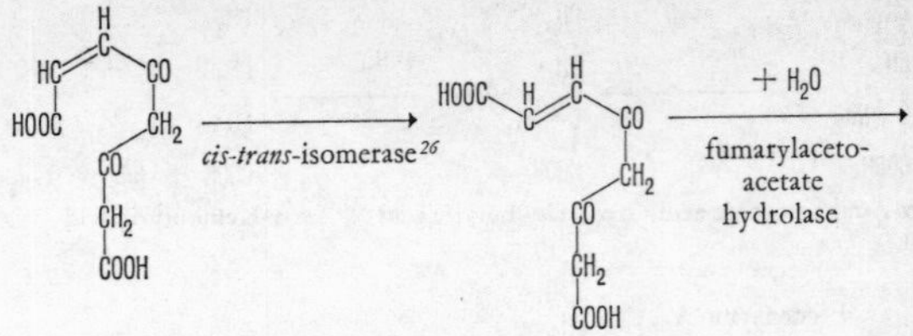

Maleylacetoacetic acid Fumarylacetoacetic acid

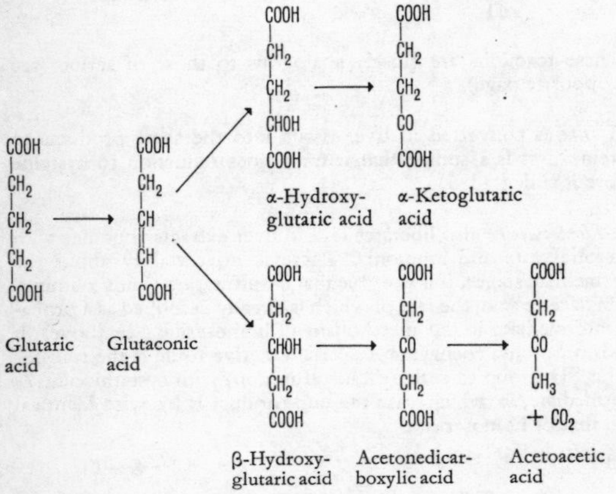

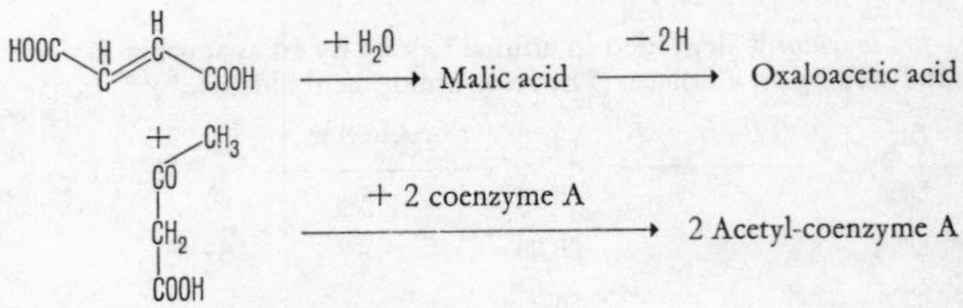

Fumaric acid + acetoacetic acid

There are three types of inborn errors of metabolism where the disorder is due to insufficient formation (or nonformation) of one of the enzyme systems of the above sequence. In phenylketonuria the conversion of phenylalanine to tyrosine is blocked. As a consequence, phenylalanine undergoes an alternative degradation to phenylpyruvic acid, which accumulates since it is not readily broken down. In tyrosinosis the block is taken to be at the stage between *p*-hydroxyphenylpyruvate and 2,5-dihydroxyphenylpyruvate. In alkaptonuria, homogentisic oxidase is deficient.

Tryptophan is incompletely burned in man and in most animals. Products of incomplete oxidation which appear in the urine are anthranilic acid, kynurenine, hydroxykynurenine, kynurenic acid and 8-hydroxykynurenic ("xanthurenic") acid. Tryptophan and 3-hydroxyanthranilic acid (but not anthranilic acid) can be converted into nicotinic acid in some animals, though only in limited quantities. This involves a fission of the benzene ring of 3-hydroxyanthranilic acid and the formation of a pyridine ring, the nitrogen of which is derived from the amino group of anthranilic acid. The side chain of tryptophan can appear in the form of alanine. An outline of the probable pathways leading to the various products is given in Figure 6. Many details are still unknown.

Intermediates which have not been isolated are the two piperideinecarboxylic acids, glutaconic acid, β-hydroxyglutaric acid and acetonedicarboxylic acid. It is noteworthy that the ε-amino group of lysine becomes the α-amino group of aminoadipic acid. The end-products – α-ketoglutarate and acetoacetate (or acetate) – have been identified. The branching of the pathways resulting in two different products is assumed to occur at the stage of glutaconic acid. The formation of both α- and β-hydroxyglutarate from glutaconate is analogous to the action of aconitase. Aconitase does not control the manner in which H and OH are attached to the double bond of *cis*-aconitic acid[23], and two different hydroxy acids, *iso*citric and citric acid, are therefore formed. By analogy, glutaconic acid would yield α- and β-hydroxyglutaric acids on hydration.

Phenylalanine and *tyrosine* are degraded in animal tissues by the reactions shown in the following scheme. Several unusual enzymes are involved. The end-products as formulated are oxaloacetic acid and acetyl-coenzyme A:

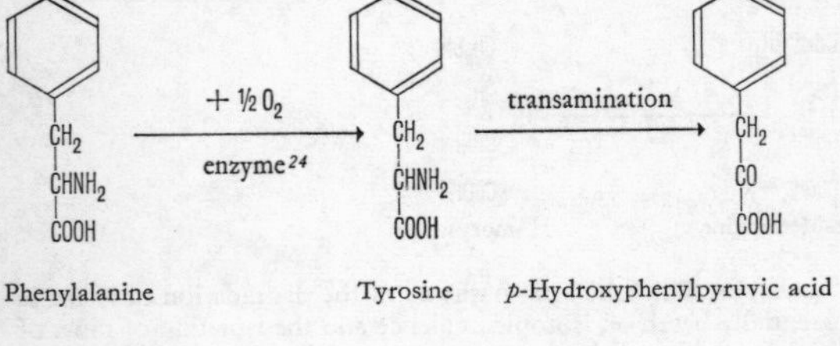

Phenylalanine Tyrosine *p*-Hydroxyphenylpyruvic acid

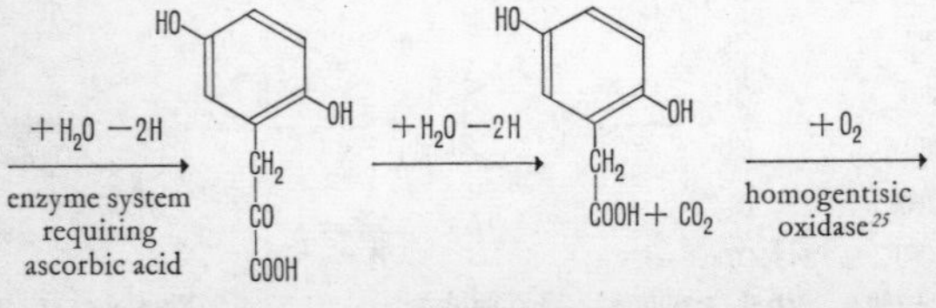

2,5-Dihydroxyphenylpyruvic acid Homogentisic acid

References

1) For reviews see Greenberg, D. M. (Ed.), *Chemical Pathways of Metabolism*, vol. II, New York, 1954; McElroy and Glass (Eds.), *A Symposium on Amino Acid Metabolism*, Baltimore, 1955; Meister, A., *Biochemistry of the Amino Acids*, New York, 1957. *2)* Strecker and Mela, *Biochim. biophys. Acta*, **17**, 580 (1955). *3)* Bachhawat et al., *J. biol. Chem.*, **216**, 727 (1955); Coon et al., in McElroy and Glass (Eds.), *A Symposium on Amino Acid Metabolism*, Baltimore, 1955, page 431. *4)* Coon et al., *J. biol. Chem.*, **199**, 75 (1954); Robinson et al., *J. biol. Chem.*, **218**, 391 (1956). *5)* Coon et al., in McElroy and Glass (Eds.), *A Symposium on Amino Acid Metabolism*, Baltimore, 1955, page 431; Kinnory et al., *J. biol. Chem.*, **212**, 385 (1955); Robinson et al., *J. biol. Chem.*, **224**, 1 (1957). *6)* Chargaff and Sprinson, *J. biol. Chem.*, **151**, 273 (1943). *7)* Carroll et al., *J. biol. Chem.*, **180**, 375 (1949). *8)* Matsuo and Greenberg, *J. biol. Chem.*, **215**, 547 (1955). *9)* Binkley and Olson, *J. biol. Chem.*, **185**, 881 (1950). *10)* Greenberg, D. M., *Chemical Pathways of Metabolism*, vol. II, New York, 1954, page 57. *11)* Braunshtein and Vilenkina, *C. R. Acad. Sci. U.S.S.R.*, **66**, 243 (1949). *12)* Meltzer and Sprinson, *J. biol. Chem.*, **197**, 461 (1952). *13)* Cf. Arnstein, H. R. V., *Advanc. Protein Chem.*, **9**, 1 (1954); Huennekens et al., *J. biol. Chem.*, **224**, 435 (1957). *14)* Shemin and Russell, *J. Amer. chem. Soc.*, **75**, 4873 (1953). *15)* Shemin, D., *Harvey Lect.*, **50**, 258 (1954–55). *16)* Neuberger and Scott, *Nature*, **172**, 1093 (1953). *17)* Rimington, C., *Brit. med. J.*, **2**, 189 (1956). *18)* Smythe, C. V., *J. biol. Chem.*, **142**, 387 (1942). *19)* Fromageot, C., in Sumner and Myrbäck (Eds.), *The Enzymes*, vol. I, part 2, New York, 1951, page 1237. *20)* Binkley, F., *J. biol. Chem.*, **191**, 531 (1951). *21)* Borsook et al., *J. biol. Chem.*, **176**, 1383 (1948). *22)* Rothstein and Miller, *J. biol. Chem.*, **206**, 243 (1954); **211**, 851 and 859 (1954). *23)* Ogston, A. G., *Nature*, **167**, 693 (1951). *24)* Udenfriend and Mitoma, in McElroy and Glass (Eds.), *A Symposium on Amino Acid Metabolism*, Baltimore, 1955, page 876; Mitoma, C., *Arch. Biochem. Biophys.*, **60**, 476 (1956); Kaufman, S., *Biochim. biophys. Acta*, **23**, 445 (1957); Kaufman, S., *J. biol. Chem.*, **226**, 511 (1957). *25)* Suda and Takeda, *J. Biochem. (Tokyo)*, **37**, 381 (1950); Crandall, D. I., *J. biol. Chem.*, **212**, 565 (1955). *26)* Knox, W. E., in McElroy and Glass (Eds.), *A Symposium on Amino Acid Metabolism*, Baltimore, 1955, page 836; Knox and Edwards, *J. biol. Chem.*, **216**, 479, 489 (1955).

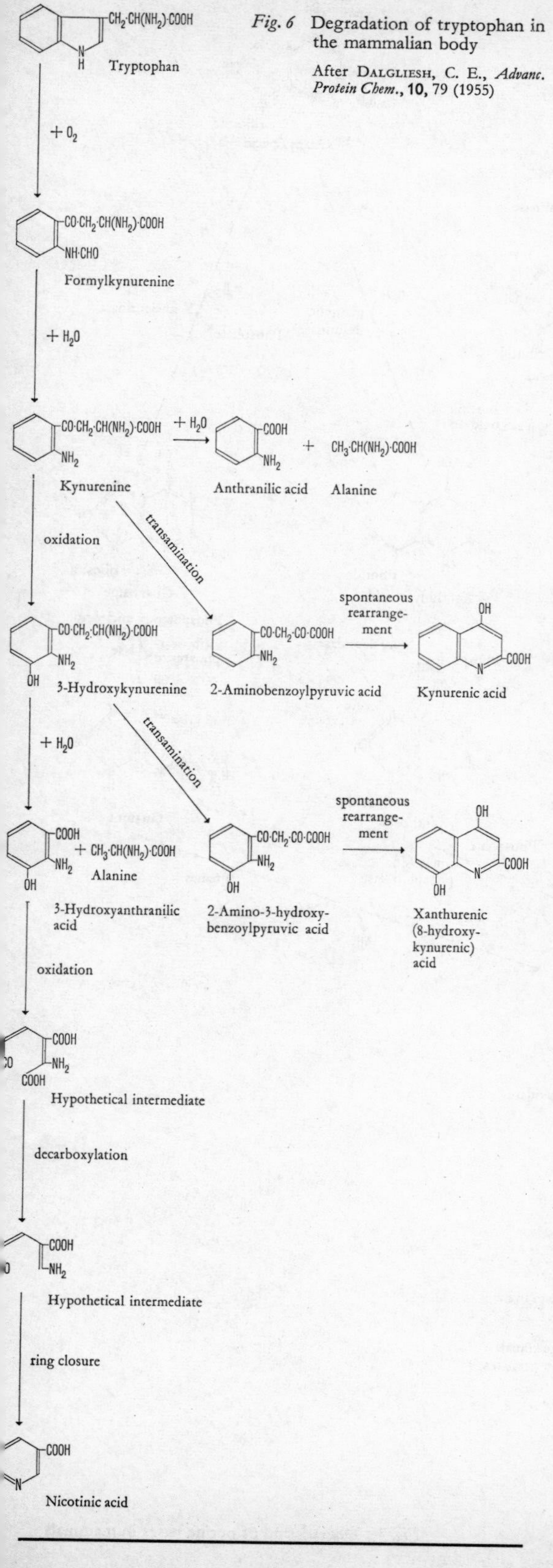

Fig. 6 Degradation of tryptophan in the mammalian body

After Dalgliesh, C. E., *Advanc. Protein Chem.*, **10**, 79 (1955)

5. Degradation of food constituents other than carbohydrate, fat and protein

Foods contain a number of substances built up from molecules other than hexoses, fatty acids or amino acids. Some of these are not broken down in the body, but others are. To the latter group belong the constituents of nucleic acids and nucleotides (pentoses, desoxypentoses, purine bases, pyrimidine bases) and part of the cholesterol molecule. Quantitatively these substances form a very small part of the food and their contribution to the supply of energy is almost negligible.

Pentoses, reacting in the form of ribose-5-phosphate, can be converted to glucose-6-phosphate and triose-phosphate by reactions of the pentose-phosphate cycle (reactions **3** to **8** of Table 19, page 430). Three molecules of ribose-5-phosphate form two molecules of glucose-6-phosphate and one molecule of glyceraldehyde phosphate.

2-Desoxyribose-5-phosphate can be split by aldolase to acetaldehyde and glyceraldehyde phosphate[1]:

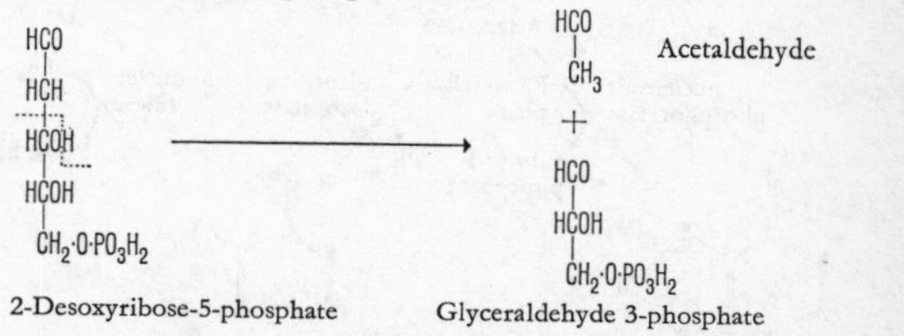

The acetaldehyde can be converted into acetyl-coenzyme A.

Purine bases are degraded in man to uric acid and in most mammals to allantoin (see page 412). *Pyrimidines* are broken down to ammonia, CO_2 and β-alanine or α-methyl-β-alanine (β-amino-*iso*butyric acid) by the reactions shown below. Both β-alanine and α-methyl-β-alanine can be further oxidized[2]. β-Alanine can enter a transamination reaction with α-ketoglutarate to form the semialdehyde of malonic acid which is probably decarboxylated to acetaldehyde, a precursor of acetyl-coenzyme A[3]:

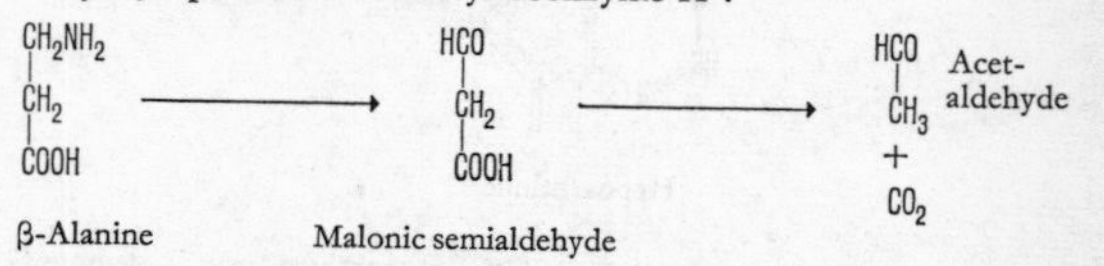

The analogous reactions of α-methyl-β-alanine would yield propionic aldehyde which is expected to form propionyl-coenzyme A and subsequently succinic acid.

About 5–10% of humans excrete α-methyl-β-alanine in the urine in quantities up to 300 mg daily[4]. This is assumed to be an inborn error of metabolism. It is probable that the defect is not due to the absence of enzymes responsible for the degradation but to a failure of tubular renal absorption[5].

Of *cholesterol*, only the side chain undergoes complete oxidation. A specific enzyme can cleave off the side chain, forming *iso*-caproic acid and leaving the ring system in the form of pregnenolone[6]. *iso*Caproic acid in turn is broken down to propionic acid and acetyl-coenzyme A[7]. The ring system of cholesterol and steroids is not oxidized to CO_2[6].

Other cell constituents which are essentially not oxidized in the body to CO_2 are the *iron porphyrins* derived from hemoglobin and cytochromes (these are excreted in the form of bile pigments and their derivatives), and the *uronic acids* contained in mucins, in hyaluronic acid and in the chondroitin sulfate of cartilage and tendons.

Degradation of pyrimidines. Cytosine and uracil are converted into β-alanine by the liver through the following reaction sequence. The evidence for these postulated reactions has not yet been fully investigated[8].

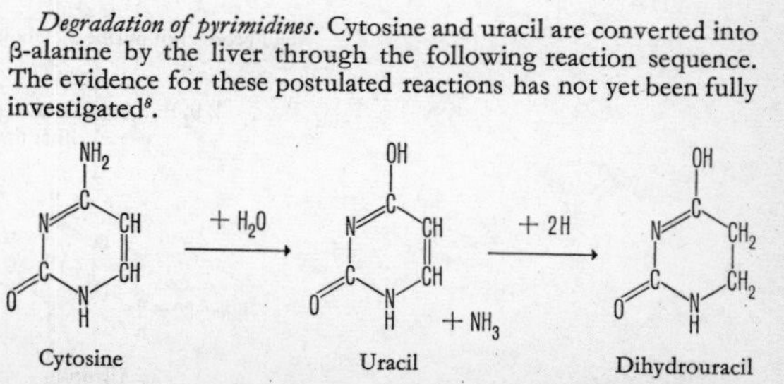

(continued on page 413)

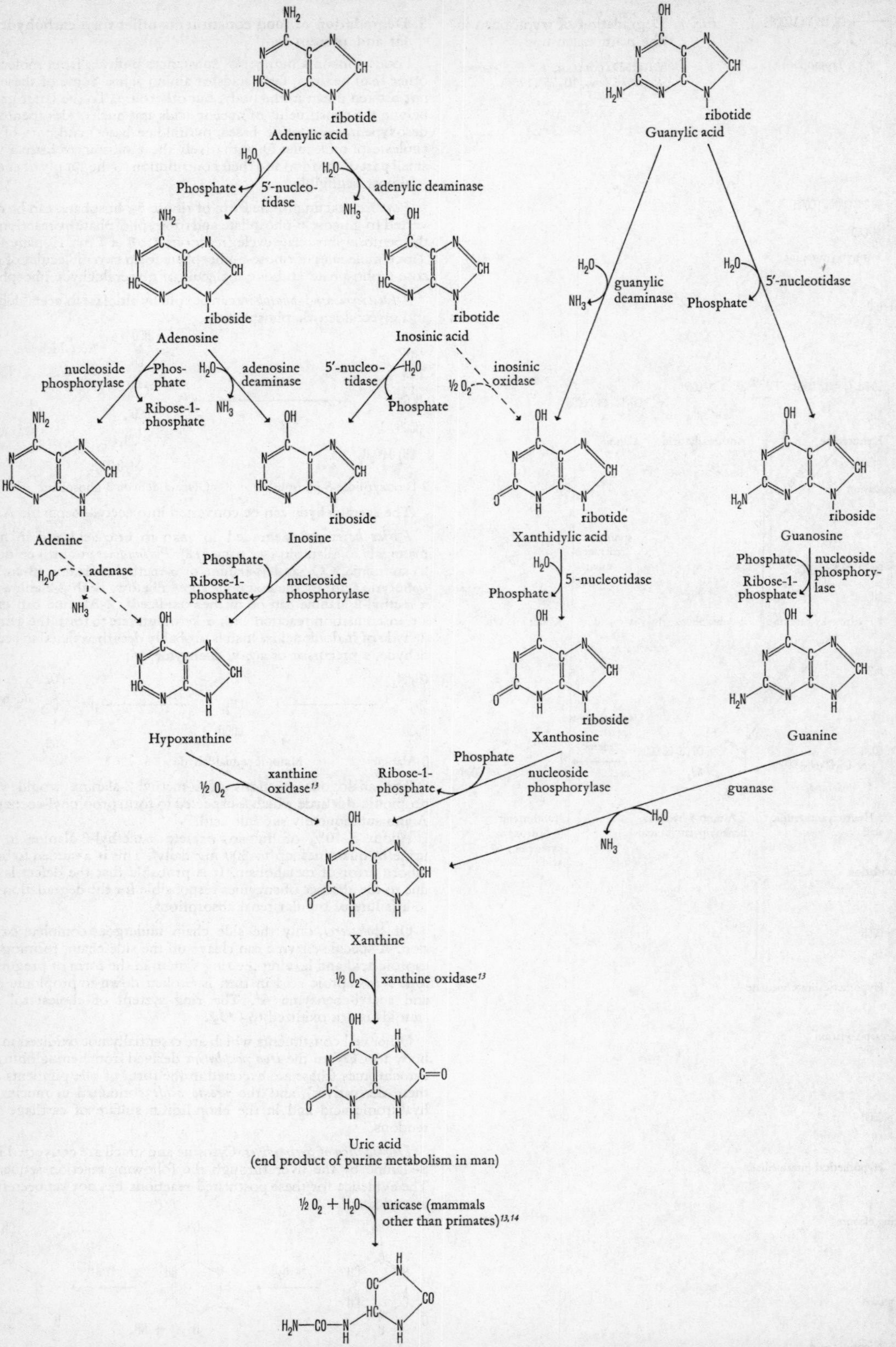

Fig. 7 Degradation of purine bases in mammals

(continued from page 411)

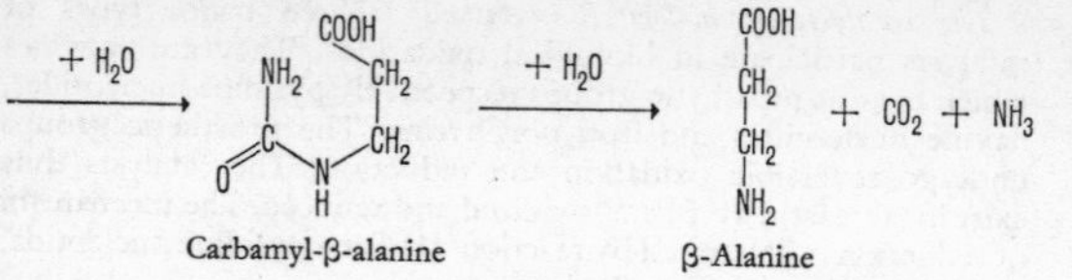

Carbamyl-β-alanine β-Alanine

Thymine, by analogous reactions[9], forms α-methyl-β-alanine in liver. Other pathways occur in bacteria[10].

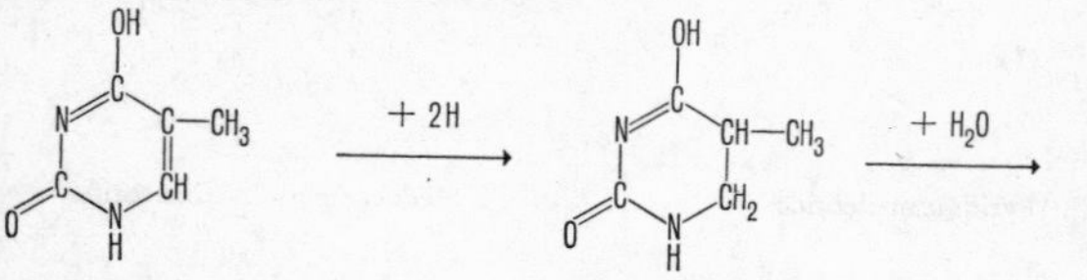

Thymine Dihydrothymine

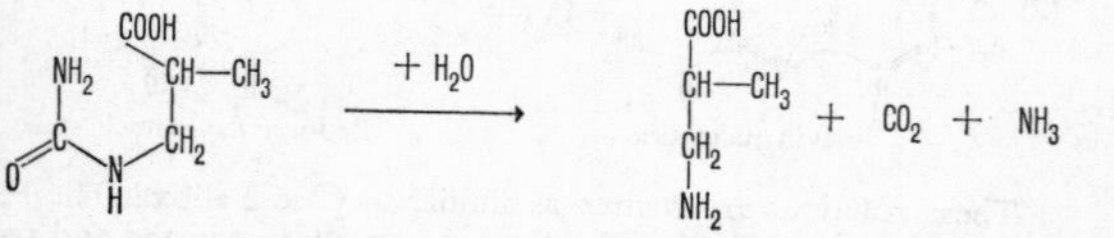

Carbamyl-β-amino*iso*butyric acid (α-methylcarbamyl-β-alanine) β-Amino*iso*butyric acid (α-methyl-β-alanine)

Degradation of purine bases in man and mammals[11]. The degradation of the purine bases adenine and guanine involves hydrolytic deamination and oxidation. Both types of reactions can be entered by the respective nucleotides and nucleosides, and by the free purine bases. Deamination precedes oxidation but there are various pathways depending on whether deamination and oxidation precede or do not precede the fission of the nucleotide or nucleoside. The end-product of purine degradation is the same, irrespective of the route. It is uric acid in man and other primates, and allantoin in other mammals. Amphibians and fish degrade allantoin further to allantoic acid, urea and glyoxylic acid. Some lower species such as crustacea degrade urea to ammonia and carbon dioxide.

The various pathways are shown in Figure 7 opposite. The relative importance of the alternatives has not been accurately assessed. Reactions which occur readily and are widespread in mammals are indicated by full arrows, those which are of limited occurrence and relatively slow are indicated by broken arrows.

Purine deaminases. Three types of enzyme – adenase, adenosine deaminase and adenylic deaminase – are known which hydrolyze adenine, adenosine and adenylic acid respectively to yield ammonia and the corresponding derivative of hypoxanthine. Of these, the occurrence of adenase (adenine deaminase) in mammals is uncertain. Adenosine deaminase occurs in most tissues of higher animals. Adenylic deaminase (adenylic acid deaminase) occurs abundantly in striated muscle but is relatively weak in other tissues, including heart muscle[12].

Three types of enzymes – guanase, guanosine deaminase, and guanylic deaminase – are known which hydrolyze guanine, guanosine and guanylic acid respectively to yield ammonia and the corresponding derivative of xanthine. Each of these enzymes occurs in many tissues of higher animals.

Purine oxidases. The oxidation of purines can occur at the ribotide level or at the free base level. The oxidation of inosinic acid to xanthidylic acid is an intermediate stage in the synthesis of guanylic acid (see page 440), but the contribution of this reaction to the degradation of purines is probably very small, the chief oxidation reactions being those attacking the free purine bases.

Xanthine oxidase catalyzes the oxidation of hypoxanthine to xanthine and of xanthine to uric acid. The enzyme occurs in milk and in many tissues[13].

Uricase oxidizes uric acid to allantoin[13, 14]. It occurs in liver and kidney of mammals other than man and primates.

Nucleotide hydrolases and nucleoside phosphorylases. The fission of nucleotides is hydrolytic, the products being nucleosides and inorganic phosphate. The fission of nucleosides in animals is phosphorolytic, the products being a purine base and ribose-1-phosphate. Microorganisms also contain nucleoside hydrolases, but these have not so far been demonstrated in higher animals.

References

1) Racker, E., *J. biol. Chem.*, **196**, 347 (1952). *2)* Roberts and Bregoff, *J. biol. Chem.*, **201**, 393 (1953). *3)* Piehl and Fritzson, *J. biol. Chem.*, **215**, 345 (1955). *4)* Crumpler et al., *Nature*, **167**, 307 (1951). *5)* Harris, H., *An Introduction to Human Biochemical Genetics*, London, 1954. *6)* Siperstein and Chaikoff, *J. biol. Chem.*, **198**, 93 (1952); Staple et al., *J. biol. Chem.*, **219**, 845 (1956). *7)* Atchley, W. A., *J. biol. Chem.*, **176**, 123 (1948). *8)* Fink et al., *J. biol. Chem.*, **197**, 441 (1952); Fink et al., *J. biol. Chem.*, **201**, 349 (1953); Fink and McGaughey, *Fed. Proc.*, **13**, 207 (1954). *9)* Fink et al., *Fed. Proc.*, **15**, 251 (1956). *10)* Hayaishi and Kornberg, *J. biol. Chem.*, **197**, 717 (1952). *11)* For reviews see Schmidt, G., in Chargaff and Davidson (Eds.), *The Nucleic Acids*, vol. I, New York, 1955, page 555; Baldwin, E., *Dynamic Aspects of Biochemistry*, London, 1952, page 347. *12)* Conway and Cooke, *Biochem. J.*, **33**, 479 (1939). *13)* Mahler, H. R., *Advanc. Enzymol.*, **17**, 233 (1956). *14)* Mahler et al., *Science*, **124**, 705 (1956).

6. Synopsis of the degradation of the principal foodstuffs

In surveying the reactions by which the basic constituents of foodstuffs are broken down it may be said that the degradation proceeds in two major stages. In the first stage the starting material – the small molecules produced by the process of digestion and consisting of several hexoses, glycerol, about twenty amino acids and a number of fatty acids – is incompletely burned. The products listed in Table 7, apart from carbon dioxide and water, are either

Table 7 Survey of the products formed by the initial oxidative degradation reactions of the basic constituents of foodstuffs

These reactions all lead to acetyl-coenzyme A and/or the intermediates of the tricarboxylic acid cycle

Starting material	Products of initial reactions (CO_2 omitted)
Glucose, other hexoses	2 Acetyl-CoA
Fatty acids (even-numbered chains of *n* C-atoms)	½ *n* Acetyl-CoA
Fatty acids (uneven-numbered chains of *n* C-atoms)	½ (*n*−3) Acetyl-CoA; 1 Succinate (via propionyl-CoA)
Glycerol, alanine, cysteine, cystine, serine	1 Acetyl-CoA
Glutamic acid, histidine, arginine, ornithine, citrulline, proline, hydroxyproline	1 α-Ketoglutarate
Aspartic acid	1 Oxaloacetate
Leucine	3 Acetyl-CoA
*iso*Leucine	1 Acetyl-CoA; 1 Succinate (via propionyl-CoA)
Valine	1 Succinate (via methyl-malonyl-CoA)
Norleucine	1 Acetyl-CoA
Norvaline	2 Acetyl-CoA; 1 Succinate (via propionyl-CoA)
α-Aminobutyric acid, homoserine, homocysteine, methionine	1 Succinate (via propionyl-CoA)
Glycine*	1 Acetyl-CoA (via serine)
Threonine	2 Acetyl-CoA (one via glycine–serine)
Lysine	α-Ketoglutarate, Acetyl-CoA
Phenylalanine, tyrosine	1 Fumarate; 2 Acetyl-CoA
Tryptophan	1 Acetyl-CoA (via alanine)**

* Glycine may also be oxidized by a special cycle (see page 409).
** Other products are formed which are not oxidizable (see page 410).

acetic acid in the form of acetyl-coenzyme A or an intermediate of the tricarboxylic acid cycle, α-ketoglutarate, succinate, fumarate or oxaloacetate. Acetic acid constitutes the main product: two-thirds of the carbon of carbohydrate and glycerol, all the carbon of the common fatty acids and about half the carbon skeleton of amino acids yield acetyl-coenzyme A. α-Ketoglutarate arises from glutamic acid, histidine, arginine, citrulline, ornithine, proline and hydroxyproline; oxaloacetate from aspartate; fumarate from part of the benzene ring of tyrosine and phenylalanine; succinate from *iso*leucine, valine, methionine, α-aminobutyric acid, propionic acid and the three terminal carbon atoms of fatty acids with an uneven number of carbon atoms.

The products of the first stage of the oxidative breakdown are completely oxidized in the second stage, the tricarboxylic acid cycle, which thus represents a common terminal pathway of oxidation shared by all foodstuffs. Almost two-thirds of the total energy released in the combustion of foodstuffs appears during the reactions of this cycle.

Any surplus oxaloacetate which is not required as a catalyst in the cycle can be decarboxylated to pyruvate, whence it is converted into acetyl-coenzyme A and undergoes complete oxidation.

In so far as substances other than carbohydrate, fat and amino acids can supply energy, their degradation follows pathways which, like those of carbohydrate, fat and amino acids, yield acetyl-coenzyme A and/or an intermediate of the tricarboxylic acid cycle.

7. Mechanism of biological oxidations

General. The degradation reactions discussed so far take place when the foodstuff molecules are "burned" by molecular oxygen. This "combustion" is not, however, a direct reaction of molecular oxygen with the substrate but a transference of electrons, mediated by several complex enzyme systems, in which oxygen is the ultimate electron acceptor. In order to understand the action of these catalysts, it has to be borne in mind that biological oxidations include three types of reaction which at first sight appear to be different but which are basically the same. The three types are illustrated by the following cases:

Case 1. Addition of oxygen atoms, for example:

$$CH_3{\cdot}CHO \xrightarrow{+O} CH_3{\cdot}COOH$$

Acetaldehyde — Acetic acid

Case 2. Removal of hydrogen atoms, for example:

$$CH_3{\cdot}CHOH{\cdot}COOH \xrightarrow{-2H} CH_3{\cdot}CO{\cdot}COOH$$

Lactic acid — Pyruvic acid

Case 3. Transformation of a metal from a lower to a higher valency state by removal of electrons, for example:

$$Fe^{++} \rightarrow Fe^{+++} + e^-$$

All three cases are seen to be basically similar – as removal of H atoms – if the participation of water is also considered:

Case 1 may then be formulated as

$$CH_3{\cdot}CHO + H_2O \rightarrow CH_3{\cdot}CH(OH)_2 \xrightarrow{-2H} CH_3{\cdot}COOH$$

Acetaldehyde — Hydrated form of acetaldehyde — Acetic acid

and *Case 3* as

$$2\,Fe^{++} + 2\,H_2O \xrightarrow{-2H} 2\,Fe^{+++} + 2\,OH^-$$

The common feature of all types of biological oxidations is a removal of electrons, although this is often either written as a removal of H (i.e. electron and proton) or as the addition of O atoms. There are instances in which neither H nor O atoms are directly involved, as in the oxidation of one heavy metal catalyst by another:

$$R{\cdot}Fe^{++} + R'{\cdot}Fe^{+++} \rightarrow R{\cdot}Fe^{+++} + R'{\cdot}Fe^{++}$$

Such reactions occur in living cells between iron porphyrins (cytochromes) in which the electrons travel more or less directly from one Fe atom to another. Because there are cases where electron transfer is the only change, the formulation of oxidation as electron transport is looked upon as the most general and fundamental description of this process.

Biological oxidations may therefore be described in terms of the transfer of electrons, and the reactions whereby electrons are transferred from substrates to molecular oxygen are usually referred to as electron transport reactions.

The catalysts of biological oxidations[1]. Three major types of catalysts participate in biological oxidations. They are enzymes which have as prosthetic groups respectively pyridine nucleotides, flavine nucleotides and iron porphyrins. The prosthetic groups undergo reversible oxidation and reduction. The catalysts thus exist in (at least) two forms, oxidized and reduced. The mechanism of reduction is illustrated by reaction (**1**) for a pyridine nucleotide, and by reaction (**2**) for a flavin nucleotide:

(**1**)

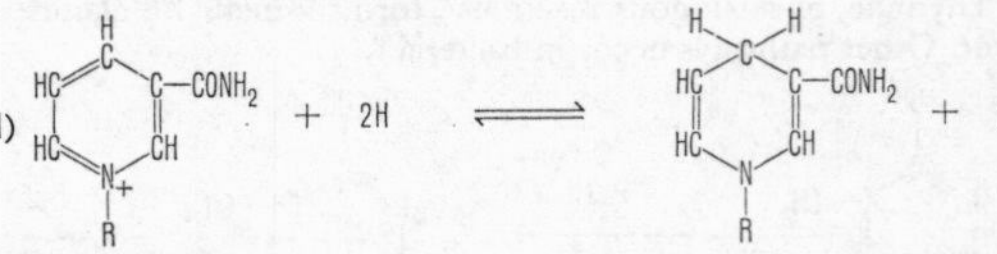

Pyridine nucleotide — Reduced pyridine nucleotide

(**2**)

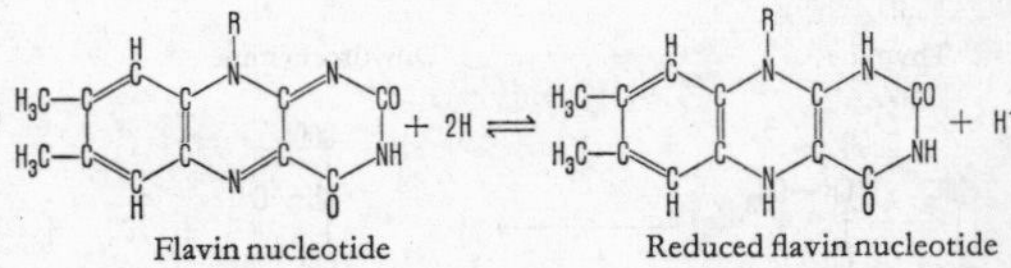

Flavin nucleotide — Reduced flavin nucleotide

These reactions are written as similar to Case 2 above. The Fe atoms of iron porphyrin enzymes are reversibly oxidized and reduced as described in Case 3 above.

When mediating the reactions between substrate and molecular oxygen, i.e. when transferring electrons (or H atoms) from substrate to oxygen, these catalysts react in a characteristic order governed by their thermodynamic properties. These properties are indicated by the oxidation–reduction potentials of the catalysts:

Catalyst	E'_0 *(volts)*
Oxygen electrode ($H_2O \rightleftharpoons \frac{1}{2}O_2 + 2H + 2e^-$)	+ 0.81
Cytochrome C	+ 0.25[2]
Flavin nucleotides (free)	– 0.20[2]
Pyridine nucleotides (free)	– 0.32[2]
Hydrogen electrode ($H_2 \rightleftharpoons 2H^+ + 2e^-$)	– 0.42

As seen from this table, the potentials of the electron carriers are such that the reduced form of pyridine nucleotides can act as reductant of the flavin nucleotides which, in turn, can act as reductant of the oxidized cytochromes. The order in which the catalysts transport electrons from the substrate to molecular oxygen may therefore be expressed in the following series of reactions:

(*a*) Substrate + pyridine nucleotide → oxidized substrate + reduced pyridine nucleotide

(*b*) Reduced pyridine nucleotide + flavin nucleotide → pyridine nucleotide + reduced flavin nucleotide

(*c*) Reduced flavin nucleotide + 2 Fe^{+++}-porphyrin → flavin nucleotide + 2 Fe^{++}-porphyrin + 2 H^+

(*d*) 2 Fe^{++}-porphyrin + 2 H^+ + ½ O_2 → 2 Fe^{+++}-porphyrin + H_2O

Sum: Substrate + ½ O_2 → oxidized substrate + H_2O

There are many variants of this basic scheme: firstly, because there are two pyridine nucleotides, many flavoproteins (some containing iron or molybdenum) and many iron porphyrins; secondly, because other types of reactions such as

flavoprotein 1 + reduced flavoprotein 2
→ reduced flavoprotein 1 + flavoprotein 2

or

ferrous iron porphyrin 1 + ferric iron porphyrin 2
→ ferric iron porphyrin 1 + ferrous iron porphyrin 2

can be interspersed in the above series; thirdly, because additional catalysts may take part. There is evidence that both vitamin E and vitamin K are links in the hydrogen transport chain[3].

References

1) For reviews see Ball, E. G., *Ann. N.Y. Acad. Sci.*, **45**, 363 (1944); Herbert, D., *Ann. Rep. Progr. Chem.*, **47**, 335 (1951); Slater, E. C., *Proceedings of the Third International Congress of Biochemistry, Brussels 1955*, New York, 1956, page 264; Mahler and Green, *Science*, **120**, 7 (1954); Mahler, H. R., *Proceedings of the Third International Congress of Biochemistry, Brussels 1955*, New York, 1956, page 252. *2*) Values from Burton, K., in Krebs and Kornberg, *Ergebn. Physiol.*, **49**, 212 (1957). *3*) Martius, C., *Biochem. Z.*, **326**, 26 (1954); Martius and Nitz-Litzow, *Biochem. Z.*, **327**, 1 (1955); Martius, C., *Proceedings of the Third International Congress of Biochemistry, Brussels 1955*, New York, 1956, page 1.

8. The key position of adenosine triphosphate (ATP) in biological energy transformations[1]

One of the outstanding advances in the understanding of energy metabolism is the appreciation of the fact that the energy derived from the degradation of foodstuffs can be utilized for most purposes only if it is first transformed into a special type of chemical energy. This is the energy residing in the pyrophosphate bonds of adenosine triphosphate (ATP) which is released when these bonds are hydrolyzed to form inorganic orthophosphate (P) or pyrophosphate (PP), adenosine diphosphate (ADP) and adenosine monophosphate (adenylic acid, AMP):

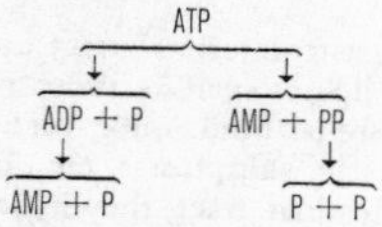

Pyrophosphate bonds release more free energy on hydrolysis (11–13 kcal according to conditions) than ester phosphate bonds (2–4 kcal). They are therefore referred to as "energy-rich". It is the hydrolysis of the pyrophosphate bonds of ATP which provides the energy necessary for the various kinds of work performed by living cells, such as the contraction of muscle, the production of secretions, the activities of the nervous system and the synthesis of cell constituents.

The pyrophosphate bonds which are used up during the activities of the cells are resynthesized at the expense of the energy liberated by the degradation of foodstuffs. The synthesis of pyrophosphate bonds may in fact be looked upon as the first major object of the biological energy transformations. Special chemical mechanisms are required for the coupling between pyrophosphate bond synthesis and foodstuff degradation. It is evident that many hundreds of separate reactions occur when foodstuffs are degraded, but owing to the special arrangement of the metabolic processes coupling between degradation and pyrophosphate bond synthesis occurs only at a few stages. In all, six types of reaction are known in which energy becomes available for the synthesis of ATP. Two such stages occur in anaerobic glycolysis: when one molecule of glucose is converted into lactic acid two molecules of ATP are resynthesized from ADP and inorganic phosphate (Table 3, page 401). There are no more than four types of steps in the course of all the oxidative reactions where ATP is synthesized. The oxidative degradation of the substrate itself, i.e. the removal of two hydrogen atoms and their transfer to pyridine nucleotide, as a rule does not supply energy. Energy is liberated when the hydrogen atoms or electrons are transferred from the pyridine nucleotides to molecular oxygen through the reactions (*b*), (*c*) and (*d*) discussed on page 414. Each of these three steps leads to the synthesis of one pyrophosphate bond ("oxidative phosphorylation"). The fourth step of the oxidative metabolism coupled with phosphorylation consists of reactions of type (*a*) (page 414) where the substrate is an α-ketonic acid. Reactions of this type where the substrate is not an α-ketonic acid do not yield appreciable amounts of energy and therefore cannot support the synthesis of pyrophosphate bonds.

The chemical mechanism by which the coupling between pyrophosphate synthesis and reactions (*b*), (*c*) and (*d*) is effected is unknown. Some information is available about the coupling mechanism between ATP synthesis and reactions of type (*a*) with α-ketonic acids as substrates. In this case an acyl-coenzyme A derivative is formed from the α-ketonic acid by the reactions described for pyruvate on page 403. Thus α-ketoglutarate yields succinyl-coenzyme A. The latter reacts as follows:

succinyl-coenzyme A + guanosine diphosphate + P
→ succinate + coenzyme A + guanosine triphosphate

Phosphoryl succinate or phosphoryl-coenzyme A may be intermediates in this reaction though neither has as yet been identified[2]. Guanosine triphosphate can transfer phosphate to ADP:

guanosine triphosphate + ADP
→ guanosine diphosphate + ATP

Adenosine triphosphate contains two "energy-rich" pyrophosphate bonds. It is probable that only the terminal bond serves as an immediate source of energy, or can be directly resynthesized. The second pyrophosphate bond is used to re-phosphorylate adenosine diphosphate according to the reaction

$$2\,ADP \rightleftharpoons AMP + ATP$$

which is catalyzed by the enzyme adenylate kinase (also called myokinase) present in all tissues. The balance of this reaction plus the hydrolysis of ATP to ADP + P represents an hydrolysis of ADP to AMP + P. In reverse the reaction represents a mechanism for the re-phosphorylation of AMP.

References

1) For bibliography see Krebs and Kornberg, *Ergebn. Physiol.*, **49**, 212 (1957).
2) Sanadi et al., *Biochim. biophys. Acta*, **13**, 146 (1954); **14**, 434 (1954); Kaufman, S., *J. biol. Chem.*, **216**, 153 (1955); Cohn, M., *Biochim. biophys. Acta*, **20**, 92 (1956).

Digestive enzymes

In this section will be described the specific enzymes the combined action of which is responsible for the process of digestion of foodstuffs. Each enzyme catalyzes the hydrolysis of one compound or of a series of closely related compounds. (For a general review of enzymes and enzyme action see pages 396–398.)

1. Proteolytic enzymes (proteases)

These are enzymes which catalyze the hydrolytic cleavage of peptide bonds:

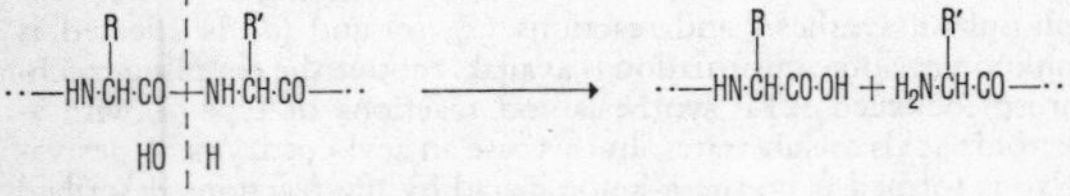

They may be divided into two main classes:

1. *Endopeptidases*, which act on proteins and peptides by hydrolyzing "internal" peptide linkages, i.e. those situated away from the ends of peptide chains.

2. *Exopeptidases*, which catalyze the hydrolysis of peptide bonds situated at the ends of peptide chains. These enzymes are specific for peptides possessing one or more free terminal α-amino or α-carboxyl groups.

Members of both classes of proteases are widely distributed in mammalian tissues. Those of the gastrointestinal tract are discussed in Tables 10 and 11, pages 417–420. The proteases of other tissues are summarized in Table 12 (page 421).

2. Glycosidases

Carbohydrates are digested by these enzymes, which catalyze the hydrolysis of glycosidic bonds:

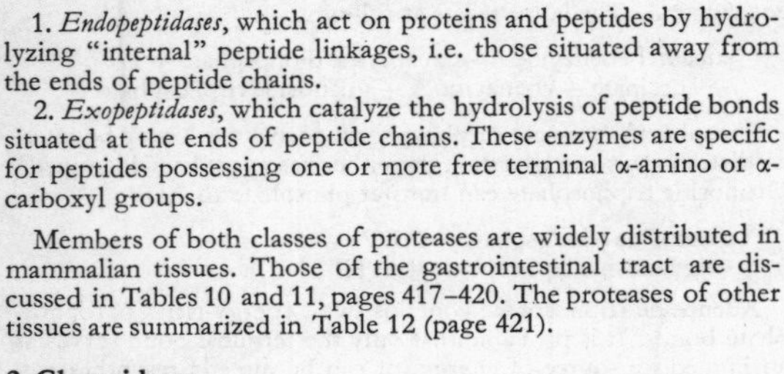

Some glycosidases act on only the glycosidic bonds of polysaccharides (polysaccharidases), others on only those of smaller carbohydrates (oligosaccharidases). A number of factors determine whether a glycosidase will act on any particular linkage. Among these factors the most important are

(*a*) the nature of the monosaccharide which donates the reducing group involved in the glycosidic bond; for example, separate enzymes act on glucosides and galactosides;

(*b*) the configuration (α or β) about the carbon atom of the potential reducing group:

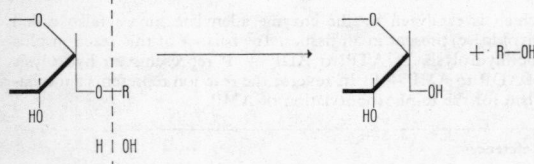

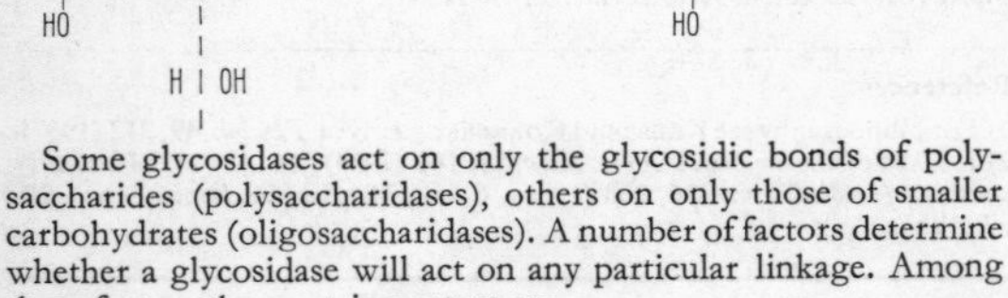

α β

(*c*) the configuration (D- or L-) of the monosaccharide bearing the potential reducing group. In general, mammalian glycosidases act only at linkages of the D-configuration;

(*d*) the size of the heterocyclic sugar ring. Usually, glycosidases which act on aldohexosides are specific for linkages in which the aldohexose is in the pyranose form, whilst those acting on ketohexosides require the substrate to be in the furanose form:

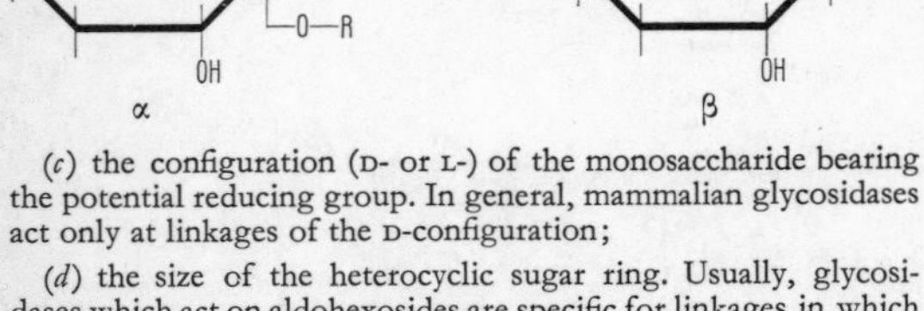

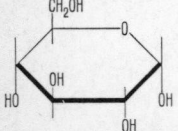

Pyranose ring (e.g. glucose) Furanose ring (e.g. fructose)

The general properties of mammalian glycosidases are described in Table 13 (pages 422 and 423).

3. Lipases and esterases

Fats and other esters are hydrolyzed by the action of enzymes which have been subdivided into *lipases*, which hydrolyze the ester linkages between both short-chain and long-chain fatty acids and glycerol, and thus act on fats, and *esterases*, which act only slowly on fats but split the ester linkages between other acids and other alcohols. The general action of this group of enzymes may be formulated as follows:

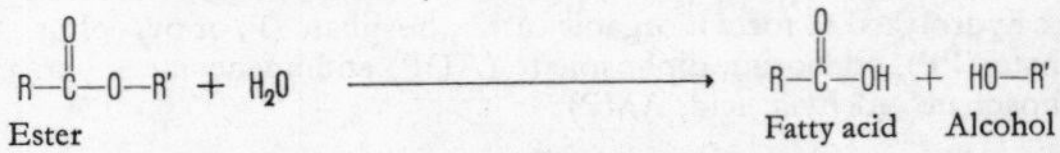

Ester Fatty acid Alcohol

The lipases of the gastrointestinal tract are discussed in Table 14 (page 423). Other lipases such as those of serum, leukocytes, erythrocytes, cerebrospinal fluid, milk, pleural effusions, lymph, liver, lung, brain, muscle, skin, testes, etc., behave similarly; like those of the gastrointestinal tract, they hydrolyze fats and short-chain fatty acid esters[1].

Phosphatases

Mammalian tissues contain a variety of unspecific esterases which have not yet been obtained in a pure form. Some of these enzymes catalyze the hydrolysis of the ester linkages between short-chain fatty acids and alcohol, others hydrolyze esters of the type R·OR′, where R is not a carboxylic acid. The largest group of these enzymes is formed by the *phosphatases*[2]. These may be further classified as:

1. *Phosphomonoesterases*, which hydrolyze monoesters of phosphoric acid:

For example, glucose-6-phosphate is hydrolyzed to glucose and phosphate.

2. *Phosphodiesterases*, which hydrolyze substrates such as nucleic acids, or the synthetic substrate diphenyl orthophosphate, at one of the ester linkages:

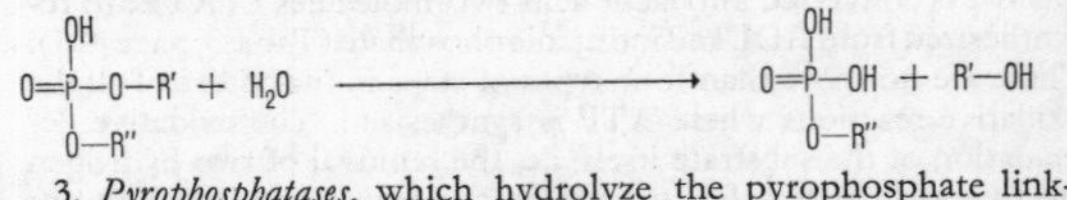

3. *Pyrophosphatases*, which hydrolyze the pyrophosphate linkages of salts of pyrophosphoric acid and of pyrophosphate esters:

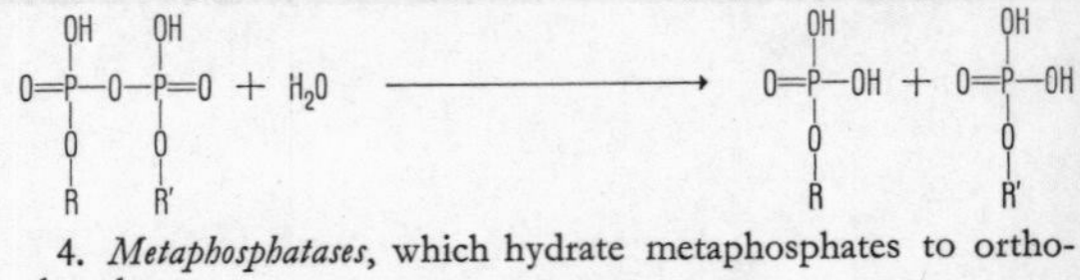

4. *Metaphosphatases*, which hydrate metaphosphates to orthophosphates:

$$(HPO_3)_n + n\,H_2O \rightarrow n\,H_3PO_4$$

These have not been demonstrated to occur in the mammalian body.

Sulfatases[3]

These enzymes catalyze the hydrolysis of esters of sulfuric acid:

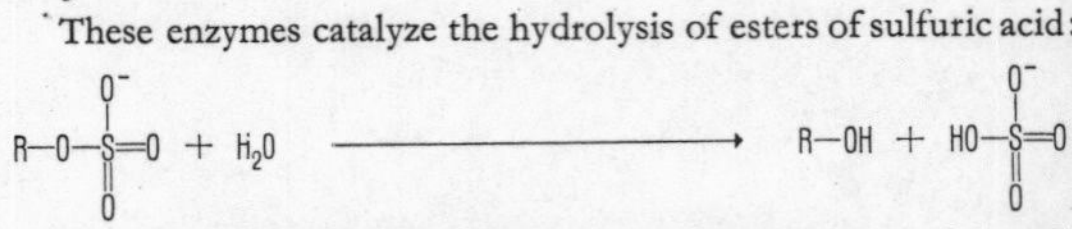

They may be distinguished according to the nature of the sulfuric acid esters which they hydrolyze.

The esterases in general are listed in Table 15 (pages 424 and 425); those acting on phospholipids and their metabolic products are further discussed in Table 16 (pages 425 and 426).

4. Ribonucleases and desoxyribonucleases

Ribonucleases (RNAases) and desoxyribonucleases (DNAases) catalyze the cleavage of ribonucleic acid (RNA) and desoxyribonucleic acid (DNA) respectively (Table 17, pages 426 and 427). They are present in most if not all tissues[4].

Of the RNAases only pancreatic RNAase has been studied extensively. The enzyme is a specific phosphodiesterase which hydrolyzes certain phosphoric ester linkages of RNA but not of DNA. The end-products of the prolonged action of pancreatic RNAase are 3′-uridylic acid, 3′-cytidylic acid, and a large number of

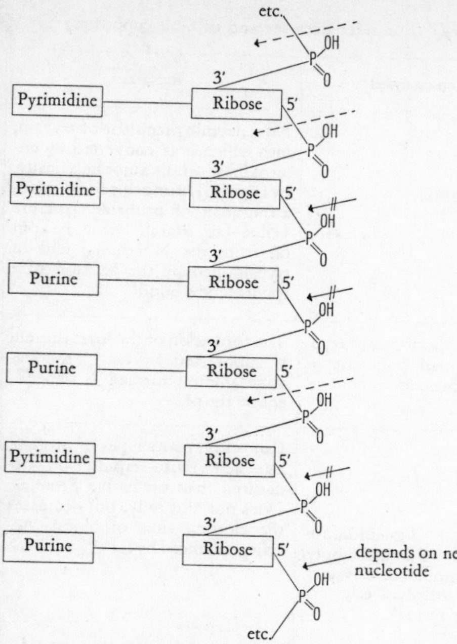

Fig. 8 The specificity of pancreatic RNAase

The 5'-ester linkages attacked are indicated by broken arrows, those not attacked are indicated by crossed arrows. The enzyme does not attack 3'-ester linkages

dialyzable polynucleotides of varying degrees of polymerization. The terminal nucleotides of these polynucleotides are all either 3'-uridylic acid or 3'-cytidylic acid. This and other evidence indicates that RNAase specifically hydrolyzes pyrimidine nucleoside-3'-phosphodiesters, with the resulting liberation of the corresponding pyrimidine nucleoside-3'-phosphates (phosphomonoesters). The mode of attack of the enzyme on a hypothetical part of an RNA molecule is shown in Figure 8. Information on the specificity of RNAases from tissues other than the pancreas is not yet available.

Several types of DNAases occur in various tissues; of these, pancreatic DNAase has been studied most extensively. The enzyme is a specific phosphodiesterase which hydrolyzes certain phosphoric ester linkages of DNA but not of RNA. The end-products of the prolonged action of DNAase on DNA are mainly di- and tri-nucleotides as well as small amounts of mononucleotides and other polynucleotides. The terminal nucleotides of the polynucleotides liberated by the enzyme are all 5'-nucleotides, and the mononucleotides liberated by the enzyme are also 5'-nucleotides. This indicates that pancreatic DNAase specifically hydrolyzes nucleoside-5'-phosphodiesters with the resulting liberation of the corresponding nucleoside-5'-phosphates (Figure 9). The enzyme also exhibits purine and pyrimidine selectivity, but the extent and type of this specificity is not known at present.

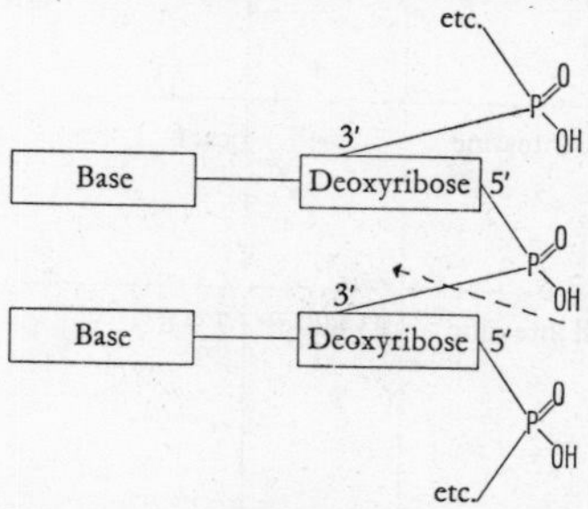

Fig. 9 The specificity of pancreatic DNAase

The ester linkage attacked by the enzyme is indicated by a broken arrow

The products of the action of RNAase and DNAase are broken down further by other phosphodiesterases and phosphatases (see Table 17, page 427) to yield nucleotides and nucleosides. The latter are then degraded by phosphorolysis to yield purines and pyrimidines and pentose-1-phosphate, or by hydrolysis to yield purines and pyrimidines, pentose and inorganic phosphate.

References

1) For a review see Ammon and Jaarma, in Sumner and Myrbäck (Eds.), *The Enzymes*, vol. I, part 1, New York, 1950, page 390. *2)* For a review see Roche, J., in Sumner and Myrbäck (Eds.), *The Enzymes*, vol. I, part 1, New York, 1950, page 473. *3)* For a review see Fromageot, C., in Sumner and Myrbäck (Eds.), *The Enzymes*, vol. I, part 1, New York, 1950, page 517. *4)* See Schmidt, G., in Chargaff and Davidson (Eds.), *The Nucleic Acids*, vol. I, New York, 1955, page 555; Davidson, J. N., *The Biochemistry of the Nucleic Acids*, 2nd ed., London, 1954; Laskowski, M., in Sumner and Myrbäck (Eds.), *The Enzymes*, vol. I, part 2, New York, 1951, page 956; McDonald, M. R., in Colowick and Kaplan (Eds.), *Methods in Enzymology*, vol. II, New York, 1955, page 427.

Table 10 Proteases and protease precursors of the gastrointestinal tract (For references see end of table, page 419)

Enzyme	Location	Approx. mol. wt.	Optimal pH of action	Reaction catalyzed*	Remarks
Pepsinogen	Chief cells of gastric mucosa	42,000	–	–	Nonenzymic precursor of pepsin, into which it is converted autocatalytically by pepsin at pH < 6, with loss of a "pepsin inhibitor" of mol. wt. ca. 5000[2]
Pepsin	Gastric juice	36,000	1.8 – 3.8 Depends on the nature of the substrate and the acid anion[3]	—CO·NH·CH(R)·CO ⁞ NH·CH(R')·CO— where R' = *p*-hydroxybenzyl or benzyl (from L-tyrosine or L-phenylalanine)	Attacks most proteins except some protamines and keratins. Denatured proteins are attacked more readily than native proteins, and the pH range of action is wider. It is assumed that the initial step of peptic hydrolysis is the unfolding of the peptide chain
Rennin	Stomach of young animals	40,000	Milk clotting: ca. 5 Proteolysis (hemoglobin): 3.7	May act by hydrolyzing phosphoamide bonds of phosphoserine and phosphothreonine; crystalline rennin shows phosphoamidase and phosphatase activities[4]	Clots milk and liberates peptones from the α-casein contained therein

* These specificity relationships are those elucidated by the action of the enzymes on synthetic peptides; they are not necessarily those of the enzymes acting on proteins[1].

Table 10 Proteases and protease precursors of the gastrointestinal tract (*continued*) (For references see end of table, opposite)

Enzyme	Location	Approx. mol.wt.	Optimal pH of action	Reaction catalyzed*	Remarks
Trypsinogen	Pancreas	23,700[5]	–	–	Nonenzymic precursor of trypsin, into which it is converted by enterokinase and, autocatalytically, by trypsin. During this conversion, a fragment of probable structure valine–(aspartate)$_4$–lysine is split off from the N-terminal end of trypsinogen by the scission of a lysyl*iso*leucyl bond[6]
Enterokinase	Small intestine	–	ca. 6	Converts trypsinogen to trypsin + a small fragment + some inert protein	The formation of the inert protein is suppressed by Ca^{++}; the relative amount formed is dependent on the pH[7]
Trypsin	Small intestine	23,800	7 – 8	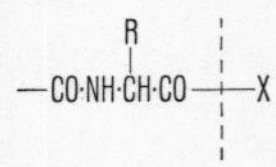 where R = δ-guanidino-*n*-propyl or ε-amino-*n*-butyl (from L-arginine or L-lysine). Can also hydrolyze esters of arginine or lysine[8]	Can act on many types of protein, but acts more rapidly on denatured than on native proteins. Does not clot milk, but decreases the clotting time of blood. Activity enhanced by Ca^{++}
α-Chymotrypsinogen	Pancreas	22,500	–	–	Nonenzymic precursor of the chymotrypsins, to which it is converted by trypsin and, autocatalytically, by chymotrypsins. It is believed[9] that the conversion of α-chymotrypsinogen to δ-chymotrypsin involves the successive action of trypsin and chymotrypsin on the peptide sequence [–leucine–serine–arginine–*iso*leucine–] within the cyclic α-chymotrypsinogen molecules. Trypsin attacks the arginyl–*iso*leucyl bond to form π-chymotrypsin; this is followed by autolysis of the leucylseryl bond to yield δ-chymotrypsin. Serylarginine is formed in this reaction. Autolytic cleavage of a tyrosyl–alanyl bond of δ-chymotrypsin then yields α-chymotrypsin, which is the enzyme normally predominant in the pancreatic juice
Chymotrypsinogen B	Pancreas	22,500	–	–	Yields chymotrypsin B on activation by trypsin. Differs from α-chymotrypsinogen in electrophoretic mobility and in the ease with which it is retained on resins[10]
Chymotrypsins: π	Pancreas	–	–	Similar in action to α-chymotrypsin	First product of tryptic digestion of α-chymotrypsinogen. Very unstable: obtained only at low temperature. Rapidly converted to δ- and α-chymotrypsins. 2–2½ times as active as α-chymotrypsin
δ	Pancreas	–	–	Similar in action to α-chymotrypsin	Derived from π-chymotrypsin, with loss of serylarginine. Unstable. Approximately 1½ times as active as α-chymotrypsin

* These specificity relationships are those elucidated by the action of the enzymes on synthetic peptides; they are not necessarily those of the enzymes acting on proteins[1].

Table 10 Proteases and protease precursors of the gastrointestinal tract (*concluded*)

Enzyme	Location	Approx. mol. wt.	Optimal pH of action	Reaction catalyzed*	Remarks
Chymotrypsins (continued):					
α	Pancreas	21,500	ca. 8	—CO—CH(R)—NH ⋮ CO—CH(R′)·NH— where R′ = *p*-hydroxyphenyl from tyrosine. If the group R′·CH(NH·)·CO· is a phenylalanine, tryptophan or methionine residue, decreased activity persists. Rupture of C–C bonds has also been reported[11]	Predominant chymotrypsin in the pancreatic secretion. Unlike trypsin, it clots milk but not blood
β	Pancreas	30,000 (probably as a dimer)	ca. 8	Similar in action to α-chymotrypsin	Produced by limited autolysis of α-chymotrypsin. Differs from α-chymotrypsin in crystalline form, solubility and rate of inactivation by acids, alkalis and urea[12]
γ	Pancreas	27,000 (probably as a dimer)	ca. 8	Similar in action to α-chymotrypsin	Probably a product of the further autolysis of β-chymotrypsin
B	Pancreas	22,500	ca. 8	Similar in action to α-chymotrypsin	Differs from the α-enzyme in crystalline form and electrophoretic mobility. Has lower activity towards casein than α-chymotrypsin

* These specificity relationships are those elucidated by the action of the enzymes on synthetic peptides; they are not necessarily those of the enzymes acting on proteins[1].

References

1) See Bergmann, M., *Advanc. Enzymol.*, **2**, 49 (1942); Fruton, J. S., *Ann. Rev. Biochem.*, **16**, 35 (1947). *2)* Herriott, R. M., *J. gen. Physiol.*, **24**, 325 (1940-41). *3)* Masch and Huchting, *Hoppe-Seyl. Z. physiol. Chem.*, **301**, 49 (1955). *4)* Holter and Li, *Acta chem. scand.*, **4**, 1321 (1950); Mattenheimer et al., *Helv. chim. Acta*, **35**, 1970 (1952). *5)* Tietze, F., *J. biol. Chem.*, **204**, 1 (1953). *6)* Davie and Neurath, *J. biol. Chem.*, **212**, 515 (1955); Desnuelle and Fabre, *Biochim. biophys. Acta*, **18**, 49 (1955). *7)* McDonald and Kunitz, *J. gen. Physiol.*, **25**, 53 (1941–42). *8)* Neurath and Schwert, *Chem. Rev.*, **46**, 69 (1950). *9)* Fruton and Mycek, *Ann. Rev. Biochem.*, **25**, 57 (1956). *10)* Laskowski, M., in Colowick and Kaplan (Eds.), *Methods in Enzymology*, vol. II, New York, 1955, page 8. *11)* Doherty, D. G., *J. Amer. chem. Soc.*, **77**, 4887 (1955). *12)* Smith, E. L., in Sumner and Myrbäck (Eds.), *The Enzymes*, vol. I, part 2, New York, 1951, page 793.

Table 11 Exopeptidases and exopeptidase precursors of the gastrointestinal tract[1] (For references see end of table, page 420)

A large number of different exopeptidases have been recognized as occurring in the gastrointestinal tract. They are distinguished from each other mainly in their specificities of action on synthetic peptides. Only a few have been purified extensively, and the list of exopeptidases here given is not complete: doubtless many more remain to be isolated and studied

Enzyme	Location	Approx. mol. wt.	Optimal pH of action	Reaction catalyzed*	Remarks
Procarboxy-peptidase	Pancreas	96,000		–	Nonenzymic precursor of carboxypeptidase. Is more acidic than carboxypeptidase, and is split by trypsin to carboxypeptidase and fragments. All the potential carboxypeptidase activity of procarboxypeptidase is retained in the smaller carboxypeptidase fragment: the larger fragment is enzymically inactive[2]
Carboxy-peptidase	Pancreas	34,000[2-4]	7.5 – 8.5	R—CO ⋮ NH—CH(R′)·COOH Wide specificity, but most active when R′ = benzyl from phenylalanine. Also acts when R′ is derived from tyrosine > tryptophan > leucine > methionine > *iso*leucine > alanine > glycine. Also acts on esters. Terminal carboxyl must be free; may also require the presence of uncharged amino groups	Contains Zn^{++} as essential constituent[4]. Strongly inhibited by sulfide, cyanide, iodoacetate; sulfhydryl groups in the protein necessary for activity. Also inhibited by aromatic D-amino acids, by aromatic and heterocyclic carboxylic acids and, most effectively, by β-phenylpropionic acid

* These specificity relationships are those elucidated by the action of the enzymes on synthetic peptides; they are not necessarily those of the enzymes acting on proteins[2].

Table 11 Exopeptidases and exopeptidase precursors of the gastrointestinal tract[1] (*continued*)

Enzyme	Location	Approx. mol. wt.	Optimal pH of action	Reaction catalyzed*	Remarks
Amino-tripeptidase (tripeptidase)	Small intestine[5]	–	7.5 – 8.5	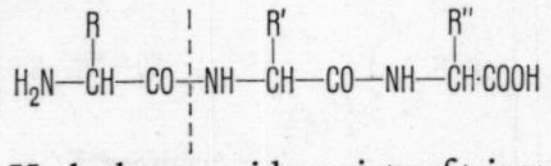 Hydrolyzes a wide variety of tripeptides. Requires free amino group	Hydrolyzes tripeptides at the bond adjacent to the essential free amino group to yield a free amino acid and a dipeptide. Has little or no action on tetra- or dipeptides
L-Leucine amino-dipeptidase	Small intestine		Prob. ca. 8	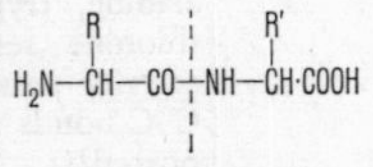 Wide specificity, but most active when R = L-leucine residue. Also attacks polypeptides, but more slowly	Activated by Mg^{++} or Mn^{++}, inhibited by anions which will bind Mg^{++} or Mn^{++}, e.g. citrate, ethylenediamine tetraacetate, pyrophosphate. Not affected by reagents reacting with sulfhydryl groups
Glycylglycine dipeptidase[6]	Small intestine	–	ca. 8	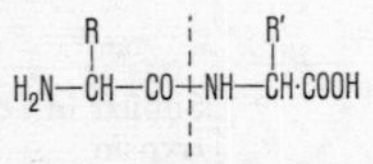 where R = glycine or sarcosine residue, R′ = glycine residue	Probably a metal enzyme: contains Co^{++} as essential constituent. It has been postulated that Co^{++} acts as a bridge in forming chelate complexes between the enzyme and its substrate
Glycyl-L-leucine dipeptidase[7]	Small intestine	–	ca. 8	Optimally specific for L-leucine. Also hydrolyzes sarcosyl-L-leucine	Activated by Mn^{++}
Imido-dipeptidase (prolidase)	Small intestine	–	ca. 8	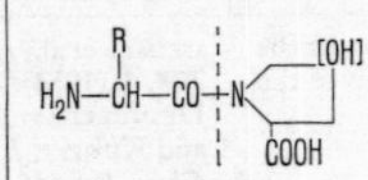 or 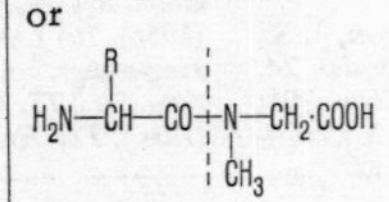	Hydrolyzes only dipeptides lacking a peptide hydrogen. Activated by Mn^{++}. Inhibited strongly by iodoacetamide and *p*-chloromercuribenzoate in the absence of, but not in the presence of, Mn^{++}: this suggests that Mn^{++} is bound to a sulfhydryl group of the protein[8]
Imino-dipeptidase (prolinase)	Small intestine	–	ca. 8	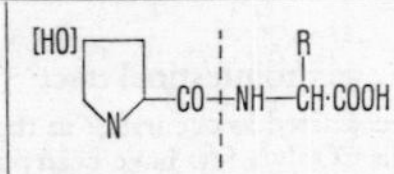 where R = any amino acid residue except glutamic or aspartic acid	Hydrolyzes dipeptides containing N-terminal proline or hydroxyproline residues. Activated by Mn^{++}

* These specificity relationship are those elucidated by the action of the enzymes on synthetic peptides; they are not necessarily those of the enzymes acting on protein[2].

References

1) For a review see Smith, E. L., in Sumner and Myrbäck (Eds.), *The Enzymes*, vol. I, part 2, New York, 1951, page 793. *2)* Bergmann, M., *Advanc. Enzymol.*, **2**, 49 (1942); Fruton, J. S., *Ann. Rev. Biochem.*, **16**, 35 (1947). *3)* Smith et al., *J. biol. Chem.*, **180**, 33 (1949). *4)* Vallee and Neurath, *J. Amer. chem. Soc.*, **76**, 5006 (1954). *5)* Ågren, G., *Acta physiol. scand.*, **9**, 248, 255, 269 (1945). *6)* Smith, E. L., in Colowick and Kaplan (Eds.), *Methods in Enzymology*, vol. II, New York, 1955, page 107. *7)* Smith, E. L., in Colowick and Kaplan (Eds.), *Methods in Enzymology*, vol. II, New York, 1955, page 105. *8)* Smith et al., in McElroy and Glass (Eds.), *The Mechanism of Enzyme Action*, Baltimore, 1954, page 291.

Table 12 Proteases of tissues other than the gastrointestinal tract (For references see end of table, opposite)

It has long been known that animal tissues other than the gastrointestinal tract contain proteolytic enzymes since, on the death of animals, extensive breakdown of tissue proteins occurs. The tissue proteinases are now referred to as cathepsins: they occur in most tissues, the liver, spleen and kidney being particularly rich in them. In addition to these proteinases, which have been only partially purified, tissues contain exopeptidases analogous to, or identical with, those of the gastrointestinal tract. The list of endo- and exo-peptidases here given cites only those enzymes which up to the present have been well characterized. The proteases of blood clotting and the proteases acting on dehydropeptides and acylpeptides (acylase I and II) are also not discussed here

Enzyme	Location	Optimal pH of action	Reaction catalyzed*	Remarks
Cathepsin A	Most animal tissues, particularly liver, spleen and kidney. The skin, uterus, lung, muscles and brain are poor in activity[1]	5.6	Similar in action to pepsin	Old name: cathepsin I. Requires no activator
Cathepsin B		ca. 5	Similar in action to trypsin	Old name: cathepsin II. Activated by compounds containing sulfhydryl groups

* These specificity relationships have been elucidated by the use of synthetic substrates; they are not necessarily those of the enzymes acting on protein[7].

Table 12 Proteases of tissues other than the gastrointestinal tract (*continued*)

Enzyme	Location	Optimal pH of action	Reaction catalyzed*	Remarks
Cathepsin C	Most animal tissues, particularly liver, spleen and kidney. The skin, uterus, lung, muscles and brain are poor in activity[1]	ca. 5 for proteolysis; ca. 7 for transamidation	Similar in action to chymotrypsins	Activated by compounds containing sulfhydryl groups. At pH 7 acts as transamidase: when acting on a peptide amide, the NH_2 group split off by water can be transferred not only to the H^+ of water (in which case a normal hydrolytic reaction occurs and ammonia is formed) but also to other NH_2 acceptors, such as H of another NH_2 group. Thus, with glycyl-L-phenylalanineamide $NH_2{\cdot}CH_2{\cdot}CO{\cdot}NH{\cdot}CH(CH_2{\cdot}C_6H_5){\cdot}CO{\cdot}NH_2$ successive transamidations occur[2], leading to the formation of insoluble polypeptides: $NH_2{\cdot}R{\cdot}CO{\cdot}NH_2 + NH_2{\cdot}R{\cdot}CO{\cdot}NH_2 \rightarrow NH_2{\cdot}R{\cdot}CO{\cdot}NH{\cdot}R{\cdot}CO{\cdot}NH_2 + NH_3$
Carboxypeptidase	Most animal tissues	ca. 7	Homospecific with pancreatic carboxypeptidase	Old name: cathepsin IV
Aminotripeptidase (tripeptidase)	Most animal tissues; has been purified from calf thymus[3] and from equine erythrocytes[4]	8.0	Similar in action to intestinal tripeptidase	Inhibited by cysteine, Cd^{++}, Hg^{++}. Rapidly inactivated in acid media
L-Leucine aminodipeptidase	Many tissues; especially abundant in kidney	8 – 9	Similar in action to the intestinal enzyme	Old name: cathepsin III. The enzyme protein, isolated from swine kidney[5], is particularly rich in leucine (8.8%). Requires activation by Mg^{++} or Mn^{++}
Glycylglycine dipeptidase	Many tissues; has been partially purified from rat muscle, human uterus and swine kidney[6]	7.6	Similar in action to the intestinal enzyme	Activity enhanced by addition of Co^{++} or, more weakly, of Mn^{++}. Preparations of this enzyme from rat muscle are exceedingly unstable, from human uterus less so[6]
Glycyl-L-leucine dipeptidase	Several tissues; has been partially purified from uterus[6]	ca. 8	Similar in action to the intestinal enzyme	Activity enhanced by Zn^{++} and phosphate
Imidodipeptidase (prolidase)	Many tissues; has been found in skeletal and smooth muscle, erythrocytes, serum, pituitary, lung and kidney, and has been partially purified from equine erythrocytes and swine kidney[6]	7.8 – 8.0	Similar in action to the intestinal enzyme	Activity enhanced by Mn^{++}
Iminodipeptidase (prolinase)	Many tissues; has been partially purified from swine kidney[6]	ca. 8	Similar in action to the intestinal enzyme	Activity enhanced by Mn^{++} and Cd^{++}
Carnosinase	Several tissues; has been partially purified from spleen, liver and swine kidney[6]	8.0 – 8.4 in presence of Mn^{++}, 7.8 – 7.9 in presence of Zn^{++}, 7.4–7.5 in absence of metal	A dipeptidase, hydrolyzing L-alanyl-L-histidine > glycyl-L-histidine > β-alanyl-L-histidine > D-alanyl-L-histidine	Activity enhanced by Zn^{++} and Mn^{++}

* These specificity relationships have been elucidated by the use of synthetic substrates: they are not necessarily those of the enzymes acting on proteins[7].

References

1) SMITH, E. L., in SUMNER and MYRBÄCK (Eds.), *The Enzymes*, vol. I, part 2, New York, 1951, page 793. *2)* DE LA HABA et al., in COLOWICK and KAPLAN (Eds.), *Methods in Enzymology*, vol. II, New York, 1955, page 64. *3)* ELLIS and FRUTON, *J. biol. Chem.*, **191**, 153 (1951). *4)* ADAMS et al., *J. biol. Chem.*, **199**, 845 (1952). *5)* SPACKMAN et al., *J. biol. Chem.*, **212**, 255 (1955). *6)* SMITH, E. L., in COLOWICK and KAPLAN (Eds.), *Methods in Enzymology*, vol. II, New York, 1955, page 93. *7)* BERGMANN, M., *Advanc. Enzymol.*, **2**, 49 (1942); FRUTON, J.S., *Ann. Rev. Biochem.*, **16**, 35 (1947).

Table 13 Glycosidases (For references see end of table, opposite)

Enzyme	Location	Optimal pH of action	Reaction catalyzed	Remarks
α-Amylase	Saliva, pancreatic juice, blood	6.9	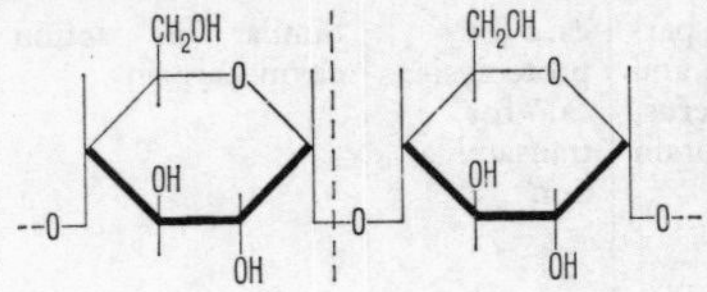	Hydrolyzes α-1,4-glucosidic bonds in polyglucosans such as amylose, amylopectin, glycogen and dextrins. The initial stage of action of the enzyme is characterized by a rapid decrease of the mol.wt. of the substrate, resulting in a rapid change of its iodine-staining properties; when starch paste is the substrate, a rapid decrease of viscosity (liquefaction) occurs. The enzyme preferentially attacks the second linkage from the reducing end of the polyglucosan molecule, producing maltose, dextrins and a small amount of glucose[1]. Activity of the enzyme is enhanced by $Cl^- > Br^- > NO_3^- > I^-$. Human salivary and pancreatic α-amylases are identical[2]
Maltase	Small intestine, pancreatic juice, blood, liver[3]	6.6	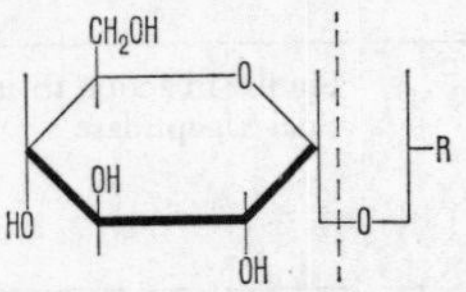 where R = glucose (in which case the above compound is maltose, 4-α-D-glucopyranosyl-D-glucose), substituted hexoses, phenols, terpenes, etc.[4]. The evidence for the rupture of the glucose–O bond rests on isotopic data[5]	An α-glucosidase: the maltose produced from the digestion of starch by α-amylase is hydrolyzed to glucose by this enzyme. Inhibited by the glucose formed. Does not act on sucrose. Claims for the existence of an animal sucrase, and its suggested identity with maltase, have been disputed[4,6]
Oligo-1,6-glucosidase	Small intestine	ca. 7	Hydrolyzes 1,6-glucoside linkages of *iso*maltose, panose, and α-amylase dextrins[7]	This enzyme is thought to complete the digestion of starch by hydrolyzing the dextrins produced by α-amylase to smaller unbranched molecules, which can be further degraded by α-amylase and maltase in the pancreatic juice
Amylo-1,6-glucosidase	Muscle	ca. 6.8	Phosphorylase limit dextrin (glycogen) → glucose + polysaccharide in which penultimate branches have become outer branches[8]	Splits the α-1,6-glucosidic bonds in the branched polysaccharides glycogen and amylopectin; it acts only after a phosphorylase has degraded the outer chains of these polysaccharides exhaustively, forming a limit dextrin. By hydrolytic action, the amylo-1,6-glucosidase then liberates glucose plus a polysaccharide which can again be degraded by phosphorylase action. Successive repetitions result in complete degradation of the polysaccharide to yield glucose and glucose-1-phosphate. This enzyme differs from oligo-1,6-glucosidase in having no action on *iso*maltose, panose or α-amylase dextrin
β-Glucosidase and β-Galactosidase	Kidney[9], liver[9], small intestine[10], blood	Varies with substrate	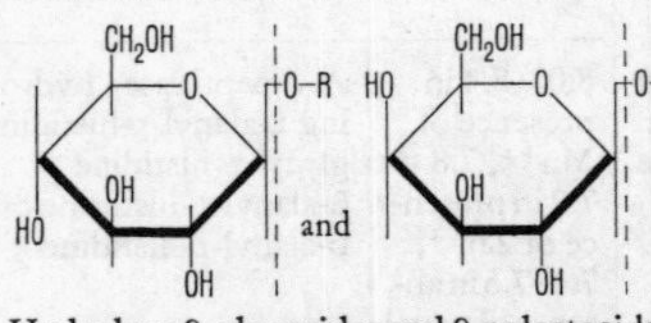 Hydrolyze β-glucosides and β-galactosides; do not act on α-glucosides	β-Glucosidase hydrolyzes gentiobiose, cellobiose, amygdalin, salicin, prunasin and arbutin. Not affected by HCN, H_2S or glutathione, inactivated by oxidizing agents. Although this enzyme is widespread in the *Rosaceae*, molds, yeasts and bacteria, its presence in mammals is still a matter for dispute, as also its possible identity with β-galactosidase. β-Galactosidase can transfer galactose residues to a variety of acceptors (such as lactose, galactose and glucose) as well as to water, and thus can catalyze transgalactosidations

Table 13 Glycosidases (*continued*)

Enzyme	Location	Optimal pH of action	Reaction catalyzed	Remarks
β-Glucuronidase	Most animal tissues, especially spleen, liver and endocrine tissues[11]	ca. 5	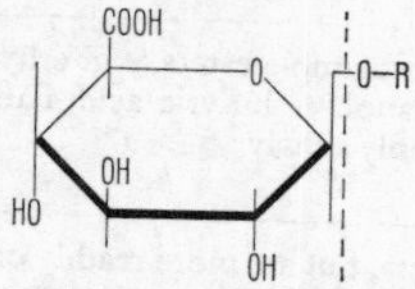 Hydrolyzes many glucuronides, does not act on α- or β-glucosides	Dilute solutions of the enzyme show enhanced activity in presence of desoxyribonucleic acid. The physiological function of the enzyme probably lies in the reverse action, i.e. the formation of glucuronides. It thus plays a role in the detoxication of toxic materials and in steroid metabolism[11]
Hyaluronidases[12]	Testes, semen, spleen, iris, cornea	ca. 7.5	Hydrolyze the glycosidic bonds involving the reducing group N-acetylglucosamine of hyaluronic acid. Also act on some chondroitin sulfates	Hydrolyze the mucopolysaccharide hyaluronic acid to disaccharides composed of N-acetylglucosamine and glucuronic acid, and oligosaccharides which are further hydrolyzed by β-glucuronidase. Increase the diffusion of materials injected into the skin
Sulfomucases[12]	Testes, liver	ca. 7.5	Act primarily on chondroitinsulfuric acid by hydrolysis of the glycosidic bonds of N-acetylgalactosamine	May be part of the hyaluronidase complex of enzymes
Heparinase[13]	Liver, kidney	5.3 – 6.8	Hydrolyzes the anti-clotting mucopolysaccharide heparin	Probably attacks the carbohydrate portion of heparin[13]
Lysozyme[12]	Mucus, lacrimal secretion, spleen[14]	5.3	Hydrolyzes glycosidic groups in bacterial mucopolysaccharides, especially those of *Micrococcus lysodeikticus*	May play a role in defending mucous surfaces against bacterial invasion
α- and β-Glucosaminidases[15]	Spleen, liver, kidney, lung, blood, heart, brain, testes	Not recorded for animal enzymes	Hydrolyze N-acetyl-α- and N-acetyl-β-glucosaminides respectively → N-acetyl-α- or N-acetyl-β-glucosamine	The β-enzyme has been shown to act on the blood-group A and O(H) substances of swine gastric mucin with the liberation of methylpentose constituents[16]. The enzyme liberates N-acetylglucosamine residues from A but not from O(H)

References

1) Bird and Hopkins, *Biochem. J.*, **56**, 86 (1954). *2)* Bernfeld et al., *Helv. chim. Acta*, **33**, 1064 (1950). *3)* Glock, G. E., *Biochem. J.*, **30**, 2313 (1936). *4)* Gottschalk, A., in Sumner and Myrbäck (Eds.), *The Enzymes*, vol. I, part 1, New York, 1950, page 551. *5)* Springhorn and Koshland, *Abstr. Amer. chem. Soc. 128th Meeting*, 1955, page 37C. *6)* Neuberg and Mandl, in Sumner and Myrbäck (Eds.), *The Enzymes*, vol. I, part 1, New York, 1950, page 527. *7)* Larner and McNickle, *J. biol. Chem.*, **215**, 723 (1955). *8)* Cori, G. T., in Colowick and Kaplan (Eds.), *Methods in Enzymology*, vol. I, New York, 1955, page 211. *9)* Neuberg and Hofmann, *Biochem. Z.*, **281**, 431 (1935). *10)* Steensholt and Veibel, *Acta physiol. scand.*, **6**, 62 (1943); Clarke et al., *J. biol. Chem.*, **131**, 135 (1939); Wallenfels et al., *Justus Liebigs Ann. Chem.*, **584**, 63 (1953). *11)* Fishman, W. H., in Sumner and Myrbäck (Eds.), *The Enzymes*, vol. I, part 1, New York, 1950, page 635. *12)* Fishman, W. H., in Sumner and Myrbäck (Eds.), *The Enzymes*, vol. I, part 2, New York, 1951, page 769. *13)* Jaques, L. B., *J. biol. Chem.*, **133**, 445 (1940); Jaques and Cho, *Biochem. J.*, **58**, XXV (1954). *14)* Jollès and Fromageot, *Biochim. biophys. Acta*, **11**, 95 (1953); **14**, 219 (1954). *15)* Kent and Whitehouse, *Biochemistry of the Aminosugars*, London, 1955, page 20. *16)* Howe and Kabat, *J. Amer. chem. Soc.*, **75**, 5542 (1953).

Table 14 Lipases of the gastrointestinal tract

The lipases catalyze the reaction $(R{\cdot}CO{\cdot}O{\cdot}R')_3 + 3\,H_2O \rightleftharpoons 3\,R{\cdot}CO{\cdot}OH + 3\,HO{\cdot}R'$, where $R{\cdot}CO{\cdot}O$ is a long-chain fatty acid and $HO{\cdot}R'$ represents one of the three alcoholic groups of glycerol

Location	Optimal pH of action	Remarks
Saliva	7.5 – 7.7	Secretion from parotid gland most active[1]. The enzyme can be found in infants as early as the first month[2]
Stomach, gastric juice	Varies with substrate: 5.5 for lower triglycerides, 7.5 for higher ones[3]	Stable in acid media. Present in embryo from the 7th to 8th month[4]
Pancreas	ca. 7.8	Pancreatic lipase was formerly called *steapsin*. Activity is enhanced by presence of bile salts, proteins and soaps: this is probably the result of facilitation of enzyme–substrate interaction by emulsification of the water-insoluble substrate. Enzyme solutions are relatively unstable in aqueous media, more stable in glycerol[5]. Attacks tri- > di- > mono-glycerides
Intestine		Weak lipase activity of the jejunum has been reported[6]. Lipase appears to be absent from the ileum[7]. Hydrolysis of tributyrin by preparations from the large bowel is due to bacterial action; such hydrolyzed fat is not absorbed

References

1) Koldajew and Pikul, *Biochem. Z.*, **212**, 53 (1929). *2)* Scheer, K., *Klin. Wschr.*, **7**, 163 (1928). *3)* Schønheyder and Volqvartz, *Acta physiol. scand.*, **11**, 349 (1946). *4)* Itoh and Kamisasanuki, *J. Biochem.* (*Tokyo*), **33**, 269 (1941). *5)* Deuel, H. J., *The Lipids*, vol. II, London, 1955, page 9. *6)* Frazer, A. C., *Physiol. Rev.*, **26**, 103 (1946). *7)* Bickel and Kanitz, *Biochem. Z.*, **270**, 378 (1934).

Table 15 Esterases (For references see end of table, opposite)

Like the lipases, some of these enzymes catalyze the reaction $R\cdot CO\cdot OR' + H_2O \rightleftharpoons R\cdot CO\cdot OH + HOR'$, but $R\cdot CO\cdot O$ is not a long-chain fatty acid. Other esterases act on esters of acids other than carboxylic acids

Enzyme	Location	Reaction catalyzed	Remarks
Tissue esterases (nonspecific or aliesterases)	Most tissues, highest activity in liver	Readily split most simple esters, e.g. ethyl butyrate ⇌ ethanol + butyric acid. Fats are hydrolyzed only slowly	Act more readily on simple esters than on acetylcholine. Inhibited by the hydrochloride of the *m*-dimethylaminophenyl ester of methylcarbamic acid[1]
Choline esterases[2] (*a*) nonspecific or pseudo	Most tissues, especially blood, pancreas, liver, ovary, placenta, heart, intestinal mucosa, skin. Not present in skeletal muscle	Split simple esters, but act more readily on those containing choline than on those not containing choline. Rate of hydrolysis increases when the acyl chain increases from 2 to 4 carbon atoms; do not act on acetyl-β-methylcholine	Inhibited by eserine, prostigmine, organophosphorus compounds. Some of these latter inhibitors act in extremely low concentrations, e.g. tetraethyl pyrophosphate effectively inhibits at a molar concentration of 10^{-10}: this appears to be irreversible[3]
(*b*) Specific, true or acetylcholine esterase	Most tissues, especially conductive tissues (e.g. brain, nerves), erythrocytes, skeletal muscle, adrenals, lung, liver, stomach, salivary glands	Hydrolyzes acetylcholine → acetate + choline. Splits other choline esters also, but an increase in the acyl chain from 2 to 3 carbon atoms does not affect the rate of hydrolysis, and butyrylcholine is only slowly attacked. Rapidly splits acetyl-β-methylcholine. Also acts on non-choline esters, but at lower rates and higher concentrations	Can be distinguished from the nonspecific choline esterases by its action on acetyl-β-methylcholine[4]. The optimum substrate concentration for acetylcholine is 4–7 micromoles per milliliter. At higher concentrations the activity decreases. If the activity is plotted against pS (the negative logarithm of substrate concentration) a bell-shaped curve results
Phosphomonoesterases (*a*) Phosphomonoesterase I (alkaline phosphatase)	Most cells, particularly zones of growth of bones, intestinal mucosa, kidney cortex, mammary gland, milk, liver, brain, white blood cells, lymphoid tissue, plasma	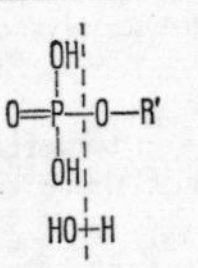	Acts optimally at pH 9.2–9.6. Activity enhanced by divalent cations, e.g. Mg^{++}, inhibited by CN^-, PO_4^{3-}, SH-compounds (e.g. cysteine). Does not attack pyrophosphates or ribonucleic acid. The enzyme also catalyzes transfer reactions, e.g. creatine phosphate + glucose → glucose-6-phosphate + creatine. The enzymes of milk, mammary gland, kidney, bone and liver are thought to be identical, and different from that of intestinal mucosa[5]
(*b*) Fructose 1,6-diphosphatase[6,7]	Liver	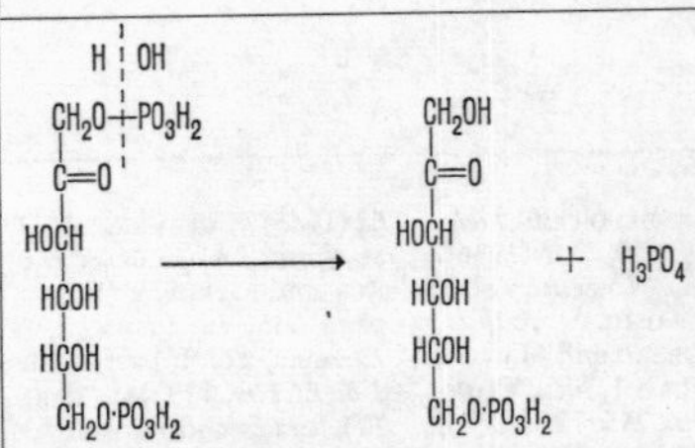 Fructose-1,6-diphosphate Fructose-6-phosphate Also slowly hydrolyzes fructose-1-phosphate and L-sorbose-1,6-diphosphate	The enzyme is optimally active at pH 9.3–9.5; its activity is enhanced by Mg^{++} or Mn^{++} and inhibited by F^- [6]. Does not hydrolyze glucose-1-phosphate, glucose-6-phosphate, fructose-6-phosphate, phosphoglyceric acid, L-sorbose-1-phosphate. Plays a role in the synthesis of glycogen from noncarbohydrate compounds (see Figure 14, page 444)
(*c*) Glucose 6-phosphatase[9]	Liver	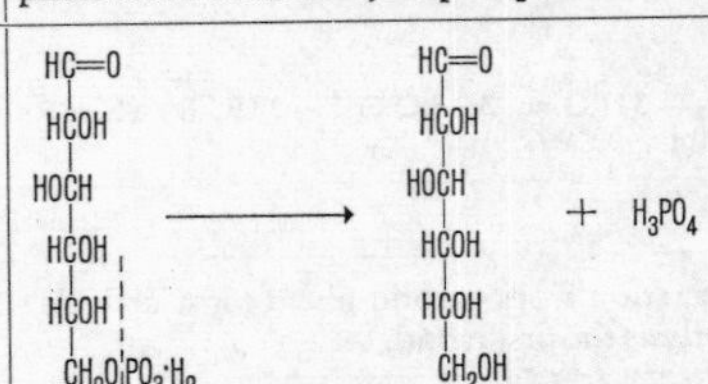 Glucose-6-phosphate Glucose	Plays a role in the formation of glucose from glycogen or from noncarbohydrate compounds (see Figure 14, page 444). Absent from, or weak in, the liver during glycogen storage disease[8]
(*d*) Phosphomonoesterase II (acid phosphatase)	Some tissues, particularly prostate[10], spleen, liver, kidney, plasma	As for phosphomonoesterase I, above	Optimally active at pH 5.3–5.6. Inhibited strongly by F^-. The prostatic phosphatase is also inhibited by ethanol; the erythrocyte enzyme is not inhibited[11]
(*e*) Acyl phosphatase	Wide variety of tissues, bacteria[12]	$R{-}CO\cdot O\cdot PO_3H_2 \longrightarrow R{-}COOH + H_3PO_4$ where $R\cdot CO\cdot$ = acetyl, propionyl, butyryl, succinyl, octanoyl, palmityl and other acyl groups[13]	Specific for acyl phosphates: does not act on α-glycerophosphate, for example. Is presumed to be a basic protein because of its solubility in acidic and its insolubility in basic solutions. Resistant to hot acidic (pH 3) solutions and to cold trichloroacetic acid. Inhibited strongly by pyrophosphate, phosphate, hexosephosphate, nucleic acid and hyaluronic acid; slightly inhibited by F^-

Table 15 Esterases (*continued*)

Enzyme	Location	Reaction catalyzed	Remarks
Phospho-diesterases See also Table 17 (Nucleases), page 427	Various tissues, particularly intestine, spleen[14]. Also present in snake venoms	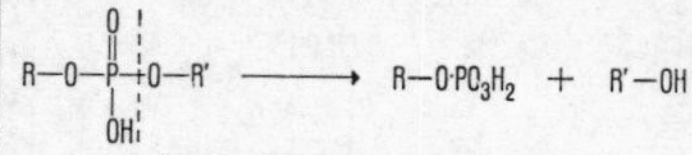 In the body the main substrates for the phosphodiesterases are the nucleic acids (see Figure 4, page 404). Some of the phospholipases (see Table 16) also more properly belong to this class of enzymes	Mammalian enzymes[14] are optimally active at about pH 7, and those of rattlesnake, viper and water moccasin venoms[15] at pH 9.3
Inorganic pyro-phosphatase	Most tissues, particularly liver	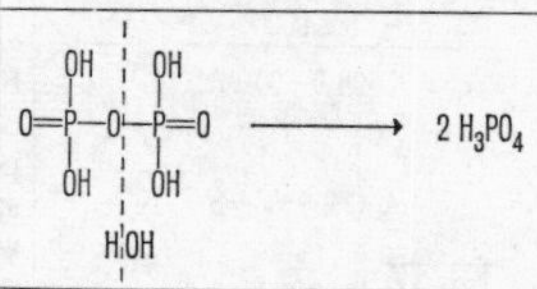	
Pyrophos-phatases	Most tissues	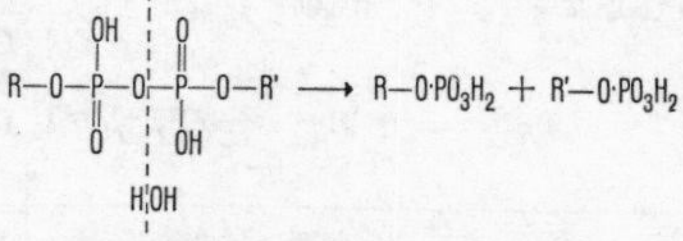 Examples of substrates are flavin adenine dinucleotide (FAD) and diphosphopyridine nucleotide (DPN+) (see Table 12, page 421)	
Phenol-sulfatases	Most tissues	Hydrolyze esters with an aromatic radical (e.g. $C_6H_5 \cdot O \cdot SO_3H$)	Act only on aryl esters in which the ester linkage is formed between a phenolic hydroxyl group and H_2SO_4. Optimally active at pH 6.1

References
1) Stedman and Stedman, *Biochem. J.*, **25**, 1147 (1931). *2)* For reviews see Nachmansohn and Wilson, *Advanc. Enzymol.*, **12**, 259 (1951); Thompson, R. H. S., *Brit. med. Bull.*, **9**, 138 (1953); Augustinsson, K.-B., in Sumner and Myrbäck (Eds.), *The Enzymes*, vol. I, part 1, New York, 1950, page 443. *3)* Mackworth and Webb, *Biochem. J.*, **42**, 91 (1948). *4)* Nachmansohn and Wilson, in Colowick and Kaplan (Eds.), *Methods in Enzymology*, vol. I, New York, 1955, page 642. *5)* Morton, R. K., in Colowick and Kaplan (Eds.), *Methods in Enzymology*, vol. II, New York, 1955, page 533. *6)* Gomori, G., *J. biol. Chem.*, **148**, 139 (1943). *7)* McGilvery, R. W., in Colowick and Kaplan (Eds.), *Methods in Enzymology*, vol. II, New York, 1955, page 543; Pogell and McGilvery, *J. biol. Chem.*, **208**, 149 (1954). *8)* Cori and Cori, *J. biol. Chem.*, **199**, 661 (1952). *9)* Fantl and Rome, *Aust. J. exp. Biol. med. Sci.*, **23**, 21 (1945). *10)* Schmidt, G., in Colowick and Kaplan (Eds.), *Methods in Enzymology*, vol. II, New York, 1955, page 523. *11)* Herbert, F. K., *Quart. J. Med.*, **15**, 221 (1946). *12)* Lipmann, F., *Advanc. Enzymol.*, **6**, 231 (1946); Shapiro and Wertheimer, *Nature*, **156**, 690 (1945). *13)* Lehninger, A. L., *J. biol. Chem.*, **162**, 333 (1946). *14)* Heppel and Hilmoe, in Colowick and Kaplan (Eds.), *Methods in Enzymology*, vol. II, New York, 1955, page 565. *15)* Butler, G. C., in Colowick and Kaplan (Eds.), *Methods in Enzymology*, vol. II, New York, 1955, page 561.

Table 16 Phospholipases[1] (For references see end of table, page 426)

Typical phospholipids, such as lecithin or cephalin, may be represented by the general formula

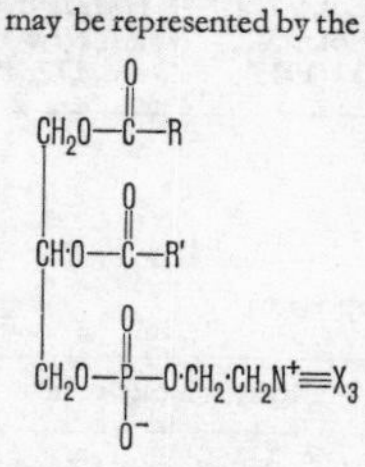

where $R\text{-}\overset{O}{\overset{\|}{C}}\text{-}O\text{-}$ is a saturated, $R'\text{-}\overset{O}{\overset{\|}{C}}\text{-}O\text{-}$ an unsaturated, long-chain fatty acid; X = CH_3 for lecithin, H for cephalin.

Enzyme	Location	Reaction catalyzed	Remarks
Phospholipase A (lecithinase A)	Pancreas, muscles, heart, liver, kidneys, adrenals, other tissues[2]	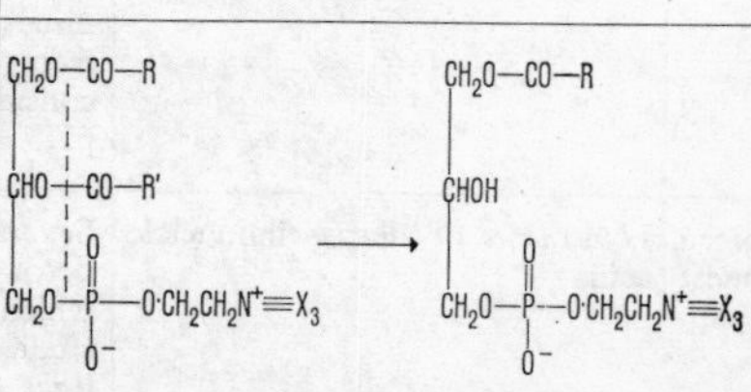	Hydrolyzes phospholipids to lysolipids, which can cause rapid hemolysis. One of the most widespread components of animal poisons, present in the poisonous secretions of snakes, echinoderms, scorpions, bees and wasps. Does not act on lipids, sphingomyelins, acetalphosphatides or cerebrosides, or on synthetic phospholipids not containing unsaturated fatty acids. Activity enhanced by Ca++. Very stable to heat: can be boiled for 5 minutes at pH 5.9 without loss of activity[3]

Table 16 Phospholipases (*continued*)

Enzyme	Location	Reaction catalyzed	Remarks
Phospholipase B (lecithinase B)	Pancreas[1], other tissues[2]	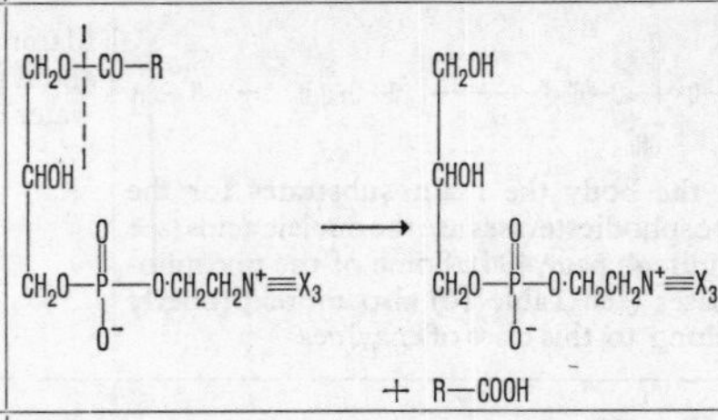	Catalyzes the hydrolytic cleavage of saturated fatty acid from lysophosphatides. Acting on lecithin, it forms glycerylphosphorylcholine, which has no hemolytic action. Less heat-stable than phospholipase A
Phospholipase C (lecithinase C)	In toxins of *Clostridium welchii*, *Cl. oedematiens*, *Cl. sordelli*. Not present in mammalian tissues	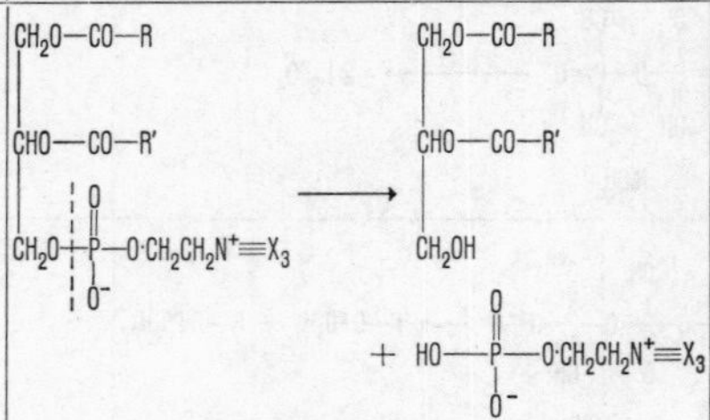	Splits phospholipids at an O–P bond. Acts on lecithin, producing a diglyceride + phosphorylcholine. Attacks lecithins and sphingomyelins (which are hydrolyzed to acylsphingosine + phosphorylcholine) but not cephalins. Activity enhanced by Ca^{++} and, to a smaller degree, by Mg^{++}, Mn^{++}, Co^{++}, Zn^{++}. Rather heat-stable: retains 50% of its activity after heating at 100°C for 10 minutes
Glycerylphosphorylcholine diesterase	Not present in animal tissues, but found in some bacteria, e.g. *Serratia*[4]	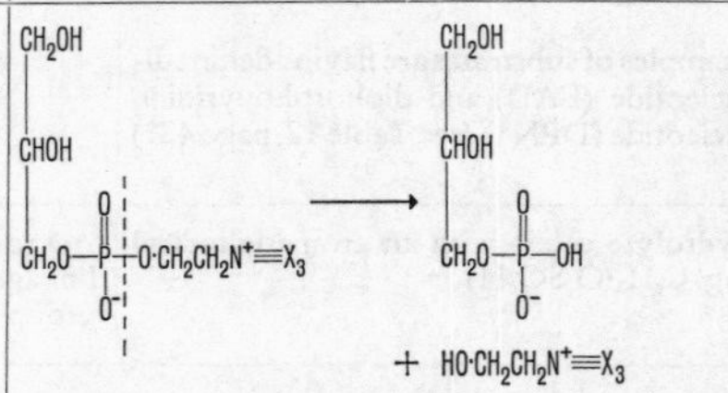	Hydrolyzes glycerylphosphorylcholine to glycerophosphate + choline. Also acts on glycerylphosphorylethanolamine. Optimally active at pH 8–9. Inhibited by Mg^{++}, Mn^{++}, Zn^{++}, ethylenediamine tetraacetate
Phospholipase D[5]	Not present in mammalian tissues; has been found in carrots and cabbage	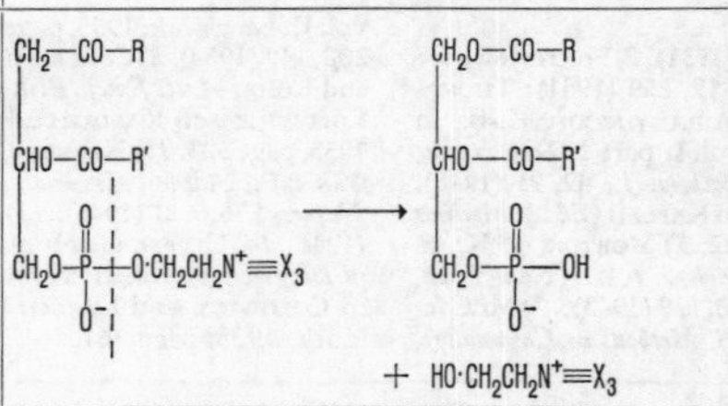	Hydrolyzes the linkage between the base and phosphoric acid to form phosphatidic acid and, in the case of lecithin, choline. Heat-stable: retains 30–40% of its activity after heating at 100°C for 15 minutes

References

1) For a review see ZELLER, E.A., in SUMNER and MYRBÄCK (Eds.), *The Enzymes*, vol. I, part 2, New York, 1951, page 986. *2*) FRANCIOLI, M., *Fermentforschung*, **14**, 241 (1935). *3*) HUGHES, A., *Biochem. J.*, **29**, 437 (1935). *4*) HAYAISHI, O., in COLOWICK and KAPLAN (Eds.), *Methods in Enzymology*, vol. I, New York, 1955, page 668. *5*) HANAHAN and CHAIKOFF, *J. biol. Chem.*, **172**, 191 (1948).

Table 17 Nucleases (For references see end of table, opposite)

Enzyme	Location	Reaction catalyzed	Remarks
Ribonucleases[1]	Most tissues, highest activity in pancreas	Hydrolysis of ribonucleic acids	Specific phosphodiesterases which hydrolyze ribonucleic acids but not desoxyribonucleic acids. Only pancreatic ribonuclease has been studied extensively. It is a digestive enzyme with an optimum pH of 7.7. Its specificity is discussed on page 417. Studies of ribonucleases from different sources show that they vary considerably in properties such as the optimum pH
Desoxyribonucleases[2]	Pancreas, thymus, spleen and various other tissues; highest activity in pancreas	Hydrolysis of desoxyribonucleic acids	Several different enzymes which hydrolyze desoxyribonucleic acid have been described, of which pancreatic desoxyribonuclease has been studied most extensively. The enzyme hydrolyzes desoxyribonucleic acids but not ribonucleic acid. Its specificity is discussed on page 417

Table 17 Nucleases (*continued*)

Enzyme	Location	Reaction catalyzed	Remarks
Phosphodiesterases	Intestine, spleen and other tissues	Hydrolysis of nucleic acid fragments	Discussed under esterases (Table 15, pages 424 and 425)
5′-Nucleotidase[3]	Seminal plasma	Hydrolysis of adenylic acid, inosinic acid, uridylic acid, cytidylic acid and nicotinamide mononucleotide to the corresponding nucleosides and orthophosphate	Desoxyribonucleotides are also attacked by this enzyme
Nucleoside phosphorylase[4]	Liver, muscle, spleen	Nucleoside + orthophosphate → pentose-1-phosphate + purine or pyrimidine	Desoxyribonucleosides are also attacked by this enzyme[5]
Adenylic deaminase[6,7]	Muscle and to a much lesser extent other tissues	Deaminates adenylic acid to inosinic acid and ammonia	Specific for 5′-adenylic acid (adenosine 5′-monophosphate); optimum pH of 5.9. Activated by citrate, chloride and other anions
Guanylic deaminase[8]	Liver	Deaminates guanylic acid to xanthidylic acid and ammonia	
Adenosine deaminase[6,7,9]	Muscle, liver, intestinal mucosa and other tissues	Deaminates adenosine to inosine and ammonia	Desoxyadenosine is also deaminated by the enzyme. Broad optimum pH range between 6 and 9
Guanosine deaminase[8,10]	Liver	Deaminates guanosine to xanthosine and ammonia	
Guanase[6,8]	Liver, muscle	Deaminates guanine to xanthine and ammonia	Guanosine and guanylic acid are not attacked by this enzyme. Acts optimally from pH 6 to 10
Xanthine oxidase[11]	Milk, liver, spleen, kidney, lung	The purified enzyme oxidizes hypoxanthine to xanthine, xanthine to uric acid, and aldehydes to acids	Contains flavin adenine dinucleotide, iron and molybdenum
Uricase[12]	Liver and kidney of mammals. Absent in man and other primates	Oxidizes uric acid to allantoin according to the overall reaction: uric acid + O_2 + 2 H_2O → allantoin + H_2O_2 + CO_2	Contains copper

References

1) McDonald, M. R., in Colowick and Kaplan (Eds.), *Methods in Enzymology*, vol. II, New York, 1955, page 427. *2)* McDonald, M. R., in Colowick and Kaplan (Eds.), *Methods in Enzymology*, vol. II, New York, 1955, page 437. *3)* Heppel and Hilmoe, in Colowick and Kaplan (Eds.), *Methods in Enzymology*, vol. II, New York, 1955, page 546. *4)* Price et al., in Colowick and Kaplan (Eds.), *Methods in Enzymology*, vol. II, New York, 1955, page 448. *5)* Friedkin and Kalckar, *J. biol. Chem.*, **184**, 437 (1950). *6)* Kalckar, H. M., *J. biol. Chem.*, **167**, 461 (1947). *7)* Schmidt, G., *Hoppe-Seyl. Z. physiol. Chem.*, **179**, 243 (1928). *8)* Schmidt, G., *Hoppe-Seyl. Z. physiol. Chem.*, **208**, 185 (1932). *9)* Kornberg and Pricer, jr., *J. biol. Chem.*, **193**, 481 (1951). *10)* Wakabayasi, Y., *J. Biochem. (Tokyo)*, **28**, 185 (1938). *11)* Mahler, H. R., *Advanc. Enzymol.*, **17**, 233 (1956). *12)* Mahler et al., *Science*, **124**, 705 (1956).

Apart from supplying energy, the products of digestion serve as precursors of many cell constituents. The mammalian body can form all cell constituents from:

1. The essential amino acids (see page 354)
2. Vitamins
3. The essential (highly unsaturated) fatty acids
4. Mineral salts
5. A bulk source of carbon (usually carbohydrate)
6. A source of nitrogen in the form of ammonia derived mainly from surplus amino acids, with small amounts supplied by purine bases, pyrimidines and amino sugars.

Carbohydrate as a bulk source of carbon can be largely replaced by protein and fat, especially in carnivores.

Much progress has been made in recent years in the elucidation of the pathways by which the basic constituents of food are converted into cell constituents, but many details still remain to be clarified. A synopsis of the available information is contained in the section which follows.

1. Formation of basic cell constituents and metabolites from glucose

The principal products, their pathways of formation and their physiological functions are summarized in Table 18 below.

The pentose-phosphate cycle

Glucose-6-phosphate (formed from glucose by the hexokinase reaction) can be oxidized in liver and some other animal tissues at the carbon atom 1 to yield 6-phosphogluconate. This initiates a sequence of reactions in which various pentose-phosphates and other sugar phosphates are formed. In the course of these reactions

Table 18 Formation of basic cell constituents and metabolites from glucose
This list is not comprehensive

Product formed	Pathway of formation	Physiological function
Glycogen	Reversal of two stages of glycolysis (reactions catalyzed by phosphorylase and phosphoglucomutase; see Table 4, page 402, reactions 1 and 2)	Storage of energy
Galactose	Reversal of reactions 4 and 5, Table 4, page 402	Constituent of lactose, cerebrosides
Lactose	Probably from uridine diphosphogalactose and glucose-1-phosphate, via lactose-1-phosphate[1]	Milk constituent
Ribose-5-phosphate	Reactions of the pentose-phosphate cycle (see above)	Constituent of nucleic acid and nucleotides
Desoxyribose-5-phosphate	Probably by aldol condensation between glyceraldehyde phosphate and acetaldehyde (reversal of the reaction shown on page 411)	Constituent of nucleic acids
Glucuronic acid	Formed via uridine diphosphoglucose (see page 430)	Constituent of mucins (hyaluronic acid and chondroitin sulfate) and of heparin; detoxicating agent
Fructose	Reactions of glycolysis and hydrolysis of fructose-6-phosphate by phosphatase	Constituent of semen
Citric acid	CO_2-fixation by pyruvate (see page 431) and reactions of the tricarboxylic acid cycle (see page 402)	Constituent of bone, milk, semen
Fatty acids	From acetyl-coenzyme A (formed via pyruvate) by reversal of the reactions causing the degradation of fatty acids (see page 403)*	Constituents of fats and phospholipids
Glycerophosphates	Reduction of dihydroxyacetone phosphate, catalyzed by glycerophosphate dehydrogenase	Constituents of phospholipids
Phospholipids	See page 431	Cell constituents
Glyceride fats	See page 432	Cell constituents
Sterols and steroids	See pages 432–436	Cell constituents; hormones
Nonessential amino acids:		
Glutamic acid	Glutamic dehydrogenase reaction (see page 436)	Constituent of proteins and special peptides (glutathione, folic acid)
Aspartic acid	CO_2-fixation by pyruvate (see page 431) and transamination between glutamate and oxaloacetate	Constituent of proteins
Alanine	Transamination between pyruvate and glutamate	Constituent of proteins
Glycine	From 3-phosphoglycerate by the reactions shown on page 436	Constituent of proteins
Serine	From 3-phosphoglycerate by the reactions shown on page 436	Constituent of proteins
Cysteine	From serine by transsulfuration from homocysteine derived from methionine (see page 409)	Constituent of proteins
Proline	From glutamic acid or ornithine (see page 436)	Constituent of proteins
Hydroxyproline	Probably by oxidation of proline (see page 436)	Constituent of proteins

* Although the intermediates in the fatty-acid synthesis from acetyl-coenzyme A are the same as those occurring in the reverse process, the enzymic mechanisms of synthesis and breakdown are different. Cf. WAKIL et al., *Biochim. biophys. Acta*, 34, 227 (1959).

References 1) GANDER et al., *Arch. Biochem. Biophys.*, 60, 259 (1956); PAZUR and TIPTON, *J. biol. Chem.*, 224, 381 (1957).

some glucose-6-phosphate is regenerated, implying a cyclic nature of the reaction sequence. The reactions of this cycle represent a partial oxidation of glucose-6-phosphate.

The main components of the cycle are eight different reactions. In the first reaction (**1**) glucose-6-phosphate is oxidized to 6-phosphogluconolactone, which is subsequently hydrolyzed by a "lactonase" to 6-phosphogluconate[1]. TPN is reduced in this reaction.

(**1**)

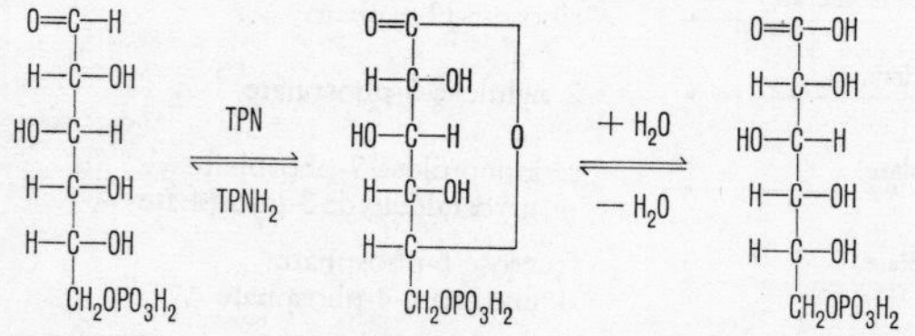

Glucose-6-phosphate — 6-Phosphogluconolactone — 6-Phosphogluconic acid

The 6-phosphogluconate formed is oxidatively decarboxylated (**2**) to yield ribulose-5-phosphate, whilst another molecule of TPN is reduced[2]:

(**2**)

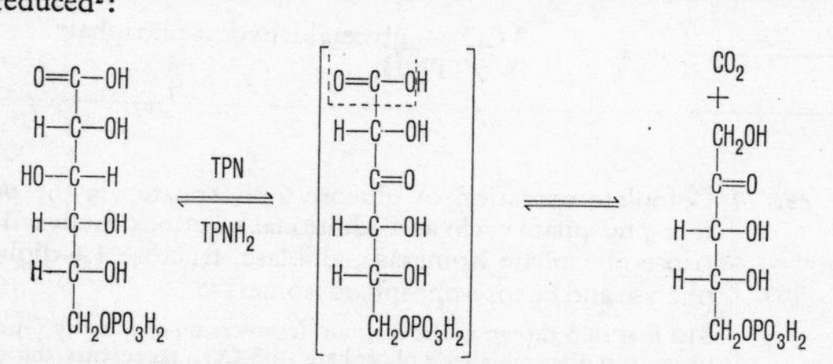

6-Phosphogluconic acid — Hypothetical intermediate (3-keto-6-phosphogluconic acid) — Ribulose-5-phosphate

Ribulose-5-phosphate undergoes two different isomerizations, one to ribose-5-phosphate (**3**) catalyzed by pentose-phosphate isomerase[3]:

(**3**)

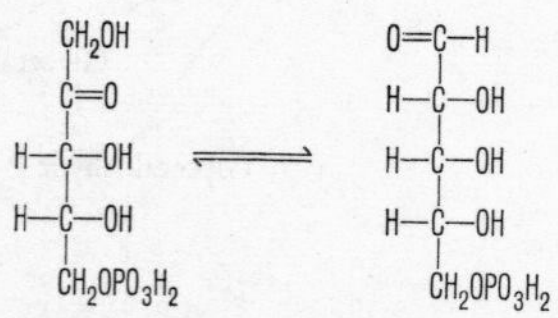

Ribulose-5-phosphate — Ribose-5-phosphate

and one (**4**) to xylulose-5-phosphate[4,5]:

(**4**)

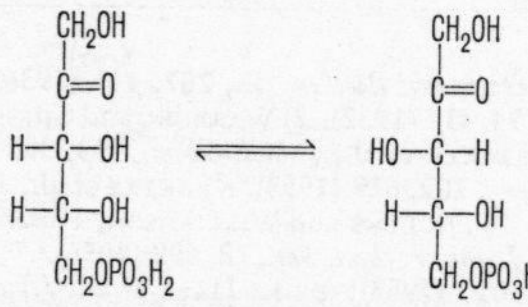

Ribulose-5-phosphate — Xylulose-5-phosphate

One molecule of xylulose-5-phosphate and one of ribose-5-phosphate, produced by reactions (**3**) and (**4**), interact to form sedoheptulose-7-phosphate and glyceraldehyde 3-phosphate (**5**)[4,6]. This reaction is catalyzed by transketolase[7], an enzyme requiring thiamine pyrophosphate (TPP) as co-factor. It is thought that an "active glycolaldehyde" may be an intermediate in this reaction. This may therefore be written as:

(**5**)

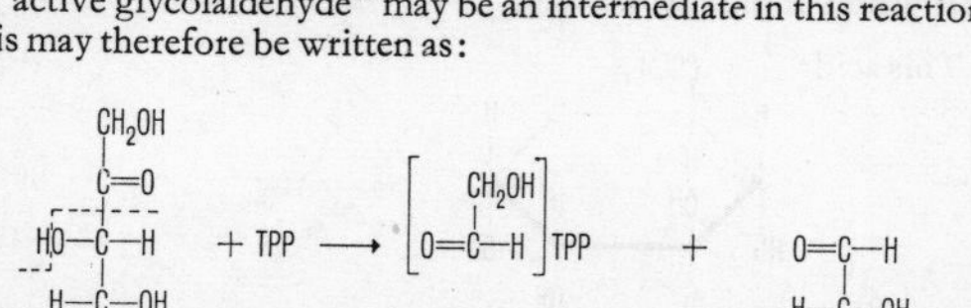

Xylulose-5-phosphate — "Active glycolaldehyde" — Glyceraldehyde 3-phosphate

(**5**)

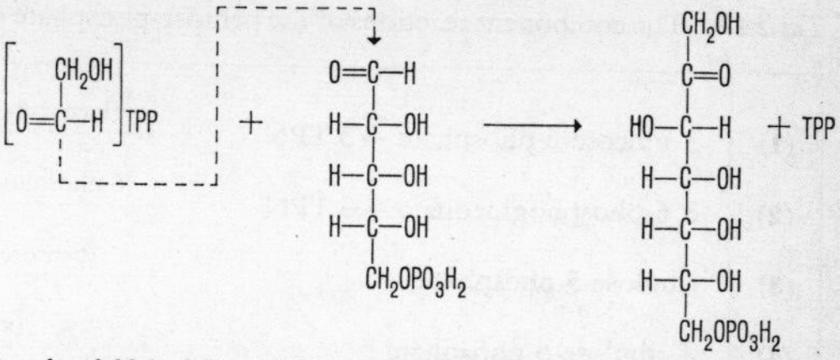

"Active glycolaldehyde" — Ribose-5-phosphate — Sedoheptulose-7-phosphate

The glyceraldehyde 3-phosphate and sedoheptulose-7-phosphate interact further in a transfer reaction under the influence of transaldolase. The action of this enzyme is analogous to that of transketolase, except that the moiety transferred is not an "active glycolaldehyde" but an "active dihydroxyacetone". In this reaction (**6**) fructose-6-phosphate and erythrose-4-phosphate are formed[8]:

(**6**)

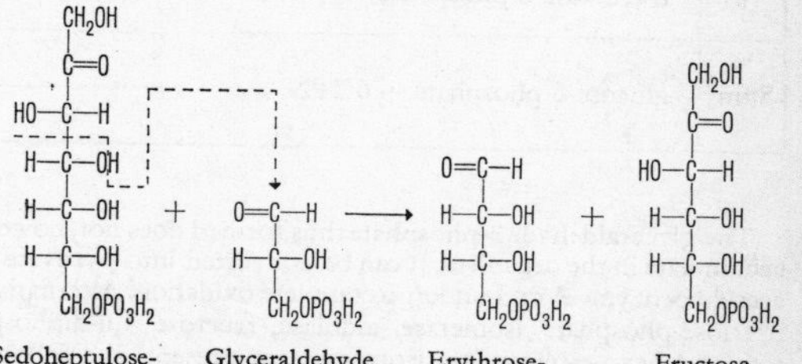

Sedoheptulose-7-phosphate — Glyceraldehyde 3-phosphate — Erythrose-4-phosphate — Fructose-6-phosphate

The erythrose-4-phosphate formed in (**6**) undergoes a transketolase reaction (**7**) with a molecule of xylulose-5-phosphate. This is analogous to reaction (**5**) and leads to fructose-6-phosphate and glyceraldehyde 3-phosphate[9]:

(**7**)

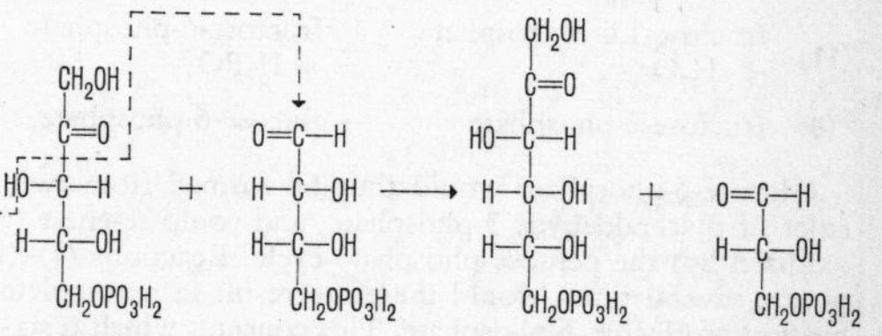

Xylulose-5-phosphate — Erythrose-4-phosphate — Fructose-6-phosphate — Glyceraldehyde 3-phosphate

The fructose-6-phosphate formed in reactions (**6**) and (**7**) is converted to glucose-6-phosphate by reaction (**8**), catalyzed by hexose-phosphate isomerase:

(**8**)

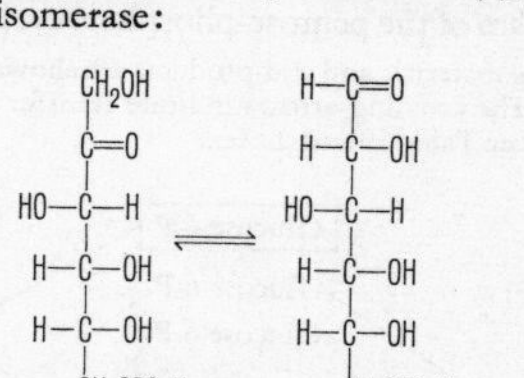

Fructose-6-phosphate — Glucose-6-phosphate

This reaction completes the cycle in that it leads to the (partial) regeneration of the starting material, glucose-6-phosphate. The interplay of the components of the cycle is somewhat complex. It is shown diagrammatically in Figure 10 and Table 19 (page 430).

In this scheme, the reactions catalyzed by transketolase and transaldolase, (**5**), (**6**) and (**7**), are indicated by crossing arrows; of the three glucose-6-phosphate molecules required for each turn of the cycle, two are regenerated. While three molecules participate in reactions (**1**) and (**2**), two are involved in reactions (**4**) and (**8**) and only one each participates in the remaining reactions.

The net effect of one revolution of the cycle, as shown in Table 19, is therefore:

glucose-6-phosphate → glyceraldehyde 3-phosphate + 3 CO_2

Table 19 The component reactions of the pentose-phosphate cycle and their quantitative relations

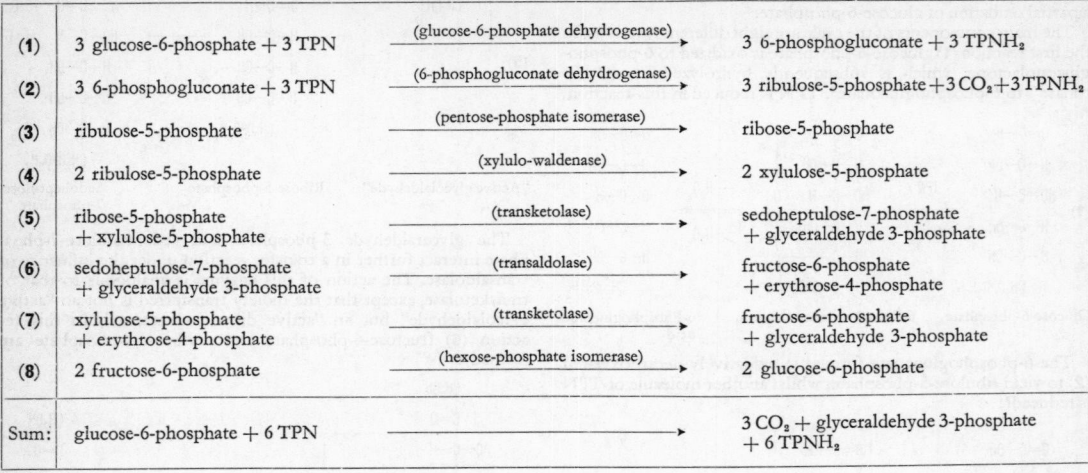

(1)	3 glucose-6-phosphate + 3 TPN	(glucose-6-phosphate dehydrogenase) →	3 6-phosphogluconate + 3 $TPNH_2$
(2)	3 6-phosphogluconate + 3 TPN	(6-phosphogluconate dehydrogenase) →	3 ribulose-5-phosphate + 3 CO_2 + 3 $TPNH_2$
(3)	ribulose-5-phosphate	(pentose-phosphate isomerase) →	ribose-5-phosphate
(4)	2 ribulose-5-phosphate	(xylulo-waldenase) →	2 xylulose-5-phosphate
(5)	ribose-5-phosphate + xylulose-5-phosphate	(transketolase) →	sedoheptulose-7-phosphate + glyceraldehyde 3-phosphate
(6)	sedoheptulose-7-phosphate + glyceraldehyde 3-phosphate	(transaldolase) →	fructose-6-phosphate + erythrose-4-phosphate
(7)	xylulose-5-phosphate + erythrose-4-phosphate	(transketolase) →	fructose-6-phosphate + glyceraldehyde 3-phosphate
(8)	2 fructose-6-phosphate	(hexose-phosphate isomerase) →	2 glucose-6-phosphate
Sum:	glucose-6-phosphate + 6 TPN	→	3 CO_2 + glyceraldehyde 3-phosphate + 6 $TPNH_2$

The glyceraldehyde 3-phosphate thus formed does not, however, accumulate in the organism. It can be converted into pyruvate and acetyl-coenzyme A and undergo complete oxidation. Alternatively, if triose-phosphate isomerase, aldolase, fructose 1,6-diphosphatase and hexose-phosphate isomerase are present, the following sequence of reactions can occur:

(9) glyceraldehyde 3-phosphate → dihydroxyacetone phosphate

(10) glyceraldehyde 3-phosphate + dihydroxyacetone phosphate → fructose-1,6-diphosphate

(11) fructose-1,6-diphosphate + H_2O → fructose-6-phosphate + H_3PO_4

(8) fructose-6-phosphate → glucose-6-phosphate

Glucose-6-phosphate would thus be formed from two molecules of glyceraldehyde 3-phosphate, and could re-enter (and be oxidized by) the pentose-phosphate cycle. Reactions **(1)**–**(11)** repeated several times would therefore result in a complete combustion of glucose-6-phosphate. This concept, which rests on the demonstration of all the required enzymes in liver[10], is illustrated in Figure 11.

Fig. 10 Diagram of the pentose-phosphate cycle

Starting materials and end-products are shown enclosed. P = phosphate. The crossing arrows indicate transfer reactions. For further details see Table 19 and the text

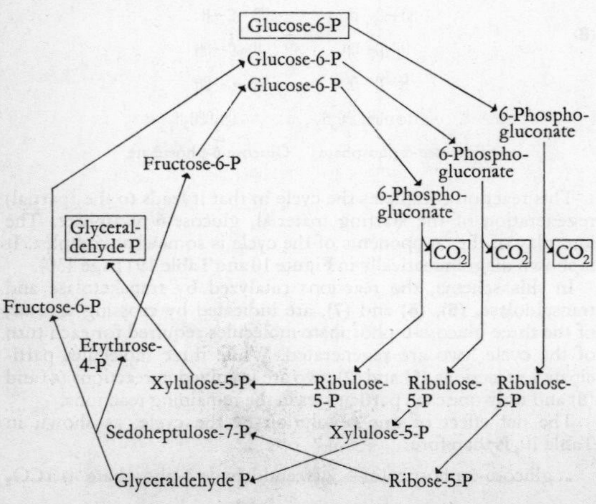

Fig. 11 Complete oxidation of glucose-6-phosphate via the pentose-phosphate cycle and additional reactions catalyzed by triose-phosphate isomerase, aldolase, fructose 1,6-diphosphatase and hexose-phosphate isomerase.

The first step shown in the diagram (conversion of glucose-6-phosphate into glyceraldehyde phosphate + 3 CO_2) represents the sum of the reactions shown in Table 19 and Figure 10. P = phosphate

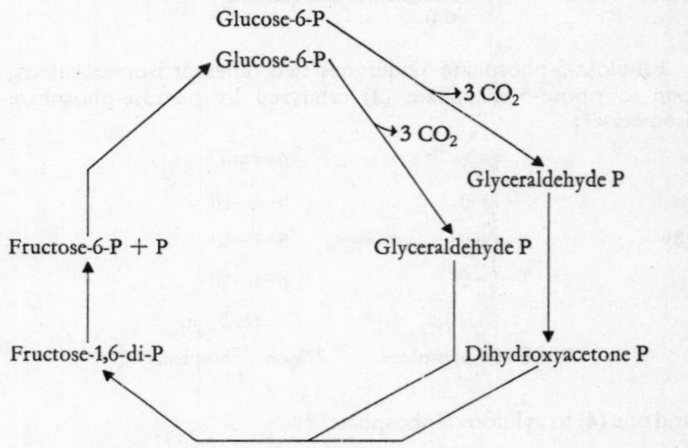

References

1) Warburg and Christian, *Biochem. Z.*, **287**, 440 (1936); Cori and Lipmann, *J. biol. Chem.*, **194**, 417 (1952). *2)* Warburg and Christian, *Biochem. Z.*, **292**, 287 (1937); Horecker et al., *J. biol. Chem.*, **193**, 383 (1951). *3)* Axelrod et al., *J. biol. Chem.*, **202**, 619 (1953). *4)* Srere et al., *Arch. Biochem. Biophys.*, **59**, 535 (1955). *5)* Dickens and Williamson, *Nature*, **176**, 400 (1955). *6)* Horecker et al., *J. Amer. chem. Soc.*, **78**, 692 (1956). *7)* Racker et al., *J. Amer. chem. Soc.*, **75**, 1010 (1953); de la Haba et al., *J. biol. Chem.*, **214**, 409 (1955). *8)* Horecker and Smyrniotis, *J. Amer. chem. Soc.*, **75**, 2021 (1953); Horecker et al., *J. biol. Chem.*, **212**, 827 (1955); Srere et al., *Fed. Proc.*, **14**, 285 (1955). *9)* Kornberg and Racker, *Biochem. J.*, **61**, iii (1955). *10)* Horecker et al., *J. biol. Chem.*, **207**, 393 (1954); Gibbs and Horecker, *J. biol. Chem.*, **208**, 813 (1954).

Formation of glucuronic acid

This acid:

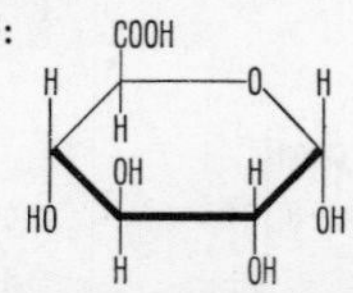

is a constituent of mucopolysaccharides as well as a coupling agent in detoxication reactions. It couples with many substances possessing hydroxyl groups, such as alcohols and substances which in the body are converted into alcohols (salicylic acid, camphor, menthol, chloral hydrate, pregnanediol) or phenols (phenol, indoxyl). It also couples with carboxyl groups attached to an aromatic nucleus (benzoic acid, phenylacetic acid)[1], and with bile pigments[2].

The reactive form of glucuronic acid in the conjugation reactions, and probably also in the synthesis of mucopolysaccharides, is uridine diphosphoglucuronic acid:

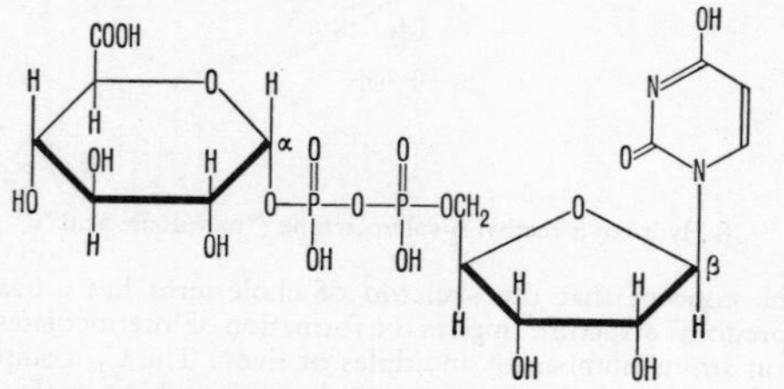

This arises from glucose by the following reactions[3]:

Glucose + ATP	→	Glucose-6-phosphate + ADP
Glucose-6-phosphate	→	Glucose-1-phosphate
Glucose-1-phosphate + uridine triphosphate	→	Uridine diphosphoglucose + pyrophosphate
Uridine diphosphoglucose + DPN	→	Uridine diphosphoglucuronic acid + $DPNH_2$

The synthesis of conjugated glucuronide may be represented as follows[4]:

Uridine diphosphoglucuronate + ROH $\xrightarrow[\text{inversion}]{\text{Walden}}$ Glucuronosyl-OR + uridine diphosphate

where ROH is an alcoholic or phenolic compound, or an aromatic carboxylic acid.

References

1) Williams, R.T., *Detoxication Mechanisms*, 2nd ed., London, 1959. *2)* Billing and Lathe, *Biochem. J.*, **63**, 6P (1956). *3)* Strominger et al., *J. Amer. chem. Soc.*, **76**, 6411 (1954). *4)* Storey and Dutton, *Biochem. J.*, **59**, 279 (1955); Smith and Mills, *Biochim. biophys. Acta*, **13**, 386 (1954).

Extension of carbon chains by carbon dioxide fixation

An important link in the building-up of the carbon skeletons of cell constituents is the addition of CO_2 to pyruvate. There are at least two CO_2-fixation reactions in animal tissues by which 4-carbon chains arise from pyruvate. The first[1] is catalyzed by the "malic" enzyme; it requires reduced triphosphopyridine nucleotide and leads to L-malic acid:

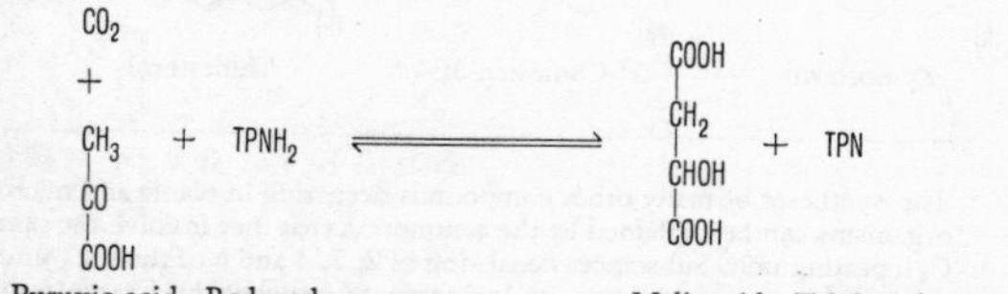

Pyruvic acid | Reduced triphosphopyridine nucleotide | L-Malic acid | Triphosphopyridine nucleotide

The second reaction[2] requires adenosine diphosphate or inosine diphosphate and consists of the binding of CO_2 by phosphopyruvate (reaction of Utter and Kurahashi); it leads to oxaloacetate:

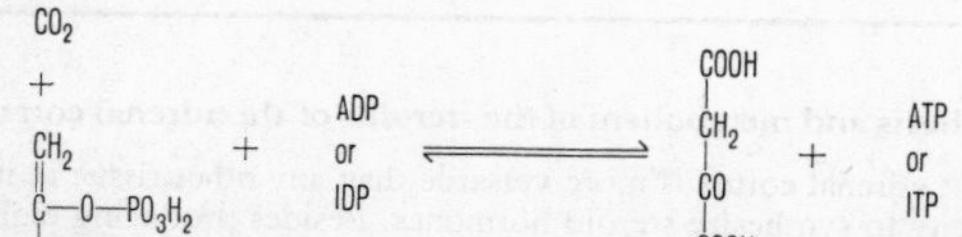

Phosphopyruvic acid | Adenosine or inosine diphosphate | Oxaloacetic acid | Adenosine or inosine triphosphate

Both reactions readily occur in liver tissue and also elsewhere. They are reversible. The malic and oxaloacetic acids formed can enter the tricarboxylic acid cycle and form citrate and α-ketoglutarate.

References

1) Ochoa et al., *J. biol. Chem.*, **174**, 979 (1948); Veiga Salles and Ochoa, *J. biol. Chem.*, **187**, 849 (1950); Harary et al., *J. biol. Chem.*, **203**, 595 (1953). *2)* Utter and Kurahashi, *J. biol. Chem.*, **207**, 821 (1954).

Formation of lecithin and cephalin

The synthesis of lecithin in animal tissues from fatty acids, glycerophosphate and choline requires the participation as cofactors of ATP, coenzyme A and cytidine triphosphate:

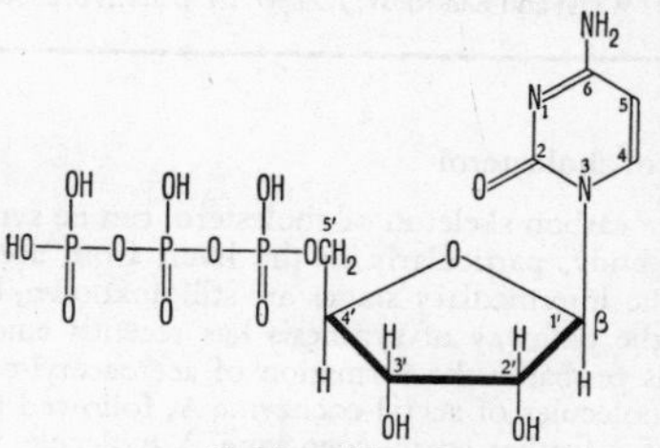

Cytidine triphosphate

The intermediary stages of the synthesis are as follows:

(*a*) "Activation" of fatty acids[1]:

$$\text{R·COOH} + \text{HSR'} + \text{ATP} \longrightarrow \text{R·CO·S·R'} + \text{AMP} + \text{pyrophosphate}$$

Fatty acid | Coenzyme A | Acyl-coenzyme A

(*b*) "Activation" of choline by choline phosphokinase[2]:

Choline | Phosphocholine

(*c*) "Activation" of phosphocholine[3]:

cytidine triphosphate + phosphocholine ⇌ cytidine diphosphocholine + pyrophosphate

(*d*) Synthesis of phosphatidic acid[3]:

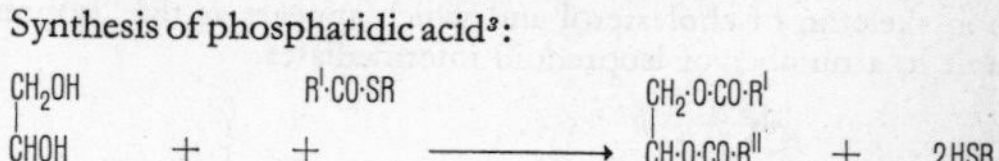

α-Glycerophosphate | 2 Acyl-coenzyme A | Phosphatidic acid | 2 Coenzyme A

(*e*) Dephosphorylation of phosphatidic acid[3]:

phosphatidic acid → D-α-β-diglyceride + phosphate

(*f*) Synthesis of lecithin[3]:

cytidine diphosphocholine + D-α-β-diglyceride → lecithin + cytidine monophosphate

(*g*) Rephosphorylation of cytidine monophosphate[4]:

cytidine monophosphate + 2 ATP → cytidine triphosphate + 2 ADP

Cephalin is synthesized by analogous reactions, choline being replaced by ethanolamine ($HO·CH_2·CH_2·NH_2$).

References

1) Kornberg and Pricer, *J. biol. Chem.*, **204**, 329 (1953). *2)* Wittenberg and Kornberg, *J. biol. Chem.*, **202**, 431 (1953). *3)* Weiss et al., *Nature*, **178**, 594 (1956); Kennedy and Weiss, *J. Amer. chem. Soc.*, **77**, 250 (1955); Kennedy and Weiss, *J. biol. Chem.*, **222**, 193 (1956); Kennedy, E. P., *J. biol. Chem.*, **222**, 185 (1956). *4)* Berg and Joklik, *J. biol. Chem.*, **210**, 657 (1954); Krebs and Hems, *Biochim. biophys. Acta*, **12**, 172 (1953); Krebs and Hems, *Biochem. J.*, **61**, 435 (1955); Lieberman et al., *J. biol. Chem.*, **215**, 429 (1955); Brumm et al., *J. biol. Chem.*, **220**, 713 (1956).

Formation of neutral fat

WEISS and KENNEDY[1] have presented evidence which suggests that the glycerol moiety of neutral fat is derived from α-glycerophosphate and that the reactions (*d*) and (*e*) of the preceding section (the synthesis of phosphatidic acid and its dephosphorylation) are also intermediary stages in the synthesis of neutral fat. They showed that liver preparations catalyze the following reaction:

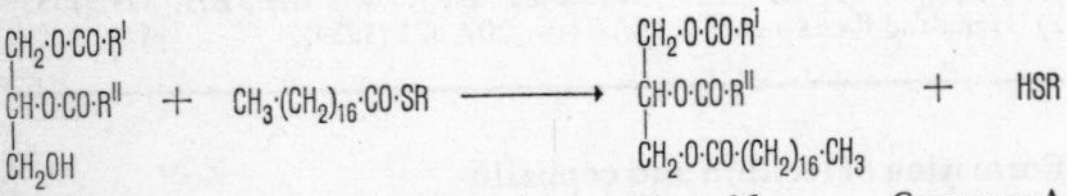

D-α-β-diglyceride Palmitoyl-coenzyme A Neutral fat Coenzyme A

Reference *1)* WEISS and KENNEDY, *J. Amer. chem. Soc.*, **78**, 3550 (1956).

Formation of cholesterol

The entire carbon skeleton of cholesterol can be synthesized in the animal body, particularly in the liver, from acetate. Many details of the intermediary stages are still unknown, but a broad outline of the pathway of synthesis has recently emerged[1]. The first stage is probably the formation of acetoacetyl-coenzyme A from two molecules of acetyl-coenzyme A, followed by the condensation of a further acetyl-coenzyme A molecule with acetoacetyl-coenzyme A to form β-hydroxy-β-methylglutaric acid or some closely related C_6 structure:

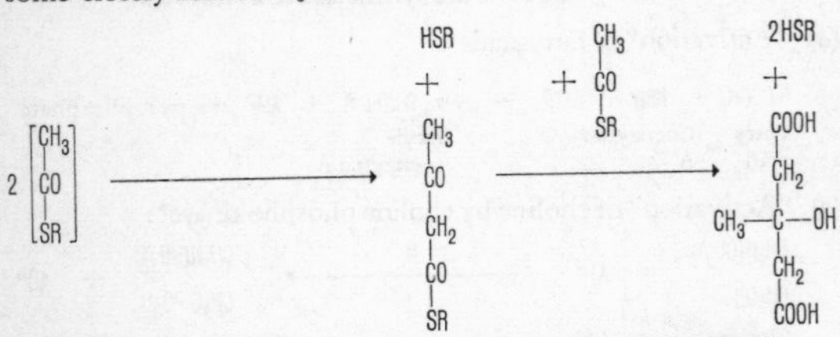

Acetyl-coenzyme A Acetoacetyl-coenzyme A β-Hydroxy-β-methylglutaric acid

In some manner as yet obscure, this C_6 compound provides the C_5 isopentane-type structural unit which is the basis of the carbon skeleton of cholesterol and which appears as the "isoprene" unit in a number of isoprenoid intermediates.

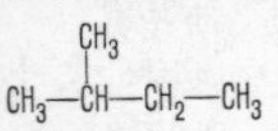

Isopentane

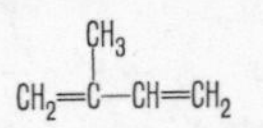

Isoprene

The above condensation reactions leading to β-hydroxy-β-methylglutaric acid are readily reversible, and in most systems the compound is also in equilibrium with 3-methylglutaconic, 3-hydroxy*iso*valeric and 3-methylcrotonic acids:

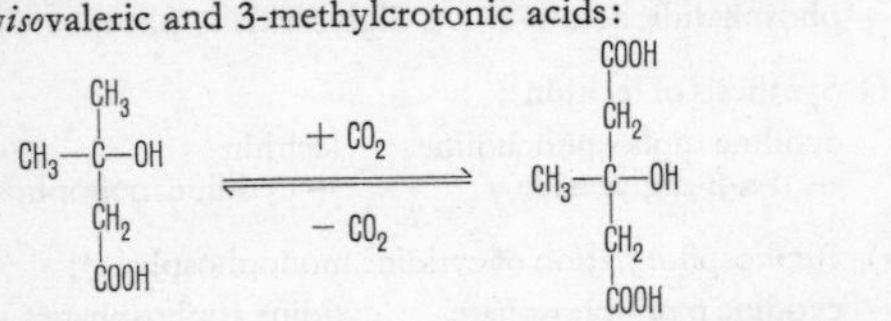

β-Hydroxy*iso*valeric acid β-Hydroxy-β-methylglutaric acid

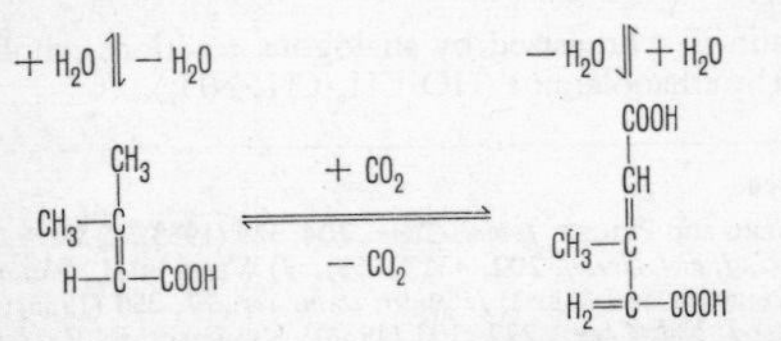

3-Methylcrotonic acid 3-Methylglutaconic acid

The rapid interconversion of these substances has made their study as precursors of cholesterol extremely difficult and their status as intermediates is still in doubt.

β-Hydroxy-β-methyl-δ-valerolactone ("mevalonic acid") is a C_6 derivative which is closely related structurally to β-hydroxy-β-methylglutaric acid and is probably more closely related to the C_5 isopentane building unit than any other substance which has been tested, since it is a far more efficient and direct precursor of cholesterol than any of the compounds mentioned above[2,3].

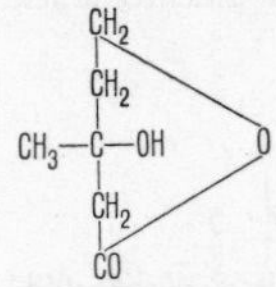

β-Hydroxy-β-methyl-δ-valerolactone ("mevalonic acid")

The concept that the skeleton of cholesterol has a basically "isoprenoid" structure implies the formation of intermediates with carbon atoms numbering multiples of five*. The C_{15} compound farnesic acid and the C_{30} compound squalene have so far been shown to behave like intermediates.

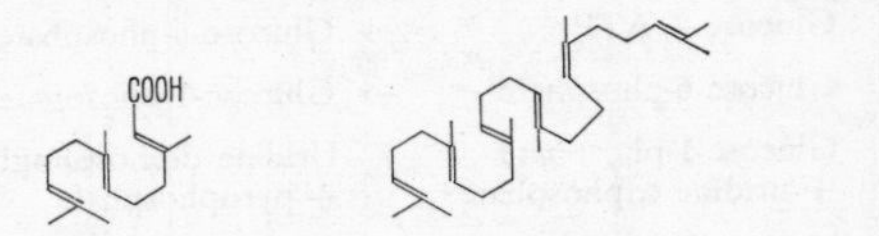

Farnesic acid Squalene

The theory that the initial condensing unit for the formation of these isoprenoid compounds may be isoprene itself has not received experimental support. The C_6 compound δ-valerolactone gives rise to squalene by some mechanism which apparently does not involve the intermediate formation of free isoprene[3].

Farnesic acid and squalene are both formed in liver homogenates from acetate, and squalene can react further in the liver to form cholesterol. The carbon skeleton of farnesic acid represents one half of the symmetric structure of squalene. Squalene in turn can be cyclized by enzymes of liver tissue to give a C_{30} trimethyl-sterol, lanosterol[4]:

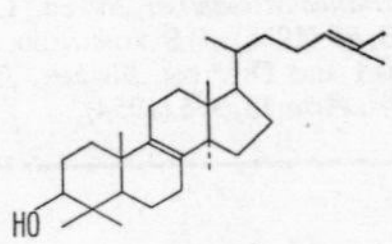

Lanosterol

which can react to yield the C_{27} compound cholesterol, probably via zymosterol and Δ^7-cholesten-3β-ol.

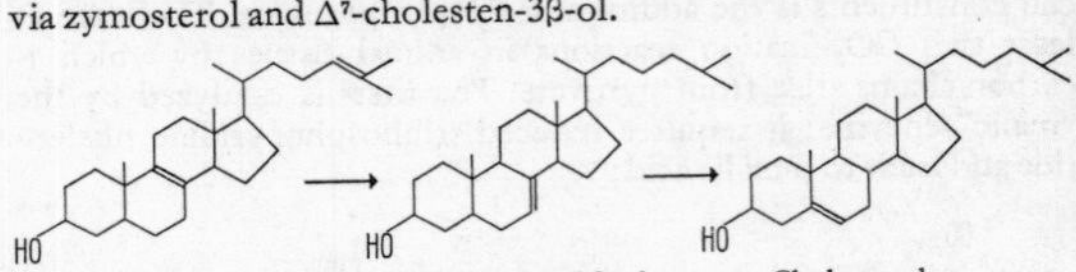

Zymosterol Δ^7-Cholesten-3β-ol Cholesterol

* The syntheses of many other compounds occurring in plants and micro-organisms can be explained by the assumption that they involve the same C_5 repeating unit. Substances consisting of 2, 3, 4 and 6 of these C_5 units are called mono-, sesqui-, di-, and tri-terpenes respectively. Examples are essential oils (citral, limonene), pigments (carotene, lycopene), vitamin A, camphor and rubber.

References

1) FRIEDMAN et al., *Ann. Rev. Biochem.*, **25**, 613 (1956). *2)* TAVORMINA et al., *J. Amer. chem. Soc.*, **78**, 4498 (1956). *3)* CORNFORTH et al., *Biochem. J.*, **69**, 146 (1958). *4)* TCHEN and BLOCH, *J. Amer. chem. Soc.*, **77**, 6085 (1955).

Synthesis and metabolism of the steroids of the adrenal cortex

The adrenal cortex is more versatile than any other tissue in its capacity to synthesize steroid hormones. Besides producing eight C_{21} steroids of known structure and proven "corticoid" activity, it also produces at least fifteen other known C_{21} steroids the physiological activity of which is not known, as well as progesterone, the estrogens and the androgens of the $C_{19}O_2$ and $C_{19}O_3$ series.

Fig. 12 Synthesis of the steroid hormones of the adrenal cortex from cholesterol

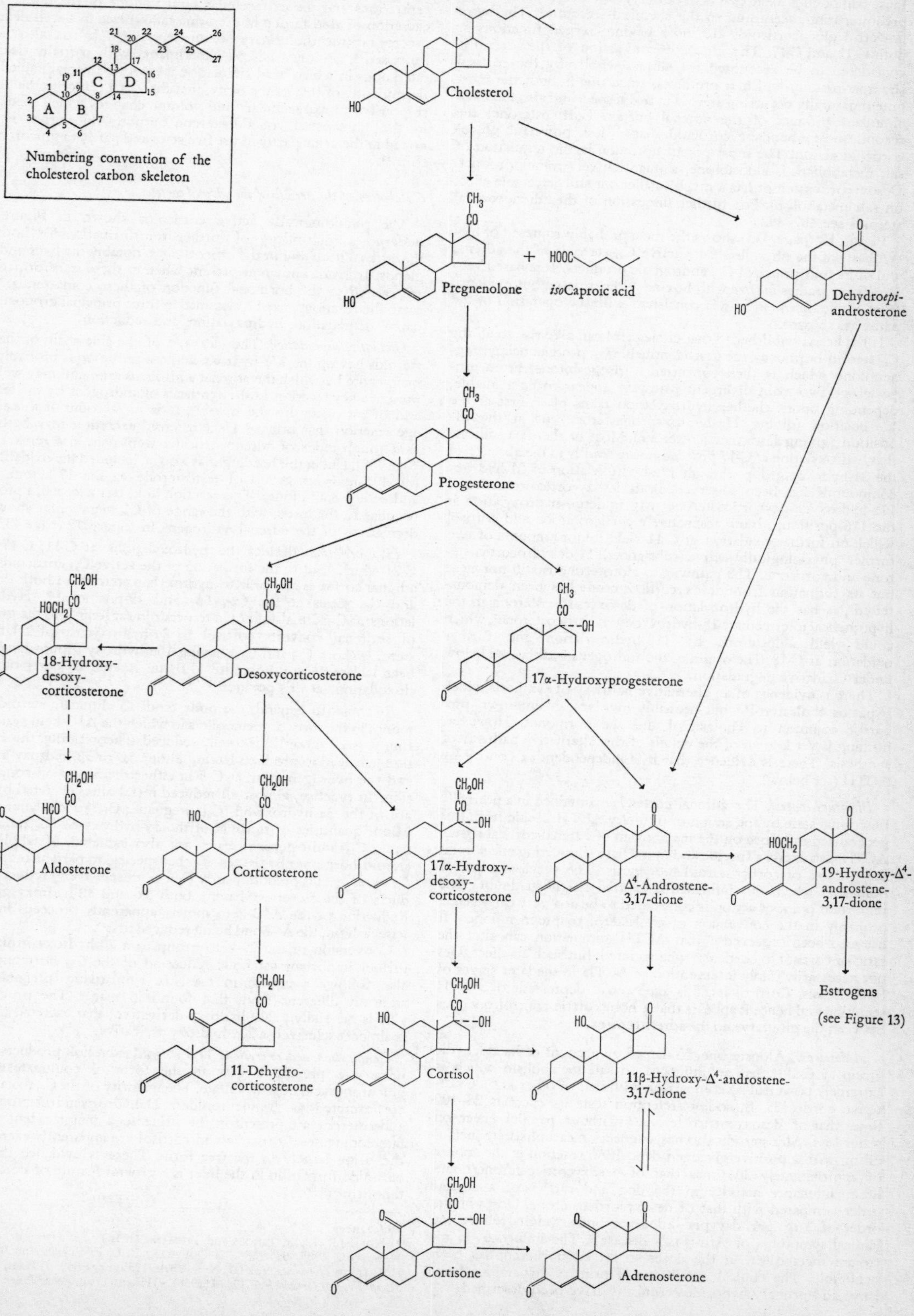

The C_{21} corticoids exert profound effects on carbohydrate and protein metabolism ("glucocorticoid" activity) and upon sodium and potassium metabolism ("mineralocorticoid" activity). Most of these compounds exert effects of both types with one or the other predominating, according to the chemical structure[1]. The more powerful glucocorticoids are those having oxygen functions at both C-11 and C-17. The glucocorticoid action of the adrenal is considered to be accounted for almost wholly by the cortisol (hydrocortisone) which it produces, since this is both the most potent naturally occurring steroid in this respect and also the most abundant product of the adrenal cortex. Corticosterone, the second most abundant corticoid, has a less powerful glucocorticoid action. The most potent hormone in the regulation of salt metabolism is aldosterone, a quantitatively minor product. Desoxycorticosterone has a much smaller but still detectable effect on salt metabolism. For further discussion of the adrenocortical steroids see 487–492.

Figure 12 (page 433) shows the most probable routes[2-4] of biosynthesis of the physiologically active C_{21} steroids of the adrenal and of its four principal C_{19} androgenic products. It is based very largely on studies *in vitro* with bovine adrenal tissue but evidence from studies *in vivo* in man is consistent with the operation of the pathways shown[5].

It has been established[3,4] that cholesterol can give rise to all the C_{21} steroid hormones, the first identifiable C_{21} product being pregnenolone which is then converted to progesterone. From progesterone two main divergent pathways appear to be available, depending upon whether hydroxylation takes place first at the 17α-position (giving 17α-hydroxyprogesterone) or at the 21-position (giving desoxycorticosterone). Most of the data indicate that hydroxylation at C-17 proceeds more readily in the absence of the 21-hydroxy group, though 17α-hydroxylation of 21-hydroxy compounds has been observed. Both desoxycorticosterone and 17α-hydroxydesoxycorticosterone may undergo hydroxylation at the 11β-position, giving respectively corticosterone and cortisol which on further oxidation at C-11 yield minor amounts of two further physiologically active substances, 11-dehydrocorticosterone and cortisone. The pathway to aldosterone is still not clear but its formation from desoxycorticosterone has been demonstrated[6], as has the hydroxylation of desoxycorticosterone to the hypothetical intermediate 18-hydroxydesoxycorticosterone[7], which could yield aldosterone by 11β-hydroxylation and further oxidation at C-18. The origin of the androgens is discussed below under Oxidative degradation.

There is evidence of an alternative pathway of synthesis which bypasses cholesterol[3,4] but probably involves an unknown precursor common to cholesterol and the hormones. However, nothing is yet known of the details of this alternative pathway of synthesis. There is evidence that it is independent of control by ACTH (see below).

Pituitary control. The adrenal cortex is maintained in a normally functional state by the action of pituitary ACTH. Aside from this generalized influence on the metabolism of adrenal cortical tissue, ACTH also exerts a specific and immediate stimulating effect upon the process of corticosteroid biogenesis. The precise point (or points) at which this influence is exerted is still in doubt. One important point of action is considered to be at a very early stage, probably in the conversion of cholesterol to pregnenolone[3]. It has also been observed[8,9] that ACTH stimulation can alter the ratio of cortisol to corticosterone secreted, but such an effect does not necessarily imply intervention of ACTH in the later stages of biosynthesis. Cortisol itself is a powerful depressant of ACTH secretion and hence it appears that a homeostatic control operates between the pituitary and the adrenal cortex.

Aldosterone. Aldosterone, so named on account of its aldehydic group at C-18[10], has an influence on salt metabolism which is extremely powerful by comparison with that of other known salt-active corticoids. In sodium-retention tests its effect is 25–100 times that of desoxycorticosterone[11] without parallel effect on water loss. Aldosterone also has an effect on carbohydrate metabolism, with a positive glycogen deposition reaction in the mouse of approximately 30 times that of desoxycorticosterone[12] and life-maintenance activity in the dog and rat[10,13] of a similar order compared with that of desoxycorticosterone. Doses of the order of 3 μg per day per kilogram body weight relieve the clinical symptoms of ADDISON's disease[14]. The influence on nitrogen metabolism in the doses so far administered has been negligible. The clinical conditions of primary hyperaldosteronism[15] and primary hypoaldosteronism[16] have been described.

The available evidence[17] indicates only a minor control of aldosterone secretion by ACTH, since aldosterone output falls by only about 30% after hypophysectomy[18]. More important and direct is probably the control by the sodium and potassium concentrations and the extracellular fluid volume of the body. The excretion of aldosterone in the urine takes place in a well-defined inverse ratio to the urinary sodium content[17]. It has also been proposed[18], on the basis of experiments with partially decapitated dogs in which head circulation was artificially maintained independently of that of the body, that there is a center in the brain responsive to extracellular fluid volume changes which mediates in the homeostasis of aldosterone output. Aldosterone is excreted in the urine partly in the free state and partly in glucuronide form[19].

Catabolism of the steroids of the adrenal cortex

The physiologically active corticoids shown in Figure 12 undergo a multiplicity of further transformations[2,20] both in the adrenal itself and in the other tissues, notably the liver and sex glands. It is not known at present whether these transformations are related to the hormonal function of these compounds. The catabolic reactions may be classified in three principal groups: oxidative degradation, hydroxylation, and reduction.

Oxidative degradation. The cleavage of the side chain of the C_{21} steroids having the 17α-hydroxy-20-keto grouping is probably the main route by which the adrenal androgens arise and may well represent a key reaction in the synthesis of androgens by the testis[21] and of estrogens by the ovary[22]. It is on account of this cleavage reaction that urinary 17-ketosteroid excretion may be taken as a rough index of adrenocortical activity (see also remarks on page 489). Under this heading may also be included the oxidation of the 17β-hydroxy group of testosterone to the 17-ketone (Δ^4-androstene-3,17-dione). This reaction links testosterone, a product peculiar to the testis, with the range of C_{19} metabolites shown as derivatives of the adrenal androgens in Figure 12 (page 433).

Hydroxylation. Besides the hydroxylations at C-11, C-17 and C-21 which lead to the formation of the active C_{21} corticoids, the adrenal cortex is also able to hydroxylate steroids of both the C_{19} and C_{21} series at the 6α-, 6β- and 19-positions[2,3]. Hydroxylations at C-6 are also known to occur in rat liver, and the guinea-pig adrenal converts cortisol to 2α-hydroxycortisol[23]. Urinary steroids (both C_{19} and C_{21}) having 16α-hydroxy groups have also been isolated[24], and hog adrenal tissue is able to carry out hydroxylations at this position[25].

Reduction. In general, the body tends to eliminate steroid hormones in the form of metabolites in which the Δ^4-3-keto system of ring A (see Figure 12) is totally reduced. Theoretically, this reduction may lead to products having either 3α- or 3β-hydroxy groups and the hydrogen atom at C-5 in either the 5α- or 5β-configuration. In practice, almost all reduced metabolites excreted by man are of the 3α-hydroxy-5β-(C_{21}: pregnane; C_{19}: etiocholane) series. Minor quantities of steroids of the 3α-hydroxy-5α-(C_{21}: allopregnane; C_{19}: androsterone) series are also excreted. Metabolism of steroid hormones by tissues of other species, in particular rat liver *(in vitro)*, yields predominantly (but not exclusively) reduced products of the 5α-series[26] having both 3α- and 3β-hydroxy groups. Reduction of the Δ^4-3-keto moiety apparently proceeds in stepwise fashion, the Δ^4-bond being reduced first[27].

Conversion of the 20-keto group to a 20-hydroxy group is a further important catabolic reduction of the C_{21} hormones and also follows a course in most *in vitro* tissue preparations[28] sterically different from that found in man[20]. The product *in vitro* is generally a 20β-hydroxy derivative; that excreted by man is almost exclusively a 20α-hydroxy derivative.

Conjugation and excretion. The steroid excretion products of the urine are present largely in the form of conjugates[20] with glucuronic acid or with sulfate. The majority of the C_{21} metabolites are excreted as β-glucuronides. Dehydro*epi*androsterone and androsterone are present in the urine to a major extent as sulfate conjugates. Cortisone and cortisol are apparently excreted in the urine largely in the free form. There is evidence that glucuronide formation in the liver is a general feature of steroid metabolism[29].

References

1) NOBLE, R. L., in PINCUS and THIMANN (Eds.), *The Hormones*, vol. III, New York, 1955, page 685. *2)* DORFMAN, R. I., in PINCUS and THIMANN (Eds.), *The Hormones*, vol. III, New York, 1955, page 589. *3)* HAYANO et al., *Recent Progr. Hormone Res.*, **12**, 79 (1956). *4)* HEARD et al., *Recent Progr. Hormone*

Fig. 13 Synthesis and metabolism of estrogens

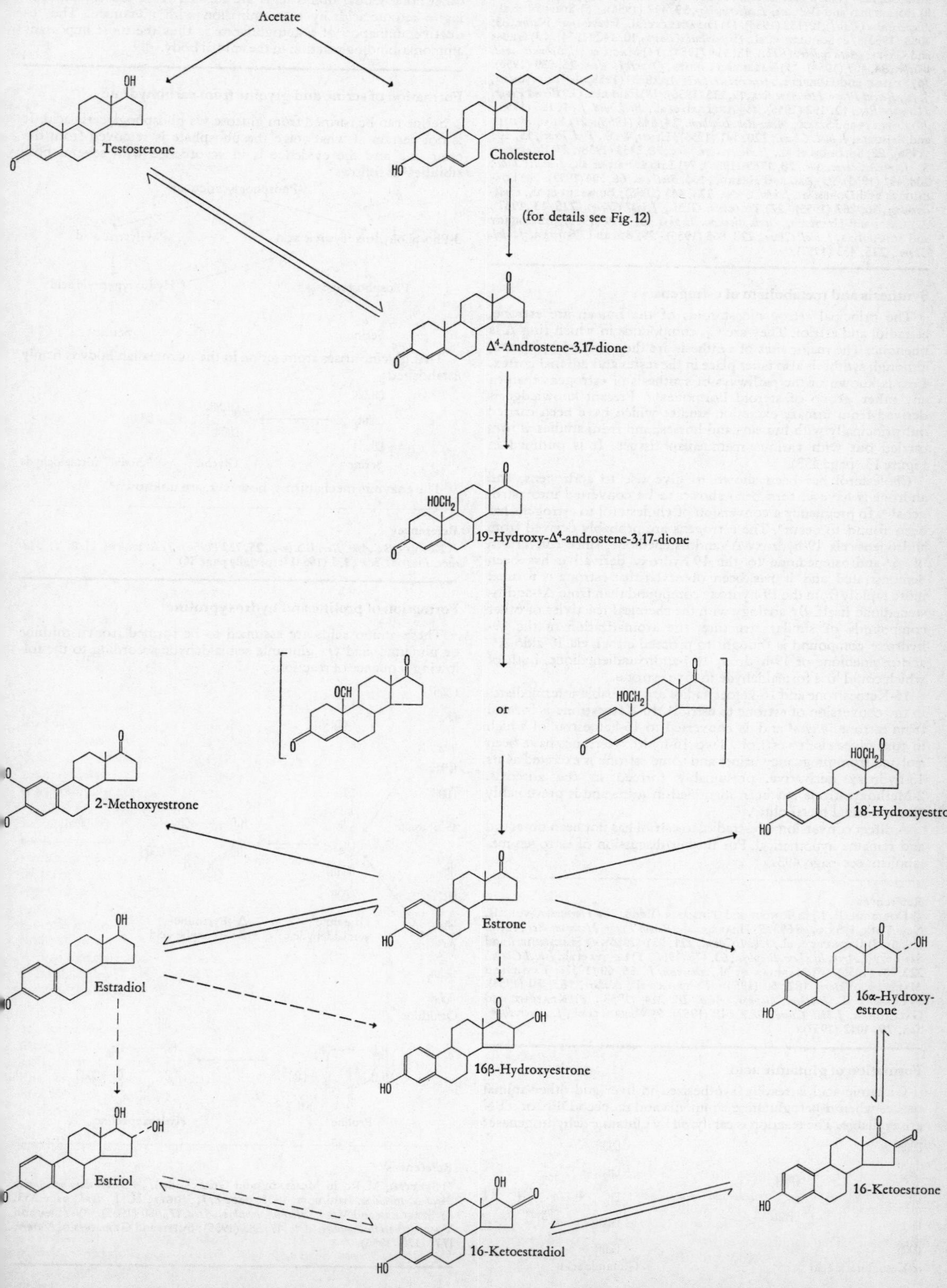

Res., **12**, 45 (1956). *5)* DORFMAN, R. I., *Ciba Foundation Colloquia on Endocrinology*, **8**, 112 (1955); CORNFORTH et al., *Proc. chem. Soc. Lond.*, **1958**, 112. *6)* KAHNT et al., *Experientia (Basel)*, **11**, 446 (1955). *7)* KAHNT et al., *Helv. chim. Acta*, **38**, 1237 (1955). *8)* KASS et al., *Proc. Soc. exp. Biol. (N.Y.)*, **85**, 583 (1954). *9)* ROSENFELD and BASCOM, *Endocrinology*, **59**, 497 (1956). *10)* SIMPSON et al., *Experientia (Basel)*, **10**, 132 (1954). *11)* DESAULLES et al., *Schweiz. med. Wschr.*, **83**, 1088 (1953). *12)* SCHULER et al., *Experientia (Basel)*, **10**, 142 (1954). *13)* GROSS and GYSEL, *Acta endocr. (Kbh.)*, **15**, 199 (1954). *14)* MACH et al., *Schweiz. med. Wschr.*, **84**, 407 (1954). *15)* EALES and LINDER, *Quart. J. Med.*, **25**, 539 (1956). *16)* SKANSE and HÖKFELT, *Acta endocr. (Kbh.)*, **28**, 29 (1958). *17)* LUETSCHER, J. A., *Recent Progr. Hormone Res.*, **12**, 175 (1956). *18)* FARRELL, G., *Recent Progr. Hormone Res.*, **12**, 192 (1956). *19)* AXELRAD et al., *Brit. med. J.*, **1**, 196 (1955). *20)* ROBERTS and SZEGÖ, *Ann. Rev. Biochem.*, **24**, 543 (1955). *21)* SLAUNWHITE and SAMUELS, *J. biol. Chem.*, **220**, 341 (1956); LYNN, W. S., *Fed. Proc.*, **15**, 305 (1956). *22)* SOLOMON et al., *J. Amer. chem. Soc.*, **78**, 5453 (1956). *23)* BURSTEIN, S., *J. Amer. chem. Soc.*, **78**, 1769 (1956). *24)* LIEBERMAN et al., *J. biol. Chem.*, **204**, 491 (1953). *25)* RAO and HEARD, *Arch. Biochem.*, **66**, 504 (1957). *26)* FORCHIELLI and DORFMAN, *J. biol. Chem.*, **223**, 443 (1956); BURSTEIN et al., *Endocrinology*, **56**, 267 (1955). *27)* TOMKINS, G. M., *J. biol. Chem.*, **225**, 13 (1957). *28)* CASPI and HECHTER, *Arch. Biochem. Biophys.*, **61**, 299 (1956); DE COURCY and SCHNEIDER, *J. biol. Chem.*, **223**, 865 (1956). *29)* SIE and FISHMAN, *J. biol. Chem.*, **225**, 453 (1957).

Synthesis and metabolism of estrogens

The principal estrogenic steroids of the human are estrone, estradiol and estriol. They are C_{18} compounds in which ring A is phenolic. The major sites of synthesis are the ovary and placenta, although synthesis also takes place in the testes and adrenal cortex. Less is known of the pathways of synthesis of estrogens than of any other group of steroid hormones[1,2]. Present knowledge is derived from urinary excretion studies which have been carried out principally with humans and horses, and from studies *in vitro* carried out with various mammalian tissues. It is outlined in Figure 13 (page 435).

Cholesterol has been shown to give rise to androgens, and androgens have in turn been shown to be converted into estrogens[2,3]. In pregnancy a conversion of cholesterol to estrogens has been found to occur[9]. The estrogens are probably derived from androgens via 19-hydroxy-Δ^4-androstenedione, since conversion of Δ^4-androstenedione to the 19-hydroxy derivative has been demonstrated and it has been observed that estrone is formed more rapidly from the 19-hydroxy compound than from Δ^4-androstenedione itself. By analogy with the chemical reactivity of other compounds of similar structure, the aromatization of the 19-hydroxy compound is thought to proceed either via 19-aldo-Δ^4-androstenedione or 19-hydroxy-$\Delta^{1,4}$-androstadienedione, both of which could lose formaldehyde to give estrone.

16-Ketoestrone and 16-ketoestradiol are probable intermediates in the conversion of estrone to estriol[1]. 16-Ketoestrone is formed from estrone *in vivo*[4] and is converted to 16-ketoestradiol which in turn gives rise to estriol[5]. Two 16-hydroxyestrones have been isolated from pregnancy urine[6] and some estrone is excreted as its 18-hydroxy derivative, presumably formed in the adrenal[7]. 2-Methoxyestrone has been identified in urine and is presumably also a normal metabolite[8].

A direct conversion of estradiol to estriol has not been observed and remains hypothetical. For further discussion of estrogen metabolism see page 493.

References

1) DORFMAN, R. I., in PINCUS and THIMANN (Eds.), *The Hormones*, vol. III, New York, 1955, page 593. *2)* HEARD et al., *Recent Progr. Hormone Res.*, **12**, 45 (1956). *3)* BAGGETT et al., *J. biol. Chem.*, **221**, 931 (1956). *4)* SLAUNWHITE and SANDBERG, *Arch. Biochem. Biophys.*, **63**, 478 (1956). *5)* LEVITZ et al., *J. biol. Chem.*, **222**, 981 (1956). *6)* MARRIAN et al., *Biochem. J.*, **66**, 60 (1957); LAYNE and MARRIAN, *Nature*, **182**, 50 (1958); BROWN et al., *Nature*, **182**, 50 (1958). *7)* LOKE et al., *Biochim. biophys. Acta*, **28**, 214 (1958). *8)* KRAYCHY and GALLAGHER, *J. biol. Chem.*, **229**, 519 (1957). *9)* WERBIN et al., *J. Amer. chem. Soc.*, **79**, 1012 (1957).

Formation of glutamic acid

Glutamic acid is readily synthesized in liver and other animal tissues when α-ketoglutarate, ammonia and reduced DPN or TPN are available. The reaction is catalyzed by glutamic dehydrogenase:

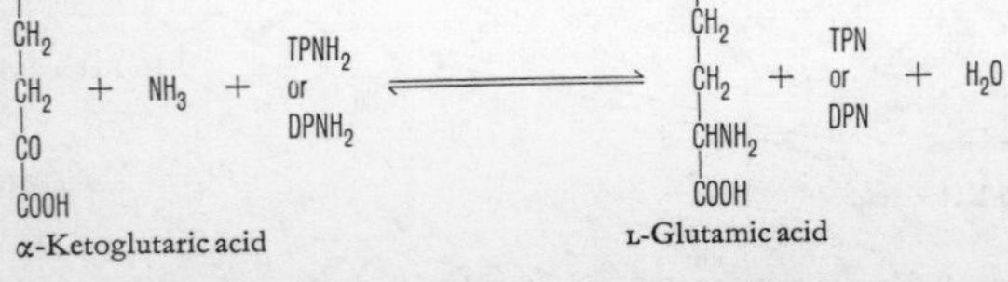

Glutamic acid is the only amino acid in animal tissues which can be directly synthesized from ammonia and the corresponding carbon skeleton (supplied in the form of the α-ketonic acid). All other nonessential amino acids are formed from the corresponding α-ketonic acids by transamination with glutamate. The reductive amination of α-ketoglutarate is thus the most important ammonia-binding reaction in the animal body.

Formation of serine and glycine from carbohydrate

Serine can be formed from glucose via phosphoglyceric acid. It is not certain at what stage the phosphate is removed from the ester link and the evidence is in accordance with several possibilities[1] as follows:

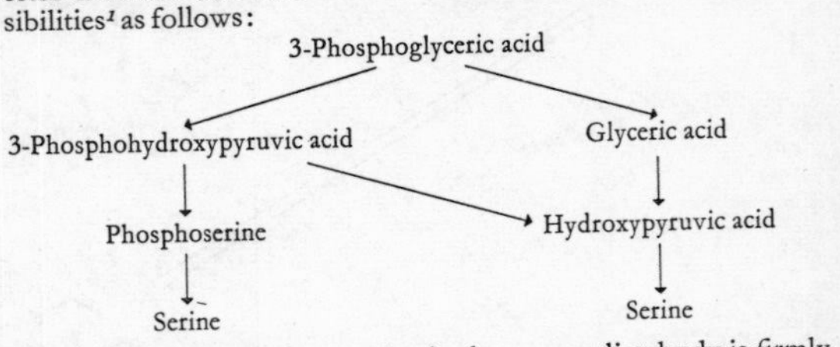

That glycine arises from serine in the mammalian body is firmly established:

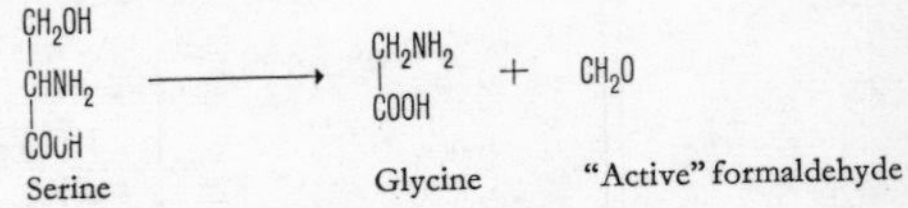

The enzymic mechanisms, however, are unknown[2].

References

1) KORKES, S., *Ann. Rev. Biochem.*, **25**, 732 (1956). *2)* ARNSTEIN, H. R. V., *Advanc. Protein Chem.*, **9**, 1 (1954) (especially page 36).

Formation of proline and hydroxyproline

These amino acids are assumed to be formed from ornithine or glutamic acid via glutamic semialdehyde according to the following sequence of reactions:

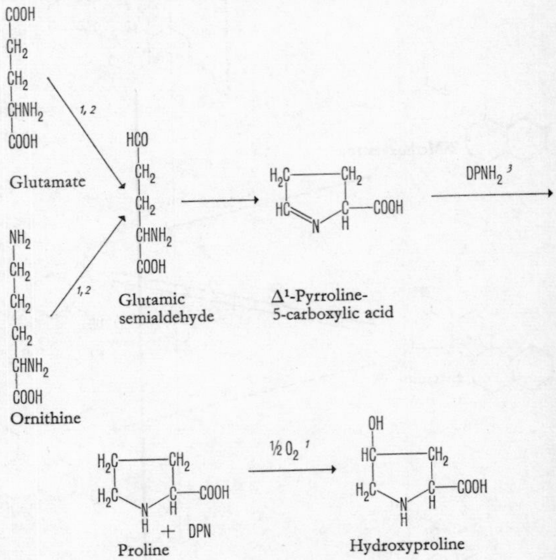

References

1) STETTEN, M. R., in MCELROY and GLASS (Eds.), *A Symposium on Amino Acid Metabolism*, Baltimore, 1955, page 277; VOGEL, H. J., *ibid.*, page 335. *2)* STRECKER and MELA, *Biochim. biophys. Acta*, **17**, 580 (1955). *3)* YURA and VOGEL, *Biochim. biophys. Acta*, **17**, 582 (1955); SMITH and GREENBERG, *Nature*, **177**, 1130 (1956).

Table 20 Formation of basic cell constituents and metabolites from amino acids
This list is not comprehensive; for carbohydrate synthesis from amino acids see page 443

Amino acid serving as starting material	Product formed	Pathway of formation	Physiological function
Glycine	Purine bases	See page 438	Constituent of nucleic acids and nucleotides
	Porphyrins	See page 440	Constituent of hemoglobin and cytochromes
	Creatine	See page 440	Precursor of creatine phosphate, an energy store in muscle and other tissues
	Glutathione	See page 441	Prosthetic group of glyoxalase, triose-phosphate dehydrogenase and probably other enzymes
	Hippuric acid and related compounds	See page 448	Detoxication product of benzoic acid
	Bile acids	See page 441	Required for digestion of fats
Serine	Ethanolamine	Decarboxylation (see Table 6, page 406)	Constituent of phospholipids
	Choline	Methylation of ethanolamine, methionine acting as a methyl group donor	Constituent of phospholipids
	Acetylcholine	Acetylation of choline by acetyl-coenzyme A[1]	Transmitter substance at nerve endings
Cysteine	Taurine	See page 441	Constituent of bile acids
	Glutathione	See page 441	See above under Glycine
Glutamic acid	Glutamine	From glutamic acid and ammonia in the presence of ATP[2]	Cell constituent. Intermediate carrier of amino groups in aminations and amidations
	γ-Aminobutyric acid	Decarboxylation (see Table 6, page 406)	Cell constituent, especially of brain
	Glutathione	See page 441	See above under Glycine
	Proline	See opposite page	Protein constituent
	Hydroxyproline	See opposite page	Protein constituent
Arginine	Creatine	See page 440	See above under Glycine
Methionine	Creatine	See page 440	See above under Glycine
	Choline	Decarboxylation (see Table 6, page 406)	See above under Serine
Histidine	Histamine	See page 406	Transmitter substance at nerve endings
Aspartic acid	Pyrimidine bases	See page 442	Constituent of nucleic acids and nucleotides
	β-Alanine	Probably by α-decarboxylation	Constituent of special peptides (anserine, carnosine, pantothenic acid)
Tyrosine	Adrenaline	See page 442	Hormone
	Noradrenaline	See page 442	Hormone and transmitter substance at nerve endings
	Thyroxine	See page 443	Hormone
	Melanins	See page 443	General pigments of hair and skin
Tryptophan	5-Hydroxytryptamine (serotonin)	See page 443	Transmitter substance at nerve endings
	Nicotinic acid	See page 411	Constituent of pyridine nucleotides
Glucogenic amino acids	Carbohydrates	See page 443	

References *1)* Korkes et al., *J. biol. Chem.*, **198**, 215 (1952). *2)* Elliott, W. H., *J. biol. Chem.*, **201**, 661 (1953).

2. Formation of basic cell constituents and metabolites from amino acids

The principal products, their pathways of formation and their physiological functions are summarized in Table 20 on page 437.

Formation of purines

Knowledge of the pathways shown below and on pages 439 and 440 is derived mainly from work done on pigeon liver. There is, however, no reason to doubt that the same pathway occurs in mammals. The purine skeleton is built up on the nitrogen atom of ribosylamine-5-phosphate. The substrates utilized in this process include glutamine, glycine, aspartic acid, carbon dioxide, and a one-carbon fragment equivalent to formaldehyde which is supplied in the form of formyltetrahydrofolic acid[1]. The first purine derivative to be formed is inosinic acid (reactions **1–11**). This is then converted into adenylic acid (reactions **12** and **13**) or into xanthidylic acid (reaction **14**) and guanylic acid (reaction **15**). Only adenine is utilized directly when the naturally occurring purines are ingested as the free bases. It is probably converted into AMP by a reaction similar to the conversion of orotic acid to orotidylic acid (see page 442)[2]. Other purine bases such as guanine, hypoxanthine and xanthine are utilized to a very small extent or not at all[3].

Formation of inosinic acid (IMP)

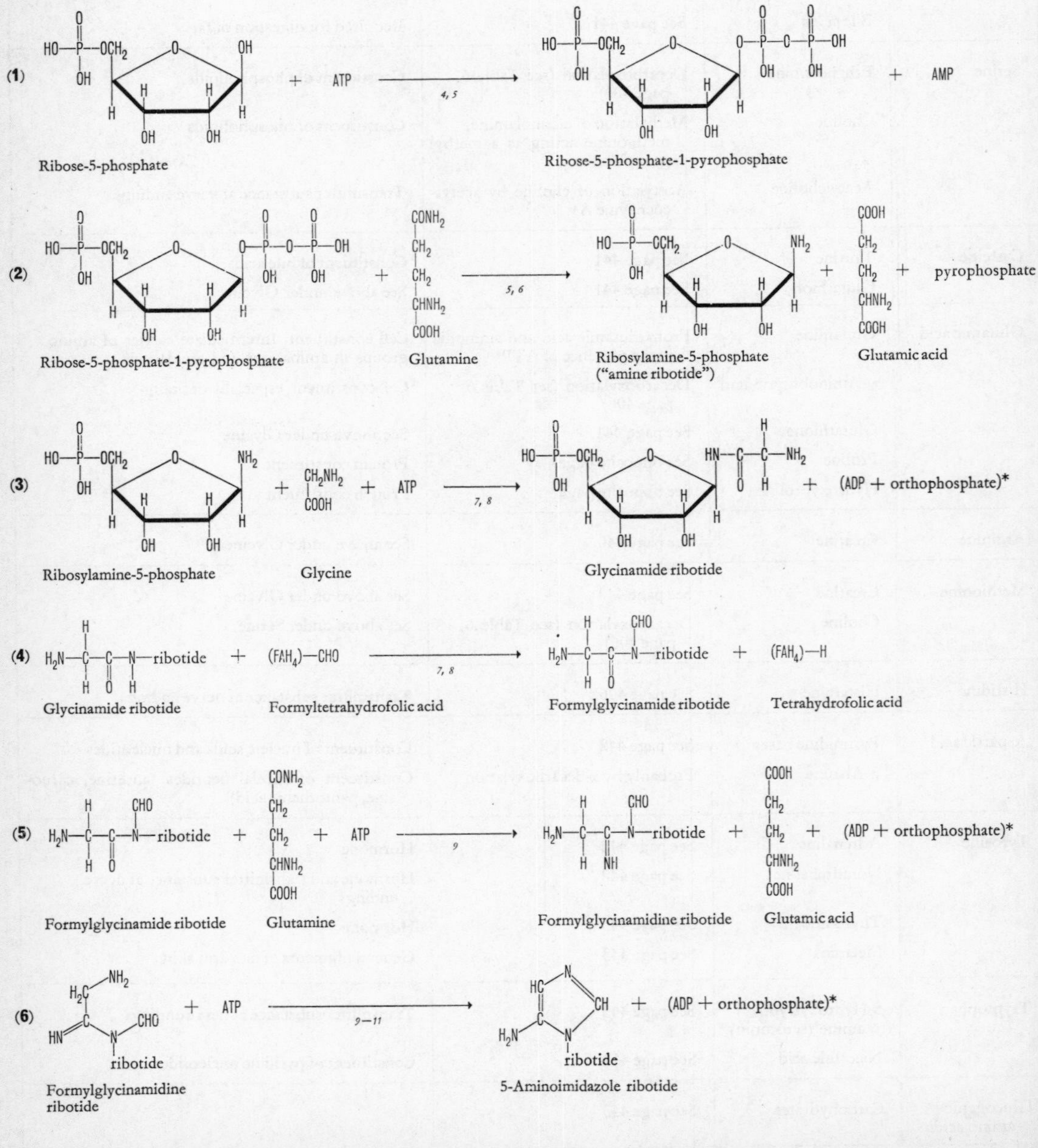

* The nature of the products given in brackets is not established with certainty.

(7)

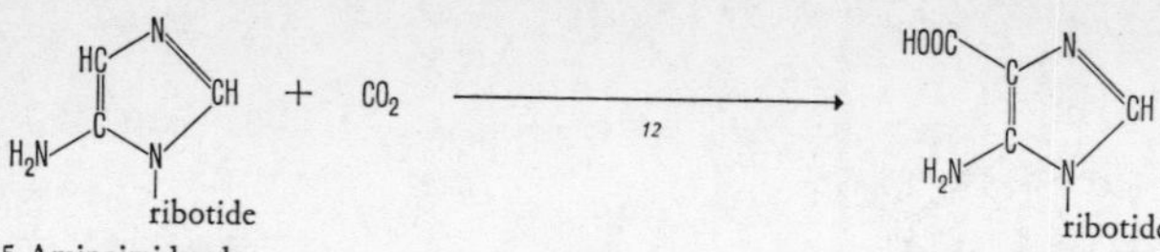

5-Aminoimidazole ribotide — 5-Amino-4-carboxyimidazole ribotide

(8)

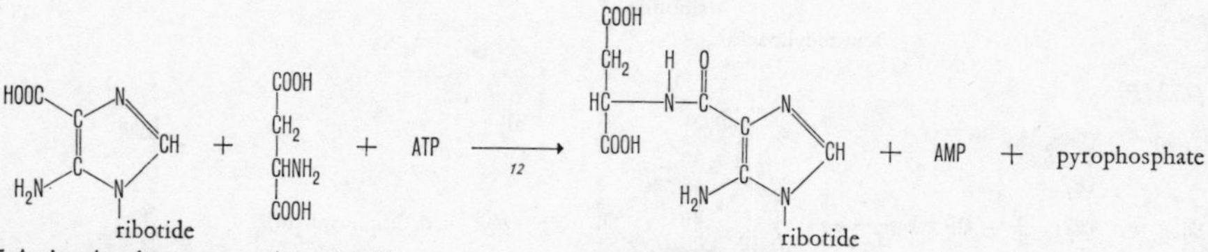

5-Amino-4-carboxy-imidazole ribotide — Aspartic acid — 5-Amino-4-succino-carboxamidoimidazole ribotide

(9)

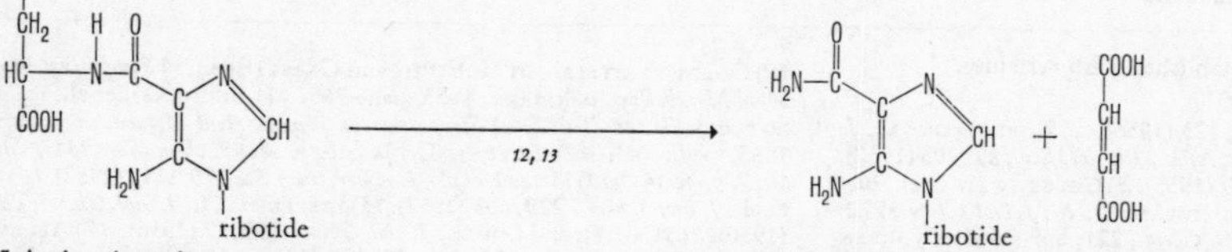

5-Amino-4-succino-carboxamidoimidazole ribotide — 5-Amino-4-carboxamido-imidazole ribotide — Fumaric acid

(10)

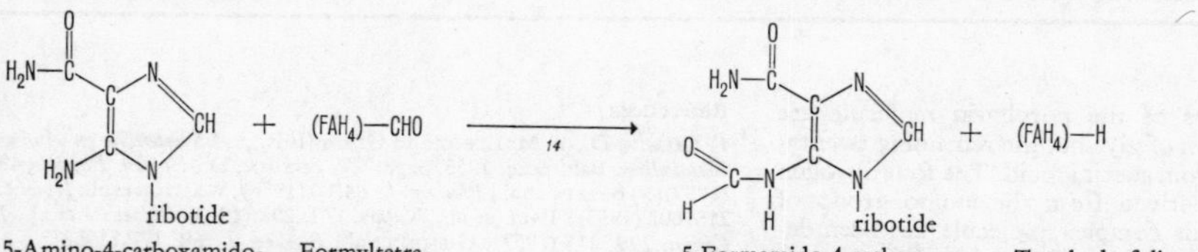

5-Amino-4-carboxamido-imidazole ribotide — Formyltetra-hydrofolic acid — 5-Formamido-4-carbox-amidoimidazole ribotide — Tetrahydrofolic acid

(11)

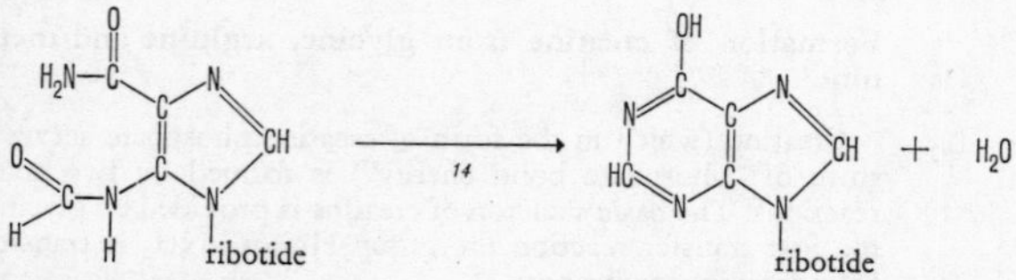

5-Formamido-4-carbox-amidoimidazole ribotide — Inosinic acid

Formation of adenylic acid (adenosine monophosphate, AMP)

(12)

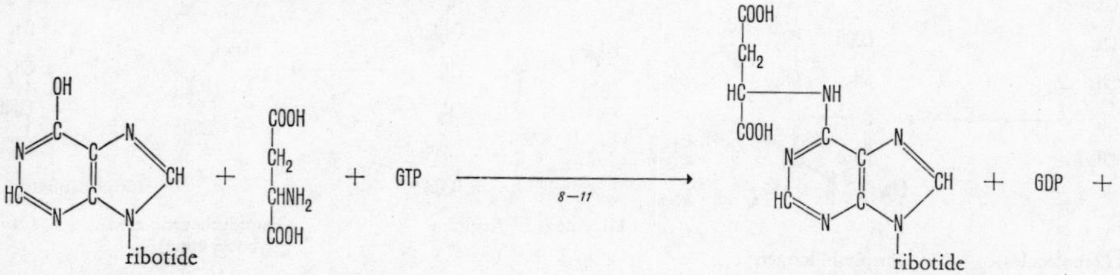

Inosinic acid (IMP) — Aspartic acid — Adenylosuccinic acid (succinyladenylic acid)

(13)

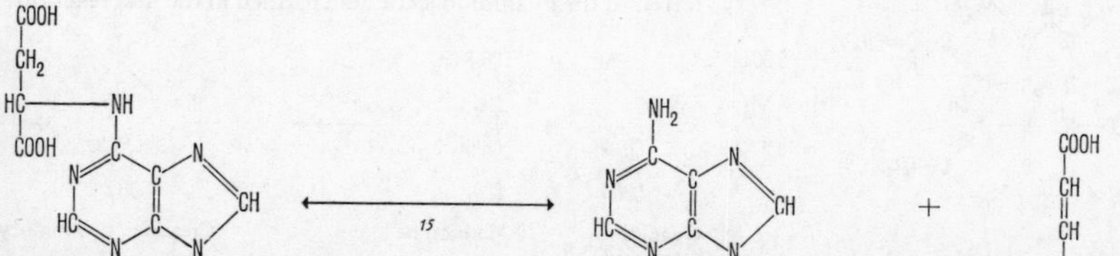

Adenylosuccinic acid (succinyladenylic acid) — Adenylic acid — Fumaric acid

Formation of xanthidylic acid (XMP)

(14)

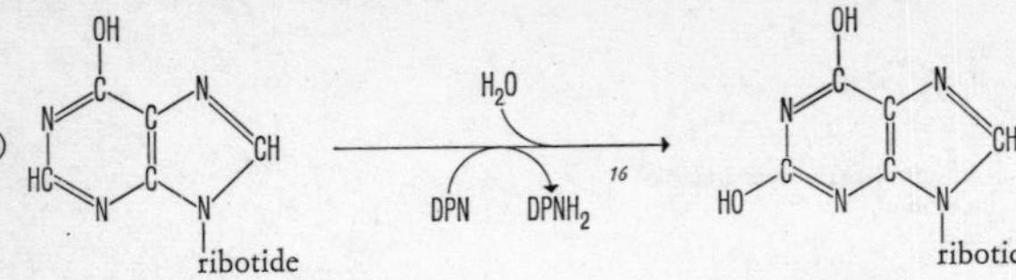

Inosinic acid (IMP) — Xanthidylic acid

Formation of guanylic acid (GMP)

(15)

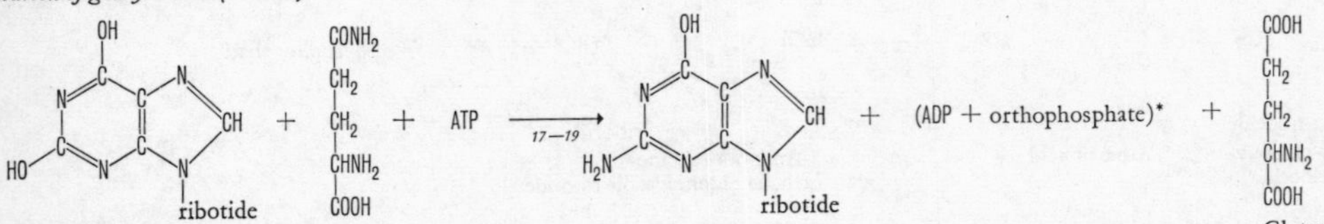

Xanthidylic acid — Glutamine — Guanylic acid — Glutamic acid

* The nature of these products is not established with certainty.

References

1) Carter, C. E., *Ann. Rev. Biochem.*, **25**, 123 (1956). *2)* Kornberg et al., *J. biol. Chem.*, **215**, 417 (1955). *3)* Christman, A. A., *Physiol. Rev.*, **32**, 303 (1952). *4)* Kornberg et al., *J. biol. Chem.*, **215**, 389 (1955). *5)* Goldthwait et al., *Biochim. biophys. Acta*, **18**, 148 (1955). *6)* Goldthwait, D. A., *J. biol. Chem.*, **222**, 1051 (1956). *7)* Goldthwait et al., *J. biol. Chem.*, **221**, 569 (1956); Warren and Buchanan, *J. biol. Chem.*, **229**, 613 (1957). *8)* Hartman et al., *J. biol. Chem.*, **221**, 1057 (1956). *9)* Levenberg and Buchanan, *J. biol. Chem.*, **224**, 1005, 1019 (1957); Melnick and Buchanan, *J. biol. Chem.*, **225**, 157 (1957). *10)* Goldthwait et al., in McElroy and Glass (Eds.), *A Symposium on Amino Acid Metabolism*, Baltimore, 1955, page 765. *11)* Buchanan et al., in McElroy and Glass (Eds.), *A Symposium on Amino Acid Metabolism*, Baltimore, 1955, page 743. *12)* Lukens, L. N., *Abstr. Amer. chem. Soc. 131st Meeting*, 1957, page 14C. *13)* Miller et al., *J. Amer. chem. Soc.*, **79**, 1513 (1957). *14)* Flaks et al., *J. biol. Chem.*, **229**, 603 (1957). *15)* Lieberman, I., *J. biol. Chem.*, **223**, 327 (1956). *16)* Carter and Cohen, *J. biol. Chem.*, **222**, 17 (1956). *17)* Abrams and Bentley, *Arch. Biochem. Biophys.*, **58**, 109 (1955). *18)* Lagerkvist, U., *Acta chem. scand.*, **9**, 1028 (1955). *19)* Gehring and Magasanik, *J. Amer. chem. Soc.*, **77**, 4685 (1955).

Formation of porphyrins

Eight of the carbon atoms of the porphyrin molecule are derived from the α-carbon atom of glycine; the remaining twenty-six carbon atoms are derived from succinic acid. The four nitrogen atoms of the molecule are derived from the amino group of glycine[1]. The formation of this complex molecule has been demonstrated to proceed via δ-aminolevulic acid and porphobilinogen[2] by the following reactions:

(1)

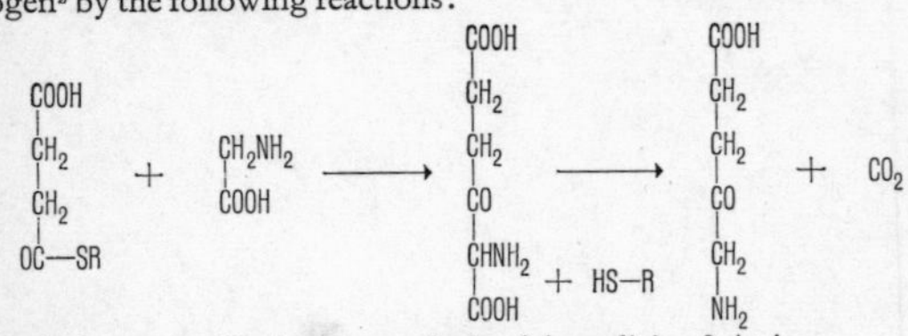

Succinyl-coenzyme A (see page 402) — Glycine — α-Amino-β-ketoadipic acid (hypothetical intermediate) — δ-Aminolevulic acid

(2)

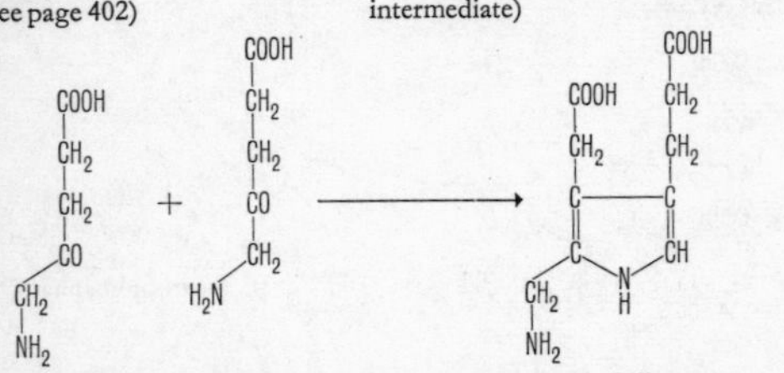

δ-Aminolevulic acid (2 molecules) — Porphobilinogen

(3)

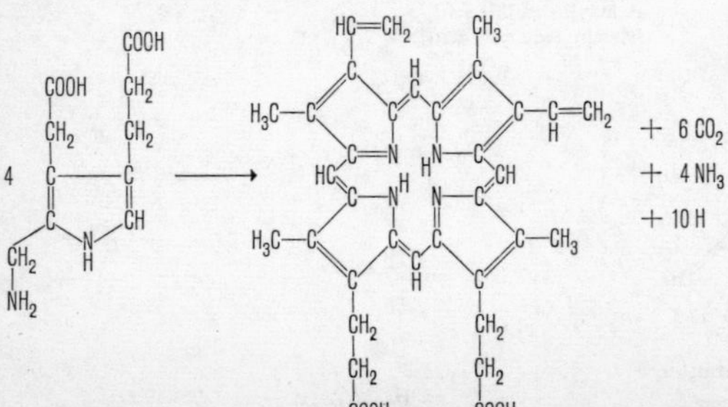

Porphobilinogen — Protoporphyrin IX

References

1) Shemin, D., in McElroy and Glass (Eds.), *A Symposium on Amino Acid Metabolism*, Baltimore, 1955, page 727; Shemin, D., *Ergebn. Physiol.*, **49**, 299 (1957). *2)* Berlin et al., *Biochem. J.*, **64**, 80 (1956); Wriston et al., *J. biol. Chem.*, **215**, 603 (1955); Falk et al., *Nature*, **172**, 292 (1953); Németh et al., *J. biol. Chem.*, **229**, 415 (1957); Gibson et al., *Biochem. J.*, **68**, 17P (1958).

Formation of creatine from glycine, arginine and methionine[1]

Creatine (which in the form of creatine phosphate serves as a store of "phosphate bond energy") is formed by two transfer reactions. The basic skeleton of creatine is provided by glycine. In the first transfer reaction the group HN=C(–)–NH_2 is transferred from arginine to glycine:

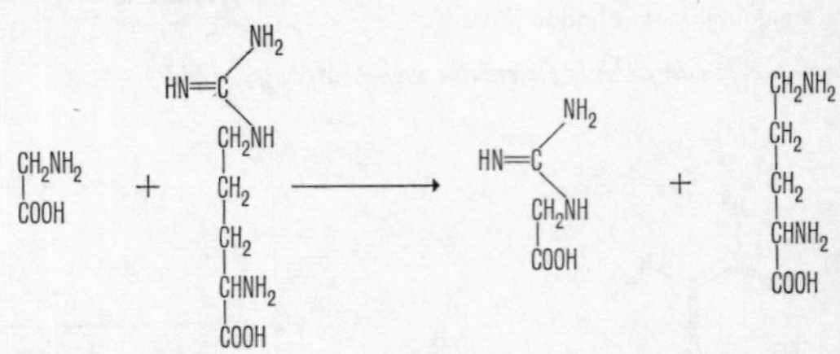

Glycine — Arginine — Guanidinoacetic acid (glycocyamine) — Ornithine

In the second reaction the methyl group of methionine is transferred to the guanidinoacetic acid formed in the first reaction:

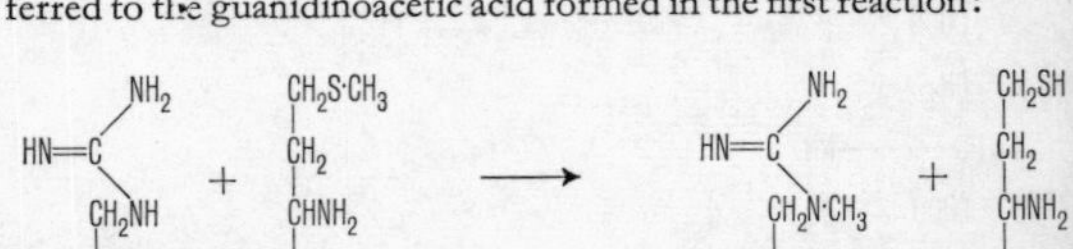

Guanidinoacetic acid — Methionine — Creatine — Homocysteine

Methionine does not react as the free amino acid but as the S-adenosyl derivative, formed from ATP and methionine[2]:

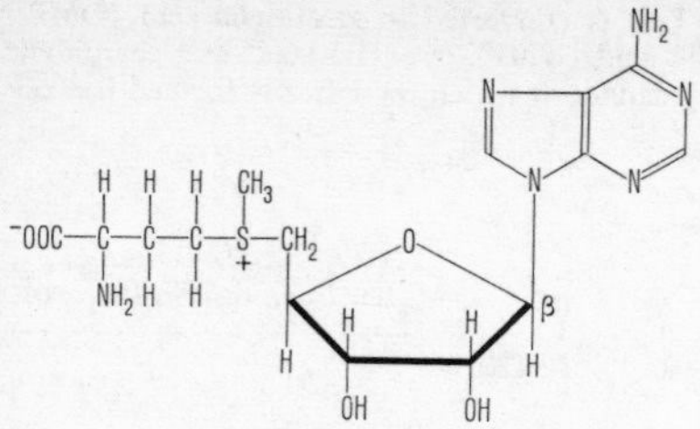

S-Adenosylmethionine

Homocysteine appears likewise as the adenosyl derivative in the transmethylation reaction formulated above[3].

Creatine interacts reversibly with ATP, especially in muscle, to form creatine phosphate:

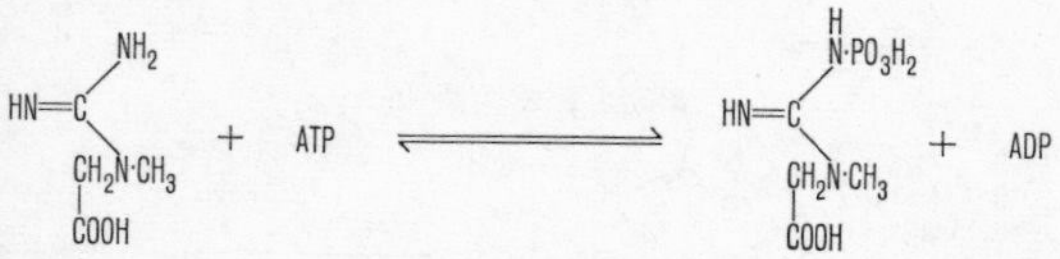

The reaction proceeds from left to right in resting muscle, and from right to left during prolonged contractions, regenerating ATP spent as an energy source in the process of contraction.

References

1) For a review see ARNSTEIN, H. R. V., *Advanc. Protein Chem.*, **9**, 1 (1954). *2)* CANTONI, G. L., *J. biol. Chem.*, **204**, 403 (1953); CANTONI and SCARANO, *J. Amer. chem. Soc.*, **76**, 4744 (1954); CANTONI and VIGNOS, *J. biol. Chem.*, **209**, 647 (1954). *3)* CANTONI and SCARANO, *J. Amer. chem. Soc.*, **76**, 4744 (1954).

Formation of glutathione

Glutathione is formed in two main steps which have been demonstrated to occur in the liver. The first of these involves the formation of the dipeptide γ-L-glutamyl-L-cysteine from glutamic acid, cysteine and ATP[1]. This is followed by the formation of glutathione itself from γ-L-glutamyl-L-cysteine, glycine and ATP[2].

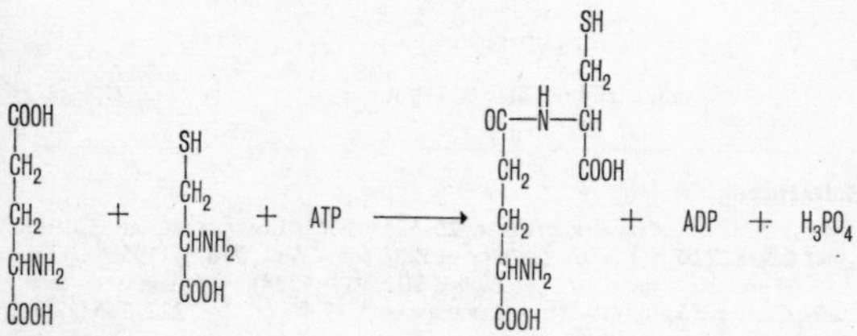

L-Glutamic acid — L-Cysteine — γ-L-Glutamyl-L-cysteine

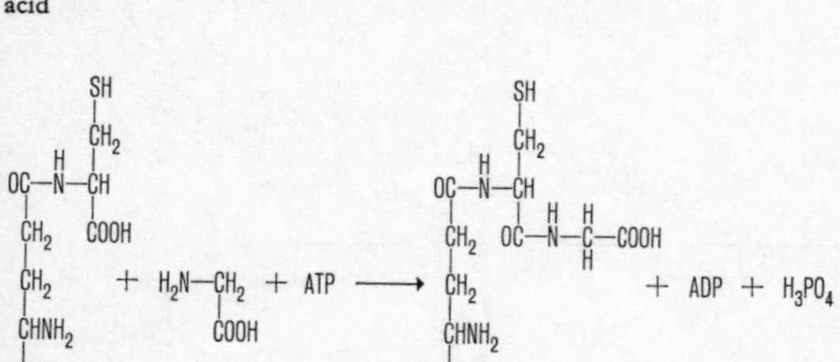

γ-L-Glutamyl-L-cysteine — Glycine — Glutathione

References

1) MANDELES and BLOCH, *J. biol. Chem.*, **214**, 639 (1955). *2)* SNOKE, J. E., *J. biol. Chem.*, **213**, 813 (1955).

Formation of bile acid conjugates[1]

Bile acids such as cholic and desoxycholic acids are excreted into the intestine in the form of glycine or taurine conjugates. The major factors controlling the ratios of glycine and taurine conjugates appear to be the availability of taurine. The specificity and activity of the enzyme systems are such as to favor the formation of taurine conjugates[2]. The reactions require the presence of coenzyme A and ATP, and presumably proceed by a mechanism similar to that involved in the activation of acetate (page 403) and aromatic acids (page 448)[3].

(1)

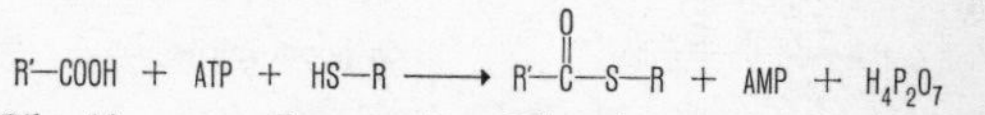

Bile acid — Coenzyme A — Bile acyl-coenzyme A — Pyrophosphoric acid

(2a)

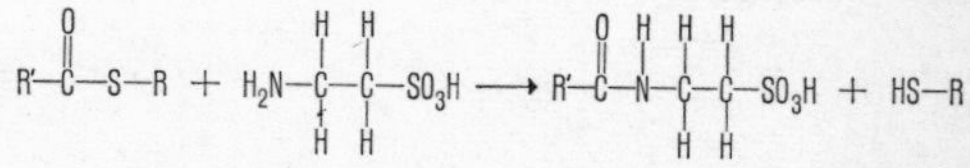

Bile acyl-coenzyme A — Taurine — Bile acid taurine conjugate (e.g. taurocholic acid) — Coenzyme A

(2b)

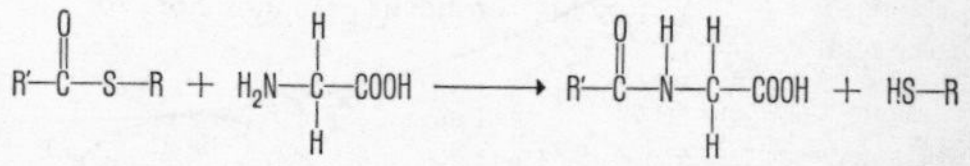

Bile acyl-coenzyme A — Glycine — Bile acid glycine conjugate (e.g. glycocholic acid) — Coenzyme A

References

1) BERGSTRÖM and BORGSTRÖM, *Ann. Rev. Biochem.*, **25**, 187 (1956). *2)* BREMER, J., *Acta chem. scand.*, **9**, 268 (1955). *3)* BREMER, J., *Acta chem. scand.*, **9**, 1036 (1955); ELLIOTT, W. H., *Biochem. J.*, **62**, 427, 433 (1955); **65**, 315 (1957).

Formation of taurine

Taurine is formed from cysteine in the liver and possibly in other organs. The pathway in mammalian tissues is via cysteinesulfinic acid and hypotaurine[1]:

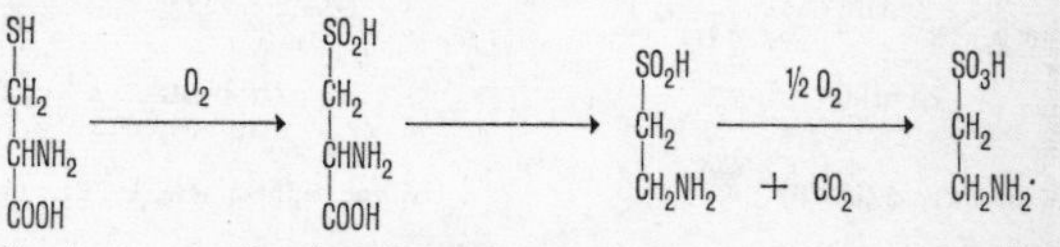

Cysteine — Cysteinesulfinic acid — Hypotaurine — Taurine

Cysteinesulfinic acid may also be formed from pyruvic acid, sulfur dioxide and glutamic acid by the following reactions[2]:

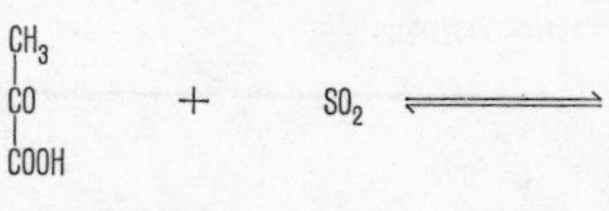

Pyruvic acid — β-Sulfinylpyruvic acid

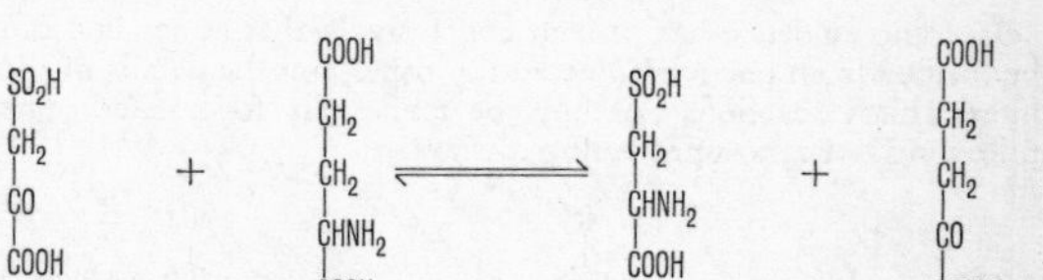

β-Sulfinylpyruvic acid — Glutamic acid — Cysteinesulfinic acid — α-Ketoglutaric acid

References

1) AWAPARA and WINGO, *J. biol. Chem.*, **203**, 189 (1953); CAVALLINI et al., *J. biol. Chem.*, **216**, 577 (1955); HOPE, B. D., *Biochem. J.*, **59**, 497 (1955); BERGERET et al., *Biochim. biophys. Acta*, **17**, 128 (1955); CHAPEVILLE and FROMAGEOT, *Biochim. biophys. Acta*, **17**, 275 (1955). *2)* CHAPEVILLE and FROMAGEOT, *Biochim. biophys. Acta*, **14**, 415 (1954).

Formation of pyrimidines

The starting materials of pyrimidine synthesis are aspartic acid and carbamyl phosphate. The pathway shown below occurs in mammals[1] and bacteria[2]. Orotic acid is the first complete pyrimidine to be formed. This is converted to orotidylic acid (OMP)[3] and then to uridylic acid (UMP), cytidylic acid[4] and thymidylic acid* (TMP). The manner in which the latter is formed has not been determined.

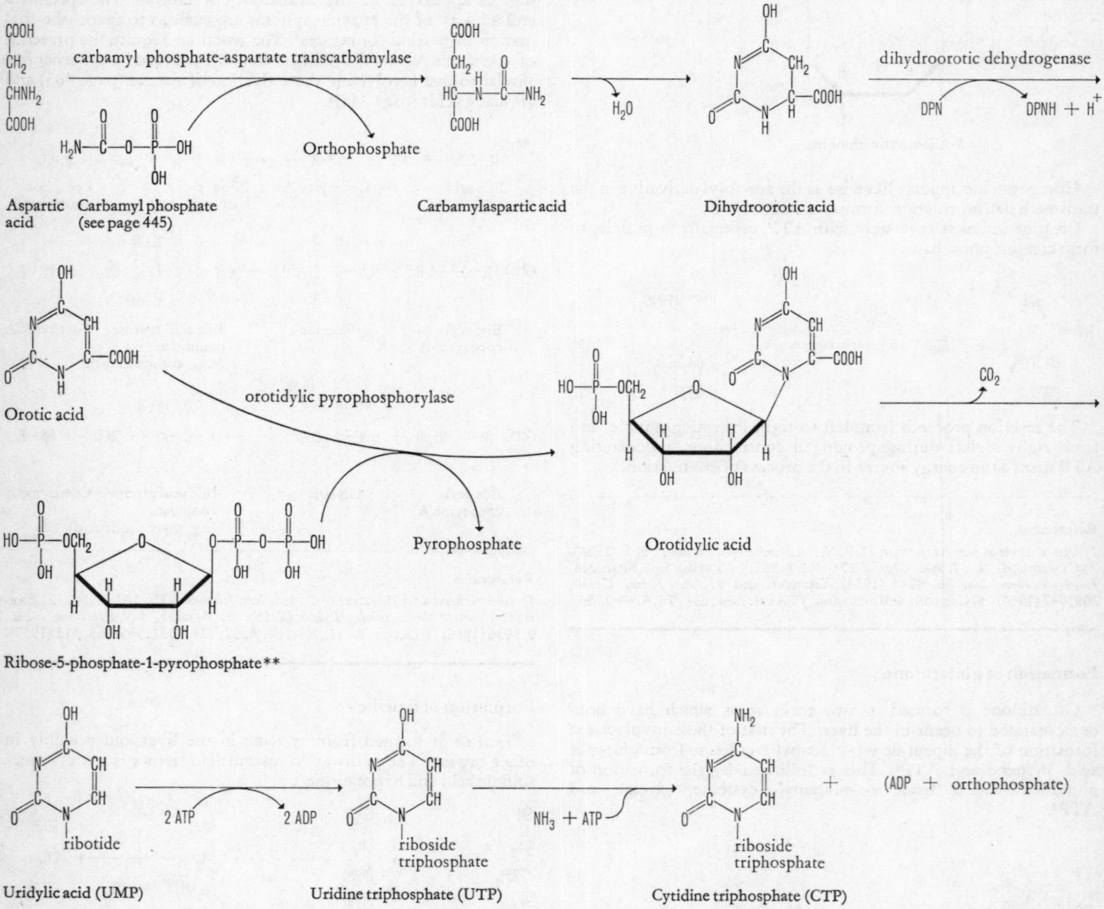

* Strictly speaking, this compound should be termed desoxythymidylic acid (DTMP) since it contains desoxyribose.

** This compound is formed by reaction (**1**), page 438.

References

1) Carter, C. E., *Ann. Rev. Biochem.*, **25**, 123 (1956); Lowenstein and Cohen, *J. biol. Chem.*, **220**, 57 (1956); Cooper et al., *J. biol. Chem.*, **216**, 37 (1955). *2)* Lieberman and Kornberg, *J. biol. Chem.*, **207**, 911 (1954). *3)* Lieberman et al., *J. biol. Chem.*, **215**, 403 (1955). *4)* Lieberman, I., *J. biol. Chem.*, **222**, 765 (1956).

Formation of adrenaline and noradrenaline from tyrosine

Isotopic evidence has proved conclusively that adrenaline can be formed from phenylalanine and tyrosine, but the details of the intermediary reactions can only be tentatively formulated. The following is the most probable pathway[1]:

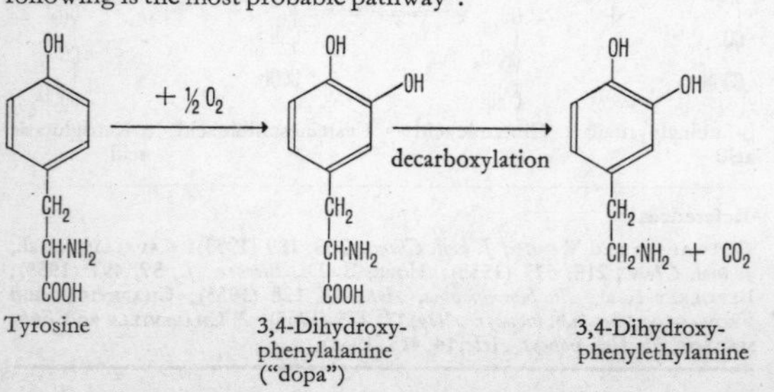

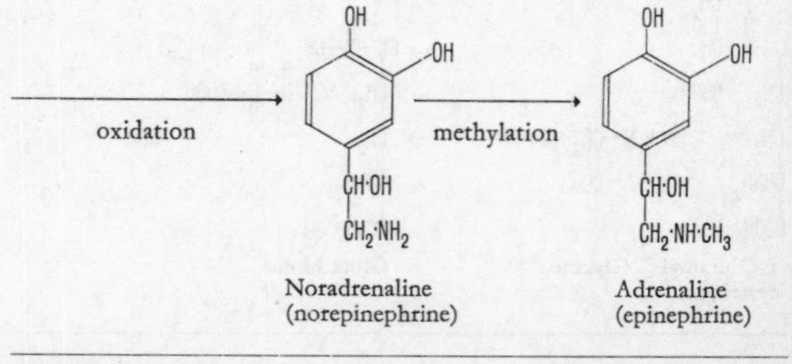

Reference

1) For alternative pathways see Dalgliesh, C. E., *Advanc. Protein Chem.*, **10**, 65 (1955).

Formation of thyroid hormones[1]

The thyroid gland has the capacity to concentrate iodide (I^-) from a blood level of about 1 μg per 100 ml to a gland level of about 10 μg per 100 g tissue. This concentration ratio may vary since it is influenced by a variety of factors such as the plasma iodide level. The incorporation of iodine into thyroid protein is a process the details of which are not yet known. It possibly occurs via free iodine (I_2) and involves the iodination of both free and protein-bound tyrosine[2]:

(1)

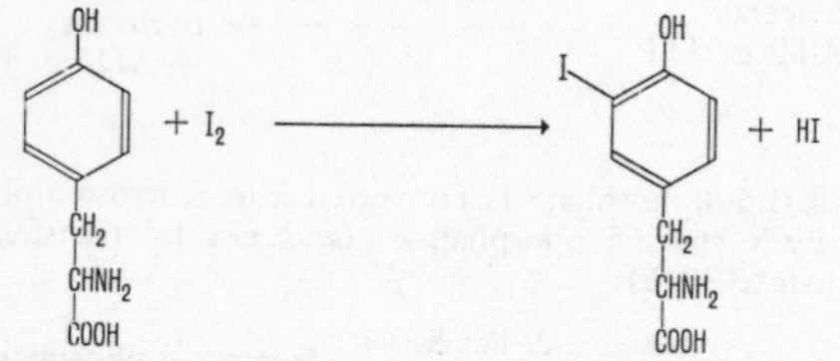

Tyrosine Monoiodotyrosine

(2)

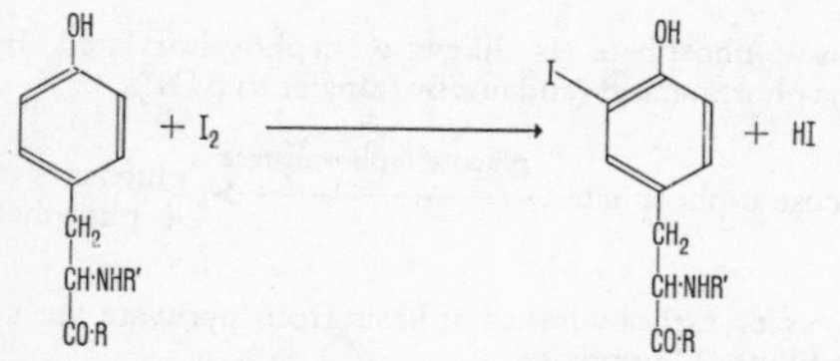

Protein-bound tyrosine Protein-bound monoiodotyrosine

(3)

Monoiodotyrosine + Protein-bound monoiodotyrosine + I_2

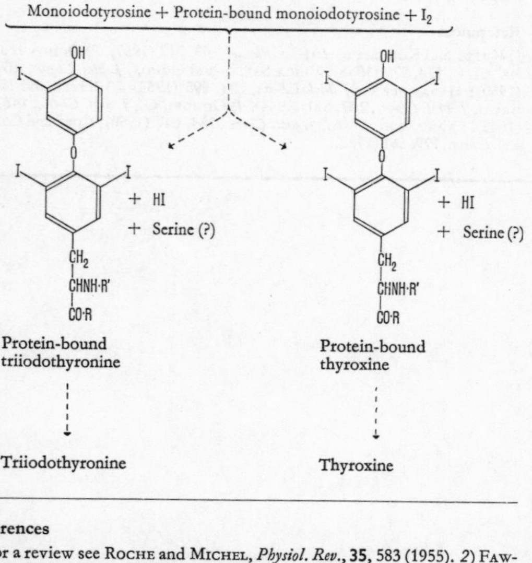

Protein-bound triiodothyronine Protein-bound thyroxine

Triiodothyronine Thyroxine

References

1) For a review see ROCHE and MICHEL, *Physiol. Rev.*, **35**, 583 (1955). *2)* FAWCETT and KIRKWOOD, *J. biol. Chem.*, **209**, 249 (1954); TAUROG et al., *J. biol. Chem.*, **213**, 119 (1955).

Formation of melanin from tyrosine[1]

Melanin is the pigment of vertebrate skin, hair, feathers and eyes. It is a complex and nonhomogeneous substance. The chief basic unit is 5,6-dihydroxyindole which undergoes polymerization and in the polymerized form combines with protein. It is formed from tyrosine, probably by the following route (this route is blocked in albinism):

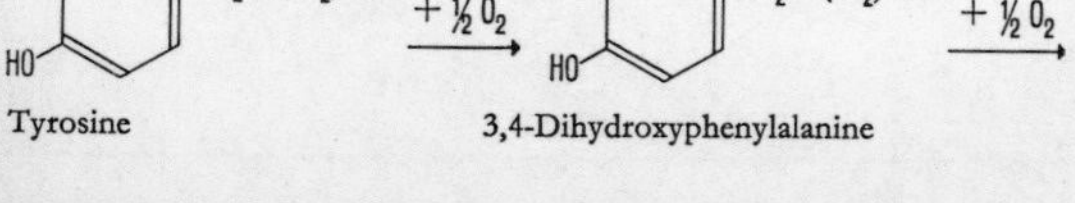

Tyrosine 3,4-Dihydroxyphenylalanine

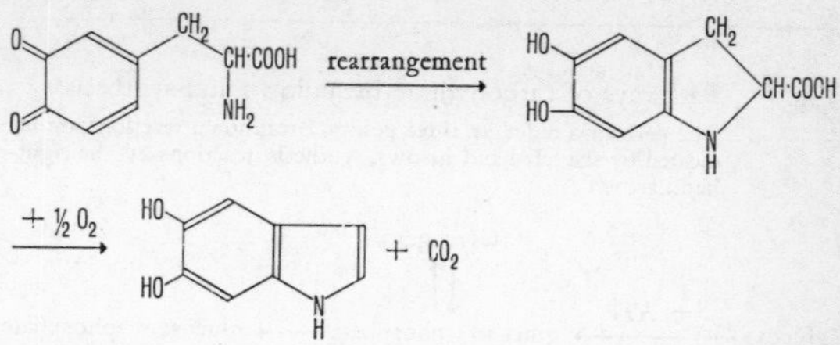

5,6-Dihydroxyindole

References

1) For a review see MASON, H. S., *Advanc. Enzymol.*, **16**, 163 (1955); DALGLIESH, C. E., *Advanc. Protein Chem.*, **10**, 65 (1955).

Formation and degradation of 5-hydroxytryptamine (serotonin)

5-Hydroxytryptamine (serotonin) is assumed to be a transmitter substance at nerve endings; it may play a role in hemostasis, in the control of renal activity, and has probably other functions[1]. It is found in relatively high concentrations in thrombocytes and in the argentaffine cells of the intestinal wall. Its degradation product, 5-hydroxyindoleacetic acid, appears in the urine in abnormal quantities in cases of tumors of the argentaffine cells (argentaffinoma, malignant carcinoid)[2]. 5-Hydroxytryptamine is assumed to be formed from tryptophan by the following reactions[3]:

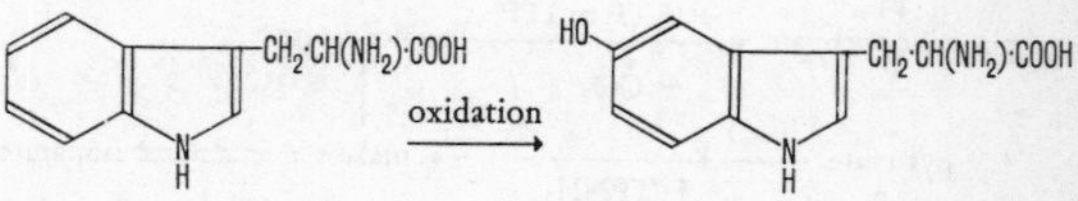

Tryptophan 5-Hydroxytryptophan

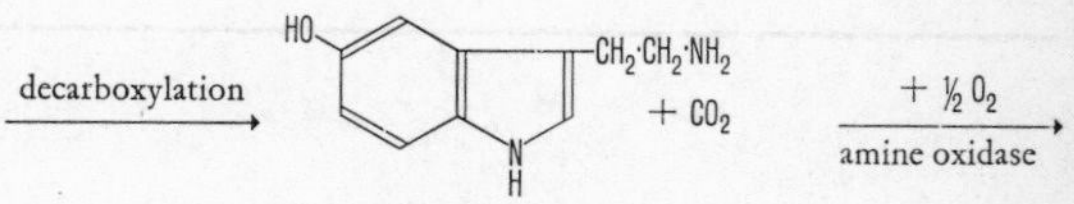

5-Hydroxytryptamine (serotonin)

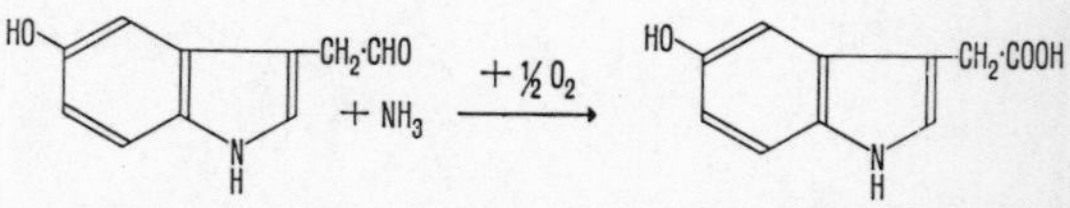

5-Hydroxyindoleacetaldehyde 5-Hydroxyindoleacetic acid

References

1) PAGE, I. H., *Physiol. Rev.*, **34**, 563 (1954); ERSPAMER, V., *Pharmacol. Rev.*, **6**, 425 (1954); SPECTOR and WILLOUGHBY, *Nature*, **179**, 318 (1957). *2)* PAGE et al., *Lancet*, **1**, 198 (1955); PERNOW and WALDENSTRÖM, *Lancet*, **2**, 951 (1954). *3)* UDENFRIEND et al., *J. Amer. chem. Soc.*, **75**, 501 (1953); DALGLIESH, C. E., *Advanc. Protein Chem.*, **10**, 103 (1955); DALGLIESH, C. E., *Biochem. J.*, **64**, 481 (1956); DALGLIESH and DUTTON, *Biochem. J.*, **65**, 21P (1957).

Synthesis of carbohydrate from amino acids and other non-carbohydrate precursors (gluconeogenesis)

Glucose can be formed from lactate, pyruvate, glycerol and a number of amino acids: glutamic acid, aspartic acid, alanine, arginine, proline, hydroxyproline, histidine, serine, glycine and valine. The common metabolic property of all glucose-formers is the ability to yield pyruvate (or phosphopyruvate). The pathway from pyruvate to glucose includes most steps of the anaerobic glycolysis (Table 3, page 401) in reverse, but at three stages special reactions occur[1]. These circumvent the energy barriers which would prevent a simple reversal of glycolysis. The three stages are:

Fig. 14 Pathways of carbohydrate breakdown and synthesis[1]

The pathways differ at three points. Breakdown reactions are indicated by the left-hand arrows, synthesis reactions by the right-hand arrows

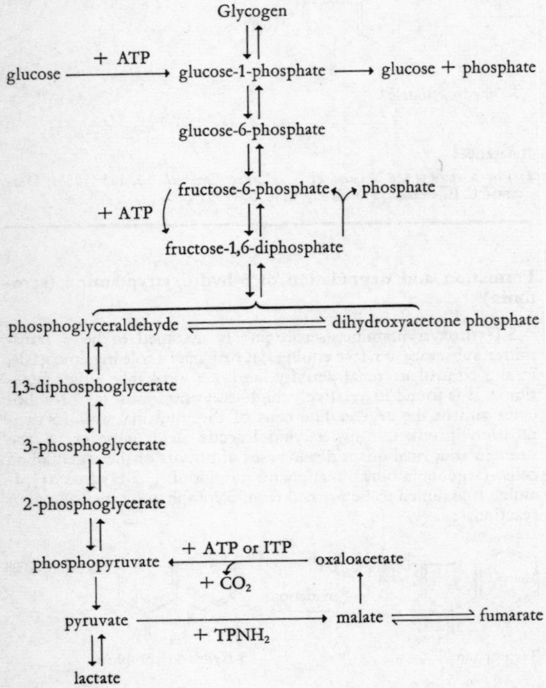

(*a*) The formation of phosphopyruvate from pyruvate. The special reactions by which phosphopyruvate is formed are:

$$\text{pyruvate} + TPNH_2 + CO_2 \xrightarrow[2]{\text{malic enzyme}} \text{malate} + TPN$$

$$\text{malate} + \tfrac{1}{2}O_2 \xrightarrow{\text{malic dehydrogenase system}} \text{oxaloacetate} + H_2O$$

$$\begin{matrix}\text{oxaloacetate} \\ + \text{ ATP or ITP}\end{matrix} \xrightarrow[3]{\text{Utter-Kurahashi enzyme}} \begin{matrix}\text{phospho-} \\ \text{pyruvate} \\ + \text{ ADP or IDP}\end{matrix}$$

(*b*) Fructose-1,6-diphosphate is converted into fructose-6-phosphate by a specific phosphatase[4] (and not by transfer of phosphate to ADP):

$$\begin{matrix}\text{fructose-1,6-} \\ \text{diphosphate}\end{matrix} \xrightarrow{\text{hexose diphosphatase}} \begin{matrix}\text{fructose-6-phosphate} \\ + \text{ phosphate}\end{matrix}$$

(*c*) Glucose-6-phosphate is likewise dephosphorylated by a specific phosphatase[5] (and not by transfer to ADP):

$$\text{glucose-6-phosphate} \xrightarrow{\text{glucose 6-phosphatase}} \begin{matrix}\text{glucose} \\ + \text{ phosphate}\end{matrix}$$

The stages of carbohydrate synthesis from pyruvate are summarized in Figure 14 opposite.

References

1) Krebs and Kornberg, *Ergebn. Physiol.*, **49**, 212 (1957). *2*) Ochoa et al., *J. biol. Chem.*, **174**, 979 (1948); Veiga Salles and Ochoa, *J. biol. Chem.*, **187**, 849 (1950); Harary et al., *J. biol. Chem.*, **203**, 595 (1953). *3*) Utter and Kurahashi, *J. biol. Chem.*, **207**, 821 (1954). *4*) Gomori, G., *J. biol. Chem.*, **148**, 139 (1943). *5*) Swanson, M. A., *J. biol. Chem.*, **184**, 647 (1950); Cori and Cori, *J. biol. Chem.*, **199**, 661 (1952).

A number of metabolic processes do not fall under the headings of either energy supply or synthesis of cell constituents. Their common feature is the disposal of potentially harmful substances. In other words they contribute towards the maintenance of the physiological environment. These metabolic processes are commonly referred to as "detoxication mechanisms".

Quantitatively the most important detoxication mechanism is the conversion of surplus nitrogen, in particular surplus ammonium ions, into urea (see below). Other detoxication reactions concern the disposal of certain ingested materials (e.g. benzoic acid) and of drugs. Information on the intermediary metabolism of detoxication mechanisms is summarized in Table 21 below and in the section which follows.

Synthesis of urea[1]

Most of the surplus nitrogen arising in the mammalian body is excreted in the form of urea. The synthesis of urea from ammonia and carbon dioxide proceeds by a cyclical mechanism. The concept of the urea cycle was originally based on the observation that ornithine, citrulline and arginine stimulate urea production in the presence of ammonia without being themselves consumed in the process[2]. Since it was proposed, this concept has received support from many other experiments[1]. The reactions of the cycle involve the stepwise building-up of the urea structure on the δ-amino group of ornithine. The building-up process is completed with the formation of arginine, which is then hydrolyzed by arginase to yield urea and ornithine.

Before one molecule each of ammonia and carbon dioxide enter the cycle, they react to form carbamyl phosphate. The synthesis of this compound requires ATP, and has been tentatively formulated as follows[3,4]:

(1) $CO_2 + NH_3 \longrightarrow H_2N{-}COOH$ (not established)

Carbamic acid

(2) $H_2N{-}COOH + 2\,ATP \rightarrow H_2N{-}\overset{\overset{\large C}{\|}}{C}{-}O{-}\overset{\overset{\large O}{\|}}{\underset{\underset{\large OH}{|}}{P}}{-}OH + 2\,ADP$ + orthophosphate

Carbamic acid — Carbamyl phosphate

Reaction (**2**) is stimulated by acetyl glutamate and by other acyl glutamates[5]. It is probable that acetyl glutamate is the compound normally involved since it occurs in mammalian liver[6]. In bacteria the stimulation by acetyl glutamate does not occur, and only one molecule of ATP is utilized per molecule of carbamyl phosphate formed. The nature of the action of acetyl glutamate is obscure. Carbamyl phosphate reacts with ornithine to yield citrulline[3,7]:

(3) 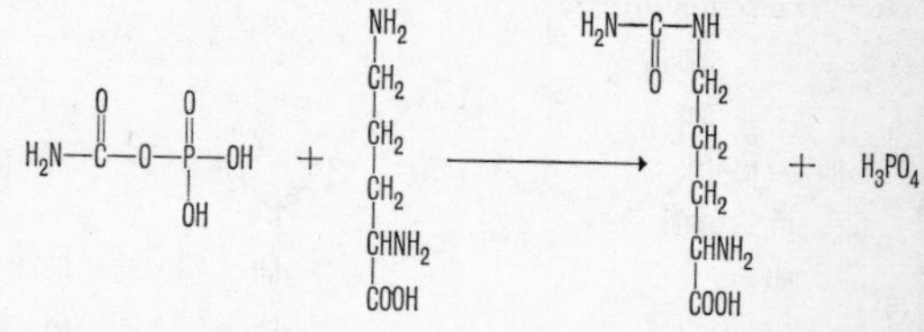

Carbamyl phosphate — Ornithine — Citrulline

Citrulline next condenses with aspartic acid to form argininosuccinic acid[8], a process which requires ATP:

(4) 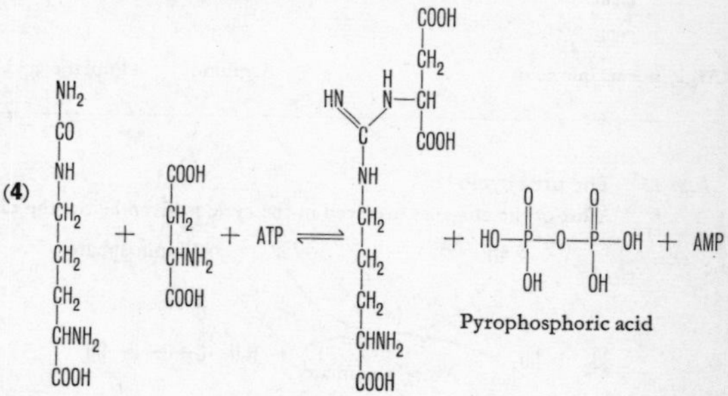

Citrulline — Aspartic acid — Argininosuccinic acid

Reaction (**4**) is freely reversible, but under physiological conditions it proceeds only from left to right because of the presence of a highly active pyrophosphatase[9]:

Table 21 Detoxication mechanisms

Reaction	Examples of compounds detoxicated	Product formed	Mechanism
Acetylation	Sulfanilamide	Acetylsulfanilamide	See page 447
Methylation	Nicotinamide	N-Methylnicotinamide	The methyl group is derived from methionine probably via S-adenosylmethionine (see page 440)
Glycine conjugation	Benzoic acid	Hippuric acid	See page 448
Alkyl- and aryl-glucuronide formation	Alcohols and phenols (menthol and phenol)	Menthyl- and phenyl-glucuronide	R·OH + uridine diphosphoglucuronic acid→ 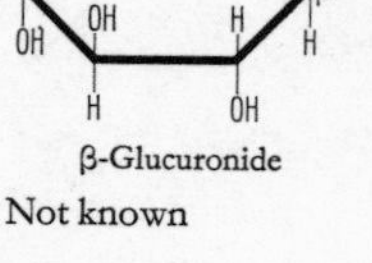 + uridine diphosphate β-Glucuronide
Acyl-glucuronide formation	Aromatic acids (benzoic acid) and branched-chain aliphatic acids	Benzoylglucuronide	Not known
Sulfate ester formation	Phenols	Phenyl sulfate	See page 448
Glutamine conjugation	Phenylacetic acid	Phenacetylglutamine	See page 448
Mercapturic acid formation	Naphthalene, alkyl halides	Naphthylmercapturic acid	See page 448

(5) 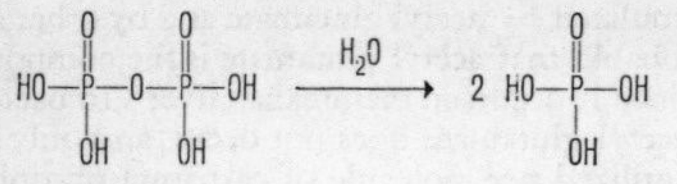

Pyrophosphoric acid Orthophosphoric acid

Argininosuccinate reacts further to give arginine and fumarate[10] by reaction (6):

(6) 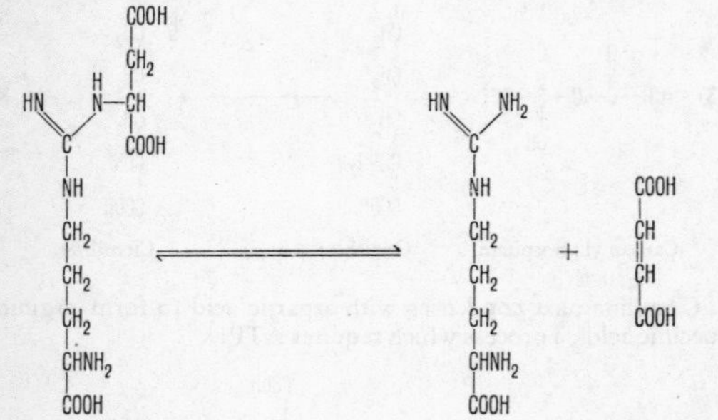

Argininosuccinic acid Arginine Fumaric acid

This is followed by the hydrolysis of arginine to ornithine and urea. Ornithine can then undergo the same sequence of reactions, starting with reaction (3):

(7) 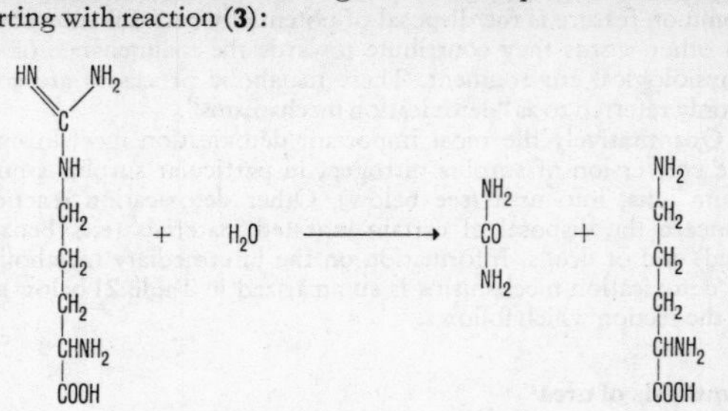

Arginine Urea Ornithine

The cyclic sequence of the reactions is shown in Figure 15, below. As formulated here, one molecule each of carbon dioxide and ammonia are utilized for every molecule of urea produced. The second nitrogen atom of the urea molecule is supplied by aspartic acid. The latter is regenerated by transamination between glutamate and oxaloacetate. Glutamate in turn can be regenerated in two ways, either by transamination between various

Fig. 15 The urea cycle

A list of the enzymes involved in the cycle is given below the diagram

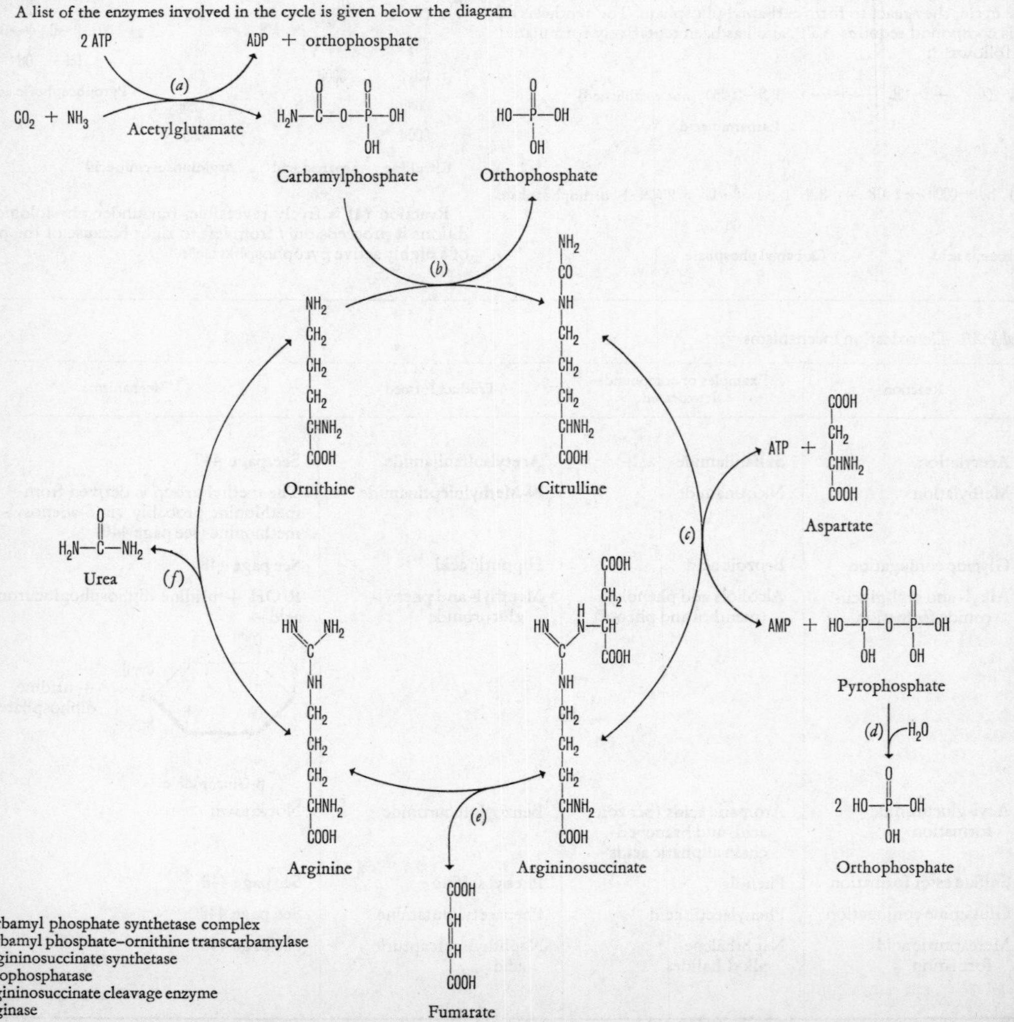

Enzymes

(*a*) Carbamyl phosphate synthetase complex
(*b*) Carbamyl phosphate–ornithine transcarbamylase
(*c*) Argininosuccinate synthetase
(*d*) Pyrophosphatase
(*e*) Argininosuccinate cleavage enzyme
(*f*) Arginase

Fig. 16 Utilization and regeneration of aspartate in the synthesis of urea

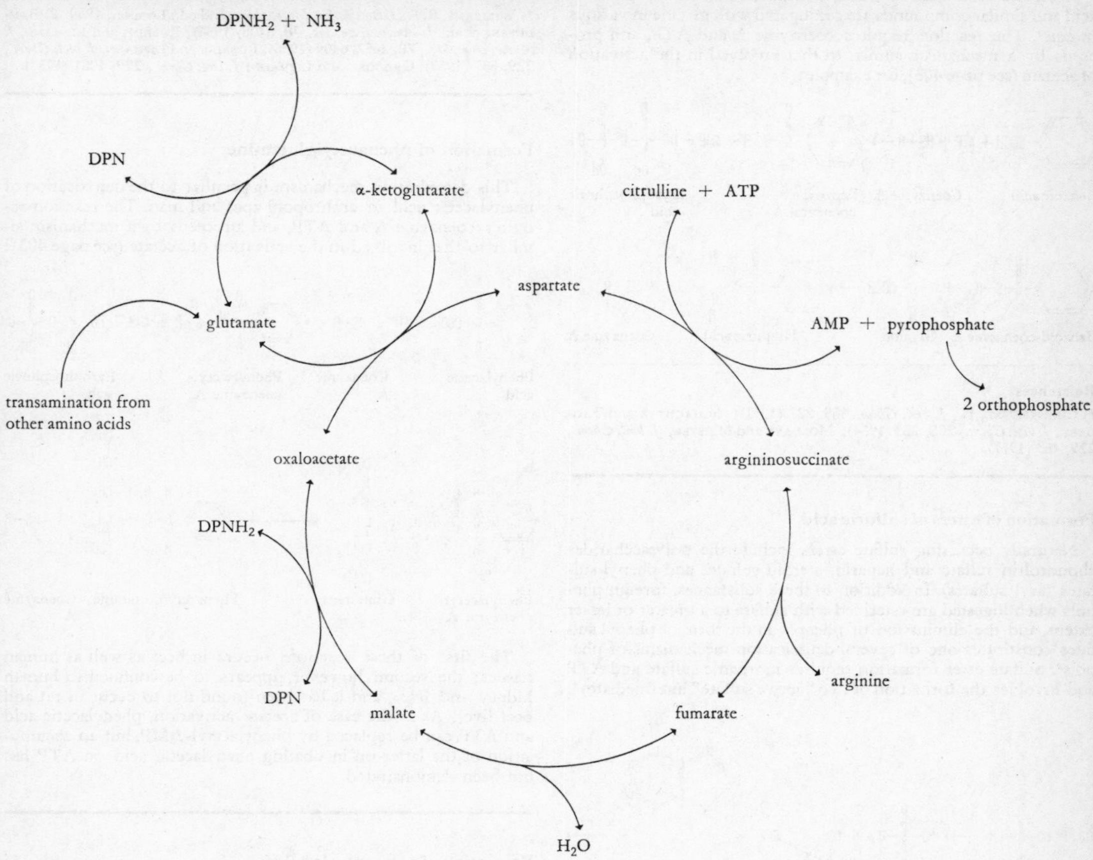

amino acids and α-ketoglutarate (see page 405) or by reductive amination from ammonia and α-ketoglutarate[11]:

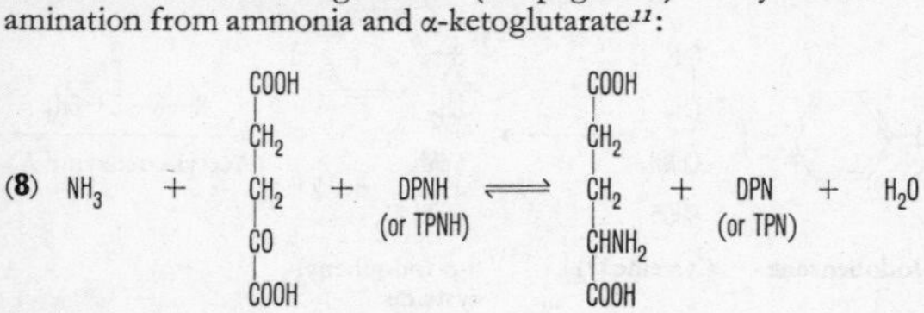

Ammonia α-Ketoglutaric acid Glutamic acid

The second nitrogen atom of urea must thus pass through glutamate and aspartate but not necessarily through the stage of ammonia. The supply of aspartate for reaction (**4**) involves two cycles which are subsidiary to the main urea cycle shown in Figure 15. These subsidiary processes are shown in Figure 16, above.

References

1) For reviews see KREBS, H. A., in SUMNER and MYRBÄCK (Eds.), *The Enzymes*, vol. II, part 2, New York, 1952, page 866; RATNER, S., *Advanc. Enzymol.*, **15**, 319 (1954). *2)* KREBS and HENSELEIT, *Hoppe-Seyl. Z. physiol. Chem.*, **210**, 33 (1932). *3)* JONES et al., *J. Amer. chem. Soc.*, **77**, 819 (1955). *4)* METZENBERG et al., *J. biol. Chem.*, **229**, 1019 (1957). *5)* GRISOLIA and COHEN, *J. biol. Chem.*, **204**, 753 (1953). *6)* HALL et al., *Nature*, **178**, 1468 (1956). *7)* BURNETT and COHEN, *J. biol. Chem.*, **229**, 337 (1957). *8)* RATNER et al., *J. biol. Chem.*, **204**, 95 (1953). *9)* RATNER and PETRACK, *Arch. Biochem. Biophys.*, **65**, 582 (1956). *10)* RATNER et al., *J. biol. Chem.*, **204**, 115 (1953). *11)* OLSON and ANFINSEN, *J. biol. Chem.*, **202**, 841 (1953).

Acetylation of amines[1]

Many aromatic and aliphatic amines are acetylated in the body. These include sulfanilamide, *p*-aminobenzoic acid, *p*-nitraniline and others[2]. In general, the acetylated amines are less toxic than the unacetylated compounds. However, in some cases the low solubility of acetylated amines can render them harmful owing to their crystallization in the urinary tract.

The acetylation reaction proceeds via acetyl-coenzyme A (see page 403), for example:

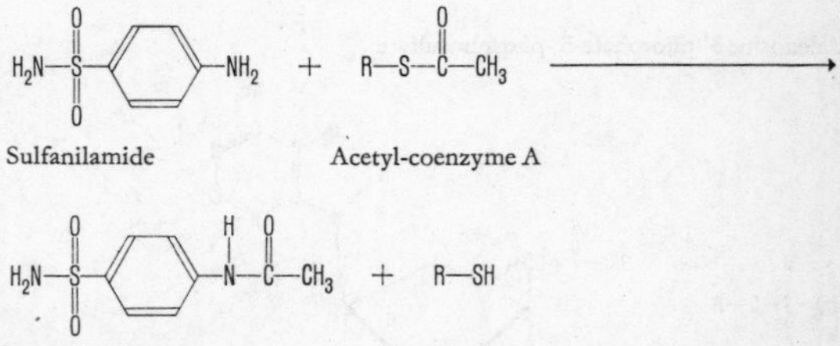

References

1) TABOR et al., *J. biol. Chem.*, **204**, 127 (1953); LIPMANN, F., *Bact. Rev.*, **17**, 1 (1953). *2)* WILLIAMS, R.T., *Detoxication Mechanisms*, 2nd ed., London, 1959.

Formation of glycine conjugates

Aromatic acids such as benzoic acid, nicotinic acid, cinnamic acid and similar compounds are conjugated with glycine in various organs[1]. The reaction requires coenzyme A and ATP, and proceeds by a mechanism similar to that involved in the activation of acetate (see page 403), for example:

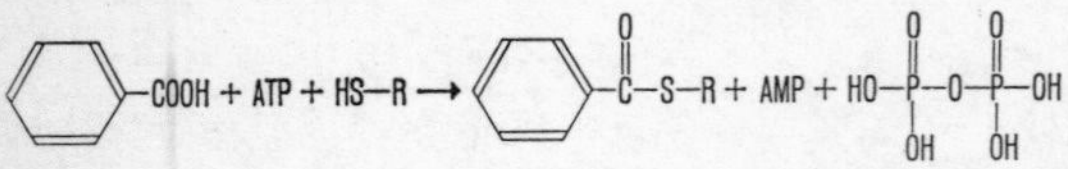

Benzoic acid Coenzyme A Benzoyl-coenzyme A Pyrophosphoric acid

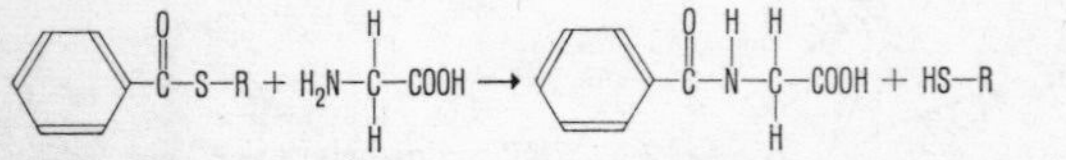

Benzoyl-coenzyme A Glycine Hippuric acid Coenzyme A

References

1) Chantrenne, H., *J. biol. Chem.*, **189**, 227 (1951); Schachter and Taggart, *J. biol. Chem.*, **208**, 263 (1954); Moldave and Meister, *J. biol. Chem.*, **229**, 463 (1957).

Formation of esters of sulfuric acid

Naturally occurring sulfate esters include the polysaccharides chondroitin sulfate and heparin, steroid sulfates and phenyl sulfates (aryl sulfates). In addition to these substances, foreign phenols when ingested are esterified with sulfate to a greater or lesser extent, and the elimination of phenols in the form of phenyl sulfates constitutes one of several detoxication mechanisms of phenols[1]. Sulfate ester formation requires inorganic sulfate and ATP and involves the formation of two "active sulfate" intermediates[2]:

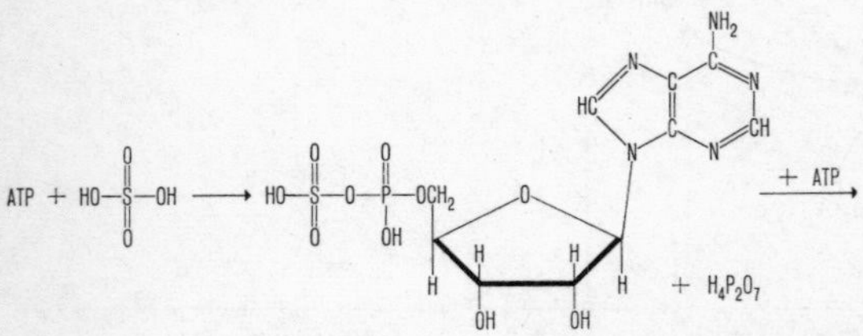

Adenosine 5′-phosphosulfate Pyrophosphoric acid

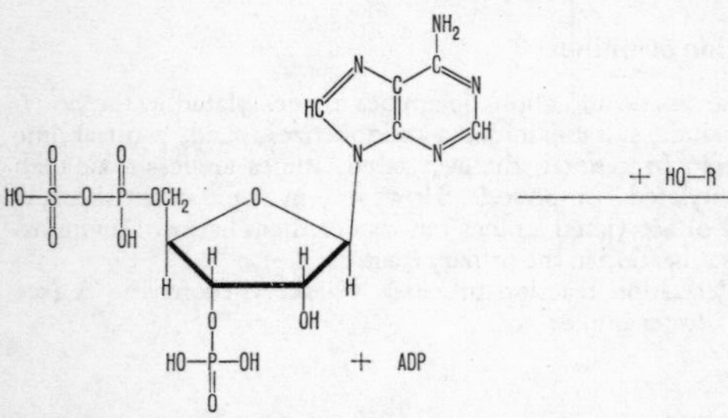

Adenosine 3′-phosphate-5′-phosphosulfate

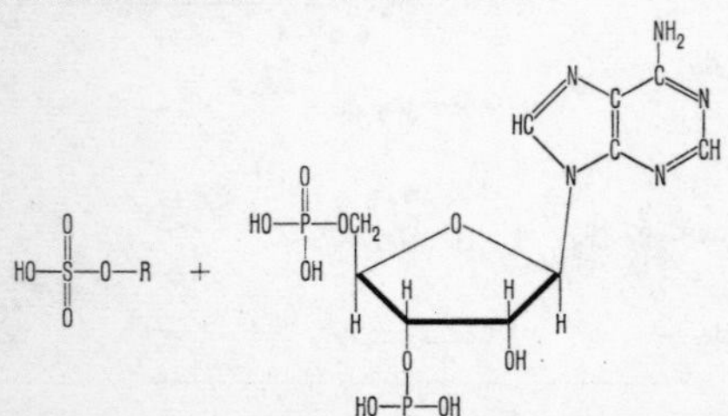

Sulfate ester Adenosine 3′,5′-diphosphate

References

1) Williams, R.T., *Detoxication Mechanisms*, 2nd ed., London, 1959. *2)* Bandurski et al., *J. Amer. chem. Soc.*, **78**, 6408 (1956); Robbins and Lipmann, *J. Amer. chem. Soc.*, **78**, 2652, 6409 (1956); Robbins and Lipmann, *J. biol. Chem.*, **229**, 837 (1957); Gregory and Lipmann, *J. biol. Chem.*, **229**, 1081 (1957).

Formation of phenacetylglutamine

This detoxication mechanism is peculiar to the detoxication of phenylacetic acid in anthropoid apes and man. The reaction requires coenzyme A and ATP, and proceeds by a mechanism similar to that involved in the activation of acetate (see page 403):

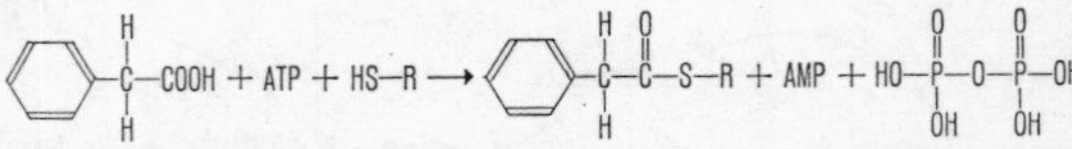

Phenylacetic acid Coenzyme A Phenylacetyl-coenzyme A Pyrophosphoric acid

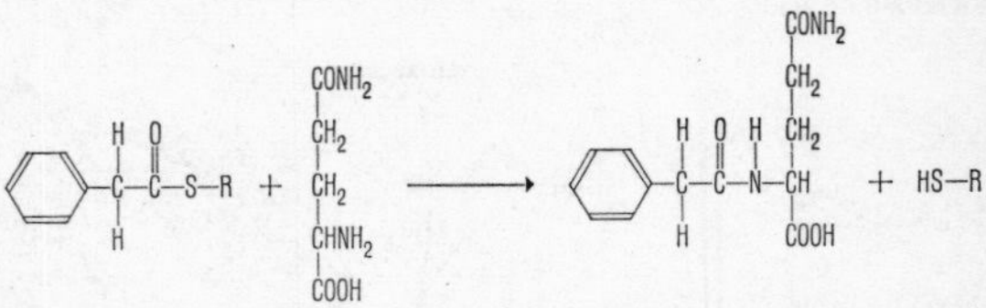

Phenylacetyl-coenzyme A Glutamine Phenacetylglutamine Coenzyme A

The first of these reactions occurs in beef as well as human tissues; the second however, appears to be confined to human kidney and liver, and it has been found not to occur in rat and beef liver. As in the case of acetate activation, phenylacetic acid and ATP can be replaced by phenylacetyl-AMP, but an accumulation of the latter on incubating phenylacetic acid on ATP has not been demonstrated.

Formation of mercapturic acids

A number of aromatic compounds (e.g. halogenobenzenes, naphthalene) give rise on ingestion to mercapturic acids (N-acetyl-S-arylcysteines)[1]. The mechanism of formation of these compounds is not known, but it probably proceeds as follows[1,2]:

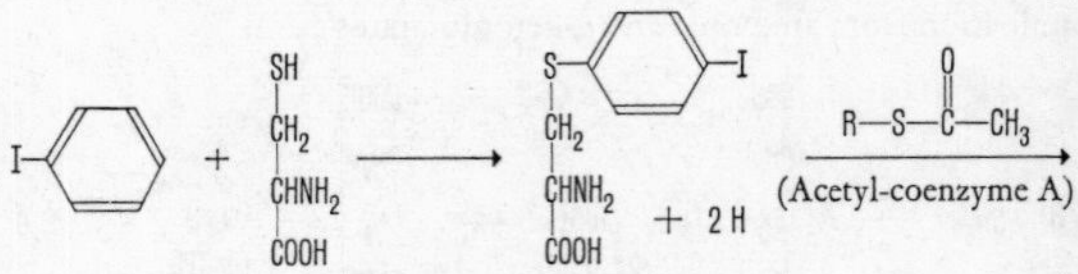

Iodobenzene Cysteine (?) S-*p*-Iodophenyl-cysteine

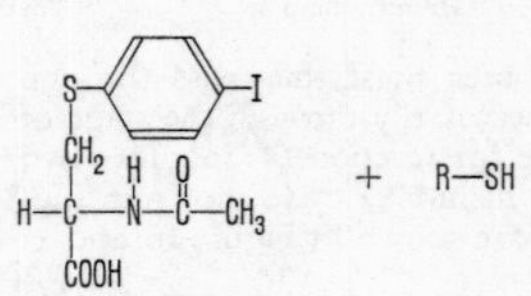

p-Iodophenylmercapturic acid (N-acetyl-S-*p*-iodophenyl cysteine) Coenzyme A

References

1) Williams, R.T., *Detoxication Mechanisms*, 2nd ed., London, 1959. *2)* Mills and Wood, *J. biol. Chem.*, **207**, 695 (1954).

In compiling this review of vitamins and related substances (pages 449–472) the editors have made use of the following standard works in addition to numerous papers from the current literature: BICKNELL and PRESCOTT, *The Vitamins in Medicine*, 2nd ed., London, 1946; CLARK, G. W., *A Vitamin Digest*, Springfield, 1953; GYÖRGY, P. (Ed.), *Vitamin Methods*, vol. II, New York, 1951; ROBINSON, F. A., *The Vitamin B Complex*, London, 1951; SEBRELL and HARRIS (Eds.), *The Vitamins*, vol. III, New York, 1954; SPECTOR, W. S. (Ed.), *Handbook of Biological Data*, Philadelphia, 1956; SUNDERMAN and BOERNER, *Normal Values in Clinical Medicine*, Philadelphia, 1950; THOMPSON and KING (Eds.), *Biochemical Disorders in Human Disease*, London, 1957; Recent Research on Vitamins, *Brit. med. Bull.*, **12**, No. 1 (1956); *Annual Review of Biochemistry*, Palo Alto, Cal.; *Vitamins and Hormones*, New York.

Vitamin A

Vitamin A occurs in nature in three or more forms (vitamers), either as free alcohol or ester. It is found only in the animal kingdom. The yellow or reddish crystalline A-vitamers are soluble in fats, insoluble in water, easily oxidized but in the absence of oxygen stable to acids, alkalis and heat.

In the vegetable kingdom only their precursors, the carotenes, occur. Carotenes can be converted into vitamin A by the animal organism; measured by biological effect, 1 part of carotene gives rise to 1 part of vitamin (see below under Physiology). Of the nine known carotenes the most important for the animal organism are α-, β- and γ-carotene and cryptoxanthine, the most active being β-carotene, with about twice the activity of the other carotenes.

β-Carotene, $C_{40}H_{56}$
Red crystals
Mol. wt. 536.89
M. p. 181–182° C
Absorpt. max. 4640, 4650 Å (benzene)
4550, 4560 Å (cyclohexane)

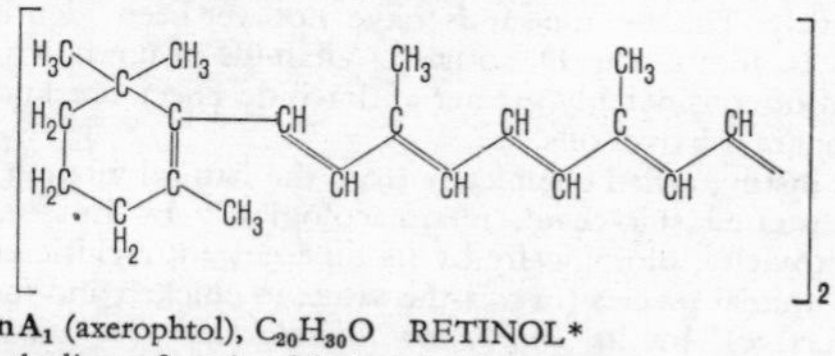

Vitamin A_1 (axerophtol), $C_{20}H_{30}O$ RETINOL*
From the liver of marine fish (cod, halibut, shark)
Mol.wt. 286.46
M.p. 63–64° C
Absorpt. max. 3280 Å

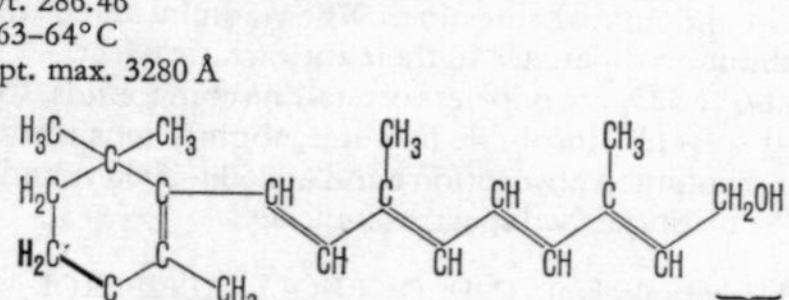

RETINAL: CHO

Vitamin A_2, $C_{20}H_{28}O$ DEHYDRORETINOL
From the liver of freshwater fish
Mol.wt. 284.44

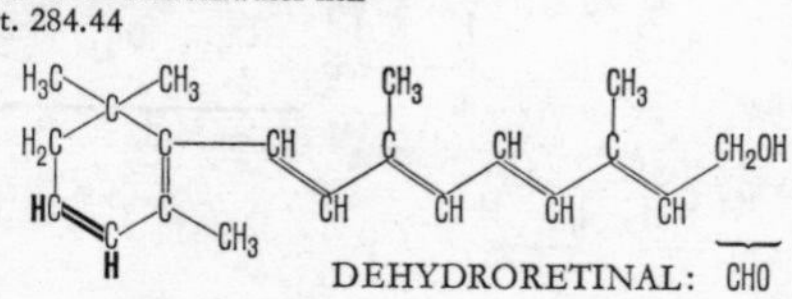

DEHYDRORETINAL: CHO

Units

Vitamin A:

1 international unit (I.U.) = 0.0003 mg pure vitamin A_1 (alcohol) = 0.000 344 mg all *trans* vitamin A_1 acetate.

1 U.S. Pharmacopeia unit (USP) = 1 international unit.

Carotene:

1 international unit = 0.0006 mg β-carotene, equivalent in activity to 1 I.U. of vitamin A.

Methods of test and assay

In the U.S.A., the growth test on standardized vitamin A deficient rats is the official test for pharmaceutical preparations. The carotenes are determined colorimetrically after chromatographic separation (modified CARR-PRICE test), the vitamin is determined by colorimetric and spectrometric methods.

Occurrence (values in I.U. of vitamin A per 100 g weight fresh)

Vitamin A:

fish liver oils: halibut 2–5 million; tunny 0.5–8 million; cod 100,000; sardines 4800–54,000.

Carotenes:

palm oil 50,000–500,000; parsley 8000; dandelion leaves 12,000; spinach 9000.

Vitamin A + carotenes:

calf liver 27,000; liver of other domesticated animals 2700–50,000; eggyolk (dark) 3200; cow's milk 130 (winter) – 1000 (summer, autumn); human milk 350; colostrum 600.

Physiology

Carotenes. The carotenes are widely distributed in the vegetable kingdom and can be converted by most vertebrates into vitamin A (exceptions are the true carnivores, such as cats, whose source of the vitamin is the liver and meat they eat). The conversion takes place in the small intestine[1] but other organs, such as the muscles and lungs, and serum also possess this function[2]. Invertebrates cannot effect this conversion.

The process consists of successive partial oxidations[3] and takes place in such a manner that out of one molecule of carotene only one molecule of the vitamin is formed instead of the two molecules which would be expected from the formulas. *Infants and young children can convert carotene into vitamin A in only very limited amounts.* The carotenoids and vitamin A of marine invertebrates are an important source of the vitamin for marine fish. The conversion of carotene into vitamin A is diminished in diseases of the intestine, liver or kidneys and also in diabetes and phosphorus poisoning.

In athyroidism and hypothyroidism the conversion is almost completely blocked[4]. It should be noted that carotene is absorbed very incompletely from vegetable foods.

The liver stores considerably more vitamin A when the latter is consumed as such than when it is consumed in the form of carotenes. The organism appears to limit its conversion of carotenes in accordance with its day to day requirements of vitamin A.

The carotene level in blood varies greatly with the diet and amounts on the average to 200–300 µg per 100 ml plasma[5, 6]. It is increased physiologically in pregnancy (parallel with the vitamin E level)[7] but decreases markedly in late pregnancy[24]. In the fetus, the vitamin A and carotene levels are both higher than in the mother. The carotene blood level is increased pathologically in athyroidism and diabetes.

Vitamin A. The absorption of vitamin A from fats, in which it occurs mainly in the form of esters, takes place efficiently and rapidly in the presence of bile acid salts (ca. 80 %), the blood level reaching a maximum about 3–4 hours after intake. During the following 8–10 hours the blood level returns to normal. The absorption of the water-soluble preparations of vitamin A, such as the crystalline acetate or the pure vitamin (alcohol), is even better, the latter being the most rapidly absorbed[8]. The average blood level amounts to 100–300 I.U./100 ml serum, the level being lower in winter. In the newborn the fetal blood level is largely independent of the mother's blood level and is often higher, although never above the normal value.

Vitamin A is stored principally in the liver (ca. 22,000 I.U. per 100 g) but also in the lungs, kidneys, gonads and adrenals; in other organs it occurs only in traces. The vitamin A content of the liver falls ca. 50 % in hypertonia, gastrointestinal ulcers, syphilis and endocarditis, even more in diseases of the blood vessels and septicemia, and most of all in chronic nephritis and diseases of the gallbladder and kidneys.

In febrile conditions there is in general a progressive loss of vitamin A. During recovery the temperature first becomes normal, then the vitamin A content, and finally the erythrocyte sedimentation rate[9]. Severe physical exertion also causes a marked decrease of the blood level of vitamin A. A fall in the liver level occurs without any increase in temperature shortly prior to death.

In the healthy organism, vitamin A is not excreted by the kidney; in disease (pneumonia, for example) however, excretion may be as high as 3000 I.U. per day.

Owing to the large reserves in the liver, deficiency of the vitamin develops only very slowly. The carotenes first disappear

* Names printed in capitals are internationally recognized names. Cf. *Commission on the Nomenclature of Biological Chemistry* (International Union of Pure and Applied Chemistry), *J. Amer. chem. Soc.*, **82**, 5575 (1960).

from the plasma, although the vitamin A level may remain normal for as long as two years. The daily requirement in health is 2500 I.U. vitamin A, or in the form of carotenes 4000 I.U. in oily solution, 7500 I.U. in green vegetables, 12,000 I.U. in cooked carrots[6]. For dietary allowances recommended by the National Research Council (U.S.A.) see page 498.

Function

The carotenes as such have no function but simply serve as the material from which vitamin A is formed.

Vitamin A aldehydes are the prosthetic groups of the photosensitive pigments in the retinal rods (dim-light vision) and cones (bright-light and color vision), the specific protein moiety being named opsin. Four pigments are known, rhodopsin (retinal and rod opsin) in land and marine animals, iodopsin (retinal and cone opsin) in land animals, porphyropsin (dehydroretinal and rod opsin) in fresh-water animals, and cyanopsin (dehydroretinal and cone opsin) in fresh-water fish. Lack of vitamin A increases the adaptation time from cone to rod vision from the normal 8 to ca. 30–45 minutes[10, 11].

Although its presence in epithelium cannot be demonstrated, vitamin A exerts a direct effect on this tissue, but whether it acts in trace amounts or as a catalyst is not known. In vitamin A deficiency, hyperkeratosis of the epithelium develops. In tissue cultures containing much vitamin A, ectoderm changes into mucosa with ciliated epithelium, while normally only epithelium is formed (metaplasia). This change is reversible[11, 12].

In the bones and teeth, as a result of changes in the osteoblasts and odontoblasts, vitamin A deficiency leads to the formation of inferior bone tissue and dentine. During growth this can cause hypoplasia of the hard tooth substance and bone deformities[13].

The blood level of vitamin A in normal women falls markedly during menstruation but later becomes normal; maximal values appear about the 14th and the 25th day of the menstrual period, corresponding to the increased requirements of the organism during the proliferation of the uterine mucosa and ovulation. In dysmenorrhea and oligomenorrhea these fluctuations may be more or less completely absent. Among its other functions vitamin A also acts as a peripheral antagonist to estrogens[14].

Lack of vitamin A has important effects in pregnancy and is a cause of infertility in animals as well as of malformations in immature offspring[15]. Animals deficient in the vitamin show a high percentage of stillbirths; in the fetus there is also a tendency to hydrocephalus, and atrophy of the optic nerve caused by bone compression has been observed[16]. Vitamin A has a prophylactic action against infections (for example, influenza) as well as antiallergic properties when given in high doses[17].

Toxicology

Vitamin A is to a certain extent toxic. The liver of the polar bear and fox is poisonous to man because of its high content of the vitamin. In prolonged treatment with high doses hypervitaminosis may appear. Clinically, signs in adults are fatigue, insomnia, pains in the bones and joints, affections of the skin and mucosa. Decalcification of the bones may lead to spontaneous fractures and internal hemorrhages[18]. In certain cases persistent headache with vertigo may simulate tumor of the brain or serous meningitis[19]. Young children show restlessness, anorexia, orthostatic disturbances, swelling of the bones of the extremities and of the diaphyses caused by swelling of the cartilage and periosteum. Alopecia and pruritus may also occur[20]. All these symptoms are reversible and disappear when vitamin A treatment is stopped[20].

MELLANBY[21] regards vitamins A (osteoclastic) and D (osteoblastic) as being more or less complementary.

Therapeutic applications

Prophylactic: In long-continued febrile diseases and in impairment of absorption, conversion or storage of the vitamin (see above). Also in prolonged cortisone therapy, since this is accompanied by a large consumption of vitamin A.

Curative:

(*a*) in hemeralopia in children and in progressively defective twilight and night vision;

(*b*) in hyperkeratosis, in inflammations and infections of the skin and mucosae and in xerophthalmia;

(*c*) in the premenstrual syndrome (hyperestrogenism)[22];

(*d*) in skin complaints (very high doses): peroral administration leads to a marked rise in the blood level, whereas the injected vitamin is stored in the liver without a substantial increase of the serum value[23].

References: *1)* THOMPSON et al., *Brit. J. Nutr.*, **3**, 50 (1949). *2)* BIERI and POLLARD, *Brit. J. Nutr.*, **8**, 32 (1954). *3)* GLOVER and REDFEARN, *Biochem. J.*, **58**, xv (1954). *4)* Editorial, *J. Amer. med. Ass.*, **137**, 91 (1948). *5)* KIRK and CHIEFFI, *J. Nutr.*, **36**, 315 (1948). *6)* HUME and KREBS, *Spec. Rep. Ser. med. Res. Coun. (Lond.)*, No. 264 (1949). *7)* DARBY et al., *Ann. N.Y. Acad. Sci.*, **52**, 328 (1949). *8)* KAGAN et al., *J. Nutr.*, **40**, 275 (1950); WEEK and SEVIGNE, *J. Nutr.*, **40**, 563 (1950). *9)* JACOBS et al., *Amer. J. clin. Nutr.*, **2**, 155 (1954). *10)* WALD, G., *Science*, **109**, 482 (1949); WALD and HUBBARD, *J. gen. Physiol.*, **32**, 367 (1949). *11)* MORTON, R. A., *J. Sci. Food Agric.*, **6**, 349 (1955). *12)* FELL and MELLANBY, *J. Physiol. (Lond.)*, **119**, 470 (1953). *13)* IRVING, J. T., *Med. Klin.*, **51**, 690 (1956); IRVING and RICHARDS, *Brit. J. Nutr.*, **10**, 7 (1956). *14)* LAURENCE and SOBEL, *J. clin. Endocr.*, **13**, 1192 (1953). *15)* WATT and BARLOW, *Vet. Rec.*, **68**, 780 (1956). *16)* MILLEN and WOOLLAM, *J. Neurol. Neurosurg. Psychiat.*, **19**, 17 (1956). *17)* UNDERDAHL and YOUNG, *Virology*, **2**, 415 (1956). *18)* ELLIOTT and DRYER, *J. Amer. med. Ass.*, **161**, 1157 (1956). *19)* GERBER et al., *Amer. J. Med.*, **16**, 729 (1954). *20)* CAFFEY, J. P., *Pediatrics*, **5**, 672 (1950); CAFFEY, J. P., *Pediatric X-Ray Diagnosis*, New York, 1950, page 747. *21)* MELLANBY, E., *J. Physiol. (Lond.)*, **94**, 380 (1938); **99**, 467 (1941). *22)* GEISENDORF, W., *Bull. Féd. Gynéc. Obstét. franç.*, **10**, 3 (1958). *23)* WULF and NIBBE, *Arzneimittel-Forsch.*, **5**, 120 (1955). *24)* BODANSKY et al., *J. clin. Invest.*, **22**, 643 (1943).

Vitamin D

Of this group, only vitamin D_3 occurs naturally in higher animals. It is formed photochemically from 7-dehydrocholesterol (animal provitamin). In plants, substances with strong antirachitic effect are known. Other substances with D-activity and of known chemical structure, vitamins D_2 (calciferol), D_4, D_5 and D_6, are artificially produced by irradiation of ergosterol, of 22-dihydroergosterol, of 7-dehydrositosterol and of 2-dehydrostigmasterol respectively. These compounds have not yet been identified in animals. In addition to D_3, other D vitamins of unknown structure and of considerably greater antirachitic effect are known to be present in fish liver oils.

D_2 is distinguished chemically from the natural vitamin D_3 by its unsaturated side-chain, pharmacologically by its somewhat greater toxicity, biologically by its different antirachitic effect in various animal species (in rats the same, in chicken and monkeys less effective), by its *antirachitic ineffectiveness when administered parenterally* and by the fact that its precursor, ergosterol, is not absorbed in the animal intestine. When administered orally, D_2 and D_3 exhibit no difference in their antirachitic effect.

D_2, D_3, D_4 and D_5 are odorless crystalline compounds, soluble in fats and fat solvents, insoluble in water, slightly sensitive to light. They have a common absorption band at 2600–2900 Å and cannot therefore be distinguished spectroscopically.

Vitamin D_3 (cholecalciferol), $C_{27}H_{44}O$ CHOLECALCIFEROL
Mol.wt. 384.65

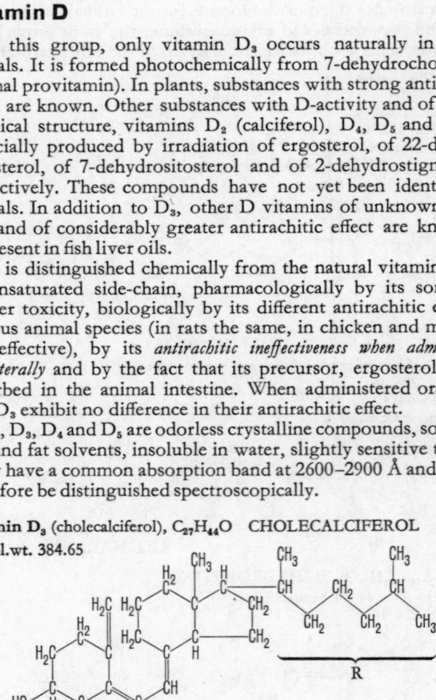

Vitamin D_2 (calciferol [irradiated ergosterol]), $C_{28}H_{44}O$
Mol.wt. 396.66 ERGOCALCIFEROL

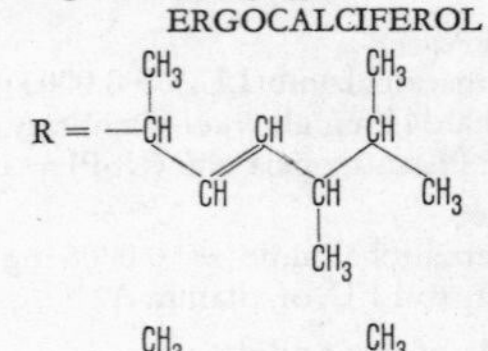

Vitamin D_4, $C_{28}H_{46}O$
Mol.wt. 398.68

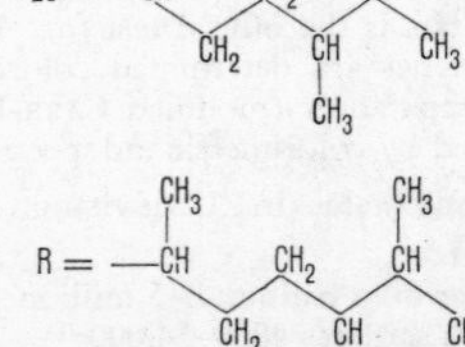

Vitamin D_5, $C_{29}H_{48}O$
Mol.wt. 412.70

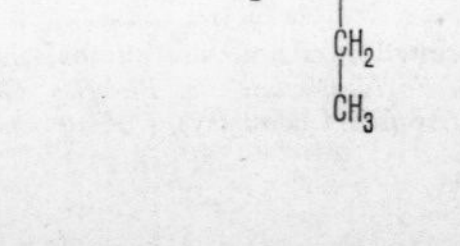

Units

Vitamin D_3:
1 international unit (I. U.) = 0.000 025 mg crystalline vitamin D_3.
1 U.S. Pharmacopeia unit = 1 international unit.
(See also International Standard for vitamin D_3, page 739)

Vitamin D_2:
1 international unit = 1 mg of the international standard preparation of irradiated ergosterol in solution in a vegetable oil.

Methods of test and assay

Antirachitic test on rats (official test in U.S.A. and United Kingdom for pharmaceuticals and foodstuffs).

Occurrence (values in I.U. per 100 g weight fresh)

Fish-liver oils (tunny) 1.6–25 millions, (halibut) 20,000–400,000, (cod) 8000–30,000; egg-yolk 1000; human milk (summer) 2.4–3.8, (winter) 0.3–1.7.

Physiology and function

In man the vitamin is formed by the action of the sun's rays in the outer layers of the skin, in furred animals and birds in the fur or feathers, whence it enters the organism through grooming or licking or by direct absorption. The origin of vitamin D in fish is unknown. As with all the fat-soluble vitamins, bile is necessary for its absorption in the organism.

A large part (up to 70%) of the vitamin ingested is excreted in the feces and some of the remainder is broken down in the liver. The rest is stored in the liver, bones, blood, intestinal wall and kidneys (in decreasing order of importance). The urine of healthy subjects contains no vitamin D. The vitamin formed in the skin is rapidly transported to other organs, the liver being able to store sufficient to meet the needs of the organism for several months. The skin readily absorbs the vitamin present in its superficial layers[1].

The blood level in children and adults is 66–165 I.U. per 100 ml, with seasonal variations. With a daily intake of 50,000–500,000 I.U. the blood level in adults rises to 9000–13,000 I.U. per 100 ml.

Vitamin D regulates calcium and phosphorus balance by direct action on phosphorus metabolism. It mobilizes the phosphorus from the soft tissues and participates in the conversion of organic into inorganic phosphorus and in phosphorus metabolism during muscular work. By its regulation of phosphorus metabolism vitamin D also regulates calcium metabolism.

It promotes calcium absorption and the formation of the calcium phosphate in the blood necessary for the growth of bone.

Deficiency of vitamin D may have the following causes:

(*a*) *Insufficient intake in food* (classical rickets). The rachitic organism is not only incapable of absorbing the calcium in food but also of incorporating calcium into bone. Bone and cartilaginous tissues grow, but with deficient mineralization. In children bone deformities occur through loss of consistency, retarded ossification, and enlargement of the synchondroses. In adults the commonest symptom is osteomalacia. Decrease of calcium and phosphorus in the blood causes secondary hyperparathyroidism[2].

(*b*) *Idiopathic or acquired resistance to vitamin D.* This kind of rickets is rare and usually hereditary. It is accompanied by severe deformity and disorganization phenomena in the skeletal bones (thickened substratum, generalized osteomalacia). Symptoms of this disease are increase of the sagittal and decrease of the transverse diameter of the skull[3].

(*c*) *Chronic intestinal disturbances* (idiopathic steatorrhea, celiac disease) which prevent the usually steady absorption of calcium through the intestinal wall. Part of the vitamin D ingested is also thought to be destroyed by the intestinal flora.

(*d*) *Disturbances of renal function.* In the *glomerular form* (renal rickets, renal dwarfism), lowered excretion of phosphate leads to increase of its blood level. Reflex hyperparathyroidism then causes fibrosis of the bones due to diminished activity of the osteoblasts (osteitis fibrosa cystica).

In the *tubular form* there is severe loss of phosphorus due to disturbance of tubular absorption. Parathyroid function remains normal. Phosphaturia may be the only symptom (idiopathic osteomalacia, MILKMAN's syndrome), or may be accompanied by loss of amino acids (FANCONI's syndrome), or by calcification of the tubules (nephrocalcinosis)[4].

It is difficult to establish a daily requirement of vitamin D. In adults the body usually produces sufficient if deficiency of sunlight does not impair its synthesis (night workers, miners, northern peoples). During vigorous skeletal growth, pregnancy and lactation the requirements of the vitamin as well as of calcium are increased, so that an increased daily dose of vitamin D and additional calcium and phosphorus are indicated. For dietary allowances recommended by the National Research Council (U.S.A.) see page 498.

Toxicology

All the D vitamins, artificial and natural, are toxic in large amounts, but specific data are very variable. In general it can be assumed that daily doses of 20,000 I.U. per kg are not toxic. According to MACH[5], daily doses of 5000 I.U. per kg should not be exceeded in prolonged therapy.

High doses of vitamin D cause mobilization of the calcium fixed in the skeleton and a marked rise of the phosphorus and calcium levels in blood and urine. Parallel with the decalcification of the bones there is abnormal deposition of calcium in the soft tissues, the kidneys and especially in the blood vessels. Symptoms of poisoning are a transitory tonic action (euphoria, increased appetite), followed by anorexia and loss of weight. Later there are nausea, vomiting, pains in the head and joints, muscular weakness, diarrhea, often also pruritus, polydipsia and dysuria. Subsequently there are deposition of calcium in the tissues and renal disturbances (albuminuria, leukocytosis, erythrocytosis).

Symptoms in children are a dry, flaccid skin, hypotonia of the muscles with fibrillary twitching, nystagmus, tremors of the extremities, often also constipation and arterial hypertension. In severe cases an initial phase of excitement and insomnia is followed by profound apathy. The sensitivity and reflexes remain unaffected[6].

Increased diuresis, vomiting and anorexia finally lead to a deficiency of salt and progressive dehydration[6].

Idiopathic hypercalcemia of children is very similar to vitamin A poisoning. Symptoms are interruption of development during the early months, loss of appetite, vomiting, obstipation. In severe cases there are also hypertension, a systolic cardiac murmur, osteosclerosis, retarded mental development, marked increase in blood calcium, uremia, hyperglobulinemia and hypercholesterinemia. The urine contains large numbers of epithelial cells.

The disease possibly has its origin in an alkaline diet combined with vitamin D and cow's milk, since the latter contains five times as much calcium and phosphorus as breast milk. An idiopathic factor and hypersensitivity to the vitamin seem to be involved. Cortisone and a calcium-free diet have a favorable effect in reducing the calcium level of the blood[7].

Therapeutic applications

1. *Prophylaxis of rickets:* Sunshine or quartz-lamp irradiation; doses of the pure vitamin (400 I.U. daily) or fish liver oil; diet rich in vegetables and moderate intake of milk; restriction of cereals since the phytic acid in them forms an insoluble compound with calcium which is not absorbed. Leavened bread need not be restricted because the greater part of the phytic acid is destroyed by yeast fermentation.

   Prophylaxis of rickets with massive doses of vitamin D is not recommended since severe poisoning may occur. The addition of calcium to the diet sometimes recommended should also be avoided. *Premature infants* definitely have deficient utilization of vitamin D and very high prophylactic doses have been recommended. Such massive dosage, however, whether given orally or parenterally, may lead to severe poisoning with hypercalcemia and deposition of salts in the tissues. Interstitial pneumonia, often fatal, has also been frequently observed[8].
2. *Treatment of rickets:* Improvement of the diet is essential, combined with 4000–5000 I.U. daily of some form of vitamin D. In rickets resistant to vitamin D very high daily doses over several months (or a single dose of up to 500,000–600,000 I.U., in severe cases repeated after 4–12 weeks) are necessary. When equilibrium is reached a daily maintenance dose of about 1500 I.U. should be given.
3. As adjunct for prevention of bone atrophy in *disturbances of renal function,* where the primary need is to prevent acidosis.
4. In the treatment of *osteomalacia* and *infantile tetany* (spasmophilia).
5. In *acute lead poisoning* together with calcium to fix the lead circulating in the blood.
6. *Lupus vulgaris* is treated with vitamin D_2 either orally or parenterally, the dose being 600,000 I.U. given in alcoholic solution 3 times during the 1st week, twice during the 2nd to 4th weeks, and once during subsequent weeks up to a total period of 12–18 months[9]. Control of nonprotein nitrogen and blood calcium is necessary. Contraindications are renal insufficiency and arteriosclerosis.

7. *After-treatment of hypoparathyroidism:* When the patient's condition returns to normal after treatment with A.T. 10*, 50,000 I.U. of vitamin D (less active than A.T. 10, but substantially cheaper) can be given three times a week. If the condition proves resistant, vitamin D_3 can be replaced by vitamin D_2 for example, or treatment with A.T. 10 resumed for a time.

References: *1)* CRUICKSHANK et al., *Proc. Nutr. Soc.*, **14**, viii (1955); GREENE et al., *Fed. Proc.*, **14**, 435 (1955). *2)* ALBRIGHT and REIFENSTEIN, *The Parathyroid Glands and Metabolic Bone Disease*, Baltimore, 1948. *3)* GREGERSEN, E., *Acta paediat. (Uppsala)*, **44**, 491 (1955). *4)* DENT, C. E., *J. Bone Jt Surg.*, **34B**, 266 (1952); GALBRAITH, D., *Med. J. Aust.*, **2**, 208 (1953). *5)* MACH, R. S., *La vitamine D et les facteurs hypercalcémiants*, Geneva, 1948. *6)* PFENNIGSDORF et al., *Arzneimittel-Forsch.*, **5**, 570 (1955). *7)* STAPLETON and EVANS, *Helv. paediat. Acta*, **10**, 149 (1955); FANCONI and SPAHR, *Helv. paediat. Acta*, **10**, 156 (1955). *8)* GLEISS, J., *Mschr. Kinderheilk.*, **102**, 177 (1954). *9)* CHARPY, J., *Ann. Derm. Syph. (Paris)*, **6**, 311 (1946).

Vitamin E

Seven forms of this vitamin, the tocopherols, are known. The activities of α-, β-, γ- and δ-tocopherol are in the proportions 100:30:20:1[1]. Recent studies indicate that the activity of ζ-tocopherol is the same as that of β-tocopherol. γ-Tocopherol has only very slight activity and δ-, ε- and η-tocopherol are probably completely inactive. Little is at present known concerning the activities of ζ-, ε- and η-tocopherol. All these compounds are very widely distributed in green plants, especially in cereals. According to their occurrence they fall into two groups: α-, β-, ε- and ζ-tocopherol (wheat germ, barley, rye) and η-, γ- and δ-tocopherol (soya beans, groundnuts, mustard, corn). Oats are exceptional in containing at least 5 tocopherols[2]. The α-, β- and γ-vitameres are viscous oils, insoluble in water, stable to light, heat and acids in the absence of oxygen, but decomposed by ultraviolet light, alkalis, oxidizing agents and rancid fats. In general their esters are more stable and possess similar biological activity. Vitamin E is not destroyed by cooking.

α-Tocopherol (5,7,8-trimethyltocol), $C_{29}H_{50}O_2$ α-TOCOPHEROL
Mol.wt. 430.72

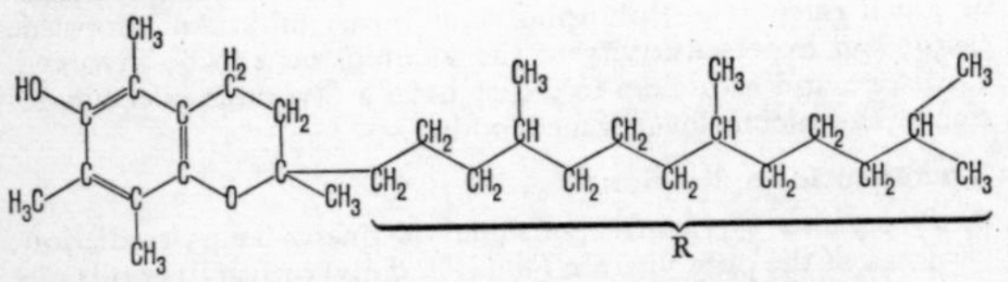

β-Tocopherol (5,8-dimethyltocol), $C_{28}H_{48}O_2$ β-TOCOPHEROL
Mol.wt. 416.69

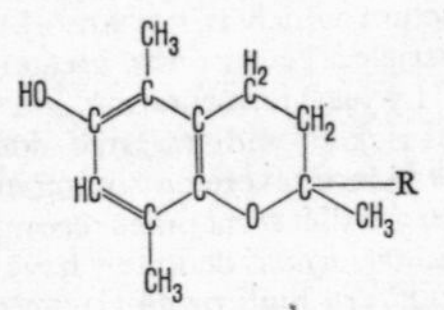

γ-Tocopherol (7,8-dimethyltocol), $C_{28}H_{48}O_2$ γ-TOCOPHEROL
Mol.wt. 416.69

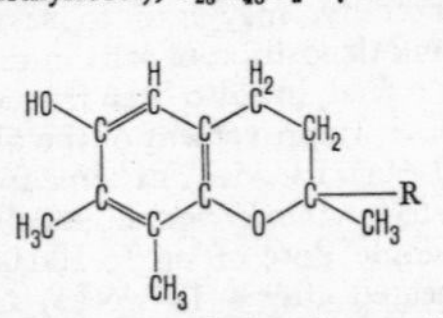

(ζ = 5,7-dimethyltocol; ε = 5-methyltocol; η = 7-methyltocol; δ = 8-methyltocol)

Unit

1 international unit (I.U.) = 1.0 mg of synthetic, racemic α-tocopherol acetate.

Methods of test and assay

Micromethod[3]; rapid method[4].

Two-dimensional paper chromatography is now usually used (sometimes one-dimensional in the absence of ε- and ζ-tocopherol)[2].

* A.T. 10 (dihydrotachysterol) is a derivative of vitamin D without antirachitic properties but with an action on calcium metabolism similar to that of parathormone. It stimulates the excretion of phosphate in the urine.

Occurrence (values in mg per 100 g)

Wheat-germ oil 320; cottonseed oil, refined, 83–92; arachis oil 26–36; wheat germ 27; wholemeal wheat flour 1.2–3.4.

Physiology and function

Nothing certain is known of the biochemistry of vitamin E. Symptoms of deficiency vary according to the species, age and sex of the experimental animal. The uncertainty regarding the role of the vitamin in the organism is increased by the fact that other compounds can replace it in certain of its functions.

The following effects have been ascribed to vitamin E:

(*a*) General antioxidative effect. The vitamin protects the unsaturated fatty acids of the organism against oxidation. In deficiency, peroxides appear which cause a stoppage of protein synthesis. Vitamin E also neutralizes the toxic effects of certain compounds such as cresol esters, carbon tetrachloride, pyridine, sodium sulfite and certain sulfonamides[5].

(*b*) Effects on the kidneys (tubular degeneration) and on the genital organs of rats and guinea pigs. The ovaries are less sensitive than the testes, which may ultimately show irreversible injuries.

(*c*) Progressive muscular dystrophy (rats, guinea pigs, rabbits) with creatinuria and internal calcification of the affected muscles.

(*d*) Participation in certain respiratory enzyme systems and protein metabolism. Possibly also a regulatory action on the utilization of muscle carbohydrate[6].

(*e*) Protective action against fatty degeneration and necrosis of the liver (swine, guinea pigs).

(*f*) Protection of the erythrocytes against hemolysis.

(*g*) Adaptation of the body to fluctuations of atmospheric pressure and protection of the lungs against the effects of anoxia and hyperoxia[7].

(*h*) An effect on the blood vessels and muscle of the heart (disputed).

(*i*) Participation together with proteins in the formation of the dental enamel and certain tissues such as liver (but no role in the formation of bone[8]).

(*k*) A relationship to the pituitary. In vitamin E deficiency the production of the follicle-stimulating hormone (FSH) and the luteinizing hormone (LH) is increased[9]. Degeneration of the uterine nerve ganglia has been attributed to this vitamin, which has been thought ultimately to be responsible for abortion or resorption of the fetus[10].

In monkeys, deficiency leads to muscular dystrophy, loss of creatinine and amino acids through urinary excretion, anemia and leukocytosis (decrease of erythrocytes and hemoglobin content, neutrophilia)[11].

Cases of deficiency in man have only recently been studied. In adults there is absence of tocopherol in the blood, xanthomatosis and cirrhosis of the gall bladder, creatinuria[12]; in children steatorrhea, very low tocopherol blood level, tendency to hemolysis of the erythrocytes. All these symptoms disappear under vitamin therapy[13].

Since it occurs in all tissues of the body, vitamin E obviously plays an important role in the organism. The daily excretion in the feces is approximately 21 mg, representing 60–70% of the amount ingested; in LAENNEC's cirrhosis of the liver the excretion falls to 7–10 mg. Vitamin E seems to be neither synthesized nor broken down in the intestine. The organism stores the vitamin mainly in the fatty tissues (0.1–1.1 mg/1 g fat). The average level in the circulating blood is 1110 μg/100 ml (range 560–1950 μg/100 ml)[14], with α-tocopherol predominating. The level rises during pregnancy and when the cholesterol level rises. It falls during disturbances of fat absorption and remains unaffected by the menstrual cycle.

Therapeutic applications

The many therapeutic studies made have given very conflicting results so that there is as yet no established vitamin E therapy. In carbon tetrachloride poisoning it is effective only during the first 24 hours, in contrast to vitamin B_{12}, which has a long-lasting favorable effect on liver regeneration. Vitamin E has been used with varying success in progressive muscular atrophy, multiple and amyotrophic lateral sclerosis, arteriosclerosis, angina pectoris, and anemia not responding to the usual treatment. It has also been used in protective liver therapy and in menopausal disturbances in which estrogens are ineffective or contraindicated.

As an antioxidant vitamin E can sometimes replace vitamin A. Oxidants, and also cod-liver oil, function as antimetabolites of vitamin E.

References: *1)* BROWN, F., *J. Sci. Food Agric.*, **4**, 161 (1953). *2)* GREEN et al. *J. Sci. Food Agric.*, **6**, 274 (1955). *3)* QUAIFE et al., *J. biol. Chem.*, **180**, 122

(1949). *4)* Farber et al., *Fed.Proc.*, **10**, 294 (1951). *5)* Hove, E. L., in *Symposium on the Antimetabolites*, Nutrition Symposium Series, No. 11, New York, 1955, page 58. *6)* Lilienthal and Zierler, in Thompson and King (Eds.), *Biochemical Disorders in Human Disease*, London, 1957, page 445. *7)* Moore, T., *Brit. med. Bull.*, **12**, 44 (1956). *8)* Irving, J. T., *Vitam. and Horm.*, **15**, 291 (1957). *9)* Griesbach et al., *Endocrinology*, **60**, 729 (1957). 10) Coujard and Daum, *C. R. Acad. Sci. (Paris)*, **238**, 840 (1954). *11)* Day and Dinning, *Fed. Proc.*, **15**, 548 (1956); *Amer. J. clin. Nutr.*, **4**, 386 (1956). *12)* Woodruff, C. W., *Amer. J. clin. Nutr.*, **4**, 597 (1956). *13)* Nitowsky et al., *Amer. J. Dis. Child.*, **92**, 164 (1956). *14)* Darby et al., *Ann. N.Y. Acad. Sci.*, **52**, 328 (1949); Quaife et al., *J. biol. Chem.*, **180**, 1229 (1949).

Vitamin K[14]

Several naturally occurring forms of vitamin K are known. Vitamin K_1 contains a singly unsaturated side chain of 20 C-atoms, the two forms of vitamin K_2 a multiply unsaturated side chain of 30 ($K_{2(30)}$) and 35 ($K_{2(35)}$) C-atoms[1]. A whole series of compounds chemically related to this vitamin and having similar biological activity have been synthesized. Vitamin K occurs in the chloroplasts of plants, where it plays an important part in photosynthesis[2]. The natural vitamins are soluble in fats, fairly stable to heat, but unstable to alkalis and light. Menadione (2-methyl-1,4-naphthoquinone), a synthetic compound with vitamin K activity, is converted in the animal organism into a compound resembling vitamins K_1 and K_2 with a side chain of 20 C-atoms[3].

Vitamin K_1, $C_{31}H_{46}O_2$
Oil, originally obtained from lucerne
Mol.wt. 450.71
M.p. – 20°C

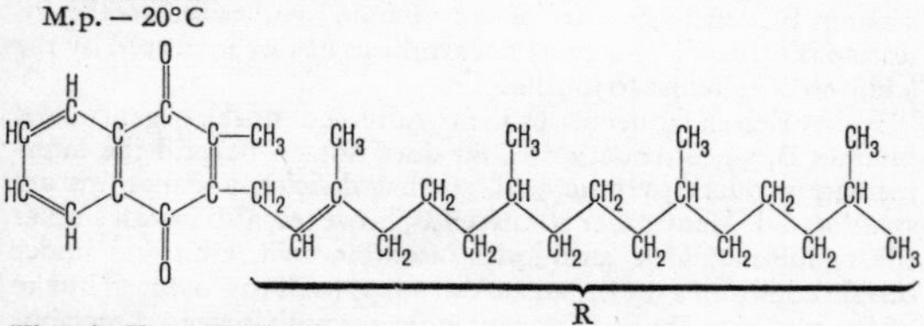

Vitamin $K_{2(35)}$, $C_{46}H_{64}O_2$
Yellow crystals, originally obtained from putrefying fish meal
Mol.wt. 649.02
M.p. 53.5–54.5°C

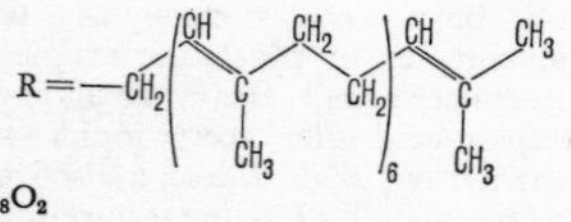

Menadione, $C_{11}H_8O_2$
Yellow crystals
Mol.wt. 172.19
M.p. 106°C

R=H

Units

No international unit has yet been established but 1 milligram of synthetic menadione has been proposed as such. 0.0008 mg menadione = 20 Dam units = 1 Ansbacher unit = the minimum quantity which in 6 hours normalizes the blood coagulation time of 70–100 g vitamin K-deficient chicks. There are in addition many other units which have no further significance now that the synthetic preparations permit definition by weight.

Methods of assay

Chemically (based on the reduction of the quinone group to hydroquinone); spectrometrically in pure solutions of K_1, K_2 and menadione; biologically on vitamin K-deficient chicks (see Ansbacher unit).

Occurrence

Chiefly in green vegetables: spinach, cabbage, Brussels sprouts. The content in tomatoes and liver is smaller and that in fruits, milk and meat minimal.

Physiology and function

Fats and bile are necessary for the absorption of vitamin K and menadione in the intestine but this does not apply to the synthetic, water-soluble preparations. It is doubtful whether the healthy adult is dependent on alimentary intake of this vitamin since it is synthesized in sufficient amount by the bacterial flora of the alimentary canal. The few cases of Kavitaminosis described in the literature can be ascribed either to changes in the intestinal bacterial flora or to injury to the liver parenchyma.

It is impossible to establish a minimal daily dose for adults. This is mainly because extremely small amounts of vitamin K cause the disappearance of hypoprothrombinemia[2]. The requirement of the organism for vitamin K increases with the external temperature.

Vitamin K is involved in the blood coagulation mechanism, not directly in clot formation but indirectly in the production of prothrombin in the liver by its action on the precursors, in particular factor VII (proconvertin)[3]. The plasma contains a group of relatively stable substances necessary for the conversion of prothrombin into thrombin, and these substances require vitamin K for the development of their activity. When the liver parenchyma is damaged or when dicoumarol derivatives are present, this function of vitamin K is inhibited[4].

A lowered prothrombin level can have the following causes:

(*a*) insufficient intestinal synthesis of vitamin K;
(*b*) poor absorption (steatorrhea, deficient fat absorption);
(*c*) damage to the liver parenchyma.

Parenteral vitamin therapy makes differential diagnosis to some extent possible. Rapid increase of prothrombin suggests intestinal disturbance or slight damage to the liver. Absence of a reaction indicates serious damage to the liver cells as a result of which they are no longer able to synthesize prothrombin[5].

Vitamin K is an antagonist of dicoumarol and its derivatives. Here vitamin K_1 is more efficient and faster-acting than menadione and is therefore preferred as an antihemorrhagic agent[6]. Continuous intravenous infusion of a 5% (50 mg/ml) emulsion of vitamin K_1 at the rate of 1 ml per minute up to a total dosage of 5–20 mg per kg body weight (360–1290 mg per patient) lowers prothrombin times of 43–85 seconds in 2 hours to 28–36 seconds and in 5 hours to 20–30 seconds[7].

The antimetabolites of the K vitamins act by changing or inhibiting the intestinal flora (sulfonamides, antibiotics), by blocking enzymes (dihydroxystearic acid glycide) or by displacement of compounds related to vitamin K from enzyme systems which are involved in the synthesis of the vitamin[8].

Therapeutic applications

Prophylactic:

(*a*) Administration to the mother before parturition for prevention of hemorrhagic diathesis of the newborn; it should be noted that there is a certain amount of placental resistance to the passage of the vitamin into the fetal circulation.
Administration of the vitamin to newborn and premature infants must be made with caution since overdosage can lead to hemolytic anemia and kernicterus, the latter due to hyperbilirubinemia. The sensitivity of infants to the vitamin may be related to the low blood level of vitamin E, which here acts as a K antagonist. For these reasons daily doses should be restricted to 1 mg or less[9].

(*b*) Preoperative treatment of patients with icterus or liver injury, in which case the prothrombin level must of course first be determined.

(*c*) In prolonged antibiotic therapy as compensation for the disturbed intestinal flora.

Curative: In all cases of prothrombinopenia due to intestinal or liver disturbance or to overdosage of anticoagulants. Intravenous injection is recommended for antagonization of dicoumarol derivatives since it is faster and more certain than intramuscular injection[10]. Dosage for fast-acting anticoagulants 5–15 mg, for anticoagulants with persistent action 15–25 mg. The effect is tested after 6–8 hours and the dose increased if no perceptible rise of the prothrombin level is observed[11].

Treatment in this way must be accompanied by control of the blood prothrombin level in order to prevent possible thrombosis due to overdosage of the vitamin. An antibacterial action has been ascribed to vitamin K[12] and it has been alleged to sensitize cells to X-rays[13].

References: *1)* Isler et al., *Helv. chim. Acta*, **41**, 786 (1958). *2)* Owen, C.A., in Sebrell and Harris (Eds.,) *The Vitamins*, vol. II, New York, 1954, page 419. *3)* Martius and Esser, *Biochem. Z.*, **331**, 1 (1958). *4)* Ratnoff, O.D., *Advanc. intern. Med.*, **9**, 107 (1958). *5)* Stein, H.B., *S. Afr. J. med. Sci.*, **9**, 111 (1944). *6)* Collentine and Quick, *Amer. J. med. Sci.*, **222**, 7 (1951). *7)* Watkin et al., *J. Lab. clin. Med.*, **37**, 269 (1951). *8)* Albert, A., *Brit. med. Bull.*, **12**, 67 (1956). *9)* Dyggve et al., *Acta paediat. (Uppsala)*, **43**, 27 (1954); Capon et al., *Brit. med. J.*, **1**, 1425 (1956); Marusich et al., *Fed. Proc.*, **15**, 562 (1956). *10)* Shoshkes and Perelman, *J. Amer. med. Ass.*, **161**, 1145 (1956). *11)* Toohey, M., *Brit. med. J.*, **1**, 1020 (1954). *12)* Kitamikado and Mori, *Bull. Japan. Soc. sci. Fisheries*, **20**, 147 and 237 (1954), quoted by Kodicek, E., *Ann. Rev. Biochem.*, **25**, 497 (1956). *13)* Kohn and Gunter, *Radiat. Res.*, **2**, 351 (1955). *14)* For a review see Isler and Wiss, *Vitam. and Horm.*, **17**, 53 (1959).

Vitamin B_1 (thiamine, aneurine)

This vitamin occurs in plants in the free form and in animals as the pyrophosphate (cocarboxylase) or protein-magnesium-cocarboxylase complex. Vitamin B_1 is soluble in water and aqueous alcohol, insoluble in fat solvents, thermostable in strongly acid solutions, thermolabile in neutral or alkaline solution. Although it is stable to atmospheric oxygen it is easily decomposed by oxidizing agents, as also by ultraviolet light. Optically inactive. Absorption maxima 233 mμm and 267 mμm. The molecule consists of a pyrimidine ring connected by a methylene bridge with a substituted thiazole.

Vitamin B_1 (thiamine hydrochloride), $C_{12}H_{18}ON_4SCl_2$ THIAMINE

Colorless monoclinic needles, nutty odor
Mol.wt. 337.29
M.p. 248–250° C

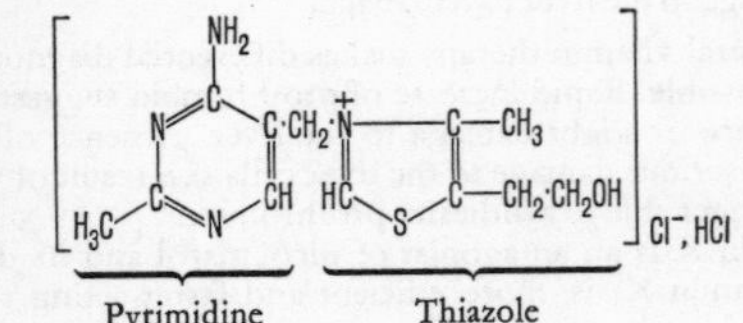

Pyrimidine residue   Thiazole residue

Cocarboxylase

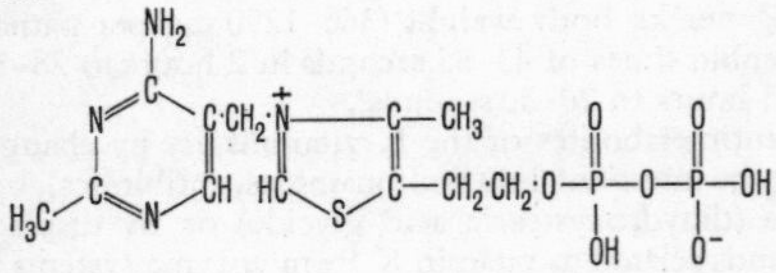

Units

1 international unit (I.U.) = 0.003 mg vitamin B_1 hydrochloride = 1 U.S. Pharmacopeia unit.

Methods of test and assay

Thiochrome method[1]: Potassium ferricyanide oxidizes vitamin B_1 to thiochrome, which shows an intense blue fluorescence in ultraviolet light (the prescribed method in U.S.A. for pharmaceuticals and foodstuffs).

Biological methods: Rat protection test, rat growth test, yeast fermentation test.

WESTENBRINK's micromethod has a sensitivity up to 0.000 05 μg of cocarboxylase and 0.0005 μg of vitamin B_1 in blood[2]. The use of alkali-washed yeast makes possible estimations with only 0.01 ml of blood[3].

Estimations with the yeast *Kloeckera brevis* B 768 are sensitive up to 0.001 μg per ml (HOFF-JØRGENSEN and HANSEN[4]).

Occurrence (values in I.U. per 100 g weight fresh)

Yeast 2000–30,000, wheat germ 600–1250, wholemeal, wheat or rye bread 75–150, soybeans 175–400, pork fat 280–400.

Physiology and function

Vitamin B_1 is synthesized by plants as well as various microorganisms. In plants its role resembles that of a hormone; it is formed in the leaves and transported to the roots, where it controls growth[5].

The animal organism is capable of forming small amounts by means of the intestinal bacterial flora but is chiefly dependent for its supply on foods of plant (free vitamin B_1) or animal (cocarboxylase) origin. The vitamin is rapidly absorbed in the alimentary tract and is phosphorylated by nucleated cells, especially in the liver, dephosphorylated in the kidneys and excreted as the free vitamin in the urine. A large part of it is decomposed in the organism and excreted in the form of organic sulfur compounds. The total amount excreted daily is approximately proportional to the amount of urine passed. Very small amounts are excreted in the sweat.

The blood contains per 100 ml about 3.5–11.5 μg of cocarboxylase[6] (in the corpuscles) and up to 1.3 μg of the free vitamin[7] (in the plasma). The cocarboxylase content of the leukocytes is ten times that of the erythrocytes. The concentration in the cerebrospinal fluid is about the same as in the plasma.

The daily requirement of the vitamin depends on the constitutional type and weight of the body, on the metabolism, on the fat content of the food, on the extent of bacterial synthesis, on the presence in the food of the enzymes which break down the vitamin, and on other factors. COWGILL[8] gives the following equation for the minimal requirement: $4.26 \times 10^{-6} \times$ body weight in kilograms $\times$ daily intake of calories = milligrams of vitamin B_1. The optimum is 50% higher than this. The requirement in children is higher than in adults and according to BEAL[9] amounts to: newborn, 0.3 mg/1000 cal; 1 year, 0.7 mg/1000 cal; 1–3 years, slow fall to 0.54 mg/1000 cal; the latter value remains unchanged up to 5 years. According to HOLT et al.[10], the maintenance dose for infants of 4–11 months with artificial feeding is 0.14–0.20 mg. For dietary allowances recommended by the National Research Council (U.S.A.) see page 498.

Cocarboxylase functions as the prosthetic group of various enzymes involved in the metabolism of α-keto acids, in which pyruvic acid occupies a key position as intermediate and decomposition product of the metabolism of amino acids, fats and carbohydrates. The neurones obtain the energy for their activity almost entirely by oxidation of carbohydrates, in which vitamin B_1 and pantothenic acid (formation of coenzyme A from pyruvate), nicotinic acid (a constituent of DPN) and riboflavin (a constituent of certain dehydrogenases) are involved[11]. Vitamin B_1 and pantothenic acid also play a part in the synthesis of acetylcholine in the nerve fibers[12]. Cocarboxylase prevents the accumulation of pyruvate and pyruvic aldehyde, both of which are toxic to the organism[11].

Vitamin B_1 has an immediate action on cells which use large amounts of carbohydrate (nerve cells), on cells with predominantly pyruvic acid metabolism (heart muscle) and on mechanisms which depend on the formation of acetylcholine (peripheral nerves). In vitamin B_1 deficiency part of the vitamin synthesized in the intestine is utilized. The intestinal synthesis can be increased by the addition of cellulose to the diet[13].

A diet rich in fat decreases the requirement of the organism for vitamin B_1 since oxidation of fat does not go beyond the intermediate product pyruvic acid, so that deficiency symptoms are ameliorated. Many other compounds, however, also have a similar effect (sulfonamides, antibiotics, ascorbic acid, etc.) and under certain conditions the organism can adapt itself to a reduced intake of the vitamin. The requirement increases with increased metabolism (fever, exertion, hyperthyroidism), during the second half of pregnancy and during lactation. In diabetes the cocarboxylase content of the blood and liver is reduced[14].

The vitamin B_1 enzymes consist chiefly of a protein-cocarboxylase-magnesium-complex in which the magnesium can be replaced by other divalent metals. Heavy metals and certain organic compounds (pyruvic acid ester, acetyl iodide, mustard gas, arsenites) block the pyruvic acid oxidase, a discovery which finally led to the synthesis of BAL (2,3-dimercaptopropanol), the antidote to certain war gases and heavy-metal poisons. Vitamin B_1 is also destroyed by certain salts (K_2HPO_4, $CaCO_3$, $MnSO_4$).

Substitution in the pyrimidine ring of vitamin B_1, as also substitution of the alcoholic hydroxyl in the thiazole component, leads to antagonists to the vitamin. Although vitamins B_1 and B_{12} are usually synergistic, antagonism appears to develop between them in certain cases[15].

Vitamin B_1 is to some extent toxic, and for this reason intravenous injections of large doses can cause shock. It is uncertain whether this is an anaphylactic phenomenon or the result of blocking of ganglia. Treatment with vitamin B_1 alone without the addition of other vitamins of the B group can cause undesirable side effects[16].

Therapeutic applications[17]

The classical symptoms of vitamin B_1 deficiency are initially anorexia, nausea and vomiting, later lassitude, debility, hypotonia of the gastrointestinal tract, disturbances of the peripheral nerves (atony of the lower extremities, hyperesthesia and paresthesia, disturbances of coordination). Mental disturbances also appear, such as depression, irritability and impairment of memory and concentration. Mental capacity remains unaffected.

Severe deficiency causes the disease known as beri-beri. This has three forms:

(*a*) The exudative form in which edema is the initial symptom. Enlargement of the heart and right-sided cardiac failure may cause sudden death.

(*b*) The "dry" form with predominance of peripheral, degenerative polyneuritis and muscular atrophy of the extremities.

(*c*) The infantile form in the infants of mothers with B_1 deficiency. This shows itself chiefly in chronic marasmus, in which cardiac failure may also lead to sudden death.

In northern latitudes polyneuritis is the chief symptom of B_1 deficiency, for example in chronic alcoholism, in which the cause lies more in the general inflammation of the gastrointestinal tract than in the alcohol itself. Alcoholic polyneuritis resembles in many ways the "dry" form of beri-beri. The increase in the pyruvic acid level of the blood and the rapid return to the normal when it is treated with vitamin B_1 suggest deficiency of the vitamin. The polyneuritic disturbances disappear slowly and often leave irreversible nervous injury.

The rare cerebral form of beri-beri shows symptoms resembling WERNICKE's encephalopathy: nystagmus, paralysis of the eye muscles, mental disorders (over-excitability, insomnia, loss of memory, disorientation, confabulation, hallucinations) and finally loss of consciousness and death. This disease is seen in Europe in chronic alcoholics and occasionally in cancer patients and can be effectively treated with vitamin B_1.

Cardiac disease is accompanied by a rapid fall in the vitamin B_1 content of the tissues and especially of the heart. The use of mercurial diuretics further depletes the reserves of the vitamin, and for this reason the additional administration of vitamin B_1 during therapy has been suggested. Deficiency of the vitamin is often the first sign of cardiac failure with decompensation.

In all forms of neuritis high doses of vitamin B_1 with other compounds of the B complex should be tried, although naturally only those forms of neuritis caused by lack of vitamin B_1 respond completely and quickly. In lead poisoning, vitamin B_1 is indicated for prevention of neuritis. In delirium tremens, nicotinamide has proved more effective than vitamin B_1.

References: *1)* HOLMAN, W. I. M., *Biochem. J.*, **38**, 388 (1944); PATRICK and WRIGHT, *Analyst*, **74**, 303 (1949). *2)* WESTENBRINK, H. G. K., *Enzymologia (Amst.)*, **8**, 97 (1940). *3)* WESTENBRINK et al., *Z. Vitaminforsch.*, **13**, 218 (1943); STEYN PARVÉ, E. P., *Onderzoekingen over splitsing en vorming van het enzyme carboxylase*, Thesis, Amsterdam, 1945. *4)* HOFF-JØRGENSEN and HANSEN, *Acta chem. scand.*, **9**, 562 (1955). *5)* BONNER, J., *Harvey Lect.*, **48**, 1 (1952–53). *6)* EVERETT, M. R., *Medical Biochemistry*, 2nd ed., New York, 1946, page 653. *7)* MEIKLEJOHN, A.P., *Biochem J.*, **31**, 1441 (1937). *8)* COWGILL, G.R., *Vitamin B Requirement of Man*, Oxford, 1934. *9)* BEAL, V.A., *J. Nutr.*, **57**, 183 (1955). *10)* HOLT et al., *J. Nutr.*, **37**, 53 (1949). *11)* SINCLAIR, H. M., *Brit. med. Bull.*, **12**, 18 (1956). *12)* MINZ, B., *Presse méd.*, **46**, 1406 (1938); *C. R. Soc. Biol. (Paris)*, **127**, 1251 (1938). *13)* NAGASE and FUJITA, *J. Vitaminol.*, **2**, 107 (1956), quoted by SARETT and MORRISON, *Ann. Rev. Biochem.*, **27**, 339 (1958); SHIMOMURA, F., *J. Vitaminol.*, **2**, 232 (1956), quoted by SARETT and MORRISON, *loc. cit.* *14)* SILIPRANDI and NAVAZIO, *Acta med. scand.*, **142**, 147 (1952). *15)* CERECEDO, L.R., *Amer. J. clin. Nutr.*, **3**, 273 (1955); FELLER and MACEK, *J. Amer. pharm. Ass.*, **44**, 662 (1955). *16)* WOLFSON and ELLIS, *Fed. Proc.*, **13**, 418 (1954). *17)* THOMPSON and CUMINGS, in THOMPSON and KING (Eds.), *Biochemical Disorders in Human Disease*, London, 1957, page 418.

Vitamin B_2 (riboflavin, lactoflavin)

Vitamin B_2, which owes its other name of riboflavin to its color and ribose content, occurs in nature either free or as component of coenzymes (flavin mononucleotide, flavine adenine dinucleotide; see page 370). The *flavoproteins* consist of these coenzymes with their apoenzymes. Vitamin B_2 is a derivative of *iso*alloxazine; it is soluble in water and alcohols and is insoluble in fat solvents, thermostable in the dry state and in acid solution, stable to atmospheric oxygen except in alkaline solution, unstable to light and alkalis. Solutions of the vitamin show an intense yellow fluorescence.

Vitamin B_2, $C_{17}H_{20}O_6N_4$ RIBOFLAVINE
Orange-yellow crystals, blackening at 240° C. Bitter taste
Mol.wt. 376.38
M. p. (decomp.) 275–282° C

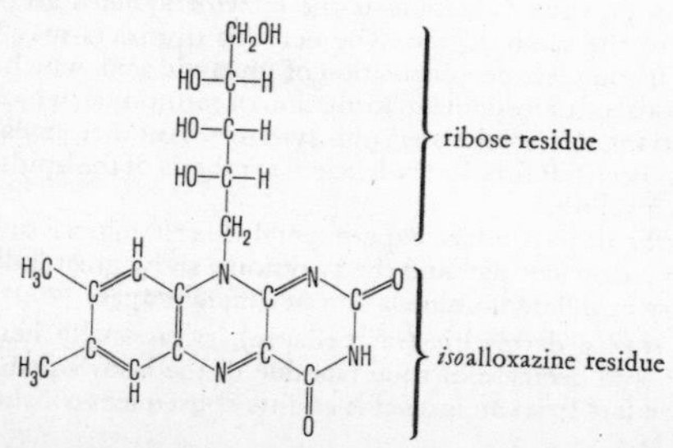

Unit

No international unit; by weight.

Methods of test and assay

Microbiologically by means of *Lactobacillus helveticus (L.casei)* and many other species, rat growth test, fluorometrically.

Occurrence (values in mg per 100 g weight fresh)

Yeast 2–4; liver of various animals 2–3.5; meat extract 1.5–2.5; kidneys 1–2; human milk 0.06 mg/100 ml[1]; widely distributed in all leaf vegetables, in flesh of warm-blooded animals and fish.

Physiology and function

In human feces the vitamin B_2 content is often higher than in the ingested food because of synthesis of the vitamin by the bacterial flora in the intestine. The extent to which the organism uses the vitamin formed in the intestine is not known. A vegetable diet, or the addition of cellulose to the food, considerably increases the bacterial synthesis[2].

Vitamin B_2 is phosphorylated in the intestinal wall and is stored in the liver, heart and kidneys. These depots are maintained as far as possible and are depleted in deficiency states only by 30–50%[3]. Deficiency of vitamin B_1 or increased intake of protein lead to increased storage and decreased excretion of vitamin B_2.

The vitamin B_2 content of the organism diminishes slowly in infancy up to the third year and then rises slightly between the third and fifth year[4]. The blood level in adults decreases during life[5]. The content of flavin coenzyme in the tissues depends on the diet, while its content in the brain remains practically constant[6].

The vitamin B_2 content of whole blood is 4.9–10.4 µg per 100 ml (average 6.68 µg per 100 ml)[7], that of the serum 0.3–1.3 µg per 100 ml (average 0.8 µg per 100 ml)[8], most of which (84.3%) is present in the form of nucleotides[7]. The content in the embryonal blood is higher than that in the maternal blood[9].

The amount excreted in normal nutrition is about 12% of the intake, but bears no constant relationship to it. The vitamin is excreted as uroflavin in the feces (0.823–1.313 mg per day, average 1.029 mg per day) and in the urine (0.543–0.913 mg per day, average 0.678 mg per day)[10]. Uroflavin is a pigment almost identical with vitamin B_2 both in composition and activity.

The human daily requirement cannot be exactly determined but seems to be in the neighborhood of 1.5–1.8 mg. The minimum is about 1.1–1.6 mg[11]. A daily dose of 0.4 mg is sufficient for the needs of the infant[12]. For dietary allowances recommended by the National Research Council (U.S.A.) see page 498.

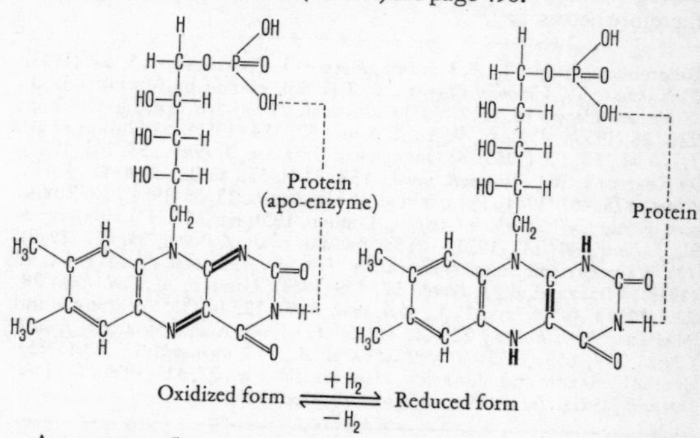

As enzymes, flavoproteins bring about hydrogen transference in various metabolic processes (see above formulas). Among other functions, they participate in a whole series of redox systems. As phosphoric acid ester (mononucleotide), vitamin B_2 forms the prosthetic group of the yellow respiratory enzyme of WARBURG, the first to be discovered of a long series of respiratory enzymes (D-amino acid oxidase, xanthine oxidase, diaphorase, cytochrome c reductase, etc.). The other respiratory enzymes differ in the nature of the prosthetic group and are up to a thousand times more active. The prosthetic group of these enzymes is an adenine dinucleotide in which the riboflavin component is esterified at position 5′ with pyrophosphate, the latter in turn linked with the 5′-position of the ribose of the adenosine molecule. The action of all these enzymes is analogous to that of the yellow respiratory enzyme.

Vitamin B_2 affects the growth and development of the fetus. Deficiency during pregnancy may cause skeletal abnormalities (shortening of the mandibles, tibia, fibula, radius and ulna, coalescences between the ribs, sternal zones of ossification in fingers and toes, brachydactylia, and occasionally cleft palate[13]. Deficiency of the vitamin manifests itself in tissues of ectodermal origin when their flavoprotein content has been very markedly reduced:

(*a*) Eyes: lacrimation, abnormal vascularization of the cornea, keratitis, cataract.
(*b*) Mucosa of the digestive tract: glossitis, inflammation of the buccopharyngeal mucosa, cheilosis, fissures of the corners of the mouth as in perlèche.
(*c*) Skin: marked pruritus, desquamation, fissures, inflammation of the flexion folds of the joints and also of the nasolabial folds, seborrhea.
(*d*) Pelvis ("anogenital syndrome"): inflammation, desquamation and marked pruritus of the anus, vulva and scrotum[14].

Vitamin B_2 has some effect on the nervous system. A decrease in the content of the vitamin has been found in most cases of schizophrenia, neurasthenia and multiple sclerosis and in 20% of cases of neurovegetative disturbances. A strikingly small decrease was noted in tuberculosis, chronic rheumatism, bronchial asthma, gastric and duodenal ulceration and chronic colitis and also in all psychosomatic disorders[7].

The vitamin appears to be involved in the release of ACTH from the pituitary[15], and its presence in the free state or as coenzyme in the retina, cornea and lens indicates that it plays a part with vitamin A and nicotinamide in the visual process.

Diagnosis and therapy of vitamin B_2 deficiency

Intestinal synthesis of the vitamin makes it difficult to bring about deficiency via the diet. On the other hand the deficiency symptoms are not very specific, although certain symptoms, or rather symptom complexes, may suggest the diagnosis, particularly seborrheic lesions, vascularization of the cornea, glossitis and fissures at the corners of the mouth. The latter also occur in deficiencies of other vitamins[14].

The endemic "shibi-gatchaki" of northern Japan is a B_2 deficiency coupled with slight pellagra which has the following symptoms: exhaustion, severe pruritus of the anus and genitals, glossitis, dermatitis, ocular disorders. It responds well to vitamins B_1 and B_2, nicotinic acid, folic acid and vitamin B_{12}[16].

Deficiency symptoms disappear after several days with daily doses of 10 mg of the vitamin. The response serves to confirm the diagnosis.

The requirements of the organism increase slightly during the first three months of pregnancy and to a considerable extent during the last six months. An additional dose of 2 mg daily is therefore necessary[17].

References: *1*) Sós, J., *Z. Vitamin-, Hormon- u. Fermentforsch.*, **1**, 369 (1948). *2*) Yasuda, T., *Vitamins (Japan)*, **6**, 7 (1953), quoted by Mickelsen, O., *Vitam. and Horm.*, **14**, 1 (1956). *3*) Kuhn et al., *Hoppe-Seylers Z. physiol. Chem.*, **232**, 36 (1935). *4*) Beal, V. A., *J. Nutr.*, **57**, 183 (1955). *5*) Schaus et al., *J. Geront.*, **10**, 170 (1955). *6*) Decker and Byerrum, *J. Nutr.*, **53**, 303 (1954). *7*) Kerppola, W., *Acta med. scand.*, **153**, 33 (1955). *8*) Burch et al., *J. biol. Chem.*, **175**, 457 (1948). *9*) Lust et al., *J. clin. Invest.*, **33**, 38 (1954). *10*) Robinson, F. A., *The Vitamin B Complex*, London, 1951, page 74. *11*) Horwitt et al., *J. Nutr.*, **41**, 247 (1950). *12*) Snyderman et al., *J. Nutr.*, **39**, 219 (1949). *13*) Warkany and Schraffenberger, *Proc. Soc. exp. Biol. (N. Y.)*, **54**, 92 (1943); Miller et al., *J. Nutr.*, **52**, 405 (1954); Giroud, A., *Biol. Rev.*, **29**, 220 (1954). *14*) Witts, L. J., *Brit. med. Bull.*, **12**, 14 (1956); Schour and Massler, *Physiol. Rev.*, **25**, 442 (1945). *15*) Forker and Morgan, *J. biol. Chem.*, **217**, 659 (1955). *16*) Masuda et al., *J. Vitaminol.*, **1**, 229 (1955), quoted by Sarett and Morrison, *Ann. Rev. Biochem.*, **27**, 339 (1958). *17*) Jansen and Jansen, *Int. Z. Vitaminforsch.*, **25**, 193 (1954).

Vitamin B_6 (pyridoxine, adermine)[1]

Vitamin B_6 occurs in nature in at least three forms, as pyridoxol, pyridoxal and pyridoxamine, of which for a long time only the first was known. Pyridoxol is soluble in water, alcohol and acetone, sparingly soluble in organic solvents, stable to heat and concentrated acids and alkalis but unstable to light. Pyridoxal and pyridoxamine are thermolabile.

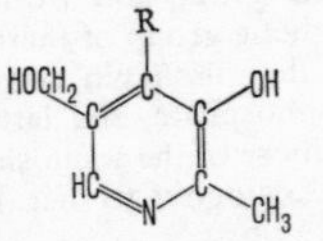

Pyridoxol (adermine), $C_8H_{11}O_3N$ — $R = CH_2OH$ — PYRIDOXOL
Mol.wt. 169.18

Pyridoxal, $C_8H_9O_3N$ — $R = CHO$ — PYRIDOXAL
Mol.wt. 167.17

Pyridoxamine, $C_8H_{12}O_2N_2$ — $R = CH_2NH_2$ — PYRIDOXAMINE
Mol.wt. 168.20

4-Pyridoxic acid, $C_8H_9O_4N$ — $R = COOH$
Mol.wt. 183.17

Units

No international unit; by weight.

Methods of test and assay

Microbiologically by means of *Lactobacillus helveticus (L. casei)*, *Streptococcus faecalis* and *Saccharomyces carlsbergensis* for pyridoxol, pyridoxal and pyridoxamine[2]. The three forms, and 4-pyridoxic acid, can be separated fluorometrically[3].

Occurrence (values in mg per 100 g weight fresh)

Dried yeast 3.6; cereal germ 0.6–1.8; liver 0.2; potatoes 0.2–0.3; widely distributed in small concentrations in all animal and plant tissues.

Physiology and function

Animal tissues contain vitamin B_6 chiefly in the form of pyridoxal and pyridoxamine, while in plants pyridoxol is also present in large quantities[4]. The three compounds are interconverted either directly or via their phosphates by some unknown enzymatic mechanism. The phosphates are carriers of the vitamin activity[5].

In man, vitamin B_6 is synthesized chiefly by the flora of the large intestine, but it is still uncertain to what extent, if at all, the organism makes use of this source of the vitamin[6]. In young children this synthesis is absent or occurs only to a very restricted extent[7].

Opinions differ greatly as to the daily requirement (the National Academy of Science[8] gives values between 0.53 and 1.21 mg). It is also known to depend on the protein content of the food. The daily excretion in the feces is 0.5–0.8 mg. About 57% of the amount ingested is excreted in the urine in the form of pyridoxal (0.2–0.3 mg per day) and 4-pyridoxic acid (3–4 mg per day), the latter being a decomposition product which has no vitamin activity[9]. The average normal level in blood is 11.2 µg per 100 ml of whole blood (range 5–20.8 µg), in plasma 7 µg per 100 ml. On a deficient diet the blood level falls after 3–4 weeks to 2–3 µg per 100 ml (expressed as pyridoxol hydrochloride) and remains at this level[10]. The skin contains about 1 µg per gram of dry weight[9]. The urinary excretion is considerably greater after ingestion of pyridoxal than after ingestion of the other forms.

Vitamin B_6 acts as a coenzyme in many mechanisms of amino acid metabolism: decarboxylation, transamination, dehydration, breakdown and resynthesis of tryptophan, breakdown of β-hydroxy-α-amino acids into glycine and aldehydes, desulfuration, racemization, etc. The active form of the vitamin is possibly a chelate with a metallic ion. Pyridoxol is a constituent of the transaminases and pyridoxal a coenzyme necessary for the glycin-serine transformation[11].

Vitamin B_6 seems also to play a part in fat metabolism since in deficiency states the organism loses the ability to convert proteins into fats, with the result that no unsaturated fatty acids are formed. The vitamin may also be involved in the synthesis of highly unsaturated fatty acids from linoleic and linolenic acids[12].

The antivitamins function by displacing pyridoxol phosphate from coenzymes in phosphorylation. In this way desoxypyridoxol blocks most enzymes with the exception of desulfurase. Isoniazid acts as an antivitamin by inhibiting the decarboxylases which contain pyridoxal phosphate[13].

Although the pyrimidine component of vitamin B_1 acts as an antivitamin, the presence of this vitamin is necessary for the effective utilization of vitamin B_6 by the organism[14].

The varying picture of B_6 deficiency is due to the fact that during progressive avitaminosis the enzyme systems are not all blocked to the same degree. The nervous disorders may be the result of incomplete decomposition of glutamic acid, which causes convulsions, or of inadequate formation of serotonine, which plays an important role in the nervous system[15]. Another explanation which has been put forward is deficient synthesis of the lipids which form the myelin[16].

It is difficult to produce experimental B_6 avitaminosis solely by means of a deficient diet and the symptoms show great individual variability in different animals and at different ages.

Rats: severe dermatitis (rat pellagra), occasionally hemolytic anemia[17], and decrease of total fats due to the body's inability to synthesize fats from amino acids and its consequent consumption of depot fats[18].

Syrian hamsters: muscular weakness, atrophy of the lymph glands and fat tissues, increased excretion of xanthurenic acid in the urine.

Rabbits: desquamative dermatitis of the ears, slight anemia, convulsions, increased blood coagulation time, creatinuria, paralytic collapse and death[19].

Dogs: seropurulent conjunctivitis, blepharitis, dermatitis with slight loss of hair on the snout and around the eyes, arteriosclerotic disorders[20].

Rhesus monkeys: arteriosclerosis as constant and dominant symptom, also dental caries, fatty degeneration or cirrhosis of the liver, sclerosis of the pancreas, disorders of the central nervous system[21].

Adult humans: the not very specific symptoms can be confused with those of most vitamin B deficiencies:

(*a*) skin and mucosa: seborrheic and desquamative dermatitis of the mouth and eyes which may also spread to the face, head, neck and pelvic region; intertrigo of the breasts and inguinal region of women; desquamation and pigmentation of the skin of the lower extremities reminiscent of pellagra; stomatitis and glossitis;

(*b*) nervous system: irritability, depression, somnolence, nausea; occasionally mental disorders and disturbances of the perception of vibrations and position; very rarely peripheral neuritis[9].

Infants: cessation of weight increase, occasionally hypochromic anemia with microcytosis[22].

In the arteriosclerosis of dogs and monkeys there is fibrosis of the intima. It is uncertain whether vitamin B_6 plays a part in arteriosclerosis in man. Nevertheless a considerable increase of the blood transaminase level has been noted in 90% of cases of myocardial necrosis, as also 36 hours after an infarct (2–10 times in latter case). In myocardial ischemia and angina pectoris the serum level remains constant, an observation which could be useful in differential diagnosis[23].

The decrease of B_6 reserves during pregnancy causes changes in the nitrogen content of the plasma (both in proteins and non-proteins) which resemble those following a toxemia of pregnancy[24].

The deficiency symptoms rapidly disappear on administration of vitamin B_6 in any one of its three forms, an exception being the degenerative arteriosclerotic changes, which are only partly reversed. Inclusion of linoleic acid in the diet suffices to terminate some of the symptoms, particularly the skin lesions[9]. Ascorbic acid, lactose and dextrin have a favorable effect. In B_6 deficiency the formation of antibodies is considerably reduced; the condition appears to be particularly favorable to the multiplication of the tubercle bacillus[25].

Therapeutic applications[9]

Vitamin B_6 has been tried in various disorders:

(*a*) In epilepsy, postencephalitic parkinsonism, progressive muscular atrophy, amyotrophic lateral sclerosis and muscular dystrophy almost no benefit has been recorded. There has been some success in arteriosclerotic parkinsonism.

(*b*) Some isolated good results have been observed in peripheral neuritis.

(*c*) There have been rare instances of improvement in chronic alcoholism and delirium tremens.

(*d*) Local application has a beneficial effect on acne and certain forms of dermatitis (oral administration is without effect). Dry seborrhea shows the best results.

(*e*) Some success has been recorded in granulocytopenia after X-ray treatment or poisoning, but in these cases the effect cannot be ascribed with certainty to the vitamin.

(*f*) The vitamin has been used empirically in hyperemesis gravidarum and vomiting after anesthetics or irradiation with X-rays. In such cases these appears to be a very high momentary increase in the requirement of the vitamin rather than a deficiency. It has been postulated that X-rays damage the enzyme system in which vitamins of the B group are involved as coenzymes.

(*g*) The vitamin has been used as supportive therapy in pellagra, as also in prolonged treatment with isoniazid, in which peripheral neuritis may occur.

A minor epidemic of convulsions in infants fed on sterilized milk has been ascribed to deficiency of vitamin B_6[26]. Sterilization in an autoclave destroys most of the vitamin and part of the remainder would be converted on storage into an inactive product[27].

References: *1)* For a review see *Vitamin B_6 in Human Nutrition*, Report of the Tenth M & R Pediatric Research Conference, Ohio, 1954. *2)* Snell and Rannefeld, *J. biol. Chem.*, **157**, 475 (1945); Snell, E. E., *J. biol. Chem.*, **157**, 491 (1945); Rabinowitz and Snell, *J. biol. Chem.*, **169**, 631 (1947). *3)* Fujita et al. *J. Vitaminol.*, **1**, 267, 275, 279, 290 (1955), quoted by Greenberg, L. D., *Ann. Rev. Biochem.*, **26**, 209 (1957). *4)* Rabinowitz and Snell, *J. biol. Chem.*, **176**, 1157 (1948). *5)* Snell, E. E., *Vitam. and Horm.*, **16**, 77 (1958). *6)* Linkswiler and Reynolds, *J. Nutr.*, **41**, 523 (1950). *7)* Coursin, D.B., *J. Amer. med. Ass.*, **154**, 406 (1954); May, C.D., *Pediatrics*, **14**, 269 (1954). *8)* National Academy of Science, *National Research Council Publication 302*, Washington, 1953. *9)* Vilter, R.W., *J. Amer. med. Ass.*, **159**, 1210 (1955). *10)* Greenberg and Rinehart, *Proc. Soc. exp. Biol. (N.Y.)*, **70**, 20 (1949). *11)* Bodansky, O., *Ann. Rev. Biochem.*, **24**, 627 (1955). *12)* Snell, E.E., *Physiol. Rev.*, **33**, 509 (1953). *13)* Makino and Koike, *Nature*, **174**, 1056 (1954); Hurwitz, J., *J. biol. Chem.*, **217**, 513 (1955). *14)* Rabinowitz and Snell, *Arch. Biochem.*, **33**, 472 (1951). *15)* Sinclair, H. M., *Brit. med. Bull.*, **12**, 18 (1956). *16)* Tower, D. B., *Amer. J. clin. Nutr.*, **4**, 329 (1956). *17)* Dann, W. J., *J. biol. Chem.*, **128**, xviii (1939). *18)* Beaton et al., *J. biol. Chem.*, **207**, 385 (1954). *19)* Hove and Herndon, *J. Nutr.*, **61**, 127 (1957). *20)* Hawkins, W. W., *Science*, **121**, 880 (1955). *21)* Rinehart and Greenberg, *Amer. J. Path.*, **25**, 481 (1949); Victor and Adams, *Amer. J. clin. Nutr.*, **4**, 346 (1956); Day and Dinning, *Amer. J. clin. Nutr.*, **4**, 386 (1956). *22)* Snyderman et al., *J. clin. Nutr.*, **1**, 200 (1953). *23)* Steinberg and Ostrow, *Proc. Soc. exp. Biol. (N.Y.)*, **89**, 31 (1955). *24)* Ross and Pike, *J. Nutr.*, **60**, 211 (1956). *25)* Charconnet-Harding and Hirsch, *Ann. Inst. Pasteur*, **91**, 120 (1956). *26)* Coursin, D. B., *Amer. J. Dis. Child.*, **90**, 344 (1955). *27)* Hodson, A. Z., *J. Agric. Food Chem.*, **4**, 876 (1956).

Nicotinic acid (niacin)

Nicotinic acid, a pyridine derivative, occurs in small quantities free in nature but chiefly as its amide (nicotinic acid amide, nicotinamide, nicotylamide). It is soluble in water and alcohol, insoluble in fat solvents, stable to heat and oxidizing agents; it is also very stable in foodstuffs and in storage.

Nicotinic acid, $C_6H_5O_2N$
White crystals or crystalline powder, odorless, acid taste
Mol.wt. 123.11
M.p. 234–237° C

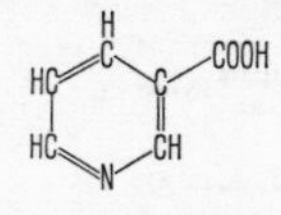

Nicotinamide (vitamin PP), $C_6H_6ON_2$ NICOTINAMIDE
Crystalline powder, odorless, bitter taste
Mol.wt. 122.13
M.p. 128–131° C

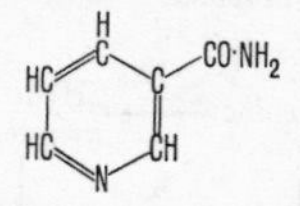

1-Methylnicotinamide chloride (nicotinamide methochloride)

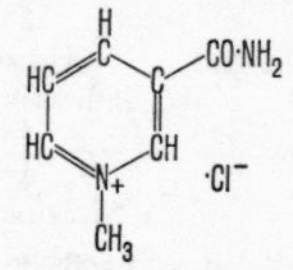

Coenzyme I, DPN (diphosphopyridine nucleotide), $C_{21}H_{27}O_{14}N_7P_2$
Mol.wt. 663.45 (see also page 369)

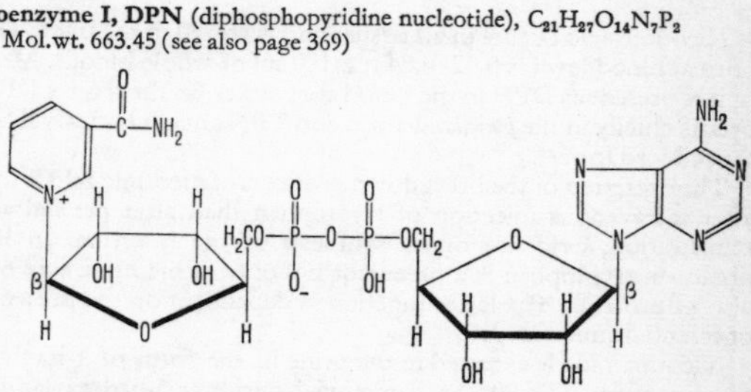

Coenzyme II, TPN (triphosphopyridine nucleotide), $C_{21}H_{28}O_{17}N_7P_3$
Mol.wt. 743.44 (see also page 369)

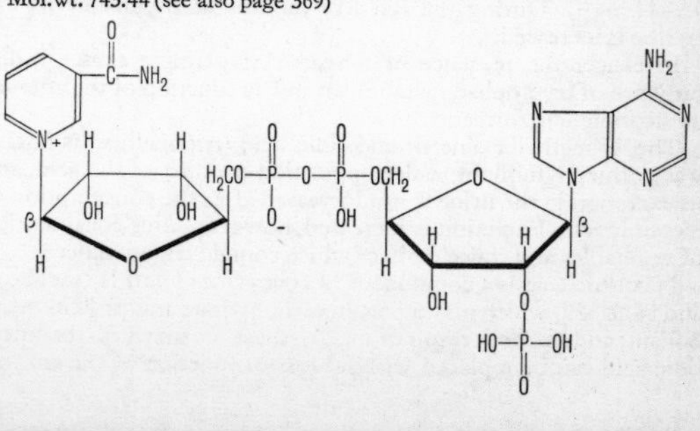

Unit

No international unit; by weight.

Methods of test and assay

Microbiologically: *Lactobacillus arabinosus* for nicotinic acid and nicotinamide, *Leuconostoc mesenteroides* for nicotinic acid alone, blacktongue curative test on dogs, growth test on chicks[1]. Colorimetrically.

Fluorometric determination of methylnicotinamide and pyridine nucleotides in blood[2]. Chromatographic separation and determination of nicotinamide[3] and pyridine nucleotides[4]. Spectrophotometric determination of di- and tri-phosphopyridine nucleotides down to 0.1 µg[5].

Occurrence (values in mg per 100 g weight fresh)

Meat extract, yeast 30–100; rice bran 30–140; liver 10–20; widely distributed in all animal and vegetable foods except pure fats. Bacterial activity during fermentation causes the nicotinic acid content of tobacco leaves to rise to 0.4%.

Physiology and function

Mammals, and also most bacteria, can synthesize nicotinic acid from tryptophan. This process occurs in the intestine but it is not certain whether it also occurs in other tissues[6]. The synthesis requires the presence of other B vitamins and proceeds as follows[7]: tryptophan → kynurenine → 3-hydroxykynurenine → 3-hydroxyanthranilic acid → 1-amino-4-formyl-1,2-dicarboxybuta-1,3-diene → quinolinic acid → nicotinic acid.

The role of the B vitamins in this synthesis is illustrated by the following scheme[8]:

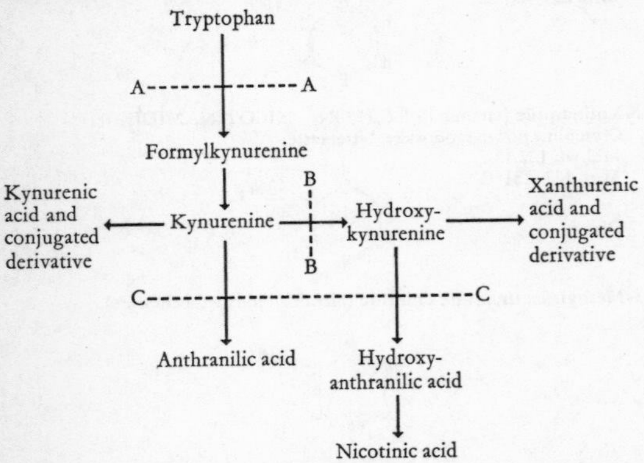

A····A = thiamine, B····B = riboflavin, C····C = pyridoxine

Nicotinic acid occurs in all tissues and is stored in the liver. The normal blood level is 0.42–0.84 mg/100 ml of whole blood[9]. Most of it is present as DPN in the blood corpuscles. In the tissues DPN occurs chiefly in the oxidized form and TPN almost exclusively in the reduced form[10].

The excretion of the breakdown products of nicotinic acid is less after intravenous injection of tryptophan than after peroral administration, evidence of its synthesis in the intestine. In the organism tryptophan is a precursor not only of nicotinic acid but also of proteins. The latter function is dependent on the presence of essential amino acids[11].

Nicotinamide is excreted in the urine in the form of 1-methylnicotinamide (73–80%), 1-methyl-2-pyridone-5-carboxylamide and other acid-hydrolysable derivatives[12] (total daily excretion 9.5–44 mg[13]). During the last five months of pregnancy its excretion is increased[14].

In cancer the presence of 5-hydroxytryptamine causes a disturbance of tryptophan metabolism and a reduction of the amount of nicotinic acid formed[15].

The N-methylbetaine of nicotinic acid (trigonelline) is not, as was formerly thought, a decomposition product of the acid, and its excretion in the urine is not increased after the consumption of nicotinic acid. Excretion is increased, however, after consumption of vegetables and coffee, both of which contain trigonelline.

Nicotinic acid is a component of coenzymes I and II (see above and page 369) which play a part in carbohydrate and protein metabolism and in cell respiration. In these coenzymes the nicotinic acid can be replaced without loss of function of the enzyme system by other pyridine derivatives, for example by nicotinic acid-N-diethylamide (nikethamide), quinolinic acid, 2,6-dimethylpyridine-3,5-dicarboxylic acid, pyrazinemonocarboxylic acid and pyrazine-2,3-dicarboxylic acid.

It is difficult to lay down the daily requirement of nicotinic acid; 4.7 mg per 1000 calories seems to be sufficient to prevent the occurrence of pellagra (the activity of tryptophan in this respect is about $^1/_{60}$ of that of nicotinic acid[16]). For dietary allowances recommended by the National Research Council (U.S.A.) see page 498.

In sprue, there is a deficiency of various vitamins, including nicotinic acid. The B avitaminoses are partly attributable to competition between bacteria and partly to disturbance of the intestinal flora.

In schizophrenia, disturbances in the metabolism of the B vitamins occur, especially in that of thiamine, riboflavin and nicotinic acid[17]. These three vitamins are concerned in enzyme reactions in the brain, for which reason deficiency of all of them leads to encephalopathies and mental disorders (cases of this kind are seen occasionally in psychiatric clinics)[18].

The classical disease due to deficiency of nicotinic acid, pellagra, has other supplementary causes, namely lack of other B vitamins, consumption by the organism of an unsuitable combination of food proteins, and also excessive exposure to the sun's rays. The symptoms are:

(*a*) A symmetrical dark-red erythema on the extremities, face, neck and all parts exposed to the air and light; the skin is ultimately dry, cracked, atrophic and pigmented brown. The lesions are characterised by atrophy of the superficial layers of the corium accompanied by dilatation of the blood vessels, keratinization of the epidermis and a tendency to separation of the latter from the corium. Injuries of any kind aggravate these symptoms[19].

(*b*) Chronic inflammation of the mucosa of the digestive tract (stomatitis, glossitis, gastritis, hypochlorhydria) and profuse, often hemorrhagic, diarrhea.

(*c*) Neurological symptoms similar to those of multiple sclerosis and mental disorders (delirium, hallucinations, confusional states). It has not been shown conclusively that nicotinic acid deficiency is directly responsible for the nervous disorders, because lack of B vitamins (thiamine, riboflavin) has similar effects, and lesions of the spinal cord are attributable, among other causes, to B_{12} deficiency.

Liability to pellagra is increased by chronic alcoholism. The best treatment is a combination of nicotinic acid, vitamins of the B complex and tryptophan. Although this brings about rapid disappearance of the skin and digestive symptoms, the nervous lesions and the mental disorders tend to persist[20].

The disease known as "kwashiorkor" which occurs in Africa and Asia in children shortly after weaning, is also due to lack of several vitamins, principally the B vitamins. Its causes are unsuitable or insufficient food proteins, their poor utilization, and intestinal parasites. The symptoms are general muscular atrophy, loss of hair pigment, marked lowering of the serum albumin level, qualitative and quantitative insufficiency of digestive enzymes, and edema. A vicious circle is established, with deficiency of essential amino acids and atrophy of the liver, pancreas and endocrine glands. The glandular atrophy may persist in adults after recovery from the disease[20].

Pharmacology

Nicotinic acid, but *not* nicotinamide, causes a marked vasodilatation in high doses, especially of the capillaries and vessels of the upper half of the body. Side effects after parenteral administration are hot flushes, sensation of pressure and heat in the region of the head and neck, vertigo, nausea, abdominal pain and sometimes deep unconsciousness. The effects of the drug are very marked but transient. It is used in the treatment of ischemia of the legs, angina pectoris and during crises in asthma. In these cases, however, it does not permanently improve the patient's condition and therefore remains an adjuvant. When given by intravenous injection it causes a marked fall of blood pressure and, in exceptional instances, anaphylactic shock.

Therapeutic applications

Nicotinic acid: in disorders of the peripheral circulation, in angina pectoris, in asthma.

Nicotinamide: in pellagra, in radiation sickness (together with the B complex). General prophylaxis of malnutrition, sprue and dermatosis of alimentary or toxic origin. Occasionally beneficial in delirium tremens.

Niascorbin: This complex of nicotinamide with ascorbic acid is more effective in the treatment of scurvy than ascorbic acid alone since the vitamin C content of the liver and adrenal glands is maintained at a maximum[21].

References: *1)* Bliss and György, in György, P. (Ed.), *Vitamin Methods*, vol. II, New York, 1951, page 210. *2)* Kring and Williams, *J. biol. Chem.*, **207**, 851 (1954). *3)* Kuznetsova and Chagovets, *Chem. Abstr.*, **49**, 14084 (1955). *4)* Hulme, A.C., *J. exp. Botany*, **6**, 153 (1955). *5)* Glock and McLean, *Biochem. J.*, **61**, 381 (1955). *6)* Henderson and Hankes, *Proc. Soc. exp. Biol. (N.Y.)*, **70**, 26 (1949); Snyderman et al., *Proc. Soc. exp. Biol. (N.Y.)*, **70**, 569 (1949); Hundley, J. M., *Proc. Soc. exp. Biol. (N.Y.)*, **70**, 592 (1949). *7)* Lusbough and Schweigert, *Ann. Rev. Biochem.*, **27**, 313 (1958). *8)* Dalgliesh, C. E., *Brit. med. Bull.*, **12**, 49 (1956). *9)* Roggen, J. C., *Ned. T. Geneesk.*, **85**, 4603 (1941); Raoul et al., *C. R. Soc. Biol. (Paris)*, **136**, 740 (1942); Kochhar, B. D., *Indian J. med. Res.*, **28**, 385 (1940). *10)* Glock and McLean, *Biochem. J.*, **61**, 388 (1955). *11)* Geiger et al., *Arch. Biochem.*, **23**, 315 (1949). *12)* Holman and Lange, *Biochem. J.*, **45**, 559 (1949). *13)* Johnson et al., *J. biol. Chem.*, **159**, 231 (1945). *14)* Frazier et al., *J. Nutr.*, **37**, 393 (1949). *15)* Thorson et al., *Amer. Heart J.*, **47**, 795 (1954); Sjoerdsma et al., *Amer. J. Med.*, **20**, 520 (1956). *16)* Horwitt, M. K., *Amer. J. clin. Nutr.*, **3**, 244 (1955); Goldsmith et al., *J. Nutr.*, **56**, 371 (1955). *17)* Zelin'skiĭ, S. P., *Chem. Abstr.*, **50**, 11494 (1956). *18)* Jolliffe, N., *J. Amer. med. Ass.*, **117**, 1496 (1941); Sydenstricker et al., *J. Amer. med. Ass.*, **118**, 1199 (1942); Sinclair, H. M., *Brit. med. Bull.*, **12**, 18 (1956). *19)* Sinclair, H. M., *Brit. med. Bull.*, **12**, 24 (1956). *20)* Passmore and Meiklejohn, in Thompson and King (Eds.), *Biochemical Disorders in Human Disease*, London, 1957, page 544. *21)* Chalopin, H., *C. R. Soc. Biol. (Paris)*, **150**, 940 (1956); Nigeon-Dureuil et al., *J. Physiol. (Paris)*, **48**, 674 (1956).

Biotin (vitamin H)

Biotin occurs naturally in two forms, α- and β-biotin. Both forms are soluble in water and alcohol, sparingly soluble in ether and chloroform, stable to heat, and inactivated by acids, alkalis, rancid fats and choline.

α-Biotin, $C_{10}H_{16}O_3N_2S$ BIOTIN
Crystallizes in rhombic prisms
Mol. wt. 244.32
M. p. 220°C

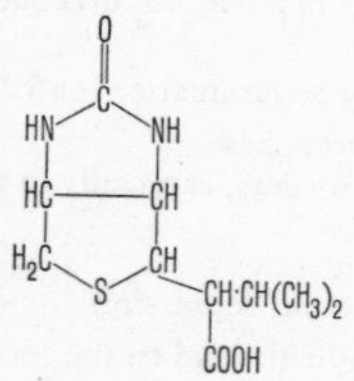

β-Biotin, $C_{10}H_{16}O_3N_2S$
Colorless crystals
Mol. wt. 244.32
M. p. 232–233°C

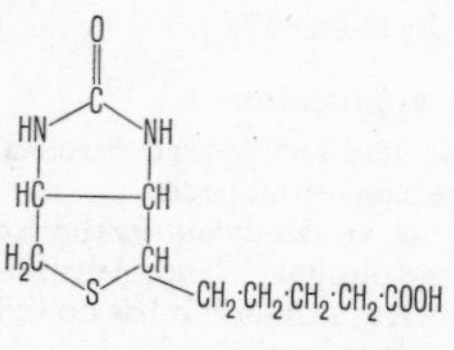

Oxybiotin, $C_{10}H_{16}O_4N_2$
Colorless crystals
Mol. wt. 228.25
M. p. 205–207°C

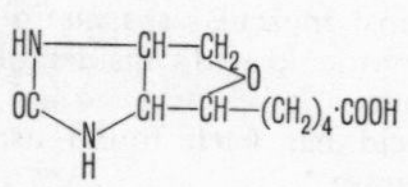

Oxybiotin, in which the sulfur atom is replaced by oxygen, possesses marked biotin activity[1].

Methods of test and assay

Microbiologically by means of *Lactobacillus helveticus (L. casei)* or *Lactobacillus arabinosus*. *Micrococcus sodonensis* is significantly more sensitive than *L. arabinosus* and has now largely replaced the latter[2]. There are no physical or chemical methods of assay.

Occurrence (values in mg per 100 g weight fresh)

Yeast *(Torula utilis)* 0.13; roasted peanuts and chocolate 0.032–0.034; dried peas and mushrooms 0.016–0.018; in small concentrations in all animal and plant tissues.

Physiology and function

Warm-blooded animals and certain bacteria require biotin for growth. Whilst many species are dependent on intake in food others can themselves synthesize enough for their needs.

Biotin is formed by the intestinal flora in such large quantities that its excretion in the feces is always 2–5 times the intake in food[3]. A diet rich in fat seems to reduce the intestinal synthesis but in general the influence of the diet on the synthesis of the vitamin in the digestive tract is very small[4]. Excretion in the urine proceeds parallel with the intake of biotin and under normal conditions is 0.33–0.75 μg (mean 0.4 μg) per day per kg body weight[5]. The biotin content of the whole blood is 0.75–1.73 μg per 100 ml (average 1.23 μg per 100 ml), that of the serum 0.95–1.66 μg per 100 ml (average 1.27 μg per 100 ml)[6]. The organism seems able to utilize the intestinal biotin, but to what extent is not known.

Nothing is yet known of the physiological function of this vitamin. It is possibly involved in the biosynthesis of oleic acid and fatty acids and also of some amino acids[7]. It seems to play no part in the breakdown of tryptophan[8].

Relationships between this vitamin and certain enzymes have also been found. It is uncertain, however, whether it acts as a coenzyme, is involved in enzyme synthesis (hexokinase), or exerts a nonspecific action on protein synthesis in general[9].

Mention should also be made of the effect of biotin on the direct carboxylation of propionates to succinates[10]. Biotin plays a coenzymatic role in the oxalacetic carboxylase system (reversible fixation of carbon dioxide)[11].

The presence of biotin is important for the proper utilization of pantothenic acid, as also for recovery from diseases due to pantothenic acid deficiency[12]. Biotin and pantothenic acid together represent a growth factor for certain animals[13] and are probably also concerned in the synthesis of nicotinic acid[14].

The relatively high concentration of a complex of factors of the B group (biotin, riboflavin, pantothenic acid, etc.) in the skin indicates that these compounds play an important part in the metabolic processes of the cutaneous cells[15].

The sulfoxides exhibit some vitamin activity. Milk contains biotin-(+)sulfoxide methyl ester. The AN-factor of *Aspergillus* is a biotin-(−)sulfoxide[16] with the formula shown below, and has vitamin activity for *Neurospora crassa*[17].

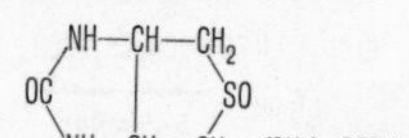

Certain homologues (homooxybiotin; biotin sulfone, in which the sulfur atom is replaced by a sulfone group) act as antivitamins[1]. The protein avidine, present in raw egg albumin, combines with biotin in the organism and is used to produce experimental avitaminosis[18].

Biotin deficiency in higher animals causes hyperactivity of the sebaceous glands, with a tendency to cutaneous inflammation and abscesses[1]. Nervous disorders also appear. When the diet is deficient in the vitamin a mild dermatitis is observed after 4 weeks, developing in up to 7 weeks into maculosquamous dermatitis of the nape, hands, arms and legs. During the 7th and 8th weeks the skin has a marked gray color and the tongue is whitish with atrophied papillae. Nervous disorders appear toward the 5th week in the form of myalgia, hyperesthesia, localized paresthesia, anorexia, nausea and depression. In the blood, in spite of normal intake of iron, a fall in the erythrocytes and in the hematocrit and hemoglobin values occurs, with a slight increase in bile pigments and a marked rise of cholesterol[19]. The experimental animal shows dermatitis, arrest of growth and loss of hair which is localized particularly around the eyes ("spectacle" alopecia).

Deficiency symptoms in the turkey are retarded growth, diarrhea, deformation of the bones (perosis), dermatitis, brittleness and loss of luster in feathers. When pantothenic acid is given the growth improves but not the other symptoms[20]. In rats, early degeneration of the testes with delayed spermatogenesis and lesions of the spermatocytes have been observed, a result of deficiency of the male sex hormone[21]. When the deficiency is severe the animal cannot synthesize nicotinic acid and 1-methylnicotinamide from tryptophan[22], and an increase of pyruvic acid occurs with slight hypoglycemia, slight fall of glucose level and marked lack of reducing sugars in the liver[23]. Treatment with 75–300 μg of biotin per day brings about disappearance of the symptoms in 3–5 days[24].

Therapeutic applications

Biotin should be given in dermatoses in which deficiency of the vitamin is suspected (seborrhea in infancy, acne, furunculosis).

When given parenterally biotin prevents the congestion which occurs after peroral administration of nicotinic acid, a single dose sufficing with decreasing efficacy for several days. Biotin treatment of acne rosacea results in an immediate marked improvement but its action is only temporary[25].

The biotin content of tumor tissues is abnormally high but experimental therapy in man based on this fact has proved unsuccessful[26].

References: *1)* Pilgrim et al., *Science*, **102**, 35 (1945). *2)* Aaronson, S., *J. Bact.*, **69**, 67 (1955). *3)* Oppel, T. W., *Amer. J. med. Sci.*, **204**, 856 (1942). *4)* Barki et al., *J. Nutr.*, **37**, 443 (1949). *5)* Spector, W. S. (Ed.), *Handbook of Biological Data*, Philadelphia, 1956, page 242. *6)* Denko et al., *Arch. Biochem.*, **13**, 481 (1947). *7)* Williams et al., *J. biol. Chem.*, **170**, 619 (1947). *8)* Dalgliesh, C. E., *Biochem. J.*, **61**, 328 (1955). *9)* Williams et al., *Arch. Biochem. Biophys.*, **66**, 234 (1957). *10)* Lardy and Peanasky, *Physiol. Rev.*, **33**, 560 (1953); Lardy and Adler, *J. biol. Chem.*, **219**, 933 (1956). *11)* Lichtstein, H. C., *J. biol. Chem.*, **212**, 217 (1955); Sitinskaya, O. N., *C. R. Acad. Sci. U.R.S.S.*, **110**, 253 (1956). *12)* Wright and Welch, *J. Nutr.*, **27**, 55 (1944). *13)* Emerson and Wurtz, *Proc. Soc. exp. Biol. (N.Y.)*, **57**, 47 (1944). *14)* Sundaram et al., *Curr. Sci.*, **22**, 211 (1953). *15)* Lee et al., *J. invest. Derm.*, **20**, 19 (1953). *16)* Melville, D.B., *J. biol. Chem.*, **208**, 495 (1954). *17)* Wright et al., *J. Amer. chem. Soc.*, **76**, 4156 (1954). *18)* Mickelsen, O., *Vitam. and Horm.*, **14**, 1 (1956). *19)* Sydenstricker et al., *Science*, **95**, 176 (1942). *20)* Robblee and Clandinin, *Poult. Sci.*, **32**, 579 (1953). *21)* Delost and Terroine, *C. R. Soc. Biol. (Paris)*, **149**, 1236 (1955). *22)* Sundaram and Sarma, *J. sci. industr. Res.*, **14c**, 193 (1955). *23)* Terroine, T., *Arch. Sci. physiol.*, **10**, 59 (1956). *24)* Sydenstricker et al., *J. Amer. med. Ass.*, **118**, 1199 (1942). *25)* Bereston, E. S., *Amer. J. clin. Nutr.*, **2**, 133 (1954). *26)* West and Woglom, *Science*, **93**, 525 (1941); *Cancer Res.*, **2**, 324 (1942).

Pantothenic acid[1]

This vitamin occurs in nature as the free acid. It is soluble in water, insoluble in benzene and chloroform, unstable to heat, alkalis and acids. Commercial preparations usually contain the water-soluble and thermostable calcium salt.

Pantothenic acid, $C_9H_{17}O_5N$ PANTOTHENIC ACID
Yellow, viscous oil
Mol.wt. 219.24

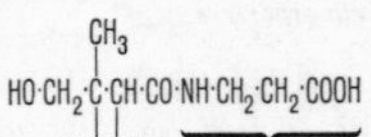

β-Alanine
residue

Calcium pantothenate, $(C_9H_{16}O_5N)_2Ca$
White crystals, odorless with a sweet taste
Mol.wt. 476.55

Unit

No international unit; by weight.

Methods of test and assay

Microbiologically by means of *Lactobacillus helveticus (L. casei)* or *L. arabinosus*; growth test on chicks or yeast.

Occurrence (values in mg per 100 g weight fresh)

Yeast 14–35; liver 7–8; dried beans, mushrooms, roasted peanuts 1–2.5; human milk 0.2 mg/100 ml[2]; widely distributed in plant and animal tissues. The food of the queen bee (gelée royale) is very rich in pantothenic acid and is in this respect surpassed only by the ovaries of fish[3].

Physiology and function

Pantothenic acid can be synthesized by plants, certain microorganisms and rodents (very probably by their intestinal flora).

It is formed in the intestine of man but it has not been proved that the organism uses this source.

All tissues contain pantothenic acid, the concentration being half that of nicotinic acid and ten times that of vitamin B_1[4]. Its biological significance is still not fully explained. It is a component of the coenzyme A necessary for acetylation (see page 370). Folic acid and biotin are necessary for the normal utilization of pantothenic acid by the organism[5].

The daily urinary excretion is 1.46–6.79 mg and is increased significantly in conditions inducing profuse sweating[6]. The normal level in whole blood is 19–32 μg/100 ml (mean 23 μg/100 ml)[7], in plasma 6–22 μg/100 ml[8]. Four hours after a test dose a marked rise in the levels in the blood and urine is observed[9]. Excretion in the feces is very variable and depends on the diet. The daily requirement is unknown.

The adrenal cortical tissue is especially sensitive to deficiency of pantothenic acid and shows a decrease of steroid production (probably due to disturbance of acetylation); in the blood the eosinophil reaction to ACTH is feeble or absent[10] and the serum shows a decrease of antibodies and complement[11].

Pantothenic acid and coenzyme A promote the growth of epidermal tissues and tissue cultures[12–14]. Coenzyme A also has a marked action on the mitochondria and on the intracellular formation of lipids[14]. A deficiency of pantothenic acid from the start of pregnancy may cause premature birth with high mortality. Survivors show maldevelopment of the eyes and brain, cardiovascular anomalies, hemorrhage and edema of the fingers, hydronephrosis, often cleft palate and clubfoot. If the deficiency is not of long duration the fetus rarely shows anomalies[15].

The external symptoms of pantothenic acid deficiency vary considerably with the species of experimental animal:

(a) Skin and mucosae: loss of hair pigment (young rats), atrophy of the skin and dermatitis (chicks), vascularization of the cornea due to large capillaries with prominent anastomoses (rats)[16].
(b) Intestine: atrophy of the intestinal mucosa (all animal species), duodenal ulceration (rats, in 60% of cases)[17], fatty degeneration of the liver (dogs)[18].
(c) General disorders: convulsions and coma (dogs)[18], increased susceptibility to stress (rats)[19].
(d) Nervous system: ataxia (monkeys)[20], degenerative changes in the spinal cord (chicks)[21], in the peripheral nerves, the spinal nerve roots and posterior columns (pigs)[22].

In man, pantothenic acid deficiency shows itself in slight lassitude, orthostatic disorders and mental disturbances (discontent and quarrelsomeness), subsequently torpor and paresthesia of the extremities, exaggerated reflexes and epigastric troubles. In addition there are increased susceptibility to infectious diseases of the respiratory passages, hypochlorhydria and a fall in the blood cholesterol level.

The symptoms may be summarized as follows:

(a) neuromotor disturbances
(b) cardiovascular disorders, especially in the erect posture
(c) digestive disorders
(d) susceptibility to infections
(e) physical weakness and depression

Addition of pantothenic acid to the food does not suppress all the symptoms; administration of vitamins of the B complex gives a considerably better result[23].

In the diabetic animal pantothenic acid produces insulin resistance[24]. In liver disorders the urinary excretion of pantothenic acid is markedly reduced[25].

Therapeutic applications

Pantothenic acid has proved practically useless in combatting graying of the hair and alopecia.

It is used as an adjuvant in the treatment of chromophobe adenoma of the pituitary gland, Addison's disease, cirrhosis of the liver and diabetes (although it has no influence on the blood sugar or blood phosphate level)[26].

Good results are observed in the treatment of post-operative intestinal atony. High peroral or parenteral doses of 500 mg seem to be active against muscular spasms in pregnancy[27]. Dressings with salts of pantothenic acid considerably accelerate the healing of sluggish wounds.

Pantothenic acid has been found useful in poisoning with isoniazid[28] and curare[29].

References: *1)* For a review see Briskas et al., *Int. Z. Vitaminforsch.*, **23**, 63 (1951). *2)* Schmidt, V., *Int. Z. Vitaminforsch.*, **22**, 21 (1950). *3)* Pearson and Burgin, *Proc. Soc. exp. Biol. (N.Y.)*, **48**, 415 (1941); Novelli, G. D., *Ann. Rev. Biochem.*, **26**, 243 (1957). *4)* Williams et al., *The Biochemistry of the B-Vitamins*, New York, 1950, quoted by Pett, L. B., *Vitam. and Horm.*, **13**, 213 (1955). *5)* Wright and Welch, *J. Nutr.*, **27**, 55 (1944); Popp and Totter, *J. biol. Chem.*, **199**, 547 (1952). *6)* Pelczar and Porter, *Proc. Soc. exp. Biol. (N.Y.)*, **47**, 3 (1941). *7)* Stanbery et al., *J. biol. Chem.*, **135**, 353 (1940). *8)* Denko et al., *Arch. Biochem.*, **13**, 481 (1947). *9)* Gounelle and Richet, *C. R. Soc. Biol. (Paris)*, **150**, 2167 (1956); **151**, 24 (1957). *10)* Dumm and Ralli, *Metabolism*, **2**, 153 (1953); *Endocrinology*, **54**, 71 (1954). *11)* Axelrod et al., *Proc. Soc. exp. Biol. (N.Y.)*, **66**, 137 (1947). *12)* Lasfargues and Wiesendanger, *C. R. Soc. Biol. (Paris)*, **147**, 978 (1953). *13)* Mouchette, R., *C. R. Soc. Biol. (Paris)*, **147**, 1306 (1953). *14)* Biesele, J. J., *J. biophys. biochem. Cytol.*, **1**, 119 (1955). *15)* Nelson et al., *J. Nutr.*, **62**, 395 (1957).

16) Bowles et al., *J. Nutr.*, **37**, 9 (1949). 17) Berg et al., *Proc. Soc. exp. Biol. (N.Y.)*, **71**, 374 (1949). 18) Schaefer et al., *J. biol. Chem.*, **143**, 321 (1942). 19) Dumm et al., *Proc. Soc. exp. Biol. (N.Y.)*, **71**, 368 (1949). 20) McCall et al., *J. Nutr.*, **31**, 685 (1946). 21) Phillips and Engel, *J. Nutr.*, **18**, 227 (1939). 22) Follis and Wintrobe, *J. exp. Med.*, **81**, 539 (1945). 23) Bean et al., *J. clin. Invest.*, **34**, 1073 (1955). 24) Hazelwood et al., *Endocrinology*, **58**, 427 (1956). 25) Ueshima et al., *J. Vitaminol.*, **2**, 299 (1956), quoted by Sarett and Morrison, *Ann. Rev. Biochem.*, **27**, 339 (1958). 26) Gershberg et al., *J. Nutr.*, **39**, 107 (1949). 27) Luraschi, C., *Acta vitamin. (Milano)*, **10**, 113 (1956); Luisi, M., *Acta vitamin. (Milano)*, **10**, 219 (1956); Schulte, F.-J., *Dtsch. med. Wschr.*, **82**, 1188 (1957). 28) Manthei, R. W., *Proc. Soc. exp. Biol. (N.Y.)*, **95**, 402 (1957). 29) Galeotto, E., *Acta vitamin. (Milano)*, **10**, 193 (1956).

Folic acid group

The name "folic acid" was given in 1941 to a vitamin-like substance isolated from spinach leaves[1]. In 1943 the crystalline compound pteroylglutamic acid was isolated from liver and yeast[2] and later shown to be related to the pteridines, the wing pigments of butterflies. In 1945 its synthesis was demonstrated by Angier[3]. In 1948 Sauberlich and Baumann described a growth factor essential to *Leuconostoc citrovorum* 8081 which they named the citrovorum factor[4]. This was later identified as 5-formyl-5,6,7,8-tetrahydropteroylglutamic acid and synthesized[5,6].

The structure of the original **"folic acid"** is unknown, and this term is today used to designate the group of pteroylglutamic acids. In common usage, however, it usually means *pteroylmonoglutamic acid* (vitamin B_c, vitamin M, factor U). Pteroyltriglutamic acid and pteroylheptaglutamic acid contain respectively three and seven glutamic acid residues in the molecule[7].

Pteroylmonoglutamic acid occurs only in the liver and in yeast. It is identical with the *Lactobacillus casei* factor isolated from the liver[8] and also with vitamin B_c[9] (the letter c is from "chicken"). It is sparingly soluble in water, insoluble in fat solvents (the sodium salt is very soluble in water), thermostable in alkaline or neutral solution, unstable to heat in acid solution. It is decomposed by light first into pteraldehyde-(6), then into 2-amino-4-hydroxypteridine-6-carboxylic acid and finally into 2-amino-4-hydroxypteridine[10].

Similar vitamin activity is shown by conjugates of folic acid which occur in nature, such as *pteroyltriglutamic acid (teropterin)*, identical with the *Lactobacillus casei* factor produced by vegetable fermentation processes; and *pteroylheptaglutamic acid*, identical with the vitamin B_c conjugate found in yeast. Still other pteridine derivatives have analogous but weaker vitamin activity, such as *rhizopterin*, which is identical with the so-called SLR-factor[11]; *xanthopterin*, the yellow pigment of butterflies[12]; *biopterin*, found in human urine; and *ichthyopterin* found in the scales of fish[13].

Folic acid (vitamin B_c, vitamin M, factor U), $C_{19}H_{19}O_6N_7$
PTEROYLMONOGLUTAMIC ACID
Orange-yellow needles or platelets, tasteless, odorless
Mol.wt. 441.42

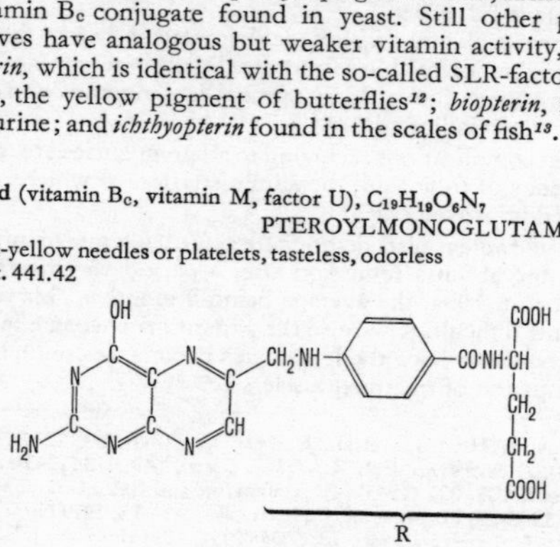

Citrovorum factor (5-formyl-5,6,7,8-tetrahydropteroylglutamic acid, leucovorin, folinic acid), $C_{20}H_{23}O_7N_7$
Mol.wt. 473.46

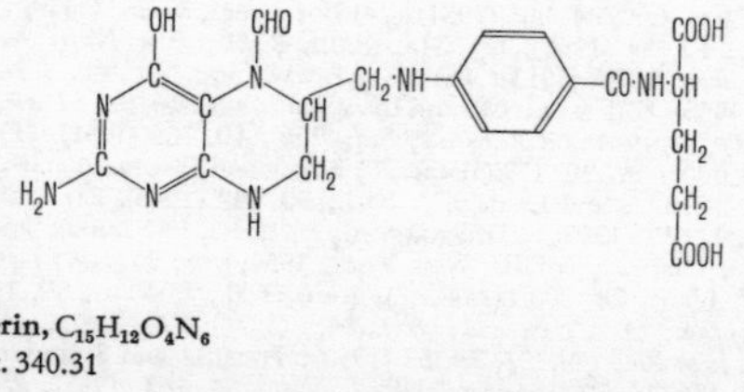

Rhizopterin, $C_{15}H_{12}O_4N_6$
Mol.wt. 340.31

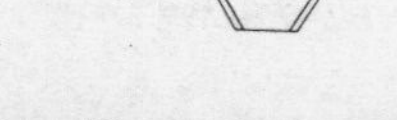

Xanthopterin, $C_6H_5O_2N_5$ R = OH
Mol.wt. 179.15

Biopterin, $C_9H_{11}O_3N_5$
Mol.wt. 237.23

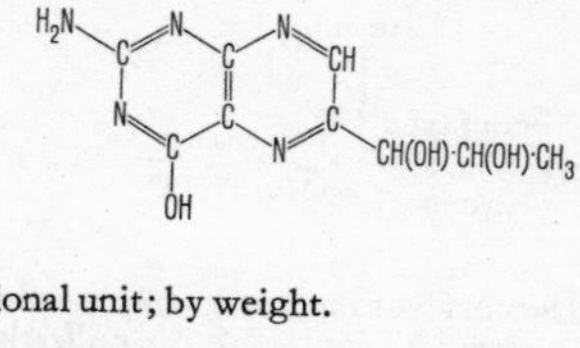

Unit

No international unit; by weight.

Methods of test and assay[14]

Citrovorum factor: *Leuconostoc citrovorum*; micro-methods[17]. Folic acid, citrovorum factor and other substances with folic acid activity: *Streptococcus faecalis, Lactobacillus helveticus (L. casei)*.

Folic acid: comparison of the urinary excretion of folic acid in the urine after identical peroral and subcutaneous doses (Girdwood's method)[15]; chromatographic separation followed by fluorimetric assay[16].

Occurrence

Citrovorum factor and folic acid: yeast and liver; *pteroylglutamic acid conjugates:* yeasts and other fungi, green leaves, grass, milk (very little); *rhizopterin:* liver, milk and cereal grains, very little in green leaves; *xanthopterin:* fish liver.

Physiology and function

Folic acid. Synthesized in large quantities by the intestinal flora. The organism appears to be able to meet its needs very largely from this synthesis since a diet deficient in folic acid continued for some time hardly affects the urinary excretion, while normally 75% of the folic acid ingested is excreted in the urine[18]. On a normal diet the urinary excretion of folic acid amounts to 3.8–23.8 µg (mean 10.8 µg) per day[19]. In health, the gastric juice converts pteroylheptaglutamic acid into another, unknown conjugate and finally into pteroylmonoglutamic acid, which appears in the blood. This process is interrupted in pernicious anemia but not in sprue[20]. Certain constituents of the intestinal flora destroy folic acid (*Streptococcus lactis R* and *S. faecalis* up to 60–80%)[21]. The blood contains folic acid conjugase[22], an enzyme which converts folic acid conjugates with more than three glutamic acid groups into pteroylmonoglutamic acid. It is not therefore absolutely necessary for folic acid conjugates to be broken down in the intestinal tract for them to become utilizable by the organism.

Man and some other animal species (rats, pigs, dogs, rabbits) seem able to meet their requirements of folic acid by their own intestinal synthesis. Many animals (monkeys, guinea pigs, mice, foxes, chickens, geese, turkeys) are entirely dependent on external sources[23]. The mouse makes only partial use of intestinal synthesis, as shown by the fact that a diet absolutely free from folic acid is unfavorable to its growth and causes loss of hair[24]. Guinea pigs require 3–6 mg of folic acid per kilogram of food, or 6 mg daily, to maintain a normal state of the white blood cells[25].

The folic acid formed in the intestine is used more or less completely by the organism. Sulfonamides show a tendency to block the intestinal synthesis, an effect which they also exert on the intestinal synthesis of other vitamins of the B complex[26].

The *citrovorum factor* is the active form of folic acid. It has not been proved that the diet must contain this factor, because in the presence of ascorbic acid it can be formed in the liver from folic acid[27]. The citrovorum factor is the only compound of this group which has an influence on blood formation. Its vitamin activity corresponds to that of pteroylmonoglutamic acid.

The folic acid conjugates are precursors of pteroylmonoglutamic acid, which in turn is the provitamin of the citrovorum factor.

In metabolic investigations it is impossible to demarcate completely the activities of folic acid and the citrovorum factor from those of vitamin B_{12} since the two groups are closely interconnected (see below). Both are concerned in the synthesis of nucleic acid but their roles are different and they are not mutually replaceable[28]. They also play a part in certain metabolic functions of the nucleoproteins. Folic acid controls the glycine–serine conversion in amino acid metabolism[29]. Derivatives of the vitamin act as coenzymes in the intermediate metabolism of purines and pyrimidines[30]. The following scheme illustrates the functions of folic acid and the citrovorum factor[31]:

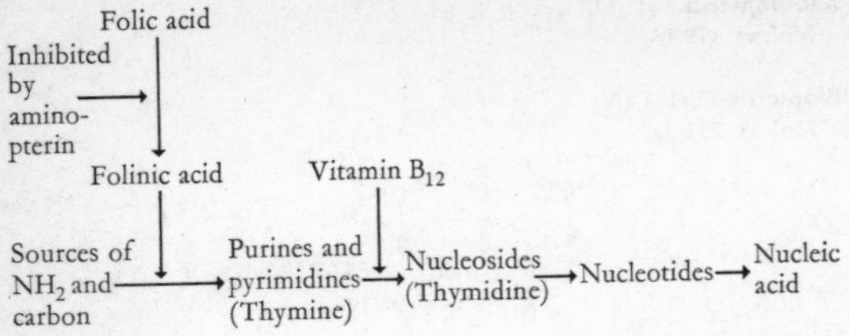

Folic acid and biotin favor the storage of pantothenic acid in the liver and are also necessary for the proper utilization of this substance in the organism[32], especially in coenzyme-A synthesis[30]. Ascorbic acid is not only concerned in the formation of the citrovorum factor from folic acid but also protects the former from oxidation in an aerobic environment[33].

Folic acid is an important factor in growth and reproduction. Its influence on the female sex organs is particularly evident after prolonged deficiency, when changes in the vaginal epithelium and endometrium appear with the result that these no longer react normally to estrogens[34, 35]. In deficiency the ovarian hormones are no longer able to maintain normal pregnancy[35, 36]. It is noteworthy that during pregnancy the serum level of folic acid, as also that of the estrogens, rises 2–8 times, and urinary excretion increases[37]. Symptoms of deficiency are much less marked in males[38]; folic acid increases the action of testosterone on the development of accessory sex organs.

Either folic acid or the citrovorum factor appears to perform some function in the differentiation of the primitive nervous system in the embryo. Lack of folic acid impairs the development of young animals[39]. Guinea pigs, for example, grow slowly and exhibit loss of appetite, leukopenia, anemia, tendency to diarrhea and poor development of the erythroblasts in the bone marrow; other effects are fatty infiltration of the liver and hemorrhages in the adrenal glands[25]. In geese, paralyses of cervical origin occur.

Vitamin B_{12} and pteroylmonoglutamic acid are essential factors for cell multiplication. Vitamin B_{12} is stored in the mitochondria while folic acid is distributed throughout the whole cell[40]. During mitosis, folic acid is necessary for the transition from the metaphase to the anaphase and the presence at this stage of the folic acid antagonist aminopterin inhibits cell-division[39]. Both vitamins occur in the chromosomes[40].

The complexity of the blood-forming and digestive processes is probably the reason for their special sensitivity to deficiency of one or other of these two vitamins. Folic acid appears in some way to lay the foundations for the action of vitamin B_{12}, which in turn has an influence on the storage and utilization of folic acid as well as protecting the nervous system against injury due to pernicious anemia. In addition to the two vitamins mentioned, various other substances play a part in erythropoiesis: amino acids, trace elements (Cu, Zn, Mo), iron, various vitamins (nicotinic acid, pantothenic acid, riboflavin, pyridoxine, etc.). In man, impairment of erythropoiesis is caused only by lack of iron, folic acid, vitamin B_{12} and possibly ascorbic acid. The part played by folic acid and vitamin B_{12} in the bone marrow has not as yet been fully explained, but they seem to exert an influence on the metabolism of the nutritional substrate[41]. In man, inadequate utilization of folic acid, or deficiency of the vitamin due to deficient intestinal synthesis or poor absorption, may result in megaloblastic anemia. If vitamin B_{12} also is deficient, some of the symptoms of pernicious anemia may appear[42].

In sprue and idiopathic steatorrhea there is impaired absorption not only of folic acid and vitamin B_{12} but also of other vitamins (A, K), iron, fats, etc. The clinical picture varies greatly according to the nature of the principal disturbance. Cytologically there is a macrocytic anemia with the appearance of megaloblasts and other intermediates in the bone marrow. A trial treatment will show which of the two vitamins or which combination of the various factors is likely to be effective therapeutically[42].

Megaloblastic anemia in young children with signs of general malnutrition is due to multiple avitaminosis caused by artificial feeding with cow's milk, which contains insufficient quantities of essential metabolites. Folic acid given together with ascorbic acid brings about rapid recovery[43]. The anemia of scurvy has a similar origin and also responds well to this treatment[44].

Megaloblastic anemia during the last 3 months of pregnancy may be due to unbalanced or insufficient nutrition, to gastrointestinal disorders or to twin-pregnancy. It disappears spontaneously after parturition, but may reappear in subsequent pregnancies. Prior to parturition, vitamin B_{12} has no effect on the anemia and folic acid only a partial one, so that this disease is more likely to be due to poor utilization of the vitamins than to lack of them[41, 45]. The anemia of epileptics is apparently due to folic acid and vitamin B_{12} antagonists which arise during prolonged treatment with phenytoin, phenobarbital and primidone[46].

True pernicious anemia (Addison-Biermer anemia) reacts to folic acid with immediate normalization of the blood picture and disappearance of the mucosal symptoms. This effect is only transient, however, and relapses eventually occur[47]. Folic acid also fails to protect the nervous system against the subacute degenerative lesions of pernicious anemia, which it may actually accelerate[48].

The antivitamins of the folic acid group can be divided into several classes according to whether they inhibit pteroylmonoglutamic acid or the citrovorum factor. These compounds have been used to produce avitaminosis, in studies of the mechanisms of vitamin metabolism and in the investigation of pernicious anemia. The most active folic acid antagonists are derivatives and analogues of pteroylmonoglutamic acid with an amino group in the 4-position (4-aminopteroylglutamic acid, 4-aminopteroylaspartic acid, etc.). They act by blocking the conversion of folic acid into the citrovorum factor and probably also by making it impossible for the organism to use the latter substance. These antagonists cause hemorrhage and necrosis of the mucosa of the digestive tract and the appearance of megaloblasts in the bone marrow[41, 49]. The other antivitamins have a marked action on bacterial growth and cause death of the fetus *in utero*, deformities, or disturbances of growth[50]. Certain 4-aminopteroylglutamic acids have found a use in the treatment of acute leukemia of infants (see below).

It is noteworthy that folic acid deficiency considerably reduces the capacity of the organism to form antibodies[51].

Therapeutic applications

1. In megaloblastic anemia (see above), which can be divided into two groups:
   (*a*) with involvement of the nervous system; these are best treated with vitamin B_{12}.
   (*b*) without involvement of the nervous system; these do not in general respond to vitamin B_{12}, so that folic acid is the drug of choice[52].
2. As adjuvant in the treatment of diseases with concomitant anemia, in which it should be combined with vitamin C in order to achieve full effect.

   In pernicious anemia, folic acid simulates a cure by the restoration of the normal blood picture. For this reason and for the reasons given above this treatment is dangerous and is absolutely contraindicated[47, 48].
3. Certain complications recurring in all pregnancies are caused by deficiency of folic acid, the administration of which results in marked improvement[53].
4. Folic acid antagonists do not cure acute leukemia of infants, but can bring about a remission after a period varying from two weeks to 6 years, the average being 8 months. This treatment presents difficulties because the patient may become intolerant, and sooner or later the leukocytes become resistant and make continuation of treatment useless[41, 49, 54].

References: *1*) Mitchell et al., *J. Amer. chem. Soc.*, **63**, 2284 (1941); **66**, 267 (1944). *2*) Stokstad, E. L. R., *J. biol. Chem.*, **149**, 573 (1943). *3*) Angier et al., *Science*, **102**, 227 (1945). *4*) Sauberlich and Baumann, *J. biol. Chem.*, **176**, 165 (1948). *5*) Flynn et al., *J. Amer. chem. Soc.*, **73**, 1979 (1951). *6*) Cosulich et al., *J. Amer. chem. Soc.*, **73**, 5006 (1951). *7*) Courtois, J. E., *Bull. Soc. Chim. biol. (Paris)*, **38**, 295 (1956). *8*) Snell and Peterson, *J. Bact.*, **39**, 273 (1940). *9*) Hogan and Parrott, *J. biol. Chem.*, **128**, xlvi (1939). *10*) Lowry et al., *J. biol. Chem.*, **180**, 389 (1949). *11*) Keresztesy et al., *Science*, **97**, 465 (1943). *12*) Schöpf and Becker, *Justus Liebigs Ann. Chem.*, **524**, 49 (1936); Becker and Schöpf, *ibid.*, **524**, 124 (1936). *13*) Tschesche and Korte, *Chem. Ber.*, **84**, 801 (1951). *14*) For a review see Witts, L. J., *Brit. med. Bull.*, **12**, 14 (1956). *15*) Girdwood, R. H., *Proc. Nutr. Soc.*, **14**, 41 (1955); *Lancet*, **2**, 53 (1953). *16*) Zakrzewski and Nichol, *J. biol. Chem.*, **205**, 361 (1953). *17*) Polonovski and Lévy, *Bull. Soc. Chim. biol. (Paris)*, **35**, 1167 (1953). *18*) Johnson and Parsons, *Fed. Proc.*, **10**, 385 (1951). *19*) Wright and Welch, *Science*, **98**, 179 (1943). *20*) Buyze and Engel, *Nature*, **163**, 135 (1949). *21*) Stokes and Larsen, *J. Bact.*, **50**, 219 (1945). *22*) Wolff et al., *Science*, **109**, 612 (1949). *23*) Stokstad, E. L. R., in Sebrell and Harris (Eds.), *The Vitamins*, vol. III, New York, 1954, page 171. *24*) Nielsen and Black, *J. Nutr.*, **28**, 203 (1944). *25*) Reid et al., *J. Nutr.*, **59**, 103 (1956). *26*) Mickelsen, O., *Vitam. and Horm.*, **14**, 1 (1956). *27*) Nichol and Welch, *Proc. Soc. exp. Biol. (N.Y.)*, **74**, 52 (1950); Heisler and Schweigert, *Fed. Proc.*, **14**, 436 (1955); Bleiler et al., *J. Nutr.*, **56**, 163 (1955). *28*) Harris, J. W., *Amer. J. Med.*, **21**, 461 (1956). *29*) Arnstein and Stanković, *Biochem. J.*, **62**, 190 (1956); Arnstein and Keglević, *Biochem. J.*, **62**, 199 (1956). *30*) Popp and Totter, *J. biol. Chem.*, **199**, 547 (1952). *31*) Girdwood, R. H.,

Brit. J. Nutr., **6**, 315 (1952); MUELLER and WILL, *Amer. J. clin. Nutr.*, **3**, 30 (1955). *32)* WRIGHT and WELCH, *J. Nutr.*, **27**, 55 (1944); GIROUD et al., *Int. Z. Vitaminforsch.*, **25**, 153 (1954). *33)* NICHOL and WELCH, *Proc. Soc. exp. Biol. (N.Y.)*, **74**, 52 (1950); NICHOL, C. A., *J. biol. Chem.*, **204**, 469 (1953). *34)* HERTZ, R., *Science*, **107**, 300 (1948); HERTZ and TULLNER, *Endocrinology*, **44**, 278 (1949). *35)* SILVER, M., *J. Endocr.*, **10**, 95 (1954). *36)* NELSON et al., *Proc. Soc. exp. Biol. (N.Y.)*, **92**, 554 (1956). *37)* BAKER et al., *Proc. Soc. exp. Biol. (N.Y.)*, **94**, 513 (1957). *38)* GOLDIN et al., *Cancer (Philad.)*, **3**, 849 (1950). *39)* JACOBSON, W., *J. Physiol. (Lond.)*, **123**, 603 and 618 (1954). *40)* UNGLEY, C. C., *Vitam. and Horm.*, **13**, 137 (1955). *41)* CALLENDER and O'BRIEN, in THOMPSON and KING (Eds.), *Biochemical Disorders in Human Disease*, London 1957, page 84. *42)* ESTREN, S., *J. Mt Sinai Hosp.*, **24**, 304 (1957); BADENOCH and CALLENDER, *Blood*, **9**, 123 (1954); CARTWRIGHT et al., *Blood*, **7**, 992 (1952). *43)* ZUELZER and OGDEN, *Amer. J. Dis. Child.*, **71**, 211 (1946); ZUELZER and RUTZKY, *Advanc. Pediat.*, **6**, 243 (1953); MAY et al., *Amer. J. Dis. Child.*, **80**, 191 (1950). *44)* JANDL and GABUZDA, *Proc. Soc. exp. Biol. (N.Y.)*, **84**, 452 (1953). *45)* MOLLIN and ROSS, *Proc. roy. Soc. Med.*, **47**, 428 (1954); GIRDWOOD, R. H., *Brit. med. J.*, **2**, 954 (1954). *46)* BADENOCH, J., *Proc. roy. Soc. Med.*, **47**, 426 (1954); GIRDWOOD and LENMAN, *Brit. med. J.*, **1**, 146 (1956). *47)* VILTER et al., *Blood*, **5**, 695 (1950). *48)* ISRAËLS and WILKINSON, *Brit. med. J.*, **2**, 1072 (1949). *49)* BURCHENAL, J. M., *Proceedings of the 2nd Conferenc on Folic Acid Antagonists in the Treatment of Leukaemia*, 1952, quoted by CALLENDER and O'BRIEN, in THOMPSON and KING (Eds.), *Biochemical Disorders in Human Disease*, London, 1957, page 84; BURCHENAL, J. H., *Cancer Res.*, **14**, 615 (1954); *Fed. Proc.*, **13**, 760 (1954). *50)* THIERSCH, J. B., *Proc. Soc. exp. Biol. (N.Y.)*, **87**, 571 (1954). *51)* AXELROD and PRUZANSKY, *Vitam. and Horm.*, **13**, 1 (1955). *52)* NIEWEG et al., *J. Lab. clin. Med.*, **44**, 118 (1954). *53)* LAWSON et al., *Med. J. Aust.*, **1**, 848 (1953). *54)* FARBER et al., *Advanc. Cancer Res.*, **4**, 1 (1956).

Para-aminobenzoic acid (vitamin H_1)

This compound occurs in nature in the free or acetylated form or in combination with peptides. It is soluble in alcohol and in boiling water, stable in acid and alkaline solutions, unstable in the presence of oxidizing agents.

***p*-Aminobenzoic acid**, $C_7H_7O_2N$ PARA-AMINOBENZOIC ACID
Yellowish-red crystals
Mol.wt. 137.14
M.p. 186–187° C

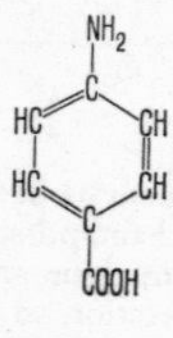

Unit

No international unit; by weight.

Methods of test and assay

Microbiologically by means of *Clostridium acetobutylicum*[1] or *Neurospora crassa*[2].

Occurrence[3] (values in mg per 100 g weight fresh)

Yeast 0.49–0.55; beef liver 0.15–0.25; mushrooms 0.13; wheat germ 0.17; spinach 0.06–0.13; oat flakes 0.033; corn meal 0.03; egg powder (whole egg) 0.02–0.036; calf liver 0.02; milk 0.015 mg per 100 ml.

Physiology and function

Man and the higher animals seem to be adapted to synthesize para-aminobenzoic acid from phenylalanine through para-aminophenylpyruvic acid and para-aminophenylacetic acid[4]. The urinary excretion is 2.0–3.0 μg/kg body weight in 24 hours (average 2.11 μg/kg); in the feces it is 1.01–8.2 μg/kg (average 3.5 μg/kg)[5].

The most characteristic property of para-aminobenzoic acid is its antagonistic action against sulfonamides, the bacteriostatic and bactericidal activity of which is inhibited; the slight antimalarial action of sulfonamides is also antagonized[6]. For this reason para-aminobenzoic acid is thought to be a constituent of some unknown enzyme of importance for bacteria which is blocked by sulfonamides via a displacement mechanism[4].

Para-aminobenzoic acid is an essential growth factor for many species of bacteria[7], but some of these can replace it more or less completely by pantothenic acid (for example *Bacterium linens*). Its metabolism is unknown, but it is thought that bacteria and possibly also other organisms can convert it into the citrovorum factor and pteroylglutamic acid.

The role of para-aminobenzoic acid in the animal organism has not yet been elucidated. In the presence of folic acid no symptoms of deficiency appear. In black rats it is important for hair pigmentation and in chickens and guinea pigs it promotes growth[8]. In certain cases it shows an activity similar to that of carotenes and in certain species often seems able to replace folic acid. Apart from the latter effect, however, there is no indication of the role played by para-aminobenzoic acid in the metabolism of man and higher animals[9]. For this reason it has been suggested that it should be removed from the vitamin series and classified among the nutritional factors essential to bacteria (such as α-lipoic acid, adenylic acid, orotic acid and certain thiazoles, purines, pyrimidines, etc.).

In high concentrations, para-aminobenzoic acid has a bacteriostatic action on the Rickettsias, but the effect is small in comparison with that of antibiotics[10].

Therapeutic applications

The esters of para-aminobenzoic acid are local anesthetics, for example procaine, the diethylaminoethyl ester. In the treatment of rheumatism, para-aminobenzoic acid reinforces the action of cortisone so that the dose of the latter can be reduced[11]. When very high doses of para-aminobenzoic acid are given, the patients excrete so much glucuronic acid in the urine that the glucose-fermentation test can no longer be carried out[12].

Good results have been obtained with para-aminobenzoic acid in the treatment of mycosis and of lymphoblastomas of the skin[13].

References: *1)* LAMPEN and PETERSON, *J. biol. Chem.*, **153**, 193 (1944). *2)* THOMPSON et al., *J. biol. Chem.*, **148**, 281 (1943). *3)* WRIGHT and TAVORMINA, in SEBRELL and HARRIS (Eds.), *The Vitamins*, vol. III, New York, 1954, page 27. *4)* NURMIKKO, V., *Ann. Acad. Sci. fenn.*, Ser. AII, No. 54 (1954). *5)* SPECTOR, W. S. (Ed.), *Handbook of Biological Data*, Philadelphia, 1956, page 242. *6)* For a review see WRIGHT and TAVORMINA, in SEBRELL and HARRIS (Eds.), *The Vitamins*, vol. III, New York, 1954, page 66. *7)* HAWKING F., *Brit. med. J.*, **1**, 425 (1954). *8)* ANSBACHER, S., *Science*, **93**, 164 (1941); MARTIN and ANSBACHER, *Proc. Soc. exp. Biol. (N.Y.)*, **48**, 118 (1941). *9)* WOODRUFF et al., *J. Nutr.*, **51**, 23 (1953); REID et al., *J. Nutr.*, **59**, 103 (1956). *10)* SCOTT, C. C., in SEBRELL and HARRIS (Eds.), *The Vitamins*, vol. III, New York, 1954, page 52. *11)* WIESEL et al., *Amer. J. med. Sci.*, **222**, 243 (1951). *12)* ZARAFONETIS and CHANDLER, *J. Lab. clin. Med.*, **37**, 425 (1951). *13)* ZARAFONETIS et al., *Cancer (Philad.)*, **7**, 190 (1954).

Vitamin B_{12} group COBALAMINS

The treatment of pernicious anemia with raw liver goes back to the year 1926[1], but the first isolation of the active substance was not possible until the year 1948[2]. Although the structure of the vitamin is known, its industrial manufacture still is based on its direct microbiological synthesis by *Streptomyces olivaceus*[3, 4] or *Bacillus megatherium*[3, 5]. It is also obtained as a by-product of the manufacture of antibiotics.

Vitamin B_{12} is a complex porphyrin derivative containing a tervalent cobalt atom and linked to a nucleotide (cf. also page 383). The term "B_{12} vitamins" is given to metabolites utilizable by vertebrates and the term "ψ-B_{12} vitamins" to those utilizable only by lower animals[6]. For a general review of the vitamin B_{12} group see LESTER SMITH[13].

Vitamin B_{12} exists in various forms designated B_{12} and $B_{12a, b, c, f, m, s}$. The a-form is formed by the action of light on an aqueous solution of the vitamin in the presence of catalysts[7]. The chemical, physical and biological properties of the different forms are practically identical except for the a-form, which presumably does not occur naturally. All are hygroscopic, stable at room temperature and to boiling in neutral aqueous solution, but unstable in alkaline or boiling acid solutions[8].

A nomenclature of the members of the vitamin B_{12} group based on the nature of the nucleotide group has been proposed[9] in which the term cobalamin is confined to those compounds in which the nucleotide contains the base 5,6-dimethylbenzimidazole. Thus vitamin B_{12}, which contains a cyano group attached to the cobalt atom, is named cyanocobalamin. Vitamins B_{12a} and B_{12b} (see Table 1, below) can be converted into cyanocobalamin by

Table 1 The cobalamins (nucleotide base: 5,6-dimethylbenzimidazole) (after LESTER SMITH[13])

Original designation	Coordinated ion or molecule	Semi-systematic name
B_{12}	CN^-	cyanocobalamin
B_{12a} }	OH^- (alkaline soln.)	hydroxocobalamin
B_{12b} }	H_2O (acid solution)	aquocobalamin
B_{12c}	ONO^-	nitritocobalamin

reaction with cyanogen ions. Many related compounds found in the feces of various animals[10], in activated sewage sludge, in soils[11], and in algae and bacteria[12] exhibit different activity and contain nucleotide bases other than 5,6-dimethylbenzimidazole (see Table 2, below). A systematic nomenclature of the compounds in the B_{12} field has been tentatively put forward by the International Union of Pure and Applied Chemistry[14]. In this system the base-free compound is designated cobamide, so that vitamin B_{12} becomes α-(5,6-dimethylbenzimidazolyl)cobamide cyanide.

Table 2 B_{12} analogues containing bases other than 5,6-dimethylbenzimidazole (after LESTER SMITH[13])

Name	Nucleotide base	Remarks
ψ-Vitamin B_{12}	adenine	Mainly active for bacteria *(Escherichia coli)*
Factor A	2-methyladenine	Active for certain bacteria, inactive for chicks. Poorly absorbed in the intestine. When given parenterally it is stored partly unchanged in the liver. Very feeble activity in pernicious anemia
Factor B (etiocobalamin)	(no nucleotide)	The nucleotide-free part of B_{12}, ψ-B_{12} and factor A. Very active for some bacteria *(E. coli)*, inactive for rats and chicks. Poorly absorbed in the intestine. Inactive in pernicious anemia
Factor C	guanine (?)	Mixture of two very similar compounds, C_1 and C_2, from calf feces. Activity for bacteria similar to factor B, into which it is slowly converted in aqueous solution
Factor D	(unknown)	Red, acid pigment from calf feces. No vitamin activity. Possibly an intermediate metabolite
Factor E	(unknown)	Red, acid pigment from feces of swine, cattle and rats. Also found in many fermentation products. Activity for bacteria similar to factor B
Factor F	2-methylmercapto-adenine (?)	Main B_{12}-active constituent of chicken feces; also found in swine feces
Factor G	hypoxanthine	Deamination product of ψ-B_{12} from calf and swine feces. Very active for *E. coli*
Factor H	2-methylhypoxanthine	Deamination product of factor A from calf and swine feces. Very active for *E. coli*
Factor I	5-hydroxybenzimidazole	Identical with the B_{12}-factor III from sewage sludge. Active for bacteria and chicks

Vitamin B_{12}, $C_{63}H_{88}O_{14}N_{14}PCo$ CYANOCOBALAMIN

Red, orthorhombic needles with marked pleochroism[15]
Blackening at 190–215° C
Mol. wt. 1355.42
M.p. < 300° C
Absorption maxima in water 2780 Å (B_{12b} 2730 Å), 3610 Å (B_{12b} 3510 Å), 5500 Å (B_{12b} 5250 Å), levorotatory

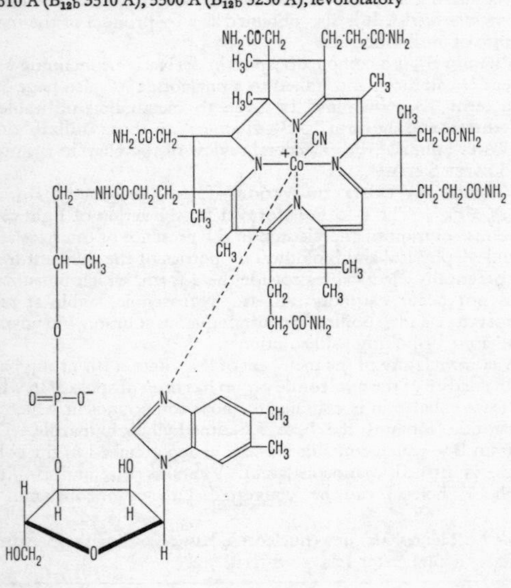

Unit

No international unit has yet been defined. 1 μg vitamin B_{12} = 11,000 LLD units (*Lactobacillus lactis* DORNER units) = 1 U.S. Pharmacopeia (liver extract) unit (the USP unit is defined as that amount which produces, when administered daily, satisfactory clinical and hematopoietic responses in Addisonian pernicious anemia). The activity of 1000 LLD units corresponds to that of about 1 ml of a good liver extract.

Methods of test and assay

There are difficulties in analysis because of the extraordinarily small amounts involved and the possibility of admixture of substances inactive against pernicious anemia and of other factors which have an action in relation to bacteria similar to that of vitamin B_{12}.

Curative tests on higher animals. Microbiologically with *Lactobacillus lactis* DORNER or *Lactobacillus leichmannii*[16] (these tests have not proved very specific[17]). The tests with *Euglena gracilis*[18, 19] and *Ochromonas malhamensis*[20] are very specific but complicated.

Physically and chemically after purification of extracts. Also spectrographically in pure solutions. Separation of individual factors and vitamins by chromatography and autography[21]. Rapid spectrophotometric methods[22].

For International Reference Preparation see page 739.

Occurrence[23] (values in μg B_{12} activity/100 g weight dry, unless otherwise stated)

Streptomyces aureofaciens (cells) 1000–1300; *Bacillus megatherium* (whole cultures) 40–80; stomach contents (rumen) of sheep: protozoal fraction (cells) 630, bacterial fraction (cells) 210, stomach flora cultivated on sterile gastric juice (cells) 400; pig's liver 180; calf liver 240; fish meal up to 389[24]; beef liver 30–100[25]; calf spleen 93; calf thymus (sweetbread) 24; meat meal 10; oysters (shelled) 280; milk 1.1–1.25 μg per 100 ml; casein 104[24]; earthworms 110; upper layers of the soil 170.

Physiology and function

Vitamin B_{12} can be synthesized only by certain microorganisms, bacteria and actinomycetes. It does not occur in yeasts or plants[26]. Contrary to earlier beliefs, algae do not synthesize the vitamin but obtain it from bacteria living symbiotically with them[12]. The phycomycetes, ascomycetes and basidiomycetes contain no cobalamins in the plasma, a fact which makes it possible to assign these organisms to the plants and also indicates that the higher plants are derived from flagellates of the type of *Chlamydomonas*[27].

Certain lower organisms require vitamin B_{12} as a growth factor, while others can do without it[28] or replace it by other metabolites. The tubers of leguminosae contain bacteria which produce cobalamins; their red color is due to a compound related to hemoglobin[29].

More highly-organized animals depend on ingested vitamin B_{12} and it is present in most of their tissues, especially the liver, kidneys and muscles, and in the milk and eggs.

Vitamin B_{12} content of various tissues (man, in µg/100 g)[30]: liver 24–74; kidney 7.1–37; spleen 3.9–39; lungs 4–5.2; brain 7–22; stomach 6.2–30; intestine 15–28; skin 1.2–1.5. The gastric juice contains ca. 0.03 µg/100 ml[19], the blood serum 0.03–0.04 µg/100 ml[16, 31].

Vitamin B_{12} is normally synthesized in large quantities by the intestinal flora, but apart from ingestion due to coprophagy, the organism does not utilize this source[32]. The minimal daily requirement of man is unknown, but 1 µg per 24 hours suffices to prevent pernicious anemia[33]. In the small intestine, chiefly in the ileum, ingested vitamin B_{12} combines with the "intrinsic factor" (CASTLE) of unknown structure which is produced by the fundic glands. This appears to be a thermolabile, nondialyzable mucoprotein (molecular weight ca. 15,000) which is stable to alkalis, unstable to acids, and precipitated by ammonium sulfate solutions[34]. In animals the intrinsic factor is not always secreted by the fundic glands and seems to have a certain species-specificity[35]. It does not function by activation of the vitamin but forms with it a complex compound resistant to bacteria which is for some unknown reason better absorbed by the intestinal wall[36].

The maximum capacity of the intestinal wall to absorb vitamin B_{12}, even when there is an excess of the intrinsic factor, does not exceed 0.7–1.3 µg daily[37]. This fact has led to the postulation of a "vitamin acceptor" in the intestinal wall. With increasing ingestion of vitamin B_{12} the intestinal absorption rapidly decreases[38]:

Vitamin intake in µg	Intestinal absorption in %
0.5	90.5 ± 5.8
1.0	81.5 ± 11.4
2.0	40.0 ± 8.1
5.0	22.0 ± 3.3
20.0	6.0 ± 1.5
50.0	3.0 ± 0.7
1000.0	less than 1%

When the concentration is very high some cobalamin diffuses through the intestinal wall without the help of the intrinsic factor. In rats, absorption of vitamin B_{12} is impaired by deficiency of vitamin B_6 but not by deficiency of vitamins B_1 and B_2 and pantothenic acid[51].

Vitamin B_{12} is stored in the liver and large quantities are found in the kidneys, the central nervous system and the myocardium. The serum contains some free vitamin B_{12} but most of it is combined with α_1-globulins (52%), α_2-globulins (21%), albumins (16%), β-globulins (7%) and γ-globulins (4%); normally the serum globulins are not saturated and can take up additional vitamin B_{12}[39].

The vitamin B_{12} of the tissues is combined with the α-globulins[40]. Since the association is weaker than that with the serum globulins the organism can if necessary maintain the serum level at the expense of the tissues[41]. The vitamin content of the leukocytes, normally greater than that of the serum, is increased in myeloid leukemia[42, 43]. Vitamin B_{12} occurs in pathological exudates (ascites, joint effusions) as well as in body fluids (pleura, peritoneum, cerebrospinal fluid). The daily excretion in the urine is 0.131 µg (mean value)[44]. The stools contain an average of 34% of the amount ingested, but this value is of little significance because of the intestinal synthesis[45].

As yet little is known of the biochemistry of vitamin B_{12}[46]. The site of action of B_{12} is indicated by its role in the metabolism of one-carbon fragments (but not in transmethylation[47]) and of thiol groups and thence of fats and carbohydrates[48]. The metabolically active form of vitamin B_{12} is a coenzyme (coenzyme B_{12}), isolated from bacterial cultures and animal livers, in which the cyano group of the vitamin is replaced by an adenine nucleoside[75].

The role of vitamin B_{12} in the metabolism of amino acids is evident from the symptoms of deficiency:

(*a*) Inhibition of the synthesis of methionine, as a result of which the formation of essential amino acids and proteins is diminished.

(*b*) Blocking of the synthesis of ribonucleic acid (a constituent of nucleoproteins).

The disturbances of protein metabolism are most marked in cells which show a high protein turnover and mitotic frequency, as also in the nervous system and during hemopoiesis; they are accompanied by an increase in the ribonucleic acid/desoxyribonucleic acid and uracil/thymine ratios. In such cases folic acid can exert a palliative effect:

(*a*) by itself contributing to desoxyribonucleic acid synthesis for a short time;

(*b*) by mobilization of the last reserves of vitamin B_{12}, after which folic acid itself becomes inactive.

Other signs of B_{12} deficiency observed are a decrease of blood lipids and tissue lipids and disturbance of carbohydrate metabolism with a tendency to hyperglycemia[49].

The interrelationship of vitamin B_{12} with other vitamins (see also above) is further illustrated by the observations that in bacteria (*E. coli*) the biosynthesis of vitamin B_6 is blocked in the presence of B_{12}[50, 51] and that in rats the uptake and utilization of carotenes is increased when B_{12} is added to the diet[52].

As a result of the body's large reserves of vitamin B_{12} and the high activity of the vitamin it is difficult to produce experimental B_{12} deficiency. The liver reserves in man are sufficient to supply the needs of the organism for 2–3 years. Deficiency in rats can only be produced with certainty by rearing them from mothers kept on a B_{12} deficient diet. The normal diet of man and animals contains sufficient of the vitamin, whereas a completely vegetarian diet which excludes all products of animal origin eventually results in deficiency in healthy persons. A supplementary intake may also be necessary in undernourished infants or in children with persistent anorexia. During pregnancy the reserves of the mother are largely used up by the fetus, whose blood level is high in comparison with that of the mother. In old people the serum level is reduced as a result of poor intestinal absorption. In neither case, however, does the serum content fall below the physiological threshold value under normal conditions.

Vitamin B_{12} is an important growth factor for many, if not all, lower organisms. Chicken embryos react to deficiency by inhibition of growth, edema and hemorrhages, necrotic foci in the liver, brain and spinal cord, and fatty infiltration of the parenchyma. Deficient chickens have an enlarged but immature thyroid gland with a poor iodine-combining capacity[53]. Administration of vitamin B_{12} does not completely eliminate deficiency symptoms in either pigs[54] or chickens[55]; antibiotics must also be given which either alter the bacterial metabolism or destroy injurious intestinal flora[56].

Vitamin B_{12} deficiency states in man may be summarized as follows[57]:

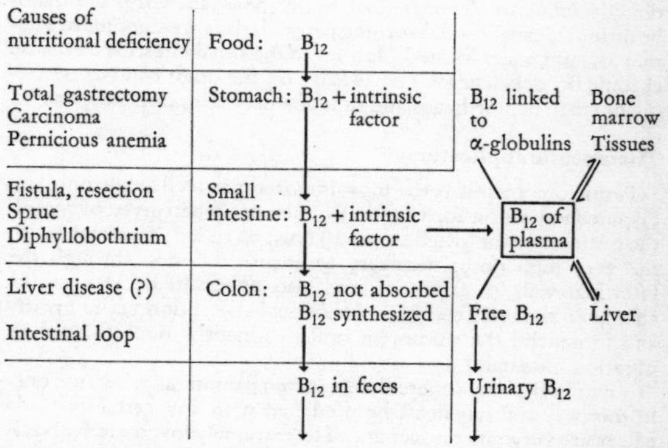

Deficiency can thus be caused either by low intake or by inadequate intestinal absorption. The latter is the case in the absence of the intrinsic factor, which may be due to an hereditary disorder (pernicious anemia) or be an acquired condition (gastrectomy)[58, 59]; ingested vitamin B_{12} then passes through the intestinal wall and all of it appears in the feces. The main cause of pernicious anemia is malformation of the stomach, and B_{12} deficiency and all other symptoms are a consequence of this[58]. As already mentioned, disturbance of protein synthesis leads to retardation of cell division in the digestive tract and bone marrow with loss of blood elements (anemia) and appearance of abnormal forms (macrocytosis). The deficiency of ribonucleic acids is particularly injurious to the axis-cylinders of the spinal neurones, which show progressive degeneration[60].

A marked fall of the vitamin B_{12} blood level is often the first sign of pernicious anemia, but it may also appear to a lesser degree in certain other diseases and in megaloblastic anemia[16]. The blood level is increased in iron-deficiency anemia[16, 61], in allergic eczema[62], in diabetes with retinopathy[63] and in myeloid leukemia[43]. It is variable or unchanged in tropical anemia[64], acute and lymphatic leukemia[43] and diabetes without ocular symptoms[63].

The growth of intestinal flora in the stomach caused by concomitant achlorhydria (normally inhibited by hydrochloric acid) is associated with the deficiency symptoms.

Serum levels of vitamin B_{12} (μg/100 ml)[67]*:*

Normal	0.02–0.09	Pernicious anemia (relapse)	0–0.005
Pernicious anemia of pregnancy	0.02–0.09	Pernicious anemia (parenteral therapy) .	0.02–0.09
Acute liver disease[65]	0.08–0.6	Pernicious anemia (incomplete oral therapy)	0.01–0.03
Biliary and portal cirrhosis of the liver[65]	0.083–0.36	Total gastrectomy ..	0–0.005
Extrahepatic obstructive jaundice	0.02–0.09	Diphyllobothrium anemia	0–0.005
Chronic myelocytic leukemia ..	0.15–1.7	Posterolateral sclerosis with or without anemia	0–0.002
Malabsorption syndrome	0.02–0.09 or 0.005–0.01	Blind loop anemia ..	0–0.005

Vitamin therapy reverses the changes in the blood and digestive tract. The nervous lesions also show a more or less marked improvement depending on their duration[66]. On the other hand, vitamin therapy has no effect on the atrophy of the stomach or on achlorhydria, and for this reason a patient with pernicious anemia must remain under treatment for his whole life[67].

The primary syndrome of poor absorption occurs in sprue, idiopathic steatorrhea, etc., and includes various symptoms of partial or complete avitaminosis (see under Folic acid, page 462). Vitamin deficiencies also occur in pellagra, and the nervous disorders of this disease are very probably attributable to deficiency of vitamin B_{12}[68].

Intestinal parasites which remove the vitamin either partially or completely from the host may also result in decreased intestinal absorption in spite of the presence of the intrinsic factor[69]. Intestinal blind loops or diverticula can harbor abnormal bacterial flora, but here it is difficult to decide whether the resulting B_{12} deficiency is due to normal competition among the bacteria or (principally) to bacterial toxins which block the vitamin or the intrinsic factor or directly influence the intestinal wall[70]. The tapeworm Diphyllobothrium is capable of absorbing particularly large amounts of vitamin B_{12} and when located high up in the small intestine can cause chronic B_{12} deficiency[71]. The Taeniae on the other hand cause frequent small hemorrhages and thus anemia due to iron deficiency[72].

Therapeutic applications[73]

Pernicious anemia is the most important as well as the only undisputed indication for vitamin B_{12} therapy. When given by mouth the intrinsic factor (dried stomach) must be added. Treatment with the very high doses necessary to ensure diffusion through the intestinal wall is expensive and also uncertain because of the change in the intestinal flora. Individual absorption varies greatly and in general the efficacy of oral treatment is doubtful and its duration uncertain.

Vitamin B_{12} is undoubtedly best given parenterally, because only in this way can its effects be predicted with any certainty. Side effects are very rare on account of its extremely low toxicity. Nasal instillations and inhalation of aerosols have also been proposed since like parenteral administration, these methods obviate the intrinsic factor and are equally effective[74].

In megaloblastic anemia of unknown origin, vitamin B_{12} should be given in order to assist differential diagnosis and to prevent the emergence or aggravation of latent nervous disorders which may be caused by folic acid. The optimum treatment of pernicious anemia consists of high initial doses of vitamin B_{12} to restore the reserves in the organs, followed by prolonged treatment with appropriate lower dosage.

The vitamin has been used with variable but mainly moderate results in various other diseases: in very high doses in nervous disorders (trigeminal and glossopharyngeal neuritis, subacute combined degeneration in the cord with or without pernicious anemia) and in diabetic neuritis. The improvements reported in lupus erythematosus, seborrheic dermatitis, leukoplakia, arthritis, lead poisoning, herpes zoster, postoperative anemia and hemophilia are doubtful.

Vitamin B_{12} has no effect in hemolytic anemia, pulmonary tuberculosis, muscle dystrophy, multiple sclerosis or osteoarthritis, or chronic malnutrition in children.

References: *1)* MINOT and MURPHY, *J. Amer. med. Ass.*, **87**, 470 (1926). *2)* RICKES et al., *Science*, **107**, 396 (1948); LESTER SMITH, E., *Nature*, **161**, 638 (1948). *3)* HESTER and WARD, *Ind. Eng. Chem.*, **46**, 238 (1954), quoted by JOHNSON and TODD, *Vitam. and Horm.*, **15**, 1 (1957). *4)* PFEIFER et al., *Ind. Eng. Chem.*, **46**, 843 (1954), quoted by JOHNSON and TODD, *loc. cit.* *5)* GARIBALDI et al., *Ind. Eng. Chem.*, **45**, 838 (1953), quoted by JOHNSON and TODD, *loc. cit.* *6)* GANT et al., *Biochem. J.*, **56**, xxxiv (1954). *7)* KACZKA et al., *J. Amer. chem. Soc.*, **71**, 1514 (1949). *8)* RICKES et al., *Science*, **108**, 134 (1948). *9)* BRINK et al., *Science*, **112**, 354 (1950); KACZKA et al., *Science*, **112**, 354 (1950). *10)* LEWIS et al., *J. biol. Chem.*, **194**, 539 (1952); **199**, 517 (1952). *11)* FRIEDRICH and BERNHAUER, *Angew. Chem.*, **65**, 627 (1953). *12)* ERICSON and LEWIS, *Ark. Kemi*, **6**, 427 (1953-54). *13)* LESTER SMITH, E., *Vitamin B_{12}*, London, 1960. *14)* International Union of Pure and Applied Chemistry, *Nomenclature of Organic Chemistry*, London, 1958, page 83. *15)* KENDREW and PERUTZ, *Ann. Rev. Biochem.*, **26**, 327 (1957). *16)* GIRDWOOD, R. H., *Brit. med. J.*, **2**, 954 (1954). *17)* SKEGGS et al., *J. biol. Chem.*, **176**, 1459 (1948); GREENE et al., *J. biol. Chem.*, **178**, 999 (1949). *18)* HUTNER et al., *Proc. Soc. exp. Biol. (N.Y.)*, **70**, 118 (1949). *19)* ROSS, G. I. M., *Nature*, **166**, 270 (1950). *20)* HAMILTON et al., *Analyst*, **77**, 618 (1952); HAMILTON et al., *J. clin. Invest.*, **31**, 636 (1952). *21)* FANTES et al., *Biochem. J.*, **46**, xxxiv (1950); BOXER and RICKARDS, *Arch. Biochem.*, **29**, 75 (1950); **30**, 372, 382, 392 (1951). *22)* FISHER, R. A., *J. Agric. Food Chem.*, **1**, 951 (1953). *23)* ZUCKER and ZUCKER, *Vitam. and Horm.*, **8**, 1 (1950). *24)* PEELER et al., *J. Nutr.*, **43**, 49 (1951). *25)* SCHWEIGERT et al., *Fed. Proc.*, **10**, 394 (1951). *26)* DARKEN, M. A., *Bot. Rev.*, **19**, 99 (1953). *27)* HUTNER and PROVASOLI, in LWOFF, A. (Ed.), *Biochemistry and Physiology of Protozoa*, vol. I, New York, 1951, page 27. *28)* BURTON and LOCHHEAD, *Canad. J. Botany*, **29**, 352 (1951). *29)* THORNTON, H. G., *Science Progr. twent. Cent.*, **42**, 185 (1954). *30)* GIRDWOOD, R. H., *Biochem. J.*, **52**, 58 (1952). *31)* CALLENDER and O'BRIEN, in THOMPSON and KING (Eds.), *Biochemical Disorders in Human Disease*, London, 1957, page 84. *32)* HAUSMANN et al., *Acta haemat. (Basel)*, **10**, 282 (1953). *33)* REISNER and WEST, *Proc. Soc. exp. Biol. (N.Y.)*, **71**, 651 (1949). *34)* TERNBERG and EAKIN, *J. Amer. chem. Soc.*, **71**, 3858 (1949). *35)* LATNER, A. L., *Lancet*, **1**, 921 (1955). *36)* DAVIDSON and GULLAND, *Pernicious Anaemia*, London, 1930; HOFF-JØRGENSEN, E., *Arch. Biochem.*, **36**, 235 (1952). *37)* CALLENDER and EVANS, *Clin. Sci.*, **14**, 387 (1955). *38)* GLASS et al., *Proc. Soc. exp. Biol. (N.Y.)*, **86**, 522 (1954); GLASS et al., *Science*, **120**, 74 (1954); ESTREN et al., *Advanc. intern. Med.*, **9**, 11 (1958). *39)* HEINRICH and ERDMANN-OEHLECKER, *Clin. chim. Acta*, **1**, 311 (1956). *40)* PITNEY et al., *J. biol. Chem.*, **207**, 143 (1954). *41)* MOLLIN and ROSS, *Brit. med. J.*, **2**, 640 (1953). *42)* ROSS and MOLLIN, *5th International Congress of Haematology*, Résumé des Rapports et Communications, Paris, 1954, page 245, quoted by UNGLEY, C.C., *Vitam. and Horm.*, **13**, 137 (1955). *43)* BEARD et al., *Ann. intern. Med.*, **41**, 323 (1954); *Blood*, **9**, 789 (1954). *44)* PITNEY and BEARD, *J. clin. Nutr.*, **2**, 89 (1954). *45)* TOTTER, J. R., *Ann. Rev. Biochem.*, **26**, 181 (1957). *46)* For reviews see BRIGGS and DAFT, *Ann. Rev. Biochem.*, **24**, 339 (1955); LESTER SMITH, E., *Brit. med. Bull.*, **12**, 52 (1956). *47)* JOHNSON et al., *Brit. J. Nutr.*, **11**, 313 (1957). *48)* FOX et al., *Proc. Soc. exp. Biol. (N.Y.)*, **93**, 501 (1956). *49)* LING and CHOW, *J. biol. Chem.*, **206**, 797 (1954). *50)* SAXENA et al., *Experientia (Basel)*, **10**, 488 (1954). *51)* HSU et al., *Fed. Proc.*, **15**, 557 (1956). *52)* POTTER et al., *Poult. Sci.*, **35**, 452 (1956); MAYFIELD and ROEHM, *J. Nutr.*, **58**, 483 (1956). *53)* FERGUSON et al., *Arch. Path. (Chicago)*, **60**, 393 (1955); *Endocrinology*, **60**, 13 (1957). *54)* BURNSIDE et al., *Proc. Soc. exp. Biol. (N.Y.)*, **74**, 173 (1950); JUKES et al., *Arch. Biochem.*, **26**, 324 (1950). *55)* STOKSTAD and JUKES, *Abstr. Amer. chem. Soc. 117th Meeting, 1950*, page 12. *56)* LUECKE et al., *Arch. Biochem.*, **26**, 326 (1950). *57)* ESTREN et al., *Advanc. intern. Med.*, **9**, 11 (1958). *58)* GRAHAM and RHEAULT, *J. Lab. clin. Med.*, **43**, 235 (1954). *59)* MOLLIN et al., *Brit. J. Haemat.*, **1**, 278 (1955). *60)* For a review see CASTLE, W.B., *New Engl. J. Med.*, **249**, 603 (1953). *61)* GOLDECK and WEISS, *Klin. Wschr.*, **31**, 860 (1953). *62)* BLOQUIAUX, S., *C. R. Soc. Biol. (Paris)*, **147**, 713 (1953). *63)* CHOW et al., *Proc. Soc. exp. Biol. (N.Y.)*, **87**, 38 (1954). *64)* NIEWEG et al., *J. Lab. clin. Med.*, **44**, 118 (1954). *65)* RACHMILEWITZ et al., *J. Lab. clin. Med.*, **48**, 339 (1956). *66)* SAMSON et al., *Arch. intern. Med.*, **90**, 4 (1952). *67)* MCALPINE and GOLDSMITH, *Arch. Middx Hosp.*, **1**, 109 (1951). *68)* MEIKLEJOHN and KARK, *New Engl. J. Med.*, **221**, 519 (1939). *69)* OXENHORN et al., *J. Mt Sinai Hosp.*, **24**, 232 (1957). *70)* HALSTED et al., *Gastroenterology*, **30**, 21 (1956). *71)* VON BONSDORFF, B., *Exp. Parasit.*, **5**, 207 (1956). *72)* GEIMAN, Q. M., *Vitam. and Horm.*, **16**, 1 (1958). *73)* For a review see BRIGGS and DAFT, *Ann. Rev. Biochem.*, **24**, 339 (1955). *74)* MONTO and REBUCK, *Arch. intern. Med.*, **93**, 219 (1954). *75)* BARKER et al., *J. biol. Chem.*, **235**, 480 (1960).

Vitamin C

Vitamin C occurs in nature in a reduced form (L-ascorbic acid) and an oxidized form (dehydroascorbic acid) in much lower concentration, both forms being biologically active, soluble in water and unstable to oxidizing agents, alkalis and certain metals. This vitamin is almost unique in nature in that it occurs in only one form and is not known to be a component of any nucleotide or coenzyme. No natural or synthetic substitutes for it are known[1].

L-Ascorbic acid, $C_6H_8O_6$ ASCORBIC ACID

White crystals, acid taste
Mol.wt. 176.13
M.p. 192°C

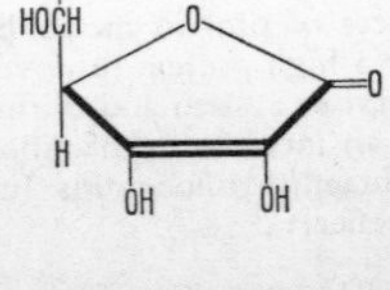

Dehydroascorbic acid, $C_6H_6O_6$
Mol.wt. 174.11

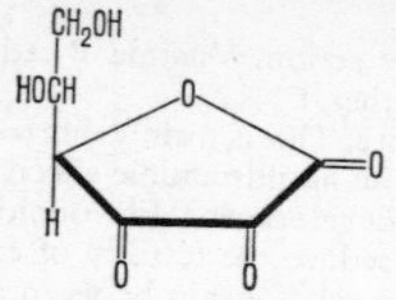

Unit

1 international unit (I.U.) = 0.05 mg crystalline ascorbic acid.

Methods of test and assay

Prophylactic scurvy test in guinea pigs. Growth test (easily carried out). Very specific microscopic examination of tooth structure. Chemical methods have now almost entirely replaced biological methods.

Chemical methods[2]: L-*ascorbic acid:* titration with 2,6-dichloroindophenol (official method in the U.S.A. for pharmaceuticals and foods); formation of the 2,4-dinitrophenylosazone. *Dehydroascorbic acid:* reduction with homocysteine and subsequent titration with 2,6-dichloroindophenol. *"Total" vitamin C* (L-ascorbic acid + dehydroascorbic acid + 2,3-diketogulonic acid, a compound closely related to vitamin C with no biological activity): formation of the 2,4-dinitrophenylosazone[2].

Occurrence

Vitamin C is very widely distributed in nature, especially in green plants and citrus fruits. It is found in most plant and animal tissues; in these its distribution shows remarkable variations, the reasons for which are unknown. Certain plants contain large amounts (black currants, guava, Brussels sprouts, cress, horse-radish, green peppers), others less (pears, celery, pomegranates, plums, figs, beetroots, mushrooms)[1]. Certain organs are also rich in vitamin C (adrenals, lens and aqueous and vitreous humors of the eye, leukocytes), while other organs have a relatively low content (erythrocytes, muscle, brain, pancreas)[1].

Values in mg per 100 g weight fresh: parsley 154–209; dandelions 30; green peppers 120; Brussels sprouts 68; kohlrabi 28–136; currants 35; lemon juice 27; orange juice 42; grapefruit juice 45. The vitamin C content is reduced considerably by cooking.

Physiology and function

The higher plants and the majority of mammals can synthesize vitamin C. Man, the primates and rather remarkably also guinea pigs are unable to do this, probably because of their lack of certain enzymes. Vitamin C is stored in certain organs of the body (see above). The concentration in whole blood is 0.2–0.7 mg per 100 ml (mean 0.62 mg per 100 ml)[3]; that in the serum 0.1–0.7 mg per 100 ml[4]. Plasma values in relation to the vitamin intake are as follows:

Daily intake in mg:	0	5	10	20	50	70	600
Plasma value in mg/100 ml:	<0.03	<0.05	<0.10	<0.10	0.31	0.55	1.02

The plasma level gradually falls during vitamin C deficiency. After ingestion in the diet it rises to a point at which excretion by the kidney commences. Subsequently there is only an insignificant further rise in the plasma level. After ingestion of 50–100 mg the plasma content after 12 days (equilibrium) is 0.97 mg (summer) and 0.89 mg (winter). Renal elimination is most rapid after intravenous administration.

Vitamin C is excreted in feces, sweat and urine. Urinary excretion is proportional to the overall body content, the daily excretion being 26.7 mg total vitamin C in summer and 31.4 mg in winter, of which 25.6 and 24.4 mg respectively consist of reduced vitamin C. The rate of excretion is affected not only by the intake but also by certain drugs (fish liver oils, salicylates, acetylsalicylic acid, barbiturates, anesthetics, estradiol, stilbestrol, sulfonamides, atropine, adrenaline, etc.). Insulin and sodium bicarbonate decrease the rate of excretion.

Excretion in the feces is fairly constant and is not related to the intake, but intestinal derangements may increase it considerably. In severe bodily exertion large amounts of vitamin C may be excreted in the sweat[5].

The vitamin C content of the organism falls in old age, a state of affairs to which bad eating habits and poorly cooked food as well as general malnutrition may contribute[6].

The daily requirement in man is difficult to establish. A daily dose of 10 mg seems to be sufficient to prevent scurvy, but the optimum daily intake is considerably higher and probably in the region of 70–75 mg, although there is little scientific evidence to support this[7]. For dietary allowances recommended by the National Research Council (U.S.A.) see page 498.

Infectious diseases, rheumatism and tuberculosis cause a marked fall in the plasma level and it is difficult to compensate for this even by very high doses.

Recent research has thrown more light on the clinical picture of scurvy: after 17 weeks of a diet completely free from vitamin C, keratosis of the hair follicles appears, with ultimately hemorrhages and the characteristic "scurvy patches"; after 26 weeks changes in the teeth and gums are observed. Further clinical symptoms are pains in the back and limbs, marked acne, ecchymosis, edema of the knee. In some patients there are cardiac disorders and an old tuberculosis may flare up. There is much individual variation in the severity of the lesions. The erythrocyte and leukocyte counts and the blood coagulation time remain normal. The usual tests for capillary resistance show no dependence on the degree of vitamin C deficiency. Eventually there is a diminished capacity for wound-healing. A daily dose of 10 mg is sufficient to abolish the symptoms of scurvy (lesions of the skin in 2 months, of the teeth and gums in 3 months). There remain a marked tendency to exhaustion and incapacity for bodily exertion which disappear only after larger doses of 30 mg[7].

The antiscorbutic action is at present the only known specific activity of vitamin C. In spite of much work in this field, the exact part played by this vitamin in normal metabolism has not yet been established. However, the following functions are recognized:

(*a*) Participation to an important extent in the redox systems of the organism.
(*b*) A role in the metabolism of tyrosine (oxidation of L-tyrosine) and of folic acid (conversion into the citrovorum factor) which would explain certain relationships between vitamin C deficiency and anemia.
(*c*) An effect on growth through its influence on the morphology of the tissues (especially bone, tooth and scartissue)[8].
(*d*) An effect on the adrenals: doses of ACTH cause hypertrophy of the adrenals with decrease of the vitamin C content. The active form of the adrenocortical hormones is possibly a complex of the corticosteroid with water-soluble vitamins and pituitary compounds[9].
(*e*) An anti-infectious action: vitamin C stimulates the activity of the phagocytes and the formation of antibodies. Its antibacterial action may be due to lysis of the membrane polysaccharides of the microorganisms or to destruction of their protective mucous envelopes.
(*f*) In general vitamin C seems to operate as an anti-stress factor which enables the organism to adapt itself better to environmental influences (chills, physical exertion, disease, etc.)[10].

Dehydroascorbic acid has a similar antiscorbutic activity to ascorbic acid. It is rapidly broken down in the organism and occurs neither in the tissues nor in the urine. For this reason its activity when given orally is about one-third of that of L-ascorbic acid[11]. In infectious diseases the blood level of ascorbic acid decreases while that of dehydroascorbic acid rises. In convalescence this relationship is reversed[12].

When injected in large doses dehydroascorbic acid seems to have a certain toxicity; in guinea pigs they cause atrophic changes in the hair, fatty degeneration of the liver and eventually death[11].

Therapeutic applications

Deficiency of vitamin C and infantile and adult scurvy[7] are the only unconditional indications for administration of the vitamin. While true scurvy is now hardly ever seen, it should not be forgotten that vitamin C deficiency often occurs without clinical symptoms. The requirement of the organism increases during pregnancy and lactation, in disease and in old age as also in newborn children who are artificially fed. Very high doses of the vitamin are useless in these cases, however, because the kidney threshold prevents an accumulation in the organism and the overstepping of a certain blood level. A daily dose of 50–100 mg meets the needs of the body and any further amount will be excreted without beneficial effect[10].

Vitamin C cannot be regarded as an effective antibacterial agent, although it is helpful in augmenting the body's defensive mechanisms and in aiding the recovery of strength during convalescence.

References: *1)* Harris, L. J., *Brit. med. Bull.*, **12**, 57 (1956). *2)* Iggo et al., *Clin. chim. Acta*, **1**, 167 (1956). *3)* Osborne et al., *J. Lab. clin. Med.*, **27**, 1135 (1942). *4)* Vitamin C Subcommittee, Medical Research Council, *Lancet*, **1**, 853 (1948). *5)* Namyslowski, L., *Chem. Abstr.*, **51**, 4518 (1956). *6)* Cass et al.,

Geriatrics, **9**, 375 (1954). *7)* Medical Research Council, *Vitamin C Requirements of Human Adults* (Special Report No. 280), London, 1953; WAIFE, S. O., *Amer. J. Clin. Nutr.*, **2**, 273 (1954). *8)* IRVING, J. T., *Vitam. and Horm.*, **15**, 291 (1957). *9)* RATSIMAMANGA and NIGEON-DUREUIL, *Bull. Soc. Chim. biol. (Paris)*, **38**, 183 (1956). *10)* PASSMORE and MEIKLEJOHN, in THOMPSON and KING (Eds.), *Biochemical Disorders in Human Disease*, London, 1957, page 544. *11)* CLAYTON et al., *Biochem. J.*, **58**, 542 (1954). *12)* CHAKRABARTI and BANERJEE, *Proc. Soc. exp. Biol. (N.Y.)*, **88**, 581 (1955).

Vitamin P (citrin)

In 1936 SZENT-GYÖRGYI and RUSZNYÁK[1] isolated a factor ("citrin") from paprika and lemon peel which had a favorable influence on capillary resistance. Later this was shown to be a mixture of compounds of the flavone group. There is thus no single "vitamin P" but rather a group of compounds with vitamin P activity, for example flavones (phenylchromone), flavanones (hesperidin, eriodictyol), flavanols (rutin), etc. All these substances are very widely distributed in nature, especially in citrus fruits and black currants.

In animals fairly large quantities occur in the thymus[2]. The vitamin P substances are soluble with difficulty in water, rather more easily in alkalis. The basic structure of the flavonoids is shown below[3]:

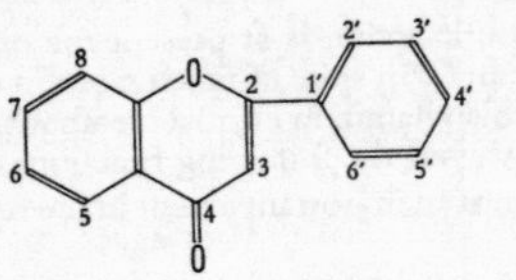

Unit None.

Methods of test and assay

No test. Dosage of the individual flavonoids.

Physiology and function

According to SZENT-GYÖRGYI, vitamin P can only be regarded as a vitamin in a restricted sense because it is required by the organism only under certain pathological conditions[2]. Its physiology and mode of action are unknown.

The following possible properties have been ascribed to vitamin P:

(*a*) Lowering of the permeability of the capillaries, with general improvement of resistance[4]. This antihemorrhagic effect is useful in the treatment of certain side effects of dicoumarol (purpura, and haemorrhages of the nose, mouth, gums, rectum and bladder)[5].

(*b*) Anti-inflammatory action. Vitamin P reduces edema or even prevents it altogether.

(*c*) Antiallergic activity. This is mainly due to reduction of edema, but is not simply an antihistaminic effect[6].

(*d*) Effect on sexual development. Flavonoids delay the onset of puberty and can reduce the fertility of experimental animals. Possibly there is a relationship between their presence in the thymus and atrophy of this gland at puberty[7].

Other effects have been claimed for vitamin P but satisfactory experimental proof of them is lacking. There is also no conclusive evidence that this group of substances possesses vitamin activity in any animal organism, and for this reason the term "vitamin P" has largely been replaced by "bioflavonoids".

Therapeutic applications

The flavonoids have disappointed all the therapeutic hopes placed in them. None of the published claims have withstood scientific control, so that these substances have very little pharmacological significance[3]. The least doubtful effect is that of increasing capillary resistance, but this is not completely reliable. However, vitamin P can be tried in the treatment of any of the hemorrhagic diatheses except thrombocytopenic purpura and diabetic retinal hemorrhage[8]. The flavonoids have also been used for the prophylaxis and treatment of apoplexy, hypertension and arteriosclerosis. Other suggested uses are in surgical operations and for the prevention of hemorrhagic side effects in prolonged treatment with dicoumarol. The flavonoids have been used for the treatment of inflammatory edema and for the prevention of erythema after irradiation by X-rays[9]. They are absolutely inactive against the common cold.

Proof of the alleged reduction of human fertility by the flavonoids is lacking but they possess a slight and therapeutically unimportant estrogenic activity.

References: *1)* RUSZNYÁK and SZENT-GYÖRGYI, *Nature*, **138**, 27 (1936). *2)* SZENT-GYÖRGYI, A., *Ann. N.Y. Acad. Sci.*, **61**, 732 (1955). *3)* PEARSON, W. N., *J. Amer. med. Ass.*, **164**, 1675 (1957). *4)* JAVILLIER and LAVOLLAY, *Helv. chim. Acta*, **29**, 1283 (1946). *5)* BRAMBEL, C. E., *Ann. N.Y. Acad. Sci.*, **61**, 678 (1955). *6)* MARTIN, G. J., *Ann. N.Y. Acad. Sci.*, **61**, 646 (1955). *7)* Annotations, *Lancet*, **1**, 443 (1955). *8)* LEVITAN, B. A., *Amer. J. med. Sci.*, **221**, 185 (1951). *9)* SOKOLOFF et al., *J. clin. Invest.*, **30**, 395 (1951).

Essential nutritional factors

The substances described in this section are not universally accepted as vitamins. Since they are active only in much larger amounts than the latter they are perhaps better described as essential nutritional factors. Choline and inositol are usually grouped in the B complex, although they have no biological relationship with it. The group of unsaturated fatty acids known as "vitamin F" should properly be classed with the fat-soluble vitamins.

Choline

Choline is a strong organic base whose derivatives, such as acetylcholine, are widely distributed in the animal and vegetable kingdoms. It is a component of phospholipids (lecithin, etc.; cf. page 387). Choline was first discovered over a century ago in bile[1], but its function as an essential metabolite was not realized until 1932[2].

Choline is very hygroscopic, soluble in water and alcohol, insoluble in ether, benzene and carbon disulfide. It is stable to heat in acid solutions, unstable in alkaline solutions.

Choline, $C_5H_{15}O_2N$ CHOLINE
White crystals, bitter taste
Mol.wt. 121.18

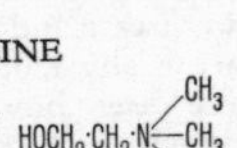

Unit

No unit defined; by weight.

Methods of test and assay

Chemically by precipitation of the reineckate[3], microbiologically by means of strains of *Neurospora crassa* irradiated by ultraviolet light[4]. For determination in the presence of the whole B complex, see BANDELIN and TUSCHHOFF[5]. Colorimetrically (not very specific)[6]. By UV-spectrometric assay of the periodide (up to 5 μg)[7]. Determination with sodium tetraphenylborate[8].

Occurrence[9] (values in mg per 100 g weight fresh, unless otherwise stated)

The choline in food occurs chiefly in eggs, meat, legumes and cereal and milk products. Vegetables, oils, refined and neutral fats, and also fruits, contain little or no choline. There is no loss in cooking.

Eggs: egg-yolk 1500–1700, egg-white very little. *Meat:* liver of various species 350–650; kidneys 100–300; muscle 70–140; lean meat 40–120 (average over 90). *Fish:* haddock 200; salmon 180; herring 127; trout 87. *Dairy products:* whole-milk powder 170; skim-milk powder 16; fresh milk 15 mg/100 ml; cheese 50. *Legumes:* soybeans 237; dried beans 181; fresh peas 55; dried peas 188. *Cereals:* wheat germ 400; oat flakes 151; wheat and oats 30–140 (average over 90); barley 139; maize 40; polished rice 88; black bread 56; white flour 52. *Various:* soya flour 280–350; groundnut flour 200–300. *Vegetables and fruits:* Brussels sprouts 103; radishes 48; spinach 38; celery 17; parsley 16; carrots 4; mushrooms 20–70; potatoes, tomatoes, onions, apples, plums, melons and grapes contain no choline.

Physiology and function

The daily requirement of man is not accurately known but is estimated at 250–600 mg. The daily intake on a normal diet is 500–1000 mg[10]. It is very probable that the intestinal flora synthesizes choline. Since the feces contain no choline, either it is completely absorbed or the part remaining unabsorbed is destroyed by intestinal microorganisms[11,12].

After oral administration of choline the blood level shows no increase and after intravenous administration it rises only for a short time[13]. Two-thirds of the amount ingested is excreted in the urine as trimethylamines (according to some authors these compounds are formed in the intestine and simply pass through the organism unchanged) and very little as choline; there is practically none in the feces[11,13].

From the intestine the choline passes chiefly into the portal circulation and is rapidly eliminated by the choline oxidase* of the liver and kidneys[14]. The normal serum level is 0.3–1.5 mg per 100 ml[16].

Choline is a quaternary ammonium base containing three methyl groups and plays an important part in metabolism in transmethylation processes such as methionine → creatine, choline → methionine (and vice versa), betaine → choline, nicotinamide → 1-methylnicotinamide.

The mitochondria of the liver cells contain an enzyme which catalyzes the formation of phospholipids from choline[17]. On the biosynthesis of lecithin and cephalin from choline[18] see page 431. In the absence of choline, betaine, methionine, thetin and proteins can to a certain extent take over the function of choline as a donator of methyl groups. The first three are apparently precursors from which the organism can synthesize choline in deficiency states[9].

Biogenesis and transference mechanism of methyl groups[19]

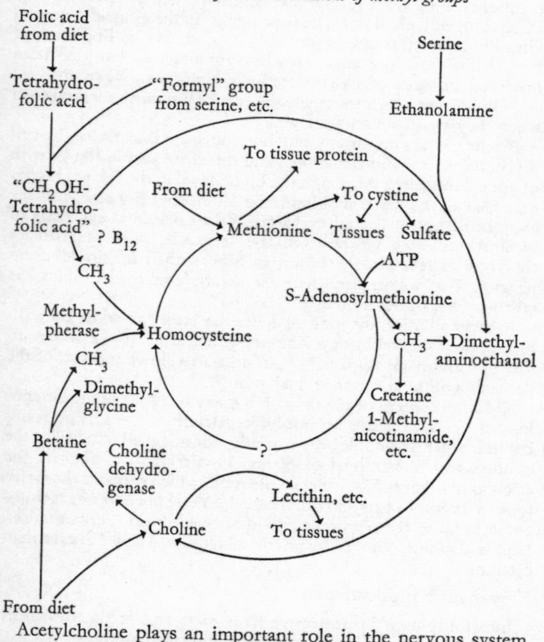

Acetylcholine plays an important role in the nervous system, particularly in the transmission of nerve impulses across synapses[20]. Two enzymes are involved in these processes, choline acetylase and choline esterase, the latter splitting acetylcholine into choline and acetic acid. A distinction is drawn between the "true" or "specific" esterase of the gray matter of the brain and the "pseudo-" or "nonspecific" esterase of the white matter, the glia and the peripheral nerves[21] (see page 425). A distinction between cholinergic and noncholinergic neurones can be made according to the distribution of acetylcholine[22]. The synthesis of acetylcholine is decreased in the absence of thiamine and pantothenic acid. Choline exhibits a qualitatively similar activity in the nervous system, but this is only $^1/_{1000}$ of that of acetylcholine.

* Composition of choline oxidase: dehydrogenase + flavin adenine dinucleotide + cytochrome c + (possibly) Mg^{++}. Enzyme activity is conditional on the presence of thiol groups[15].

In the liver, choline protects the tissues from accumulation of fats, and on a choline deficient diet central fatty infiltration of the liver soon occurs (after 24–48 hours in rats and mice). This is in contrast to protein deficiency, when infiltration is periportal[23]. Long-continued fat accumulation results in diffuse fibrosis and finally cirrhosis (dogs[24], rats), with the formation of malignant tumors of the liver (rats)[25,26]. Simultaneous deficiency of choline, essential fatty acids and vitamin B_{12} considerably accelerates the appearance of such tumors. For a review see SCHWARZ [27].

In animals deficient in choline the following symptoms are also observed: hemorrhage of the kidneys (swine[28], calves[29]) with hypertension[30] and lesions of the eyes[31,32], involution of the thymus[31,33], muscular weakness[28] or dystrophy[34], cardiovascular lesions[35] (rats), bone deformities[36] (chickens, ducks, turkeys).

The protective action of choline is conditional on the presence of essential fatty acids[37]. Nothing is yet known of the precise mechanism but it is assumed that the choline converts the fats into phospholipids and thus prevents their accumulation in the liver[38].

Little is known about the mode of action of choline in the circulatory system. In rats deficient in choline there is fatty infiltration of the myocardium which ultimately causes an infarct. In addition, sclerosis of the MÖNCKEBERG type has been observed with more or less calcified lipid deposits in the media (and also intima) of the aorta and coronary vessels. Since the kidneys simultaneously show similar pathological changes (fat deposits, necrotic areas) it is difficult to distinguish between cause and effect in these two manifestations[39]. The condition appears to improve on administration of cholesterol, essential fatty acids and antithyroid substances but it remains uncertain whether lipotropic substances such as choline, methionine and inositol have any effect on the cholesterol level in blood. Observations made so far on the human organism have been extremely contradictory[40].

Deficiency of choline has no effect on the intestinal absorption of fats[41] but causes a decrease of serum albumin and an increase of phospholipids and of α- and β-globulins[42].

Choline is an essential growth factor for a number of microorganisms but can be replaced by certain of its analogues. In the higher animals, on the other hand, the latter may have an antagonistic effect under certain conditions. The favorable effect of choline on development, on reproduction, on pregnancy, and on the growth of the offspring is not confined to lower organisms. Together with vitamin B_{12} it augments the reproductive capacity of mice and lowers the mortality among gravid females and the litter[43]. Symptoms of choline deficiency in lower animals are as follows:

Guinea pigs[44]: retardation of growth, anemia, high mortality among the young, pale and atrophic kidneys (no hemorrhages), no fatty infiltration of the liver.

Rabbits[45]: retardation of growth, anemia, fatty degeneration and cirrhosis of the liver, necrosis of the tubules of the kidneys, creatinuria, progressive muscular dystrophy, death.

Birds[46]: small eggs poor in fats, inhibition of the growth of chicks. In choline deficiency, administration of growth hormone tends to cause exacerbation of the renal symptoms[47].

Choline deficiency lowers the capacity of the liver to store carotene but not its capacity to store vitamin A, the distribution of which in the organism remains unaltered[48].

In the vegetable kingdom choline occurs as its oxidation product betaine. This accumulates particularly in the leaves and green stems, is a source of choline for herbivorous animals and occasionally lessens the requirement of choline[49]. Choline synthesis in plants is promoted by nitrates, ammonium and potassium[50].

Pharmacology

Choline is a vasodilator but is greatly excelled in this respect by acetylcholine.

Therapeutic applications

Choline can be used to protect the liver in toxic lipomatosis and forms of infectious hepatitis, but here its activity is considerably less than that of methionine, vitamin E or proteins. Given intravenously with other lipotropic substances (vitamin E; B complex, especially vitamin B_{12}) in diseases of the liver, choline can shorten the course of the disease and of convalescence. It is also indicated in dietary treatment for protection of the liver and in toxic cirrhosis of the liver.

References: *1*) STRECKER, A., *Justus Liebigs Ann. Chem.*, **70**, 149 (1849); **123**, 353 (1862). *2*) BEST et al., *Amer. J. Physiol.*, **101**, 7 (1932). *3*) BEATTIE, F. J. R., *Biochem. J.*, **30**, 1554 (1936); JACOBI et al., *J. biol. Chem.*, **138**, 571

(1941); ENGEL, R. W., *J. biol. Chem.*, **144**, 701 (1942); GLICK, D., *J. biol. Chem.*, **156**, 643 (1944). *4)* HOROWITZ and BEADLE, *J. biol. Chem.*, **150**, 325 (1943). *5)* BANDELIN and TUSCHHOFF, *J. Amer. pharm. Ass.*, **40**, 245 (1951). *6)* SAMUELSSON, G., *J. Pharm. (Lond.)*, **5**, 239 (1953). *7)* APPLETON et al., *J. biol. Chem.*, **205**, 803 (1953). *8)* MARQUARDT and VOGG, *Hoppe-Seylers Z. physiol. Chem.*, **291**, 143 (1952). *9)* For a review see BEST et al., *Brit. med. Bull.*, **12**, 9 (1956). *10)* RIDOUT et al., *Biochem. J.*, **52**, 79 (1952). *11)* DE LA HUERGA et al., *J. clin. Invest.*, **32**, 1117 (1953). *12)* BENNETT, M. A., *J. biol. Chem.*, **163**, 247 (1946); BENNETT and TOENNIES, *J. biol. Chem.*, **163**, 235 (1946). *13)* GABUZDA, G. J., *J. Amer. med. Ass.*, **160**, 969 (1956). *14)* ROHSE and SEARLE, *Fed. Proc.*, **12**, 118 (1953). *15)* KENNEDY and WEISS, *J. Amer. chem. Soc.*, **77**, 250 (1955). *16)* SCHLEGEL, J. U., *Proc. Soc. exp. Biol. (N.Y.)*, **70**, 695 (1949). *17)* ARTOM, C., *J. biol. Chem.*, **213**, 681 (1955). *18)* ROTHSCHILD et al., *J. biol. Chem.*, **208**, 41 (1954). *19)* JUKES, M., *Proceedings of the 6th Congress of the International Society of Haematology*, quoted by BROQUIST, H. P., *Ann. Rev. Biochem.*, **27**, 285 (1958). *20)* For a review see FELDBERG, W. S., *Brit. med. Bull.*, **6**, 312 (1950). *21)* NACHMANSOHN and ROTHENBERG, *J. biol. Chem.*, **158**, 653 (1945); FELDBERG, W. S., *Pharmacol. Rev.*, **6**, 85 (1954); HEBB and WAITES, *J. Physiol. (Lond.)*, **132**, 667 (1956). *22)* MENDEL and RUDNEY, *Science*, **100**, 499 (1944). *23)* HARTROFT, W. S., *Anat. Rec.*, **106**, 61 (1950); BUCKLEY and HARTROFT, *Arch. Path. (Chicago)*, **59**, 185 (1955). *24)* CHAIKOFF and CONNOR, *Proc. Soc. exp. Biol. (N.Y.)*, **43**, 638 (1940). *25)* COPELAND and SALMON, *Amer. J. Path.*, **22**, 1059 (1946). *26)* ENGEL et al., *Ann. N.Y. Acad. Sci.*, **49**, 49 (1947); SCHAFFER et al., *Cancer Res.*, **10**, 786 (1950). *27)* SCHWARZ, K. (Ed.), *Ann. N.Y. Acad. Sci.*, **57**, art. 6 (1954). *28)* NEUMANN et al., *J. Nutr.*, **38**, 195 (1949). *29)* JOHNSON et al., *J. Nutr.*, **43**, 37 (1951). *30)* HARTROFT and BEST, *Brit. med. J.*, **1**, 423 (1949). *31)* GRIFFITH and WADE, *J. biol. Chem.*, **131**, 567 (1939). *32)* BELLOWS and CHINN, *Arch. Ophthal. (Chicago)*, **30**, 105 (1943). *33)* CHRISTENSEN, K., *J. biol. Chem.*, **133**, xx (1940). *34)* HOVE and COPELAND, *J. Nutr.*, **53**, 391 (1954). *35)* WILGRAM and HARTROFT, *Brit. J. exp. Path.*, **36**, 298 (1955); WILGRAM et al., *Proc. Soc. exp. Biol. (N. Y.)*, **91**, 620 (1956). *36)* JUKES and ALMQUIST, *Ann. Rev. Biochem.*, **11**, 511 (1942). *37)* ENGEL, R. W., *J. Nutr.*, **24**, 175 (1942). *38)* DILUZIO and ZILVERSMIT, *J. biol. Chem.*, **205**, 867 (1953). *39)* WILGRAM et al., *Science*, **119**, 842 (1954); *Brit. med. J.*, **2**, 1 (1954); *Proc. Soc. exp. Biol. (N. Y.)*, **91**, 620 (1956); WISSLER et al., *Arch. Path. (Chicago)*, **57**, 333 (1954); BAXTER and GOODMAN, *Proc. Soc. exp. Biol. (N.Y.)*, **89**, 682 (1955). *40)* MORRISON, L. M., *Angiology*, **4**, 123 and 130 (1953); *Geriatrics*, **8**, 649 (1953); GREENBERG and BRUGER, *Proc. Soc. exp. Biol. (N.Y.)*, **84**, 87 (1953); DUFF and MEISSNER, *Arch. Path. (Chicago)*, **57**, 329 (1954); GOLDBLOOM et al., *Amer. J. dig. Dis.*, **21**, 152 (1954). *41)* STEGGERDA, F. R., *Ann. Rev. Physiol.*, **17**, 129 (1955). *42)* FISCHER and GARRITY, *J. biol. Chem.*, **204**, 759 (1953); **206**, 345 (1954). *43)* MIRONE, L., *Amer. J. Physiol.*, **179**, 49 (1954). *44)* REID, M. E., *Fed. Proc.*, **13**, 474 (1954). *45)* HOVE et al., *J. Nutr.*, **53**, 377 (1954); HOVE and COPELAND, *J. Nutr.*, **53**, 391 (1954). *46)* BURNS and ACKERMAN, *Proc. Soc. exp. Biol. (N.Y.)*, **89**, 420 (1955). *47)* HALL and BIERI, *Endocrinology*, **53**, 661 (1953). *48)* CLAYTON and BAUMANN, *J. Nutr.*, **27**, 155 (1944); DAVIS et al., *J. Dairy Sci.*, **39**, 440 (1956). *49)* CROMWELL and RENNIE, *Biochem. J.*, **55**, 189 (1953); **58**, 318 (1954). *50)* AHMAD and KARIM, *Biochem. J.*, **55**, 817 (1953).

myo-Inositol (inositol, mesoinositol)[1]

Inositol occurs in nature either free or in compounds (phytic acid). It is soluble in water, insoluble in organic solvents, stable to acids and alkalis.

myo-**Inositol**, $C_6H_{12}O_6$ MESOINOSITOL

White crystals, sweet taste
Mol.wt. 180.16
M.p. 225–226° C

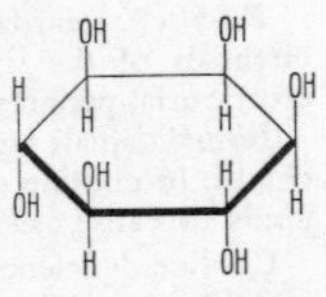

Of the eight possible *cis-trans*-isomers, the optically active D- and L-forms, the racemate and some other isomers occur in nature.

Unit

No unit defined; by weight.

Methods of test and assay

Chemically[2], or biologically with white mice[3]. Microbiologically by means of *Saccharomyces cerevisiae*[4], *S. carlsbergensis*[5], *Neurospora crassa*[6], *Kloeckera brevis*[7], etc. Chromatographic separation of the phosphate[8]. Spectrophotometric assay[9].

Occurrence (values in mg per 100 g weight fresh, unless otherwise stated)

Yeast 500, crude liver extracts 200–300, beef liver 340, beef brain 149, white flour 110, oats 100, black bread 64, milk 50 mg/100 ml.

Physiology and function

Inositol is very widely distributed in the plant kingdom, chiefly as phytic acid (hexaphosphate) and the calcium magnesium salt of the latter (phytin). Inositol monophosphate and triphosphate also occur in nature.

In animals, the brain and lymph nodes contain twice as much inositol as the blood serum, mainly as phospholipids and the diphosphoinositide of cephalin. In muscle, inositol appears to be combined with a protein. In the tissues and serum most of it is combined with lipids[10]. The spermatozoa and secretion of the seminal vesicles of hogs contain large quantities of inositol[11].

Ingested inositol is taken up very quickly by the liver, lungs, brain, pancreas and especially by the kidneys. Very probably the body cells are able to synthesize inositol in certain circumstances[12]. For certain microorganisms it is an indispensable growth factor, as also for some higher animals (mouse, rat, guinea pig, hamster, chicken). Its significance in human nutrition is still rather obscure[13]; the daily requirement is estimated to be about 1 mg per 2500 calories[14].

The plasma level is 0.37–0.76 mg per 100 ml[15]. An average of 0.65 mg per day is excreted in the sweat and 22–30 mg/l in the urine[26]. In diabetes with glycosuria, urinary excretion is markedly increased. Elimination of the glycosuria normalizes the urinary excretion, so that there must be an absorption mechanism in the kidneys which is blocked by the increase in the glucose concentration[17].

The high inositol content of the brain and cerebrospinal fluid indicates its involvement in the intermediary metabolism of the central nervous system[18]. It has no influence on the seminal cells and seems to function in the spermatozoa only as a regulator of osmotic pressure. The spermatozoal content can be used for estimating the secretory activity of the seminal vesicles[11].

In general metabolism inositol takes part in the transport of fats in the form of phospholipids. Its derivatives function as intermediates in the conversion of aliphatic into aromatic compounds[19]. The activity of α-amylase is markedly reduced when there is a deficiency of inositol[20].

The lipotropic action of inositol is peculiar in that it is manifested only on a *fat-free diet*, and it is then effective against infiltration with cholesterol but not against infiltration with neutral fats. The protective action probably depends on the liberation of methionine from proteins. This lipotropic action has also been observed in cases of gastrointestinal carcinoma. When inositol and choline are given together, the results are more marked than when they are given separately[21].

Inositol is an important but not indispensable factor in cell division (normal and cancerous) and therefore also in the growth of young animals[22]. Although the blood level in the fetus is higher than that in the maternal blood, the latter does not rise, and the absence of transplacental exchange and of placental synthesis of inositol indicates synthesis in the fetus. In twin pregnancies the inositol level in the blood is higher than in single pregnancies. Two weeks after birth the serum level of the infant has fallen to that of the mother[23].

In rats and mice, the inositol deficiency state caused by the antimetabolite γ-hexachlorocyclohexane leads after 10–12 weeks to loss of weight and alopecia[20, 24], in dogs to a slowing down of the peristalsis of the stomach and jejunum[25].

The high content of phytic acid in many cereals is of importance in that this acid forms an insoluble calcium salt, with the result that the organism is able only partially – or not at all – to utilize the calcium and phosphorus of plants. Phytic acid can also fix the calcium of other foods, for example milk, which explains the rachitogenic action of oats and other cereals. Yeast bread is not rachitogenic because the phytic acid is destroyed during fermentation. Iron is also immobilized by phytic acid, but to a lesser degree than calcium.

Therapeutic applications

Inositol is used in protective liver diets and in the treatment of steatosis, arteriosclerosis and gastrointestinal atony.

References: *1)* For a brief review see CLARK, G. W., *A Vitamin Digest*, Springfield, 1953, page 200. *2)* GREGORY, R. A., *Biochem. J.*, **29**, 2798 (1935). *3)* WOOLLEY, D. W., *J. biol. Chem.*, **136**, 113 (1940); **139**, 29 (1941); *J. Nutr.*, **21**, suppl., 17 (1941). *4)* WOOLLEY, D. W., *J. biol. Chem.*, **140**, 453 (1941); *J. exp. Med.*, **75**, 277 (1942). *5)* ATKIN et al., *Industr. Engng. Chem. Anal. Ed.*, **15**, 141 (1943). *6)* BEADLE, G. W., *J. biol. Chem.*, **156**, 683 (1944). *7)* BURKHOLDER et al., *J. Bact.*, **48**, 385 (1944). *8)* CONSDEN et al., *Biochem. J.*, **41**, 590 (1947); HECHT and MINK, *Biochim. biophys. Acta*, **8**, 641 (1952); HACK, M. H., *Biochem. J.*, **54**, 602 (1953). *9)* LEBARON et al., *Fed. Proc.*, **16**, 209 (1957). *10)* MAIBAUER, D., *Naunyn-Schmiedeberg's Arch. exp. Path. Pharmak.*, **225**, 131 (1955); HERKEN and MAIBAUER, *Klin. Wschr.*, **32**, 1113 (1954). *11)* MANN, T., *Proc. roy. Soc. B*, **142**, 21 (1954). *12)* AGRANOFF, B. W., *Fed. Proc.*, **16**, 379, (1957). *13)* PETT, L. B., *Vitam. and Horm.*, **13**, 213 (1955). *14)* WILLIAMS, R. J., *J. Amer. med. Ass.*, **119**, 1 (1942). *15)* SONNE and SOBOTKA, *Arch. Biochem.*, **14** 93 (1947). *16)* JOHNSON et al., *J. biol. Chem.*, **161**, 357 (1945). *17)* DAUGHADAY and LARNER, *J. clin. Invest.*, **33**, 326 (1954). *18)* HERKEN and MAIBAUER, *Klin. Wschr.*, **32**, 1113 (1954). *19)* CORNATZER and SIMONSON, *Abstr. Amer. chem. Soc. 126th Meeting*, 1954, page 54C; BARKER and BOURNE, *Advanc. Carbohydr. Chem.*, **7**, 137 (1952). *20)* RAMACHANDRAN and SARMA, *Indian J. med. Res.*, **42**, 201 (1954). *21)* BEST, C. H., *Diabetes and Insulin and the Lipotropic Factors*, Springfield, 1948; HARTMANN, F., *Naturwissenschaften*, **41**, 231 (1954); ABELS et al., *Proc. Soc. exp. Biol. (N.Y.)*, **54**, 157 (1943). *22)* EAGLE et al., *Science*, **123**, 845 (1956). *23)* CAMPLING and NIXON, *J. Physiol. (Lond.)*, **126**, 71 (1954). *24)* WOOLLEY, D. W., *Science*, **92**, 384 (1940); *J. biol. Chem.*, **139**, 29 (1941). *25)* MARTIN et al., *Amer. J. dig. Dis.*, **8**, 290 (1941); **9**, 268 (1942). *26)* MALANGEAU, P., *Bull. Soc. Chim. biol. (Paris)*, **38**, 729 (1956).

Essential fatty acids (EFA, vitamin F)[1]

These substances are a group of higher unsaturated fatty acids which were found to have a curative effect on liver damage caused by a fat-free diet[2]. The most important members of this group are linoleic acid and arachidonic acid. So far only linoleic acid has been synthesized[3].

Linoleic acid, $C_{18}H_{32}O_2$
Colorless oil
Mol.wt. 280.45

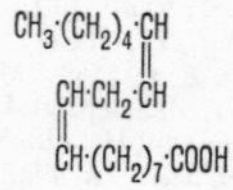

Arachidonic acid, $C_{20}H_{32}O_2$
Mol.wt. 304.48

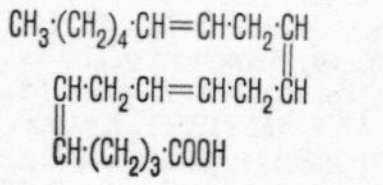

Unit. No unit defined.

Methods of test and assay[4]

Chemical. Spectrophotometric (very sensitive), chiefly for vegetable products, not always practicable for animal products.

GREENBERG's growth test: comparison of the biological activity of the material with that of a standardized essential fatty acid. This method depends on the fact that the increase in weight and size of the experimental animal are roughly proportional to the amount and activity of the EFA[5]. THOMASSON's method: based on disturbances of water balance appearing in deficiency states[6].

Occurrence

The EFA occur in all animal and vegetable fats. The latter contain only linoleic acid, the former also arachidonic acid[7].

Linoleic acid content of fats (per cent)[8]:

Animal body fats	Animal milk fats	Vegetable seed fats
Domestic fowl . 18	Cow 4	Coconut 1
Hens' egg yolk . 9	Horse 8	Palm kernel . . . 1
Hog, back 7	Goat 4	Olive fruit 7
Sheep 5	Man 8	Peanut 26
Ox 2		Cotton 45
Man 8		Corn 53
		Soybean 51
		Sunflower 65
		Safflower 77

Physiology and function

Not all polyunsaturated fatty acids possess "vitamin" activity; linolenic acid, contrary to general belief, has no biological activity. This is apparently confined to acids which contain the grouping $CH_3{\cdot}(CH_2)_4{\cdot}CH{:}CH{\cdot}CH_2{\cdot}CH{:}CH$[6,8]. The animal body meets its needs of EFA and especially of linoleic acid, mainly from vegetable sources.

In the organism, linoleic acid is probably important as a precursor of arachidonic acid, which is formed from it by condensation with acetate[9]. Pyridoxine may be involved in this reaction[17].

The EFA are stored in the form of phospholipids and are so sparingly used by the organism that even after a year on a deficient diet 50 % of the liver reserves still remain in spite of a massive reduction of the body fats. The exact daily requirement is unknown, but it varies with the mode of nutrition and is in general higher in males than in females[10].

In the form of enzymes, the EFA play a part in oxidative phosphorylation in the mitochondria of the liver cells[11].

The lowering of the serum cholesterol level by certain fats is due to their content not only of EFA but also of other polyunsaturated acids. The current view is that although linoleic and arachidonic acids are effective in this respect when present in adequate amount, this action of these acids has nothing to do with the specific growth-promoting properties to which they owe the name "essential"[8]. It has also been observed that the EFA improve the capillary resistance of the skin[12].

The protective action of the EFA against injury by X-rays seems to be due to their regenerative action on the tissues[13].

Deficiency of EFA in rats and mice retards growth, which ceases altogether after 8–10 weeks[5]. After a long period of progressive wasting, death occurs. Accompanying symptoms are increase of basal metabolism, disturbances of fat and water metabolism, lesions of the skin (dermatitis), falling out of hair and alopecia, kidney degeneration and loss of sexual function. In young dogs deficient in EFA the epithelial cells and organs of the skin (hairs, sebaceous and sweat glands) showed delayed maturation.

The EFA play an important part in reproduction, which is retarded in deficiency states both by sterility of the male and poor lactation. Conception remains possible but the number of stillbirths and the mortality of the newborn during the first few days are markedly increased[14].

In man it is impossible to produce deficiency of EFA by dietary restriction alone, and all that is achieved is a marked fall in the blood level. Eczema is sometimes attributed to a partial deficiency and a decrease of blood fats in this condition has in fact been observed[15].

Therapeutic applications

The beneficial effect of EFA on the cicatrization of wounds is exploited in the treatment of ulcers, burns and certain forms of eczematous dermatitis. They are also employed as a lipotropic factor[16].

References: *1)* For a review see STANGL, E., *Int. Z. Vitaminforsch.*, **23**, 164 (1951). *2)* BURR and BURR, *J. biol. Chem.*, **82**, 345 (1929). *3)* RAPHAEL and SONDHEIMER, *J. chem. Soc.*, **1950**, 2100; WALBORSKY et al., *J. Amer. chem. Soc.*, **73**, 2590 (1951); GENSLER and THOMAS, *J. Amer. chem. Soc.*, **73**, 4601 (1951). *4)* For a review see DEUEL and REISER, *Vitam. and Horm.*, **13**, 29 (1955). *5)* DEUEL et al., *J. Nutr.*, **40**, 351 (1950). *6)* THOMASSON, H. J., *Int. Z. Vitaminforsch.*, **25**, 62 (1953). *7)* DEUEL, H. J., *Progr. Chem. Fats and other Lipids*, **2**, 99 (1954). *8)* HILDITCH and JASPERSON, *Lipids in Relation to Arterial Disease*, Liverpool, 1959. *9)* MEAD et al., *J. biol. Chem.*, **218**, 401 (1956); STEINBERG et al., *J. biol. Chem.*, **220**, 257 (1956). *10)* GREENBERG et al., *J. Nutr.*, **41**, 473 (1950). *11)* KLEIN and JOHNSON, *J. biol. Chem.*, **211**, 103 (1954). *12)* KRAMÁR and LEVINE, *J. Nutr.*, **50**, 149 (1953). *13)* CHENG and DEUEL, *Fed. Proc.*, **12**, 410 (1953); CHENG et al., *J. Nutr.*, **52**, 637 (1954); **54**, 201 (1954). *14)* EVANS et al., *J. biol. Chem.*, **106**, 431, 441, 445 (1934); DEUEL et al., *J. Nutr.*, **54**, 193 (1954). *15)* HANSEN and WIESE, *Proc. Soc. exp. Biol. (N.Y.)*, **52**, 205 (1943). *16)* ROTH, O. A., *Med. Welt*, **20**, 1103 (1951). *17)* TULPULE and WILLIAMS, *J. biol. Chem.*, **217**, 229 (1955).

α-Lipoic acid (thioctic acid)[1]

This lipotropic factor was discovered in 1941 in yeast and in liver extracts[2]. Certain growth factors in cultures of various microorganisms have also been identified as α-lipoic acid. It is a component of enzymes and has been given various names: factor II (liver extracts), acetate replacing factor[3] or pyruvate oxidase factor (bacterial cultures)[4], protogen A or protogen B (enzymes)[5]. The acid has been prepared in the pure state[6] and also synthesized[7].

α-Lipoic acid (dithiooctanoic acid), $C_8H_{14}O_2S_2$
Mol.wt. 206.33

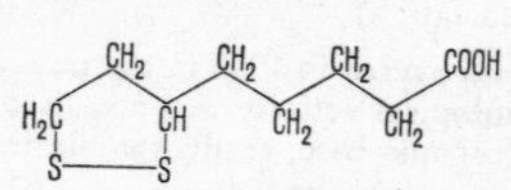

The disulfide form is easily reduced to the dithiol form, so that a redox system arises.

Unit

No unit defined; by weight.

Occurrence

In small quantities in most plants and in all animal tissues except the thyroid gland.

Physiology and function

α-Lipoic acid has been thought to play a role in plant photosynthesis but this is still disputed[8]. In the animal organism its primary role is in oxidations associated with coenzyme A[9] in which it transfers the acetyl group of pyruvic acid to coenzyme A and is then oxidized back to the disulfide form by DPN (see page 403). Other mechanisms in which it is involved are the phosphorylation of glucose, glycolysis and gluconeogenesis, and the conversion of lactic into pyruvic acid[10]. It also accelerates acetylation in the liver and takes part in the metabolism of lipids and in the synthesis of fatty acids.

After injection of α-lipoic acid only 10-15% enters the blood stream[11] and after two hours all has been excreted in the urine[12].

Although α-lipoic acid has been shown to function as a growth factor for certain microorganisms a similar activity in higher animals (rats, chicks) has not been demonstrated with certainty[13, 14]. The variable results obtained with chicks are possibly due to variable composition of the intestinal flora[15]. Chick embryos can synthesize α-lipoic acid[14].

Deficiency of α-lipoic acid, which may arise in severe forms of hepatitis, affects the activity of coenzyme A. α-Lipoic acid also has an antisteatogenous and necrotropic action similar to that of cysteine, but in high doses this can be reversed[16].

Therapeutic applications

α-Lipoic acid is a highly-active antidote in acute mercury, arsenic and thallium poisoning (superior to BAL) and in subacute phosphorus, carbon tetrachloride, potassium cyanide and aniline poisoning but is inactive in lead, uranium, benzene and alcohol poisoning. α-Lipoic acid prevents the development of alloxan diabetes in animals.

In severe hepatitis, α-lipoic acid has given variable results. According to some authors it has a favorable effect on the vegetative symptoms and thus brings about a subjective improvement and a general stimulation of the patient. In hepatic coma, which is probably the result of intoxication of the brain cells by abnormal products of metabolism, high doses may restore consciousness but the improvement is only transitory. In such cases the blood level of α-ketoglutarate, pyruvate and ammonium derivatives remains constant, so that it is not possible to decide to what extent the administration of α-lipoic acid is logically justified[17]. It is a powerful diuretic, especially in hepatic obstruction.

The therapeutic dose is $^1/_{100}$ of the lethal dose[11]. The usual dose is 10–60 mg given subcutaneously or better intravenously.

References: *1)* For a review see Roth and Cruchaud, *Rev. méd. Suisse rom.*, **77**, 574 (1957). *2)* Dewey, V. C., *Proc. Soc. exp. Biol. (N.Y.)*, **46**, 482 (1941); Dewey and Kidder, *Fed. Proc.*, **12**, 196 (1953). *3)* Guirard et al., *Arch. Biochem.*, **9**, 381 (1946). *4)* Dolin, M. I., *J. Bact.*, **69**, 51 (1955). *5)* Snell and Broquist, *Arch. Biochem.*, **23**, 326 (1949); Patterson et al., *J. Amer. chem. Soc.*, **76**, 1823 (1954). *6)* Reed, L. J., *Physiol. Rev.*, **33**, 544 (1953); Reed and Niu, *J. Amer. chem. Soc.*, **77**, 416 (1955). *7)* Brockmann et al., *J. Amer. chem. Soc.*, **74**, 3455 (1952). *8)* Calvin, M., *Fed. Proc.*, **13**, 697 (1954); *Angew. Chem.*, **68**, 253 (1956); Bradley and Calvin, *Proc. nat. Acad. Sci. (Wash.)*, **41**, 563 (1955); Grisebach, H., *Dtsch. med. Wschr.*, **81**, 145 (1956). *9)* Seaman, G. R., *J. Amer. chem. Soc.*, **76**, 1712 (1954). *10)* Bornstein and Hartman, *Nature*, **176**, 788 (1955); Gunsalus et al., *J. Amer. chem. Soc.*, **78**, 1763 (1956). *11)* Covello, M., *Prod. pharm.*, **12**, 87 (1957). *12)* Patterson et al., *Amer. J. clin. Nutr.*, 4, 269 (1956). *13)* DeBusk and Williams, *Arch. Biochem.*, **55**, 587 (1955). *14)* Stokstad et al., *Proc. Soc. exp. Biol. (N.Y.)*, **92**, 88 (1956). *15)* Supplee et al., *Arch. Biochem.*, **61**, 140 (1956). *16)* Larizza, P., *Minerva med. (Torino)*, **47** I, 581 (1956); Larizza and Grignani, *Minerva med. (Torino)*, **47** II, 527 (1956). *17)* Rausch, F., *Arzneimittel-Forsch.*, **5**, 32 (1955); Steigmann and Canahuati, *Fed. Proc.*, **15**, 487 (1956); Summerskill et al., *Amer. J. Med.*, **23**, 59 (1957).

Vitamins of indefinite character

Little is known of the biological activity of the substances described in this section and few of them have been isolated.

Vitamins B_3, B_4, B_5

The existence of these vitamins is still very controversial. B_3 may be identical with pantothenic acid[1] and B_5 with pyridoxine or nicotinic acid[2]. B_4 can be replaced biologically by a mixture of arginine, glycine and cystine[3].

Vitamin B_{13} (polished rice factor)

This factor has been isolated from polished rice and liver extracts, but it has not yet been prepared in crystalline form. It activates the growth of rats and is effective in a daily dose of 2 µg.

That there is a relationship between this factor and orotic acid is indicated by their common activity in *Lactobacillus bulgaricus* and in most other microorganisms and even in higher animals (rats, chickens, swine, etc.). Orotic acid, however, is effective only in milligram concentrations, indicating that it is probably a constituent of vitamin B_{13}[4].

In rats, orotic acid is converted into uridine 5′-phosphate, a precursor of ribonucleic acid and other compounds[2].

Vitamin B_{14}

This substance has been obtained in crystalline form from human urine. Its structure is still unknown; it contains 19.4% of nitrogen, 4% of phosphorus, but no sulfur or cobalt. It has a stimulating influence on cell division (curative effect in anemia caused by sulfonamides)[5].

Vitamin B_T (carnitine)

Carnitine was discovered in 1905 in the muscle tissue of vertebrates, but its biological activity was not discovered until 1952. It is a very hygroscopic base, easily soluble in water and ethyl alcohol.

DL-Carnitine, $C_7H_{15}O_3N$
Levorotatory crystals
Mol.wt. 161.21
M.p. 195–197° C

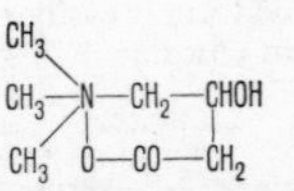

Methods of test and assay

Chemical determination. Biologically with *Tenebrio molitor* by measurement of the growth and survival rate of the larvae. Other species of *Tenebrio* have also been used.

Occurrence[6]

Almost universal. The chief source of carnitine is the muscle tissue of vertebrates, which at birth contains 48–260 mg per 100 g fresh weight.

Physiology and function

Carnitine is essential to certain bacteria and can be synthesized by practically all organisms in which it has been identified.

Apart from its role in the utilization of fats by animals, little is known of the biological activity of carnitine. There is no evidence that it is concerned in methylation processes.

Extracts of the pancreas contain much carnitine. Here it appears to promote secretion both by stimulation of the vagus and by direct action on the gland cells. In muscle its action is analogous to that of acetylcholine, its esters inhibiting the contraction and promoting the relaxation of muscle[7]. In this respect it can be replaced by the synthetic product dicarnitine, which inhibits ganglionic transference and acts on the sympathetic synapses as a parasympatheticomimetic[8].

Although carnitine as such has only a slight pharmacological activity it may be a precursor of highly active substances. Some authors consider that it is one of the sources of acetylcholine.

Carnitine is a growth factor for insects and also promotes the growth *in vitro* of cultures of bone tissue.

Carnitine does not protect rats deficient in choline from fatty infiltration of the liver and cannot, in spite of its close relationship with choline, replace the latter in organisms which need it.

Therapeutic applications

Carnitine has been used with good results to stimulate the appetite and digestive secretion in premature and very young children. Its very low toxicity permits daily doses of 10–30 mg per kg over several months.

References: *1)* Williams and Waterman, *J. biol. Chem.*, **78**, 311 (1928). *2)* Carter et al., *Biochem. J.*, **24**, 1844 (1930); Macrae and Edgar, *Biochem. J.*, **31**, 2225 (1937). *3)* Reader, V., *Biochem. J.*, **23**, 689 (1929); Briggs et al., *J. biol. Chem.*, **150**, 11 (1943). *4)* For a review see Haüge, S.M., *Symposium on B-Vitamins*, Abstracts, Austin, Tex., 1953, quoted by Johnson, B. C., *Ann. Rev. Biochem.*, **24**, 419 (1955). *5)* Norris and Majnarich, *Science*, **109**, 32 (1949). *6)* For a review see Stekol, J. A., *Ann. Rev. Biochem.*, **26**, 611 (1957). *7)* Strack and Försterling, *Hoppe-Seylers Z. physiol. Chem.*, **295**, 377 (1953). *8)* Leclercq, J., *Biochim. biophys. Acta*, **13**, 160 (1954).

Gonadotropins[1]

The gonadotropic hormones are water-soluble glycoproteins with a molecular weight ranging from 30,000 to 100,000 and containing hexosamine as component. They are not stored in the organism but are either inactivated in the blood or, with the exception of the serum gonadotropin of pregnant mares, excreted in the urine.

Gonadotropins of the anterior pituitary

Follicle stimulating hormone

(FSH, follicle ripening hormone, prolan A, gonadotropin I, gametokinetic hormone, gametogenic hormone, thylakentrin)

Site of formation

Basophil cells of the anterior pituitary.

Source

Pituitary of man, horse, sheep and swine.

Unit and assay

No international unit. Assay by measurement of follicle ripening[2] or increase in weight of testes in hypophysectomized rats treated with an excess of chorion gonadotropin[3]; by increase in weight of ovaries in infantile rats treated with chorion gonadotropin[2,4].

Function

Women: Stimulates the ripening of the follicles; does not cause rupture of the follicles or estrogen formation. Overdosage causes formation of follicular cysts.

Men: Stimulates spermiohistogenesis up to the formation of ripe sperm cells and the growth of the seminal tubules; has no effect on the interstitial tissue and therefore none on testosterone formation.

Luteinizing hormone

(LH, interstitial cell-stimulating hormone, ICSH, prolan B, gonadotropin II, corpus luteum ripening hormone, metakentrin)

Site of formation

Eosinophil cells of the anterior pituitary.

Source

Pituitary of sheep and swine.

Unit and assay

No international unit. Assay by measurement of repair of interstitial tissue[2], or of increase in weight of ovaries[5], prostate[6,7] or seminal vesicles[7] in infantile hypophysectomized rats. Feather pigmentation test in weaverbirds[8].

Function

Women: Stimulates rupture of the follicles and the formation of the corpora lutea; together with FSH stimulates estrogen formation and together with prolactin progesterone formation.

Men: Stimulates synthesis and secretion of testosterone; promotes growth of the seminal tubules and accessory sex organs.

Prolactin (luteomammotropic hormone, LMTH; see page 476) has a component with luteotropic activity. Rats require this hormone for progesterone formation. In man the gonadotropic activity of prolactin is uncertain.

Gonadotropins of extrapituitary origin

These are found in man and in some simian and equine species.

Chorionic gonadotropin

(human chorionic gonadotropin, HCG or CG; pregnancy urine hormone, PU; anterior pituitary-like hormone, APL)

Site of formation

LANGHANS' cells of the chorionic villi of the placenta.

Source

Blood or urine in pregnancy, placenta.

Unit and assay

1 international unit (IU) = 0.1 mg of the international standard preparation (see page 739). Assay by measurement of increase in weight of the prostate[9], vesicular glands[10] or both together[11] in infantile rats. The pregnancy test on toads and frogs[23,26–30] (see below) can also be used for assay.

Function

Takes over the function of LH in pregnancy as a result of blocking of the pituitary secretion of LH by estrogens and progesterone. When HCG is given during the lutein phase in doses of 5000 to 20,000 IU the cycle is prolonged by two weeks and the uterine mucosa becomes decidual (pseudopregnancy).

Serum gonadotropin of pregnant mares

(PMS)

Site of formation

Chorion cells and endometrium.

Source

Serum and endometrium of pregnant mares.

Unit and assay

1 international unit (IU) = 0.25 mg of the international standard preparation (see page 739). Assay by measurement of the increase in weight of the uterus and ovaries of infantile rats and mice[12].

Function

The physiological role of PMS is uncertain since in contrast to the human pituitary that of the horse continues to secrete gonadotropins during pregnancy. It is remarkable that in spite of its relatively low molecular weight of ca. 30,000, PMS is not excreted in the urine. This is of importance in therapy[13].

Pathological gonadotropins

Gonadotropic hormones are known to be formed in chorioepithelioma of both sexes, in hydatid mole, and in seminoma and carcinoma of the testes[14].

Regulation of gonadotropin secretion

In men the basal secretion is constant, in women subject to cyclic variations[15]. The amount of gonadotropins secreted by the pituitary is inversely proportional to the amount of sex hormones formed, which explains for example the very high gonadotropin titer of castrated men. From the clinical point of view, this is important in that the administration of sex hormones in large amounts inhibits gonadotropin secretion by the pituitary and thus depresses gametogenesis.

Both the constant and cyclic basal secretion are subject to the influence of emotional and sensory changes. There is a "chain reaction" between the pituitary, the hypothalamic sexual center and the periphery. In all probability the link with the anterior pituitary is by means of adrenergic substances. It can be blocked in a first phase by parasympatholytic agents (atropine) and in a second phase by adrenaline-blocking drugs[16]. The central regulation of gonadotropin secretion is also affected by barbiturates, an effect also observed in man[17].

Figures 1 and 2 illustrate the regulation of gonadotropin secretion and the reactive formation of sex hormones in the ovaries during the normal menstrual cycle and in pregnancy (after G. WERTH, *Arzneimittel-Forsch.*, 5, 738 [1955]).

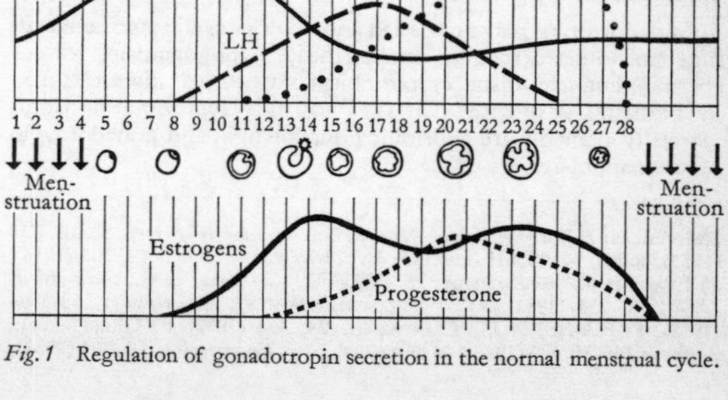

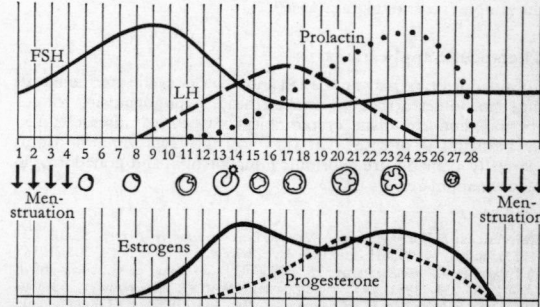

Fig. 1 Regulation of gonadotropin secretion in the normal menstrual cycle.

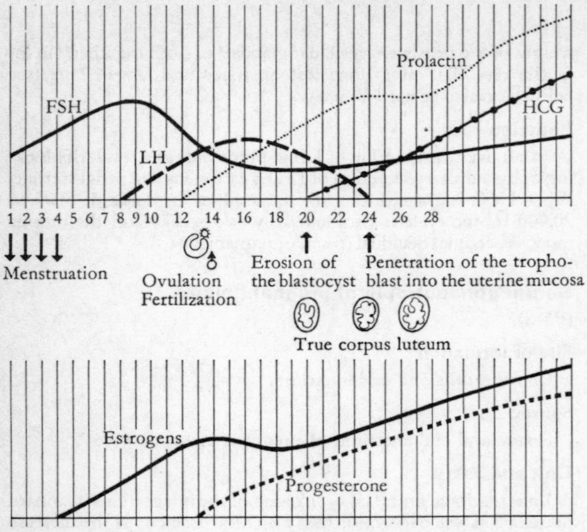

Fig. 2 Regulation of gonadotropin secretion during pregnancy. When the LH curve falls after fertilization the HCG curve commences to rise. HCG appears in the urine at the earliest on the 10th day of pregnancy. Erosion of the blastocyst has already occurred on the 6th day, and implantation of the trophoblast in the uterine mucosa has started on the 9th day. It is therefore possible that HCG formation only commences slowly between the 6th and 9th days after fertilization, i.e. between the 20th and 24th days after the last menstruation, and thus fails to appear in the urine. The increasing formation of HCG stimulates the secretion of prolactin in the anterior pituitary, thus making possible the growth and maintenance in the ovary of the corpus luteum of pregnancy and the increased output of sex hormones.

Relation of the pituitary to the various hormone systems

This is not known in detail, although it has been shown that the secretion of gonadotropins is reduced in stress and in nonfunctioning of the thyroid (i.e. when there is excessive production of ACTH or thyrotropin). Hyperthyroidism can also lead to a cessation of gonadotropin secretion.

Diagnostic application

Determination of the gonadotropin titer can be used as an early test for pregnancy and for the diagnosis of hydatid mole and chorio-epithelioma (uterus, ovaries, testes, metastases).

Pregnancy tests

On rabbits: The FRIEDMAN test[18] consists of 2 injections at a 24-hour interval of 10 ml each of the urine sample in the ear veins of female rabbits. The test is positive when hemorrhage of a follicle is observed 48 hours after the second injection.

On rats: Injection of the urine into immature female rats, positive when followed by hyperemia of the ovaries (modified ASCHHEIM-ZONDEK test)[19].

On frogs and toads: Injection of the urine or serum into the dorsal lymph sac, positive when followed by appearance of spermatozoa in the urine of the animal. The original GALLI-MAININI test was on *Bufo arenarum*[20, 21]; other species employed are *Rana pipiens*[22, 23], *R. nigromaculata*[24], *R. esculenta*[25, 26], *Bufo bufo*[27], *B. marinus*[28], *B. viridis*[29]. With *Xenopus laevis* the test is positive when injection of the sample causes ovulation[24, 30, 31].

Therapeutic applications

Gonadotropins may be tried in anovulatory cyclic uterine bleeding, menometrorrhagia, amenorrhea, hypogonadism, oligospermia, eunuchoidism, cryptorchism, SIMMONDS' disease[32]; also in FROMMEL's disease (CHIARI-FROMMEL syndrome)[33]. Commercially available are chorionic gonadotropin and gonadotropin of pregnant mares.

References: *1)* For reviews see WERTH, G., *Arzneimittel-Forsch.*, **5**, 409, 735 (1955), and **6**, 79 (1956); LORAINE, J. A., *Vitam. and Horm.*, **14**, 305 (1956). *2)* EVANS et al., *Endocrinology*, **25**, 529 (1939). *3)* PAESI et al., *Acta endocr. (Kbh.)*, **8**, 251 (1951). *4)* STEELMAN and POHLEY, *Endocrinology*, **53**, 604 (1953). *5)* FEVOLD, H. L., *Endocrinology*, **24**, 435 (1939). *6)* GREEP et al., *Endocrinology*, **30**, 635 (1942); MCARTHUR, J.W., *Endocrinology*, **50**, 304 (1952); LORAINE and BROWN, *Acta endocr. (Kbh.)*, **17**, 250 (1954), and *J. Endocr.*, **13**, 1 (1955). *7)* MCARTHUR, J. W., *Endocrinology*, **50**, 304 (1952); LORAINE and BROWN, *Acta endocr. (Kbh.)*, **17**, 250 (1954). *8)* WITSCHI, E., *Proc. Soc. exp. Biol. (N.Y.)*, **35**, 484 (1936); ALBERT, A., *Recent Progr. Hormone Res.*, **13**, 227 (1956). *9)* LORAINE, J. A., *J. Endocr.*, **6**, 319 (1950). *10)* WATTS and ADAIR, *Amer. J. Obstet. Gynec.*, **46**, 183 (1943). *11)* DICZFALUSY, E., *Acta endocr. (Kbh.)*, **17**, 58 (1954). *12)* HAMBURGER, C., in EMMENS, C. W. (Ed.), *Hormone Assay*, New York, 1950, page 173. *13)* CATCHPOLE et al., *Amer. J. Physiol.*, **112**, 21 (1935); EVANS and SIMPSON, in PINCUS and THIMANN (Eds.), *The Hormones*, vol. II, New York, 1950, page 351. *14)* ZONDEK, H., *Die Krankheiten der endocrinen Drüsen*, 3rd ed., Basle, 1953, page 197; MCCORMICK, J. B., *Obstet. and Gynec.*, **3**, 58 (1954); HAMBURGER, C., *Ciba Found. Coll. Endocr.*, **12**, 190, 200 (1958). *15)* RAKOFF, A. E., *Med. Clin. N. Amer.*, **26**, 1915 (1942). *16)* MARKEE et al., *Recent Progr. Hormone Res.*, **7**, 139 (1952); SAWYER, C. H., *Recent Progr. Hormone Res.*, **7**, 161 (1952); WERTH, G., *Arzneimittel-Forsch.*, **5**, 735 (1955). *17)* WESTMAN, A., *Recent Progr. Hormone Res.*, **7**, 160 (1952) (discussion of MARKEE et al., *ibid.*, **7**, 139 (1952). *18)* FRIEDMAN and LAPHAM, *Amer. J. Obstet. Gynec.*, **21**, 405 (1931); KELLY and WOODS, *J. Amer. med. Ass.*, **108**, 615 (1937). *19)* KELSO, R. E., *Amer. J. clin. Path.*, **10**, 293 (1940); SALMON et al., *J. clin. Endocr.*, **2**, 167 (1942), and *Endocrinology*, **30**, Suppl., 1039 (1942); KUPPERMAN et al., *J. clin. Endocr.*, **3**, 548 (1943); ZONDEK et al., *J. Amer. med. Ass.*, **128**, 939 (1945); ALBERT, A., *J. clin. Endocr.*, **8**, 619 (1948); ALBERT and BERKSON, *J. clin. Endocr.*, **11**, 805 (1951); BEHRMAN and NIEMANN, *Fertil. and Steril.*, **6**, 236 (1955); BERMAN, R. L., *Fertil. and Steril.*, **7**, 276 (1956). *20)* GALLI-MAININI, C., *Sem. méd. (B. Aires)*, **1**, 337 (1947). *21)* GALLI-MAININI, C., *J. clin. Endocr.*, **7**, 653 (1947). *22)* WILTBERGER and MILLER, *Science*, **107**, 198 (1948); BRODY, H., *Amer. J. Obstet. Gynec.*, **57**, 581 (1949); MAIER, E. C., *West. J. Surg.*, **57**, 558 (1949); GARDNER and HARRIS, *Amer. J. Obstet. Gynec.*, **59**, 350 (1950); GREENBLATT et al., *J. clin. Endocr.*, **10**, 265 (1950), and *Fertil. and Steril.*, **1**, 533 (1950); BENITEZ et al., *U.S. armed Forces med. J.*, **5**, 815 (1954). *23)* HASKINS and SHERMAN, *Endocrinology*, **44**, 542 (1949), and *J. clin. Endocr.*, **12**, 385 (1952). *24)* FREYTAG et al., *J. Lab. clin. Med.*, **42**, 646 (1953). *25)* JAUBERT et al., *Concours méd.*, **74**, 377 (1952); KOCH, O., *Thesis*, Zurich, 1953. *26)* LAJOS et al., *Schweiz. med. Wschr.*, **81**, 815 (1951). *27)* THORBORG and HANSEN, *Acta endocr. (Kbh.)*, **6**, 51 (1951). *28)* WANNAN, J. S., *Med. J. Aust.*, **2**, 83 (1952). *29)* BUKOVICS and WOHLZOGEN, *Acta endocr. (Kbh.)*, **14**, 273 (1953); WOHLZOGEN, F. X., *Naunyn-Schmiedeberg's Arch. exp. Path. Pharmak.*, **217**, 482 (1953). *30)* HOBSON, B. M., *Quart. J. exp. Physiol.*, **37**, 191 (1952). *31)* SHAPIRO and ZWARENSTEIN, *Med. J. S. Afr.*, **9**, 202 (1935); ROBBINS et al., *New Engl. J. Med.*, **234**, 784 (1946); DITTEBRANDT, M., *Amer. J. clin. Path.*, **19**, 284 (1949). *32)* RUSSELL, C. S., *Practitioner*, **180**, 77 (1958). *33)* CHRISTIANSEN, E. G., *Acta Endocr. (Kbh.)*, **24**, 407 (1957).

Corticotropin

(corticotropic hormone, adrenocorticotropin, adrenocorticotropic hormone, ACTH)

Chemistry[1, 2]

In the pituitary, ACTH is contained in a protein of molecular weight of the order of 10,000 to 20,000 from which it can be separated by the action of acid or pepsin. The structures of the following have so far been elucidated: α-corticotropin (sheep), β-corticotropin (swine), corticotropin A (swine), corticotropin B (swine) and an ACTH from cattle[3]. All these peptides have very similar amino acid sequences. That of β-corticotropin is as follows[4]:

Ser . [Tyr] . Ser [. Met . Glu . His . Phe . Arg . Try . Gly] . Lys .
[Pro] . Val . Gly . Lys . Lys . Arg . Arg . Pro . Val . Lys . Val .
Tyr . Pro . Asp . Gly . Ala . Glu . Asp . Glu(NH_2) . Leu . Ala .
Glu . Ala . Phe . Pro . Leu . Glu . Phe

It is noteworthy that this structure is similar to that of the melanocyte-stimulating hormone, MSH (see page 478) – shown boxed-in in the above formula – a similarity which is reflected in an MSH-activity shown by ACTH. A polypeptide with activity equal to natural ACTH and containing 23 amino acid residues has recently been synthesized.

Units

1 USP unit = 1 international unit (IU) = 0.88 mg of the international standard preparation (1.14 IU/mg; see page 739). Other units are also in use[5, 7].

Methods of assay[7]

The ascorbic acid test of SAYERS et al.[6] is rapid and sensitive. It consists in the measurement of the decrease in the ascorbic acid content of the adrenals of hypophysectomized rats after injection of the extract under test.

Site of formation

Basophil cells of the anterior lobe of the pituitary[8], possibly also the placenta[9–11] and the posterior lobe of the pituitary[8, 12].

Physiology

The ACTH content of the pituitary in man is about 2.5 mg/g of tissue (dry substance). The ACTH concentration in the blood is small and may be less then 0.5 milliunit per 100 ml[13]. Higher values for normal tissues often reported in the literature should be regarded with scepticism[14], but they are observed in pathological conditions[15] (for example in untreated cases of ADDISON's disease).

ACTH given intravenously to rats has a half-life of about 5 minutes[16].

Function

1. Stimulation of the growth of the adrenal glands. Hypophysectomy causes atrophy of these glands.
2. Stimulation of the activity of the adrenal cortex. ACTH promotes the secretion of corticosteroids (cortisol, corticosterone, cortexone). It appears to have an effect on the cholesterol-pregnenolone stage in the biosynthesis of corticosteroids[17] (probably by stimulation of the adrenal phosphorylase involved[20]), the subsequent stages being mainly due to the presence of hydroxylating enzymes[18].

   The secretion of aldosterone is increased to some extent by ACTH[19], an effect which seems to be due to an increased secretion of corticosterone or cortexone as precursors of aldosterone.
3. ACTH has an influence on the ascorbic acid content of the adrenals. Administration of ACTH causes an increased discharge of ascorbic acid into the blood[21]. This is used as a test for ACTH (see above).
4. ACTH, like cortisol, causes a decrease of eosinophils in the blood (see page 490). Injection of ACTH, followed by an eosinophil count, serves as a test of the function of the adrenal cortex (THORN test).
5. The extra-adrenal effects of ACTH are qualitatively similar to those which result from stimulation of the adrenal cortex or from the administration of cortisol; quantitatively, however, they are different[22]. Like the growth hormone, ACTH causes mobilization of fats (transitory ketosis is possible in man[23]) and is diabetogenic (antagonistic to insulin). For a more detailed description of the metabolic effects see under Adrenocortical Hormones, pages 487–491.

Control of ACTH secretion[24, 25]

(*a*) *Hormonal auto-regulation.* The secretion of ACTH by the pituitary varies in inverse proportion to the corticosteroid titer of the blood. Here the pituitary does not react uniformly to the whole adrenocorticosteroid spectrum but principally to the 11-17-oxycorticosteroids.

(*b*) *Nervous control.* Apart from this obligate hormonal control, an important part is probably also played by central nervous control, very probably via the hypothalamus. This view is strengthened by the fact that morphine, reserpine and chlorpromazine – whose point of attack is probably the hypothalamus – can block the secretion of ACTH.

Adrenaline and histamine stimulate secretion of ACTH, possibly by the elimination of naturally occurring ACTH inhibitors.

Nothing certain is yet known either about the way in which the hypothalamus is stimulated or of its relation to the pituitary. Possibly a hormone-like factor, often designated the Corticotropin Releasing Factor (CRF), is responsible. Different suggestions have been made about the nature of this factor. Vasopressin, for example, has CRF properties[26], but does not seem to be the true CRF[27]. The control of ACTH secretion by the corticosteroid content of the blood may also have a central nervous origin in that the secretion of CRF is blocked or hindered by corticosteroid action via the CNS[28].

A nervous or nervous and hormonal control by the hypothalamus seems to be very important in the reaction of the pituitary to unfavorable environmental conditions[29]. When stress* occurs, perfect functioning of the adrenal cortex is indispensable to recovery. Under such conditions a secretion of ACTH sufficient to ensure stimulation of the production of adrenal cortical hormones is essential, particularly since the adrenal cortex is unable to store large quantities of hormones[30]. The reaction of the pituitary to a "neural stress" depends possibly on nervous control, while in a "systemic stress" there must be a direct influence via the blood circulation since after severance of the pituitary stalk the secretion of ACTH, which continues, is unaffected by nervous reflexes but may be influenced by injuries to the tissues. The increased secretion of adrenaline observed under stress[31] does not play any significant part in the stimulation of ACTH secretion[32].

Therapeutic applications[33]

Corticotropin-zinc hydroxide, given parenterally, is more slowly absorbed than ACTH alone. When the hormone is given intramuscularly it is partially inactivated by muscle enzymes. Its range of application is similar to that of the adrenal steroids so long as the adrenal cortex continues to function. An occasional side effect is increased pigmentation of the skin (due to the MSH activity). ACTH is contraindicated in cases in which its secretion is already increased (ADDISON's disease, adrenogenital syndrome in children).

* The following are included under stress: Strong emotions, strenuous muscular effort, all major forms of trauma (accidental, obstetric, surgical, pharmacological, etc.; mechanical, hemorrhagic, electrical, toxic; burns, freezing; trauma due to high acceleration, large changes in pressure, etc.), exposure to cold, heat and ionizing radiation, diathermy, ultrasound, anoxia, hemorrhages, infections, effects of allergens, overdosage of hormones, malnutrition, hunger, thirst, severe atmospheric influences, excessive exposure to the sun, etc. For a review of stress see SELYE[32].

References: *1)* LI, C. H., *Advanc. Protein Chem.*, **11**, 101 (1956). *2)* BEHRENS and BROMER, *Ann. Rev. Biochem.*, **27**, 57 (1958); ONCLEY, J. L., *Rev. mod. Physics*, **31**, 30 (1959). *3)* LI et al., *J. Amer. chem. Soc.*, **80**, 2587 (1958). *4)* SHEPHARD et al., *J. Amer. chem. Soc.*, **78**, 5067 (1956). *5)* MUNSON et al., *Fed. Proc.*, **9**, 208 (1950). *6)* SAYERS et al., *Endocrinology*, **42**, 379 (1948). *7)* GREENSPAN et al., in EMMENS, C. W. (Ed.), *Hormone Assay*, New York, 1950, page 205. *8)* ROCHEFORT and SAFFRAN, *Canad. J. Biochem.*, **35**, 471 (1957). *9)* JAILER and KNOWLTON, *J. clin. Invest.*, **29**, 1430 (1950). *10)* JAILER, J. W., *Clinical ACTH*, vol. I, New York, 1951, page 77. *11)* TARANTINO, C., *Folia endocr. (Pisa)*, **4**, 197 (1951). *12)* MIALHE-VOLOSS, C., *Acta endocr. (Kbh.)*, **28**, Suppl. 35 (1958). *13)* SNYDOR et al., *J. clin. Endocr.*, **13**, 891 (1953). *14)* SAYERS, G., *J. clin. Endocr.*, **15**, 754 (1955). *15)* LORAINE, J. A., *Ciba Found. Coll. Endocr.*, **11**, 19 (1957). *16)* GREENSPAN et al., *Endocrinology*, **46**, 261 (1950). *17)* HAYANO et al., *Recent Progr. Hormone Res.*, **12**, 79 (1956). *18)* DODDS et al., *Ann. Rev. Med.*, **7**, 41 (1956). *19)* LUETSCHER, J. A., *Recent Progr. Hormone Res.*, **12**, 175 (1956). *20)* HAYNES, R. C., *Fed. Proc.*, **17**, 376 (1958). *21)* SLUSHER and ROBERTS, *Endocrinology*, **61**, 98 (1957). *22)* ASTWOOD, E. B., in PINCUS and THIMANN (Eds.), *The Hormones*, vol. III, New York, 1955, page 235. *23)* KINSELL et al., *Clinical ACTH*, vol. I, New York, 1951, page 308. *24)* LONG, C. N. H., *Ann. Rev. Physiol.*, **18**, 409 (1956). *25)* SAYERS et al., *Ann. Rev. Physiol.*, **20**, 243 (1958). *26)* SAFFRAN and SAFFRAN, *Ann. Rev. Physiol.*, **21**, 403 (1959). *27)* GUILLEMIN et al., *Proc. Soc. exp. Biol. (N.Y.)*, **101**, 107 (1959). *28)* SHAPIRO et al., *Amer. J. Physiol.*, **192**, 58 (1958). *29)* HARRIS, G. W., *Neural Control of the Pituitary Gland*, London, 1955. *30)* VOGT, M., *J. Physiol. (Lond.)*, **113**, 129 (1951). *31)* ELMADJIAN et al., *Recent Progr. Hormone Res.*, **14**, 513 (1958). *32)* SELYE, H., *Stress*, Montreal, 1950. *33)* For a review see STRONG, J. A., *Practitioner*, **180**, 41 (1958).

Thyrotropin

(thyrotropic hormone, thyroid-stimulating hormone, TSH)[1]

Chemistry[2]

TSH is a protein of molecular weight over 10,000 containing carbohydrate. The most active preparation so far obtained from beef pituitary has a molecular weight of 25,000 and an activity of 30–50 USP units per milligram[3].

Units and assay

1 USP unit = 1 international unit (IU) = 13.5 mg of the international standard preparation (see page 739). 1 JUNKMANN-SCHÖLLER unit[4] is the minimum amount which when administered to guinea pigs weighing 100–150 g causes a histological reaction after 3 days. Other methods of assay depend on the increase in weight of the thyroid in guinea pigs and on changes in the basal metabolic rate or in the iodine content of the thyroid (including tracer methods with ^{131}I)[1, 4, 5].

Physiology

TSH is formed in the basophil cells of the anterior pituitary. Variations in the TSH content during growth and pregnancy differ in different animal species. In man the content appears to be independent of age[6]. In guinea pigs exposure to cold results in increased TSH formation[7] and thus in an increase in basal metabolic rate. In normal human plasma a level of 50 milliunits per 100 ml has been reported[9]. In myxedema it has been found in the albumin fraction[8]. After intravenous injection the hormone disappears rapidly from the circulating blood, and as studies with the ^{35}S-labeled hormone have shown, is taken up by the thyroid, reproductive glands, liver and possibly muscles. The hormone appears to be inactivated by the cells of the thyroid.

Function

1. Maintenance of thyroid function is dependent upon secretion of TSH by the pituitary. Lack of TSH results eventually in atrophy of the thyroid and storage of colloid, while thyroidectomy causes hypertrophy of the anterior pituitary and specific changes in the basophil cells (thyroidectomy cells).
2. TSH controls the iodine metabolism of the thyroid in two different ways: (*a*) directly by regulating the rate of formation of the enzymes involved in the synthesis of thyroid hormone, and (*b*) indirectly by regulating the ability of the thyroid to concentrate iodide[11]. The immediate effect of TSH is an acceleration of the release of preformed thyroid hormone stored in the form of colloid.

A connection between TSH and exophthalmic goiter (Graves' disease) has not been demonstrated with certainty[10]. Excessive administration of TSH causes changes in the eye socket with exophthalmos, and the existence of an "exophthalmos-producing substance", not identical with TSH, has been postulated.

The production of TSH by the anterior pituitary and its release are regulated on the one hand antagonistically by the blood level of thyroid hormone ("feed-back mechanism")[12] and on the other by an assumed nervous action[13]. As in the case of ACTH (see page 475), participation of the hypothalamus is likely, and a lowering of TSH production after cutting the pituitary stalk has often been observed[10]. Injury to the hypothalamus has also been found to result in decreased stimulation of the thyroid[14]. The observed disturbance of thyroid function in stress (see page 475) has been ascribed to interference with the release of TSH and to interdependence of the release mechanisms of TSH and of ACTH at the level of the pituitary[15]. However, the latter assumption does not appear to be valid in all cases.

Human urine may contain a substance with an inhibitory action on the activity of TSH[16].

Therapeutic applications

Acetylated TSH, an antagonist of TSH, has been found to have a favorable effect in exophthalmic goiter and in cancer of the thyroid[17].

References: *1)* Sonenberg, M., *Vitam. and Horm.*, **16**, 205 (1958). *2)* Behrens and Bromer, *Ann. Rev. Biochem.*, **27**, 57 (1958). *3)* Bates and Condliffe, *Recent Progr. Hormone Res.*, **16**, 309 (1960). *4)* Hays and Steelman, in Pincus and Thimann (Eds.), *The Hormones*, vol. III, New York, 1955, page 201. *5)* Turner, C. W., in Emmens, C. W. (Ed.), *Hormone Assay*, New York, 1950, page 215. *6)* Blumenthal, H. T., *Arch. Path. (Chicago)*, **57**, 481 (1954). *7)* Stevens et al., *Endocrinology*, **56**, 143 (1955). *8)* Querido et al., *Proc. roy. Soc. Med.*, **49**, 209 (1956). *9)* Bates, R. W., *Fed. Proc.*, **17**, 187 (1958). *10)* Pitt-Rivers and Tata, *The Thyroid Hormones*, London, 1959. *11)* Taurog et al., *Ciba Found. Coll. Endocr.*, **10**, 59 (1957). *12)* Brown-Grant, K., *Ciba Found. Coll. Endocr.*, **10**, 97 (1957). *13)* Greer, M. A., *Ciba Found. Coll. Endocr.*, **10** 34 (1957). *14)* D'Angelo, S. A., *Fed. Proc.*, **17**, 32 (1958). *15)* Harris, G. W., *Ciba Found. Coll. Endocr.*, **8**, 531 (1955). *16)* Lepp, A., *Proc. soc. exp. Biol. (N.Y.)*, **100**, 683 (1959). *17)* Sonenberg et al., *Trans. Ass. Amer. Phycns*, **70**, 192 (1957).

Prolactin

(lactogenic hormone, luteotropin, mammotropin, prolactin hormone, PH, luteotropic hormone, LTH, luteomammotropic hormone, LMTH)

Chemistry[1]

Prolactin can be isolated in good yield from sheep pituitary as a protein of molecular weight ca. 25,000 with an isoelectric point at pH 5.73. In aqueous solution it is remarkably insensitive to heat. The percentage amino acid composition is known, the terminal-N amino acid being threonine. A terminal-C amino acid does not appear to be present, indicating the presence of a ring (with disulfide bridge as in oxytocin).

Unit and assay

1 international unit (IU) = 0.1 mg of the international standard preparation (see page 739). Assay is by the crop proliferation test on young pigeons[2] and other birds[3].

Physiology and function[4]

The hormone is formed in the eosinophil cells of the anterior pituitary. Normally the prolactin content is the same in both the male and female pituitary; during pregnancy it is augmented at an increasing rate. Prolactin also appears to be present in the blood, placenta and urine[5].

Prolactin possesses a luteotropic action similar to that of the gonadotropic hormones (see page 473), as well as mammotropic and lactogenic activity. In pigeons it stimulates the growth and activity of the crop. The mammotropic activity consists in stimulation of the development of the breasts and of lactation[6–8].

Development of the mammary glands

This proceeds under the synergistic effect of several hormones. Under the influence of the gonadotropic hormones the ovaries secrete estrogens, which together with the growth hormone and the corticosteroids (the latter released by the action of ACTH) promote growth of the milk ducts. Full development of the lobules and alveoli requires the additional presence of prolactin and progesterone. Since the secretion of progesterone is stimulated by prolactin, the latter participates both directly and indirectly in breast development.

Lactation

Lactation commences after the estrogen level has fallen and is controlled by prolactin and progesterone. In high dosage, estrogens have an inhibitory effect on lactation.

Hormone effects in the maintenance of lactation (galactopoiesis) are not fully understood. Prolactin is known to play an important part, but corticosteroids and the thyroid and parathyroid hormones also appear to be necessary.

Lactation is also subject to nervous regulation by the suckling stimulus, which causes an increase in the production of the necessary hormones. The primary effect is probably the secretion of oxytocin by the hypothalamus (see page 478), which in turn stimulates the production of prolactin by the pituitary.

Milk ejection

The phase of *milk secretion*, in which the milk is formed in the alveolar cells and then transferred from the cytoplasm of these cells to the milk ducts, is distinct from that of the *release of milk*, which consists of a passive and an active component, the latter known as *milk ejection*[9].

The greater part of the milk in the breasts is contained in the alveoli and narrow ducts and only a small part in the wider ducts and glands. The latter can be extracted passively either by sucking or pumping, but the former must first be actively displaced from the alveoli and ducts by a contraction of the tissues in response to the suckling stimulus (reflex contraction of the myoepithelium). This nervous control of milk ejection, which is also brought about by tactile stimulation of the uterine cervix and by vagus stimulation, is probably due to an increase of oxytocin secretion as in the case of lactation. Here, however, the oxytocin released into the blood stream has a direct effect on milk ejection[10]. This effect is extremely specific and sensitive, and the injection of 0.01 IU of oxytocin has a perceptible effect on the mammary glands of lactating women[11].

References: *1)* Li, C. H., *Advanc. Protein Chem.*, **12**, 269 (1957). *2)* Riddle et al., *Amer. J. Physiol.*, **105**, 191 (1933). *3)* Meites and Turner, in Emmens, C. W. (Ed.), *Hormone Assay*, New York, 1950, page 237; Turner, C. W., in Emmens, C. W. (Ed.), *Hormone Assay*, New York, 1950, page 261. *4)* Cowie and Folley, in Pincus and Thimann (Eds.), *The Hormones*, vol. III, New York, 1955, page 309. *5)* Hadfield, G., *Lancet*, **1**, 1058 (1957); **1**, 568 (1958). *6)* Linzell, J. L., *Physiol. Rev.*, **39**, 534 (1959). *7)* Folley, S. J., *Brit. med. Bull.*, **11**, 145 (1955). *8)* Lyons et al., *Recent Progr. Hormone Res.*, **14**, 219 (1958). *9)* Cowie and Folley, in Heller, H. (Ed.), *The Neurohypophysis*, London, 1957, page 183. *10)* Berde, B., *Recent Progress in Oxytocin Research*, Springfield, 1959. *11)* Beller et al., *Acta endocr. (Kbh.)*, **29**, 1 (1958).

Growth hormone[1]

(somatropin, somatotropic hormone, STH)

Chemistry[2, 3]

The growth hormone can be isolated as a protein from the pituitary of various animals (cattle, apes, etc.) and of man. That from ox pituitary has a molecular weight of 46,000 (396 amino acid residues) and an isoelectric point at pH 6.85, that from human pituitary a molecular weight of 27,000 (241–245 amino acid residues) and an isoelectric point at pH 5.5[4]. The terminal-C and terminal-N amino acid in the hormone of man and apes is phenylalanine. The amino acid composition is known but not the amino acid sequence.

Units and assay

1 USP unit = 1 international unit (IU) = 1 mg of the international standard preparation (see page 739). The EVANS unit is that quantity which when administered daily to 21-30-day-old hypophysectomized albino rats produces in 10 days an increase in weight of 10 g[5,6]. The tibia cartilage test[7,8] is more specific and more rapid than the EVANS test. Other methods are also in use[1,6].

Physiology

STH is formed in the eosinophil cells of the anterior pituitary. The adult human pituitary contains 3.7–6.0 mg of STH[9]. Only traces of the hormone are present in normal plasma, and in normal human serum 0.2–0.5 µg per milliliter has been detected by an immunological method[10,11]. Higher levels have been reported in gigantism and acromegaly[11]. Normal STH secretion appears to be dependent on normal functioning of the thyroid[12]. In blood the hormone is rapidly inactivated by the enzyme plasmin[13].

Function[14,15]

STH possesses a high activity which is species specific[16], and preparations from nonprimate animals are inactive in man. Treatment of the ox hormone with chymotrypsin results in a protein with similar physicochemical and physiological properties to the human hormone[17].

Of all the hormones which affect the growth or size of organs, only STH promotes the growth of the whole body and has a continuous effect on almost all organs. For normal growth both STH and thyroxine appear to be essential, their action being complementary[12] in that STH promotes growth but not maturation while thyroxine promotes maturation with only a slight effect on growth.

The primary site of action of STH is the epiphysial cartilage. In young persons excesssive production of STH before epiphysial fusion results in pituitary gigantism, after epiphysial fusion in acromegaly. Overproduction of STH can arise from hyperplasia, adenoma or more rarely from carcinoma of the eosinophil cells. Pituitary dwarfism can be caused not only by lack of STH but also by hypofunction of the whole pituitary. Another variety of pituitary dwarfism is the LORAIN type, often caused by a craniopharyngioma. On growth disturbances due to malfunctioning of the pituitary see ESCAMILLA[18].

The growth-promoting action of STH is closely related to its effect on metabolism, reflected in:

1. Increase in protein synthesis (increase in plasma protein level), lowering of the blood amino acid level and increase in nitrogen retention[19]. The stimulation of protein synthesis is dependent on the presence of sufficient insulin and on an adequate supply of exogenous protein (or amino acids) and vitamins. Inadequate protein intake rapidly depletes the pituitary in STH and acidophil cells[20].

2. Decrease in the fat content of tissues as a result of increased oxidation of fat (increase in the formation of acetone bodies in the liver). At the same time the level of free fatty acids in the plasma is increased[11,19,21].

3. Increase in the salt and water content of tissues (in acromegaly, for example, there is a marked increase in the total and also in the extracellular water content[22]).

4. Increase in the blood sugar and inhibition of sugar breakdown in muscle. Like ACTH, STH is an antagonist of insulin, and the insulin sensitivity shown by hypophysectomized rats can be counteracted by STH. In normal animals with slight induced diabetes, administration of STH in large amounts causes hyperglycemia and glucosuria (somatropin diabetes). The glucose output of the liver, and with it the insulin activity of the plasma, are increased. Somatropin diabetes is possibly due to insulin exhaustion of the beta cells of the pancreas.

5. Increase in the blood levels of alkaline phosphatase and inorganic phosphate, particularly in the active phase of acromegaly.

Therapeutic applications

STH preparations from nonprimates are inactive in man. Human STH has been used successively in hypopituitarism[23], and in a case of pituitary dwarfism in a 17-year-old youth[11].

References: *1)* For a review see SMITH et al. (Eds.), *The Hypophyseal Growth Hormone*, New York, 1955. *2)* LI, C.H., *Advanc. Protein Chem.*, **11**, 101 (1956). *3)* BEHRENS and BROMER, *Ann. Rev. Biochem.*, **27**, 57 (1958). *4)* LI and PAPKOFF, *Science*, **124**, 1293 (1956). *5)* EVANS et al., *Endocrinology*, **22**, 483 (1938). *6)* GREENSPAN et al., in EMMENS, C.W. (Ed.), *Hormone Assay*, New York, 1950, page 273. *7)* GESCHWIND and LI, in SMITH et al. (Eds.), *The Hypophyseal Growth Hormone*, New York, 1955, page 28. *8)* LOSTROH and LI, *Endocrinology*, **60**, 308 (1957). *9)* GEMZELL and HEIJKENSKJÖLD, *Endocrinology*, **59**, 681 (1956). *10)* READ and STONE, *Amer. J. Dis. Child.*, **95**, 538 (1958). *11)* RABEN, M.S., *Recent Progr. Hormone Res.*, **15**, 71 (1959). *12)* RUSSELL and WILHELMINI, *Ann. Rev. Physiol.*, **20**, 43 (1958). *13)* MIRSKY et al., *J. clin. Invest.*, **38**, 14 (1959). *14)* ASTWOOD, E.B., in PINCUS and THIMANN (Eds.), *The Hormones*, vol. III, New York, 1955, page 235. *15)* WEIL, R., *Arch. intern. Med.*, **95**, 739 (1955); DE BODO and ALTSZULER, *Vitam. and Horm.*, **15**, 205 (1957). *16)* KNOBIL and GREEP, *Recent Progr. Hormone Res.*, **15**, 1 (1959). *17)* FORSHAM et al., *Metabolism*, **7**, 762 (1958). *18)* ESCAMILLA, R.F., *Recent Progr. Hormone Res.*, **12**, 321 (1956). *19)* ENGEL et al., *Proc. Soc. exp. Biol. (N.Y.)*, **100**, 699 (1959). *20)* SREBNIK et al., *Proc. Soc. exp. Biol. (N.Y.)*, **101**, 97 (1959). *21)* RABEN and HOLLENBERG, *J. clin. Invest.*, **38**, 484 (1959). *22)* IKKOS et al., *J. clin. Invest.*, **33**, 989 (1954). *23)* Medical Research Council, *Lancet*, **1**, 7 (1959).

Oxytocin[1]

(pitocin, lactagogin)

Vasopressin[2]

(pitressin, antidiuretin, antidiuretic hormone, ADH)

Chemistry[3,4]

The posterior pituitary hormones oxytocin and vasopressin are octapeptides of known structure both of which have been synthesized. Oxytocin has the same structure in all the species from which it has so far been obtained, while swine vasopressin differs from that of other species in having lysine instead of arginine in the side chain (lysine vasopressin and arginine vasopressin):

Oxytocin
Mol.wt. 1007
Isoelectric point pH 7.7

S————————————————S (disulfide bridge between the two Cy residues)

Cy . Tyr . Ileu . Glu(NH$_2$) . Asp(NH$_2$) . Cy . Pro . Leu . Gly(NH$_2$)

Lysine vasopressin
Mol.wt. 1056

S————————————————S

Cy . Tyr . Phe . Glu(NH$_2$) . Asp(NH$_2$) . Cy . Pro . Ly . Gly(NH$_2$)

Arginine vasopressin
Mol.wt. 1084
Isoelectric point pH 10.9

S————————————————S

Cy . Tyr . Phe . Glu(NH$_2$) . Asp(NH$_2$) . Cy . Pro . Arg . Gly(NH$_2$)

Under physiological conditions, both oxytocin and vasopressin may be linked to a protein[5,6], although the available chemical evidence rather suggests the contrary[7].

Arginine vasotocin, consisting of the oxytocin ring linked to the arginine vasopressin side chain, has been synthesized, and there is now evidence that it occurs in nonmammals[8].

Units and assay

1 USP posterior pituitary unit = 1 international posterior pituitary unit = 0.5 mg of the international standard oxytocic, vasopressor and antidiuretic substances (posterior ox pituitary) (see page 739).

Determination of oxytocin activity: contraction measurements on the surviving uterus of virgin guinea pigs[9].

Determination of vasopressin activity: blood pressure measurements on cats or dogs[9], or on chickens[10].

Determination of antidiuretic action: diuretic studies on dogs, rats and rabbits[9].

Physiology

The posterior pituitary hormones are almost certainly formed in the large-celled hypothalamic nuclei. The neuropituitary is thus merely the storage organ for these hormones, although it may possibly provide a carrier substance for their transport from hypothalamus to pituitary.

The proportion of vasopressin to oxytocin in both the hypothalamic nuclei and the posterior pituitary varies with different animal species. In the human posterior pituitary it is ca. 1.2 : 1[6]. The proportion shows characteristic changes in certain physiological conditions, for example during lactation in dogs and menstruation in rats.

Both hormones have often been shown to be present in blood and urine, although claims to this effect should be regarded with reserve if not based on reliable chemical methods (the data reported often relate to substances not yet clearly defined which possess activity similar to oxytocin or vasopressin[11]). In man, a vasopressin blood level of ca. 37 micro-units per milliliter has been reported[12], and during lactation an oxytocin blood level of 0–80 micro-units per milliliter[13]. In women the oxytocin level appears to undergo no increase during lactation, but in goats and cows an increase during milking has been observed[14]. Oxytocin and vasopressin are always secreted together, irrespective of the nature of the stimulus[15]. The proportions vary with the stimulus, but there is always more of the former hormone than of the latter.

Little is known of the metabolism of the posterior pituitary hormones. Vasopressin is excreted by the kidneys, but is also inactivated in this organ and in the liver[16]. Oxytocin is broken down by the enzyme oxytocinase which is formed in the placenta during pregnancy. Parenteral oxytocin has a half-life of ca. 9 minutes in pregnant women[17].

Function

The four principal functions of the posterior pituitary hormones are:

1. Contraction of the uterus[2, 18]
2. Milk ejection[2, 19]
3. Antidiuresis[3]
4. Vasoconstriction

Both oxytocin and vasopressin exhibit all the above functions, but to a varying extent. Oxytocin is primarily responsible for uterine contraction and milk ejection, and vasopressin possesses only 5% and 20% respectively of the activity of oxytocin in respect of these functions. In birds, oxytocin shows also a hypotensive effect (vasopressin 15% of this activity). Vasopressin is primarily responsible for the antidiuretic and hypertensive activity, while oxytocin shows only 0.5% and 1% respectively of these activities[20].

Oxytocin not only initiates uterine contraction but also promotes the spontaneous activity of the uterus. The sensitivity of the uterus to this hormone increases with the duration of pregnancy and reaches a maximum immediately prior to parturition. In animals a change in sensitivity during the estrous cycle has been observed, with a maximum during the estrus. During the luteal phase the uterus is completely insensitive to oxytocin. In pregnant mice injection of estrone has been found to increase sensitivity. Oxytocin appears to play some role in the initiation of parturition, although the latter can also proceed after hypophysectomy. The explanation of this apparent contradiction is probably that the hypothalamus contains a sufficient reserve of the hormone. If injury in the region of the hypothalamus has completely severed the nervous connections of the posterior pituitary, disturbances of the birth process are observed.

During coitus there is an increase in the woman's secretion of oxytocin. The resultant uterine contractions possibly assist in the transport of the spermatozoa towards the ovum.

Oxytocin is responsible for milk ejection from the lactating mammary gland and probably has an indirect effect on lactogenesis (see page 476).

Vasopressin has a direct antidiuretic action on the kidneys, the capacity of the distal tubules to reabsorb water being increased; it is also possible that the osmotic activity of the salts in the proximal tubules undergoes a change which enables them to transport more water than usual. The release of vasopressin from the neuropituitary is probably controlled by the total osmotic concentration of electrolytes in the extracellular fluid. Thus when loss of water by the body causes the osmotic concentration to rise, more antidiuretic hormone is released, more water is reabsorbed in the kidneys, and a more concentrated urine is produced. Excessive intake of water has the opposite effect and a very dilute urine is produced (water diuresis). However, the osmotic concentration undergoes only slight variations, so that it is assumed that the hypothalamus contains "osmoreceptors" which react to the slightest variation.

The antidiuretic action described above is abolished by severance of the pituitary stalk, but an increased excretion of water only takes place so long as the anterior lobe of the pituitary remains intact. In man, lesions in the region of the pituitary which cause destruction or degeneration of the posterior lobe can result in diabetes insipidus when the functioning of the anterior lobe is maintained, with polyuria up to 20 liters per day and severe polydipsia. The relationships between the anterior pituitary, the corticosteroids and the antidiuretic hormone in respect of diuresis are not fully understood[21]. The corticosteroids appear to have a direct effect on the activity of the neuropituitary, and it is possible that they are also involved in the inactivation of the hormones of the posterior lobe. There also appears to be some connection between vasopressin and the formation of ACTH (see page 475).

A further effect of vasopressin is vasoconstriction of the peripheral vessels, with slowing of the heart beat, diminution of the minute volume, and increase of blood pressure. This effect resembles that of adrenaline but the mechanism is different, and ergotamine or ergotoxin, for example, has no effect on this action of vasopressin. Vasopressin also causes contraction of the smooth muscles of the intestine, gallbladder and urinary bladder.

Therapeutic applications

Posterior pituitary preparation: diabetes insipidus. *Vasopressin:* diabetes insipidus. *Oxytocin:* primary and secondary insufficiency of labor, atonic uterine bleeding, postoperative paralysis of the intestine and bladder.

References: *1)* For reviews see LANDGREBE et al., in PINCUS and THIMANN (Eds.), *The Hormones*, vol. III, New York, 1955, page 389; BERDE, B., *Recent Progress in Oxytocin Research*, Springfield, 1959. *2)* For reviews see LANDGREBE et al., *loc. cit.*; THORN, N. A., *Physiol. Rev.*, **38**, 169 (1958). *3)* BEHRENS and BROMER, *Ann. Rev. Biochem.*, **27**, 57 (1958). *4)* ONCLEY, J. L., *Rev. mod. Physics*, **31**, 30 (1959). *5)* VAN DYKE et al., *J. Pharmacol. exp. Ther.*, **74**, 190 (1942). *6)* VAN DYKE et al., in HELLER, H. (Ed.), *The Neurohypophysis*, London, 1957, page 65. *7)* ACHER and FROMAGEOT, in HELLER, H. (Ed.), *The Neurohypophysis*, London, 1957, page 39. *8)* KATSOYANNIS and DU VIGNEAUD, *Nature*, **184**, 1465 (1959). *9)* THORP, R. H., in EMMENS, C. W. (Ed.), *Hormone Assay*, New York, 1950, page 109. *10)* *Pharmacopeia of the United States*, 15th Rev., Easton, 1955, page 555. *11)* CROXATTO, H., in HELLER, H. (Ed.), *The Neurohypophysis*, London, 1957, page 51. *12)* MACFARLANE and ROBINSON, *J. Physiol. (Lond.)*, **135**, 1 (1957). *13)* HAWKER, R. W., *J. clin. Endocr.*, **18**, 54 (1958). *14)* HAWKER and ROBERTS, *Brit. vet. J.*, **113**, 459 (1957). *15)* HARRIS, G. W., *Neural Control of the Pituitary Gland*, London, 1955. *16)* HELLER, H., in HELLER, H. (Ed.), *The Neurohypophysis*, London, 1957, page 77. *17)* CALDEYRO-BARCIA and POSEIRO, *Ann. N.Y. Acad. Sci.*, **75**, 813 (1958). *18)* FITZPATRICK, R. J., in HELLER, H. (Ed.), *The Neurohypophysis*, London, 1957, page 203. *19)* COWIE and FOLLEY, in HELLER, H. (Ed.), *The Neurohypophysis*, London, 1957, page 183. *20)* VAN DYKE et al., *Recent Progr. Hormone Res.*, **11**, 1 (1955). *21)* GAUNT et al., in HELLER, H. (Ed.), *The Neurohypophysis*, London, 1957, page 233.

Melanocyte-stimulating hormone (MSH)[1]

(chromatophore hormone, melanophore hormone, intermedin, B hormone, pigment hormone)

Chemistry[2]

The melanocyte-stimulating hormones so far isolated are polypeptides. β-MSH (swine) has an isoelectric point at pH 5.2. The amino acid sequences of the following have been worked out: α-MSH (swine)[3], β-MSH (swine)[4], β-MSH (ox)[5] and β-MSH (man)[6]. Interest in the isolation and structure of MSH has been stimulated by work on ACTH, which possesses some MSH activity. α-MSH has recently been synthesized.

β-MSH isolated from the human pituitary by ion-exchange chromatography has the following amino acid structure[6]:

Ala . Glu . Lys . Lys . Asp . Glu . Gly . Pro . [Tyr] . Arg .
[Met . Glu . His . Phe . Arg . Try . Gly] . Ser . [Pro] . Pro . Lys . Asp

The structure shared with ACTH (page 474) is shown boxed-in.

Units

The activity of MSH is measured in relation to that of the international standard posterior pituitary preparation (see page 739)[7]. Assay is by measurement of the change in the skin color of cold-blooded animals[7]. The LANDGREBE-WARING[7] and SHIZUME[8] units are also in use.

Physiology

MSH is formed in the intermediate lobe of the pituitary but has also been found in the anterior and posterior lobes. There is some doubt as to the occurrence in the anterior lobe in view of the known MSH activity of ACTH. This also applies to animals in which the intermediate lobe is absent (whale, chicken) but in which the presence of MSH in the anterior lobe has been reported[1,9]. Normally, similar concentrations of MSH are found in the pituitary of men and women. During pregnancy the level increases steadily until parturition and then falls to normal in a few days. In ADDISON's disease the blood and urine levels are greatly increased but can be depressed by administration of cortisone. In such cases the MSH activity of ACTH must of course be taken into account.

Function

MSH causes expansion of the chromatophores and in cold-blooded animals adaptation of the skin color to the environment. The function of chromatophore expansion in warm-blooded animals is unknown. In man, subcutaneous doses of MSH increase sensitivity to light and shorten the time required for dark adaptation of the eye. It has been claimed that MSH increases the rate of regeneration of visual purple in the retina. An increase in pigmentation has been observed several hours after administration of large doses.

Pigmentation appears to be subject to the control of several hormones, MSH being concerned in the conversion of tyrosine into dihydroxyphenylalanine under the action of tyrosinase (see page 443). The action is an indirect one involving re-location of the enzymically active particles inside the cell[10]. In the frog, pigment formation in the chromatophores is stimulated by very small amounts of hormone: 10^{-11} mol of swine α-MSH, 2×10^{-11} mol of swine β-MSH, and 3×10^{-10} mol of swine ACTH[11].

References: *1)* For reviews see LANDGREBE et al., in PINCUS and THIMANN (Eds.), *The Hormones*, vol. III, New York, 1955, page 389; LI, C. H., *Advanc. Protein Chem.*, **12**, 269 (1957). *2)* BEHRENS and BROMER, *Ann. Rev. Biochem.*, **27**, 57 (1958). *3)* ONCLEY, J. L., *Rev. mod. Physics*, **31**, 30 (1959); HARRIS, J. I., *Biochem. J.*, **71**, 451 (1959). *4)* HARRIS and ROOS, *Biochem. J.*, **71**, 434 (1959). *5)* GESCHWIND et al., *J. Amer. chem. Soc.*, **79**, 1003 (1957). *6)* HARRIS, J. I., *Nature*, **184**, 167 (1959). *7)* LANDGREBE and WARING, in EMMENS, C. W. (Ed.), *Hormone Assay*, New York, 1950, page 141. *8)* LI, C. H., *Advanc. Protein Chem.*, **12**, 269 (1957). *9)* DODDS et al., *Ann. Rev. Med.*, **7**, 41 (1956). *10)* LERNER, A. B., *Nature*, **184**, 674 (1959). *11)* LEE and LERNER, *J. biol. Chem.*, **221**, 943 (1956); LERNER and CASE, *J. invest. Derm.*, **32**, 211 (1959).

Thyroid hormone[1]

Chemistry

The normal thyroid contains 0.007–0.18% of iodine, or some 20% of the body's total iodine. That of the thyroid is 90% organically combined in the form of the protein complex thyroglobulin, containing thyroxine and triiodothyronine together with their precursors mono- and diiodotyrosine. Thyroglobulin has a molecular weight of ca. 700,000 and an isoelectric point at pH 5. Its iodine content varies from one animal species to another between 0.1 and 0.8%, but the ratio of thyroxine iodine to total iodine is fairly constant at 0.25–0.32[2]. For chemical and physical properties of thyroxine see the table on page 358.

L-3-Monoiodotyrosine, $C_9H_{10}NO_3I$
Mol.wt. 307.10
M.p. 204° C

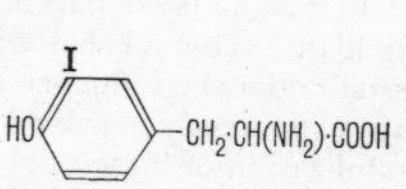

L-3,5-Diiodotyrosine, $C_9H_9NO_3I_2$
Mol.wt. 433.00
M.p. 200° C

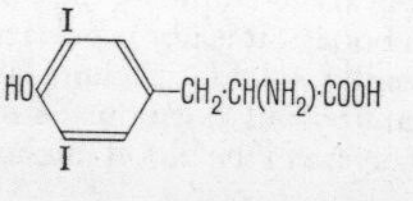

L-3,5,3'-Triiodothyronine, $C_{15}H_{12}NO_4I_3$
Mol.wt. 651.00
M.p. 201° C

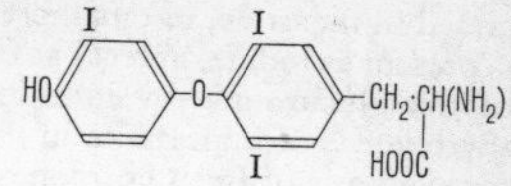

L-Thyroxine, $C_{15}H_{11}NO_4I_4$
Mol.wt. 776.90
M.p. 232° C

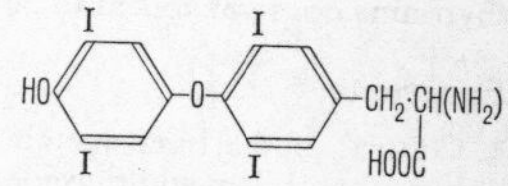

Hormonal activity is possessed only by thyroxine and triiodothyronine. The latter is present in very low concentration, so that effectively the hormonal activity of the thyroid is equivalent to that of the thyroxine present.

Methods of test and assay

Chemical: For reviews see PITT-RIVERS[4] and CHANEY[5].

Biological[6]: Acceleration of the metamorphosis of amphibian larvae; increase of basal metabolic rate in rats. The units are based on these tests.

Physiology

Biosynthesis of thyroxine (see also page 443) takes place in the following stages[3]:

1. Iodide in the blood stream is taken up and stored by the thyroid.
2. The iodide is oxidized to iodine and combines with tyrosine to form first mono- and then diiodotyrosine.
3. Two molecules of tyrosine combine to form thyroxine.
4. Triiodothyronine arises either by coupling of diiodotyrosine with the monoiodo-derivative or by the partial deiodination of thyroxine.

A high level of iodine in the blood inhibits the incorporation of iodide in organic compounds; a low level results in increased synthesis of triiodothyronine[7].

Although tissues other than the thyroid can combine iodide with tyrosine to form diiodotyrosine, only the thyroid is capable of forming thyroxine and triiodothyronine. The iodine-storing capacity of the thyroid is dependent on its physiological condition: it is increased in hyperthyroidism and decreased in myxedema. The functioning of the thyroid can be determined by investigating its iodine retention by means of radioactive iodine (see also page 276).

The thyroid hormones are stored in the thyroid colloid in the form of thyroglobulin and their release into the blood stream requires hydrolysis of this protein by a protease present in the thyroid. Under normal conditions only thyroxine and triiodothyronine are released into the blood. The daily release of iodine from the adult human thyroid at a mean iodine content of 5.26 mg is ca. 56 μg[8]. Both the formation and release of thyroid hormone are controlled by thyrotropin (see page 476). Administration of thyroxine lowers the response of the thyroid to thyrotropin[7].

In the blood stream thyroxine and triiodothyronine are linked in a nonpeptide form with a protein[9,10] (probably prealbumin and α-globulin). The serum thyroxine level is dependent on the activity of the thyroid: in normal functioning 3.0–6.5 μg/100 ml, in hypofunction 0–3.5 μg/100 ml, in hyperfunction over 6.5 μg/100 ml[11]. A similar relationship is shown by the level of protein-bound iodine in plasma: in normal functioning 4–8 μg/100 ml, in hypofunction 0–4 μg/100 ml, in hyperfunction up to 22 μg/100 ml[12]. The mean ratio of thyroxine iodine to protein-bound iodine is normally 0.58 and increases with increasing thyroid activity[11]. The determination of the level of protein-bound iodine or thyroxine in plasma is of clinical importance as an indication of the condition of the thyroid. During pregnancy the iodine-combining capacity of the plasma proteins is increased while the thyroxine level is decreased[10]. The half-life of thyroxine in the blood stream is ca. 6–11 days, of triiodothyronine ca. 2–3 days[3].

The metabolism of the thyroid hormones is dependent on the metabolic state of the body. In hyperthyroid conditions the breakdown of thyroxine is accelerated. From the blood stream thyroxine passes into various tissues; it is taken up rapidly by the stomach, liver and kidneys, slowly by the intestine, muscles and skin. The inactivation and excretion of thyroxine takes place first in the liver and later in the bile. In the liver, thyroxine is partly converted into the glucuronide. In man the iodine is mostly excreted in the urine, in rats mostly in the feces. In urine the iodine is present as iodide, in feces as free thyroxine following hydrolysis of the glucuronide by intestinal bacteria. The deiodination of thyroxine is of importance in that the iodide liberated is available for synthesis of fresh hormone (ca. 20% is thus re-used). Little is known of the enzymes responsible for deiodination, and triiodothyronine does not appear to be an intermediate in the process[13].

Functions

1. Control of the basal metabolic rate. The BMR is lowered in hypothyroidism and myxedema and after thyroidectomy, raised in thyrotoxicosis and after administration of thyroid hormone. When the ambient temperature falls, the thyroid hormones regulate the body temperature by stimulating energy production. The mechanism of the regulation of the BMR, however, is unknown. Possibly the effect is an indirect one on enzymes concerned in respiration and energy exchange, the hormone causing structural changes in the mitochondrial membrane which affect their entry into the cell[3]. The increase of the BMR is accompanied by an increase in the level of free fatty acids in the plasma[14].
2. Independently of its stimulation of energy metabolism, thyroxine has an influence on growth and differentiation which is particularly marked in lower animals (cf. the metamorphosis test for thyroxine). The hormone is essential for normal growth in the early stages of life of man and many animals, a function which appears to be dependent on the presence of the growth hormone (see page 477). Of particular importance is the ability of thyroxine to stimulate growth of the cerebral cortex during the critical phases of development.
3. The effects of thyroxine on circulation, water balance, the gonads and the cortical centers are probably secondary results of the regulation of energy metabolism, in the last case also of the stimulation of growth and cell development.

Hormonal activity is shown only by the L-forms of thyroxine and triiodothyronine (see the table below), both of which possess the diphenyl ether structure. Mono- and diiodotyrosine, which do not possess this structure, are inactive. The action of the hormones, particularly that of thyroxine, is preceded by a latent period: after removal of the thyroid and injection of thyroxine an effect is observed only after hours or days. The action of thyroxine is probably not direct but via a series of reactions.

Biological activity of the thyroid hormones
(after Pitt-Rivers and Tata[3])

	Animal species	Physiological test: Oxygen consumption	Growth and differentiation	Thyrotropin antagonism
L-Thyroxine	all	100	100	100
D-Thyroxine	man	10– 16	–	–
Triiodo-L-thyronine	man	90–140	–	280–540
	rat	100–200	500	–
Triiodo-D-thyronine	rat	–	–	14

Compounds with a thyrostatic action include thiocyanates, perchlorates, thiouracil, thiocarbamide and mercaptoimidazole. Their administration lowers the blood thyroxine level and increases thyrotropin formation, which in turn causes hyperplasia of the thyroid. Perchlorates and thiocyanates act by inhibiting the iodide trapping mechanism of the thyroid, an effect reversible by administering iodide. Thiocarbamide and its derivatives and imidazoles act by inhibiting oxidation of iodide and thus the iodination of tyrosine, an effect reversible by administering thyroxine. In endemic goiter the primary cause is thought to be deficiency of exogenous iodine but natural thyrostatica in foods may also be responsible. Cabbage and kohlrabi, for example, contain progoitrin, a substance broken down by intestinal bacteria to the thyrostatic compound L-5-vinyl-2-thiooxazolidone[15].

Therapeutic applications[16]

L-Thyroxine and L-triiodothyronine, as well as whole thyroid preparations, are used in the treatment of hypothyroidism, disturbances of growth and development, thyrogenous obesity and polyglandular insufficiency.

References: *1)* For reviews see Rawson et al., in Pincus and Thimann (Eds.), *The Hormones*, vol. III, New York, 1955, page 433; Werner, S.C. (Ed.), *The Thyroid*, New York, 1955; Pitt-Rivers and Tata, *The Thyroid Hormones*, London, 1959. *2)* Werner, S. C., *loc. cit.* *3)* Pitt-Rivers and Tata, *loc. cit.* *4)* Pitt-Rivers, R., in Emmens, C. W. (Ed.), *Hormone Assay*, New York, 1950, page 514. *5)* Chaney, A. L., *Advanc. clin. Chem.*, **1**, 81 (1958). *6)* Reineke and Turner, in Emmens, C. W. (Ed.), *Hormone Assay*, New York, (1950), page 489. *7)* Söderberg, U., *Physiol. Rev.*, **39**, 777 (1959). *8)* Nodine et al., *J. clin. Endocr.*, **17**, 832 (1957). *9)* Tata, J. R., *Nature*, **183**, 877 (1959). *10)* Robbins and Nelson, *J. clin. Invest.*, **37**, 153 (1958); Vannotti and Béraud, *Expos. ann. Biochim. méd.*, **21**, 57 (1959). *11)* Whitehead and Beale, *Clin. chim. Acta*, **4**, 710 (1959). *12)* Astwood et al., *Ciba Found. Coll. Endocr.*, **11**, 95 (1957). *13)* Tata, J. R., *Biochim. biophys. Acta*, **28**, 95 (1958). *14)* Rich et al., *J. clin. Invest.*, **38**, 275 (1959). *15)* Greer and Deeney, *J. clin. Invest.*, **38**, 1465 (1959). *16)* Martin, L., *Practitioner*, **180**, 50 (1958).

Parathyroid hormone[1]

(parathormone, PTH)

Chemistry

Protein preparations from the parathyroid (ox preparations) can be separated either chromatographically or electrophoretically into two fractions[2]: parathormone A, molecular weight 4000–6000, activity 75–100 USP parathyroid units per milligram; and parathormone B, molecular weight ca. 10,000, activity 220 USP parathyroid units per milligram. The amino acid composition of parathormone B is known[3]. Parathyroid hormone is rapidly inactivated by digestive enzymes. Part of its physiological activity appears to be due to a lipid fraction of the parathyroid of steroid nature[4].

Units and assay[5]

1 USP unit = $^1/_{100}$ of the amount required to raise the calcium content of 100 ml of the serum of 8–16-kg dogs 1 mg within 16–18 hours after administration.

1 Collip unit = 5 USP units.

Physiology and function

The hormone is formed in the epithelial bodies of the parathyroid but nothing definite is known of the mechanism of its release. Possibly its production is stimulated by a fall in the blood calcium level via a central nervous mechanism[6].

The sites of action of parathyroid hormone are the *kidneys* (increase of phosphate excretion) and the *bones* (mobilization of calcium). It is not known for certain whether the hormone acts independently at these two sites, or whether the primary effect is on the kidneys with secondary action on the bones, or whether the reverse is the case. The present tendency is to regard both effects as primary, even though calcium mobilization and phosphate excretion are interdependent.

In general an excess of the hormone promotes phosphate excretion, i.e. decreases tubular reabsorption. However, this phosphate diuresis seems to occur only when the serum phosphate level is high[7]. Infusion of calcium lowers phosphate excretion, an effect probably due to inhibition of the release of parathyroid hormone[8].

It is now clearly established that parathyroid hormone has an influence on the blood calcium level and on calcium mobilization in the bones. Injection of the hormone causes an increase in the calcium blood level, and high doses over a long period result in proliferation of osteoclasts, rarefaction of the bone, and replacement of the bone substance by soft tissue (osteitis fibrosa)[9]. Mobilization of bone calcium is accompanied by that of bone phosphate. There appears to be a balance between the serum calcium level and the mobilization of bone calcium which is independent of the parathyroid hormone, as evidenced by the fact that even after removal of the epithelial bodies the blood calcium level remains constant at 7 mg/100 ml[10]. Maintenance of the normal level of 10 mg/100 ml, however, depends on the presence of parathormone.

Citric acid plays a part in calcium mobilization which is not fully elucidated. This substance is possibly formed from glucose in bone tissue under the influence of parathyroid hormone and vitamin D and is apparently involved in the form of a calcium complex in the mobilization of bone calcium into the blood stream[11]. Apart from promoting citric acid formation, parathyroid hormone also appears to stimulate the formation of lactic acid from pyruvic acid in bone[12]. It is not yet clear whether the enrichment in bone of the readily soluble calcium citrate or lactate under the influence of parathyroid hormone is sufficient to account for the observed increase in the blood calcium level[12].

The hypercalcemic effects of parathyroid hormone and of vitamin D probably differ in their mechanisms, particularly in view of the effect of vitamin D on citric acid metabolism. The effect of the vitamin on calcium mobilization is probably proportional to its intake, while that of parathyroid hormone is a synergistic one. However, since the release of the hormone is regulated by the blood calcium level it maintains the balance between calcium intake, calcium excretion and the regulatory action of vitamin D[13].

Other effects of parathyroid hormone in animals are promotion of the breakdown of the organic structure of bone[14], regulation of calcium concentration in the mammary glands[15], and stimulation of calcium and phosphate absorption in the intestine[16]. These very various and to some extent independent effects of the hormone indicate the likelihood of its consisting of a complex of several hormones[17].

Therapeutic applications

Parathyroid hormone is used in the treatment of hypoparathyroid conditions (replaceable by dihydrotachysterol; see under Vitamin D, page 452), and for distinguishing between idiopathic hypoparathyroidism (atrophy or absence of the parathyroid) and pseudo-hypoparathyroidism (nonreaction of the body to the hormone)[18]. On hyperparathyroidism see NORDIN[7] and HARDY[19].

References: *1)* For a review see GREEP and KENNY, in PINCUS and THIMANN (Eds.), *The Hormones*, vol. III, New York, 1955, page 153. *2)* RASMUSSEN, H., *J. biol. Chem.*, **229**, 781 (1957). *3)* SPACKMAN et al., *Analyt. Chem.*, **30**, 1190 (1958). *4)* RAOUL and MARNAY, *Expos. ann. Biochim. méd.*, **21**, 169 (1959). *5)* BIERING, A., *Acta Pharmacol. (Kbh.)*, **6**, 40 (1950); THORP, R. H., in EMMENS, C. W. (Ed.), *Hormone Assay*, New York, 1950, page 77. *6)* BENETATO et al., *Probl. Endokr. Gormonoter.*, **3**, 26 (1957). *7)* NORDIN, B. E. C., *Advanc. intern. Med.*, **9**, 81 (1958). *8)* HIATT and THOMPSON, *J. clin. Invest.*, **36**, 573 (1957). *9)* LEUTHARDT, F., *Lehrbuch der physiologischen Chemie*, 14th ed., Berlin, 1959. *10)* COPP, D. H., *Amer. J. Med.*, **22**, 275 (1957). *11)* NEUMAN and NEUMAN, *The Chemical Dynamics of Bone Mineral*, Chicago, 1958. *12)* FIRSCHEIN et al., *Recent Progr. Hormone Res.*, **15**, 427 (1959). *13)* MCLEAN and BUDY, *Ann. Rev. Physiol.*, **21**, 69 (1959). *14)* ENGEL, M. B., *Arch. Path. (Chicago)*, **53**, 339 (1952). *15)* MUNSON et al., *J. dent. Res.*, **33**, 676 (1954). *16)* TALMAGE and ELLIOT, *Fed. Proc.*, **17**, 160 (1958). *17)* DENT, C. E., *Proc. roy. Soc. Med.*, **46**, 291 (1953); NEUMAN and NEUMAN, *Amer. J. Med.*, **22**, 123 (1957); MUNSON, P. L., *Ann. N.Y. Acad. Sci.*, **60**, 776 (1955). *18)* MOLDAWER, M., *Practitioner*, **180**, 88 (1958). *19)* HARDY, J. D., *Ann. Rev. Med.*, **10**, 183 (1959).

Noradrenaline (norepinephrine)[1]

Adrenaline (epinephrine)[2]

Chemistry

Noradrenaline and adrenaline are catecholamine derivatives whose very similar chemical and physical properties make them difficult to separate. They are soluble with difficulty in water but readily soluble in most organic solvents and aqueous alkalis and acids. Their salts are easily soluble in water.

The naturally occurring hormones are both levorotatory, the synthetic products being racemates with only 3–4% of the biological activity of the natural hormones. Both are readily oxidized to the corresponding adrenochromes. The difference in the rate of oxidation of the two hormones in acid solution is used for their separation: at pH 4, for example, adrenaline is almost completely oxidized by 0.1-N iodine solution, noradrenaline only about 10%[3]; at pH 6 both are completely oxidized.

Noradrenaline, $C_8H_{11}O_3N$
Mol.wt. 169.18

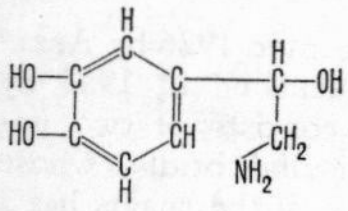

Noradrenochrome

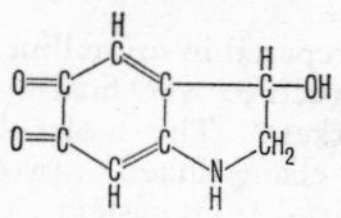

Noradrenolutin

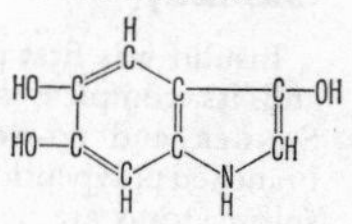

Adrenaline, $C_9H_{13}O_3N$
Mol.wt. 183.21

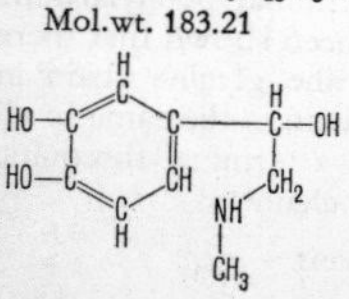

Adrenochrome

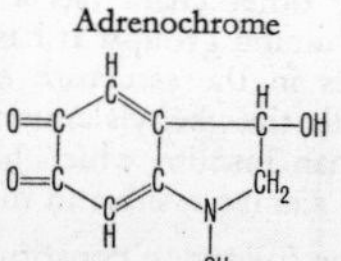

Adrenolutin

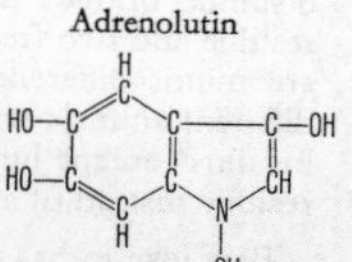

Units. None; by weight.

Methods of test and assay

The following methods are suitable for determining adrenaline and noradrenaline together or singly:

1. *Biological:* By blood pressure changes in chloralized cats sensitized with cocaine[4] (sensitivity up to 0.2 µg noradrenaline), or by changes in the surviving rat uterus[5] (sensitivity for adrenaline up to 0.001 µg, for noradrenaline 75–300 times less so). Other biological methods are also in use[6].

2. *Chemical:* (*a*) Colorimetrically[3] (sensitivity up to 10 µg noradrenaline or adrenaline); (*b*) fluorometrically[7] as adrenolutin and/or noradrenolutin (sensitivity up to 0.01 µg), or by condensation of adrenochrome and/or noradrenochrome with ethylenediamine[8] (sensitivity up to 0.001 µg for adrenaline and 0.005 µg for noradrenaline). Other methods are also in use[9]. Adrenaline, noradrenaline and their metabolites are best determined individually after chromatographic separation.

Physiology

Formation and occurrence[10]. Starting from phenylalanine, biosynthesis is via tyrosine, dihydroxyphenylalanine (dopa), which appears to occupy a key position, and dihydroxyphenylethylamine (see also page 442). Most of the latter compound is converted into dihydroxyphenylacetic acid but a small part is oxidized to noradrenaline, a part of which is methylated to adrenaline in the argentaffine cells. Apart from the adrenal medulla, the hormones are synthesized in the sympathetic nerves and ganglia, the main product in the nerves being noradrenaline.

The most important end-product of the metabolism of adrenaline and noradrenaline is 3-methoxy-4-hydroxymandelic acid, intermediate products being *m*-O-methyladrenaline, *m*-O-methylnoradrenaline and dihydroxymandelic acid[11, 12].

The concentration of the hormones in the adrenals varies from species to species between 0.12 and 14 mg/g[27]; the human adrenals contain 0.27–1 mg/g. Stress lowers the concentration in the adrenal medulla. The proportion of adrenaline to noradrenaline in the medulla also varies with the species of animal; in man it is 4:1. In the fetus there is no adrenaline in the medulla. After birth the adrenaline content rises slowly. Both hormones are stored in various cells of the medulla, where they appear to be linked to bodies resembling the mitochondria.

Apart from the adrenals, noradrenaline and adrenaline are found in the sympathetic nervous system and in the argentaffine cells of various organs and tissues. In man the sympathetic nervous system contains 1–3 µg noradrenaline per gram of tissue (thoracic and lumbar ganglia)[27]; the adrenaline content is only a small fraction of this amount. Noradrenaline and to a lesser extent adrenaline are also found in the spleen, heart, bone marrow and placenta. The noradrenaline content of organs and tissues appears to be closely connected with the numbers of adrenergic nerve fibers with which they are supplied. Tumors of argentaffine cells contain up to 8.4 mg/g noradrenaline and 2.3 mg/g adrenaline[13].

The peripheral venous plasma of resting persons contains less than 0.5 µg/l noradrenaline and less than 0.1 µg/l adrenaline[14]. In insulin hypoglycemia the adrenaline level can rise to ten times this amount, and in patients with catecholamine-producing tumors noradrenaline levels 100 times greater than normal have been observed[14].

The catecholamine hormones are released directly into the blood stream, the release being promoted by various factors such as stimulation of the sympathetic nerves, low blood sugar level, trauma, drugs (reserpine, morphine, etc.) and stress[26]. Normally the medulla secretes the two hormones in a constant ratio but in some conditions, such as hypoglycemia, the proportion of adrenaline is increased[15].

Apart from the two hormones, dihydroxyphenylalanine, dihydroxyphenylethylamine and isopropylnoradrenaline are found in the adrenals, dihydroxyphenylalanine, dihydroxyphenylethylamine, dihydroxyphenylacetic acid and dihydroxymandelic acid in the adrenergic neurones, and dihydroxyphenylethylamine, dihydroxyphenylacetic acid and dihydroxymandelic acid in the serum and in various organs[10].

Excretion. The injected hormones disappear very rapidly from the plasma and are taken up by various organs which partly store them and partly break them down; the amounts excreted in the urine are 0.5–2% of adrenaline and 3–6% of noradrenaline[15]. The adrenaline normally present in urine appears to come mainly from the medulla, the noradrenaline mainly from the sympathetic nerves, as indicated by the observation that destruction of the adrenals reduces the excretion of adrenaline but not that of noradrenaline[26]. A small part of the hormones is excreted in conjugated form, more of the noradrenaline than of the adrenaline. The former appears to be conjugated as glucuronide[15].

The 24-hour urine contains 25–50 µg free noradrenaline and 4–8 µg free adrenaline; the total amounts are 1.5–3 times the amounts of the free hormones[27]. The urine also contains dihydroxyphenylethylamine and dihydroxyphenylacetic acid[10] as well as 3-methoxy-4-hydroxymandelic acid (6.1 mg/24 h[16]).

An increased excretion of the hormones is observed in various conditions: of adrenaline and noradrenaline in stress (see page 475), after operations[17] and following stimulation of the sympathetic nervous system[15]; of adrenaline in insulin hypoglycemia; of noradrenaline after injection of methacholine.

The increased excretion of noradrenaline in active and agressive emotional states and of adrenaline in passive anxiety states indicate that a psychological factor is involved in the release of the hormones from the adrenal medulla[15].

Tumors of argentaffine cells are accompanied by the excretion of large amounts of the hormones and their metabolites: of adrenaline up to 0.25 mg/24 h[13], of noradrenaline up to 8.8 mg/24 h[13], of *m*-O-methylnoradrenaline up to 30 mg/24 h[12], of 3-methoxy-4-hydroxymandelic acid up to 60 mg/24 h[18].

Function

The high concentration of noradrenaline in various tissues and the similarity of its effects to those of stimulation of the sympathetic nerves has led to the postulation of this hormone, or of its mixture with a smaller amount of adrenaline, as the transmitter of nerve impulses in the sympathetic nervous system. The actions of both noradrenaline and adrenaline are blocked by various substances such as ergotamine, tetraethylammonium chloride, N,N-dibenzyl-β-chloroethylamine (antiadrenergic substances).

Effects on blood circulation. In man, continuous intravenous infusion of the hormones (0.1–0.3 µg/min per kg body weight) can have the following effects as revealed by catheterization of the right heart (Fick principle) and other methods[19, 20]: *Noradrenaline:* immediate increase of the mean blood pressure (increase of both systolic and diastolic pressure) due to increase of the peripheral resistance (vasoconstriction). The performance of the heart is unchanged or only slightly impaired. Owing to the absence of any subjective symptom the changes are not usually noticed by the patient. *Adrenaline:* Increase of the mean blood pressure due to over-compensation of the depression of the peripheral circulation (always observed) by increased beat output and beat rate. The subjective symptoms are unpleasant: tachycardia, palpitations and psychic disturbances.

Noradrenaline and adrenaline thus both cause a rise in blood pressure, but in different ways. Noradrenaline causes vasoconstriction, reduced blood supply to all organs, increase of peripheral resistance, no change in cardiac performance. Adrenaline causes an increase in cardiac performance, vasodilatation, increased blood supply to all organs (except kidneys, see below), decrease of peripheral resistance[20, 21]. In pathological hyperactivity of the medulla, for example in pheochromocytoma, intravenous doses of adrenaline larger than 0.3 µg/min/kg cause *vasoconstriction* like noradrenaline[22]. At physiological dosage (intravenous up to 0.3 µg/min/kg) the circulatory effects of the two hormones cancel each other out.

Effects on the kidneys. Both hormones cause a marked reduction in the renal blood circulation, renal plasma circulation and glomerular filtration rate[23].

Metabolic effects. Adrenaline increases oxygen consumption and thus raises the body temperature and the BMR[24]. It also causes a short-lived increase in blood sugar as a result of increased gluconeogenesis, particularly from liver fat and through mobilization of muscle glycogen. The metabolic effects of adrenaline are almost entirely absent in noradrenaline[19, 22].

Effects on the central nervous system. Noradrenaline is without effect on the CNS; adrenaline causes restlessness and feelings of oppression and anxiety.

Effect on the pituitary. Adrenaline stimulates the production and release of ACTH and thus indirectly the production of the corticosteroids.

Comparison of the effects of intravenous adrenaline (0.1–0.3 µg/min/kg) *and intravenous noradrenaline* (0.1–0.325 µg/min/kg)[19, 25]

\+ or – = nature and degree of effect □ = slight or insignificant effect

	Noradrenaline	Adrenaline
Pulse frequency	–	+
Cardiac performance	⊟	+++
Systolic blood pressure	+++	+++
Diastolic blood pressure	++	⊞
Total peripheral resistance	+++	– –
Basal metabolic rate	⊞	++
Blood sugar	⊞	+++
Effects on central nervous system	□	+
Eosinopenia	□	+

Therapeutic applications

As a sympathomimetic drug without side effects, *noradrenaline* is used (by intravenous infusion) for maintenance of blood pressure in surgical and nonsurgical shock, in acute hypotension, hemorrhage and central vasomotor depression. *Adrenaline* is used in the treatment of anaphylactic or allergic reactions (urticaria, hay fever, serum sickness and particularly asthma), in insulin overdosage, for reduction of hemorrhage in surgical operations, and as an additive to local anesthetics to prevent absorption and localize their effects. Adrenaline is given intravenously and is inactive when taken orally.

References: *1*) For reviews see Gaddum and Holzbauer, *Vitam. and Horm.*, **15**, 151 (1957); Von Euler, U. S., *Noradrenaline*, Springfield, 1956. *2*) For a review see Gaddum and Holzbauer, *loc. cit.* *3*) Von Euler and Hamberg, *Acta physiol. scand.*, **19**, 74 (1949). *4*) Von Euler and Luft, *Acta endocr. (Kbh.)*, **3**, 323 (1949). *5*) Gaddum, J. H., *Meth. med. Res.*, **3**, 116 (1950). *6*) West, G. B., in Emmens, C. W. (Ed.), *Hormone Assay*, New York, 1950, page 91. *7*) Lund, A., *Acta pharmacol. (Kbh.)*, **6**, 137 (1950). *8*) Weil-Malherbe and Bone, *Biochem. J.*, **51**, 311 (1952). *9*) Persky, H., in Glick, D. (Ed.), *Methods of Biochemical Analysis*, vol. II, New York, 1955, page 57. *10*) Von Euler, U. S., *Recent Progr. Hormone Res.*, **14**, 483 (1958). *11*) Kirshner et al., *Proc. Soc. exp. Biol. (N. Y.)*, **98**, 627 (1958); Goodall et al., *J. clin. Invest.*, **38**, 707 (1959); Axelrod, J., *Physiol. Rev.*, **39**, 751 (1959). *12*) Sjoerdsma et al., *J. clin. Invest.*, **38**, 31 (1959). *13*) Von Euler, U. S., *Ciba Found. Coll. Endocr.*, **12**, 268 (1958). *14*) Von Euler, U. S., *Ciba Found. Coll. Endocr.*, **11**, 379 (1957). *15*) Elmadjian et al., *Recent Progr. Hormone Res.*, **14**, 513 (1958). *16*) Sandler and Ruthven, *Lancet*, **2**, 1034 (1959). *17*) Halme et al., *Acta endocr. (Kbh.)*, **24**, Suppl. 32 (1957). *18*) Sandler and Ruthven, *Lancet*, **2**, 114 (1959). *19*) Goldenberg et al., *Amer. J. Med.*, **5**, 792 (1948). *20*) Wakim and Essex, *Circulation (N.Y.)*, **5**, 370 (1952). *21*) Swan, H. J. C., *Lancet*, **2**, 508 (1949); Kappert et al., *Acta cardiol. (Brux.)*, **5**, 121 (1950); Barcroft and Konzett, *J. Physiol. (Lond.)*, **110**, 194 (1949); Barnett et al., *Clin. Sci.*, **9**, 151 (1950). *22*) Goldenberg et al., *Arch. intern. Med.*, **86**, 823 (1950). *23*) Moyer and Handley, *Circulation (N.Y.)*, **5**, 91 (1952). *24*) Griffith, F. J., *Physiol. Rev.*, **31**, 151 (1951). *25*) Goldenberg, M., *Amer. J. Med.*, **10**, 627 (1951); Cori and Buchwald, *Amer. J. Physiol.*, **95**, 71 (1930); Madison, L. L., *J. clin. Invest.*, **29**, 789 (1950); Rein, H., *Physiologie des Menschen*, 12th ed., Berlin, 1956. *26*) Gaddum and Holzbauer, *Vitam. and Horm.*, **15**, 151 (1957). *27*) Von Euler, U.S., *Noradrenaline*, Springfield, 1956.

Insulin

Discovered by Banting and Best[1] in 1921, insulin was first used clinically in the treatment of diabetes by the same workers in 1922[2]. For a current review of all aspects of this hormone see the collection of papers in *British Medical Bulletin*, **16**, No. 3 (1960).

Chemistry

Insulin was first prepared in crystalline form in 1926 by Abel[3] and its complete structure was finally elucidated in 1955 by Sanger and co-workers[4]. The molecule consists of two unbranched polypeptide chains linked by two disulfide bridges whose sulfur atoms are derived from cysteine. One of the chains has a terminal glycine residue, four free amino groups and its own disulfide bridge; the other chain has a terminal phenylalanine residue and two free amino groups. It has been shown that there are minor differences in the structure of the glycine chain in different animals while the phenylalanine chain is the same in all insulins[5] except human insulin, which has a terminal threonine residue instead of an alanine residue in this chain[6].

Beef insulin has the following constitution:

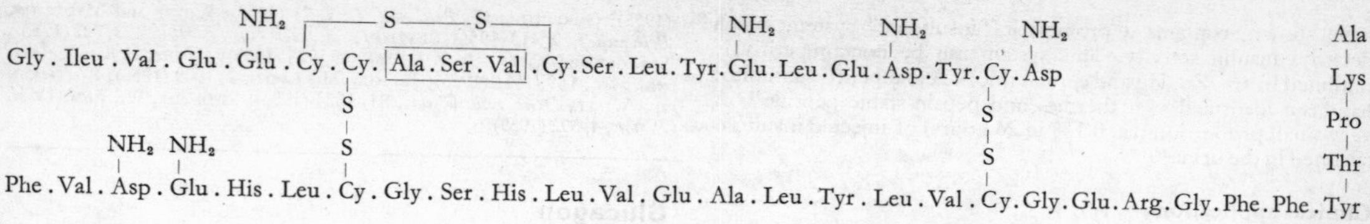

In human[6], hog and whale insulins the boxed-in portion in the above structure is replaced by Thr. Ser. Ileu, in sheep insulin by Ala. Gly. Val, in horse insulin by Thr. Gly. Ileu.

Molecular weight:	5807	(man)
	5733	(beef)
	5777	(hog, whale)
	5703	(sheep)
	5747	(horse)

The natural products are dimers or polymers of this unit.

Absorption maximum 276 mμm

Insulin crystallizes in rhombi or prisms and is soluble in water and 60–80% alcohol. On heating in solution at pH values below 3.5 its structure becomes filamentous[7]. It is inactivated by pepsin, trypsin, cysteine (distinction from glucagon), glutathione, thioglycollic acid, thiosalicylic acid, dimercaprol (BAL) and ultraviolet light and partly inactivated by radioactive irradiation.

Site of formation

β-Cells of the LANGERHANS islets of the pancreas.

Unit

1 international unit (IU) = 1 USP unit = 0.04167 mg of the international standard preparation (see page 739) which thus contains 24 IU per milligram.

Methods of test and assay

Biological: Measurement of fall in blood sugar in rabbits. 1 IU of insulin depresses the blood sugar of a 2-kg, 24-hour fasting rabbit to 45 mg/100 ml in 3 hours. Other tests utilize mice and rats[8].

Serological: Insulin acts as an antigen in almost all immunized animals as well as in most diabetics requiring insulin, so that detection of the antibodies provides a method of assay of microgram quantities of insulin[9].

Biochemical: Measurement of glucose uptake by the isolated rat diaphragm[10]. Oxidation of glucose-1-^{14}C in adipose tissue of the rat to $^{14}CO_2$ (sensitivity 10 micro-units per milliliter)[11].

Physiology and function

The continuous basal secretion of the β-cells of the pancreas amounts to 0.005–0.035 IU/kg/hour[12]. The normal plasma level in man is $0.1–3.0 \times 10^{-3}$ IU/ml[13].

Insulin promotes the uptake of glucose by the liver and muscles[14] and the penetration of glucose into muscle cells but not into brain cells or erythrocytes[15]. The storage of glucose as glycogen in liver and muscle cells and the oxidation of glucose in the peripheral tissues and muscles is increased. The formation of fats from glucose is increased[11], the respiratory quotient is raised towards unity, and there is increased heat production. Oxidative processes are accelerated and the breakdown of fats and amino acids is lessened.

Lack of insulin causes a corresponding increase of glycogenolysis in the liver and an increase in blood sugar.

It may be necessary to revise the earlier assumption that the diabetic organism cannot store or utilize exogenous glucose. Recent studies[16] indicate that during prolonged glucose infusion the nonketotic diabetic utilizes as much glucose as the nondiabetic but that this takes place at a higher blood sugar level.

Fructose can be utilized by adolescent ketotic diabetics but not by adult nonketotic diabetics[17]. Radioactive tracer studies have shown that the hyperglycemia observed in insulin deficiency is due as much to increased gluconeogenesis as to poor utilization of glucose[18]. When the kidney threshold for glucose is exceeded glucosuria occurs, with consequent increase of water excretion and disturbances of electrolyte and water balance. The increased breakdown of fats and amino acids leads to increased nitrogen excretion and gluconeogenesis. The BMR rises and the respiratory quotient falls. The result is the classical clinical picture: thirst, dry, red tongue, flushed face, polyuria, polydipsia and polyphagia. The increased breakdown of fats is accompanied by defective fat synthesis[19] and results in the accumulation of β-hydroxybutyric acid and acetoacetic acid, the latter giving rise to acetone by decarboxylation. Ketonemia and ketonuria ensue, and the consequent metabolic acidosis with lowered blood bicarbonate and pH leads to progressive metabolic upset and increased metabolic breakdown in the tissues reflected in the liberation of phosphate and associated cations and their excretion in the urine. Loss of water and electrolytes leads to hemoconcentration, decrease of blood volume, collapse of the peripheral blood vessels, failure of kidney function and finally shock[20]. The toxicity of the acetone bodies causes a reduction of cerebral metabolism with lowered oxygen uptake and eventually loss of consciousness[21].

The mechanism of the metabolic action of insulin is shown in the accompanying diagram.

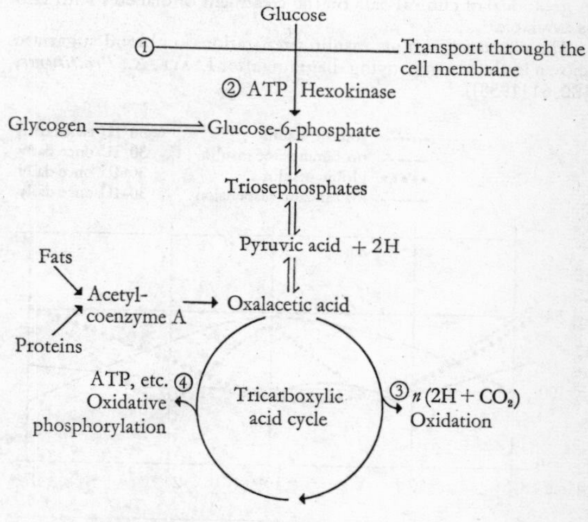

The four points at which insulin intervenes appear to be the following[19]:

1. Transport of glucose through the cell membrane.
2. The reaction: glucose $\xrightarrow[\text{hexokinase}]{\text{ATP}}$ glucose-6-phosphate (see also page 401).
3. Oxidations in the tricarboxylic acid cycle (see page 403).
4. Reactions involved in the formation of compounds with "energy-rich" phosphate bonds (ATP, creatine phosphate, etc.) (see pages 415 and 440).

It is not yet known with certainty how the production of insulin by the β-cells is regulated; nervous, metabolic and hormonal (for example, glucagon) factors are all involved and these again may be stimulated by hyperglycemia and insulin deficiency[22]. Anastomosis experiments on dogs have shown that release of insulin (hyperglycemia) follows injection of D-glucose, D-galactose, D-ribose and D-arabinose into the pancreatic vein. D-Fructose, D-mannose, D-xylose, L-arabinose, 3-methylglucose, D-glucosamine, galacturonic acid and sodium chloride had no such effect[23].

Distribution, breakdown and excretion

Studies with insulin-^{131}I have shown that the hormone is accumulated in the liver, muscles and renal tubuli, while the brain and blood contain only traces[24]. In the main, insulin is broken down in the liver, which as experiments with liver homogenates have shown, contains a proteolytic "insulinase" system which destroys insulin activity. This system can be noncompetitively inhibited by Cu, Zn, Hg and certain thiols. A competitive inhibitor has been identified as a thermo- and pepsin-stable peptide[25]. A very small proportion (ca. 0.1% in 24 hours) of injected insulin is excreted in the urine[24, 26].

Clinical applications

Therapeutic: In the treatment of diabetes mellitus and in hypoglycemic shock therapy (schizophrenia); to stimulate appetite in severe emaciation and as adjuvant in liver disease.

Diagnostic: In hyperinsulinism due to β-cell tumors, plasma insulin concentrations up to 73×10^{-3} IU/ml have been measured[27].

Insulin preparations

Since insulin is rapidly broken down in the organism, insulin preparations with protracted action have been developed. Thus insulin has been combined with protamine and zinc[28] and with globin[29]. More recently it has been combined with zinc in an acetate buffer as insulin zinc suspension (IZS)[30], the reaction time of which can be varied by varying the method of preparation. If the pH value is rapidly increased during preparation an amorphous precipitate of IZS is obtained which is fairly quickly absorbed in the body; when the pH is carefully controlled at 4.8–5.7 the insoluble crystalline IZS is obtained which is only slowly absorbed. These two varieties can be mixed in any desired proportions[31]. A great deal of clinical data on the treatment of diabetes with IZS is available[32].

The effects of various insulin preparations on blood sugar are shown in the accompanying diagram (after Lyall, A., *Practitioner*, **180**, 61 [1958]).

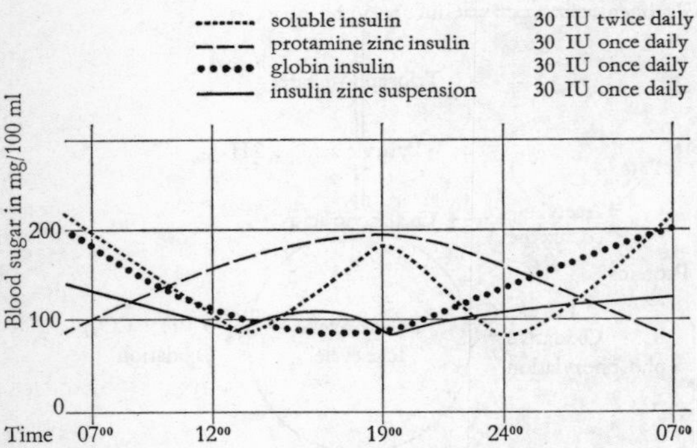

References: *1)* Banting and Best, *J. Lab. clin. Med.*, **7**, 464 (1922). *2)* Best, C. H., *Brit. med. Bull.*, **16**, 179 (1960). *3)* Abel et al., *Proc. nat. Acad. Sci. (Wash.)*, **12**, 132 (1926); *J. Pharmacol. exp. Ther.*, **31**, 65 (1927). *4)* Sanger et al., *Biochem. J.*, **59**, 509 (1955); Ryle et al., *Biochem. J.*, **60**, 541 (1955). *5)* Brown et al., *Biochem. J.*, **60**, 556 (1955); Sanger, F., *Ciba Found. Coll. Endocr.*, **9**, 110 (1956); Oncley, O. L., *Rev. mod. Physics*, **31**, 30 (1959); Stetten, D., *Rev. mod. Physics*, **31**, 563 (1959). *6)* Nicol and Smith, *Nature*, **187**, 483 (1960). *7)* Waugh, D. F., *Ciba Found. Coll. Endocr.*, **9**, 122 (1956). *8)* Randle, P. J., *Ciba Found. Coll. Endocr.*, **11**, 115 (1957). *9)* Arquilla and Stavitsky, *J. clin. Invest.*, **35**, 458 and 467 (1956). *10)* Groen et al., *J. clin. Invest.*, **31**, 97 (1952); Vallance-Owen and Hurlock, *Lancet*, **1**, 68 (1954); Randle, P. J., *Lancet*, **1**, 441 (1954), and *J. Endocr.*, **14**, 82 (1956). *11)* Renold et al., *Mod. Probl. Pediat.*, **4**, 119 (1959). *12)* Houssay et al., *C. R. Soc. Biol. (Paris)*, **101**, 239 (1929). *13)* Randle, P. J., *Ciba Found. Coll. Endocr.*, **11**, 115 (1957). *14)* de Duve, C., *Ciba Found. Coll. Endocr.*, **9**, 203 (1956). *15)* Park et al., *Ciba Found. Coll. Endocr.*, **9**, 240 (1956). *16)* Lestradet, H., *Mod. Probl. Pediat.*, **4**, 553 (1959). *17)* Felber et al., *Mod. Probl. Pediat.*, **4**, 467 (1959). *18)* Feller et al., *J. biol. Chem.*, **187**, 571 (1950); Stetten et al., *ibid.*, **192**, 817 (1951). *19)* Stadie, W. C., *Physiol. Rev.*, **34**, 52 (1954); *Amer. J. Med.*, **19**, 257 (1955). *20)* Guest, G. M., *Amer. J. Med.*, **7**, 630 (1949). *21)* Kety, S., *Proc. Amer. Diabetes Ass.*, **8**, 259 (1948). *22)* Foà, P. P., *Ciba Found. Coll. Endocr.*, **9**, 55 (1956). *23)* Grafe and Meythaler, *Naunyn-Schmiedeberg's Arch. exp. Path. Pharmak.*, **131**, 80 (1928); Foà et al., *Mod. Probl. Pediat.*, **4**, 382 (1959). *24)* Elgee et al., *J. clin. Invest.*, **33**, 1252 (1954). *25)* Mirsky, I. A., *Metabolism*, **5**, 138 (1956); *Recent Progr. Hormone Res.*, **13**, 429 (1957). *26)* Mirsky et al., *J. clin. Invest.*, **27**, 515 (1948). *27)* Groen et al., *Ciba Found. Coll. Endocr.*, **12**, 255 (1958). *28)* Hagedorn et al., *J. Amer. med. Ass.*, **106**, 177 (1936). *29)* Reiner et al., *Proc. Soc. exp. Biol. (N.Y.)*, **171**, 40 (1939). *30)* Hallas-Møller et al., *Ugeskr. Læg.*, **113**, 1761 (1951). *31)* Peck et al., *Diabetes*, **3**, 261 (1954). *32)* Fitzgerald et al., *Lancet*, **1**, 187 (1954); Melton, G., *Brit. med. J.*, **2**, 448 (1954); Mangold, R., *Schweiz. med. Wschr.*, **84**, 1041 (1954); Swoboda and Zweymüller, *Schweiz. med. Wschr.*, **85**, 231 (1955); Gurling et al., *Brit. med. J.*, **1**, 71 (1955); Wolff and Maddison, *Brit. med. J.*, **2**, 413 (1955); Slayton et al., *New Engl. J. Med.*, **253**, 722 (1955); Sprague and Kilby, *Amer. J. Med.*, **19**, 925 (1955); Haunz, E. A., *J. Amer. med. Ass.*, **159**, 1611 (1955); Jersild, M., *Lancet*, **2**, 1009 (1956); Rottmann and Wille, *Dtsch. med. Wschr.*, **81**, 1324 (1956); Swoboda, W., *Mod. Probl. Pediat.*, **4**, 592 (1959).

Glucagon

The classification of glucagon as a hormone is still a matter of discussion, since undisputed and lasting symptoms either from excess or lack of it are as yet unknown[1].

More than thirty years ago MacLeod[2] and Collip[3] described the hyperglycemic effect of their original pancreatic extracts. Kimball and Murlin[4] then suggested the existence of a second pancreatic hormone for which they coined the name glucagon. Staub et al.[5] succeeded further in preparing glucagon in a state of high purity and in elucidating its structure completely.

Glucagon obtained from hogs is a straight-chain polypeptide built up of 29 residues of 15 different amino acids with an N-terminal histidine residue:

His.Ser.Glu(-NH_2).Gly.Thr.Phe.Thr.Ser.Asp.Tyr.Ser.
Lys.Tyr.Leu.Asp.Ser.Arg.Ala.Glu(-NH_2).Asp.Phe.Val.
Glu(-NH_2).Try.Leu.Met.Asp(-NH_2).Thr

Empirical formula	$C_{153}H_{227}N_{43}O_{49}S$
Molecular weight	3485
Absorption maximum	278 mμm

Glucagon crystallizes in white rhombic dodecahedra; in acid solution it readily changes into a filamentous form resembling insulin. It is inactivated by ultraviolet light.

Glucagon cannot be a degradation product of insulin since they have no more than two amino acids in common arranged in the same order[6]. Glucagon differs from all other known protein hormones in lacking cystine, proline and isoleucine. Its activity is destroyed by incubation with pepsin, trypsin, chymotrypsin, subtilysin, leucine-aminopeptidase and carboxypeptidase, but not by incubation with cysteine. Glucagon can be obtained free from insulin by incubation with cysteine.

Site of formation

Destruction of the pancreatic β-cells by alloxan has no effect on the glucagon content of the pancreas, whilst gradual diminution of glucagon activity follows damage to the α-cells by cobalt chloride or other compounds[7]. Glucagon can be isolated from those parts of the dog's pancreas which contain α-cells, but not from the uncinate process, which lacks α-cells[7]. Thus it is highly probable that the α-cells in the pancreatic islets of Langerhans are the site of glucagon production. It has not yet been proved that glucagon is identical with the substances having a hyperglycemic action which have been isolated from skin, lymph nodes, tongue, spleen and gastric mucosa[8]: their action may perhaps be due to serotonin[9]. Glucagon has also been obtained from the human pancreas, where it is found to be more concentrated in the female than in the male[10].

Unit and assay

No international unit; by weight.

Assay is always by measurement of glycogenolysis, either by estimating the hyperglycemia of starved, anesthetized cats or dogs (accuracy about 15–20%)[11], or by means of intact liver slices[12] or liver homogenates[13]. A combination of the last two methods has also been described[14].

Physiology and function

Glucagon causes a transient rise in the blood sugar concentration. The magnitude of the rise and its duration depend on the dose, its mode of administration and the nutritional state of the subject. Hyperglycemia due to glucagon has been observed in most of the mammals, in birds and in reptiles; it is accompanied by a rapid fall in the glycogen content of the liver and an increase in liberation of glucose from the liver. The glycogen loss from the liver is of short duration, and 24 hours after a single dose of glucagon its glycogen content has returned to its original value owing to reactive secretion of insulin. Daily administration of glucagon does not therefore lead to any change in the glycogen content of the liver.

The mode of action of glucagon on liver glycogen has been in large measure elucidated by studies on tissue slices of liver[15] and certain fractions of liver homogenates[13, 16]. The first step is the reaction of glucagon with a certain liver fraction (probably cyclic adenosine-3′,5′-phosphate), ATP and Mg^{++}, resulting in the formation of an active adenine ribonucleotide. This in turn leads to an increase in concentration of effective phosphorylase in the phosphorylase system of the liver, either by an activation of dephospho-phosphorylase-kinase (DPPK) or by a suppression of liver phosphorylase-phosphatase (LPP) (see the diagram below).

The hyperglycemia induced by glucagon is followed by the release of insulin and adrenal cortical hormones, which again bring about an increase of liver glycogen.

The course of the reaction in liver homogenates is of interest as affording proof that a hormone can act in the absence of undamaged cells. In this connection it is worthy of note that two such widely different compounds as glucagon and adrenaline are able to bring about the production of an active factor needed to raise the concentration of liver phosphorylase.

Glucagon retards contractions of the stomach and colon, and also the secretion of gastric juice[17]; it causes a reduction of adrenal ascorbic acid[18], an increase in the excretion of 17-hydroxycorticosteroids[19] and a 200–500% increase of sodium, potassium, chloride, iodide and phosphate ions[20]. Very high doses of glucagon over long periods have a diabetogenic effect in rats (hyperglycemia and

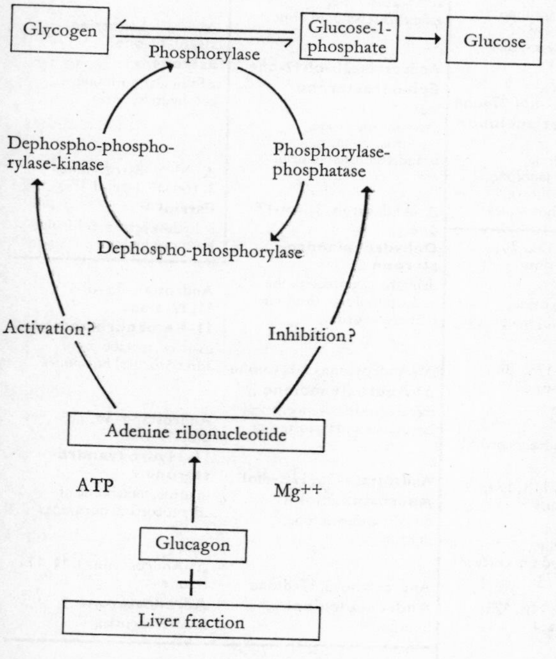

glycosuria), which continues throughout the treatment and is increased by cortisone[21].

The action of glucagon on the glycogen of muscle, on the peripheral utilization of glucose, and on the metabolism of fats and ketone bodies has not yet been fully elucidated[1].

Breakdown and excretion

Glucagon is destroyed in the kidneys, liver and other organs, and in the blood. Experiments with glucagon-^{131}I have shown that immediately following its injection glucagon becomes concentrated in the following organs (in decreasing order of amount stored): kidneys, liver, pituitary, spleen, lungs, salivary glands, adrenals, pancreas, thyroid, heart, duodenum, lymph nodes[22]. It has been possible to show by hepatectomy and nephrectomy that the liver and kidneys are the main sites of destruction of glucagon[22]. A proteolytic glucagonase of limited specificity is said to take part in the destruction. This enzyme contains SH groups and is inhibited by insulin, growth hormone, α-ACTH and α-casein[23]. Injected glucagon is thus quickly destroyed, and it is therefore unlikely to be identical with the glycogenolytic substances or those with hyperglycemic action which are found in the urine of normal individuals, diabetics and schizophrenics[24].

Clinical applications

A connection of glucagon with the KIMMELSTIEL-WILSON syndrome[25], with α-cell carcinoid tumor[26], with schizophrenia[27], with spontaneous hypoglycemia[28] and with peptic ulcer[29] has been suggested but remains unproven. Glucagon can exert an influence on the clinical course of diabetes in man[30] and also in pancreatectomized birds[31], but the connection here also is still not clear[1, 32].

Glucagon tests can be used diagnostically for the investigation of liver function[33], in glycogenosis and the MAURIAC syndrome[34], and in ADDISON's disease[35].

References: *1)* FOÀ et al., *Recent Progr. Hormone Res.*, **13**, 473 (1957), and *Mod. Probl. Paediat.*, **4**, 237 (1959); BEHRENS and BROMER, *Vitam. and Horm.*, **16**, 263 (1958). *2)* MACLEOD, J. J. R., *J. metab. Res.*, **2**, 149 (1922). *3)* COLLIP, J. B., *Amer. J. Physiol.*, **63**, 391 (1923). *4)* KIMBALL and MURLIN, *J. biol. Chem.*, **58**, 337 (1923). *5)* STAUB et al., *Science*, **117**, 628 (1953), and *J. biol. Chem.*, **214**, 619 (1955); BROMER et al., *Diabetes*, **6**, 234 (1957), and *J. Amer. chem. Soc.*, **78**, 3858 (1956); **79**, 2807 (1957). *6)* SANGER, F., *Ciba Found. Coll. Endocr.*, **9**, 110 (1956). *7)* BENCOSME et al., *Proc. Soc. exp. Biol. (N.Y.)*, **90**, 387 (1955); *Canad. J. Biochem.*, **35**, 1197 (1957); *Endocrinology*, **61**, 1 (1957). *8)* SUTHERLAND and DE DUVE, *J. biol. Chem.*, **175**, 663 (1948); SUTHERLAND et al., *J. biol. Chem.*, **180**, 825 (1949); FOÀ et al., *Science*, **117**, 82 (1953); RABEN, M., *Recent Progr. Hormone Res.*, **8**, 471 (1953); RAJA RAMA RAO and DE, *Nature*, **174**, 229 (1954), and *Acta endocr. (Kbh.)*, **18**, 299 (1955); WEITZEL et al., *Hoppe-Seylers Z. physiol. Chem.*, **303**, 161 (1956). *9)* SIREK, A., *Nature*, **179**, 376 (1957). *10)* KENNY, A. J., *J. clin. Endocr.*, **15**, 1089 (1955). *11)* STAUB and BEHRENS, *J. clin. Invest.*, **33**, 1629 (1954); STAUB et al., *Fed. Proc.*, **15**, 361 (1956). *12)* SUTHERLAND and DE DUVE, *J. biol. Chem.*, **175**, 663 (1948); VUYLSTEKE and DE DUVE, *Arch. int. Pharmacodyn.*, **111**, 437 (1957). *13)* BERTHET et al., *J. biol. Chem.*, **229**, 351 (1957); RALL et al., *J. biol. Chem.*, **224**, 463 (1957). *14)* UI et al., *Endocr. jap.*, **3**, 191 (1956). *15)* RALL et al., *J. biol. Chem.*, **218**, 483 (1956); SUTHERLAND and RALL, *J. biol. Chem.*, **232**, 1077 (1958). *16)* SUTHERLAND and RALL, *J. Amer. chem. Soc.*, **79**, 3608 (1957). *17)* STUNKARD et al., *Proc. Soc. exp. Biol. (N.Y.)*, **89**, 258 (1955); EARLE et al., *Ann. Surg.*, **146**, 124 (1957); LIN and ALPHIN, *Fed. Proc.*, **17**, 97 (1958). *18)* COSTA et al., *Proc. Soc. exp. Biol. (N.Y.)*, **91**, 308, 574 (1956). *19)* KIRTLEY et al., *Diabetes*, **2**, 345 (1953). *20)* STAUB et al., *Fed. Proc.*, **15**, 361 (1956), and *Proc. Soc. exp. Biol. (N.Y.)*, **94**, 57 (1957); ELRICK et al., *New Engl. J. Med.*, **256**, 742 (1957). *21)* SALTER et al., *Fed. Proc.*, **15**, 160 (1956), and *Diabetes*, **6**, 248 (1957); CAVALLERO et al., *Nature*, **173**, 585 (1954); ELRICK et al., *Diabetes*, **7**, 129 (1958); LAZARUS and VOLK, *Fed. Proc.*, **17**, 444 (1958). *22)* COX et al., *Endocrinology*, **60**, 277 (1957); NARAHARA and WILLIAMS, *Endocrinology*, **60**, 258 (1957); BERSON et al., *J. Lab. clin. Med.*, **49**, 331 (1957). *23)* TYBERGHEIM et al., *J. biol. Chem.*, **222**, 945 (1956). *24)* FOÀ et al., *Recent Progr. Hormone Res.*, **13**, 473 (1957). *25)* DANA et al., *Bull. Johns Hopk. Hosp.*, **90**, 98 (1952). *26)* WEISBERG and SCHAEFER, *Amer. J. clin. Path.*, **22**, 1169 (1952). *27)* MORGAN and PILGRIM, *Proc. Soc. exp. Biol. (N.Y.)*, **79**, 106 (1952). *28)* MCQUARRIE, T., *Amer. J. Dis. Child.*, **87**, 399 (1954); BIERICH and KORNATZ-STEGMANN, *Mschr. Kinderheilk.*, **102**, 49 (1954). *29)* ZOLLINGER and ELLISON, *Ann. Surg.*, **142**, 709 (1955). *30)* HAWKINS et al., *Canad. med. Ass. J.*, **74**, 972 (1956). *31)* MIAHLE, P., *Acta endocr. (Kbh.)*, **28**, Suppl. 36, (1958). *32)* HUG, G., *Mod. Probl. Paediat.*, **4**, 277 (1959). *33)* KENNY, A. J., *J. clin. Endocr.*, **15**, 1089 (1955); VAN ITALLIE and BENTLEY, *J. clin. Invest.*, **34**, 1730 (1955). *34)* CARSON and KOCK, *J. Pediat.*, **47**, 161 (1955); HUBBLE, D., *Lancet*, **1**, 235 (1954), and *Diabetes*, **4**, 197 (1955); VASSELLA, F., *Helv. paediat. Acta*, **12**, 331 (1957); DENYS et al., *Mod. Probl. Paediat.*, **4**, 197 (1959); GITZELMANN, P., *Mod. Probl. Paediat.*, **4**, 288 (1959). *35)* ALIVISATOS and MCCULLAGH, *J. Amer. med. Ass.*, **159**, 1098 (1955).

Hormones of the gastrointestinal tract[1]

Secretin[2]. A peptide formed in the duodenal mucosa. Molecular weight ca. 5000. Increases the pancreatic secretion and the flow of bile, but not the formation of pancreatic enzymes.

Gastrin. Formed in the gastric mucosa (around the pylorus). Promotes the secretion of gastric juice.

Cholecystokinin. Present in the mucosa of the small intestine. Causes contraction of the gallbladder.

Enterogastrone. Formed in the mucosa of the small intestine. Inhibits the secretion of gastric juice and the contraction of the stomach.

Pancreozymin. Formed in the mucosa of the upper small intestine. Promotes enzyme secretion by the pancreas.

All the above substances are peptides or proteins of unknown constitution. They arise through chemical or mechanical stimulation of the gastrointestinal tract and are rapidly released following onset of the stimulus. Their secretion ceases immediately on cessation of the stimulus.

References: *1)* For a review see GREENGARD, H., in PINCUS and THIMANN (Eds.), *The Hormones*, vol. I, New York, 1948, page 201. *2)* GROSSMAN, M. I., *Vitam. and Horm.*, **16**, 179 (1958).

Nomenclature of steroids occurring in the human organism

Grotesque type = systematic chemical name*	♀ = estrogenic activity	○ = adrenocortical-hormonal activity	
Grotesque type, bold = trivial name*	♂ = androgenic activity	× = no hormonal activity	
Small type = synonyms, etc.	● = progestational activity	? = activity unknown	

Chemical names derived from

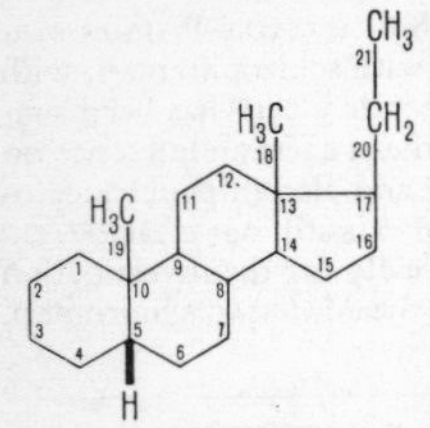

Pregnane
(5β-Pregnane**)

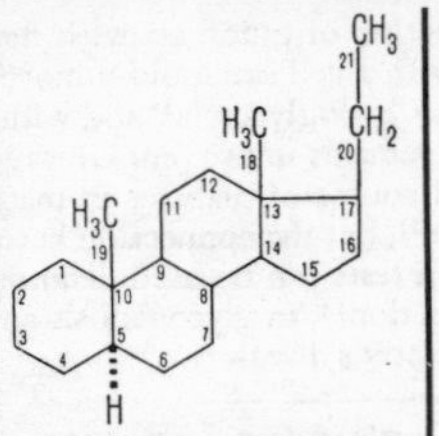

Allopregnane
(5α-Pregnane**)

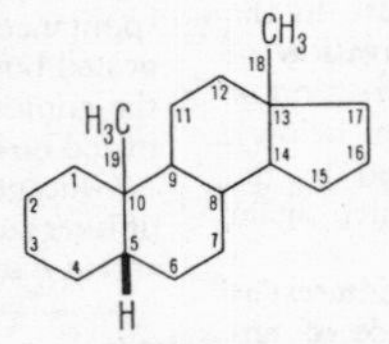

Etiane
(5β-Androstane**)

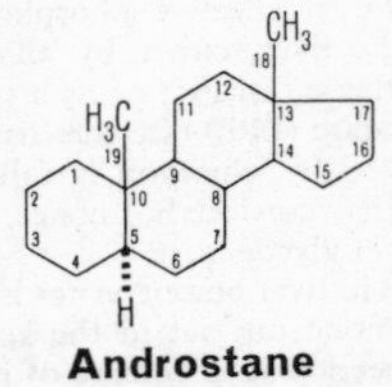

Androstane
(5α-Androstane**)

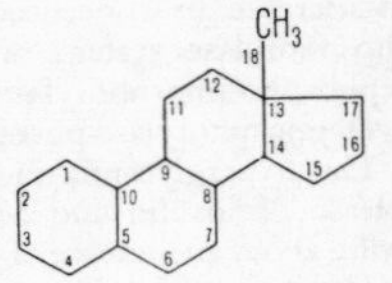

Estrane

Pregnane column

Δ^4-Pregnene-3, 20-dione
Progesterone ●
corpus luteum hormone, luteohormone, corporin

Δ^4-Pregnen-20α-ol-3-one
20α-Hydroxy-progesterone ●
metabolite of progesterone

Δ^4-Pregnen-20β-ol-3-one
20β-Hydroxy-progesterone ●
metabolite of progesterone

Δ^4-Pregnen-17α-ol-3,20-dione
17-Hydroxy-progesterone ♂ ●
in adrenals

Pregnane-3, 20-dione
Pregnanedione ×
in urine

Pregnan-3α-ol-20-one
α-Pregnanolone ×
epipregnanolone; in urine

Pregnane-3α, 20α-diol
Pregnanediol ×
in urine, metabolite of progesterone and adrenocortical hormones

Pregnane-3α, 17α, 20α-triol
Pregnanetriol ×
in urine, metabolite of adrenocortical hormones

Allopregnane column

Allopregnane-3α, 20α-diol
α-Allopregnanediol ×
in urine, metabolite of progesterone and adrenocortical hormones

Allopregnane-3β, 20α-diol
β-Allopregnanediol ×
in urine

Allopregnan-3α-ol-20-one
α-Allopregnanolone ×
in urine

Allopregnan-3β-ol-20-one
β-Allopregnanolone ×
in urine

Allopregnane-3α, 11β, 17α, 21-tetraol-20-one
Allotetra-hydrocortisol ×
in urine, metabolite of adrenocortical hormones

Etiane column

Etian-3α-ol-17-one
α-Etianolone ×
α-etiocholanolone; metabolite of testosterone and adrenocortical hormones

Etian-3α-ol-11,17-dione
11-Ketoetianolone ×
11-ketoetiocholanolone; in urine, metabolite of adrenocortical hormones

Etiane-3α,11β-diol-17-one
11-Hydroxyetianolone ×
etianediolone, etiocholanediolone, hydroxyetiocholanolone; in urine, metabolite of adrenocortical hormones

Pregnane derivatives (below Allopregnane and Etiane)

Pregnane-3α, 17α, 21-triol-11, 20-dione
Tetrahydrocortisone ×
urocortisone; in urine, metabolite of adrenocortical hormones

Pregnane-3α, 11β, 17α, 21-tetraol-20-one
Tetrahydrocortisol ×
urocortisol; in urine, metabolite of adrenocortical hormones

Pregnane-3α, 11β, 21-triol-20-one
Tetrahydrocortico-sterone ×
in urine, metabolite of adrenocortical hormones

Pregnane-3α-17α-21-triol-20-one
Tetrahydro-cortexolone ×
in urine, metabolite of adrenocortical hormones

Pregnane-3α, 17α, 20α, 21-tetraol-11-one
Cortolone ×
α-cortolone; in urine, metabolite of adrenocortical hormones

Pregnane-3α, 17α, 20β, 21-tetraol-11-one
β-Cortolone ×
in urine, metabolite of adrenocortical hormones

Pregnane-3α, 11β, 17α, 20α, 21-pentaol
Cortol ×
α-cortol; in urine, metabolite of adrenocortical hormones

Pregnane-3α, 11β, 17α, 20β, 21-pentaol
β-Cortol ×
in urine, metabolite of adrenocortical hormones

Androstane column

Δ^4-Androsten-17β-ol-3-one
17β-Testosterone ♂
dehydroandrostan-17-ol-3-one, *trans*-testosterone

Androstan-3α-ol-17-one
Androsterone ♂
cis-androsterone, *epi*androsterone; in urine

Androstan-3β-ol-17-one
Epiandrosterone
weak ♂
trans-androsterone, *n*-androsterone, *iso*androsterone; in urine

Δ^5-Androsten-3β-ol-17-one
Dehydroepiandro-sterone ♂
dehydro*iso*androsterone, androstenolone; in adrenal cortex and urine

Δ^4-Androstene-3, 17-dione
Δ^4-Androstenedione ♂
metabolite of adrenocortical hormones and testosterone

Androstane-3α, 17β-diol
Androstanediol ♂
dihydroandrosterone; in urine

Androstane-3, 17-dione
Androstanedione ♂
in urine

Estrane column

$\Delta^{1,3,5(10)}$-Estratriene-3, 17β-diol
17β-Estradiol ♀
dihydro-follicular hormone, dihydro-folliculin, dihydroxyestrin, *trans*-estradiol, α-dihydroxyestrin

$\Delta^{1,3,5(10)}$-Estratrien-3β-ol-17-one
Estrone ♀
α-follicular hormone, ketohydroxyestrin

$\Delta^{1,3,5(10)}$-Estratriene-3, 16α, 17β-triol
Estriol ♀
trihydroxyestrin, follicular hormone hydrate

Androstan-3α-ol-11, 17-dione
11-Ketoandrosterone ♂
in urine, metabolite of adrenocortical hormones

Androstane-3α, 11β-diol-17-one
11-Hydroxyandro-sterone ?
in urine, metabolite of adrenocortical hormones

Δ^4-Androstene-3, 11, 17-trione
Adrenosterone ♂
in adrenal cortex

Adrenocortical hormones

Δ^4-Pregnene-17α, 21-diol-3, 11, 20-trione
Cortisone ○
17-hydroxy-11-dehydro-corticosterone, compound E (Kendall), substance Fa (Reichstein), compound F (Wintersteiner)

Δ^4-Pregnen-21-ol-3, 20-dione
Cortexone ○
desoxycorticosterone, 21-hydroxyprogesterone, substance Q (Reichstein)

Δ^4-Pregnene-11β,17α, 21-triol-3, 20-dione
Cortisol ○
hydrocortisone, 17-hydroxycorticosterone, compound F (Kendall), substance M (Reichstein)

Δ^4-Pregnene-17α, 21-diol-3, 20-dione
Cortexolone ○
17-hydroxy-11-desoxy-corticosterone, substance S (Reichstein)

Δ^4-Pregnen-21-ol-3,11, 20-trione
11-Dehydrocorti-costerone ○
compound A (Kendall)

Δ^4-Pregnene-11β, 21-diol-3, 20-dione
Corticosterone ○
compound B (Kendall), substance H (Reichstein)

Δ^4-Pregnen-18-al-11β, 21-diol-3, 20-dione
Aldosterone ○
electrocortin

Systematic chemical names

The symbol Δ indicates a double bond between two carbon atoms. When these atoms have successive numbers (for example 5 and 6) only the lower number is affixed to this symbol (thus Δ^5). When the carbon atoms have nonsuccessive numbers, the second (higher) number is added in brackets (thus a double bond between carbon atoms 5 and 10 is indicated by $\Delta^{5(10)}$).

Numbers = carbon atom to which the substituent group (hydroxyl group, keto group, etc.) is attached.

di, tri, tetra, penta = 2, 3, 4, 5 bonds or groups

al = aldehydo group			
an(e) = saturated bond	desoxy = one O-atom less		
en(e) = double bond	anhydro = one H_2O less		
ol = hydroxyl group	dehydro = two H-atoms less		
on(e) = keto group	dihydro = two H-atoms more		

* For explanation of the α- and β-configurations see opposite (valid only for the *systematic* and *trivial* names in this table, not for the synonyms).

** Systematic nomenclature according to the definitive rules for nomenclature of steroids adopted by the International Union of Pure and Applied Chemistry (*Nomenclature of Organic Chemistry*, London, 1957, page 73).

Steroid hormones

Chemical nomenclature

The sex hormones and adrenocortical hormones belong to the group of compounds known as steroids. The skeleton of the steroid molecule consists of three six-membered rings A, B and C and a five-membered ring D (Fig. 1), with methyl groups at positions C-10 and C-13. In the estrogens the methyl group at C-10 is lacking and the ring A is aromatic (Fig. 2).

The steroids with two methyl groups may be classified according to the total number of carbon atoms in the molecule:

"C_{19}-steroids" with no side-chain at C-17: among these are testosterone and its metabolites (androgens), and the 17-ketosteroids (keto group at C-17). See Figure 3.

"C_{21}-steroids" with a side-chain of 2 C-atoms at C-17: among these are progesterone and the adrenocortical hormones. See Figure 4.

"C_{24}-steroids" with a branched side-chain of 5 C-atoms at C-17: this is characteristic of the bile acids. See Figure 5.

"C_{27}-steroids" with a branched side-chain of 8 C-atoms at C-17: among these are cholesterol and the precursors of vitamin D_3. See Figure 6.

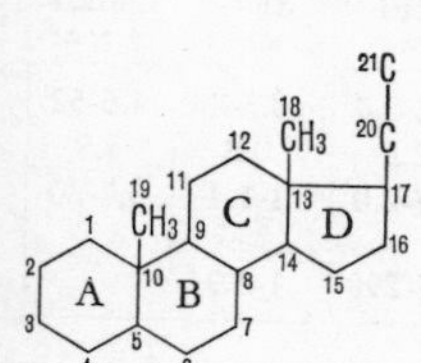

Fig. 1

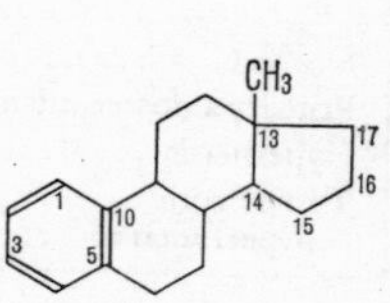

Fig. 2

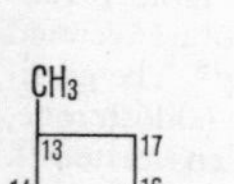

Fig. 3

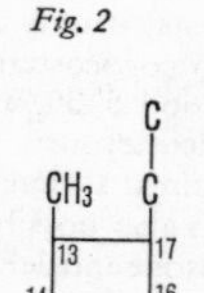

Fig. 4

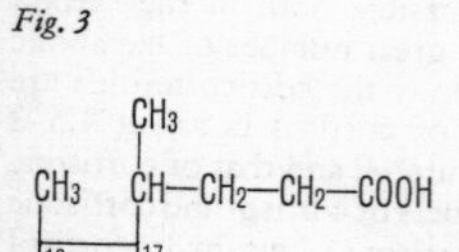

Fig. 5

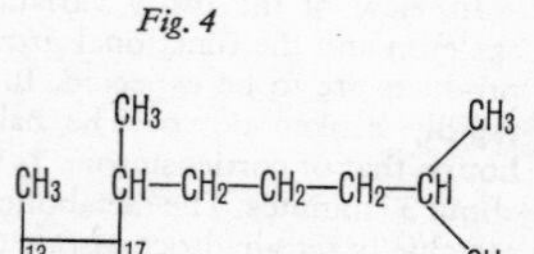

Fig. 6

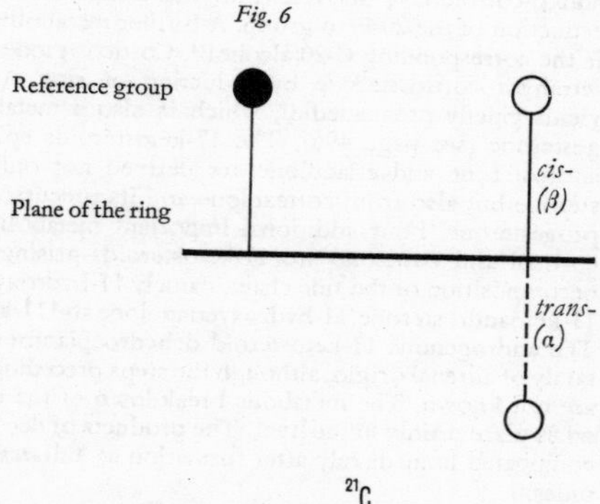

Fig. 7

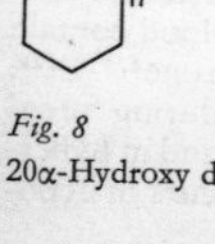

Fig. 8
20α-Hydroxy derivative

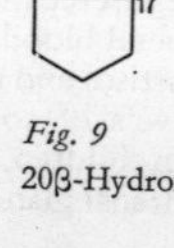

Fig. 9
20β-Hydroxy derivative

Stereochemical designations

Since the biological activity of many hormones is markedly dependent on the stereochemical configuration, precise designation in this respect is necessary. The symbols α and β are used to designate those forms in which certain substituents stand in *trans*- or *cis*-relationship respectively to the methyl groups at C-10 or C-13 as reference groups. The *cis*-configuration indicates one in which the substituent is located spatially on the same side of the plane of the ring system as the reference group, the *trans*-configuration one in which the two groups are on different sides of this plane. In the structural formulas in this chapter, the *cis*(β)-position is indicated by a full line and the *trans*(α)-position by a broken line (see Fig. 7). The methyl group at C-10 is arbitrarily regarded as being situated *above* the plane of the ring. In the steroids the configuration of the methyl group at C-13, which serves as reference group, is with very few exceptions the same as that of the methyl group at C-10.

In steroid nomenclature the symbols α and β are also used to denote a different type of stereoisomerism which arises when the C-20 atom is asymmetrically substituted. This is illustrated by Figures 8 and 9.

Biosynthesis and metabolism

The biosynthesis and metabolism of the steroid hormones are described on pages 432–434.

Bibliography (chemistry and metabolism of steroid hormones): FIESER and FIESER, *Steroids*, New York, 1959; INHOFFEN, H. H. (Ed.), *Über Sterine, Gallensäuren und verwandte Naturstoffe*, vols. I and II, Stuttgart, 1954 and 1959; KLYNE, W., *The Chemistry of the Steroids*, London and New York, 1957; ROBERTS and SZEGÖ, *Ann. Rev. Biochem.*, **24**, 543 (1955); DORFMAN, R.I., *Ann. Rev. Biochem.*, **26**, 523 (1957); KATZMAN et al., *Ann. Rev. Biochem.*, **28**, 257 (1959); PINCUS and THIMANN (Eds.), *The Hormones*, vols. I, II, III, New York, 1948, 1950, 1955. Also *Recent Progr. Hormone Res.*, **1** (1947), and subsequent volumes; *Vitam. and Horm.*, **1** (1943), and subsequent volumes.

Adrenocortical hormones (corticosteroids)

The adrenocortical hormones are C_{21}-steroids and are therefore closely related chemically to the other steroid hormones. This close relationship is also shown biologically by the fact that in non-functioning of the cortex the sex hormones are able to prolong life and that certain cortical substances and metabolites of the adrenocortical hormones show androgenic, progestational and estrogenic activity. Thus dysfunction of the cortex due to hyperplasia or neoplasms, for example, can bring about the adrenogenital syndrome (interrenalism) in women, interrenal feminization in men (rare), or pubertas praecox.

More than 40 different steroids have so far been isolated from the adrenal cortex. The following steroids have a substitutive action in survival tests on adrenalectomized animals and are thus characterized as adrenocortical hormones: cortisol (hydrocortisone), cortisone, corticosterone, dehydrocorticosterone, cortexone (desoxycorticosterone) and cortexolone (17-hydroxy-11-desoxycorticosterone). In 1953 the steroid aldosterone, which has a remarkable effect on mineral metabolism (see page 492), was isolated from the so-called amorphous fraction of the adrenocortical steroids[1]. Subsequently the amorphous fraction yielded other steroids, some with interesting physiological properties[2,3].

In the literature a distinction is often made between "*mineralo*-" (cortexone, aldosterone) and "*gluco*-" (cortisol, cortisone) corticosteroids. This distinction has no valid basis since the actions of the individual hormones on mineral and carbohydrate metabolism show only quantitative differences and moreover considerably overlap (see also under Biological action, page 490). A better classification of the corticosteroids is on the basis of their chemical structure, which also shows some parallelism with their metabolic action:

11-Oxycorticosteroids, so-named on account of the oxygen atom linked to the carbon atom at position 11: cortisol, corticosterone, 11-dehydrocorticosterone, cortisone, aldosterone (in contrast, cortexone [desoxycorticosterone] and cortexolone [17-hydroxy-11-desoxycorticosterone] have no oxygen atom linked to the C-11 atom), and *11-17-oxycorticosteroids*, which have oxygen atoms linked to both the C-11 and C-17 atoms: cortisol and cortisone.

The 11-oxycorticosteroids have a more marked effect on carbohydrate metabolism than cortexone (and usually also on organic metabolism as a whole); the greatest effect is shown by the 11-17-oxycorticosteroids.

Cortisol (hydrocortisone), $C_{21}H_{30}O_5$
Mol.wt. 362.47
M.p. 218–221°C

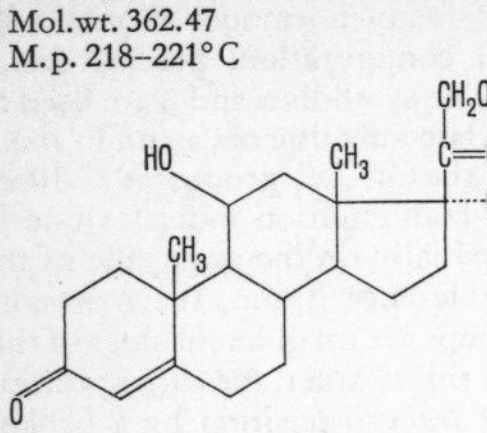

Cortisone, $C_{21}H_{28}O_5$
Mol.wt. 360.46
M.p. 218–220°C

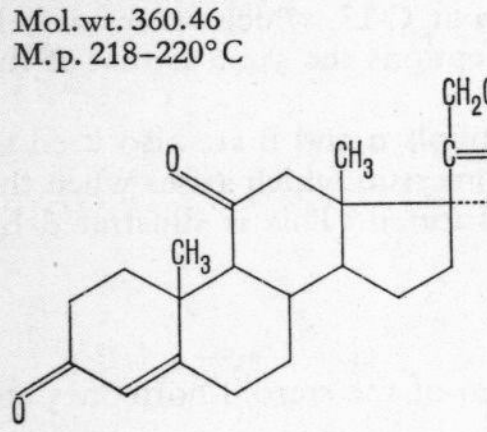

Corticosterone, $C_{21}H_{30}O_4$
Mol.wt. 346.47
M.p. 180–182°C

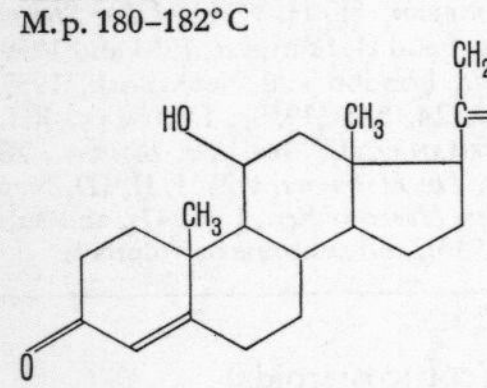

Dehydrocorticosterone, $C_{21}H_{28}O_4$
Mol.wt. 344.46
M.p. 177–180°C

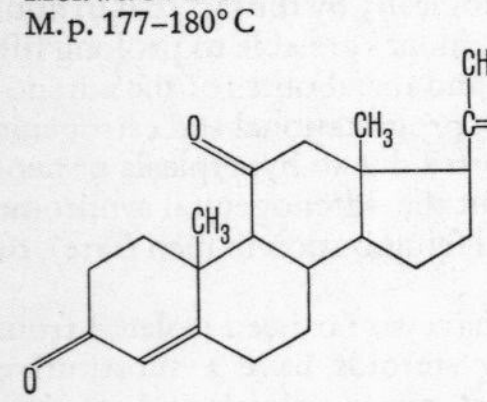

Cortexolone (17-hydroxy-11-desoxycorticosterone), $C_{21}H_{30}O_4$
Mol.wt. 346.47
M.p. 213–217°C

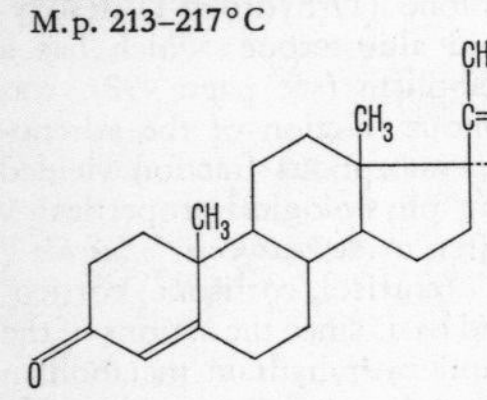

Cortexone (desoxycorticosterone), $C_{21}H_{30}O_3$
Mol.wt. 330.47
M.p. 141–142°C

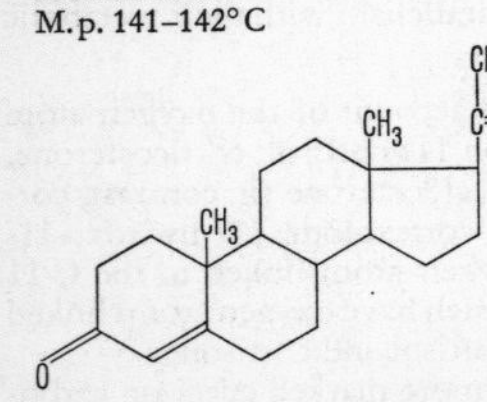

Unit

No international unit; by weight.

Methods of test and assay

Chemical: The individual corticosteroids are best separated and determined by chromatographic methods[5]. There are also various nonspecific methods[4] of estimating functional groups or characteristic side-chains, for example SILBER and PORTER's method for the 17,21-dihydroxy-20-ketosteroids[6] and NORYMBERSKI's method for the 17-ketogenic steroids (17-hydroxycorticosteroids which can be oxidized to 17-ketosteroids by sodium bismuthate or chromic acid)[8]. The values obtained by these methods, however, are comparable only to a limited extent.

Biological: Many different tests are available[7].

Formation and occurrence

The corticosteroids are formed in the adrenal cortex: in the outermost layer (zona glomerulosa) the hormones, which affect salt and water metabolism, in the middle layer (zona fasciculata) the glucogenic steroids, and in the innermost layer (zona reticularis) the androgens. The reciprocal mechanism between the pituitary (secretion of ACTH; see page 475) and the adrenal cortex seems mainly to involve only the zona fasciculata. On the stimulation of corticosteroid secretion by ACTH see page 475. The biosynthesis of the corticosteroids is described on pages 432–434.

Corticosteroid content of the adrenal cortex in micrograms
(after NEHER[5])

	Cortisol	Corti-sone	Aldo-sterone	Cortico-sterone
Normal.............	8-30.6	0.2-2.0	<0.3-2.0	4.6-52
Primary aldosteronism ..	67.7	2.5	0.8	5.9
Hyperplasia	23.4-30	0.7-2.0	1-1.4	3.7-20
Tumor with hyperfunction	41.6-160	7.7-290	1-3.9	

The composition of the corticosteroids is species-specific and in man they consist mainly of cortisol and corticosterone. The ratio of cortisol to corticosterone in the adrenals is 0.29–3.8, in the peripheral blood 5–30, an indication of the more rapid breakdown of corticosterone[5]. Normally 5–60 mg of cortisol are secreted daily[9], in maximal stimulation by ACTH ca. 240 mg[10]. The corticosteroids are also possibly formed in the placenta (aldosterone, cortisol, cortisone and dehydrocorticosterone have been isolated[11]).

Metabolism

In view of the many variations possible both in the carbon skeleton and the functional groups, a great number of metabolic products are to be expected. In the body the corticosteroids are rapidly broken down. The half-life of cortisol is about 1.5–3 hours, that of corticosterone 1–1.5 hours[9, 12] and that of cortisone about 30 minutes. The metabolic products of cortisol and cortisone are chiefly tetrahydrocortisone (urocortisone), tetrahydrocortisol (urocortisol) and *allo*-tetrahydrocortisol[13] – all formed by reduction of ring A of the steroid nucleus – and α- and β-cortol and α- and β-cortolone[14], derived from the tetrahydro-compounds by reduction of the 20-keto group. A further metabolite of cortisone is the corresponding C-20 alcohol[15]. Corticosterone yields chiefly tetrahydrocorticosterone by reduction of ring A[16]. Cortexone yields chiefly pregnanediol, which is also a metabolite of progesterone (see page 496). The 17-ketosteroids epiandrosterone, androsterone and etianolone are derived not only from testosterone but also from cortexolone and its precursor 17-hydroxyprogesterone. Four additional important metabolic products of cortisol and cortisone are 17-ketosteroids arising by oxidative decomposition of the side chain, namely 11-hydroxyandrosterone, 11-ketoandrosterone, 11-hydroxyetianolone and 11-ketoetianolone. The androgenous 17-ketosteroid dehydroepiandrosterone is certainly of adrenal origin, although the steps preceding its formation are not known. The metabolic breakdown of the corticosteroids takes place mainly in the liver. The products of decomposition are conjugated immediately after formation as sulfates or β-glucuronides.

For details of corticosteroid metabolism see pages 432–434.

Corticosteroids in blood[5, 17, 18]

There are wide discrepancies in data on the corticosteroid content of the peripheral blood. On an average, 100 ml blood contain about 10 μg of cortisol and at least 1 μg of corticosterone[6, 9, 12, 19]. Higher blood levels of corticosteroids are found during pregnancy, in newborn children, after ingestion of ACTH and in hyperfunction of the adrenal glands; a lower blood level occurs in hypofunction of the pituitary. There is a marked daily rhythm in which the corticosteroid blood level in the morning may rise up to four times the daily minimum in the evening. The active corticosteroids in the blood are free but their metabolites are conjugated, chiefly as glucuronides. The corticosteroids, but not their conjugated metabolites, are normally bound to a protein ("transcortin", probably an α-globulin), cortisol being more firmly bound than corticosterone[20]. The combining capacity of the plasma proteins is apparently limited, since part of the steroids are present uncombined in the plasma when the corticosteroid level is increased.

Corticosteroids in urine[5,18]

About 100 different steroids are excreted in the urine. The majority must be metabolic products of the cortical hormones since they are also found after castration. The active corticosteroids are chiefly excreted in the free state, but their metabolites are conjugated as sulfates or β-glucuronides.

After infusion of radioactive cortisol, 87% of the labeled material is found in the urine in conjugated form, 4% as free metabolites and less than 1% as unchanged cortisol. The metabolism is slowed down in liver diseases (increase in the level of unchanged corticosteroids in the urine). In men at least 50% of the 17-ketosteroid fraction consists of metabolites of the adrenocortical hormones, in women and children it consists almost wholly of these metabolites (see also under 17-Ketosteroids, page 495).

Pregnanetriol in urine derives from 17-hydroxyprogesterone, a precursor of the corticosteroids. In adrenal hyperplasia its excretion is increased due to failure in hydroxylation of 17-hydroxyprogesterone to cortisol[21]. Relationships between important urinary metabolites of the adrenocortical and testicular steroids are shown in the diagram below.

The urinary excretion of the individual corticosteroids and their metabolites and some physiological and pathological changes in the excretion of 17,21-dihydroxy-20-ketosteroids and 17-ketosteroids are shown in the adjacent tables. In contrast to the natural corticosteroids, the synthetic analogues prednisone and prednisolone are excreted mainly unchanged in the urine.

Urinary excretion of individual corticosteroids and their metabolites in adults

	Urinary excretion in μg/24 hours Range	Mean	Reference
Cortisol (women)	10–50		*22*
(men)	10–80	34.5	*23*
Cortisone (men)	20–200	91.5	*23*
Corticosterone (men)	2.2–9.0	5.8	*24*
Tetrahydrocortisol (men)	900–1900	1300	*13*
allo-Tetrahydrocortisol (men)	600–2100	1300	*13*
Tetrahydrocortisone (men)	1600–5300	3100	*13*
Pregnanetriol (men and women)	200–1800		*25*

Urinary excretion of 17,21-dihydroxy-20-ketosteroids and 17-ketosteroids in various physiological and pathological conditions[26]

	17,21-Dihydroxy-20-ketosteroids mg/24 hours	17-Keto-steroids mg/24 hours
Normal child	1–5	1–12
Normal female	3–10*	8–20
Normal male	5–16*	12–24
Senility	0–5	4–12
Pregnancy	5–20	12–36
ADDISON's disease	0–5	0–8
Hypopituitarism	0–4	0–6
Anorexia nervosa	3–8	6–12
Myxedema	3–5	2–12
Thyrotoxicosis	8–20	4–14
Dwarfism	8–18	6–12
Eunuchoidism (male)	3–10	6–12
Hirsutism	3–10	8–30
Acromegaly	3–18	4–20
Liver diseases	3–8	5–12
Rheumatoid arthritis	3–8	5–10
Diabetes mellitus	3–10	5–12
Diabetes insipidus	3–10	5–12
Castrates (female)	3–10	3–12
CUSHING's disease (pituitarian)	30–80	30–100
CUSHING's syndrome (adrenal)	10–80	12–28
Adrenal tumor	15–80	30–2000
Testicular tumor	3–20	30–2000
Pseudohermaphroditism	3–16	12–100
Hypertension	3–12	6–12
Debilitating disease	0–5	6–12
Arrhenoblastoma	5–18	8–20
Dysgerminoma	3–10	8–20
Chorionepithelioma	8–25	12–24
Hydatidiform mole	5–20	8–18
Pituitary tumor	5–40	8–50
Retinitis pigmentosa	1–5	3–8
Obesity	1–5	5–10
Pubertas praecox	6–12	10–20
Migraine	3–16	10–20

* Corresponding values for 17-ketogenic steroids[27]: women 4.6–13.4 mg/24 hours, men 9.6–19.2 mg/24 hours.

Clinical significance of the assay of 17-ketosteroids and corticosteroids

Determination of the 17-ketosteroid fraction alone allows only limited conclusions to be drawn concerning the functional state of the adrenal cortex since these substances can also arise in the

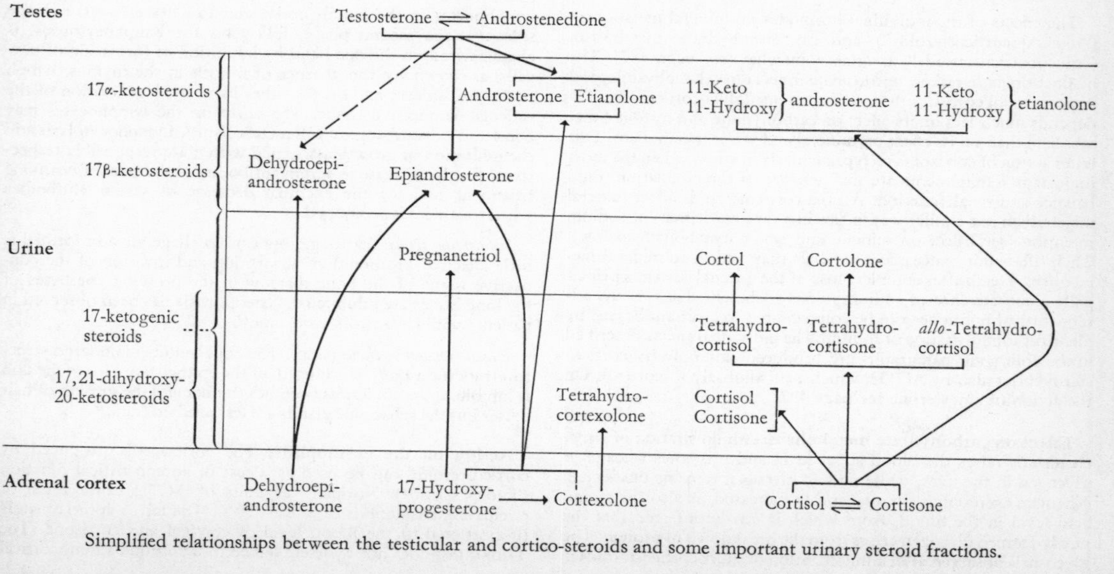

Simplified relationships between the testicular and cortico-steroids and some important urinary steroid fractions.

testes and ovaries. There is also no relation between the formation of cortisol and the excretion of 17-ketosteroids, as indicated for example by the small change in the excretion of 17-ketosteroids in the CUSHING syndrome. Hyperfunction of the cortex can be recognized by the increased excretion of cortisol, hypofunction by the decreased excretion of tetrahydrocortisone and tetrahydrocortisol[28]. The assay best suited to routine clinical studies[4] would appear to be the determination of the 17-ketogenic steroids by NORYMBERSKI's method[8], which unlike the SILBER-PORTER assay[6] also embraces cortol, cortolone and pregnanetriol. This assay, however, shows correlation with the daily cortisol formation only when cortical activity is increased[28].

For clinical purposes, determination of the corticosteroids in blood is now preferred since in the blood about half the hormones are present in the active form and thus better reflect the state of hormone production. However, there are considerable technical difficulties due to the large amounts of blood required.

Biological action[29]

The adrenocortical hormones are in the widest sense concerned with the maintenance of homeostasis. They enable the organism to react to internal and external stress by sensitizing it and calling forth appropriate defense reactions, although they are not specific for these reactions. The regulation of hormone production by the ACTH of the pituitary is of special importance in connection with this function of the corticosteroids (see page 475).

The corticosteroids show marked differences in the nature and intensity of their activity, as illustrated in the following table (there are conspicuous differences in their action in the various animal species, especially between rats and man):

Comparative effects of corticosteroids
(after FRUTON and SIMMONDS[30])

	$Na^+:K^+$ in urine (rats)	Growth and maintenance of life (rats)	Maintenance of life (dogs)	Muscular work (rats)	Liver glycogen (rats)
Cortisone	0.6	2.5	0.5	10	10
Cortisol	0.8	0.5		19	16
Corticosterone..	1.4	1.7			5
Dehydro-corticosterone		1.0		5	5
Cortexolone....	0.8			0.2	
Cortexone	10	10	10	0.2	0.1
Aldosterone....	1000		250		3

The effects of the individual hormones on mineral metabolism ("mineralocorticosteroids") and on carbohydrate metabolism ("glucocorticosteroids") overlap somewhat (see page 487). The distinction is a rather unfortunate one since the physiological importance of cortisol – the most important "glucocorticosteroid" – depends much less on its effect on carbohydrate and nitrogen metabolism than on its effect on mineral and water metabolism. This latter action of cortisol is seen particularly in stress, when the most important requirements are maintenance of the circulation, fluid balance and renal function. All the corticosteroids affect mineral metabolism in a similar way in causing varying degrees of sodium retention (see Effect on mineral and water metabolism, below). Their life-maintenance effect parallels their action on mineral metabolism. Death after complete loss of the adrenal cortex is principally a consequence of sodium impoverishment. Lack of the adrenocortical hormones can be compensated to a certain degree by plentiful administration of sodium. The individual effects described in the following paragraphs are produced not only by corticosteroids but also by ACTH, which acts similarly to cortisol. On the action of aldosterone see page 492.

Effect on carbohydrate metabolism. Administration of corticosteroids raises the blood sugar level and promotes storage of glycogen in the liver, while muscle glycogen remains unaffected. Nitrogen excretion is simultaneously increased, as also the amino acid level in the blood, from which it can be inferred that the newly-formed glycogen arises from the breakdown of protein. The glycosuria observed after administration of glucocorticosteroids is a result of hyperglycemia and increased clearance[31]. In rare cases diabetes may develop[32], or a pre-existing diabetes may be exacerbated[33]. Normally, however, the capacity of the islets is sufficient to neutralize the diabetogenic action of corticosteroids.

Effect on nitrogen metabolism. Corticosteroids have an anti-anabolic effect in that they inhibit protein synthesis and thus lead to *intensified protein metabolism with negative nitrogen balance*. The non-protein nitrogen of the blood, especially the amino acid fraction, is increased[34]. In man the extent of the negative nitrogen balance depends on the dosage[35]. It can be prevented or corrected by administration of testosterone[36] (see page 494) or by increasing calorie[37] or amino acid[38] intake.

During corticosteroid treatment there is a sharp increase in uric acid excretion. This is less the result of increased nitrogen metabolism than of increased kidney clearance. The excretion of amino acids is also increased[34].

Effect on fat metabolism. Corticosteroids have a fat-mobilizing action in the subcutaneous tissues. On a carbohydrate-rich diet liver fat is increased. Transitory ketosis may occur[39, 40].

Effect on mineral and water metabolism. The corticosteroids all cause retention of sodium and an increase in the excretion of potassium and water. This property is very marked with aldosterone and, to a lesser extent, cortexone. The primary action of these two steroids appears to be promotion of sodium reabsorption and of tubular clearance of potassium.

Cortisol has an effect on mineral and water metabolism different from that of aldosterone and cortexone. This substance regulates the distribution of water and salts in the body independently of the renal excretion of sodium. The decrease in water diuresis seen in adrenocortical insufficiency can be reversed by administration of cortisol but not of aldosterone. Cortisol appears to be necessary for maintenance of a tubular function adequate for normal water diuresis but on the other hand does not inhibit the activity of the antidiuretic hormone of the posterior pituitary[41]. Overdosage of cortisol can result in a condition similar to diabetes insipidus.

In the tissues the following electrolyte displacements have been observed[42]: *muscle:* increase of extracellular sodium, chloride and water; decrease of intracellular potassium and phosphate; no change in intracellular sodium; *erythrocytes:* sodium increased, chloride unchanged and potassium decreased.

Histomorphological effect on various organs. The corticosteroids mainly affect the tissues derived from the primitive mesenchyma: lymphatic tissues, bone marrow, connective tissues and synovial membranes.

The corticosteroids cause marked involution of the lymphatic organs which involves both the cells of the parenchyma and of the reticular connective tissue[43]. In the first phase there is characteristic cytolysis of the thymocytes in the thymus and of the lymphocytes in the lymph nodes and to a lesser degree in the spleen[44]. The second phase, following the lymphocytolysis, is characterized on the one hand by inhibition of formation of new cells, as shown by the absence of mitosis in the thymus, lymph nodes and spleen, and on the other hand by degeneration of the reticular connective tissue. The effect on the lymphocytes may consist in a disturbance of cell metabolism[45]. Lymphocytolysis and the inhibition of growth associated with it are responsible respectively for the increase in serum antibodies at the start of hormone treatment and for the eventual decrease of serum antibodies when treatment is prolonged.

Supporting tissues (cartilage, bones). Cartilage already formed is little affected. Proliferation, absorption and invasion of the connective tissue of the bone marrow in the growing epiphyses of the long bones are inhibited[46]. Osteoporosis has been observed in patients with CUSHING's syndrome[47].

Elastic connective tissue (skin). The collagen fibers undergo structural modification[48]. The growth of the epithelial organs of the skin is inhibited, the epidermis becomes thinner and the growth of hair ceases but the sebaceous glands are less affected (rats)[46].

Action on the eosinophils. The eosinopenia produced by corticosteroids can be used as a test of adrenocortical function (THORN's test[49]). Normally 25 units of ACTH cause a fall of circulating eosinophils of at least 50%. The fall is approximately proportional to the blood level of cortisol and cortisone. The THORN test does not by itself suffice to determine adrenocortical function and for this purpose should be combined with a chemical determination of corticosteroids in the blood or urine[29].

The fall in eosinophils after administration of corticosteroids to adrenalectomized mice can be used for their biological determination[50]. The advantage of this method is that untreated urine can be used.

Effect on reactive processes. *ACTH, cortisol and cortisone have an inhibitory or suppressive effect on most inflammatory processes of toxic, allergic, infectious and other origin, combined with a marked analgesic effect.* The mechanism of this action is not known. It is *purely symptomatic*, since the process underlying the inflammation continues unaffected.

Action on the pituitary. The corticosteroids inhibit the secretion of ACTH by the pituitary (see page 475).

Synthetic steroids with corticosteroid-like action

In recent years numerous steroids have been synthesized in an effort to find compounds with biological activity superior to the natural corticosteroids and with fewer undesirable side effects, especially sodium retention[51]. In the following table the effects of various synthetic steroids are compared with those of cortisol and cortisone[52]:

	Anti-inflam-matory activity	Sodium reten-tion	Potas-sium ex-cretion	Effect on carbo-hydrate meta-bolism
Cortisone	1	1	1	1
Cortisol	1–1.25	1–1.25	1	1.25
Prednisone (1-dehydrocortisone)	3–5	none	slight	3–5
Prednisolone (1-dehydrocortisol)	3–5	none	slight	3–5
6α-Methylprednisolone	3–5	none	slight	3–5
9α-Fluorocortisol	10–15	300-900	10–25	10–25
Triamcinolone (9α-fluoro-16α-hydroxyprednisolone)	3–5	none	slight	3–5
Dexamethasone (9α-fluoro-16α-methylprednisolone)	15–28	none	slight	30

Therapeutic applications of "gluco"- corticosteroids[51, 53]

1. In adrenocortical insufficiency due to adrenalectomy, ADDISON's disease, or WATERHOUSE-FRIEDRICHSEN syndrome; in adrenocortical insufficiency in the newborn or in patients whose normal defensive capacity is almost exceeded, e.g. by operation stress, severe trauma, burn shock; in pituitary hypofunction.
2. In the adrenogenital syndrome in adolescence.
3. In metabolic disturbances: spontaneous hypoglycemia in adolescence.
4. Symptomatic, on the basis of their inhibitory effect on inflammation and their analgesic and anti-allergic action: in bronchial asthma, allergic dermatitis, dermatitis medicamentosa, pemphigus vulgaris, systemic lupus erythematosus, acquired hemolytic anemia, the early stage of periarteritis nodosa, allergic and inflammatory diseases of the eyes, sprue, nonpurulent inflammation of the thyroid, bursitis, rheumatic fever (carditis, pericarditis), arthritis.
5. Improvement is often observed in immunization reactions, hypersensitivity to drugs, acute allergic conditions (transfusion reactions, angioneurotic edema, urticaria), the shoulder–hand syndrome, contact dermatitis, dermatomyositis, nephrosis, delirium tremens, hay fever, emphysema of the lungs, the REITER syndrome, WERLHOF's disease, tropical sprue, some cases of leukemia.
6. Corticosteroids have been used to reduce formation of scar tissue, to prevent fibrosis of the lungs after irradiation or berylliosis, in skin grafts, in infections with poor response to antibiotics[54], in viral hepatitis[55] and in tuberculosis[56].

Therapeutic applications of "mineralo"- corticosteroids[57]

In ADDISON's disease and bilateral adrenalectomy as dictated by the extent of the electrolyte imbalance.

Side effects and contraindications

1. CUSHING's syndrome: the syndrome is completely reversible and often appears only after treatment lasting longer than three weeks.
2. Increase of weight.
3. In view of the disturbance of electrolyte balance caused by corticosteroids (sodium retention and increased potassium excretion) the urine must be examined regularly until the balance is restored and the patient placed on a *low-sodium, high-potassium diet*. Corticosteroids should be given cautiously when there is danger of apoplexy or severe cardiac or circulatory failure, although these conditions do not constitute an absolute contraindication. *Edema should not be treated with diuretics since they greatly increase the potassium loss.*
4. Disturbances of carbohydrate metabolism: although diabetes is rare during treatment, sugar levels in blood and urine should be kept under observation. There is no contraindication for diabetics[41]. As a result of overproduction of insulin, hypoglycemia may briefly follow cessation of treatment.
5. Suppression of the function of the gonads may occur, possibly due to inhibition of secretion of gonadotropins in the pituitary. In women there is often cessation of menstruation and in men decrease of libido.
6. In the gastrointestinal tract corticosteroids cause ulceration. Gastric and intestinal ulcers may spontaneously perforate or perforations arise without a history of ulceration. *A careful investigation should therefore be made when even the slightest abdominal pain occurs during treatment with corticosteroids.*
7. Neuropsychic reactions are euphoria and occasionally depression and convulsions.
8. In respect of blood coagulation there is an increased susceptibility to thrombosis.
9. Exogenous corticosteroids may reactivate and propagate latent infections (for example, tuberculosis and malaria) and their inhibitory action on inflammations and their analgesic effects may mask intercurrent diseases.
10. Exogenous corticosteroids cause hypofunction of the anterior pituitary and consequently atrophy of the adrenal cortex, which is therefore only capable of producing small amounts of corticosteroids on termination of treatment. The dosage should therefore be reduced slowly and ACTH given.

In contrast to the results of experiments on animals, corticosteroids do not seem to delay the healing of wounds to a dangerous degree in man.

References: *1)* SIMPSON et al., *Experientia (Basel)*, **9**, 333 (1953). *2)* NEHER and WETTSTEIN, *Helv. chim. Acta*, **39**, 2062 (1956); NEHER et al., *Helv. chim. Acta*, **41**, 1667 (1958). *3)* VON EUW et al., *Helv. chim. Acta*, **41**, 1516 (1958). *4)* RAFTOPOULO et al., *Clin. chim. Acta*, **4**, 463 (1959). *5)* NEHER, R., *Advanc. clin. Chem.*, **1**, 127 (1958). *6)* SILBER and PORTER, in GLICK, D. (Ed.), *Methods of Biochemical Analysis*, vol. IV, New York, 1957, page 139. *7)* DORFMAN, R. I., in EMMENS, C. W. (Ed.), *Hormone Assay*, New York, 1950, page 325. *8)* NORYMBERSKI et al., *Lancet*, **1**, 1276 (1953). *9)* PETERSON, R. E., *Recent Progr. Hormone Res.*, **15**, 231 (1959). *10)* Editorial, *J. Amer. med. Ass.*, **171**, 1439 (1959). *11)* BERLINER et al., *J. biol. Chem.*, **223**, 1043 (1956). *12)* PETERSON R. E., *Ann. N. Y. Acad. Sci.*, **82**, 246 (1959). *13)* ROMANOFF et al., *J. clin. Endocr.*, **17**, 434 (1957). *14)* FUKUSHIMA et al., *J. biol. Chem.*, **212**, 449 (1955). *15)* LOMBARDO and HUDSON, *J. biol. Chem.*, **229**, 181 (1957). *16)* DYRENFURTH et al., *J. clin. Endocr.*, **18**, 391 (1958). *17)* BORTH, R., *Vitam. and Horm.*, **15**, 259 (1957). *18)* DORFMAN, R. I., *Ann. Rev. Biochim.*, **26**, 523 (1957). *19)* AYRES et al., *Ciba Found. Coll. Endocr.*, **11**, 309 (1957). *20)* SANDBERG et al., *Recent Progr. Hormone Res.*, **13**, 209 (1957); SLAUNWHITE and SANDBERG, *J. clin. Invest.*, **38**, 384 (1959); SANDBERG and SLAUNWHITE, *J. clin. Invest.*, **38**, 1290 (1959). *21)* BONGIOVANNI, A. M., *J. clin. Invest.*, **37**, 1342 (1958). *22)* MEYERHEIM and HÜBENER, *Naturwissenschaften*, **39**, 482 (1952). *23)* DE COURCY et al., *J. Endocr.*, **9**, 401 (1953). *24)* AYRES et al., *Biochem. J.*, **65**, 639 (1957). *25)* WILKINS et al., *Ciba Found. Coll. Endocr.*, **8**, 460 (1955). *26)* SULMAN, F. G., *Acta endocr. (Kbh.)*, **22**, 107 (1956). *27)* SCHOEN and SÜDHOF, *Biochemische Befunde in der Differentialdiagnose innerer Krankheiten*, Stuttgart, 1960, page 324. *28)* COPE and BLACK, *Brit. med. J.*, **2**, 1117 (1959). *29)* For a review see NOBLE, R. L., in PINCUS and THIMANN (Eds.), *The Hormones*, vol. III, New York, 1955, page 685. *30)* FRUTON and SIMMONDS, *General Biochemistry*, 2nd ed., New York, 1958, page 947. *31)* FROESCH et al., *J. clin. Invest.*, **37**, 524 (1958). *32)* CONN et al., *J. Lab. clin. Med.*, **33**, 651 (1948). *33)* BROWN et al., *J. clin. Endocr.*, **10**, 1363 (1950). *34)* BORDEN et al., *Fed. Proc.*, **10**, 376 (1951). *35)* SPRAGUE, R. G., *Amer. J. Med.*, **10**, 567 (1951). *36)* SPRAGUE et al., *Arch. intern. Med.*, **85**, 199 (1950). *37)* PEARSON et al., *Cancer (Philad.)*, **2**, 943 (1949). *38)* ENGEL, F. L., *Recent Progr. Hormone Res.*, **6**, 277 (1951). *39)* THORN et al., *Trans. Ass. Amer. Phys.*, **62**, 233 (1949). *40)* KINSELL et al., *Clinical ACTH*, vol. I, New York, 1951, page 308. *41)* RAISZ et al., *J. clin. Invest.*, **36**, 767 (1957). *42)* ELIEL et al., *Clinical ACTH*, vol. I, New York, 1951, page 196. *43)* BAKER et al., *Amer. J. Anat.*, **88**, 313 (1951). *44)* DOUGHERTY and WHITE, *Amer. J. Anat.*, **77**, 81 (1945). *45)* BLECHER and WHITE, *Recent Progr. Hormone Res.*, **15**, 391 (1959). *46)* BAKER, B. L., *Recent Progr. Hormone Res.*, **7**, 331 (1952). *47)* SISSONS, H. A.

J. Bone Jt Surg., **38B**, 418 (1956). *48)* Baker et al., *Anat. Rec.*, **102**, 313 (1948). *49)* Thorn and Forsham, *Recent Progr. Hormone Res.*, **4**, 229 (1949). *50)* Speirs et al., *Clinical ACTH*, vol. I, New York, 1951, page 32. *51)* Report, *Brit. med. J.*, **1**, 109 (1959). *52)* Liddle, G.W., *Ann. N. Y. Acad. Sci.*, **82**, 854 (1959); Tolksdorf, S., *Ann. N. Y. Acad. Sci.*, **82**, 829 (1959); Frawley et al., *Ann. N. Y. Acad. Sci.*, **82**, 868 (1959); Fried and Borman, *Vitam. and Horm.*, **16**, 303 (1958); Soffer and Orr, *Metabolism*, **7**, 383 (1958). *53)* Beckman, H., *Drugs, their Nature, Action and Use*, Philadelphia, 1958; Spence, A. W., *Practitioner*, **180**, 22 (1958); Hart, F. D., *Practitioner*, **180**, 31 (1958). *54)* Kass and Finland, *Advanc. intern. Med.*, **9**, 45 (1958); Rentchnick, P., *Antibiot. et Chemother. (Basel)*, **7**, 59 (1960); Robinson, H. J., *Antibiot. et Chemother. (Basel)*, **7**, 199 (1960). *55)* Zollikofer, H., *Antibiot. et Chemother. (Basel)*, **7**, 241 (1960). *56)* Mlczoch, F., *Antibiot. et Chemother. (Basel)*, **7**, 302 (1960). *57)* Richardson, J. S., *Practitioner*, **180**, 58 (1958).

Aldosterone (electrocortin)[1]

As early as 1934 Wintersteiner et al.[2] had observed that an amorphous fraction of adrenal extract showed high activity in maintaining vital processes following adrenalectomy. The isolation from this fraction of a steroid hormone in a pure crystalline form, and the determination of its structure, were carried out in 1953 by Simpson et al.[3]. It was given the name aldosterone on account of its aldehyde group. Its complete synthesis was finally accomplished by Wettstein's group in 1955[4].

Aldosterone (monohydrate), $C_{21}H_{28}O_5 \cdot H_2O$
Mol. wt. 378.47
M. p. 120° C and 157–163° C

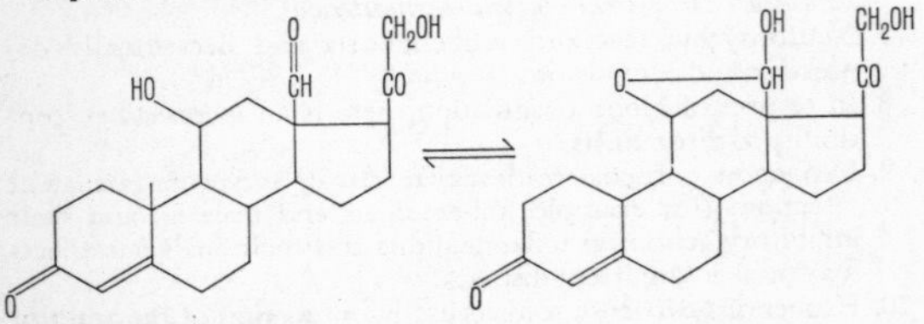

Site of formation

Adrenal cortex.

Sources

Extracts of the adrenal bodies[3,5,6], blood from the adrenal veins[7], urine of normal individuals[8] and of those recently operated on[9], and urine of patients with nephroses[10]. Aldosterone is formed when cortexone is incubated with adrenocortical enzymes[11].

Unit

No international unit; by weight.

Methods of test and assay

Biologically by determination of the $Na^+ : K^+$ ratio[5] or the $^{24}Na^+ : {}^{42}K^+$ ratio[12]; by estimation of sodium retention and potassium excretion[13] in adrenalectomized rats. Survival test in adrenalectomized dogs[14]. Physicochemically (accuracy ± 20%)[15].

Physiology and function

Compared with other "mineralocorticosteroids", aldosterone exerts a very considerable influence on the electrolyte balance of the body, while its glucocorticosteroid activity as measured by various tests varies from one-quarter of that of cortisone to equality with cortisone[12,16]. The following table summarizes its activity compared to cortexone:

Test	Activity of cortexone = 1	Reference
$Na^+ : K^+$ ratio in urine of adrenalectomized rats	~ 100	*5*
$^{24}Na^+ : {}^{42}K^+$ ratio in urine of adrenalectomized rats	120 ± 10	*12*
Sodium retention in adrenalectomized rats	25	*13*
Potassium excretion in adrenalectomized rats	5	*13*
Survival test in adrenalectomized dogs	25–30	*14*
Na-K equilibrium in Addison's disease	~ 30	*17*

The normal concentration in plasma has been determined by means of [16-³H]-aldosterone and is approximately 0.03 µg/100 ml. Under normal conditions the daily production is 170 to 190 µg, but it is increased to 780 µg on a sodium-free diet (urinary sodium excretion 7 mEq Na per day). The half-life of aldosterone in blood is 18 minutes. About 50% of injected aldosterone could be identified in the urine by the isotope method[18].

Aldosterone occurs in urine in the free state and also as the β-glucuronide. Its excretion in urine is inversely proportional to sodium excretion and directly proportional to potassium excretion[19].

Differing values for the normal urinary excretion, ranging from 0.5 to 12.5 µg/24 hours, have been reported[19,20]. The mean daily excretion from 43 patients recently operated on was 8 µg[9]. The excretion is greatly influenced by administration of sodium and potassium, and also by renal and extrarenal elimination of water[21].

Production of aldosterone is probably controlled by the sodium and potassium concentration of the extracellular fluid. Experiments on dogs following hypophysectomy showed a reduction in aldosterone formation to 66% of the normal value; following partial or complete decapitation, however, it was reduced to 25% of normal, showing that ACTH has a relatively minor influence on aldosterone formation but that the control by sodium and potassium already mentioned must itself be under the influence of some center situated in the brain[22].

Clinical significance

A transient state of hyperaldosteronism follows an operation, and this may be correlated with the postoperative retention of sodium and loss of potassium which is already well known[9,23].

During pregnancy the excretion of aldosterone rises to a maximum of 34 µg daily shortly before delivery and falls to normal afterwards[24]. Production of aldosterone is also increased in conditions of stress[25] and in idiopathic edema[26].

In 1955 Conn[27] described the syndrome of primary aldosteronism which is known by his name. The features are increased excretion of aldosterone, reduced potassium level and increased sodium level in blood, alkalosis, polydipsia, polyuria, hypertension, muscular weakness, intermittent tetany. The cause of the disease is hyperplasia, adenoma or carcinoma of the adrenal bodies, and it disappears following operative removal of the tumor[28].

The clinical characteristics of primary hypoaldosteronism, with raised blood potassium and Stokes-Adams attacks, have also been described[29].

The disturbances in electrolyte and water balance which occur in Addison's disease can be remedied by daily administration of 150–180 µg aldosterone[17,30].

References: *1)* For reviews see Muller and O'Connor (Eds.), *An International Symposium on Aldosterone*, London, 1957; Gaunt et al., *J. clin. Endocr.*, **15**, 621 (1955); Simpson and Tait, *Recent Progr. Hormone Res.*, **11**, 183 (1955); Wettstein, A., in Inhoffen, H. H. (Ed.), *Über Sterine, Gallensäuren und verwandte Naturstoffe*, vol. II, 2nd ed., Stuttgart, 1959, page 588. *2)* Wintersteiner et al., *J. biol. Chem.*, **105**, C (1934); Pfiffner et al., *J. biol. Chem.*, **111**, 585 (1935). *3)* Simpson et al., *Experientia (Basel)*, **9**, 333 (1953), and **10**, 132 (1954); *Helv. chim. Acta*, **37**, 1163, 1200 (1954). *4)* Schmidlin et al., *Experientia (Basel)*, **11**, 365 (1955); Vischer et al., *Experientia (Basel)*, **12**, 50 (1956). *5)* Mattox et al., *Proc. Mayo Clin.*, **28**, 569 (1953); *J. Amer. chem. Soc.*, **75**, 4869 (1953). *6)* Wettstein et al., *Ciba Found. Coll. Endocr.*, **8**, 170 (1953); Wettstein, A., *Experientia (Basel)*, **10**, 397 (1954). *7)* Simpson et al., *Lancet*, **263**, 226 (1952); Farrell and Richards, *Proc. Soc. exp. Biol. (N.Y.)*, **83**, 628 (1953). *8)* Luetscher and Johnson, *J. clin. Invest.*, **32**, 585 (1953), and **33**, 276 (1954). *9)* Llaurado et al., *Clin. chim. Acta*, **1**, 236 (1956). *10)* Luetscher et al., *Experientia (Basel)*, **10**, 456 (1954). *11)* Kahnt et al., *Experientia (Basel)*, **11**, 446 (1955); Ayres et al., *Ciba Found. Coll. Endocr.*, **11**, 309 (1957). *12)* Speirs et al., *Endocrinology*, **55**, 233 (1954). *13)* Kagawa et al., *Proc. Soc. exp. Biol. (N.Y.)*, **80**, 281 (1952); Desaulles et al., *Schweiz. med. Wschr.*, **83**, 1088 (1953). *14)* Gross and Gysel, *Acta endocr. (Kbh.)*, **15**, 199 (1954); Swingle et al., *Proc. Soc. exp. Biol. (N.Y.)*, **86**, 147 (1954). *15)* Simpson et al., *Helv. chim. Acta*, **37**, 1163 (1954); Neher and Wettstein, *Acta endocr. (Kbh.)*, **18**, 386 (1955); *J. clin. Invest.*, **35**, 800 (1956). *16)* Gaunt et al., *Endocrinology*, **55**, 236 (1954); Schuler et al., *Experientia (Basel)*, **10**, 142 (1954); Gross and Gysel, *Acta endocr. (Kbh.)*, **15**, 199 (1954). *17)* Mach et al., *Schweiz. med. Wschr.*, **84**, 407 (1954); Mach and Fabre, *Ciba Found. Coll. Endocr.*, **8**, 361 (1955). *18)* Ayres et al., *Ciba Found. Coll. Endocr.*, **11**, 309 (1957). *19)* Axelrad et al., *Brit. med. J.*, **1**, 196 (1955); Luetscher, J. A., *Recent Progr. Hormone Res.*, **12**, 175 (1956). *20)* Venning et al., *J. clin. Endocr.*, **16**, 1326 (1956); Wolff et al., *Klin. Wschr.*, **34**, 366 (1956); Wettstein, A., in Inhoffen, H.H. (Ed.), *Über Sterine, Gallensäuren und verwandte Naturstoffe*, vol. II, 2nd ed., Stuttgart, 1959, page 588. *21)* Falbriard et al., *Schweiz. med. Wschr.*, **85**, 1218 (1955); Luetscher and Curtis, *Ann. intern. Med.*, **43**, 658 (1955); Mach et al., *Schweiz. med. Wschr.*, **85**, 1229 (1955). *22)* Farrell, G., *Recent Progr. Hormone Res.*, **12**, 192 (1956). *23)* Llaurado and Woodruff, *Surgery*, **42**, 313 (1957). *24)* Venning et al., *J. clin. Endocr.*, **17**, 473

(1957). *25)* VENNING et al., *J. clin. Endocr.*, **17**, 1005 (1957). *26)* LUETSCHER and LIEBERMANN, *Trans. Ass. Amer. Phycns*, **70**, 158 (1957). *27)* CONN, J. W., *J. Lab. clin. Med.*, **45**, 3 (1955). *28)* CONN, J. W., *J. Lab. clin. Med.*, **45**, 661 (1955); MADER and ISERI, *Amer. J. Med.*, **19**, 976 (1955); CRANE et al., *J. Lab. clin. Med.*, **48**, 1 (1956); MILNE and MUEHRCKE, *Proc. roy. Soc. Med.*, **49**, 883 (1956); VAN BUCHEM et al., *Acta endocr. (Kbh.)*, **23**, 313 (1956); HEWLETT et al., *J. Amer. med. Ass.*, **164**, 719 (1957); HUDSON et al., *Aust. Ann. Med.*, **6**, 250 (1957); SKANSE et al., *Acta med. scand.*, **158**, 181 (1957). *29)* HUDSON et al., *New Engl. J. Med.*, **257**, 529 (1957); SKANSE and HOKFELT, *Acta endocr. (Kbh.)*, **28**, 29 (1958). *30)* KEKWICK and PAWAN, *Lancet*, **2**, 162 (1954); SALASSA et al., *Proc. Mayo Clin.*, **32**, 201 (1957).

Estrogens

Chemistry

The naturally occurring estrogens are all derived from estrane (see page 486) and are unsaturated compounds readily soluble in the common organic solvents and vegetable oils but insoluble in water. As a result of their phenolic character they are easily soluble in aqueous alkalis, a property which is used for their separation from the androgens present in the same urinary fraction.

Estradiol, $C_{18}H_{24}O_2$
Mol.wt. 272.39
M.p. 176–178° C

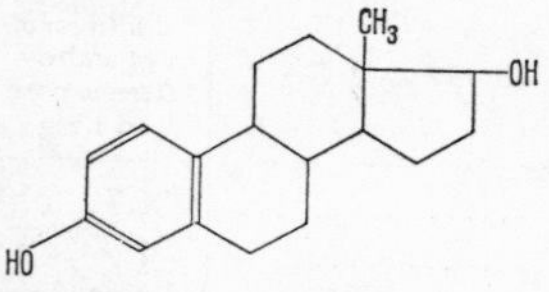

Estriol, $C_{18}H_{24}O_3$
Mol.wt. 288.39
M.p. 280° C

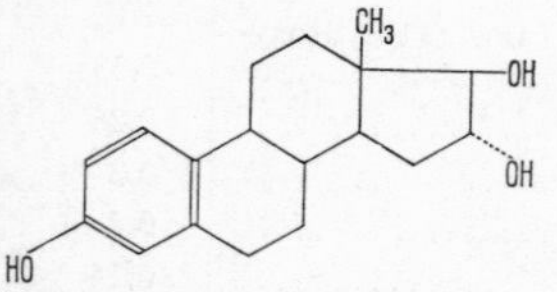

Estrone, $C_{18}H_{22}O_2$
Mol.wt. 270.37
M.p. 259° C

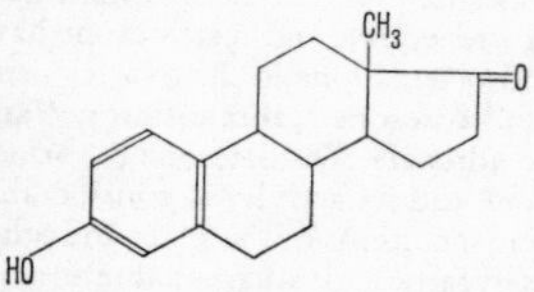

Synthetic compounds with estrogenic activity are ethinyl-estradiol and the nonsteroid compounds benzestrol, chlorotrianisene, dienestrol, diethylstilbestrol (stilbestrol) hexestrol, etc. Estradiol esters have a more protracted action than the free compound since they are more slowly absorbed.

Unit

No international units; by weight.

Methods of assay

Biological: On castrated female mice or rats by the ALLEN-DOISY method[1].

Chemical: As total estrogens[2] colorimetrically (KOBER reaction) or fluorometrically; separately by chromatographic separation[3] (comparison with U.S.P. Reference Standards in the case of estradiol and estrone). See also [7].

Physiology[11]

Estradiol occurs in two forms, the active 17β-form and the inactive 17α-form. Estradiol and to a lesser extent estrone act on the corpora lutea, while estriol stimulates the cervix, vagina and vulva to a much greater extent than the other two estrogens. The relative activities of estriol, estrone and estradiol measured by the biological method (subcutaneous administration) are 1:103:1000.

The biosynthesis and metabolism of the estrogens are described on pages 435 and 436. They are formed in the ovaries, placenta, testes and adrenals, the primary products being estradiol and estrone while estriol is probably a metabolite of these two compounds. During pregnancy the secretion of estrogens is increased. The following amounts have been isolated from the placenta at full term: estradiol 51 µg/kg, estrone 170 µg/kg, estriol 314 µg/kg; from semen: estradiol 1 µg/100 ml, estrone 6 µg/100 ml, estriol 3 µg/100 ml. Estriol is also present in bile, meconium and probably the corpus luteum. This hormone appears to be confined to man and chimpanzees.

Estrogen secretion is regulated by the gonadotropins (see page 473). In plasma the estrogen found in the greatest amount is estriol, probably conjugated as the glucuronide; for the most part it is linked to the plasma proteins. The estrone and estradiol of plasma are mainly in the free form[4]. Of all the steroids the estrogens are those most strongly bound to the plasma proteins[5].

Normally the estrogens can barely be detected in plasma. The estrone and estriol levels in men and women are below 0.2 µg/100 ml, while estradiol cannot be detected[6]. On estrogens in blood see also BORTH[7].

During pregnancy the high level of placental secretion of estrogens causes an increase in the level in plasma and, to an even greater extent, in urine.

Blood estrogens and urinary estriol excretion during pregnancy[8]

Week of pregnancy	Estrogens in blood (µg/100 ml)	Estriol in urine (mg/24 hours) Range	Mean
12	0.8		<1
16	1.6		2
20	3.3	4–9	6
24	5.4	6–13	8
28	7.1	8–22	13
32	9.7	12–43	19
36	(12.7)	14–45	24
40	(9.0)	19–46	32

Estrogen levels in plasma during late pregnancy are as follows[6]: estradiol 1.3–2.9 µg/100 ml, estrone 2.7–10.3 µg/100 ml, estriol 4.3–17.5 µg/100 ml. During the second and third trimesters the estrone and estriol levels are fairly constant but the estradiol level shows large fluctuations[9].

The estrogens disappear very rapidly from the blood (more quickly than the corticosteroids), the half-life being between 2 and 4 minutes[10]. They are metabolized mainly in the liver. In urine they are excreted almost entirely as sulfates or glucuronides. Shortly before parturition, however, estriol appears in the free form in the urine.

The urinary excretion of estrogens shows characteristic fluctuations during the course of the menstrual cycle[11]. It is lowest during the first week, begins to rise on the 7th day and reaches a maximum on about the 13th day (ovulation peak). It then falls suddenly and begins to rise again to a second peak on about the 21st day (luteal maximum), after which it falls again just prior to menstruation. The ratio of estradiol to estrone remains fairly constant at 1:2 during the cycle.

Excretion of individual estrogens in urine (in µg/24 hours)[11]

	Total estrogens	Estrone	Estradiol	Estriol
Men, 25–35 years......	9– 25	0–11	0– 7	1–12
Women, postmenopausal	3– 11	1– 3	0– 4	1– 9
Women, onset of menstruation	4– 25	4– 7	0– 3	0–15
Women, ovulation peak .	30– 79	11–31	4–14	15–34
Women, luteal maximum	22–105	10–23	4–10	8–72
Women, uterine carcinoma	up to 1400	up to 896	0	up to 504
Men, benign adrenal tumor	158	86	15	57
Men, castrated	10	5	1	4
Women, 1 week antepartum	30800	1400	520	29000

During pregnancy[11] there is a rapid increase in the urinary excretion of all estrogens, the amounts of estrone and estradiol just prior to parturition being 100 times the luteal maximum with a fairly constant ratio between the two hormones of 3:1. The excretion of estriol rises about 1000-fold and this is by far the most abundant estrogen during pregnancy. The urinary excretion of estrogens begins to rise rapidly about seven weeks after the last menstruation. During lactation it remains low.

In the newborn only estriol is excreted and the level falls sharply after the first week[12]. In children the estrogen excretion remains less than in adults up to puberty[13].

Function. See under Functions of the sex hormones, pages 496 and 497.

References: *1)* Emmens, C. W., *Hormone Assay*, New York, 1950, page 391. *2)* Bates, R. W., *Recent Progr. Hormone Res.*, **9**, 95 (1954); Haslewood, G. A. D., in Emmens, C.W. (Ed.), *Hormone Assay*, New York, 1950, page 443; Jayle et al., *Clin. chim. Acta*, **4**, 276 (1959). *3)* Axelrod, L. R., *Recent Progr. Hormone Res.*, **9**, 69 (1954); Bauld and Greenway, in Glick, D. (Ed.), *Methods of Biochemical Analysis*, vol.V, New York, 1957, page 337. *4)* Loraine, J. A., *Ciba Found. Coll. Endocr.*, **11**, 335 (1957). *5)* Sandberg et al., *Recent Progr. Hormone Res.*, **13**, 209 (1957). *6)* Aitken and Preedy, *Ciba Found. Coll. Endocr.*, **11**, 331 (1957). *7)* Borth, R., *Vitam. and Horm.*, **15**, 259 (1957). *8)* Kellar et al., *J. Obstet. Gynaec. Brit. Emp.*, **66**, 804 (1959). *9)* Slaunwhite and Sandberg, *Proc. Soc. exp. Biol. (N.Y.)*, **101**, 544 (1959). *10)* Pearlman, W. H., *Ciba Found. Coll. Endocr.*, **11**, 233 (1957). *11)* Merrill, R. C., *Physiol. Rev.*, **38**, 463 (1958). *12)* Diczfalusy et al., *Ciba Found. Coll. Endocr.*, **11**, 249 (1957). *13)* Nathanson et al., *Endocrinology*, **28**, 851 (1941).

Androgens[1]

The androgens are those steroid hormones which exhibit a typically viriligenic activity in the capon comb growth test. Structurally, they are derivatives of androstane (see page 486).

Testosterone, $C_{19}H_{28}O_2$

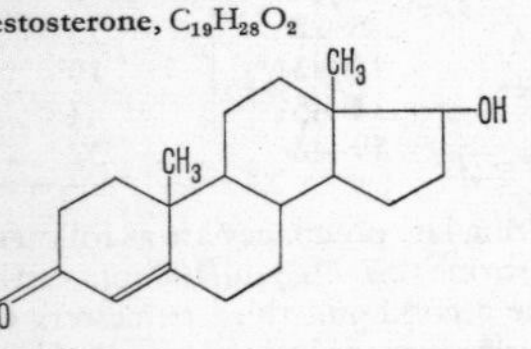

Mol.wt. 288.43
M.p. 155° C

Androstan-3α-ol-17-one (androsterone), $C_{19}H_{30}O_2$

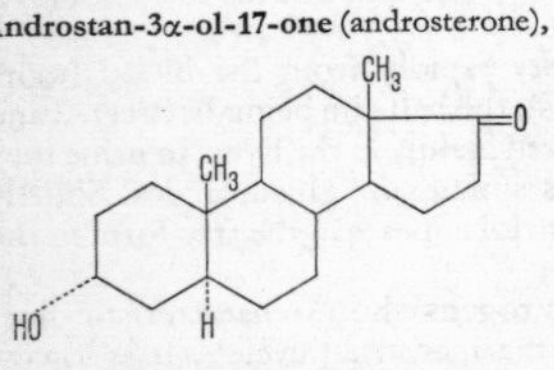

Mol.wt. 290.45
M.p. 184–185° C

Δ⁴-Androstene-3,17-dione, $C_{19}H_{26}O_2$

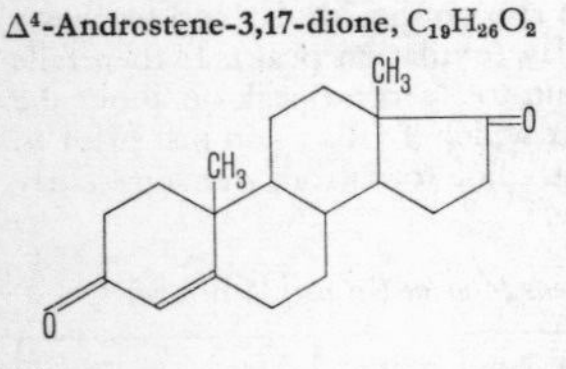

Mol.wt. 286.42
M.p. 174° C

Androstane-3,17-dione, $C_{19}H_{28}O_2$

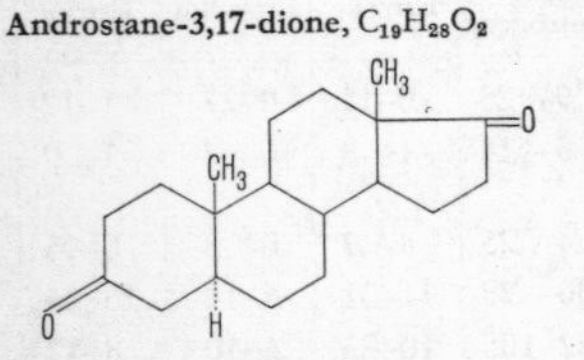

Mol.wt. 288.43
M.p. 132–134° C

Dehydroepiandrosterone, $C_{19}H_{28}O_2$

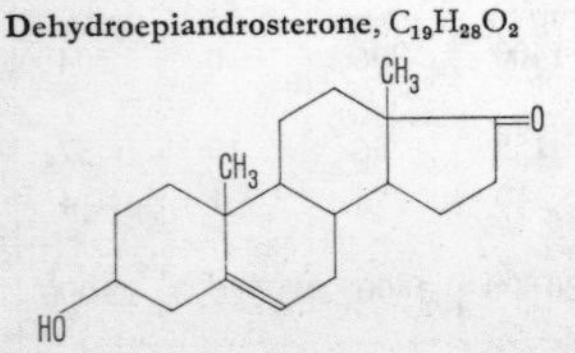

Mol.wt. 288.43
M.p. (two forms) 128° C and 141° C

Synthetic compounds with androgenic activity are 17-methyltestosterone and 9α-fluoro-11β-hydroxy-17-methyltestosterone. Androgen esters (for example with propionic acid) have considerably greater activity than the free androgens.

Units

No international unit; by weight. The *biological unit* of androgenic activity is the capon unit and is the minimum amount which when given on two successive days causes a 20% enlargement of the capon comb; it corresponds roughly to the activity of 0.1 mg androsterone.

Methods of test and assay

Biological: On the capon comb (see above), cockscomb, etc.[1,2].

Chemical: In the 17-ketosteroid fraction by Zimmermann's method (nonspecific; see page 495); individually by chromatographic separation[3] (comparison with U.S.P. Reference Standard in the case of testosterone).

Physiology

The following are the principal steroids with androgenic activity (in order of decreasing activity)[4]:

	Milligrams of androsterone corr. to 1 mg
Testosterone	6.7
Androsterone	1
Δ⁴-Androstene-3,17-dione	0.83
Androstane-3,17-dione	0.83–0.77
Dehydroepiandrosterone	0.5
Androstane-3α, 11β-diol-17-one (11-hydroxyandrosterone)	0.33
Androstane-3α,17α-diol	0.28
Adrenosterone	0.2
17-Hydroxyprogesterone	0.2
Epiandrosterone	0.14

The biosynthesis and metabolism of the androgens are described on pages 433 and 434. The hormones are found in the testes, adrenals and ovaries. Thus in man, androstenedione and testosterone have been identified in the testes[5], androstenedione in the ovaries[6], and androstenedione[12], 11-hydroxyandrosterone[12], adrenosterone[13] and dehydroepiandrosterone[7] in the adrenals. Testosterone is formed in the Leydig cells of the testes[8] and its activity is considerably increased by the admixture of acid secretions of the testes and other organs (X-substances) as well as by fatty acids such as palmitic acid, which occurs free in large amounts in bovine testes. Androsterone is a metabolite of 17-hydroxyprogesterone in the adrenals and of testosterone, the intermediate products being androstenedione and androstanedione.

The secretion of the androgenic hormones is regulated by the gonadotropins of the anterior pituitary (see page 473). In men, the normal daily production of testosterone is about 17 mg[9], the normal plasma level of dehydroepiandrosterone (representing 50–70% of the total 17-ketosteroids) 40–110 µg/100 ml, of androsterone 20–30 µg/100 ml[10]. In women the levels are somewhat lower. The plasma androgen level in the newborn is as high as or higher than in adults but falls sharply after the first week. Before puberty, 17-ketosteroids cannot be detected in the plasma. In old age the plasma androgen level falls, and in the 70-year-old man dehydroepiandrosterone and androsterone have practically disappeared from the plasma[11]. No precise data on the half-lives of the androgens are available, but that of testosterone is probably about 4 minutes[9].

In urine the androgens are mainly in the 17-ketosteroid fraction. Testosterone is excreted only in traces. The most important metabolites of testosterone are androsterone and α-etianolone. Excretion of dehydroepiandrosterone is increased following the growth of adrenal tumors. In men the excretion of androgens decreases gradually with age while that of estrogens and corticosteroids remains constant. In women the excretion of androgens also decreases gradually with age while that of estrogens falls abruptly at the menopause. On the excretion of androgens see also under 17-Ketosteroids, below.

Function. See under Functions of the sex hormones, pages 496 and 497.

References: *1)* Dorfman and Shipley, *Androgens*, New York, 1956. *2)* Dorfman, R. I., in Emmens, C.W. (Ed.), *Hormone Assay*, New York, 1950, page 291. *3)* Lakshmanan and Lieberman, *Arch. Biochem.*, **53**, 258 (1954); Robinson, A. M., *Recent Progr. Hormone Res.*, **9**, 163 (1954); Rubin et al., *Recent Progr. Hormone Res.*, **9**, 213 (1954); Savard, K., *Recent Progr. Hormone Res.*, **9**, 185 (1954). *4)* Staudinger, H., in Rauen, H. M. (Ed.), *Biochemisches Taschenbuch*, Berlin, 1956, page 957; Fieser and Fieser, *Steroids*, New York, 1959, page 519. *5)* Anliker et al., *Helv. chim. Acta*, **40**, 1517 (1957). *6)* Zander, J., *J. biol. Chem.*, **232**, 117 (1958). *7)* Bloch et al., *J. biol. Chem.*, **224**, 737 (1957). *8)* Leach et al., *Recent Progr. Hormone Res.*, **12**, 377 (1956). *9)* Pearlman, W. H., *Ciba Found. Coll. Endocr.*, **11**, 233 (1957). *10)* Borth, R., *Vitam. and Horm.*, **15**, 259 (1957). *11)* Migeon et al., *J. clin. Endocr.*, **17**, 1051 (1957). *12)* Von Euw and Reichstein, *Helv. chim. Acta*, **24**, 879 (1941). *13)* Reichstein, T., *Helv. chim. Acta*, **19**, 223 (1936).

17-Ketosteroids

The 17-ketosteroids, so named on account of the keto group at C-17 (see page 487), fall into two subgroups which are of some significance clinically, the 3α-hydroxy- and 3β-hydroxy-17-ketosteroids, usually termed α- and β-17-ketosteroids.

Methods of assay

Total ketosteroids: colorimetrically by the methods of Zimmermann[1] and others[2]; α- and β-ketosteroids separately by various methods[3]; individual ketosteroids by chromatographic separation (for references see under Androgens, above).

For ketosteroid levels in plasma see under Androgens, opposite.

Urinary excretion

Total 17-ketosteroids. The heavy line in the adjacent diagrams is the mean 24-hour urinary excretion, the shaded area the range in which 97–98% of cases fall.

During the first two weeks of life the daily excretion of ketosteroids is 1.2–2.5 mg and falls to 0.5 mg by the third or fourth week; the excretion begins to rise at about 8 years[5, 6].

α-17-Ketosteroids

The total daily urinary excretion (in milligrams) *in young adults* (19–35 years) is as follows[7]:

Men	Women
Range* *8.2–15.8*; mean **12.0**	Range* *6.8–14.0*; mean **10.4**
Standard deviation $s = 1.9$	Standard deviation $s = 1.8$

The most important α-ketosteroids in urine are given in the following table[7]:

	Excretion in mg/24 hours					
	Men			Women		
	Mean	Range*	*s*	Mean	Range*	*s*
α-Etianolone	**3.89**	*2.71–5.07*	0.59	**3.05**	*1.93–4.17*	0.56
Androsterone	**3.36**	*2.22–4.50*	0.57	**3.80**	*2.62–4.98*	0.59
11-Hydroxy-androsterone.....	**0.73**	*0.47–0.99*	0.13	**0.78**	*0.52–1.04*	0.13
11-Ketoetianolone ..	**0.51**	*0.37–0.65*	0.07	**0.49**	*0.25–0.73*	0.12
11-Hydroxy-etianolone	**0.35**	*0.13–0.57*	0.11	**0.29**	*0.15–0.43*	0.07
11-Ketoandrosterone	**0.35**	*0.23–0.47*	0.06	**0.21**	*0.15–0.27*	0.03

β-17-Ketosteroids

The total daily urinary excretion (in milligrams) is as follows[8]:

Men	Women
Range 0.4–10.0; mean 4.4	Range 0.0–6.4; mean 1.7

In healthy men the proportion of β-17-ketosteroids in the total 17-ketosteroids averages 31%, in healthy women 22%[8]. The predominant constituents of this fraction are dehydroepiandrosterone (in men 2.7 mg mean) and epiandrosterone (in men 1.7 mg mean)[8]. Dehydroepiandrosterone appears to be the most important 17-ketosteroid in the fetal meconium[9].

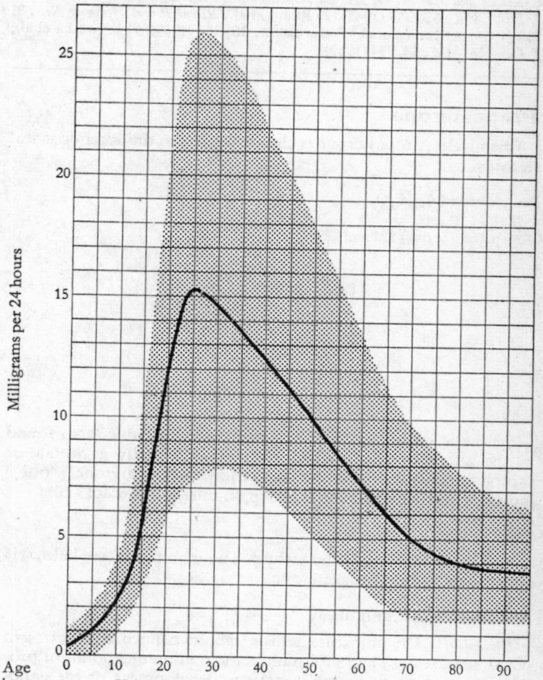

Urinary excretion of 17-ketosteroids in men[4]

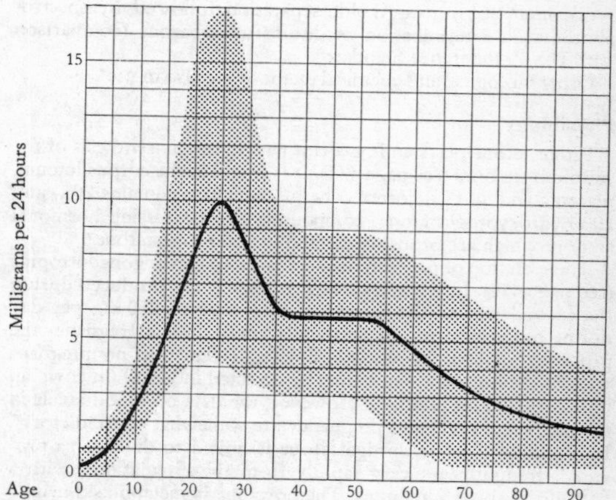

Urinary excretion of 17-ketosteroids in women[4]

Clinical significance

In men at least 50% and in women the greater part of the urinary 17-ketosteroids are metabolites of the adrenocortical steroids. In men some of the degradation products of testosterone also appear in the 17-ketosteroid fraction. The total excretion of 17-ketosteroids is therefore a direct measure of adrenocortical activity (see also under Adrenocortical hormones, page 489).

The β-fraction is increased up to 50% in malignant tumors of the adrenal cortex and is therefore an important indication in differential diagnosis. In hyperplasia of the adrenal cortex, in which the total fraction is always greatly increased, the proportion of β-17-ketosteroids remains normal. There are characteristic changes in the urinary excretion of individual ketosteroids in the Cushing syndrome[8].

* On the normal range see footnote, page 517.

References: *1)* ZIMMERMANN, W., *Hoppe-Seylers Z. physiol. Chem.*, **233**, 257 (1935), and **300**, 141 (1955). *2)* MUNSON and KENNY, *Recent Progr. Hormone Res.*, **9**, 135 (1954). *3)* HASLAM and KLYNE, *Lancet*, **1**, 285 (1952); BUTT et al., *Biochem. J.*, **42**, 447 (1948). *4)* HAMBURGER, C., *Acta endocr. (Kbh.)*, **1**, 19 (1948). *5)* WILKINS, L., *Diagnosis and Treatment of Endocrine Disorders in Childhood and Adolescence*, 2nd ed., Springfield, 1957. *6)* TALBOT et al., *Amer. J. Dis. Child.*, **65**, 364 (1943). *7)* RUBIN et al., *Recent Progr. Hormone Res.*, **9**, 213 (1954). *8)* JAILER et al., *J. clin. Invest.*, **38**, 357 (1959). *9)* KINSELLA et al., *J. Lab. clin. Med.*, **54**, 834 (1959).

Progesterone

Chemically, progesterone is closely related to the adrenocortical steroids.

Progesterone, $C_{21}H_{30}O_2$
Mol.wt. 314.47
M.p. (two forms) 121 and 129° C

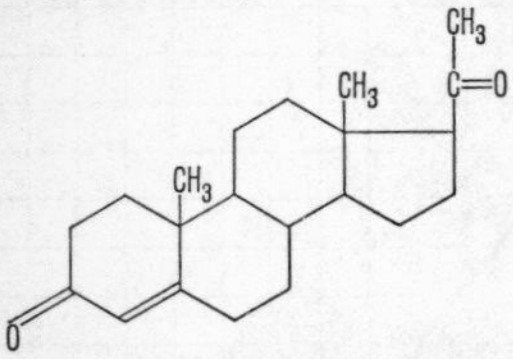

Synthetic analogues are 17α-hydroxyprogesterone (also found in the adrenal cortex), which can be taken orally as acetate or caproate, ethinyltestosterone and ethinylnortestosterone ("nor-" indicates absence of a methyl group, in this case that at C-10).

Unit

No international unit; by weight. The rabbit unit (see below) is equal to ca. 0.6 mg progesterone.

Methods of test and assay

Biological[1]: On immature female rabbits primed with estrogen (CLAUBERG test). The rabbit unit is the minimum amount of progesterone which causes characteristic development of the endometrium.

Chemical[2]: Chromatographic separation followed by spectrophotometric determination as dithiosemicarbazone (comparison with U.S.P. Reference Standard).

Other biological and chemical methods are also in use[7].

Physiology

Progesterone plays an important part in the biosynthesis of the steroid hormones (see page 434). It is found in the corpus luteum, placenta and adrenal cortex. The placenta also contains 20α- and 20β-hydroxyprogesterone, compounds also possessing hormonal activity which are probably metabolites of progesterone[3].

The secretion of progesterone is regulated by the gonadotropins (see page 473). In women ca. 20 mg per day are produced during the second half of the menstrual cycle and ca. 250 mg per day during pregnancy (mainly by the placenta)[4]. In late pregnancy the progesterone level in blood is 2–15 μg/100 ml[4]. In nonpregnant women the hormone can barely be detected in blood (in cows up to 0.2 μg/100 ml plasma[5]). However, the data on blood levels in the menstrual cycle and pregnancy are somewhat contradictory[7]. In blood, 99% of the progesterone is linked to the plasma proteins[6]. It disappears very rapidly from the circulation[4], with a half-life of about 2 minutes. The hormone is metabolized mainly in the liver, which explains the high progesterone blood levels observed in patients with liver disease.

Urinary excretion

In urine, progesterone appears mainly in the form of the glucuronates of its breakdown products pregnane-3α, 20α-diol and allopregnane-3α, 20α-diol, a mixture which is determined by the usual methods of assay as "pregnanediol". The data given below under this description refer in all cases to the mixture of these two substances.

The pregnanediol of urine is derived not only from progesterone but also from cortexone, but since the latter substance is produced in the body only in very small quantities its contribution to the pregnanediol excretion may normally be neglected. During therapy with exogenous cortexone, however, the pregnanediol excretion may be considerably increased, a factor which must be taken into account when using pregnanediol excretion as a pregnancy test.

Normal urinary excretion of pregnanediol[8]

	Pregnanediol in urine (mg/24 hours)	
	Range	Mean
Males	0.38–1.42	0.92
Females		
proliferative phase	0.78–1.50	1.12
luteal phase	2.1 –4.2	3.3
postmenopausal	0.28–0.86	0.63

Urinary excretion of pregnanediol during pregnancy[9]

Week of pregnancy	Number of estimations	Pregnanediol in urine (mg/24 hours) Mean	s
8	6	8.2	1.4
12	12	10.7	2.7
16	11	13.0	4.3
20	12	15.7	4.7
24	11	22.4	5.2
26	11	29.0	8.2
28	14	34.8	8.5
30	12	41.3	9.4
32	12	44.0	10.6
36	12	45.1	15.8
40	11	43.0	10.3

Several workers have reported a fall in the excretion of pregnanediol 1–2 weeks before parturition but this does not appear to be a regular phenomenon.

Various methods are available for determination of pregnanediol in urine[8, 12, 13], as also in plasma[11].

The excretion of pregnanetriol, which is generally considered to be a metabolite of the adrenocortical hormones, also varies with the stage of the menstrual cycle[10] and during pregnancy[14], so that it may be derived in part from precursors in the ovaries and placenta.

Function. See under Functions of the sex hormones, below.

References: *1)* EMMENS, C.W., in EMMENS, C.W. (Ed.), *Hormone Assay*, New York, 1950, page 419. *2)* PEARLMAN, W. H., *Recent Progr. Hormone Res.*, **9**, 27 (1954). *3)* ZANDER et al., *J. clin. Endocr.*, **18**, 337 (1958). *4)* PEARLMAN, W. H., *Ciba Found. Coll. Endocr.*, **11**, 233 (1957). *5)* SHORT, R. V., *Ciba Found. Coll. Endocr.*, **11**, 362 (1957). *6)* WESTPHAL, U., *Endocrinology*, **57**, 456 (1955). *7)* BORTH, R., *Vitam. and Horm.*, **15**, 259 (1957). *8)* KLOPPER et al., *J. Endocr.*, **12**, 209 (1955). *9)* SHEARMAN, R. P., *J. Obstet. Gynaec. Brit. Emp.*, **66**, 1 (1959). *10)* PICKETT et al., *Lancet*, **2**, 829 (1959). *11)* SOMMERVILLE and DESHPANDE, *J. clin. Endocr.*, **18**, 1223 (1958). *12)* HASLEWOOD, G. A. D., in EMMENS, C. W. (Ed.), *Hormone Assay*, New York, 1950, page 443. *13)* EBERLEIN and BONGIOVANNI, *J. clin. Endocr.*, **18**, 300 (1958). *14)* RONAN et al., *J. clin. Endocr.*, **20**, 355 (1960).

Functions of the sex hormones[1]

From the close similarity in the chemical structure of the three principal hormones (testosterone, estradiol, progesterone) it is highly probable that their chemical relationship is of biological and phylogenetic origin. Hormones of these three types occur in both sexes and are found throughout the vertebrates: they are specific neither for sex nor species. Experimentally the direction and intensity of the hormonal effect is a question of dosage, of the proportions in which they are mixed, of the stage of the menstrual cycle and of the organ on which they act. Although the extent to which absence of the sex hormones affects the development of the sex organs is the greater the earlier the stage of fetal development, it is quite certain that these hormones have no effect on sex differentiation. It has been shown that the development of female sex characteristics is inherent in both sexes, i.e. that the development is automatically in the female direction unless it is diverted in the male direction by the testes anlage. The effect of the latter is not, however, exercised through the male sex hormone, since after removal of the testes anlage the development of female characteristics cannot be hindered by administering male sex hormone. It appears rather to be an inductive effect of unknown nature exercised by the testes anlage on the surrounding primitive tissues (transplantation of a testes anlage on to an embryo is likewise followed by female development)[2].

In addition to its sexual activity testosterone shows a marked anabolic action (protein-forming with concomitant effect on

Male organism	Androgens	Estrogens	Progesterone
Development of primary sex organs:			
General, especially testes, prostate, penis	+++	antagonist	
Muscles and connective tissue of accessory glands	?	+	
Development of secondary sex characteristics	++++	antagonist	
Emotional behavior: libido, masculine activity	++++	antagonist	
Female organism			
Development of primary sex organs:			
General, especially uterus and ovaries	partial antagonist	+++	0
Organs of the orgasm	+	+++	0
Development of secondary sex characteristics	antagonist	++++	?
Emotional behavior: frigidity	antagonist	++++	+
libido	+++	+	partial antagonist
Menstrual cycle	Always present in large quantities, not subject to cyclic variation		
Maturation of ovum	?	+++	+
Proliferation phase	?	++++	+
Secretion phase	?	+	++++
Migration of ovum, nidation	?	++	+++
Pregnancy			
Inhibition of maturation of further follicles; quiescence of the uterus; relaxation of the uterine muscles (1); lowering of the Na:K ratio in blood; lowering of the sympathetic tonus (2)	?	antagonist to (1), synergist to (2)	++++
Indispensable for maintenance of pregnancy	?	++	++
Relaxation of the pelvic girdle; increase of tonus of uterine muscles towards end of pregnancy (3)	?	+++	antagonist to (3)
Growth of mammary tissue	?	++*	++*
Inhibition of lactation until parturition	?	++	+
Post partum			
Maintenance of lactation	?	++*	++*
Inhibition of lactation at high therapeutic dosage	++	+++++	0
Involution of the uterus and preparation for fresh menstrual cycle	?	+++	0

* See also under Prolactin, page 476.

energy metabolism), and may therefore be used therapeutically for the normalization of nitrogen balance disturbed by ACTH or adrenocortical hormone therapy. The estrogens also possess, to a lesser extent, an anabolic action in respect of protein metabolism. Progesterone, on the other hand, has a weakly catabolic action[3, 4], but in contrast to the catabolic properties of the corticosteroids, has little effect on the amino acid levels in plasma and urine. In addition, progesterone must be regarded as an antagonist of aldosterone inasmuch as it causes an increased excretion of sodium chloride. These metabolic effects of progesterone may possibly play an important role during pregnancy.

The individual hormone types, particularly the estrogens and progesterone, act either antagonistically or synergistically according to the stage of the menstrual cycle and the organ affected. In the phase in which each of these hormones predominates, however, it requires the cooperation of the opposite hormone in order that the organs affected may remain capable of functioning biologically[5] (see the table above). The effect is greatly enhanced by the presence of traces of the opposite hormone: threatened abortion (operative removal of the ovaries) at the commencement of pregnancy can for example be held off with the aid of much smaller doses of progesterone if a little estradiol is added to it. A similar remarkable synergism exists between androgens and estrogens: provided that sufficient follicular hormone is present, androgens have a libido-increasing effect on women, whereas they are otherwise typical female antagonists.

In addition to gonadotropic hormones (see pages 473 and 474) the developing placenta produces increasing quantities of progesterone and estrogens during pregnancy, rapidly surpassing the ovaries in this respect. In nonfunctioning of the ovaries and pituitary the hormone production of the placenta suffices to prevent miscarriage. This defensive mechanism of the human embryo in late pregnancy is rare among mammals and has otherwise been observed only in the horse and guinea pig.

Therapeutic applications

Androgens[6]: In menorrhagia, the premenstrual syndrome, frigidity in women, certain cases of glandular-cystic hyperplasia of the endometrium, endometriosis, dysmenorrhea, mastalgia.

On account of their lower tendency to cause virilization, the 19-nortestosterone derivatives are particularly indicated for the normalization of negative metabolic balance during ACTH or adrenocortical hormone therapy or in senile osteoporosis.

Androgens in high dosage are indicated prior to the menopause in inoperable mammary carcinoma with diffuse bone metastases; after the menopause and particularly in women over 60, estrogens are preferable.

Side effects are virilization in women, salt and water retention, depression of spermatogenesis, exacerbation of carcinoma of the prostate.

Progestational hormones[7]: In habitual abortion, endometriosis; combined with estrogens in menstrual irregularities, metrorrhagia and essential uterine hemorrhage.

Estrogens[8]: In carcinoma of the prostate, postmenopausal mammary carcinoma, the menopausal syndrome[9], senile kraurosis, atrophic vaginitis; combined with androgens in senile osteoporosis in women. Estrogens are usually ineffective in amenorrhea and oligomenorrhea, effective when combined with progestational hormones in menstrual irregularities, metrorrhagia and essential uterine hemorrhage.

References: *1)* For a review see Pincus, G., in Pincus and Thimann (Eds.), *The Hormones*, vol. III, New York, 1955, page 665. *2)* Moore, C. R., in Gordon, E. S. (Ed.), *Steroid Hormones*, University of Wisconsin, 1950, page 393. *3)* Landau et al., *J. clin. Endocr.*, **15**, 1194 (1955). *4)* Kyle and Hess, *J. Lab. clin. Med.*, **47**, 278 (1956). *5)* Courrier, R., *Vitam. and Horm.*, **8**, 179 (1950). *6)* Crooke, A. C., *Practitioner*, **180**, 13 (1958); Bishop, P. M. F., *Brit. med. J.*, **1**, 184 (1960). *7)* MacGregor, T. N., *Practitioner*, **180**, 83 (1958); Swyer, G. I. M., *Brit. med. J.*, **1**, 48, 121 (1960). *8)* Bishop, P. M. F., *Practitioner*, **180**, 5 (1958). *9)* Jeffcoate, T. N. A., *Brit. med. J.*, **1**, 340 (1960).

	Age in years	Weight lb.	Weight *kg*	Height in.	Height *cm*	Calories kcal	Proteins g	Calcium g	Iron mg	Vitamins A I.U.	B_1 mg	B_2 mg	Nicotinic acid* mg	C mg	D I.U.
Men	25	154	70	69	175	3200	70	0.8	10	5000	1.6	1.8	21	75	–
	45	154	70	69	175	3000	70	0.8	10	5000	1.5	1.8	20	75	–
	65	154	70	69	175	2550	70	0.8	10	5000	1.3	1.8	18	75	–
Women	25	128	58	64	163	2300	58	0.8	12	5000	1.2	1.5	17	70	–
	45	128	58	64	163	2200	58	0.8	12	5000	1.1	1.5	17	70	–
	65	128	58	64	163	1800	58	0.8	12	5000	1.0	1.5	17	70	–
	Pregnant (second half)					+ 300	+ 20	1.5	15	6000	1.3	2.0	+ 3	100	400
	Lactating (850 ml daily)					+ 1000	+ 40	2.0	15	8000	1.7	2.5	+ 2	150	400
Infants**	0–1/12**	–	–	–	–	–	–	–	–	–	–	–	–	–	–
	2/12–6/12	13	6	24	60	kg × 120	–	0.6	5	1500	0.4	0.5	6	30	400
	7/12–12/12	20	9	28	70	kg × 100	–	0.8	7	1500	0.5	0.8	7	30	400
Children	1–3	27	12	34	87	1300	40	1.0	7	2000	0.7	1.0	8	35	400
	4–6	40	18	43	109	1700	50	1.0	8	2500	0.9	1.3	11	50	400
	7–9	60	27	51	129	2100	60	1.0	10	3500	1.1	1.5	14	60	400
	10–12	79	36	57	144	2500	70	1.2	12	4500	1.3	1.8	17	75	400
Boys	13–15	108	49	64	163	3100	85	1.4	15	5000	1.6	2.1	21	90	400
	16–19	139	63	69	175	3600	100	1.4	15	5000	1.8	2.5	25	100	400
Girls	13–15	108	49	63	160	2600	80	1.3	15	5000	1.3	2.0	17	80	400
	16–19	120	54	64	162	2400	75	1.3	15	5000	1.2	1.9	16	80	400

* Nicotinic acid equivalents include dietary sources of the preformed vitamin and the precursor, tryptophan (1 mg nicotinic acid ≡ 60 mg tryptophan).

** The Board recognizes that human milk is the natural food for infants and feels that breast feeding is the best and desired procedure for meeting nutrient requirements in the first months of life. No allowances are stated for the first month of life. Breast feeding is particularly indicated during the first month when infants show handicaps in homeostasis due to different rates of maturation of digestive, excretory and endocrine functions. Recommendations as listed pertain to nutrient intake as afforded by cow's milk formulas and supplementary foods given the infant when breast feeding is terminated. Allowances are not given for protein during infancy.

1) From Food and Nutrition Board, National Research Council, *Recommended Daily Dietary Allowances, revised 1958*, Washington, 1958. The allowances are intended for persons normally active in a temperate climate and are designed to cover individual variations among most normal persons as they live in the United States under usual environmental stresses. The recommended allowances can be attained with a variety of common foods, providing other nutrients for which human requirements have been less well defined.

Calories

In the United States, recommended calorie allowances are based on a reference man and woman, 25 years of age, living in a temperate climate at 20° C, physically fairly active, and weighing 70 and 58 kilograms respectively. Adjustments can be made for variations in age, body weight, physical activity and climate for persons differing from these specifications. The Food and Nutrition Board recommends a 3% reduction in the calorie allowance per decade between the ages of 30 and 50 and a 7.5% reduction per decade between the ages of 50 and 70. A further decrement of 10% is recommended for the years between 70 and 80. Each 10° C increase in average temperature above the basic 20° C calls for a reduction of 5% in calorie intake. The calorie allowance should be increased by 5% for the first 10° decrease below the standard 20° C and by 3% for each additional 10° decrease; it should be reduced by 5% for each increase of 10° C above the standard temperature. The calorie allowances for men and women who differ from the standard body weight can be calculated with the aid of the following formulas:

$$\text{Calories for men} = 0.95\,(815 + 36.6\,W)$$
$$\text{Calories for women} = 0.95\,(580 + 31.1\,W)$$

where W = desirable body weight in kilograms. Calorie allowances should always be based on the body weight which is desirable for the individual's height, not on his actual weight, which may be above or below normal. For desirable weights of men and women see page 624.

Adjustment for activity. Persons engaged in heavy labor will have enhanced requirements, but the allowance probably need seldom be increased more than 25% above the standard allowance. Those who expend less physical energy will have reduced requirements because of relatively sedentary existence. For all persons the allowance is best judged for adequacy or pertinence by observation of weight change and health.

Relation of daily calorie requirement to physical work[1]

	Men	Women
Light work	2650 kcal	2400 kcal
Medium heavy work	3200 kcal	2800 kcal
Heavy work	3800 kcal	3000 kcal
Very heavy work	4750 kcal	–

1) From Kraut, H., in Verzár, F. (Ed.), *Gegenwartsprobleme der Ernährungsforschung*, Basle, 1953.

Carbohydrate

Evidence is not available to provide a basis for establishing a recommended allowance for carbohydrate. Note that alcohol consumed in beverages may contribute importantly as a source of carbohydrate in the diet and should not be excluded from calculations in diet planning or analysis.

Fats

It is not yet possible to state definitely a reasonable allowance for fat in the diet or to indicate the characteristics of a fatty acid mixture most favorable to health. A diet selected from a wide variety of foodstuffs, both vegetable and animal, is most likely to maintain good health. The unsaturated fatty acids such as linoleic and arachidonic acids are essential in the nutrition of experimental animals and possibly also for man (see page 471).

Water

The requirement for water is determined by body heat production, renal solute load, the concentrating capacity of the kidney, and losses due to sweating. Water requirements are intimately related to salt requirements. The daily requirement of a 70-kg man ingesting 3200 kcal daily is of the order of 2300 to 3100 ml. Under desert conditions, the requirement may be much greater, since losses from sweating may be as great as 1200 ml per hour. The water requirements of young infants under ordinary environmental conditions are met by milk mixtures supplying 150 ml of water per 100 kcal.

Physiologic mechanisms controlling thirst closely control water intake in most normal individuals, but under conditions of extreme heat and excessive sweating the sensation of thirst may not allow for sufficient intake of water and more careful observation and control of intake may be necessary.

Sodium

In the United States the daily sodium intake has been estimated to be 3–7 g per person per day. Ingested sodium is rapidly absorbed and distributed throughout the extracellular fluid. Sodium may be rapidly lost after ingestion, thus making it possible to maintain body concentrations. Sodium is excreted in urine, sweat and feces, the urinary excretion being by far the greatest. Urinary sodium loss declines, however, when intake of this mineral is restricted. Loss of sodium in sweat is variable and depends on the environmental temperature and humidity as well as body temperature. There is insufficient information available to establish the sodium requirement.

Potassium

According to recent studies, 0.8–1.3 g potassium per day would appear to be very close to a potassium requirement.

A mixed diet of both animal and vegetable foods like those usual in the United States will contain 2.5–4.5 g potassium per 3000 kcal.

Phosphorus

Phosphorus allowances should be at least equal to those of calcium in the diet of children and of women during the latter part of pregnancy or during lactation. For other adults, the phosphorus allowances should be approximately one and a half times those for calcium. In general, it is safe to assume that if the calcium and protein needs are met through common foods, the phosphorus requirement also will be covered, because the common foods richest in calcium and protein are also the best sources of phosphorus.

Magnesium

It has been estimated that a young child requires about 13 mg magnesium per kg body weight to satisfy growth needs. The adult requirement has been estimated at 250–300 mg per day.

Copper

Balance studies in man reveal that an intake of 2 mg of copper per day will maintain adults in balance. Infants and children require about 0.05 mg per kg body weight. The American diet usually supplies more than the indicated requirements.

Iodine

The intake averages about 150 μg per day. The need for iodine is increased in adolescence and pregnancy. The use of iodized table salt will provide an adequate iodine intake.

Fluorine

Extensive evidence indicates that during development of the teeth a controlled intake of fluoride results in substantial protection against dental caries. The practice of adding fluoride to water supplies at the rate of 1 part per million is highly desirable as a public health practice in areas where the content of fluoride in natural water is low. For a brief review of this much debated question see Annotations, *Lancet*, **1**, 563 (1959).

Trace elements

A number of elements are regularly found in trace amounts in plant and animal tissues. In some cases the element has been found to be an essential part of the structure of a complex compound, like cobalt in vitamin B_{12}. In others a close association with the functioning of an endocrine gland is suggested, for example the occurrence of zinc with insulin.

Trace elements are most frequently associated with enzyme systems. The amounts needed are exceedingly small and would appear to be provided by mixed diets. There is a growing body of evidence that antagonisms between trace elements may occur with relatively small increments in intake. In the absence of specific evidence of deficiency, therefore, the diet should not be supplemented with trace elements. There is evidence that cobalt, zinc, manganese, molybdenum and perhaps bromine are essential to man.

Vitamins

For vitamins not listed in the table opposite see pages 449–472.

Essential amino acid* requirements of infants[1] and adults[2]

(assuming that the nitrogen intake is adequate for the formation of the non-essential amino acids)

Amino acid	Infants: Minimum requirement mg/kg/day	Adults: Minimum requirement (young men) g/day	Adults: Definitely safe intake** g/day
L-Histidine	34	0	0
L-Tryptophan	22	0.25	0.5
L-Phenylalanine	90++	1.10***	2.2
L-Lysine	103	0.80	1.6
L-Threonine	87	0.50	1.0
L-Methionine	45+	1.10***	2.2
L-Leucine	150	1.10	2.2
L-Isoleucine	126	0.70	1.4
L-Valine	105	0.80	1.6

* Essential amino acids are those which are constituents of human proteins and which the body either cannot synthesize or can synthesize only in inadequate amount. They are therefore essential constituents of the diet. See also pages 354 sq.

** Higher figures are recommended during pregnancy and lactation. Elderly men may require more of a particular acid or acids[2].

*** 70–75% of the requirement of phenylalanine can be covered by tyrosine, 80–90% of that of methionine by cystine.

\+ In the presence of cystine.

++ In the presence of tyrosine.

1) From Holt et al., *Protein and Amino Acid Requirements in Early Life*, New York, 1960. *2)* From Rose, W. C., *Fed. Proc.*, **8**, 546 (1949), and *Nutr. Abstr. Rev.*, **27**, 631 (1957). *2)* Tuttle et al., *Metabolism*, **6**, 564 (1957).

Daily calorie and protein intakes in childhood and adolescence[1]

Age (years)	Calorie intake (kcal/day)						Protein intake (g/day)					
	Boys			Girls			Boys			Girls		
	Mean	s	Experimental range	Mean	s	Experimental range	Mean	s	Experimental range	Mean	s	Experimental range
1– 2	1287	198	800–1700	1273	173	850–1800	43.6	7.7	25.0– 60.0	44.3	7.0	32.5– 57.5
2– 3	1403	205	800–1900	1377	188	950–1800	46.1	8.1	27.5– 62.5	46.9	8.3	30.5– 72.5
3– 4	1544	210	1050–2000	1483	183	1050–1950	50.0	8.4	32.5– 70.0	49.1	8.4	29.0– 70.0
4– 5	1629	208	1200–2200	1605	251	1150–2500	53.2	8.6	32.5– 72.5	53.6	9.3	34.0– 80.0
5– 6	1792	252	1200–2400	1704	245	1200–2350	57.7	9.8	40.0– 77.5	56.7	10.2	33.0– 85.0
6– 7	1971	304	1450–2800	1845	276	1350–2450	63.6	11.7	42.5– 97.5	60.3	11.8	35.0– 90.0
7– 8	2013	299	1450–2650	1930	297	1250–2650	65.4	11.5	45.0– 97.5	63.4	12.9	37.5–100.0
8– 9	2159	391	1400–3925	2026	291	1400–2800	69.5	12.9	45.0–107.5	65.4	10.9	40.0– 85.0
9–10	2235	388	1500–3225	2125	376	1350–3300	72.5	13.9	45.0–105.0	69.4	14.3	37.5–110.0
10–11	2403	427	1700–3800	2264	407	1400–3400	77.9	15.7	50.0–127.5	73.6	14.4	45.0–105.0
11–12	2619	474	1750–3775	2450	373	1900–3250	82.8	15.7	55.0–120.0	76.5	14.3	50.0–120.0
12–13	2878	482	1950–3850	2529	466	1800–4000	87.4	13.3	60.0–113.5	78.2	13.7	57.5–132.5
13–14	3117	493	1900–4400	2575	479	1625–3850	96.4	16.8	55.0–142.5	81.4	14.5	45.0–122.5
14–15	3338	674	2100–5700	2592	502	1500–4400	101.7	20.7	57.5–165.0	80.9	15.0	60.0–140.0
15–16	3467	668	1700–5070	2575	522	1600–4350	106.6	22.9	70.0–175.0	81.6	18.5	52.5–145.0
16–17	3443	631	2275–5350	2437	505	1400–3900	107.8	20.7	62.5–145.0	77.7	15.9	50.0–130.0
17–18	3532	718	1900–5000	2390	464	1775–3475	110.6	24.4	65.0–185.0	76.8	16.5	52.5–135.0

1) From Burke et al., *Pediatrics*, **24**, Suppl. 923 (1959). The intakes were measured on 125 children (64 boys and 61 girls) born in the United States of parents of predominantly Northern European stock, and formed part of a study of individual patterns of intakes. The data are based on 2707 dietary histories taken at 6-month intervals up to 6 years of age and at one-year intervals thereafter. Note that the average intakes (especially of protein and more so for boys than for girls) tend to be higher than the "Recommended Dietary Allowances" of the Food and Nutrition Board, National Research Council, given in the table opposite.

The data on the chemical composition of foods given in the tables on pages 501–513 have been assembled mainly from the sources listed below. An attempt has been made to give representative values, but it must be borne in mind that the actual value of a food in respect of any particular constituent may for various reasons depart from the value given. Factors which may affect some or all of the constituents listed are species and variety (especially in the case of vegetable products), quality (for example the degree of fattening of domestic animals), season of the year, climate and geographical location (differences in soil constitution and manuring). The manner in which foodstuffs are stored is important in respect of the conservation of the water and vitamin content; loss of water results in a concentration of all the nutrients.

The values in the tables relate unless otherwise stated to 100 g of the edible, uncooked portion of foods, i.e. after removal of the usual rind, husk, shell, etc. Allowances must therefore be made for the cooking of foods which are normally eaten raw, as for any other unusual method of preparation. Cooking of foods may result in loss of nutrients. Apart from loss of water-soluble vitamins and minerals (when the cooking water is not used) vitamins may be destroyed by heating (vitamin B_1, pantothenic acid) or oxidation (vitamins A, C, D and E).

For the calculation of the energy content (in calories) of the foods listed from their protein, fat and carbohydrate content (any organic acids present have been ignored) use has been made of specific factors for the different groups of foods which take account of their different digestibility and energy value (see *Energy Yielding Components of Food and Computation of Caloric Values*, Food and Agriculture Organization, Nutrition Division, Washington, 1947).

In the column headed "Other vitamins" the abbreviations PA for pantothenic acid and FA for folic acid have been used in addition to the usual letters denoting vitamins. The contents of vitamins A and D are given in international units, all other vitamins in milligrams. The values for vitamin A include the calculated vitamin A equivalents of the various precursors (mainly β-carotene).

A zero value (0) indicates that there is no detectable content of the constituent concerned. A dash (–) indicates that no data are available, *not* a zero value. Plus signs (+) are indefinite indications of content in relation to other forms of the food concerned.

Bibliography (pages 501–513)

Asenjo and Muñiz, *Food Res.*, **20**, 47 (1955); Braekkan and Probst, *Fiskeridir. Skr., Ser. teknol. Undersøkelser*, **2**, No. 13 (1953); Brandt et al., *Statens Husholdningsråds Faglige Medd.*, No. 5, 19 (1953); Cailleau, R., *Bull. Acad. nat. Méd. (Paris)*, **133**, 204 (1949); Catel and Schuphan, *Mschr. Kinderheilk.*, **101**, 473 (1953); Clifford, P. A., *J. Amer. diet. Ass.*, **31**, 21 (1955); Clouse, R. C., *J. Amer. diet. Ass.*, **19**, 496 and 746 (1943); Evans et al., *Poultry Sci.*, **32**, 680 (1953); Fisher and Dodds, *Food Res.*, **20**, 247 (1955); Van Koetsveld, E. E., *Nature*, **171**, 483 (1953); Hall et al., *Food Res.*, **18**, 574 (1953), and **21**, 362 (1956); Hayes and Rose, *J. Amer. diet. Ass.*, **33**, 26 (1957); Holman, W. I. M., *Nutr. Abstr. Rev.*, **26**, 277 (1956); Martinek and Wolman, *J. Amer. med. Ass.*, **158**, 1030 (1955); Munsell, H. E., *Milbank mem. Fd Quart.*, **21**, 102 (1943); Neseni and Köprich, *Milchwissenschaft*, **3**, 186 (1948); Okey, R., *J. Amer. diet. Ass.*, **21**, 341 (1945); Piatkowska and Smereczynska, *Rocz. Panstwowego zakt. Hig.*, **4**, 497 (1953); Randoin and Causeret, *Bull. Soc. sci. Hyg. aliment. (Paris)*, **43**, 227 (1955); Reith et al., *J. Sci. Food Agric.*, **6**, 317 (1955); Schweigert and Guthneck, *J. Nutr.*, **51**, 283 (1953); Sherman and Gettler, *J. biol. Chem.*, **11**, 323 (1912); Thomas and Lewis, *J. Amer. diet. Ass.*, **30**, 327 (1954); Booher et al., *A Compilation of the Vitamin Values of Foods in Relation to Processing and other Variants*, U.S. Department of Agriculture Circ. 638, Washington, 1942, page 153; Bowes and Church, *Food Values of Portions Commonly Used*, Philadelphia, 1944; Bridges and Mattice, *Food and Beverage Analysis*, London, 1942; Chatfield, C., *Food Composition Tables for International Use*, Food and Agriculture Organization of the United Nations, Washington, 1949; Chatfield, C., *Food Composition Tables for International Use—Minerals and Vitamins*, Food and Agriculture Organization of the United Nations, Rome, 1954; Chatfield and Adams, *Proximate Composition of American Food Materials*, U. S. Department of Agriculture Circ. 549, Washington, 1940; Cheldelin and Williams, *Univ. Texas Publ.*, No. 4237 (1942); Demole et al., *Ernährungslehre und Diätetik*, Berne, 1948; Elvehjem and Pavcek, *Table of Proximate Mineral and Vitamin Composition of Foods*, Committee on Food and Nutrition Board, National Research Council, Washington, 1948; Heupke and Rost, *Was enthalten unsere Nahrungsmittel?*, 2nd ed., Frankfurt a. M., 1958; Hodgman et al. (Eds.), *Handbook of Chemistry and Physics, 1960–61*, 42nd ed., Cleveland, 1960; Lange and Forker (Eds.), *Handbook of Chemistry*, 10th ed., Sandusky, 1961; McLester and Darby, *Nutrition and Diet in Health and Disease*, 6th ed., Philadelphia, 1952; *Mayo Clinic Diet Manual*, Committee on Dietetics of the Mayo Clinic, 2nd ed., Philadelphia, 1954; Osmond and Wilson, *Tables of Composition of Australian Foods*, Nutrition Committee of the National Health and Medical Research Council, Canberra, 1954; Proudfit and Robinson, *Nutrition and Diet Therapy*, New York, 1946; Schall, H., *Nahrungsmitteltabelle*, 16th ed., Leipzig, 1954; Sherman, H. C., *Chemistry of Food and Nutrition*, New York, 1954; Sherman, H.C., *Food Products*, 4th ed., New York, 1948; Stern, F., *Applied Dietetics*, Baltimore, 1943; Turner, D., *Handbook of Diet Therapy*, Chicago, 1946; Waller, D.S., *Nutritive Values of Foods*, Ann Arbor, 1933; Watt and Merill, *Composition of Foods*, U. S. Department of Agriculture Handbook No. 8, Washington, 1950.

Amino acid contents of foods

From Harvey, D., *Tables of the Amino Acids in Foods and Feedingstuffs*, Commonwealth Agricultural Bureaux Technical Communication No. 19, Farnham Royal, 1958

	Grams per 100 g protein																	
	Alanine	Arginine	Aspartic acid	Cystine	Glutamic acid	Glycine	Histidine	Leucine	Isoleucine	Lysine	Methionine	Phenyl-alanine	Proline	Serine	Threonine	Tryptophan	Tyrosine	Valine
Human milk	3.5	2.9	8.6	1.5	18.3	2.2	1.9	9.2	5.0	5.9	–	3.8	8.0	4.5	4.4	1.8	4.2	5.0
Cow's milk	3.6	3.7	8.1	0.8	22.3	1.9	2.8	10.1	5.5	8.4	2.1	5.3	9.8	5.7	4.8	1.1	5.6	6.7
Eggs (fowl)	–	6.4	–	2.2	–	–	2.0	–	–	5.2	5.2	5.8	–	–	3.9	1.4	4.8	–
Protein (cooked)	–	5.7	–	1.9	–	–	1.4	–	–	4.9	6.6	6.2	–	–	4.0	1.4	4.5	–
Egg yolk (cooked)	–	6.8	–	2.2	–	–	1.5	–	–	5.7	3.0	4.4	–	–	3.5	1.4	4.7	–
Beef	7.3	5.4	9.8	1.3	15.9	4.5	3.8	8.2	5.2	9.3	2.9	4.5	3.6	4.5	4.7	–	4.1	5.0
Pork	–	5.7	8.9	1.5	14.5	6.1	3.6	7.8	4.8	8.1	2.5	3.7	4.2	4.1	5.2	1.4	3.5	5.0
Heart (pig)	–	5.9	–	–	–	–	2.5	9.2	5.7	8.5	2.3	4.7	–	–	4.6	1.2	–	5.6
Kidney (pig)	–	5.9	–	–	–	–	2.6	9.0	5.7	7.8	2.2	4.9	–	–	4.5	1.4	–	6.2
Liver (pig)	–	5.8	–	–	–	–	2.8	9.7	6.0	8.7	2.3	5.3	–	–	4.7	1.4	–	6.5
Herrings	–	5.9	–	–	–	–	2.0	8.0	6.4	8.2	2.2	4.5	–	–	4.5	0.7	2.2	5.1
Rye	–	5.3	–	–	–	–	2.2	6.0	3.9	4.0	1.6	4.2	–	–	3.3	1.2	–	5.0
Wheat	–	4.5	–	–	–	–	2.2	6.5	4.1	2.5	1.6	5.0	–	–	2.7	1.3	–	4.6
Carrots	–	3.4	–	–	–	–	1.4	5.8	4.2	5.8	1.3	3.4	–	–	3.7	1.1	–	5.3
Potatoes	–	5.3	–	–	–	–	1.4	4.6	3.7	5.1	1.5	3.1	–	–	2.5	1.8	–	4.8
Spinach	–	2.7	–	–	–	–	1.1	4.3	2.4	3.1	0.9	2.6	–	–	2.4	2.1	–	3.0
Green beans	–	4.1	–	–	–	–	2.1	6.2	4.4	5.8	1.2	3.5	–	–	3.8	1.1	–	4.9
Peas (dried)	–	7.3	–	–	–	–	1.2	7.2	4.7	3.2	0.8	3.0	–	–	3.3	0.7	–	3.3
Soya beans	–	3.4	–	–	–	–	1.1	3.8	2.4	1.8	0.5	2.5	–	–	1.9	0.5	–	2.6
Brewer's yeast	9.2	5.0	10.6	2.1	20.2	6.0	4.1	7.5	4.5	6.7	1.4	1.9	3.9	3.6	8.2	–	4.1	9.4

Content per 100 grams edible portion (unless otherwise stated)	Water g	Proteins g	Fats: Total g	Fats: Cholesterol g	Carbohydrates: Total g	Carbohydrates: Fiber g	Calories kcal	Vitamins: A* IU	Vitamins: B_1 mg	Vitamins: B_2 mg	Vitamins: Nicotinic acid mg	Vitamins: C mg	Other vitamins*** mg	Malic acid mg	Citric acid mg	Oxalic acid mg	Uric acid mg	Purine bases mg	Excess acid ml**	Excess base ml**	Sodium Na mg	Potassium K mg	Calcium Ca mg	Magnesium Mg mg	Manganese Mn mg	Iron Fe mg	Copper Cu mg	Phosphorus P mg	Sulfur S mg	Chlorine Cl mg
Fruit, Fruit Juices																														
Apples (sweet)																														
fresh	84	0.3	0.4	0.007	15.0	0.9	58	90	0.04	0.02	0.2	3–30	E 0.72; B_6 0.1; PA 0.2	270	70	trace	0	0	0	2.8	1	116	6	6	0.084	0.3	0.071	10	5	4
per lb. as purchased	*335*	*1.2*	*1.6*	*0.028*	*59.8*	*3.6*	*231*	*359*	*0.16*	*0.08*	*0.08*	*12-120*	*E 2.9; B_6 0.45; PA 0.9*	*1080*	*280*	*trace*	*0*	*0*	*0*	*10.8*	*4*	*463*	*24*	*24*	*0.34*	*1.2*	*0.28*	*40*	*20*	*16*
1 apple, 2½" dia.	*111*	*0.4*	*0.5*	*0.009*	*20.0*	*1.2*	*77*	*119*	*0.05*	*0.03*	*0.3*	*4–40*	*E 1.0; B_6 0.1; PA 0.3*	*356*	*90*	*trace*	*0*	*0*	*0*	*3.7*	*1.3*	*153*	*8*	*8*	*0.11*	*0.4*	*0.093*	*13*	*7*	*5*
dried	20	3	0.7	—	73.6	4.0	281	0	0.05	0.08	0.5	6-60†	—	—	0	0	0	0	0	+	—	—	24	—	—	1.4	—	42	—	—
Apple juice, fresh	87	0.1	0	—	13	—	50	57	0.02	0.03	trace	3–30	B_6 0.16	—	—	0	0	0	0	+	1	100	6	—	—	0.5	—	10	—	—
Apple sauce, sweetened	79.8	0.2	0.1	—	19.7	0.6	72	60	0.01	0.01	trace	1.6	—	—	—	0	0	0	0	+	0.3	55	4	—	—	0.2	< 0.05	6	—	—
Apricots																														
fresh	85.3	0.9	0.2	0.003	12.9	0.6	51	2790	0.03	0.04	0.7	8	—	—	—	14	0	0	0	10.9	0.6	440	16	9	—	0.5	0.11	23	6	2
per lb. as purchased	*363*	*3.8*	*0.9*	*0.013*	*54.5*	*2.6*	*217*	*11900*	*0.13*	*0.17*	*3*	*34*	—	—	—	*60*	*0*	*0*	*0*	*46.3*	*2.6*	*1880*	*68*	*38*	—	*2.1*	*0.47*	*98*	*26*	*9*
1 apricot, medium	*30*	*0.3*	*0.07*	*0.001*	*4.3*	*0.2*	*18*	*980*	*0.01*	*0.01*	*0.2*	*2.8*	—	—	—	*4.9*	*0*	*0*	*0*	*3.6*	*0.2*	*154*	*5*	*3*	—	*0.2*	*0.04*	*8*	*2*	*1*
canned, sweetened	77.3	0.6	0.1	—	21.4	0.4	89	1350	0.02	0.02	0.3	4.4	—	330	1060	trace	0	0	0	+	2	65	10	—	—	0.3	—	15	—	—
dried	24.0	5.2	0.4	—	66.9	2.6	262	7430	0.01	0.16	3.3	12	—	810	350	trace	0	0	0	+	11	1700	86	65	—	4.9	0.4	119	—	47
cooked	67	1.3	0.1	—	31	0.7	120	2000	0.01	0.1	0.9	2	—	—	—	—	0	0	0	+	—	—	24	—	—	1.4	—	34	—	—
Avocados																														
fresh	65	1.7	26.4	—	5.1	1.8	245	290	0.06	0.13	1.1	16	PA 1.0	—	—	—	—	—	0	7.5	3	340	10	30	4.2	0.6	0.4	38	25	10
per lb. as purchased	*221*	*5.8*	*89.8*	—	*17.4*	*6.1*	*833*	*987*	*0.20*	*0.44*	*3.7*	*54*	*PA 3.4*	—	—	—	—	—	*0*	*25.6*	*10*	*1157*	*34*	*102*	*14.3*	*2.0*	*1.4*	*129*	*85*	*34*
Bananas																														
fresh	73.5	1.3	0.4	0.008	24.0	0.5	94	430	0.09	0.06	0.6	10	E 0.37; B_6 0.5; PA 0.20	500	150	6.4	0	0	0	7.7	1	420	8	31	0.64	0.6	0.20	28	12	125
per lb. as purchased (1 banana, 6" = ca. 100 g edible portion)	*223*	*3.9*	*1.2*	*0.024*	*73*	*1.5*	*285*	*1310*	*0.27*	*0.18*	*1.8*	*30*	*E 1.1; B_6 1.5; PA 0.61*	*1520*	*455*	*19*	*0*	*0*	*0*	*23.1*	*3*	*1275*	*24*	*94*	*1.95*	*1.8*	*0.61*	*85*	*36*	*380*
Blackberries																														
fresh	84	1.2	1.1	—	11.9	4.1	56	200	0.03	0.04	0.31	21	—	160	trace	18	0	0	0	4.8	4	181	32	24	0.59	1.0	0.11	34	17	15
canned, sweetened	79	0.7	0.2	—	19	2.5	85	180	0.01	0.03	0.18	6	—	—	—	—	0	0	0	+	19	—	15	—	—	0.7	—	19	—	—
Blueberries																														
fresh	83.4	0.6	0.6	—	15.1	1.2	61	280	0.03	0.07	0.3	16	—	100	1560	15	0	0	0	1.6	1	65	16	10	2.3	0.8	0.11	13	11	8
canned, sweetened	73	0.4	0.4	—	26	1.0	109	100	0.02	0.07	0.18	5	—	—	—	—	0	0	0	+	1	—	10	—	—	0.5	—	10	—	—
Cantaloups																														
fresh	94	0.6	0.2	—	4.6	0.6	20	3420	0.05	0.04	0.5	33	—	—	—	—	—	—	0	6.4	12	230	17	17	0.04	0.4	0.04	16	1.7	41
per lb. as purchased	*200*	*1.3*	*0.4*	—	*9.8*	*1.3*	*43*	*7290*	*0.10*	*0.09*	*1.1*	*70*	—	—	—	—	—	—	*0*	*13.0*	*23*	*490*	*36*	*36*	*0.09*	*0.9*	*0.09*	*34*	*3.6*	*90*
Cherries																														
fresh	83.4	1.1	0.4	—	14.6	0.5	60	1000	0.05	0.06	0.14	8	—	1250	10	0	0	0	0	7.8	2	260	19	14	—	0.5	0.07	20	8	3
per lb. as purchased	*355*	*4.7*	*1.7*	—	*62*	*2.1*	*255*	*4260*	*0.21*	*0.26*	*0.6*	*34*	—	*5320*	*43*	*0*	*0*	*0*	*0*	*33.6*	*8.5*	*1110*	*81*	*60*	—	*2.1*	*0.3*	*85*	*34*	*13*
candied	12	0.5	0.2	—	87.0	0.5	352	—	—	—	—	—	—	—	—	—	—	—	0	0	—	—	—	—	—	—	—	—	—	—
canned, sweetened	78.1	0.6	0.1	—	20.8	—	80	870	0.03	0.02	0.18	4.1	—	—	—	0	0	0	0	+	2	77	11	—	—	0.3	< 0.05	14	—	—
Cranberries																														
fresh	87.4	0.4	0.7	—	11.3	1.4	48	40	0.03	0.02	0.1	12	—	—	—	—	—	—	0	1.8	1	65	14	8	0.3	0.6	0.09	11	7	5
dried	4.9	2.8	6.6	—	84.3	8.7	368	300	0.19	0.18	0.9	34	—	—	—	—	—	—	0	+	—	—	82	—	—	3.4	—	22	—	—
Cranberry sauce	48.1	0.1	0.3	—	51.4	0.4	198	30	0.02	0.02	0.1	2	—	—	—	—	—	—	0	+	1	17	8	—	—	0.3	—	7	—	—

* Vitamin A activity due to vitamin A + carotenes (see page 449): 1 IU vitamin A = 0.0006 mg β-carotene. ** Milliliters of N-acid or N-base. *** PA = pantothenic acid. † Unsulfurated.

Content per 100 grams edible portion (unless otherwise stated)	Water	Proteins	Fats: Total	Fats: Cholesterol	Carbohydrates: Total	Carbohydrates: Fiber	Calories	Vitamins: A*	Vitamins: B₁	Vitamins: B₂	Vitamins: Nicotinic acid	Vitamins: C	Vitamins: Other vitamins***	Other organic constituents: Malic acid	Other organic constituents: Citric acid	Other organic constituents: Oxalic acid	Other organic constituents: Uric acid	Other organic constituents: Purine bases	Excess acid	Excess base	Elements: Sodium Na	Elements: Potassium K	Elements: Calcium Ca	Elements: Magnesium Mg	Elements: Manganese Mn	Elements: Iron Fe	Elements: Copper Cu	Elements: Phosphorus P	Elements: Sulfur S	Elements: Chlorine Cl
	g	g	g	g	g	g	kcal	IU	mg	mg	mg	mg	mg	mg	mg	mg	mg	mg	ml**	ml**	mg	mg	mg	mg	mg	mg	mg	mg	mg	mg
Currants (red currants) fresh	83.7	1.4	0.4	—	13.9	3.2	58	120	0.05	0.14	0.3	35	B_6 0.03	50	2300	19	0	0	0	5.2	2	261	36	15	—	0.7	0.11	38	29	13
Dates dried	20	2.2	0.6	—	75	2.4	284	60	0.08	0.05	2.18	0	—	—	—	—	0	0	0	12.3	0.9	790	65	65	0.15	2.1	0.21	72	65	283
Figs fresh	71.7	1.2	0.4	0.01	16.1	1.4	65	75	0.09	0.08	0.63	2	—	trace	340	—	0	0	0	5.4	2	190	50	21	—	0.8	0.07	40	12	16
dried	21.1	3.1	0.2	—	73.0	3.4	270	60	0.13	0.11	1.72	0	—	—	—	—	0	0	0	21.7	34	780	162	82	—	4.0	0.4	116	69	105
Fruit cocktail canned	81	0.4	0.2	—	18.6	0.4	70	160	0.01	0.01	0.4	2	—	—	—	—	—	—	0	+	5	160	9	—	—	0.4	—	12	—	—
Gooseberries fresh	89.9	0.8	0.5	—	8.3	1.2	35	290	0.15	—	—	25	—	1400	+	13	0	0	0	3.2	1	149	35	9	0.04	0.5	0.08	31	15	9
Grapes fresh	81.6	0.8	0.4	0.006	16.7	4.3	68	80	0.05	0.03	0.4	4	B_6 0.1; PA 0.08	650	—	0	0	0	0	6.1	2.0	254	17	7	0.083	0.6	0.098	21	9	2
Grape juice	81	0.4	0	—	18	0	67	—	0.03	0.08	0.2	2	B_6 0.08; PA 0.08	310	20	0	0	0	0	+	1	120	10	—	—	0.3	0.02	10	—	—
Grapefruit fresh	89.0	0.6	0.2	—	9.8	0.5	39	trace	0.04	0.02	0.2	40	E 0.25; P; PA 0.2	—	1460	0	0	0	0	5.3	2	198	17	10	0.01	0.3	0.02	18	5.1	3
per lb. as purchased	*267*	*1.8*	*0.6*	—	*29*	*1.5*	*117*	*trace*	*0.12*	*0.06*	*0.6*	*120*	*E 0.75; P; PA 0.6*	—	*4380*	*0*	*0*	*0*	*0*	*16.1*	*6*	*594*	*51*	*30*	*0.03*	*0.9*	*0.06*	*54*	*15.3*	*9*
½ grapefruit, 4¼" dia.	*167*	*1.1*	*0.4*	—	*18.4*	*0.9*	*73*	*trace*	*0.08*	*0.04*	*0.4*	*75*	*E 0.5; P; PA 0.4*	—	*2750*	*0*	*0*	*0*	*0*	*9.7*	*3.8*	*372*	*32*	*19*	*0.02*	*0.6*	*0.04*	*34*	*10*	*6*
canned, sweetened	79.8	0.6	0.2	—	19.1	0.3	72	trace	0.03	0.02	0.2	30	—	—	—	0	0	0	0	3.4	2	150	13	8	—	0.3	—	14	15	2
Grapefruit juice, fresh	89.4	0.4	0.1	—	10	0.1	36	trace	0.04	0.02	0.2	45	—	—	—	0	0	0	0	4.3	2	139	8	8	—	0.4	—	7	5	2
Lemons fresh	89.3	0.9	0.6	—	8.7	0.9	32	0	0.04	trace	0.1	45	PA 0.1	290	6080	0	0	0	0	4.8	6	148	40	9	0.04	0.6	0.26	22	8	4
1 lemon, 2" dia.	*55*	*0.6*	*0.4*	—	*5.4*	*0.6*	*21*	*0*	*0.02*	*trace*	*0.06*	*28*	*PA 0.05*	*190*	*3770*	*0*	*0*	*0*	*0*	*3.2*	*4*	*92*	*26*	*6*	—	*0.4*	*0.17*	*14*	*5*	*2*
Lemon juice	91.4	0.4	0.2	—	7.7	—	24	0	0.04	trace	0.1	27	PA 0.1	300	6000	—	—	—	0	3.4	1	130	14	9	—	0.1	—	11	9	4
Lime juice	91	0.4	—	—	8.3	—	24	0	0.04	trace	0.1	27	—	—	—	—	—	—	0	+	1	100	14	—	—	0.1	—	11	—	—
Melons, honeydew fresh	90.5	0.5	—	—	8.5	0.4	32	40	0.05	0.03	0.2	23	—	—	—	—	—	—	0	+	—	—	17	12	—	0.4	0.07	16	14	41
water	92.1	0.5	0.2	0.017	6.9	0.6	28	590	0.05	0.05	0.2	6	—	—	—	0	0	0	0	2.7	0.3	121	7	10	0.02	0.2	0.07	12	9	8
Olives green	75	1.5	13.5	—	4.0	1.2	132	300	—	—	—	—	—	—	—	—	—	—	0	+	2400	55	87	—	1.2	—	1.6	17	32	1877
Oranges fresh	87.1	0.9	0.2	0.014	11.3	0.8	45	190	0.08	0.03	0.2	49	E 0.23; PA 0.2; B_6 0.12	trace	980	24	0	0	0	4.8	0.3	170	33	10	0.025	0.4	0.076	23	8	4
per lb. as purchased	*284*	*2.9*	*0.7*	*0.045*	*36.9*	*2.6*	*147*	*620*	*0.26*	*0.10*	*0.7*	*160*	*E 0.75; PA 0.7; B_6 0.4*	*trace*	*3200*	*78*	*0*	*0*	*0*	*15.3*	*1*	*555*	*108*	*33*	*0.08*	*1.3*	*0.25*	*75*	*26*	*13*
1 orange, 3" dia.	*135*	*1.4*	*0.3*	*0.021*	*17.5*	*1.2*	*70*	*290*	*0.12*	*0.05*	*0.3*	*76*	*PA 0.3; E 0.4; B_6 0.18*	*trace*	*1520*	*37*	*0*	*0*	*0*	*7.4*	*0.5*	*260*	*51*	*15*	*0.04*	*0.6*	*0.12*	*35*	*12*	*6*
Orange juice, fresh	86	0.6	0.1	—	12.9	0.1	49	100	0.07	0.02	0.2	42†	—	—	—	—	0	0	0	4.6	0.5	190	19	10	0.025	0.4	0.076	23	8	4
Peaches fresh	86.6	0.8	0.2	0.006	11.8	0.6	47	880	0.02	0.05	0.9	8.7	—	370	370	trace	0	0	0	3.5	0.5	160	8	11	0.11	0.6	0.01	22	7	5
per lb. as purchased (1 peach, 2½" dia. = ca. 100 g edible port.)	*346*	*3.2*	*0.8*	*0.024*	*47.1*	*2.4*	*188*	*3510*	*0.08*	*0.2*	*3.6*	*35*	—	*1480*	*1480*	*trace*	*0*	*0*	*0*	*13.7*	*2*	*638*	*32*	*44*	*0.44*	*2.4*	*0.04*	*88*	*28*	*20*
canned, sweetened	80.9	0.4	0.1	—	18.2	0.2	68	450	0.01	0.02	0.7	3.4	—	690	50	trace	0	0	0	+	5	31	5	—	—	0.4	—	14	—	—
dried	24	3.0	0.6	—	69.4	3.5	265	3250	0.01	0.2	5.4	19	—	—	—	—	0	0	0	+	12	1100	44	—	—	6.9	0.3	126	—	—

* Vitamin A activity due to vitamin A + carotenes (see page 449): 1 IU vitamin A = 0.0006 mg β-carotene. ** Milliliters of N-acid or N-base. *** PA = pantothenic acid. † In canned juice 12.

Content per 100 grams edible portion (unless otherwise stated)	Water g	Proteins g	Fats: Total g	Fats: Cholesterol g	Carbohydrates: Total g	Carbohydrates: Fiber g	Calories kcal	Vitamins: A* IU	Vitamins: B_1 mg	Vitamins: B_2 mg	Vitamins: Nicotinic acid mg	Vitamins: C mg	Vitamins: Other vitamins*** mg	Other organic constituents: Malic acid mg	Citric acid mg	Oxalic acid mg	Uric acid mg	Purine bases mg	Excess acid ml**	Excess base ml**	Elements: Sodium Na mg	Potassium K mg	Calcium Ca mg	Magnesium Mg mg	Manganese Mn mg	Iron Fe mg	Copper Cu mg	Phosphorus P mg	Sulfur S mg	Chlorine Cl mg
Pears																														
fresh	83.2	0.5	0.4	0.014	15.5	1.5	61	20	0.02	0.04	0.1	4	B_6 0.15; PA 0.3	120	70	3	0	0	0	3.3	3	129	13	9	0.064	0.3	0.134	16	7	4
per lb. as purchased	*313*	*1.9*	*1.5*	*0.053*	*58*	*5.6*	*230*	*75*	*0.08*	*0.15*	*0.4*	*15*	*B_6 0.56; PA 1.1*	*452*	*260*	*11*	—	—	*0*	*12.3*	*11.3*	*485*	*49*	*34*	*0.24*	*1.1*	*0.5*	*60*	*26*	*15*
1 pear, 2½" dia.	*125*	*0.8*	*0.6*	*0.021*	*23.4*	*2.3*	*92*	*30*	*0.03*	*0.06*	*0.2*	*6*	*B_6 0.23; PA 0.5*	*180*	*110*	*5*	*0*	*0*	*0*	*5.2*	*4.5*	*195*	*20*	*14*	*0.10*	*0.5*	*0.22*	*24*	*11*	*6*
canned, sweetened	81.1	0.2	0.1	—	18.4	0.8	68	trace	0.01	0.02	0.1	1.7	—	—	—	—	0	0	0	+	2	52	8	—	—	0.2	—	10	—	—
dried	24	2.3	0.4	0.06	72	6.1	301	45	0.07	0.15	—	0	—	—	—	—	0	0	0	+	—	—	30	—	—	5.4	—	165	—	91
Pineapple																														
fresh	86.7	0.4	0.2	—	12.2	0.5	47	130	0.08	0.02	0.2	24	PA 0.1	—	—	—	0	0	0	5.1	0.3	210	16	11	1.07	0.3	0.07	11	2.5	46
canned, sweetened	78.0	0.4	0.1	—	21.1	0.3	78	80	0.07	0.02	0.2	8.8	—	120	840	6.3	0	0	0	+	1	120	29	—	—	0.6	—	7	—	—
Pineapple juice, canned	86.2	0.3	0.1	—	13.0	0.1	49	80	0.05	0.02	0.2	9	—	—	—	—	0	0	0	+	0.5	140	15	—	—	0.5	—	8	—	—
Plums																														
fresh	85.7	0.7	0.2	—	12.9	0.5	50	350	0.15	0.03	0.6	5	PA 0.03	920	30	10	0	0	0	4.5	0.6	170	17	11	0.096	0.5	0.08	20	5	2
per lb. as purchased	*369*	*3.0*	*0.9*	—	*56*	*2.2*	*215*	*1510*	*0.65*	*0.13*	*2.6*	*22*	*PA 0.13*	*3960*	*129*	*43*	*0*	*0*	*0*	*19.2*	*2.6*	*732*	*73*	*47*	*0.41*	*2.2*	*0.34*	*86*	*22*	*9*
1 plum 2" dia.	*49*	*0.4*	*0.1*	—	*7.4*	*0.3*	*32*	*200*	*0.09*	*0.02*	*0.3*	*3*	*PA 0.02*	*530*	*17*	*6*	*0*	*0*	*0*	*2.6*	*0.3*	*97*	*10*	*6*	*0.06*	*0.3*	*0.046*	*11*	*3*	*1*
canned, sweetened	78.6	0.4	0.1	—	20.4	0.3	76	230	0.03	0.03	0.4	1.8	—	—	—	—	0	0	0	+	18	110	8	—	—	1.1	—	12	—	—
dried	24.0	2.3	0.6	—	71.0	1.6	268	1890	0.10	0.16	1.7	3	—	—	—	—	0	0	0	20.6	5	848	54	40	—	3.9	—	85	28	9
Prunes																														
cooked, sweetened	55	1.0	0.2	—	43.2	0.6	165	750	0.03	0.06	0.6	1	—	—	—	—	—	—	0	+	—	—	22	—	—	1.5	—	34	—	—
dried, uncooked	24	2.3	0.6	—	71.0	1.6	268	1890	0.10	0.16	1.7	3	—	—	—	—	—	—	0	+	—	—	54	—	—	3.9	—	85	—	—
Quinces	84.0	0.3	0	0	14.1	—	52	—	—	—	—	10	—	—	—	—	—	—	0	0	—	—	14	—	—	0.3	—	—	—	—
Raisins																														
dried	24	2.3	0.5	—	71.2	1.8	268	50	0.15	0.08	0.5	trace	—	—	—	0	0	0	0	10.2	31	708	78	6	—	3.3	0.2	129	42	103
Raspberries																														
fresh	83	1.1	0.6	—	14.4	2.8	66	150	0.03	0.07	0.3	25	—	40	1300	—	0	0	0	5.3	3	190	49	23	0.51	1.0	0.13	37	18	22
canned, sweetened	71	0.6	0.5	—	28.0	1.9	119	100	0.02	—	—	—	—	—	—	—	0	0	0	+	2	—	20	—	—	0.5	—	20	—	—
Raspberry juice, fresh	88	0.2	0	—	11.0	—	45	100	0.03	—	—	25	—	—	—	—	0	0	0	4.6	5	134	20	18	0.36–7.0	—	—	10	9	10
Strawberries																														
fresh	90	0.8	0.6	0.009	8.1	1.2	37	60	0.03	0.07	0.3	60	K 0.1	160	1080	6	0	0	0	3.4	2	145	28	12	0.06	0.8	0.13	27	12	11
canned, sweetened	71	0.5	0.2	—	28.0	0.7	116	—	—	—	—	—	—	—	—	—	0	0	0	+	1	80	25	12	0.1	1.0	0.06	—	—	10
Tangerines	87	0.8	0.3	—	10.9	1.0	44	420	0.07	0.03	0.2	31	—	—	—	—	—	—	0	3.3	2.2	110	33	11	0.04	0.4	0.1	23	10	2
per lb. as purchased	*280*	*2.6*	*1.0*	—	*35.1*	*3.2*	*142*	*1353*	*0.23*	*0.10*	*0.6*	*100*	—	—	—	—	—	—	*0*	*10.7*	*7.1*	*354*	*106*	*35*	*0.13*	*1.3*	*0.32*	*74*	*33.2*	*6*
Vegetables																														
Artichokes, fresh	83.7	3.0	0.2	—	11.8	1.9	51	200	0.08	0.03	—	9	—	170	100	—	+	—	0	8.5	43	430	40	27	—	1.0	—	90	20	57
Asparagus																														
fresh	92.9	2.1	0.2	0.01	4.1	0.8	21	800	0.12	0.17	1.2	36	—	100	110	5.2	24	8	0	0.7	2	240	23	12	0.190	0.9	0.141	60	46	36
per lb. as purchased	*316*	*7.1*	*0.7*	*0.03*	*13.9*	*2.7*	*71*	*2720*	*0.41*	*0.58*	*4.1*	*122*	—	*340*	*374*	*18*	*81*	*27*	*0*	*2.4*	*6.8*	*816*	*78*	*41*	*0.65*	*3.1*	*0.48*	*204*	*156*	*122*
canned	93.6	1.6	0.3	—	3.0	0.5	17	600	0.06	0.09	0.8	15	—	—	—	+	+	+	0	+	410	130	20	—	—	1.9	—	53	—	—
Beans																														
kidney, fresh	12	21.4	1.6	—	61.6	4.0	338	0	0.67	0.23	2.2	2	PA 0.2	—	—	—	—	—	0	+	1.0	1300	163	—	—	6.9	0.7	437	—	—
per lb. as purchased	*54*	*97.2*	*7.3*	—	*279.4*	*18.1*	*1533*	*0*	*3.04*	*1.04*	*10.0*	*9*	*PA 0.9*	—	—	—	—	—	*0*	+	*4.5*	*5896*	*740*	—	—	*31.3*	*3.2*	*1984*	—	—
lima, fresh	67	7.5	0.8	—	23.5	1.5	128	280	0.21	0.11	1.4	32	PA 0.9	—	—	—	—	—	0	11.9	1.0	680	63	66	—	2.3	0.86	158	60	9
canned	75	5	0.4	—	18.3	2.0	95	180	0.03	0.05	0.5	6	—	—	—	—	—	—	0	+	2.0	210	29	—	—	1.7	—	77	—	—

* Vitamin A activity due to vitamin A + carotenes (see page 449): 1 IU vitamin A = 0.0006 mg β-carotene. ** Milliliters of N-acid or N-base. *** PA = pantothenic acid.

Content per 100 grams edible portion (unless otherwise stated)	Water g	Proteins g	Fats: Total g	Fats: Cholesterol g	Carbohydrates: Total g	Carbohydrates: Fiber g	Calories kcal	Vitamins: A* IU	Vitamins: B_1 mg	Vitamins: B_2 mg	Vitamins: Nicotinic acid mg	Vitamins: C mg	Other vitamins*** mg
Beans													
snap, fresh	89	2.4	0.2	—	7.7	1.4	35	630	0.08	0.11	0.5	19	—
canned	93	1.4	0.2	—	4.7	0.5	22	500	0.04	0.05	0.4	5	—
wax, fresh	89	2.4	0.2	—	7.7	1.4	35	150	0.08	0.11	0.5	19	—
canned	93	1.4	0.2	—	4.7	0.5	22	120	0.04	0.05	0.4	5	—
Beets (beetroots)													
peeled, fresh	87.6	1.6	0.1	—	9.6	0.9	42	6	0.03	0.04	0.3	5.5	—
tops	90.4	2.0	0.3	—	5.6	1.4	33	6700	0.05	0.17	0.3	34	—
Broccoli, fresh	90	3.3	0.2	—	5.5	1.3	29	3500	0.10	0.21	1.1	118	—
Brussels sprouts													
fresh	84.8	4.7	0.5	—	8.7	1.2	47	400	0.09	0.16	0.5	68	B_6 0.1
per lb. as purchased	*296*	*16.4*	*1.7*	—	*30.4*	*4.2*	*164*	*1397*	*0.31*	*0.56*	*1.7*	*238*	*B_6 0.35*
Cabbage													
fresh	91.8	1.6	0.1	—	5.7	1.0	25	100	0.06	0.05	0.26	40–70†	E 0.1; B_6 0.29; PA 0.16
per lb. as purchased	*304*	*5.3*	*0.3*	—	*18.9*	*3.3*	*83*	*331*	*0.20*	*0.17*	*0.86*	*130–230*	*E 0.3; B_6 0.96; PA 0.6*
dried	8.8	13.7	1.8	—	68.8	—	346	520	0.41	0.37	2.4	189	—
Carrots††													
fresh	88.6	1.1	0.2	0.001	9.1	1.0	40	2000–12000	0.13	0.06	0.64	4.3	E 0.45; PA 0.8; B_6 0.19; K 0.1
per lb. as purchased	*253*	*3.1*	*0.6*	*0.003*	*26.0*	*2.9*	*114*	*5200–34000*	*0.37*	*0.17*	*1.8*	*12*	*E 1.3; PA 2.3; B_6 0.54; K 0.3*
1 carrot, 6″	*44*	*0.5*	*0.1*	*0.0005*	*4.5*	*0.5*	*20*	*6000*	*0.06*	*0.03*	*0.3*	*2*	*E 0.2; PA 0.4 B_6 0.10; K 0.05*
canned	92.2	0.5	0.4	—	6.1	0.6	30	17570	0.03	0.02	0.3	0.8	—
dried	5.6	4.0	1.4	—	83.1	—	361	60000	0.29	0.28	3.2	11	—
Cauliflower, fresh	91.7	2.4	0.2	0.02	4.9	0.9	25	90	0.10	0.11	0.6	69	B_6 0.2; FA 0.2; PA 1.1; E 2.0; K 0.08–3
Celery													
leaves	93.3	1.1	0.2	—	4.3	0.9	20	0	0.03	0.04	0.3	7	E 0.46
stalk	88	1.7	0.3	—	9	1.4	46	—	—	—	—	4.9	—
Chicory and endives	93.1	1.7	0.2	—	4.1	0.9	20	3600	0.10	0.20	0.72	14	—
Corn (sweet)													
fresh	74	3.2	1.2	0.1	20.5	0.8	92	400‡	0.15	0.12	1.7	12	—
per lb. as purchased	*128*	*5.5*	*2.1*	*0.18*	*35.3*	*1.4*	*159*	*700‡*	*0.26*	*0.20*	*2.9*	*20*	—
canned, drained solids	76	2.7	0.7	—	20.2	1.1	85	230‡	0.03	0.06	0.9	5	—
Cucumbers													
fresh	95.6	0.8	0.1	—	3.0	0.6	13	200	0.04	0.05	0.18	10	—
1 cucumber 7½″ × 2″	*277*	*2.3*	*0.3*	—	*8.7*	*1.7*	*28*	*580*	*0.12*	*0.14*	*0.5*	*29*	—

Content per 100 grams edible portion (unless otherwise stated)	Other organic constituents: Malic acid mg	Citric acid mg	Oxalic acid mg	Uric acid mg	Purine bases mg	Excess acid ml**	Excess base ml**	Elements: Sodium Na mg	Potassium K mg	Calcium Ca mg	Magnesium Mg mg	Manganese Mn mg	Iron Fe mg	Copper Cu mg	Phosphorus P mg	Sulfur S mg	Chlorine Cl mg
Beans																	
snap, fresh	—	—	—	—	—	0	+	1.0	300	65	—	—	1.1	—	44	—	—
canned	—	—	—	—	—	0	+	—	—	36	—	—	1.7	—	23	—	—
wax, fresh	—	—	—	—	—	0	+	1.0	—	65	—	—	1.1	—	44	—	—
canned	—	—	—	—	—	0	+	—	—	36	—	—	1.7	—	23	—	—
Beets (beetroots)																	
peeled, fresh	—	—	338	—	—	0	1.3	11	350	30	23	0.577	1.0	0.187	78	78	61
tops	—	—	916	—	—	0	+	130	570	118	—	—	3.2	—	45	—	—
Broccoli, fresh	—	—	—	—	—	0	+	15	400	130	24	—	1.3	—	76	137	—
Brussels sprouts																	
fresh	200	240	5.9	0	0	0	+	12	400	26	—	—	1.0	—	50	184	—
per lb. as purchased	*700*	*840*	*20.7*	—	—	*0*	+	*42*	*1400*	*91*	—	—	*3.5*	—	*175*	*643*	—
Cabbage																	
fresh	100	140	7.3	6	2	0	4.6	15	294	43	12	0.114	0.6	0.099	23	67	39
per lb. as purchased	*330*	*460*	*24*	*19*	*7*	*0*	*15.3*	*49.7*	*974*	*142*	*40*	*0.377*	*2.0*	*0.33*	*76*	*222*	*129*
dried	—	—	—	+	+	0	+	—	—	374	—	—	4.7	—	274	—	—
Carrots††																	
fresh	240	90	33	0	2	0	8.9	48	311	41	17	0.247	0.9	0.111	34	21	42
per lb. as purchased	*686*	*257*	*94*	*0*	*5.7*	*0*	*25.1*	*137*	*889*	*117*	*49*	*0.71*	*2.6*	*0.317*	*97*	*60*	*121*
1 carrot, 6″	*120*	*45*	*16*	*0*	*1*	*0*	*4.4*	*24*	*155*	*20*	*8*	*0.12*	*0.4*	*0.06*	*17*	*10*	*21*
canned	—	—	—	0	(+)	0	+	280	110	22	—	—	0.6	—	24	—	30
dried	—	—	—	0	(+)	0	+	—	—	242	—	—	5.9	—	102	—	—
Cauliflower, fresh	390	210	0	24	8	0	5.3	16	400	22	6.6	0.17	1.1	0.14	72	29	30
Celery																	
leaves	170	10	50	15	5	0	8.6	96	291	50	27	—	0.5	—	40	22	137
stalk	—	—	620	+	+	0	+	100	300	50	—	—	0.8	—	70	—	—
Chicory and endives	—	—	27.3	+	+	0	10.8	18	400	104	13	—	—	—	38	32	71
Corn (sweet)																	
fresh	—	—	—	—	—	0	1.2	0.4	300	9	38	0.15	0.5	0.06	120	32	14
per lb. as purchased	—	—	—	—	—	*0*	*2.1*	*0.7*	*517*	*16*	*66*	*0.26*	*0.9*	*1.03*	*207*	*55*	*24*
canned, drained solids	—	—	—	—	—	0	+	2	200	5	—	—	0.6	—	52	—	—
Cucumbers																	
fresh	—	—	0	8	0	0	2.1	5	140	10	9	0.15	0.3	0.06	21	12	30
1 cucumber 7½″ × 2″	—	—	*0*	*23*	*0*	*0*	*6.2*	*2.3*	*410*	*29*	*26*	*0.43*	*0.9*	*0.17*	*61*	*35*	*87*

* Vitamin A activity due to vitamin A + carotenes (see page 449): 1 IU vitamin A = 0.0006 mg β-carotene. ** Milliliters of N-acid or N-base. *** PA = pantothenic acid; FA = folic acid.
† Inner parts richer in vitamin C. †† Vitamin A content in dark varieties 12,000, in light varieties 2000. ‡ Based on yellow corn; white contains only a trace.

Content per 100 grams edible portion (unless otherwise stated)	Water g	Proteins g	Fats: Total g	Fats: Cholesterol g	Carbohydrates: Total g	Carbohydrates: Fiber g	Calories kcal	Vitamins: A* IU	Vitamins: B_1 mg	Vitamins: B_2 mg	Vitamins: Nicotinic acid mg	Vitamins: C mg	Other vitamins*** mg	Other organic constituents: Malic acid mg	Citric acid mg	Oxalic acid mg	Uric acid mg	Purine bases mg	Excess acid ml**	Excess base ml**	Elements: Sodium Na mg	Potassium K mg	Calcium Ca mg	Magnesium Mg mg	Manganese Mn mg	Iron Fe mg	Copper Cu mg	Phosphorus P mg	Sulfur S mg	Chlorine Cl mg
Dandelion greens, fresh	85.8	2.7	0.7	—	8.8	1.8	44	13650	0.19	0.14	0.8	30	—	—	—	24.6	+	+	0	18.4	76	430	187	36	0.30	3.1	0.15	70	17	99
Eggplant, fresh	93	1.1	0.2	0.002	5.5	0.9	24	30	0.04	0.05	0.6	5	—	—	—	—	—	—	0	2.8	0.9	190	15	10	0.11	0.4	0.07	37	9	24
Kale, fresh	87	3.9	0.6	—	7.2	1.2	40	7540	0.10	0.26	2.0	115	E 2–3; B_6 0.1–0.3; PA 0.1–1.4	—	—	—	—	—	0	15.3	110	410	225	37	0.5	2.2	0.09	62	115	122
Kohlrabi																														
leaves	89.3	3.1	0.4	—	5.4	1.2	30	9540	0.10	0.56	0.8	136	E 2.2	—	—	+	+	+	0	17.1	10	440	259	19	—	1.5	—	50	54	92
tubers	90.5	2.1	0.2	—	6.2	1.1	29	trace	0.06	0.06	0.5	28	PA 0.1	230	0	1.8	33	11	0	3.6	37	230	40	16	0.083	0.5	0.085	34	58	52
Leeks, leaves	90	1.8	0.4	0	4	1.3	24	6500	0.12	—	—	25	—	—	—	—	—	—	0	11.1	40	260	120	20	—	2	—	34	23	50
Lentils, dried	10	25.7	1.0	0.04	59.2	3.7	339	570	0.50	0.32	3.10	5	PA 0.9	—	—	—	162	54	5.9	0	3	1200	59	86	—	8.6	0.7	438	277	60
Lettuce, headed, fresh	94.8	1.3	0.2	—	2.8	0.6	15	540	0.06	0.07	0.2	8	E 0.45; PA 0.1	170	20	7.1	9	3	0	1.3	12	140	22	11	0.777	0.5	0.069	25	18	73
Mushrooms (field mushrooms)	90	4	0.15	0	3.3	0.8	26	+	0.15	—	1	—	biotin 0.017; PA 1.75; PAB 0.13	—	—	—	15	—	0	2.9	70	230	3	2	—	—	—	37	52	25
Onions																														
fresh, ripe	88.8	1.4	0.2	—	9.0	0.8	40	50	0.03	0.02	0.1	12	E 0.27; PA 0.13	170	20	23	0	0	1.5	0	1	130	32	15	0.363	0.5	0.13	44	68	24
1 onion 2½"	*98*	*1.5*	*0.2*	—	*9.9*	*0.9*	*44*	*55*	*0.03*	*0.02*	*0.1*	*13*	*E 0.3; PA 0.14*	*187*	*22*	*25*	*0*	*0*	*1.6*	*0*	*1*	*140*	*35*	*16*	*0.39*	*0.5*	*0.14*	*48*	*75*	*26*
dried	9.9	10.1	1.0	—	75.2	—	350	20	0.23	0.15	1.1	37	—	—	—	—	0	0	+	0	—	—	158	—	—	3.1	—	256	—	—
Parsley, fresh	84	3.7	1.0	—	9.0	1.8	50	8230	0.11	0.28	1.4	181	—	—	—	165	+	+	0	16.3	28	880	190	52	0.94	3.2	0.21	80	190	156
Parsnips, fresh	79	1.5	0.5	—	18.2	2.2	78	0	0.08	0.12	0.2	18	—	—	—	—	—	—	0	6.6	16.5	342	57	22	0.03–0.34	0.7	0.10	80	26	30
Peas, green, fresh, unripe	75.0	6.7	0.4	—	17.0	2.2	90	690	0.30	0.18	1.9	26	E 2.1; B_6 0.18; K 0.3; FA 0.3	80	110	0	54	18	0	1.2	0.9	380	22	27	0.41	2.0	0.23	118	56	33
canned	82.3	3.4	0.4	—	12.9	1.3	69	540	0.11	0.06	0.9	9.4	—	—	—	0	+	+	0	+	270	96	25	—	—	1.8	—	67	—	—
dried	10.0	24.5	1.0	—	61.7	4.4	354	370	0.87	0.29	3.0	2	biotin 0.017	—	—	0	++	++	0	+	42	880	73	140	1.99	6.0	0.802	397	196	44
Peppers, green, fresh	92.8	1.2	0.2	—	5.3	1.4	24	630	0.07	0.04	0.4	120	PA 0.2; E 2.5	—	—	16	+	+	0	3.2	0.5	186	11	12	0.126	0.4	0.107	25	19	13–19
Potato chips	3	6.7	37.1	—	49.1	1.1	544	50	0.18	0.11	3.2	11	—	—	—	—	—	—	0	+	340	880	30	—	—	1.9	—	152	—	—
Potatoes, raw	77.8	2.0	0.1	0.003	19.1	0.4	85	40	0.10	0.04	1.0	23	E 0.06; B_6 0.2; FA 0.1; PA 0.3; K 0.08	0	510	5.7	6	1	0	7.8	0.8	410	14	27	0.173	0.8	0.164	52	29	35
per lb. as purchased	*296*	*7.6*	*0.4*	*0.01*	*73*	*1.5*	*324*	*152*	*0.38*	*0.15*	*3.8*	*88*	*E 0.23; B_6 0.76; FA 0.4; PA 1.2; K 0.28*	*0*	*1940*	*21.7*	*23*	*3.8*	*0*	*27.2*	*3*	*1560*	*53*	*103*	*0.66*	*3.0*	*0.62*	*198*	*110*	*133*
dried	7.2	7.1	0.7	—	82.0	—	363	400	0.25	0.10	4.8	26	—	0	—	—	0	(+)	.0	+	—	—	25	—	—	3.7	—	103	—	—
Pumpkins, fresh	95.0	0.8	0.1	—	3.5	0.6	15	3400	0.05	0.08	0.6	8	—	—	—	—	0	0	0	8.8	1	457	21	12	0.04	0.8	0.1	44	13	49
Radishes, fresh	93.7	1.1	0.1	—	4.2	0.7	20	30	0.04	0.04	0.1	24	—	—	—	0	15	5	0	4.0	8	229	37	15	0.05	1.0	0.13	31	37	37
Rhubarb, fresh	94.9	0.5	0.1	—	3.8	0.7	16	30	0.01	—	0.1	9	—	1770	410	100–900	12	—	0	10.1	15	358	51	16	—	0.5	0.05	25	8	53
Soybeans, dried	7.5	34.9	18.1	—	35.0	4.4	331	110	1.14	0.31	2.1	trace	E10; B_6 0.5; PA 1.4	—	—	—	+	+	0	32.4	4	1900	227	310	—	8.0	0.12	586	240	30

* Vitamin A activity due to vitamin A + carotenes (see page 449): 1 IU vitamin A = 0.0006 mg β-carotene. ** Milliliters of N-acid or N-base. *** PA = pantothenic acid; FA = folic acid; PAB = para-aminobenzoic acid.

Content per 100 grams edible portion (unless otherwise stated)	Water	Proteins	Fats: Total	Fats: Cholesterol	Carbohydrates: Total	Carbohydrates: Fiber	Calories	Vitamins: A*	Vitamins: B_1	Vitamins: B_2	Vitamins: Nicotinic acid	Vitamins: C	Other vitamins***	Other organic constituents: Malic acid	Citric acid	Oxalic acid	Uric acid	Purine bases	Excess acid	Excess base	Elements: Sodium Na	Potassium K	Calcium Ca	Magnesium Mg	Manganese Mn	Iron Fe	Copper Cu	Phosphorus P	Sulfur S	Chlorine Cl
	g	g	g	g	g	g	kcal	IU	mg	mg	mg	mg	mg	mg	mg	mg	mg	mg	ml**	ml**	mg	mg	mg	mg	mg	mg	mg	mg	mg	mg
Spinach																														
fresh	92.1	2.2	0.3	0.006	3.9	0.7	22	9420	0.08	0.20	0.5	59	B_6 0.08–0.5; PA 0.7; E 6.0; FA 0.28; PAB 0.1	90	80	320–900	72	24	0	16.9	42	489	87	55	0.828	3.0	0.197	45	27	65
per lb. as purchased	*343*	*8.2*	*1.1*	*0.02*	*14.5*	*2.6*	*82*	*35040*	*0.3*	*0.74*	*1.9*	*219*	*B_6 0.3–1.9; PA 2.6; E 22; FA 1.0; PAB 0.35*	*334*	*298*	*1190–3340*	*267*	*89*	*0*	*63*	*305*	*1560*	*324*	*205*	*3.07*	*11.2*	*0.73*	*168*	*100*	*242–275*
canned	92.3	2.3	0.4	—	3.0	0.6	22	7630	0.02	0.08	0.3	14	—	—	—	+++	++	+	0	+	300	260	90	—	—	1.6	—	33	—	—
Sweet potatoes																														
fresh	69	1.8	0.7	—	27.9	1.0	123	7700	0.09	0.05	0.6	22	PA 0.3	—	—	—	—	—	0	7.2	4.0	530	30	12	0.15–0.52	0.7	0.15	49	14.9	85
canned	72	2.0	0.1	—	25.0	1.0	107	8850	0.05	0.04	0.5	14	—	—	—	—	—	—	0	+	48	200	25	—	—	0.8	—	41	—	—
Sauerkraut	93.2	1.1	0.2	—	3.4	1.4	20	trace	0.03	0.20	0.2	18	—	—	—	—	+	+	0	+	730	490	46	—	—	0.5	—	31	—	—
Tomatoes																														
fresh	94.1	1.0	0.3	—	4.0	0.6	23	1100	0.06	0.04	0.6	23	E 0.27; PA 0.1	150	390	0–5	—	—	0	4.9	4	268	11	12	0.189	0.6	0.097	27	14	40
1 tomato, 2½" dia.	*141*	*1.5*	*0.4*	—	*6.0*	*0.9*	*34*	*1650*	*0.09*	*0.06*	*0.9*	*34*	*E 0.4; PA 0.15*	*225*	*585*	*11*	—	—	*0*	*7.3*	*6*	*400*	*16*	*18*	*0.28*	*0.9*	*0.15*	*40*	*21*	*60*
canned	94.2	1.0	0.2	—	3.9	0.5	21	1050	0.05	0.03	0.7	16	—	—	—	—	—	—	0	+	18	130	11	—	—	0.6	—	27	—	—
Tomato catsup	69.5	2.0	0.4	—	24.5	0.4	98	1880	0.09	0.07	1.8	28	—	—	—	—	—	—	0	+	1300	800	12	—	—	0.8	—	18	—	—
Tomato juice, canned	93.5	1.0	0.2	—	4.3	0	23	1050	0.05	0.03	0.7	15.6	—	23	336	—	—	—	0	5.1	230	230	7	10	—	0.4	—	15	5	380
Turnips																														
fresh	91	1.1	0.2	—	7.1	1.1	32	trace	0.05	0.07	0.5	28	B_6 0.1; PA 0.3	—	—	—	—	—	0	5.4	37	230	40	7	0.04	0.5	0.07	34	22	41
greens	90	2.9	0.4	—	5.4	1.2	30	9540	0.09	0.46	0.8	136	—	—	—	—	—	—	0	15.0	10	440	260	19	1.42	2.4	0.09	50	54	168
Water cress	95	1.7	0.5	—	3.7	0.5	22	4000	0.10	0.27	0.8	75	PA 0.2	—	—	—	+	+	0	5.9	60	301	187	17	0.54	2.0	0.04	46	147	109
Nuts																														
Almonds, dried	4.7	18.6	54.1	0.05	19.6	2.0	596	75	0.25	0.67	4.6	trace	PA 0.4	—	—	—	—	—	0	11.4	3.0	690	254	252	1.94	4.4	0.14	475	150	2
Brazil nuts	5	14.4	65.9	—	11.0	2.1	646	10	0.5	—	—	—	—	—	—	—	—	—	12.6	0	16	601	120	225	0.32	2.8	1.09	600	198	81
Cashew nuts, roasted or cooked	4	18.5	48.2	—	27.0	1.3	578	—	0.63	0.19	2.1	—	—	—	—	—	—	—	0	0	14	560	46	267	—	5.0	—	428	—	—
Chestnuts																														
fresh	48	3.4	1.9	0.02	45.6	1.3	213	80	0.23	—	1.17	6	—	—	—	—	—	—	0	6.7	7	410	30	42	3.7	0.7	0.06	90	48	11
dried	9	6.7	4.1	—	79	2.5	380	—	—	—	—	—	—	—	—	—	—	—	0	+	—	—	—	—	—	—	—	—	—	—
Coconuts																														
fresh	48	4.2	34.0	—	12.8	3.3	351	—	0.09	0.02	0.4	2	E 2.7	—	—	—	—	—	0	6.1	30	363	20	39	1.31	2.7	0.32	100	32	13
dried	3.3	3.6	39.1	—	53.2	4.1	579	0	0.03	trace	trace	0	PA 0.2	—	—	—	—	—	0	+	53	693	43	77	—	3.6	—	191	76	225
Hazelnuts	6	12.7	60.9	—	18	3.4	671	100	0.40	—	—	3	—	—	—	—	—	—	0	1.0	19	618	290	140	4.2	4.1	1.35	350	198	67
Peanuts, roasted	5.2	30.6	46.1	—	18.2	3.3	560	360	0.30	0.15	21.6	0	B_6 12; E 16; biotin 0.03; PA 1.75	—	—	—	—	—	13.5	0	2.0	740	74	167	1.51	1.9	0.27	393	377	41
Pecans	3	9.4	73.0	—	13.0	2.2	696	50	0.72	0.11	0.9	2	—	—	—	—	—	—	+	0	0.3	420	74	152	3.48	2.4	1.36	324	5.6	50
Walnuts	3.3	15.0	64.4	—	15.6	2.1	654	30	0.26	0.14	1.0	3	B_6 1.0; FA 0.16; PA 0.7	—	—	—	—	—	7.7	0	4	450	83	134	1.8	2.1	0.31	380	146	36

* Vitamin A activity due to vitamin A + carotenes (see page 449): 1 IU vitamin A = 0.0006 mg β-carotene. ** Milliliters of N-acid or N-base. *** PA = pantothenic acid; FA = folic acid; PAB = para-aminobenzoic acid.

Content per 100 grams edible portion (unless otherwise stated)	Water g	Proteins g	Fats: Total g	Fats: Cholesterol g	Carbohydrates: Total g	Carbohydrates: Fiber g	Calories kcal	Vitamins: A* IU	Vitamins: B_1 mg	Vitamins: B_2 mg	Vitamins: Nicotinic acid mg	Vitamins: C mg	Other vitamins*** mg	Other organic constituents: Malic acid mg	Citric acid mg	Oxalic acid mg	Uric acid mg	Purine bases mg	Excess acid ml**	Excess base ml**	Elements: Sodium Na mg	Potassium K mg	Calcium Ca mg	Magnesium Mg mg	Manganese Mn mg	Iron Fe mg	Copper Cu mg	Phosphorus P mg	Sulfur S mg	Chlorine Cl mg
Cereals, Cereal products																														
Barley, pearled	12	9.0	1.4	—	76.5	0.8	346	0	0.12	0.08	3.1	0	—	0	0	0	0	0	14.2	0	3	160	16	37	1.684	2.0	0.753	189	116	105
Bread																														
Boston, enriched, brown	45	4.8	2.1	—	46.0	0.3	219	140	0.08	0.12	1.4	0	—	—	—	—	—	—	+	0	—	—	185	—	—	2.5	—	158	—	—
corn or muffins, enriched	49	6.7	4.7	—	36.6	0.2	219	130	0.17	0.23	1.3	0	—	—	—	—	—	—	+	0	—	—	139	—	—	1.9	—	155	—	—
raisin, enriched	30	7.1	3.1	—	57.8	0.2	284	10	0.07	0.11	0.9	0	—	—	—	—	—	—	+	0	—	—	80	—	—	1.8	—	104	—	—
rye, American	35	9.1	1.2	—	52.4	0.4	244	0	0.18	0.08	1.5	0	—	—	—	—	—	—	+	0	600	160	72	—	—	1.6	—	147	—	—
white, enriched, 4% nonfat milk solids	35	8.5	3.2	—	51.8	0.2	275	0	0.24	0.15	2.2	0	—	—	—	—	—	—	+	0	600	180	79	—	—	0.6	—	92	—	—
toasted	26	9.7	3.7	—	59.0	0.2	313	0	0.22	0.18	2.5	0	—	—	—	—	—	—	+	0	—	—	90	—	—	2.1	—	105	—	—
whole-wheat	37	9.3	2.6	—	49.0	1.5	240	0	0.30	0.13	3.0	0	—	—	—	—	—	—	+	0	600†	230	96	—	—	2.2	—	263	—	—
Bread rolls																														
plain, unenriched	29	9.0	5.5	—	55.1	0.2	1.9	0	0.06	0.11	1.0	0	—	—	—	—	—	—	+	0	—	—	55	—	—	0.7	—	96	—	—
sweet, unenriched	28	8.5	7.8	—	53.8	0.2	323	0	0.05	0.13	1.0	0	—	—	—	—	—	—	+	0	—	—	63	—	—	0.6	—	104	—	—
Cornflakes	4	7.9	0.7	—	80.3	0.6	359	0	0.16	0.08	1.6	0	—	0	0	0	0	0	+	0	660	160	10	—	—	1.0	0.19	56	—	—
Cornstarch	12	0.5	0.3	—	86.9	0.2	362	0	0	0	0	0	—	0	0	0	0	0	+	0	4	4	trace	—	—	trace	—	trace	—	—
Crackers																														
graham	6	8.0	10.0	—	74.3	0.8	393	0	0.30	0.12	1.5	0	—	—	—	—	—	—	+	0	710	330	20	—	—	1.9	—	203	—	—
saltines	5	9.2	11.8	—	71.1	0.4	431	0	0.06	0.04	1.0	0	—	—	—	—	—	—	+	0	—	—	19	—	—	1.0	—	92	—	—
soda	6	9.6	9.6	—	72.7	0.2	420	0	0.06	0.05	1.1	0	—	—	—	—	—	—	+	0	1100	120	20	—	—	1.1	—	96	—	—
Flour																														
buckwheat, light	12	6.3	1.1	—	79.7	0.5	354	0	0.31	0.08	2.1	0	—	0	0	0	0	0	2.4	0	1	132	11	48	—	1.0	0.7	88	71	12
corn, whole, unbolted	12	9.2	3.9	—	73.7	1.6	355	510	0.38	0.11	2.0	0	PA 0.05; B_6 1.0	—	—	—	—	—	+	0	2	120	10	86	—	2.4	—	256	127	—
rice	12	7.4	0.5	—	80	0.4	354	0	0.04	—	0.1-0.3	0	E 0.35	0	0	0	0	0	+	0	—	79	10	28	—	0.9	—	100	—	6
rye, dark	12	11.0	1.9	—	73.1	—	319	0	0.47	0.21	1.7	0	—	0	0	0	0	0	3.8	0	61	450	61	155	3.067	4.8	0.656	369	146	40
self-raising, enriched	12	9.2	1.0	—	73.8	0.4	350	0	0.44	0.26	3.5	0	—	—	—	—	—	—	+	0	—	90	272	—	—	2.9	—	484	—	—
soybean, full fat	9	35.9	20.6	—	29.9	2.3	347	140	0.77	0.28	0.3	0	—	—	—	—	++	++	+	0	—	—	195	223	—	12.1	—	553	300	24
medium fat	9	42.5	6.5	—	37.2	2.6	264	110	0.82	0.34	0.25	0	—	0	0	0	++	++	+	0	0.6	1700	244	—	—	13.0	—	610	290	24
wheat, whole	12	12.2	2.3	—	71.8	2.1	334	0	0.56	0.12	1–4	0	E 2.2; B_6 0.4; PA 2	0	0	0	0	0	+	0	—	324	38	122	4.28	2.3	0.435	385	124	177
white, unenriched	12	10.8	1.1	—	75.5	0.3	370	0	0.07	0.03	0.06–0.08	0	E 1.2	0	0	0	0	0	8.7	0	1	130	19	21	0.713	0.7	0.147	93	109	71
Macaroni, unenriched, dry	9	12.8	1.4	—	76.5	0.4	377	0	0.09	0.06	2.0	0	—	—	—	—	—	—	10.9	0	5	160	22	36	—	1.5	—	165	136	52
Muffins, unenriched	37	8.0	8.4	—	42.1	0.1	280	100	0.05	0.13	0.4	0	—	—	—	—	—	—	+	0	—	—	206	—	—	0.6	—	191	—	—
Noodles, unenriched, dry	10	12.6	3.4	—	73.2	0.4	381	200	0.20	0.11	2.3	0	—	—	—	—	—	—	+	0	10	—	22	—	—	2.1	—	199	—	—
Oatflakes	10.0	13.0	7.5	—	67.8	1.9	385	0	0.55	0.14	1.1	0	PA 1.0; E 1.9; B_6 0.75; PAB 0.03	0	0	0	0	0	13.7	0	2	340	54	145	4.945	5.2	0.738	365	199	49
cooked	85	2.8	0.5	—	11.5	0.2	62	0	—	—	—	0	—	0	0	0	0	0	+	0	—	—	11	—	—	0.6	—	65	—	—
Pancakes, wheat, unenriched	55	6.8	9.2	—	26.6	0.1	218	200	0.06	0.13	0.3	trace	—	—	—	—	—	—	+	0	—	—	158	—	—	0.6	—	154	—	—
Pie crust, plain, unenriched	10	7.5	26.9	—	53.1	0.2	487	0	0.03	0.02	0.5	0	—	—	—	—	—	—	+	0	—	—	11	—	—	0.5	—	65	—	—
Popcorn, popped	4	12.7	5.0	—	76.7	2.2	386	0	0.39	0.12	2.2	0	—	—	—	—	—	—	+	0	3	240	11	—	—	2.7	—	281	—	—
Pretzels	8	8.8	3.2	—	74.5	0.3	369	0	0.01	0.04	0.7	0	—	—	—	—	—	—	+	0	1700	130	12	—	—	0.7	—	71	—	—

* Vitamin A activity due to vitamin A + carotenes (see page 449): 1 IU vitamin A = 0.0006 mg β-carotene. ** Milliliters of N-acid or N-base. *** PA = pantothenic acid; PAB = para-aminobenzoic acid.
† Varies with amount of added salt.

Content per 100 grams edible portion (unless otherwise stated)	Water	Proteins	Fats		Carbohydrates		Calories	Vitamins						Other organic constituents					Excess acid	Excess base	Elements									
			Total	Cholesterol	Total	Fiber		A*	B_1	B_2	Nicotinic acid	C	Other vitamins***	Malic acid	Citric acid	Oxalic acid	Uric acid	Purine bases			Sodium Na	Potassium K	Calcium Ca	Magnesium Mg	Manganese Mn	Iron Fe	Copper Cu	Phosphorus P	Sulfur S	Chlorine Cl
	g	g	g	g	g	g	kcal	IU	mg	mg	mg	mg	mg	mg	mg	mg	mg	mg	ml**	ml**	mg	mg	mg	mg	mg	mg	mg	mg	mg	mg
Rice																														
polished, raw	11.8	8.2	0.46	0.027	79.3	0.2	363	0	0.07	0.03	3.4	0	PA 0.5	0	0	0	0	0	6.1	0	2	79	24	28	1.014	1.4	0.183	104	79	6
cooked	74	2.2	0.1	—	22.5	0.1	100	0	0.01	0.01	0.4	0	—	0	0	0	0	+	+	0	—	—	8	—	—	0.2	—	45	—	—
whole	12	7.5	1.7	—	77.7	0.6	356	0	0.29	0.05	4.6	0	—	0	0	0	0	4	+	0	—	342	39	119	—	5.5	—	303	—	23
Rice bran	9	11.6	10.1	—	64	2.2	393	—	2.20	0.23	96.6	0	—	0	0	0	—	—	+	0	—	—	60	—	—	16.0	—	1450	—	—
Rice flakes	4	5.9	0.6	—	87.7	0.5	392	0	0.08	0.08	0.9	0	—	—	—	—	—	—	+	0	720	180	21	—	—	1.8	—	116	—	—
Semolina, corn	12	8.3	1.2	—	78.0	—	356	300	0.15	0.06	0.9	0	—	0	0	0	0	0	7.2	0	0.6	213	10	84	—	0.2	—	140	111	146
Spaghetti, unenriched, dry	9	12.8	1.4	—	76.5	0.4	377	0	0.09	0.06	2.0	0	—	—	—	—	—	—	+	0	5	—	22	—	—	1.5	—	165	—	—
Tapioca, dry	12.6	0.6	0.2	—	86.4	0.1	350	0	—	0.10	—	0	—	0	0	0	0	0	0	0	4	20	12	2	—	1.0	—	12	4	16
Waffles, baked, unenriched	40	9.3	10.6	—	37.8	0.1	287	360	0.06	0.18	0.4	0	—	—	—	—	—	—	+	0	—	—	192	—	—	1.0	—	204	—	—
Wheat																														
flakes	4	10.8	1.6	—	80.2	1.7	355	0	0.08	0.18	4.8	0	—	—	—	—	—	—	+	0	1300	320	46	—	—	3.0	—	329	—	—
germ	11	25.2	10	—	49.5	2.5	389	0	2.05	0.80	4.6	0	E 27; B_6 3.7; PA 2.0; PAB 0.17	0	0	0	—	—	+	0	2	780	84	—	4.2	8.1	1.3	1096	—	—
Confectionery, Sugar																														
Chocolate																														
sweetened, milk	1	6.0	33.5	—	54.0	0.5	542	183	0.10	0.04	0.8	0	E 5.3; biotin 0.03	—	—	35	—	—	4.0	0	86	420	216	58	—	4.0	—	400	67	151
plain	1	2.0	29.8	0.06	62.7	1.4	471	30	0.03	0.15	0.6	0	E 5.3; biotin 0.03	—	—	80	—	—	3.3	0	30	230	63	107	—	2.8	—	287	32	71
unsweetened	2.3	5.5	52.9	—	18	—	570	30	0.03	0.24	1.1	0	E 5.3; biotin 0.03	—	—	80	—	—	4.4	0	10	442	95	107	—	6.8	—	343	95	71
Dextrose, anhydrous	trace	0	0	—	99.5	0	387	0	0	0	0	0	—	0	0	0	0	0	0	0	0	0	0	0	0	0	0	0	0	0
Honey	20	0.3	0	—	79.5	—	294	0	trace	0.04	0.2	4	PA 0.2	—	50	—	—	—	0	0.1	5	10	5	6	0.209	0.9	0.2	16	5	trace
Jams	28	0.5	0.3	—	70.8	0.6	278	10	0.02	0.02	0.2	6	—	—	—	—	—	—	0	+	13	13	12	—	—	0.3	—	12	—	—
Jellies	34.5	0.2	0	—	65.0	0	252	10	0.02	0.02	0.2	4	—	—	—	—	—	—	0	0	12	—	12	—	12	0.3	—	12	—	—
Molasses	24	2.4	0	—	60	0	240	0	0.08	0.16	2.8	0	PA 0.5	—	—	—	—	—	0	34	43	1238	273	81	—	6.7	—	51	50	501
Sirup (chiefly corn sirup)	25	0	0	—	74.0	—	286	0	0	0.01	0.1	0	—	—	—	—	—	—	0	+	68	—	46	10	—	4.1	—	16	—	74
Sugar																														
brown	3	0	0	—	96	—	377	0	0	0	0	0	—	0	0	0	0	0	0	+	24	230	76	—	—	2.6	—	40	—	76
cane or beet, white	trace	0	0	—	99.5	0	387	0	0	0	0	0	—	0	0	0	0	0	0	0	0.3	0.5	0	0	0	0	0	0	0	0
Fats, Oils†																														
Butter	15.5	0.6	81	0.28	0.4	0	716	3300	trace	0.01	0.1	0	D 60 IU††; B_6 0.15; E 2.4	0	0	0	0	0	+	0	10	14	16	1	6	0.2	—	16	9	—
Cod-liver oil	0	0	100	0.85	0	0	902	ca. 10^5	0	0	0	0	D 8000–30,000 IU	0	0	0	0	0	0	0	0	0	0	0	0	0	0	0	0	0
Lard	trace	0	100	—	0	0	900	0	0	0	0	0	D 2800; E 2.0	0	0	0	0	0	0	0	1	10	0.6	0.2	0	4	trace	0	0	0
Mayonnaise	16	1.5	78	—	3.0	0	720	10–210	0.02	0.02	0.2	6	—	0	0	0	0	0	+	—	600	17	19	—	—	1.0	—	60	—	—
Olive oil	trace	0	100	—	0	0	900	—	0	0	0	0	E 8.0	0	0	0	0	0	0	0	0	0	0	0	0	0	0	0	0	0
Peanut butter	2	26.1	47.8	—	21.0	2.0	576	0	0.12	0.13	16.2	0	—	—	—	—	—	—	+	0	5	820	74	178	—	1.9	—	393	225	—

* Vitamin A activity due to vitamin A + carotenes (see page 449): 1 IU vitamin A = 0.0006 mg β-carotene. ** Milliliters of N-acid or N-base. *** PA = pantothenic acid; PAB = para-aminobenzoic acid.
† Margarine is not included in this table because of the variability of its composition. †† In summer; in winter less.

Content per 100 grams edible portion (unless otherwise stated)	Water g	Proteins g	Fats: Total g	Fats: Cholesterol g	Carbohydrates: Total g	Carbohydrates: Fiber g	Calories kcal	Vitamins: A* IU	Vitamins: B_1 mg	Vitamins: B_2 mg	Vitamins: Nicotinic acid mg	Vitamins: C mg	Vitamins: Other vitamins*** mg	Other organic constituents: Malic acid mg	Citric acid mg	Oxalic acid mg	Uric acid mg	Purine bases mg	Excess acid ml**	Excess base ml**	Elements: Sodium Na mg	Potassium K mg	Calcium Ca mg	Magnesium Mg mg	Manganese Mn mg	Iron Fe mg	Copper Cu mg	Phosphorus P mg	Sulfur S mg	Chlorine Cl mg
Dairy products, Eggs																														
Butter. See under Fats, above																														
Cheese																														
Camembert	51	19.7	25.2	0.14	0	0	306	3610	0	0.83	1.6	0	E 1.0	0	0	0	0	0	+	0	340	90	680	—	—	0.9	—	500	—	—
Cheddar	37	25.0	32.2	0.16	2.1	0	398	1400	0.02	0.42	trace	0	—	—	—	—	—	—	+	0	700	92	725	—	—	1.0	—	495	—	—
Cottage	77	19.5	0.5	—	2.0	0	95	20	0.02	0.31	0.1	0	—	—	—	—	—	—	+	0	20	72	96	—	—	0.3	—	189	—	—
Cream	53	7.1	36.9	0.14	2.0	0	368	2000	0.02	0.20	0.06	0	E 1.0	0	0	0	0	0	+	0	340	90	30	—	—	0.1	—	40	—	—
Limburger	38	23.5	32.4	0.135	1.0	0	390	2000	0.02	0.2	0.06	0	E 1.0	0	0	0	0	0	+	0	400	100	440	—	—	0.6	—	570	—	—
Parmesan	29	36.3	27.4	0.19	2	0	400	1350	0.03	0.53	0.11	0	E 1.0	0	0	0	0	0	+	0	880	131	1220	—	—	1.9	—	770	218	1350
Roquefort	37	21.7	33.2	0.135	1	0	390	4010	0.03	0.45	1.24	0	E 1.0	0	0	0	0	0	+	0	—	—	700	—	—	1.0	—	360	—	—
Swiss (Emmentaler)	34	28.6	31.3	0.145	2	0	404	4010	0.03	0.45	1.24	0	E 1.0	0	0	0	0	0	+	0	420	110	1090	—	—	1.2	—	810	—	—
Cream																														
light	73	2.5	20.0	0.10	4.0	0	206	1250	0.03	0.13	0.1	1	D 50 IU	—	—	0	0	0	0	1.1	40	130	90	10	—	0.2	—	80	30	80
heavy	59	2.3	35.0	0.13	3	0	336	2250	0.03	0.15	0.1	1	D 100 IU	—	—	0	0	0	0	+	30	91	90	10	—	0.2	—	70	—	—
Eggs																														
whole, raw	74	12.8	11.5	0.463	0.7	—	158	1140	0.12	0.34	0.1	0	B_6 0.3; B_{12} 0.7 µg; FA 0.008; PA 2.7; D 170 IU; K 0.2; E 1.1; biotin 0.04	0	0	0	0	0	17.9	0	130	100	54	13	0.033	2.7	0.253	210	197	144
Egg white, raw	87.8	10.8	—	0	1.0	—	47	0	0	0.23	0.08	0	B_6 0.2; B_{12} 0.08 µg; FA 0.002; PA 0.3; biotin 0.007	0	0	0	0	0	8.2	0	150	100	6	11	—	0.2	—	17	208	161
Egg yolk, raw	49.4	16.3	31.9	1.3	0.7	—	355	3210	0.32	0.52	0.02	0	E 1.1; B_6 0.3; B_{12} 1.8 µg; FA 0.022; PA 3; D 1000 IU; biotin 0.05	0	0	0	0	0	36.7	0	85	100	147	16	—	7.2	0.4	564	194	124
1 egg, medium (48 grams)	*35.5*	*6.1*	*5.5*	*0.22*	*0.35*	—	*76*	*547*	*0.06*	*0.16*	*0.05*	*0*	(Calculate from 100 gram data above)	*0*	*0*	*0*	*0*	*0*	*8.6*	*0*	*62*	*48*	*26*	*6*	*0.016*	*1.3*	*0.12*	*101*	*95*	*48*
1 egg white, medium (31 grams)	*27*	*3.3*	—	*0*	*0.3*	—	*15*	*0*	*0*	*0.07*	*0.02*	*0*	(Calculate from 100 gram data above)	*0*	*0*	*0*	*0*	*0*	*2.5*	*0*	*47*	*31*	*2*	*3*	—	*0.06*	—	*5*	*64*	*48*
1 egg yolk, medium (17 grams)	*8.5*	*2.8*	*5.4*	*0.22*	*0.05*	—	*61*	*547*	*0.06*	*0.88*	*0.03*	*0*	(Calculate from 100 gram data above)	*0*	*0*	*0*	*0*	*0*	*6.2*	*0*	*15*	*17*	*25*	*3*	—	*1.2*	*0.07*	*96*	*32*	*21*
Egg powder	2	48.2	43.3	2.14	2.6	—	593	4460	0.35	1.23	0.2	0	PA 10	0	0	0	0	0	+	0	—	—	187	—	—	7.4	—	800	—	—
Milk (cow's)† [1]																														
pasteurized, whole	87.3	3.3	4.01	0.01	4.94	0	65	130‡‡	0.04	0.16	0.09	1.8	See page 514	—	250	0	0	0	0	2.2	58	138	125	13	0.002	0.1‡	0.03	99	30	103
buttermilk, cultured	90.5	3.5	0.1	—	4.8	0	36	trace	0.04	0.18	0.1	1	—	—	—	0	0	0	0	+	130	140	105	15	—	0.3	—	97	—	100
canned, evaporated (unsweetened)††	73.7	7.0	7.9	—	9.9	0	139	400	0.05	0.36	0.2	1	E 0.30	—	—	0	0	0	0	+	100	270	243	—	—	0.2	—	195	—	—
condensed (sweetened)	27	8.1	8.4	—	54.8	0	327	430	0.05	0.39	0.2	1	—	—	—	0	0	0	0	+	140	340	273	—	—	0.2	—	228	—	—
dried, whole	3.5	25.8	26.7	0.1	38.0	0	496	1400	0.29	1.1–2.0	0.5–1.6	10	—	—	—	0	0	0	0	+	410	1100	949	—	—	0.6	—	728	—	—
nonfat	3.5	35.6	1.0	0.004	52.0	0	359	40	0.35	1.96	1.1	7	—	—	—	0	0	0	0	+	525	—	1300	—	—	0.6	<0.05	1030	—	—

* Vitamin A activity due to vitamin A + carotenes (see page 449): 1 IU vitamin A = 0.0006 mg β-carotene.
** Milliliters of N-acid or N-base.
*** PA = pantothenic acid; FA = folic acid.

1) For a review of the literature see Kon and Henry, *J. Dairy Res.*, **18**, 317 (1951).

† **Values per 100 g:**

	pH	Spec. grav.	Casein	Albumin	Total protein	Nonprotein nitrogen	Ash
Camel's milk	—	1.031	—	—	3.4–3.7 g	—	0.68 g
Cow's milk	6.60	1.031	2.80 g	0.40 g	2.0–6.0 g	13–14 mg	0.72 g
Breast milk	6.97	1.031	0.40 g	0.30 g	1.0–6.0 g	32.4 mg	0.21 g
Sheep's milk	6.54	1.036	4.17 g	0.98 g	4.5–5 g	42.5 mg	0.93 g
Goat's milk	—	1.031	2.87 g	0.89 g	3.6–3.8 g	—	0.85 g

See also pages 514 and 515

(pH values measured on very fresh samples)

†† U.S. Standard.

‡ In commercial milk; less in fresh milk.

‡‡ In winter; in summer and autumn up to 1000.

Content per 100 grams edible portion (unless otherwise stated)	Water	Proteins	Fats: Total	Fats: Cholesterol	Carbohydrates: Total	Carbohydrates: Fiber	Calories	Vitamins: A*	Vitamins: B_1	Vitamins: B_2	Vitamins: Nicotinic acid	Vitamins: C	Vitamins: Other vitamins***	Other organic constituents: Malic acid	Citric acid	Oxalic acid	Uric acid	Purine bases	Excess acid	Excess base	Elements: Sodium Na	Potassium K	Calcium Ca	Magnesium Mg	Manganese Mn	Iron Fe	Copper Cu	Phosphorus P	Sulfur S	Chlorine Cl
	g	g	g	g	g	g	kcal	IU	mg	mg	mg	mg	mg	mg	mg	mg	mg	mg	ml**	ml**	mg	mg	mg	mg	mg	mg	mg	mg	mg	mg
Breast milk †, ††	87.58	2.01	3.8	0.01	6.5	0	62	350	0.04	0.06	0.26	6	See page 514	—	150	0	0	0	0	0–5	13	45	35	5	—	0.7	0.06	20	11	50
Goat's milk ††	86.88	3.76	4.07	—	4.64	0	71	170	0.06	0.07	0.25	1	—	—	—	0	0	0	0	4.2	34	180	128	13.3	0.08	0.2	0.04	103	37	14
Mare's milk	89	1.8	1.4	—	6.7	—	—	—	—	—	—	—	—	—	—	—	—	—	0	+	—	—	—	—	—	—	—	—	—	—
Sheep's milk ††	83.57	5.15	6.18	—	4.17	0	93	—	—	—	—	3.6	—	—	130	0	0	0	0	+	33	188	207	8.3	—	—	—	125	—	95
Meat, Poultry (raw unless otherwise stated)																														
Bacon																														
medium fat, cooked	13	25.0	55.0	—	1.1	0	607	0	0.48	0.31	4.8	0	—	—	—	—	—	—	+	0	—	—	25	—	—	3.3	—	255	—	—
fat, salted	8	3.9	85	—	0	0.5	481	0	0.18	0.09	0.7	0	—	—	—	0	++	++	+	0	2900	—	2	—	—	0.6	< 0.05	42	—	—
Beef (medium fat)																														
hamburger, cooked	47	22.0	30.0	—	0	0	364	0	0.08	0.19	4.8	0	—	—	—	—	+	+	+	0	—	—	9	—	—	2.8	—	158	—	—
rib roast, cooked	51	24.0	24.0	—	0	0	319	0	0.06	0.18	4.3	0	—	—	—	—	+	+	+	0	—	—	10	—	—	3.0	—	185	—	—
rump, cooked	46	21.0	32.0	—	0	0	378	0	0.04	0.15	3.1	0	—	—	—	—	+	+	+	0	—	—	8	—	—	2.5	—	85	—	—
sirloin, cooked	54	23.0	22.0	—	0	0	297	0	0.06	0.19	4.8	0	—	—	—	—	+	+	+	0	—	—	10	—	—	2.9	—	175	—	—
canned, corned	57.3	24.4	15.0	—	0	0	232	0	0.02	0.19	2.7	0	—	—	—	0	++	++	+	0	1700	400	29	—	—	4.0	—	113	—	—
dehydrated, salted	47.7	34.3	6.3	—	0	0	199	0	0.11	9.22	3.7	0	—	—	—	0	+++	+++	+	0	3900	1000	20	—	—	5.1	—	370	—	—
brain	81	10.0	8.3	2.36	0.8	0	117	0	—	—	4.5	—	—	—	—	0	84	28	+	0	90	340	11	—	—	1.6	0.2	360	—	—
heart	75.4	16.5	6.3	0.15	0.7	0	108	30	0.54	0.89	6.8	6	PA 2.0	—	—	0	++	++	19.6	0	85	380	10	40	—	6.2	—	236	296	122
kidneys	75	15.0	8.1	0.41	1.0	0	140	1000	0.25	2.10	7.4	11	PA 6–25; E 0.5; K 0.1–1.0	—	—	0	240	80	16.2	0	246	238	10	21	—	6.5	0.1	260	190	246
liver	70.9	19.8	4.2	0.32	3.6	0	136	19200	0.27	2.80	16.1	31	$B_6$1; B_{12}0.03–0.1; PA5; FA0.05; E1.0; K0.1–1.0; biotin0.2; B_{12} 0.03; PAB 0.2	—	—	0	279	93	26.4	0	130	298	8	22	0.3	12.1	2.08	373	251	101
tongue	68	16.4	15.0	—	0.4	0	207	0	0.22	0.27	5.0	0	—	—	—	—	++	++	+	0	80	260	30	—	—	6.9	—	119	—	—
tripe, cooked	79	19.1	2.0	0.15	0	0	99	—	0.01	—	3.0	—	—	—	—	0	++	++	+	0	46	19	10	—	—	1.6	—	130	—	—
Calf (see also Veal, page 512)																														
brain	81	10.0	8.3	2.1	0	0	117	—	—	—	4.5	—	—	—	—	0	75	26	+	0	110	305	11	—	—	1.5	—	360	—	—
heart	76	15.4	7.1	0.18	1	0	134	—	0.60	—	10.60	—	—	—	—	0	++	++	21.2	0	71	370	11	35	—	6.2	—	240	296	125
kidney	76	16.9	6.4	0.5	0	0	129	1200	0.26	2.4	7.40	10	—	—	—	0	+++	+++	+	0	—	—	9	—	—	4.1	—	171	—	—
liver	71	19.0	4.9	0.36	4.0	0	141	27000	0.4	3.3	12.0	32	$B_6$1; B_{12}0.24; PA6; FA0.05; E1.0; K0.1–1.0; D200IU; biotin0.2; PAB0.02	—	—	0	260	88	18.0	0	87	298	11	22	0.341	5.4	15	210	251	101
sweetbreads	75	19.6	3.1	0.28	0	0	111	—	0.06	0.27	4.10	—	B_{12} 0.024	—	—	0	990	330	+	0	—	—	11	—	—	1.6	—	—	—	—
Chicken																														
broilers and roasters	68	20.0	11.0	0.09	0	0	185	0	0.1	0.2	6.2	—	E 0.22	—	—	0	87	29	16.5	0	75	372	10	27	—	3.0	—	220	252	79
broiled	66	20.2	12.6	0.09	0	0	199	0	0.11	0.18	8.6	—	—	—	—	0	++	++	+	0	—	—	16	—	—	1.9	—	218	—	—
canned	62	29.8	8.0	—	0	0	199	0	0.04	0.16	6.4	0	—	—	—	—	—	—	+	0	—	—	14	—	—	1.8	—	148	—	—
liver	70	22.1	4.0	—	3.0	0	141	24000	0.40	2.50	14.6	35	PA 2.2	—	—	0	279	93	+	0	85	—	20	—	—	—	—	240	—	—
Duck, medium fat	54	16.0	28.6	0.07	0	0	321	—	0.13	0.41	7.89	8	—	—	—	0	81	20	+	0	82	285	10	—	—	1.7	0.4	197	—	85

* Vitamin A activity due to vitamin A + carotenes (see page 449): 1 IU vitamin A = 0.0006 mg β-carotene. ** Milliliters of N-acid or N-base. *** PA = pantothenic acid; FA = folic acid; PAB = para-aminobenzoic acid.
† See also pages 514 and 515. †† See also footnote †, page 509.

Content per 100 grams edible portion (unless otherwise stated)	Water g	Proteins g	Fats: Total g	Fats: Cholesterol g	Carbohydrates: Total g	Carbohydrates: Fiber g	Calories kcal	Vitamins: A* IU	Vitamins: B_1 mg	Vitamins: B_2 mg	Vitamins: Nicotinic acid mg	Vitamins: C mg	Vitamins: Other vitamins*** mg
Goose, medium fat	51	16.4	31.5	—	0	0	349	—	0.16	0.24	—	13	—
liver	67	16.5	10.0	—	5	0	180	—	0.03	—	3.6	—	—
Ham													
boiled	48	22.8	22.7	—	0	0	302	0	1.01	0.26	5.1	0	—
smoked, cooked	39	23.0	33.0	—	0.4	0	397	0	0.54	0.21	4.2	0	—
canned, spiced	55	14.9	24.3	—	1.5	0.2	289	0	0.32	0.22	2.8	0	—
Hare	73	21.0	5.0	0.08	0	0	134	—	0.05	0.06	12.7	—	—
Horse flesh, lean	73	22	2.5	—	0.8	—	122			—	4.5	—	D 130 IU
Lamb (medium fat)													
leg roast, cooked	56	24.0	19.0	—	0	0	274	0	0.14	0.25	5.1	0	—
rib chop, cooked	40	24.0	35.0	0.07	0	0	418	0	0.14	0.26	5.6	0	—
shoulder roast, cooked	50	21.0	28.0	—	0	0	342	0	0.12	0.22	4.6	0	—
Meat extract	35	17.6	0	—	47	0	258	0	0.02	2.0	65	0	—
Mutton, medium fat	63.7	18	17.5	0.07	0	0	235	20	0.21	0.26	5.9	0	—
Pork (see also Bacon and Ham)													
medium fat	67.1	18.1	14.9	0.09	0	0	224	0	1.04	0.20	4.4	0	B_6 0.10; PA 0.47; FA 0.08; B_{12} 0.003; biotin 0.005; E 0.63
cutlets, cooked	53	14.6	32	0.105	0	0	350	0	0.18	0.04	0.9	0	B_6
loin or chops, cooked	50	23.0	26.0	—	0	0	333	35	0.83	0.24	5.0	0	PA 0.47; B_6 0.10; biotin 0.005; FA 0.08; B_{12} 0.003
canned, strained	76	17.1	6.0	—	0	0	127	0	0.35	0.28	4.7	0	—
heart	77	16.9	4.8	—	0.4	0	119	30	0.43	1.24	6.0	6	PA 2.4
kidneys	77	16.3	4.6	—	0.8	0	118	130	0.58	1.74	10	13	PS 3.1
liver	72	19.6	4.8	0.42	2.0	0	135	2700	0.43	2.7	15.5	27	B_6 1; B_{12} 0.18; PA 6; FA 0.05; K 0.1–1.0; D 180 IU; biotin 0.2
Rabbit	68	20.8	10.2	0.05	0	0	180	—	0.05	0.06	12.7	4	—
Sausages													
beef	55	16	28	—	0	0	320	0	0.10	0.13	4.3	0	—
bologna	62.4	14.8	15.9	—	0	0	217	0	0.31	0.30	3.0	0	—
frankfurter	64.3	15.2	14.1	—	0	0	205	0	0.19	0.23	2.4	0	—
liver	59	16.7	20.6	—	2.0	0	263	10000	0.19	1.3	5.2	—	—
pork	41.9	10.8	44.8	—	0	0	450	0	0.22	0.15	2.3	0	—
salami	31	23.9	36.8	—	0	0	427	—	0.24	0.21	2.91	—	—
Sheep (see also Lamb and Mutton)													
liver	71	21.0	3.9	—	2.9	0	136	50500	0.40	3.28	16.9	33	PA 6.5
kidneys	78	16.6	3.3	—	1.0	0	105	1150	0.51	2.42	7.4	13	—
offal (values as for calf's offal)													
Turkey, medium fat	58.3	20.1	20.2	0.015	0	0	268	trace	0.12	0.19	7.9	—	—

Content per 100 grams edible portion (unless otherwise stated)	Other organic constituents: Malic acid mg	Citric acid mg	Oxalic acid mg	Uric acid mg	Purine bases mg	Excess acid ml**	Excess base ml**	Elements: Sodium Na mg	Potassium K mg	Calcium Ca mg	Magnesium Mg mg	Manganese Mn mg	Iron Fe mg	Copper Cu mg	Phosphorus P mg	Sulfur S mg	Chlorine Cl mg
Goose, medium fat	—	—	0	99	33	+	0	85	420	10	—	—	2.0	0.3	180	—	120
liver	—	—	0	260	85	+	0	—	—	10	—	—	—	—	180	—	—
Ham																	
boiled	—	—	—	—	—	+	0	—	—	9	—	—	2.7	—	92	—	—
smoked, cooked	—	—	—	—	—	+	0	—	—	10	—	—	2.9	—	166	—	—
canned, spiced	—	—	—	—	—	+	0	—	—	9	—	—	2.2	—	161	—	—
Hare	—	—	0	++	38	+	0	—	—	10	—	—	3.2	—	239	—	—
Horse flesh, lean	—	—	0	++	++	0	4.5	175	176	4	4	—	50	—	44	10	260
Lamb (medium fat)																	
leg roast, cooked	—	—	—	—	—	+	0	—	—	10	—	—	3.1	—	257	—	—
rib chop, cooked	—	—	—	—	—	+	0	—	—	11	—	—	3.0	—	200	—	—
shoulder roast, cooked	—	—	—	—	—	+	0	—	—	9	—	—	2.6	—	188	—	—
Meat extract	—	—	—	+++	+++	+	0	27,000	1500	40	—	—	4.2	—	510	—	—
Mutton, medium fat	—	—	0	++	++	14.1	0	84	301	10	24	—	2.7	—	194	211	85
Pork (see also Bacon and Ham)																	
medium fat	—	—	0	123	41	13.8	0	69	280	10	20	0.01	2.5	0.1	177	206	69
cutlets, cooked	—	—	0	++	++	10.7	0	42	169	8	12	—	2.2	—	157	115	38
loin or chops, cooked	—	—	—	—	—	+	0	70	280	11	20	0.01	3.0	0.3	235	—	63
canned, strained	—	—	—	—	—	+	0	—	—	14	—	—	1.7	—	180	—	—
heart	—	—	0	+	+	+	0	—	—	35	—	—	27	—	132	—	—
kidneys	—	—	0	+	+	+	0	—	—	11	—	—	8.0	—	246	—	—
liver	—	—	0	+++	+++	+	0	77	350	10	—	—	18.0	—	210	—	—
Rabbit	—	—	0	++	++	+	0	40	390	10	—	—	3.1	—	220	—	—
Sausages																	
beef	—	—	—	++	++	+	0	—	—	9	—	—	2.4	—	172	—	—
bologna	—	—	—	++	++	+	0	—	—	9	—	—	2.2	—	160	—	—
frankfurter	—	—	—	++	++	+	0	—	—	9	—	—	2.3	—	164	—	—
liver	—	—	—	114	38	+	0	—	—	10	—	—	2.5	—	180	—	—
pork	—	—	—	++	++	+	0	740	140	6	—	—	1.6	—	116	—	—
salami	—	—	—	++	23	+	0	—	—	10	—	—	3.6	—	260	—	—
Sheep (see also Lamb and Mutton)																	
liver	—	—	—	—	—	+	0	—	—	8	—	—	12.6	—	364	—	—
kidneys	—	—	—	—	—	+	0	—	—	13	—	—	9.2	—	237	—	—
offal (values as for calf's offal)																	
Turkey, medium fat	—	—	0	++	++	22.8	0	66	367	23	28	—	3.8	0.2	320	234	123

* Vitamin A activity due to vitamin A + carotenes (see page 449): 1 IU vitamin A = 0.0006 mg β-carotene. ** Milliliters of N-acid or N-base. *** PA = pantothenic acid; FA = folic acid.

Content per 100 grams edible portion (unless otherwise stated)	Water g	Proteins g	Fats: Total g	Fats: Cholesterol g	Carbohydrates: Total g	Carbohydrates: Fiber g	Calories kcal	Vitamins: A* IU	Vitamins: B_1 mg	Vitamins: B_2 mg	Vitamins: Nicotinic acid mg	Vitamins: C mg	Vitamins: Other vitamins*** mg	Other organic constituents: Malic acid mg	Citric acid mg	Oxalic acid mg	Uric acid mg	Purine bases mg	Excess acid ml**	Excess base ml**	Elements: Sodium Na mg	Potassium K mg	Calcium Ca mg	Magnesium Mg mg	Manganese Mn mg	Iron Fe mg	Copper Cu mg	Phosphorus P mg	Sulfur S mg	Chlorine Cl mg
Veal, medium fat	69	19.2	11.0	0.065	0	0	181	0	0.18	0.27	6.3	0	D 140 IU; E 0.9	—	—	0	114	38	14.3	0	48	359	11	23	—	2.9	—	207	203	77
cutlet, cooked	60	28.0	11.0	—	0	0	219	30	0.08	0.28	6.1	0	D 140 IU; E 0.9	—	—	—	+	+	+	0	—	—	12	—	—	3.5	—	258	—	—
shoulder roast, cooked	59	28.0	12.0	—	0	0	228	0	0.13	0.31	7.9	0	—	—	—	—	+	+	+	0	—	—	12	—	—	3.6	—	258	—	—
stew meat, cooked	53	25.0	21.0	—	0	0	296	0	0.05	0.24	4.6	0	—	—	—	—	+	+	+	0	—	—	11	—	—	3.0	—	124	—	—
lean, roasted	—	32.2	11.3	—	0	0	239	—	0.24	0.26	7.6	—	D 100 IU	—	—	0	++	++	+	0	—	—	20	—	—	3.6	—	290	—	—
Venison	73	20.0	6.0	—	0	0	139	—	—	—	—	—	—	—	—	0	117	39	+	0	—	—	11	—	—	3.0	—	—	220	—
Whalemeat	74	22.8	1.4	0.015	—	—	—	80	0.03	0.10	4.4	0	B_{12} 0.002; B_6 0.15; PA 0.3	—	—	—	—	—	+	0	—	—	12	—	—	2.4	—	—	—	—
Sea food (raw unless otherwise stated)																														
Carp	—	7.5	3.9	—	—	—	67	600	0.20	0.05	—	1.0	—	—	—	—	++	++	+	0	—	—	4.5	—	—	1.5	—	115	—	—
Caviar, pressed	36	34.4	16.7	0.49	0	0	288	—	—	—	—	—	—	—	—	—	0	0	+	0	2200	640	140	—	—	—	—	180	—	1819
Clams, long and round	80	12.8	1.4	—	3.4	—	81	110	0.10	0.18	1.6	—	PA 0.6	—	—	—	—	—	+	0	180	240	96	89	—	7.0	—	139	219	—
Cod	82.6	16.5	0.4	0.05	0	0	70	0	0.10	0.07	2.17	2	—	—	—	—	114	38	13.5	0	96	339	18	22	—	0.9	0.55	189	203	150
Crab, canned or cooked, meat only	77	16.9	2.9	0.145	1.3	—	104	—	0.05	0.06	2.5	—	—	—	—	—	—	—	+	0	1000	110	45	—	—	0.9	—	182	—	—
Eel	72	18.6	9.1	—	0	0	162	1800	0.28	0.37	1.4	1.7	—	—	—	—	—	—	+	0	32	241	18	18	—	0.7	—	202	135	35
smoked	50	18.6	27.8	—	0	0	325	2500	0.14	0.07	—	—	—	—	—	—	81	27	+	0	—	—	0.02	—	—	1.0	—	210	—	—
Flounder	83	14.9	0.5	0.06	0	0	64	—	0.08	0.20	3.84	—	—	—	—	—	++	++	13.4	0	68	311	30	25	—	1.0	0.15	160	217	151
Frog legs	82	16.4	0.3	—	0	0	68	—	—	—	—	—	—	—	—	—	++	++	+	0	—	—	20	—	—	0.4	—	190	—	—
Haddock	77	16.8	0.3	—	0	0	74	0	0.09	0.12	0.90	0	E 0.35	—	—	—	117	39	18.4	0	99	314	19	26	0.015	0.9	0.216	190	238	241
Halibut	75.5	18.6	5.2	—	0	0	121	10	0.09	0.17	3	—	—	—	—	—	++	++	15.2	0	56	340	20	24	0.01	0.9	0.160	213	212	88
Herring	73	19.0	6–12	—	0	0	136	100–700	0.01	0.33	3.9	—	B_{12} 0.014; B_6 1.3; PA 2; D 5000–50,000 IU	—	—	—	207	69	+	0	100	—	20	26	—	1.1	—	220	202	122
smoked	61	22.2	12.9	—	0	0	211	0	trace	0.28	2.9	—	—	—	—	—	—	—	+	0	—	—	66	—	—	1.4	—	254	—	—
Lobster	79	16.2	1.9	0.145	1	0	86	—	0.15	0.18	—	—	PA 0.35	—	—	—	66	22	+	0	210	180	60	—	—	0.8	16.7	280	—	—
canned	77	18.4	1.3	0.12	0.4	0	86	—	0.15	0.18	2.2	—	—	—	—	—	59	++	+	0	—	—	60	—	—	0.8	0.73	280	—	—
Mackerel	68	18.7	12.0	0.08	0	0	188	50	0.15	0.35	8	—	PA1.0; B_{12} 0.01	—	—	—	—	—	+	0	—	412	5	33	0.02	1.0	0.07	239	197	170
Oysters	87.1	6.0	1.2	0.23	3.7	—	50	320	0.18	0.23	1.2	3.0	B_{12} 0.28	—	—	—	87	29	7.3	0	471	204	68	39	0.295	7.1	3.623	172	180	628
Pike	80	18.7	0.6	—	0	0	80	—	0.09	0.07	1.7	—	—	—	—	—	135	45	15.5	0	75	350	20	25	—	1.1	—	220	220	105
Salmon																														
Pacific, cooked	65	28.0	5.6	0.06	0.2	0	170	—	0.10	0.28	8.1	—	—	—	—	—	—	—	+	0	—	—	—	—	—	1.2	0.2	417	—	—
red	66	22.0	12.3	0.06	0	0	203	285	0.21	0.20	7.1	9	D 8000 IU; B_6 1.5	—	—	—	72	24	+	0	45	396	24	29	—	0.8	—	253	226	—
canned	67.4	20.6	9.6	—	0	0	169	80	0.03	0.18	6.5	0	—	—	—	—	++	++	+	0	540	330	67	30	—	1.3	—	286	260	—
Sardines, canned in oil,																														
solids and liquid	47.1	21.1	27.0	—	1.0	0	331	710	0.05	0.10	4.3	0	—	—	—	—	354	118	+	0	760	260	29	—	—	1.5	—	299	—	—
drained solids	57.4	25.7	11.0	—	1.2	0	207	290	0.06	0.12	5.2	0	—	—	—	—	+++	+++	+	0	820	310	35	—	—	1.8	—	365	—	—

* Vitamin A activity due to vitamin A + carotenes (see page 449); 1 IU vitamin A = 0.0006 mg β-carotene. ** Milliliters of N-acid or N-base. *** PA = pantothenic acid.

Content per 100 grams edible portion (unless otherwise stated)	Water	Proteins	Fats		Carbo-hydrates		Calories	Vitamins						Other organic constituents					Excess acid	Excess base	Elements									
			Total	Cholesterol	Total	Fiber		A*	B_1	B_2	Nicotinic acid	C	Other vitamins***	Malic acid	Citric acid	Oxalic acid	Uric acid	Purine bases			Sodium Na	Potassium K	Calcium Ca	Magnesium Mg	Manganese Mn	Iron Fe	Copper Cu	Phosphorus P	Sulfur S	Chlorine Cl
	g	g	g	g	g	g	kcal	IU	mg	mg	mg	mg	mg	mg	mg	mg	mg	mg	ml**	ml**	mg	mg	mg	mg	mg	mg	mg	mg	mg	mg
Scallops	80	14.8	0.1	—	3.4	0	78	0	0.04	0.10	1.4	—	—	—	—	—	—	—	+	0	—	—	26	—	—	1.8	0.23	208	—	—
Shrimps, canned, drained	78.8	17.8	0.8	0.15	0.8	0.15	82	60	0.01	0.03	1.9	0	PA 0.2	—	—	—	60	20	+	0	140	404	75	74	—	2.0	0.4	210	339	—
Trout	78	19.2	2.1	—	0	0	96	12	0.09	0.05	3.50	—	—	—	—	—	168	56	15.9	0	80	334	20	26	—	1.1	—	220	224	105
Tunny, canned	57.7	27.7	11.8	0.07	0	0	217	70	0.04	0.13	10.6	0	—	—	—	—	++	++	+	0	540	480	34	—	—	1.7	—	290	—	—
Miscellaneous																														
Gelatin, dry, plain	13	85.6	0.1	—	0	0	343	0	0	0	0	0	—	0	0	0	—	—	0	0	27	22	11	—	—	0	—	0	—	—
Yeast, compressed, baker's	70.9	13.3	0.4	—	13.0	0.3	109	0	0.45	2.07	28.2	0	—	—	—	—	—	—	0	0	4	360	25	—	—	4.9	—	605	—	—
dried, brewer's	7.0	46.1	1.6	0.68	37.4	0.8	348	0	9.69	5.45	36.2	0	B_6 3.6	—	—	—	—	—	0	0	180	1900	106	—	—	18.2	—	1893	—	—
Beverages, nonalcoholic																														
Carbonated soft drinks	—	0	0	0	12	0	48	0	0	0	0	0	—	—	—	—	—	—	0	0	—	—	—	—	—	—	—	—	—	—
Cocoa, dry powder	4.3	9.0	18.8	—	31	—	329	0	0.09	0.45	1.5	0	E 3.1	—	—	500	—	—	8.5	0	60	900	160	420	—	2.7	4.3	709	203	51
Coffee, per cup (125 ml)	Caffeine 95–125 mg Trigonelline ~ 120 mg Acetic acid ~ 24 mg Formic acid ~ 15 mg Chlorogenic acid ~ 200 mg													Malic acid ~ 23 mg Citric acid ~ 36 mg Phenolic acids (other than chlorogenic acid) ~ 60 mg Nicotinic acid 2 mg																
Tea, per cup (150 ml)	Caffeine 60–90 mg																													
Beverages, alcoholic			Alcohol†																											
Beer	90	0.6	4.4		4.0	0	50	0	0	0.03	0.79	—	—	—	—	—	—	—	0	0	8	46	10	8	—	0	—	20	—	—
Brandy	—	—	40		—	0	250	0	0	0	0	0	—	0	0	0	0	0	0	0	—	—	—	—	—	—	—	—	—	—
Fruit wine	—	0	5.2		1.0	0	41	—	—	—	—	—	—	+	+	0	0	0	0	+	4	75	—	—	—	—	—	—	—	—
Port wine	—	0.3	15.0		14.0	0	163	—	—	—	—	—	—	+	+	+	0	0	0	0	—	—	—	—	—	—	—	—	—	—
Rum	56	0	43.9		0	0	312	0	0	0	0	0	—	0	0	0	0	0	0	0	—	—	—	—	—	—	—	—	—	—
Whisky	58	0	42.2		0	0	301	0	0	0	0	0	—	0	0	0	0	0	0	0	—	—	—	—	—	—	—	—	—	—
Wine	—	—	7.5		0.1	0	53	0	1–5 µg	0.01–0.03	0.05–0.2	0	B_6 0.03; PA 0.02	+	+	+	0	0	0	204	7	104	10	7	—	0	—	10	15	2

* Vitamin A activity due to vitamin A + carotenes (see page 449): 1 IU vitamin A = 0.0006 mg β-carotene. ** Milliliters of N-acid or N-base. *** PA = pantothenic acid. † Alcohol has a calorific value of 7 cal/g.

Composition of Breast Milk

(and of cow's milk)

Values are in **milligrams per 100 ml** unless otherwise stated. For references and footnotes see opposite page

	Mature milk (15 days to 20 months post partum)			Transitional milk (5–10 days post partum)			Colostrum (first 5 days post partum)			Cow's milk		
	Mean	Range	References	Mean	Range	References	Mean	Range	References	Mean	Range	References
Calories (kcal)	65	–	*1*	63	–	*1*	57	–	*1*	65	–	*1*
Specific gravity	1.031	1.026–1.037	*2*	1.035	1.034–1.036	*2*	–	–	–	1.031	1.028–1.033	*3*
Solids, total	12.9 g	10.3–17.5 g	*2*	13.3 g	10.5–15.6 g	*2*	12.8 g	10.0–16.7 g	*2*	12.43 g	11.89–14.24g	*3*
Ash, total	202	160–266	*2*	267	231–338	*2*	308	247–350	*2*	715	681–771	*4*
Minerals												
Cations, total	4.1 mEq	–	*2*	5.5 mEq	–	*2*	6.8 mEq	–	*2*	–	–	–
Sodium	17.2	6.4–43.6	*2*	29.4	19.2–53.9	*2*	50.1	26.5–136.5	*2*	76.8	39.2–139.2	*5*
Potassium	51.2	37.3–63.5	*2*	63.6	52.8–76.9	*2*	74.5	65.8–87.0	*2*	143	38–287	*6*
Calcium	34.4	17.3–60.9	*2*	46.4	23.0–62.8	*2*	48.1	24.2–65.6	*2*	137	56–381	*6*
Magnesium	3.5	1.8–5.7	*2*	3.5	2.6–5.4	*2*	4.2	3.1–8.2	*2*	13	7–22	*6*
Manganese	trace	–	*7*	–	–	–	trace	–	*8*	3.5 μg	3.3–3.6 μg	*9*
Iron	0.03	0.02–0.09	*6*	0.04	0.02–0.05	*6*	0.04	0.02–0.05	*6*	0.04	0.03–0.07	*6*
Copper	0.05	0.04–0.06	*10*	0.05	0.04–0.07	*6*	0.04	0.02–0.05	*6*	0.008	0.005–0.015	*6*
Anions, total	2.8 mEq	–	*2*	3.7 mEq	–	*2*	4 mEq	–	*2*	–	–	–
Phosphorus	14.1	6.8–26.8	*2*	19.8	9.7–31.7	*2*	15.7	8.5–25.1	*2*	91	56–112	*6*
Sulfur	14	5–30	*2*	20	15–23	*2*	23	20–26	*2*	30	24–36	*6*
Chlorine	37.5	8.8–73.4	*2*	45.7	30.5–72.1	*2*	58.6	43.5–100.7	*2*	108	93–141	*6*
Total ions (ash)	6.9 mEq	–	*2*	9.2 mEq	–	*2*	10.8 mEq	–	*2*	–	–	–
Alkaline excess	1.3 mEq	–	*2*	1.8 mEq	–	*2*	2.8 mEq	–	*2*	–	–	–
Proteins total*	1060	730–2000	*2*	1590	1270–1890	*2*	2290	1460–6800	*2*	3246	2816–3676	*11*
Casein*	370	140–680	*2*	510	420–590	*2*	2058	726–5172	*12*	2493	2185–2800	*11*
Lactalbumin*	360	140–600	*2*	780	690–860	*2*	–	–	–	236	144–328	*11*
Amino acids, total**	1280	900–1600	*1*	940	600–1000	*1*	1200	700–4000	*1*	3300	2700–4100	*1*
Arginine	43.3	27.8–63.7	*2,13*	62.8	47.7–73.4	*2,14*	74.4	62.0–95.8	*2,14*	140	120–160	*15*
Histidine	23.7	12.4–30.2	*2,13*	38.3	28.8–44.9	*2,14*	41.2	34.9–46.3	*2,14*	120	110–113	*15*
Isoleucine	61.0	40.9–92.3	*2,13*	97.0	73.2–120.9	*2,14*	101.1	88.2–114.9	*2,14*	250	210–290	*15*
Leucine	96.6	65.3–147.0	*2,13*	151.2	113.2–197.0	*2,14*	165.6	133.4–214.4	*2,14*	360	320–390	*15*
Lysine	70.1	36.2–92.9	*2,13*	112.6	87.7–148.4	*2,14*	117.7	95.0–141.0	*2,14*	270	230–310	*15*
Methionine	11.6	6.5–16.0	*2,13*	24.1	15.7–34.4	*2,14*	25.3	18.6–36.2	*2,14*	75	60–90	*15*
Phenylalanine	40.4	24.3–57.8	*2,13*	62.4	48.4–71.3	*2,14*	70.0	59.9–84.1	*2,14*	185	150–220	*15*
Threonine	51.8	29.7–65.6	*2,13*	78.1	60.6–90.7	*2,14*	84.8	75.2–103.9	*2,14*	175	130–220	*15*
Tryptophan	19.2	14.2–26.0	*2,13*	28.2	23.0–31.6	*2,14*	32.2	25.3–42.2	*2,14*	60	40–80	*15*
Valine	72.5	44.7–114.2	*2,13*	104.9	77.4–136.0	*2,14*	116.9	97.8–148.7	*2,14*	260	240–280	*15*
Nonprotein nitrogen, total	32.4	17.3–60.4	*2*	47.9	42.5–53.3	*2*	91	51–127	*12*	25.2	18.1–32.3	*11*
Urea-N	18.0	12.7–23.5	*2*	11.1	–	*2*	–	–	–	13.27	6.13–20.4	*11*
Uric acid-N	2.2	1.3–4.1	*2*	–	–	–	–	–	–	2.41	1.13–3.69	*11*
Creatinine-N	1.1	0.8–1.9	*2*	–	–	–	–	–	–	0.705	0.19–1.22	*11*
Creatine-N	1.1	0.2–4.1	*2*	–	–	–	–	–	–	4.035	2.45–5.62	*11*
Amino acid-N	5.0	2.8–11.3	*2*	4.4	4.2–4.7	*2*	–	–	–	0.68	0.17–1.19	*11*
Lactose												
(direct estimation)	7100	4900–9500	*2*	6400	6100–6700	*2*	5700	1100–7900	*16*	4700	4500–5000	*4*
(by difference)	6800	5000–9200	*2*	6400	6000–6800	*2*	–	–	–	–	–	–
Fats, total	4540	1340–8290	*2*	3520	2730–5180	*2*	2950	2470–3180	*2*	3800	3400–6100	*3*
Fatty acids, essential	346	–	*1*	–	–	–	246	–	*1*	99	–	*1*
Vitamins (values are in μg per 100 ml unless otherwise stated)												
Vitamin A, total	61	15–226	*2*	88	58–183	*2*	161	75–305	*2*	27	17–38	*3*
Vitamin B_1	14.2	8.1–22.7	*2*	5.9	2.3–10.5	*2*	1.9	0.9–3.4	*2*	43	28–90	*3*
Vitamin B_2	37.3	19.8–79.0	*2*	36.9	27.5–49.0	*2*	30.2	12.0–45.3	*2*	156	116–202	*3*
Vitamin B_{12}	trace	–	*17*	0.036	0.003–0.070	*17*	0.045	0.010–0.15	*17*	0.66	0.32–1.24	*17*
Vitamin C	5200	0–11 200	*2*	7100	4500–9000	*2*	7200	4700–10 400	*2*	1100	300–2300	*3*
Vitamin D	–	0.4–10.0 IU	*18*	–	–	–	–	–	–	–	0.5–4.0 IU	*18*
Vitamin E	240	100–480	*22*	890	400–1850	*21*	1480	280–3000	*19*	60	20–100	*21*
Nicotinic acid***	183	66–330	*2*	175	60–360	*2*	75	50–145	*2*	74	50–86	*20*
Pantothenic acid	246	86–584	*2*	288	135–412	*2*	183	29–302	*2*	340	220–550	*20*
Pyridoxine	18	10–22	*2*	–	–	–	–	–	–	51	40–63	*6*
Biotin	0.81	0.04–4.22	*2*	0.35	0.02–1.77	*2*	0.06	0.03–0.31	*2*	2.17	1.4–2.9	*20*
Folic acid	0.14	0.09–0.18	*17*	0.02	0.015–0.025	*17*	0.05	0.010–0.15	*17*	0.13	0.02–0.4	*17*
Inositol	44.9 mg	38.6–55.5 mg	*2*	–	–	–	–	–	–	8 mg	6–12 mg	*6*
Choline	8.9 mg	5.4–14.5 mg	*2*	–	–	–	–	–	–	10 mg	4–16 mg	*6*

Amino acid composition of casein, whey and whole milk

(in milligrams per 100 ml of a sample of mature milk)

From Beach et al., *J. biol. Chem.*, **139**, 57 (1941)

	Casein	Whey	Whole milk
Nitrogen	48.6	77.0	125.6
Histidine	6.0	6.3	12.3
Arginine	11.0	29.0	40.0
Lysine	17.3	32.4	49.7
Tyrosine	20.4	29.2	49.6
Tryptophan	5.7	13.0	18.7
Cystine	2.5	17.3	19.8
Methionine	7.2	10.9	18.1
Cystine-S	0.7	4.6	5.3
Methionine-S	1.5	2.3	3.8
Cystine-S + methionine-S	2.2	6.9	9.1

Fatty acid composition of total milk fat

From Baldwin and Longenecker, *J. biol. Chem.*, **154**, 255 (1944)

	Percentage by weight			Molar percentage		
	Mature milk	Colostrum		Mature milk	Colostrum	
		1st and 2nd day	3rd day		1st and 2nd day	3rd day
Saturated fatty acids						
Butyric acid	0.4	0.2	0.3	1.1	0.7	0.8
Caproic acid	0.1	0.1	0.1	0.1	0.3	0.2
Caprylic acid	0.3	0.8	0.1	0.6	1.5	0.1
Capric acid	2.2	3.5	0.9	3.3	5.3	1.4
Lauric acid	5.5	0.9	2.6	7.1	1.2	3.4
Myristic acid	8.5	2.8	4.9	9.6	3.3	5.7
Palmitic acid	23.2	24.6	27.8	23.4	25.4	28.9
Stearic acid	6.9	9.9	7.7	6.3	9.2	7.2
Remaining saturated fatty acids calculated as arachidic acid	1.1	4.9	2.7	0.9	4.1	2.3
Saturated fatty acids, total	48.2	47.7	47.1	52.4	51.0	50.0
Unsaturated fatty acids						
Decenoic acid	0.1	0.2	0.1	0.1	0.3	0.1
Dodecenoic acid	0.1	0.1	0.1	0.1	0.1	0.1
Tetradecenoic acid	0.6	0.1	0.2	0.7	0.1	0.2
Hexadecenoic acid	3.0	1.8	2.9	3.0	1.9	3.0
Oleic acid	36.5	66.0	37.1	33.3	33.8	35.1
Octadecadienoic acid	7.8	7.5	6.2	7.2	7.1	5.9
Octadecatrienoic acid	0.4	0.3	0.3	0.4	0.3	0.2
Eicosatetraenoic acid	0.9	1.8	1.6	0.8	1.5	1.4
Remaining unsaturated fatty acids calculated as eicosadienoic acid	2.4	4.6	4.7	2.0	3.9	4.0
Unsaturated fatty acids, total	51.8	52.4	53.2	47.6	49.0	50.0

References (table on opposite page)

1) Albritton, E. C. (Ed.), *Standard Values in Nutrition and Metabolism*, Philadelphia, 1954, page 111. *2)* Macy, I. G., *Amer. J. Dis. Child.*, **78**, 589 (1949). *3)* Dahlberg et al., *Sanitary Milk Control in Relation to Sanitary, Nutritive, and Other Qualities of Milk*, National Research Council Publication 250, Washington, 1952. *4)* Meigs and Marsh, *J. biol. Chem.*, **16**, 147 (1913/14). *5)* Jones and Davies, *Biochem. J.*, **29**, 978 (1935). *6)* Macy, I. G., unpublished values, quoted by Macy et al., *The Composition of Milks*, National Research Council Publication 254, Washington, 1953. *7)* Dingle and Sheldon, *Biochem. J.*, **32**, 1078 (1938). *8)* Castellanos and Lizarralde, *Rev. Asoc. argent. Diet.*, **1**, 199 (1943). *9)* Kemmerer and Todd, *J. biol. Chem.*, **94**, 317 (1931). *10)* Hess et al., *J. biol. Chem.*, **57**, 725 (1923). *11)* Shahani and Sommer, *J. dairy Sci.*, **34**, 1010 (1951). *12)* Waller et al., *Biochem. J.*, **35**, 272 (1941). *13)* Miller and Ruttinger, *Proc. Soc. exp. Biol. (N.Y.)*, **77**, 96 (1951). *14)* Miller et al., *J. Nutr.*, **40**, 499 (1950). *15)* Sarkar et al., *J. dairy Sci.*, **32**, 671 (1949). *16)* Widdows et al., *Biochem. J.*, **29**, 1145 (1935). *17)* Collins et al., *J. Nutr.*, **43**, 313 (1951). *18)* Lawrence et al., *Amer. J. Dis. Child.*, **70**, 193 (1945). *19)* Neuweiler, W., *Int. Z. Vitaminforsch.*, **20**, 108 (1948). *20)* Lawrence et al., *J. Nutr.*, **32**, 73 (1946). *21)* Abderhalden, R., *Biochem. Z.*, **318**, 47 (1948). *22)* Harris et al., *J. Nutr.*, **46**, 459 (1952).

* Calculated by multiplying the appropriate N content by 6.37.

** The following also occur in mature breast milk (milligrams per 100 ml): aspartic acid 88.7–98.2, glutamic acid 197.0–200.0, glycine 22.9–24.0, alanine 35.5–40.6, serine 46.6–50.8, cystine 23.0, proline 83.8–87.6, tyrosine 46.3–46.5, ammonia 28.1–33.6. (From Soupart et al., *J. biol. Chem.*, **206**, 699 [1954], in agreement with Cheung et al., *Pediatrics*, **12**, 353 [1953].)

*** Nicotinic acid + nicotinamide.

Composition of the Body and Organs[1]

For other elements see the table on pages 252–262

Content per 100 g	Percentage of total body weight: Newborn	Adults	Water	Fats: Total	Phospholipids	Sterols	Elements (on fat-free basis): Sodium Na	Potassium K	Calcium Ca	Magnesium Mg	Chlorine Cl	Phosphorus P	Sulfur S	Manganese Mn	Lead Pb	Tin Sn	Aluminum Al	Copper Cu	Silver Ag
Whole body			g	g	g	g	g	g	g	g	g	g	g	mg	mg	mg	mg	mg	mg
Fetus 3–4 months	....	....	93	0.5	–	–	–	–	0.34	0.018	0.27	0.214	–						
Fetus 5 months	....	....	91	1.2	–	–	0.258	0.20	0.59	0.021	0.25	0.358	0.148						
Fetus 6 months	....	....	87	2.5	–	–	0.216	0.162	0.62	0.021	0.25	0.382	0.180						
Fetus 7 months	....	....	86	2.5	–	–	0.214	0.188	0.62	0.022	0.26	0.382	0.153						
Premature 7th month	....	....	85	3.0	–	–	0.242	0.171	0.75	0.022	0.27	0.382	–						
Newborn	....	....	80	12.0	–	–	0.178	0.190	0.92	0.027	0.20	0.540	0.246						
Adults	....	....	72	18.0	–	–	0.109	0.265	2.01	0.036	0.156	1.16	0.196						
Adult organs																			
Muscle	25.1	43.0	79	7.5	1	0.15/0.06‡	0.072	0.360	0.007	0.023	0.066	0.220	0.250	0.050	0.010	0.011	0.015	0.125	0.00
Skeleton	13.7	17.5	44	10.0	0.3	–	0.18	0.061	11.0	0.105	0.19	5.05	–	0.3/0.17*	1.88/0.470*	0.08/0.05*	0.5/0.24*	1.19/0.410*	0.00/0.01*
Blood serum	6.5	7.0	92	0.6	0.3	0.210	0.335	0.020	0.011	0.003	0.370	0.015	0.0001	0.015	0.025	0.012	0.013	0.185–0.229	–
Erythrocytes			65	0.6			0.023	0.42	–	0.006	0.193	0.1	0.0001					–	–
Skin	19.7**	26.3**	73	15.0	0.3	1.40	0.16	0.107	0.020	0.014	0.30	0.065	–	–	–	0.5–1.0	–	–	–
Brain	12.3	2.2	90	12.6	9.0/4.0†	4.0/1.0†	0.17	0.33	0.012	0.016	0.15	0.38	0.13	0.030	0.013	0.00	0.004	0.400	0.003
Liver	4.6	2.7	79	21.3	2.5	0.350	0.19	0.215	0.012	0.022	0.16	0.21	0.19	0.205	0.130	0.060	0.160	0.710	0.005
Intestines	2.1	2.2	85	6.5	1	–	–	0.29	0.014	0.008	0.065	0.100	0.120	0.035	0.023	0.016	0.087	0.110	0.002
Lungs	1.8	1.5	78	1.7	1.5	0.375	0.25	0.15	0.017	0.007	0.26	0.12	0.127	0.022	0.028	0.045	5.94	0.110	0.004
Kidneys	0.8	0.5	80	5.2	2.5	0.430	0.175	0.175	0.020	0.021	0.22	0.14	–	0.060	0.027	0.020	0.042	0.166	0.00
Heart	0.8	0.5	77	8.3	1.5	–	0.185	0.250	0.010	0.017	0.135	0.270	–	0.032	0.038	0.022	0.056	0.190	0.00
Spleen	0.3	0.2	77	3.0	1	0.250	–	–	0.010	0.015	0.16	0.38	0.17	0.022	0.030	0.022	0.130	0.085	0.00
Pancreas	0.1	0.1	80	10.5	2	0.310	0.087	0.226	0.017	0.019	0.18	0.34	–	0.115	–	–	–	–	–
Thyroid	–	–	75	4.4	–	–	–	–	0.034	0.01	0.18	0.34	–	–	–	–	–	–	–
Testes	–	–	–	4.5	2	–	–	–	0.009	0.010	0.24	–	–	–	–	–	–	–	–
Uterus	–	–	–	–	–	–	0.145	0.145	0.022	0.016	0.26	0.057	–						
Adrenals	–	–	–	–	2	5.0	–	0.103	0.016	0.010	0.24	–	–						

Iodine 7–180 mg

* *first value:* long bones; *second value:* ribs
** skin and subcutaneous tissue
† *first value:* grey matter; *second value:* white matter
‡ *first value:* smooth muscles; *second value:* striated muscles

1) From SHOHL, A.T., *Mineral Metabolism*, American Chemical Society Monograph Series, No. 82, New York, 1939; KEHOE et al., *J. Nutr.*, **19**, 579 (1940); GROSSE-BROCKHOFF, F., *Einführung in die pathologische Physiologie*, Berlin, 1950; EVERETT, M. R., *Medical Biochemistry*, 2nd ed., New York, 1946; TOMPSETT, R., *Biochem. J.*, **28**, 1544 (1934).

Unless otherwise stated, the values given refer to unstimulated total saliva, obtained in the morning from healthy, fasting adults (total resting saliva). "Saliva" without further qualification in the literature referred to here has been taken to mean total resting saliva.

Normal values in **mg/100 ml** unless otherwise stated

	Mean*	Range*	*s*	Sources	Remarks
Appearance	–	See remarks	–		Colorless, transparent or translucent, somewhat viscid, of low viscosity and tasteless.
Daily volume	–	1–2 liters	–	HOPPE-SEYLER[1], page 357.	The saliva secretion never ceases entirely. In the adult it amounts to about 15 ml per hour between meals (HOUSSAY et al., *Physiologie humaine*, Paris, 1950, page 479). In infancy it is about 4 ml per hour (HUNGERLAND et al., *Klin. Wschr.*, **33**, 44 [1955]).
Water	99.5%	–	–		
Specific gravity	–	1.002–1.008	–	HOPPE-SEYLER[1], page 358.	
Freezing-point depression	–	0.2–0.4°C	–	HOPPE-SEYLER[1], page 358.	
pH value					
Adults	**5.97**	*5.17–6.77*	0.40	OSTER et al., *J. appl. Physiol.*, **6**, 348 (1953).	Mean value of 385 determinations on 195 subjects. Some authors give wider ranges: 3.25–8.0 (SUNDERMAN and BOERNER, *Normal Values in Clinical Medicine*, Philadelphia, 1950, page 699).
Children	**7.32**	*6.40–8.24*	0.46	TURNER et al., *J. dent. Res.*, **33**, 55 (1954).	Mean value of determinations on 315 children, of whom some had caries.
Mucin		up to 200	–	HOPPE-SEYLER[1], page 361.	Mucin is a glycoprotein. It contains the specific blood group substances, which are present in saliva.
Total proteins	**262**	*0–538*	138	DREVON and DONIKIAN, *C. R. Soc. Biol. (Paris)*, **150**, 1206 (1956).	Determinations made on the *parotid* saliva of 25 healthy subjects.
Nonprotein nitrogen	–	17–58	–	HOPPE-SEYLER[1], page 360.	
Ammonia	–	2–10	–	HOPPE-SEYLER[1], page 358.	
Amino acids	–	See remarks	–		WOLDRING, M. G., *J. dent. Res.*, **34**, 248 (1955), found the following free amino acids in saliva stimulated by paraffin chewing: taurine, aspartic acid, threonine, serine, glutamic acid, proline, glycine, alanine, cystine, valine, methionine, isoleucine, leucine, tyrosine, phenylalanine, histidine, lysine and arginine. KIRCH et al., *J. dent. Res.*, **26**, 297 (1947), arrived at similar results except that they also found tryptophan but no taurine, alanine or aspartic acid. According to TURNER and CROWELL, *J. dent. Res.*, **26**, 99 (1947), patients with caries have no tryptophan in their saliva, while KIRCH et al., *J. dent. Res.*, **26**, 297 (1947), found that the saliva of healthy persons contained the same amino acids as that of caries sufferers.
Urea					
Adults	–	75–90% of the content in blood	–	HOPPE-SEYLER[1], page 361.	
Children	–	20–36	–	SCARPULLA, G., *Riv. Clin. pediat.*, **31**, 811 (1933).	
Uric acid	1.5	–	–	SUNDERMAN and BOERNER, *Normal Values in Clinical Medicine*, Philadelphia, 1950, page 697.	
Sugars	0	–	–		Data on the sugar content of saliva are contradictory. See in particular HOPPE-SEYLER[1], page 361.
Lactic acid	–	2.5–10.0		Mean value from the literature; see in particular HOPPE-SEYLER[1], page 361.	
Citric acid	–	up to 1.92	–	ZIPKIN and MCCLURE, *J. dent. Res.*, **28**, 613 (1949).	According to HOPPE-SEYLER[1], page 361, the citric acid content of saliva increases somewhat with age.

* When a range given is a *normal range* (see page 154), i.e. calculated from the formula: mean ± (2 × standard deviation *s*), it is printed in *italics*, with the mean in **bold** figures. Otherwise the data given are experimental results which have not been tested statistically.

1) LANG et al. (Eds.), *Hoppe-Seyler/Thierfelder Handbuch der physiologisch- und pathologisch-chemischen Analyse*, 10th ed., vol. V, *Untersuchung der Organe, Körperflüssigkeiten und Ausscheidungen*, Berlin, 1953.

Synopsis of Saliva (continued)

Normal values in mg/100 ml unless otherwise stated

	Mean*	Range*	s	Sources	Remarks
Enzymes					The total saliva always contains dead epithelial cells, bacteria and leukocytes which are themselves rich in various enzymes (lipase, proteinase, peptidase, etc.). See also under Digestive Enzymes, pages 416 et seq.
α-Amylase (ptyalin)...	–	0–300 or more (see remarks)	–	CLAYCOMB et al., *J. dent. Res.*, **35**, 391 (1956).	The authors examined the saliva of 1228 subjects by a method which gave the results directly in milligrams of α-amylase. In 55% of the subjects the α-amylase content varied between 0 and 150 mg/100 ml, in 31% between 150 and 300 mg/100 ml, while in the remaining 14% it was over 300 mg/100 ml. The parotid saliva is considerably richer in α-amylase than saliva from the other glands (SCHNEYER, L. H., *J. appl. Physiol.*, **9**, 453 [1956]). See also page 422.
Histamine...........	14.56 μg /100 ml	10.65–18.10 μg/100 ml	–	SANDERS, S. G., *J. oral Surg.*, **13**, 193 (1955).	Mean of 48 determinations on 24 healthy subjects. No appreciable variations during the course of the day are found.
Vitamins					
Vitamin C..........	**0.218**	*0.058–0.378*	0.080	HESS and SMITH, *J. dent. Res.*, **28**, 507 (1949).	The mean of determinations on 54 subjects with caries does not differ significantly from the normal mean given here.
Other vitamins.......	–	See remarks	–		GLAVIND et al., *Int. Z. Vitaminforsch.*, **20**, 234 (1948), found the following further vitamins: B_1, B_2, B_6, nicotinic acid, pantothenic acid, folic acid and biotin.
Chloride					
Adults..............	**102.8**	*40.4–165.2*	31.2	WHITE et al., *J. clin. Invest.*, **34**, 246 (1955).	Mean value from 73 healthy subjects. THAYSEN et al., *Amer. J. Physiol.*, **178**, 155 (1954), showed that the chloride content of saliva varies according to the minute volume: with a secretion of 0.31 ml/min they found 35.5 mg/100 ml, with a secretion of 3.66 ml/min a content of 152.5 mg/100 ml.
Children	**57.62**	*24.78–90.46*	16.42	ANDERS, J. T., *J. appl. Physiol.*, **8**, 659 (1956).	Measurements on 431 children.
Phosphorus					
Total...............	**20.4**	*12.0–28.8*	4.2	LURA, H. E., *J. dent. Res.*, **26**, 203 (1947).	Mean value from 120 men, women and children without caries.
Organic............	**5.5**	*0–13.3*	3.9		Mean value from 50 men, women and children without caries.
Inorganic..........	**14.9**	*8.1– 21.7*	3.4		Mean value from 180 men, women and children without caries.
Sulfur...............	7.6		–	SUNDERMAN and BOERNER, *Normal Values in Clinical Medicine*, Philadelphia, 1950, page 697.	
Potassium	**77.0**	*46.4–107.6*	15.3	WHITE et al., *J. clin. Invest.*, **34**, 246 (1955).	Mean value from 73 healthy subjects. The values found by THAYSEN et al., *Amer. J. Physiol.*, **178**, 155 (1954), and by PRADER et al., *Helv. paediat. Acta*, **10**, 29 (1955), agree with those given here. The potassium content of saliva fluctuates during the course of the day: as a rule it is lowest in the morning and reaches a maximum during the afternoon (DE TRAVERSE and COQUELET, *C. R. Soc. Biol. [Paris]*, **146**, 1099 [1952]). It is markedly higher than in blood plasma and independent of age (in adults), sex, method of stimulation and rate of secretion (PRADER et al., *Helv. paediat. Acta*, **10**, 29 [1955]). The potassium content of saliva in *children* is higher than in adults (HUNGERLAND et al., *Klin. Wschr.*, **33**, 44 [1955]). See also under Sodium and Sodium/potassium ratio.
Sodium...............		Fluctuates according to the rate of secretion (see remarks)			PRADER et al., *Helv. paediat. Acta*, **10**, 29 (1955), found that the sodium content of saliva increases with the rate of secretion in accordance with the following relation: y (milligrams sodium/100 ml) = 18.19 x + 19.04, where x is the minute volume in milliliters; the correlation coefficient is 0.72. When $x = 0.25$ (resting saliva), $y = 23.6$ mg/100 ml; when $x = 1, y = 37.2$; when $x = 2, y = 55.4$; when $x = 3, y = 73.6$. The sodium content of saliva also varies according to the time of day: as a rule it is highest in the morning and lowest in the afternoon, the reverse therefore of the trend of potassium values (DE TRAVERSE and COQUELET, *C. R. Soc. Biol. [Paris]*, **146**, 1099 [1952]). It is markedly lower than in blood plasma and independent of age (in adults), sex and method of stimulation (PRADER et al., *Helv. paediat. Acta*, **10**, 29 [1955]). The sodium content of saliva is higher in children than in adults (HUNGERLAND et al., *Klin. Wschr.*, **33**, 44 [1955]). See also under Potassium and Sodium/potassium ratio.

* When a range given is a *normal range* (see page 154), i.e. calculated from the formula: mean ± (2 × standard deviation *s*), it is printed in *italics*, with the mean in **bold** figures. Otherwise the data given are experimental results which have not been tested statistically.

Synopsis of Saliva (concluded)

Normal values in **mg/100 ml** unless otherwise stated

	Mean*	Range*	*s*	Sources	Remarks
Sodium/potassium ratio		See remarks			Most authors assume that the ratio of sodium to potassium in saliva is in some way controlled by the pituitary-adrenal axis. In healthy subjects the sodium/potassium ratio is as a rule highest in the morning, reaches its lowest point in the course of the afternoon, and begins to rise again in the evening (GRAD, B., *J. Geront.*, **9**, 276 [1954]). Since the potassium content of saliva, in contrast to the sodium content, is independent of the rate of secretion, the sodium/potassium ratio must rise with the rate of secretion, as shown by PRADER et al., *Helv. paediat. Acta*, **10**, 29 (1955). These authors give the following relation: $y = 0.48\,x + 0.38$, where x is the minute volume in milliliters and y the sodium/potassium ratio when the concentration of the elements is given in milliequivalents per liter. When $x = 0.25$ (resting saliva), $y = 0.50$; when $x = 1$, $y = 0.86$; when $x = 2$, $y = 1.34$; when $x = 3$, $y = 1.82$. The same authors also found that the sodium/potassium ratio is independent of age, sex and method of stimulation. According to THORN et al., *Amer. J. Med.*, **10**, 595 (1951), the rise in the sodium/potassium ratio characteristic of adrenocortical insufficiency (observed particularly in ADDISON's disease) does not occur when the *serum* sodium level remains below 300 mg/100 ml.
Bicarbonate	5.5 vol % CO_2	–	–	SAND, H. F., *J. appl. Physiol.*, **4**, 66 (1951).	The bicarbonate content of saliva varies with the rate of secretion. In stimulated saliva values up to 80 vol% are found. According to LILIENTHAL, B., *J. dent. Res.*, **34**, 516 (1955), the buffering capacity of saliva depends mainly on the presence of bicarbonates and to a lesser extent on the phosphates; the other components of saliva, even mucin, play no part.
Calcium	–	4.5–10	–	Mean value from the literature; see in particular HOPPE-SEYLER[1], page 358, and SUNDERMAN and BOERNER, *Normal Values in Clinical Medicine*, Philadelphia, 1950, page 697.	
Cobalt	7.04 µg /100 ml	–	–	DREIZEN et al., *J. dent. Res.*, **31**, 137 (1952).	The authors examined 37 saliva samples: only 10 contained cobalt (in the mean concentration given in the adjoining column). This concentration is insufficient to prevent the *in vitro* growth of *Lactobacillus acidophilus*.
Copper	25.60 µg /100 ml	–	–	DREIZEN et al., *J. dent. Res.*, **31**, 137 (1952).	The average of 48 random subjects without regard to the state of their teeth. According to the authors the copper content of saliva is 25–30 times higher than that of plasma. It is insufficient to prevent the *in vitro* growth of *Lactobacillus acidophilus*.
Magnesium	–	0.5–1.0	–	Mean value from the literature; see in particular HOPPE-SEYLER[1], page 358, and SUNDERMAN and BOERNER, *Normal Values in Clinical Medicine*, Philadelphia, 1950, page 697.	
Bromine	–	0.02–0.71	–	HOPPE-SEYLER[1], page 359.	
Fluorine		10–20 µg/100 ml	–	HOPPE-SEYLER[1], page 359.	
Iodine	10.2 ± 5 µg /100 ml	3.5–24.0 µg/100 ml	–	BRUGER et al., *J. Lab. clin. Med.*, **26**, 1942 (1941), quoted by HOPPE-SEYLER[1], page 359.	
Thiocyanate	–	11.7–33.0	–	HOPPE-SEYLER[1], page 358.	The thiocyanate content of saliva is higher in smokers and in pregnant women than in other persons. The functional significance of this anion is not clear.

* When a range given is a *normal range* (see page 154), i.e. calculated from the formula: mean ± (2× standard deviation *s*), it is printed in *italics*, with the mean in **bold** figures. Otherwise the data given are experimental results which have not been tested statistically.

1) LANG et al. (Eds.), *Hoppe-Seyler/Thierfelder Handbuch der physiologisch- und pathologisch-chemischen Analyse*, 10th ed., vol. V, *Untersuchung der Organe, Körperflüssigkeiten und Ausscheidungen*, Berlin, 1953.

Synopsis of Gastric Juice

Normal values, fasting, unless otherwise stated

	Normal values	Sources	Remarks
Color	Pearl-gray to colorless		The gastric juice can be yellowish or greenish in color if it contains bile, more or less intensely red if containing fresh blood or dark brown if containing old blood. Traces of fresh *blood* can be caused by trauma during passage of the gastric tube. The presence of *bile* in gastric juice, fasting or after a test meal, is of little diagnostic significance; on the other hand the gastric juice should not contain any further bile during fractional aspiration after the first aspiration.
Odor	None, or acid and penetrating		A fetid odor of the gastric juice indicates disease.
Specific gravity	1.004–1.010		
Freezing-point depression	0.30–0.82° C		
Daily volume	2–4 liters		Contrary to previous statements, the secretion of gastric juice does not cease completely at night; usually the secretion between 3 and 7 a.m. no longer contains acid (Papayannopoulos et al., *Amer. J. dig. Dis.*, **21**, 41 [1954], and Perry et al., *Proc. Soc. exp. Biol. [N. Y.]*, **92**, 237 [1956]). The volume following an injection of *histamine* (0.25–0.5 mg s.c.) is up to 70 ml during the 10 minutes after injection and a total of 150–200 ml during the 2 hours after the injection (see also page 522).
Residual volume (fasting)			
Adults	40–50 ml average		More than 100 ml indicates hypersecretion, retention, or regurgitation of fluid from the duodenum.
Children	0.4–80 ml	Wolman, I. J., *Amer. J. Dis. Child.*, **71**, 394 (1946).	
Proteins	Mean value **214.1** mg/100 ml Standard deviation 64.7 mg/100 ml Normal range* *84.7–343.5* mg/100 ml	Teichmann, W., *Z. ges. inn. Med.*, **7**, 908 (1952).	The values given by Richmond et al., *Gastroenterology*, **29**, 1017 (1955), and by Gilligan et al., *J. nat. Cancer Inst.*, **12**, 657 (1951) agree with these.
Total nitrogen	67.58 mg/100 ml	Norpoth, L., *Klin. Wschr.*, **26**, 406 (1948).	Mean value in 59 healthy subjects.
Nonprotein nitrogen	24–47 mg/100 ml	Mean values from the literature.	
Histamine	0.7–4.8 μg/100 ml	Faredin et al., *Gastroenterologia (Basel)*, **79**, 185 (1953).	
Uric acid	0.8–2.0 mg/100 ml		
Hexoses (total)	32.1 mg/100 ml	Richmond et al., *Gastroenterology*, **29**, 1017 (1955). Mean value of 16 cases	The investigators found that in cancer of the stomach and in pernicious anemia the content of hexoses in the gastric juice rises. For the chemistry of sialic acid see Blix et al., *Nature*, **175**, 340 (1955).
Hexosamines	32.7 mg/100 ml	Mean value of 10 cases	
Sialic acid	7.31 mg/100 ml	Mean value of 13 cases	
Glucuronic acid	2.0 mg/100 ml	Mean value of 12 cases	
Lactic acid	None		Lactic acid is formed during fermentations which can only take place if hydrochloric acid is almost or completely absent.
Mucus	Trace		Depends on the amount of saliva swallowed.
Enzymes			Normal gastric juice contains two proteolytic enzymes, pepsin (greatest activity at about pH 2) and cathepsin (greatest activity at about pH 4.7), a lipase (certainly in children) and lysozyme (Richmond et al., *Gastroenterology*, **29**, 1017 [1955]). There is no decisive evidence that the stomach produces lab ferment (rennin) and opinions vary greatly on this point. It is certain, however, that pepsin also can cause coagulation of milk. Martin, L., *Bull. Johns Hopk. Hosp.*, **52**, 166 (1933), has demonstrated the presence of urease in gastric juice. See also under Digestive Enzymes, pages 416 et seq.
pH value	1.2 ± 0.3 1.7 ± 0.1	Everett, M. R., *Medical Biochemistry*, 2nd ed., New York, 1946.	The first value refers to pure gastric juice obtained through a gastric fistula; the second to juice obtained 1 hour after an Ewald test meal (2 slices of bread and 2 tumblers of water). The mean pH value in children is somewhat higher.
Total acids	2–80, mEq/l	Harrison, G. A., *Chemical Methods in Clinical Medicine*, 4th ed., London, 1957, page 484.	In healthy subjects the total acidity varies with age and sex on the one hand (see pages 521–523) and with the time of day on the other. It is greatest at about 6 p.m.; at this time some acid can be detected even in patients who show a histamine-fast achylia in the morning (Schunk and Schmitt, *Dtsch. med. Wschr.*, **80**, 347 [1955]). See also remarks under Daily volume, above.

* For definition of the normal range see footnote, page 517.

Normal values, fasting, unless otherwise stated

	Normal values	Sources	Remarks
Free hydrochloric acid	0–66, mean 32 mEq/l	After BERNSTEIN, R. E., *J. Lab. clin. Med.*, **40**, 707 (1952).	The values given by HARRISON, G. A., *Chemical Methods in Clinical Medicine*, 4th ed., London, 1957, page 484, agree with these (see also below and pages 522 and 523). In the histamine test (contraindicated in allergic individuals) the free acid reaches a maximum 30–60 minutes after the injection. The presence or absence of free hydrochloric acid in the stomach can be demonstrated by having the subject ingest a synthetic resin containing quinine in combination. If the gastric juice is sufficiently acid, the H^+ ions displace the quinine, which begins to be excreted in the urine about 15 minutes after ingestion. At present this method gives only qualitative results. For details see HARKNESS and DURANT, *J. clin. Path.*, **6**, 178 (1953).
Chloride	500–600 mg/100 ml	Mean values from the literature.	
Ammonia	0.5–4.0 mg/100 ml	STREHLER, E., *Helv. med. Acta*, **22**, 83 (1955).	
Calcium	4.0–9.6, mean 7.2 mg/100 ml	BERNSTEIN, R. E., *J. Lab. clin. Med.*, **40**, 707 (1952).	
Iron	0.3 mg/100 ml	RECHENBERGER, J., *Z. ges. inn. Med.*, **2**, 764 (1947).	The iron is in the ferrous form.
Hydrogen sulfide	Small amounts	CHRISTENSEN and WONG, *Proc. Soc. exp. Biol. (N. Y.)*, **47**, 54 (1941).	
Potassium	14.1–138.8 mg/100 ml	HOLLANDER, F., *Fed. Proc.*, **11**, 706 (1952).	
Sodium	43.0–160.0, mean 112.7 mg/100 ml	BERNSTEIN, R. E., *J. Lab. clin. Med.*, **40**, 707 (1952).	Mean of the values in 50 fasting healthy subjects.
Thiocyanate	0	TEICHMANN, W., *Dtsch. Z. Verdau.- u. Stoffwechselkr.*, **13**, 203 (1953).	Thiocyanate in the gastric juice indicates that it contains saliva.

Normal and mean values for free and total acids

From VANZANT et al., *Arch. intern. Med.*, **49**, 345 (1932)

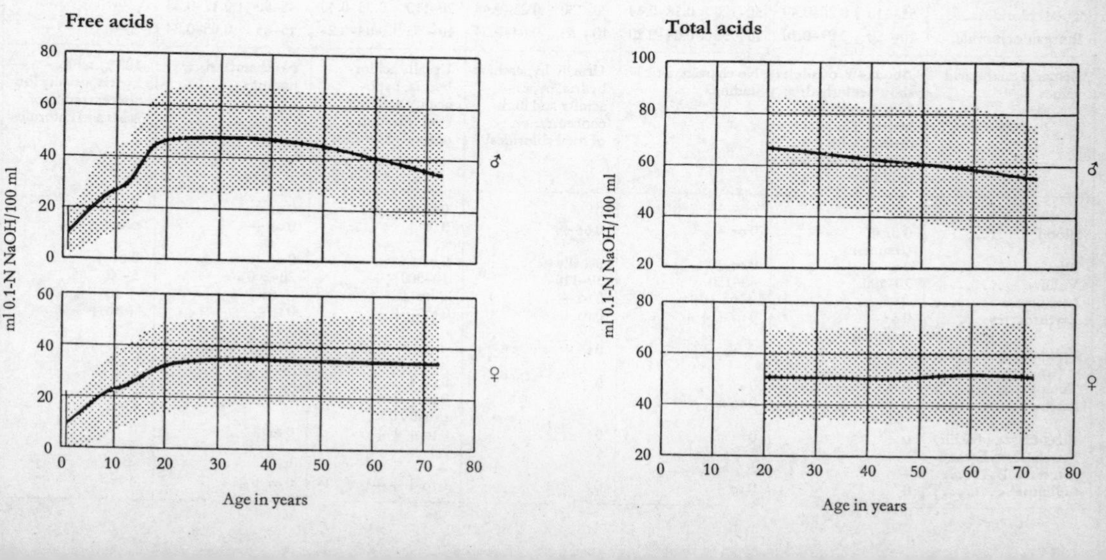

Normal mean values and standard deviations for free and total acids, volume and achlorhydria in adults

From Vanzant et al., *Arch. intern. Med.*, **52**, 616 (1933). Results from 3764 normal subjects after a test meal of 400 ml of water and 8 arrowroot biscuits

Age in years	Men								Women							
	Free acids ml 0.1-N NaOH/100 ml		Total acids		Volume ml		Achlorhydria %		Free acids ml 0.1-N NaOH/100 ml		Total acids		Volume ml		Achlorhydria %	
	Mean	Standard deviation	Mean	Standard deviation	Mean	Standard deviation	Absolute	Apparent	Mean	Standard deviation	Mean	Standard deviation	Mean	Standard deviation	Absolute	Apparent
20–24	46.7	16.5	63.5	16.5	118.0	49.5	....	....	32.0	14.5	49.7	14.5	100.5	39.0	2.0	3.0
25–29	47.0	17.0	63.0	16.2	116.5	50.5	....	2.0	33.0	14.0	50.0	14.2	100.0	39.0	4.5	6.5
30–34	47.0	16.7	62.5	16.2	113.5	50.0	3.0	5.2	33.0	13.7	50.5	14.7	99.0	39.0	7.3	10.0
35–39	47.0	16.5	61.7	16.4	109.5	48.5	6.3	8.5	33.0	14.0	50.5	15.1	97.7	39.0	10.0	13.5
40–44	46.5	16.5	60.7	17.2	105.0	46.0	9.5	11.7	33.0	13.8	50.5	15.2	96.0	39.0	12.7	17.0
45–49	45.5	16.7	59.5	18.4	101.0	43.0	12.7	15.0	33.0	13.5	50.5	14.2	94.0	38.5	14.5	20.5
50–54	43.7	17.6	58.3	19.1	97.5	41.0	16.0	18.5	33.0	14.0	50.5	14.7	92.0	37.5	18.2	24.0
55–59	41.5	18.7	57.0	19.2	95.0	42.0	19.3	21.5	33.5	15.0	50.5	15.3	89.5	37.0	21.0	27.5
60–64	39.3	19.4	55.5	18.8	93.5	45.0	22.0	25.0	33.5	16.0	50.5	16.0	87.0	36.0	23.5	31.0
65–69	37.3	18.5	53.7	17.5	92.0	47.0	22.5	26.0	33.5	16.0	50.5	16.7	84.0	35.0	26.3	31.5
70–79	33.5	17.0	50.5	16.7	91.0	50.5	17.0	21.0	33.5	15.2	50.5	17.2	79.0	33.0	24.0	28.7

Normal values for basal secretion per minute and free and total acids in children after histamine injection

From Wolman, I. J., *Amer. J. med. Sci.*, **207**, 782 (1944)

Age	Basal secretion per min ml	Free acids	Total acids	pH	Age	Basal secretion per min ml	Free acids	Total acids	pH
		ml 0.1-N NaOH/100 ml					ml 0.1-N NaOH/100 ml		
Premature	0.12–0.15	0	0– 8	4.7	1 to 2 years	0.70–1.80	15– 95	26–106	1.2–2.0
Newborn	0.20–0.45	0– 20	15– 40	2.3–3.6	2 to 5 years	0.50–2.20	20– 90	38–102	1.4–2.0
2 weeks to 6 months	0.25–1.10	0– 59	5– 71	1.5–3.4	5 to 10 years	0.10–3.30	53–113	61–145	1.4–2.0
7 to 12 months	0.40–1.50	12– 80	25–105	1.5–2.2	10 to 15 years	2.70–3.60	49–115	61–128	1.4–2.0

Characteristics of the gastric juice in various diseases

Modified from Harrison, G.A., *Chemical Methods in Clinical Medicine*, 4th ed., London, 1957

	Normal		Ulcer gastric		Ulcer duodenal		Cancer		Chronic dyspepsia and/or gastritis		Pernicious anemia	
	ml 0.1-N NaOH per 100 ml	g/100 ml as HCl	ml 0.1-N NaOH per 100 ml	g/100 ml as HCl	ml 0.1-N NaOH per 100 ml	g/100 ml as HCl	ml 0.1-N NaOH per 100 ml	g/100 ml as HCl	ml 0.1-N NaOH per 100 ml	g/100 ml as HCl	ml 0.1-N NaOH per 100 ml	g/100 ml as HCl
Free hydrochloric acid	0– 70	0.00–0.26	0– 70	0.00–0.26	0– 95	0.00–0.35	0– 70	0.00–0.25	0–70	0.00–0.25	0	0.00
Total acids	5–100	0.02–0.36	10–100	0.04–0.36	15–110	0.05–0.40	3– 80	0.01–0.29	3–55	0.01–0.20	0–40	0.00–0.15
Total chloride	55–110	0.20–0.40	50–120	0.18–0.44	70–130	0.25–0.48	20–110	0.08–0.40	45–90	0.17–0.33	—	—
Inorganic chloride	20– 50	0.07–0.18	10– 55	0.04–0.20	10– 65	0.04–0.24	10– 65	0.04–0.24	15–65	0.05–0.24	—	—
Remarks on the acid values	About 4% of adults show achlorhydria, 10% hypochlorhydria. The percentage with achlorhydria rises in old age		No characteristic findings		Usually hyperchlorhydria, hyperacidity and high concentration of total chlorides		Usually achlorhydria, hypoacidity and low concentration of total chlorides		No characteristic findings		100% achlorhydria, usually low concentration of acids and chlorides	
Lactic acid	0		0		0		0 or +		0 or +		0 or +	
Blood	0 or + (trauma)		0 or +		0 or +		0 or +		0 or +		often +	
Bile	0 or +		0 or +		usually +		0 or +		0 or +		0 or +	
Volume	20–100		40–150		30–110		10–500		20–200		5–50	
Leukocytes	+		+ to ++		0 to +		+ to +++		+ to +++		+ to +++	
Erythrocytes	0 or + (trauma)		0 to +++		0 to +		0 to +++		0 to +		+ to +++	
Epithelial cells (scales excepted)	0		+ to ++		0 to +		+ to +++		+ to ++		+ to ++	
Tumor cells	0		0		0		0 or +		0		0	
Sarcinae	0		0 to +		0		0 to +++ usually 0		0 to ++		0	
Boas-Oppler bacilli	0		0		0		0 to +++		0 to +		0	
Starch (from Ewald test meal)	+		+		+		+		+		+	
Cellulose	0		0 to +		0		0 to +++		0 to +++		0	

Stomach emptying time and total acidity for various foods

From Hawk et al., *Practical Physiological Chemistry*, 12th ed., Philadelphia, 1947, page 322

Food 100 g portions, unless otherwise stated	Number of observations	Mean of maximum total acidity ml 0.1-N NaOH per 100 ml	Mean emptying time h.	min.	Food 100 g portions, unless otherwise stated	Number of observations	Mean of maximum total acidity ml 0.1-N NaOH per 100 ml	Mean emptying time h.	min.
Bread and cereals	75	80	2	40	Vegetables	124	75	2	15
Cakes	29	90	3	00	Water ices	4	65	2	35
Eggs and egg dishes	90	80	2	40	Yoghurt	4	65	2	25
Ice cream	7	105	3	15	Tarts	29	90	2	30
Meat					Milk				
Fish	75	130	2	50	cow's 400 ml	50	100	2	30
Chicken	20	125	3	15	cow's 75 ml	3	45	1	15
Veal	7	140	2	50	human 150 ml	5	60	1	40
Beef	25	120	3	00	human 225 ml	2	90	2	25
Mutton	14	135	3	00	Nuts (25–50 g)	22	100	3	30
Pork	31	120	3	15	Milk pudding	23	90	2	20
Turkey	2	140	3	30	Sugar and candies	28	70	2	05
Fruit jellies	5	70	2	00					

Synopsis of Pancreatic Juice

	Normal values	Sources	Remarks
Appearance	watery, clear or slightly opaque		Pure pancreatic juice is generally considered to be colorless. Nevertheless certain authorities state that it may have a faint yellowish color even in the absence of bile.
Daily volume	30–1770 ml, mean 700 ml	Sunderman and Boerner, *Normal Values in Clinical Medicine*, Philadelphia, 1950, page 279.	The secretion of pancreatic juice never ceases completely during the course of the day, but the volume varies greatly and may fall to a few drops a minute. Goetze and Piechowski, *Z. ges. inn. Med.*, **7**, 1009 (1952), have demonstrated that in healthy subjects the secretion shows a rhythmic variation, the volume of juice secreted by the pancreas reaching a peak value every 55–180 minutes. Injections of secretin or pancreozymin (stimulating hormones secreted by the mucous membrane of the duodenum and the first part of the jejunum) cause profuse secretion of a watery juice in which electrolytes predominate; stimulation of the vagus nerve, on the other hand, produces small amounts of a viscous juice rich in digestive enzymes (Snyder and Lium, *Surg. Gynec. Obstet.*, **62**, 57 [1936]).
Water	98–99%		
Dry residue	1–2 g/100 ml		
Specific gravity	1.007–1.012	Mean values from the literature.	
Freezing-point depression	0.61–0.62° C		
pH value	7.5–8.0	Miller and Wiper[1].	The values in the literature vary considerably. The normal pH of pancreatic juice is given various values between 7.0 and 9.0 by different authorities. See Snyder and Lium, *Surg. Gynec. Obstet.*, **62**, 57 (1936).
Total protein	190–340 mg/100 ml	Miller and Wiper[1].	According to Di Sant'Agnese et al., *Pediatrics*, **19**, 252 (1957), the mucoproteins of normal pancreatic juice are almost always soluble in water, while an insoluble mucoprotein is often secreted in fibrocystic disease of the pancreas.
	480–530 mg/100 ml	Bartelheimer et al., *Klin. Wschr.*, **33**, 160 (1955).	
	1200 mg/100 ml	Sunderman and Boerner, *Normal Values in Clinical Medicine*, Philadelphia, 1950, page 284.	
Albumin	60 mg/100 ml	Miller and Wiper[1].	
Globulin	40 mg/100 ml	Miller and Wiper[1].	
Nitrogen			
Total nitrogen	233 mg/100 ml	Mangeot et al., *Ann. Méd.*, **54**, 604 (1953).	Determined in a single case.
Nonprotein nitrogen	14.3 mg/100 ml	Miller and Wiper[1].	

1) Miller and Wiper, *Ann. Surg.*, **120**, 852 (1944). The results are based on a study of 3 patients with external pancreatic fistulas. The authors consider the values quoted above to be normal.

	Normal values	Sources	Remarks
Urea nitrogen	5.0 mg/100 ml	MILLER and WIPER[1].	MANGEOT et al., *Ann. Méd.*, **54**, 604 (1953) give a value about 5 times greater: 0.5 g urea/l, corresponding to 23.3 mg urea-N/100 ml.
Ammonia nitrogen ...	10–15 mg/100 ml	SUNDERMAN and BOERNER, *Normal Values in Clinical Medicine*, Philadelphia, 1950, page 284.	
Uric acid	0.2 mg/100 ml	MILLER and WIPER[1].	
Cholesterol	0	MILLER and WIPER[1].	
Sugars	0	MILLER and WIPER[1].	

Pancreatic enzymes

The three main classical pancreatic enzymes are trypsin (protease), steapsin (lipase) and amylase (JONES, J. A., *J. Pediat.*, **49**, 672 [1956], MILLER and WIPER[1], etc.), but in fact more than three exist. According to THOMAS, J. E., *Acta gastro-ent. belg.*, **15**, 811 (1952), the pancreas produces at least two proteases (trypsin and chymotrypsin), one peptidase, one lipase and one or possibly two amylases. Other authorities have described also pancreatic carboxypeptidases and polynucleotidases. The general opinion is that the pancreatic juice in fibrocystic disease of the pancreas contains neither trypsin, lipase nor amylase (JONES, J. A., *J. Pediat.*, **49**, 672 [1956]). See also under Digestive Enzymes, pages 416 et seq.

Trypsin and chymotrypsin. According to the classical theory, which is that most widely accepted (see in particular HOUSSAY et al., *Physiologie humaine*, Paris, 1950, page 501), the pancreas secretes two proenzymes (zymogens), trypsinogen and chymotrypsinogen. These are not converted into active enzymes until they reach the duodenum. Trypsinogen is activated by enterokinase at pH 5.2 to 6.0, then by trypsin itself (autocatalytic reaction) at pH 7.9. Chymotrypsinogen is converted to chymotrypsin by the action of trypsin (but not of enterokinase). Some authors, notably MANGEOT et al., *Ann. Méd.*, **54**, 604 (1953), nevertheless claim to have found in *pure* pancreatic juice, extracted by a catheter in the duct of WIRSUNG, active trypsin and not trypsinogen. If this is true, the theory can no longer be held that acute hemorrhagic pancreatitis is caused by an activation of trypsinogen in the pancreatic tissue itself. DI SANT'AGNESE et al., *Pediatrics*, **19**, 252 (1957), using the viscosimetric method of NORTHROP and HOUSSAY, found that the normal mean value for the activity of trypsin in the adult was 250 viscosimetric units per milliliter of pancreatic juice, or at all events was above 100 such units; in fibrocystic disease of the pancreas the value falls to zero.

	Normal values	Sources	Remarks
Calcium	4.4–6.4 mg/100 ml	MILLER and WIPER[1].	
Potassium	20–60 mg/100 ml	Mean values from the literature.	Some authorities give lower values (TRIA and FABRIANI, *Atti R. Accad. Ital.*, **2**, 381 [1941], quoted by HOPPE-SEYLER[2], page 389, give 10.24 mg/100 ml) others much higher (MANGEOT et al., *Ann. Méd.*, **54**, 604 [1953] give 144 mg/100 ml).
Sodium	276–322 mg/100 ml	COOKE and CROWLEY, *New Engl. J. Med.*, **246**, 637 (1952).	
Bicarbonate	60–75 mEq/l	MILLER and WIPER[1].	Some authors have found much lower values: LESSER and PAREIRA, *Ann. Surg.*, **138**, 846 (1953), give 7.9 mEq/l.
Chloride	213–284 mg/100 ml	MILLER and WIPER[1].	
Other mineral constituents			
Silicic acid	5.15 mg/100 ml	HOPPE-SEYLER[2], page 389.	
Magnesium	0.17 mg/100 ml	HOPPE-SEYLER[2], page 389.	
Sulfur	6.7 mg/100 ml	HOPPE-SEYLER[2], page 389.	
Sulfate	0	MILLER and WIPER[1].	

Intestinal Juice

Little is known about the composition of the intestinal juice in healthy subjects since there is no practical method of extracting the juice unchanged. Most of the values given here are taken from SUNDERMAN and BOERNER, *Normal Values in Clinical Medicine*, Philadelphia, 1950, pages 243–248, and from HOPPE-SEYLER[2], pages 383–389.

			100 ml intestinal juice contain
Specific gravity	1.005–1.010	Water	98 g
Freezing-point depression	0.62° C	Dissolved substances	2 g
Daily volume	ca. 200 ml	Calcium	5–12.8 mg, mean 7.7 mg
pH (after meals):		Sodium	230–320 mg
Duodenum	4.7–6.5	Potassium	20–60 mg
Upper jejunum	6.2–6.7	Phosphorus	4.5–13.2 mg, mean 6.8 mg
Lower jejunum	6.2–7.3	Sodium chloride	0.4–0.6 g
Ileum	6.1–7.3	Sodium bicarbonate	0.1–1.2 g
Enzymes	See pages 416 et seq.	Proteins	0.8 g
		Total nitrogen	35–200 mg

1) MILLER and WIPER, *Ann. Surg.*, **120**, 852 (1944). The results are based on a study of 3 patients with external pancreatic fistulas. The authors consider the values quoted above to be normal.

2) LANG et al. (Eds.), *Hoppe-Seyler/Thierfelder Handbuch der physiologisch- und pathologisch-chemischen Analyse*, 10th ed., vol. V, *Untersuchung der Organe, Körperflüssigkeiten und Ausscheidungen*, Berlin, 1953.

Synopsis of Bile

For definition of the normal range see footnote, page 517

	Bile in liver	Sources	Bile in gallbladder	Sources
Color	Golden yellow to orange		Dark brown to greenish brown	
Daily volume	700–1200 ml	*8*	–	–
Specific gravity	1.008–1.016	*11*	1.008–1.059	*10*
Freezing-point depression	0.56–0.61°C	*13*	–	–
pH value	5.7–8.6	*8*	Mean value **7.35** Standard deviation 0.624 Normal range *6.10–8.60*	*5*
Water	97–98%	*13*	84%	*4*
Bile acids, total	1.24–1.72%	*6*, page 264	2.3–7.7%	*12*
Conjugated bile acids	0.96–1.2%	*6*, page 264	1.8–6.2%	*12*
Free bile acids	0.28–0.52%	*6*, page 264	20%	*12*
Cholic acid	0.39–0.63%	*6*, page 264	1.2–3.3%	*12*
Desoxycholic acid	0.85–0.88%	*6*, page 264	1.1–4.3%	*12*
Bilirubin	17–71 mg/100 ml	*10*	50–1000 mg/100 ml	*10*
Cholesterol*	86–176 mg/100 ml	*9*	100–900 mg/100 ml	*13*
Choline, total	Mean value **57** mg/100 ml Standard deviation 17.5 mg/100 ml Normal range *22.0–92.0* mg/100 ml	*1* and *2*	550 mg/100 ml	*1*
Mucin	–	–	1–4%	*6*, page 276
Proteins	180 mg/100 ml	*1*	450 mg/100 ml	*1*
Total nitrogen	77 mg/100 ml	*1*	490 mg/100 ml	*1*
Fatty acids	0.02–0.14% Mean value **269.3** mg/100 ml Standard deviation 84.3 mg/100 ml Normal range *100.7–437.9* mg/100 ml	*6*, page 264 *1* and *2*	80–1600 mg/100 ml 2400 mg/100 ml	*6*, page 275 *1*
Lecithins	250 mg/100 ml	*1*	350 mg/100 ml	*1*
Carbohydrates, total	61 mg/100 ml	*3*	239 mg/100 ml	*3*
Reducing sugars	30 mg/100 ml	*1* and *3*	80 mg/100 ml	*1*
Bases	80–90 mEq/l	*14*	280–300 mEq/l	*14*
Bicarbonate	20–25 mEq/l	*14*	8–12 mEq/l	*14*
Calcium	8–11 mg/100 ml	*7*	25–28 mEq/l	*14*
Chloride	90–100 mEq/l	*14*	16–19 mEq/l	*14*
Phosphorus	Mean value **14.8** mg/100 ml Standard deviation 4.4 mg/100 ml Normal range *6.0–23.6* mg/100 ml	*1* and *2*	140 mg/100 ml	*1*

* Occurs in its nonesterified form in bile.

1) Polonovski and Bourrillon, *Bull. Soc. Chim. biol. (Paris)*, **34**, 703 (1952) } or calculated from the numerical data of these authors.
2) Polonovski and Bourrillon, *Bull. Soc. Chim. biol. (Paris)*, **34**, 712 (1952) }
3) Polonovski and Bourrillon, *Bull. Soc. Chim. biol. (Paris)*, **34**, 720 (1952) }
4) Hammarsten, O., *Ergebn. Physiol.*, **4**, 1 (1905).
5) Calculated from the data of Crawford and Brooke, *Lancet*, **1**, 1096 (1955).
6) Sunderman and Boerner, *Normal Values in Clinical Medicine*, Philadelphia, 1950.
7) Lang et al. (Eds.), *Hoppe-Seyler/Thierfelder Handbuch der physiologisch- und pathologisch-chemischen Analyse*, 10th ed., vol. V, *Untersuchung der Organe, Körperflüssigkeiten und Ausscheidungen*, Berlin, 1953, page 391.
8) Popper and Schaffner, *Liver: Structure and Function*, New York, 1957, page 80.
9) Jacobi et al., *Amer. J. dig. Dis.*, **9**, 264 (1942).
10) Elton, N. W., *Amer. J. clin. Path.*, **6**, 81 (1936).
11) Brugsch and Horsters, *Z. ges. exp. Med.*, **38**, 367 (1923).
12) Colp and Doubilet, *Arch. Surg. (Chicago)*, **33**, 913 (1936).
13) Horrall, O. H., *Bile, its Toxicity and Relation to Disease*, Chicago, 1938, quoted by Popper and Schaffner, *Liver: Structure and Function*, New York, 1957, page 80.
14) Walters and Snell, *Diseases of the Gallbladder and Bile Ducts*, Philadelphia, 1940, page 68.

Daily quantity[2]

Adults
- mixed diet .... 60–250 g
- vegetable diet .... 370 g
- meat diet .... 54–64 g
- prolonged fasting .... 9.5–22 g
- in disease .... 500–1200 g

Infants .... 4–120 g
Young children .... 60–150 g

pH value[2]

The feces are usually alkaline or neutral, but the pH value depends on the diet, on the rate of passage through the intestine, on the intestinal flora, etc. Variations of pH 4.6 to pH 8.8 have been observed in healthy subjects.

Composition (approximate)[2]

Water		75 %
Dry substance		
Cellulose	Food residues	2 %
Muscle fiber, nitrogenous substances	Food residues	2 %
Fats	Food residues	6 %
Bacterial substances		8 %
Other constituents		7 %

Nitrogen[2]

The nitrogen content amounts to ca. 1 g/day (food residues, bacteria, desquamated epithelium, exudate of the intestinal mucosa). In illness the nitrogen content is often greatly increased (incomplete digestion, poor absorption). High values are mainly found in diarrhea and pancreatic disease.

Urobilinogen[3]

	Mean mg/day	Range mg/day
Men	101	57–200
Women	40	8–150

The fecal urobilinogen concentration provides a rough measure of the rate of hemoglobin turnover[3].

Fats (unregulated diet)[4]

	Mean	Range
Dry substance, per cent of fresh feces	21.1	4.6–38.0
Total fat, per cent of dry substance	17.5	7.3–27.6
Neutral fat, per cent of dry substance	7.3	2.5–11.8
Free fatty acids, per cent of dry substance	5.6	1.1–10.0
Fatty acids, combined as soaps, per cent of dry substance	4.6	0.5–11.4

Salts and minerals[5]

	Average total excretion per day	Comparative amounts excreted in urine and in feces: Urine % of total excretion	Feces % of total excretion
Chlorides	0.09 g	98	2
Lead	0–0.4 mg	–	–
Potassium	0.47 g	79	21
Calcium	0.64 g	12	88
Magnesium	0.20 g	31	69
Sodium	0.12 g	95	5
Phosphorus	0.51 g	57	43
Sulfur	0.13 g	83	17

Average number of stools per day in infants[6]

Days	Breast milk	Cow's milk	Irradiated dried milk
1	3.8	3.1	2.9
2	4.0	4.0	5.0
3	4.9	4.9	5.3
4	5.3	5.5	6.6
5	5.4	5.3	6.0
6	4.8	5.1	4.4
7	3.9	4.2	5.2
8	4.1	4.1	4.6
9	3.9	3.8	4.5
10	3.8	4.1	3.6
11	3.7	3.3	4.1
12	3.0	3.4	3.9
13	2.8	3.1	3.7
14	2.7	3.0	3.7
Weeks			
3	2.53	2.70	3.01
4	2.28	2.51	2.99
5	2.06	2.33	2.71
6	1.84	2.16	2.45
7	1.47	2.08	2.40
8	1.24	1.99	2.19
9	1.40	1.84	2.12
10	1.10	1.80	2.08
11	1.15	1.69	2.03
12	1.15	1.69	1.95
13	1.19	1.66	1.93

Color

Normal: *brown*, mainly due to stercobilin; darker on low-residue meat diets, lighter on high-residue vegetable diets. Darkens on exposure to air (oxidation of urobilinogen to urobilin). *Golden yellow* in breast-fed infants (unchanged bilirubin). *Green* color is due to chlorophyll (spinach) or biliverdin (change in infants' stools). *Black* color is due to plant juices (blueberry), carbon, iron (iron sulfide). *Pitchblack* color is due to high hematin content (consumption of black pudding, hemorrhage of stomach or upper intestine). *Light gray* color is due to undigested fats following inadequate bile secretion (neutral fats, calcium soaps).

Effects of drugs on the color of feces[2]

Drug	Dose causing abnormal color	Color
Bismuth salts	5 g	Black
Calomel	130–140 mg	Green
Iron	65–70 mg	Gray-black, darkening in air
Methylene blue	130–140 mg	Blue, especially on contact with air
Manganese dioxide	130–140 mg	Dark brown to black
Hematoxylin	1 g	Reddish brown
Rhubarb extract	2 ml	Yellow
Senna extract	4 ml	Deep yellow
Santonin	65–70 mg	Deep yellow

References

1) For a review and bibliography see Krzywanek and Flaschenträger, in Flaschenträger and Lehnartz (Eds.), *Physiologische Chemie*, vol. II, part 2b, Berlin, 1957, page 202. *2)* From Harrison, G. A., *Chemical Methods in Clinical Medicine*, 4th ed., London, 1957, page 507. *3)* Balikov, B., *Clin. Chem.*, 3, 145 (1957). *4)* Fowweather, F. S., *Brit. J. exp. Path.*, 7, 15 (1926). *5)* Shohl, A. T., *Mineral Metabolism*, American Chemical Society Monograph No. 82, New York, 1939. *6)* Gonce and Lewis, *Amer. J. Dis. Child.*, **80**, 274 (1950).

Normal values in **milligrams per 24-hour urine** in adults on a normal balanced diet (unless otherwise stated)

Physicochemical properties

Appearance: At the moment of voiding the urine is clear and transparent; after a rich meal which turns the urine alkaline, however, it can sometimes be more or less turbid. If clear urine is allowed to stand for some time *nubeculae* appear, i.e. cloudy opacities formed by mucin from the urinary passages and, in alkaline urine, by various crystals (phosphates of alkaline-earth metals). The urine can also be turbid when fats are present.

Odor: The faint and usually aromatic odor is due to unidentified substances. Following ingestion of thymol or asparagus, for instance, the odor changes completely.

Color: Normally the urine is more or less deep yellow in color, due mainly to the presence of urochrome. In certain diseases and after ingestion of various substances (drugs, foodstuffs, etc.) it can assume many shades of red, dark brown or blue as shown in the following scheme (see also Lagrue, G., *Vie méd. [Paris]*, **37**, 203 [1956]; Hoppe-Seyler[1], page 184; Sunderman and Boerner, *Normal Values in Clinical Medicine*, Philadelphia, 1950, page 350):

Red urine:	Blood, aminopyrine, aniline dyes (in candies), etc.
Dark brown urine:	Hemoglobinuria, poisoning by phenol or cresol, melanin, alkaptonuria, etc.
Blue urine:	Methylene blue, indigo blue.

	Mean*	Range*	s	Sources	Remarks
Daily volume					
Newborn					
(1–2 days old)	–	30– 60 ml/24 h	–	Rubin, M.I., in Nelson, W. E. (Ed.), *Textbook of Pediatrics*, 7th ed., Philadelphia, 1959, page 1010.	
Infants of					
3– 10 days	–	100– 300 ml/24 h	–		
10– 60 days	–	250– 450 ml/24 h	–		
60–365 days	–	400– 500 ml/24 h	–		
Children of					
1– 3 years	–	500– 600 ml/24 h	–		
3– 5 years	–	600– 700 ml/24 h	–		
5– 8 years	–	650–1000 ml/24 h	–		
8–14 years	–	800–1400 ml/24 h	–		
Adults	–	600–1600 ml/24 h	–	Weisberg, H. F., *Water, Electrolyte and Acid-Base Balance*, Baltimore, 1953.	See also under Water and Electrolyte Balance, pages 544 and 545. The urine volume is physiologically increased after excessive water intake, increased salt intake and high protein intake; it is decreased after low water intake and excessive exercise and sweating. There is a well-known day/night periodicity in the volumes of urine produced by adults: the largest volumes are produced between 3 and 6 p.m., the smallest between 3 and 6 a.m. (Metz and Mours-Laroche, *C. R. Soc. Biol. [Paris]*, **149**, 1026 [1955]).
Old people	853 ml /24 h	250–2400 ml/24 h	–	Howell, T.H., *J. Geront.*, **11**, 61 (1956).	This mean value of measurements on 27 old people (20 women, 7 men) over 90 years of age shows that oliguria can be caused by old age.
Specific gravity					
Newborn (first few days)	1.012	–	–	Rubin, M. I., in Nelson, W. E. (Ed.), *Textbook of Pediatrics*, 7th ed., Philadelphia, 1959, page 1011.	
Infants	–	1.002–1.006	–		
Adults	–	1.001–1.030	–	Sunderman and Boerner, *Normal Values in Clinical Medicine*, Philadelphia, 1950, page 351.	
Freezing-point depression	–	0.075–2.6° C	–	Hoppe-Seyler[1], page 184.	Usually between 1.3–2.3° C.
Viscosity	–	See remarks	–		Posner, C., *Berl. klin. Wschr.*, **52**, 1106 (1915), gives the following figures: (see table below)
pH	**6.25**	*5.53–6.97*	0.36	Calculated from Yarbro, C. L., *J. Urol. (Baltimore)*, **75**, 216 (1956).	Determinations on 54 healthy students. According to Violle, P.-L., *Rev. Prat.*, **7**, 644 (1957), the pH value shows a rhythmical variation during the 24-hour period: the maximum pH (i.e. least acidity) in adults is in the morning; it then falls progressively until about 1 p.m., rises until about 5 p.m. and falls until about 11 p.m., after which it rises again until the morning. The values vary as a rule between pH 5 and 6; individual variations are not much more than pH 0.2 or 0.3.
Temperature coefficient between 24 and 38° C, in pH units per degree Centigrade					
Acid urine (10 tests)	**-0.0047**	*-0.0013 to -0.0081*	0.0017	Wesson, L. G., *J. appl. Physiol.*, **5**, 619 (1953).	The temperature coefficient of a buffer solution such as urine is the number of pH units by which the pH value of the solution falls (or rises) when the temperature rises 1° C.
Alkaline urine (4 tests)	**-0.0053**	*-0.0035 to -0.0071*	0.0009		

Dilution test (Volhard's test) (normal values, adults after single intake of 1000 ml water)

Hours	Urine volume (ml)	Spec. grav.
1	140	1.008
2	500	1.002
3	270	1.003
4	90	1.010
Volume over first 4 hours: 1000 ml		
6	40	1.020
8	45	1.026
10	85	1.025
12	30	1.031

Viscosity (Posner):

Specific gravity	Viscosity	
1.005	1.0	
1.016	1.02	Viscosity of distilled water = 1.00
1.022	1.09	
1.024	1.14	

* When a range given is a *normal range* (see page 154), i.e. calculated from the formula: mean ± (2 × standard deviation *s*), it is printed in *italics*, with the mean in **bold** figures. Otherwise the data given are experimental results which have not been tested statistically.

1) Lang et al. (Eds.), *Hoppe-Seyler/Thierfelder Handbuch der physiologisch- und pathologisch-chemischen Analyse*, 10th ed., vol. V, *Untersuchung der Organe, Körperflüssigkeiten und Ausscheidungen*, Berlin, 1953.

Normal values in **milligrams per 24-hour urine** in adults on a normal balanced diet (unless otherwise stated)

	Mean*	Range*	s	Sources	Remarks
Dry weight	–	55.0–70.0 g/24 h	–	SUNDERMAN and BOERNER, *Normal Values in Clinical Medicine*, Philadelphia, 1950, page 368.	Can be calculated approximately from the specific gravity by multiplying the 2nd and 3rd figure after the decimal point by 2.6 (or by 1.6 in small children). Example: specific gravity 1.020; dry weight $\cong$ 20 × 2.6 = 52 g/24 h (for adults). After HOPPE-SEYLER[1], page 183.
Proteins					
Total proteins	–	20–100	–	Mean values from the literature; see especially SUNDERMAN and BOERNER, *Normal Values in Clinical Medicine*, Philadelphia, 1950, page 355.	These small concentrations of protein in urine cannot be determined by ordinary laboratory methods, which explains why it was held for a long time that no proteins were present in urine. The protein concentration rises after hard physical activity; see JAVITT and MILLER, *J. appl. Physiol.*, **4**, 834 (1952), GARDNER, K. D., *J. Amer. med. Ass.*, **161**, 1613 (1956), and ALYEA and BOONE, *Sth. med. J. (Bgham, Ala.)*, **50**, 905 (1957). In various illnesses – especially multiple myelomatosis, sometimes also leukemia and osteomalacia – the characteristic BENCE-JONES protein occurs in urine. SANDKÜHLER, S., *Amer. J. clin. Path.*, **22**, 282 (1952), has described a simple and exact test for its determination.
Mucoproteins					
Men	**146.0**	*98.6–193.4*	23.7	ANDERSON and MACLAGAN, *Biochem. J.*, **59**, 638 (1955).	Mucoproteins are substances containing a mucopolysaccharide firmly linked to a peptide and with a hexosamine content of more than 4%.
Women	**106.0**	*65.8–146.2*	20.1		
Glycoproteins	–	1–11 mg/100 ml	–	ANDERSON and MACLAGAN, *Biochem. J.*, **59**, 638 (1955).	Glycoproteins are substances containing less than 4% of hexosamine and ca. 1–2% of firmly bound carbohydrate.
Nitrogen					
Total nitrogen	**15.3 g /24 h**	*10.26–20.34 g /24 h*	2.52 g /24 h	KUHL et al., *Metabolism*, **4**, 143 (1955).	Approximate distribution of total nitrogen: Urea-N 84 %; Amino acid-N 4.8%; Ammonia-N 4.6%; Creatinine-N 4.4%; Uric acid-N 1.8%; Hippuric acid-N 0.4%
Ammonia-N	–	0.4–1.0 g/24 h	–	SUNDERMAN and BOERNER, *Normal Values in Clinical Medicine*, Philadelphia, 1950, page 352, and HOPPE-SEYLER[1], page 183.	To obtain true values, ammonia must be estimated in fresh urine since otherwise fermentations take place which considerably increase the concentration of ammonia.
Amino acid-N, total	**349**	*267–431*	41	KALANT and DUCCI, *J. clin. Endocr.*, **15**, 481 (1955).	BERGER, H., *Schweiz. med. Wschr.*, **86**, 711 and 729 (1956), has shown that a physiological increase of amino acids in urine occurs in the newborn, old people, pregnant women (especially in the second half of pregnancy) and during puberty.
Amino acids					
Alanine	27.1 µg/ml	–	–	Calculated from SUTTON and VANDENBERG, *Hum. Biol.*, **25**, 318 (1953).	
β-Aminoisobutyric acid	6.52 µg/ml	–	–	Calculated from SUTTON and VANDENBERG, *Hum. Biol.*, **25**, 318 (1953).	
Arginine					
Total: Men	**47.0**	*37.2–56.8*	4.9	Calculated (in part) from ULRICH, J. A., *Proc. Mayo Clin.*, **29**, 210 (1954).	
Total: Women	**33.4**	*17.0–49.8*	8.2		
Free: Men	**24.0**	*0.4–47.6*	11.8		
Free: Women	**17.4**	*6.2–28.6*	5.6		
Aspartic acid					
Total: Men	**113.4**	*16.4–210.4*	48.5	Calculated (in part) from ULRICH, J. A., *Proc. Mayo Clin.*, **29**, 210 (1954).	
Total: Women	**91.5**	*30.1–152.9*	30.7		
Free: Men	**74.8**	*0–155.2*	40.2		
Free: Women	**54.0**	*21.0–87.0*	16.5		
Cystine (free)	**87.7**	*37.7–137.7*	25.0	HIER, S. W., *Trans. N.Y. Acad. Sci.*, **10**, 280 (1948).	
Glutamine	32.2 µg/ml	–	–	SUTTON and VANDENBERG, *Hum. Biol.*, **25**, 318 (1953).	

Frequency of excretion of various amino acids in human urine (determinations by paper chromatography on urine from 100 males and females). After SCHÖNENBERG, H., *Klin. Wschr.*, **34**, 442 (1956). This table shows the percentage of specimens in which the respective acids could be detected.

	%		%
Glycine	100	Taurine	63
Serine	99	Phenylalanine	56
Glutamic acid	91	Tyrosine	54
Valine	82	Lysine	48
Alanine	81	Cysteine	31
Aspartic acid	69	Arginine	27
Leucine or Isoleucine	69	Glutamine	26
		Threonine	20
Proline	69	3-Methylhistidine	19

The fact that the same amino acids are not present in the urine of all individuals may explain why the values given in the literature for the concentration of the various amino acids in urine often show considerable discrepancies (cf. especially STEIN, W. H., *J. biol. Chem.*, **201**, 45 [1953]; EADES and POLLACK, *J. nat. Cancer Inst.*, **15**, 421 [1954]; HIER, S. W., *Trans. N. Y. Acad. Sci.*, **10**, 280 [1948]). The figures given here should therefore be regarded as approximations, not as absolute values.

* When a range given is a *normal range* (see page 154), i.e. calculated from the formula: mean ± (2 × standard deviation *s*), it is printed in *italics*, with the mean in **bold** figures. Otherwise the data given are experimental results which have not been tested statistically.

1) LANG et al. (Eds.), *Hoppe-Seyler/Thierfelder Handbuch der physiologisch- und pathologisch-chemischen Analyse*, 10th ed., vol. V, *Untersuchung der Organe, Körperflüssigkeiten und Ausscheidungen*, Berlin, 1953.

Synopsis of Urine (continued)

Normal values in **milligrams per 24-hour urine** in adults on a normal balanced diet (unless otherwise stated)

	Mean*	Range*	s	Sources	Remarks
Glutamic acid					
Total: Men	**249.9**	*15.1–484.7*	117.4	Calculated (in part) from ULRICH, J. A., *Proc. Mayo Clin.*, **29**, 210 (1954).	According to STEIN, W. H., *J. biol. Chem.*, **201**, 45 (1953), *fresh* urine contains glutamine but no free glutamic acid.
Women	**248.7**	*45.1–452.3*	101.8		
Free: Men	**235.4**	*107.8–363.0*	63.8		
Women	**201.9**	*55.9–347.9*	73.0		
Glycine					
Total	**405.0**	*139.4–670.6*	132.8	EADES and POLLACK, *J. nat. Cancer Inst.*, **15**, 421 (1954).	
Free	**226.0**	*131.2–320.8*	47.4		
Histidine					
Total: Men	**284.0**	*69.2–498.8*	107.4	Calculated (in part) from ULRICH, J. A., *Proc. Mayo Clin.*, **29**, 210 (1954).	Urine also contains 3-methylhistidine (~ 50 mg per 24-hour urine), which occurs in plasma only in minute concentrations (less than 0.1 mg/100 ml according to TALLAN et al., *J. biol. Chem.*, **206**, 825 [1954]).
Women	**170.0**	*57.0–283.0*	56.5		
Free: Men	**255.6**	*82.4–428.8*	86.6		
Women	**162.3**	*38.1–286.5*	62.1		
Hydroxyproline					
Total	23.05	–	–	Calculated from ZIFF et al., *J. clin. Invest.*, **35**, 579 (1956).	
Free	0.55	–	–		
Isoleucine					
Total: Men	**11.3**	*6.5–16.1*	2.4	Calculated (in part) from ULRICH, J. A., *Proc. Mayo Clin.*, **29**, 210 (1954).	
Women	**11.7**	*4.3–19.1*	3.7		
Free: Men	**7.8**	*3.0–12.6*	2.4		
Women	**6.3**	*1.9–10.7*	2.2		
Leucine					
Total: Men	**27.9**	*11.9–43.9*	8.0	Calculated (in part) from ULRICH, J. A., *Proc. Mayo Clin.*, **29**, 210 (1954).	
Women	**21.9**	*10.7–33.1*	5.6		
Free: Men	**20.0**	*6.2–33.8*	6.9		
Women	**13.4**	*4.4–22.4*	4.5		
Lysine					
Total: Men	**102.0**	*44.4–159.6*	28.8	Calculated (in part) from ULRICH, J. A., *Proc. Mayo Clin.*, **29**, 210 (1954).	
Women	**97.2**	*29.0–165.4*	34.1		
Free: Men	**57.4**	*15.2–99.6*	21.1		
Women	**57.4**	*6.6–108.2*	25.4		
Methionine					
Total: Men	**6.6**	*3.8–9.4*	1.4	Calculated (in part) from ULRICH, J. A., *Proc. Mayo Clin.*, **29**, 210 (1954).	
Women	**5.5**	*1.7–9.3*	1.9		
Free: Men	**3.9**	*1.1–6.7*	1.4		
Women	**2.8**	*0.6–5.0*	1.1		
Phenylalanine					
Total: Men	**28.7**	*13.5–43.9*	7.6	Calculated (in part) from ULRICH, J. A., *Proc. Mayo Clin.*, **29**, 210 (1954).	
Women	**23.7**	*10.9–36.5*	6.4		
Free: Men	**18.6**	*13.0–24.2*	2.8		
Women	**14.9**	*3.7–26.1*	5.6		
Proline					
Total: Men	**43.3**	*24.5–62.1*	9.4	Calculated (in part) from ULRICH, J. A., *Proc. Mayo Clin.*, **29**, 210 (1954).	
Women	**49.5**	*20.3–78.7*	14.6		
Free: Men	**35.4**	*18.8–52.0*	8.3		
Women	**33.2**	*6.2–60.2*	13.5		
Serine					
Total	–	0.35–1.4 mg per kilogram of body weight per day	–	SPECTOR, W. S. (Ed.), *Handbook of Biological Data*, Philadelphia, 1956, page 242.	
Free	–	0.21–0.52 mg per kilogram of body weight per day	–		
Taurine	156	–	–	STEIN, W. H., *J. biol. Chem.*, **201**, 45 (1953).	
Threonine					
Total: Men	**83.2**	*41.6–124.8*	20.8	Calculated (in part) from ULRICH, J. A., *Proc. Mayo Clin.*, **29**, 210 (1954).	
Women	**64.2**	*26.8–101.6*	18.7		
Free: Men	**59.8**	*28.0–91.6*	15.9		
Women	**52.3**	*10.3–94.3*	21.0		

* When a range given is a *normal range* (see page 154), i.e. calculated from the formula: mean ± (2 × standard deviation *s*), it is printed in *italics*, with the mean in **bold** figures. Otherwise the data given are experimental results which have not been tested statistically.

Normal values in **milligrams per 24-hour urine** in adults on a normal balanced diet (unless otherwise stated)

	Mean*	Range*	s	Sources	Remarks
Tryptophan					
Total: Men	**22.9**	*13.1–32.7*	4.9	Calculated (in part) from ULRICH, J. A., *Proc. Mayo Clin.*, **29**, 210 (1954).	
Women	**16.6**	*8.4–24.8*	4.1		
Free: Men	**20.7**	*9.7–31.7*	5.5		
Women	**16.0**	*4.8–27.2*	5.6		
Tyrosine					
Total: Men	**55.5**	*38.1–72.9*	8.7	Calculated (in part) from ULRICH, J. A., *Proc. Mayo Clin.*, **29**, 210 (1954).	According to TALLAN et al., *J. biol. Chem.*, **217**, 703 (1955), about half the tyrosine in urine occurs as a double sulfate of tyrosine and potassium.
Women	**41.1**	*18.7–63.5*	11.2		
Free: Men	**44.2**	*31.8–56.6*	6.2		
Women	**32.9**	*18.7–47.1*	7.1		
Valine					
Total: Men	**30.1**	*15.5–44.7*	7.3	Calculated (in part) from ULRICH, J. A., *Proc. Mayo Clin.*, **29**, 210 (1954).	
Women	**27.8**	*12.8–42.8*	7.5		
Free: Men	**20.1**	*7.7–32.5*	6.2		
Women	**16.7**	*5.5–27.9*	5.6		
Organic bases					
Allantoin	–	25–30 mg/liter	–	LARSON, H. W., *J. biol. Chem.*, **94**, 727 (1931/32).	
Choline	–	5.6–9.0	–	LUECKE and PEARSON, *J. biol. Chem.*, **153**, 259 (1944).	Choline occurs in urine in the free form only.
Creatine					
Adults: Men	–	almost absent	–	TAUSSKY and BRAHEN, in SELIGSON, D. (Ed.), *Standard Methods in Clinical Chemistry*, vol. III, New York, 1961, page 99; HOWELL, T. H., *J. Geront.*, **11**, 61 (1956).	The creatine excretion is higher in growing children (CLARK et al., *Amer. J. Dis. Child.*, **81**, 774 [1951]). It fluctuates with the menstrual cycle up to the menopause. The excretion is increased during pregnancy and the early puerperium. A pathological increase is observed in muscle diseases and under ACTH and corticosteroid therapy.
Women	–	0–50	–		
Old people (men and women over 90)	90	25–230	–		
Creatinine					
Adults	**2.145** g/24 h	*1.071–3.219* g/24 h	0.537 g/24 h	KUHL et al., *Metabolism*, **4**, 143 (1955).	The creatinine of urine is of endogenous origin in the healthy human, so that variations of diet, provided that they remain within normal limits, have no notable influence on the amount of this compound excreted daily (SUNDERMAN and BOERNER, *Normal Values in Clinical Medicine*, Philadelphia, 1950, page 353). At the present time the clearance of "endogenous" creatinine is hardly ever determined since in man (though not in animals) it apparently fails to give any exact indication of glomerular filtration (BRADLEY, S. E., *Ann. Rev. Physiol.*, **19**, 521 [1957]). JAFFÉ's test is often used but it is not absolutely specific: the sodium salt of pyruvic acid for instance also gives a positive reaction. For the quantitative and qualitative determination of creatinine see especially PAGET et al., *Ann. Biol. clin.*, **13**, 535 (1955), and TAUSSKY, H. H., *Clin. chim. Acta (Amst.)*, **1**, 210 (1956).
Old people					
Men (7 subjects)	0.48 g/24 h	0.26–0.69 g/24 h	–	HOWELL, T. H., *J. Geront.*, **11**, 61 (1956).	
Women (20 subjects)	0.46 g/24 h	0.035–1.0 g/24 h	–		
Ethanolamine	3.18 µg/ml	–	–	SUTTON and VANDENBERG, *Hum. Biol.*, **25**, 318 (1953).	According to SCHÖNENBERG, H., *Klin. Wschr.*, **34**, 442 (1956), ethanolamine occurs in only 24–48% of human urines.
Guanidine	–	10–20	–	WEBER, C. J., *J. biol. Chem.*, **78**, 465 (1928).	
Guanidinoacetic acid	30	–	–	EVERETT, M. R., *Medical Biochemistry*, 2nd ed., New York, 1946, page 434.	
Hippuric acid	0.7 g/24 h	0.1–1.0 g/24 h	–	KILDUFFE, R. A., *Clinical Urinalysis and its Interpretation*, Philadelphia, 1937, quoted by SUNDERMAN and BOERNER, *Normal Values in Clinical Medicine*, Philadelphia, 1950, page 355.	
Imidazoles					
On low-protein diet (40 g/day)	286.1	150–300	–	KAUFFMANN and ENGEL, *Z. klin. Med.*, **114**, 405 (1930).	The amounts excreted vary with the protein (especially histidine) content of the ingested food.
On high-protein diet (118 g/day)	443	320–600	–		

* When a range given is a *normal range* (see page 154), i.e. calculated from the formula: mean ± (2 × standard deviation *s*), it is printed in *italics*, with the mean in **bold** figures. Otherwise the data given are experimental results which have not been tested statistically.

Synopsis of Urine (continued)

Normal values in **milligrams per 24-hour urine** in adults on a normal balanced diet (unless otherwise stated)

	Mean*	Range*	*s*	Sources	Remarks
Indican (3-indoxylsulfuric acid)	–	5–10	–	BRADLEY, S. E., *Med. Clin. N. Amer.*, **29**, 1314 (1945).	Much increased by putrefaction of bowel contents, especially in obstruction.
Kynurenine					
Average age:					
20 years	**0.096** /100 ml	*0.014–0.178* per 100 ml	0.041	ŠPAČEK, M., *Canad. J. Biochem.*, **33**, 14 (1955).	Kynurenine is a metabolite of tryptophan (see pages 410 and 411).
47 years	**0.207** /100 ml	*0.017–0.431* per 100 ml	0.112		
Purine bases	–	10–60	–	BRADLEY, S. E., *Med. Clin. N. Amer.*, **29**, 1314 (1945).	
Urea	–	20–35 g/24 h	–	HOPPE-SEYLER[1], page 187.	The excretion of urea in urine is increased by a diet rich in protein and also by increased protein catabolism (for instance in fever); it is decreased by inanition, by certain diets and in various renal diseases.
Uric acid (see also Purine bases)	**528**	*80–976*	224	KUHL et al., *Metabolism*, **4**, 143 (1955).	Values in 20 healthy adults on a normal diet. According to SALA et al., *Reumatismo*, **7**, 223 (1955), the clearance of uric acid in normal adults is 9.25 ± 0.75 ml/min, whilst in 9 patients with gout it was found to be reduced to 3.59 ± 0.3 ml/min.
Blood pigments and other pigments					
Hemoglobin	0	–	–		This is *free* hemoglobin in urine. For hemoglobin contained in erythrocytes see page 534. The threshold for the excretion of free hemoglobin by the kidneys is approximately 150 mg per 100 ml of blood.
Methemoglobin	0	–	–		
Myohemoglobin	0	–	–		
Porphyrins (and related compounds)	–	–	–		On porphyrins in general see pages 376–384.
δ-Aminolevulic acid (mg/liter)	**2.9**	*0.1–5.7*	1.4	HAEGER-ARONSEN, B., *Scand. J. clin. Lab. Invest.*, **12**, Suppl. 47 (1960).	Increased in porphyria acuta intermittens, porphyria cutanea tarda and some other types of porphyria, as also in lead poisoning. The determination of the urinary δ-aminolevulic acid gives an early and reliable indication of increased lead absorption. Concentrations above the range 13–20 mg/liter (corresponding to 150–200 µg lead per liter urine) indicate a level of lead absorption at which the danger of poisoning is increased.
Porphobilinogen (mg/liter)	**1.0**	*0.0–2.0*	0.5	HAEGER-ARONSEN, B., *Scand. J. clin. Lab. Invest.*, **12**, Suppl. 47 (1960).	Increased in porphyria but not in lead poisoning. Slightly increased in liver disease.
Coproporphyrins (mg/liter)	**0.07**	*0–0.15*	0.04	HAEGER-ARONSEN, B., *Scand. J. clin. Lab. Invest.*, **12**, Suppl. 47 (1960).	Increased in porphyria, liver disease and lead poisoning.
Uroporphyrins (µg/liter)	–	0–15	–	HAEGER, B., *Lancet*, **2**, 606 (1958).	Increased in porphyria.
Urobilinogen	–	0–4	–	WATSON, C. J., *Arch. intern. Med.*, **59**, 196 (1937).	The quantities found vary greatly according to the method of determination. See SUNDERMAN and BOERNER, *Normal Values in Clinical Medicine*, Philadelphia, 1950, page 362.
Bilirubin	5	–	–	NAUMANN, H. N., *Biochem. J.*, **30**, 762 (1936).	The urinary bilirubin is conjugated. Cf. remarks on pages 559 and 560.

* When a range given is a *normal range* (see page 154), i.e. calculated from the formula: mean ± (2 × standard deviation *s*), it is printed in *italics*, with the mean in **bold** figures. Otherwise the data given are experimental results which have not been tested statistically.

1) LANG et al. (Eds.), *Hoppe-Seyler/Thierfelder Handbuch der physiologisch- und pathologisch-chemischen Analyse*, 10th ed., vol. V, *Untersuchung der Organe, Körperflüssigkeiten und Ausscheidungen*, Berlin, 1953.

Normal values in **milligrams per 24-hour urine** in adults on a normal balanced diet (unless otherwise stated)

Carbohydrates and related substances	Mean*	Range*	*s*	Sources	Remarks
"Sugars"	–	500–1500	–	BRADLEY, S. E., *Med. Clin. N. Amer.*, **29**, 1314 (1945).	The classical methods (FEHLING, TROMMER, BENEDICT, NYLANDER) for the quantitative and qualitative determination of "sugars" are based on the reducing properties of certain carbohydrates. These methods are not specific and give positive results also with various other constituents of urine such as uric acid, creatinine, glucuronic acid, homogentisic acid, fructose, lactose, pentoses, vitamin C. Positive results may also be obtained in patients undergoing treatment with certain antibiotics (penicillin, streptomycin, chlortetracycline, oxytetracycline, tetracycline hydrochloride, but not dihydrostreptomycin or chloramphenicol; cf. FISHER et al., *Ann. paediat. [Basel]*, **185**, 254 [1955]). See also below under Glucose, and WRIGHT, W. T., *New Engl. J. Med.*, **254**, 570 (1956).
Glucose	72	16–132	–	FROESCH and RENOLD, *Diabetes (N. Y.)*, **5**, 1 (1956).	These results were obtained by a method based on a specific enzyme reaction (only xylose and mannose take part in a similar reaction), namely the conversion of β-glucose into gluconic acid by glucose oxidase. Determinations of "sugars" by the authors in the same urine samples (24-hour urine) using the classical methods gave as the mean daily amount 511 mg, with a range from 242 to 845 mg.
Pentoses					
Ribulose	~1 mg/l	–	–	FUTTERMAN and ROE, *J. biol. Chem.*, **215**, 257 (1955).	Values from determinations on 2 healthy men only. On essential pentosuria see FLYNN, F. V., *Brit. med. J.*, **1**, 391 (1955).
Xylulose	~4 mg/l	–	–		
Inositols					
Total	–	~35–85 mg/l	–	MALANGEAU, P., *Bull. Soc. Chim. biol. (Paris)*, **38**, 729 (1956).	Values from chromatographic determinations on 200 specimens of urine. The author notes that scyllitol was present in 67% of the samples only but that all the samples contained myoinositol. See also under Myoinositol, page 470.
Myoinositol	–	~22–30 mg/l	–		
Scyllitol	–	~15–22 mg/l	–		
Glucuronic acid (total)					
Men	**6.00**	*5.394–6.606*	0.303	DIFERRANTE and RICH, *J. Lab. clin. Med.*, **48**, 491 (1956).	The daily amount varies with the diet (HOPPE-SEYLER[1], page 245).
Women	**3.77**	*3.29–4.25*	0.24		
Boys	**7.45**	*6.822–8.078*	0.314		
Girls	**5.80**	*4.952–6.648*	0.424		
Amino sugars	**84**	*60–108*	12	BOAS et al., *J. clin. Invest.*, **34**, 782 (1955).	
Lipids					
Free fatty acids	–	8–50	–	HOPPE-SEYLER[1], page 183.	
Cholesterol					
Complete urine	–	20–140 μg/100 ml	–	HOPPE-SEYLER[1], page 250.	
Urine without sediment	–	20–90 μg/100 ml	–		
Intermediary metabolites					
Acetone bodies (as acetone)	19.4	14.5–23.5	–	BEHRE, J. A., *J. biol. Chem.*, **92**, 679 (1931).	Mean of determinations made during 32 days on 12 normal subjects. The quantities excreted vary during the course of the day: they are greatest in the evening, smallest in the morning; during fasting they increase. Acetone bodies give a positive reaction with sodium nitroprusside (LEGAL's test), but only when their concentration is at least the equivalent of 3–5 mg acetoacetic acid/100 ml urine (BEHRE, J. A., *loc. cit.*). According to DEUEL and GULICK, *J. biol. Chem.*, **96**, 25 (1932), during the first days of a fasting period the urinary excretion of acetone bodies increases considerably, more in women than in men. The amount excreted by the females averaged about 3 to 4 times as much as in the males, from 10 times on the first day to twice as much on the fourth day.
Citric acid	**678**	*128–1228*	275	Calculated from YARBRO, C. L., *J. Urol. (Baltimore)*, **75**, 216 (1956).	Determinations on 54 healthy students on a normal diet. The excretion of citric acid continues during a fast, suggesting that this constituent has an endogenous origin. In women a reduced amount is excreted during menstruation (SUNDERMAN and BOERNER, *Normal Values in Clinical Medicine*, Philadelphia, 1950, page 357).

* When a range given is a *normal range* (see page 154), i.e. calculated from the formula: mean ± (2 × standard deviation *s*), it is printed in *italics*, with the mean in **bold** figures. Otherwise the data given are experimental results which have not been tested statistically.

1) LANG et al. (Eds.), *Hoppe-Seyler/Thierfelder Handbuch der physiologisch- und pathologisch-chemischen Analyse*, 10th ed., vol. V, *Untersuchung der Organe, Körperflüssigkeiten und Ausscheidungen*, Berlin, 1953.

Normal values in **milligrams per 24-hour urine** in adults on a normal balanced diet (unless otherwise stated)

	Mean*	Range*	*s*	Sources	Remarks
Homogentisic acid	0	–	–	HOUSSAY et al., *Physiologie humaine*, Paris, 1950, page 669.	Homogentisic acid (alkapton) is occasionally found in rather high concentrations in the urine of individuals who are otherwise normal. If such urine is allowed to stand for some time it becomes dark; it also reduces FEHLING's solution. Homogentisic acid is a metabolite of phenylalanine and tyrosine (see page 410).
Lactic acid	–	100–600	–	HOPPE-SEYLER[1], page 202.	
Oxalic acid	–	20–40	–	YARBRO and SIMPSON, *J. Lab. clin. Med.*, **48**, 304 (1956).	
Phenols	437	260–636	–	VOLTERRA, M., *Amer. J. clin. Path.*, **12**, 525 (1942).	The author describes in detail the methods of estimating phenols in urine.
Pyruvic acid	100	–	–	HOPPE-SEYLER[1], page 203.	
Succinic acid	–	2.5–10.8	–	HOPPE-SEYLER[1], page 202.	
Hormones					
See under the respective hormones on pages 473–497.					
Vitamins					
See under the respective vitamins on pages 449–468.					
Enzymes					
Amylase	**3095** U /24 h	*1047–5143* U /24 h	1024 U/24h	SMITH and ROE, *J. appl. Physiol.*, **4**, 666 (1952).	The classical description of acute pancreatitis includes increased excretion of amylase in the urine. However, various authors have shown that there are considerable variations in the amount of this enzyme excreted, independent of the diet. They conclude that the determination of the amylase concentration in urine has no diagnostic value (MCCOLLUM, J. K., *Brit. med. J.*, **2**, 1482 [1955]).
	These are standard units. In clinical laboratories the results are usually given in WOHLGEMUTH units/ml. Normal values are 24–76 WOHLGEMUTH units/ml; values above 128 WOHLGEMUTH units/ml indicate definite disease (HOPPE-SEYLER[1], page 292).				
Jropepsin .... (as tyrosine)	417	98–835	–	BOLT et al., *J. Lab. clin. Med.*, **43**, 335 (1954).	For the determination of uropepsin it is allowed to react with hemoglobin under standard conditions, when the amount of tyrosine liberated in a certain time is measured (BUCHER, G. R., *Gastroenterology*, **8**, 627 [1947]).
)ther enzymes		See remarks			Urine contains also a large number of digestive enzymes (cathepsin, trypsin, other proteases), acid and alkaline phosphatase (HOPPE-SEYLER[1], page 293), arylsulfatases A and B (DODGSON and SPENCER, *Clin. chim. Acta [Amst.]*, **1**, 478 [1956]), histaminase and cadaverinase (KAPELLER-ADLER and RENWICK, *Clin. chim. Acta [Amst.]*, **1**, 197 [1956]), and other enzymes.
norganic constituents					
:hloride	7368	–	–	BURRILL et al., *J. biol. Chem.*, **157**, 297 (1945).	The amounts excreted vary considerably according to the diet. The value given here is the mean of determinations carried out daily for 3 weeks on 6 healthy men living on a fixed diet, namely (per day) 2750 kcal, 3.29 g sodium, 3.27 g potassium, 4.93 g chloride, 5 g NaCl as seasoning.
hosphorus	1100	–	–	SUNDERMAN and BOERNER, *Normal Values in Clinical Medicine*, Philadelphia, 1950, page 361.	The phosphorus content varies with the diet; 96–99% of the amount given here occurs in the inorganic form.
ılfur (as SO_3)					
Total	–	2000–3400	–	HARROW, B., *Textbook of Biochemistry*, 4th ed., Philadelphia, 1946, page 465.	In cystinuria the sulfur of cystine occurs in the organic (neutral) fraction.
Inorganic	–	1700–2700	–		
Organic (neutral).....	–	200–400	–		
Alkylsulfuric acids.... (conjugated or esterified sulfuric acids)	–	150–300	–		

When a range given is a *normal range* (see page 154), i.e. calculated from the formula: mean ± (2 × standard deviation *s*), it is printed in *italics*, with the mean in **bold** figures. Otherwise the data given are experimental results which have not been tested statistically.

LANG et al. (Eds.), *Hoppe-Seyler/Thierfelder Handbuch der physiologisch- und pathologisch-chemischen Analyse*, 10th ed., vol. V, *Untersuchung der Organe, Körperflüssigkeiten und Ausscheidungen*, Berlin, 1953.

Normal values in **milligrams per 24-hour urine** in adults on a normal balanced diet (unless otherwise stated)

	Mean*	Range*	s	Sources	Remarks
Calcium	–	141.1–364.9	–	WEBER, R. J., *Proc. Soc. exp. Biol. (N.Y.)*, **37**, 55 (1937).	The threshold value for the excretion of calcium in the urine lies between 9.5 and 10.5 mg/100 ml of blood. If its concentration falls below 8 mg/100 ml, almost none will be excreted in the urine (SUNDERMAN and BOERNER, *Normal Values in Clinical Medicine*, Philadelphia, 1950, page 358). For methods of calcium determination see BERGER, E.Y., *Clin. Chem.*, **1**, 249 (1955).
Potassium	2740	–	–	BURRILL et al., *J. biol. Chem.*, **157**, 297 (1945).	See remarks under Chloride, page 533.
Magnesium	103	32.5–307	–	WALKER and WALKER, *J. Lab. clin. Med.*, **21**, 713 (1936).	The concentration of magnesium in plasma shows a regular diurnal increase between 3 a.m. and 9 a.m. (METZ and MOURS-LAROCHE, *C.R. Soc. Biol. [Paris]*, **149**, 579 [1955]).
Sodium	4615	–	–	BURRILL et al., *J. biol. Chem.*, **157**, 297 (1945).	See remarks under Chloride, page 533.
Aluminum	**78 µg/l**	*14–142 µg/l*	32 µg/l	KEHOE et al., *J. Nutr.*, **19**, 579 (1940).	Mean value from determinations on 94 healthy subjects.
Lead	**27 µg/l**	*0–55 µg/l*	14 µg/l	KEHOE et al., *J. Nutr.*, **19**, 579 (1940).	Mean value from determinations on 107 healthy subjects.
Iron	0.045	–	–	PLÖTNER and PETZEL, *Klin. Wschr.*, **32**, 821 (1954).	The results vary according to the method of determination.
Iodine	–	0.018–0.483	–	BRUGER et al., *J. Lab. clin. Med.*, **26**, 1942 (1941).	
Copper					
Adults	**0.018**	*0.00354–0.03246*	0.00723	BUTLER and NEWMAN, *J. clin. Path.*, **9**, 157 (1956).	There are regular variations in the course of 24 hours with a maximum in the afternoon. It is important tha[t] determinations of copper should be carried out i[n] Pyrex vessels, since all other laboratory glassware con[-] tains copper (BUTLER and NEWMAN, *J. clin. Path.*, **9**, 157 [1956]). In children suffering from WILSON's dis[-] ease (familial juvenile hepatolenticular degeneration) the urinary excretion of copper is considerably in[-] creased (BEARN and KUNKEL, *J. clin. Invest.*, **33**, 40[0] [1954]).
Children	**0.048**	*0.0154–0.0806*	0.0163	BEARN and KUNKEL, *J. clin. Invest.*, **33**, 400 (1954).	
Manganese	10 µg/l	–	–	KEHOE et al., *J. Nutr.*, **19**, 579 (1940).	
Nickel	0.1 mg/l		–	STANLEY, E. L., personal communication; SUNDERMAN and BOERNER, *Normal Values in Clinical Medicine*, Philadelphia, 1950, page 361.	Mean value from determinations on 8 healthy subject[s] by a polarographic method.
Silver	–	trace	–	KEHOE et al., *J. Nutr.*, **19**, 579 (1940).	Result of determinations on 94 healthy subjects.
Tin	**11 µg/l**	*0–31 µg/l*	10 µg/l	KEHOE et al., *J. Nutr.*, **19**, 579 (1940).	Mean value from determinations on 94 healthy sub[-] jects. It is noteworthy that in the urine samples of c[a.] 20% of these subjects (included in the calculations) no tin at all could be found.
Zinc	0.457	–	–	VALLEE et al., *Ann. intern. Med.*, **50**, 1077 (1959).	The urinary excretion of zinc is markedly increased i[n] cirrhosis of the liver (mean 1.03 mg/24 hours).
Cells					
Bacteria		See remarks			According to PHILPOT, V. B., *J. Urol. (Baltimore)*, **7**[...] 562 (1956), the bacteria found in the urine of healt[hy] persons consist mainly of Micrococcaceae.
Erythrocytes		See remarks			According to WATSON-WILLIAMS, E. J., *Brit. med. J.*, [...] 1511 (1955), the urine of men can contain up to 2 eryth[-] rocytes/ml and that of women up to 50 erythrocyte[s/] ml without the urine being considered as abnorma[l.] This author also describes a simple method for detectin[g] microscopic hematuria which can be carried out at th[e] bedside.

* When a range given is a *normal range* (see page 154), i.e. calculated from the formula: mean ± (2 × standard deviation *s*), it is printed in *italics*, with th[e] mean in **bold** figures. Otherwise the data given are experimental results which have not been tested statistically.

Macroscopic examination: *Uric acid* and *urates* dissolve on warming to about 60° C and on addition of alkalis. *Phosphates* dissolve on addition of acetic acid, *oxalates* on addition of hydrochloric acid (for further differentiation see below). *Pus cells* clump together on warming, especially after addition of a little alkali.

Microscopic examination: The urine is allowed to stand in a sedimentation glass and the sediment layer then withdrawn by a pipette and centrifuged for 5 minutes. Where there is suspicion of kidney disease clear urine should also be centrifuged, since casts and other organized elements can be present.

Urinary sediments may be classified as follows:

1. **Organized elements** (erythrocytes, leukocytes, epithelial cells, bacteria).
2. **Casts** from the uriniferous tubules (hyaline, granular, waxy, epithelial, erythrocyte, hemoglobin, leukocyte or cylindroid casts).
3. **Amorphous and crystalline chemical sediments** (see below and on page 536).
4. **Miscellaneous** (mucus, spermatozoa, parasites [*Schistosoma haematobium* or *japonicum*, filaria, echinococci], foreign bodies [starch granules from face powder, mostly in urine of infants and women; hairs, textile fibers], oily substances [catheter lubricants]).

Amorphous and crystalline chemical sediments

Sediment	Characteristics	Occurrence (alkaline or acid urine)	Solubility (○ = readily soluble, ● = sparingly soluble)						
			Heating	Alkalis	Mineral acids	Acetic acid	Alcohol	Acetone	Ether
Uric acid	Crystals mostly, but not always, colored yellow by absorption of urinary pigments. Colorless crystals are usually smaller than colored crystals	acid urine	○ (60° C)	○	●	●	●	●	●
Urates	Calcium, magnesium and potassium urates, mostly amorphous, in concentrated acid-urine. Color and chemical behavior as for uric acid	Ammonium urate in alkaline urines. All other urates in acid urines	○ (60° C)	○	●	●	●	●	●
Phosphates									
Star-shaped calcium phosphate crystals	Rare	alkaline urine	●	●	○	○	●	●	●
Ammonium magnesium phosphate	Commoner	alkaline urine	●	●	○	○	●	●	●
Calcium oxalate	Size about that of erythrocytes	Usually in acid urine, also in neutral and weakly alkaline	●	●	○	●	●	●	●
Cystine	Colorless crystals (distinction from uric acid crystals, when of similar form). Must be looked for in fresh urine since cystine is rapidly destroyed by bacteria	acid urine	●	○ esp. ammonia	○	●	●	●	●
Tyrosine	Often yellow-colored since they are associated with jaundice. Mostly accompanied by leucine. Occur in acute yellow atrophy of the liver, also in cirrhosis, acute phosphorus poisoning, leukemia	acid urine	● relative	○	○ precipitated on neutralization	○	●	●	●
Leucine	See tyrosine. Crystals in urine are impure. Pure leucine crystallizes in hexagonal platelets	acid urine	○ relative	○	○	○	●	●	●
Bilirubin (hematoidin)	Colors any uric acid crystals present and changes their shape	acid urine	●	○	○	○	●	○	●
				readily soluble in chloroform					
Indigotin	Rare. Also colors other crystals and thus appears to crystallize in various forms. Pure indigo in urine is amorphous or as (*b*) in the figure on page 536. Crystallizes from chloroform as (*c*) in this figure	alkaline or acid urine	very soluble in chloroform				●	–	○
Cholesterol	Very rare	acid urine	very soluble in chloroform				●	–	○
Hippuric acid	Very rare		○	○	●	●	●	–	●
Sulfonamides	Easily distinguished from uric acid crystals by solubility in acetone		–	–	–	–	–	○	–

Amorphous and crystalline chemical sediments[1]

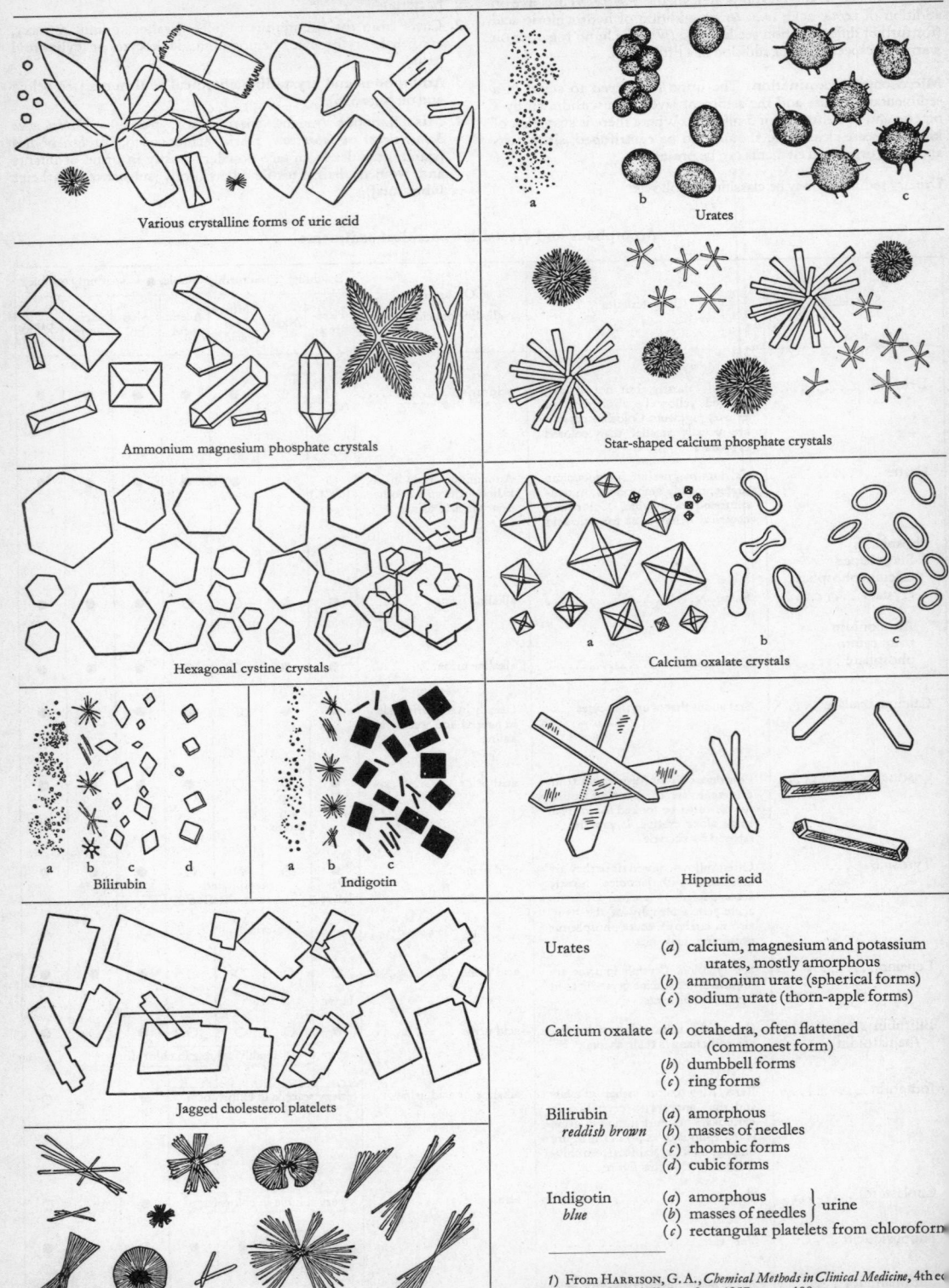

Various crystalline forms of uric acid

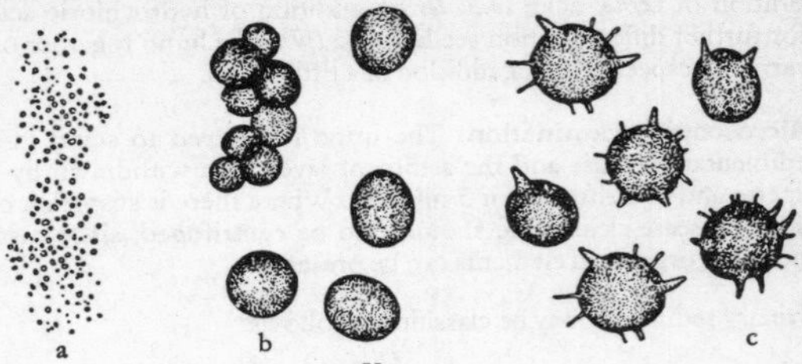

Urates

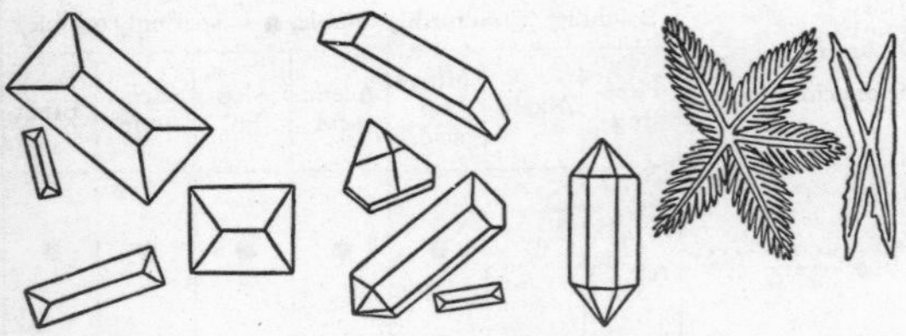

Ammonium magnesium phosphate crystals

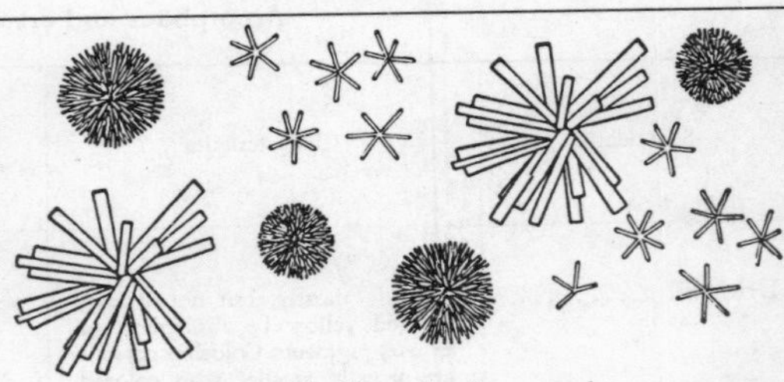

Star-shaped calcium phosphate crystals

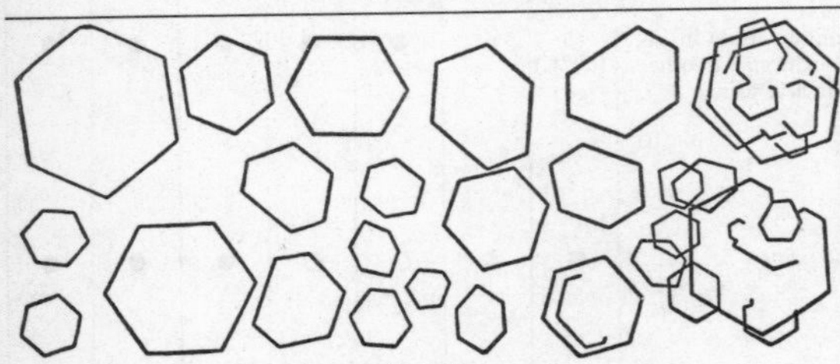

Hexagonal cystine crystals

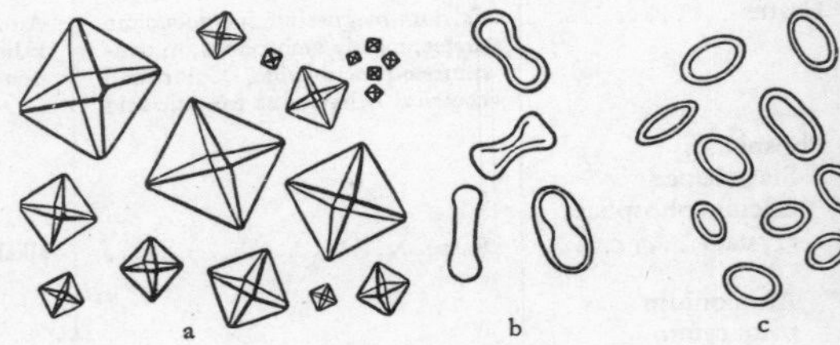

Calcium oxalate crystals

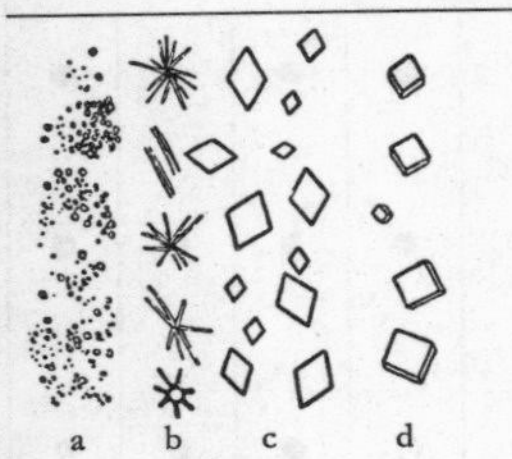

Bilirubin

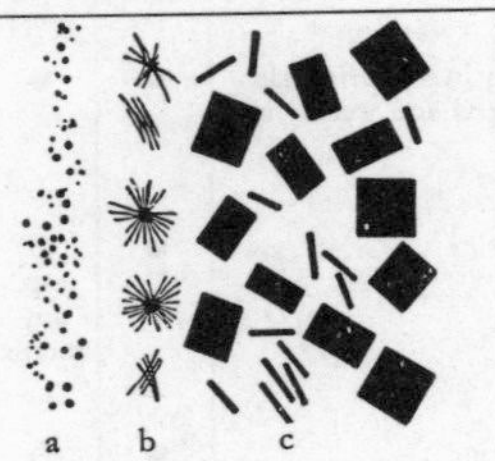

Indigotin

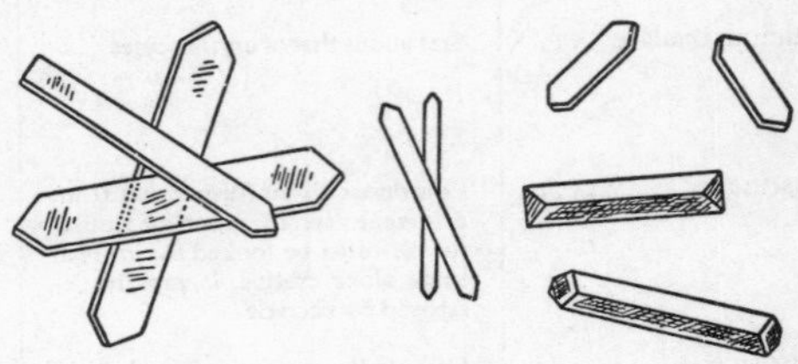

Hippuric acid

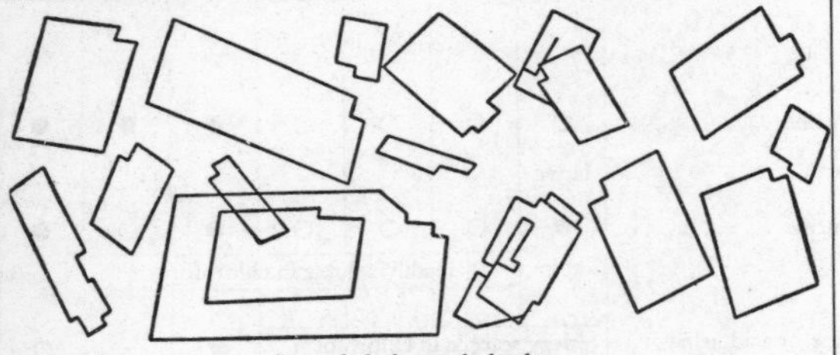

Jagged cholesterol platelets

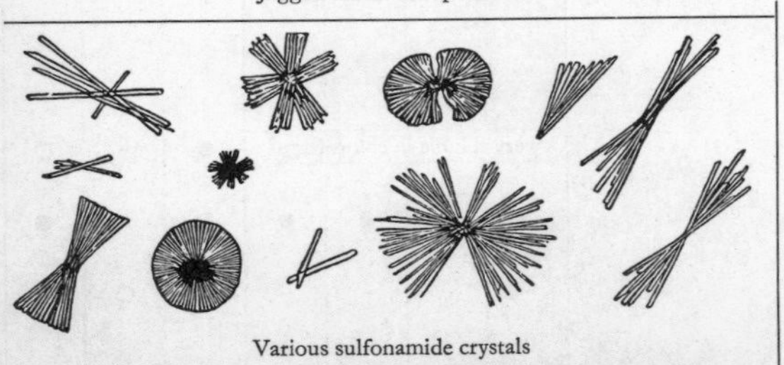

Various sulfonamide crystals

Urates (*a*) calcium, magnesium and potassium urates, mostly amorphous
(*b*) ammonium urate (spherical forms)
(*c*) sodium urate (thorn-apple forms)

Calcium oxalate (*a*) octahedra, often flattened (commonest form)
(*b*) dumbbell forms
(*c*) ring forms

Bilirubin *reddish brown* (*a*) amorphous
(*b*) masses of needles
(*c*) rhombic forms
(*d*) cubic forms

Indigotin *blue* (*a*) amorphous } urine
(*b*) masses of needles } urine
(*c*) rectangular platelets from chloroforn

1) From Harrison, G. A., *Chemical Methods in Clinical Medicine*, 4th e
J. and A. Churchill, London, 1957, pages 100 et seq.

Only tests requiring a minimum of laboratory equipment are described

Proteins

Acetic acid test (heat test)

5 ml of clear urine, filtered if necessary, are heated to boiling for ca. ½ minute with 0.5 ml SØRENSEN's acetate buffer solution. SØRENSEN's acetate buffer: 56.5 g glacial acetic acid and 118.0 g sodium acetate cryst. dissolved in 1 liter distilled water.

Interpretation: When the urine contains more than traces of protein a fine flocculation appears. With a protein content of less than 1‰ an opalescent turbidity first appears, developing into a fine flocculation after several minutes standing or on further boiling.

Alkaline-earth phosphates or urates give no precipitate in this test, which is also independent of the pH value of the urine.

Sulfosalicylic acid test

(highly sensitive test for very small protein concentrations): 0.5 ml 25% sulfosalicylic acid solution are added dropwise to 5 ml of clear, slightly acid urine, filtered if necessary.

Interpretation: In the presence of proteins a white turbidity is formed, not cleared on warming. If it is difficult to decide whether turbidity has formed or not, compare the treated sample against the light with an untreated one. The test is positive for protein concentrations of 0.015‰ upwards. If the urine is somewhat alkaline, rather more sulfosalicylic acid must be added.

In certain circumstances (rare) uric acid can simulate a positive reaction, but in this case the turbidity, in contrast to that due to proteins, disappears on warming.

"Sugars"

(see also page 532)

FEHLING's test

5 ml of urine in one test tube and 5 ml of a mixture of equal parts of FEHLING's solutions I and II in another test tube are heated almost to boiling (avoid boiling) over the same flame, and the FEHLING's solution then poured slowly into the urine. Very concentrated urine should be diluted beforehand. FEHLING's *solution I:* 3.5 g copper sulfate dissolved in 50 ml distilled water. FEHLING's *solution II:* 17.5 g potassium sodium tartrate (Rochelle salt) and 5 g sodium hydroxide dissolved in 50 ml distilled water.

Interpretation: In the presence of sugar a more or less abundant precipitate of yellowish-red cuprous oxide, according to the amount of reducing substances present, is formed. On further heating the mixture a greenish precipitate sometimes appears, indicating the presence in the urine of strongly alkaline substances.

BENEDICT's test

5 ml of BENEDICT's reagent are mixed with 0.5 ml urine and the mixture boiled vigorously for 2 minutes. BENEDICT's *reagent:* 173 g sodium citrate and 100 g anhyd. sodium carbonate are dissolved in ca. 600 ml distilled water and 17.3 g cryst. copper sulfate in a separate receptacle in ca. 100 ml distilled water. The latter solution is then added with constant stirring to the former, the mixture filtered if not clear, and made up to 1000 ml with distilled water. The reagent may be stored indefinitely.

Interpretation: In the presence of sugar a yellowish or reddish precipitate is formed. In certain circumstances (rare) alkaline-earth phosphates can simulate a positive reaction by giving a whitish or grayish precipitate.

Acetone bodies

ROTHERA's test

(modification of LEGAL's test):

10 ml of urine are mixed with ca. 2 ml of concentrated ammonia and ca. 2 g of a dry powdered mixture of 100 parts ammonium sulfate and 1 part sodium nitroprusside, and the test tube stoppered, shaken vigorously and allowed to stand.

Interpretation: In the presence of acetone, acetoacetic acid or both, a characteristic purple coloration (resembling permanganate) is developed, the intensity of which is proportional to the concentration of acetone bodies. The test is more sensitive to acetoacetic acid than to acetone.

GERHARDT's test

for acetoacetic acid:

The test must be made with the freshest possible urine since acetoacetic acid is readily decomposed into carbon dioxide and acetone. 5 ml of urine are mixed with ca. 2–3 ml of a 10% ferric chloride solution.

Interpretation: In the presence of acetoacetic acid the mixture turns a wine-red color. This coloration is also produced by salicylic acid or drugs such as acetylsalicylic acid but since these substances, in contrast to acetoacetic acid, are not destroyed by boiling, their presence may be detected by repeating the test using boiled urine. If the result of this second test is negative then the coloration in the first test can be ascribed to acetoacetic acid.

For literature references and bibliography see page 545

This chapter should be read in conjunction with that on "Aqueous Solutions" on pages 324–334, where definitions and conversion factors of the important units mole and gram equivalent (Eq) will be found, together with a detailed discussion of infusion solutions and parenteral fluid and electrolyte replacement therapy.

Functionally, water balance and electrolyte balance are inseparable since the chemically uncombined water of the body is for practical purposes an isotonic solution with a relatively constant electrolyte content and a somewhat less constant content of organic substances. Changes in any one component therefore inevitably result in changes in the others, a functional dependence which should be kept in mind when making use of the data given in this chapter of the *Tables*. For the sake of clarity the general discussion of body water precedes that of its electrolytic constitution.

I. Water balance

A. Distribution of water

The distribution of water between the various parts of the body (intra- and extra-cellular water, etc.) provides a basis for calculating their respective contents of dissolved minerals. Sodium and chloride ions are found mainly in the extracellular fluid, a circumstance which must be taken into consideration when making calculations. A deficiency of these ions is therefore revealed by their serum concentration. Potassium ions, on the other hand, are concentrated mainly inside the cell and the extent of a deficiency cannot simply be deduced from the serum concentration. Potassium deficiency is indicated by clinical symptoms but can be accurately estimated only by measurements of electrolyte balance.

The following may be regarded as **clinical norms** for water content and distribution (for details see the tables and text below):

	Men	Women	
Total water	60%	55%	of body weight
Extracellular water	15%	15%	of body weight
Intracellular water	45%	40%	of body weight

B. Daily water intake and water loss

The **water intake** is made up of the water content of the liquid and solid food together with the "water of oxidation" arising from intermediary metabolism. 100 g of fat yield ca. 100 ml, 100 g of protein ca. 40 ml and 100 g carbohydrate ca. 60 ml of water of oxidation. For a simplified clinical water balance the water of oxidation may be regarded as equal to the water of the feces, provided that there is no diarrhea. For patients in bed on a normal diet, without fever or sweating, the water content of the solid food is sufficient to meet the extrarenal water loss via the skin and lungs (insensible perspiration).

The following may be regarded as **clinical norms** (rest, moderate climate, no fever, no sensible perspiration):

Water intake, total .... 2500 ml
as liquid .... 1500 ml
with food (including 300 ml water of oxidation) .... 1000 ml

Under normal conditions the water intake is controlled very closely by thirst to meet the actual water requirements of the body. The sensation of thirst is dependent on various factors such as the water content of the cells (in turn dependent on the electrolyte concentration of the extracellular water), the plasma volume (maintenance of the blood circulation), etc.

Total body water
Average values for adults

	Percentage of body weight: Mean	Range
Heavy water method[1]		
Men, 17–34 years	61.1	53.3–70.3
57–86 years	54.3	47.8–62.8
Women, 20–31 years	51.2	45.6–59.9
60–82 years	46.2	42.0–53.4
Antipyrine method[2]		
Men	53.6	–
Women	46.2	–

The more accurate heavy water method gives higher values than the simpler antipyrine method, particularly in edema[6].

The percentage water content is more closely related to body area than to body weight[4] and varies inversely with the fat content of the body[1,5]. This explains the general difference in water content between men and women. The relative water content of infants is considerably higher than that of adults[6], which diminishes with increasing age[1]. For children up to 20 kg, total water content (in liters) = (0.55 × body weight in kilograms) + 0.51[6].

Extracellular water
Average values for adults

	Percentage of body weight: Mean	Range
(*a*) *Total extracellular water* (inc. plasma water)		
Thiosulfate method (men)[7]	16.6	–
Inulin method[8]	15	–

The water in which thiosulfate or inulin is distributed does not include the "trans-cellular" water[9], i.e. the cerebrospinal fluid and water of the glandular and intestinal cavities, renal pelvis, etc.

	Mean	Range
(*b*) *Plasma volume*		
Evans blue method of Gibson[10]		
Men	4.3	3.2–5.8
Women	4.1	3.3–5.2

For other methods see page 547

Calculation of plasma water from plasma volume[4]:

$$\text{Plasma water in milliliters} = \frac{\text{Plasma vol. (ml)} \times (98.400 - [0.718 \times \text{protein content in g/100 ml serum}])}{100}$$

(*c*) *Interstitial water*
Obtained as the difference between total extracellular water and plasma water.

Intracellular water

Obtained as the difference between total body water and extracellular water.

Average value for adults (antipyrine distribution volume minus inulin distribution volume)[11]: 40% of body weight.

The distribution of water in the various parts of the body, like the total water content, is more closely related to the body surface area than to the body weight[4].

None of the methods described above is normally suitable for clinical purposes. The state of hydration must usually be judged by other criteria, such as the elasticity of the skin and subcutaneous tissues, blood pressure, specific gravity of urine, etc. Since the relative volume of the intracellular water is a function of the effective osmotic pressure of the extracellular water the elasticity of the skin and subcutaneous tissues primarily indicates not the level of the intracellular water but that of the extracellular water.

The proportion of intra- to extra-cellular water can be estimated from the sodium content of the serum; the plasma volume can be calculated from the hematocrit value, the erythrocyte count or the hemoglobin content. Although reductions in the extracellular water and the blood concentration often run parallel, exceptions to this are so frequent that only a careful assessment of the whole clinical picture allows reliable conclusions to be drawn.

When rapid changes in the state of hydration occur, useful indications are provided by comparisons between body weight and erythrocyte count or serum protein content.

The **water loss** is made up of the losses via the skin and lungs (insensible perspiration), the feces and the urine.

The following may be regarded as **clinical norms** (rest, moderate climate, no fever, no sensible perspiration):

Water loss, total	2500 ml		
(*a*) via the skin	500 ml	(*c*) in feces	100 ml
(*b*) via the lungs ...	400 ml	(*d*) in urine	1500 ml

(*a*) *Water loss via the skin*

Rest, moderate climate, no fever, no sensible perspiration[12–14]	400– 600 ml
Working in the tropics (DILL, quoted by GAMBLE[15])	8000–10,000 ml
Rest, moderate climate, body naked and exposed to the sun (DILL, quoted by GAMBLE[15])	400 ml

(*b*) *Water loss via the lungs*

Rest, moderate climate[13, 16]	400 ml

Water loss via the skin and lungs = insensible perspiration, (*a*) + (*b*)

Rest in bed, no fever, no sensible perspiration[13, 17]	800– 1000 ml
Rest in bed, fever, mild sweating[17]	1500 ml
Rest in bed, fever, profuse sweating[17]	2000 ml

(*c*) *Water loss via the intestinal tract*

Feces: the normal water content is ca. 75%, or 4 ml water per 100 calories food intake. The total excretion per day[20] amounts to 60–250 g on a mixed diet, up to 370 g on a vegetable diet, only 54–64 g on a meat diet (see also page 526).

Intestinal water circulation[21, 22] (loss only by surgical drainage):

	Range (ml)
Saliva	500– 1500
Gastric juice	1000– 5000
Bile	100– 1000
Pancreatic juice	700– 1000
Intestinal juice	700– 3000
Total	3000–11,500

(*d*) *Water loss by the kidneys*[22] (see page 544): 600*–1600 ml

The loss of heat by evaporation amounts to ca. 24% of the total loss of heat[18]. Assuming the heat of vaporization of water at 37°C to be 0.58 kcal/ml, the extrarenal water loss, except in excessive sweating, can be calculated from the calorie consumption by means of the following formula[18]:

* Normal minimum excretion.

Water loss by evaporation (in ml)
= 0.414 × calorie consumption

Thus with a calorie consumption of 2000 kcal, for example, a water loss via the skin and lungs of ca. 825 ml is to be expected. The calorie consumption cannot be assumed to be the same as the calorie intake. In fever, for example, the calorie consumption (heat production) is usually greater than the calorie intake.

Water loss by evaporation in warm weather and that due to the water requirement of a deficient kidney (lowered concentration capacity) are often underestimated.

II. Osmotic relations of the body fluids

The osmotic relationships are of importance with regard to the distribution of water between the extra- and intra-cellular spaces, between the vascular and perivascular spaces, and for the filtration processes of the body.

The water equilibrium between the *intracellular* and the interstitial space depends on the respective concentrations of osmotically active particles (molecules and ions).

The distribution of water between the *vascular* and the interstitial space depends on the following factors[4]:

(*a*) Capillary pressure; Oncotic pressure of the interstitial fluid	(*b*) Tissue tension; Oncotic pressure of the plasma
Lymph drainage	

where the factors (*a*) favor transudation from the capillaries and the factors (*b*) retard this transudation. The interstitial fluid is an ultrafiltrate of the plasma and differs from the plasma only in its much lower protein concentration.

Osmotic pressure of plasma at 38°C:
7.70 atm or 5852 mm Hg.

This osmotic pressure corresponds to a **freezing-point depression** of 0.56°C or an **osmolality** (concentration of all osmotically active particles) of 301.4 mmol.

For conversion of freezing-point depression into osmotic concentration and osmotic pressure and vice versa see page 326. For conversion of pressure units see pages 215 and 227.

The osmotic concentration (ideal osmolality) **calculated** from the chemical composition on the assumption of *complete dissociation* of the strong electrolytes (mineral salts, mainly NaCl) amounts to ca. 325 mmol per 1000 g serum water (see Figure 1). The difference between this value and the **actual** effective osmotic concentration of ca. 300 mmol per 1000 g serum water (real osmolality) is accounted for by the fact that the dissociation of the electrolytes is somewhat less in serum.

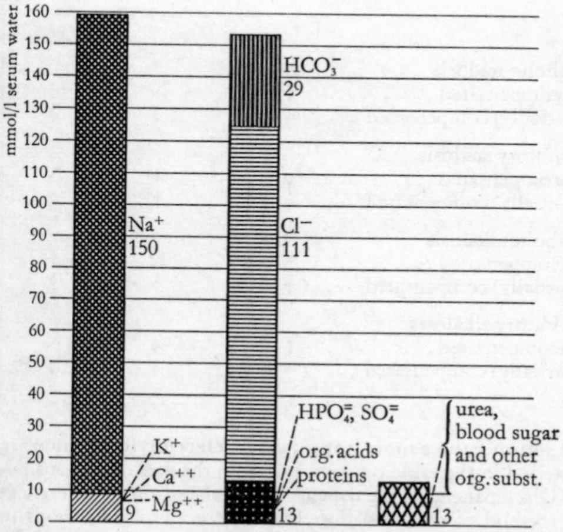

Fig. 1. **Concentration of the osmotically active components of serum** in mmol/l (or mmol/1000 g) serum water, calculated from the analytical values of JEANNERET et al.[23] on the assumption of complete dissociation.

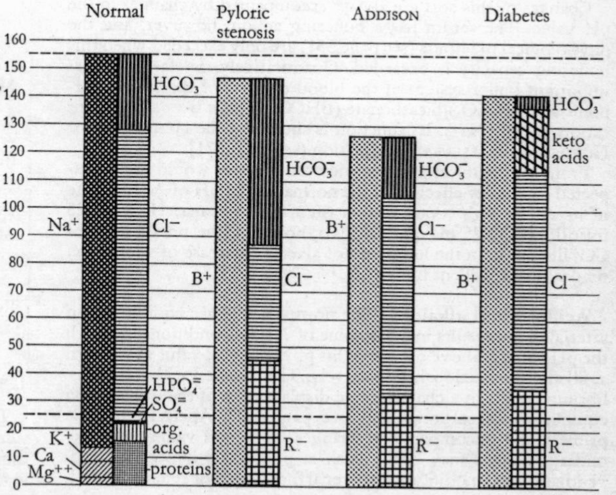

Fig. 2. **Ionic concentration in blood serum** (GAMBLE's ionogram[15]). B+ = total cations, R− = anions other than bicarbonate and chloride. The weakly dissociated carbonic acid is not included. Cf. the following page.

Capillary pressure (after LANDIS[59]):
mean values in the hand held at the level of the heart:

32 mm Hg (43.5 cm H_2O) in the arterial limb
12 mm Hg (16.3 cm H_2O) in the venous limb

Cf. also page 634.

Oncotic pressure (colloid-osmotic pressure) of serum:
20.60–35.31 mm Hg (28–48 cm H_2O)

For abnormal combinations of plasma proteins the *oncotic pressure* can be calculated from KEYS' formula[24]:

Oncotic pressure (in mm water) $= f_c\,(45.2\,A + 18.86\,G) \times T/273.16$, where A = albumins in g/100 ml serum, G = globulins in g/100 ml serum, T = absolute temperature in °K = 273.16 + °C, and f_c is a factor which varies with the total protein content in the following way:

Total protein content of serum								
in g/100 ml:	1	2	3	4	5	6	7	8
f_c:	0.88	0.92	0.98	1.03	1.09	1.17	1.28	1.45

On account of its high molecular weight fibrinogen exerts practically no osmotic pressure so that the oncotic pressures of the serum and the plasma can be considered as equal. Cf. also page 548.

III. Serum levels of the clinically important electrolytes

Electrolyte relationships and calculations involving them are based on the chemical unit "gram equivalent" (Eq). The gram equivalent is calculated by dividing the molecular weight of the ions (in grams) by their valency (see pages 324–326 and the conversion tables for electrolytes on pages 328–330). Conversion factors for concentrations in mg per 100 ml (or g per 100 ml or vol%) and mEq per liter are given in the two right-hand columns of the table on page 542.

When the concentrations of the serum electrolytes are expressed in milligram equivalents per liter they can be represented in the now usual form of an ionogram (first due to GAMBLE[15], see Figure 2, page 539), in which the sums of the cations* and of the anions* are represented by columns. Since in serum, as in all other electrolytic solutions, the positive and negative valencies are in equilibrium (electrical neutrality) the columns are of equal height. When changes in the ionic constitution of one column occur, or when there is a change in the total cation or anion content, the heights of the two columns remain the same. A rise or fall in the chloride level, for example, is balanced by a corresponding opposite movement in the bicarbonate level, changes in the sodium content result in corresponding changes in the sum of the anions, and so on.

Changes of this sort are always accompanied by changes in the pH value. The serum has a buffering action, however, and the physiological pH limits (see page 551) are only exceeded when this buffering capacity is exceeded. Quantitatively, by far the most important buffer system of the blood consists of the system carbonic acid (H_2CO_3)/bicarbonate ($BHCO_3$, where B = a univalent cation, mainly Na^+). Its function is shown by the HENDERSON or HENDERSON-HASSELBALCH equation (see page 571).

From the chemical point of view this system would not be expected to be very effective at the normal blood pH of 7.41 in spite of its rather high concentration (in arterial plasma: H_2CO_3 1.25 mEq/l, HCO_3^- 25 mEq/l). In vivo, however, the possibilities of CO_2 liberation in the lungs and of alveolar increase of ventilation render it an excellent buffer[15, 25].

Acidosis and alkalosis. The normal acid–base equilibrium in arterial blood results in a pH value of 7.41[25]. Conditions in which the pH value is above or below this physiological value are known as alkalosis and acidosis respectively. The changed acid–base equilibrium results in a characteristic displacement of the dissociation equilibrium of carbonic acid (see page 571). Apart from these primary and uncompensated changes in the pH value other secondary changes may occur, such as pulmonary hyper- or hypoventilation and modifications of renal function (base retention, etc.), which counteract the primary changes. The alkalosis or acidosis is then said to be compensated and the pH value does not change to any marked extent.

(Primary) **metabolic acidosis** arises from the *accumulation of large quantities of acids* stronger than H_2CO_3 as a result of increased acid production (in hunger, extreme physical exertion, diabetes mellitus, etc.), of exogenous administration of acids (e.g. ammonium chloride) and of acid retention (kidney disease), or as a result of *severe loss of bases* (diarrhea, intestinal or biliary drainage or fistulas, ADDISON's disease). (Primary) **metabolic alkalosis** arises as a result of *severe loss of acids* (vomiting, gastric drainage, etc.) or as a result of *excessive intake of alkalizing salts* (sodium bicarbonate, lactate, etc.).

(Primary) **respiratory acidosis** occurs when the *expiration of CO_2 is impeded* (stenoses of the upper respiratory passages, hypopnea of central origin, pulmonary emphysema, etc.), (primary) **respiratory alkalosis** in *hyperventilation* (e.g. salicylate poisoning).

Disturbances of acid–base equilibrium can be measured by determining the components in the dissociation equation for carbonic acid (see page 571 and the nomogram on the opposite page).

A measure of the bicarbonate content (denominator in the HENDERSON equation) which is usually adequate for clinical purposes is provided by the so-called **alkali reserve** of serum (CO_2 combining capacity, etc.; for definition and determination, see page 571). This can be expressed either as bicarbonate-CO_2 in vol% or as bicarbonate ions (HCO_3^- in mEq). Since the measurement is made at constant CO_2 pressure, however, the alkali reserve reflects only metabolic and not respiratory changes. The latter can be measured by determining two of the components in the dissociation equation for carbonic acid (for example pH and CO_2 pressure). The table below shows the directions in which the measured values change in disturbances of acid–base equilibrium. In cases of uncompensated alkalosis or acidosis with only slight change in the pH value and where the initial value is unknown it may be necessary not only to take account of the whole clinical picture but also to determine other factors, such as organic acids and phosphate in the plasma or ammonia and pH in the urine.

Changes in the most important measured values in acid–base equilibrium accompanying acidosis and alkalosis
(after SCHWAB and KÜHNS[25])

N = normal value, ↑ = value increases, ↓ = value decreases

	In arterial blood		Standard bicarbonate value mEq/l plasma **25** (22–28)
	pH **7.41** (7.38--7.44)	CO_2 pressure mm Hg **40** (36–45)	
Metabolic acidosis			
uncompensated	↓ ↓	N	↓
(partially) compensated ...	(↓) ↓	↓	↓
Respiratory acidosis			
uncompensated	↓ ↓	↑	N
(partially) compensated ...	(↓) ↓	↑	↑
Metabolic alkalosis			
uncompensated	↑ ↑	N	↑
(partially) compensated ...	(↑) ↑	↑	↑
Respiratory alkalosis			
uncompensated	↑ ↑	↓	N
(partially) compensated ...	(↑) ↑	↓	↓

The **serum values most important in electrolyte balance** are summarized in the table on page 542 from the data of various authors. Discrepancies in the data are partly the result of differences in the method of determination. Flame-photographic methods in general give somewhat higher values. Although lying inside the limits of physiological variation the serum value for Na (142 mEq/l) and the total ionic concentration (155 mEq/l) in GAMBLE's ionogram[15] are probably somewhat too high.

* In physiology, the cations are often erroneously called "bases", the anions "acids". According to the definition of BRØNSTEDT, acids are proton (hydrogen ion) donors and bases proton acceptors.

Nomogram for acid–base equilibrium of human blood at 37° C (from SINGER and HASTINGS[19])

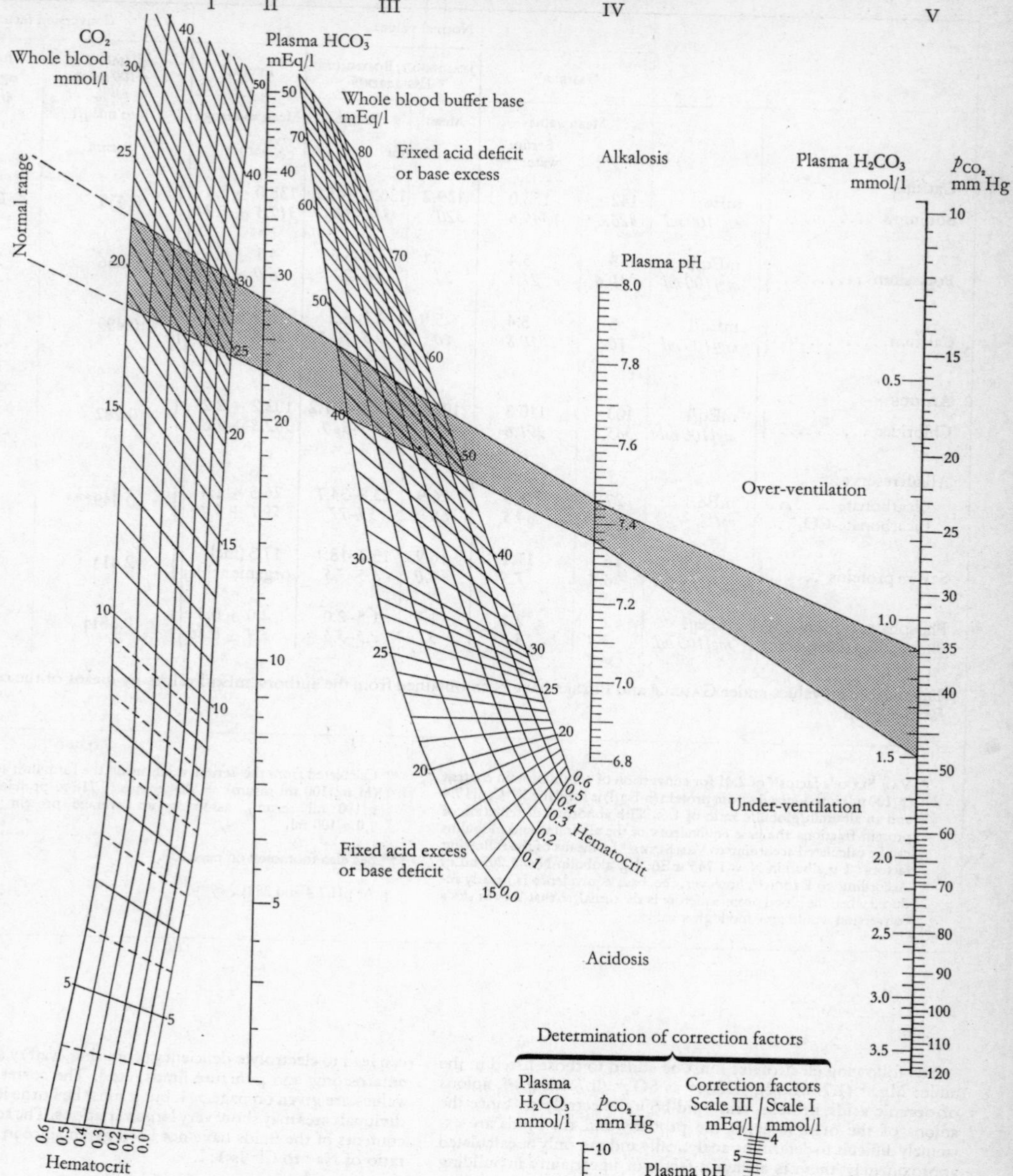

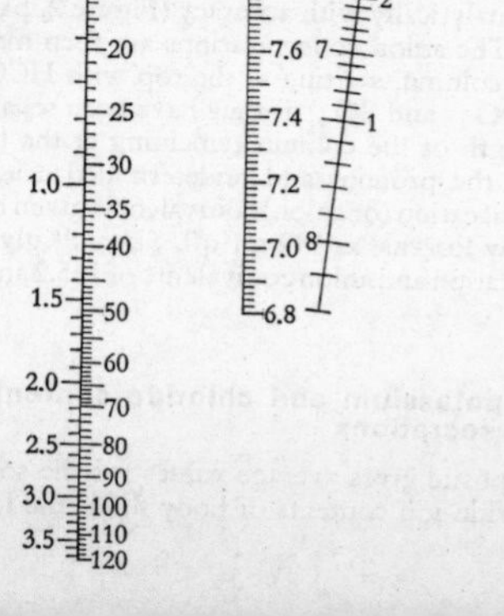

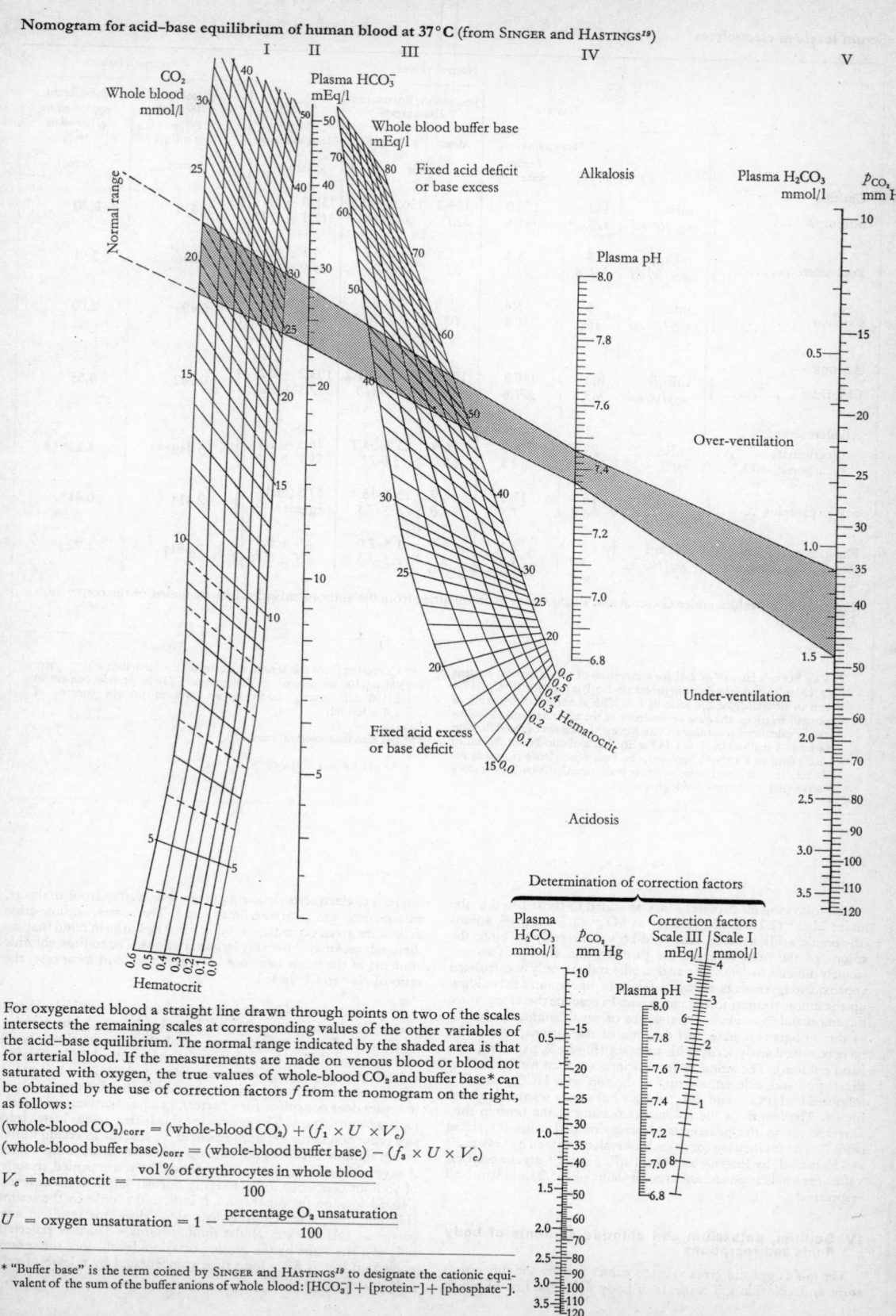

For oxygenated blood a straight line drawn through points on two of the scales intersects the remaining scales at corresponding values of the other variables of the acid–base equilibrium. The normal range indicated by the shaded area is that for arterial blood. If the measurements are made on venous blood or blood not saturated with oxygen, the true values of whole-blood CO_2 and buffer base* can be obtained by the use of correction factors *f* from the nomogram on the right, as follows:

$$(\text{whole-blood } CO_2)_{corr} = (\text{whole-blood } CO_2) + (f_1 \times U \times V_c)$$

$$(\text{whole-blood buffer base})_{corr} = (\text{whole-blood buffer base}) - (f_3 \times U \times V_c)$$

$$V_c = \text{hematocrit} = \frac{\text{vol \% of erythrocytes in whole blood}}{100}$$

$$U = \text{oxygen unsaturation} = 1 - \frac{\text{percentage } O_2 \text{ unsaturation}}{100}$$

* "Buffer base" is the term coined by SINGER and HASTINGS[19] to designate the cationic equivalent of the sum of the buffer anions of whole blood: $[HCO_3^-] + [\text{protein}^-] + [\text{phosphate}^-]$.

Serum levels of electrolytes

		Normal values					Conversion factors	
		GAMBLE[15]		JEANNERET, ROSENMUND, ESSELLIER[23]		PETERS[4]	*mg/100 ml* or *g/100 ml* or *vol%* into mEq/l	mEq/l into *mg/100 ml* or *g/100 ml* or *vol%*
		Mean values		Mean	Range	Mean and range		
		Serum	Serum water**	Serum		Serum	Serum	Serum
Cations								
Sodium	mEq/l	142	152.0	139.2	136.6–141.8	138.0 ± 3.4	0.435	2.30
	mg/100 ml	*326.6*	*349.6*	*320*	*314–326*	*317.5 ± 7.8*		
Potassium	mEq/l	5	5.4	5.1	4.1–5.6	4.1 ± 0.3	0.256	3.91
	mg/100 ml	*19.6*	*21.1*	*20*	*16–22*	*16.0 ± 1.2*		
Calcium	mEq/l	5	5.4	5.0	4.7–5.2	5.3 ± 0.3	0.499	2.00
	mg/100 ml	*10*	*10.8*	*10*	*9.5–10.5*	*10.6 ± 0.6*		
Anions								
Chlorides	mEq/l	103	110.3	102.9	97.3–107.2	102.2 ± 2.2	0.282	3.55
	mg/100 ml	*365.7*	*391.6*	*365*	*345–380*	*362.8 ± 7.8*		
Alkali reserve:								
Bicarbonate	mEq/l	27	28.9	26.9	23.8–34.7	26.5 ± 1.4	0.449***	2.23***
Bicarbonate-CO_2	*vol %*	*60.2*	*64.5*	*60*	*53–77*	*59.1 ± 3.1*		
Serum proteins	mEq/l	16	17.1	16.9	15.7–18.1	17.3 (incl. organic acids)	2.41*	0.41*
	g/100 ml	*6.6*	*7.5*	*7.0*	*6.5–7.5*			
Phosphates (inorganic)	mEq/l	2	2.1	1.7	1.5–2.0	2.0 ± 0.5	0.581†	1.72†
Phosphorus (inorganic)	*mg/100 ml*	*3.4*	*3.6*	*3*	*2.5–3.5*	*3.4 ± 0.86*		

The mg/100 ml values under GAMBLE and PETERS have been obtained from the authors' mEq/l values by means of the conversion factors given.

* VAN SLYKE's factor[28] of 2.41 for conversion of serum protein content (g/100 ml) into ionized serum protein (mEq/l) is valid for 38° C, pH 7.4 and an albumin/globulin ratio of 1.6. With abnormal distribution of protein fractions the base equivalents of the albumins and globulins can be calculated according to VAN SLYKE[28] by means of the following factors: 1 g albumin-N = 1.745 mEq, 1 g globulin-N = 1.205 mEq. According to BROCH[29], however, the base equivalence is greatly reduced when the blood protein picture is abnormal, so that VAN SLYKE's conversion would give too high a value.

** Calculated from the serum value using the formula[4]: serum water (in ml/100 ml serum) = 98.4 minus (0.718 × protein content in g/100 ml serum), assuming an average protein content of 7.0 g/100 ml.

*** See also footnote* on page 330.

† At pH 7.4 and 38° C.

The following electrolytes must be added to those listed in the table: Mg^{++} (1.7 mEq/l), sulfates as SO_4^{--} (0.7 mEq/l)[27], anions of organic acids, protein- and lipid-bound electrolytes. Since the anions of the organic acids, the proteins and the lipids are extremely difficult to determine analytically and can only be calculated approximately, there is always a factor of uncertainty in building up the anion column in the ionogram. In practice therefore, since the anion and cation columns must be of equal height, the height of the ionogram is based on the sum of the cations, which can be determined analytically with accuracy (Figure 2, page 539, left-hand column). The anion concentrations are then marked off on the right-hand column, starting at the top with HCO_3^- and Cl^-, followed by HPO_4^{--} and SO_4^{--} if they have been separately determined. The length of the column remaining at the bottom then corresponds to the proteins and undetermined acids ("residual acids"). The total cation (or anion) equivalent is given by GAMBLE[15] as 155 mEq/l, by PETERS[4] as 149 mEq/l. SHOHL[30] gives analytical values for total cation and anion equivalents of 155.2 and 150 mEq/l respectively.

IV. Sodium, potassium and chloride contents of body fluids and secretions

The table opposite gives average values for the sodium, potassium and chloride ion contents of body fluids the loss of which can lead to electrolyte deficiency (vomiting, watery stool, drainage, enterostomy and puncture fluids, etc.). The corresponding urine values are given on page 544, but it must be borne in mind that individual cases may show very large variations. The sodium chloride contents of the fluids have not been given since in most cases the ratio of Na^+ to Cl^- is 1:1.

A rational electrolyte replacement therapy is particularly important in disturbances of renal function in which the tubular regulation of water and mineral metabolism is impaired (postoperative conditions, etc.). In view of the practical difficulties involved in even a rough determination of electrolyte balance it might well be asked why a determination of the electrolyte values in serum does not suffice for a correct, i.e. quantitatively adequate, replacement therapy. The reason for this is that *sodium* losses lead to a reduction in the extracellular fluid, so that the lowering of the serum sodium level does not correspond to the actual sodium loss. A severe loss of body water can therefore be accompanied, in spite of sodium deficiency, by a roughly normal serum sodium level. *Chloride* loss, on the other hand, is indicated at once by the serum chloride level, since chloride loss alone does not result in any particular loss of extracellular fluid. *Potassium* deficit is reflected only at a late stage by the serum potassium level, since the serum potassium loss is for a long time compensated by release of cell potassium.

Sodium, potassium and chloride contents of body fluids and secretions

	Na+		K+		Cl−	
	mEq/l	mg/100 ml	mEq/l	mg/100 ml	mEq/l	mg/100 ml
1. Mean values in serum water, after GAMBLE[15] (see the table opposite)	152	350	5.4	21	110	392
2. Serum ultrafiltrate	139	320	4.4	17	114.2	405
3. Serum transudates	144	331	4.9	19	112	397
4. Sweat[31], mean	**58.4**	**134**	**10.0**	**39**	**45.4**	**161**
standard deviation	*15.7*	*36*	*2.4*	*9*	*15.5*	*55*
5. Saliva[32], mean	**33.1**	**76**	**19.5**	**76**	**33.9**	**120**
standard deviation	*13.4*	*31*	*3.4*	*13*	*10.2*	*36*
6. Gastric juice, total[13], mean	59.0	136	9.3	36	89.0	316
²/₃ of cases	31–90	71–107	4.3–12.0	17–47	52–124	184–440
after COOKE and CROWLEY[33]	20–80	46–184	5–20	20–78	100–150	355–532
7. Gastric juice, fundus[30]	35	80	15	59	160	567
Gastric juice, pyloric[30]	160	368	25	98	140	496
8. Bile[13], average	145.3	334	5.2	20	99.9	354
²/₃ of cases	134–156	308–359	3.9–6.3	15–25	83–110	294–390
after COOKE and CROWLEY[33]	120–140	276–322	5–15	20–59	80–120	284–425
9. Pancreatic juice[13]	141.1	324	4.6	18	76.6	272
after COOKE and CROWLEY[33]	120–140	276–322	5–15	20–59	40–80	142–284
10. Intestinal juice[13], MILLER-ABBOTT catheter average	104.9	240	5.1	20	98.9	350
²/₃ of cases	72–128	166–296	3.5–6.8	14–27	69–127	245–451
after COOKE and CROWLEY[33]	100–140	230–322	5–15	20–59	90–130	319–461
11. Ileal secretion[13], MILLER-ABBOTT catheter	116.7	268	5.0	20	105.8	376
from a fresh ileostomy, average	129.5	298	16.2	63	109.7	389
²/₃ of cases	112–142	258–326		18–55	93–122	330–433
12. Cecostomy secretion[13], average	79.6	183	20.6	81	48.2	171
²/₃ of cases	48–116	110–266	11.1–28.3	43–111	35–70	124–248
13. Formed stools (values relate to the water content)[18] Calculated average	35	81	72	282	73	259
Extreme values	7–96	16–221	34–150	133–587	17–164	60–582

In view of the large variations in the composition of the fluids of the digestive tract, prior determination of the Na-, K- and Cl-ion contents is essential for an effective electrolyte replacement therapy.

Serum ultrafiltrate. The values for serum ultrafiltrate have been calculated from the mean values in serum water using PETERS' ratios for serum ultrafiltrate/serum water (Na^+: 0.91, K^+: 0.82, Cl^-: 1.03)[18]. The concentrations are largely the same as those in the nearly protein-free interstitial fluid.

Serum transudates. The ratios of the electrolyte concentrations in serum water and transudates are 0.96 for Na, 0.92 for K, 1.03 for Cl[18, 34]. The values given have been calculated from the mean values in serum water using these ratios, on the assumption of an average protein content in transudates of 2 g/100 ml.

Sweat. The values given are for sweat samples from the forearm obtained by warming artificially. After adaptation to a hot climate the Na and Cl values are much lower[35]. According to AHLMAN et al.[31] the Na/Cl ratio is 1.32 ± 0.15, according to BERENSON and BURCH[36] 1.14 average. In contrast to saliva, there is no diagnostically significant Na/K ratio in sweat[31, 36]. During a sweating test the Na and Cl concentrations rise in the course of an hour to double the initial values[36]. The values given are the maximum values observed after one hour's sweating.

Saliva. According to FRAWLEY and THORN[37] the ratio of Na/K in saliva averages 1.3 ± 0.5 with a range of 0.33–2.1. In ADDISON's disease this ratio averages 1.8 in treated cases and 5 in untreated cases. If the Na level in serum lies below 132 mEq/l this characteristic increase of the Na/K ratio may not be observed[38]. The values for this ratio[37] and those given above for Na[32] were measured after normal alimentary salt intake and after stimulation of salivation by chewing of paraffin wax. Saliva obtained by simple aspiration, i.e. without stimulation, has a markedly lower Na content (mean value 8.3 mEq/l, range 4.8–14.6 mEq/l)[39].

Gastric juice. The average fasting values given (after RANDALL[13]) are based on 130 measurements on gastric juice ranging from anacidity to hyperacidity. The Na/Cl ratio in a hyperacid gastric juice can fall to one-third of the normal value. In anacidity the total gastric juice can contain as many chloride ions as sodium ions, not, however, in the form of HCl but as salts[13, 40]. A high sodium content can also be due to a reflux of duodenal juice. RANDALL's potassium value[13] of 9.3 mEq/l is low; according to MARTIN[41] the potassium concentration averages 16.5 mEq/l, according to SAEMUNDSSON[42] 17.1–21.8 mEq/l, according to MACH[43] 22–29 with mean 26 mEq/l.

Bile and pancreatic juice. The values (from RANDALL[13]) are for surgical fistula fluids.

Ileal secretion. In ileostomy a lowering of the electrolyte content of the secretion eventually occurs[44].

Cecostomy secretion. The Na and Cl concentrations are about half those in the ileostomy secretion[44].

Stools. The values given relate to the water in the feces (mEq/l water). The normal electrolyte excretion can also be expressed as a percentage of the total excretion (feces + urine); the values are then roughly 5% for Na, 21% for K, 2% for Cl[30].

In *diarrhea* it is difficult to estimate the electrolyte loss via the feces; the more watery the stool the more nearly the electrolyte concentration approaches that of the ileal secretion[13]. According to BARTLETT et al. (quoted by MADDOCK[45]) the mean value for Cl is 73 mEq/l (63–89 mEq/l). The usually higher potassium loss in diarrhea is of greater practical significance. In artificial diarrhea due to anthraquinone laxatives[46], potassium concentrations in the stool of 50–55 mEq/l have been observed, in cases of ulcerative colitis[47] 38–43 mEq/l. According to DARROW and PRATT[56], diarrhea stools of infants contain ca. 64 mEq/l Na, 44 mEq/l Cl and 32 mEq/l K, with fecal quantities of ca. 250 ml per day.

V. Renal function values

Table (a) below gives a summary of average values in health for the filtration, reabsorption and excretion of important electrolytes. These values demonstrate the high filtration capacity of the kidneys for sodium and chloride, which are present in high concentration in serum, and the markedly smaller filtration capacity for potassium and phosphate, of which the serum levels are low. These data, and the fact that 137 liters per day are filtered by the glomeruli, explain why the retention of sodium, chloride and water, so long as a diuresis persists, must be due to increased tubular reabsorption. The data also show that if the glomerular filtration is reduced, retention of phosphate must soon occur but not of sodium or chloride.

Potassium excretion, like that of the other electrolytes, is regulated by the tubular reabsorption. Potassium can, however, be eliminated by tubular secretion[48], so that a hyperpotassemia can arise only in cases of severe oliguria.

Under (b) the clinically important relations between specific gravity, osmotic concentration and diuresis are briefly discussed.

Under (c) will be found normal values for various quantitative tests of renal function. This summary has been included since the results of renal function tests are usually reported in the literature without normal values being given.

(a) Excretion of electrolytes

	1 Concentration in serum ultrafiltrate mg/100 ml	2 Concentration in urine mg/100 ml	3 Glomerular filtration in 24 hours g	4 Urinary excretion in 24 hours g	5 Tubular reabsorption %
Cations					
Sodium	320	385	438	4.62	99
Potassium	17	228	23.3	2.74	88
Calcium		20.8		0.25	
Magnesium		8.3		0.10	
Ammonium (as N)		58		0.70	
Anions					
Chloride	405	614	555	7.37	99
Phosphate (as P)	4.3	92	5.9	1.10	81
Sulfate (as SO_3)		183		2.20	
Organic acids				see pages 532 and 533	

Column 1: Values from the table on page 543; the phosphate concentration in the ultrafiltrate has been calculated from that in the serum water (table on page 542) by using the value of 1.2 (GAMBLE[15]) for the ratio of the phosphate concentration in the ultrafiltrate to that in the serum water.
Column 2: Calculated from the values in column 4 on the assumption of a 24-hour urinary volume of 1200 ml.
Column 3: Obtained by multiplying the rate of glomerular filtration (137 l/24 hours; see the opposite page) by the concentration in the serum ultrafiltrate in column 1.
Column 4: Normal values from the section Synopsis of Urine, pages 533 and 534.
Column 5: Obtained by dividing the amount reabsorbed (column 3 minus column 4) by the amount in the glomerular filtrate given in column 3.

(b) Specific gravity

The specific gravity of urine is a measure of the total weight of dissolved substances, while the osmolality expresses the number of osmotically active particles present in the solution. The specific gravity and osmolality (*the latter measured in practice by means of the quotient freezing-point depression/1.858*; cf. page 326) do not therefore necessarily run parallel. A sodium chloride solution has a lower specific gravity than an osmotically equivalent urea solution, i.e. one containing roughly the same number of particles. Various "concentration tests" have been devised[58] to assess the maximum concentration capacity of the kidneys. The proper measure of this function is the highest osmotic concentration which is attained. In clinical practice, however, it is more expedient to measure the specific gravity than the freezing-point depression (SCHADE[49]), and the osmolalities corresponding to various specific gravities are therefore shown in the adjacent table. The maximum concentration capacity of the kidneys[50] amounts to ca. 1400 mosm/l, corresponding to a freezing-point depression of 2.6°C. In evaluating the results of concentration tests in albuminuria, 1 unit of specific gravity must be subtracted per 3.9 g/l protein and per 2.7 g/l glucose[51].

Approximate osmolalities and corresponding specific gravities of urine on a normal diet

mosm/l	Specific gravity	mosm/l	Specific gravity
200	1.006	800	1.024
400	1.012	1000	1.030
600	1.018	1200	1.036

The table below shows for any given concentration capacity the minimum quantities of urine which are necessary for the excretion of the urinary constituents. The values are based on the graphical representation of DARROW and PRATT[57] and a normal value of 1200 mosm of urinary constituents excreted per 24 hours on a normal diet (GAMBLE[15]). The amount of these substances is greatest on a protein-rich diet, smallest on a carbohydrate-rich diet. In fasting, ca. 800 millimoles of urinary constituents are eliminated[22]; on a high-calorie, high-carbohydrate, low-protein diet, on which the breakdown of the body proteins is reduced, the amount of these substances excreted may be even lower.

Urinary concentration		Minimum quantity of urine in ml required for excretion of the urinary constituents from an intake of 100 calories		Minimum quantity of urine in ml required for excretion of 1200 millimoles of urinary constituents
Specific gravity	Milliosmoles per liter	Pure carbohydrate diet	Mixed diet	
1.006	ca. 200	ca. 105	ca. 160	ca. 6000
1.012	400	60	100	3000
1.018	600	40	70	2000
1.024	800	25	50	1500
1.030	1000	20	40	1200
1.036	1200	18	35	1000

(c) **Quantitative glomerular and tubular function tests and renal plasma flow**

Glomerular filtration

(after SMITH[52], not including the 24-hour glomerular filtrate of CAMARA et al.[53]; all values for a body surface area of 1.73 m^2):

Glomerular filtration, inulin clearance method, short-duration tests:
men 131 ± 21.5 ml/min
women 117 ± 15.6 ml/min

Glomerular filtration in 24 hours, creatinine clearance method, normal physical activity[8]:
137 (113–158) liters
or 95.5 ml/min

Plasma urea clearance with a diuresis of *over* 2 ml/min = maximum clearance (*Cm*):
70.7 ml/min

The *Cm* value of 75 ml/min of PETERS and VAN SLYKE[54] which is often quoted relates to the *whole-blood* urea clearance in the determination of blood urea, and not the usual *plasma* urea clearance. The ratio of urea-*Cm* to glomerular filtrate, the latter measured by the inulin clearance method, is ca. 0.6. The urea-*Cm* is therefore not a measure of glomerular filtration like inulin clearance, since urea is in part reabsorbed by the tubules. With adequate tubular flow (*Cm*), however, the tubular urea reabsorption does not vary greatly, so that the urea clearance may be used clinically in assessing the glomerular filtration capacity. The "standard clearance" (*Cs*) with a diuresis of *less than* 2 ml/min bears no constant relation to the glomerular filtration and has therefore no diagnostic value.

Maximum values for tubular function

(after SMITH[52]; all values for a body surface area of 1.73 m^2):

Maximum tubular para-aminohippurate excretory capacity (PAH-Tm):
men 79.8 ± 16.7 ml/min
women 77.2 ± 10.8 ml/min

Maximum tubular reabsorption of glucose (glucose-Tm):
men 375 ± 79.7 ml/min
women 303 ± 55.3 ml/min

These tests are a measure of the total mass of functioning tubular tissue.

Renal plasma flow

(after SMITH[52], as above):

Plasma minute-volume in functional kidney tissue (PAH-clearance):
men 654 ± 163 ml/min
women 592 ± 153 ml/min

Tubular excretion of phenol red

According to SMITH[52] the phenol-red clearance amounts to 394 ± 45 ml/min. ROWNTREE and GERAGHTY's excretion test (quoted by SUNDERMAN and BOERNER[51]) can be performed in various ways[51, 55] and is based on the measurement of the percentage of an injected quantity of 6 mg phenol red which is excreted in the urine during a certain period of time. During the first 65–70 minutes after injection, 40–60% of the dye is normally excreted, during the next hour 20–25%.

References

1) EDELMAN et al., *Surg. Gynec. Obstet.*, **95**, 1 (1952). *2)* SCRIBANTE et al., *Helv. physiol. pharmacol. Acta*, **10**, 224 (1952). *3)* HURST et al., *J. Lab. clin. Med.*, **39**, 36 (1952). *4)* PETERS, J. P., *Water Balance in Health and Disease*, in GARFIELD, G. P. (Ed.), *Diseases of Metabolism*, Philadelphia, 1953. *5)* SOBERMAN et al., *J. biol. Chem.*, **179**, 31 (1949). *6)* FRIIS-HANS et al., *Pediatrics*, **7**, 321 (1951). *7)* CARDOZO and EDELMAN, *J. clin. Invest.*, **31**, 280 (1952). *8)* LEVITT and GAUDINO, *Amer. J. Med.*, **9**, 208 (1950). *9)* EDELMAN et al., *Science*, **115**, 447 (1952). *10)* GIBSON and EVANS, *J. clin. Invest.*, **16**, 317 (1937). *11)* BERGER et al., *Amer. J. Physiol.*, **162**, 318 (1950). *12)* NEWBURGH and JOHNSTON, *Physiol. Rev.*, **22**, 1 (1942). *13)* RANDALL, H. T., *Surg. Clin. N. Amer.*, **32**, 445 (1952). *14)* WIGGERS, C. J., *Physiology in Health and Disease*, 5th ed., Philadelphia, 1949. *15)* GAMBLE, J. L., *Chemical Anatomy, Physiology and Pathology of Extracellular Fluid*, 6th ed., Cambridge, Mass., 1954. *16)* MARIOTT, H. L., *Water and Salt Depletion*, Springfield, 1950. *17)* SCRIBNER et al., *J. Amer. med. Ass.*, **144**, 1167 (1950). *18)* PETERS, J. P., *Body Water. The Exchange of Fluids in Man*, Springfield, 1935. *19)* SINGER and HASTINGS, *Medicine (Baltimore)*, **27**, 223 (1948). *20)* SUNDERMAN and BOERNER, *Normal Values in Clinical Medicine*, Philadelphia, 1950, page 255. *21)* MCCANCE, R. A., *Lancet*, **1**, 704 (1936). *22)* WEISBERG, H. F., *Water, Electrolyte and Acid-Base Balance*, Baltimore, 1953. *23)* JEANNERET et al., *Helv. med. Acta*, **21**, 191 (1954). *24)* KEYS, A., *J. Phys. Chem.*, **42**, 11 (1938). *25)* SCHWAB and KÜHNS, *Die Störungen des Wasser- und Elektrolyt-Stoffwechsels*, Berlin, 1959. *26)* ASTRUP, P., *Klin. Wschr.*, **35**, 749 (1957). *27)* ALBRITTON, E. C., *Standard Values in Blood*, Philadelphia, 1952. *28)* VAN SLYKE et al., *J. biol. Chem.*, **79**, 768 (1928). *29)* BROCH, O. J., *Scand. J. clin. Lab. Invest.*, **5**, 9 (1954). *30)* SHOHL, A. T., *Mineral Metabolism*, New York, 1939. *31)* AHLMANN et al., *J. clin. Endocr.*, **13**, 773 (1953). *32)* WHITE et al., *J. clin. Invest.*, **29**, 1445 (1950). *33)* COOKE and CROWLEY, *New Engl. J. Med.*, **246**, 637 (1952). *34)* FOLK et al., *Amer. J. Physiol.*, **153**, 381 (1948). *35)* CONN, J. W., *Arch. intern. Med.*, **83**, 416 (1949). *36)* BERENSON and BURCH, *J. Lab. clin. Med.*, **42**, 58 (1953). *37)* FRAWLEY and THORN, *Proceedings of the Second Clinical ACTH Conference*, vol. I, Philadelphia, 1951, page 115. *38)* THORN et al., *Amer. J. Med.*, **10**, 595 (1951). *39)* WARMING-LARSEN et al., *Acta endocr. (Kbh.)*, **11**, 400 (1952). *40)* MACH, R. S., *Les troubles du métabolisme du sel et de l'eau*, Lausanne, 1946. *41)* MARTIN, L., *Gastroenterology*, **15**, 326 (1950). *42)* SAEMUNDSEN, J., *Acta med. scand.*, Suppl. 208 (1948). *43)* MACH, R. S., *Schweiz. med. Wschr.*, **84**, 113 (1954). *44)* LOCKWOOD and RANDALL, *Bull. N. Y. Acad. Med.*, **25**, 228 (1949). *45)* MADDOCK, W. G., *Ohio St. med. J.*, **45**, 462 (1949). *46)* SCHWARTZ and RELMAN, *J. clin. Invest.*, **32**, 258 (1953). *47)* POLLARD and BOLT, *Gastroenterology*, **22**, 564 (1952). *48)* BERLINER et al., *Amer. J. Med.*, **11**, 274 (1951). *49)* SCHADE, H., *Die physikalische Chemie in der inneren Medizin*, 3rd ed., Dresden and Leipzig, 1923. *50)* PITTS and SARTORIUS, *Pharmacol. Rev.*, **2**, 161 (1950). *51)* SUNDERMAN and BOERNER, *Normal Values in Clinical Medicine*, Philadelphia and London, 1950, page 338. *52)* SMITH, H. W., *The Kidney: Structure and Function in Health and Disease*, New York, 1951. *53)* CAMARA et al., *J. Lab. clin. Med.*, **37**, 743 (1951). *54)* PETERS and VAN SLYKE, *Quantitative Clinical Chemistry*, vol. I, *Interpretations*, 2nd ed., Baltimore, 1946. *55)* SPUEHLER, O., Quantitative Nierenfunktionsprüfungen, in *Schweizerisches medizinisches Jahrbuch*, Basle, 1951, page liii. *56)* DARROW and PRATT, *J. Amer. med. Ass.*, **143**, 432 (1950). *57)* DARROW and PRATT, *J. Amer. med. Ass.*, **143**, 365 (1950). *58)* WELLER, J. M., in MILLER, S. E. (Ed.), *A Textbook of Clinical Pathology*, 6th ed., Baltimore, 1960, page 350. *59)* LANDIS, E. M., *Heart*, **15**, 209 (1930).

Bibliography

GAMBLE, J. L., *Chemical Anatomy, Physiology and Pathology of Extracellular Fluid*, 6th ed., Cambridge, Mass., 1954; MARIOTT, H. L., *Water and Salt Depletion*, Springfield, 1950; PETERS, J. P., *Body Water. The Exchange of Fluids in Man*, Springfield, 1935; PETERS, J. P., *Water Balance in Health and Disease*, in GARFIELD, G. P. (Ed.), *Diseases of Metabolism*, Philadelphia, 1953; WEISBERG, H. F., *Water, Electrolyte and Acid-Base Balance*, Baltimore, 1953; ELKINTON and DANOWSKI, *The Body Fluids*, Baltimore, 1955; HOEBER, R., *Physikalische Chemie der Zellen und Gewebe*, Berne, 1947; SCHADE, H., *Die physikalische Chemie in der inneren Medizin*, 3rd ed., Dresden and Leipzig, 1923; DARROW and PRATT, *J. Amer. med. Ass.*, **143**, 365, 432 (1950); LEUTHARDT, *Lehrbuch der physiologischen Chemie*, 14th ed., Berlin, 1959; MACH, R. S., *Les troubles du métabolisme du sel et de l'eau*, Lausanne, 1946.

Nomogram for the calculation of hemoglobin and hematocrit values and plasma protein content from specific gravities of whole blood and plasma (or approximately from specific gravity of whole blood alone)

From VAN SLYKE et al., *J. biol. Chem.*, **183**, 349 (1950)

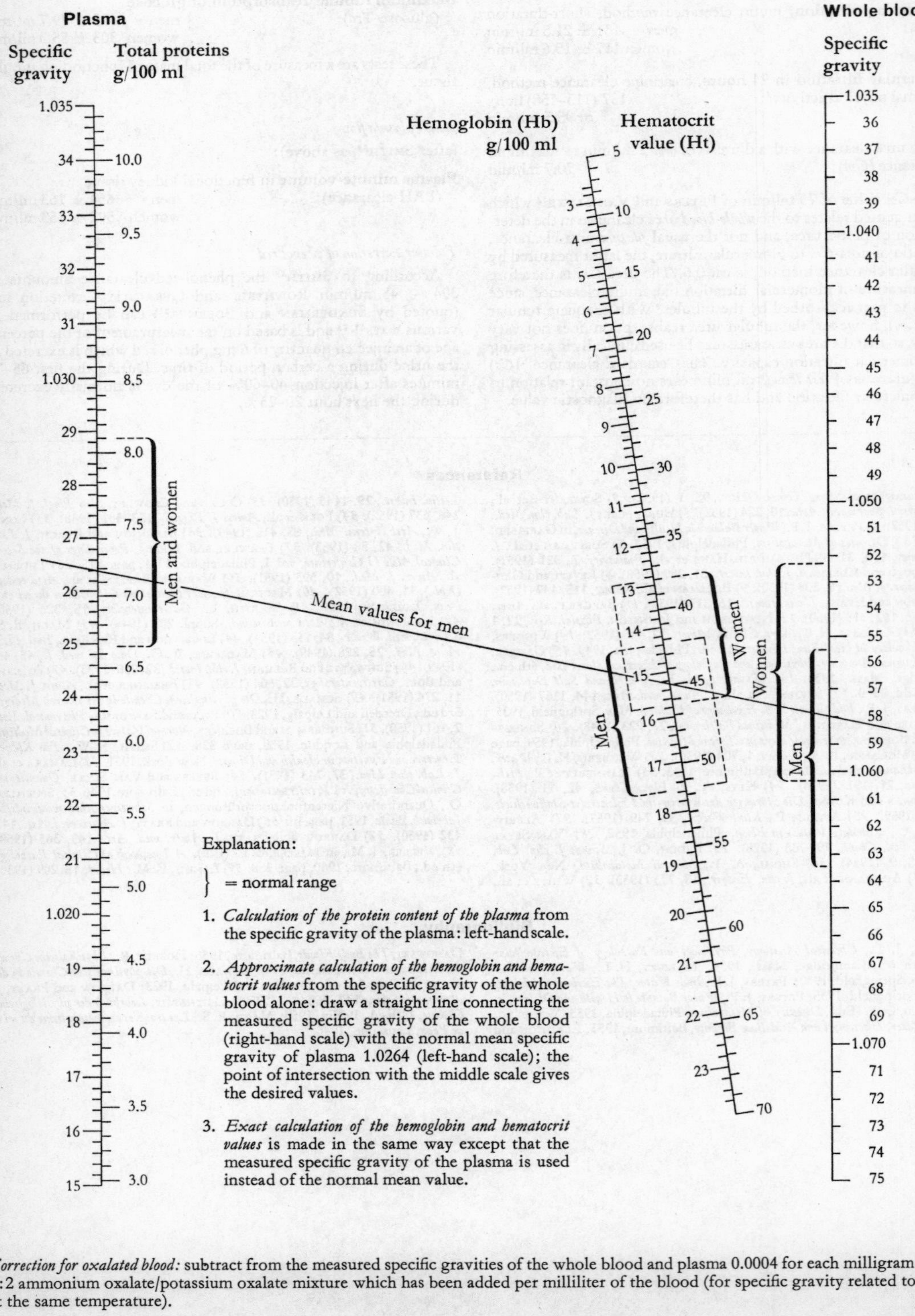

Explanation:

} = normal range

1. *Calculation of the protein content of the plasma* from the specific gravity of the plasma: left-hand scale.

2. *Approximate calculation of the hemoglobin and hematocrit values* from the specific gravity of the whole blood alone: draw a straight line connecting the measured specific gravity of the whole blood (right-hand scale) with the normal mean specific gravity of plasma 1.0264 (left-hand scale); the point of intersection with the middle scale gives the desired values.

3. *Exact calculation of the hemoglobin and hematocrit values* is made in the same way except that the measured specific gravity of the plasma is used instead of the normal mean value.

Correction for oxalated blood: subtract from the measured specific gravities of the whole blood and plasma 0.0004 for each milligram of the 3:2 ammonium oxalate/potassium oxalate mixture which has been added per milliliter of the blood (for specific gravity related to water at the same temperature).

Normal values (for definition of the normal range see footnote, page 517)

Specific gravity (20/20°C)

	Value	Method	Remarks
Whole blood			
Men	1.055–1.064	Copper sulfate method of PHILLIPS et al., *J. biol. Chem.*, **183**, 305 (1950); values from VAN SLYKE et al., *J. biol. Chem.*, **183**, 349 (1950).	The specific gravity of the blood is dependent on the total number of cellular elements (mean specific gravity of erythrocytes 1.084–1.117; see page 576).
Women	1.050–1.056		
Plasma	1.025–1.029		The specific gravity of the plasma and serum is mainly dependent on the protein content and is therefore a measure of this. *Specific gravity lowered:* (blood) in anemia; (plasma) in marasmus, hydropic renal disease. *Specific gravity increased:* (blood) polycythemia; (plasma) cholera, dysentery, severe burns, plasmacytoma.
Serum	1.024–1.028	LEAKE et al., *Amer. J. Physiol.*, **81**, 493 (1927).	

Specific gravity – Serum water – Solid constituents (After SUNDERMAN, F.W., *J. biol. Chem.*, **113**, 1 [1936])

The following table allows the conversion of

(*a*) the concentration of a substance in 1 liter of serum into its concentration in 1 kg of serum water, i.e. the molality (multiplication by the factor in column 6), and

(*b*) the concentration of a substance in 1 kg of serum water into its concentration in 1 liter of serum (multiplication by the factor in column 4 and division by 1000).

Specific gravity	Water per kilogram serum (grams)	Solid constituents per kilogram serum (grams)	Water per liter serum (grams)	Solid constituents per liter serum (grams)	Multiplication factor
1.015	952	48	966	34	1.035
1.016	948	52	964	36	1.038
1.017	945	55	961	39	1.040
1.018	942	58	959	41	1.043
1.019	939	61	957	43	1.045
1.020	936	64	954	46	1.048
1.021	932	68	952	48	1.051
1.022	929	71	949	51	1.053
1.023	926	74	947	53	1.056
1.024	923	77	945	55	1.059
1.025	919	81	942	58	1.061
1.026	916	84	940	60	1.064
1.027	913	87	938	62	1.067
1.028	910	90	935	65	1.069
1.029	906	94	933	67	1.072
1.030	903	97	930	70	1.075
1.031	900	100	928	72	1.078
1.032	897	103	925	75	1.081
1.033	894	106	923	77	1.083
1.034	890	110	921	79	1.086

Volume

Total volume in milliliters per kilogram body weight (men and women as one group)

Method	Mean	Range	*s*
		Whole blood	
(1)	**65.6**	*51.0–81.2*	7.3
(2)	**71.4**	*55.6–87.2*	7.9
(3)	**69.8**	*53.2–86.4*	8.3
		Erythrocytes	
(1)	**25.8**	*20.4–31.2*	2.7
(2)	**30.3**	*19.1–41.5*	5.6
(3)	**27.7**	*20.5–34.9*	3.6
		Plasma	
(1)	**39.8**	*27.6–52.0*	6.1
(2)	**41.1**	*29.9–52.3*	5.6
(3)	**42.1**	*30.5–53.7*	5.8
		Ratio of total hematocrit to venous hematocrit	
(4)	**0.910**	*0.858–0.962*	0.026

Methods and sources

(1) Determined by means of ^{32}P-labeled erythrocytes. Values from WASSERMAN et al., *J. Lab. clin. Med.*, **37**, 342 (1951).

(2) Determined by simultaneous labeling of the erythrocytes with radioactive sodium chromate and of the plasma with radioactive chromic chloride. After GRAY and FRANK, *J. clin. Invest.*, **32**, 1000 (1953).

(3) Determined by the dyestuff dilution method. Values from WASSERMAN et al., *loc. cit.* Literature on dyestuff methods: Geigy Blue 536: SOMOGYI, J. C., *Schweiz. med. Wschr.*, **71**, 225 (1941); SCHNEIDER, J. A., *Z. ges. inn. Med.*, **5**, 124 (1950); Evans blue (T 1824): GREGERSEN et al., *Amer. J. Physiol.*, **113**, 54 (1935); CROOKE and MORRIS, *J. Physiol. (Lond.)*, **101**, 217 (1942); WASSERMAN et al., *loc. cit.* CO-method (marking of the erythrocytes with CO) and also a comparison with dyestuff methods: HOPPER et al., *J. clin. Invest.*, **23**, 628 and 636 (1944). ^{32}P-Method: WASSERMAN et al., *loc. cit.*; MUKHERJEE and ROWLANDS, *Lancet*, **2**, 98 (1951).

(4) After CHAPLIN et al., *J. clin. Invest.*, **32**, 1309 (1953), in agreement with others. The measurements were made on 28 persons of whom only 4 were healthy, the remainder having various diseases, mainly erythremia and varieties of anemia. For the 4 healthy subjects the limiting values were 0.878 and 0.909 with a mean of 0.8895.

The ^{32}P-methods are more accurate than the dyestuff methods for determination of total blood volume since centrifuging is avoided. The latter methods give rather larger values than those using ^{32}P.

Normal values (for definition of the normal range see footnote, page 517)

Volume *(continued)*

Remarks

Physiological variations: the total blood volume at birth is about 300 ml and doubles itself during the first year of life[1]. Subsequently it increases gradually in proportion to bodily development up to puberty. Values are equal for boys and girls up to puberty, subsequently those for boys increase more rapidly than those for girls. The total blood and plasma volumes are closely dependent on bodily dimensions and bear little relation to age[2]. Blood and plasma volumes of Negroes are less than those of whites[3], those of Eskimos greater[4].

The total blood volume remains relatively constant; after oral or intravenous intake of liquid the normal level is regained rapidly[5]. Rest in bed brings about a reduction in the total blood volume, mainly as a result of diminished plasma volume[6]. In both men and women athletic pursuits lead to an increased total blood volume and an increase in hemoglobin[7]. Plasma and blood volumes both increase during pregnancy[8, 9] (see page 604). On the effect of heat and cold on blood volume see Bass and Henschel[4].

Pathological variations: greatly increased total blood and erythrocyte volumes are characteristic signs of erythremia[10, 11]. Total erythrocyte volumes of 48.8–93.9 ml/kg body weight have been observed in this disease[12], with a simultaneous reduction of plasma volume to 29 ml/kg on the average. Plasma volume is increased in nephrosis and under corticotropin or adrenocortical hormone therapy, as also in cardiac disease with severe decompensation[13]. A marked reduction in total blood volume accompanies shock, acute hemorrhages and dehydration; mercury diuretics bring about a decrease, theophylline derivatives an increase, of plasma volume[14]. Earlier data (prior to ca. 1935) on blood volume variations in pathological conditions should be treated with reserve since former methods of measurement lacked the accuracy of the present-day isotope and dyestuff methods[15].

The ratio of the *total erythrocyte volume to the total blood volume* **(total hematocrit value)** is less than the venous hematocrit value (cf. page 576). If the total blood volume is calculated from the total plasma volume and the venous hematocrit value, the latter must accordingly be multiplied by the correction factor 0.91. It is safer, however, to determine simultaneously the total plasma and erythrocyte volumes by method (2) above.

For reviews of **blood volume** see Sjöstrand, T., *Physiol. Rev.*, **33**, 202 (1953); Berlin et al., *New Engl. J. Med.*, **247**, 675 (1952); Gregersen and Rawson, *Physiol. Rev.*, **39**, 307 (1959).

Other physical data

		Methods and sources	Remarks
Osmotic pressure (at 0° C) (serum)	6.47–6.72 atm; mean 6.62 atm equal to 4922–5106 mm Hg; mean 5030 mm Hg	Calculated from the freezing-point depression (cf. pages 324–326) or measured directly.	Mainly due to the crystalloid constituents; ca. 0.5% of the total osmotic pressure is due to the colloidal constituents.
Colloid-osmotic pressure (at 0° C) (serum or plasma)	20.60–35.31 mm Hg; mean 24.27 mm Hg equal to 280–480 mm H_2O; mean 330 mm H_2O	Values from Keys and Hill, *J. exp. Biol.*, **11**, 28 (1934), in agreement with more recent measurements. Osmotic balance method: Julander and Svedberg, *Nature (Lond.)*, **153**, 523 (1944); osmometer methods: Bourdillon, J., *J. biol. Chem.*, **127**, 617 (1939); Clément, P., *Bull. Soc. chim. Fr.*, 5th Series, **16**, 781 (1949); Holm-Jensen, I., *Scand. J. clin. Lab. Invest.*, **1**, 87 (1949).	The colloid-osmotic pressure (COP) amounts to ca. 1/200 of the total osmotic pressure and can be calculated approximately from the serum albumin and globulin values by means of Keys' formula[16] (see under Oncotic pressure of serum, page 540). Most of the colloid-osmotic pressure is due to albumin; fibrinogen exerts no measurable COP. In the organism it is maintained constant; Wuhrmann and Wunderly[17, 21], in common with other workers[18–20], ascribe this to regulation of the serum albumin level.
Freezing-point depression (serum)	0.535–0.555° C; mean 0.547° C	By cryoscope. Values from Sunderman and Boerner, *Normal Values in Clinical Medicine*, Philadelphia, 1950, page 99. Gram, H. C., *Amer. J. med. Sci.*, **168**, 511 (1924), found range 0.555–0.570 with mean 0.562° C.	On osmotic pressure and freezing-point depression see pages 324–326. Crawford and Nicosia, *J. Lab. clin. Med.*, **40**, 907 (1952), describe a relatively simple method using only 5 ml of serum.

Viscosity

(1) **Relative viscosity** (viscosity of water = 1) measured *in vitro*

Whole blood	3.6–5.4; mean: women 4.5, men 5.0
Plasma	1.9–2.3
Serum	1.7–2.0

(2) **Absolute viscosity** *in vivo*, expressed in **centipoises:**

Whole blood	*2.46–2.94*; mean **2.70**, standard deviation 0.12

1) Brines et al., *J. Pediat.*, **18**, 447 (1941). *2)* Russell, S. J. M., *Arch. Dis. Childh.*, **24**, 88 (1949). *3)* Bass et al., *J. appl. Physiol.*, **14**, 801 (1959). *4)* Bass and Henschel, *Physiol. Rev.*, **36**, 128 (1956). *5)* Kaltreider and Meneely, *J. clin. Invest.*, **19**, 627 (1940). *6)* Taylor et al., *Amer. J. Physiol.*, **144**, 227 (1945). *7)* Kjellberg et al., *Acta physiol. scand.*, **19**, 146 (1949). *8)* Thomson et al., *Amer. J. Obstet. Gynec.*, **36**, 48 (1938). *9)* Caton et al., *Amer. J. Obstet. Gynec.*, **57**, 471 (1949). *10)* Gibson et al., *J. clin. Invest.*, **18**, 621 (1939). *11)* Haden, R. L., *Amer. J. med. Sci.*, **196**, 493 (1938). *12)* Berlin et al., *Amer. J. Med.*, **9**, 747 (1950). *13)* Gunton and Paul, *J. clin. Invest.*, **34**, 879 (1955). *14)* Spühler et al., *Helv. med. Acta*, **15**, 95 (1948). *15)* Wintrobe, M. M., *Clinical Hematology*, Philadelphia, 1952, page 280. *16)* Keys, A., *J. phys. Chem.*, **42**, 11 (1938). *17)* Wuhrmann and Wunderly, *Schweiz. med. Wschr.*, **75**, 234 (1945). *18)* Bjørneboe, M., *Acta path. microbiol. scand.*, **22**, 323 (1945). *19)* Bjørneboe, M., *Acta med. scand.*, **123**, 393 (1946). *20)* Bing, J., *Hygiea (Stockh.)*, **107**, quoted in *Nord. Med.*, **27**, 1455 (1945). *21)* Wuhrmann and Wunderly, *Die Bluteiweisskörper des Menschen*, 3rd ed., Basle, 1957, page 83.

Normal values (for definition of the normal range see footnote, page 517)

Viscosity *(continued)*

Methods

(1) By Hess viscosimeter with Gram's temperature correction (Hess, W., *Vjschr. naturf. Ges. Zürich*, **51**, 236 [1906]; values from Gram, H. C., *Amer. J. med. Sci.*, **168**, 511 [1924], and Wintrobe, M. M., *Clinical Hematology*, 3rd ed., Philadelphia, 1952, page 283). (2) Method of Pirofsky, B., *J. clin. Invest.*, **32**, 292 (1953). For rheoviscosimetric method see Krosch and Heidelmann, *Klin. Wschr.*, **33**, 947 (1955).

Remarks

The relative viscosity of whole blood measured *in vitro* by Hess's method is not always in agreement with the absolute viscosity *in vivo*, and cannot therefore be used in hemodynamic calculations. The absolute viscosity *in vivo* may be measured quite simply by Pirofsky's method.

The viscosity of whole blood is primarily dependent on the blood corpuscle content, i.e. in health on the erythrocyte content. The viscosity of plasma is due to the protein content, primarily the fibrinogen and globulins.

The viscosity is also affected by the CO_2 content (venous blood is more viscous than arterial blood), by the form of the erythrocytes, the presence of abnormal plasma proteins, and other factors.

The viscosity is increased in erythremia[1], in leukemia[2], in cryoglobulinemia[3], by changes in the plasma protein values[4], in sickle-cell anemia[5], in hypercholesterinemia[6], in hyperglycemia[7].

The blood of women has normally a somewhat lower viscosity than that of men, and that of children a lower viscosity than that of adults.

1) Nygaard et al., *Amer. J. Physiol.*, **114**, 128 (1935). *2)* Stephens, D. J., *Proc. Soc. exp. Biol. (N. Y.)*, **35**, 251 (1936). *3)* Petersen, W. E., *J. Lab. clin. Med.*, **42**, 641 (1953). *4)* Chopra and Choudhury, *Indian J. med. Res.*, **16**, 939 (1928/29). *5)* McCord et al., *Proc. Soc. exp. Biol. (N. Y.)*, **69**, 19 (1948). *6)* Burton-Opitz, R., *J. exp. Med.*, **8**, 240 (1906). *7)* Fishberg, E. H., *J. biol. Chem.*, **85**, 465 (1929/30).

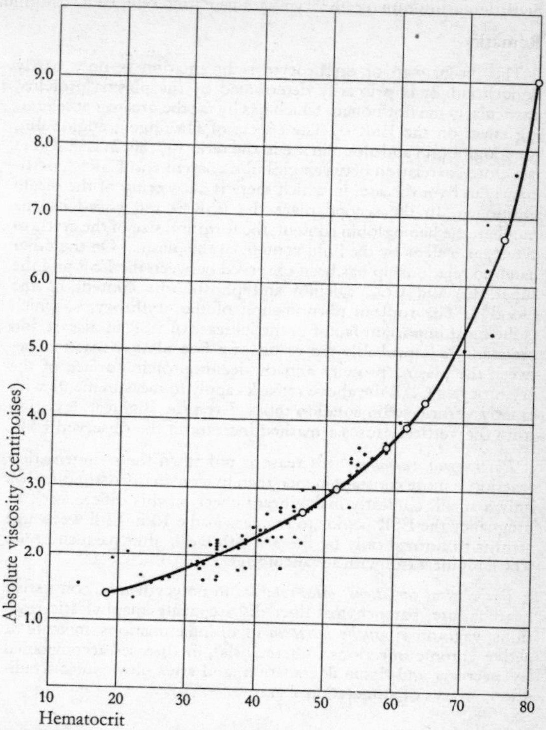

Relation between hematocrit value and absolute viscosity of normal blood (after Pirofsky, B., *J. clin. Invest.*, **32**, 292 [1953]).

Sedimentation rate (erythrocyte sedimentation rate, ESR) (mornings, fasting)

	Westergren methods			
	Original[1]	"Wide tube" modification[2]	Wintrobe's modification[3]	Linzenmeier's method[4]
Sedimentation tube				
Blood column	200 mm	100 mm	100 mm	50 mm
Diameter	2.5 mm	5 mm	2.5 mm	5 mm
Anticoagulant	Sodium citrate 3.8% solution	Sodium citrate 3.8% solution	2 parts potassium oxalate + 3 parts ammonium oxalate dry	Sodium citrate 5% solution
Quantity (mg/100 ml mixture)	760	760	200	1000
Resulting dilution of blood	20%	20%	0	20%
Method of reading	Sedimentation in 1, 2 or 24 hours	Sedimentation in 1 or 2 hours	Sedimentation in 1 hour	Time for a sedimentation of 18 mm
Normal values 1 hour				
Adults: Men	up to 5 mm	up to 6 mm	up to 6.5 mm; mean 3.7 mm	200–600 minutes
Women	up to 8 mm	up to 7 mm	up to 15 mm; mean 9.6 mm	200–600 minutes
Adolescents 12–20 years	–	–	up to 20 mm; mean 4.7 mm[5]	–
Newborn	up to 2 mm[6]	–	up to 2 mm[6]	see below
Normal values 2 hours				
Adults: Men	about twice the 1-hour values	up to 18 mm		
Women	about twice the 1-hour values	up to 20 mm		
Normal values 24 hours				
Adults: Men	up to 90 mm			
Women	up to 110 mm			

Values for infants by Linzenmeier's method[7]

Age	Mean (hours)	Range (hours)
1 day	106	30–185
2 days	57	3–180
4 days	45	6–120
6 days	20	5–100
8 days	14	4– 37
9–14 days	10	4– 24
9–12 months	1¼	–

Micro-methods (Westergren): Cutler[8], Smith[6], etc.

1) Wuhrmann and Wunderly, *Die Bluteiweisskörper des Menschen*, 3rd ed., Basle and Stuttgart, 1957, pages 141 and 142. *2)* Wuhrmann and Wunderly, *loc. cit.*, pages 141 and 190. *3)* Wintrobe and Landsberg, *Amer. J. med. Sci.*, **189**, 102 (1935). *4)* Linzenmeier, G., *Arch. Gynäk.*, **113**, 608 (1920). *5)* Gallagher, J. R., *Amer. J. med. Sci.*, **188**, 450 (1934). *6)* Smith, C. H., *Amer. J. med. Sci.*, **192**, 73 (1936). *7)* Hurwitz et al., *J. Pediat.*, **12**, 785 (1938). *8)* Cutler, J.W., *J. Lab. clin. Med.*, **26**, 542 (1940).

Normal values (for definition of the normal range see footnote, page 517)

Sedimentation rate (erythrocyte sedimentation rate, ESR) (mornings, fasting) *(continued)*

Remarks

The mechanism of erythrocyte sedimentation is only partly understood. It is primarily determined by the plasma proteins, particularly the fibrinogen, which has by far the greatest accelerating effect on the ESR[1,2]. The effects of fibrinogen, euglobulin, pseudoglobulin and albumin are in the ratio 100:20:2:1.5[3]. There is a close correlation between globulin content and ESR[4,5], particularly in liver disease, in which there is a lowering of the serum fibrinogen. In the second place the ESR is influenced by the number, the hemoglobin content, the form and size of the erythrocytes[6], as well as by the lipid content of the plasma. On the other hand no relationship has been observed between the ESR and the sugar, O_2 and CO_2, calcium and phosphorus content of the blood[7,8]. The rouleau phenomenon of the erythrocytes, which is the most important factor in the increase of ESR in disease and pregnancy[9], is probably the result of a flocculation reaction between the plasma proteins and the lecithoprotein surface of the erythrocytes[10]. All the above remarks apply to measurements with exactly vertical sedimentation tubes. Even the slightest deviation from the vertical causes a marked increase in the observed ESR.

Physiological variations: for reasons unknown the sedimentation reaction is more constant in men than in women (menstruation has only a small, clinically insignificant effect on this difference[9]). In pregnancy the ESR begins to increase at the 10th–12th week and returns to normal only by the 3rd–4th week after parturition[7,8]. The ESR increases with advancing age[11].

Pathological variations: often retarded in polycythemia, congestive heart failure, parenchymal liver disease, acute anaphylactic reactions, vagotonia; *usually increased* in all inflammations, in acute or active chronic infections (tuberculosis), in diseases accompanied by necrosis and tissue degradation, and after ultra-violet irradiation, X-rays or stimulation therapy.

Guiding principles[12] ("wide-tube" Westergren method)

1. In principle no more information can be expected from the ESR than this *simple, nonspecific, routine test* is capable of offering. Even when the ESR is normal a thorough examination of the patient should be made. In contrast to other blood tests which can be rapidly carried out, measurement of the ESR usually involves a *delay of 20–30 hours.*
2. In the great majority of cases an *increase in the ESR* is due to a *displacement in the blood proteins*; only rarely is it due to cellular changes (number, form, surface area, etc. of erythrocytes). Marked increases in γ-globulins may also be observed in decompensation without an increase in the ESR.
3. The ESR shows hardly any variation during the course of the day so that any *major changes* are of significance; the usual *1- and 2-hour values* generally suffice, the normal values varying somewhat according to the method. In view of the differences between individuals it is important to know exactly the patient's minimum values. Greatly increased 2-hour values with normal 1-hour values are rare and are typical of liver disease. *Upper limits of ESR* in a tube 5 mm dia. and 100 mm long ("wide-tube" method): *men:* 2–6 mm in 1st hour, 5–18 mm in 2nd hour; *women:* 3–7 mm in 1st hour, 6–20 mm in 2nd hour. The so-called micro-methods generally give unreliable results.
4. A marked increase in the ESR indicates a *pathological process* under any circumstances, but not necessarily a disease (it may persist during convalescence, for example). Where no obvious cause can be found, the examination must be taken a stage further. In the case of large increases, such as 1-hour values of 60 mm or more, the 2-hour values are very little higher.
5. An *exceptionally large initial increase in ESR*, where a maximum value of 70 mm or more is reached in 15–20 minutes, points strongly to a *plasmacytoma* or to macroglobulinemia.
6. A *normal ESR* never excludes the possibility of disease, even a severe progressive one such as *tuberculosis* or *cancer*; in particular the increase in ESR may be delayed for a considerable time by decompensation. *Exceptionally low* ESR values (1–3 mm in the 1st and 2nd hours) are often observed in *dystonia of the involuntary muscles.*
7. Absence of an increase in ESR should be interpreted as confirmation of an otherwise negative clinical picture, and the ESR value deserves to be more widely used in routine medical examinations.
8. A single measurement of ESR can be misleading in several ways: *too little citrate accelerates*, too much retards. *High temperatures* usually have an accelerating effect. In case of doubt it may be advisable to repeat the test at short intervals.
9. The full significance of an ESR measured at the *climax of a disease* is only apparent in comparison with later measurements; in an acute disease there is little point in making an ESR measurement if it can only be evaluated by waiting until the ESR has in any case returned to normal (note the analogy with measurement of temperature in fever).
10. An "ESR neurosis" should not be created in the patient by over-emphasis of the importance of the test or its too frequent repetition.
11. The ESR is often less affected by the basic disease than by the *secondary complications, such as pneumonia, pleurisy, thrombophlebitis, arthritic components, intercurrent infections*, etc. Generally speaking, the ESR is not directly influenced by drugs, including anticoagulants.
12. Since the ESR yields diagnostic indications it is valuable both in prognosis and therapy, and it is one of the most useful aids in triage.
13. The *secondary results* of an ESR measurement, such as the appearance of the plasma in the sedimentation tube, presence of pathological cell aggregations (e.g. in leukemia), may yield valuable supplementary indications; thus the plasma is *golden-yellow* in hemolysis, *unusually clear* in iron-deficiency anemia, *straw-colored* in pernicious anemia, *cloudy* in nephrosis and diabetes owing to increase in lipids and pathological proteins, and after ingestion of fats.

		Methods and sources	Remarks
Surface tension			
16–18°C (serum)	57–58 dyn cm^{-1}	Cf. Loiseleur, J., *Techniques de laboratoire*, Paris, 1947, page 52.	
37°C (serum)	47 dyn cm^{-1}		
Refractive index			
(fasting)	1.348 46–1.351 32 (adults)	Using the Abbé refractometer. Values from Wuhrmann and Wunderly, *Die Bluteiweisskörper des Menschen*, 2nd ed., Basle, 1952, page 61.	
(serum at 20°C)	1.345 75–1.347 98 (newborn)		

1) Gilligan and Ernstene, *Amer. J. med. Sci.*, **187**, 552 (1934). *2)* Lucia et al., *Amer. J. med. Sci.*, **192**, 179 (1936). *3)* Gordon and Wardley, *Biochem. J.*, **37**, 393 (1943). *4)* Bendien and Snapper, *Biochem. Z.*, **235**, 14 (1931). *5)* Ham and Curtis, *Medicine (Baltimore)*, **17**, 447 (1938). *6)* Thygesen, J. E., *Acta med. scand.*, Suppl. 134 (1942). *7)* Katz and Leffkowitz, *Ergebn. inn. Med. Kinderheilk.*, **33**, 266 (1928). *8)* Wintrobe, M. M., *Int. Clin.*, **2**, 34 (1936). *9)* Wintrobe, M. M., *Clinical Hematology*, Philadelphia, 1952, page 292. *10)* Hirschboeck, J. S., *Blood*, **2**, 578 (1947). *11)* Olbrich, O., *Edinb. med. J.*, **55**, 100 (1948). *12)* Wuhrmann and Wunderly, *Die Bluteiweisskörper des Menschen*, 3rd ed., Basle, 1957, page 190. *13)* Malmros and Blix, *Acta med. scand.*, Suppl. 170, 280 (1946).

Normal values (for definition of the normal range see footnote, page 517)

Nomogram for the calculation of total serum cations from specific conductivity and total protein content of serum

From Lufkin and Sunderman, *Techn. Bull. Registry med. Technologists*, **7**, 118 (1946), supplement to *Amer. J. clin. Path.*, **16** (1946)

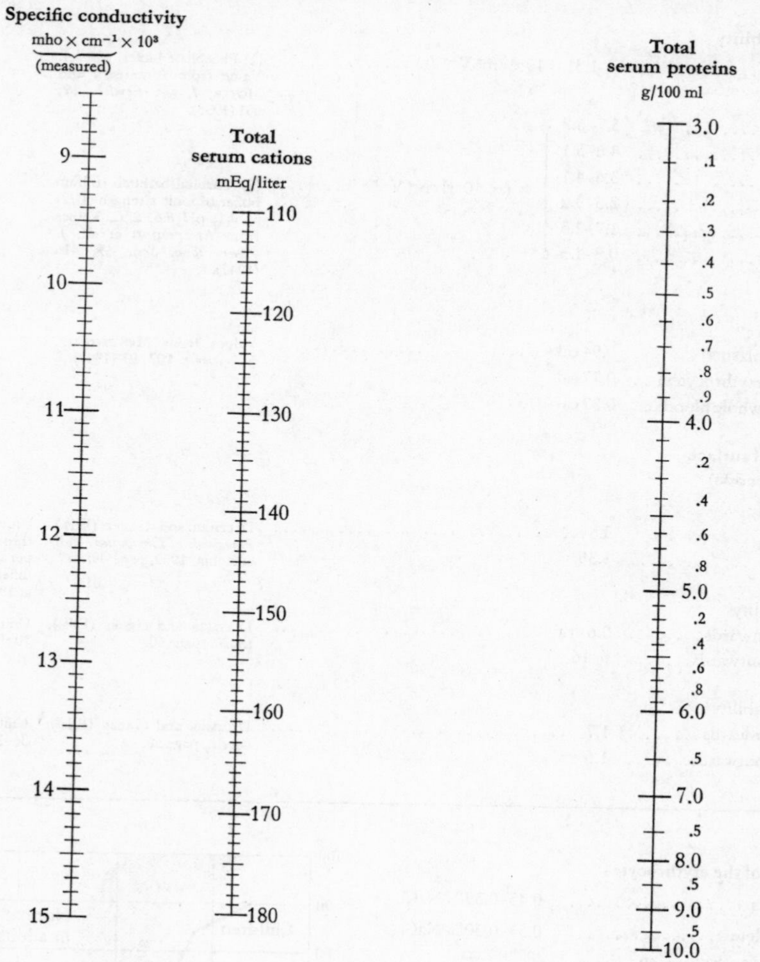

		Methods and sources	Remarks
Specific conductivity (serum) (at 25° C)	0.011 73–0.012 29 mho × cm⁻¹ mean 0.011 90 mho × cm⁻¹	Values from Sunderman, F. W., *Amer. J. clin. Path.*, **15**, 219 (1945).	The specific conductivity and the total protein content of the serum enable the total serum bases to be readily calculated (see the nomogram above).

Hydrogen-ion concentration (pH)

	Arteries (plasma)	Veins (plasma)	Capillaries (plasma)	Methods and sources	Remarks
Children (boys and girls)					
Birth to 10 days	–	*7.30–7.46* mean **7.38**	*7.31–7.53* mean **7.42**	Values from Singer and Hastings, *Acid-Base Data for Human Blood: Normal Standards and Some Physiological Variations*, Washington, 1950, quoted by Albritton, E. C. (Ed.), *Standard Values in Blood*, Philadelphia, 1952, page 124.	See pages 571 and 572.
1 month to 2 years	–	mean 7.38	–		
6–15 years	*7.33–7.47* mean **7.40**	*7.32–7.44* mean **7.38**	–		
Men 16–50 years	*7.33–7.45* mean **7.39**	*7.27–7.43* mean **7.35**	*7.33–7.45* mean **7.39**	Methods of determination: Graig et al., *Fed. Proc.*, **10**, 301 (1951); by indicator or electrometric methods, or calculated from the ratio of carbonate to bicarbonate ions (see pages 571 and 572). For equipment for serial pH determinations on arterial blood see Holaday, D. A., *J. Lab. clin. Med.*, **44**, 149 (1954).	
Women 16-50 years	–	*7.31–7.43* mean **7.37**	*7.35–7.47* mean **7.41**		
Men over 50	*7.32–7.52* mean **7.42**	–	*7.32–7.46* mean **7.39**		
Women over 50	*7.34–7.50* mean **7.42**	–	–		

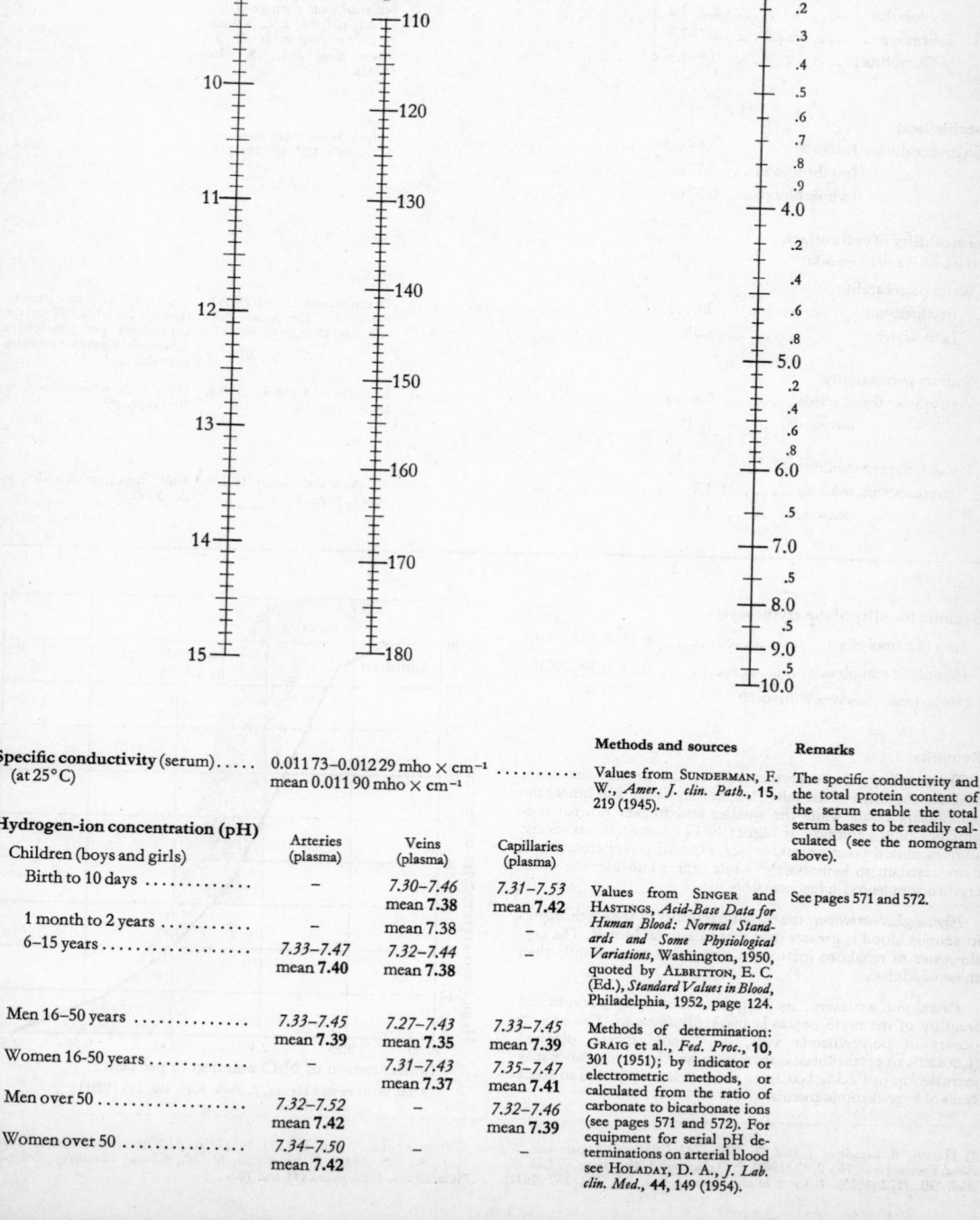

Normal values (for definition of the normal range see footnote, page 517)

	Value	Methods and sources	Remarks
Electric charge (per erythrocyte)			
in electrostatic units	0.007 34 esu	Value from ABRAMSON and MOYER, *J. gen. Physiol.*, **19**, 601 (1936).	Calculated from the electrophoretic mobility on the basis of an erythrocyte surface area of 163 μm² per cell.
Electrophoretic mobility			
(1) Erythrocytes	− 1.31 × 10⁻⁴ cm² V⁻¹ s⁻¹	(1) Phosphate buffer, pH 7.4. Value from ABRAMSON and MOYER, *J. gen. Physiol.*, **19**, 601 (1936).	
(2) Plasma proteins			
Albumins	5.7–6.2 × (− 10⁻⁵) cm² V⁻¹ s⁻¹	(2) Barbital/barbital sodium buffer of ionic strength (Γ/2) = 0.1, pH 8.6, 2° C. Values from ARMSTRONG et al., *J. Amer. chem. Soc.*, **69**, 416 (1947).	
α_1-Globulins	4.6–5.1 × (− 10⁻⁵) cm² V⁻¹ s⁻¹		
α_2-Globulins	3.6–4.1 × (− 10⁻⁵) cm² V⁻¹ s⁻¹		
β-Globulins	2.5–3.2 × (− 10⁻⁵) cm² V⁻¹ s⁻¹		
Fibrinogen	1.7–2.3 × (− 10⁻⁵) cm² V⁻¹ s⁻¹		
γ-Globulins	0.8–1.3 × (− 10⁻⁵) cm² V⁻¹ s⁻¹		
Specific heat			
in gram calories (plasma)	0.94 cal	Values from MENDLOWITZ, M., *Science*, **107**, 97 (1948).	
(erythrocytes)	0.77 cal		
(whole blood)	0.87 cal		
Permeability of cell surface (for units see under remarks)			
Water permeability			
Erythrocytes	3.6	DITTMER and GREBE (Eds.), *Handbook of Circulation*, Philadelphia, 1959, page 49.	Unit: μm³ of water passing through 1 μm² of cell surface per minute per atmosphere difference in osmotic pressure at 18–22° C.
Leukocytes	1.35		
Sodium permeability			
Erythrocytes, inwards	0.6–1.6	DITTMER and GREBE (Eds.), *loc. cit.*, page 50.	Unit: (ionic velocity) cm/h × 10⁻⁶ at 36–38° C.
outwards	6–16		
Potassium permeability			
Erythrocytes, inwards	1.7	DITTMER and GREBE (Eds.), *loc. cit.*, page 50.	Unit: mmol/cm²/h × 10⁻⁷ at 36–38° C.
outwards	1.6		

Osmotic fragility of the erythrocytes

Start of hemolysis	0.45–0.39 % NaCl
Hemolysis complete	0.33–0.30 % NaCl

(Method and values after WINTROBE[7])

Remarks

The fragility of the erythrocytes is the greater the more globular the shape of the cells[1,2]. Spherocytes are thus nearer the hemolyzing point while the smaller and thicker normal corpuscules only hemolyze at higher NaCl concentrations. Some authors regard young erythrocytes, especially reticulocytes, as more resistant to hemolysis[2,3] while others consider the older erythrocytes as more resistant[4,5].

Physiological variations: the osmotic fragility of the erythrocytes in venous blood is greater than that in arterial blood[6]. The erythrocytes of newborn infants are somewhat more fragile than those of adults[7].

Pathological variations: in congenital hemolytic jaundice the fragility of the erythrocytes is markedly *increased.* The *opposite* occurs in polycythemia vera, in "Mediterranean disease" (COOLEY's or erythroblastic anemia, in which the resistance may increase up to 0.03 % NaCl), in sickle-cell anemia and in some cases of hypochromic anemia.

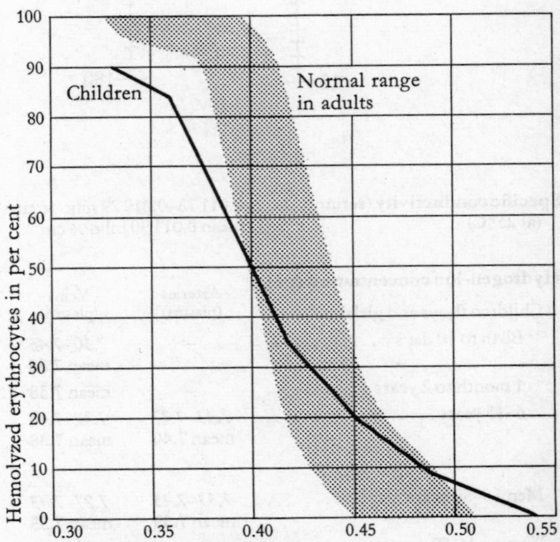

(After WHITBY and HYNES, *J. Path. Bact.*, **40**, 219 [1935].)

1) HADEN, R. L., *Amer. J. med. Sci.*, **188**, 441 (1934). *2)* DAMESHEK, W., *Blood*, Special Issue, No. 2, 43 (1948). *3)* DALAND and WORTHLEY, *J. Lab. clin. Med.*, **20**, 1122 (1935). *4)* CRUZ et al., *Amer. J. med. Sci.*, **202**, 157 (1941). *5)* STEWART et al., *J. exp. Med.*, **91**, 147 (1950). *6)* WHITBY and HYNES, *J. Path. Bact.*, **40**, 219 (1935). *7)* WINTROBE, M. M., *Clinical Hematology*, 3rd ed., Philadelphia, 1952, pages 161 and 162.

Synopsis of Blood – Plasma Proteins

Normal values (for definition of the normal range see footnote, page 517)

Plasma protein concentrations in adults

Fraction	Electrophoretic method (Tiselius[1]): % plasma (g/100 g plasma) mean*	% total proteins (g/100 g total proteins of plasma) mean**	g/100 ml plasma: Mean	Range	*s*	References	Salt fractionation method (Howe[2]) with sodium sulfate followed by Kjeldahl determination[6,13]: % plasma (g/100 g plasma) mean*	% total proteins (g/100 g total proteins of plasma) mean**	g/100 ml plasma: Mean	Range	*s*	References
Total proteins	6.55	100	**6.72**	*6.02 –7.42*	0.35	Calculated from 4a–f	7.02	100	**7.2**	*6.5 –7.9*	0.35	*3*
Albumins	3.94	60	**4.04**†	*3.50 –4.58*	0.27	4a	5.07	72.2	**5.2**	*4.7 –5.7*	0.25	*3*
Globulins	2.28	35	**2.34**	*1.90 –2.78*	0.22	Calculated from 4b–e	1.95	27.8	**2.0**	*1.46–2.54*	0.27	*3*
α-Globulins	0.77	11.8	**0.79**	*0.596–0.984*	0.097	Calculated from 4b–c	–	–	–	–	–	
α_1-Globulins	0.30	4.6	**0.31**	*0.208–0.412*	0.051	4b	–	–	–	–	–	
α_2-Globulins	0.47	7.1	**0.48**	*0.314–0.646*	0.083	4c	–	–	–	–	–	
β-Globulins	0.79	12.1	**0.81**	*0.558–1.062*	0.126	4d	–	–	–	–	–	
γ-Globulins	0.72	11.0	**0.74**†	*0.438–1.042*	0.151	4e	–	–	–	–	–	
Euglobulins	–	–	–	–	–		0.195	2.8	**0.2**	*0 –0.42*	0.11	*3*
Pseudoglobulin I	–	–	–	–	–		1.27	18.1	**1.3**	*0.84–1.76*	0.23	*3*
Pseudoglobulin II	–	–	–	–	–		0.487	6.9	**0.5**	*0.18–0.82*	0.16	*3*
							Determined gravimetrically					
Fibrinogen	0.33	5.1	**0.34**	*0.222–0.458*	0.059	4f	0.26	–	**0.27**	*0.17–0.37*	0.051	*5*
Ratio albumins: globulins	mean *** 1.73						mean *** 2.6					

Exchangeable albumin pool[14]: total 259 ± 40 g; per square meter body surface 232 ± 34 g

* Calculated from mean values in g/100 ml plasma assuming normal specific gravity of plasma (1.026).

** Calculated from mean values in g/100 ml plasma assuming that a normal total protein content of 6.72 g/100 ml plasma = 100%.

*** Calculated from the mean values given in g/100 ml plasma.

† In agreement with Lever et al., *J. clin. Invest.*, **30**, 99 (1951).

The standard deviations of the values from references 4a–f, 4b–e, 4b–c have been calculated from the formula $\sigma = \sqrt{\sigma_1^2 + \sigma_2^2 + \cdots}$

Plasma and serum protein concentrations in children

Total proteins (in g/100 ml)

	Age	Kjeldahl[6,13]: Mean	Range	References	Refractometric[7]: Mean	Range	References
Plasma	Premature births						
	3–5 days	4.62	3.62–5.36	*12*			
	8–18 days	4.42	3.80–5.02	*12*			
	At birth	5.89	5.46–6.31	*8*			
Serum	Umbilical blood	6.4	5.3 –7.7	*9*	6.04	5.15–7.43	*10*
	At birth	5.52	4.36–6.68	*11*			
	1–2 days	–	–	–	6.03	5.10–7.02	*10*
	3–4 days	–	–	–	5.89	5.15–6.67	*10*
	5–6 days	–	–	–	6.02	5.10–7.01	*10*
	7–8 days	–	–	–	5.93	5.10–6.60	*10*
	5–6 months	6.29	5.63–6.95	*11*			

Protein fractions (in g/100 ml)

Fraction	Age	Salt fractionation method (Howe[2]) with sodium sulfate followed by Kjeldahl[6,13]: Mean	Range	*s*	References
Serum					
Total proteins	At birth	**5.52**	*4.36–6.68*	0.58	*11*
Albumins	At birth	**3.73**	*3.11–4.35*	0.31	*11*
Globulins	At birth	**1.78**	*0.88–2.68*	0.45	*11*
Ratio albumins: globulins	At birth	**2.16**	*1.42–2.90*	0.37	*11*
Total proteins	5–6 months	**6.29**	*5.63–6.95*	0.33	*11*
Albumins	5–6 months	**4.28**	*3.52–5.04*	0.38	*11*
Globulins	5–6 months	**2.01**	*1.33–2.69*	0.34	*11*
Ratio albumins: globulins	5–6 months	**2.14**	*1.26–3.02*	0.44	*11*

Concentrations of sodium sulfate and sulfite required for precipitation of the various protein fractions

Fraction	Sodium sulfate[2]: mol/liter	g/100 ml	Sodium sulfite[18]: mol/liter	g/100 ml
Fibrinogen	0.76	10.6	0.906	11.4
Euglobulins	1.00	14.2	1.131	14.25
Pseudoglobulins I and II	1.25	17.7	1.355	17.1
Total globulins	1.50	21.5	1.58	19.95

The electrophoretic and sodium sulfate fractions are related as follows: In *normal* serum the electrophoretic picture is usually unchanged after precipitation of the euglobulins (13.5% sodium sulfate); precipitation of the euglobulins + pseudoglobulins (17.4% sodium sulfate) removes ca. 50% of the α-globulins and 25% of the β-globulins (no γ-globulins). 21.5% sodium sulfate removes all the γ-globulins, 75% of the β-globulins and 50% of the α-globulins.

1) Tiselius, A., *Trans. Faraday Soc.*, **33**, 524 (1937); *Svensk kem. Tidskr.*, **50**, 58 (1938); *Kolloid-Z.*, **85**, 129 (1938); *Harvey Lect.*, **35**, 37 (1939/40). *2)* Howe, P. E., *J. biol. Chem.*, **49**, 93 and 109 (1921). *3)* Gutman et al., *J. clin. Invest.*, **20**, 765 (1941) (36 healthy subjects). *4)* a–f: Dole, V. P., *J. clin. Invest.*, **23**, 708 (1944). *5)* Smith et al., *Fed. Proc.*, **10**, 370 (1951) (975 measurements). *6)* Hiller et al., *J. biol. Chem.*, **176**, 1401 (1948). *7)* See page 550. *8)* Pommerenke (1936), quoted by Sunderman and Boerner, *Normal Values in Clinical Medicine*, Philadelphia, 1950, page 104. *9)* Andersch and Oberst (1936), quoted by Sunderman and Boerner, *loc. cit.*, page 104. *10)* Denzer et al. (1939), quoted by Sunderman and Boerner, *loc. cit.*, page 105. *11)* Darrow and Cary, *J. Pediat.*, **3**, 573 (1933). *12)* Young et al. (1941), quoted by Sunderman and Boerner, *loc. cit.*, page 105. *13)* For micro-Kjeldahl methods see Pregl and Roth, *Die quantitative organische Mikroanalyse*, 4th ed., Berlin, 1935, page 105. *14)* Sterling, K., *J. clin. Invest.*, **30**, 1228 (1951).

Synopsis of Blood – Plasma Proteins (continued)

Normal values (for definition of the normal range see footnote, page 517)

Plasma protein fractions of COHN[1,2] (fractional precipitation method[3])

Electrophoretic fractions	COHN fraction	Approximate plasma content g/100 ml	Sedimentation constant	Molecular weight	Approximate molecular size in ångströms: Length	Diameter
Serum albumins	V	3.2	4.6	69,000	150	38
α_1-Globulins	IV-1	0.2	5.0	200,000	300	50
	IV-4	0.1	4-5	(70,000)	–	–
α_2-Globulins	IV-6	0.1	9.0	(300,000)	–	–
β_1-Globulins	IV-7	0.2	5.5	90,000	190	37
	III-0, III-2	0.2	7.0	(150,000)	–	–
	III-0	0.1	20.0	500,000–1,000,000	–	–
	III-0	0.2	–	1,300,000	185	185
β_2-Globulins	III-1	0.2	7.0	(150,000)	–	–
γ-Globulins	II	0.5	7.2	156,000	235	44
	II	0.1	10.0	(300,000)	–	–
Fibrinogen	I-2	0.2	9.0	400,000	700	38

1) COHN et al., *J. Amer. chem. Soc.*, **68**, 459 (1946); COHN, E. J., *Experientia (Basel)*, **3**, 125 (1947). *2)* COHN, E. J., Plasma Fractionation, in ANDRUS et al. (Eds.), *Advances in Military Medicine; the History of the Committee on Medical Research*, Boston, 1948. *3)* COHN et al., *J. Amer. chem. Soc.*, **72**, 465 (1950).

The rapid method of plasma fractionation of LEVER et al.[1], based on COHN's method (see above) for small quantities of blood yields the following 4 fractions in 3 stages (without destruction of the biological activity of the proteins in the fractions):

COHN fractions[2]	VI	IV+V	I+III	II
Percentage of total plasma proteins	0.2–3.3; mean 2.2	59.8–71.7; mean 65.6	15.8–32.0; mean 22	9.3–14.0; mean 10.8
Cholesterol content of the fraction as percentage of total cholesterol	not measurable	18.0–33.3; mean 26.6	54.8–83.1; mean 71.4	1.5–6.9; mean 4.0
Phospholipid content of the fraction as percentage of total phospholipids	not measurable	33.0–57.0; mean 46.7	51.0–56.6; mean 52.8	0.8–2.3; mean 1.5
Carbohydrates (hexoses) in mg/100 ml	0.52	11.5	17.6	0.64
Electrophoretic fractions as percentage of the fraction (mean values)	– – – – – – –	**Albumins 81.3** α_1-Globulins 7.8 α_2-Globulins 4.7 β_1-Globulins 5.5 β_2-Globulins 0.7 Fibrinogen 0 γ-Globulins 0	Albumins 0.5 α_1-Globulins 3.5 α_2-Globulins 13.3 **β_1-Globulins 49.4** **β_2-Globulins**, **Fibrinogen** } 26.5 γ-Globulins 6.8	Albumins 3.1 α_1-Globulins 0.1 α_2-Globulins 0 β_1-Globulins 0 β_2-Globulins 3.8 **γ-Globulins 93.0**
Other components or components contained in the above	Traces of fraction IV+V α_1-Glycoproteins α_2-Proteins Other small proteins and peptides Urea Glucose	β_1-Metal-combining protein α_2-Glycoproteins α_2-Mucoproteins α_1-Lipoproteins Iodoproteins Cholinesterase Alkaline phosphatase	β_1-Lipoproteins β_1-Lipid-poor euglobulins Ceruloplasmin Isoagglutinins Plasminogen Cold-insoluble proteins Prothrombin	Antibodies

1) LEVER et al., *J. clin. Invest.*, **30**, 99 (1951). *2)* COHN et al., *J. Amer. chem. Soc.*, **72**, 465 (1950).

Amino acid, nitrogen and sulfur contents of albumins, γ-globulins and fibrinogen[1]

	Albumins %	γ-Globulins %	Fibrinogen %
Glycine	1.6	4.2	5.6
Alanine	–	–	3.7
Valine	7.7	9.7	4.1
Leucine	11.0	9.3	7.10
Isoleucine	1.7	2.7	4.8
Proline	5.1	8.1	5.7
Phenylalanine	7.8	4.6	4.6
Cysteine	0.70	0.70	0.41
Cystine	5.58	2.37	2.23
Methionine	1.28	1.06	2.52
Tryptophan	0.19	2.86	3.29
Arginine	6.15	4.80	7.8
Histidine	3.5	2.50	2.6
Lysine	12.3	8.1	9.2

	Albumins %	γ-Globulins %	Fibrinogen %
Aspartic acid	10.4	8.8	13.1
Glutamic acid	17.4	11.8	14.5
Serine	3.7	11.4	7.0
Threonine	5.0	8.4	6.10
Tyrosine	4.66	6.75	5.5
Total N	15.95	16.03	16.90
Total S	1.96	1.02	1.26
Amido N	0.880	1.11	–
Indole N	0.013	0.20	–
Guanidine N	1 500	1.16	–
Iminazole N	0.641	0.45	–
Peptide N	11.555	12.22	–

1) After BRAND, E., *Ann. N. Y. Acad. Sci.*, **47**, 187 (1946), with additional data from BRAND and EDSALL, *Ann. Rev. Biochem.*, **16**, 223 (1947), and TRISTRAM, G. R., *Advanc. Protein Chem.*, **5**, 142 (1949).

Normal values (for definition of the normal range see footnote, page 517)

Properties and interactions of plasma protein components (according to COHN[1])

	Estimated percentage of plasma proteins	Sedimentation constant	Approx. isoelectric point	Specific chemical interaction with
Serum albumins...	52	4.6	4.9	Fatty acids, dyes, bile salts, drugs, mercury
(Mercaptalbumins)	(34)			
α_2-Glycoproteins..	1.2	9	4.9	Carbohydrates and barium
α_2-Mucoproteins..	0.5	9	4.9	(Carbohydrates and barium)
Fibrinogen	4	9	<5.3	Thrombin
α_1-Lipoproteins...	3	5	5.2	Steroids and carotenoids
β_1-Lipoproteins...	5	7	5.4	(Steroids and carotenoids)
β_1-Lipid-poor euglobulins.....	2 1	7 20	5.5	
β_1-Metal-combining protein	3	5.0	5.8	Iron and copper
β_2-Globulins......	3	7	6.3	
γ-Globulins	11	7 10	6.3 7.3	Antigens Antibodies
Complement components ...	0.4			Antigen-antibody complex
α_1-Small acid proteins........	0.5	2.9	3.0	
Cold-insoluble globulin	0.15		<5.3	

	Estimated percentage of plasma proteins	Sedimentation constant	Approx. isoelectric point	Specific chemical interaction with
Prothrombin	0.1			Calcium and thromboplastin
Plasminogen				Streptokinase
Hypertensinogen .				Renin
Iodoproteins				Thyroxine, iodine
Isoagglutinins	(0.03)		6.3	Incompatible erythrocytes
Properdin*	0.03	24–27		
Amylase				Starch
Cholinesterase	0.005		4.5	Choline esters
Alkaline phosphatase				Phosphate esters
Peptidase				L-Leucylglycylglycine
β-Glucuronidase ..				β-Glucuronides
Ceruloplasmin			4.4	Copper
α_1-Bilirubin globulin	0.05		4.7	Bilirubin
α_2-Proteins	0.1	2.9		Barium
β_1-Proteins	0.05	5		
Plasmin inhibitor..				Plasmin
Heparin complement				Heparin
Clotting Factor V..				Prothrombin

* Properdin is a recently discovered euglobulin which plays an important part in acquired or inherited resistance mechanisms. Its molecular weight is 8 times that of the γ-globulins. Its activity is dependent on the presence of Mg ions and complement substances (properdin system). For reviews see DELAUNAY et al., *Presse méd.*, **64**, 65 (1956), and ISLIKER, H. C., *Vox Sang. (Basel)*, **1**, 8 (1956).

1) COHN et al., *J. Amer. chem. Soc.*, **72**, 465 (1950), with additional data from RIVA, G., *Das Serumeiweissbild*, Berne, 1957, page 160.

Remarks on plasma proteins

Earlier clinical and experimental observations[1–4] indicated that the plasma proteins were in the main synthesized by the liver. Perfusion experiments with ^{14}C-lysine on the surviving liver have since confirmed this[5] (the whole of the albumins and fibrinogen, 80% of the globulins). The synthetic capacity of the liver suffices to replace daily ca. 9% of the liver proteins and ca. 25% of the circulating plasma proteins[5]. Direct measurement of the exchangeable albumin pool by albumin labeled with iodine-131, for example, gives an albumin turnover rate of $6.7 \pm 0.93\%$ per day (17.2 ± 2.7 g per day total or 15.4 ± 2 g per day per m^2 body surface)[6]. This exclusive synthesis of the albumins (and of the fibrinogen) by the liver, together with the partial extrahepatic synthesis of the globulins, provides an explanation of the inverted albumin/globulin ratio occurring in advanced cirrhosis of the liver with symptoms of portal obstruction[5].

The plasma protein fractions (albumins, globulins, fibrinogen) bear a close relationship to one another, expressed by the formula[7]:

$$K = A^{0.62} \times G^{0.328} \times F^{0.052}$$

$$\text{or } \log K = 0.62 \log A + 0.328 \log G + 0.052 \log F$$

where A, G and F are respectively the albumin, globulin and fibrinogen contents and K is a constant. 80 TISELIUS electrophoresis diagrams on healthy subjects aged 20–45 have given the value $K = 0.442$ ($\pm$ 0.002 range of physiological variation)[7]. In the age groups 0–45 and 70–95 the corresponding values for K are 0.441 ($\pm$ 0.005) and 0.435 respectively. The value of 0.442 (+) for the age group 20–45 represents a maximum. A change in the content of any fraction results in a lowering of this maximum[7], a fact which justifies the assumption of a central regulation of the plasma protein picture in which the controlling variable is possibly the colloid-osmotic pressure[8]. The albumins can be regarded as the principal agent in this regulation. In disease there can be a decrease in their concentration but never an increase[9].

Total protein content

Strictly speaking, the total protein content can only be judged in relation to the total plasma volume. In relation to the hematocrit value it may be misleading since an increase in the blood plasma concentration can be simulated by a thickening or thinning of the blood, or conversely an abnormal protein content can be masked by such changes. In practice it is sufficient to determine the hemoglobin content and make an erythrocyte count[9]. In health the total protein concentration is rather variable, so that only changes of considerable magnitude have any clinical significance. *The total protein content* is increased through salt loss in cholera and other diseases accompanied by severe diarrhea, after severe vomiting (albumins and globulins increased in proportion), in many infectious diseases (for example, kala-azar), and in plasmacytoma (increase mainly in globulins).

The total protein content is diminished in kidney diseases, particularly nephrosis, in undernourishment (nutritional edema), in some cases of diabetes (in all these cases it is principally the albumin content which is lowered), in wasting diseases such as cancer and tuberculosis. A sudden fall in plasma proteins, particularly the albumins, follows operations (irrespective of the type of operation and subsequent nursing). This is soon followed by an increase in the globulins up to and beyond the preoperative level[10] (cf. also under Blood chlorides, page 567).

1) MADDEN and WHIPPLE, *Physiol. Rev.*, **20**, 194 (1940). 2) WHIPPLE and MADDEN, *Medicine (Baltimore)*, **23**, 215 (1944). 3) JANSSEN, L. W., *Verh. Akad. Wet. Amst., Afd. Natuurk.*, Sect. 2, Deel **47**, No. 3 (1951). 4) WHIPPLE, G. H., *Amer. J. Physiol.*, **33**, 50 (1941). 5) MILLER et al., *J. exp. Med.*, **94**, 431 (1951). 6) STERLING, K., *J. clin. Invest.*, **30**, 1228 (1951). 7) ECKER and FRACKELTON, *Fed. Proc.*, **10**, 353 (1951). 8) WUNDERLY and WUHRMANN, *Gastroenterologia (Basel)*, **69**, 121 (1944). 9) WUHRMANN and WUNDERLY, *Die Bluteiweisskörper des Menschen*, 3rd ed., Basle, 1957. 10) WILKINSON et al., *Lancet*, **1**, 315 (1951).

Total protein content *(continued)*

Guiding principles in clinical applications[1]

1. The readily determined total protein content of serum or plasma is generally of little clinical importance in acute diseases or those of short duration.

2. Only variations *of considerable magnitude* have any clinical value, and it may be assumed that the more marked the hyper- or hypo-proteinemia is, the more pronounced will be the changes within the fractions.

3. Of major clinical importance is the *overall diminution of proteins* in blood in chronic disease, above all in wasting diseases such as cancer and tuberculosis, as also in many chronic liver diseases, particularly cirrhosis of the liver and chronic inanition.

4. The lowest blood protein levels occur in the nephrotic syndrome.

5. The highest blood protein levels, occasionally up to double the normal value, occur mainly in cases of plasmacytoma.

6. The total protein value itself is largely *independent of changes in the ESR, the various turbidity and flocculation reactions, the coagulation threshold and electrophoretic patterns.*

7. The electrolyte balance, particularly the serum calcium and potassium levels, should be kept under observation when there are marked changes in the total protein content.

8. Sufficient indication of thickening or thinning of the patient's blood is provided in practice by regular determination of the hemoglobin content, erythrocyte number and water balance, and the hematocrit determination can be dispensed with.

Plasma protein fractions

(See also the remarks on the previous page)

Many methods are now available for fractionating plasma proteins[2]. Broadly they comprise the following:

1. Electrophoretic methods (TISELIUS method, one- or two-dimensional paper electrophoresis, column electrophoresis).

2. Physicochemical precipitation methods (addition of ammonium sulfate, of sodium sulfate [HOWE method], or of ether, COHN methods).

3. Ultracentrifuging (and "flotation") and ultrafiltration.

4. Immunobiological methods (for example, OUCHTERLONY plates).

Of these methods the commonest are electrophoresis, COHN's method No. 10, ultracentrifuging, and sodium sulfate precipitation. The first and the last of these are suitable clinical methods, the other two are relatively complicated and usually confined to research laboratories.

The following fractions can be separated by the usual electrophoretic methods: albumins, globulins (α_1, α_2, β and γ) and fibrinogen. Intensive studies have extended fractionation much further than this, and 17 fractions have been described in healthy plasma[13].

The HOWE method (precipitation with sodium sulfate at various concentrations) yields albumin and globulin fractions. Euglobulins and pseudoglobulins I and II can be differentiated in the latter fraction (fibrinogen is eliminated beforehand by coagulation).

The complicated method No. 10 of COHN yields various fractions denoted by numbers (IV–1, III–2, etc.) which have not yet been clearly related to the above electrophoretic or precipitation fractions. This method was developed for the assessment of large quantities of plasma (blood banks) and is little used clinically.

Ultracentrifuging separates the plasma proteins in accordance with their sedimentation or flotation constants.

Physiological changes in plasma proteins are exemplified by the increase in globulins and decrease in albumins observed during pregnancy (see page 605) and stress. *Pathological changes* in the proteins occur in a great many diseases of such diverse nature as inflammation, irreversible changes in organs, endocrinological disturbances and cancer[3,4]. The fact that the albumins, in contrast to the globulins, may decrease but never increase greatly detracts from the clinical significance of the albumin/globulin ratio. It is clear that a pathological change in the protein spectrum can occur in spite of a "normal" albumin/globulin ratio. The measurement of the ESR and the various flocculation and turbidity reactions are easily and rapidly carried out and provide more exact indications.

Chemical, physical and biological data on the plasma proteins and the amounts of the individual fractions are given on pages 553–555. A brief description of the three principal fractions follows.

1. **Albumins.** The total plasma volume (see page 548) and the colloid osmotic pressure of the plasma (see page 548) are primarily dependent on the albumins. Owing to their relatively small molecular size they possess a very large surface area, enabling them to act as carriers of a great variety of substances in the blood. In general, there is a decrease in the albumins in all pathological conditions.

2. **Globulins.** The more coarsely dispersed globulins are separated by electrophoresis into a large number of subfractions the functions of which vary extremely widely. The α- and β-lipoglobulins, carriers of ca. 75% of the plasma lipids[5], are increased in all diseases in which the blood lipid content is increased (see also remarks under Blood Lipids, page 562). The γ-globulins, carriers of antibodies, are increased in all infectious diseases and in other conditions in which immunization processes are set in motion. This is the reason for the almost *stereotyped increase of the globulin fraction in practically all diseases.*

It should be noted, however, that hyperproteinemia is by no means always accompanied by hyperglobulinemia[6] (cf. the increase during pregnancy, page 605). Cases of hereditary or acquired agammaglobulinemia are known[7].

3. **Fibrinogen.** The fibrinogen is best determined gravimetrically by precipitation as fibrin, since salt fractionation simultaneously precipitates other coarsely dispersed proteins, particularly in pathological conditions, with the result that these are determined as fibrin. Extensive studies[8] (975 tests on 333 individuals) have shown that the *fibrinogen content* is doubled or even quadrupled 3–7 days after the start of an acute bacterial lung infection, 4–5 days after operations, 5 days after the start of anticoagulant therapy using bishydroxycoumarin, in acute pancreatitis, in untreated cancer, and 3–4 days after radiological treatment. In *virus infections* the fibrinogen content begins to *fall* in the second week and remains below the normal level for up to 7 months. *Fibrinopenia* is usually observed in injury to the liver parenchyma (particularly in acute yellow atrophy of the liver), in hepatic disturbances following extensive burns, in leukemia, in liver obstruction and in cardiac failure[12]. Constitutional afibrinogenemia is rare[1], as is also constitutional fibrinopenia[9,10] and (acquired) fibrinasthenia[11,12] (functionally defective fibrinogen). On fibrinogen and sedimentation see page 550.

---

1) WUHRMANN and WUNDERLY, *Die Bluteiweisskörper des Menschen*, 3rd ed., Basle, 1957, page 185. *2)* For reviews see WUHRMANN and WUNDERLY, *loc. cit.*, and RIVA, G., *Das Serumeiweissbild*, Berne, 1957. *3)* WUHRMANN and WUNDERLY, *Gastroenterologia (Basel)*, **69**, 121 (1944). *4)* LEINWAND, I., *J. Lab. clin. Med.*, **37**, 532 (1951). *5)* ONCLEY et al., *J. Amer. chem. Soc.*, **72**, 458 (1950). *6)* FEINSTEIN and PETERSDORF, *Ann. intern. Med.*, **44**, 899 (1956). *7)* FAVOUR, C. B., *Stanf. med. Bull.*, **14**, 172 (1956). *8)* SMITH et al., *Fed. Proc.*, **10**, 370 (1951). *9)* RISAK, E., *Z. klin. Med.*, **128**, 605 (1935). *10)* GLANZMANN et al., *Schweiz. med. Wschr.*, **70**, 1243 and 1261 (1940). *11)* FANCONI, G., *Schweiz. med. Wschr.*, **71**, 255 (1941). *12)* FANCONI, G., *Schweiz. med. Wschr.*, **76**, 791 (1946). *13)* BERRY and CHANUTIN, *J. clin. Invest.*, **34**, 1513 (1955).

Normal values in **mg/100 ml**, unless otherwise stated

Nitrogen	Whole blood g/100 ml	Plasma or serum g/100 ml	Method	Remarks
Total N (chemically combined)	2.6–4.3	1.1–1.4	Kjeldahl	*Whole blood:* mean usually 3%. Protein N is 99% of total N (over 96% in *plasma* or *serum*). On increase and decrease of nitrogen see under Plasma Proteins, pages 555 and 556.
Total protein N ...... (For nitrogen as N_2 see Blood Gases, page 572)	2.5–4.3	1.0–1.4	Kjeldahl	

Nonprotein nitrogen[1]	Whole blood Range*	Whole blood Mean*	Cells Range*	Cells Mean*	Plasma or serum Range*	Plasma or serum Mean*
Total	28–39	32	38–55	44	22–29	25
Urea N	8.9–15.2	12	8–13	10	9.6–17.6	12
Non-urea N	16–26	20	25–45	33	6–18	12
Amino acid N	4.6–6.8	5.6	6.5–9.6	7.4	3.4–5.0	4.4
Creatine N	1.0–1.6	1.3	1.9–3.2	2.6	–	–
Creatinine N.........	0.4–0.6	0.5	–	–	0.4–0.5	0.4
Uric acid N..........	0.3–1.3	0.7	–	–	0.7–1.3	1.3
Glutathione N	4.4–4.8	4.6	9.5–10.5	10.0	–	–
Nucleotide N	4.4–7.4	5.8	10–16	13	–	–
Ergothioneine N	*0.3–6.3*	**3.3** *s* 1.5	*1–11.8*	**6.4** *s* 2.7	–	–
Ammonia N	0.1–0.3	–	–	–	0.1–0.2	–

Remarks

Serum: the nonprotein N is increased in renal insufficiency, also in extrarenal disturbances such as hypochloremia and ADDISON's disease.

Serum nonprotein N is made up of nitrogen of urea, free amino acids, creatine, creatinine, guanidinoacetic acid, purine derivatives, indican, phenols, bilirubin, urobilin, choline, histamine, glutathione, etc. (see under these substances below and on pages 558 and 559).

See also remarks under Urea, below.

1) SUNDERMAN and BOERNER, *Normal Values in Clinical Medicine*, Philadelphia, 1950, page 110.

Nonprotein N components	Whole blood Mean*	Whole blood Range*	Whole blood *s*	Plasma or serum Mean*	Plasma or serum Range*	Plasma or serum *s*
Urea						
(1) Men	–	–	–	**27.1**	*18.1–36.1*	4.5
(2) Women	–	–	–	**26.4**	*10.2–42.6*	8.1
(3) Men and women as one group	25.6	19–32.5	–	**26.8**	*14.2–39.4*	6.3
Urea level in relation to protein intake (young males)						
(4) 0.5 g prot. per kg body weight per day	–	–	–	**19.3**	*13.5–25.1*	2.9
(4) 1.5 g prot. per kg body weight per day	–	–	–	**38.6**	*24.4–52.8*	7.1
(4) 2.5 g prot. per kg body weight per day	–	–	–	**45.5**	*31.1–59.9*	7.2
Free amino acids (total) (nonprotein amino acids)	50	38–53	–	–	–	–
Alanine	**4.0**	*2.76–5.24*	0.62	**3.97**	*2.57–5.37*	0.7
Arginine	**0.99**	*0.43–1.55*	0.28	**2.34**	*1.10–3.58*	0.62
Aspartic acid	–	–	–	0.58	–	–
Citrulline	–	–	–	0.5	0.38–0.59	–
Cystine	**0.94**	*0.62–1.26*	0.16	**1.47**	*0.89–2.05*	0.29
Glutamine	–	–	–	**5.78**	*2.68–8.88*	1.55
Glutamic acid.......	–	–	–	**3.41**	*0.63–6.19*	1.39
Glycine	**2.02**	*1.74–2.30*	0.14	**1.77**	*1.25–2.29*	0.26
Histidine...........	**1.24**	*1.04–1.44*	0.20	**1.42**	*1.06–1.78*	0.18
Isoleucine	**1.10**	*0.76–1.44*	0.17	**1.60**	*0.98–2.22*	0.31
Leucine	**1.70**	*1.38–2.02*	0.16	**1.91**	*1.23–2.59*	0.34
Lysine	**1.80**	*1.28–2.32*	0.26	**2.95**	*2.11–3.79*	0.42
Methionine.........	**0.52**	*0.32–0.72*	0.10	0.85	0.46–1.48	–
Phenylalanine.......	**0.99**	*0.75–1.23*	0.12	**1.38**	*0.74–2.02*	0.32
Proline	–	–	–	2.36	–	–
Threonine..........	**1.63**	*1.23–2.03*	0.20	**2.02**	*1.12–2.92*	0.45
Tryptophan	**0.79**	*0.53–1.05*	0.13	**1.08**	*0.66–1.50*	0.21
Tyrosine	**1.05**	*0.71–1.39*	0.17	**1.48**	*0.74–2.22*	0.37
Valine	**2.36**	*1.84–2.88*	0.26	**2.83**	*2.15–3.51*	0.34

Methods and sources

Urea: Urease: GENTZKOW, C. J., *J. biol. Chem.*, **143**, 531 (1942); OWINGS and MANDEL, *Proc. Soc. exp. Biol. (N. Y.)*, **78**, 363 (1951). Another (simple) method: KIBRIK and SKUPP, *Proc. Soc. exp. Biol. (N. Y.)*, **73**, 432 (1950). Values (1), (2): KREBS, H. A., *Ann. Rev. Biochem.*, **19**, 409 (1950); (3) *plasma:* calculated from (1) and (2). *Whole blood:* SUNDERMAN and BOERNER, *Normal Values in Clinical Medicine*, Philadelphia, 1950, page 110. (4) ADDIS et al., *J. clin. Invest.*, **26**, 869 (1947).

Free amino acids: Microbiological method: SELIGSON et al., *J. Lab. clin. Med.*, **35**, 640 (1950). Values: *whole blood:* GUTMAN and ALEXANDER, *J. biol. Chem.*, **168**, 527 (1947); JOHNSON and BERGEIM, *J. biol. Chem.*, **188**, 833 (1951); *plasma:* summary in KREBS, H. A., *Ann. Rev. Biochem.*, **19**, 409 (1950); JOHNSON and BERGEIM, *J. biol. Chem.*, **188**, 833 (1951); STEIN and MOORE, *J. biol. Chem.*, **211**, 915 (1954); HIER and BERGEIM, *J. biol. Chem.*, **163** 129 (1946).

Remarks

Serum: urea constitutes the main component of the nonprotein N (ca. 50%). At the start of *renal insufficiency* the urea (and uric acid) increases not only absolutely but also relatively to the nonprotein N increase and usually then amounts to more than 50% of the total. If the insufficiency becomes severe the percentage of urea in the nonprotein N falls while that of the amino acids and creatinine, derived from increased and modified protein breakdown, increases. In acute nephritis only the urea and uric acid levels rise.

See also under Urea and Nonprotein N. – Apart from the amino acids listed, serine and hydroxyproline are thought to be present since their existence in animal sera has been demonstrated.

Nonprotein N and ACTH (or cortisol or cortisone) therapy. As a result of the antianabolic action of ACTH, cortisol and cortisone, the blood level of all nonprotein N components is as a rule slightly increased during treatment with these hormones. This applies particularly to the free amino acids. Cf. BERGENSTAL et al., in MOTE, J. R. (Ed.), *Proceedings of the Second Clinical ACTH Conference*, vol. I, New York, 1951, page 250.

* When a range given is a *normal range* (see page 154), i.e. calculated from the formula: mean ± (2 × standard deviation *s*), it is printed in *italics*, with the mean in **bold** figures. Otherwise the data given are experimental results which have not been tested statistically.

Normal values in mg/100 ml, unless otherwise stated

	Whole blood			Plasma or serum			Methods and sources	Remarks
	Mean*	Range*	*s*	Mean*	Range*	*s*		
Creatine								
(1) Men and women as one group	4.0	3.0–5.0	–	0.49	0.32–0.72	–	Values: (1) *whole blood:* SUNDERMAN and BOERNER, *Normal Values in Clinical Medicine*, Philadelphia, 1950, page 110; *serum:* ALLINSON, M. J. C., *J. biol. Chem.*, **157**, 169 (1945); (2) TIERNEY and PETERS, *J. clin. Invest.*, **22**, 595 (1943); for details of the method see PETERS, J. H., *J. biol. Chem.*, **146**, 179 (1942).	See also remarks under Nonprotein N, page 557. – ALLINSON's method depends on the use of a creatine-destroying enzyme, TIERNEY and PETERS' is photo-electric.
(2) Men	–	–	–	–	0.17–0.50	–		
(2) Women	–	–	–	–	0.35–0.93	–		
Creatinine								
(1) Men and women as one group	1.3	1.2–1.5	–	0.89	0.62–1.02	–	Values: (1) *whole blood:* SUNDERMAN and BOERNER, *Normal Values in Clinical Medicine*, Philadelphia, 1950, page 110; *serum:* ALLINSON, M. J. C., *J. biol. Chem.*, **157**, 169 (1945). (2) Range from CAMARA et al., *J. Lab. clin. Med.*, **37**, 743 (1951); mean from ADDIS et al., *J. clin. Invest.*, **30**, 206, 1951. On methods see TAUSSKY, H. H., in SELIGSON, D. (Ed.), *Standard Methods of Clinical Chemistry*, vol. III, New York and London, 1961, page 99; OWEN et al., *Biochem. J.*, **58**, 426 (1954).	See also remarks under Nonprotein N and Urea, page 557. – The creatinine level in blood is relatively constant and does not vary with the nutrient protein intake except when the latter is in large amounts in the form of meat.
(2) Men	–	–	–	1.03	0.95–1.29	–		
(2) Women	–	–	–	0.79	0.77–0.98	–		
Ammonia (as N)	**0.0795**	*0.0741–0.0849*	0.00268	–	–	–	CALKINS, W. G., *J. Lab. clin. Med.*, **47**, 343 (1956).	Increased in liver disease.
Guanidinoacetic acid ..	–	–	–	0.26	0.24–0.28	–	Values from HOBERMAN, H. D., *J. biol. Chem.*, **167**, 721 (1947), and LEVEDAHL and SAMUELS, *ibid.*, **176**, 327 (1948).	
Methylguanidine	0.25	0.2–0.3	–	–	–	–	Values from PFIFFNER and MYERS, *J. biol. Chem.*, **87**, 345 (1930).	
Uric acid	2.0	1.0–3.0	–	–	–	–	Serum values from YÜ, T. F., quoted by GUTMAN, A. B., *Ann. intern. Med.*, **39**, 1062 (1953).	See remarks under Urea, page 557. – In gout the value increases up to 18 mg. For another method see BIDMEAD, D. S., *J. clin. Path.*, **4**, 370 (1951).
Men.............	–	–	–	**5.3**	*1.9–8.7*	1.7		
Women...........	–	–	–	**4.3**	*2.3–6.3*	1.0		
Allantoin	–	–	–	–	0.3–0.6	–	Values from ARCHIBALD, R. M., *J. biol. Chem.*, **156**, 121 (1944).	
Nucleotides and related compounds								
Nucleotides	41	31–52	–	–	–	–	JACKSON, H., *J. biol. Chem.*, **57**, 121 (1923).	
Pyridine nucleotides .. (as DPN)	**3.6**	*2.6–4.6*	0.5	0.07	0.02–0.12	–	LEVITAS et al., *J. biol. Chem.*, **167**, 169 (1947).	DPN = diphosphopyridine nucleotide, TPN = triphosphopyridine nucleotide (cf. page 369). The ratio DPN:TPN in erythrocytes has been estimated to be 8:1.
	(erythrocytes:)							
	7.7	*6.1–9.3*	0.8					
Ribonucleic acid (RNA)...........	–	–	–	4.9	3.9–5.9	–	MANDEL and MÉTAIS, *C. R. Soc. Biol. (Paris)*, **142**, 241 (1948).	
Desoxyribonucleic acid (DNA)	–	–	–	0.8	0–1.6	–	MANDEL and MÉTAIS, *C. R. Soc. Biol. (Paris)*, **142**, 241 (1948).	
Adenosine triphosphate (ATP)								
Men.............	46	38–54	–	–	–	–	BUELL, M. V., *J. biol. Chem.*, **108**, 273 (1935).	
Women...........	39	30–48	–	–	–	–		
Adenosine + adenylic acid (AMP)........ (as adenosine)	–	–	–	**1.09**	*0.32–1.86*	0.385	GREEN et al., *Clin. Sci.*, **8**, 65 (1949).	

* When a range given is a *normal range* (see page 154), i.e. calculated from the formula: mean ± (2 × standard deviation *s*), it is printed in *italics*, with the mean in **bold** figures. Otherwise the data given are experimental results which have not been tested statistically.

Normal values in **mg/100 ml**, unless otherwise stated

	Whole blood			Plasma or serum			Methods and sources	Remarks
	Mean*	Range*	*s*	Mean*	Range*	*s*		
Choline								
Total	–	–	–	–	26–35	–	LUECKE and PEARSON, *J. biol. Chem.*, **153**, 259 (1944). Plasma values from APPLETON et al., *Fed. Proc.*, **10**, 157 (1951).	In some individuals constant over long periods. In disease, values are normal, except in kidney diseases, when the value lies on or above the upper limit of the normal range. When the level in blood is normal no choline appears in the urine. Choline injected intravenously is eliminated inside one hour (APPLETON et al., *loc. cit.*).
Free	2.5	1.0–4.0	–	–	0.2–2	–		
Acetylcholine								
Healthy subjects	–	–	–	**0.00128**	*0–0.00368*	0.0012	Values from SCUDAMORE, H. H., *J. Lab. clin. Med.*, **37**, 860 (1951).	See also under Cholinesterase, page 564. – The ratio of acetylcholine to choline on the erythrocyte surface is 1:300 (MARQUARDT and HIRSCH, *Hoppe-Seylers Z. physiol. Chem.*, **289**, 131 [1952]).
Asthmatics	–	–	–	**0.00397**	*0.00109–0.00685*	0.00144		
Histamine	–	–	–	–	0.002–0.008	–	Values from CODE, C. F., *Physiol. Rev.*, **32**, 47 (1952), in agreement with ROSE, B., *Recent Progr. Hormone Res.*, **7**, 375 (1952).	Histamine is probably contained in the polymorphonuclear leukocytes, whence the greatly increased blood histamine content in leukemia (VALENTINE and LAWRENCE, *Amer. J. med. Sci.*, **216**, 619 [1948]), *but definitely not in the eosinophils* (HERBERT et al., *J. Allergy*, **21**, 12 [1950]). Cf. ROSE, B., *loc. cit.*
Glutathione	35.4	26.9–41.4	–	0	0	–	CAREN and CARNE, *Amer. J. med. Sci.*, **221**, 307 (1951).	See also under Glucose, page 560. – *Increased* in diabetes mellitus (unaffected by insulin); *lowered* both in healthy and diabetic subjects during ACTH, cortisol or cortisone therapy.
Ergothioneine	**9.6**	*8.96–10.24*	*0.32*	0	0		FRASER, R. S., *J. Lab. clin. Med.*, **37**, 199 (1951) (94 tests, average age 29½ years).	Significantly *lowered* only in hypothyroidism, *increased* in acute appendicitis, anemia, coronary sclerosis and circulatory diseases, nephrosis and nephritis, dermatitis, fractures, nontuberculous lung infections, acute infections of the nasopharynx, cholecystitis and cholelithiasis (cf. FRASER, R. S., *loc. cit.*).
Indican (3-indoxylsulfuric acid)	–	–	–	–	0.026–0.085	–	Values from TOWNSEND, S. R., *J. Lab. clin. Med.*, **23**, 809 (1938).	Increased in obstipation and renal insufficiency. In uremia the level of phenols always exceeds 2.0 mg/100 ml (GABERMAN et al., *J. Lab. clin. Med.*, **37**, 544 [1951]).
Phenols	–	2–8	–	–	1–2	–	STOUGHTON, R. W., *J. biol. Chem.*, **115**, 293 (1936).	
Bilirubin								
Direct-reacting bilirubin								
(1) Adults	–	–	–	0.10	0.05–0.24	–	VAN DEN BERGH diazo reaction, VAN DEN BERGH, A. A. H., *Der Gallenfarbstoff im Blut*, Leipzig, 1918. Values from (1) NOSSLIN, B., *Scand. J. clin. Lab. Invest.*, **12**, Suppl. 49 (1960), (2) OBRINSKY et al., *Amer. J. Dis. Child.*, **87**, 305 (1954).	The direct-reacting bilirubin is approximately identical with conjugated bilirubin. For a discussion of the role of the direct reaction in clinical diagnosis see WITH, T. K., *Biologie der Gallenfarbstoffe*, Stuttgart, 1960, and NOSSLIN, B., *Scand. J. clin. Lab. Invest.*, **12**, Suppl. 49 (1960). See also the remarks below and on page 560.
Total bilirubin								
(1) Adults	–	–	–	0.60	0.26–1.4	–		
(2) Full term infants								
1st day	–	–	–	**2.68**	*0–6.00*	1.66		
3rd day	–	–	–	**5.85**	*0.25–11.45*	2.80		
5th day	–	–	–	**6.08**	*0.12–12.04*	2.98		
7th day	–	–	–	**5.00**	*0.14–9.86*	2.43		

Bilirubin[1–6] (for references see page 560)

The bilirubin of the organism is mainly a product of the degradation of hemoglobin when the erythrocytes have reached senescence. Normally 10–30% of the bilirubin formed is derived from sources other than hemoglobin degradation. Under pathological conditions such as pernicious anemia and congenital porphyria this fraction may constitute an even greater proportion of the total bilirubin. The degradation of hemoglobin to bilirubin (see page 382) takes place in the reticuloendothelial system and the bilirubin is discharged into the plasma, where it becomes bound to plasma proteins, mainly albumin. The level of bilirubin in the plasma is determined by the relative rates at which bilirubin enters and leaves the circulation. The precise upper limit of normality is difficult to define but may be assumed to be 1.5 mg/100 ml in adults.

The bilirubin is taken up from the plasma proteins by the liver cells. There, conjugation of bilirubin – primarily with glucuronic acid but also with sulfate and perhaps other substances – converts the lipid-soluble unconjugated bilirubin into water-soluble conjugates. The conjugation with glucuronic acid yields bilirubin monoglucuronide (pigment I) and bilirubin diglucuronide (pigment II). The former is probably formed also in extrahepatic tissues and is not present in normal human plasma.

The direct VAN DEN BERGH reaction provides a reasonable

* When a range given is a *normal range* (see page 154), i.e. calculated from the formula: mean ± (2 × standard deviation *s*), it is printed in *italics*, with the mean in **bold** figures. Otherwise the data given are experimental results which have not been tested statistically.

Normal values in **mg/100 ml**, unless otherwise stated

Bilirubin[1–6] *(continued)*

approximation of the total amount of conjugated bilirubin ("direct bilirubin"). The nonconjugated bilirubin ("indirect bilirubin") is given by the difference between total bilirubin and conjugated bilirubin. The conjugated bilirubin is excreted from the liver mainly in the bile. At normal serum levels the urine contains only traces of conjugated bilirubin and no unconjugated bilirubin.

In the colon, bilirubin undergoes a series of reductive reactions by bacterial action which result in the formation of a group of compounds known collectively as "urobilinogens". Some of the urobilinogen formed in the colon is reabsorbed and returned to the liver. This urobilinogen is ultimately re-excreted in the bile but a small amount may be excreted in the urine.

Bilirubin metabolism and jaundice

When bilirubin enters the circulation more rapidly than it is removed, it accumulates in the plasma and tissues, ultimately staining the latter by combining with tissue protein to produce jaundice. Three basic mechanisms are involved in the production of jaundice: (*a*) increased production of bilirubin; (*b*) impairment of the capacity of the liver to take up, conjugate or excrete bilirubin; and (*c*) regurgitation of bilirubin from the bile into the plasma (see also page 382). For clinical purposes it is more convenient to classify jaundice on the basis of its pathogenesis, i.e. as being mainly of hemolytic, hepatocellular or biliary obstructive origin. The distribution of bile pigments in different forms of jaundice is shown in the table below.

Distribution of bile pigments in jaundice[2]

Type of jaundice	Plasma			Urine
	Bilirubin	Pigment I	Pigment II	Conjugated bilirubin
Cirrhosis, hepatitis, and chronic obstruction	+	+++	++	++
Acute biliary obstruction	+	++	+++	+++
Hemolytic jaundice in adults	+	(+)	(+)	–
Neonatal jaundice	++	–	–	–
Hemolytic disease of the newborn	+++	–	–	–
Inspissated bile syndrome	+++	++	+	+
Familial hyperbilirubinemia				
GILBERT's disease	++	–	–	–
CRIGLER and NAJJAR's disease	+++	–	–	–
Chronic idiopathic jaundice	++	+	+	+

Neonatal jaundice. Jaundice is commonly observed in newborn infants. It is likely that 40% of infants have a serum bilirubin level of at least 4 mg/100 ml ("physiological jaundice of the newborn"). In premature infants, jaundice is more pronounced than in normal infants, suggesting that the accumulation of unconjugated bilirubin might be due to a defect in the bilirubin conjugating mechanism in the immature liver, probably by a deficiency of glucuronyl transferase activity. Extremely high bilirubin serum levels – up to 40 mg/100 ml or more – are found in hemolytic disease of the newborn.

Kernicterus. The danger of hyperbilirubinemia lies in the development of cerebral nuclear jaundice (kernicterus), but it is unlikely to occur at bilirubin levels below 20 mg/100 ml serum. The damage to the central nervous system in kernicterus is probably a result of the direct toxic action of unconjugated bilirubin. One of the reasons that kernicterus is almost exclusively found in the neonatal period may be an immaturity of the blood-brain barrier for bilirubin.

1) KLATSKIN, G., *Ann. Rev. Med.*, **12**, 211 (1961). *2)* BILLING, B. H., *Advanc. clin. Chem.*, 2, 267 (1959). *3)* ARIAS, I. M., *Med. Clin. N. Amer.*, **44**, 607 (1960). *4)* ARIAS, I. M., *Advanc. clin. Chem.*, **3**, 35 (1960). *5)* CLAIREAUX, A. E., *Brit. med. J.*, **1**, 1528 (1960). *6)* WITH, T. K., *Biologie der Gallenfarbstoffe*, Stuttgart, 1960.

Carbohydrates and related substances	Whole blood			Plasma or serum			Methods and sources	Remarks
	Mean*	Range*	*s*	Mean*	Range*	*s*		
Glucose								
(*a*) Adults, fasting								
Venous blood	**83**	*75–91*	4	97	61–130	–	MILLER and VAN SLYKE, *J. biol. Chem.*, **114**, 583 (1936); SOMOGYI, M., *J. biol. Chem.*, **174**, 189 and 597 (1948).	Apart from glucose the most important reducing substance in blood is glutathione (see page 559), which is linked to the erythrocytes. In determining glucose in *venous* blood a tourniquet should not be used in venepuncture since this may cause fluctuations in the blood sugar level (CHESROW and BLEYER, *Geriatrics*, **9**, 276 [1954]). Blood sugar is increased in diabetes, decreased in hyperinsulinism, ADDISON's disease and glycogen storage disease. In old age the level is somewhat higher.
Capillary blood	**92**	*86–98*	3	–	max. 180	–		
(*b*) Newborn (1–12 hours)	–	–	–	–	30–75	–	CREERY and PARKINSON, *Arch. Dis. Childh.*, **28**, 134 (1953).	The blood sugar level falls during the first hours of life, then rises slowly for at least 10 days. Cf. FARQUHAR, J. W., *Arch. Dis. Childh.*, **29**, 519 (1954).
Glycogen	5.5	1.2–16.2	–	0	0	–	WAGNER, R., *Arch. Biochem.*, **11**, 249 (1946).	
Protein-bound carbohydrates								
Hexoses (galactose + mannose)	–	–	–	121	–	–	WINZLER, R. J., *Meth. biochem. Anal.*, **2**, 279 (1955).	In disease, the serum level of glycoproteins is often increased (e.g. in tuberculosis, cancer, pneumonia, bacterial endocarditis, rheumatic fever). A decrease is rare (e.g. in lipoid nephrosis). For a review see WINZLER, R. J., *loc. cit.*
Hexosamines (glucosamine + galactosamine)	–	–	–	83.4	–	–		
Fucose	–	–	–	8.9	–	–		
Neuraminic acid	–	–	–	60	–	–		

* When a range given is a *normal range* (see page 154), i.e. calculated from the formula: mean $\pm$ (2 $\times$ standard deviation *s*), it is printed in *italics*, with the mean in **bold** figures. Otherwise the data given are experimental results which have not been tested statistically.

Normal values in mg/100 ml, unless otherwise stated

	Whole blood			Plasma or serum			Methods and sources	Remarks
	Mean*	Range*	s	Mean*	Range*	s		
Pentoses								
total	–	–	–	**2.55**	*1.81–3.29*	0.37	Green et al., *Clin. Sci.*, **8**, 65 (1949); Stoner and Green, *J. Path. Bact.*, **61**, 114 (1949); Green et al., *J. Path. Bact.*, **61**, 101 (1949).	The first value (total pentoses) corresponds to free pentoses, nucleotide- and nucleoside-pentoses, the second (phosphorylated pentoses) to nucleotide-pentoses alone.
phosphorylated	–	–	–	**2.19**	*1.59–2.79*	0.30		
Hexuronates (as glucuronic acid)	6.7	4.1–9.3	–	–	0.4–1.4	–	*Whole blood:* Ratish and Bullowa, *Arch. Biochem.*, **2**, 381 (1943), quoted in Albritton, E. C. (Ed.), *Standard Values in Blood*, Philadelphia, 1952, page 89. *Serum:* Deichmann and Dierker, *J. biol. Chem.*, **163**, 753 (1946).	Values are for substances giving a color reaction with naphthoresorcinol.

* When a range given is a *normal range* (see page 154), i.e. calculated from the formula: mean ± (2 × standard deviation s), it is printed in *italics*, with the mean in **bold** figures. Otherwise the data given are experimental results which have not been tested statistically.

Lipids

Serum lipoprotein fractions and their composition[1]

	Average concentration* mg/100 ml	Density	S_f **	$-S$ **	Cohn fraction method 10	Lipoprotein composition						
						Protein, %	Lipids, %	Lipid composition as per cent total lipids				
								Neutral fats	Phospholipids	Cholesterol ester	Free cholesterol	NEFA***
Chylomicrons	0–50	< 0.96	10^4–10^5		I + II	1	99	88	8	3	1	–
Low-density (β) lipoproteins												
LDF 1	150	0.96 –1.006	20–400	> 70	I + II	7	93	56	20	15	8	1
LDF 2	50	1.006–1.019	12–20	40–70	I + III	11	89	29	26	34	9	1
LDF 3	350	1.019–1.063	0–12	20–40	III	21	79	13	28	48	10	1
High-density (α) lipoproteins												
HDL 2	50	1.063–1.125		4–20	IV + V	33	67	16	43	31	10	–
HDL 3	300	1.125–1.210		0–4	IV + V	57	43	13	46	29	6	6
Albumin-NEFA***	4000				V	99	1	0	0	0	0	100

* Concentrations are average postabsorptive values for a healthy and well-nourished 40-year-old male.

** S_f = Svedberg flotation units ($-S \times 10^{-13}$ sec) at density 1.063 and $t = 26°$C; $-S$ = Svedberg flotation units at density 1.21 and $t = 26°$C.

*** NEFA = Nonesterified fatty acids.

1) Olson and Vester, *Physiol. Rev.*, **40**, 677 (1960).

Serum lipids in newborn infants (Sweden)[1] and adults (Germany)[2]

(values in mg/100 ml)

Age group	Number	Total lipids		Neutral fats		Total cholesterol		Free cholesterol		Phospholipids	
		Mean	Range	Mean	Range	Mean	Range	Mean	Range	Mean	Range
Newborn infants											
cord blood	50	347	210–600			75	50–110	22	13– 34	75	48–133
capillary blood 1–6 days after birth		591	340–890			138	98–200	50	25–105	131	70–178
Adults, male											
18–30 years	30	743	570–900	305	163–477	177	112–210	62	30– 93	177	118–224
31–45 years	31	793	720–900	313	211–405	199	160–238	76	56–103	191	150–221
46–60 years	31	806	670–900	320	218–433	205	150–275	79	57–106	190	158–260
Adults, female											
18–30 years	30	703	530–840	260	118–347	180	118–246	67	42– 92	180	127–221
31–45 years	29	757	600–870	288	173–409	192	148–248	72	46– 96	189	133–237
46–60 years	29	812	565–930	328	264–431	204	124–250	79	48–108	189	118–248

1) Rafstedt and Swahn, *Acta paediat. (Uppsala)*, **43**, 229 (1954).
2) Böhle et al., *Dtsch. Arch. klin. Med.*, **203**, 29 (1956).

Total serum cholesterol and serum phospholipids[1]

(mean values in mg/100 ml in individuals selected at random from a healthy group of industrial workers and their dependents of low-middle income, predominantly of Italian and Irish origin, in Staten Island, New York)

Age group	Males				Females			
	Number	Total cholesterol	Number	Phospholipids	Number	Total cholesterol	Number	Phospholipids
3– 7	34	179.8	29	227.1	36	209.0	31	261.9
8–12	54	180.4	50	233.2	55	196.4	51	241.7
13–17	46	175.5	40	220.6	53	182.9	46	235.5
18–22	22	185.2	20	217.0	24	192.6	21	243.7
23–27	16	194.5	16	249.4	40	201.9	38	249.0
28–32	38	243.1	34	285.3	50	200.1	45	241.4
33–37	53	231.0	45	270.0	72	206.9	67	255.0
38–42	57	246.9	49	289.4	64	224.5	61	270.2
43–47	77	237.2	61	280.9	56	238.9	50	275.2
48–52	63	238.8	47	287.5	34	249.5	31	290.9
53–57	45	239.7	41	282.8	28	285.8	26	313.7
58–62	34	236.2	30	275.3	20	263.8	18	298.3
63–67	19	249.7	19	298.4	14	259.9	14	317.1
68–72	6	242.5	6	279.8	3	241.8	3	279.3

1) ADLERSBERG et al., *J. Amer. med. Ass.*, **162**, 619 (1956).

Serum bile acids in adults[1]

(values in mg/100 ml from 30 healthy subjects aged 22–76 years)

	Mean	Range
Trihydroxycholanic acid (cholic acid)	0.14	0–0.34
Dihydroxycholanic acids (chenodesoxycholic and desoxycholic acids)	0.08	0–0.19

1) CAREY, J. B., *J. clin. Invest.*, **37**, 1494 (1958).

Remarks*

The major part of the lipids in serum is linked to proteins (see also page 555). The upper table on page 561 gives a comparison of the lipoprotein fractions obtained by various methods of separation. The fractions obtained by flotation in the ultracentrifuge are characterized by their flotation constants S_f (GOFMAN) or $-S$ (LEWIS).

The serum lipid level is dependent upon numerous factors, including age, sex, race, nutrition, hormones, stress, climate and occupation. Newborn children have a considerably lower serum lipid level than adults. (For changes in the serum lipid level during pregnancy see page 604.) There is a positive correlation between the serum lipid level (in particular the levels of triglycerides, cholesterol and some of the lipoprotein fractions[1]) and the occurrence of atherosclerosis, although no causal connection has yet been satisfactorily demonstrated. However, it would appear desirable so to adjust the diet that the serum lipid level does not rise excessively.

Blood cholesterol exists in a free form and an ester form. Free cholesterol is equally distributed between the serum and erythrocytes, while the ester form occurs only in the plasma. The serum cholesterol level is affected by the same factors that affect the total lipid level. It is less affected by the cholesterol content of the diet (the major part of the cholesterol is of endogeneous origin) than by the fat content of foods. A diet rich in polyunsaturated fatty acids can depress the serum cholesterol level (see also the remarks on the essential fatty acids on page 471). For a review of the extensive literature on serum cholesterol see KEYS et al.[2], ADLERSBERG et al.[3], and LEWIS et al.[4].

Fatty acid composition of serum lipids[1]

(mean values from 16 normal subjects aged 18–41 years)

	Neutral fat	Cholesterol ester	Phospholipids
Total, mg/100 ml serum	173	224	209
Fatty acids, mg/100 ml serum	144	72	111
Fatty acids as per cent of total fatty acids			
Myristic acid	1.6	1.1	0.9
Palmitic acid	28.1	12.1	30.7
Palmitoleic acid	7.6	6.8	3.3
Stearic acid	3.7	2.6	11.9
Oleic acid	36.8	18.9	15.1
Linoleic acid	12.2	47.1	21.5
Triene acids (C_{18} and C_{20})	0.9	0.9	0.8
Arachidonic acid	3.1	5.0	8.8
Pentaene acids (C_{20} and C_{22})	1.2	1.4	2.0
Hexaene acids (C_{22})	1.9	1.9	3.1
Other fatty acids	2.9	2.2	2.1

1) SCHRADE, W., *Medizin und Ernährung*, **1**, 267 (1960).

Individual serum phospholipids in adults[1]

(mean values from 7 subjects)

Lipid phosphorus, mg/100 ml	10.0	
Phospholipids as per cent of total lipid phosphorus		
Cephalin	4.6	includes plasmalogen and phospholipids containing inositol
Lecithin	69.1	includes plasmalogen
Sphingomyelin	19.0	
Lysolecithin	7.1	

1) PHILLIPS, G. B., *Biochim. biophys. Acta*, **29**, 594 (1958).

Pathological changes in the serum lipid pattern

(↑ = increase, ↓ = decrease, N = no change)

	Total lipids	Cholesterol	Phospholipids	Triglycerides	α-Lipoproteins	β-Lipoproteins
Essential hyperlipemia	↑↑	↑	↑	↑↑	(↑)	↑↑
Essential hypercholesterolemia	↑	↑↑	↑	(↑)	(↑)	↑↑
Hyperthyroidism	↓	(↓)	(↑)	(↓)	N	(↓)
Hypothyroidism	↑	↑	(↑)	(↑)	(↑)	↑
Diabetes mellitus	↑	↑	↑	↑↑	(↑)	↑↑
Nephrotic syndrome	↑	↑	↑	↑↑	(↑)	↑↑
Acute hepatitis	N	(↓)*	N	N	(↓)	(↑)
Chronic hepatitis	N	N, (↓)*	N	N	(↓), (↑)	(↓), (↑)
Liver cirrhosis	N	(↓)*	N	N	(↓)	N
Biliary cirrhosis	↑↑	N	↑↑	N	(↓)**	↑↑
Biliary obstruction	↑	(↑)	↑	N	(↓)**	↑

* Ester cholesterol only.
** In liver damage abnormal lipoproteins may be present because of impairment of the capacity of the liver to synthesize α-lipoproteins.

* For a general classification and description of the lipids see pages 385–389.

1) GOFMAN, J. D., in HOMBURGER and BERNFELD (Eds.), *The Lipoproteins: Methods and Clinical Significance*, Basle, 1958, page 47. 2) KEYS et al., *Clin. Chem.*, **1**, 34 (1955). 3) ADLERSBERG et al., *J. Amer. med. Ass.*, **162**, 619 (1956). 4) LEWIS et al., *Circulation*, **16**, 227 (1957).

Normal values in **mg/100 ml**, unless otherwise stated

Intermediary metabolites	Whole blood			Plasma or serum			Methods and sources	Remarks
	Mean*	Range*	*s*	Mean*	Range*	*s*		
Acetone bodies .... (nonfasting blood)	–	–	–	–	–	–		The content of acetone bodies in the erythrocytes is very low, while the concentration in whole blood is ca. 20% less than that in plasma. They are *greatly increased* in ketosis, diabetes and fasting, and may be increased in pregnancy (see page 604). The acetone bodies consist of 80% β-hydroxybutyric acid and 20% acetoacetic acid; acetone is present only in traces.
Total (as β-hydroxybutyric acid)	0.5	–	–	–	0.3–0.9	–	Weichselbaum and Somogyi, *J. biol. Chem.*, **140**, 5 (1941).	
Acetoacetic acid	–	–	–	–	0.08–0.28	–	Rosenthal, S. M., *J. biol. Chem.*, **179**, 1235 (1949).	
Total α-keto acids								
Adults	1.3	0–3.1	–	–	0.6–2.1	–	*Whole blood* (adults): Friedemann and Haugen, *J. biol. Chem.*, **147**, 415 (1943). *Whole blood* (newborn): Allibone and Finch, *Arch. Dis. Childh.*, **21**, 165 (1946). *Serum:* Westerkamp, H., *Biochem. Z.*, **263**, 239 (1933).	
Newborn	0.8	0.6–1.0	–	–	–	–		
α-Ketoglutaric acid	0.13	0.05–0.27	–	0.8	–	–	*Whole blood:* Cavallini et al., *Nature*, **164**, 792 (1949); *serum:* Krebs, H. A., *Biochem. J.*, **32**, 108 (1938).	See Pyruvic acid, below.
Pyruvic acid	**0.76**	*0.414–1.106*	0.173	**1.1**	*0.5–1.7*	0.3	*Whole blood:* Klein, J. R., *J. biol. Chem.*, **145**, 35 (1942); *serum:* Kirk and Chieffi, *J. Nutr.*, **38**, 353 (1949) (249 tests). Bonting, S. L., *Arch. Biochem.*, **58**, 100 (1955), describes a colorimetric method which allows determination of microgram quantities of pyruvic acid. For a review of methods see Biserte and Dassonville, *Clin. chim. Acta*, **1**, 49 (1956).	Other keto acids such as α-ketoisovaleric, α-ketoisocaproic and α-keto-β-methylvaleric acids have been detected in blood, so that the values given here for pyruvic and α-ketoglutaric acids are probably too high (cf. Kaeser et al., *Rev. franç. Et. clin. biol.*, **4**, 138 [1959]). The pyruvic acid level in blood does not change with age. It is *increased* (together with all α-keto acids and lactic acid) in vitamin B_1 deficiency (see page 455), after muscular activity, great emotional excitement, in alkalosis, dyspnea, cardiovascular disturbances, thyrotoxicosis. For estimation of vitamin B_1 deficiency see Horwitt and Kreisler, *J. Nutr.*, **37**, 411 (1949).
Lactic acid	**9.9**	*4.7–15.1*	2.6	**11.5**	*6.1–16.9*	2.7	Gibbs et al., *J. biol. Chem.*, **144**, 325 (1942).	See Pyruvic acid, above.
Citric acid								
Adults	1.9	1.3–2.3	–	2.4	1.6–3.2	–	*Whole blood:* Wolcott and Boyer, *J. biol. Chem.*, **172**, 729 (1948); *serum:* Natelson et al., *J. clin. Invest.*, **27**, 446 (1948).	
Children	–	–	–	2.8	1.8–3.8	–		
Newborn	–	–	–	–	3–6	–		
Malic acid	0.46	0.24–0.75	–	0.5	0.1–0.9	–	Hummel, J. P., *J. biol. Chem.*, **180**, 1225 (1949).	
Succinic acid	–	–	–	0.5	–	–	Krebs, H. A., *Ann. Rev. Biochem.*, **9**, 417 (1950).	
Fumaric acid	<0.3	–	–	–	–	–	Marshall et al., *J. biol. Chem.*, **179**, 1127 (1949).	
Phenols. See page 559								
Vitamins See pages 449–472								
Hormones See pages 473–497								

* When a range given is a *normal range* (see page 154), i.e. calculated from the formula: mean ± (2 × standard deviation *s*), it is printed in *italics*, with the mean in **bold** figures. Otherwise the data given are experimental results which have not been tested statistically.

Normal values in the units stated

Enzymes and coenzymes	Whole blood Mean*	Whole blood Range*	Whole blood *s*	Plasma or serum Mean*	Plasma or serum Range*	Plasma or serum *s*	Methods and sources	Remarks
Adenosinepoly-phosphatase (μmol phosphorus per hour per 100 ml serum at pH 4.8 [acid] and pH 8.9 [alkaline])								
acid	–	–	–	41	21–61	–	MEISTER, A., *Science*, **106**, 167 (1947); *J. clin. Invest.*, **27**, 263 (1948).	
alkaline	–	–	–	30	10–50	–		
Aldolase (μg fructose diphosphate per hour per 100 ml serum at pH 8.6 and 38° C)	–	–	–	490	350–800	–	Method of SIBLEY and LEHNINGER, *J. biol. Chem.*, **177**, 859 (1949). Values from SIBLEY and LEHNINGER, *J. nat. Cancer Inst.*, **9**, 303 (1949).	
Amylase (diastase) (mg glucose formed from the starch per 100 ml serum or plasma)	–	–	–	–	40–145 (15 min incubation)	–	LEWISON, E. F., *Surg. Gynec. Obstet.*, **72**, 202, (1941); ANDERSCH, M. A., *J. biol. Chem.*, **166**, 705 (1946). For methods see STREET and CLOSE, *Clin. Chim. Acta*, **1**, 256 (1956).	*Increased* in pancreatic disease and in severe renal insufficiency; also in mumps meningoencephalitis and other salivary gland diseases (WALLMAN and VIDOR, *Lancet*, **1**, 1105 [1955]). Of importance in *differential diagnosis* is the fact that *opiates* (e.g. codeine sulfate) can *markedly increase* the serum amylase (and lipase) content for 24 hours after administration (GROSS et al., *Proc. Mayo Clin.*, **26**, 81 [1951]).
	–	–	–	–	95–250 (30 min incubation)	–		
Arginase (authors' units)	2000	800–3400	–	–	–	–	KOCHAKIAN et al., *Conference on Metabolic Aspects of Convalescence, Transactions of the 17th Meeting*, New York, 1948, page 187; KOCHAKIAN, C. D., *J. biol. Chem.*, **155**, 579 (1944).	The arginase content is lowered in undernourishment.
Cadaverinase ("permanganate" units)								
Men	–	–	–	0.48	0–1.1	–	KAPELLER-ADLER and RENWICK, *Clin. chim. Acta*, **1**, 197 (1956).	The cadaverinase content is increased during pregnancy.
Women	–	–	–	0.65	0.1–1.5	–		
Catalase (authors' units)								
Men	**19.73**	*12.29–27.17*	3.72	**13.90**	*9.74–18.06*	2.08	Calculated from the data of YAMAGATA et al., *Tohoku J. exp. Med.*, **57**, 85 (1952).	
Women	**15.94**	*10.26–21.62*	2.84	**14.30**	*9.96–18.64*	2.17		
Ceruloplasmin (μmol oxygen used per milliliter serum per hour)	–	–	–	**3.60**	*2.14–5.06*	0.73	BEARN and KUNKEL, *J. clin. Invest.*, **33**, 400 (1954).	Ceruloplasmin is an α_2-globulin containing ca. 0.32% copper. It has a molecular weight of ca. 151,000 and the molecule contains 8 atoms of copper. It has properties similar to those of oxidase. In WILSON's disease (hepatolenticular degeneration) the serum level is decreased, during pregnancy and in chronic infections it is increased (MARKOWITZ et al., *J. clin. Invest.*, **34**, 1498 [1955]).
Cholinesterase (fall in pH units per hour per 100 ml)	(erythrocytes:) **0.67**	*0.47–0.87*	0.10	**0.94**	*0.56–1.32*	0.19	SCUDAMORE, H. H., *J. Lab. clin. Med.*, **37**, 860 (1951).	Serum cholinesterase is often given the name *pseudocholinesterase* (but see also page 424). In contrast to acetylcholine (see page 559), cholinesterase is not increased in asthma.
Cocarboxylase (thiamine pyrophosphate) (μg/100 ml)								
(1) Children								
0–3 years	**12.6**	*5.5–19.7*	3.55	–	–	–	Methods: (1) *Manometric:* values calculated from data of RÄIHÄ and FORSANDER, *Acta paediat. (Uppsala)*, **42**, 514 (1953).	See also under Vitamin B_1, page 454.
3–11 years	**10.5**	*5.32–15.68*	2.59	–	–	–		
(1) Adolescents 11–25 years	**9.7**	*6.32–13.08*	1.69	–	–	–	(2) *Microbiological:* values from BEERSTECHER and SPANGLER, in ALBRITTON, E. C. (Ed.), *Standard Values in Blood*, Philadelphia, 1952, page 116. (3) Values from SMITS and FLORIJN, *Biochim. biophys. Acta*, **3**, 44 (1949).	
(2) Men	8.9	–	–	–	–	–		
(2) Women	7.6	–	–	–	–	–		

* When a range given is a *normal range* (see page 154), i.e. calculated from the formula: mean ± (2 × standard deviation *s*), it is printed in *italics*, with the mean in **bold** figures. Otherwise the data given are experimental results which have not been tested statistically.

Normal values in the units stated

	Whole blood Mean*	Whole blood Range*	Whole blood *s*	Plasma or serum Mean*	Plasma or serum Range*	Plasma or serum *s*	Methods and sources	Remarks
Cocarboxylase *(continued)* (μg/100 ml)								
	(erythrocytes:)							
(2) Men	10.0	7–14	–	–	–	–		
(2) Women	6.5	5–8	–	–	–	–		
(3) As free thiamine	(per 10^{11} erythrocytes:)							
Men	**1.5**	*1.34–1.66*	0.08	–	–	–		
Women	**1.3**	*1.12–1.48*	0.09	–	–	–		
(3) As free thiamine	(per 10^{11} leukocytes:)							
Men	**290**	*184–396*	53	–	–	–		
Women	**270**	*202–338*	34	–	–	–		
Coenzyme A (mg of bound pantothenic acid per 100 ml)	–	(erythrocytes:) 0.210-0.280	–	–	–	–	KAPLAN and LIPMANN, *J. biol. Chem.*, **174**, 37 (1948).	
Dehydropeptidase (μmol NH_3 per half-hour per 100 ml serum; substrate DL-alanyldehydroalanine at pH 8.1 and 37° C)	–	–	–	359	191–527	–	MEISTER and GREENSTEIN, *J. nat. Cancer Inst.*, **8**, 169 (1948).	
Desoxyribonuclease I (depolymerase) (μg phosphodesoxypentose per milliliter serum after 1 hour incubation)	–	–	–	**0.46**	*0.34–0.58*	0.06	KOWLESSAR and MCEVOY, *J. clin. Invest.*, **35**, 1325 (1956).	Increased in acute hemorrhagic pancreatitis.
Flavin adenine dinucleotide (FAD) (mg/100 ml)	(erythrocytes:) 0.075	–	–	0.010	–	–	KLEIN and KOHN, *J. biol. Chem.*, **136**, 177 (1940).	See also under Vitamin B_2, page 455.
β-Glucuronidase (μg phenolphthalein per hour per 100 ml serum, substrate phenolphthalein-glucuronide at pH 4.5 and 37° C)								
Men	–	–	–	–	0–181	–	FISHMAN et al., *J. biol. Chem.*, **173**, 449 (1948).	
Women	–	–	–	–	37–230	–		
Glutamate-oxalacetate transaminase (SGOT) (spectrophotometric units per ml)	–	–	–	–	8–40	–	WRÓBLEWSKI, F., *Amer. J. Med.*, **27**, 911 (1959)	
Glutamate-pyruvate transaminase (SGPT) (spectrophotometric units per ml)	–	–	–	–	5–35	–	WRÓBLEWSKI, F., *Amer. J. Med.*, **27**, 911 (1959)	
Glyoxalase (ml CO_2 per 20 min per 100 ml whole blood; substrate methylglyoxal at pH 7.2 and 26° C)	611.6	425–705	–	–	–	–	COHEN and SOBER, *Cancer Res.*, **5**, 631 (1945).	
	(erythrocytes:) 1398	1320–1500	–	–	–	–		
Histaminase (μg histamine per 100 ml destroyed in 90 min at 37° C)	36	30–40	–	18	0–36	–	WERLE and EFFKEMANN, *Klin. Wschr.*, **19**, 717 (1940).	Increased in pregnancy.

Range of SGOT and SGPT values in disease states (WRÓBLEWSKI, *loc. cit.*)

	SGOT	SGPT
Transmural myocardial infarction	50–600	5–150
Subendocardial infarction	20–150	5–50
Viral and/or homologous serum hepatitis		
Non-icteric phase	50–300	60–400
Increasing icteric phase	500–2500	600–3500
Toxic hepatitis	50–27,000	50–20,000
LAENNEC's cirrhosis, progressive	50–250	30–200
Biliary cirrhosis, progressive	50–350	30–300
Extrahepatic biliary tract obstruction	40–300	50–400
Metastatic and primary hepatic carcinoma	40–250	20–150
Skeletal muscle trauma	30–500	20–150
Progressive muscular dystrophy; Pseudohypertrophic muscular dystrophy; Dermatomyositis	40–250	20–100

* When a range given is a *normal range* (see page 154), i.e. calculated from the formula: mean ± (2 × standard deviation *s*), it is printed in *italics*, with the mean in **bold** figures. Otherwise the data given are experimental results which have not been tested statistically.

Normal values in the units stated

	Whole blood			Plasma or serum			Methods and sources	Remarks
	Mean*	Range*	*s*	Mean*	Range*	*s*		
Lactic dehydrogenase (LDH) (spectrophotometric units per ml)	–	–	–	–	200–680	–	WRÓBLEWSKI, F., *Ann. N. Y. Acad. Sci.*, **75**, 322 (1958).	Increased 2–5 times in myocardial infarction, moderately increased in acute viral hepatitis and muscular dystrophy.
Lipase (ml 0.05-N NaOH per 24 hours per 100 ml serum; substrate olive oil emulsion)	–	–	–	–	0–150	–	COMFORT and OSTERBERG, *Med. Clin. N. Amer.*, **24**, 1137 (1940).	The serum lipase level varies in a similar manner to the amylase level. See page 564.
Lysozyme (µg crystalline lysozyme per milliliter whole blood)	**5.64**	*1.54–9.74*	2.05	–	–	–	FOGELSON et al., *Amer. J. Digest. Dis.*, **21**, 327 (1954).	
Malic dehydrogenase (MDH) (spectrophotometric units per ml)	–	–	–	–	50–104	–	BING et al., *J. Amer. med. Ass.*, **164**, 647 (1957).	Increased in myocardial infarction.
Pepsinogen (µg "tyrosine" liberated per milliliter plasma at pH 1.5)								
Men								
0– 9 years	–	–	–	**391**	*338.2-443.2*	26.1	Calculated from the data of MIRSKY et al., *J. Lab. clin. Med.*, **40**, 188 (1952).	The plasma pepsinogen level shows little change either during the course of the day or from day to day. Usually increased in patients with *duodenal* ulcer (in 60% according to HIRSCHOWITZ, B. I., *J. Lab. clin. Med.*, **46**, 568 [1955], who also reports that of 15 patients with *gastric* ulcer 13 had a normal blood pepsinogen level). Decreased in pernicious anemia.
10–19 years	–	–	–	**521**	*441.2-600.8*	39.9		
20–59 years	–	–	–	**636**	*540.2-731.8*	47.9		
60–89 years	–	–	–	**703**	*592.4-813.6*	55.3		
Women								
0– 9 years	–	–	–	**449**	*396.8-501.2*	26.1		
10–19 years	–	–	–	**471**	*425.8-516.2*	22.6		
20–59 years	–	–	–	**601**	*537.0-665.0*	32.0		
60–89 years	–	–	–	**636**	*516.4-755.6*	59.8		
Phenolsulfatase (authors' units)	–	–	–	–	30–1550	–	HUGGINS and SMITH, *J. biol. Chem.*, **170**, 391 (1947).	
Phosphatase (KING and ARMSTRONG units per 100 ml serum)								
Acid								
"Total"	–	–	–	–	0.5–5.0	–	FISHMAN et al., *J. clin. Invest.*, **32**, 1034 (1953).	Phosphatase activity is usually expressed in BODANSKY or KING-ARMSTRONG units, respectively the amount of phosphatase which liberates 1 mg of phosphorus as phosphorus ion after 1 hour incubation on a substrate of sodium β-glycerophosphate (at ca. pH 5 for acid and ca. pH 10 for alkaline phosphatase), and the amount which when allowed to act on an excess of disodium phenyl phosphate liberates 1 mg of phenol after 15 minutes incubation at 37° C (at ca. pH 5 for acid and pH 9.8 for alkaline phosphatase). One BODANSKY unit corresponds to ca. 2.5 KING-ARMSTRONG units (KING, E. J., *Brit. med. Bull.*, **9**, 160 [1953]). On phosphatases in general see COLOWICK and KAPLAN, *Methods in Enzymology*, vol. II, New York, 1955, pages 523–561; JONES, J. H., in GYÖRGY, P. (Ed.), *Vitamin Methods*, vol. II, New York, 1951, page 379. The highest concentrations of ***alkaline phosphatase*** are found in the prostate, bone marrow, kidneys, liver, intestinal mucosa and erythrocytes. Serum alkaline phosphatase is increased in active bone disease, rickets and obstructive jaundice. Serum ***acid phosphatase*** is usually increased in prostate carcinoma bone metastases; the level is reduced to normal after a few weeks' estrogen treatment. TUCHMAN et al., *J. Mt Sinai Hosp.*, **23**, 227 (1956), have described 8 cases of GAUCHER's disease in which the serum acid phosphatase level was increased.
"Prostatic"	–	–	–	–	0–0.5	–		
Alkaline								
Children	–	–	–	17	11–20	–	KING, E. J., *Brit. Med. Bull.*, **9**, 160 (1953).	
Adults	–	–	–	7.8	3–13	–		
Profibrinolysin (fibrinolysin units per 100 ml plasma)	–	–	–	–	50–125	–	GUEST et al., *Amer. J. Physiol.*, **150**, 661 (1947).	
Pteroylglutamic acid conjugase (folic acid conjugase) (µg folic acid per 100 ml serum produced in 90 min from yeast extract at pH 4.5 and 37° C)	–	–	–	–	80–100	–	WOLFF et al., *Science*, **109**, 612 (1949).	
Pyridine nucleotides. See under Nucleotides and related compounds, page 558.								

* When a range given is a *normal range* (see page 154), i.e. calculated from the formula: mean ± (2 × standard deviation *s*), it is printed in *italics*, with the mean in **bold** figures. Otherwise the data given are experimental results which have not been tested statistically.

Synopsis of Blood – Inorganic Constituents

Normal values in **mg/100 ml**, unless otherwise stated

Inorganic constituents (other than trace elements)	Whole blood Mean*	Whole blood Range*	Whole blood *s*	Plasma or serum Mean*	Plasma or serum Range*	Plasma or serum *s*	Methods and sources	Remarks
Phosphorus, P								
(1) Total (as P)	–	28–48	–	12.1	10.0–14.1	–	(1) STEARNS and WARWEG, *J. biol. Chem.*, **102**, 749 (1933). (2) *Whole blood:* HELVE, O., *Acta med. scand.*, **125**, 505 (1946); *serum:* WERTHEIM et al., *J. clin. Invest.*, **33**, 565 (1954). (3) BULLOCK, J. K., *Amer. J. Dis. Child.*, **40**, 725 (1930).	The plasma inorganic phosphorus level in adolescence is markedly higher than in adults owing to the requirements of bone calcification (cf. Growth hormone, page 476). The level is *lowered* in rickets and often in osteomalacia, osteitis fibrosa, hyperparathyroidism and during insulin treatment. *Increased* in chronic nephritis, in diabetic coma and after severe bone fractures.
Inorganic (as P) (2) Adults	2.9	2.1–3.8	–	**3.36**	*2.56–4.16*	0.40		
(erythrocytes:)	2.4	0.91–3.3	–	–	–	–		
(3) Children (1–19 years)	–	–	–	4.8	3.6–5.9	–		
Organic or ester phosphorus (as P) ..	23.1	18.6–28.6	–	0.6	0–4	–	*Whole blood* and *erythrocytes:* HELVE, O., *Acta med. scand.*, **125**, 505 (1946); *serum:* STEARNS and WARWEG, *J. biol. Chem.*, **102**, 749 (1933).	= acid-soluble phosphates, except inorganic orthophosphates.
(erythrocytes:)	49.7	38.5–58.7	–	–	–	–		
Lipid phosphorus (as P)	11.2	8–18	–	8.0	6.1–9.9	–	STEARNS and WARWEG, *J. biol. Chem.*, **102**, 749 (1933).	= organic phosphates soluble in ether-alcohol or ether. Lipid-P × 25 = lecithin; Lipid-P × 23.5 = phospholipids
Adenosine triphosphate (ATP) phosphorus (as P) ..	8.1	5.1–10.4	–	–	–	–	KERR and DAOUD, *J. biol. Chem.*, **109**, 301 (1935).	For adenosine triphosphate content of blood see page 558.
Diphosphoglycerate phosphorus (as P) ..	12.4	8.1–16.7	–	–	–	–	HELVE, O., *Acta med. scand.*, **125**, 505 (1946).	
Nucleotide phosphorus (as P)	2.8	2.2–3.4	–	–	–	–	KERR and DAOUD, *J. biol. Chem.*, **109**, 301 (1935).	
Hexose-phosphate phosphorus (as P) ..	3.2	1.4–5.0	–	–	–	–	HELVE, O., *Acta med. scand.*, **125**, 505 (1946).	
Sulfur, S (other than protein-S)								
Total (as S)	–	3.84–5.06	–	3.38	2.95–3.75	–	STURM and POTHMANN, *Z. klin. Med.*, **137**, 467 (1940).	
Inorganic (as S)	–	0.28–0.65	–	1.57	1.00–1.85	–	STURM and POTHMANN, *Z. klin. Med.*, **137**, 467 (1940).	Increased in renal insufficiency.
Esterified (as S)	–	0.07–0.96	–	0.39	0.25–0.65	–	STURM and POTHMANN, *Z. klin. Med.*, **137**, 467 (1940).	= organic substances from which sulfates are liberated by acid hydrolysis (= sulfuric esters of carbohydrates and phenols).
Neutral (as S)	–	3.19–4.32	–	1.42	0.90–1.95	–	STURM and POTHMANN, *Z. klin. Med.*, **137**, 467 (1940).	= substances which are converted into sulfates by oxidation (S-containing amino acids, taurine, thiosulfate, thiocyanate, thiamine).
Silicon, Si (as SiO_2).....	**0.83**	*0.35–1.31*	0.24	–	–	–	Values from WORTH, G., *Klin. Wschr.*, **30**, 82 (1952).	No significant differences due to age, sex or disease (including silicosis).
Chlorides (as Cl)**								
in mEq/liter	–	77.0–90.6	–	–	100.0–107.4	–	*Whole blood:* GRAM, H. C., *Amer. J. med. Sci.*, **168**, 511 (1924); *serum:* SNYDER and KATZENELBOGEN, *J. biol. Chem.*, **143**, 223 (1942), in agreement with HALD et al., *J. clin. Invest.*, **26**, 983 (1947); GRAM, H. C., *Amer. J. med. Sci.*, **168**, 511 (1924). For another method see HÜBENER and SCHMIDT, *Hoppe-Seylers Z. physiol. Chem.*, **289**, 67 (1952).	*Reduced* after severe vomiting, severe burns, in ADDISON's disease, mercury poisoning, pneumonia. *Increases* have no diagnostic significance. After *operations* there is an immediate drop in the whole-blood chloride level, accompanied by a variable reduction in the plasma level and followed by a rise in the whole-blood level above the normal value. Similar changes occur in the sodium content of whole blood (WILKINSON et al., *Lancet*, **1**, 315 [1951]). The increase in chlorides is due to stimulation of the pituitary-adrenal system.
in mg/100 ml	–	273–321	–	–	355–381	–		

* When a range given is a *normal range* (see page 154), i.e. calculated from the formula: mean ± (2 × standard deviation *s*), it is printed in *italics*, with the mean in **bold** figures. Otherwise the data given are experimental results which have not been tested statistically.

** As soon as whole blood comes into contact with air, CO_2 migrates from the erythrocytes and is replaced by Cl ions from the plasma ("chloride shift"). The true chloride content of plasma can therefore only be determined when the whole process up to the separation of the erythrocytes is carried out in the absence of air.

Normal values in **mg/100 ml**, unless otherwise stated

	Whole blood			Plasma or serum			Methods and sources	Remarks
	Mean*	Range*	*s*	Mean*	Range*	*s*		
Total cations								
in mEq/liter	–	–	–	152.5	147.6-156.0	–	From TALBOTT, quoted by SUNDERMAN and BOERNER, *Normal Values in Clinical Medicine*, Philadelphia, 1950, page 154.	Sum of all the cations. Higher in premature infants (mean 159 mEq/l) according to REARDEN et al., *Amer. J. Dis. Child.*, **79**, 372 (1950).
in mEq/liter	–	–	–	146.5	144.0-149.0	–	From SUNDERMAN, quoted by SUNDERMAN and BOERNER, *loc. cit.*, page 154.	Calculated from the electrical conductivity (see page 551).
Sodium, Na								
in mEq/liter	85.4	79.3–91.0	–	**144.7**	*134.7-154.7*	5	Method of MOSHER et al., *Amer. J. clin. Path.*, **19**, 461 (1949). Values from *(whole blood)* HALD, J., *J. biol. Chem.*, **163**, 429 (1946); *(serum)* ELLIOTT and HOLLEY, *Fed. Proc.*, **10**, 180 (1951), (400 tests) in agreement with SMITH et al., *Amer. J. clin. Path.*, **20**, 263 (1950); MARINIS et al., *J. Lab. clin. Med.*, **32**, 1208 (1947); OVERMAN et al., *J. biol. Chem.*, **168**, 641 (1947); HALD, P. M., *J. biol. Chem.*, **167**, 499 (1947).	See remarks under Chlorides and Potassium.
	(erythrocytes:)							
	21.2	15.7–25.3	–	–	–	–		
	(whole blood:)							
in mg/100 ml	196.5	182.3-209.2	–	**333**	*310–356*	11.5		
	(erythrocytes:)							
	48.7	36.1–58.2	–	–	–	–		
Magnesium, Mg	4.24	–	–	1.99	1.34–3.82	–	Values calculated from PAIXAO and YOE, *Clin. chim. Acta*, **4**, 507 (1959), using the following assumed specific gravities: whole blood 1.060, plasma 1.026, erythrocytes 1.100.	Increased in starvation up to 40% (SUNDERMAN, F. W., *Amer. J. clin. Path.*, **17**, 169 [1947]). Reduced in delirium tremens and chronic alcoholism with delirium (FLINK et al., *J. Lab. clin. Med.*, **43**, 169 [1954]).
	(erythrocytes:)							
	7.13	2.93–12.32	–	–	–	–		
Potassium, K								
in mEq/liter	**43.0**	*32.2–53.8*	5.4	**4.3**	*3.3–5.3*	0.5	Values from VIDEBAEK and ACKERMANN, *J. Geront.*, **8**, 63 (1953).	Potassium is mainly intracellular, sodium extracellular. *Increased* (serum) in ADDISON's disease and in uremia with renal retention. *Lowered* in diarrhea, in diseases accompanied by acute tissue breakdown, in kidney injury, in alimentary vitamin K deficiency, inter alia through intravenous feeding without vitamin K (MARTIN et al., *Calif. Med.*, **72**, 133 [1950]; 390 cases).
	(erythrocytes:)							
	94.6	*81.8–107.4*	6.4	–	–	–		
in mg/100 ml	**168.1**	*125.9–210.3*	21.1	**16.8**	*12.88-20.72*	1.96		
	(erythrocytes:)							
	369.9	*319.9-419.9*	25.0	–	–	–		
Calcium, Ca								
Total		6	–	9.5	8.8–10.4	–	HUNTER, G., *Nature*, **182**, 263 (1958).	*Lowered* in tetany (infantile, rachitic or following parathyroidectomy) and vitamin D deficiency. *Increased* after excessive doses of parathyroid hormone or vitamin D overdosage of long duration and in benign or malignant infantile idiopathic hypercalcemia. The erythrocytes contain practically no calcium.
Ionized			–	4.8	4.25–5.25	–	MCLEAN and HASTINGS, *Amer. J. med. Sci.*, **189**, 601 (1935). Titrimetric method, see BUCKLEY et al., *J. Lab. clin. Med.*, **38**, 751 (1951).	
Iron, Fe								
(1) Men	–	44–56	–	–	–	–	(1) (2) SACHS et al., *Arch. intern. Med.*, **52**, 366 (1933); **55**, 227 (1935); **71**, 489 (1943). (3) CHALOUPKA and LEVERTON, *Fed. Proc.*, **10**, 377 (1951) (orthophenanthrolene method). (4) FOWLER and BARER, *Amer J. med. Sci.*, **223**, 633 (1952). (5) SMITH et al., *Amer. J. clin. Path.*, **20**, 263 (1950).	*Plasma and serum:* in well-nourished subjects hourly variations of 0.02 to 0.03 mg are observed, so that values of over 0.06 mg/100 ml must be regarded as normal. There is no correlation between the serum iron content and the Hb content of the blood (CHALOUPKA and LEVERTON, *loc. cit.*). The level is *lowered* in iron deficiency anemia, *increased* in untreated macrocytic anemia and severe hepatitis. According to BUTZENGEIGER and LANGE, *Ärztl. Wschr.*, **7**, 250 (1952), the ratio of serum Fe to serum Cu is the best criterion for distinguishing between parenchymatous and obstructive jaundice. In severe hepatitis the serum Fe is greatly increased, the serum Cu less so, while in obstructive jaundice the *converse* is the case; the only inflammatory diseases which interfere are those such as tuberculosis or rheumatoid arthritis in which the serum Fe is lowered. On iron metabolism in children see STURGEON, P., *Pediatrics*, **13**, 107 (1954).
(2) Women	–	42–48	–	–	–	–		
(3) Women, aged 17–25, on an optional diet	–	–	–	0.125	–	–		
(3) Women, aged 30–40, on an optional diet	–	–	–	0.119	–	–		
(3) Women, aged 40–50, on an optional diet	–	–	–	0.113	–	–		
(3) Women, aged 50–60, on an optional diet	–	–	–	0.122	–	–		
(3) Women, aged 60–70, on an optional diet	–	–	–	0.110	–	–		
(3) Women, aged 70–80, on an optional diet	–	–	–	0.095	–	–		
(3) Women, aged 80–86, on an optional diet	–	–	–	0.093	–	–		
(4) Men and women as one group	–	–	–	**0.1062**	*0–0.2288*	0.0613		
(5) Men and women as one group (determined spectrographically)	–	–	–	**0.190**	*0.050-0.330*	0.070		

* When a range given is a *normal range* (see page 154), i.e. calculated from the formula: mean ± (2 × standard deviation *s*), it is printed in *italics*, with the mean in **bold** figures. Otherwise the data given are experimental results which have not been tested statistically.

Nomogram for calculation of calcium ions (Ca^{++}) from total protein and total calcium content of serum or plasma

From McLean and Hastings, *Amer. J. med. Sci.*, **189**, 601 (1935)

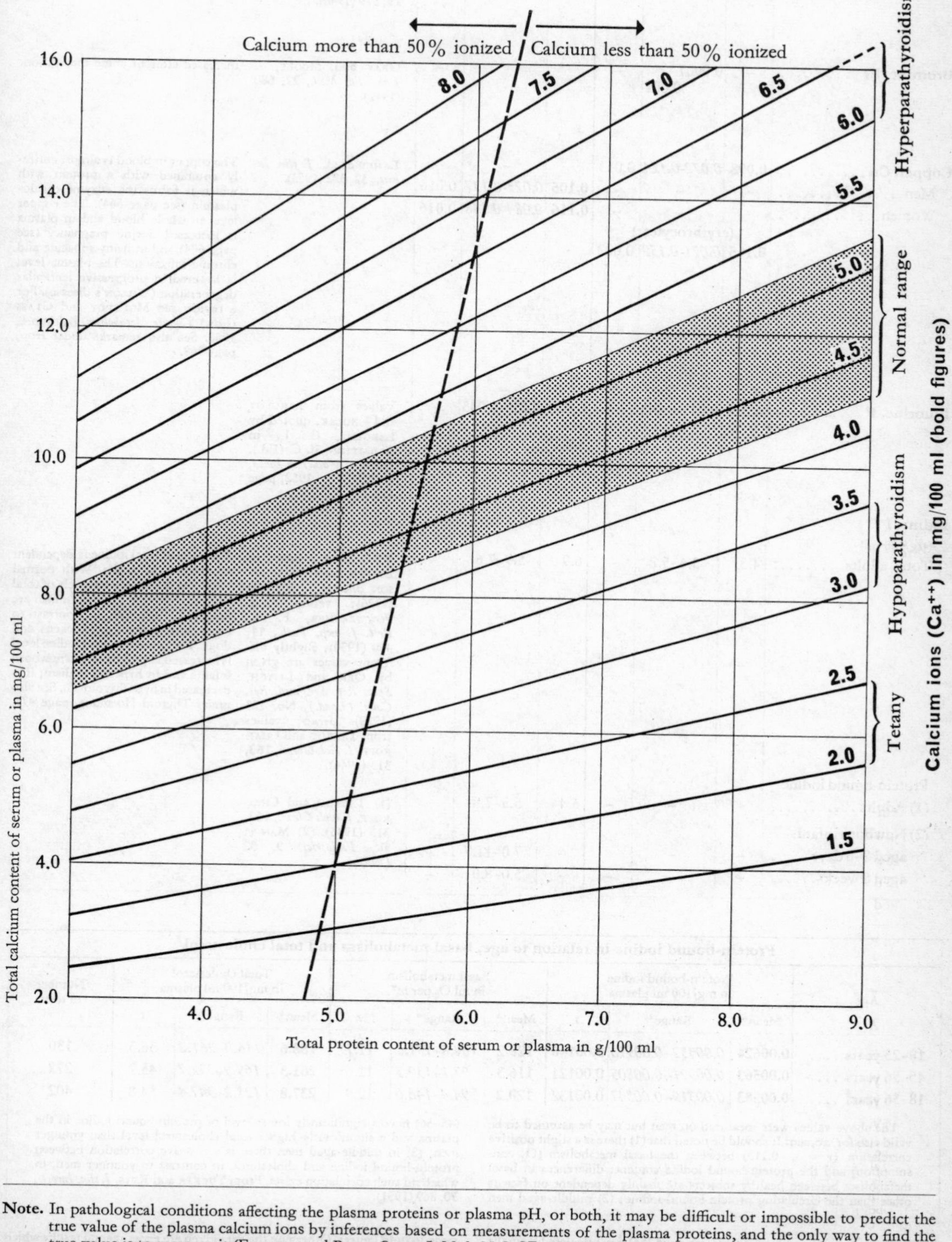

Note. In pathological conditions affecting the plasma proteins or plasma pH, or both, it may be difficult or impossible to predict the true value of the plasma calcium ions by inferences based on measurements of the plasma proteins, and the only way to find the true value is to measure it (Fanconi and Rose, *Quart. J. Med.*, N. S. **27**, 463 [1958]).

Normal values in **mg/100 ml**, unless otherwise stated

	Whole blood Mean*	Whole blood Range*	Whole blood s	Plasma or serum Mean*	Plasma or serum Range*	Plasma or serum s	Methods and sources	Remarks
Trace elements								
Aluminum, Al	0.013	up to 0.035	–	0.024	up to 0.048	–	KEHOE et al., *J. Nutr.*, **19**, 579 (1940).	Mainly in the serum.
Bromine, Br	–	0.0007–0.001	–	–	–	–	GRAY and MOORE, *J. Lab. clin. Med.*, **27**, 680 (1942).	Increased after bromine medication.
Copper, Cu	**0.098**	*0.072-0.124*	0.013	–	–	–	LAHEY et al., *J. clin. Invest.*, **32**, 322 (1953).	The copper in blood is almost entirely combined with a protein with which it forms the enzyme ceruloplasmin (see page 564). The copper level in whole blood and in plasma is increased during pregnancy (see page 604) and in many subacute and chronic infections. The plasma level is lowered in progressive lenticular degeneration (WILSON's disease). For a review see MCELROY and GLASS (Eds.), *Copper Metabolism*, Baltimore, 1950. See also remarks under Iron, page 568.
Men	–	–	–	**0.105**	*0.073-0.137*	0.016		
Women	–	–	–	**0.116**	*0.084-0.148*	0.016		
	(erythrocytes:) **0.115**	*0.071-0.159*	0.022	–	–	–		
Fluorine, F	0.028	0.011-0.045	–	0.028	0.010-0.045	–	Values from LARGENT and CHOLAK, quoted by LARGENT, E. J., in ALBRITTON, E. C. (Ed.), *Standard Values in Blood*, Philadelphia, 1952, page 119.	
Iodine, I (µg/100 ml)								
Total, adults	4.3	3.6–5.2	–	6.9	5.9–7.6	–	*Whole blood:* method of LEITCH and HENDERSON, *Biochem. J.*, **20**, 1003 (1926); values from FOWWEATHER, F. S., *Brit. J. exp. Path.*, **11**, 400 (1930); slightly different values are given by ORR and LEITCH, *Spec. Rep. Ser. med. Res. Coun. (Lond.)*, No. 123 (1929). *Serum:* values from TAUROG and CHAIKOFF, *J. biol. Chem.*, **163**, 313 (1946).	The level of total iodine is dependent on the iodide intake. With normal iodide intake the serum levels of total and protein-bound iodine in man are practically identical, in contrast to other species such as chickens and dogs. The protein-bound iodine level is increased in pregnancy, in newborn infants and in hyperthyroidism; it is decreased in hypothyroidism. See also under Thyroid Hormone, page 479.
Protein-bound iodine								
(1) Adults	–	–	–	6.4	5.5–7.8	–	(1) TAUROG and CHAIKOFF, *J. biol. Chem.*, **163**, 313 (1946). (2) MAN et al., *Pediatrics*, **9**, 32 (1952).	
(2) Newborn infants aged 2–6 days	–	–	–	–	7.0–11.7	–		
aged 8 weeks	–	–	–	–	5.0–8.0	–		

Protein-bound iodine in relation to age, basal metabolism and total cholesterol

Age	Protein-bound iodine in mg/100 ml plasma			Basal metabolism in ml O_2 per m²			Total cholesterol in mg/100 ml plasma			Number of tests
	Mean*	Range*	s	Mean*	Range*	s	Mean*	Range*	s	
18–25 years	**0.00624**	*0.00332–0.00916*	0.00146	**128.2**	*104.8–151.6*	11.7	**188.6**	*116.0–261.2*	36.3	130
45–56 years	**0.00563**	*0.00321–0.00805*	0.00121	**116.3**	*93.1–139.5*	11.6	**261.3**	*169.9–352.7*	45.7	272
18–56 years	**0.00583**	*0.00319–0.00847*	0.00132	**120.2**	*94.4–146.0*	12.9	**237.8**	*128.2–347.4*	54.8	402

The above values were measured on men but may be assumed to be valid also for women. It should be noted that (1) there is a slight positive correlation ($r = + 0.113$) between the basal metabolism (O_2 consumption) and the protein-bound iodine content; differences in basal metabolism between healthy subjects are mainly dependent on factors other than the circulating protein-bound iodine; (2) middle-aged men (45–56) have a significantly lower level of protein-bound iodine in the plasma and a significantly higher total cholesterol level than younger men; (3) in middle-aged men there is a positive correlation between protein-bound iodine and cholesterol, in contrast to younger men, in which no such correlation exists. From TUCKER and KEYS, *J. clin. Invest.*, **30**, 869 (1951).

* When a range given is a *normal range* (see page 154), i.e. calculated from the formula: mean ± (2 × standard deviation *s*), it is printed in *italics*, with the mean in **bold** figures. Otherwise the data given are experimental results which have not been tested statistically.

	Whole blood Mean*	Whole blood Range*	Whole blood s	Plasma or serum Mean*	Plasma or serum Range*	Plasma or serum s	Methods and sources	Remarks
Lead, Pb	0.025	0.015-0.035	–	0.0015	up to 0.0041	–	KEHOE et al., *J. Nutr.*, **19**, 579 (1940), and **20**, 85 (1940).	According to KEHOE, R. A., *Industrial Hygiene and Toxicology*, vol. II, New York, 1949 (in agreement with SCHMIDT, P., *Über die Diagnostik der Bleivergiftung im Lichte moderner Forschung*, Jena, 1933, page 37; BRUGSCH, T., *Lehrbuch der inneren Medizin*, 13th ed., vol. II, Berlin, 1948, page 1531; PORTHEINE, F., *Klin. Wschr.*, **30**, 83 [1952]), the upper limit of the normal range for lead in blood is 0.060 mg/100 ml whole blood. An increase above this level indicates an abnormal exposure to or intake of lead without recognizable pathological changes necessarily becoming immediately or later apparent. Values under 0.060 mg/100 ml are to be regarded as normal, over 0.060 as critical, 0.080 or more as dangerous. With values of over 0.080 mg/100 ml, further contact with lead should be forbidden, even if there are no obvious symptoms of lead poisoning. When the lead level in blood has fallen to 0.050 mg/100 ml, contact with lead may be resumed.
(erythrocytes:)	0.024	0.012-0.036	–	–	–	–		
Manganese, Mn	0.015	up to 0.033	–	0.004	up to 0.010	–	KEHOE et al., *J. Nutr.*, **19**, 579 (1940).	Mainly in the erythrocytes.
Tin, Sn	0.012	up to 0.032	–	0.002	up to 0.0028	–	KEHOE et al., *J. Nutr.*, **19**, 579, (1940), and **20**, 85 (1940).	Mainly in the erythrocytes.
Zinc, Zn	0.880	0.488-1.272	–	0.300	0–0.613	–	VALLEE and GIBSON, *J. biol. Chem.*, **176**, 445 (1948).	
(erythrocytes:)	1.440	0.911-1.979	–	–	–	–		
(per 10^8 leukocytes:)	0.0032	–	–	–	–	–		

* When a range given is a *normal range* (see page 154), i.e. calculated from the formula: mean ± (2 × standard deviation s), it is printed in *italics*, with the mean in **bold** figures. Otherwise the data given are experimental results which have not been tested statistically.

Blood gases (see page 572)

Oxygen capacity

The *oxygen capacity* is the oxygen content of blood saturated with O_2; it consists of two fractions, oxygen combined chemically (with hemoglobin) and oxygen in solution. However, the oxygen capacity is usually taken as equal to the hemoglobin-combined oxygen and is calculated instead of measured (see note 3 on page 572).

Carbon dioxide capacity and alkali reserve

The *carbon dioxide capacity* is the CO_2 content of whole blood or plasma in equilibrium with CO_2 at 40 mm Hg (= partial pressure of CO_2 in alveolar air). In practice only the CO_2 capacity of plasma is determined: arterial blood is drawn with exclusion of air and allowed to stand until coagulated. The plasma is then separated and after equilibration with CO_2 the ionically bound CO_2 is liberated by weak acid and measured. The measured gas volume is reduced to normal conditions (STPD = 0°C, 760 mm Hg, dry; cf. page 300).

The *total* CO_2 extractable from plasma so treated represents the total CO_2 capacity of the plasma and consists of two fractions, that present as bicarbonate ion and that present in physical solution (also referred to as carbonic acid, H_2CO_3), known respectively as the *combined capacity* and *free capacity*. The combined capacity is usually designated the **alkali reserve.** The CO_2 of the alkali reserve is also known as "bicarbonate CO_2".

The pH of the blood is primarily dependent on the ratio of carbonic acid to bicarbonate (H_2CO_3:$BHCO_3$), represented by HENDERSON's equation

$$[H^+] = K[H_2CO_3]/[BHCO_3]$$

or by the logarithmic form of HENDERSON and HASSELBACH

$$pH = pK + \log\,[BHCO_3] - \log\,[H_2CO_3]$$

where [ ] indicates molar concentration, K = dissociation constant of carbonic acid, and $pH = -\log\,[H^+]$, $pK = -\log K$.

The denominator in the HENDERSON equation may be obtained with sufficient accuracy for most clinical purposes by determining the alkali reserve. For more precise measurements determination of the *actual CO_2 content* and pH of a blood sample under complete exclusion of air must be made. On alkalosis and acidosis see under Water and Electrolyte Balance, page 540.

The **O_2 content, CO_2 content and related values** refer to the actual O_2 and CO_2 contents of blood (plasma) *drawn and examined with complete exclusion of air*. They must not be confused with the gas capacities described above, which always relate to blood (plasma) either saturated with or in equilibrium with these gases.

Diagram: pH value of blood and distribution of the total CO_2 content

Example: At pH 7.39 the total CO_2 content consists of 0.05 (5%) as carbonic acid and 0.95 (95%) as bicarbonate. With a total CO_2 content of say 60 vol% and pH 7.39 the blood sample therefore contains $0.05 \times 60 = 3$ vol% (= 1.4 mmol/l*) carbonic acid CO_2 and $0.95 \times 60 = 57$ vol% (= 25.6 mmol/l*) bicarbonate CO_2 (the latter corresponding to 25.6 mEq/l* HCO_3^- ions.

For a method of determining simultaneously pH, CO_2 content and packed cell volume in 0.1 ml aliquots of blood see SINGER et al., *Clin. Chem.*, **1**, 287 (1955).

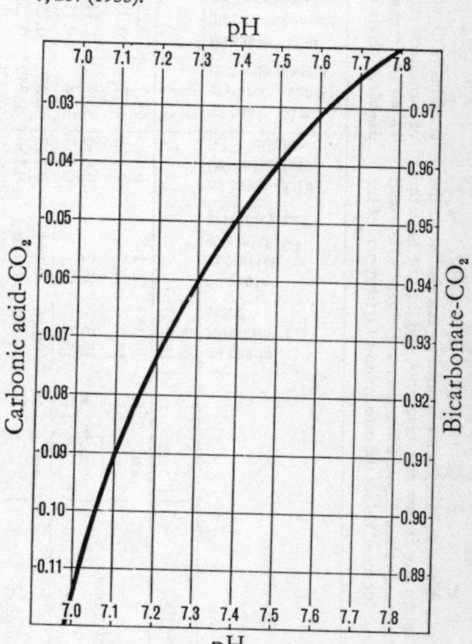

After SUNDERMAN and BOERNER, *Normal Values in Clinical Medicine*, Philadelphia, 1950, page 158.

* Conversion factor for vol% into mmol/l (and mEq/l) = 1/2.226 = 0.449.

Many of the values in this table have been obtained by calculation on the basis of assumed values for factors and constants, and do not have the same validity as measured values. Those for women are in general less well established than those for men. Values for carbamino-CO_2 (that part of the combined CO_2 which is combined with protein) in particular indicate order of magnitude rather than exact magnitude. The data under Nos. 1–13 and 17–40 are from a summary based on 50 sources in ALBRITTON, E. C. (Ed.), *Standard Values in Blood*, Philadelphia, 1952, page 120; those under Nos. 14–16 are from (for whole blood) HARRISON, G. A., *Chemical Methods in Clinical Medicine*, 4th ed., London, 1957, page 369, and (for plasma) GUEST, G. M., in NELSON, W. E. (Ed.), *Textbook of Pediatrics*, 7th. ed., Philadelphia, 1959, page 177, in general agreement with other authors.

	No.	Blood gases			ml gas in 100 ml whole blood	ml gas in 45.0 ml (M)[1] or 40.0 ml (F)[1,2] erythrocytes	ml gas in 55.0 ml (M)[1] or 60.0 ml (F)[1,2] plasma	ml gas in 100 ml erythroc. in contact with plasma	ml gas in 100 ml plasma in contact with erythrocytes	Blood gas pressure (tension) mm Hg	Factors and constants
Oxygen, O_2	1	**Capacity**[3]		M	20.4[4]			45.3[6]			
				F	18.0[4,5]			45.3[7]			
	2	Total content	art.	M	20.3[8,9]	20.1	0.142	44.7	0.258	94	5.00 } Difference arterial O_2 — venous O_2
	3			F	17.9	17.7	0.155	44.7	0.258	94[7]	4.20
	4		ven.[10]	M	15.3	15.2	0.060	33.9	0.110	40[11]	
	5			F	13.7	13.6	0.068	34.4	0.113	41[11]	
	6	In solution ("free" O_2)	art.	M	0.285	0.144	0.142	0.319	0.258	94	factor[12] 0.0258[12]; factor[13] 0.02089[13]
	7			F	0.282	0.126	0.156	0.319	0.258	94[7]	
	8		ven.[10]	M	0.122	0.061	0.061	0.136	0.110	40[11]	
	9			F	0.124	0.055	0.068	0.139	0.113	41[11]	
	10	Combined (hemoglobin-O_2)	art.	M	20.0	20.0	0	44.4	0	94	98 } Hemoglobin O_2 saturation in %
	11			F	17.6	17.6	0	44.4	0	94[7]	98
	12		ven.[10]	M	15.2	15.2	0	33.6	0	40[11]	73.5
	13			F	13.6	13.6	0	34.3	0	41[11]	74.5
Carbon dioxide, CO_2	14	**Capacity**		M, F	43-56[14]				53-68[14]		Note: the plasma values are for plasma not in contact with erythrocytes
	15	Free capacity (in sol.)		M, F	2.7[14]				2.4-3.4[14]		
	16	Combining power or alkali reserve (total combined CO_2)		M, F	41-53[14]				50-65[14] 22-30 mEq HCO_3		
	17	Total content	art.	M	49.0	16.2	32.8	36.0	59.6	41	1.217 } factor[15]; 4.1 } Difference arterial CO_2 — venous CO_2
	18			F	48.0[17]	13.6	34.4	34.3	57.0[17]	39[18,19]	1.187; 3.4
	19		ven.[10]	M	53.1	18.0	35.1	40.1	63.8	46.5[19]	1.201
	20			F	51.4	14.9	36.5	37.7	60.4[17]	43[19]	1.175
	21	In solution (free CO_2 content = carbonic acid-CO_2)	art.	M	3.384	1.820	1.564	2.356	2.844	41	0.4399 } factor[20] erythrocytes; 0.5311 } factor[20] plasma
	22			F	2.532	0.891	1.641	2.250	2.717	39[18,19]	
	23		ven.[10]	M	2.997	1.211	1.786	2.690	3.248	46.5[19]	
	24			F	2.785	0.965	1.820	2.437	3.013	43[19]	
	25	Combined, total	art.	M	45.6	14.4	31.2	33.6	56.8	41	7.19 } erythrocytes; 7.40 } plasma } pH values
	26			F	45.5	12.7	32.8	32.1	54.3	39	7.20; 7.40[7]
	27		ven.[10]	M	50.1	16.8	33.3	37.4	60.5[8]	46.5	7.17; 7.37[21]
	28			F	48.7	14.0	34.7	35.3	57.4	43	7.18; 7.38[19]
	29	Carbamino-CO_2	art.	M	2.2[8]	1.7	0.4	3.9	0.8	41	0.115 } factor erythrocytes[22]; 0.014 } factor plasma[22]
	30			F	1.9[8]	1.5	0.5	3.7	0.8	39	0.116; 0.014
	31		ven.[10]	M	3.1	2.6	0.5	5.8	0.8	46.5	0.154; 0.014
	32			F	2.7	2.2	0.5	5.5	0.8	43	0.156; 0.014
	33	Bicarbonate-CO_2	art.	M	43.4	12.6	30.8	29.8	56.0	41	
	34			F	43.5	11.2	32.3	28.3	53.5	39	
	35		ven.[10]	M	47.0	14.2	32.8	31.6	59.7	46.5	
	36			F	46.0	11.8	34.2	29.8	56.6	43	
Nitrogen, N_2	37	(in solution)	art.	M	0.979	0.494	0.484	1.099	0.881	572[23]	0.0146 } factor[24] erythrocytes; 0.0117 } factor[24] plasma
	38			F	0.970	0.437	0.534	1.103	0.884	574[23]	
	39		ven.[10]	M	0.979	0.494	0.484	1.099	0.881	572[23]	
	40			F	0.970	0.437	0.534	1.103	0.884	574[23]	

1) The hematocrit values used here are somewhat lower than the normal clinical values given on page 576, in part due to the greater plasma volume in recumbent posture (v. standing). *2)* The exact values used for this table are 39.6 (hematocrit) and 60.4 (100 minus hematocrit = plasma per 100 ml whole blood). *3)* O_2 capacity = grams Hb × 1.36. This factor is based on a Hb-Fe content of 0.339%. See also footnote *1*. *4)* Based on Hb contents of 15 g (M) and 13.2 g (F), both somewhat lower than the clinical values given on page 578. See also footnote *1*. *5)* Exact value used in subsequent calculations: 17.95. *6)* Equivalent to 33.3 g Hb/100 ml (= 20 mmol/l) erythrocytes. *7)* Assumed to be equal to the value for men. *8)* Any apparent discrepancies in sums or differences are due to rounding off *after* calculations were made. *9)* Arithmetical mean of 9 mean values from the literature = 19.5, equivalent to a Hb content of 14.34 g. *10)* Mixed venous blood. *11)* Available mean values for mixed venous blood of men average slightly less, viz. 38. *12)* Dissolved O_2 content (in ml) in 100 ml human erythrocytes = 100 × 0.0258 × O_2 pressure/760. *13)* Dissolved O_2 content (in ml) in 100 ml (horse) plasma = 100 × 0.02089 × O_2 pressure/760. *14)* See remarks on CO_2 capacity and related values on page 571. *15)* Plasma CO_2 = F × whole-blood CO_2, F being a factor depending on pH, O_2 capacity and Hb-O_2 saturation per cent. *16)* Arterio-venous CO_2 difference calculated as arterio-venous O_2 difference multiplied by the normal respiratory quotient of 0.82. *17)* The blood CO_2 content in women is ca. 1 ml lower than in men (antecubital vein blood). *18)* May be still lower prior to menstruation. *19)* Calculated from the equation: $pH = 6.10 + (A - kB)kB$, where pH = values in lines 25–28 (plasma column), k = 0.0314 = plasma factor (lines 21–24) × 100/2.226 × 760, A = total CO_2 content in 100 ml plasma (in contact) × 2.226, B = CO_2 pressure. *20)* ml CO_2 (inc. H_2CO_3) dissolved in 100 ml erythrocytes = 0.4399 × 100 × CO_2 pressure/760. For plasma, substitute 0.5311 for 0.4399. *21)* Calculated from the arterial value for men, using the standard arterio-venous pH difference of 0.03. *22)* Carbamino-CO_2 = total combined CO_2 × this factor. The values of this factor are provisional as other factors on which it is based have not yet all been determined for human blood. *23)* The arterial and venous N_2 pressures are assumed to be both equal to the alveolar air N_2 pressure, the latter calculated as the difference between 760 and the sum of the following: O_2 = 100; CO_2 = (M) 41, (F) 39; water vapor = 47 mm Hg. Note that the total of blood gases and water vapor varies with atmospheric pressure (normal 760 mm Hg). *24)* ml N_2 dissolved in 100 ml erythrocytes = 0.0146 × 100 × N_2 pressure/760. For plasma, substitute 0.0117 for 0.0146.

Genealogy (of the formed elements of the blood of adults)

Modified neo-unitarian (monophyletic) theory of DOWNEY[1]

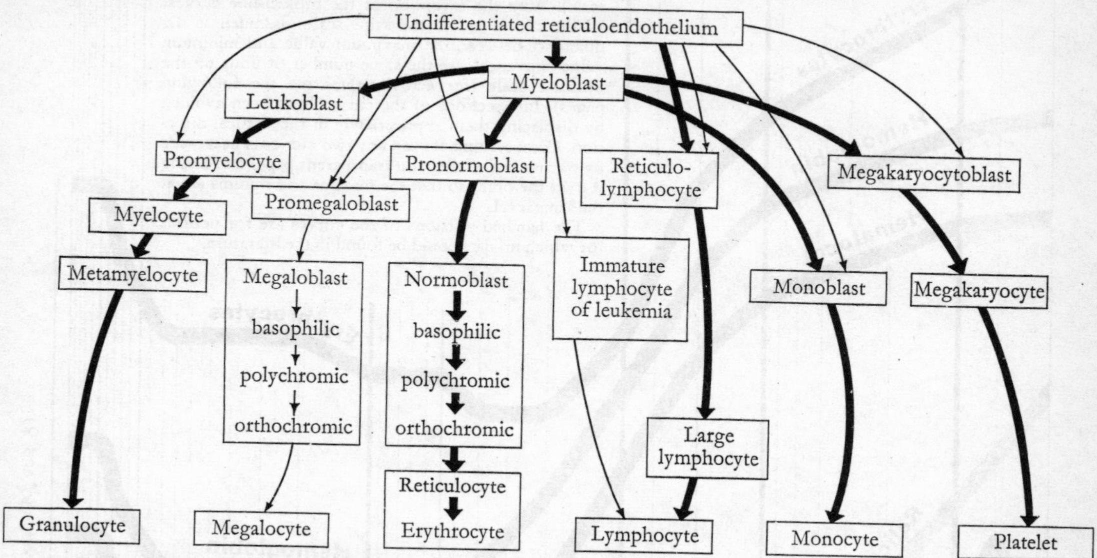

Legend: The thick lines indicate the development of blood cells in the normal human adult, the thin lines the various possibilities under pathological and experimental conditions.

Polyphyletic (dualist) theory of DOAN[2]

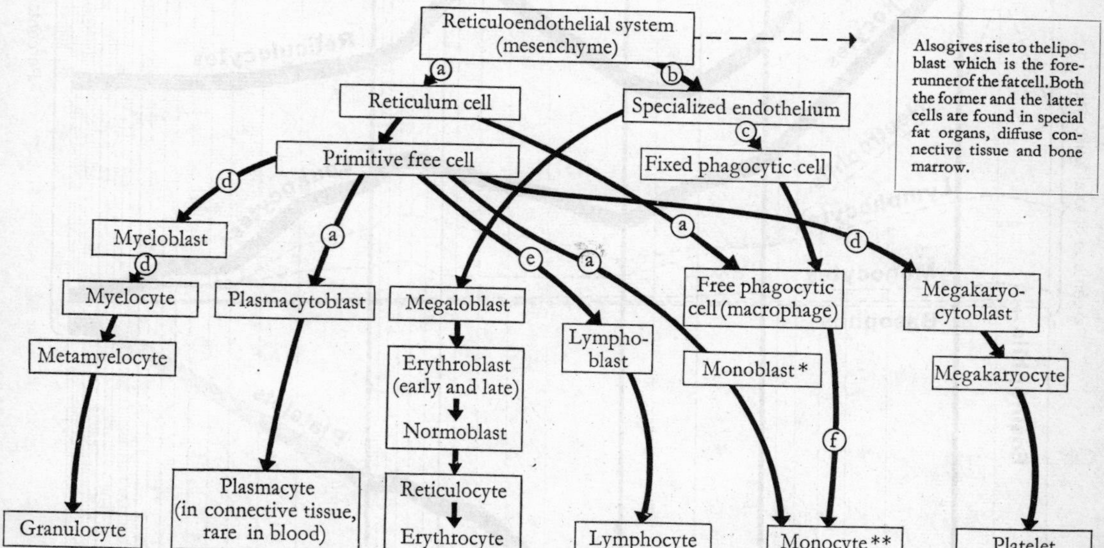

Legend: (a) In diffuse connective tissue and organ parenchyma; (b) in bone marrow, lymph nodes, spleen, KUPFFER cells of liver; (c) in lymph nodes, spleen, KUPFFER cells of liver; (d) in bone marrow; (e) in lymph nodes and spleen; (f) on demand, the macrophage may also give rise to fat cells or vice versa.

* Monoblasts may give rise to myeloblasts in tissue cultures.

** Monocytes may give rise to fibroblast-like cells in tissue cultures and may revert to monoblasts on demand. Monocytes may also give rise to epithelioid cells in fatty degeneration (in tuberculosis caseation) and to the LANGHANS or foreign-body giant cells.

1) After JONES, O. P., in ALBRITTON, E. C. (Ed.), *Standard Values in Blood*, Philadelphia, 1952, page 68. See also DOWNEY, H., in DOWNEY, H. (Ed.), *Handbook of Hematology*, New York, 1938, vol. II, page 1275, and vol. III, page 1965; SUNDBERG and DOWNEY, *Amer. J. Anat.*, **70**, 455 (1942); JONES, O. P., *Arch. Path. (Chicago)*, **35**, 752 (1943). *2)* DOAN, C. A., in ALBRITTON, E. C. (Ed.), *Standard Values in Blood*, Philadelphia, 1952, page 69. See also DOAN et al., *Contributions to Embryology*, No. 83, Publn. 361 of the Carnegie Institution, Washington, 1925; CUNNINGHAM et al., *Contributions to Embryology*, No. 84, Publn. 361 of the Carnegie Institution, Washington, 1925; DOAN, C. A., *Medicine*, **10**, 323 (1931); DOAN, C. A., *Bull. N.Y. Acad. Med.*, **15**, 668 (1939); DOAN, C. A., *J. Lab. clin. Med.*, **26**, 89 (1940).

Diagrammatic comparison of fluctuations of the formed elements during growth

The curves have been obtained by plotting the percentage of the maximum value (maximum value between birth and 20 years) against age (logarithmic scale). With the exception of the broken-line curves, all the curves are to the same scale inasmuch as the difference between the maximum value and minimum value is in each case the same number of units on the ordinate scale (for actual values see the following pages). Intersections of the curves have been avoided by displacing them appropriately in the vertical direction. Comparison between any two curves is best made by tracing one of them on transparent paper and laying it over the other so that the maxima and minima are at the same level.

The hatched portions of the curves are for periods for which no data could be found in the literature.

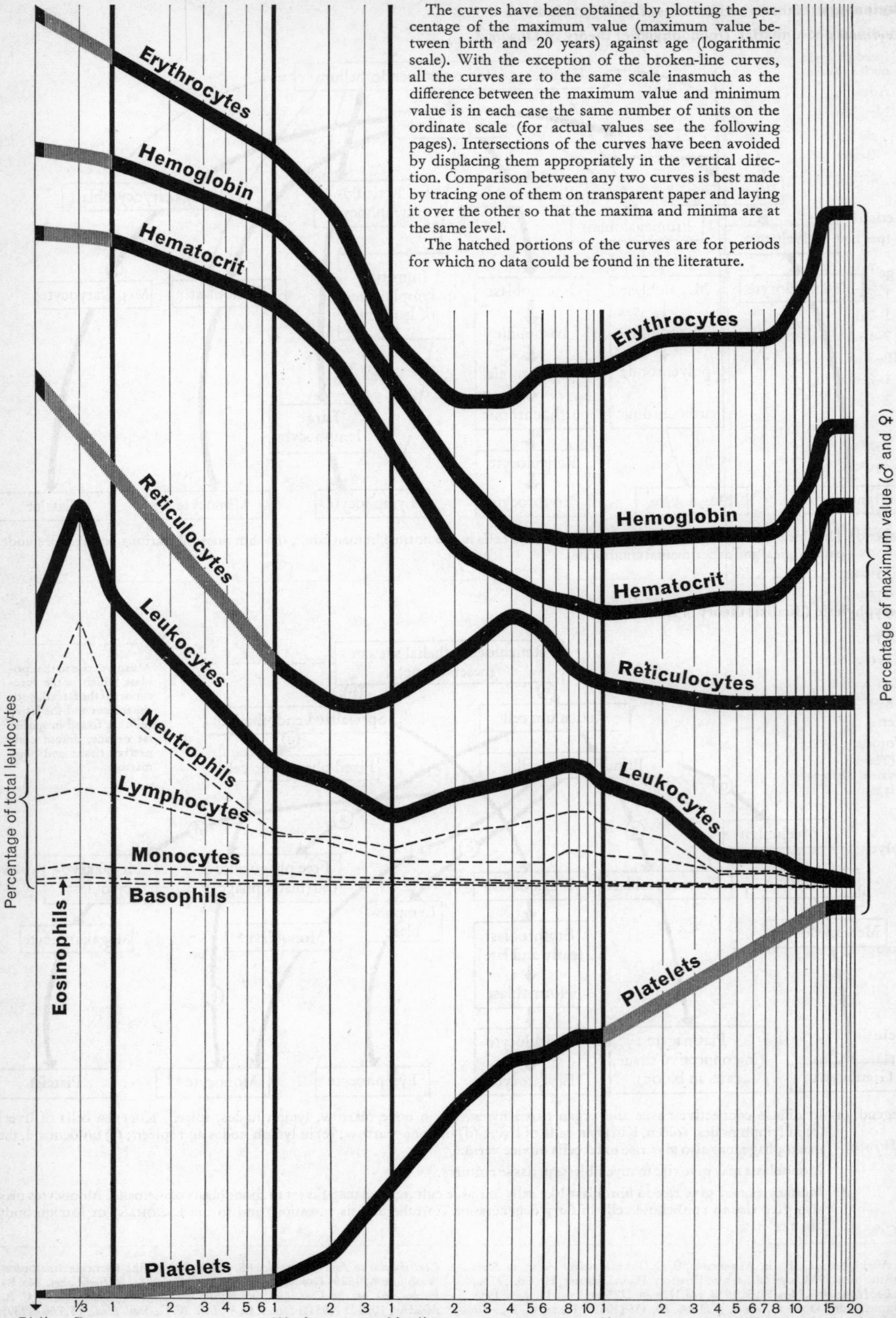

Erythrocyte forms (for genealogy of erythrocytes see page 573)

Erythroblasts (percentage of total nucleated cells)	Normal values	Methods and sources	Remarks
Adults	0	From SMITH et al., in NELSON, W. E. (Ed.), *Textbook of Pediatrics*, 7th ed., Philadelphia, 1959, page 932.	In respect of shape, staining, hemoglobin content and size, the *normoblasts* which first appear in the blood in erythroblastosis bear a marked resemblance, except for the nucleus, to erythrocytes. Erythroblastosis is related (with exceptions) to increase of the erythrocytes. It is a sign, however, of a dysfunction rather than a hyperfunction of hematopoiesis. For evolution of erythroblasts see page 573.
Newborn			
At birth	1–5		
2 days old	2		
Subsequently	0		

Reticulocytes (per 1000 erythrocytes)

Methods and sources: Counting in smears. *Adult values* from WATSON, C. J., *Arch. intern. Med.*, **86**, 797 (1950) (values for the group ♂ + ♀ corrected to a sex ratio of 1:1). *Values for children* from DE CHASTONAY, E., *Helv. paediat. Acta*, **6**, 257 (1951), in agreement with WASHBURN, A. H., *Amer. J. Dis. Child.*, **62**, 530 (1941).

Remarks: Reticulocytes, or reticulated erythrocytes, are young erythrocytes showing a basophilic reticulum under vital staining. Usually somewhat larger than the average erythrocyte and more resistant to hemolysis. There is an average difference of 3‰ between men and women. *Increased* in blood regeneration during the reparative phase of anemia. An abrupt increase of 4% up to 40% indicates a reticulocytic crisis, e.g. after starting treatment of pernicious or severe hypochromic anemia. The number of reticulocytes in the blood is usually a measure of its regenerative activity. For the relation between the number of reticulocytes and the erythrocyte coproporphyrin see page 579. For comparison between the variation in the reticulocyte count and other blood values in adolescence see the diagram on the opposite page. *Physiologically higher* in children; *permanent pathological increase* (up to 20%) in congenital hemolytic jaundice.

Age	Mean*	Range*	*s*
1–24 hours	39.2	–	–
1–7 days	22.3	–	–
7–10 days	10.6	–	–
10–30 days	**7.9**	*0.3–15.5*	3.8
1–2 months	**12.9**	*0–27.7*	7.4
2–6 months	**10.6**	*0–24.8*	7.1
6–12 months	**7.5**	*0–17.3*	4.9
1 year	**7.5**	*0–16.3*	4.4
2 years	**7.1**	*0–15.1*	4.0
3 years	**7.2**	*0–15.4*	4.1
4 years	**8.1**	*0–18.1*	5.0
5 years	**8.2**	*0–17.2*	4.5
6 years	**7.5**	*0–15.5*	4.0
7 years	**7.6**	*0.6–14.6*	3.5
8 years	**6.8**	*0.4–13.2*	3.2
9 years	**7.5**	*0.9–14.1*	3.3
10 years	**7.6**	*1.2–14.0*	3.2
11–15 years	**7.4**	*0–15.4*	4.0
Men and women as one group	**7.5**	*1.3–13.7*	3.1
Men	**6**	*1.6–10.4*	2.2
Women	**9**	*2.6–15.4*	3.2
(The difference between the values for men and women is significant)			

Form	Methods and sources	Remarks
Polychromatic erythrocytes	Staining with basic dyes.	*Polychromatophilia* = appearance of diffuse bluish color, varying in intensity from erythrocyte to erythrocyte, on staining with basic dyes. It parallels reticulation and like the latter is a sign of increased regeneration. Polychromatic erythrocytes are mostly macrocytes.
Basophilic granulated erythrocytes	As above	Likewise a sign of increased (but degenerative) regeneration: in adults basophilic stippling is not a normal stage in the development of the erythrocytes like reticulation and polychromatophilia and does not run at all parallel with these. Occurs mainly in and after lead poisoning.
Inclusion bodies		
HEINZ bodies	Vital staining	On staining with Nile blue sulfate HEINZ bodies appear as blue granules on the edge of the erythrocyte, more rarely in the middle. They are observed in poisoning (aniline, phenylhydrazine, sulfonamides, etc.) and frequently also after splenectomy.
HOWELL-JOLLY bodies	Staining with nuclear stains.	Granules of diameter 1–2 µm, staining deeply with nuclear stains, observed occasionally in erythrocytes. Very probably of nuclear derivation. They appear occasionally (very few) in anemia, in large numbers after splenectomy.
CABOT's rings		Threadlike rings and convolutions in the erythrocytes of hemopathic patients. Occur occasionally in conjunction with polychromatophilia and HOWELL-JOLLY bodies. Very probably nuclear membrane remnants.

* When a range given is a *normal range* (see page 154), i.e. calculated from the formula: mean ± (2 × standard deviation *s*), it is printed in *italics*, with the mean in **bold** figures. Otherwise the data given are experimental results which have not been tested statistically.

Erythrocytes	Mean*	Range*	s	Methods and sources	Remarks
Specific gravity $\left(\frac{25}{4}°C\right)$	–	1.084-1.117	–	LANG et al. (Eds.), *Hoppe-Seyler/Thierfelder Handbuch der physiologisch- und pathologisch-chemischen Analyse*, vol. V, *Untersuchung der Organe, Körperflüssigkeiten und Ausscheidungen*, Berlin, 1953, page 1.	The specific gravity of whole blood is a result mainly of the relatively high specific gravity of the erythrocytes. Cf. specific gravity of blood and plasma (page 547) and hemoglobin content of erythrocytes (opposite). With a water content of 60–67% the erythrocytes are among the "driest" cells of the organism.
pH value	7.36	7.28–7.41	–	GRAM, H. C., *Amer. J. med. Sci.*, **168**, 511 (1924).	
Lifetime (days)					
Men and women as one group	115	–	–	LONDON et al., *J. biol. Chem.*, **179**, 463 (1949); CALLENDER et al., *J. Path. Bact.*, **57**, 129 (1945).	Determined by means of glycine tagged with radioactive ^{15}N. Corresponds to an erythrocyte replacement rate of ca. 0.83% per day. Pathologically, only decreases are observed in the lifetime. For a review see BERLIN et al., *Physiol. Rev.*, **39**, 577 (1959).
Men	120	–	–		For further physical and chemical data on erythrocytes see pages 547–550, 552, 557–560, 563–568 and 570–572.
Women	109	–	–		
Erythrocyte count (red blood count, RBC) (millions p. cubic millim. of peripheral venous blood)					
Age					
(1) At birth (2 series)	**4.82**	*4.04–5.60*	0.39	(1) From DEMARSH et al., *Amer. J. Dis. Child.*, **75**, 860 (1948); (2) MERRITT and DAVIDSON, *Amer. J. Dis. Child.*, **46**, 990 (1953); (3) WINTROBE, M. M., *Clinical Hematology*, 3rd ed., Philadelphia, 1952, page 95, in agreement with GUEST et al., *Amer. J. Dis. Child.*, **56**, 529 (1938); (4) JUDY and PRICE, *J. Amer. med. Ass.*, **167**, 563 (1958).	*Newborn* (1 week): The erythrocyte count of the cutaneous (capillary) blood is greater than that of the blood of the sagittal sinus. If the umbilical cord is not tied until after the expulsion of the placenta the erythrocyte count is ca. 560,000/mm³ greater than if the cord is tied immediately after the birth (DEMARSH et al., *J. Amer. med. Ass.*, **116**, 2568 [1941]). *Physiologically increased* in acclimatization to high altitudes. Measurements made with the aid of ^{32}P-tagged erythrocytes have given markedly lower figures for the total erythrocytes circulating in the body than those calculated from counts of peripheral venous blood. The erythrocyte concentration in peripheral venous blood is diagnostically reliable only when used in conjunction with a measurement of the total blood volume: an increase in the latter, for example, can increase the total number of erythrocytes in the body (polycythemia) while the concentration in peripheral venous blood remains normal. In hydremia, on the other hand, a subnormal erythrocyte concentration in peripheral venous blood may be accompanied by a normal total of erythrocytes in the body. See also the diagram on page 574.
	5.50	*4.58–6.42*	0.46		
(2) 1 day	5.95	4.6–6.8	–		
(2) 1 month	5.19	3.9–5.9	–		
(2) 2 months	4.74	3.7–5.9	–		
(2) 3 months	4.65	3.9–5.4	–		
(2) 4 months	4.61	3.6–5.2	–		
(2) 5 months	4.67	3.9–5.5	–		
(2) 6 months	4.73	3.8–5.2	–		
(2) 7 months	4.70	3.9–5.3	–		
(2) 8 months	4.65	3.8–5.3	–		
(2) 9 months	4.79	4.2–6.3	–		
(2) 10 months	4.74	4.2–5.6	–		
(2) 11 months	4.70	3.9–5.4	–		
(2) 12 months	4.67	4.1–5.3	–		
(3) 1 year	4.5	–	–		
(3) 2 years	4.6	–	–		
(3) 3 years	4.5	–	–		
(3) 4 years	**4.6**	*3.4–5.8*	0.6		
(3) 5 years	4.6	–	–		
(3) 6–10 years	4.7	–	–		
(3) 11–15 years	4.8	–	–		
(3) Men	**5.4**	*3.8–7.0*	0.8		
(3) Women	**4.8**	*3.6–6.0*	0.6		
(4) Women (11-68 yrs.)	**4.37**	*3.81–5.03*	0.282		
Hematocrit value (Ht, packed cell volume, PCV) (volume percentage of erythrocytes in peripheral venous blood)					
Age					
At birth	56.6	–	–	By centrifuging; by calculation from specific gravities of whole blood and plasma (see page 546). Values from (children) GLASER, K., in ALBRITTON, E. C. (Ed.), *Standard Values in Blood*, Philadelphia, 1952, page 38; (adults) WATSON, C. J., *Arch. intern. Med.*, **86**, 797 (1950).	The hematocrit value or packed cell volume is primarily a function of the erythrocyte concentration, so that the above considerations equally apply. It is also influenced by the shape and size of the erythrocytes. This largely relative nature of the hematocrit value must be borne in mind when the value is used diagnostically. For a method of determining simultaneously PCV, pH and CO_2 in 0.1 ml aliquots of blood see SINGER et al., *Clin. Chem.*, **1**, 287 (1955). See also the diagram on page 574.
1 day	56.1	–	–		
1 week	52.7	–	–		
2 weeks	49.6	–	–		
3 weeks	46.6	–	–		
4 weeks	44.6	–	–		
2 months	38.9	–	–		
4 months	36.5	–	–		
6 months	36.2	–	–		
8 months	35.8	–	–		
10 months	35.5	–	–		
12 months	35.2	–	–		
2 years	35.5	–	–		
4 years	37.1	–	–		
6 years	37.9	–	–		
8 years	38.9	–	–		
10 years	39.0	–	–		
12 years	39.6	–	–		
Men and women as one group	**42.9**	*35.9–49.9*	3.5		
Men	**46.2**	*43.2–49.2*	1.5		
Women	**40.6**	*35.8–45.4*	2.4		

* When a range given is a *normal range* (see page 154), i.e. calculated from the formula: mean ± (2 × standard deviation *s*), it is printed in *italics*, with the mean in **bold** figures. Otherwise the data given are experimental results which have not been tested statistically.

Mean corpuscular volume (MCV)
(cubic microns, μm^3)

	Mean*	Range*	*s*
Adults	86	78–94	–
Children			

Methods and sources

Values: (adults) from WHITBY and BRITTON, *Disorders of the Blood*, 5th ed., London, 1946, page 57; (children) GLASER, K., in ALBRITTON, E. C. (Ed.), *Standard Values in Blood*, Philadelphia, 1952, page 38.

Remarks

MCV in cubic microns = (hematocrit value in milliliters per 100 ml blood divided by erythrocyte count per cubic millimeter in millions) × 10. The mean corpuscular (erythrocyte) volume may be regarded as an absolute value. The only factor which could militate against this would be the shape of the erythrocytes and this is unlikely in view of the plasticity of the cells and the high pressure exerted on them in the hematocrit.

Children

Age	Mean	Age	Mean	Age	Mean	Age	Mean
At birth	106	4 weeks	91	10 months	77	6 years	80
1 day	106	2 months	85	12 months	77	8 years	80
1 week	101	4 months	79	2 years	78	10 years	80
2 weeks	96	6 months	78	4 years	80	12 years	81
3 weeks	93	8 months	77				

Mean diameter
(microns, μm)

Age	Mean*	Range*	*s*
At birth	8.6	–	–
14–60 days	8.1	–	–
3–5 months	7.7	–	–
6–11 months	7.4	–	–
1 year	7.3	–	–
3–10 years	7.4	–	–
Adults	**7.5**	*6.9–8.1*	0.3

Methods, sources, remarks

Determination: Direct microscopic measurement.

Values from WINTROBE, M. M., *Clinical Hematology*, 3rd ed., Philadelphia, 1952, page 95.

Remarks: Size distribution of erythrocytes: *normocytes*, 6.5–8.5; *microcytes*, under 5; *macrocytes*, over 10. Predominance of either of the latter sizes is known respectively as *micro-* and *macrocytosis*. The standard deviation of the erythrocyte diameter is a measure of the *anisocytosis*, i.e. the degree of exaggeration of the usual size variation. For calculation of the standard deviation see page 159.

Microcytosis (without marked anisocytosis) occurs particularly in compensated hemolytic jaundice, *macrocytosis* (without marked anisocytosis) appears relatively rapidly in liver diseases (mean value in infectious hepatitis **8.15**, *s* 0,64; in cirrhosis of the liver **8.45**, *s* 0.66) without increase of poikilocytes; in pernicious anemia; in vitamin B_1 deficiency (after LÜDIN, H., *Helv. med. Acta*, **17**, 340 [1950]). Marked *anisocytosis* occurs principally in iron-deficiency anemia.

Reduction of the erythrocyte diameter, in conjunction with a parallel reduction in hemoglobin content, causes physiological *microcytosis* combined with *hypochromia* in infants of 3–3½ months, a condition which is normalized by the 7th month.

Numerical eccentricity ε
(percentage of erythrocytes)

	Mean*	Range*	*s*
82 %	0.00	–	–
9.2%	–	0.01–0.70	–
8.2%	–	0.71–0.80	–
0.3%	–	0.81–0.90	–
0.2%	–	0.91–0.98	–

Measurement: $\varepsilon = \sqrt{1-(b/a)^2}$ (a = major axis, b = minor axis).

Values from ZINI and LEUBNER, *Schweiz. med. Wschr.*, **81**, 382 (1951).

Remarks: A predominance of oval forms is known as *elliptocytosis* (ovalocytosis).

Constitutional elliptocytosis is very rare (0.04% of persons). It is characterized by elliptocytes (ovalocytes) of uniform shape and is not associated with disease.

Symptomatic elliptocytosis with non-uniform elliptocytes and combined with a parallel increase in poikilocytes occurs in many diseases which are accompanied by blood changes (hemoglobin, erythrocyte count, displacement of the PRICE-JONES curve), particularly in pernicious anemia and leukemia, but also in pulmonary tuberculosis, for example. Symptomatic elliptocytosis is of value prognostically and in assessment of the course of a disease, since it is only normalized on complete return to health (after ZINI and LEUBNER, *Schweiz. med. Wschr.*, **81**, 382 [1951]).

Poikilocytosis, in which there is complete irregularity of erythrocyte form, is very probably due to abnormal deformability (cf. symptomatic elliptocytosis, above).

Sickle cells present a special form of poikilocytosis and are found almost exclusively in Negroes or in individuals whose blood contains an admixture of Negro blood (ca. 10% of Negroes show the sickling trait). Their presence is usually but not always associated with a form of hereditary chronic hemolytic anemia known as *sickle-cell* or *drepanocytic anemia*.

Thickness
(microns, μm)

	Mean*	Range*	*s*
Thickness	–	1.84–2.05	–

Determination: Direct microscopic measurement.

Values from WINTROBE, M.M., *Medicine (Baltimore)*, **9**, 195 (1930).

Remarks: *Spherocytes* have a greater thickness, i.e. a more spherical form. *Spherocytosis* is usually a sign of lowered osmotic resistance of the erythrocytes (spherocytes are intermediate in shape between normal and hemolyzed erythrocytes) and therefore appears prominently in hemolysis. In 5% NaCl solution the erythrocytes are nearly all completely spherical with thickness and diameter of ca. 4–5 μm, the volume thus remaining fairly constant. After DAMESHEK, W., *Blood*, Special Issue No. 2, 43 (1948).

Surface area
(square microns, μm^2)

	Mean*	Range*	*s*
Surface area	~140	–	–

Value from WINTROBE, M.M., *Clinical Hematology*, 3rd ed., Philadelphia, 1952, page 86.

Remarks: The average total surface area of the erythrocytes in the human body amounts to ca. 3820 sq. meters, or 2000 times the surface area of the body.

Hemoglobin (Hb) content
(grams per 100 ml of peripheral venous blood)

Age	Mean*	Range*	*s*
(1) At birth	**19.5**	*9.5–29.5*	5.0
(1) 2–3 days	19.0	–	–
(1) 4–8 days	**18.3**	*10.3–26.3*	4.0
(1) 9–13 days	16.5	–	–

Determination: By hemometer (colorimetrically), spectrometrically, from the O_2-combining capacity, from the Fe content, from specific gravities of plasma and serum.

Values: (1) from WINTROBE, M.M., *Clinical Hematology*, 3rd ed., Philadelphia, 1952, page 95; (2) from JUDY and PRICE, *J. Amer. med. Ass.*, **167**, 563 (1958).

Remarks: *Newborn* (1 week): the hemoglobin content of the cutaneous (capillary) blood is greater than that of the blood of the sagittal sinus. If the umbilical cord is not tied until after the expulsion of the placenta the hemoglobin content is ca. 2.6 g/100 ml greater than if the cord is tied immediately after the birth. The hemoglobin content falls during pregnancy (PAABY, P., *Acta obstet. gynec. scand.*, **37**, 69 [1958]), but a hemoglobin level below 12 mg/100 ml should be

* When a range given is a *normal range* (see page 154), i.e. calculated from the formula: mean ± (2 × standard deviation *s*), it is printed in *italics*, with the mean in **bold** figures. Otherwise the data given are experimental results which have not been tested statistically.

Hemoglobin (Hb) content *(continued)*

Age	Mean*	Range*	*s*
(1) 14–60 days	**14.0**	*7.4–20.6*	3.3
(1) 3–5 months	**12.2**	*7.6–16.8*	2.3
(1) 6–11 months	11.8	–	–
(1) 1 year	11.2	–	–
(1) 2 years	11.5	–	–
(1) 3 years	12.5	–	–
(1) 4–5 years	12.6	–	–
(1) 6–10 years	12.9	–	–
(1) 11–15 years	13.4	–	–
(1) Men	**16.0**	*12.0–20.0*	2.0
(1) Women	**14.0**	*10.0–18.0*	2.0
(2) Women (11–68 yrs.)	**12.55**	*10.2–14.8*	1.15

Methods, sources, remarks

regarded as abnormal (Camilleri, A. P., *J. Obstet. Gynaec. Brit. Emp.*, **65**, 266 [1958]). The fetal hemoglobin (Hb-F) differs from normal adult hemoglobin (Hb-A) in amino acid composition (cf. White and Beaven, *Brit. med. Bull.*, **15**, 33 [1959]). At birth the Hb-F content is 50% of the total hemoglobin, after which it falls rapidly. Hb-F is found in adult blood in thalassemia (Cooley's anemia, Mediterranean disease). Of the very large number of other genetic hemoglobin variants, differing only in the amino acid composition, the following are important: Hb-S (sickle-cell hemoglobin, common in Negroes), Hb-E (in 10% of the population of Thailand and Burma), and Hb-D (in about 1% of the population of India). For a review see Lehmann, H., *Brit. med. Bull.*, **15**, 40 (1959).

The hemoglobin content of blood is primarily a function of the erythrocyte concentration and thus rises and falls with the erythrocyte count. Since the structure of hemoglobin is not known, present methods of determination depend on the use of empirical factors, for example that 1 gram Hb combines with 1.34 ml O_2 or that 1 gram Hb contains 0.335% Fe. These factors were originally obtained from measurements on hemoglobin from other species. Measurements by Bernhart and Skeggs, *J. biol. Chem.*, **147**, 19 (1943), on human hemoglobin have given values of 1.36 ml O_2 and 0.340% Fe per gram hemoglobin. Values for hemoglobin content obtained by the use of the earlier factors are therefore presumably ca. 1.5% too high.

See also the diagram on page 574.

Determination of hemoglobin by hemoglobinometer

Clinical hemoglobinometers are based on various norms and on practical grounds must be read before conversion of the hemoglobin into acid hematin takes place. Data on hemoglobin content given in the literature are derived from the use of a variety of hemoglobinometers and are thus only to a limited extent comparable, and then only when the method, including the reading time, is clearly laid down. The determination of hemoglobin from the specific gravities of blood and plasma usually gives more comparable values, not because the method itself is more accurate but because it is less subject to technical and subjective sources of error (see under Specific gravity of blood, pages 546 and 547).

Mean corpuscular hemoglobin (MCH or Hb_E) content (micromicrograms, $\mu\mu g = 10^{-12}$ gram)

Mean*	Range*	
31.2	27.4–35.0	(at sea level)
–	28.2–37.8	(at 3730 m)
–	28.9–38.9	(at 4540 m)
		(men and women; for children see the table below)

Determination: (*Hemoglobin* in g/100 ml blood divided by *erythrocyte count* in millions per cubic millimeter) × 10 (see adjacent nomogram).

Values from Hurtado et al., *Arch. intern. Med.*, **75**, 284 (1945).

Remarks: Hemoglobin contents below, above and within the normal range are denoted respectively as hypo-, hyper- and normo-chromic. The mean corpuscular (erythrocyte) hemoglobin content provides a reliable and comparable measure of hypo-, normo- and hyper-chromia.

The so-called **Color index** (hemoglobin content as % of normal divided by erythrocyte count as % of normal) should give the same information but does so only when (1) separate norms are used for men and women, and (2) when the norms for hemoglobin content and erythrocyte count are in the relation 15.8:5. Color index data in the literature are only comparable when they have been calculated on a uniform basis and in accordance with a clearly defined method. Expression of the mean corpuscular hemoglobin in micromicrograms is therefore much to be preferred and renders the color index superfluous.

Mean corpuscular hemoglobin concentration (MCHC) (grams per 100 ml erythrocytes = %)

Mean*	Range*	
34.1	31.3–36.9	(at sea level)
–	33.0–36.6	(at 3730 m)
–	32.7–36.7	(at 4540 m)
		(men and women; for children see the table below)

Determination: (*Hemoglobin* in g/100 ml blood divided by *hematocrit value*) × 100.

Values from Hurtado et al., *Arch. intern. Med.*, **75**, 284 (1945).

Mean corpuscular hemoglobin and mean corpuscular hemoglobin concentration in children

Age	MCH μμg	MCHC %	Age	MCH μμg	MCHC %
At birth	38	38	8 months	26	33.8
1 day	38	37.8	10 months	26	33.5
1 week	37	37.2	12 months	25	33.0
2 weeks	35	36.3	2 years	25	33.0
3 weeks	34	35.6	4 years	27	34.0
4 weeks	33	35.0	6 years	27	33.5
2 months	30	34.2	8 years	27	33.2
4 months	27	34.0	10 years	27	33.3
6 months	27	34.0	12 years	28	33.8

From Albritton, E.C. (Ed.), *Standard Values in Blood*, Philadelphia, 1952, page 38.

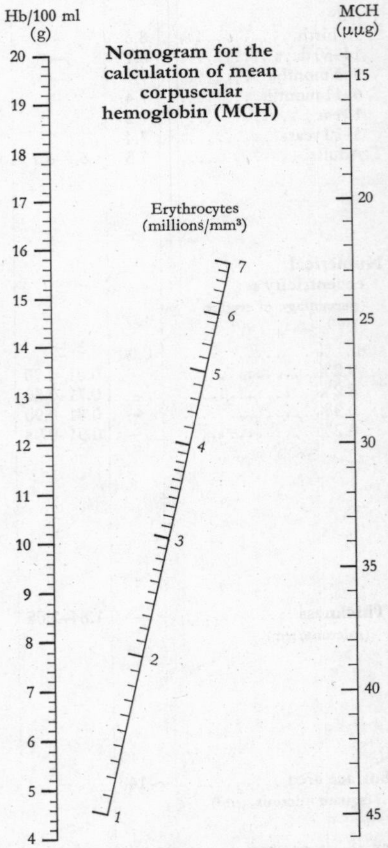

A line is drawn connecting the measured hemoglobin content (left-hand scale) with the measured erythrocyte count (middle scale). The intersection of this line with the right-hand scale gives the mean corpuscular hemoglobin.

Hemoglobin content of plasma 0–0.5 mg/100 ml (men and women)

Determination: Spectrometrically.

Remarks: Always increased in hemolysis due to any cause. The renal threshold value for hemoglobin in serum is ca. 150 mg/100 ml, so that pronounced hemoglobinemia is possible without necessarily resulting in hemoglobinuria.

* When a range given is a *normal range* (see page 154), i.e. calculated from the formula: mean ± (2 × standard deviation *s*), it is printed in *italics*, with the mean in **bold** figures. Otherwise the data given are experimental results which have not been tested statistically.

	Mean*	Range*	s	Methods and sources	Remarks
Carboxyhemoglobin .. (percentage of the hemoglobin)	3.4	0.0–8.2	2.4	PACE et al., *Amer. J. Physiol.*, **147**, 352 (1946).	See also page 379.
Expressed as **volume per cent** of CO in whole blood	**0.15**	*0.05–0.25*	0.05	EVERETT, M. R., *Medical Biochemistry*, 2nd ed., New York, 1946, page 532.	
Methemoglobin (hemiglobin, ferrihemoglobin) (percentage of the hemoglobin)	0.4	0.0–1.1	–	VAN SLYKE et al., *J. biol. Chem.*, **166**, 121 (1946).	See also page 379.
Protoporphyrin IX (micrograms per 100 ml erythrocytes)				....	See pages 376 and 377. The protoporphyrin content of the erythrocytes is not so closely correlated with the reticulocyte count as is the case with coproporphyrin. The protoporphyrin content is slightly increased in hemolytic anemia (60–120 μg), greatly increased in iron-deficiency anemia (180–390 μg) and has the highest values in lead poisoning (200–1300 μg). Values are normal in pernicious anemia.
Men and women as one group	**36.4**	*19.4–53.4*	8.5	WATSON, C. J., *Arch. intern. Med.*, **86**, 797 (1950).	
Men } Sex difference	**28.5**	*19.5–37.5*	4.5		
Women } very significant	**41.7**	*29.9–53.5*	5.9		
Coproporphyrin III (micrograms per 100 ml erythrocytes)				....	See pages 376 and 378. The coproporphyrin content is closely correlated with the reticulocyte count and is highest in diseases involving retarded hemoglobin synthesis, such as hemolytic anemia (30–50 μg) and lead poisoning (2–60 μg). Absent in pernicious anemia, it increases with the reticulocyte count, but more rapidly, after treatment with vitamin B_{12} (after WATSON, *loc. cit.*). The urinary excretion of coproporphyrin III is not correlated with the coproporphyrin content of the erythrocytes.
Men and women as one group	**0.5**	*0–1.58*	0.54	WATSON, C. J., *Arch. intern. Med.*, **86**, 797 (1950).	
Men	**0.3**	*0–1.08*	0.39		
Women	**0.7**	*0–1.9*	0.6		
Verdohemoglobin ..... (percentage of the hemoglobin)	–	5–8	–	HAVEMANN, R., *Klin. Wschr.*, **20**, 543 (1941).	

Thrombocytes (platelets; for genealogy see page 573; for thrombocytes and other blood values in adolescence see page 574)

	Mean*	Range*	s	Methods and sources	Remarks
Thrombocyte count (thousands per cubic millimeter whole blood)					
Cutaneous blood					
Age					
At birth	227	140–290	–	Direct method of WOOD et al., *Laboratory Technique*, 3rd ed., New York, 1929, page 26. Values from MERRITT and DAVIDSON, *Amer. J. Dis. Child.*, **46**, 990 (1933).	The number of platelets is ca. 15% higher in venous blood than in cutaneous blood, and ca. 12% higher in arterial blood than in venous blood. In women the platelet count falls before menstruation, then rises again afterwards (see diagram). After the age of 60 the number of platelets is markedly reduced. The platelet count and distribution are also dependent on physical constitution, physical exertion, altitude and environmental temperature.
1 week	233	160–320	–		
2 weeks	242	170–370	–		
3 weeks	269	160–380	–		
1 month	277	200–370	–		
2 months	320	200–470	–		
3 months	348	200–480	–		
4 months	324	180–450	–		
5 months	345	200–470	–		
6 months	350	200–480	–		
7 months	330	200–460	–		
8 months	346	220–480	–		
9 months	333	200–440	–		
10 months	340	200–450	–		
11 months	361	220–480	–		
12 months	339	250–470	–		
Adults	–	273–545	–	Direct values from AGGELER et al., *Blood*, **1**, 472 (1946).	
Adults	250	180–358	–	Direct method. Values from TOCANTINS, L. M., *Medicine (Baltimore)*, **17**, 155 (1938); *Amer. J. med. Sci.*, **192**, 150 (1936).	
Adults	–	500–900	–	Indirect method. Values from DAMESHEK, W., *Arch. intern. Med.*, **50**, 579 (1932).	
Venous blood	310	150–690	–	Direct method. Values from TOCANTINS, L. M., *Medicine (Baltimore)*, **17**, 155 (1938).	
Diameter (microns, μm)					
13-18% of thrombocytes	1.8	–	–		
72% of thrombocytes	2.3	–	–		
9-10% of thrombocytes	3.6	–	–		
Volume (cubic microns, μm^3)					
After VAN ALLEN, C. M., *Münch. med. Wschr.*, **24**, 141 (1927)	0.49	0.35–0.67	–		
After HORWITZ, S., *Klin. Wschr.*, **10**, 1613 (1931)	5	2.5–10	–		
After TOCANTINS, L. M., *Medicine (Baltimore)*, **17**, 155 (1938) ..	–	10–12	–		

Thrombocyte count during the menstrual cycle
After POHLE, F. J., *Amer. J. med. Sci.*, **197**, 40 (1939)

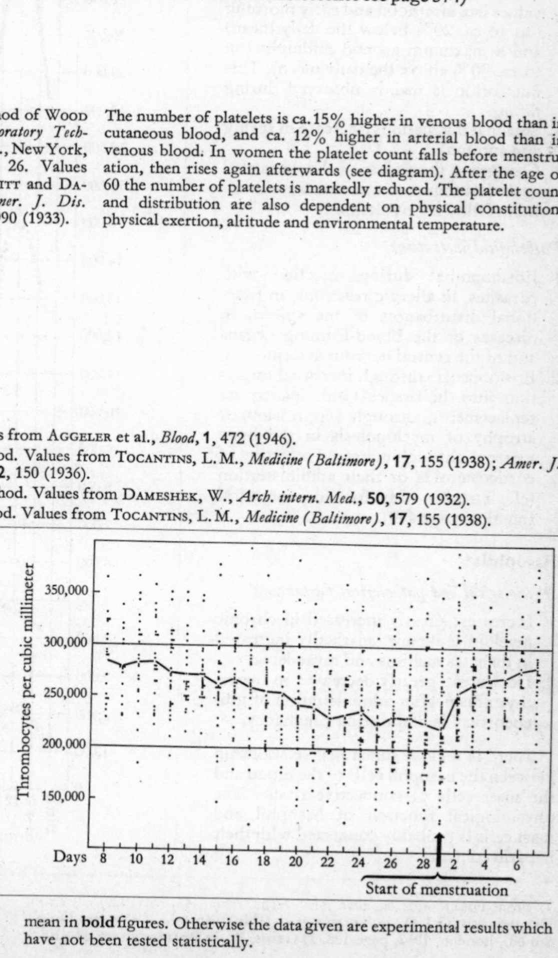

* When a range given is a *normal range* (see page 154), i.e. calculated from the formula: mean ± (2 × standard deviation *s*), it is printed in *italics*, with the mean in **bold** figures. Otherwise the data given are experimental results which have not been tested statistically.

Synopsis of Blood – Leukocytes

(See also pages 573 and 574)

Variation with age of the leukocyte count and distribution

Age	Total leukocytes	Neutrophils		Eosinophils		Basophils		Lymphocytes		Monocytes		Neutrophilic myelocytes	
	Number per mm³	Number per mm³	%	Number per mm³	%	Number per mm³	%	Number per mm³	%	Number per mm³	%	Number per mm³	%
1 day[1]	15,250-45,000	8628-33,525	53-82.5	0- 921	0 - 6	0-636	0-2	2000-8722	9-36	696-5175	3.0-11.5	0-1908	0-13
3–5 days[1]	4000-18,000	1800-10,152	32 -59	168-1110	1.5-13	0-215	0-2	600-5184	15-44.5	920-4324	10 -23	0- 174	0-1.5
6–8 days[1]	7600-16,400	2156- 8528	26.5-67	160- 727	1.5- 7	0-196	0-1.5	1292-7015	17-61	760-2362	7 -19.5	0- 437	0-3
9–11 days[1]	8100-16,500	1976- 6141	18.5-46	205- 873	1.5-6.5	0-269	0-2	2937-9453	22-69	1164-3738	8.5-28	0- 102	0-1
3 months to 3 years[2]	7500-14,000	2000- 7000	40 -50	25- 700	0.5- 5	0- 50	0-0.5	4000-9000	50-60	25- 700	0.5- 5	–	–
3–5 years[2]	6000-12,500	3000- 8000	50 -60	50- 700	1- 5	0- 50	0-0.5	2500-6000	40-50	25- 700	0.5- 5	–	–
5–15 years[2]	5500-10,800	3000- 7000	55 -65	50- 500	1- 5	0- 50	0-0.5	1500-4500	30-40	25- 600	0.5- 6	–	–
Adults[2]	5000-10,000	3000- 7000	60 -70	50- 400	1- 4	0- 50	0-0.5	1000-3000	20-30	100- 600	2 - 6	–	–
Adults, mean	7000	4500	66	100	1.5	25	0.5	1800	26	450	6	–	–

Eosinophils[3]

Physiological fluctuations

1. Repeated fluctuations of short duration at intervals of a few minutes and of a magnitude exceeding the range of error of the method of measurement.
2. A marked daily periodicity with low values late afternoon and early morning (up to ca. 20% below the daily mean) and a maximum around midnight (up to ca. 30% above the daily mean). This fluctuation is mainly observed during *fasting*.
3. Seasonal fluctuations (increase in spring and autumn).
4. Changes in the course of the menstrual cycle (maximum at menstruation, minimum following ovulation).

Pathological fluctuations

1. Eosinophilia: during infection with parasites, in allergic reactions, in functional disturbances of the spleen, in diseases of the blood-forming organs and of the central nervous system.
2. Eosinopenia: through increased migration into the tissues (with inadequate replacement), through suppression or atrophy of myelopoiesis in the bone marrow, through increased secretion of corticosteroids or their administration (cf. Thorn's test for adrenocortical function, page 490).

Basophils[4]

Physiological and pathological fluctuations

1. Increases: greatly increased in chronic myeloid leukemia, markedly increased in diabetes mellitus and myxedema.
2. Decreases: greatly decreased in hyperthyroidism, after administration of glucocorticoids and during pregnancy.

There is a close functional relationship between the basophil cells of the blood and the mast cells of connective tissue. The physiological function of basophil and mast cells is probably connected with their heparin content.

Fall in leukocyte count between birth and 15 years

After Kato, K., *J. Pediat.*, 7, 7 (1935)

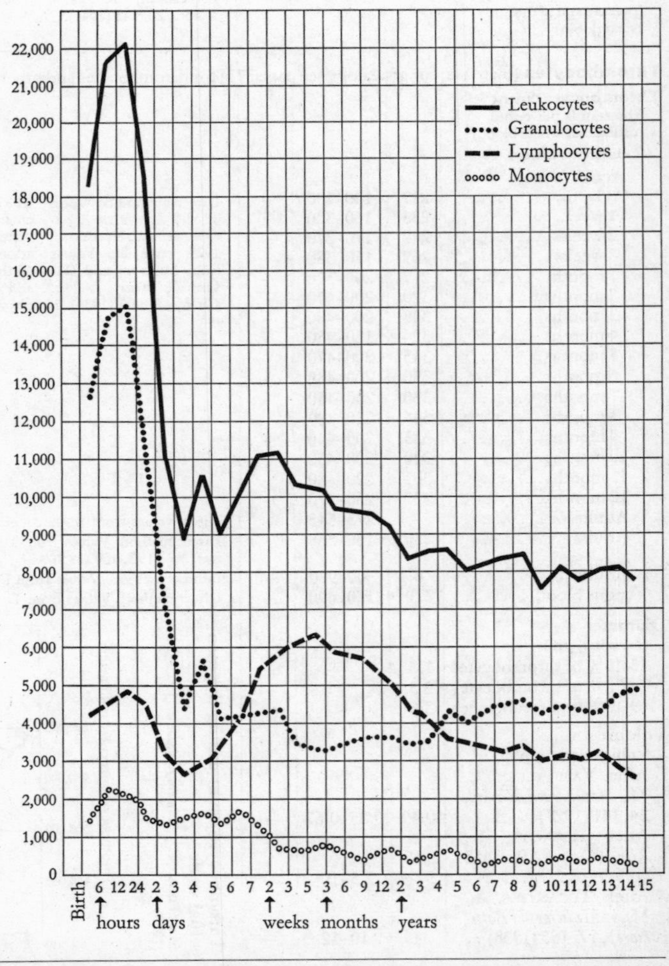

1) From Forkner, C. E., *Bull. Johns Hopk. Hosp.*, **45**, 75 (1929). *2)* From Zarafonetis, C. J. D., in Kolmer et al. (Eds.), *Approved Laboratory Technic*, 5th ed., London, 1952, page 103. *3)* Gross, R., in Braunsteiner, H. (Ed.), *Physiologie und Physiopathologie der weissen Blutzellen*, Stuttgart, 1959, page 1. *4)* Braunsteiner, H., in Braunsteiner, H. (Ed.), *loc. cit.*, page 49.

SCHILLING's hemogram

Normal ratio of immature neutrophils (myelocytes + juveniles + band cells) to mature (segmented) neutrophils = 1 : 13 or more	Basophils	Eosinophils	Myelocytes	Neutrophils: juveniles	Neutrophils: band cells	Neutrophils: segmented cells	Lymphocytes	Monocytes
Normal range (%)	0.5–1.5	2–4	0	0–1	3–5	51–67	20–30	5–10

Classifications of ARNETH and SCHILLING (modified from HADEN, R. L., *Principles of Hematology*, 2nd ed., Philadelphia, 1940)

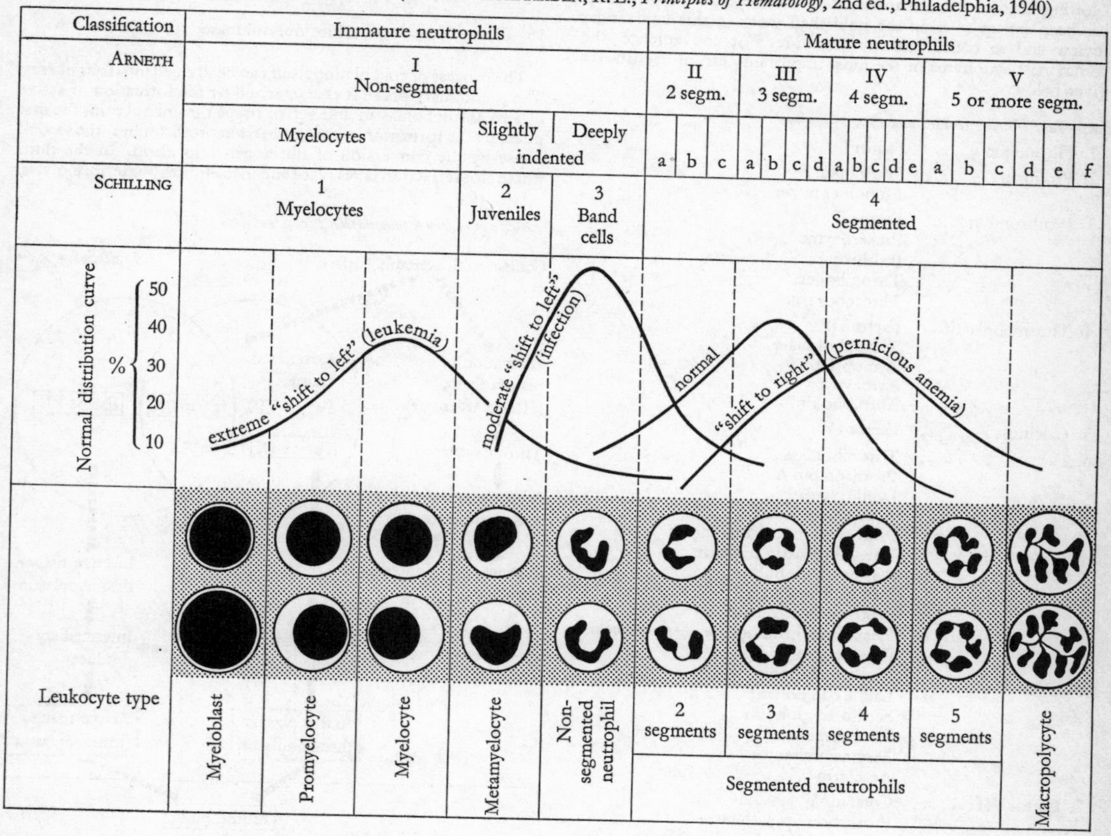

Bone marrow (see also genealogy of the blood corpuscles, page 573)

Myelogram (sternal marrow)[1]: men and women as one group

Cell types			Mean* %	Normal range** %
Red series 19.1 %	Early erythroblasts 2.9 %	Proerythroblasts	0.5	0.2 – 4.0
		Early normoblasts........................	2.4	1.5 – 5.8
	Late erythroblasts 16.2 %	Intermediate normoblasts	11.7	5.0 –26.4
		Late normoblasts........................	4.5	1.6 –21.5
White series and others 70 % ...	Granulocytes 57.4 %	Myeloblasts	1.2	0.3 – 3.1
		Progranulocytes	3.0	0.5 – 4.5
		Myelocytes........................	8.7	0.9 –20.3
		Metamyelocytes	11.0	5.6 –22
		Band cells........................	17.9	6.1 –36
		Segmented cells........................	15.6	8.7 –27
	Others 12.6 %	Lymphocytes........................	9.8	2.7 –24
		Monocytes........................	1.4	0.7 – 2.8
		Megakaryocytes	0.2	0.03– 0.4
		Plasmacytes	0.6	0.1 – 1.5
		Reticulum cells	0.6	0.03– 1.6
Not identifiable 10.9 %	Not identifiable 10.9 %	Unclassified cells	1.7	0.02– 3.3
		Disintegrated cells	9.2	1.1 –20.8

* Mean of authors' means. ** Range of authors' means.
1) From 21 authors (750 individuals), in ALBRITTON, E. C. (Ed.), *Standard Values in Blood*, Philadelphia, 1952, page 72.

Synopsis of Blood – Blood Coagulation

By Dr. C. Montigel, Research Laboratories of J. R. Geigy S.A., Basle (Switzerland)

Theoretical aspects

The complicated processes which take place in the coagulation of blood are still not fully understood. Most hematologists are agreed on the basic processes involved but there is considerable disagreement concerning the details. In addition to this, an understanding of the process is made even more difficult by the frequent use of different names for one and the same factor. For this reason the International Committee on the Nomenclature of Blood Clotting Factors (Chairman: Prof. Irving Wright, New York) has been set up to keep the published work in this field under review and to coordinate nomenclature. For convenience, the commonest synonyms of the most important clotting factors are given below.

Important clotting factors and their synonyms

1. Fibrinogen	Factor I
2. Profibrin	Fibrinogen B Monomer fibrin
3. Prothrombin	Factor II Prosérozyme Prothrombin B Thrombogen Thrombozyme
4. Thromboplastin ..	Factor III Thrombokinase Zymoplastin Zytozyme Thrombokinin
5. Calcium	Factor IV
6. Factor V	Thrombogène Prothrombin A Labile factor Accelerator factor Prothrombin accelerator Thromboplastin cofactor Plasma-ac-globulin Proprothrombinase Prothrombinogenase Plasma prothrombin conversion factor Proaccelerin Prothrombinokinase Labile component Serum-ac-globulin Prothrombinase Serum accelerator Accelerin
7. Factor VII	Cofactor V Prothrombin accelerator Prothrombin conversion factor Prothrombin converting factor Cothromboplastin Plasma precursor Proconvertin Prothrombinogen Sérozyme Stable component Serum prothrombin conversion accelerator Serum prothrombin converting factor Convertin
8. Factor VIII	Antihemophilic globulin Antihemophilic globulin A Antihemophilic factor Plasmakinin Thromboplastinogen Thrombocytolysin Thrombokatalysin Thromboplastic plasma component Prothrombokinase Antihemophilic factor A Plasma thromboplastic factor Plasma thromboplastic factor A
9. Factor IX	Christmas factor Plasma thromboplastin component Plasma factor X Antihemophilic factor B Plasma thromboplastic factor B
10. Factor X	Stuart-Prower factor
11. Rosenthal factor.	Plasma thromboplastic antecedent
12. Hageman factor..	Plasma thromboplastic factor E
13. Profibrinolysin ...	Plasminogen Proplasmin Prolysin Lytic factor
14. Fibrinolysin	Plasmin Lysin
15. Fibrinokinase	Fibrinolysokinase

The process of coagulation itself can be divided into four phases. The preliminary phase is characterized by the formation of active plasma thromboplastin and active tissue thromboplastin, the first phase by the formation of thrombin from prothrombin, the second phase by the conversion of fibrinogen into fibrin. In the third phase clot retraction takes place and in the fourth phase fibrinolysis.

Diagram of blood coagulation processes

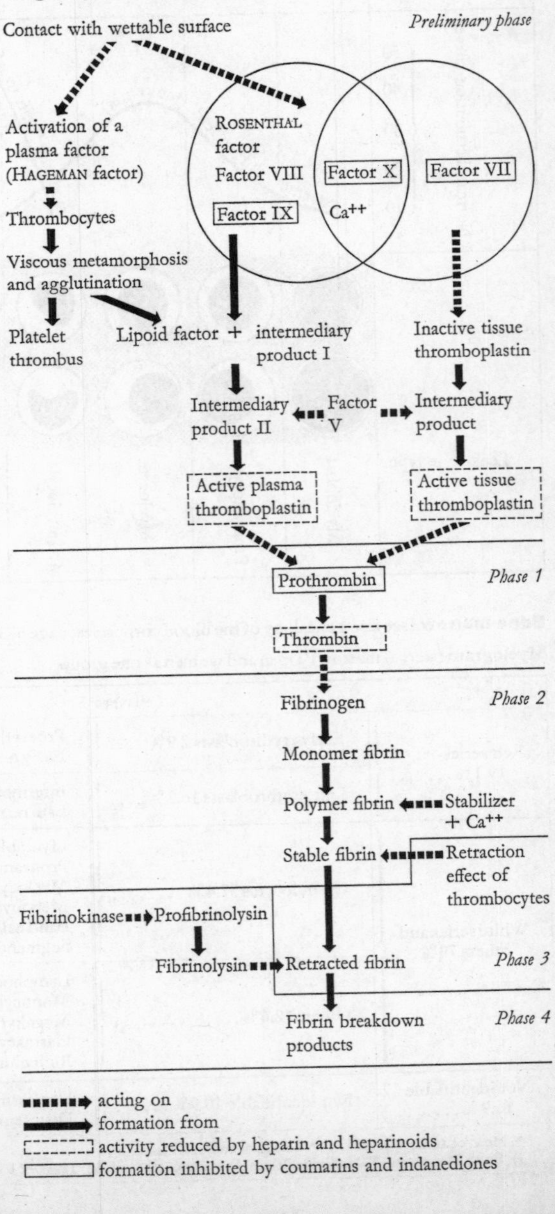

Normally, coagulation of blood begins when injury causes it to escape from a vessel and come into contact with a foreign, wettable surface (tissue). In the presence of calcium ions, contact with such a surface on the one hand activates a plasma factor (presumably the HAGEMAN factor) which in some unknown manner causes metamorphosis of the thrombocytes, and on the other brings about a reaction between antihemophilic globulin (factor VIII), Christmas factor (factor IX) and ROSENTHAL factor with the formation of the intermediary product I. Metamorphosis of the thrombocytes renders them labile, with the result that they agglutinate not only with each other but also with the wettable surface and with other cells. In this way a platelet thrombus is formed and various active substances are released. Among the latter a lipoid factor combines with the intermediary product I to form another intermediary product II which is transformed into active plasma thromboplastin under the influence of factor V.

Simultaneously with these processes, active tissue thromboplastin is being formed in the injured tissue. In the presence of calcium ions, factor VII and the STUART-PROWER factor (factor X) act on the inactive thromboplastin of the tissue fluids to form an intermediary product which is converted by factor V into active tissue thromboplastin. The processes taking place up to this point constitute the preliminary phase of coagulation.

The two active thromboplastins (plasma and tissue thromboplastin) act on prothrombin during the first phase of coagulation and bring about its conversion into thrombin. Heparin is an inhibitor of the activity of the thromboplastins as well as of thrombin. Other inhibitors about which little is as yet known also enter into the coagulation process.

In the second phase of coagulation, thrombin converts fibrinogen into soluble monomeric fibrin. This substance then polymerizes and is converted under the influence of a stabilizer and calcium ions into stable fibrin.

In the third phase the fibrin clot retracts under the action of the thrombocytes and in the fourth phase is finally broken down by the fibrinolytic enzyme system of the blood. The last process gives rise to soluble breakdown products of fibrin. The active agent fibrinolysin is a rather nonspecific, proteolytic enzyme which under pathological conditions is also capable of breaking down fibrinogen and other proteins involved in the coagulation process. It is formed from an inactive precursor, profibrinolysin, by the action of fibrinokinase, which in turn is inhibited by antifibrinokinase. The action of fibrinolysin is also subject to an inhibitor, antifibrinolysin.

Practical applications*

Bleeding time

This is the time which elapses before the arrest of bleeding not only from the capillaries but also from the small veins and arterioles. The arrest of bleeding is mainly due to the formation of a platelet thrombus.

Methods: Puncture of the lobe of the ear or of the ball of a finger with a needle or lancet. This should always be to the same depth (ca. 3 mm) and is followed by one of the following procedures:

(*a*) Soaking up the emergent blood in filter paper at regular intervals of a few seconds[1,2];

(*b*) Immersion of the finger in physiological salt solution and measurement of the interval elapsing before the thread of emergent blood breaks[3–5];

(*c*) The same procedure as (*b*) but with the capillaries kept open by the use of a pressure cuff at 40 mm Hg[6].

Normal values: By method (*a*): 0–7.5 min[1]; mean 2.5 min. By method (*b*): 2.5–7 min[5].

Remarks: The bleeding time measured by methods (*a*) and (*b*) is determined mainly by the retraction of the capillaries; in method (*c*) it is independent of the capillary effect.

1) DUKE, W. W., *J. Amer. med. Ass.*, **55**, 1185 (1910).
2) DUKE, W. W., *Arch. intern. Med.*, **10**, 445 (1912).
3) ROSKAM, J., *C. R. Soc. Biol. (Paris)*, **112**, 1245 (1933).
4) MARX and KÖPPEL, *Sangre (Santiago)*, **2**, 142 (1957).
5) IVY et al., *Surg. Gynec. Obstet.*, **60**, 781 (1935).
6) TOCANTINS, L. M., *Amer. J. clin. Path.*, **6**, 160 (1936); COPLEY and LALICH, *J. clin. Invest.*, **21**, 145 (1942).

Coagulation time

This is the time required for the complete coagulation in vitro at 37°C of blood drawn by means of a silicone- or paraffin-coated hypodermic needle.

Methods: Venous blood is drawn by a silicone- or paraffin-coated needle, transferred to a test tube, and the time required for complete solidification at 37°C measured[1,4]. One modification of this method uses capillary blood[2], another a silicone-coated test tube[3].

Normal values: Ordinary test tube, venous blood: 6–12 min[4]. Ordinary test tube, capillary blood: 1.5–3 min[2]. Silicone-coated test tube, venous blood: 18–25 min[3].

Remarks: It must be borne in mind that the blood coagulation time is dependent on a great many external factors, for example the nature of the glass, the manner in which the blood is drawn, the rate at which the test tube is tilted, etc. In expert hands this test can give indications of the presence of a hemorrhagic diathesis and of its nature.

1) LEE and WHITE, *Amer. J. med. Sci.*, **145**, 495 (1913).
2) DALE and LAIDLAW, *J. Path. Bact.*, **16**, 351 (1911).
3) BIGGS and MACFARLANE, *Human Blood Coagulation and its Disorders*, 2nd ed., Oxford, 1957.
4) JÜRGENS and STUDER, *Helv. physiol. pharmacol. Acta*, **6**, 130 (1948).

Recalcification time

This is the coagulation time of the citrated or oxalated plasma measured after recalcification.

Methods: Blood is drawn by venipuncture and mixed in the syringe with one-fifth of its volume of isotonic sodium citrate solution or with one-tenth of its volume of isotonic sodium oxalate solution. After centrifuging, 0.2 ml of the plasma is recalcified by mixing with 0.2 ml of isotonic calcium chloride solution and the time which elapses between the addition of the latter and the onset of coagulation measured (HOWELL time).

Normal values: 1.5–4 min[1].

1) BIGGS and MACFARLANE, *Human Blood Coagulation and its Disorders*, 2nd ed., Oxford, 1957.

* Detailed descriptions of all methods used in the study of blood coagulation will be found in (inter alia) BIGGS and MACFARLANE, *Human Blood Coagulation and its Disorders*, 2nd ed., Oxford, 1957, and JÜRGENS and BELLER, *Klinische Methoden der Blutgerinnungsanalyse*, Stuttgart, 1959.

Recalcification time *(continued)*

Remarks .... Measurement of the recalcification time in whole blood gives similar results. For very small amounts of blood the recalcification time can be measured in ammonium oxalate plasma[1]. When the recalcification time is very long it is better to use diluted plasma (0.2 ml plasma + 1 ml physiological salt solution)[1].

1) JÜRGENS and BELLER, *Klinische Methoden der Blutgerinnungsanalyse*, Stuttgart, 1959.

Prothrombin time

The recalcification time is measured in oxalated or citrated blood or plasma after addition of a thromboplastin preparation, which has the effect of greatly reducing the time.

Methods .... Citrated or oxalated blood or plasma is mixed with an appropriate amount of a thromboplastin preparation, recalcified, and the time up to onset of coagulation measured (first thread of fibrin). QUICK's method[1] uses 1 ml of plasma, as do numerous modifications of it[2, 3]. Other methods use smaller quantities of plasma or whole blood[4].

Normal values ...... With human brain thromboplastin: 10–12 s.
With rabbit brain thromboplastin: 12–14 s.
With lung thromboplastin: 14–16 s.

Remarks .... The prothrombin time of normal plasma or blood depends on the activity of the thromboplastin preparation used and on its mechanism of action. The test is used principally for checking the activity of coumarin and indanedione preparations in anticoagulant therapy. In interpreting the results it is essential to know to which of the coagulation factors concerned (factors II, V, VII and X) the thromboplastin preparation reacts[5].

1) QUICK et al., *Amer. J. med. Sci.*, **190**, 501 (1935).
2) SCHULTZE, H. E., *Naunyn-Schmiedeberg's Arch. exp. Path. Pharmak.*, **207**, 173 (1949).
3) MONTIGEL and PULVER, *Schweiz. med. Wschr.*, **82**, 132 (1952).
4) MONTIGEL, C., *Ther. Umsch.*, **9**, 17 (1952); FIECHTER, N., *Schweiz. med. Wschr.*, **70**, 259 (1940); JÜRGENS, J., *Z. klin. Med.*, **146**, 516 (1950); MARX and BAYERLE, *Hoppe-Seylers Z. physiol. Chem.*, **283**, 243 (1948).
5) MONTIGEL, C., *Schweiz. med. Wschr.*, **89**, 1259 (1959).

Clot retraction

When coagulation is complete the clot retracts and exudes serum. The process commences 10–30 min after coagulation and is complete in 2–3 hours.

Methods .... These are based on
1. Measurement of the volume of the retraction[1, 2];
2. Measurement of retraction time;
3. Measurement of the force of retraction, expressed in dynes[3].
Retraction measurements are also made using capillary blood[4, 5].

Normal values ...... Amount of serum liberated[1]: 48–64 vol%, mean 54.7 vol%.

Retractive force (lead shot method)[6]: 224–558 mg, corresponding to 220–547 dyn.
Interval elapsing up to the extrusion of a droplet of serum from a drop of blood suspended in castor oil[4]: 20–45 min, mean 33 min.

Remarks .... Clinically, the measurement of retraction is of interest in that the process is delayed in certain diseases affecting the thrombocytes or coagulation in general, as well as in heparin therapy.

1) MACFARLANE, R. G., *Lancet*, **1**, 1199 (1939).
2) JÜRGENS, J., *6th Congress of the European Society of Hematology*, Transactions, Copenhagen, 1957; FONIO, A., *Ergebn. inn. Med. Kinderheilk.*, **4**, 1 (1953).
3) BAYERLE et al., *Klin. Wschr.*, **27**, 237 (1949).
4) HIRSCHBOECK, J. S., *J. Lab. clin. Med.*, **33**, 347 (1948).
5) MATIS, P., *Dtsch. med. Wschr.*, **74**, 618 (1949); MATIS and GROSS, *Med. Welt*, **20**, 492 (1951).
6) FONIO, A., *Schweiz. med. Wschr.*, **84**, 372 (1954); *Acta haemat. (Basel)*, **11**, 251 (1954).

Heparin tolerance test

This test can be carried out in vitro[1] to provide a measure of the coagulability of blood, the principle of the method being the determination of the recalcification time after the addition of definite quantities of heparin (delayed coagulation). A similar method is the sodium chloride tolerance test[2] in which sodium chloride replaces heparin. The heparin tolerance test can be carried out in vivo after injection of definite amounts of heparin.

Methods .... Blood from a normal control person must always be drawn simultaneously with that of the patient and the two samples centrifuged together at 1000 r.p.m. The heparin is then added at 37°C and the recalcification time measured. Accuracy can be increased by using 3 graded heparin concentrations in parallel. The test can also be carried out on whole blood. When the test is performed in vivo, the recalcification time is measured 10 min after injection of the heparin. The sodium chloride tolerance test is carried out in vitro by measuring the recalcification time of the patient's blood after addition of sodium chloride at 37°C.

Normal values ...... Heparin tolerance test in vitro: 1 IU heparin per 0.5 ml plasma: 8–12 min.

Heparin tolerance test in vivo: 25 mg heparin i.v.: 40–49 min.
10 mg heparin i.v.: 5–7 min (at room temperature).

Sodium chloride tolerance test: 0.1 ml plasma + 0.1 ml 2.5% NaCl solution: 2–2.25 min[2].

Remarks .... Heparin tolerance test in vitro: the difference between the recalcification time of the control blood and that of the patient's blood provides information as to the so-called coagulability of the latter, a longer time indicating hypocoagulability, a shorter time hypercoagulability. In the sodium chloride tolerance test it is sufficient to measure the time in the patient's blood and compare it with the recognized normal value.

1) SOULIER and LE BOLLOCH, *Sem. Hôp. Paris*, **26**, 3702 (1950); *Rev. Hémat.*, **5**, 148 (1950); WAUGH and RUDDICK, *Canad. med. Ass. J.*, **50**, 547 (1944).
2) JÜRGENS, J., *Blut*, **2**, 301 (1956).

Synopsis of Blood – Blood Groups

By Dr. L. P. Holländer, Municipal Blood Transfusion Service (Swiss Red Cross), Basle (Switzerland)

(For bibliographical references see page 593)

General[1]

The blood groups are the result of the possession by the erythrocytes of characters identifiable serologically as antigens by means of specific antibodies. These characters are inherited in the form of genes according to mendelian rules. The blood group of an individual does not change during his lifetime and it is influenced neither by climatic and other external factors nor, in general, by illness. The individual blood group characteristics are classified into systems each of which is inherited by way of a separate chromosome (see Fig. 1). The following systems have been recognized up to the present: **ABO, MNSs, P, Rh, Lutheran, Kell, Lewis, Duffy** and **Kidd***. Certain systems consist simply of a single pair of allelomorphic genes, such as the **Lutheran** and **Kidd** systems, others of closely linked pairs of genes, such as the **MNSs** system and in the view of British workers the **Rh** system. The individual systems are transmitted to offspring independently of one another.

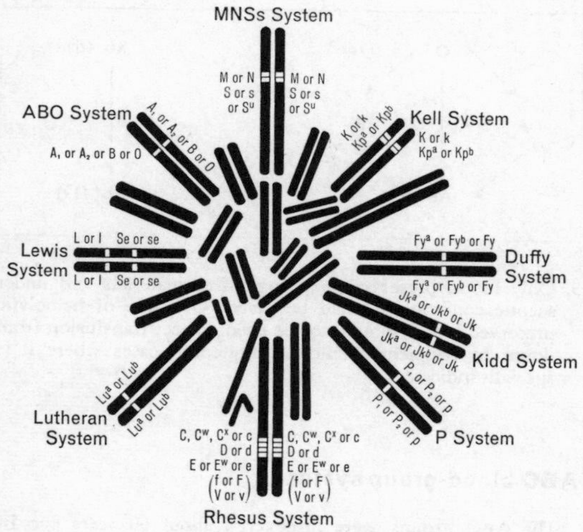

Fig. 1 Diagram of human chromosomes

The antibodies serve to determine the blood group antigens and are either iso- or hetero-antibodies**. In man they are present either "spontaneously" as the so-called naturally occurring antibodies, that is to say, without the antigenic stimulus being recognized, or as immune antibodies as a result of an immunization process, i.e. of pregnancy or of transfusion or injection of blood of a different group. Sera containing antibodies which are used for testing erythrocytes for the presence or absence of a certain blood-group antigen are known as test sera. The reaction of the antibodies with the erythrocytes carrying the antigens results in the agglutination, and in some circumstances in the lysis, of the erythrocytes.

Table 1

	Reaction with erythrocytes in physiological saline	Reaction with erythrocytes in 20–30% beef albumin solution†
Agglutinins (synonyms: complete antibodies, saline agglutinins, bivalent antibodies)	+	+
Incomplete antibodies†† (synonyms: blocking antibodies, univalent antibodies, glutinins, hyperimmune antibodies, albumin antibodies)	–	+

† Other viscous media, such as human serum, gum arabic, gelatin, macromolecular solutions, etc., can also be used.

†† The so-called cryptagglutinoids are incomplete antibodies whose presence can be detected only by the indirect Coombs test.

The antibodies are classified as agglutinins or incomplete antibodies according to the type of reaction they produce (Table 1). Agglutinins are antibodies which are active against the corresponding erythrocytes suspended in saline (erythrocytes carrying the antigen corresponding to the antibody), causing them to become agglutinated. Incomplete antibodies in these circumstances cause agglutination when the erythrocytes are suspended in a viscous medium, for example a 20% solution of beef albumin.

A sensitive method of detecting incomplete antibodies is the antiglobulin test of Coombs, Mourant and Race[2], commonly known as the Coombs test. It is based on the fact that incomplete antibodies (γ-globulins) are adsorbed on the erythrocytes but do not agglutinate them. The erythrocytes are then agglutinated by means of an antiglobulin serum usually produced by injecting γ-globulin repeatedly into rabbits (Fig. 2).

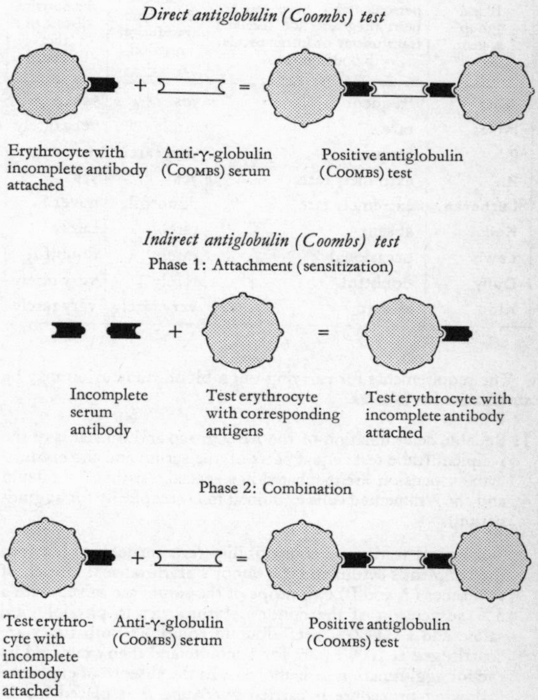

Fig. 2 Diagrammatic representation of direct and indirect antiglobulin tests

A further method of detecting incomplete antibodies consists of the prior treatment of the erythrocytes with proteolytic enzymes such as trypsin[3], papain[4], ficin proteinase[5], etc. Erythrocytes treated in this way and suspended in physiological saline are agglutinated by corresponding incomplete antibodies. Combination of this method with the antiglobulin test constitutes a particularly sensitive method of detection of incomplete antibodies[6].

* Other systems, for example Diego and Sutter, are being investigated. The antigens, however, appear to be confined to the members of certain races.

** Iso = of the same kind, hetero = of a different kind.

Clinical aspects

The blood groups are of great importance in *blood transfusions.* In spite of the large number of blood group antigens carried by the erythrocytes, initially at least only the antigens A, B and D (Rh_0) are taken into consideration in blood transfusions. If it were necessary to consider all the known blood groups before giving a transfusion the work of a blood transfusion service would become impossible. When repeated transfusions are given or blood is injected intramuscularly, antibodies (immune antibodies) to other blood groups may appear in the recipient's blood. In such cases the blood for transfusion must be chosen very carefully with the aid of a sensitive serological compatibility test. In women, pregnancy can also result in the formation of immune antibodies, a circumstance responsible for the occurrence of hemolytic disease of the newborn: a particular blood group factor (usually the Rh factor D = Rh_0) is *absent* in the mother but is inherited from the father by the fetus, whence it passes into the body of the mother and gives rise to the corresponding antibodies; the latter in turn pass the placental barrier and cause injury to the fetus. Table 2 shows which particular antibodies of the several blood group systems are capable of causing a hemolytic transfusion reaction and to what extent they play a part in the development of hemolytic disease of the newborn.

Table 2

Blood group system	Occurrence of antibodies in persons who have neither been pregnant nor received transfusions or intramuscular blood injections	Causes hemolytic transfusion reaction	Causes hemolytic disease of the newborn
ABO	frequent	yes	yes
MNSs	rare	rarely	very rarely
P	frequent	very rarely	never
Rh	extremely rare	yes	yes
Lutheran	extremely rare	doubtful	never
Kell	absent	rarely	rarely
Lewis	occasional	rarely	doubtful
Duffy	doubtful	rarely	very rarely
Kidd	absent	very rarely	very rarely

The requirements for carrying out a blood transfusion may be summarized as follows:

1. Reliable determination of the ABO group and Rh status of the recipient (tube test: equal parts of the serum and the erythrocyte suspension are incubated in a special test-tube 7 × 50 mm and the sedimented cells examined microscopically for agglutination).

2. Serological testing of compatibility (crossmatching) between the recipient's serum and the donor's erythrocytes: in each of two tubes (A and B) two drops of the serum are mixed with a 5% suspension of the donor's erythrocytes in physiological saline and a 20–30% beef albumin solution. Both tubes are centrifuged at 1000 r.p.m. for 1 minute and then examined by eye for agglutination or hemolysis. In the absence of either the following procedure is carried out: tube A is placed for 15 minutes in a water bath at 37°C, then centrifuged again at 1000 r.p.m. and the sedimented erythrocytes examined microscopically for agglutination. Agglutination indicates incompatibility. Tube B is then subjected to the indirect Coombs test after being placed in the water bath at 37°C for 15 minutes. A positive result indicates incompatibility.

3. In emergency cases the following procedure is carried out: rapid ABO- and Rh-grouping by the slide test[7]; compatibility test as follows: 2 drops of the recipient's serum are mixed with a 5% suspension of the donor's erythrocytes in physiological saline and with a 20–30% beef albumin solution in each of several tubes and centrifuged for 1 minute at 1000 r.p.m.; the tubes are then examined for agglutination or hemolysis.

4. In principle only *blood of the same group character* is given by transfusion, as shown by the following scheme:

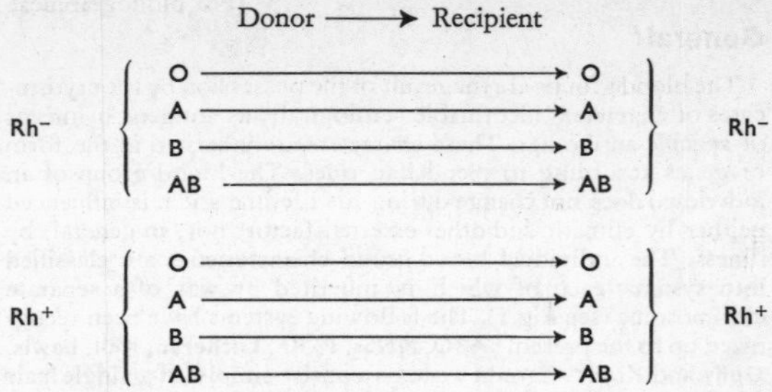

When blood of the same group character is not available the *possibilities remaining open* are shown by the following schemes:

For A, B, O For Rh⁻ (d) and Rh⁺ (D)

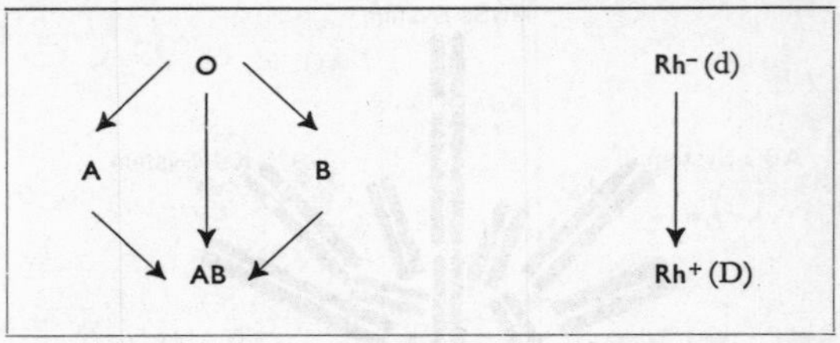

5. Only blood preserved in pyrogen-free materials and under aseptic conditions should be given. Over-age or hemolytic preserved blood should not be used. Direct transfusion from donor to recipient should be limited to cases where it is specially indicated.

ABO blood-group system

The ABO groups were discovered about 60 years ago by Landsteiner[8], and later group A was divided into groups A_1 and A_2 by von Dungern and Hirschfeld[9]. The exact manner in which the ABO groups are inherited was first described by the mathematician Bernstein[10], whose so-called three-gene theory was later expanded into a four-gene theory in order to take account of the A-subdivision of Thomsen et al.[11]. Friedenreich[12] has described a special subgroup of group A known as A_3. During the first world war, H. and L. Hirschfeld[13] discovered that people of different races had different distributions of the ABO groups, an observation which marked the beginning of the science of seroanthropology. The frequencies of the individual genes can be calculated for any particular racial group. The strict regularity of their inheritance made it possible to use blood-group determination in deciding cases of disputed ancestry and other forensic questions. The clinical significance of the discovery is shown in Table 2. Incompatibility in the ABO system is the cause of most hemolytic accidents in transfusions including the most serious ones.

Determination of the ABO groups on the erythrocytes is made with the help of the isoagglutinins anti-A and anti-B normally and regularly present in human sera (Table 3).

Table 3

Reaction with				
anti-A	–	+	–	+
anti-B	–	–	+	+
Blood group..........	O	A	B	AB

The erythrocytes are carriers of the antigens, while only the antibodies corresponding to the opposite antigens are found in the serum (Table 4).

Table 4

Blood group	Antigens on the erythrocytes	Antibodies in the serum
O	—	anti-A + anti-B
A	A	anti-B
B	B	anti-A
AB	A and B	none

Almost all anti-A sera (from donors of group B) contain two components, anti-A and anti-A_1. With the help of anti-A_1, an A blood can be more accurately identified as A_1 or A_2, an AB blood as A_1B or A_2B. anti-A_1 reacts only with erythrocytes of groups A_1 and A_1B, while anti-A reacts with A_1 as well as A_2 and with A_1B as well as A_2B. This subdivision of group A increases the number of possible blood groups to 6, namely A_1, A_2, B, A_1B, A_2B and O. There are 10 genotypes corresponding to these 6 phenotypes (Table 5).

Table 5

Phenotypes	Genotypes
A_1	A_1A_1, A_1A_2, A_1O
A_2	A_2A_2, A_2O
B	BB, BO
A_1B	A_1B
A_2B	A_2B
O	OO

Since there is no specific antibody available which is effective against the antigen "O", the group O can be identified only by its negative reaction with the anti-A and anti-B antisera. Serologically it is also impossible to distinguish between the genotypes AA and AO or BB and BO. The most important serological characteristics of the A_1A_2BO blood group are summarized in Table 6.

Intensive research on the blood groups has thrown more light on the nature of the ABO system. Thus from the genetic aspect it is now known that there are so-called modifying genes which modify the phenotypic character of the ABO groups[14], while the antigens A and B have been shown to be present also on thrombocytes and leukocytes[15]. The chemistry of the blood-group substances has been largely elucidated[16]. Certain plant extracts have been found to act like specific agglutinins[17]. Still awaiting full explanation are the exact genetic relationship between the ABO and Lewis groups (see page 590) and the nature of certain rare variants of the A and B factors (A_x[18], A_m[19], A_g[20], B_3[21] and B_w[22]).

Table 6

Blood group	Reaction with test serum: anti-A	anti-A_1	anti-B	Antibodies regularly present in the serum	Antibodies occasionally present in the serum
O	—	—	—	anti-A (+ anti-A_1) anti-B	—
A_1	+	+	—	anti-B	—
A_2	+	—	—	anti-B	anti-A_1 in ca. 2%
B	—	—	+	anti-A (+ anti-A_1)	—
A_1B	+	+	+	none	—
A_2B	+	—	+	none	anti-A_1 in ca. 25%

Secretors and nonsecretors

The blood-group substance H is peculiar to all human erythrocytes and is a basic substance from which the substances A and B probably arise under the action of the A and B genes. O-Erythrocytes contain the most H-substance, and A_2-, A_2B-, B-, A_1- and A_1B-erythrocytes decreasing quantities in that order. The fact that A_1B-erythrocytes also possess the H-substance is a proof that H is not identical with O.

The antigens A, B and H are in many cases also detectable in saliva and other body fluids[23]. This is due to the presence of a gene pair which is inherited according to mendelian rules[24]. Persons in whom the substances A, B and H are present in the body fluids are known as secretors, those in whom these substances are absent from the body fluids as nonsecretors (symbols Se and se respectively). Two kinds of antigen substances have been distinguished[25], (1) water-soluble antigens not carried on the erythrocytes but present in the body fluids of secretors as a result of their possessing the secretor gene (Se), and (2) alcohol-soluble antigens present in all tissues (except brain tissue), especially the erythrocytes, but absent from the body fluids; they are not influenced by the Se gene. The Se and se genes are inherited independently of the genes of the ABO system. It has been shown[26] that the phenomenon of secretion is closely related to the Lewis system (see page 590). The proportion of secretors among the general population (Liverpool, England) is about 75%[27].

The MNSs blood-group system

The antigens M and N of human erythrocytes were discovered in 1927 by Landsteiner and Levine[28] in experiments with immune sera from rabbits which had been injected with human blood containing the antigen M or N. Tests on families made by the same authors revealed that the characters M and N are inherited according to mendelian rules[29] and the gene frequencies for M and N were calculated[30]. The relationships in the MN groups are shown in Table 7.

Table 7

Reaction with:			
anti-M	+	+	—
anti-N	—	+	+
Phenotype (or group) . . .	M	MN	N
Genotype	MM	MN	NN

In 1947 it became apparent that the MN system was not as simple as had been thought. This followed the discovery[31] of a human serum containing an immune antibody against an antigen closely related to M and N[32]. This antigen was called S and the antibody anti-S. In 1951 Levine et al.[33] discovered an antibody which reacted with the antigen s whose existence had already been postulated. The antibodies anti-M and anti-N also occur in human sera as irregular specific cold agglutinins. It has not been found possible to produce the antisera anti-S and anti-s in animals by immunization. The following genotypes (Table 8) can be distinguished by reactions to the four antisera anti-M, anti-N, anti-S and anti-s:

Table 8

	MS/MS	MS/Ms	Ms/Ms	MS/NS	MS/Ns*	Ms/NS*	Ms/Ns	NS/NS	NS/Ns	Ns/Ns
anti-M	+	+	+	+	+	+	+	—	—	—
anti-N	—	—	—	+	+	+	+	+	+	+
anti-S	+	+	—	+	+	+	—	+	+	—
anti-s	—	+	+	—	+	+	+	—	+	+

* The genotypes MS/Ns and Ms/NS cannot be distinguished by reactions to the four antisera anti-M, anti-N, anti-S and anti-s.

Rare forms of the M and N antigens are the antigens N_2[34] and M_2[35], which are characterized by their failure to react with all anti-N or anti-M sera respectively. Also reported[36] is an antigen M^c which not only reacts with most anti-M sera but also with some anti-n sera. The M^c gene is regarded as being intermediate between N and M. The extremely rare antigen M^g is of interest in that it reacts neither with anti-M nor anti-N[37]. The specific antibody anti-M^g is a naturally occurring agglutinin which appears to be by no means uncommon in human sera, about 3% of which possess it.

While the antigens M and N as well as S and s form closely coupled allelomorphic pairs of genes, the genetic locations of the factors Hu[38] and He[39] as also Mi^a[40] and Vw[41], all of which clearly belong to the MNSs system, have not yet been elucidated. The antigen Hu occurs mainly in the blood of Negroes, the antigen He exclusively so. Mi^a and Vw were originally regarded as "private" antigens (see page 591) but it is now known that they belong to the MNSs system, although their exact genetic location is likewise unknown. The most recently described antigen, Vr, also belongs to the MNSs system[42] but the position in the chromosome of the corresponding gene could not be established.

WIENER et al.[43] have described an antibody which was the cause of a fatal transfusion reaction and which they have named anti-U. This antibody was later shown[44] to possess Ss specificity, the erythrocytes of the individuals producing it possessing neither S nor s but being homozygotic S^uS^u. An anti-S^u has not yet been discovered.

Although the MNSs system is genetically complicated and not yet thoroughly understood, it is not of great importance clinically as can be seen from Table 2 on page 586.

The P blood-group system

The P antigen was discovered in 1927 by LANDSTEINER and LEVINE[45] in the course of the immunization experiments on rabbits which led to the discovery of the MN groups. P-negative individuals frequently produce anti-P antibodies which are of low titer and only active in the cold. Good anti-P test sera are often of animal origin[46]. Since no anti-p serum has been found, human blood has been divided simply into P-positive and P-negative, with the inheritance of the character P assumed to be dominant[47]. P-positive blood is of the genotype PP or Pp, while P-negative blood is regarded as pp (see Table 9). In 1951 LEVINE et al.[48] described the antigen Tj^a. At first regarded as a "public" antigen (see page 591), Tj^a was recognized by SANGER[49] in 1955 as belonging to the P system.

Table 9

		Phenotype	Genotype
anti-P	+	P^+	PP or Pp
	–	P^-	pp

The current conception of the P blood group system is that it is analogous to the A_1A_2O system and consists of three allelomorphic genes P_1 (the earlier P), P_2 (the earlier p) and p (the earlier Tj^b). This is shown in Table 10.

Table 10

Reaction with			
anti-P + P_1 (Tj^a)	+	+	–
anti-P_1 (P)	+	–	–
Genotype	P_1P_1 (PP) P_1P_2 (Pp) P_1p (PTj^b)	P_2P_2 (pp) P_2p (pTj^b)	pp (Tj^bTj^b)

The bracketed symbols are those in use prior to 1955.

The very rare pp (Tj^bTj^b) individuals regularly exhibit anti-P (the earlier anti-Tj^a) antibodies in their serum. anti-P consists of the two components, anti-P_1 and anti-P_2. In analogy with A_2 individuals with anti-A_1, P_2P_2 (earlier pp) individuals occasionally produce in their serum anti-P_1 (earlier anti-P) antibodies.

The P system is not of any great clinical importance (see Table 2, page 586), and transfusion accidents due to anti-P_1 have only rarely been reported[50–52].

The Rhesus blood-group system

In 1940 LANDSTEINER and WIENER[53] discovered that the antibodies arising from the immunization of rabbits and guinea pigs with the blood of the monkey *Macacus rhesus* would agglutinate not only the erythrocytes of these monkeys but also those of 85% of the white inhabitants of New York. These individuals were called Rh-positive (Rh^+) and the remaining 15% who showed a negative reaction Rh-negative (Rh^-). In 1939 LEVINE and STETSON[54] had already reported the case of a woman pregnant for the second time who had given birth to a stillborn child and had then suffered a transfusion reaction with her husband's blood as a result of her immunization by the fetus. Later it was shown that the immune antibodies concerned were identical in specificity with the Rh antibodies. WIENER and PETERS[55] then demonstrated that anti-Rh antibodies occurred in the sera of persons who had suffered incompatible transfusion reactions in spite of the use of blood of the correct ABO type. Intensive research since 1941 has shown that the Rh blood groups form a complicated system. Its genetic interpretation is still a matter of discussion, a circumstance reflected in the use of two different systems of nomenclature. The Rh^+ antigen of LANDSTEINER and WIENER is now known as D or Rh_0 and the original anti-Rh as anti-D or anti-Rh_0.

Structure of the Rh system

WIENER[56] views the Rh blood-group system as being inherited through a *single* series of multiple allelomorphs, while RACE[57] and FISHER consider that there are *several closely linked* allelomorphic gene pairs. According to WIENER there is an antigen (complex

Table 11 Rh chromosomes discovered up to 1955, with their nomenclatures according to FISHER and RACE and to WIENER and the corresponding short symbols.

FISHER and RACE	WIENER	Short symbol
CDe	R^1	R_1
cDE	R^2	R_2
cDe	R^0	R_0
CDE	R^z	R_z
Cde	r'	R'
cdE	r''	R''
CdE	r^y	R_y
cde	r	r
C^wDe	R^{1w}	R_1^w
C^wde	r'^w	R'^w
C^wdE	–	R_y^w
C^wDE	–	R_z^w
C^uDe	–	–
c^vDE	–	–
C^xDe	–	–
CD^ue	R^1	R_1^u
cD^uE	R^2	R_2^u
cD^ue	R^0	R_0^u
CD^uE	–	R_z^u
C^wD^ue	–	–
cDE^u	–	–
cde^x	–	–
cDE^w	–	–
-D-	R^{0x}	–
cD-	R^{0u}	–

agglutinogen) corresponding to each gene, this antigen consisting of several factors which react with the specific antibodies. FISHER and RACE take the view that antigens corresponding to the genes are located on the erythrocytes and react with the corresponding antibodies. The same symbols are used for gene, antigen and antibody. The most important gene pairs are C–c, D–d and E–e. Three closely linked genes on the chromosome correspond to WIENER's gene complex (Table 11). This table also gives the short symbols which facilitate the verbal expression of the FISHER-RACE nomenclature.

Table 12 shows the difference between the views of WIENER and of FISHER and RACE as illustrated by the example of the Rh chromosome R^1 or CDe.

Table 12 (after RACE and SANGER, *Blood Groups in Man*, 3rd ed., Oxford, 1958, page 159)

	Gene	Agglutinogen	Factor	Antibody
WIENER	R^1	Rh_1	Rh_0	anti-Rh_0
			rh′	anti-rh′
			hr″	anti-hr″
FISHER and RACE	C	C		anti-C
	D	D		anti-D
	e	e		anti-e

The present state of knowledge of the Rh blood-group system, according to the genetic conception of FISHER and RACE, can be summarized as follows:

Gene	Antiserum
D	anti-D
D^u	
d	
C	anti-C
c	anti-c
C^w	anti-C^w
C^u	
C^x	anti-C^x
c^v	

Gene	Antiserum
E	anti-E
e	anti-e
E^u	
E^w	anti-E^w
f	anti-f
F	
V	anti-V
v	

The genes grouped in brackets are allelomorphs, that is to say, a chromosome can carry for example either C or c but not both. The order of the genes on the Rh chromosome appears to be D, C, E. It is not yet certain whether the gene V forms a further gene pair with the hypothetical v, and it is possible that V is an allelomorph of f.

The allelomorphic Rh genes, and the corresponding antigens, can be divided into three groups:

1. Those which can be detected directly by means of the specific antibodies, viz., D, C[58], c[59], C^w[60], C^x[61], E[62], e[63], E^w[64], f[65] and V[66].
2. Those for which there are no specific antibodies, viz., the antigens D^u[67], C^u[68], E^u[69] and c^v[68] which differ from D, C, E and c in that they show absence of a reaction in some cases when tested with several antisera of the same specificity.
3. Antigens which cannot be detected serologically: thus d denotes absence of D and D^u, F absence of f, v absence of V.

In 1950 the Rh chromosome -D- was described for the first time[70]. The erythrocytes of individuals of the genotype -D-/-D- carry simply the antigen D, and all other Rh antigens are lacking. A defective Rh chromosome, denoted by R^{ou} (cD-), has also been described[71].

RACE et al.[72] have observed a position effect in the Rh system. With the genotypes C and E on the same chromosome (cis-position) the antigen C is depressed, with the genotypes C and E on opposite chromosomes (trans-position) the antigen E is depressed. In the same way there is marked depression of the D antigen, under the influence of Cde, in the genotype CDe/Cde[73].

The Rh antigens recognized up to the present make possible 288 different chromosome combinations and some 42,000 genotype combinations. Some antigens are extremely rare or absent altogether in Europeans. The V antigen has been found only in Negroes.

Since the f and V antigens are clinically unimportant, these and the very rare allelomorphs of C and E have been disregarded in the discussion which follows. Most of the anti-CD sera are considered to be specific for an Rh-antigen "G"[74].

The Rh blood-group system in clinical practice

For clinical purposes the simple division into Rh-positive and Rh-negative is generally adequate, the notation $Rh^+ = D^+ = Rh_0^+$ indicating that a blood sample has given a positive reaction with anti-D (anti-Rh_0) serum. In some cases it is important to know also the genotype, and this is determined by testing against the antisera anti-C, anti-D, anti-E, anti-c and anti-e (most anti-C sera are also active against the C^w antigen; when "pure" anti-C sera are used, tests must also be made against anti-C^w serum). Table 13 shows the extent to which the phenotype, when established, yields information on the genotype. In many cases the true genotype is only revealed by family tests, and if these are not possible the genotype is referred to as the "most probable". Thus for the reactions anti-C^+, anti-D^+, anti-E^-, anti-c^+, anti-e^+ there are three possible genotypes, CDe/cDe, CDe/cde and cDe/CDe. Since the genotype CDe/cde is much more frequent than the other two (see Table 13), this is assumed to be the true genotype until such time as family tests show that this is not so.

When a woman is Rh-negative and has produced Rh antibodies it is important in the interests of future children to know either the Rh genotype of the husband or his homo- or hetero-zygoticity with respect to the D antigen. The most important 36 genotype combinations are listed in Table 14.

Table 13 Frequencies of Rh genotypes*

Reaction with anti- -C	-D	-E	-c	-e	Possible genotypes	Frequency in per cent
−	−	−	+	+	cde/cde	15.10
−	+	−	+	+	cDe/cde cDe/cDe	2.0 0.07
−	−	+	+	+	cdE/cde	0.92
−	−	+	+	−	cdE/cdE	0.01
−	+	+	+	−	cDE/cDE cDE/cdE	1.99 0.34
−	+	+	+	+	cDE/cDe cDE/cde cDe/cdE	0.72 10.97 0.06
+	−	−	+	+	cde/Cde	0.76
+	+	−	+	+	CDe/cDe CDe/cde cDe/Cde	2.09 31.68 0.05
+	+	+	+	+	CDe/cDE CDe/cdE cDE/Cde cde/CDE cDe/CDE	11.50 0.97 0.28 0.19 0.01
+	+	+	+	−	cDE/CDE cdE/CDE	0.07 0.0058
+	−	−	−	+	Cde/Cde	0.0097
+	+	+	−	+	CDe/CDE Cde/CDE	0.20 0.0048
+	+	+	−	−	CDE/CDE	0.0006

* Modified from the original table of RACE et al., *Blood*, 3, 689 (1948). The frequencies relate to the population of the British Isles and do not differ to any marked extent from those in other European countries.

Table 14

CDe/CDe	cde/cde	cDE/cDE	cDe/cDe	cdE/cdE	Cde/Cde	CDE/CDE	CdE/CdE
CDe/cde	←	←	←	←	←	←	←
CDe/cDE	cde/cDE	←	←	←	←	←	←
CDe/cDe	cde/cDe	cDE/cDe	←	←	←	←	←
CDe/cdE	cde/cdE	cDE/cdE	cDe/cdE	←	←	←	←
CDe/Cde	cde/Cde	cDE/Cde	cDe/Cde	cdE/Cde	←	←	←
CDe/CDE	cde/CDE	cDE/CDE	cDe/CDE	cdE/CDE	Cde/CDE	←	←
CDe/CdE	cde/CdE	cDE/CdE	cDe/CdE	cdE/CdE	Cde/CdE	CDE/CdE	←

Naturally occurring Rh antibodies are extremely rare. They are acquired by immunization, that is to say, by incompatible pregnancy, transfusion or intramuscular blood injection. In the great majority of cases the Rh antibodies are specific for anti-D, often combined as anti-CD or more rarely as anti-DE. Individuals who produce Rh antibodies are mostly Rh-negative (cde/cde). anti-E and anti-c are produced more often than anti-C. The Rh antigens possess differing antigenic activities; thus in this respect D > E, C > c, e > (d). The Rh antigen D^u is of importance in practice: thus Rh-negative recipients of D^u blood can react by forming Rh antibodies, while on the other hand D^u individuals can form anti-D. The D^u antigen is not a simple one: some types can be distinguished from D only by the absence of a reaction with certain agglutinating anti-D sera ("high-grade D^u") while others are detectable by only a few anti-D sera in the indirect Coombs test ("low-grade D^u").

Like the ABO system, the Rh system is of great clinical importance. Most cases of hemolytic disease of the newborn are due to anti-D, and these antibodies are the principal cause, apart from the ABO system, of hemolytic transfusion reactions. The establishment of Rh compatibility is therefore an absolute necessity before giving blood transfusions. However, Rh antibodies are not formed by all persons even after incompatible transfusions or pregnancy. In general, blood transfusion constitutes a strong stimulus to the formation of immune antibodies, especially when repeated at intervals of several months. The amount of blood given is here immaterial. When immunization results from pregnancy the first child (provided the mother has not already been sensitized by a transfusion) is usually unaffected. Exceptions to this are rare. Injury to the child increases with each subsequent pregnancy. When an individual has once been immunized, the antibodies may remain in his blood as long as he lives. When a woman has once given birth to a child with hemolytic disease and the father is homozygotic, the birth of healthy children can *no longer* be expected. The antibody titer of a pregnant woman's serum has no reliable prognostic value with respect to the health of the child. When the father is heterozygotic there is a 50% chance of the children being Rh-negative and therefore without hemolytic disease.

There is no effective antenatal prophylaxis for hemolytic disease of the newborn. The best treatment is an exchange transfusion given as soon as possible after birth[75]. The indications for this are (1) clinical and hematological findings (bilirubin and hemoglobin values), and (2) serological findings (Rh antagonism between mother and child with Rh antibodies in the mother's serum, cord blood giving positive result with the direct Coombs test).

The Lutheran blood-group system

In 1946 Callender and Race[76] described an antibody which gave positive reactions with about 8% of blood samples from the population of Great Britain. The antigen could not be assigned to any of the known blood-group systems. The "new" blood-group system was named "Lutheran" after the donor of the blood which had caused the formation of the new antibody. The nomenclature of the system[77] (see Table 15), as well as that of the later Lewis, Duffy and Kidd systems, was unified in accordance with the newer conceptions in this field. Ten years later an antibody was discovered which reacted with the antigen of the allelomorph Lu^b whose existence had already been postulated[78]. The phenotype Lu(a−b−) had not previously been found. Present knowledge of the Lutheran blood-group system is summarized in Table 15.

Table 15

Genes	Lu^a, Lu^b
Antigens	Lu^a, Lu^b
Genotypes	Lu^aLu^a, Lu^aLu^b, Lu^bLu^b
Phenotypes	Lu(a+b−), Lu(a+b+), Lu(a−b+)
Antibodies	anti-Lu^a, anti-Lu^b

The Lutheran system is of little clinical importance, and the part played by anti-Lu^a in causing hemolytic transfusion reactions is questionable. No case of hemolytic disease of the newborn due to antibodies of this system has been reported. Of interest genetically is the suggestion that the system is linked with the Lewis blood-group system[79].

The Kell blood-group system

Shortly after its description was published, the antiglobulin test resulted in the discovery in the serum of a mother of antibodies of a hitherto unknown specificity[80]. The antibodies reacted with about 9% of the blood samples tested and were named anti-Kell (anti-K). The existence of a hypothetical antigen reacting with an antibody anti-k and of a gene k was then assumed, and later[81] antibodies with anti-k specificity were actually discovered and reported under the name anti-Cellano. The Kell blood-group system is shown in Table 16.

Table 16

Reaction with:			
anti-K	+	+	−
anti-k (Cellano)	−	+	+
Phenotype	K	Kk	kk
Genotype	KK	Kk	kk

anti-K only rarely causes agglutination of K-positive erythrocytes suspended in physiological saline. Almost all anti-K are incomplete antibodies and are best detected by means of the indirect antiglobulin test. The Kell system is of considerable clinical importance since anti-K have been known to cause both severe hemolytic disease of the newborn and severe to fatal hemolytic transfusion reactions.

anti-k is rarely found, and this is understandable in view of the fact that the KK individuals who could form such antibodies constitute only about 0.2% of the population. The first anti-k reported was the cause of a mild case of hemolytic disease of the newborn.

Further antigens of the Kell system have recently been reported. Kp^a[82] and Kp^b[83] are interpreted[82] as an additional pair of allelomorphic genes on the chromosome of the Kell system, although the possibility has also been suggested[84] that Kp^a is an allelomorph of K and k and that anti-Kp^b corresponds to an antibody anti-Kk (in analogy with the anti-Ss of the MNSs system).

The Lewis blood-group system

An antibody reacting with 22% of blood samples from English people was discovered by Mourant[85] in 1946, and the antigen thus recognized was named Le^a. Two years later the antibody anti-Le^b was found[86] and the same worker showed that Le^a in adults was a recessive mendelian character[86]. Soon afterwards the important discovery was made[87] that individuals on whose erythrocytes the Le^a antigen can be demonstrated secreted no ABH-substances in their saliva (see page 587). However, up to the present the exact inheritance of the Lewis blood groups and their genetical relationship to the ABO system and the secretor-nonsecretor genes have defied all efforts at elucidation. It is now thought probable that the Lewis system is an antigen system not of the erythrocytes but of the saliva and serum, and that the Lewis substances only attach themselves in a secondary manner to the erythrocytes. According to CEPPELLINI[88], the dominant L gene is responsible for the secretion of Le^a substance in saliva. The secretor gene pair responsible for the secretion of the ABH-substance Se-se is not linked to L-l. The genetic location of the Le^b antigens is still uncertain but they are probably a combined product of the genes Se and L. The very plausible genetic theory of the Lewis blood groups due to CEPPELLINI is summarized in Table 17 (from RACE and SANGER[89]).

Table 17

Genotypes	Phenotypes			
	Saliva			Erythrocytes
	ABH	Le^a	Le^b	
SeSe LL SeSe Ll Sese LL Sese Ll	+	+	+	Le(a−b+)
sese LL sese Ll	−	+	−	Le(a+b−)
SeSe ll Sese ll	+	−	−*	Le(a−b−)
sese ll	−	−	−	

* According to GRUBB[87].

Lewis antibodies can cause severe hemolytic transfusion reactions[90], and they have also been held responsible for hemolytic disease of the newborn[91].

The Duffy blood-group system

The antibody anti-Fy^a was described in 1950 by CUTBUSH et al.[92] and the antibody anti-Fy^b in 1951 by IKIN et al.[93]. These antibodies react with two antigens, Fy^a and Fy^b, of human erythrocytes. The corresponding genes Fy^a and Fy^b are an allelomorphic pair. Subsequently the phenotype Fy(a−b−) was discovered in Negroes[94], leading to the assumption of the existence of a third allelomorph. Since the corresponding antibodies have not yet been found, this allelomorph is denoted by the symbol Fy. The phenotype Fy(a−b−) appears to be absent among members of the white races. The present state of knowledge of the Duffy system is summarized in Table 18.

Table 18

Genes	Fy^a, Fy^b, [Fy]
Antigens	Fy^a, Fy^b, [Fy]
Phenotypes...	Fy(a+b−), Fy(a+b+), Fy(a−b+), [Fy(a−b−)]
Genotypes ...	Fy^aFy^a, Fy^aFy^b, Fy^bFy^b, [Fy^aFy, Fy^bFy, FyFy]

[ ] indicates presence only in Negroes.

The samples of anti-Fy^a so far found are with few exceptions active in vitro only in the indirect antiglobulin test. The clinical significance of the Duffy blood groups is shown in Table 2.

The Kidd blood-group system

The antibody anti-Jk^a which led to the discovery of the Kidd blood groups was first described by ALLEN et al.[95] in 1951. Two years later anti-Jk^b was found by PLAUT et al.[96]. Anti-Jk^a is usually most effective in the antiglobulin test. Sera containing anti-Jk^b are very rare. The Kidd system consists of two allelomorphic genes, Jk^a and Jk^b. The phenotype Jk(a−b−) was found in a Philippine woman[97] and is certainly very rare. Table 19 summarizes present knowledge of the Kidd system.

The Kidd antibodies are only rarely responsible for hemolytic disease of the newborn or hemolytic transfusion reactions (Table 2).

Table 19

Genes	Jk^a, Jk^b, [Jk]
Antigens	Jk^a, Jk^b, [Jk]
Phenotypes ..	Jk(a+b−), Jk(a+b+), Jk(a−b+), [Jk(a−b−)]
Genotypes ...	Jk^aJk^a, Jk^aJk^b, Jk^bJk^b, [Jk^aJk, Jk^bJk, JkJk]
Antibodies ...	anti-Jk^a, anti-Jk^b

[ ] indicates occurrence not yet reported in white or Negro individuals.

Antigens of limited distribution (private family antigens)

Apart from the nine well-established blood-group systems, antigens are known whose occurrence is limited, often to the members of a single family. The antibodies concerned have usually been found in a mother and the corresponding antigens in a child and its father. The genetic classification of these private family antigens is difficult, and is usually limited to a demonstration of their independence of the other known blood-group systems. Particulars of the family antigens so far discovered are given in Table 20.

Table 20 Modified from RACE and SANGER, *Blood Groups in Man*, 3rd ed., Oxford, 1958, page 235.

Name of antigen	Discoverer	Origin of antibodies	Earlier private antigens excluded
Levay	CALLENDER and RACE[98], 1946	Transfusion	
Jobbins	GILBEY[99], 1947	Pregnancy	
Becker	ELBEL and PROKOP[100], 1951	Pregnancy	
Ven	VAN LOGHEM and VAN DER HART[101], 1952	Pregnancy	Gr*
Wr^a	HOLMAN[102], 1953	Pregnancy	Levay, Gr*, Ven
Be^a	DAVIDSOHN et al.[103], 1953	Pregnancy	
Ca	WIENER and BRANCATO[104], 1953	Pregnancy	Be^a
Rm	VAN DER HART et al.[105], 1954	Pregnancy	Ven, Wr^a
By	SIMMONS and WERE[106], 1955	Pregnancy	Levay, Gr*, Becker, Ven, Wr^a, Be^a, Ca, Rm

* Gr = Vw (see MNSs system, page 587).

The antigen Di^a (LAYRISSE et al.[107]) should also be mentioned. Often found in colored races like the South American Indians, it is in general not detectable in members of white races.

Antigens of wide distribution (public antigens)

In 1952 SUSSMAN and MILLER[108] described an antibody which gave a negative reaction with only 4 out of 10,000 blood samples with which it was tested. This anti-Vel, as it was named, was the cause of a hemolytic transfusion reaction.

Another antibody of this type, the anti-Yt^a discovered by EATON et al.[109], reacted with trypsin-treated erythrocytes in the indirect antiglobulin test. At 37°C, 99.7% of the blood samples tested gave a positive reaction. The anti-Yt^a antibody probably arises after repeated transfusions.

Antigens of human erythrocytes

Present knowledge of the antigens of human erythrocytes is summarized in Table 21. The table lists the 60 antigens which are recognized by means of antibodies together with a further 7 antigens whose existence has been postulated. The antigens of human erythrocytes can be classified into 10 separate genetic systems. It is possible that some of those now classified as private or public antigens may later be more closely defined and either assigned to one or other of the established blood-group systems or form an additional system.

Table 21 Modified from RACE and SANGER, *Blood Groups in Man*, 3rd ed., Oxford, 1958, page 276.

Blood-group system	Antigens detected by: positive reaction with specific antibody	Antigens detected by: positive reaction with one antibody, negative with another	Antigens assumed to exist because of negative reactions, but no specific antibody yet found
A_1A_2BO	A_1, B, H	A_2, A_3, A_x	
MNSs	M, N, S, s, Mi^a, Vw, Hu, He, M^g, Vr	M_2, N_2, M^c	S^u
P	P_1, P^k	P_2	p
Rh	D, C, c, C^w, C^x, E, e, E^w, f, V	D^u, C^u, c^v, E^u	d, F, v
Lutheran	Lu^a, Lu^b		
Kell	K, k, Kp^a		
Lewis	Le^a, Le^b		
Duffy	Fy^a, Fy^b		Fy
Kidd	Jk^a, Jk^b		Jk
Diego	Di^a		
"Private"	Levay, Gr, Becker, Ven, Wr^a, Be^a, Ca, Rm, By, Di^a		presumably "allelic" antigens exist
"Public"	Vel, Yt^a		presumably "allelic" antigens exist

Antibodies with blood-group specificity

Blood-group system	Specificity	Occurrence and characteristics
ABO	anti-A	In all B- and O-individuals
	anti-A_1	In about 1–2% of A_2- and 25% of A_2B-individuals
	anti-B	In all A_1-, A_2- and O-individuals
	anti-O	1. Very rare. 2. Regularly present in the rare "Bombay" bloods
	anti-H	Normal cold agglutinins
MNSs	anti-M, anti-N	Rare occurrence as specific cold antibodies in man. Produced by immunization of animals
	anti-S	Immune antibody, occurring rarely as irregular antibody active at 20°C
	anti-s	Immune antibody
	anti-U	Immune antibody in Negroes
	anti-Hu, anti-He	Produced by immunizing animals with erythrocytes of Negroes
	anti-Mi^a, anti-Vw	Occur as irregular natural antibodies or as immune antibodies
	anti-Mg	Naturally occurring antibody in about 1–3% of sera
	anti-Ve	Accompanies anti-S
P	anti-P_1	Naturally occurring, "irregular" antibody or produced by immunizing animals
	anti-P+P_1(Tj^a)	Occurs regularly in the very rare pp-individuals
Rh	anti-D	Commonest immune antibody after anti-A and anti-B
	anti-C	Often accompanies anti-D. Usually recognizes the antigen C^w
	anti-C^w	Immune antibody or naturally occurring antibody
	anti-c	Immune antibody, often accompanying anti-E
	anti-C^x	Rare immune antibody
	anti-E	Commonest Rh antibody after anti-D, also a natural antibody. Often occurs in combination with anti-D or anti-c
	anti-E^w	Found so far in only one blood sample
	anti-e	Immune antibody, often accompanying anti-C
	anti-f	Probably anti-c + e
	anti-V	The antigen V recognized by this antibody occurs mainly in Negroes (West Africans 90%, Englishmen 0.5%)
	anti-G	Specific for anti-CD
Lutheran	anti-Lu^a	Immune character doubtful
	anti-Lu^b	Rare immune antibody
Kell	anti-K, anti-k	Immune antibodies
	anti-Kp^a, anti-Kp^b	Rare immune antibodies
Lewis	anti-Le^a, anti-Le^b	Specific cold antibodies which can also occur as hemolysins and complement-fixing incomplete antibodies. anti-Le^b is weaker and rarer
	anti-X	Assumed to be anti-Le^a + Le^b
Duffy	anti-Fy^a	Immune antibody, usually active only in the antiglobulin test
	anti-Fy^b	Very rare immune antibody
Kidd	anti-Jk^a	Immune antibody reacting in the antiglobulin test with complement addition or in the combined trypsin-antiglobulin test
	anti-Jk^b	Rare immune antibody
Diego, Sutter	anti-Di^a, anti-Js^a	The antigens recognized by these antibodies are found only in individuals of certain races
Private	anti-Levay	Produced after blood transfusion
	anti-Jobbins, anti-Becker, anti-Ven	Found in mothers of children suffering from hemolytic disease of the newborn
	anti-Wr^a	Found in about 1% of sera as naturally occurring irregular antibody
	anti-Be^a, anti-Ca	Found in mothers of children suffering from hemolytic disease of the newborn
	anti-Rm, anti-By	Produced in pregnancy
	anti-I	Cold-specific antibody
Public	anti-Vel	Reacted negatively with only 4 out of 10,000 blood samples
	anti-Yt^a	Best detected by the trypsin-antiglobulin test since it does not react with all antiglobulin sera

References

1) Some recent publications on blood groups and their applications are the following: Boorman and Dodd, *An Introduction to Blood Group Serology*, London, 1957; Boyd, W. C., *Tab. biol. (Amst.)*, **17**, 113 (1939); Dunsford and Bowley, *Techniques in Blood Grouping*, Springfield, 1956; James, J. D., *Practical Blood Transfusion*, Oxford, 1958; Mollison, P. L., *Blood Transfusion in Clinical Medicine*, 2nd ed., Oxford, 1956; Mourant, A. E., *The Distribution of the Human Blood Groups*, Oxford, 1954; Race and Sanger, *Blood Groups in Man*, 3rd ed., Oxford, 1958; Stratton and Renton, *Practical Blood Grouping*, Oxford, 1958; Wiener, A. S., *Blood Groups and Transfusion*, 3rd ed., Springfield, 1943; Wiener and Wexler, *Heredity of the Blood Groups*, New York, 1958. See also Blood groups, *Brit. med. Bull.*, **15**, No. 2 (1959).
2) Coombs et al., *Brit. J. exp. Path.*, **26**, 255 (1945); *Lancet*, **1**, 264 (1946); Coombs and Roberts, *Brit. med. Bull.*, **15**, 113 (1959).
3) Morton and Pickles, *Nature*, **159**, 779 (1947); Wheeler et al., *J. Immunol.*, **65**, 39 (1950).
4) Kuhns and Bailey, *Amer. J. clin. Path.*, **20**, 1067 (1950); Stratton, F., *Vox Sang. (Basel)*, New series, **3**, 43 (1953); Stratton, F., *Lancet*, **1**, 1169 (1953).
5) Haber and Rosenfield, *P. H. Andresen, Papers in Dedication of his 60th Birthday*, Copenhagen, 1957, page 45.
6) Unger, L. J., *J. Lab. clin. Med.*, **37**, 825 (1951).
7) Diamond and Abelson, *J. Lab. clin. Med.*, **30**, 204 (1945).
8) Landsteiner, K., *Zbl. Bakt., I. Abt. Orig.*, **27**, 357 (1900); *Wien. klin. Wschr.*, **14**, 1132 (1901).
9) Von Dungern and Hirschfeld, *Z. Immun.-Forsch.*, **8**, 526 (1911).
10) Bernstein, F., *Klin. Wschr.*, **3**, 1495 (1924).
11) Thomsen et al., *Acta path. microbiol. scand.*, **7**, 157 (1930).
12) Friedenreich, V., *Z. Immun.-Forsch.*, **89**, 409 (1936).
13) Hirschfeld and Hirschfeld, *Lancet*, **2**, 675 (1919).
14) Race and Sanger, *P. H. Andresen, Papers in Dedication of his 60th Birthday*, Copenhagen, 1957, page 172.
15) Dausset, J., *Immuno-hématologie biologique et clinique*, Paris, 1956, pages 459 and 594.
16) Kabat, E. A., *Blood Group Substances*, New York, 1956; Morgan and Watkins, *Brit. med. Bull.*, **15**, 109 (1959).
17) Krüpe, M., *Blutgruppenspezifische pflanzliche Eiweisskörper (Phytagglutinine)*, Stuttgart, 1956.
18) Fischer and Hahn, *Z. Immun.-Forsch.*, **84**, 177 (1935).
19) Wiener and Gordon, *Brit. J. Haemat.*, **2**, 305 (1956).
20) Van Loghem et al., *Vox Sang. (Basel)*, New series, **2**, 16 (1957).
21) Moullec et al., *Rev. Hémat.*, **10**, 574 (1955).
22) Levine et al., *Proceedings of the 6th Congress of the International Society of Blood Transfusions*, Paris, 1958, page 132.
23) Lehrs, H., *Z. Immun.-Forsch.*, **66**, 175 (1930); Putkonen, T., *Acta Soc. Med. «Duodecim»*, **A 14**, Fasc. 2, 1 (1932).
24) Schiff and Sasaki, *Klin. Wschr.*, **11**, 1426 (1932).
25) Friedenreich and Hartmann, *Z. Immun.-Forsch.*, **92**, 141 (1938).
26) Grubb, R., *Acta path. microbiol. scand.*, **28**, 61 (1951).
27) Clarke, C. A., *Brit. med. J.*, **2**, 725 (1956).
28) Landsteiner and Levine, *Proc. Soc. exp. Biol. (N.Y.)*, **24**, 600 and 941 (1927).
29) Landsteiner and Levine, *J. exp. Med.*, **48**, 731 (1928).
30) Landsteiner and Levine, *J. exp. Med.*, **47**, 757 (1928).
31) Walsh and Montgomery, *Nature*, **160**, 504 (1947).
32) Sanger and Race, *Nature*, **160**, 505 (1947).
33) Levine et al., *Proc. Soc. exp. Biol. (N.Y.)*, **78**, 218 (1951).
34) Crome, W., *Dtsch. Z. ges. gerichtl. Med.*, **24**, 167 (1935); Friedenreich, V., *Dtsch. Z. ges. gerichtl. Med.*, **25**, 358 (1935).
35) Friedenreich and Lauridsen, *Acta path. microbiol. scand.*, Suppl. 38, 155 (1938).
36) Dunsford et al., *Nature*, **172**, 688 (1953).
37) Allen et al., *Vox Sang. (Basel)*, New series, **3**, 81 (1958).
38) Landsteiner et al., *J. Immunol.*, **27**, 469 (1934); Chalmers et al., *Brit. med. J.*, **2**, 175 (1953).
39) Ikin and Mourant, *Brit. med. J.*, **1**, 456 (1951).
40) Levine et al., *Proc. Soc. exp. Biol. (N.Y.)*, **77**, 402 (1951).
41) Van der Hart et al., *Vox Sang. (Basel)*, **4**, 108 (1954).
42) Van der Hart et al., *Vox Sang. (Basel)*, New series, **3**, 261 (1958).
43) Wiener et al., *J. Amer. med. Ass.*, **153**, 1444 (1953).
44) Greenwalt et al., *Proc. nat. Acad. Sci. (Wash.)*, **40**, 1126 (1954).
45) Landsteiner and Levine, *Proc. Soc. exp. Biol. (N.Y.)*, **24**, 941 (1927).
46) Landsteiner and Levine, *J. Immunol.*, **20**, 179 (1931).
47) Landsteiner and Levine, *J. Immunol.*, **18**, 87 (1930); **20**, 179 (1931).
48) Levine et al., *Proc. Soc. exp. Biol. (N.Y.)*, **77**, 403 (1951).
49) Sanger, R., *Nature*, **176**, 1163 (1955).
50) Wiener and Peters, *Ann. intern. Med.*, **13**, 2306 (1940).
51) Wiener, A. S., *Amer. J. clin. Path.*, **12**, 302 (1942).
52) Moureau, P., *Rev. belge Sci. méd.*, **16**, 258 (1945).
53) Landsteiner and Wiener, *Proc. Soc. exp. Biol. (N.Y.)*, **43**, 223 (1940), quoted by Race and Sanger, *Blood Groups in Man*, 3rd ed., Oxford, 1958, page 116.
54) Levine and Stetson, *J. Amer. med. Ass.*, **113**, 126 (1939).
55) Wiener and Peters, *Ann. intern. Med.*, **13**, 2306 (1940).
56) Wiener, A. S., *Proc. Soc. exp. Biol. (N.Y.)*, **54**, 316 (1943).
57) Race, R. R., *Nature*, **153**, 771 (1944).
58) Landsteiner and Wiener, *J. exp. Med.*, **74**, 309 (1941).
59) Levine et al., *Amer. J. Obstet. Gynec.*, **42**, 925 (1941).
60) Callender and Race, *Ann. Eugen. (Lond.)*, **13**, 102 (1946/47).
61) Stratton and Renton, *Brit. med. J.*, **1**, 962 (1954).
62) Race et al., *Nature*, **152**, 563 (1943).
63) Mourant, A. E., *Nature*, **155**, 542 (1945).
64) Greenwalt and Sanger, *Brit. J. Haemat.*, **1**, 52 (1955).
65) Rosenfield et al., *Brit. med. J.*, **1**, 975 (1953).
66) DeNatale et al., *J. Amer. med. Ass.*, **159**, 247 (1955).
67) Stratton, F., *Nature*, **158**, 25 (1946).
68) Race et al., *Nature*, **161**, 316 (1948).
69) Ceppellini et al., *Boll. Ist. sieroter. milan.*, **29**, 123 (1950).
70) Race et al., *Nature*, **166**, 520 (1950).
71) Wiener et al., *Amer. J. hum. Genet.*, **4**, 363 (1952).
72) Race et al., *Nature*, **174**, 460 (1954).
73) Ceppellini et al., *Proc. nat. Acad. Sci. (Wash.)*, **41**, 283 (1955).
74) Allen and Tippett, *Vox Sang. (Basel)*, New series, **3**, 321 (1958).
75) Wallerstein, H., *Science*, **103**, 583 (1946).
76) Callender and Race, *Ann. Eugen. (Lond.)*, **13**, 102 (1946/47).
77) Report, *Nature*, **163**, 580 (1949).
78) Cutbush and Chanarin, *Nature*, **178**, 855 (1956).
79) Mohr, J., *Acta path. microbiol. scand.*, **28**, 207 (1951).
80) Coombs et al., *Lancet*, **1**, 264 (1946).
81) Levine et al., *Science*, **109**, 464 (1949).
82) Allen and Lewis, *Vox Sang. (Basel)*, New series, **2**, 81 (1957).
83) Allen et al., *Vox Sang. (Basel)*, New series, **3**, 1 (1958).
84) Race and Sanger, *Blood Groups in Man*, 3rd ed., Oxford, 1958, page 197.
85) Mourant, A. E., *Nature*, **158**, 237 (1946).
86) Andresen, P. H., *Acta path. microbiol. scand.*, **25**, 728 (1948).
87) Grubb, R., *Nature*, **162**, 933 (1948).
88) Ceppellini, R., *Proceedings of the 6th Congress of the International Society of Blood Transfusions*, Paris, 1955, page 207.
89) Race and Sanger, *Blood Groups in Man*, 3rd ed., Oxford, 1958, page 208.
90) For a review see Holländer and Hässig, *P. H. Andresen, Papers in Dedication of his 60th Birthday*, Copenhagen, 1957, page 10.
91) Schwenzer and Spielmann, *Vox Sang. (Basel)*, New series, **2**, 428 (1957).
92) Cutbush et al., *Nature*, **165**, 188 (1950).
93) Ikin et al., *Nature*, **168**, 1077 (1951).
94) Sanger et al., *Brit. J. Haemat.*, **1**, 370 (1955).
95) Allen et al., *Nature*, **167**, 482 (1951).
96) Plaut et al., *Nature*, **171**, 431 (1953).
97) Pinkerton et al., *Vox Sang. (Basel)*, New series, **4**, 155 (1959).
98) Callender and Race, *Ann. Eugen. (Lond.)*, **13**, 102 (1946/47).
99) Gilbey, B. E., *Nature*, **160**, 362 (1947).
100) Elbel and Prokop, *Z. Hyg. Infekt.-Kr.*, **132**, 120 (1951).
101) Van Loghem and van der Hart, *Bulletin van het Centraal Laboratorium van de Bloedtranfusiedienst van het Nederlandse Rode Kruis*, **2**, 225 (1952).
102) Holman, C. A., *Lancet*, **2**, 119 (1953).
103) Davidsohn et al., *Blood*, **8**, 747 (1953).
104) Wiener and Brancato, *Amer. J. hum. Genet.*, **5**, 350 (1953).
105) Van der Hart et al., *Vox Sang. (Basel)*, **4**, 108 (1954).
106) Simmons and Were, *Med. J. Austral.*, **42**, 55 (1955).
107) Layrisse et al., *Acta med. venez.*, **3**, 132 (1955).
108) Sussman and Miller, *Rev. Hémat.*, **7**, 368 (1952).
109) Eaton et al., *Brit. J. Haemat.*, **2**, 333 (1956).

	Normal values*	Sources[1]	Remarks
Physicochemical properties			
Appearance	water-white, clear		*Coloration* or *cloudiness* of the spinal fluid is *pathological* unless due to hemorrhage caused by the lumbar puncture. *Cloudiness* of the fluid begins when the number of leukocytes exceeds about 200 per cubic millimeter. The usual colors observed are red, yellow and brown. A *red* color (erythrochromia) indicates the admixture of blood either at the time of the puncture or not more than 5–6 hours previously; when the number of erythrocytes is less than 30 per cubic millimeter the coloration is not obvious to the naked eye. A *yellow* color (xanthochromia) results from admixture of blood more than 6 hours before the puncture, or when the permeability of the meninges to various colored substances (bilirubin, carotenes, lipochromes) is increased, as for instance in all types of meningitis and when the circulation of spinal fluid is blocked by tumors. A *brown* color is seen in cases of melanosarcoma of the central nervous system or of the meninges.
Volume	100–150 ml		This is the volume which can be removed by lumbar puncture.
Pressure	6–20 cm H_2O = 4.5–15 mm Hg		The pressure of the cerebrospinal fluid is extremely variable; the values given here are regarded as the limits of normal for a subject lying on his side. Many factors affect the value obtained, especially the position of the subject (causing variations of 5–10 cm H_2O), inhalation of various gases (CO_2: rise of 20–30 cm H_2O; cf. Rich et al., *Circ. Res.*, **1**, 389 [1953]), hyperventilation (mean fall of 6 cm H_2O; cf. Rich et al., *loc. cit.*), ingestion of $NaHCO_3$ (mean rise of 12.5 cm H_2O; cf. Rich et al., *loc. cit.*). The movements of respiration and heart beats also cause rhythmic variations with an amplitude of several millimeters H_2O in the pressure of spinal fluid.
Queckenstedt's test: The pressure of spinal fluid rises when the two jugular veins are compressed and returns to normal when the pressure is released. Rise of pressure when only one jugular vein is compressed indicates thrombosis of the lateral sinus on the opposite side.			
Number of cells	0–3 per cubic millimeter		These few cells are usually lymphocytes. The presence of erythrocytes is fundamentally abnormal, except that a few are almost always introduced during the puncture. If more than 4 cells per cubic millimeter are present the fluid is abnormal.
Specific gravity	1.005–1.009	Sunderman and Boerner, *Normal Values in Clinical Medicine*, Philadelphia, 1950, page 315.	
pH value	Mean: **7.32** Standard deviation: 0.09 Normal range**: *7.14–7.50*	Cooper et al., *Amer. J. Med.*, **18**, 613 (1955).	Mean of 20 normal subjects. The values given by Reichner, H., *Z. Ges. Neurol. Psychiat.*, **123**, 434 (1930), agree with those given here.
Freezing-point depression	0.56–0.60°C	Lickint, F., *Z. ges. Neurol. Psychiat.*, **120**, 148 (1929).	Plasma and spinal fluid are isotonic within ca. 2 mmol. A depression of the freezing point of 0.56°C corresponds to a tonicity, i.e. a total concentration of osmotically active particles, of 301.4 mmol/1000 g H_2O (see also pages 324–326). The small difference in tonicity between plasma and spinal fluid is caused by the higher protein content of plasma (the tonicity of all other osmotically active particles is identical in the two liquids).
Refractive index	1.33494–1.33510	Hallmann, L., *Klinische Chemie und Mikroskopie*, 6th ed., Stuttgart, 1950.	
Surface tension (at 20°C)			
dynamic	62.1–65.1, mean 63.3 dyn cm^{-1}	Künzel, O., *Dtsch. Z. Nervenheilk.*, **139**, 265 (1936).	The static surface tension rises to the same value as the dynamic 2 hours after drawing of the sample.
static	59.5–62.5, mean 61.0 dyn cm^{-1}		
Viscosity (at 38°C)	1.020–1.027 (water = 1.000)	Levinson, A., *Cerebrospinal Fluid in Health and Disease*, St. Louis, 1919.	
Electrical conductivity			
at 18°C	1.198×10^{-2} mho × cm^{-1}	Teschler, L., *Dtsch. Z. Nervenheilk.*, **103**, 87 (1928).	
at 25°C	1.425×10^{-2} to 1.549×10^{-2} mho × cm^{-1}	Eckel, J. L., *Human Cerebrospinal Fluid*, New York, 1926, page 143.	

* The values given in this table apply to cerebrospinal fluid obtained by *lumbar* puncture in normal *adults*. For the principal characteristics of the cerebrospinal fluid of infants, and the differences between the fluid obtained in adults by lumbar, cisternal and ventricular puncture, see the tables on page 597.

** When a range given is a *normal range* (see page 154), i.e. calculated from the formula: mean ± (2 × standard deviation *s*), it is printed in *italics*, with the mean in **bold** figures. Otherwise the data given are experimental results which have not been tested statistically.

1) The following sources have been used in addition to those given in this column: Davson, H., *Physiology of the Ocular and Cerebrospinal Fluids*, London, 1956; Merritt and Fremont-Smith, *Cerebrospinal Fluid*, Philadelphia, 1937; Lups and Haan, *The Cerebrospinal Fluid*, New York, 1954; Lang et al. (Eds.), *Hoppe-Seyler/Thierfelder Handbuch der physiologisch- und pathologisch-chemischen Analyse*, 10th ed., vol. V, *Untersuchung der Organe, Körperflüssigkeiten und Ausscheidungen*, Berlin, 1953.

	Normal values*	Sources[1]	Remarks
Alkali reserve	59.5 vol% CO_2	PINCUS and KRAMER, *J. biol. Chem.*, **57**, 463 (1923).	Mean value from the only available determination on two subjects in undoubted good health. Many authorities give only very vague limits: 40–60 vol% CO_2.
Organic constituents			
Proteins			
Total	20–40 mg/100 ml	Mean values from the literature.	For exact determinations: Micro-Kjeldahl or method of WU and LING, *Chin. J. Physiol.*, **1**, 161 (1927). For review of methods see LINDENMEYER, E., *Mschr. Psychiat. Neurol.*, **109**, 57 (1944).
Percentage composition		MÉTAIS et al., *Ann. Biol. clin.*, **15**, 398 (1957). Determination by electrophoresis after removal of inorganic fraction and concentration.	The concentration of proteins in spinal fluid can be determined more or less exactly by various reactions which are easy to carry out. Amongst those used most frequently are the NONNE-APELT and PANDY reactions, which when positive indicate increased globulin, and the colloid reactions (using colloidal benzoin, gum mastic or colloidal gold) which indicate modifications in the albumin: globulin ratio. According to GUILLAIN et al., *C. R. Soc. Biol. (Paris)*, **83**, 1380 (1920), the reaction with colloidal benzoin is much more sensitive than that with gum mastic; it is also simpler and less subject to error than LANGE's colloidal gold reaction (GUILLAIN and LECHELLE, *Rev. neurol. [Paris]*, **28**, 80 [1921]).
X-Proteins	0 – 4.4%		
Albumins	51.3–60.0%		
α_1-Globulins	4.7– 8.0%		
α_2-Globulins	7.5–11.6%		
β-Globulins	9.2–18.0%		
Fibrinogen	0 – 8.0%		
γ-Globulins	5.6–10.0%		
Albumin: globulin ratio	approx. 4 : 1	HOPPE-SEYLER[3], page 310.	Very variable. Usually increased in chronic diseases and normal in acute infections[2].
Nitrogen			
Total	15.7–22.0 Mean 18.5 mg/100 ml	HOPPE-SEYLER[3], page 321.	
Nonprotein-N	11–20 mg/100 ml	HOPPE-SEYLER[3], page 321.	
Amino acids (as N)	1.6–2.7 Mean 2.2 mg/100 ml	HOPPE-SEYLER[3], page 336.	25 different amino acids are regularly found in normal spinal fluid and the quantitative variations are large, so that qualitative analysis of the free acids is of no diagnostic value (KNAUFF, H. G., *Nature*, **182**, 937 [1958]).
Urea	10–30 mg/100 ml	Mean values from the literature.	No known clinical significance.
Uric acid	0.5–2.6 mg/100 ml	LUPS and HAAN[2], page 66.	
Creatine	0.46–1.87 mg/100 ml	HOPPE-SEYLER[3], page 324.	
Creatinine	0.54–1.91 Mean 1.11 mg/100 ml	COCKRILL, J. R., *Arch. Neurol. Psychiat. (Chicago)*, **25**, 1297 (1931).	
Glucose	45–80 mg/100 ml	Mean values from the literature.	For practical purposes the spinal fluid contains no reducing substances other than glucose. The sugar concentration is usually *reduced* in meningitis of meningococcal, tuberculous, influenzal and acute secondary syphilitic origin, and in progressive paralysis; it is usually *increased* in the following diseases: mumps meningitis, abscesses, tumors and hemorrhage of the brain, congenital syphilis, tabes, polyneuritis, poliomyelitis, encephalitis lethargica, renal diseases, arteriosclerosis and diabetes (GREENFIELD and CARMICHAEL, *The Cerebrospinal Fluid in Clinical Diagnosis*, New York, 1925).
Inositol	2.7 mg/100 ml	NIXON, D. A., *J. Physiol. (Lond.)*, **119**, 18 P (1953).	Mean value from measurements on 17 healthy subjects. The average concentration of inositol in the plasma of these 17 subjects was 0.6 mg/100 ml, i.e. approx. 4.5 times less than in the spinal fluid.
Pyruvic acid	Mean value: **0.905** mg/100 ml Standard deviation: 0.177 Normal range**: *0.551–1.259* mg/ml	LASCH, F., *Klin. Wschr.*, **31**, 941 (1953).	Mean value in 20 cases. These values agree with those given by AMATUZIO and NESBITT, *J. clin. Invest.*, **29**, 1486 (1950).

* The values given in this table apply to cerebrospinal fluid obtained by *lumbar* puncture in normal *adults*. For the principal characteristics of the cerebrospinal fluid of infants, and the differences between the fluid obtained in adults by lumbar, cisternal and ventricular puncture, see the tables on page 597.

** When a range given is a *normal range* (see page 154), i.e. calculated from the formula: mean ± (2 × standard deviation *s*), it is printed in *italics*, with the mean in **bold** figures. Otherwise the data given are experimental results which have not been tested statistically.

1) The following sources have been used in addition to those given in this column: DAVSON, H., *Physiology of the Ocular and Cerebrospinal Fluids*, London, 1956; SUNDERMAN and BOERNER, *Normal Values in Clinical Medicine*, Philadelphia, 1950; MERRITT and FREMONT-SMITH, *Cerebrospinal Fluid*, Philadelphia, 1937. *2)* LUPS and HAAN, *The Cerebrospinal Fluid*, New York, 1954. *3)* LANG et al. (Eds.), *Hoppe-Seyler/Thierfelder Handbuch der physiologisch- und pathologisch-chemischen Analyse*, 10th ed., vol. V, *Untersuchung der Organe, Körperflüssigkeiten und Ausscheidungen*, Berlin, 1953.

	Normal values*	Sources[1]	Remarks
Lactic acid	11–27 Mean 19 mg/100 ml	GLASER, J., *J. biol. Chem.*, **69**, 539 (1926).	Determinations on 13 healthy individuals.
Aldehydes and ketones (substances reacting with bisulfites)	0.42–3.07 mg/100 ml	HOPPE-SEYLER[3], page 326.	Acetone, β-hydroxybutyric acid and acetoacetic acid are normally absent from spinal fluid.
Succinic acid	0.3–0.4 mg/100 ml	THUNBERG, T., *Acta med. scand.*, Suppl. 90, 122 (1938).	
Citric acid	4.5 mg/100 ml	BENNI, B., *Biochem. Z.*, **221**, 270 (1930).	
Ethanol	7.3 mg/100 ml	GABRIEL and NOVOTNY, *Arch. Psychiat. Nervenkr.*, **108**, 279 (1938).	
Cholesterol	0.06–0.5 mg/100 ml	Mean values from the literature.	
Fatty acids	1–5 mg/100 ml	HOPPE-SEYLER[3], page 328.	
Histamine	0.2–3.0 Mean 0.97 μg/100 ml	JACKSON and ROSE, *J. Lab. clin. Med.*, **34**, 250 (1949).	The greater the number of leukocytes in spinal fluid, the higher is its concentration of histamine.
Vitamins	–		Vitamin C (always in its reduced form), vitamin B_1 and nicotinic acid have been found in spinal fluid. See HOPPE-SEYLER[3], page 334 et seq.
Enzymes	–		Numerous enzymes have been found in normal spinal fluid but their clinical significance is not yet known with certainty. Important enzymes present are cholinesterase and pseudocholinesterase (JEFFERSON, M., *Clin. Sci.*, **13**, 599 [1954]), lactic acid dehydrogenase (FLEISHER et al., *Proc. Mayo Clin.*, **32**, 188 [1957]), phosphohexoisomerase and phosphoriboisomerase (BRUNS et al., *Clin. chem. Acta [Amst.]*, **1**, 63 [1956]), ribonuclease (KOVÁCS, E., *Canad. J. med. Sci.*, **31**, 437 [1953]), glutamic oxalacetic transaminase (FLEISHER et al., *Proc. Mayo Clin.*, **32**, 188 [1957]). See also HOPPE-SEYLER[3], page 332.

Inorganic constituents

	Normal values*	Sources[1]	Remarks
Aluminum	12.5 μg/100 ml	HOPPE-SEYLER[3], page 306.	
Bromine	100–400 μg/100 ml	Mean values from the literature. See also HOPPE-SEYLER[3], page 307.	
Calcium	4.1–5.9, mean 5.0 mg/100 ml, or 2.0–2.9, mean 2.45 mEq/l	COHN et al., *J. Lab. clin. Med.*, **24**, 609 (1939).	This concentration corresponds to the concentration of diffusible calcium in the blood.
Chloride	410–470 mg/100 ml	LUPS and HAAN[2], page 85.	As NaCl: 710–780 mg/100 ml.
Copper	Mean value: **6.2** μg/100 ml Standard deviation: 2.4 Normal range**: *1.4–11.0* μg/100 ml	GUBLER et al., *J. clin. Invest.*, **36**, 1208 (1957).	
Iron	23–52 μg/100 ml	LUPS and HAAN[2], page 89.	
Iodine	7–18 μg/100 ml	HOPPE-SEYLER[3], page 307.	The data given in the literature are very inconsistent. Other values for the normal concentration of iodine in spinal fluid are 0.58 μg/100 ml (SUNDERMAN and BOERNER, *Normal Values in Clinical Medicine*, Philadelphia, 1950) and 0.2 μg/100 ml (GILDEA and MAN, *Arch. Neurol. Psychiat. [Chicago]*, **49**, 93 [1943]).
Magnesium	1–3 mg/100 ml	Mean values from the literature according to STARY et al., *Z. ges. exp. Med.*, **66**, 671 (1929).	Most authors consider that magnesium is present in higher concentration in spinal fluid than in blood.

* The values given in this table apply to cerebrospinal fluid obtained by *lumbar* puncture in normal *adults*. For the principal characteristics of the cerebrospinal fluid of infants, and the differences between the fluid obtained in adults by lumbar, cisternal and ventricular puncture, see the tables on page 597.

** When a range given is a *normal range* (see page 154) i.e. calculated from the formula: mean ± (2 × standard deviation *s*), it is printed in *italics*, with the mean in **bold** figures. Otherwise the data given are experimental results which have not been tested statistically.

1) The following sources have been used in addition to those given in this column: DAVSON, H., *Physiology of the Ocular and Cerebrospinal Fluids*, London, 1956; SUNDERMAN and BOERNER, *Normal Values in Clinical Medicine*, Philadelphia, 1950; MERRITT and FREMONT-SMITH, *Cerebrospinal Fluid*, Philadelphia, 1937. *2)* LUPS and HAAN, *The Cerebrospinal Fluid*, New York, 1954. *3)* LANG et al. (Eds.), *Hoppe-Seyler/Thierfelder Handbuch der physiologisch- und pathologisch-chemischen Analyse*, 10th ed., vol. V, *Untersuchung der Organe, Körperflüssigkeiten und Ausscheidungen*, Berlin, 1953.

	Normal values*	Sources[1]	Remarks
Phosphorus			
Total	1.37–2.15 mg/100 ml	TROPP et al., *Biochem. Z.*, **290**, 320 (1937).	
Inorganic	1.0–1.5 Mean 1.4 mg/100 ml	COHN et al., *J. Lab. clin. Med.*, **24**, 609 (1939).	
Lead	14–38 µg/100 ml	HOPPE-SEYLER[2], page 306.	
Potassium	Mean value: **11.57** mg/100 ml = **2.96** mEq/l Standard deviation: 1.76 mg/100 ml = 0.45 mEq/l Normal range**: *8.05–15.09* mg/100 ml = *2.06–3.86* mEq/l	COOPER et al., *Amer. J. Med.*, **18**, 613 (1955).	Determination by flame photometer on 20 healthy subjects. The values given here agree with those of SHAW and HOLLEY, *J. Lab. clin. Med.*, **38**, 574 (1951). The mean concentration of potassium in the serum of the 20 subjects investigated by COOPER et al. was 17.44 mg/100 ml, or 4.46 mEq/l (see also remarks under Sodium).
Sodium	Mean value: **324.6** mg/100 ml = **141.2** mEq/l Standard deviation: 13.8 mg/100 ml = 6.0 mEq/l Normal range**: *297.0–352.2* mg/100 ml = *129.2–153.2* mEq/l	COOPER et al., *Amer. J. Med.*, **18**, 613 (1955).	Determination by flame photometer on 20 healthy subjects. The values given here agree with those of SHAW and HOLLEY, *J. Lab. clin. Med.*, **38**, 574 (1951). The mean concentration of sodium in the serum of the 20 subjects investigated by COOPER et al. was 323.3 mg/100 ml, or 140.6 mEq/l, or less than the concentration in spinal fluid. While the potassium level in the spinal fluid is relatively independent of the potassium level in the blood, the sodium level varies according to the sodium level in the blood except in very severe disorders of the central nervous system (COOPER et al., *Amer. J. Med.*, **18**, 613 [1955]).
Sulfur			
Total	47.2–60.0 mg/100 ml		
Sulfate..............	18.6–26.5 mg/100 ml	FÜRTH et al., *Biochem. Z.*, **251**, 161 (1932).	
Thiocyanate	30–290 µg/100 ml	HOPPE-SEYLER[2], page 308.	

* The values given in this table apply to cerebrospinal fluid obtained by *lumbar* puncture in normal *adults*. For the principal characteristics of the cerebrospinal fluid of infants, and the differences between the fluid obtained in adults by lumbar, cisternal and ventricular puncture, see the tables below.

** When a range given is a *normal range* (see page 154), i.e. calculated from the formula: mean ± (2×standard deviation *s*), it is printed in *italics*, with the mean in **bold** figures. Otherwise the data given are experimental results which have not been tested statistically.

1) The following sources have been used in addition to those given in this column: DAVSON, H., *Physiology of the Ocular and Cerebrospinal Fluids*, London, 1956; SUNDERMAN and BOERNER, *Normal Values in Clinical Medicine*, Philadelphia, 1950; MERRITT and FREMONT-SMITH, *Cerebrospinal Fluid*, Philadelphia, 1937; LUPS and HAAN, *The Cerebrospinal Fluid*, New York, 1954. *2)* LANG et al. (Eds.), *Hoppe-Seyler/Thierfelder Handbuch der physiologisch- und pathologisch-chemischen Analyse*, 10th ed., vol. V, *Untersuchung der Organe, Körperflüssigkeiten und Ausscheidungen*, Berlin, 1953.

*Principal characteristics of the spinal fluid in infants from birth to 6 months**
(modified from LUPS and HAAN, *The Cerebrospinal Fluid*, New York, 1954, page 109)

Age in months	Cells per cubic millimeter	PANDY's reaction	Proteins Total mg/100 ml	Globulins mg/100 ml	Albumins mg/100 ml	Glucose mg/100 ml	Chloride mg/100 ml
0–0.5	3	+ or ++	40–80	10–30	25–55	30–70 often reduced	680–850[1]
0.5–1	3	opalescence or +	30–50	10–20	20–40	very variable: 55–70	
1–2	2	opalescence or +	25–45	5–15	15–40	55–70	
2–3	2	– or opalescence	20–40	5–10	15–30	55–70	700–770[1]
3–6	1	– or opalescence	20–40	2–10	10–30	55–70	
over 6	1	–	20–40	2–10	10–20	55–70	

* In children over 6 months the composition of the spinal fluid is the same as in adults.

1) From LANG et al. (Eds.), *Hoppe-Seyler/Thierfelder Handbuch der physiologisch- und pathologisch-chemischen Analyse*, 10th ed., vol. V, *Untersuchung der Organe, Körperflüssigkeiten und Ausscheidungen*, Berlin, 1953, page 307.

Composition of spinal fluid in relation to the site of puncture

In the table the fluid with the highest concentration of the particular constituent is given the number 1, that with the next highest the number 2, and that with the lowest concentration the number 3.

	Proteins	Albumins	Globulins	Albumin: globulin ratio	Cell content	Colloidal reactions	Glucose	Density
Ventricular fluid	3	3	3	3	3	negative	1	less dense
Cisternal fluid	2	2	2	2	2	sometimes very weakly +	2	
Lumbar fluid	1	1	1	1	1	sometimes weakly +	3	more dense

In disease the changes are often much more marked in the lumbar fluid than in the cisternal fluid, while in the latter they are more marked than in the ventricular fluid.

Fresh semen

	Normal values	Sources	Remarks
Volume of the ejaculate	Mean: **3.4** ml Normal range (mean $\pm 2s$): *0.2–6.6* ml Standard deviation s: 1.62 ml	MacLeod, J., *Fertil. and Steril.*, **2**, 115 (1951) (1000 cases).	After at least 3 days continence. Very variable in the same individual. The volume diminishes on repeated coitus; it can reach 13 ml after long continence. A normal volume appears to be important from the point of view of buffering the acidity of the vaginal secretions; in relation to fertility too great a volume is not a good sign (greater dilution of the spermatozoa and loss due to escape from the vagina). After Hotchkiss, R. S., *Etiology and Diagnosis in the Treatment of Infertility in Men*, Springfield, 1952, page 31.
Secretions of the glands involved in ejaculation	The volume of the ejaculate is primarily dependent on the secretions of the prostate and the seminal vesicles. The contribution of the Cowper's glands and the epididymis is small, that of the testes (inc. the spermatozoa) even smaller.	Hotchkiss, R. S., *Fertility in Men*, Philadelphia, 1944; *Etiology and Diagnosis in the Treatment of Infertility in Men*, Springfield, 1952, page 30.	Prior to an ejaculation, 1–2 drops of a clear, colorless liquid, the secretion of the Cowper's glands, first appear. This neutralizes the acidity of the urethra in preparation for the subsequent ejaculation. Then follows first the milky prostate secretion, usually free of spermatozoa, then the part containing the spermatozoa, and finally the gelatinous, highly viscous secretion of the seminal vesicles, often of a tapioca-like consistency.
Color and appearance	Milky-turbid, slightly opalescent, with viscous filaments and grains resembling tapioca. The opalescence is proportional to the spermatozoal concentration.		
Coagulation	Takes place immediately after ejaculation. The mechanism is unknown.		According to Oettle, A. G., *Fertil. and Steril.*, **5**, 227 (1954), clotting occurs even before ejaculation, contrary to the general opinion.
Liquefaction	After a few minutes, liquefaction starts and is complete in about 15 minutes with the exception of a number of the tapioca-like grains, which may maintain their consistency up to an hour.	Mann, T., *The Biochemistry of Semen*, London, 1954; Oettle, A. G., *Fertil. and Steril.*, **5**, 227 (1954).	Liquefaction occurs under the influence of proteolytic enzymes (chiefly of the prostate) and leads to a relatively high concentration of free amino acids. In some cases of azoospermia, liquefaction is greatly delayed.

Semen, 15 minutes and more after ejaculation

Viscosity	6.54 (at 20° C) (water = 1)	Zagami, V., *Arch. Sci. biol. (Bologna)*, **25**, 208 (1939).	According to Hotchkiss, R. S., *Fertility in Men*, Philadelphia, 1944, pages 69 and 105, the viscosity is of some importance in judging semen, especially when the spermatozoa show reduced vitality and motility. Hotchkiss describes several simple methods of assessing the viscosity, one of which, using a glass rod and a test tube (at room temperature), is illustrated below.
Surface tension	66 dyn cm^{-1} (20° C) 52–59.5 dyn cm^{-1} (15° C)	Zagami, V., *loc. cit.* Shedlovsky et al., *Proceedings of the 2nd Conference on Biology of the Spermatozoa*, National Committee on Maternal Health, USA, 1940.	
pH value	7.2–7.39	Hotchkiss, R. S., *Fertility in Men*, Philadelphia, 1944, pages 69 and 102.	When loss of CO_2 from the sample is not prevented the semen will be somewhat more alkaline ca. pH 7.6–8.0. The motility of the spermatozoa is dependent on the pH value, and in contact with the acid vaginal secretion (pH 3.5–4.2) they are rapidly immobilized (see under Volume, above). Normally however, the (fertilizing) spermatozoa hardly come into contact with the vaginal secretion since those deposited at the uterus are rapidly drawn into the upper neck of the cervix (pH 7.8) by the sucking action of the cervix actuated by the orgasm. There they have been observed as little as 3 minutes after ejaculation. The spermatozoa are certainly not capable of such rapid movement with their own unaided motility. This circumstance may explain the diminished capacity for conception generally shown by frigid women.
Specific gravity	1.020–1.040	Belonoschkin, B., *Zeugung beim Menschen*, Stockholm, 1949, page 117.	
Freezing-point depression	0.56–0.58° C after 1 hour 0.74–0.78° C after 16 hours	Zagami, V., *Arch. Sci. biol. (Bologna)*, **25**, 208 (1939).	
Electrical conductivity	0.0088–0.0107 mho × cm^{-1} (20° C)	Zagami, V., *loc. cit.*	

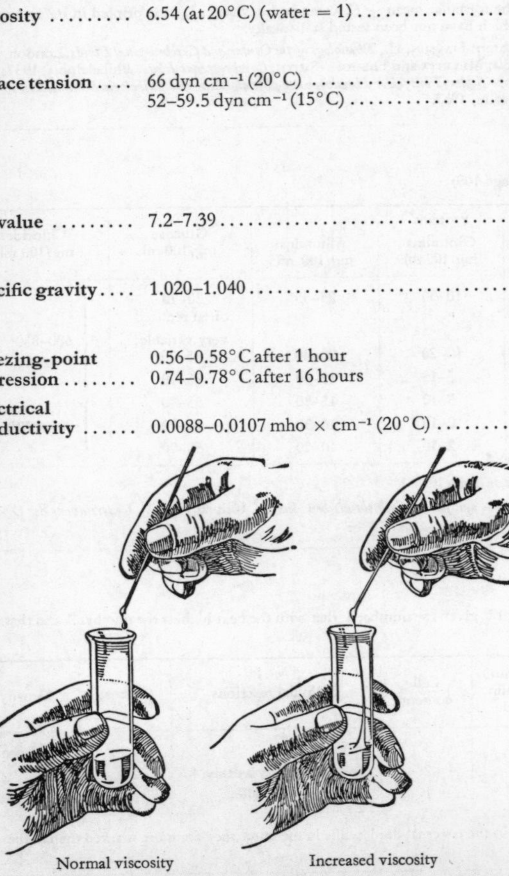

Normal viscosity — Increased viscosity

Seminal fluid

(without spermatozoa, unless otherwise stated)

	Normal values mg/100 ml, unless otherwise stated	Sources	Remarks
Dry residue	10–20% (1–2% salts, 8–10% organic matter, 2–6% proteins, 0.21% ether-soluble)	WEISMAN, A. I., *Spermatozoa and Sterility*, New York, 1941.	
Proteins	1.58–1.80 g	SHEDLOVSKY et al., *Proceedings of the 2nd Conference on Biology of the Spermatozoa*, National Committee on Maternal Health, USA, 1940.	According to MANN, T., *The Biochemistry of Semen*, London, 1954, the proteins of semen consist mainly of albumins, globulins (α, β, γ), mucoproteins, nucleoproteins, thromboplastin and various enzymes (fibrinolysin, fibrinogenase, amino acid oxidase, proteolytic enzymes, phosphatases and others).
Nonprotein nitrogen	55–80	HUGGINS and JOHNSON, *Amer. J. Physiol.*, **103**, 574 (1933).	
Amino acids	up to 100	MACLEOD, J., *Fertil. and Steril.*, **7**, 368 (1956).	The following amino acids have been found: glycine, alanine, serine, threonine, leucine, lysine, valine, cystine, proline, tyrosine, phenylalanine, aspartic acid, glutamic acid (LUNDQUIST, F., *Acta physiol. scand.*, **25**, 178 [1952], and MANN, T., *The Biochemistry of Semen*, London, 1954).
Ergothioneine	1.5	HAAG and MACLEOD, *J. appl. Physiol.*, **14**, 27 (1959).	
Glutathione	30	INFANTELLINA, F., *Boll. Soc. ital. Biol. sper.*, **20**, 322 (1945).	
Spermine and spermidine	90–200 mg/100 ml (in body tissues 1–30 mg/100 g)	EVERETT, M. R., *Medical Biochemistry*, 2nd ed., New York, 1946, page 362.	The spermine originates mainly in the prostate. After ejaculation, it reacts with phosphoric acid to form spermine phosphate, which may crystallize out after a time.
Urea	72	GOLDBLATT, M. W., *Biochem. J.*, **29**, 1346 (1935).	
Fructose	91–520	MANN, T., *The Biochemistry of Semen*, London, 1954, page 32.	The fructose content of semen is very variable and originates mainly from the seminal vesicles. No fructose is present before puberty or after castration. It appears to be important in the metabolism of the spermatozoa (in anaerobic glycolysis; oxygen is toxic) as a source of energy for their motility. In diabetics the fructose content of semen is markedly higher (MACLEOD, J., *Fertil. and Steril.*, **7**, 368 [1956]).
Lactic acid	36–51; 4.0–5.6 mEq/l	SHEDLOVSKY et al., *Proceedings of the 2nd Conference on Biology of the Spermatozoa*, National Committee on Maternal Health, USA, 1940.	GOLDBLATT, M. W., *Biochem. J.*, **29**, 1346 (1935), gives 90–100 mg/100 ml.
Citric acid	96–1430	MANN, T., *The Biochemistry of Semen*, London, 1954, page 32.	Little is known of the physiological significance of the citric acid content.
Cholesterol	103	SCOTT, W. W., *J. Urol. (Baltimore)*, **53**, 712 (1945).	The cholesterol originates mainly in the prostate.
Phospholipids	84	SCOTT, W. W., *loc. cit.*	The phospholipids originate mainly in the prostate.
Choline	up to 2120	KAHANE and LÉVY, *Bull. Soc. Chim. biol. (Paris)*, **19**, 959 (1937); MANN, T., *The Biochemistry of Semen*, London, 1954, page 168.	No free choline is present immediately after ejaculation. Choline is liberated gradually from the phosphorylcholine and glycerylphosphorylcholine of the seminal vesicles by the action of the phosphatase of the prostate and reaches a level of 2120 mg/100 ml after 6 hours.
Vitamin C	13	BERG et al., *Amer. J. Physiol.*, **133**, 82 (1941).	
Estrogens	See page 493.		
Phosphorus inorganic	40–50	GOLDBLATT, M. W., *Biochem. J.*, **29**, 1346 (1935).	
acid-soluble	95	GOLDBLATT, M. W., *loc. cit.*	
Chloride	100–203	MANN, T., *The Biochemistry of Semen*, London, 1954, page 32.	

	Normal values mg/100 ml, unless otherwise stated	Sources	Remarks
Sodium	240–319	MANN, T., *The Biochemistry of Semen*, London, 1954, page 32.	
Potassium	66–107	MANN, T., *loc. cit.*	
Calcium	21–28	MANN, T., *loc. cit.*	
Magnesium	14	MANN, T., *loc. cit.*	
Carbon dioxide	41–60 vol%	MANN, T., *loc. cit.*	See under pH value, page 598.
Phosphatase acid	540–4000 KING and ARMSTRONG units	GUTMAN and GUTMAN, *Endocrinology*, **28**, 115 (1941).	Originates mainly in the prostate. The phosphatase content of different ejaculations of the same individual is fairly constant but there are large differences between different individuals. According to GUTMAN and GUTMAN, *Proc. Soc. exp. Biol. (N.Y.)*, **39**, 529 (1938), and GUTMAN et al., *Amer. J. Cancer*, **28**, 485 (1936), the phosphatase content of the prostate per gram of tissue is 1–2 units at 4 years, 73 units at puberty, and 522–2284 units in adults. The phosphatase content of the prostate thus exceeds that of the liver, bones, kidneys or duodenal mucosa.
alkaline (pH 9)	0.1–1 KING and ARMSTRONG units	GUTMAN and GUTMAN, *loc. cit.*	Originates mainly in the seminal vesicles.
Hyaluronidase (in semen plus spermatozoa)	100 units	1 unit is that quantity of hyaluronidase in 1 ml of semen (with spermatozoa) which is sufficient to depolymerize 2.5 mg of hyaluronic acid (MCCLEAN, D., *Biochem. J.*, **37**, 169 [1943], and KURZROK et al., *Amer. J. Med.*, **1**, 491 [1946]).	The hyaluronidase is loosely attached to the cell surface around the heads of the spermatozoa and is readily released into the seminal fluid. The hyaluronidase content increases with increasing spermatozoal content but a direct correlation exists only between 50 and 100 millions per milliliter; below 50 millions the hyaluronidase content is zero or negligibly small, above 100 millions it no longer rises in proportion to the spermatozoal content. There is no connection between the form of the spermatozoa and the hyaluronidase content. The enzyme is absent in testes lacking ripe spermatozoa.
Formed elements	Apart from spermatozoa, semen contains the following bodies: giant cells, SERTOLI's cells, epithelial cells, leukocytes, prostate cells, lecithin bodies, BÖTTCHER's crystals, CHARCOT-NEUMANN crystals, fat cristals, spermine phosphate, testicular cylinders, corpora amylacea, mucus, bacteria.		See Prostate secretion, below.

Prostate secretion

From HUGGINS, C., *Physiol. Rev.*, **25**, 281 (1945)

	Normal values per 100 ml		Normal values per 100 ml
pH value	6.3–6.45 (37° C)	Ether-soluble substances	62–105 mg
Specific gravity	1.022	Cholesterol	86–618 mg
Water	92.7–93.6 g	Citric acid	0.48–2.68 g
Sodium	14.9–15.8 mEq	Acid phosphatase	255–1727 KING and ARMSTRONG units
Potassium	2.87–6.14 mEq	Alkaline phosphatase	286 KING and ARMSTRONG units
Calcium	2.87–3.27 mEq	Vitamin C	0.54 mg
Chloride	3.48–4.61 mEq		
Phosphorus, acid-soluble	0.065–0.177 mEq		
Carbon dioxide (as bicarbonate)	0.31–0.54 mEq		
Total nitrogen	295–511 mg		
Nonprotein nitrogen	30–90 mg		
Total proteins	2.46–2.64 g		
Glucose	trace–16.4 mg		

Formed elements. *Lecithin bodies* (small rounded refracting particles up to the size of erythrocytes), which are regarded, however, by SCOTT, *J. Urol.*, **53**, 712 (1945), as fat granules; *corpora amylacea*, light yellow to brown spheres, ca. 250 μm diameter, consisting mainly of protein and nucleic acids, and weakly acidophile; *epithelial cells*; a few *leukocytes*; *granulated prostate cells*, large, round or irregularly formed, giving the impression that they consist solely of granulations.

The prostate secretion also contains fibrinolysin or fibrinogenase (HUGGINS and NEAL, *J. exp. Med.* **76**, 527 [1942], and HUGGINS and VAIL, *Amer. J. Physiol.*, **139**, 129 [1943]), spermine and free amino acids (especially glutamic acid). The zinc content of the prostate is 68 mg/100 g dry substance and thus greater than that of any other tissue (MAWSON and FISCHER, *Canad. J. med. Sci.*, **30**, 336 [1952]).

Seminal vesicle secretion

From MANN, T., *The Biochemistry of Semen*, London, 1954, with additional data from MACLEOD, J., *Fertil. and Steril.*, **7**, 368 (1956)

pH value	7.29	Nonprotein nitrogen	99 mg/100 ml
Water	89.0 g/100 g	Proteins	7.78 g/100 ml
Potassium	17.8 mEq/l	Fructose	315 mg/100 ml
Phosphorus, acid-soluble	14.7 mEq/l	Citric acid	125 mg/100 ml
Nitrogen, total	1.28 g/100 ml	Vitamin C	5 mg/100 ml

The sodium content of the seminal vesicle secretion is low, the bicarbonate content high. The yellow color of the secretion is due to the presence of flavins. Ergothioneine is present in low concentration. Inositol is usually below 0.1%.

Morphology. See the adjacent diagram and the normal and abnormal spermatozoa illustrated on page 603. On studies with the electron microscope see HAMMEN et al., *Fertil. and Steril.*, **5**, 411 (1954), and MACLEOD, J., *ibid.*, **7**, 368 (1956).

Chemistry. Spermatozoa contain about 50% of solid matter. The total lipid content (containing a high proportion of acetal phosphatides) is about 13% of the dry substance; it is three times higher in the tail than in the head or middle part. The lipids are responsible for the opalescence of spermatozoa. The sulfur content of 1.8% of the dry substance is due to the high cystine and methionine content, the phosphorus content of 3.1% of the dry substance to desoxyribonucleic acids. The zinc content amounts to 2 mg/g of dry substance. Other components are enzymes (especially hyaluronidase), cytochromes (a, b, c), free amino acids (especially arginine), heptacosane and androsterone.

Spermatogenesis and vitamins. The relationship between these is still unexplained. No vitamin has yet been shown to have a (directly) favorable effect, although spermatogenesis is impaired in severe vitamin deficiency.

Spermatogenesis and hormones. Testosterone has a marked inhibitory effect on spermatogenesis and is therefore only indicated in cases where infertility is attributable to underdevelopment of the copulatory organs or to impotence.

It has been observed that several months (up to 16–27 months) after temporary azoospermia provoked by testosterone in oligospermic men the number of spermatozoa showed a sudden increase (e.g. from 10 millions before treatment up to 160 millions). Cf. HECKEL and MCDONALD, *Fertil. and Steril.*, **3**, 49 (1952); CHARNY, C. W., *J. Amer. med. Ass.*, **160**, 98 (1956).

According to HOTCHKISS, R. S., *Etiology and Diagnosis in the Treatment of Infertility in Men*, Springfield, 1952, page 7, there is no evidence that gonadotropic hormones (pituitary or placental) have any markedly favorable effect. In cases of hypothyroidism a favorable effect on fertility is shown by thyroxine (or thyrotropic hormone), and a trial is indicated even in cases where there is no obvious disturbance of thyroid function (cf. TAYMOR and SELENKOW, *Fertil. and Steril.*, **9**, 560 [1958]).

Fertility and spermatozoal concentration (cf. the nomogram on page 602). Although there is no absolute correlation between spermatozoal concentration and fertility (or infertility) the two are probably related insofar as the spermatozoal content of the ejaculate of infertile men is in general lower. In addition, a small ejaculate volume represents an absolute diminution in the number of spermatozoa, an excessive ejaculate volume a lowering of the spermatozoal concentration.

According to KAUFMAN, S. A., *Hum. Fertil.*, **11**, 3 (1946), the normal spermatozoal content amounts to 28–225 millions per milliliter. Many authorities regard 60 millions as the lower limit for a fertile semen. The spermatozoal concentration in any individual can vary greatly and is adversely affected by severe emotional stress and by physical exertion. It is also diminished in certain cases by prolonged continence, which increases above all the proportion of abnormal spermatozoa, and when the temperature of the testes is too high (cause of their degeneration in cryptorchism). Seasonal variations have also been observed (lowered spermatozoal concentration during the warm months) but are not statistically significant. In assessing the spermatozoal concentration the volume of the ejaculate must also be taken into account.

Fertility and morphology (cf. the nomogram on page 602). Infertile men show on the average a markedly higher proportion of abnormal spermatozoa. According to HOTCHKISS, R. S., *Fertility in Men*, Philadelphia, 1944, page 117, the average spermatozoal composition of semen is as follows:

Form of spermatozoa	Mean	Range
Oval (normal)	89.8%	66–99%
Tapering	3.6%	0–24%
Round	1.6%	0– 9%
Duplicate	1.8%	0–11%
Giant and pinhead	0.6%	0– 8%
Amorphous	2.1%	0–12%

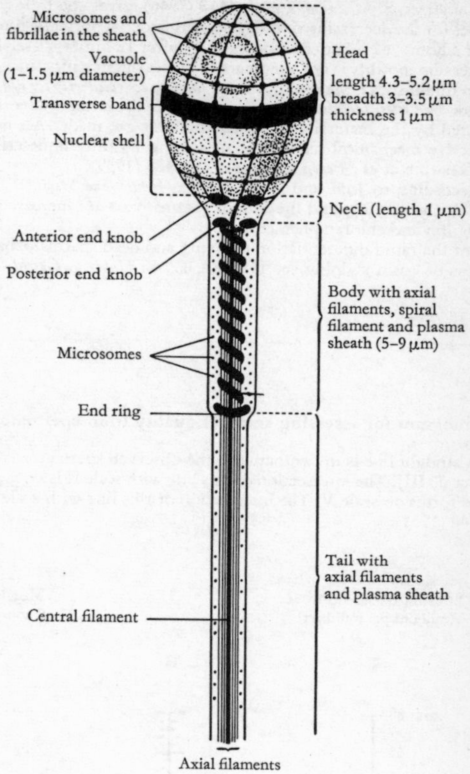

After STIEVE, H., *Harn- und Geschlechtsapparat*, in VON MÖLLENDORFF, W. (Ed.), *Handbuch der mikroskopischen Anatomie des Menschen*, vol. VII, part 2, Berlin, 1930, page 104

KAUFMAN, S. A., *Hum. Fertil.*, **11**, 3 (1946), found an average of 89.4% of normal forms in healthy subjects, and the same figure is given by MACLEOD, J., *Conference on Diagnosis in Sterility*, National Committee on Maternal Health, USA, 1946. According to MOENCH, G. L., *Amer. J. Obstet. Gynec.*, **32**, 406 (1936), 8–10% of tapering forms represents the limit for a fertile semen.

According to MACLEOD, J., *loc. cit.*, however, there is no relation between a high content of abnormal forms and an abnormal course of pregnancy.

Fertility and chemical composition. The content of desoxyribonucleic acids (DNS), the basic constituents of the chromosomes, is constant in the spermatozoa of men of normal fertility and varies little from one individual to another. In men with impaired fertility, on the other hand, the DNS content varies greatly both in a single individual and from one individual to another (cf. WEIR and LEUCHTENBERGER, *Fertil. and Steril.*, **8**, 373 [1957]).

Motility and lifetime. In freshly ejaculated semen the spermatozoa are relatively immobile. As liquefaction proceeds the motility increases and is then maintained constant for 3–5 hours at room temperature. In the cervical secretion the motility is maintained much longer as a result of the presence there of substances essential to spermatozoal metabolism which are lacking in vitro. Heat increases the motility but reduces the lifetime (increased consumption of nutrient reserves owing to increased activity). According to WEISMANN, A. I., *Spermatozoa and Sterility*, New York, 1941, spermatozoa may be classified according to their motility as follows (figures are normal percentages): 1. nonmotile (dead), 15%; 2. only slightly motile 15%; 3. moderately to very motile, at least 75%.

The rate at which normally motile spermatozoa move in vivo is about 3 mm per minute, in vitro only 0.7–0.9 mm per minute.

Kaufman, S. A., *Hum. Fertil.*, 11, 3 (1946), gives the following values for the decreasing motility of spermatozoa: normally motile after 3 hours, 61%; after 6 hours, 46%; after 12 hours, 28%. The decreasing motility is not a measure of decreasing fertility since the latter diminishes more rapidly. *Semen samples collected with the aid of a condom are useless for assessment of motility* since the latter is adversely affected by the materials of which condoms are made. A simple objective mechanical method of measuring motility is described by Gassner et al., *Fertil. and Steril.*, 10, 488 (1959).

According to Joël and Kornhauser, *Fertil. and Steril.*, 7, 430 (1956), the motility and lifetime of spermatozoa are increased by penicillin and chloramphenicol.

For the rapid differentiation of living and dead spermatozoa by means of eosin staining see Heinke, E., *Z. Haut- u. Geschl.-Kr.*, 10, 254 (1951), and Joël and Kwiat, *Schw. med. Wschr.*, 85, 428 (1955).

Assessment of fertility. In the present state of knowledge it is impossible to assess absolutely the fertility or infertility of semen except in cases where repeated tests have confirmed azoo- or necro-spermia. In the case of sterile marriages, however, where the circumstances are otherwise normal, abnormal values have been repeatedly observed for ejaculate volume, spermatozoal composition and concentration, and above all for abnormal, poorly motile, nonmotile and short-lived spermatozoa. It is therefore highly probable that sterility is here due to the poor quality of the ejaculate.

Nomogram for assessing seminal quality from spermatozoal number, motility and head normality

A straight line is drawn between the observed spermatozoal number (on scale I) and the observed percentage of motile spermatozoa (on scale III). The intersection of this line with scale II is now connected by another straight line with the observed percentage of normal head forms on scale V. The intersection of this line with scale IV gives the fertility index. From Page and Houlding, *Fertil. and Steril.*, 2, 140 (1951).

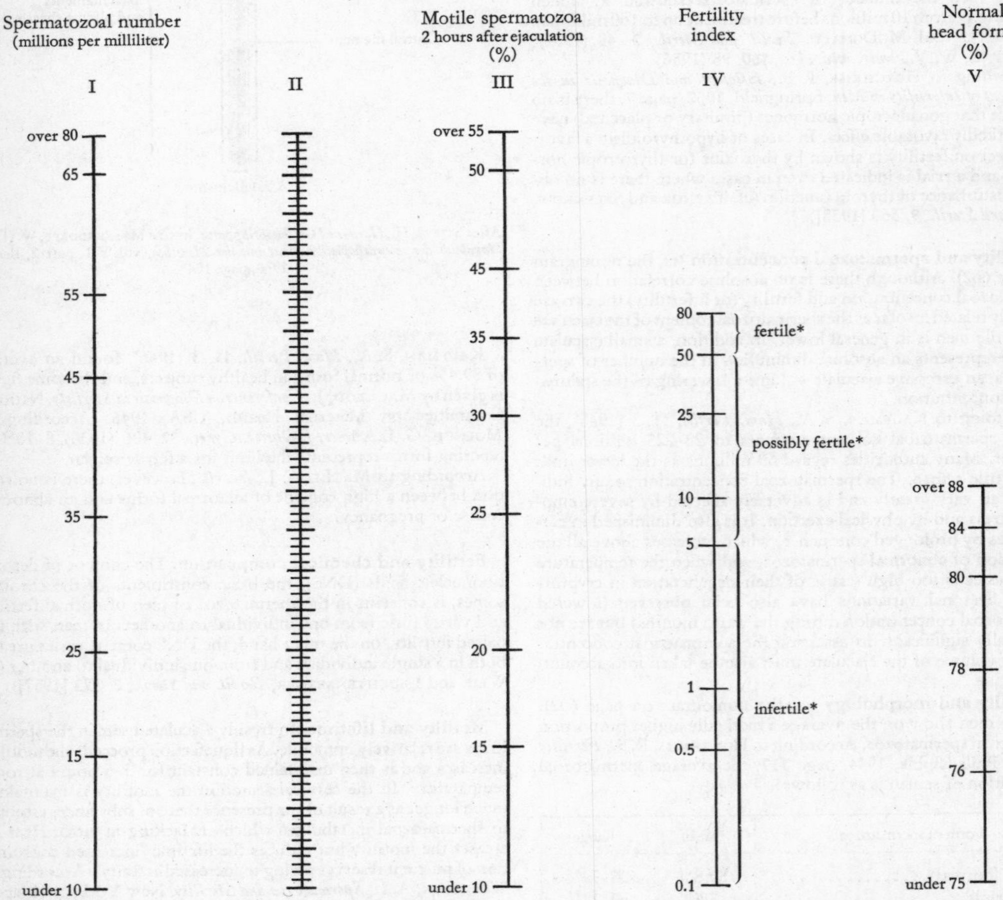

* This assessment must be regarded as relative and in no sense absolute.

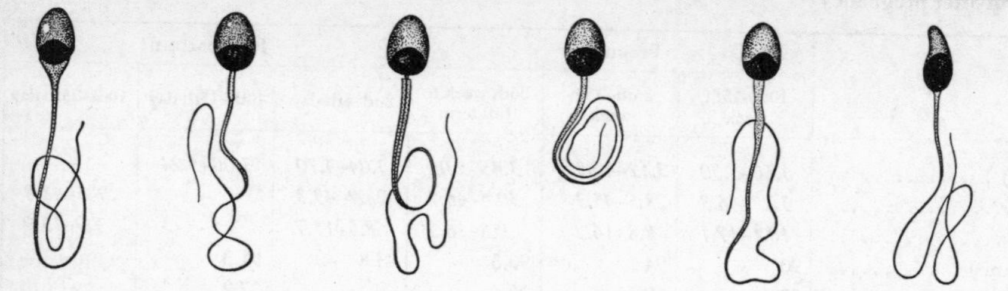

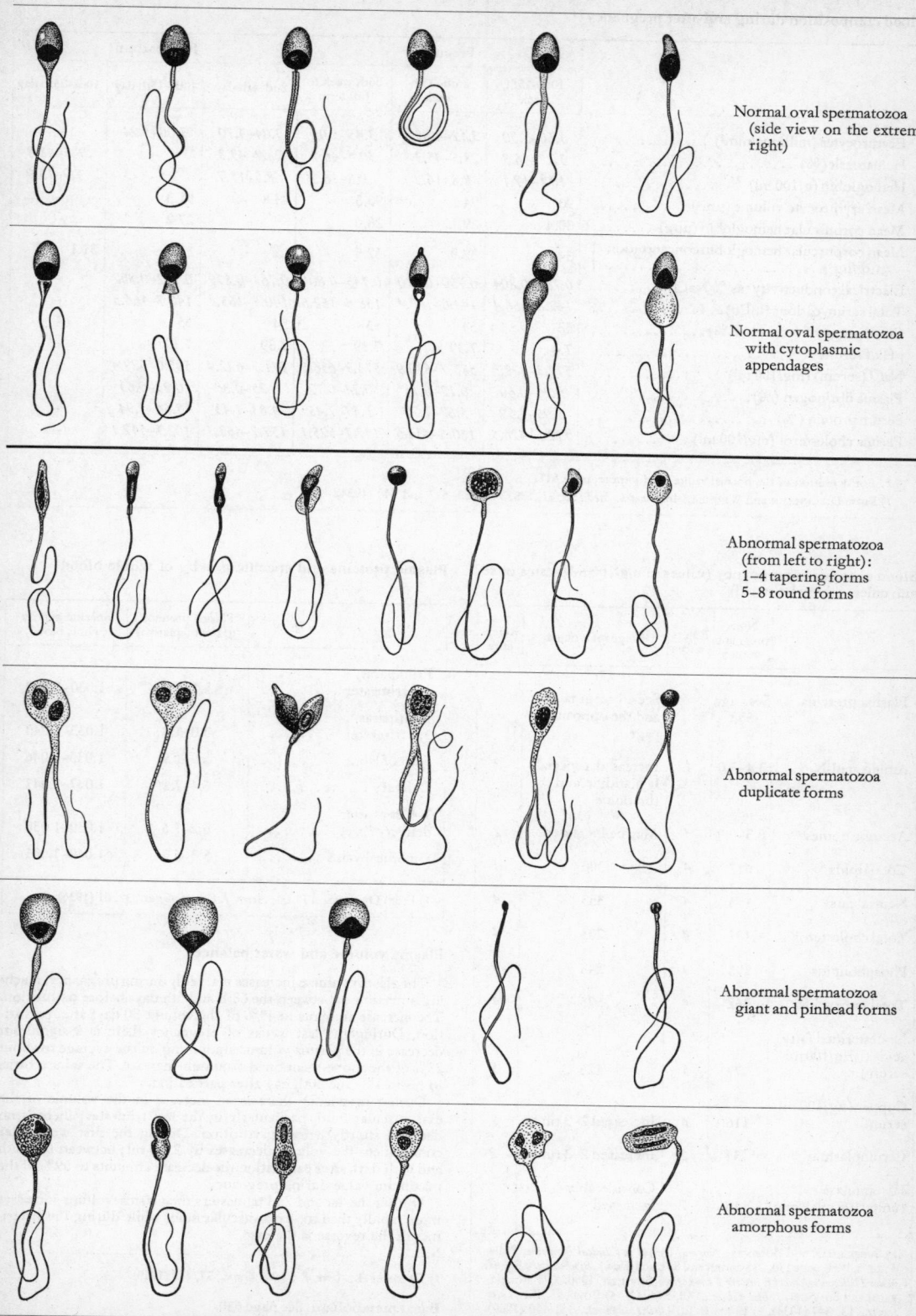

Normal oval spermatozoa (side view on the extreme right)

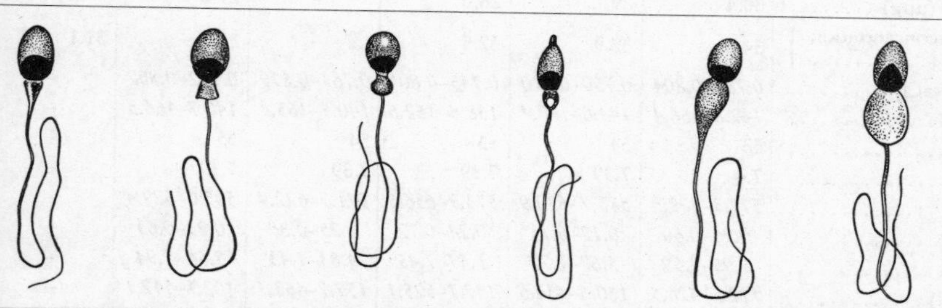

Normal oval spermatozoa with cytoplasmic appendages

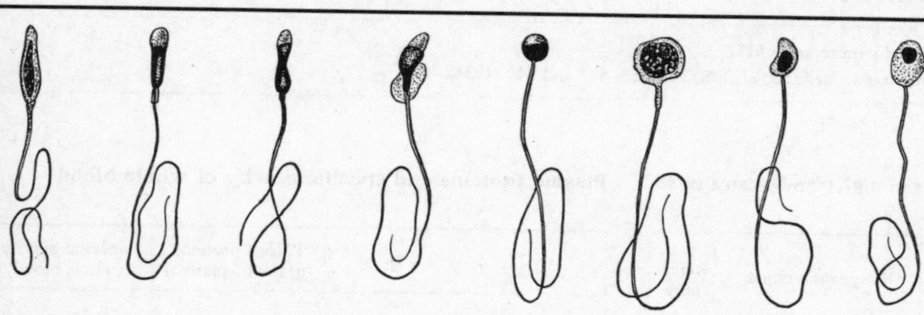

Abnormal spermatozoa (from left to right):
1–4 tapering forms
5–8 round forms

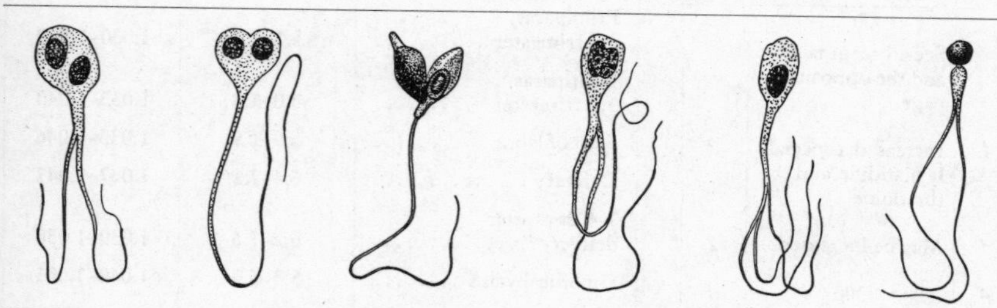

Abnormal spermatozoa duplicate forms

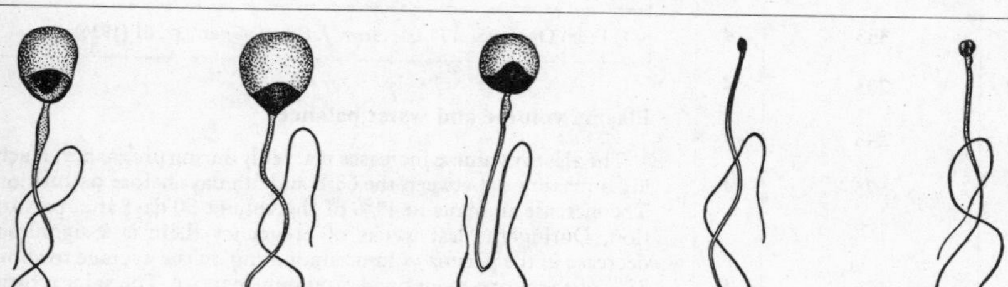

Abnormal spermatozoa giant and pinhead forms

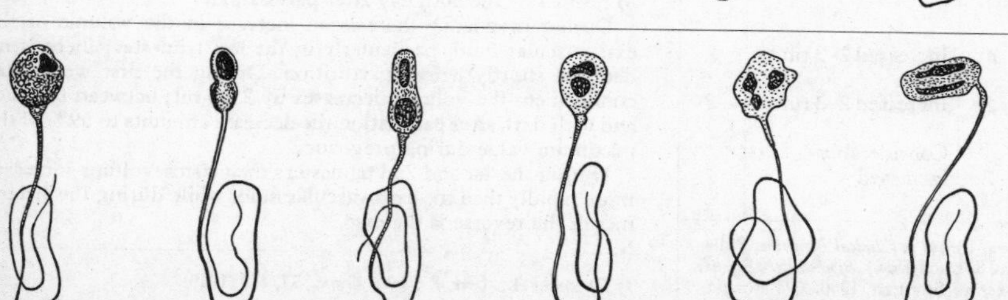

Abnormal spermatozoa amorphous forms

1) From Hotchkiss, R.S., *Fertility in Men*, Philadelphia, 1944, page 117.

Blood composition during and after pregnancy*[1]

	Pregnancy			Post partum		
	10th–15th week	26th–35th week	36th week to full term	2nd–6th day	10th–15th day	10th–25th day
Erythrocytes (millions/mm³)	*3.60–5.30*	*3.12–4.65*	*3.45–5.05*	*3.04–4.70*	*3.00–5.24*	–
Hematocrit (%)	*32.9–46.3*	*28.5–45.3*	*30.4–46.2*	*28.2–43.8*	–	*26.6–48.8*
Hemoglobin (g/100 ml)	*10.1–17.1*	*8.8–16.2*	*9.8–16.2*	*8.5–15.7*	–	*7.9–15.9*
Mean erythrocyte volume (μm³)	90	94	90.3	93.8	91.3	–
Mean corpuscular hemoglobin (μμg)	30.4	29.7	28.6	–	27.2	–
Mean corpuscular hemoglobin concentration (μμg/μg³)	34.2	32.9	32.5	–	–	31.1
Electrical conductivity (as % NaCl)	*0.756–0.804*	*0.750–0.810*	*0.745–0.801*	*0.763–0.819*	*0.762–0.802*	–
Total serum cations (mEq)	*142.8–166.4*	*144.0–160.4*	*138.6–162.6*	*140.5–165.3*	*140.7–166.3*	–
CO_2 content of serum (vol %)	53	54	53	54	55	–
pH of serum	7.4	7.39	7.39	7.39	7.39	–
NaCl (serum) (mg/100 ml)	*577.3–629.3*	*583.7–630.9*	*573.7–636.5*	*571.7–622.9*	*585.0–629.4*	–
Plasma fibrinogen (%)	*0.20–0.60*	*0.13–0.73*	*0.24–0.72*	*0.25–0.85*	*0.23–0.63*	–
Serum protein (%)	*5.95–7.59*	*5.62–7.22*	*5.57–7.45*	*4.83–7.43*	*5.66–7.94*	–
Plasma cholesterol (mg/100 ml)	*112.5–426.5*	*180.6–434.6*	*137.1–525.1*	*157.7–463.7*	*102.1–512.1*	–

* For definition of the normal range see footnote, page 517.
1) From Dieckmann and Wegner, *Arch. intern. Med.*, **53**, 71, 188, 345, 353, 527 and 540 (1934).

Blood changes in pregnancy (values in mg/100 ml plasma or serum unless otherwise stated)

	Non-pregnant women	Reference	Pregnant women	Reference
Plasma proteins	See page 553		See adjacent table and the opposite page	
Amino acid-N	3.4–5.0	*1*	Increased, especially histidine and threonine	*2*
Acetone bodies	0.3–0.9	*3*	May be increased	*2*
Total lipids	617	*4*	900	*4*
Neutral fats	154	*4*	353	*4*
Total cholesterol	181	*4*	205	*4*
Phospholipids	195	*4*	248	*4*
Total fatty acids	362	*4*	595	*4*
Nonesterified fatty acids (μEq/100 ml serum)	77	*5*	125	*5*
Copper (μg/100 ml serum)	116	*6*	Increased 2–3 times	*2*
Ceruloplasmin	34	*2*	Increased 2–3 times	*2*
Histaminase (units/100 ml serum)	18	*7*	Considerably increased	*7*

1) Sunderman and Boerner, *Normal Values in Clinical Medicine*, Philadelphia, 1950, page 110. *2*) Schoen and Südhof (Eds.), *Biochemische Befunde in der Differentialdiagnose innerer Krankheiten*, Stuttgart, 1960. *3*) Weichselbaum and Somogyi, *J. biol. Chem.*, **140**, 5 (1941). *4*) Boyd, E. M., *J. clin. Invest.*, **13**, 347 (1934). *5*) Burt, R. L., *Obstet. Gynecol.*, **15**, 460 (1960). *6*) Lahey et al., *J. clin. Invest.*, **32**, 322 (1953). *7*) Werle and Effkemann, *Klin. Wschr.*, **19**, 717 (1940).

Plasma proteins and specific gravity of whole blood[1]

	Plasma proteins (g/100 ml plasma)	Specific gravity (whole blood)
Primiparas, 3rd trimester	5.1–7.3	1.030–1.040
Multiparas, 3rd trimester	5.0–7.3	1.033–1.040
Start of labor	5.9–6.9	1.033–1.046
Delivery	6.4–7.1	1.037–1.047
7–9 days after delivery	6.2–7.6	1.039–1.050
Umbilical veins	5.3–6.7	1.040–1.051

1) From Oberst and Plass, *Amer. J. Obstet. Gynec.*, **31**, 61 (1936).

Plasma volume and water balance[1]

The plasma volume increases markedly during pregnancy, reaching a maximum between the 68th and 5th days before parturition. The increase amounts to 49% of the volume 30 days after parturition. During the last weeks of pregnancy there is a significant decrease in the plasma volume amounting on the average to about 25% of the above-mentioned maximum increase. The value returns to normal by the 30th day after parturition.

During pregnancy there is an increase in the volume of the extravascular fluid, particularly in the last trimester; there is no decrease shortly before parturition. During the first week after confinement the volume decreases by 2500 ml; between the 26th and 66th days after parturition the decrease amounts to 59% of the maximum value during pregnancy.

During the 1st and 2nd trimesters the plasma volume increases more rapidly than the extravascular fluid, while during the 3rd trimester the reverse is the case.

1) Caton et al., *Amer. J. Obstet. Gynec.*, **57**, 471 (1949).

Basal metabolism. See page 630.
Breast milk. See pages 514 and 515.
Hormones. See under the respective hormones, pages 473–497.

Plasma protein fractions (from Mack, H. C., *The Plasma Proteins in Pregnancy*, Springfield, 1955) (values in grams per 100 ml)

	Number of subjects	Number of estimations	Albumin	Globulins					Albumin/globulin ratio	Total protein
				Alpha$_1$	Alpha$_2$	Beta	Gamma	Fibrinogen		
Nonpregnant women	12	22								
Mean			4.65	0.36	0.68	1.01	0.97	0.51	1.32	8.18
Range			3.92–5.31	0.26–0.53	0.54–0.92	0.83–1.22	0.77–1.26	0.38–0.68	1.16–1.56	6.87–9.62
Pregnant women										
First trimester (4–7 weeks)	3	3								
Mean			4.22	0.40	0.70	0.96	0.73	0.55	1.26	7.56
Range			3.79–4.62	0.32–0.45	0.67–0.76	0.90–1.04	0.64–0.87	0.51–0.57	1.20–1.34	6.88–8.06
Second trimester (17–26 weeks)	7	7								
Mean			3.89	0.44	0.77	1.20	0.69	0.58	1.06	7.57
Range			3.27–4.41	0.34–0.53	0.65–1.00	0.92–1.48	0.56–0.83	0.49–0.73	0.94–1.21	6.57–8.70
Third trimester (28–41 weeks)	14	15								
Mean			3.43	0.51	0.87	1.36	0.68	0.65	0.84	7.50
Range			2.43–4.07	0.32–0.72	0.66–1.15	0.94–1.95	0.46–0.90	0.50–0.92	0.64–1.11	5.96–8.68
Delivery	16	16								
Mean			3.41	0.48	0.94	1.40	0.62	0.70	0.82	7.55
Range			2.51–4.60	0.40–0.66	0.46–1.32	1.11–1.93	0.32–0.87	0.45–1.07	0.59–0.96	5.86–10.26
Post partum										
12–24 hours	3	3								
Mean			2.68	0.54	0.86	1.22	0.50	0.67	0.71	6.47
Range			2.45–2.91	0.43–0.66	0.58–1.10	1.17–1.29	0.44–0.56	0.61–0.76	0.68–0.75	5.93–7.23
5–6 days	9	9								
Mean			3.15	0.69	1.10	1.38	0.54	0.69	0.72	7.55
Range			2.78–3.58	0.59–0.77	0.71–1.29	1.17–1.57	0.27–0.64	0.54–0.90	0.63–0.85	6.67–8.48
6–12 weeks	13	13								
Mean			4.07	0.42	0.66	1.05	0.78	0.43	1.22	7.41
Range			3.40–4.71	0.33–0.51	0.59–0.89	0.83–1.29	0.27–1.15	0.28–0.65	1.06–1.60	6.26–8.20
Maternal venous blood (delivery)	11	11								
Mean			3.46	0.49	0.97	1.41	0.64	0.73	0.82	7.71
Range			2.59–4.60	0.40–0.66	0.79–1.32	1.11–1.93	0.32–0.87	0.45–1.07	0.59–0.96	6.80–10.26
Corresponding cord blood	11	11								
Mean			3.73	0.32	0.54	0.57	0.87	0.43	1.36	6.47
Range			2.95–4.57	0.18–0.55	0.38–0.76	0.37–0.91	0.60–1.16	0.29–0.65	1.14–1.79	5.44–8.60

Remarks (for a bibliographical review see Alha[1])

In general these largely quantitative plasma protein changes[2,3] may be seen as adaptations of the maternal organism made in response to the physiological stresses of pregnancy and designed to meet the needs of the growing fetus. The fall in the albumin level and the rise in the total globulin level start in the 1st trimester and progress until delivery. The latter is unable to compensate for the former, so that the overall picture is one of a fall in the total protein level. However, because of the increase in the total blood volume during pregnancy (see opposite) this does not mean that there is necessarily a deficiency of available total protein or albumin in the blood. In fact, the total amount of circulating protein in the body may even be increased compared to the pre-pregnant state.

The changing protein levels may be caused by the readier diffusion of the smaller albumin molecules into the tissues and across the placental membranes, and to failure of albumin synthesis to keep up with albumin utilization. On the whole, a state approaching protein deficiency is to be expected as a result of the enormously increased protein demand in pregnancy. Clinically, therefore, it is important that ample protein intake be maintained and debilitating states avoided as far as possible.

The plasma protein relations in *cord blood* correspond more nearly to those of nonpregnant women than to those of the maternal blood. The changes in the latter may thus be seen as contriving to provide the infant at birth with a normal blood pattern adequate to its needs. The fetal plasma protein picture is to some extent dependent on maternal nutrition[4–6].

The rise in the level of *total globulins* aids in compensating osmotically for the lesser number of albumin molecules and thus in preventing fluid losses to the tissues (edema of pregnancy). The α- and β-*globulins* carry most of the plasma lipids and the increase in the levels of these two fractions may therefore be related to the lipemia and hypercholesteremia of pregnancy.

In view of the association of the γ-*globulins* with antibodies, the diminished concentration of this fraction is of clinical significance in pregnancy from the point of view of impairment both of acquired immunity and of the ability to form antibodies to acquired infection[7]. This is borne out by the high incidence of puerperal sepsis following undernourished pregnancies and by the susceptibility of pregnant women to the paralyzing effects of the poliomyelitis virus. The γ-globulin level in cord blood is markedly higher than in the maternal blood and it is noteworthy that intra-uterine transplacental transmission of poliomyelitis to the fetus is rare. The high fetal γ-globulin level is acquired at the expense of the maternal blood via the placenta and may be due to selective filtration of γ-globulins by the latter. It probably contributes to the relatively high resistance shown by newborn infants to the ordinary bacterial and virus infections. There is a relationship between immune mechanisms and plasma γ-globulin levels in the newborn[8,9].

The high level of *fibrinogen* in the maternal plasma and the low level in cord blood are no doubt due to the poor diffusibility of these large and asymmetric molecules. The result is that the maternal organism is provided with some protection against hemorrhage whereas the newborn infant (also deficient in prothrombin[10]), and especially the premature one, is peculiarly susceptible to hemorrhagic diatheses. The high fibrinogen level may also account for the tendency of pregnant women to develop phlebothromboses.

1) Alha, A.-L., *Ann. Chir. Gynaec. Fenn.*, **39**, Suppl. 4 (1950). *2)* Coryell et al., *J. clin. Invest.*, **29**, 1559 (1950). *3)* Macy and Mack, *Physiological Changes in Plasma Proteins Characteristic of Human Reproduction*, Children's Fund of Michigan, Detroit, 1952. *4)* Dieckmann et al., *J. Amer. diet. Ass.*, **27**, 1046 (1951). *5)* Smith et al., *Obstet. and Gynec.*, **1**, 46 (1953). *6)* Toverud et al., *Maternal Nutrition and Child Health*, Bulletin No. 123 of the National Research Council, Washington, 1950. *7)* Cannon, P. R., in Youmans, J. B. (Ed.), *Symposia on Nutrition of the Robert Gould Research Foundation*, vol. II: *Plasma Proteins*, Springfield, 1950. *8)* Smith, C. A., *The Physiology of the Newborn Infant*, 3rd ed., Oxford, 1959. *9)* Brambell et al., *Antibodies and Embryos*, London, 1951. *10)* Straumfjord and Quaife, *Proc. Soc. exp. Biol. (N.Y.)*, **61**, 369 (1946).

Normal weight changes[1]

	Per cent of weight at start of pregnancy
Increase up to 40th week of pregnancy	24.10
Loss before parturition	1.58
Loss during parturition	7.74
Loss during first 10 days post partum	3.77
Loss during following 5 weeks post partum	1.11

Involution of the uterus after parturition[2]

Days post partum	Height (cm)	Breadth (cm)
1	10.91	11.00
2	13.55	12.27
3	11.16	10.93
4	10.21	10.27
5	9.29	9.66
6	8.22	8.96
7	7.61	8.32
8	7.32	8.19

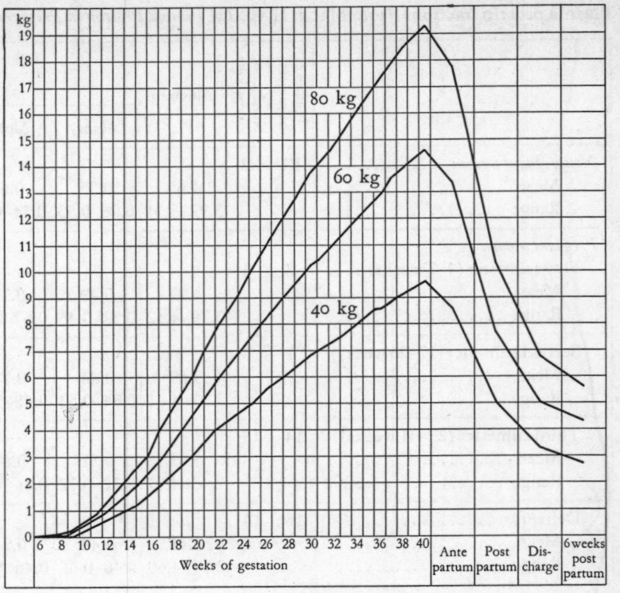

Normal weight changes during pregnancy (for weights at commencement of pregnancy of 40, 60 and 80 kg). From Stander and Pastore[1].

Development of the uterus during pregnancy[2]

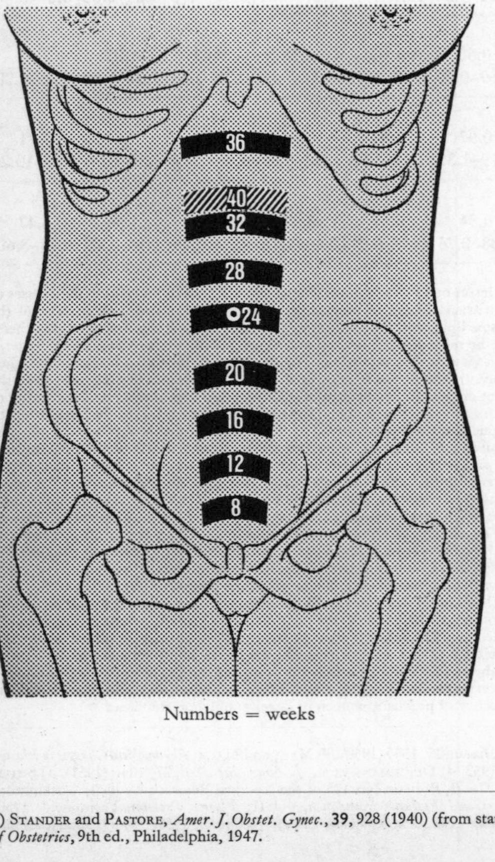

Numbers = weeks

Height of the uterus post partum[2] (bladder empty)

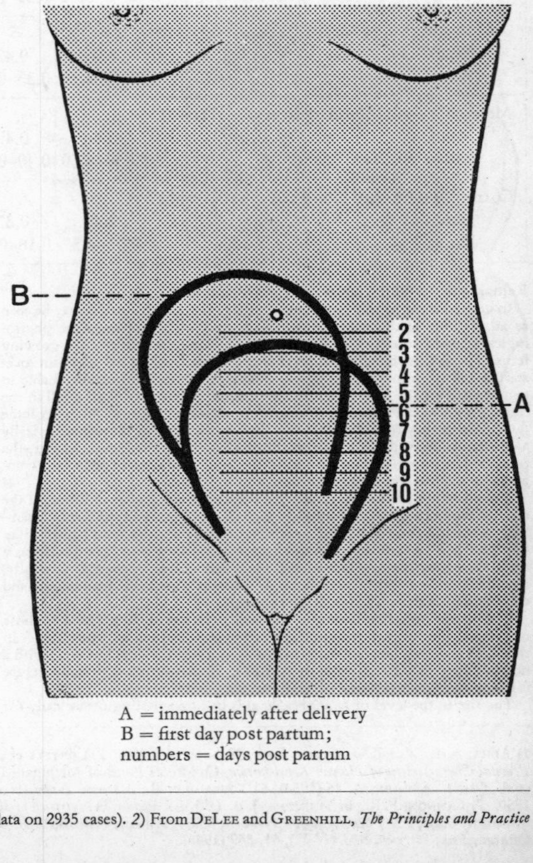

A = immediately after delivery
B = first day post partum;
numbers = days post partum

1) Stander and Pastore, *Amer. J. Obstet. Gynec.*, **39**, 928 (1940) (from statistical data on 2935 cases). *2)* From DeLee and Greenhill, *The Principles and Practice of Obstetrics*, 9th ed., Philadelphia, 1947.

Obstetric Norms[1]

(measurements in centimeters)

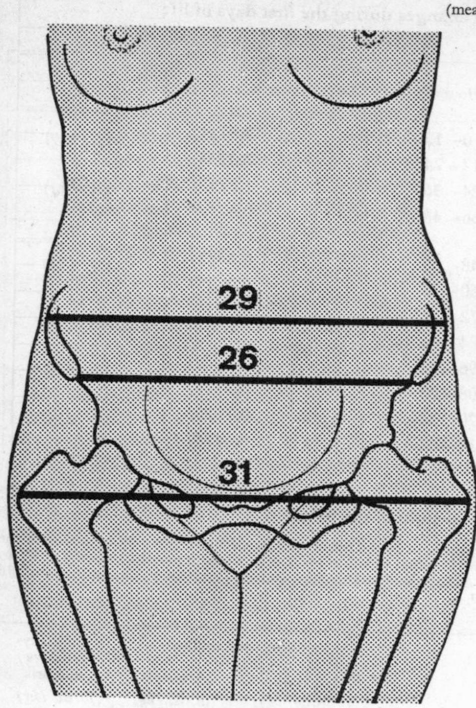

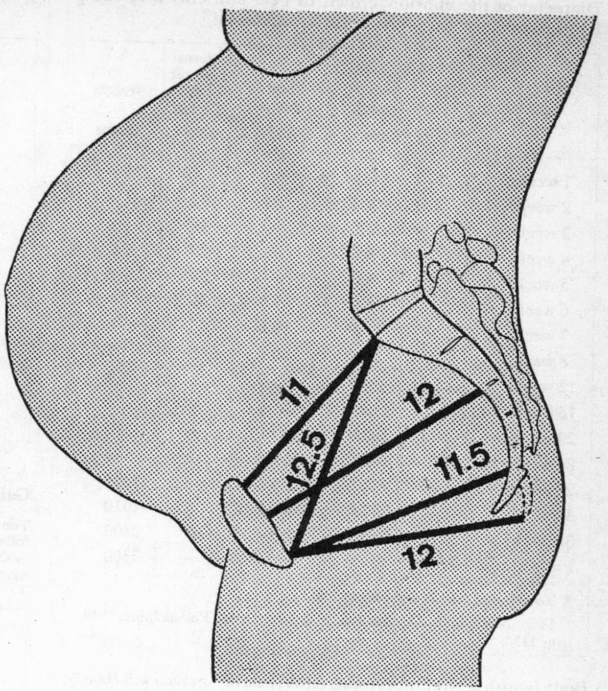

external measurements

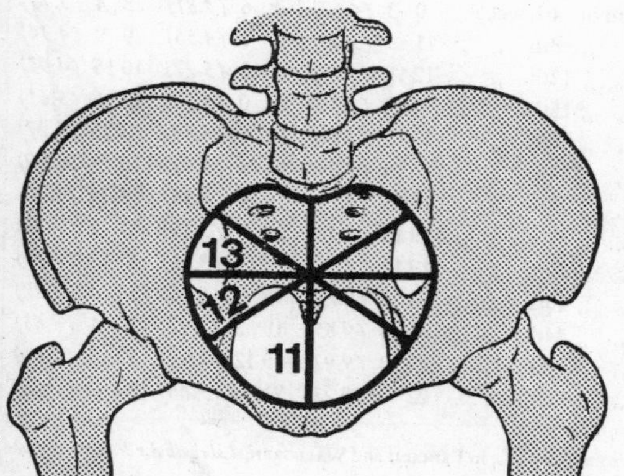

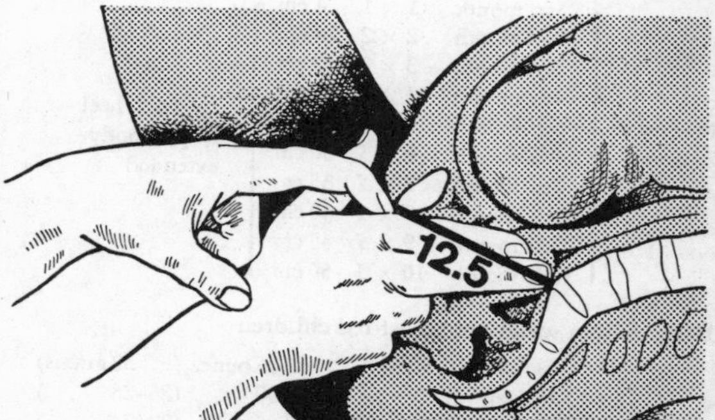

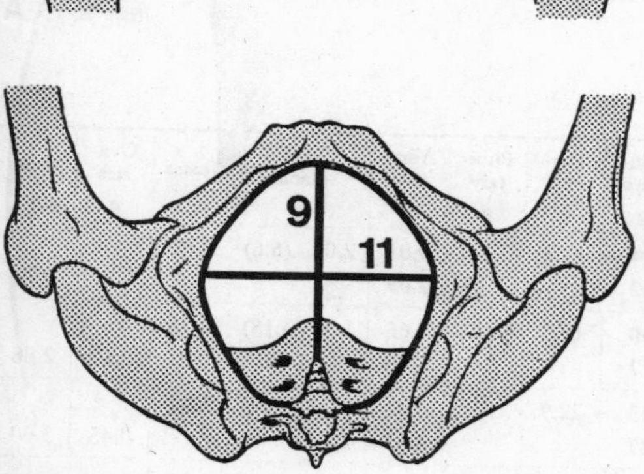

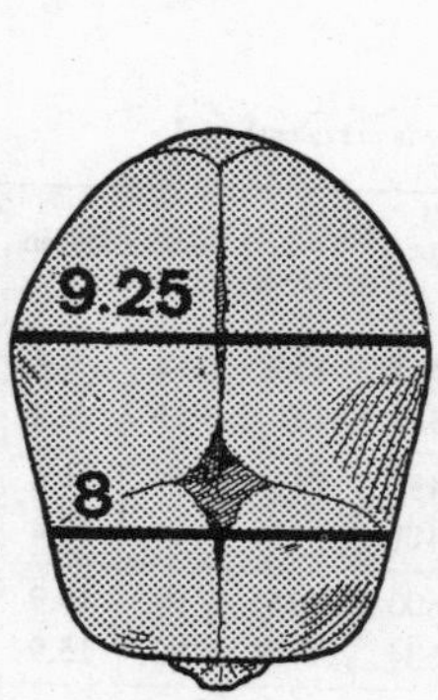

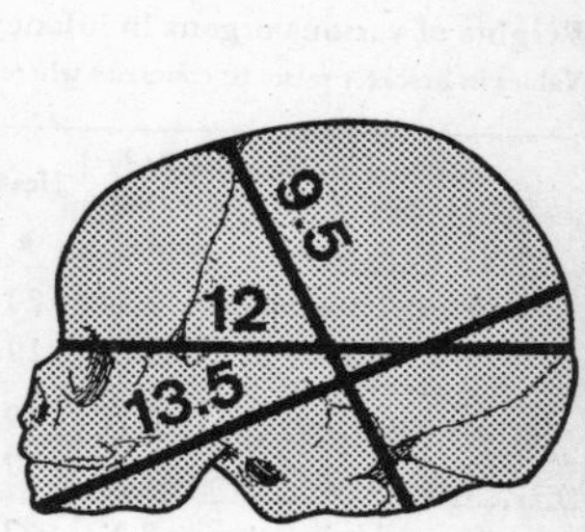

1) From Bumm, E., *Grundriss zum Studium der Geburtshilfe*, Munich, 1921, and DeLee and Greenhill, *The Principles and Practice of Obstetrics*, 9th ed., Philadelphia, 1947.

Diameter of the chorion, crown to heel and crown to rump lengths, and weight of the embryo and fetus[1]

Fetal age	Crown to rump length mm	Crown to heel length mm	External diameter of the chorion mm	Weight grams
1 week	0.1*	–	0.2	–
2 weeks	0.2*	–	3	–
3 weeks	2.0	–	10	–
4 weeks	5.0	–	20	0.02
5 weeks	8.0	–	25	–
6 weeks	12.0	–	30	–
7 weeks	17.0	19.0	40	–
8 weeks	23.0	30.0	50	1
12 weeks	56.0	73.0	–	14
16 weeks	112.0	157.0	–	105
20 weeks	160.0	239.0	–	310
24 weeks	203.0	296.0	–	640
28 weeks	242.0	355.0	–	1080
32 weeks	277.0	409.0	–	1670
36 weeks	313.0	458.0	–	2400
Full term (266 days)	350.0	500.0	–	3300

* Total length of the embryonic disk.

1) From AREY, L. B., *Developmental Anatomy*, 5th ed., Philadelphia, 1949, page 115.

Body length of the embryo and fetus (Rule of AHLFELD and HAASE) (From SUNDERMAN and BOERNER, *Normal Values in Clinical Medicine*, Philadelphia, 1950, page 422.)

Months of 28 days	1st month	1 × 1	1 cm	crown to heel length, body extended
	2nd month	2 × 2	4 cm	
	3rd month	3 × 3	9 cm	
	4th month	4 × 4	16 cm	
	5th month	5 × 5	25 cm	
	6th month	6 × *5*	30 cm	
	7th month	7 × *5*	35 cm	
	8th month	8 × *5*	40 cm	
	9th month	9 × *5*	45 cm	
	10th month	10 × *5*	50 cm	

Daily gain in weight of breast-fed children

Up to	4th week	ca.	1.06 ounce	(30 grams)
From	5th to 12th „	„	0.92–0.99 „	(26–28 „)
„	13th „ 20th „	„	0.71–0.85 „	(20–24 „)
„	21st „ 36th „	„	0.56–0.63 „	(16–18 „)
„	37th „ 52nd „	„	0.35–0.28 „	(10–15 „)

Weight changes during the first days of life

Hours	Days	Loss ounces *(grams)*	
0– 12	1st	2.8 *(81)*	4.8 *(139)*
12– 24		2.0 *(58)*	
24– 36	2nd	1.8 *(52)*	2.2 *(64)*
36– 48		0.4 *(12)*	
		Gain	
48– 60	3rd	0.3 *(8)*	1.2 *(33)*
60– 72		0.9 *(25)*	
72– 84	4th	0.7 *(20)*	1.8 *(50)*
84– 96		1.1 *(30)*	
96–108	5th	0.9 *(25)*	1.8 *(50)*
108–120		0.9 *(25)*	
120–132	6th	0.7 *(20)*	1.3 *(36)*
132–144		0.6 *(16)*	

Gain in weight of the infant

The ideal weight of the infant may be calculated roughly by means of the following formula: weight at birth + ($a \times$ age in months), where $a = 21$ oz. (600 g) during the first 6 months, and 17½ oz. (500 g) during the second 6 months[1].

	Breast-fed children boys lb. oz. *(kg)*	Breast-fed children girls lb. oz. *(kg)*	Artificially-fed boys and girls lb. oz. *(kg)*
Weight at birth ..	7 11 *(3.48)*	7 2 *(3.24)*	7 8 *(3.39)*
End of 4th week .	9 3 *(4.17)*	8 6 *(3.81)*	8 4 *(3.73)*
„ „ 8th „ .	11 3 *(5.08)*	10 1 *(4.56)*	9 9 *(4.34)*
„ „ 12th „ .	12 15 *(5.87)*	11 10 *(5.27)*	10 15 *(4.95)*
„ „ 16th „ .	14 8 *(6.58)*	13 0 *(5.90)*	12 6 *(5.61)*
„ „ 20th „ .	15 12 *(7.14)*	14 6 *(6.52)*	13 13 *(6.27)*
„ „ 24th „ .	16 14 *(7.65)*	15 4 *(6.92)*	15 3 *(6.90)*
„ „ 28th „ .	17 15 *(8.14)*	16 4 *(7.38)*	16 1 *(7.30)*
„ „ 32nd „ .	18 13 *(8.54)*	17 3 *(7.80)*	17 1 *(7.75)*
„ „ 36th „ .	19 10 *(8.90)*	17 14 *(8.09)*	17 15 *(8.13)*
„ „ 40th „ .	20 5 *(9.22)*	18 8 *(8.40)*	18 4 *(8.27)*
„ „ 44th „ .	21 4 *(9.65)*	19 3 *(8.72)*	19 1 *(8.65)*
„ „ 48th „ .	22 0 *(9.97)*	19 12 *(8.97)*	19 10 *(8.91)*
„ „ 52nd „ .	22 9 *(10.21)*	21 5 *(9.66)*	22 0 *(9.98)*

1) From SALMI, T., in FANCONI and WALLGREN, *Lehrbuch der Pädiatrie*, Basle, 1954, page 1.

Weights of various organs in infancy[1]

(Values in brackets relate to countries where goiter is prevalent)

Age	Body weight kg	Heart g	Brain g	Liver g	Lungs g	Spleen g	Kidneys g	Thymus g	Pituitary g	Adrenals g	Thyroid gland g	Testes g	Ovaries g	Uterus g
Newborn, boys	3.54	20	353	134	52	9.4	24	11.2	0.121	9.01	2.09 (6.6)	0.67		
girls	3.43	19	347	137	51	9.4	22			9.03			0.29	4.70
0– 3 months, boys .	5.92	19	435	143	69	14.6	30	19.3	0.161	4.66	1.71 (3.18)	0.91		
girls ..	5.62	17	411	133	64	11.4	27			4.60			0.63	2.88
3– 6 months, boys .	8.4	27	600	184	94	18.9	43	22.9		3.61	2.11 (4.4)	1.12		
girls ..	7.9	25	534	178	93	15.9	37			4.37			0.45	3.00
6–12 months, boys .	10.8	37	877	261	135	24	61	22.1		4.97	2.04 (3.44)	1.39		
girls ..	10.6	33	726	250	128	21	55			4.60			0.74	4.83

1) From SPECTOR, W. S. (Ed.), *Handbook of Biological Data*, Philadelphia, 1956, page 162.

Skeletal development

Various methods for the assessment of skeletal development have been devised. They usually consist of examination of a particular skeletal region, e.g. the hand or foot (see pages 610 and 611), on the assumption that its development is representative of the ossification of the whole skeleton. Such methods are not always reliable since the rates of ossification in the different regions of the body are not always the same. CAFFEY (*Pediatric X-Ray Diagnosis*, 3rd ed., Chicago, 1956) therefore recommends the method of SONTAG et al. (*Amer. J. Dis. Child.*, **58**, 949 [1939]) for the determination of the skeletal age. The technique is as follows: X-ray photographs of the whole of the left half of the body, including the scapula, are taken, the ossification centers counted (see diagrams below), and the numbers compared with the ideal values given in the adjacent table. In counting the centers all those present in the long bones of the arms, hands, legs and feet, in the carpal and tarsal bones and in the coracoid of the scapula are included, and in older children also that of the trochanter major femoris.

Age in months	Numbers of ossification centers					
	Boys			Girls		
	Mean*	Range*	*s*	Mean*	Range*	*s*
1	**4.11**	*1.29– 6.93*	1.41	**4.58**	*1.06– 8.10*	1.76
3	**6.63**	*2.91–10.35*	1.86	**7.78**	*3.46–12.10*	2.16
6	**9.61**	*5.71–13.51*	1.95	**11.44**	*6.38–16.50*	2.53
9	**11.88**	*6.56–17.20*	2.66	**15.36**	*5.52–25.20*	4.92
12	**13.96**	*6.04–21.88*	3.96	**22.40**	*8.54–36.26*	6.93
18	**19.27**	*6.05–32.49*	6.61	**34.10**	*17.22–50.98*	8.44
24	**29.21**	*13.01–45.41*	8.10	**43.44**	*30.14–56.74*	6.65
30	**37.59**	*22.79–52.39*	7.40	**48.91**	*35.91–61.91*	6.50
36	**43.42**	*32.74–54.10*	5.34	**52.73**	*41.77–63.69*	5.48
42	**47.06**	*36.54–57.58*	5.26	**56.61**	*48.65–64.57*	3.98
48	**51.24**	*42.06–60.42*	4.59	**57.94**	*50.12–65.76*	3.91
54	**53.94**	*45.24–62.64*	4.35	**59.89**	*53.17–66.61*	3.36
60	**56.24**	*48.10–64.38*	4.07	**61.52**	*56.14–66.90*	2.69

* For definition of the normal range see footnote, page 517.

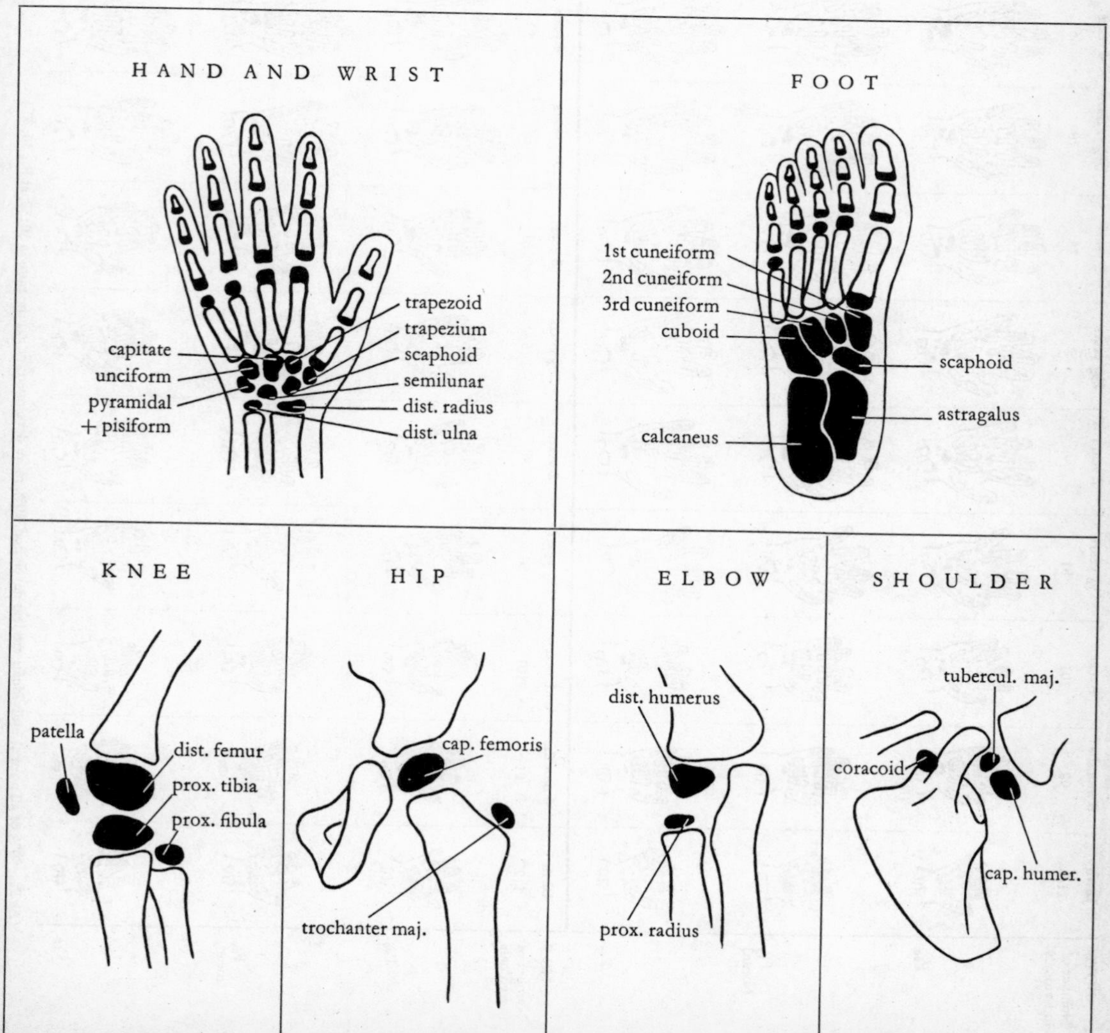

Appearance of the Secondary Ossification Centers – Hand

From VOGT and VICKERS, *Radiology*, **31**, 441 (1938)

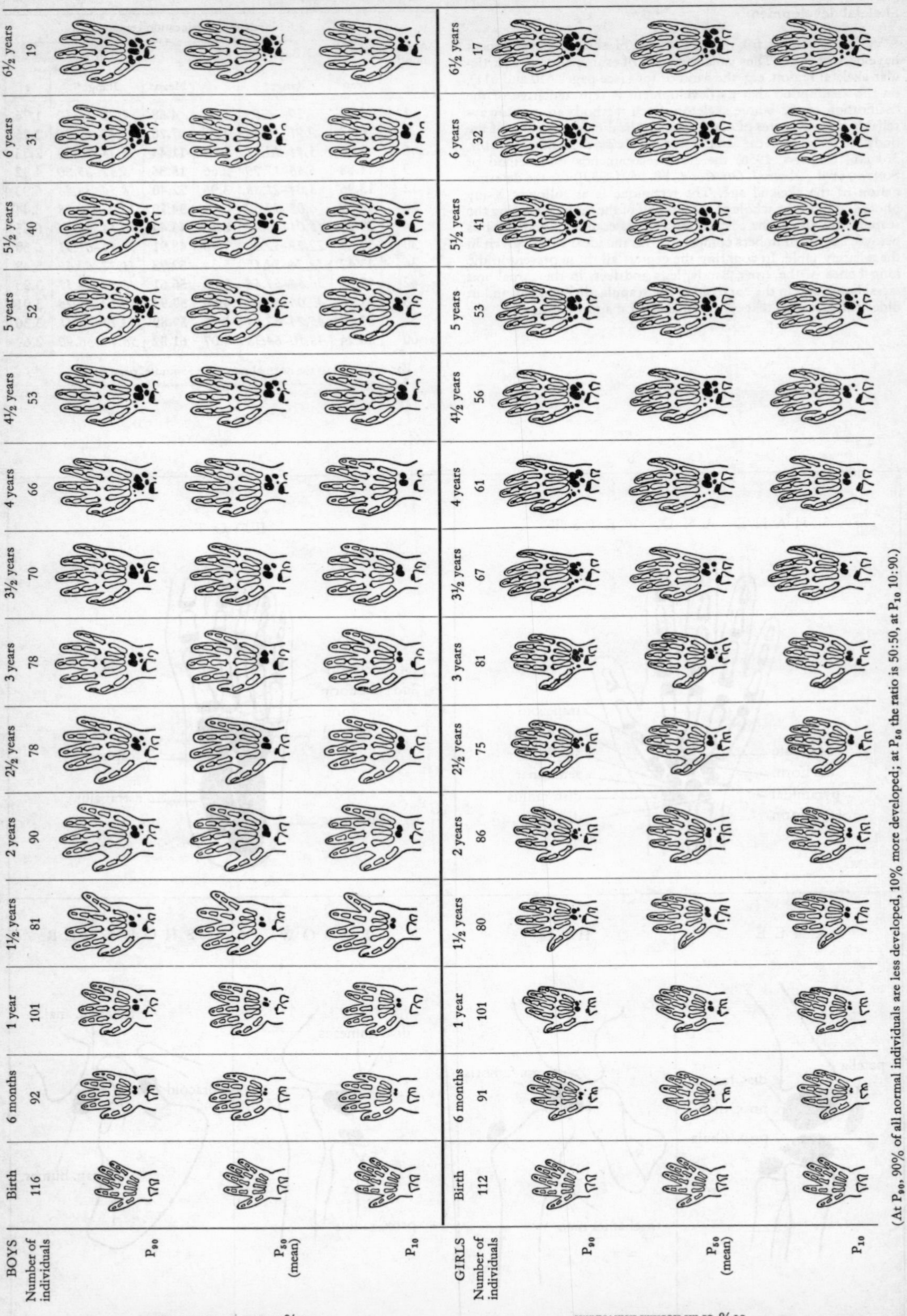

BOYS
Number of individuals
Birth 116
6 months 92
1 year 101
1½ years 81
2 years 90
2½ years 78
3 years 78
3½ years 70
4 years 66
4½ years 53
5 years 52
5½ years 40
6 years 31
6½ years 19
GIRLS
Number of individuals
Birth 112
6 months 91
1 year 101
1½ years 80
2 years 86
2½ years 75
3 years 81
3½ years 67
4 years 61
4½ years 56
5 years 53
5½ years 41
6 years 32
6½ years 17
P_{90}
P_{50} (mean)
P_{10}
80% of all normal individuals

(At P_{90}, 90% of all normal individuals are less developed, 10% more developed; at P_{50} the ratio is 50:50, at P_{10} 10:90.)

Appearance of the Secondary Ossification Centers – Foot

From Vogt and Vickers, *Radiology*, **31**, 441 (1938)

(At P_{90}, 90% of all normal individuals are less developed, 10% more developed; at P_{50} the ratio is 50:50, at P_{10} 10:90.)

From SCHOUR and MASSLER, *J. Amer. dent. Ass.*, **28**, 1153 (1941)

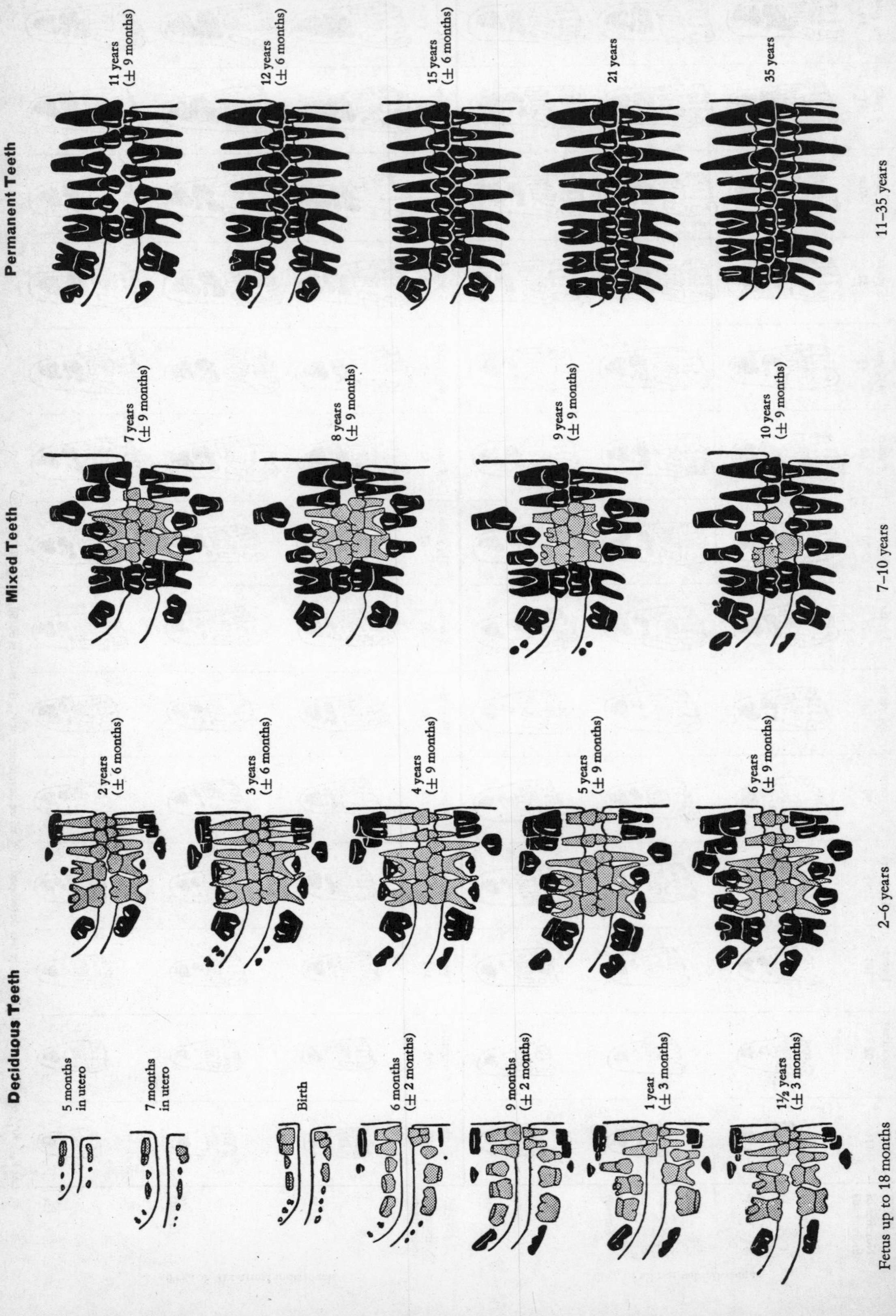

The tables[1] are based on the measurements of two groups of children in the United States of almost exclusively western European descent. The two groups cover respectively the periods from birth to 4½ years and from 5 to 18 years. The values for sitting height are from a separate study. Weights are in pounds and *kilograms*, length measurements in inches and *centimeters*. In order to simplify presentation, pounds and inches are given to the first decimal place. P = Percentile division (see page 159).

Boys

	P_{3}	P_{10}	P_{25}	P_{50}	P_{75}	P_{90}	P_{97}
	94% of the values for all normal individuals						
		80% of all values					
			50% of all values				
				Mean			
Birth							
Weight	5.8 *2.63*	6.3 *2.86*	6.9 *3.13*	**7.5** *3.4*	8.3 *3.76*	9.1 *4.13*	10.1 *4.58*
Length	18.2 *46.3*	18.9 *48.1*	19.4 *49.3*	**19.9** *50.6*	20.5 *52.0*	21.0 *53.3*	21.5 *54.6*
Pelvic breadth	2.8 *7.1*	2.9 *7.4*	3.0 *7.7*	**3.2** *8.1*	3.3 *8.4*	3.4 *8.7*	3.5 *9.0*
Head circ.	13.0 *33.0*	13.2 *33.5*	13.5 *34.4*	**13.9** *35.3*	14.3 *36.2*	14.6 *37.0*	14.8 *37.5*
Chest circ.	11.7 *29.8*	12.0 *30.6*	12.5 *31.8*	**13.1** *33.2*	13.5 *34.4*	14.1 *35.7*	14.5 *36.8*
3 Months							
Weight	10.6 *4.81*	11.1 *5.03*	11.8 *5.35*	**12.6** *5.72*	13.6 *6.17*	14.5 *6.58*	16.4 *7.44*
Length	22.4 *56.8*	22.8 *57.8*	23.3 *59.3*	**23.8** *60.4*	24.3 *61.8*	24.7 *62.8*	25.1 *63.7*
Pelvic breadth	3.9 *9.8*	3.9 *10.0*	4.0 *10.2*	**4.2** *10.6*	4.4 *11.2*	4.5 *11.5*	4.8 *12.1*
Head circ.	15.2 *38.7*	15.4 *39.2*	15.7 *40.0*	**16.1** *40.9*	16.3 *41.5*	16.6 *42.1*	17.0 *43.2*
Chest circ.	14.8 *37.6*	15.1 *38.3*	15.5 *39.3*	**16.0** *40.6*	16.4 *41.6*	16.9 *42.9*	17.4 *44.1*
Abdominal circ.	13.2 *33.6*	14.0 *35.5*	14.5 *36.8*	**15.2** *38.5*	15.7 *39.8*	16.3 *41.4*	17.1 *43.5*
6 Months							
Weight	14.0 *6.35*	14.8 *6.71*	15.6 *7.08*	**16.7** *7.58*	18.0 *8.16*	19.2 *8.71*	20.8 *9.43*
Length	24.8 *63.0*	25.2 *63.9*	25.7 *65.2*	**26.1** *66.4*	26.7 *67.8*	27.3 *69.3*	27.7 *70.4*
Sitting height	16.3 *41.4*	16.7 *42.3*	17.1 *43.4*	**17.6** *44.8*	18.2 *46.2*	18.7 *47.4*	19.1 *48.4*
Pelvic breadth	4.1 *10.5*	4.3 *10.8*	4.4 *11.2*	**4.6** *11.6*	4.7 *12.0*	4.9 *12.4*	5.2 *13.1*
Head circ.	16.6 *42.1*	16.8 *42.7*	17.0 *43.3*	**17.3** *43.9*	17.6 *44.8*	17.9 *45.4*	18.1 *45.9*
Chest circ.	15.8 *40.1*	16.4 *41.6*	16.7 *42.5*	**17.2** *43.7*	17.7 *45.0*	18.2 *46.3*	18.6 *47.2*
Abdominal circ.	14.3 *36.4*	15.1 *38.4*	15.7 *39.8*	**16.3** *41.4*	17.0 *43.2*	17.7 *45.0*	18.1 *46.0*
9 Months							
Weight	16.6 *7.53*	17.8 *8.07*	18.7 *8.48*	**20.0** *9.07*	21.5 *9.75*	22.9 *10.39*	24.4 *11.07*
Length	26.7 *67.7*	27.0 *68.6*	27.5 *69.8*	**28.0** *71.2*	28.7 *72.9*	29.2 *74.2*	29.9 *75.9*
Pelvic breadth	4.3 *11.0*	4.5 *11.5*	4.7 *11.9*	**4.8** *12.3*	5.0 *12.7*	5.2 *13.1*	5.4 *13.7*
Head circ.	17.2 *43.8*	17.5 *44.5*	17.8 *45.1*	**18.1** *46.0*	18.3 *46.5*	18.5 *47.1*	18.8 *47.8*
Chest circ.	16.5 *42.0*	17.2 *43.7*	17.6 *44.8*	**18.1** *46.0*	18.7 *47.5*	19.3 *48.9*	19.6 *49.9*
Abdominal circ.	15.0 *38.1*	15.8 *40.1*	16.4 *41.7*	**17.1** *43.4*	18.0 *45.6*	18.7 *47.6*	19.1 *48.4*

Girls

	P_{3}	P_{10}	P_{25}	P_{50}	P_{75}	P_{90}	P_{97}
	94% of the values for all normal individuals						
		80% of all values					
			50% of all values				
				Mean			
Birth							
Weight	5.8 *2.63*	6.2 *2.81*	6.9 *3.13*	**7.4** *3.36*	8.1 *3.67*	8.6 *3.9*	9.4 *4.26*
Length	18.5 *47.1*	18.8 *47.8*	19.3 *49.0*	**19.8** *50.2*	20.1 *51.0*	20.4 *51.9*	21.1 *53.6*
Pelvic breadth	2.8 *7.0*	2.8 *7.2*	2.9 *7.4*	**3.0** *7.7*	3.2 *8.2*	3.3 *8.5*	3.5 *8.9*
Head circ.	12.8 *32.5*	13.1 *33.4*	13.3 *33.9*	**13.7** *34.7*	13.9 *35.4*	14.2 *36.0*	14.4 *36.6*
Chest circ.	11.8 *30.0*	12.1 *30.8*	12.5 *31.8*	**13.0** *32.9*	13.4 *34.0*	13.8 *35.0*	14.2 *36.0*
3 Months							
Weight	9.8 *4.45*	10.7 *4.85*	11.4 *5.17*	**12.4** *5.62*	13.2 *5.99*	14.0 *6.35*	14.9 *6.76*
Length	22.0 *55.8*	22.4 *56.9*	22.8 *57.9*	**23.4** *59.5*	23.9 *60.7*	24.3 *61.7*	24.8 *63.1*
Pelvic breadth	3.7 *9.4*	3.8 *9.6*	3.9 *9.9*	**4.1** *10.4*	4.3 *10.9*	4.5 *11.4*	4.8 *12.2*
Head circ.	14.9 *37.9*	15.2 *38.5*	15.4 *39.2*	**15.7** *40.0*	16.1 *40.8*	16.4 *41.7*	16.7 *42.3*
Chest circ.	14.4 *36.5*	14.8 *37.6*	15.3 *38.8*	**15.7** *39.8*	16.1 *40.9*	16.5 *42.0*	16.9 *43.0*
Abdominal circ.	12.7 *32.3*	13.5 *34.4*	14.5 *36.8*	**15.1** *38.4*	15.9 *40.4*	16.4 *41.7*	16.8 *42.7*
6 Months							
Weight	12.7 *5.76*	14.1 *6.4*	15.0 *6.8*	**16.0** *7.26*	17.5 *7.94*	18.6 *8.44*	20.0 *9.07*
Length	24.1 *61.1*	24.6 *62.5*	25.1 *63.7*	**25.7** *65.2*	26.2 *66.6*	26.7 *67.8*	27.1 *68.8*
Sitting height	15.7 *40.0*	16.1 *41.0*	16.6 *42.1*	**17.0** *43.3*	17.5 *44.5*	18.0 *45.6*	18.4 *46.8*
Pelvic breadth	4.1 *10.3*	4.1 *10.5*	4.3 *10.8*	**4.4** *11.3*	4.6 *11.8*	4.9 *12.4*	5.2 *13.2*
Head circ.	16.1 *40.9*	16.3 *41.4*	16.5 *42.0*	**16.9** *42.8*	17.2 *43.6*	17.5 *44.5*	17.9 *45.4*
Chest circ.	15.5 *39.4*	16.0 *40.6*	16.5 *41.8*	**16.9** *43.0*	17.4 *44.2*	17.9 *45.4*	18.3 *46.6*
Abdominal circ.	14.3 *36.2*	14.9 *37.9*	15.6 *39.5*	**16.3** *41.4*	17.1 *43.5*	17.7 *45.0*	18.2 *46.2*
9 Months							
Weight	15.1 *6.85*	16.6 *7.53*	17.7 *8.03*	**19.2** *8.71*	20.8 *9.43*	22.4 *10.16*	24.2 *10.98*
Length	25.7 *65.4*	26.4 *67.0*	26.9 *68.4*	**27.6** *70.1*	28.2 *71.7*	28.7 *72.9*	29.2 *74.1*
Pelvic breadth	4.3 *11.0*	4.4 *11.3*	4.5 *11.5*	**4.7** *12.0*	4.9 *12.5*	5.2 *13.1*	5.4 *13.8*
Head circ.	16.8 *42.6*	17.0 *43.2*	17.2 *43.8*	**17.6** *44.6*	17.9 *45.4*	18.2 *46.3*	18.6 *47.2*
Chest circ.	16.4 *41.7*	16.8 *42.7*	17.3 *44.0*	**17.9** *45.4*	18.3 *46.6*	18.9 *47.9*	19.4 *49.2*
Abdominal circ.	15.0 *38.0*	15.7 *39.9*	16.3 *41.3*	**17.1** *43.4*	18.0 *45.7*	18.8 *47.7*	19.4 *49.2*

1) Quoted by STUART and STEVENSON, in NELSON, W. E. (Ed.), *Textbook of Pediatrics*, 7th ed., Philadelphia, 1959, pages 50-61.

Normal Body Measurements During Growth[1] – 12 Months to 2 Years

(Weights are in pounds and *kilograms*, length measurements in inches and *centimeters*)

Boys								Girls						
94% of the values for all normal individuals								94% of the values for all normal individuals						
	80% of all values								80% of all values					
		50% of all values								50% of all values				
			Mean								Mean			
P_3	P_{10}	P_{25}	P_{50}	P_{75}	P_{90}	P_{97}		P_3	P_{10}	P_{25}	P_{50}	P_{75}	P_{90}	P_{97}
							12 Months							
18.5 *8.39*	19.6 *8.89*	20.9 *9.48*	**22.2** *10.07*	23.8 *10.8*	25.4 *11.52*	27.3 *12.38*	Weight	16.8 *7.62*	18.4 *8.35*	19.8 *8.98*	**21.5** *9.75*	23.0 *10.43*	24.8 *11.25*	27.1 *12.29*
28.1 *71.3*	28.5 *72.4*	29.0 *73.7*	**29.6** *75.2*	30.3 *76.9*	30.7 *78.1*	31.6 *80.3*	Length	27.1 *68.9*	27.8 *70.6*	28.5 *72.3*	**29.2** *74.2*	29.9 *75.9*	30.4 *77.1*	31.0 *78.8*
17.8 *45.1*	18.1 *46.1*	18.7 *47.4*	**19.2** *48.7*	19.7 *50.1*	20.2 *51.2*	20.6 *52.4*	Sitting height	17.4 *44.2*	17.8 *45.2*	18.2 *46.3*	**18.7** *47.5*	19.2 *48.7*	19.6 *49.8*	20.0 *50.9*
4.5 *11.4*	4.7 *11.9*	4.9 *12.4*	**5.0** *12.8*	5.2 *13.2*	5.4 *13.7*	5.6 *14.2*	Pelvic breadth	4.5 *11.4*	4.6 *11.7*	4.7 *12.0*	**4.9** *12.4*	5.1 *13.0*	5.4 *13.6*	5.7 *14.4*
17.7 *44.9*	17.9 *45.5*	18.3 *46.5*	**18.6** *47.3*	18.8 *47.8*	19.1 *48.4*	19.3 *48.9*	Head circ.	17.2 *43.6*	17.4 *44.3*	17.7 *45.0*	**18.0** *45.8*	18.4 *46.7*	18.8 *47.7*	19.1 *48.4*
17.1 *43.5*	17.8 *45.1*	18.2 *46.3*	**18.7** *47.6*	19.4 *49.3*	20.0 *50.7*	20.4 *51.9*	Chest circ.	17.0 *43.1*	17.4 *44.2*	18.0 *45.6*	**18.5** *47.0*	19.0 *48.2*	19.5 *49.5*	20.0 *50.9*
15.5 *39.3*	16.2 *41.1*	16.9 *42.9*	**17.6** *44.6*	18.5 *47.0*	19.3 *48.9*	19.7 *50.0*	Abdominal circ.	15.2 *38.7*	16.1 *40.9*	16.7 *42.4*	**17.5** *44.5*	18.5 *46.9*	19.4 *49.2*	20.1 *51.1*
							15 Months							
19.8 *8.98*	21.0 *9.53*	22.4 *10.16*	**23.7** *10.75*	25.4 *11.52*	27.2 *12.34*	29.4 *13.33*	Weight	18.1 *8.21*	19.8 *8.98*	21.3 *9.66*	**23.0** *10.43*	24.6 *11.16*	26.6 *12.07*	29.0 *13.15*
29.3 *74.4*	29.8 *75.6*	30.3 *77.0*	**30.9** *78.5*	31.6 *80.3*	32.1 *81.5*	33.1 *84.2*	Length	28.3 *71.9*	29.0 *73.7*	29.8 *75.6*	**30.6** *77.6*	31.3 *79.4*	31.8 *80.8*	32.6 *82.8*
4.6 *11.8*	4.9 *12.4*	5.0 *12.8*	**5.2** *13.3*	5.4 *13.7*	5.6 *14.2*	5.8 *14.7*	Pelvic breadth	4.6 *11.6*	4.8 *12.1*	4.9 *12.4*	**5.1** *12.9*	5.3 *13.5*	5.6 *14.1*	5.8 *14.8*
18.0 *45.6*	18.2 *46.3*	18.5 *47.1*	**18.9** *48.0*	19.1 *48.5*	19.4 *49.2*	19.6 *49.8*	Head circ.	17.4 *44.3*	17.7 *44.9*	18.0 *45.6*	**18.3** *46.5*	18.7 *47.4*	19.1 *48.4*	19.3 *49.1*
17.6 *44.7*	18.1 *46.1*	18.6 *47.3*	**19.1** *48.6*	19.7 *50.1*	20.4 *51.7*	20.8 *52.8*	Chest circ.	17.5 *44.1*	17.8 *45.1*	18.3 *46.5*	**18.9** *47.9*	19.4 *49.2*	19.9 *50.5*	20.4 *51.9*
15.7 *40.0*	16.4 *41.7*	17.1 *43.5*	**17.8** *45.1*	18.7 *47.4*	19.4 *49.3*	19.9 *50.5*	Abdominal circ.	15.5 *39.3*	16.3 *41.5*	16.9 *43.0*	**17.7** *45.0*	18.6 *47.3*	19.6 *49.8*	20.4 *51.8*
							18 Months							
21.1 *9.57*	22.3 *10.12*	23.8 *10.8*	**25.2** *11.43*	26.9 *12.2*	29.0 *13.15*	31.5 *14.29*	Weight	19.4 *8.8*	21.2 *9.62*	22.7 *10.3*	**24.5** *11.11*	26.2 *11.88*	28.3 *12.84*	30.9 *14.02*
30.5 *77.5*	31.0 *78.8*	31.6 *80.3*	**32.2** *81.8*	33.0 *83.7*	33.5 *85.0*	34.7 *88.2*	Length	29.5 *74.9*	30.2 *76.8*	31.1 *79.0*	**31.9** *80.9*	32.6 *82.9*	33.3 *84.5*	34.1 *86.7*
19.0 *48.3*	19.4 *49.2*	19.8 *50.3*	**20.3** *51.6*	20.8 *52.9*	21.3 *54.1*	21.8 *55.4*	Sitting height	18.5 *47.1*	18.9 *48.1*	19.4 *49.2*	**19.8** *50.4*	20.3 *51.6*	20.7 *52.7*	21.2 *53.9*
4.8 *12.1*	5.0 *12.8*	5.2 *13.2*	**5.4** *13.7*	5.6 *14.2*	5.8 *14.7*	6.0 *15.2*	Pelvic breadth	4.6 *11.8*	4.9 *12.4*	5.0 *12.8*	**5.2** *13.3*	5.5 *13.9*	5.7 *14.5*	6.0 *15.2*
18.2 *46.2*	18.5 *47.0*	18.8 *47.7*	**19.2** *48.7*	19.4 *49.2*	19.6 *49.9*	19.9 *50.6*	Head circ.	17.7 *44.9*	17.9 *45.5*	18.2 *46.2*	**18.5** *47.1*	18.9 *48.0*	19.3 *49.0*	19.6 *49.8*
18.1 *45.9*	18.5 *47.0*	19.0 *48.2*	**19.5** *49.5*	20.0 *50.9*	20.7 *52.6*	21.1 *53.7*	Chest circ.	17.7 *45.0*	18.1 *46.0*	18.6 *47.3*	**19.2** *48.8*	19.8 *50.2*	20.2 *51.4*	20.8 *52.9*
16.0 *40.6*	16.6 *42.2*	17.3 *44.0*	**17.9** *45.5*	18.8 *47.8*	19.5 *49.6*	20.0 *50.9*	Abdominal circ.	15.7 *39.8*	16.6 *42.1*	17.2 *43.6*	**17.9** *45.5*	18.7 *47.6*	19.8 *50.3*	20.7 *52.5*
							2 Years							
23.3 *10.57*	24.7 *11.2*	26.3 *11.93*	**27.7** *12.56*	29.7 *13.47*	31.9 *14.47*	34.9 *15.83*	Weight	21.6 *9.8*	23.5 *10.66*	25.3 *11.48*	**27.1** *12.29*	29.2 *13.25*	31.7 *14.38*	34.4 *15.6*
32.6 *82.7*	33.1 *84.2*	33.8 *85.8*	**34.4** *87.5*	35.2 *89.4*	35.9 *91.1*	37.2 *94.6*	Height	31.5 *80.1*	32.3 *82.0*	33.3 *84.7*	**34.1** *86.6*	35.0 *88.9*	35.8 *91.0*	36.7 *93.3*
19.9 *50.6*	20.2 *51.4*	20.7 *52.5*	**21.2** *53.8*	21.7 *55.1*	22.2 *56.3*	22.7 *57.6*	Sitting height	19.4 *49.2*	19.8 *50.2*	20.2 *51.4*	**20.7** *52.7*	21.3 *54.0*	21.7 *55.2*	22.2 *56.4*
5.0 *12.8*	5.3 *13.5*	5.5 *13.9*	**5.7** *14.4*	5.9 *15.0*	6.1 *15.5*	6.3 *16.1*	Pelvic breadth	4.9 *12.5*	5.2 *13.1*	5.3 *13.5*	**5.6** *14.1*	5.8 *14.7*	6.0 *15.3*	6.3 *16.1*
18.5 *47.0*	18.9 *48.0*	19.2 *48.7*	**19.6** *49.7*	19.8 *50.2*	20.1 *51.0*	20.4 *51.7*	Head circ.	18.0 *45.8*	18.3 *46.4*	18.6 *47.2*	**18.9** *48.1*	19.3 *49.1*	19.7 *50.1*	20.0 *50.9*
18.7 *47.4*	19.1 *48.4*	19.5 *49.5*	**20.0** *50.8*	20.6 *52.2*	21.2 *53.9*	21.6 *54.9*	Chest circ.	18.2 *46.3*	18.7 *47.4*	19.1 *48.6*	**19.7** *50.1*	20.4 *51.8*	20.9 *53.0*	21.3 *54.2*
16.4 *41.6*	17.1 *43.4*	17.6 *44.8*	**18.2** *46.2*	19.1 *48.4*	19.8 *50.2*	20.3 *51.5*	Abdominal circ.	16.0 *40.7*	16.9 *42.8*	17.5 *44.4*	**18.2** *46.3*	19.1 *48.5*	20.2 *51.4*	21.1 *53.5*

1) Quoted by STUART and STEVENSON, in NELSON, W. E. (Ed.), *Textbook of Pediatrics*, 7th ed., Philadelphia, 1959, pages 50–61.

Normal Body Measurements During Growth[1] – 2½ to 4 Years

(Weights are in pounds and *kilograms*, length measurements in inches and *centimeters*)

Boys and Girls: P₃–P₉₇ = 94% of the values for all normal individuals; P₁₀–P₉₀ = 80% of all values; P₂₅–P₇₅ = 50% of all values; P₅₀ = Mean

	Boys P_3	Boys P_{10}	Boys P_{25}	Boys P_{50} (Mean)	Boys P_{75}	Boys P_{90}	Boys P_{97}	Girls P_3	Girls P_{10}	Girls P_{25}	Girls P_{50} (Mean)	Girls P_{75}	Girls P_{90}	Girls P_{97}
2½ Years														
Weight	25.2	26.6	28.4	**30.0**	32.2	34.5	37.0	23.6	25.5	27.4	**29.6**	31.9	34.6	38.2
	11.43	*12.07*	*12.88*	*13.61*	*14.61*	*15.65*	*16.78*	*10.7*	*11.57*	*12.43*	*13.43*	*14.47*	*15.69*	*17.33*
Height	34.2	34.8	35.5	**36.3**	37.0	37.9	39.2	33.3	34.0	35.2	**36.0**	36.9	38.0	38.9
	86.9	*88.5*	*90.2*	*92.1*	*94.1*	*96.2*	*99.5*	*84.5*	*86.3*	*89.3*	*91.4*	*93.8*	*96.4*	*98.7*
Sitting height	20.6	20.9	21.3	**21.9**	22.4	22.9	23.4	20.0	20.4	20.9	**21.4**	21.9	22.4	23.0
	52.2	*53.1*	*54.2*	*55.6*	*56.9*	*58.1*	*59.5*	*50.9*	*51.9*	*53.1*	*54.4*	*55.7*	*57.0*	*58.3*
Pelvic breadth	5.4	5.6	5.7	**5.9**	6.2	6.4	6.6	5.2	5.4	5.6	**5.8**	6.1	6.3	6.7
	13.6	*14.2*	*14.6*	*15.1*	*15.7*	*16.2*	*16.7*	*13.2*	*13.7*	*14.2*	*14.8*	*15.4*	*16.1*	*16.9*
Head circ.	18.7	19.1	19.4	**19.8**	20.0	20.3	20.6	18.2	18.5	18.8	**19.2**	19.6	20.0	20.3
	47.5	*48.5*	*49.2*	*50.2*	*50.9*	*51.6*	*52.3*	*46.3*	*47.0*	*47.8*	*48.8*	*49.8*	*50.8*	*51.5*
Chest circ.	19.0	19.4	19.8	**20.4**	20.9	21.6	22.0	18.6	19.1	19.6	**20.2**	20.8	21.4	21.9
	48.2	*49.3*	*50.3*	*51.7*	*53.2*	*54.9*	*55.8*	*47.3*	*48.4*	*49.7*	*51.2*	*52.8*	*54.3*	*55.5*
Abdominal circ.	16.5	17.3	17.9	**18.4**	19.3	20.0	20.5	16.4	17.2	17.8	**18.5**	19.4	20.7	21.5
	42.0	*44.0*	*45.5*	*46.7*	*49.1*	*50.7*	*52.0*	*41.7*	*43.6*	*45.2*	*47.0*	*49.4*	*52.6*	*54.7*
3 Years														
Weight	27.0	28.7	30.3	**32.2**	34.5	36.8	39.2	25.6	27.6	29.6	**31.8**	34.6	37.4	41.8
	12.25	*13.02*	*13.74*	*14.61*	*15.65*	*16.69*	*17.78*	*11.61*	*12.52*	*13.43*	*14.42*	*15.69*	*16.96*	*18.96*
Height	35.7	36.3	37.0	**37.9**	38.8	39.6	40.5	34.8	35.6	36.8	**37.7**	38.6	39.8	40.7
	90.6	*92.3*	*93.9*	*96.2*	*98.5*	*100.5*	*102.8*	*88.4*	*90.5*	*93.4*	*95.7*	*98.1*	*101.1*	*103.5*
Sitting height	21.1	21.5	21.9	**22.5**	23.0	23.5	24.1	20.6	21.0	21.5	**22.0**	22.6	23.1	23.6
	53.5	*54.5*	*55.6*	*57.1*	*58.5*	*59.7*	*61.1*	*52.2*	*53.4*	*54.6*	*56.0*	*57.4*	*58.7*	*60.0*
Pelvic breadth	5.6	5.8	6.0	**6.2**	6.5	6.7	6.9	5.4	5.6	5.8	**6.1**	6.3	6.6	7.0
	14.2	*14.8*	*15.2*	*15.8*	*16.4*	*16.9*	*17.4*	*13.8*	*14.3*	*14.8*	*15.4*	*16.1*	*16.8*	*17.7*
Head circ.	18.9	19.3	19.5	**19.8**	20.2	20.4	20.7	18.4	18.7	19.1	**19.4**	19.8	20.1	20.5
	47.9	*48.9*	*49.6*	*50.4*	*51.3*	*51.9*	*52.7*	*46.8*	*47.5*	*48.4*	*49.3*	*50.3*	*51.1*	*52.0*
Chest circ.	19.3	19.6	20.1	**20.6**	21.3	22.0	22.4	18.9	19.4	19.9	**20.4**	21.1	21.7	22.3
	48.9	*49.9*	*51.0*	*52.4*	*54.1*	*55.8*	*57.0*	*47.9*	*49.3*	*50.5*	*51.9*	*53.5*	*55.1*	*56.7*
Abdominal circ.	16.6	17.6	18.1	**18.6**	19.5	20.1	20.7	16.8	17.5	18.1	**18.8**	19.8	21.1	22.0
	42.1	*44.6*	*46.0*	*47.2*	*49.6*	*51.1*	*52.7*	*42.7*	*44.5*	*46.0*	*47.7*	*50.2*	*53.6*	*55.8*
3½ Years														
Weight	28.5	30.4	32.3	**34.3**	36.7	39.1	41.5	27.5	29.5	31.5	**33.9**	37.0	40.4	45.3
	12.93	*13.79*	*14.65*	*15.56*	*16.65*	*17.74*	*18.82*	*12.47*	*13.38*	*14.29*	*15.38*	*16.78*	*18.33*	*20.55*
Height	37.1	37.8	38.4	**39.3**	40.4	41.1	41.9	36.2	37.1	38.1	**39.2**	40.2	41.5	42.5
	94.3	*96.0*	*97.5*	*99.8*	*102.5*	*104.5*	*106.5*	*92.0*	*94.2*	*96.9*	*99.5*	*102.0*	*105.4*	*108.0*
Sitting height	21.6	22.0	22.4	**23.1**	23.6	24.1	24.6	21.1	21.6	22.1	**22.6**	23.2	23.7	24.3
	54.8	*55.8*	*57.0*	*58.6*	*60.0*	*61.2*	*62.6*	*53.6*	*54.8*	*56.1*	*57.5*	*59.0*	*60.3*	*61.6*
Pelvic breadth	5.8	6.0	6.2	**6.4**	6.7	6.9	7.0	5.7	5.9	6.1	**6.3**	6.6	6.9	7.2
	14.7	*15.3*	*15.7*	*16.3*	*16.9*	*17.4*	*17.9*	*14.4*	*14.9*	*15.4*	*16.0*	*16.7*	*17.4*	*18.3*
Chest circ.	19.5	19.9	20.3	**20.9**	21.6	22.3	22.8	19.1	19.7	20.2	**20.7**	21.3	22.0	22.9
	49.6	*50.5*	*51.6*	*53.1*	*54.9*	*56.6*	*58.0*	*48.5*	*50.1*	*51.2*	*52.5*	*54.1*	*55.8*	*58.1*
4 Years														
Weight	30.1	32.1	34.0	**36.4**	39.0	41.4	44.3	29.2	31.2	33.5	**36.2**	39.6	43.5	48.2
	13.65	*14.56*	*15.42*	*16.51*	*17.69*	*18.78*	*20.09*	*13.25*	*14.15*	*15.2*	*16.42*	*17.96*	*19.73*	*21.86*
Height	38.4	39.1	39.7	**40.7**	41.9	42.7	43.5	37.5	38.4	39.5	**40.6**	41.7	43.1	44.2
	97.5	*99.3*	*100.8*	*103.4*	*106.5*	*108.5*	*110.4*	*95.2*	*97.6*	*100.3*	*103.2*	*105.8*	*109.6*	*112.3*
Sitting height	22.0	22.5	23.0	**23.6**	24.2	24.6	25.2	21.6	22.1	22.6	**23.2**	23.8	24.3	24.4
	56.0	*57.1*	*58.3*	*60.0*	*61.4*	*62.6*	*64.0*	*54.9*	*56.1*	*57.4*	*58.9*	*60.4*	*61.7*	*62.1*
Pelvic breadth	6.0	6.2	6.4	**6.7**	6.9	7.1	7.3	5.9	6.1	6.3	**6.5**	6.8	7.0	7.4
	15.2	*15.8*	*16.2*	*16.9*	*17.5*	*18.0*	*18.5*	*15.0*	*15.4*	*15.9*	*16.5*	*17.2*	*17.9*	*18.9*
Chest circ.	19.7	20.1	20.6	**21.1**	21.9	22.5	23.2	19.4	20.0	20.4	**20.9**	21.5	22.2	23.2
	50.1	*51.1*	*52.2*	*53.7*	*55.5*	*57.2*	*58.9*	*49.2*	*50.7*	*51.7*	*53.1*	*54.7*	*56.5*	*59.0*

1) Quoted by Stuart and Stevenson, in Nelson, W. E. (Ed.), *Textbook of Pediatrics*, 7th ed., Philadelphia, 1959, pages 50–61.

Normal Body Measurements During Growth[1] – 4½ to 6 Years

(Weights are in pounds and *kilograms*, length measurements in inches and *centimeters*)

Boys: 94% of the values for all normal individuals lie between P_3 and P_{97}; 80% of all values between P_{10} and P_{90}; 50% of all values between P_{25} and P_{75}; Mean = P_{50}. Girls: the same.

Boys P_3	Boys P_{10}	Boys P_{25}	Boys P_{50} (Mean)	Boys P_{75}	Boys P_{90}	Boys P_{97}		Girls P_3	Girls P_{10}	Girls P_{25}	Girls P_{50} (Mean)	Girls P_{75}	Girls P_{90}	Girls P_{97}
							4½ Years							
31.6 *14.33*	33.8 *15.33*	35.7 *16.19*	**38.4** *17.42*	41.4 *18.78*	43.9 *19.91*	47.4 *21.5*	Weight	30.7 *13.93*	32.9 *14.92*	35.3 *16.01*	**38.5** *17.46*	42.1 *19.1*	46.7 *21.18*	50.9 *23.09*
39.6 *100.6*	40.3 *102.4*	40.9 *104.0*	**42.0** *106.7*	43.3 *109.9*	44.2 *112.3*	45.0 *114.3*	Height	38.6 *98.1*	39.7 *100.9*	40.8 *103.6*	**42.0** *106.8*	43.0 *109.3*	44.7 *113.5*	45.7 *116.2*
22.5 *57.1*	23.0 *58.3*	23.5 *59.6*	**24.1** *61.3*	24.7 *62.8*	25.2 *64.0*	25.7 *65.4*	Sitting height	22.1 *56.1*	22.6 *57.4*	23.1 *58.7*	**23.7** *60.2*	24.3 *61.7*	24.8 *63.1*	25.4 *64.5*
6.2 *15.7*	6.4 *16.2*	6.5 *16.6*	**6.8** *17.3*	7.1 *18.0*	7.3 *18.5*	7.5 *19.1*	Pelvic breadth	6.1 *15.5*	6.3 *15.9*	6.5 *16.4*	**6.7** *17.0*	7.0 *17.7*	7.3 *18.5*	7.6 *19.4*
20.0 *50.7*	20.4 *51.7*	20.8 *52.9*	**21.4** *54.4*	22.2 *56.3*	22.8 *58.0*	23.3 *59.3*	Chest circ.	19.6 *49.8*	20.2 *51.3*	20.6 *52.3*	**21.1** *53.7*	21.8 *55.4*	22.6 *57.3*	23.5 *59.6*
							5 Years							
34.5 *15.65*	36.6 *16.6*	39.6 *17.96*	**42.8** *19.41*	46.5 *21.09*	49.7 *22.54*	53.2 *24.13*	Weight	33.7 *15.29*	36.1 *16.37*	38.6 *17.51*	**41.4** *18.78*	44.2 *20.05*	48.2 *21.86*	51.8 *23.5*
40.2 *102.1*	41.5 *105.3*	42.6 *108.3*	**43.8** *111.3*	45.0 *114.2*	45.9 *116.7*	47.0 *119.5*	Height	40.4 *102.6*	41.3 *105.0*	42.2 *107.2*	**43.2** *109.7*	44.4 *112.9*	45.4 *115.4*	46.5 *118.0*
22.9 *58.2*	23.4 *59.5*	24.0 *60.9*	**24.6** *62.6*	25.3 *64.2*	25.7 *65.4*	26.3 *66.8*	Sitting height	22.6 *57.3*	23.1 *58.6*	23.6 *59.9*	**24.2** *61.4*	24.8 *63.0*	25.4 *64.4*	25.9 *65.9*
	6.7 *17.0*	6.9 *17.6*	**7.2** *18.3*	7.4 *18.9*	7.7 *19.6*		Pelvic breadth		6.7 *17.0*	6.9 *17.4*	**7.1** *18.0*	7.4 *18.7*	7.6 *19.4*	
	20.3 *51.6*	20.8 *52.8*	**21.5** *54.5*	22.1 *56.2*	22.6 *57.5*		Chest circ.		19.8 *50.2*	20.2 *51.4*	**20.8** *52.9*	21.5 *54.6*	22.2 *56.5*	
	8.3 *21.0*	8.5 *21.7*	**8.9** *22.6*	9.3 *23.6*	9.7 *24.6*		Calf circ.		8.3 *21.1*	8.6 *21.8*	**9.0** *22.8*	9.4 *23.8*	9.7 *24.7*	
							5½ Years							
	38.8 *17.6*	42.0 *19.05*	**45.6** *20.68*	49.3 *22.36*	53.1 *24.09*		Weight		38.0 *17.24*	40.8 *18.51*	**44.0** *19.96*	47.2 *21.41*	51.2 *23.22*	
	42.6 *108.3*	43.8 *111.2*	**45.0** *114.4*	46.3 *117.5*	47.3 *120.1*		Height		42.4 *107.8*	43.4 *110.2*	**44.4** *112.8*	45.7 *116.1*	46.8 *118.9*	
23.3 *59.3*	23.9 *60.7*	24.4 *62.1*	**25.2** *63.9*	25.8 *65.6*	26.3 *66.8*	26.9 *68.2*	Sitting height	23.1 *58.6*	23.6 *59.9*	24.1 *61.2*	**24.7** *62.7*	25.3 *64.3*	25.9 *65.8*	26.5 *67.3*
	6.9 *17.4*	7.1 *18.0*	**7.4** *18.7*	7.6 *19.4*	7.9 *20.1*		Pelvic breadth		6.9 *17.4*	7.0 *17.8*	**7.2** *18.4*	7.5 *19.1*	7.9 *20.0*	
	20.6 *52.4*	21.1 *53.6*	**21.8** *55.3*	22.5 *57.1*	23.0 *58.5*		Chest circ.		20.0 *50.9*	20.6 *52.2*	**21.1** *53.7*	21.9 *55.5*	22.6 *57.4*	
	8.4 *21.4*	8.7 *22.2*	**9.1** *23.1*	9.5 *24.1*	9.9 *25.2*		Calf circ.		8.5 *21.5*	8.8 *22.3*	**9.2** *23.3*	9.6 *24.3*	10.0 *25.3*	
							6 Years							
38.5 *17.46*	40.9 *18.55*	44.4 *20.14*	**48.3** *21.91*	52.1 *23.63*	56.4 *25.58*	61.1 *27.71*	Weight	37.2 *16.87*	39.6 *17.96*	42.9 *19.46*	**46.5** *21.09*	50.2 *22.77*	54.2 *24.58*	58.7 *26.63*
42.7 *108.5*	43.8 *111.2*	44.9 *114.1*	**46.3** *117.5*	47.6 *120.8*	48.6 *123.5*	49.7 *126.2*	Height	42.5 *108.0*	43.5 *110.6*	44.6 *113.2*	**45.6** *115.9*	47.0 *119.3*	48.1 *122.3*	49.4 *125.4*
23.8 *60.4*	24.3 *61.8*	24.9 *63.3*	**25.7** *65.2*	26.3 *66.9*	26.9 *68.2*	27.4 *69.6*	Sitting height	23.6 *59.9*	24.1 *61.2*	24.6 *62.5*	**25.2** *64.1*	25.8 *65.6*	26.4 *67.1*	27.0 *68.7*
	7.0 *17.7*	7.2 *18.4*	**7.5** *19.1*	7.8 *19.8*	8.1 *20.5*		Pelvic breadth		7.0 *17.7*	7.2 *18.2*	**7.4** *18.8*	7.7 *19.5*	8.1 *20.5*	
	20.9 *53.2*	21.4 *54.4*	**22.1** *56.1*	22.8 *57.9*	23.4 *59.5*		Chest circ.		20.3 *51.5*	20.8 *52.9*	**21.5** *54.5*	22.2 *56.3*	22.9 *58.2*	
	8.6 *21.8*	8.9 *22.6*	**9.3** *23.6*	9.7 *24.6*	10.1 *25.7*		Calf circ.		8.6 *21.9*	8.9 *22.7*	**9.4** *23.8*	9.8 *24.8*	10.2 *25.8*	

1) Quoted by Stuart and Stevenson, in Nelson, W. E. (Ed.), *Textbook of Pediatrics*, 7th ed., Philadelphia, 1959, pages 50–61.

Normal Body Measurements During Growth[1] – 6½ to 8 Years

(Weights are in pounds and *kilograms*, length measurements in inches and *centimeters*)

Boys

94% of the values for all normal individuals (P₃–P₉₇); 80% of all values (P₁₀–P₉₀); 50% of all values (P₂₅–P₇₅); Mean (P₅₀)

	P_3	P_{10}	P_{25}	P_{50} (Mean)	P_{75}	P_{90}	P_{97}
6½ Years							
Weight		43.4 *19.69*	47.1 *21.36*	**51.2** *23.22*	55.4 *25.13*	60.4 *27.4*	
Height		44.9 *114.1*	46.1 *117.2*	**47.6** *120.8*	48.9 *124.2*	50.0 *127.0*	
Sitting height	24.2 *61.5*	24.8 *62.9*	25.4 *64.5*	**26.1** *66.4*	26.9 *68.2*	27.4 *69.6*	28.0 *71.0*
Pelvic breadth		7.1 *18.1*	7.4 *18.8*	**7.7** *19.5*	8.0 *20.2*	8.3 *21.0*	
Chest circ.		21.3 *54.1*	21.8 *55.3*	**22.4** *57.0*	23.2 *58.9*	23.9 *60.6*	
Calf circ.		8.7 *22.2*	9.1 *23.1*	**9.5** *24.1*	9.9 *25.2*	10.4 *26.3*	
7 Years							
Weight	43.0 *19.5*	45.8 *20.77*	49.7 *22.54*	**54.1** *24.54*	58.7 *26.63*	64.4 *29.21*	69.9 *31.71*
Height	44.9 *114.0*	46.0 *116.9*	47.4 *120.3*	**48.9** *124.1*	50.2 *127.6*	51.4 *130.5*	52.5 *133.4*
Sitting height	24.6 *62.6*	25.2 *64.1*	25.9 *65.8*	**26.6** *67.6*	27.3 *69.4*	28.0 *71.0*	28.5 *72.4*
Pelvic breadth		7.3 *18.5*	7.6 *19.2*	**7.8** *19.9*	8.1 *20.6*	8.4 *21.4*	
Chest circ.		21.6 *54.9*	22.1 *56.1*	**22.8** *57.8*	23.5 *59.8*	24.3 *61.6*	
Calf circ.		8.9 *22.6*	9.3 *23.5*	**9.7** *24.6*	10.1 *25.7*	10.6 *26.9*	
7½ Years							
Weight		48.5 *22.0*	52.6 *23.86*	**57.1** *25.9*	62.1 *28.17*	68.7 *31.16*	
Height		47.2 *120.0*	48.6 *123.5*	**50.0** *127.1*	51.5 *130.9*	52.7 *133.9*	
Sitting height	25.1 *63.7*	25.7 *65.4*	26.4 *67.0*	**27.1** *68.8*	27.8 *70.7*	28.5 *72.3*	29.1 *73.8*
Pelvic breadth		7.4 *18.9*	7.7 *19.6*	**8.0** *20.3*	8.3 *21.0*	8.6 *21.9*	
Chest circ.		22.0 *55.8*	22.5 *57.1*	**23.1** *58.8*	24.0 *61.0*	24.8 *62.9*	
Calf circ.		9.1 *23.1*	9.5 *24.1*	**9.9** *25.2*	10.4 *26.3*	10.9 *27.6*	
8 Years							
Weight	48.0 *21.77*	51.2 *23.22*	55.5 *25.17*	**60.1** *27.26*	65.5 *29.71*	73.0 *33.11*	79.4 *36.02*
Height	47.1 *119.6*	48.5 *123.1*	49.8 *126.6*	**51.2** *130.0*	52.8 *134.2*	54.1 *137.3*	55.2 *140.2*
Sitting height	25.6 *64.9*	26.2 *66.6*	26.9 *68.2*	**27.6** *70.0*	28.3 *72.0*	29.0 *73.6*	29.6 *75.1*
Pelvic breadth		7.6 *19.2*	7.8 *19.9*	**8.1** *20.7*	8.4 *21.4*	8.8 *22.3*	
Chest circ.		22.3 *56.7*	22.8 *58.0*	**23.5** *59.8*	24.4 *62.1*	25.2 *64.1*	
Calf circ.		9.3 *23.6*	9.7 *24.6*	**10.1** *25.7*	10.6 *26.8*	11.1 *28.2*	

Girls

94% of the values for all normal individuals (P₃–P₉₇); 80% of all values (P₁₀–P₉₀); 50% of all values (P₂₅–P₇₅); Mean (P₅₀)

	P_3	P_{10}	P_{25}	P_{50} (Mean)	P_{75}	P_{90}	P_{97}
6½ Years							
Weight		42.2 *19.14*	45.5 *20.64*	**49.4** *22.41*	53.3 *24.18*	57.7 *26.17*	
Height		44.8 *113.7*	45.7 *116.2*	**46.9** *119.1*	48.3 *122.6*	49.4 *125.6*	
Sitting height	24.1 *61.2*	24.6 *62.5*	25.1 *63.8*	**25.7** *65.4*	26.3 *66.9*	26.9 *68.4*	27.6 *70.0*
Pelvic breadth		7.1 *18.1*	7.3 *18.6*	**7.6** *19.2*	7.9 *20.0*	8.3 *21.1*	
Chest circ.		20.6 *52.2*	21.1 *53.7*	**21.8** *55.3*	22.5 *57.2*	23.3 *59.2*	
Calf circ.		8.8 *22.3*	9.1 *23.2*	**9.6** *24.3*	10.0 *25.4*	10.4 *26.4*	
7 Years							
Weight	41.3 *18.73*	44.5 *20.19*	48.1 *21.82*	**52.2** *23.68*	56.3 *25.54*	61.2 *27.76*	67.3 *30.53*
Height	44.9 *114.0*	46.0 *116.8*	46.9 *119.2*	**48.1** *122.3*	49.6 *125.9*	50.7 *128.9*	51.9 *131.7*
Sitting height	24.6 *62.5*	25.1 *63.7*	25.6 *65.0*	**26.2** *66.6*	26.9 *68.2*	27.4 *69.7*	28.1 *71.3*
Pelvic breadth		7.2 *18.4*	7.4 *18.9*	**7.7** *19.6*	8.0 *20.4*	8.5 *21.6*	
Chest circ.		20.8 *52.8*	21.4 *54.4*	**22.1** *56.1*	22.8 *58.0*	23.7 *60.1*	
Calf circ.		8.9 *22.7*	9.3 *23.7*	**9.8** *24.8*	10.2 *25.9*	10.6 *27.0*	
7½ Years							
Weight		46.6 *21.14*	50.6 *22.95*	**55.2** *25.04*	59.8 *27.13*	65.6 *29.76*	
Height		47.0 *119.5*	48.0 *122.0*	**49.3** *125.2*	50.7 *128.8*	51.9 *131.8*	
Sitting height	25.0 *63.6*	25.6 *64.9*	26.1 *66.2*	**26.7** *67.8*	27.3 *69.4*	27.9 *70.9*	28.6 *72.6*
Pelvic breadth		7.4 *18.8*	7.6 *19.3*	**7.9** *20.1*	8.2 *20.9*	8.7 *22.1*	
Chest circ.		21.1 *53.5*	21.7 *55.1*	**22.4** *57.0*	23.2 *59.0*	24.1 *61.2*	
Calf circ.		9.1 *23.1*	9.5 *24.2*	**10.0** *25.3*	10.4 *26.4*	10.9 *27.7*	
8 Years							
Weight	45.3 *20.55*	48.6 *22.04*	53.1 *24.09*	**58.1** *26.35*	63.3 *28.71*	69.9 *31.71*	78.9 *35.79*
Height	46.9 *119.1*	48.1 *122.1*	49.1 *124.8*	**50.4** *128.0*	51.8 *131.6*	53.0 *134.6*	54.1 *137.4*
Sitting height	25.4 *64.6*	25.9 *65.9*	26.5 *67.3*	**27.1** *68.9*	27.8 *70.5*	28.4 *72.1*	29.1 *73.8*
Pelvic breadth		7.5 *19.1*	7.8 *19.7*	**8.1** *20.5*	8.4 *21.3*	8.9 *22.6*	
Chest circ.		21.3 *54.2*	22.0 *55.8*	**22.8** *57.8*	23.6 *59.9*	24.5 *62.3*	
Calf circ.		9.3 *23.5*	9.7 *24.6*	**10.2** *25.8*	10.6 *26.9*	11.1 *28.3*	

1) Quoted by Stuart and Stevenson, in Nelson, W. E. (Ed.), *Textbook of Pediatrics*, 7th ed., Philadelphia, 1959, pages 50–61.

Normal Body Measurements During Growth[1] – 8½ to 10 Years

(Weights are in pounds and *kilograms*, length measurements in inches and *centimeters*)

Boys								Girls						
94% of the values for all normal individuals								94% of the values for all normal individuals						
	80% of all values								80% of all values					
		50% of all values								50% of all values				
			Mean								Mean			
P_3	P_{10}	P_{25}	P_{50}	P_{75}	P_{90}	P_{97}	**8½ Years**	P_3	P_{10}	P_{25}	P_{50}	P_{75}	P_{90}	P_{97}
	53.8 *24.4*	58.3 *26.44*	**63.1** *28.62*	68.9 *31.25*	77.0 *34.93*		Weight		50.6 *22.95*	55.5 *25.17*	**61.0** *27.67*	66.9 *30.35*	74.5 *33.79*	
	49.5 *125.7*	50.8 *129.1*	**52.3** *132.8*	53.9 *137.0*	55.1 *140.0*		Height		49.1 *124.6*	50.1 *127.3*	**51.4** *130.5*	52.9 *134.4*	54.1 *137.5*	
26.0 *66.0*	26.7 *67.7*	27.3 *69.3*	**28.0** *71.2*	28.8 *73.2*	29.4 *74.8*	30.1 *76.4*	Sitting height	25.8 *65.5*	26.3 *66.8*	26.9 *68.2*	**27.5** *69.8*	28.1 *71.4*	28.8 *73.1*	29.5 *74.9*
	7.7 *19.6*	8.0 *20.3*	**8.3** *21.1*	8.6 *21.8*	8.9 *22.7*		Pelvic breadth		7.6 *19.4*	7.9 *20.1*	**8.2** *20.9*	8.6 *21.8*	9.1 *23.1*	
	22.7 *57.6*	23.2 *59.0*	**23.9** *60.8*	24.9 *63.3*	25.7 *65.4*		Chest circ.		21.6 *54.9*	22.2 *56.5*	**23.1** *58.7*	24.0 *60.9*	25.0 *63.5*	
	9.5 *24.1*	9.9 *25.1*	**10.4** *26.3*	10.8 *27.4*	11.4 *28.9*		Calf circ.		9.4 *23.9*	9.8 *25.0*	**10.4** *26.3*	10.8 *27.5*	11.4 *28.9*	
							9 Years							
52.5 *23.81*	56.3 *25.54*	61.1 *27.71*	**66.0** *29.94*	72.3 *32.8*	81.0 *36.74*	89.8 *40.73*	Weight	49.1 *22.27*	52.6 *23.86*	57.9 *26.26*	**63.8** *28.94*	70.5 *31.98*	79.1 *35.88*	89.9 *40.78*
48.9 *124.2*	50.5 *128.3*	51.8 *131.6*	**53.3** *135.5*	55.0 *139.8*	56.1 *142.6*	57.2 *145.3*	Height	48.7 *123.6*	50.0 *127.0*	51.1 *129.7*	**52.3** *132.9*	54.0 *137.1*	55.3 *140.4*	56.5 *143.4*
26.4 *67.0*	27.0 *68.6*	27.7 *70.3*	**28.4** *72.2*	29.2 *74.2*	29.9 *76.0*	30.6 *77.6*	Sitting height	26.1 *66.3*	26.7 *67.7*	27.2 *69.1*	**27.8** *70.7*	28.5 *72.4*	29.2 *74.1*	29.9 *76.0*
	7.8 *19.9*	8.1 *20.6*	**8.4** *21.4*	8.7 *22.2*	9.1 *23.0*		Pelvic breadth		7.8 *19.7*	8.1 *20.5*	**8.4** *21.3*	8.7 *22.2*	9.3 *23.5*	
	23.0 *58.4*	23.6 *59.9*	**24.3** *61.8*	25.4 *64.4*	26.3 *66.7*		Chest circ.		21.9 *55.5*	22.5 *57.2*	**23.5** *59.6*	24.4 *61.9*	25.5 *64.7*	
	9.6 *24.5*	10.1 *25.6*	**10.6** *26.8*	11.0 *28.0*	11.6 *29.5*		Calf circ.		9.5 *24.2*	10.0 *25.4*	**10.6** *26.8*	11.1 *28.1*	11.6 *29.5*	
							9½ Years							
	58.7 *26.63*	63.7 *28.89*	**69.0** *31.3*	76.0 *34.47*	85.5 *38.78*		Weight		54.9 *24.9*	60.4 *27.4*	**67.1** *30.44*	74.8 *33.93*	84.4 *38.28*	
	51.4 *130.6*	52.8 *134.0*	**54.3** *137.9*	55.9 *142.1*	57.1 *145.1*		Height		50.9 *129.4*	52.0 *132.2*	**53.5** *135.8*	55.1 *139.9*	56.4 *143.2*	
26.7 *67.9*	27.4 *69.5*	28.0 *71.2*	**28.8** *73.1*	29.6 *75.2*	30.4 *77.1*	31.0 *78.8*	Sitting height	26.4 *67.1*	27.0 *68.5*	27.6 *70.0*	**28.2** *71.7*	28.9 *73.4*	29.6 *75.2*	30.4 *77.1*
	8.0 *20.2*	8.3 *21.0*	**8.5** *21.7*	8.9 *22.6*	9.3 *23.5*		Pelvic breadth		7.9 *20.1*	8.2 *20.9*	**8.6** *21.8*	9.0 *22.8*	9.5 *24.1*	
	23.3 *59.3*	24.0 *60.9*	**24.8** *62.9*	25.8 *65.5*	26.8 *68.1*		Chest circ.		22.1 *56.2*	22.8 *58.0*	**23.8** *60.5*	24.9 *63.2*	26.0 *66.1*	
	9.8 *24.9*	10.2 *26.0*	**10.7** *27.3*	11.2 *28.5*	11.9 *30.1*		Calf circ.		9.7 *24.7*	10.2 *25.9*	**10.7** *27.3*	11.3 *28.6*	11.9 *30.2*	
							10 Years							
56.8 *25.76*	61.1 *27.71*	66.3 *30.07*	**71.9** *32.61*	79.6 *36.11*	89.9 *40.78*	100.0 *45.36*	Weight	53.2 *24.13*	57.1 *25.9*	62.8 *28.49*	**70.3** *31.89*	79.1 *35.88*	89.7 *40.69*	101.9 *46.22*
50.7 *128.7*	52.3 *132.8*	53.7 *136.3*	**55.2** *140.3*	56.9 *144.4*	58.1 *147.5*	59.2 *150.3*	Height	50.3 *127.7*	51.9 *131.7*	53.0 *134.6*	**54.6** *138.6*	56.1 *142.6*	57.5 *146.0*	58.8 *149.3*
27.1 *68.8*	27.7 *70.3*	28.3 *72.0*	**29.1** *73.9*	30.0 *76.1*	30.7 *78.1*	31.5 *79.9*	Sitting height	26.7 *67.8*	27.3 *69.4*	28.0 *71.1*	**28.7** *72.8*	29.3 *74.5*	30.0 *76.3*	30.8 *78.3*
	8.0 *20.4*	8.4 *21.3*	**8.7** *22.0*	9.0 *22.9*	9.4 *23.9*		Pelvic breadth		8.1 *20.5*	8.3 *21.2*	**8.7** *22.2*	9.2 *23.3*	9.7 *24.6*	
	23.7 *60.1*	24.3 *61.8*	**25.2** *63.9*	26.2 *66.6*	27.3 *69.4*		Chest circ.		22.4 *56.9*	23.1 *58.7*	**24.2** *61.4*	25.4 *64.4*	26.5 *67.4*	
	10.0 *25.3*	10.4 *26.4*	**10.9** *27.7*	11.4 *29.0*	12.1 *30.7*		Calf circ.		9.9 *25.1*	10.4 *26.3*	**10.9** *27.7*	11.5 *29.1*	12.2 *30.9*	

1) Quoted by Stuart and Stevenson, in Nelson, W. E. (Ed.), *Textbook of Pediatrics*, 7th ed., Philadelphia, 1959, pages 50–61.

Normal Body Measurements During Growth[1] – 10½ to 12 Years

(Weights are in pounds and *kilograms*, length measurements in inches and *centimeters*)

	Boys								Girls						
	94% of the values for all normal individuals	80% of all values	50% of all values	Mean					94% of the values for all normal individuals	80% of all values	50% of all values	Mean			
	P_3	P_{10}	P_{25}	P_{50}	P_{75}	P_{90}	P_{97}		P_3	P_{10}	P_{25}	P_{50}	P_{75}	P_{90}	P_{97}
10½ Years															
		63.7 *28.89*	69.0 *31.3*	**74.8** *33.93*	83.4 *37.83*	94.6 *42.91*		Weight		59.9 *27.17*	66.4 *30.12*	**74.5** *33.79*	84.1 *38.15*	95.1 *43.14*	
		53.2 *135.1*	54.5 *138.4*	**56.0** *142.3*	57.8 *146.8*	58.9 *149.7*		Height		52.9 *134.4*	54.1 *137.5*	**55.8** *141.7*	57.4 *145.9*	58.9 *149.7*	
	27.4 *69.6*	28.0 *71.0*	28.6 *72.7*	**29.4** *74.6*	30.3 *76.9*	31.1 *78.9*	31.8 *80.8*	Sitting height	27.0 *68.6*	27.7 *70.4*	28.4 *72.2*	**29.1** *73.9*	29.8 *75.7*	30.6 *77.6*	31.3 *79.6*
		8.2 *20.8*	8.5 *21.6*	**8.8** *22.3*	9.1 *23.2*	9.6 *24.4*		Pelvic breadth		8.3 *21.0*	8.5 *21.7*	**9.0** *22.9*	9.4 *24.0*	10.0 *25.3*	
		24.0 *60.9*	24.7 *62.8*	**25.6** *64.9*	26.7 *67.7*	27.8 *70.7*		Chest circ.		22.8 *57.8*	23.6 *59.9*	**24.7** *62.8*	25.9 *65.8*	27.2 *69.0*	
		10.1 *25.7*	10.6 *26.8*	**11.1** *28.1*	11.6 *29.5*	12.4 *31.4*		Calf circ.		10.1 *25.6*	10.6 *26.8*	**11.1** *28.3*	11.8 *29.9*	12.5 *31.8*	
11 Years															
	61.8 *28.03*	66.3 *30.07*	71.6 *32.48*	**77.6** *35.2*	87.2 *39.55*	99.3 *45.04*	111.7 *50.67*	Weight	57.9 *26.26*	62.6 *28.4*	69.9 *31.71*	**78.8** *35.74*	89.1 *40.42*	100.4 *45.54*	112.9 *51.21*
	52.5 *133.4*	54.1 *137.3*	55.3 *140.5*	**56.8** *144.2*	58.7 *149.2*	59.8 *151.8*	60.8 *154.4*	Height	52.1 *132.3*	53.9 *137.0*	55.2 *140.3*	**57.0** *144.7*	58.7 *149.2*	60.4 *153.4*	62.0 *157.4*
	27.6 *70.2*	28.2 *71.7*	28.9 *73.4*	**29.6** *75.3*	30.6 *77.6*	31.4 *79.8*	32.2 *81.7*	Sitting height	27.4 *69.6*	28.1 *71.5*	28.9 *73.4*	**29.6** *75.3*	30.4 *77.2*	31.2 *79.2*	32.0 *81.2*
		8.3 *21.1*	8.6 *21.8*	**8.9** *22.6*	9.3 *23.5*	9.8 *24.8*		Pelvic breadth		8.4 *21.4*	8.7 *22.2*	**9.3** *23.5*	9.7 *24.6*	10.2 *26.0*	
		24.3 *61.7*	25.1 *63.7*	**25.9** *65.9*	27.1 *68.8*	28.3 *71.9*		Chest circ.		23.1 *58.6*	24.1 *61.1*	**25.3** *64.2*	26.5 *67.2*	27.8 *70.5*	
		10.2 *26.0*	10.7 *27.1*	**11.2** *28.5*	11.8 *30.0*	12.6 *32.0*		Calf circ.		10.2 *26.0*	10.7 *27.3*	**11.4** *28.9*	12.0 *30.6*	12.8 *32.6*	
11½ Years															
		69.2 *31.39*	74.6 *33.84*	**81.0** *36.74*	91.6 *41.55*	104.5 *47.4*		Weight		66.1 *29.98*	74.0 *33.57*	**83.2** *37.74*	94.0 *42.64*	106.0 *48.08*	
		55.0 *139.8*	56.3 *142.9*	**57.8** *146.9*	59.6 *151.4*	60.9 *154.8*		Height		55.0 *139.8*	56.3 *143.1*	**58.3** *148.1*	60.2 *152.9*	61.8 *157.0*	
	27.9 *70.9*	28.5 *72.5*	29.2 *74.2*	**30.0** *76.2*	30.9 *78.5*	31.8 *80.7*	32.6 *82.8*	Sitting height	27.8 *70.7*	28.7 *72.8*	29.4 *74.8*	**30.2** *76.8*	31.1 *78.9*	31.9 *81.0*	32.8 *83.2*
		8.5 *21.5*	8.7 *22.2*	**9.1** *23.1*	9.4 *24.0*	10.0 *25.3*		Pelvic breadth		8.6 *21.9*	9.0 *22.8*	**9.5** *24.2*	10.0 *25.4*	10.6 *26.8*	
		24.6 *62.5*	25.4 *64.6*	**26.3** *66.9*	27.5 *69.9*	28.8 *73.1*		Chest circ.		23.5 *59.6*	24.6 *62.5*	**25.8** *65.5*	27.0 *68.5*	28.4 *72.2*	
		10.4 *26.4*	10.9 *27.6*	**11.4** *29.0*	12.0 *30.6*	12.9 *32.8*		Calf circ.		10.5 *26.6*	11.0 *27.9*	**11.6** *29.5*	12.3 *31.2*	13.1 *33.2*	
12 Years															
	67.2 *30.48*	72.0 *32.66*	77.5 *35.15*	**84.4** *38.28*	96.0 *43.55*	109.6 *49.71*	124.2 *56.34*	Weight	63.6 *28.85*	69.5 *31.52*	78.0 *35.38*	**87.6** *39.74*	98.8 *44.82*	111.5 *50.58*	127.7 *57.92*
	54.4 *138.1*	56.1 *142.4*	57.2 *145.2*	**58.9** *149.6*	60.4 *153.5*	62.2 *157.9*	63.7 *161.9*	Height	54.3 *137.8*	56.1 *142.6*	57.4 *145.9*	**59.8** *151.9*	61.7 *156.6*	63.2 *160.6*	64.8 *164.6*
	28.2 *71.6*	28.9 *73.3*	29.5 *75.0*	**30.4** *77.2*	31.3 *79.6*	32.2 *81.9*	33.1 *84.2*	Sitting height	28.3 *72.0*	29.2 *74.2*	30.1 *76.4*	**31.0** *78.7*	31.8 *80.8*	32.6 *82.9*	33.5 *85.1*
		8.6 *21.9*	8.9 *22.6*	**9.3** *23.5*	9.6 *24.5*	10.2 *25.8*		Pelvic breadth		8.8 *22.4*	9.2 *23.4*	**9.8** *24.9*	10.3 *26.2*	10.9 *27.6*	
		24.9 *63.3*	25.8 *65.5*	**26.7** *67.8*	27.9 *70.9*	29.2 *74.2*		Chest circ.		23.9 *60.6*	25.1 *63.8*	**26.3** *66.7*	27.4 *69.7*	29.1 *73.8*	
		10.6 *26.8*	11.0 *28.0*	**11.6** *29.5*	12.3 *31.2*	13.2 *33.5*		Calf circ.		10.7 *27.1*	11.2 *28.5*	**11.9** *30.1*	12.5 *31.8*	13.3 *33.8*	

1) Quoted by Stuart and Stevenson, in Nelson, W. E. (Ed.), *Textbook of Pediatrics*, 7th ed., Philadelphia, 1959, pages 50–61.

Normal Body Measurements During Growth[1] – 12½ to 14 Years

(Weights are in pounds and *kilograms*, length measurements in inches and *centimeters*)

Boys

	94% of the values for all normal individuals						
		80% of all values					
			50% of all values				
				Mean			
	P_3	P_{10}	P_{25}	P_{50}	P_{75}	P_{90}	P_{97}
12½ Years							
Weight		74.6 *33.84*	80.6 *36.56*	**88.7** *40.23*	102.0 *46.27*	116.4 *52.8*	
Height		56.9 *144.5*	58.1 *147.5*	**60.0** *152.3*	61.9 *157.2*	63.6 *161.6*	
Sitting height	28.5 *72.4*	29.2 *74.1*	29.9 *76.0*	**30.8** *78.3*	31.9 *81.0*	32.8 *83.4*	33.9 *86.0*
Pelvic breadth		8.8 *22.3*	9.1 *23.1*	**9.5** *24.1*	9.9 *25.1*	10.4 *26.5*	
Chest circ.		25.3 *64.2*	26.2 *66.5*	**27.2** *69.1*	28.5 *72.4*	29.8 *75.8*	
Calf circ.		10.7 *27.3*	11.3 *28.6*	**11.9** *30.1*	12.6 *32.0*	13.5 *34.2*	
13 Years							
Weight	72.0 *32.66*	77.1 *34.97*	83.7 *37.97*	**93.0** *42.18*	107.9 *48.94*	123.2 *55.88*	138.0 *62.6*
Height	56.0 *142.2*	57.7 *146.6*	58.9 *149.7*	**61.0** *155.0*	63.3 *160.8*	65.1 *165.3*	66.7 *169.5*
Sitting height	28.9 *73.3*	29.5 *75.0*	30.3 *77.0*	**31.3** *79.6*	32.5 *82.5*	33.6 *85.4*	34.7 *88.1*
Pelvic breadth		8.9 *22.7*	9.3 *23.6*	**9.7** *24.6*	10.1 *25.6*	10.7 *27.2*	
Chest circ.		25.6 *65.0*	26.5 *67.4*	**27.7** *70.3*	29.1 *73.8*	30.5 *77.4*	
Calf circ.		10.9 *27.8*	11.5 *29.2*	**12.1** *30.8*	12.9 *32.7*	13.7 *34.8*	
13½ Years							
Weight		82.2 *37.29*	89.6 *40.64*	**100.3** *45.5*	115.5 *52.39*	130.1 *59.01*	
Height		58.8 *149.4*	60.3 *153.1*	**62.6** *158.9*	64.8 *164.6*	66.5 *168.9*	
Sitting height	29.3 *74.3*	30.0 *76.1*	30.9 *78.4*	**32.0** *81.2*	33.2 *84.3*	34.4 *87.4*	35.4 *89.9*
Pelvic breadth		9.1 *23.2*	9.5 *24.1*	**9.9** *25.2*	10.4 *26.4*	10.9 *27.8*	
Chest circ.		26.1 *66.3*	27.1 *68.8*	**28.5** *72.4*	29.8 *75.8*	31.3 *79.4*	
Calf circ.		11.2 *28.5*	11.8 *29.9*	**12.4** *31.6*	13.1 *33.4*	13.9 *35.3*	
14 Years							
Weight	79.8 *36.2*	87.2 *39.55*	95.5 *43.32*	**107.6** *48.81*	123.1 *55.84*	136.9 *62.1*	150.6 *68.31*
Height	57.6 *146.4*	59.9 *152.1*	61.6 *156.5*	**64.1** *162.7*	66.3 *168.4*	67.9 *172.4*	69.7 *177.1*
Sitting height	29.8 *75.6*	30.5 *77.4*	31.5 *80.0*	**32.6** *82.9*	33.9 *86.1*	35.2 *89.3*	36.0 *91.4*
Pelvic breadth		9.3 *23.6*	9.7 *24.6*	**10.2** *25.8*	10.7 *27.1*	11.1 *28.3*	
Chest circ.		26.6 *67.6*	27.6 *70.2*	**29.3** *74.5*	30.6 *77.8*	32.0 *81.4*	
Calf circ.		11.5 *29.1*	12.0 *30.6*	**12.7** *32.3*	13.4 *34.1*	14.1 *35.8*	

Girls

	94% of the values for all normal individuals						
		80% of all values					
			50% of all values				
				Mean			
	P_3	P_{10}	P_{25}	P_{50}	P_{75}	P_{90}	P_{97}
12½ Years							
Weight		74.7 *33.88*	83.7 *37.97*	**93.4** *42.37*	104.9 *47.58*	118.0 *53.52*	
Height		57.4 *145.9*	58.8 *149.3*	**60.7** *154.3*	62.6 *159.1*	64.1 *162.7*	
Sitting height	29.0 *73.7*	29.9 *76.0*	30.8 *78.2*	**31.6** *80.3*	32.4 *82.4*	33.3 *84.6*	34.2 *86.8*
Pelvic breadth		9.1 *23.0*	9.4 *24.0*	**10.0** *25.5*	10.6 *26.8*	11.1 *28.3*	
Chest circ.		24.3 *61.8*	25.6 *64.9*	**26.7** *67.7*	27.9 *70.9*	29.6 *75.3*	
Calf circ.		10.9 *27.7*	11.5 *29.1*	**12.1** *30.7*	12.8 *32.4*	13.5 *34.3*	
13 Years							
Weight	72.2 *32.75*	79.9 *36.24*	89.4 *40.55*	**99.1** *44.95*	111.0 *50.35*	124.5 *56.47*	142.3 *64.55*
Height	56.6 *143.7*	58.7 *149.1*	60.1 *152.6*	**61.9** *157.1*	63.6 *161.5*	64.9 *164.8*	66.3 *168.4*
Sitting height	29.6 *75.2*	30.5 *77.5*	31.4 *79.7*	**32.2** *81.8*	33.0 *83.8*	33.9 *86.0*	34.7 *88.2*
Pelvic breadth		9.3 *23.6*	9.7 *24.6*	**10.2** *26.0*	10.8 *27.4*	11.4 *29.0*	
Chest circ.		24.8 *62.9*	25.9 *65.9*	**27.0** *68.6*	28.3 *72.0*	30.2 *76.7*	
Calf circ.		11.1 *28.2*	11.7 *29.7*	**12.3** *31.2*	13.0 *32.9*	13.7 *34.8*	
13½ Years							
Weight		85.5 *38.78*	94.6 *42.91*	**103.7** *47.04*	115.4 *52.35*	128.9 *58.47*	
Height		59.5 *151.1*	60.8 *154.4*	**62.4** *158.4*	64.0 *162.6*	65.3 *165.9*	
Sitting height	30.2 *76.6*	31.1 *78.9*	31.9 *81.0*	**32.7** *83.1*	33.5 *85.0*	34.3 *87.0*	35.1 *89.1*
Pelvic breadth		9.5 *24.2*	9.9 *25.2*	**10.4** *26.5*	10.9 *27.8*	11.6 *29.5*	
Chest circ.		25.1 *63.8*	26.2 *66.6*	**27.3** *69.3*	28.7 *72.9*	30.6 *77.7*	
Calf circ.		11.3 *28.7*	11.9 *30.2*	**12.4** *31.6*	13.1 *33.4*	13.8 *35.1*	
14 Years							
Weight	83.1 *37.69*	91.0 *41.28*	99.8 *45.27*	**108.4** *49.17*	119.7 *54.29*	133.3 *60.46*	150.8 *68.4*
Height	58.3 *148.2*	60.2 *153.0*	61.5 *156.1*	**62.8** *159.6*	64.4 *163.7*	65.7 *167.0*	67.2 *170.7*
Sitting height	30.7 *77.9*	31.5 *80.0*	32.2 *81.9*	**33.1** *84.0*	33.8 *85.9*	34.6 *87.8*	35.4 *89.8*
Pelvic breadth		9.8 *24.8*	10.2 *25.8*	**10.6** *26.9*	11.1 *28.1*	11.8 *29.9*	
Chest circ.		25.4 *64.6*	26.5 *67.2*	**27.5** *69.9*	29.0 *73.7*	30.9 *78.6*	
Calf circ.		11.5 *29.2*	12.0 *30.6*	**12.6** *32.0*	13.3 *33.8*	13.9 *35.4*	

1) Quoted by STUART and STEVENSON, in NELSON, W. E. (Ed.), *Textbook of Pediatrics*, 7th ed., Philadelphia, 1959, pages 50–61.

Normal Body Measurements During Growth[1] – 14½ to 16 Years

(Weights are in pounds and *kilograms*, length measurements in inches and *centimeters*)

Boys

94% of the values for all normal individuals (P3–P97); 80% of all values (P10–P90); 50% of all values (P25–P75); Mean (P50)

	P3	P10	P25	P50 (Mean)	P75	P90	P97
14½ Years							
Weight		93.3 *42.32*	101.9 *46.22*	**113.9** *51.66*	129.1 *58.56*	142.4 *64.59*	
Height		61.0 *155.0*	62.8 *159.4*	**65.1** *165.3*	67.2 *170.7*	68.7 *174.6*	
Sitting height	30.3 *77.0*	31.1 *78.9*	32.2 *81.7*	**33.3** *84.7*	34.5 *87.7*	35.7 *90.7*	36.5 *92.7*
Pelvic breadth		9.5 *24.1*	9.9 *25.1*	**10.4** *26.3*	10.8 *27.5*	11.3 *28.7*	
Chest circ.		27.3 *69.4*	28.5 *72.3*	**30.0** *76.3*	31.3 *79.6*	32.7 *83.1*	
Calf circ.		11.7 *29.8*	12.3 *31.3*	**13.0** *32.9*	13.6 *34.6*	14.3 *36.2*	
15 Years							
Weight	91.3 *41.41*	99.4 *45.09*	108.2 *49.08*	**120.1** *54.48*	135.0 *61.23*	147.8 *67.04*	161.6 *73.3*
Height	59.7 *151.7*	62.1 *157.8*	63.9 *162.3*	**66.1** *167.8*	68.1 *173.0*	69.6 *176.7*	71.6 *181.8*
Sitting height	30.9 *78.5*	31.7 *80.6*	32.8 *83.4*	**34.0** *86.3*	35.1 *89.2*	36.2 *91.9*	36.9 *93.7*
Pelvic breadth		9.7 *24.6*	10.1 *25.6*	**10.5** *26.7*	11.0 *27.9*	11.5 *29.1*	
Chest circ.		28.0 *71.1*	29.3 *74.4*	**30.7** *78.0*	32.0 *81.3*	33.4 *84.8*	
Calf circ.		12.0 *30.4*	12.6 *31.9*	**13.1** *33.4*	13.8 *35.1*	14.4 *36.6*	
15½ Years							
Weight		105.2 *47.72*	113.5 *51.48*	**124.9** *56.65*	139.7 *63.37*	152.6 *69.22*	
Height		63.1 *160.3*	64.8 *164.7*	**66.8** *169.7*	68.8 *174.8*	70.2 *178.2*	
Sitting height	31.6 *80.3*	32.5 *82.5*	33.5 *85.0*	**34.5** *87.7*	35.6 *90.4*	36.5 *92.8*	37.2 *94.6*
Pelvic breadth		9.9 *25.1*	10.2 *26.0*	**10.7** *27.1*	11.1 *28.2*	11.6 *29.4*	
Chest circ.		28.7 *72.8*	29.8 *75.8*	**31.3** *79.4*	32.6 *82.9*	34.0 *86.3*	
Calf circ.		12.2 *30.9*	12.7 *32.3*	**13.3** *33.8*	14.0 *35.5*	14.6 *37.0*	
16 Years							
Weight	103.4 *46.9*	111.0 *50.35*	118.7 *53.84*	**129.7** *58.83*	144.4 *65.5*	157.3 *71.35*	170.5 *77.34*
Height	61.6 *156.5*	64.1 *162.8*	65.8 *167.1*	**67.6** *171.6*	69.5 *176.6*	70.7 *179.7*	73.1 *185.6*
Sitting height	32.3 *82.0*	33.1 *84.1*	34.0 *86.4*	**35.0** *88.9*	36.0 *91.4*	36.9 *93.6*	37.5 *95.3*
Pelvic breadth		10.1 *25.6*	10.4 *26.4*	**10.8** *27.4*	11.2 *28.4*	11.7 *29.6*	
Chest circ.		29.3 *74.4*	30.4 *77.2*	**31.8** *80.7*	33.3 *84.5*	34.6 *87.8*	
Calf circ.		12.3 *31.3*	12.9 *32.7*	**13.5** *34.2*	14.1 *35.8*	14.7 *37.3*	

Girls

94% of the values for all normal individuals (P3–P97); 80% of all values (P10–P90); 50% of all values (P25–P75); Mean (P50)

	P3	P10	P25	P50 (Mean)	P75	P90	P97
14½ Years							
Weight		94.2 *42.73*	102.5 *46.49*	**111.0** *50.35*	121.8 *55.25*	135.7 *61.55*	
Height		60.7 *154.1*	61.8 *156.9*	**63.1** *160.4*	64.7 *164.3*	66.0 *167.6*	
Sitting height	31.1 *79.1*	31.9 *80.9*	32.6 *82.7*	**33.3** *84.7*	34.1 *86.6*	34.8 *88.4*	35.5 *90.2*
Pelvic breadth		9.9 *25.2*	10.3 *26.2*	**10.7** *27.2*	11.2 *28.4*	11.9 *30.3*	
Chest circ.		25.6 *65.1*	26.7 *67.7*	**27.7** *70.4*	29.2 *74.2*	31.2 *79.2*	
Calf circ.		11.7 *29.6*	12.2 *30.9*	**12.7** *32.3*	13.4 *34.1*	14.1 *35.7*	
15 Years							
Weight	89.0 *40.37*	97.4 *44.18*	105.1 *47.67*	**113.5** *51.48*	123.9 *56.2*	138.1 *62.64*	155.2 *70.4*
Height	59.1 *150.2*	61.1 *155.2*	62.1 *157.7*	**63.4** *161.1*	64.9 *164.9*	66.2 *168.1*	67.6 *171.6*
Sitting height	31.5 *80.0*	32.2 *81.7*	32.8 *83.4*	**33.5** *85.2*	34.3 *87.0*	34.9 *88.7*	35.6 *90.4*
Pelvic breadth		10.1 *25.6*	10.4 *26.5*	**10.8** *27.5*	11.3 *28.7*	12.0 *30.6*	
Chest circ.		25.8 *65.5*	26.8 *68.1*	**27.9** *70.9*	29.4 *74.7*	31.4 *79.8*	
Calf circ.		11.8 *29.9*	12.2 *31.1*	**12.8** *32.6*	13.5 *34.3*	14.1 *35.9*	
15½ Years							
Weight		99.2 *45.0*	106.8 *48.44*	**115.3** *52.3*	125.6 *56.97*	139.6 *63.32*	
Height		61.3 *155.7*	62.3 *158.2*	**63.7** *161.7*	65.1 *165.3*	66.4 *168.6*	
Sitting height	31.8 *80.7*	32.4 *82.3*	33.0 *83.9*	**33.7** *85.6*	34.4 *87.4*	35.0 *89.0*	35.6 *90.5*
Pelvic breadth		10.2 *25.9*	10.5 *26.7*	**10.9** *27.8*	11.4 *29.0*	12.1 *30.8*	
Chest circ.		25.9 *65.8*	26.9 *68.4*	**28.1** *71.3*	29.6 *75.1*	31.6 *80.2*	
Calf circ.		11.9 *30.1*	12.4 *31.4*	**13.0** *32.9*	13.6 *34.5*	14.2 *36.1*	
16 Years							
Weight	91.8 *41.64*	100.9 *45.77*	108.4 *49.17*	**117.0** *53.07*	127.2 *57.7*	141.1 *64.0*	157.7 *71.53*
Height	59.4 *150.8*	61.5 *156.1*	62.4 *158.6*	**63.9** *162.2*	65.2 *165.7*	66.5 *169.0*	67.7 *172.0*
Sitting height	32.0 *81.2*	32.6 *82.7*	33.1 *84.2*	**33.8** *85.9*	34.5 *87.6*	35.1 *89.1*	35.7 *90.6*
Pelvic breadth		10.3 *26.1*	10.6 *26.9*	**11.0** *28.0*	11.5 *29.2*	12.2 *31.0*	
Chest circ.		26.0 *66.1*	27.0 *68.7*	**28.2** *71.6*	29.7 *75.4*	31.7 *80.5*	
Calf circ.		11.9 *30.3*	12.4 *31.6*	**13.0** *33.1*	13.6 *34.6*	14.3 *36.3*	

[1] Quoted by Stuart and Stevenson, in Nelson, W. E. (Ed.), *Textbook of Pediatrics*, 7th ed., Philadelphia, 1959, pages 50–61.

Normal Body Measurements During Growth[1] – 16½ to 18 Years

(Weights are in pounds and *kilograms*, length measurements in inches and *centimeters*)

94% of the values for all normal individuals: P_3–P_{97}; 80% of all values: P_{10}–P_{90}; 50% of all values: P_{25}–P_{75}; Mean: P_{50}

Boys

Age	Measurement	P_3	P_{10}	P_{25}	P_{50} (Mean)	P_{75}	P_{90}	P_{97}
16½ Years	Weight		114.3 *51.85*	121.6 *55.16*	**133.0** *60.33*	147.9 *67.09*	161.0 *73.03*	
	Height		64.6 *164.2*	66.3 *168.4*	**68.0** *172.7*	69.8 *177.4*	71.1 *180.7*	
	Sitting height	32.8 *83.2*	33.5 *85.2*	34.4 *87.5*	**35.4** *89.8*	36.3 *92.1*	37.1 *94.2*	37.8 *95.9*
	Pelvic breadth		10.2 *25.9*	10.5 *26.7*	**10.9** *27.6*	11.3 *28.6*	11.7 *29.8*	
	Chest circ.		29.7 *75.4*	30.7 *78.1*	**32.1** *81.6*	33.6 *85.4*	35.0 *88.8*	
	Calf circ.		12.4 *31.5*	13.0 *32.9*	**13.5** *34.4*	14.2 *36.1*	14.8 *37.6*	
17 Years	Weight	110.5 *50.12*	117.5 *53.3*	124.5 *56.47*	**136.2** *61.78*	151.4 *68.67*	164.6 *74.66*	175.6 *79.65*
	Height	62.6 *159.0*	65.2 *165.5*	66.8 *169.7*	**68.4** *173.7*	70.1 *178.1*	71.5 *181.6*	73.5 *186.6*
	Sitting height	33.0 *83.9*	33.9 *86.0*	34.8 *88.4*	**35.6** *90.4*	36.5 *92.7*	37.2 *94.6*	38.0 *96.4*
	Pelvic breadth		10.3 *26.1*	10.6 *26.9*	**10.9** *27.8*	11.3 *28.7*	11.8 *29.9*	
	Chest circ.		30.1 *76.4*	31.1 *78.9*	**32.5** *82.5*	33.9 *86.2*	35.3 *89.7*	
	Calf circ.		12.5 *31.7*	13.0 *33.1*	**13.6** *34.6*	14.3 *36.3*	14.9 *37.8*	
17½ Years	Weight		118.8 *53.89*	125.8 *57.06*	**137.6** *62.41*	153.6 *69.67*	166.8 *75.66*	
	Height		65.3 *165.9*	67.0 *170.1*	**68.5** *174.1*	70.3 *178.5*	71.7 *182.0*	
	Sitting height	33.2 *84.4*	34.1 *86.5*	35.0 *88.8*	**35.7** *90.7*	36.7 *93.1*	37.4 *94.9*	38.1 *96.7*
	Pelvic breadth		10.4 *26.3*	10.6 *27.0*	**11.0** *27.9*	11.3 *28.8*	11.8 *30.0*	
	Chest circ.		30.3 *77.0*	31.3 *79.4*	**32.7** *83.0*	34.1 *86.7*	35.5 *90.2*	
	Calf circ.		12.5 *31.8*	13.1 *33.3*	**13.7** *34.8*	14.4 *36.5*	15.0 *38.0*	
18 Years	Weight	113.0 *51.26*	120.0 *54.43*	127.1 *57.65*	**139.0** *63.05*	155.7 *70.62*	169.0 *76.66*	179.0 *81.19*
	Height	62.8 *159.6*	65.5 *166.3*	67.1 *170.5*	**68.7** *174.5*	70.4 *178.9*	71.8 *182.4*	73.9 *187.6*
	Sitting height	33.3 *84.7*	34.2 *86.8*	35.0 *89.0*	**35.8** *90.9*	36.8 *93.4*	37.4 *95.0*	38.1 *96.8*
	Pelvic breadth		10.4 *26.5*	10.7 *27.1*	**11.0** *28.0*	11.4 *28.9*	11.9 *30.1*	
	Chest circ.		30.5 *77.5*	31.4 *79.8*	**32.8** *83.4*	34.3 *87.1*	35.7 *90.7*	
	Calf circ.		12.6 *31.9*	13.1 *33.4*	**13.7** *34.9*	14.4 *36.6*	15.0 *38.1*	

Girls

Age	Measurement	P_3	P_{10}	P_{25}	P_{50} (Mean)	P_{75}	P_{90}	P_{97}
16½ Years	Weight		101.9 *46.22*	109.4 *49.62*	**118.1** *53.57*	128.4 *58.24*	142.2 *64.5*	
	Height		61.5 *156.2*	62.5 *158.8*	**63.9** *162.4*	65.3 *165.9*	66.6 *169.2*	
	Sitting height	32.0 *81.4*	32.6 *82.9*	33.2 *84.4*	**33.9** *86.1*	34.5 *87.7*	35.1 *89.2*	35.7 *90.7*
	Pelvic breadth		10.3 *26.2*	10.6 *27.0*	**11.1** *28.2*	11.5 *29.3*	12.2 *31.1*	
	Chest circ.		26.1 *66.3*	27.2 *69.0*	**28.3** *71.9*	29.8 *75.7*	31.8 *80.7*	
	Calf circ.		12.0 *30.5*	12.5 *31.8*	**13.1** *33.3*	13.7 *34.8*	14.4 *36.5*	
17 Years	Weight	93.9 *42.59*	102.8 *46.63*	110.4 *50.08*	**119.1** *54.02*	129.6 *58.79*	143.3 *65.0*	159.5 *72.35*
	Height	59.4 *151.0*	61.5 *156.3*	62.6 *159.0*	**64.0** *162.5*	65.4 *166.1*	66.7 *169.4*	67.8 *172.2*
	Sitting height	32.1 *81.6*	32.7 *83.1*	33.3 *84.6*	**33.9** *86.2*	34.6 *87.8*	35.2 *89.3*	35.7 *90.8*
	Pelvic breadth		10.4 *26.3*	10.7 *27.1*	**11.1** *28.3*	11.6 *29.4*	12.3 *31.2*	
	Chest circ.		26.1 *66.4*	27.2 *69.2*	**28.4** *72.1*	29.9 *75.9*	31.9 *80.9*	
	Calf circ.		12.0 *30.6*	12.6 *31.9*	**13.1** *33.4*	13.7 *34.9*	14.4 *36.6*	
17½ Years	Weight		103.2 *46.81*	110.8 *50.26*	**119.5** *54.2*	130.2 *59.06*	143.9 *65.27*	
	Height		61.5 *156.3*	62.6 *159.0*	**64.0** *162.5*	65.4 *166.1*	66.7 *169.4*	
	Sitting height	32.2 *81.7*	32.8 *83.2*	33.3 *84.7*	**34.0** *86.3*	34.6 *87.9*	35.2 *89.4*	35.7 *90.8*
	Pelvic breadth		10.4 *26.4*	10.7 *27.2*	**11.2** *28.4*	11.6 *29.5*	12.3 *31.3*	
	Chest circ.		26.2 *66.5*	27.3 *69.3*	**28.4** *72.2*	29.9 *76.0*	31.9 *81.0*	
	Calf circ.		12.1 *30.7*	12.6 *32.0*	**13.2** *33.5*	13.8 *35.0*	14.4 *36.7*	
18 Years	Weight	94.5 *42.87*	103.5 *46.95*	111.2 *50.44*	**119.9** *54.39*	130.8 *59.33*	144.5 *65.54*	160.7 *72.89*
	Height	59.4 *151.0*	61.5 *156.3*	62.6 *159.0*	**64.0** *162.5*	65.4 *166.1*	66.7 *169.4*	67.8 *172.2*
	Sitting height	32.2 *81.7*	32.8 *83.2*	33.3 *84.7*	**34.0** *86.3*	34.6 *87.9*	35.2 *89.4*	35.7 *90.8*
	Pelvic breadth		10.4 *26.4*	10.7 *27.2*	**11.2** *28.4*	11.6 *29.5*	12.3 *31.3*	
	Chest circ.		26.2 *66.6*	27.3 *69.4*	**28.5** *72.3*	30.0 *76.1*	31.9 *81.1*	
	Calf circ.		12.1 *30.8*	12.6 *32.1*	**13.2** *33.6*	13.8 *35.1*	14.5 *36.8*	

1) Quoted by Stuart and Stevenson; in Nelson, W. E. (Ed.), *Textbook of Pediatrics*, 7th ed., Philadelphia, 1959, pages 50–61.

Average Weights of Adults[1]

Height (in shoes)		Average weights in pounds and *kilograms* (in indoor clothing)															
		15–16 years		17–19 years		20–24 years		25–29 years		30–39 years		40–49 years		50–59 years		60–69 years	
ft in	*cm*	lb	*kg*	lb	*kg*	lb	*kg*	lb	*kg*	lb	*kg*	lb	*kg*	lb	*kg*	lb	*kg*
Men																	
5 0	152.4	98	44.5	113	51.3	122	55.3	128	58.1	131	59.4	134	60.8	136	61.7	133	60.3
5 0½	153.7	100	45.4	114.5	51.9	123.5	56	129.5	58.7	132.5	60.1	135.5	61.5	137.5	62.4	134.5	61
5 1	154.9	102	46.3	116	52.6	125	56.7	131	59.4	134	60.8	137	62.1	139	63	136	61.7
5 1½	156.2	104.5	47.4	117.5	53.3	126.5	57.4	132.5	60.1	135.5	61.5	138.5	62.8	140.5	63.7	137.5	62.4
5 2	157.5	107	48.5	119	54	128	58.1	134	60.8	137	62.1	140	63.5	142	64.4	139	63
5 2½	158.8	109.5	49.7	121	54.9	130	59	136	61.7	139	63	142	64.4	143.5	65.1	140.5	63.7
5 3	160	112	50.8	123	55.8	132	59.9	138	62.6	141	64	144	65.3	145	65.8	142	64.4
5 3½	161.3	114.5	51.9	125	56.7	134	60.8	139.5	63.3	143	64.9	146	66.2	147	66.7	144	65.3
5 4	162.6	117	53.1	127	57.6	136	61.7	141	64	145	65.8	148	67.1	149	67.6	146	66.2
5 4½	163.8	119.5	54.2	129	58.5	137.5	62.4	142.5	64.6	147	66.7	150	68	151	68.5	148	67.1
5 5	165.1	122	55.3	131	59.4	139	63	144	65.3	149	67.6	152	68.9	153	69.4	150	68
5 5½	166.4	124.5	56.5	133	60.3	140.5	63.7	146	66.2	151	68.5	154	69.9	155	70.3	152	68.9
5 6	167.6	127	57.6	135	61.2	142	64.4	148	67.1	153	69.4	156	70.8	157	71.2	154	69.9
5 6½	168.9	129.5	58.7	137	62.1	143.5	65.1	149.5	67.8	155	70.3	158.5	71.9	159.5	72.3	156.5	71
5 7	170.2	132	59.9	139	63	145	65.8	151	68.5	157	71.2	161	73	162	73.5	159	72.1
5 7½	171.5	134.5	61	141	64	147	66.7	153	69.4	159	72.1	163	73.9	164	74.4	161	73
5 8	172.7	137	62.1	143	64.9	149	67.6	155	70.3	161	73	165	74.8	166	75.3	163	73.9
5 8½	174	139.5	63.3	145	65.8	151	68.5	157	71.2	163	73.9	167	75.8	168	76.2	165.5	75.1
5 9	175.3	142	64.4	147	66.7	153	69.4	159	72.1	165	74.8	169	76.7	170	77.1	168	76.2
5 9½	176.5	144	65.3	149	67.6	155	70.3	161	73	167.5	76	171.5	77.8	172.5	78.2	170.5	77.3
5 10	177.8	146	66.2	151	68.5	157	71.2	163	73.9	170	77.1	174	78.9	175	79.4	173	78.5
5 10½	179.1	148	67.1	153	69.4	159	72.1	165	74.8	172	78	176	79.8	177.5	80.5	175.5	79.6
5 11	180.3	150	68	155	70.3	161	73	167	75.8	174	78.9	178	80.8	180	81.6	178	80.8
5 11½	181.6	152	68.9	157.5	71.4	163.5	74.2	169.5	76.9	176.5	80.1	180.5	81.9	182.5	82.8	180.5	81.9
6 0	182.9	154	69.9	160	72.6	166	75.3	172	78	179	81.2	183	83	185	83.9	183	83
6 0½	184.2	156.5	71	162	73.5	168	76.2	174.5	79.2	181	82.1	185	83.9	187	84.8	185.5	84.1
6 1	185.4	159	72.1	164	74.4	170	77.1	177	80.3	183	83	187	84.8	189	85.7	188	85.3
6 1½	186.7	161.5	73.3	166	75.3	172	78	179.5	81.4	185.5	84.1	189.5	86	191.5	86.9	190.5	86.4
6 2	188	164	74.4	168	76.2	174	78.9	182	82.6	188	85.3	192	87.1	194	88	193	87.5
6 2½	189.2	166.5	75.5	170	77.1	176	79.8	184	83.5	190.5	86.4	194.5	88.2	196.5	89.1	195.5	88.7
6 3	190.5	169	76.7	172	78	178	80.8	186	84.4	193	87.5	197	89.4	199	90.3	198	89.8
6 3½	191.8	–	–	174	78.9	179.5	81.4	188	85.3	196	88.9	200	90.7	202	91.6	201	91.2
6 4	193	–	–	176	79.8	181	82.1	190	86.2	199	90.3	203	92.1	205	93	204	92.5
Women																	
4 10	147.3	97	44	99	44.9	102	46.3	107	48.5	115	52.2	122	55.3	125	56.7	127	57.6
4 10½	148.6	98.5	44.7	100.5	45.6	103.5	46.9	108.5	49.2	116	52.6	123	55.8	126	57.2	128	58.1
4 11	149.9	100	45.4	102	46.3	105	47.6	110	49.9	117	53.1	124	56.2	127	57.6	129	58.5
4 11½	151.1	101.5	46	103.5	46.9	106.5	48.3	111.5	50.6	118.5	53.8	125.5	56.9	128.5	58.3	130	59
5 0	152.4	103	46.7	105	47.6	108	49	113	51.3	120	54.4	127	57.6	130	59	131	59.4
5 0½	153.7	105	47.6	107	48.5	110	49.9	114.5	51.9	121.5	55.1	128.5	58.3	131.5	59.6	132.5	60.1
5 1	154.9	107	48.5	109	49.4	112	50.8	116	52.6	123	55.8	130	59	133	60.3	134	60.8
5 1½	156.2	109	49.4	111	50.3	113.5	51.5	117.5	53.3	124.5	56.5	131.5	59.6	134.5	61	135.5	61.5
5 2	157.5	111	50.3	113	51.3	115	52.2	119	54	126	57.2	133	60.3	136	61.7	137	62.1
5 2½	158.8	112.5	51	114.5	51.9	116.5	52.8	120.5	54.7	127.5	57.8	134.5	61	138	62.6	139	63
5 3	160	114	51.7	116	52.6	118	53.5	122	55.3	129	58.5	136	61.7	140	63.5	141	64
5 3½	161.3	115.5	52.4	118	53.5	119.5	54.2	123.5	56	130.5	59.2	138	62.6	142	64.4	143	64.9
5 4	162.6	117	53.1	120	54.4	121	54.9	125	56.7	132	59.9	140	63.5	144	65.3	145	65.8
5 4½	163.8	119	54	122	55.3	123	55.8	127	57.6	133.5	60.6	141.5	64.2	146	66.2	147	66.7
5 5	165.1	121	54.9	124	56.2	125	56.7	129	58.5	135	61.2	143	64.9	148	67.1	149	67.6
5 5½	166.4	123	55.8	125.5	56.9	127	57.6	131	59.4	137	62.1	145	65.8	150	68	151	68.5
5 6	167.6	125	56.7	127	57.6	129	58.5	133	60.3	139	63	147	66.7	152	68.9	153	69.4
5 6½	168.9	126.5	57.4	128.5	58.3	130.5	59.2	134.5	61	140.5	63.7	149	67.6	154	69.9	155	70.3
5 7	170.2	128	58.1	130	59	132	59.9	136	61.7	142	64.4	151	68.5	156	70.8	157	71.2
5 7½	171.5	130	59	132	59.9	134	60.8	138	62.6	144	65.3	153	69.4	158	71.7	159	72.1
5 8	172.7	132	59.9	134	60.8	136	61.7	140	63.5	146	66.2	155	70.3	160	72.6	161	73
5 8½	174	134	60.8	136	61.7	138	62.6	142	64.4	148	67.1	157	71.2	162	73.5	163	73.9
5 9	175.3	136	61.7	138	62.6	140	63.5	144	65.3	150	68	159	72.1	164	74.4	165	74.8
5 9½	176.5	–	–	140	63.5	142	64.4	146	66.2	152	68.9	161.5	73.3	166.5	75.5	–	–
5 10	177.8	–	–	142	64.4	144	65.3	148	67.1	154	69.9	164	74.4	169	76.7	–	–
5 10½	179.1	–	–	144.5	65.5	146.5	66.5	150.5	68.3	156.5	71	166.5	75.5	171.5	77.8	–	–
5 11	180.3	–	–	147	66.7	149	67.6	153	69.4	159	72.1	169	76.7	174	78.9	–	–
5 11½	181.6	–	–	149.5	67.8	151.5	68.7	155.5	70.5	161.5	73.3	171.5	77.8	177	80.3	–	–
6 0	182.9	–	–	152	68.9	154	69.9	158	71.7	164	74.4	174	78.9	180	81.6	–	–

1) Insured persons in the United States. From Society of Actuaries, *Build and Blood Pressure Study*, vol. I, Chicago, 1959, page 16, with interpolations by the editors of these *Scientific Tables*.

Desirable Weights of Adults[1]

Height (in shoes)			Desirable weight in pounds and *kilograms* (in indoor clothing), ages 25 and over					
			Small frame		Medium frame		Large frame	
ft	in	*cm*	lb	*kg*	lb	*kg*	lb	*kg*
					Men			
5	2	*157.5*	112–120	*50.8–54.4*	118–129	*53.5–58.5*	126–141	*57.2–64*
5	3	*160*	115–123	*52.2–55.8*	121–133	*54.9–60.3*	129–144	*58.5–65.3*
5	4	*162.6*	118–126	*53.5–57.2*	124–136	*56.2–61.7*	132–148	*59.9–67.1*
5	5	*165.1*	121–129	*54.9–58.5*	127–139	*57.6–63*	135–152	*61.2–68.9*
5	6	*167.6*	124–133	*56.2–60.3*	130–143	*59 –64.9*	138–156	*62.6–70.8*
5	7	*170.2*	128–137	*58.1–62.1*	134–147	*60.8–66.7*	142–161	*64.4–73*
5	8	*172.7*	132–141	*59.9–64*	138–152	*62.6–68.9*	147–166	*66.7–75.3*
5	9	*175.3*	136–145	*61.7–65.8*	142–156	*64.4–70.8*	151–170	*68.5–77.1*
5	10	*177.8*	140–150	*63.5–68*	146–160	*66.2–72.6*	155–174	*70.3–78.9*
5	11	*180.3*	144–154	*65.3–69.9*	150–165	*68 –74.8*	159–179	*72.1–81.2*
6	0	*182.9*	148–158	*67.1–71.7*	154–170	*69.9–77.1*	164–184	*74.4–83.5*
6	1	*185.4*	152–162	*68.9–73.5*	158–175	*71.7–79.4*	168–189	*76.2–85.7*
6	2	*188*	156–167	*70.8–75.7*	162–180	*73.5–81.6*	173–194	*78.5–88*
6	3	*190.5*	160–171	*72.6–77.6*	167–185	*75.7–83.5*	178–199	*80.7–90.3*
6	4	*193*	164–175	*74.4–79.4*	172–190	*78.1–86.2*	182–204	*82.7–92.5*
					Women			
4	10	*147.3*	92– 98	*41.7–44.5*	96–107	*43.5–48.5*	104–119	*47.2–54*
4	11	*149.9*	94–101	*42.6–45.8*	98–110	*44.5–49.9*	106–122	*48.1–55.3*
5	0	*152.4*	96–104	*43.5–47.2*	101–113	*45.8–51.3*	109–125	*49.4–56.7*
5	1	*154.9*	99–107	*44.9–48.5*	104–116	*47.2–52.6*	112–128	*50.8–58.1*
5	2	*157.5*	102–110	*46.3–49.9*	107–119	*48.5–54*	115–131	*52.2–59.4*
5	3	*160*	105–113	*47.6–51.3*	110–122	*49.9–55.3*	118–134	*53.5–60.8*
5	4	*162.6*	108–116	*49 –52.6*	113–126	*51.3–57.2*	121–138	*54.9–62.6*
5	5	*165.1*	111–119	*50.3–54*	116–130	*49 –59*	125–142	*49.4–64.4*
5	6	*167.6*	114–123	*51.7–55.8*	120–135	*54.4–61.2*	129–146	*58.5–66.2*
5	7	*170.2*	118–127	*53.5–57.6*	124–139	*56.2–63*	133–150	*60.3–68*
5	8	*172.7*	122–131	*55.3–59.4*	128–143	*58.1–64.9*	137–154	*62.1–69.9*
5	9	*175.3*	126–135	*57.2–61.2*	132–147	*59.9–66.7*	141–158	*64 –71.7*
5	10	*177.8*	130–140	*59 –63.5*	136–151	*61.7–68.5*	145–163	*65.8–73.9*
5	11	*180.3*	134–144	*60.8–65.3*	140–155	*63.5–70.3*	149–168	*67.6–76.2*
6	0	*182.9*	138–148	*62.6–67.1*	144–159	*65.3–72.1*	153–173	*69.4–78.5*

1) Weights of insured persons in the United States associated with lowest mortality. From *Metropolitan Life Insurance Company Statistical Bulletin*, **40**, Nov.–Dec. 1959.

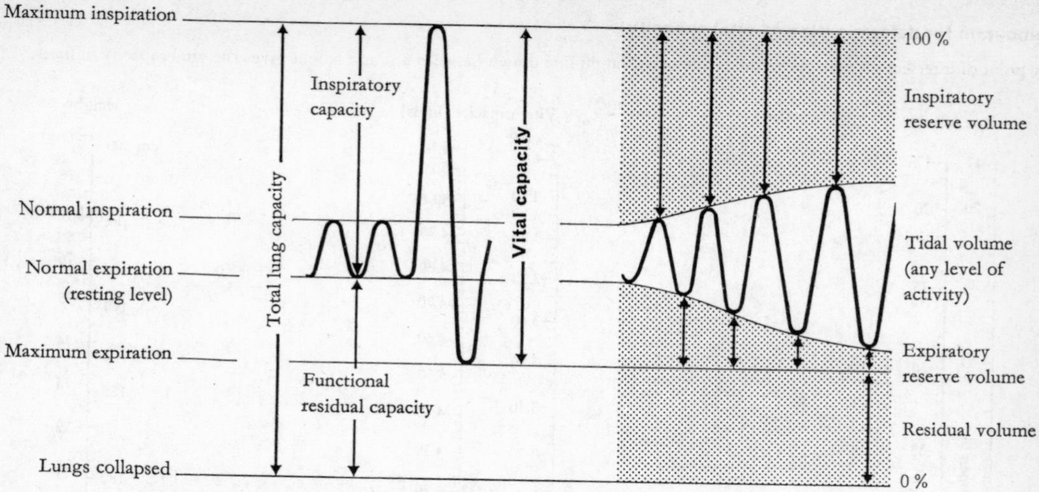

Definition of lung volume and standardized terms (from Comroe et al., *Fed. Proc.*, **9**, 602 [1950])

Normal lung volume of resting adults

From Kaltreider et al., *Amer. Rev. Tuberc.*, **37**, 662 (1938)

	50 men		50 women	
	Mean	*s*	Mean	*s*
Age (years)	22.9	3.3	23.1	3.4
Height (cm)	176.2	5.1	163.4	4.2
Weight (kg)	72.5	11.2	57.2	9.4
Inspiratory capacity (liters)	3.79	0.52	2.42	0.36
Expiratory reserve volume (liters)	0.98	0.26	0.73	0.19
Vital capacity (liters)	4.78	0.59	3.14	0.41
Residual volume (liters)	1.19	0.35	1.10	0.30
Functional residual capacity (liters)	2.18	0.50	1.82	0.39
Total lung capacity (liters)	5.97	0.81	4.24	0.57

Lung ventilation

Values for children from Spector, W. S. (Ed.), *Handbook of Biological Data*, Philadelphia, 1956, page 267; values for adults from Taylor, C., *Amer. J. Physiol.*, **135**, 27 (1941–42)

	Respiration frequency		Tidal volume		Minute volume*	
	Rate per minute		Milliliters		Liters	
	Mean	Range	Mean	Range	Mean	Range
Premature	33	–	12.4	8.4–17.3	0.41	0.28–0.58
Newborn, asleep	43	24–116	16.7	10.0–27	0.72	0.43–1.41
Adults						
Men (3 subjects):						
resting	11.7	10.1–13.1	750	757–895	7.4	5.8–10.3
light work	17.1	15.7–18.2	1670	1510–1770	29	27–31
heavy work	21.2	18.6–23.3	2030	1900–2110	60	50–90
Women (2 subj.):						
resting	11.7	10.4–13.0	339	285–393	4.5	4.0–7.0
light work	19	–	860	836–885	16.3	15.9–16.8
heavy work**	30	25–33	880	490–1270	24.5	17.3–32.0

* Minute volume = respiratory frequency × tidal volume.
** One subject near collapse at end.

Vital capacity of normal boys and girls

From Stewart C. A., *Amer. J. Dis. Child.*, **24**, 451 (1922)

Age in years	Number of cases	Height (cm)	Vital capacity in milliliters: Average	Minimum	Maximum	*s*
Normal boys						
4	6	103.4	792	500	900	
5	20	106.8	927	600	1150	
6	62	112.2	1154	800	1600	182
7	112	116.9	1290	900	2200	194
8	98	121.8	1468	1050	2100	220
9	110	129.9	1715	1200	2300	246
10	87	133.4	1872	1400	2650	262
11	113	137.8	1991	1300	2800	270
12	114	142.4	2182	1300	3300	340
13	132	148.7	2458	1700	4000	430
14	177	154.8	2712	1400	4300	484
15	155	159.9	3145	1850	4400	551
16	67	167.2	3425	2100	4300	573
17	23	171.4	3776	2400	4500	
Normal girls						
4	9	95.4	664	350	850	
5	26	106.4	888	600	1200	
6	62	111.5	1085	700	1600	163
7	81	114.4	1228	900	1800	181
8	76	121.0	1401	800	1950	199
9	73	127.0	1513	1000	2250	229
10	117	132.1	1672	900	2400	273
11	119	135.9	1799	1250	2550	241
12	135	144.0	2053	1400	2900	343
13	162	151.4	2349	1550	3600	409
14	192	156.6	2607	1900	3800	361
15	131	157.8	2702	1900	3700	413
16	29	160.1	2778	2050	3500	
17	7	162.6	2943	2250	3400	

For diminution of vital capacity with age in adults see the nomogram on the following page.

Nomogram for determination of vital capacity[1]

The point of intersection with the middle scale of a straight line drawn between age and height gives the vital capacity in liters.

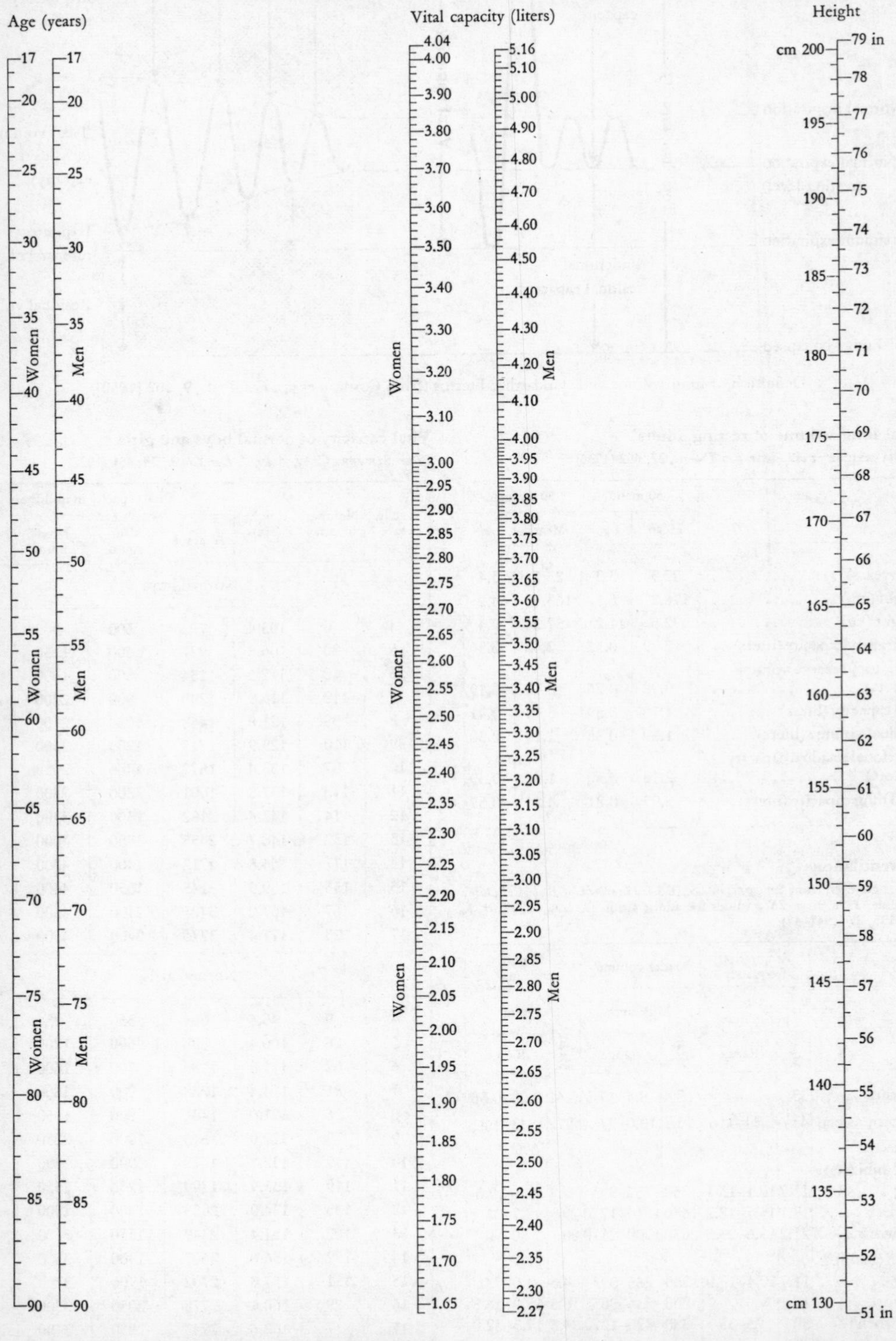

* Reproduction only by permission of the publishers of these *Scientific Tables.*

1) From the formula of COURNAND, A., quoted by ROSSIER et al., *Physiologie und Pathophysiologie der Atmung*, 2nd ed., Berlin, 1958, page 95: vital capacity of men = $[27.63 - (0.112 \times A)] \times H$; vital capacity of women = $[21.78 - (0.101 \times A)] \times H$ (in liters, A = age in years, H = height in centimeters).

Definition

The basal metabolism (or basic metabolic rate, B.M.R.) is the minimal heat produced by the fasting individual, physically and mentally at rest, at room temperature (ca. 20° C). It represents the energy expended to maintain the vegetative functions, such as respiration, circulation, body temperature, etc.

The basal metabolism is primarily dependent on the surface area of the body and secondarily on age and sex (see the ideal values of various standards on the following pages). It is physiologically increased during menstruation and pregnancy (see the diagram below and page 630).

Variations up to ± 10% of the ideal value are regarded as normal, occasionally also larger variations (the probability of the normality of an observed B.M.R. value can be read off directly from the nomogram on page 631).

The basal metabolism is usually pathologically increased in hyperthyroidism and fever and often in leukemia; it is depressed in hypothyroidism and certain forms of asthenia.

The determination of basal metabolism is widely regarded as the principal aid in the differential diagnosis of hyperthyroidism. It is unreliable for this purpose, however, since there are numerous exceptions to the rule, both in the positive and negative sense, e.g. increase of basal metabolism in hyperactivity of the adrenal cortex, in which even hypoactivity of the thyroid can occur. In practice it is almost impossible to establish the conditions necessary for an accurate determination of basal metabolism (complete physical and mental relaxation), especially with children. The diagnosis of hypo- and hyper-thyroidism is therefore coming more and more to depend on other methods, such as determination of the protein-bound iodine or, preferably, the reaction of the thyroid to the accumulation of radioactive iodine (see pages 479 and 276). It must be emphasized that the basal metabolism is no criterion in the diagnosis of hyperthyroidism and is only of value as a part of the overall clinical picture.

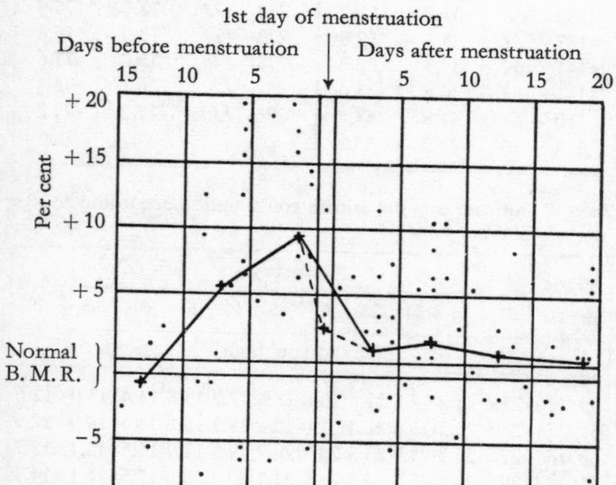

Cyclic changes in basal metabolism
From Wakeham, G., *J. biol. Chem.*, **56**, 555 (1923)

Determination of basal metabolism

The calorimetric determination of basal metabolism requires complicated apparatus. In practice, therefore, it is usually calculated from the oxygen consumption, the CO_2 production, and in certain cases where great accuracy is required, from the amount of urea eliminated in the urine.

The ratio of the CO_2 formed to the oxygen consumed is known as the **respiratory quotient (RQ):**

$$\frac{\text{vol. } CO_2 \text{ formed}}{\text{vol. } O_2 \text{ consumed}} = RQ$$

The RQ is a measure of the metabolism of the organism.

1. **Approximate determination of basal metabolism** by measuring the oxygen consumption alone (on the assumption of a mean RQ of 0.82 and neglecting the nitrogen metabolism): 1 liter of O_2 consumed = a basal metabolism of 4.825 kilocalories; for conversion into oxygen consumption per square meter per minute and use of the nomogram see page 631. This method is simple and rapid but not very reliable.
2. **A more exact method** is by measurement of the oxygen consumption and the RQ, neglecting the nitrogen metabolism: From the observed value for the RQ, Table 2 (page 628) gives the number of calories per liter of oxygen consumed, and thence the calories per hour. This method is usually of sufficient accuracy (with a normal diet) for clinical purposes.
3. **Accurate determination** of the basal metabolism, taking into account the nitrogen metabolism:
   (*a*) The urea excretion is measured on the basis of the 24-hour urine volume. 1 gram of urea excreted per hour corresponds to the production of 26.54 kilocalories per hour (Loewy) and to an oxygen consumption of 5.939 liters per hour (in the nitrogen metabolism). These two values are designated **kcal/hour$_{(N)}$** and **O_2/hour$_{(N)}$**.
   (*b*) The RQ and the oxygen consumption are now measured in the normal way and the latter value converted into liters per hour, designated **O_2/hour$_{(total)}$**. Subtracting: **O_2/hour$_{(total)}$** minus **O_2/hour$_{(N)}$** = **O_2/hour$_{(carbohydrates + fats)}$**.
   (*c*) The calorie value corresponding to the O_2/hour$_{(CH+F)}$ is obtained from Table 2 (page 628) from the observed RQ value = cal/hour$_{(CH+F)}$.

The basal metabolism is given by
kcal/hour$_{(CH+F)}$ + kcal/hour$_{(N)}$ = kcal/hour$_{(total)}$

These methods are not valid for diabetics
(exact determination only possible by means of calorimetry)
The measured oxygen volumes must always be reduced to normal (see page 300) before being converted into calories

Comparison of measured basal metabolism with normal standards (ideal values)

Various standards are in use, the commonest (for adults) being those of Harris and Benedict, Aub and Du Bois, and Boothby et al. There are special standards for children (see the following pages). It is now recognized that the older standards are at too high a level owing to their having been based on tests on untrained subjects.

(*a*) Harris-Benedict *Standard* (page 628). This is based on biometric measurements. Bases of comparison: total calories per hour and height, weight and age of the subject.

(*b*) *Standards giving the calorie values per square meter body surface per hour* (Boothby et al., Aub and Du Bois, etc.; see the following pages).
Bases of comparison: calories per square meter per hour, age and sex of the subject.
For calculation of body surface from height and weight see the nomograms on pages 632 and 633.

Table 1 Calorie values, oxygen consumption and carbon dioxide liberation per gram of proteins, fats and carbohydrates consumed in the body, and per gram of urea excreted in the urine[1]

1 gram	Oxygen consumed cm³	Carbon dioxide formed cm³	RQ	Calories (kcal) after Rubner	after Loewy	per liter oxygen	per liter carbon dioxide
Proteins	966.3	773.9	0.801	4.10	4.316	4.485	5.579
Urea	5939.0	4757.0	0.801	25.63	26.54	4.485	5.579
Fats	2019.3	1427.3	0.707	9.3	9.461	4.686	6.629
Carbohydrates	828.8	828.8	1.000	4.1	4.182	5.047	5.047

1) Peters and Van Slyke, *Quantitative Clinical Chemistry*, 2nd ed., vol. I, Baltimore, 1946, page 7.

Table 2 RQ, calories per liter oxygen consumed, and percentage participation of carbohydrates and fats in oxygen consumption and in calorie production[1]

Respiratory quotient	Percentage participation in total oxygen consumption		Percentage participation in total calorie production		Calories per liter oxygen	
	Carbohydrates (1)	Fats (2)	Carbohydrates (3)	Fats (4)	kcal (5)	$\log_{10}$
0.707	0	100.0	0	100.0	4.686	0.67080
0.71	1.02	99.0	1.10	98.9	4.690	0.67114
0.72	4.44	95.6	4.76	95.2	4.702	0.67228
0.73	7.85	92.2	8.40	91.6	4.714	0.67342
0.74	11.3	88.7	12.0	88.0	4.727	0.67456
0.75	14.7	85.3	15.6	84.4	4.739	0.67569
0.76	18.1	81.9	19.2	80.8	4.751	0.67682
0.77	21.5	78.5	22.8	77.2	4.764	0.67794
0.78	24.9	75.1	26.3	73.7	4.776	0.67906
0.79	28.3	71.7	29.9	70.1	4.788	0.68018
0.80	31.7	68.3	33.4	66.6	4.801	0.68129
0.81	35.2	64.8	36.9	63.1	4.813	0.68241
0.82	38.6	61.4	40.3	59.7	4.825	0.68352
0.83	42.0	58.0	43.8	56.2	4.838	0.68463
0.84	45.4	54.6	47.2	52.8	4.850	0.68573
0.85	48.8	51.2	50.7	49.3	4.862	0.68683
0.86	52.2	47.8	54.1	45.9	4.875	0.68793
0.87	55.6	44.4	57.5	42.5	4.887	0.68903
0.88	59.0	41.0	60.8	39.2	4.899	0.69012
0.89	62.5	37.5	64.2	35.8	4.911	0.69121
0.90	65.9	34.1	67.5	32.5	4.924	0.69230
0.91	69.3	30.7	70.8	29.2	4.936	0.69339
0.92	72.7	27.3	74.1	25.9	4.948	0.69447
0.93	76.1	23.9	77.4	22.6	4.961	0.69555
0.94	79.5	20.5	80.7	19.3	4.973	0.69663
0.95	82.9	17.1	84.0	16.0	4.985	0.69770
0.96	86.3	13.7	87.2	12.8	4.998	0.69877
0.97	89.8	10.2	90.4	9.58	5.010	0.69984
0.98	93.2	6.83	93.6	6.37	5.022	0.70091
0.99	96.6	3.41	96.8	3.18	5.035	0.70197
1.00	100.0	0	100.0	0	5.047	0.70303

$$\text{Column 1: percentage} = 100\,\frac{RQ-0.707}{0.293}$$

$$\text{Column 2: percentage} = 100\,\frac{1-RQ}{0.293}$$

$$\text{Column 3: percentage} = \frac{504.7\,(RQ-0.707)}{5.047\,(RQ-0.707)+4.686\,(1-RQ)}$$

$$\text{Column 4: percentage} = \frac{468.6\,(1-RQ)}{5.047\,(RQ-0.707)+4.686\,(1-RQ)}$$

$$\text{Column 5: calories (kcal)} = 4.686 + \frac{RQ-0.707}{0.293}\times 0.361$$

1) Zuntz and Schumburg, modified by Lusk, G., *J. biol. Chem.*, **59**, 41 (1924).

Table 3 Calories according to weight

Weight		Total kcal per hour		Weight		Total kcal per hour	
lb	*kg*	Males	Females	lb	*kg*	Males	Females
22	*10*	8.5	–	159	*72*	44.0	56.0
26	*12*	9.7	–	163	*74*	45.2	56.8
31	*14*	10.8	–	167	*76*	46.3	57.6
35	*16*	12.0	–	172	*78*	47.5	58.4
40	*18*	13.1	–	176	*80*	48.6	59.2
44	*20*	14.3	–	181	*82*	49.7	60.0
48	*22*	15.4	–	185	*84*	50.9	60.8
53	*24*	16.6	–	190	*86*	52.0	61.6
57	*26*	17.7	37.6	194	*88*	53.2	62.4
62	*28*	18.8	38.4	198	*90*	54.3	63.2
66	*30*	19.9	39.2	203	*92*	55.5	64.0
70	*32*	21.1	40.0	207	*94*	56.6	64.8
75	*34*	22.2	40.8	212	*96*	57.8	65.6
79	*36*	23.4	41.6	216	*98*	58.9	66.4
84	*38*	24.5	42.4	220	*100*	60.1	67.2
88	*40*	25.7	43.2	225	*102*	61.2	68.0
93	*42*	26.8	44.0	229	*104*	62.4	68.8
97	*44*	28.0	44.8	234	*106*	63.5	69.6
101	*46*	29.1	45.6	238	*108*	64.7	70.4
106	*48*	30.3	46.4	242	*110*	65.8	71.2
110	*50*	31.4	47.2	247	*112*	67.0	72.0
115	*52*	32.6	48.0	251	*114*	68.1	72.8
119	*54*	33.7	48.8	256	*116*	69.3	73.6
123	*56*	34.9	49.6	260	*118*	70.4	74.4
128	*58*	36.0	50.4	264	*120*	71.6	75.2
132	*60*	37.2	51.2	269	*122*	72.7	76.0
137	*62*	38.3	52.0	273	*124*	73.9	76.8
141	*64*	39.5	52.8	278	*126*	75.0	77.6
146	*66*	40.6	53.6	282	*128*	76.1	78.4
150	*68*	41.8	54.4	286	*130*	77.2	79.2
154	*70*	42.9	55.2				

Table 4 Adjustments for calorie consumption according to age and height

Height in	*cm*	Age in years 20	25	30	35	40	45	50	55	60	65	70
		Men (kcal per hour)										
59	*150*	25.6	24.2	22.8	21.4	20.0	18.6	17.2	15.8	14.4	13.0	11.6
61	*155*	26.6	25.2	23.8	22.4	21.0	19.6	18.2	16.8	15.4	14.0	12.6
63	*160*	27.7	26.3	24.9	23.5	22.1	20.7	19.3	17.9	16.5	15.1	13.7
65	*165*	28.7	27.3	25.9	24.5	23.1	21.7	20.3	18.9	17.5	16.1	14.7
67	*170*	29.8	28.4	27.0	25.6	24.2	22.8	21.4	20.0	18.6	17.2	15.8
69	*175*	30.8	29.4	28.0	26.6	25.2	23.8	22.4	21.0	19.6	18.2	16.8
71	*180*	31.9	30.4	29.1	27.6	26.2	24.8	23.4	22.0	20.6	19.2	17.8
73	*185*	32.9	31.5	30.1	28.7	27.3	25.9	24.5	23.1	21.7	20.3	18.9
75	*190*	34.0	32.5	31.2	29.7	28.3	26.9	25.5	24.1	22.7	21.3	19.9
77	*195*	35.0	33.6	32.2	30.8	29.4	28.0	26.6	25.2	23.8	22.4	21.0
79	*200*	36.1	34.6	33.2	31.8	30.4	29.0	27.6	26.2	24.8	23.4	22.0
		Women (kcal per hour)										
59	*150*	7.7	6.7	5.7	4.7	3.8	2.8	1.8	0.9	0.0	–1.0	–2.0
61	*155*	8.1	7.1	6.1	5.1	4.2	3.2	2.2	1.2	0.2	–0.7	–1.7
63	*160*	8.5	7.5	6.5	5.5	4.5	3.6	2.6	1.6	0.6	–0.3	–1.3
65	*165*	8.8	7.8	6.9	5.9	4.9	4.0	3.0	2.0	1.0	0.0	–0.9
67	*170*	9.2	8.2	7.3	6.3	5.3	4.3	3.4	2.4	1.4	0.5	–0.5
69	*175*	9.6	8.6	7.6	6.7	5.7	4.7	3.7	2.8	1.8	0.8	–0.2
71	*180*	10.0	9.0	8.0	7.0	6.1	5.1	4.1	3.2	2.2	1.2	0.2
73	*185*	10.4	9.4	8.4	7.5	6.5	5.5	4.5	3.5	2.6	1.6	0.6
75	*190*	10.8	9.8	8.8	7.8	6.8	5.9	4.9	3.9	3.0	2.0	1.0
77	*195*	11.2	10.2	9.2	8.2	7.2	6.2	5.3	4.3	3.3	2.4	1.4
79	*200*	11.5	10.5	9.6	8.6	7.6	6.7	5.7	4.7	3.7	2.7	1.8

Harris-Benedict Standard[1] of normal (total) calorie consumption per hour (Tables 3 and 4)

The tables are based on the following equation:

Men: $C = 66.473 + 13.7516\,W + 5.0033\,H - 6.7550\,A$

Women: $C = 655.0955 + 9.5634\,W + 1.8496\,H - 4.6756\,A$

(C = total kilocalories in 24 hours, W = weight in kilograms, H = height in centimeters, A = age in years.)

The normal calorie consumption per hour is obtained by adding together the appropriate values from Tables 3 and 4. In Table 3 the values corresponding to the odd weight figures are obtained by interpolation.

1) Harris and Benedict, *A Biometric Study of Basal Metabolism in Man*, Publication No. 279 of the Carnegie Institution of Washington, 1919.

Standards of normal calorie consumption per square meter body surface per hour

(For calculation of body surface according to the Du Bois and Du Bois formula see pages 632 and 633)

Standard of AUB and DU BOIS (14–80 years)

Arch. intern. Med., **19**, 823 (1917)

Age	kcal per m² per hour	
	Males	Females
14–16	46.0	43.0
16–18	43.0	40.0
18–20	41.0	38.0
20–30	39.5	37.0
30–40	39.5	36.5
40–50	38.5	36.0
50–60	37.5	35.0
60–70	36.5	34.0
70–80	35.5	33.0

Standard of BOOTHBY, BERKSON and DUNN (6–69 years)

Amer. J. Physiol., **116**, 468 (1936)

Males		Females	
Age	kcal per m² per hour	Age	kcal per m² per hour
6	53.00	6	50.62
7	52.45	6½	50.23
8	51.78	7	49.12
8½	51.20	7½	47.84
9	50.54	8	47.00
9½	49.42	8½	46.50
10	48.50	9–10	45.90
10½	47.71	11	45.26
11	47.18	11½	44.80
12	46.75	12	44.28
13–15	46.35	12½	43.58
16	45.72	13	42.90
16½	45.30	13½	42.10
17	44.80	14	41.45
17½	44.03	14½	40.74
18	43.25	15	40.10
18½	42.70	15½	39.40
19	42.32	16	38.85
19½	42.00	16½	38.30
20–21	41.43	17	37.82
22–23	40.82	17½	37.40
24–27	40.24	18–19	36.74
28–29	39.81	20–24	36.18
30–34	39.34	25–44	35.70
35–39	38.68	45–49	34.94
40–44	38.00	50–54	33.96
45–49	37.37	55–59	33.18
50–54	36.73	60–64	32.61
55–59	36.10	65–69	32.30
60–64	35.48		
65–69	34.80*		

* By extrapolation.

Cf. graphical representations of the Boothby and Harris-Benedict standards on page 630. A comparison shows at once that the Boothby standard follows the aging processes more closely than the Harris-Benedict or Du Bois standards, both of which show a more or less constant diminution of basal metabolism.

Standard of SHOCK (11½–17½ years)

Amer. J. Dis. Child., **64**, 19 (1942)

Age	kcal per m² per hour	
	Boys	Girls
11½	43.63	41.65
12	45.03	40.99
12½	44.37	40.43
13	44.13	39.90
13½	43.22	38.82
14	43.46	37.96
14½	42.91	36.45
15	42.82	35.68
15½	41.41	34.35
16	41.13	34.23
16½	40.96	34.62
17	40.96	33.44
17½	40.63	33.39

Standard of LEWIS, DUVAL and ILIFF (2–15¾ years)

J. Pediat., **23**, 1 (1943)

Age	kcal per m² per hour		Age	kcal per m² per hour	
	Boys	Girls		Boys	Girls
2	56.9	52.9	9	45.0	42.7
2¼	56.2	52.4	9¼	44.6	42.4
2½	55.6	52.0	9½	44.3	42.1
2¾	55.0	51.6	9¾	44.0	41.7
3	54.5	51.3	10	43.6	41.4
3¼	53.9	50.9	10¼	43.2	41.1
3½	53.4	50.6	10½	42.8	40.8
3¾	53.0	50.2	10¾	42.5	40.6
4	52.6	49.9	11	42.2	40.4
4¼	52.2	49.5	11¼	41.9	40.3
4½	51.8	49.1	11½	41.7	40.2
4¾	51.4	48.7	11¾	41.6	39.9
5	51.0	48.4	12	41.5	39.7
5¼	50.6	48.0	12¼	41.5	39.4
5½	50.3	47.6	12½	41.4	39.1
5¾	50.0	47.2	12¾	41.4	38.7
6	49.6	46.9	13	41.4	38.4
6¼	49.2	46.5	13¼	41.3	38.0
6½	48.9	46.2	13½	41.2	37.6
6¾	48.6	45.8	13¾	41.2	37.2
7	48.2	45.5	14	41.1	36.8
7¼	47.8	45.1	14¼	41.0	36.4
7½	47.4	44.7	14½	40.9	36.0
7¾	47.0	44.3	14¾	40.7	35.6
8	46.6	44.0	15	40.5	35.2
8¼	46.2	43.6	15¼	40.2	34.8
8½	45.8	43.3	15½	39.8	34.5
8¾	45.4	43.0	15¾	39.5	34.1

Standard of FLEISCH (1–80 years)

Helv. med. Acta, **18**, 23 (1951)

Age	kcal per m² per hour		Age	kcal per m² per hour	
	Boys	Girls		Men	Women
1	53.0	53.0	17	40.8	36.3
2	52.4	52.4	18	40.0	35.9
3	51.3	51.2	19	39.2	35.5
4	50.3	49.8	20	38.6	35.3
5	49.3	48.4	25	37.5	35.2
6	48.3	47.0	30	36.8	35.1
7	47.3	45.4	35	36.5	35.0
8	46.3	43.8	40	36.3	34.9
9	45.2	42.8	45	36.2	34.5
10	44.0	42.5	50	35.8	33.9
11	43.0	42.0	55	35.4	33.3
12	42.5	41.3	60	34.9	32.7
13	42.3	40.3	65	34.4	32.2
14	42.1	39.2	70	33.8	31.7
15	41.8	37.9	75	33.2	31.3
16	41.4	36.9	80	33.0	30.9

Standard of ROBERTSON and REID (3–75 years)

Lancet, **1**, 940 (1952)

Age	kcal per m² per hour		Age	kcal per m² per hour	
	Boys	Girls		Men	Women
3	60.1*	54.5*	17	39.7	35.3
4	57.9	53.9	18	39.2	34.9
5	56.3	53.0	19	38.8	34.5
6	54.2	51.8	20	38.4	34.3
7	52.1	50.2	25	37.1	34.0
8	50.1	48.4	30	36.4	34.1
9	48.2	46.4	35	35.9	33.5
10	46.6	44.3	40	35.5	32.6
11	45.1	42.4	45	34.1	32.2
12	43.8	40.6	50	33.8	31.9
13	42.7	39.1	55	33.4	31.6
14	41.8	37.8	60	33.1	31.3
15	41.0	36.8	65	32.7	31.0
16	40.3	36.0	70	32.4*	30.7
			75	32.0*	—

* Extrapolated or based on less than 7 subjects.

Basal metabolism before, during and after pregnancy. The upper curve gives the total calories, the lower curve the calories per square meter of body surface calculated from the Du Bois and Du Bois formula. After Sandiford and Wheeler, *J. biol. Chem.*, 62, 329 (1924).

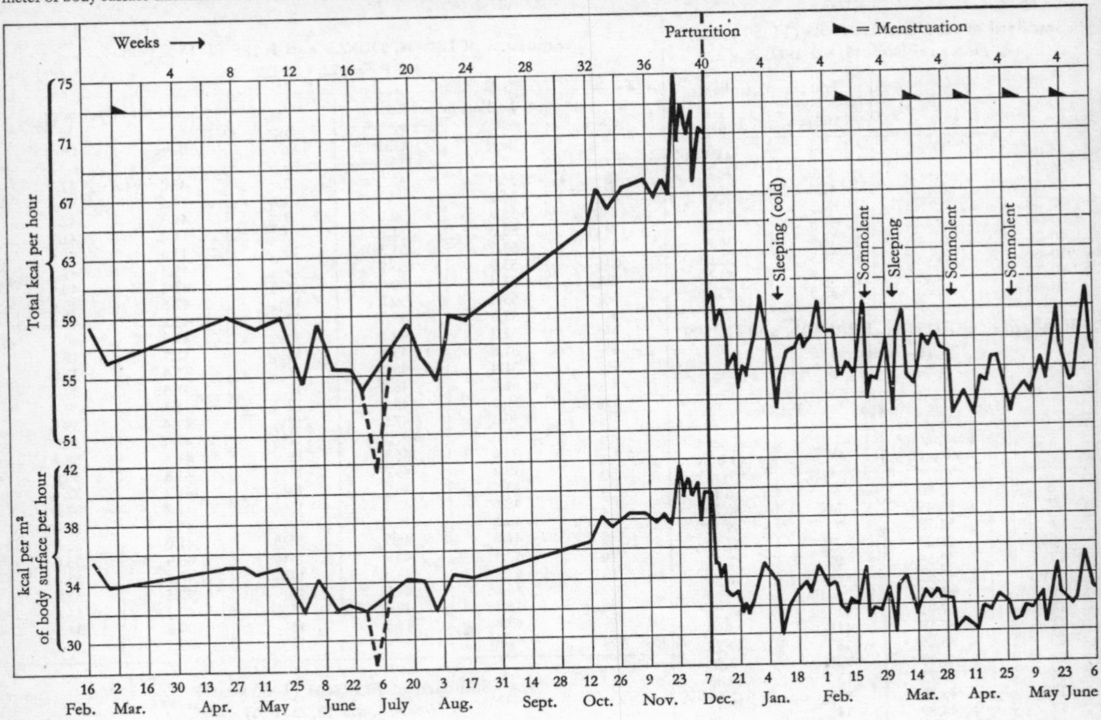

Variation of basal metabolism with age

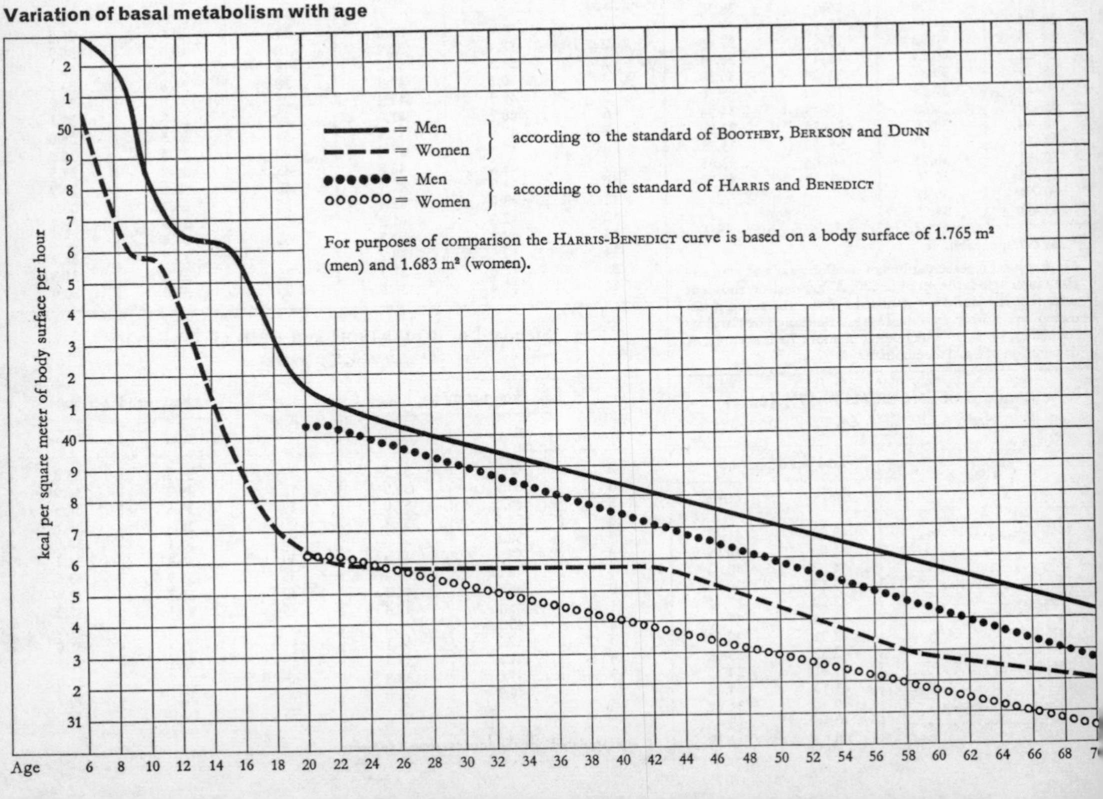

Nomogram for the Determination of Basal Metabolism and Percentage Probable Normality

From Boothby, Berkson and Dunn, *Amer. J. Physiol.*, **116**, 468 (1936)

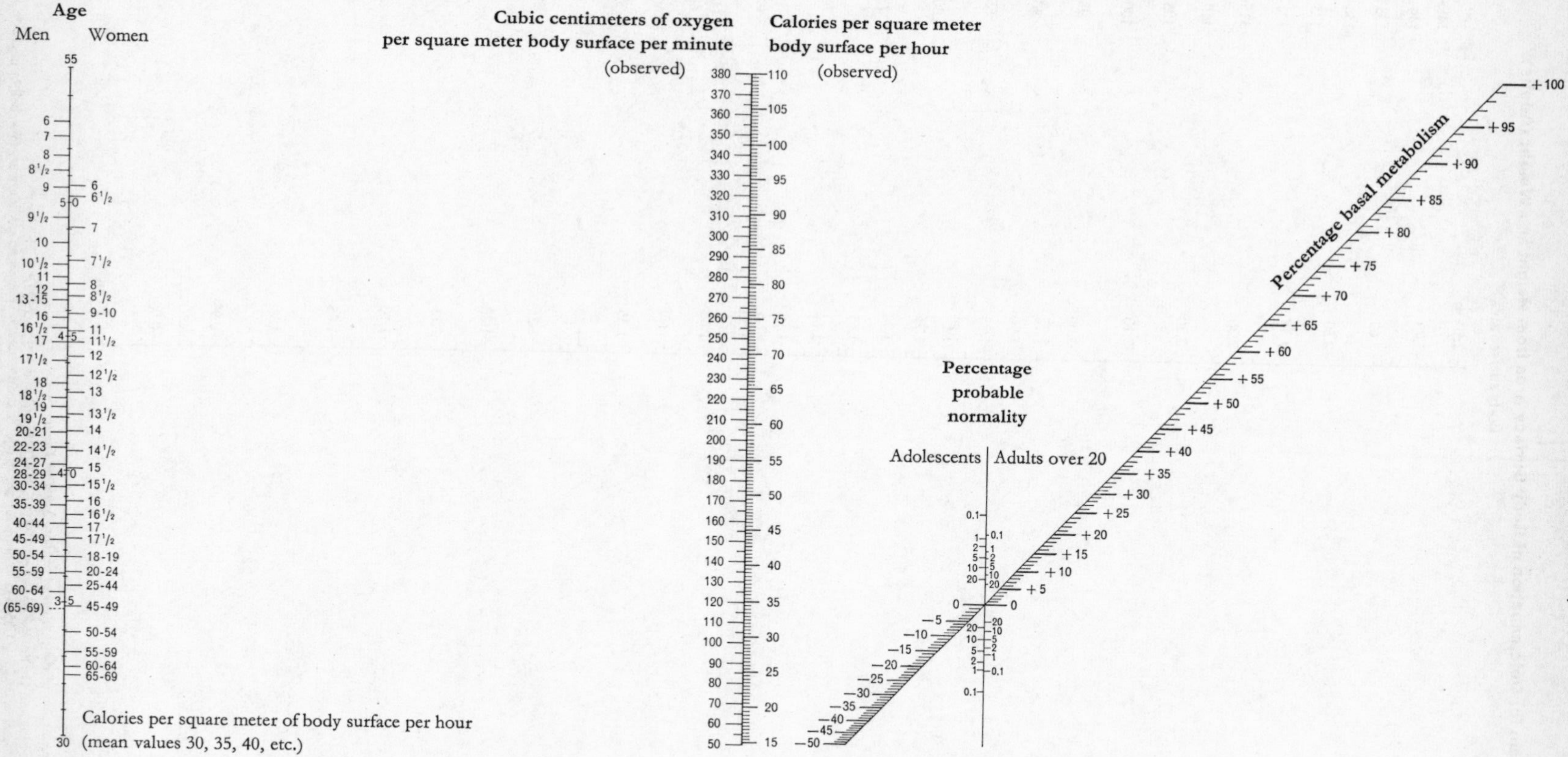

Use of the nomogram:

1. *Determination of the percentage basal metabolism on the assumption of an average RQ.* Draw a straight line between the appropriate point on the age scale and the observed oxygen consumption per square meter per minute. The point at which this line intersects the right-hand oblique scale gives the percentage basal metabolism.

2. *Determination of the basal metabolism from the calories per square meter per hour* (i.e. taking the RQ into account, and either neglecting or allowing for the nitrogen metabolism). Draw a line through the appropriate points and read off as for 1.

3. *Probable normality.* This is given by the intersection of the straight lines of 1. and 2. with the small vertical scale on the right. A probable normality of 0.1%, for example, means that in the examination of 1000 normal persons the observed basal metabolism value is to be expected in the case of one person.

Nomogram for Determination of Body Surface Area from Height and Weight (Adults)[1]

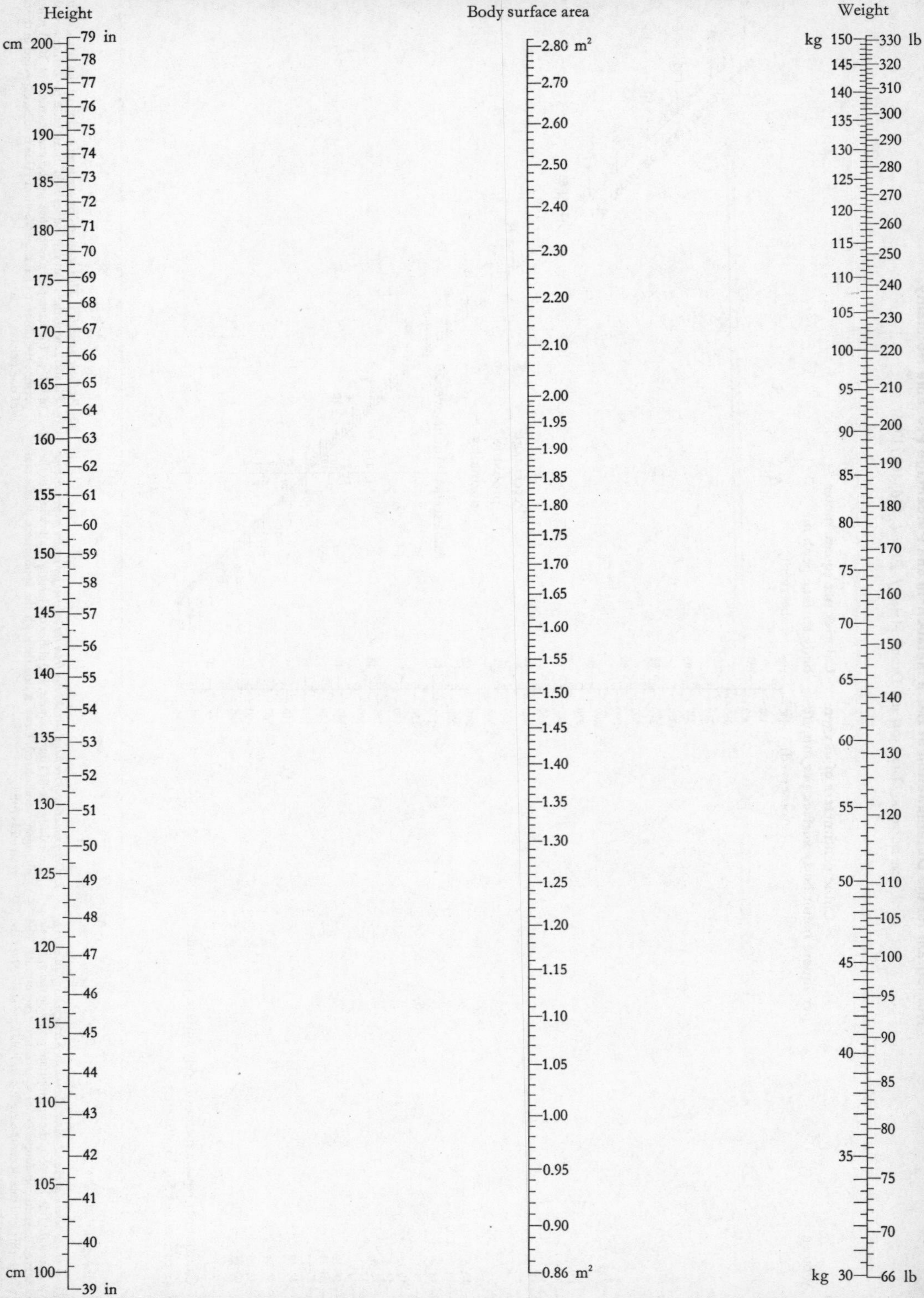

* Reproduction only by permission of the publishers of these *Scientific Tables*.

1) From the formula of Du Bois and Du Bois, *Arch. intern. Med.*, 17, 863 (1916): $S = W^{0.425} \times H^{0.725} \times 71.84$, or $\log S = \log W \times 0.425 + \log H \times 0.725 + 1.8564$ (S = body surface in square centimeters, W = weight in kilograms, H = height in centimeters).

Nomogram for Determination of Body Surface Area from Height and Weight (Children)[1]

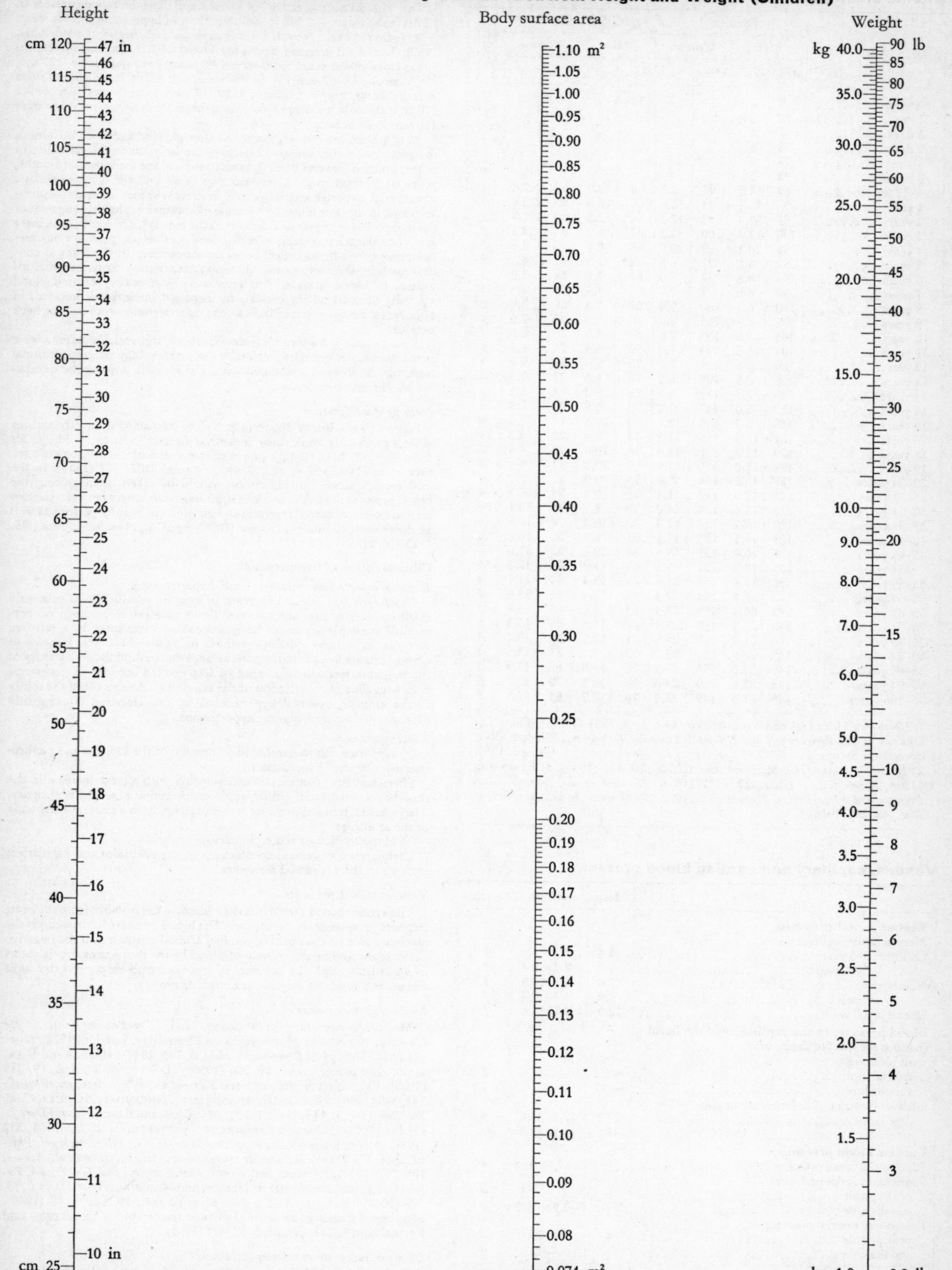

* Reproduction only by permission of the publishers of these *Scientific Tables.*

1) From the formula of Du Bois and Du Bois, *Arch. intern. Med.*, **17**, 863 (1916): $S = W^{0.425} \times H^{0.725} \times 71.84$, or $\log S = \log W \times 0.425 + \log H \times 0.725 + 1.8564$ (S = body surface in square centimeters, W = weight in kilograms, H = height in centimeters).

Normal values in mm Hg

Arterial blood pressure

Age	Systolic				Diastolic				Sources
	Men		Women		Men		Women		
	Mean	*s*	Mean	*s*	Mean	*s*	Mean	*s*	
Newborn	69	6			38				*1*
1 day	70	5							*1*
3 days	72	6							*1*
9 days	73	6							*1*
3 weeks	77	5							*1*
3 months	86	5							*1*
6–12 months	89	14.5	93	9.1	60	10.0	62	9.3	*2*
1 year	96	15.2	95	11.9	66	12.3	65	15.0	*2*
2 years	99	12.4	92	12.2	64	12.3	60	11.7	*2*
3 years	100	12.4	100	11.2	67	11.7	64	8.3	*2*
4 years	99	10.1	99	10.6	65	5.1	66	9.8	*2*
5 years	92	6.0	92	6.5	62	7.5	62	6.5	*3*
6 years	94	6.5	94	7.0	64	7.5	64	7.0	*3*
7 years	97	6.5	97	7.0	65	7.5	66	7.5	*3*
8 years	100	6.5	100	7.0	67	7.0	68	7.0	*3*
9 years	101	6.5	101	7.0	68	6.5	69	7.0	*3*
10 years	103	6.5	103	7.0	69	6.0	70	6.5	*3*
11 years	104	6.5	104	7.0	70	5.5	71	6.5	*3*
12 years	106	6.5	106	7.0	71	5.0	72	7.0	*3*
13 years	108	6.5	108	6.5	72	5.0	73	7.5	*3*
14 years	110	6.5	110	6.5	73	5.0	74	8.5	*3*
15 years	112	7.0	112	7.0	75	5.5	76	9.5	*3*
16 years	118	12.2	116	12.1	73	10.3	72	9.6	*4*
17 years	121	12.9	116	11.5	74	9.4	72	9.2	*4*
18 years	120	12.0	116	11.4	74	10.0	72	8.6	*4*
19 years	122	15.0	115	11.9	75	10.3	71	8.9	*4*
20–24 years	123	13.8	116	11.8	76	9.9	72	9.7	*4*
25–29 years	125	12.6	117	11.4	78	9.0	74	9.1	*4*
30–34 years	126	13.6	120	14.0	79	9.7	75	10.8	*4*
35–39 years	127	14.2	124	13.9	80	10.4	78	10.0	*4*
40–44 years	129	15.1	127	17.1	81	9.5	80	10.6	*4*
45–49 years	130	16.9	131	19.5	82	10.8	82	11.6	*4*
50–54 years	135	19.2	137	21.3	83	11.3	84	12.4	*4*
55–59 years	138	18.8	139	21.4	84	11.4	84	11.7	*4*
60–64 years	142	21.1	144	22.3	85	12.4	85	13.0	*4*
65–69 years	143	26.0	154	29.0	83	9.9	85	13.8	*5*
70–74 years	145	26.3	159	25.8	82	15.3	85	15.3	*5*
75–79 years	146	21.6	158	26.3	81	12.9	84	13.1	*5*
80–84 years	145	25.6	157	28.0	82	9.9	83	13.1	*5*
85–89 years	145	24.2	154	27.9	79	14.9	82	17.3	*5*
90–94 years	145	23.4	150	23.6	78	12.1	79	12.1	*5*
95–106 years	145	27.5	149	23.5	78	12.7	81	12.5	*5*

1) (Systolic) Holland and Young, *Brit. med. J.*, **2**, 1331 (1956); (Diastolic) Dexter et al., *Preeclamptic and Eclamptic Toxemia of Pregnancy*, Boston, 1941, quoted by Smith, C. A., *The Physiology of the Newborn Infant*, Oxford, 1959. *2*) Allen-Williams, G. M., *Arch. Dis. Childh.*, **20**, 125 (1945). *3*) Faber and James, *Amer. J. Dis. Child.*, **22**, 7 (1921). *4*) Master et al., *Normal Blood Pressure and Hypertension*, Philadelphia, 1952. *5*) Master et al., *Ann. intern. Med.*, **48**, 284 (1958).

Venous, capillary and cardiac blood pressure

	Mean	Range	Sources
Venous blood pressure			
Median basilic vein (at elbow)			
Children, 3–5 years	3.4	2.2– 4.6	*1*
5–10 years	4.3	2.4– 5.4	*1*
Adults, men	7.4	3.7–10.3	*1*
women	6.9	4.4– 9.4	*1*
Dorsal pedal veins	12.9	9.1–15.4	*1*
Blood pressure in the capillaries of the hand			
(hand at the level of the heart)			
with bleeding			
arterial limb	~32	–	*2*
venous limb	~12	–	*2*
without bleeding (2500 measurements)			
capillaries	27.2	22.8–31.6	*3*
arterioles	47.1	44.9–49.3	*3*
Cardiac blood pressure			
Right atrial mean pressure	–	−2 to +5	*4*
Right ventricular pressure			
peak systole	–	17 –31.5	*4*
end diastole	–	−0.5 to +7	*4*
Pulmonary arterial pressure			
peak systole	–	11–29	*4*
end diastole	–	4–13	*4*

1) Burch, G. E., *A Primer of Venous Pressure*, Philadelphia, 1950, quoted by Dittmer and Grebe (Eds.), *Handbook of Circulation*, Philadelphia, 1959, page 111. *2*) Landis, E. M., *Heart*, **15**, 209 (1930). *3*) Küchmeister, H., *Ergebn. inn. Med. Kinderheilk.*, **4**, 463 (1953). *4*) From measurements on a total of 72 subjects, summarized by Fowler et al., *Amer. Heart. J.*, **46**, 264 (1953).

Arterial blood pressure

The "clinical normal range" of systolic and diastolic blood pressure in adults is the mean ± 1.282 *s*; the lower limit of hypertension is the mean ± 2 *s* (Master et al., *Normal Blood Pressure and Hypertension*, Philadelphia, 1952). The blood pressure ranges associated with the highest life expectation (men 30–59 years, women 20–49 years) are: systolic 98–127 mm Hg, diastolic 48–67 mm Hg (from Society of Actuaries, *Build and Blood Pressure Study*, vol. I, Chicago, 1959). With a systolic pressure under 170 mm there is no danger of hemorrhage. A diastolic pressure over 130 mm is dangerous.

Blood pressure is temporarily increased after physical exercise (5–10 min), in emotional excitement (systolic pressure only, duration variable), in acute nephritis (several weeks), in eclampsia, in the menopause (months, years or permanently). *Continuous high blood pressure* is characteristic of essential hypertension; also seen in certain kidney diseases (nephrosclerosis, in the later stages of subacute glomerular nephritis, as a result of pyelonephritis or in pressure damage to the kidneys, e.g. owing to urinary stasis or enlarged prostate); in endocrine disturbances (pituitary or adrenals; excessive adrenocortical hormone production usually leads to continuous high-level adrenaline liberation rather than to paroxysmal increases of blood pressure); in arteriosclerosis; with increased blood viscosity (e.g. in polycythemia); in increased intracranial pressure; in obesity; in certain myocardiac lesions (right atrium) as a result of back pressure.

Blood pressure is temporarily lowered in shock and collapse, after severe hemorrhages, in diarrhea; *continuous low pressure* may be constitutional (asthenia, debility) or due to endocrine disturbances, myocardiac degeneration, chronic anemia.

Methods of measurement

Indirect (Riva-Rocci apparatus). Values measured indirectly do not differ significantly from those measured directly (Steele, J. M., *J. Mt Sinai Hosp.*, **8**, 1042 [1942]). *Direct measurement* with the manometric apparatus of Hamilton et al., *Amer. J. Physiol.*, **107**, 427 (1934). In the initial examination the precaution should be taken of measuring the blood pressure in both arms since significant differences between the two arms are often observed (systolic and diastolic) in healthy persons as well as those with circulatory disease (Rueger, M. J., *Ann. intern. Med.*, **35**, 1023 [1951]).

Clinical forms of hypertension

Essential hypertension (genuine, "red" hypertension)

Characteristics: marked increase in systolic pressure with relatively small increase in diastolic pressure (large pressure difference); no perceptible renal participation, fairly amenable to treatment by a salt-free diet, rest in bed and sedatives; reddish or reddish-blue face. Increase of blood pressure in essential hypertension is due to diminished elasticity of the large arteries and to a more or less marked increase in peripheral resistance (due to constriction of the arterioles). As a result of the injury to the kidneys, essential hypertension of long duration is eventually accompanied by nephrogenic hypertension.

Renal hypertension

(*a*) Hypertension in chronic inflammation of the kidneys and nephrosclerosis ("white" hypertension).

Characteristics: continuous hypertension with a large increase in the *diastolic* pressure, facial pallor, angiospastic retinitis, renal insufficiency. The increase in blood pressure is due principally to a general narrowing of the arterioles.

(*b*) Hypertension in acute glomerular nephritis.

Characteristics: general constriction of the arterioles and capillaries; increase in the peripheral resistance.

Venous blood pressure

The venous blood pressure is dependent on the distance from the heart (highest pressure at the periphery). The blood pressure in the veins is the algebraic sum of the positive residual arterial pressure and the negative pressure exerted on the column of blood by the thoracic cavity. It varies in accordance with the position of the vein with respect to the right atrium as a result of the different effect of gravity.

Methods of measurement

Membrane manometers: Wiggers, C. J., *The Pressure Pulses in the Cardiovascular System*, Monographs on Physiology, London, 1928; Müller et al., *Helv. physiol. pharmacol. Acta*, **6**, 783 (1948); Hansen and Warburg, *Acta physiol. scand.*, **19**, 306 (1950); Hansen, A. T., *ibid.*, **19**, 333 (1950). Photoelectric manometers: Rein et al., *Pflüg. Arch. ges. Physiol.*, **243**, 329 (1940). Piezoelectric manometers: Langevin and Gomez, *C. R. Soc. Biol.* (*Paris*), **113**, 1123 (1933); MacLeod and Cohn, *Amer. Heart J.*, **21**, 345 (1941). Induction manometers: Wetterer, E., *Z. Biol.*, **101**, 332 (1943). Magnetoelectric manometers: Hampel, A., *Pflüg. Arch. ges. Physiol.*, **244**, 171 (1941). Resistance manometers: Braunstein et al., *Science*, **105**, 267 (1947); Lambert and Wood, *Proc. Soc. exp. Biol.* (*N.Y.*), **64**, 186 (1947). Capacity manometers: Hansen and Warburg, *Amer. Heart J.*, **33**, 709 (1947); Hansen, A. T., *Acta physiol. scand.*, **19**, Suppl. 68 (1949). Membrane manometers with electronic transmission: Clemedson and Pettersson, *J. Lab. clin. Med.*, **38**, 631 (1951).

Blood pressure in the capillaries of the hand

The venous blood pressure in the capillaries is lower than the osmotic pressure of the plasma.

Cardiac blood pressure

Pressures in the right heart measured by catheterization by the method of Cournand and Ranges, *Proc. Soc. exp. Biol.* (*N.Y.*), **46**, 462 (1941).

As originally defined by WAKSMAN[1], the term antibiotic denotes a substance produced by microorganisms – usually bacteria or molds – which in dilute solution is capable of inhibiting or destroying other microorganisms. Of the several hundred antibiotics which have so far been isolated, about 20 are clinically useful and available. The most extensively used are the penicillins, streptomycin (and its chemical derivative dihydrostreptomycin), chloramphenicol, erythromycin and the tetracyclines (tetracycline, chlortetracycline, oxytetracycline), and today this group of substances undoubtedly constitutes the most powerful weapon in the doctor's armory. Their manufacture has become an immense industry – in the USA in 1960, for example, nearly 3 million pounds were produced, equivalent to two-thirds in value of the entire production of pharmaceuticals.

According to their activity in vitro, antibiotics can be classified as bactericidal (penicillins, streptomycin, bacitracin, neomycin) or bacteriostatic (tetracyclines, chloramphenicol, erythromycin)[2].

Unfortunately, the efficacy and ease of administration of antibiotics have resulted in their indiscriminate use and even misuse, coupled with a frequent disregard of the hazards involved. It is authoritatively considered that upwards of 50% of antibiotic applications are unwarranted in that the infections concerned are either not amenable to antibiotic therapy, are capable of being adequately treated with other drugs, or are of a severity not justifying any medication. Apart from the associated dangers of allergic reactions, superinfections and blood dyscrasia, this misuse has been largely responsible for the emergence of widespread bacterial resistance to antibiotics.

Hazards of antibiotic therapy[3]

All antibiotics can produce drug reactions in certain patients, the commonest being of an allergic nature. Penicillin, which is practically nontoxic, causes dermatitis on prolonged contact in about 5% of persons so exposed. This antibiotic occasionally results in a kind of "serum sickness" which may appear from 30 minutes up to several weeks after administration. Urticaria and angioneurotic edema are other secondary manifestations characteristic of penicillin which may occur rapidly in patients already sensitized by a previous dose. Benzathine penicillin G has been known to cause exfoliative dermatitis in some patients after long-term treatment. The most serious hazard of penicillin therapy, however, is anaphylactic shock. This is fortunately rare, its incidence being only 0.1–0.3 per million injections but with a mortality of about 10%[4]. Very small doses of penicillin can cause sensitization, and the latent period can extend from several weeks to 8 years. Anaphylactic shock results most often from intramuscular injection and is much more rare after oral administration. It has also been observed following the use of the tetracyclines.

Another severe hazard associated with antibiotics is the *superimposed infection* which occurs particularly as a sequel to the administration of the broad-spectrum tetracyclines. The most serious of such superinfections are staphylococcal enterocolitis (mortality ca. 40%), due to disturbance of the natural balance of bacterial flora, and wound infections in hospitals, where resistant organisms take the place of the sensitive strains eliminated by the antibiotic. Apart from staphylococcal infections (see also under Staphylococci, pages 661 and 662), moniliasis is important in this respect (see page 702).

Blood dyscrasia is another serious condition which may follow the use of antibiotics, particularly of chloramphenicol. The commonest manifestations are agranulocytosis and aplastic anemia, the latter being very often fatal[5]. For this reason the use of chloramphenicol should be restricted to infections where it is specifically indicated, viz. typhoid and other *Salmonella* infections, and to staphylococcal infections resistant to other available antibiotics.

In addition to causing contact dermatitis, streptomycin may damage the vestibular branch of the eighth nerve (equilibrial dysfunction), while dihydrostreptomycin may affect the auditory branch (deafness). These lesions may be irreversible, so that in prolonged treatment dosage should be limited as far as possible to 500 mg per day (adults) of either preparation. The combination of streptomycin with dihydrostreptomycin offers no advantage in respect of reduced toxicity since the mixture has been shown to be more likely to cause deafness than streptomycin alone[6].

Of the lesser used antibiotics, both neomycin and polymyxin are neurotoxic in sufficient dosage, while bacitracin, like neomycin, may impair renal function.

Finally, and this is not the least of the dangers of antibiotic therapy, there is the possibility of actually increasing the patient's susceptibility to illness by depriving him of the immunity to subsequent infection which he would have acquired had the infection been allowed to run its course[7].

Bacterial resistance to antibiotics[8]

The resistance acquired by bacteria to antibiotics is still on the increase, and this factor undoubtedly constitutes the major limitation to the usefulness of these drugs. The development of resistant mutants by an organism may be stepwise, i.e. by successive small increments of resistance, as in the case of resistance to penicillin; alternatively, the organism may acquire a sudden high degree of resistance following a single exposure to the antibiotic, as in the case of streptomycin. Resistance displayed to a particular antibiotic is usually also displayed to all antibiotics with a similar mechanism of action *(cross resistance)*, a circumstance which constitutes one of the reasons for limiting the use of combinations of antibiotics (see below). The staphylococci, in particular, have developed resistance to all the antibiotics used to combat them; the consequent difficulty of controlling staphylococcal infections, especially in hospitals, at one time caused serious consideration to be given to the legislative restriction of the use of erythromycin with the aim of limiting the spread of staphylococcal strains resistant to this antibiotic[9].

Theoretically, the development of resistance by bacteria may be countered in two ways: 1. By administering the antibiotic concerned in high dosage, i.e. sufficient to maintain concentrations high enough to inhibit the resistant mutants. This is naturally only applicable to antibiotics which are of low toxicity (penicillins, erythromycin, tetracyclines) and which cause stepwise development of resistance and not to those like streptomycin which are highly toxic or to which bacteria react with a sudden high degree of resistance. 2. By the use of two antibiotics simultaneously (combined therapy, see below), on the assumption that there is negligible probability of the emergence of doubly resistant mutants.

Combined therapy with antibiotics[10]

The claim that the in vivo development of resistance is delayed or prevented more efficiently by the use of a *combination* of antibiotics as distinct from straightforward *substitution* of one antibiotic by another using the dosages known to be most effective has not as yet been fully substantiated for any pair of antibiotics, although one extensive trial[11] indicates that the resistance of some strains of hospital staphylococci to penicillin can be reduced in this manner. (The combination of streptomycin with the chemotherapeutic agents isoniazid or para-aminosalicylic acid is known to delay the emergence of resistant tubercle bacilli [see page 678].) Other advantages which have been advanced for purely antibiotic combinations are synergistic action (claimed in particular for various commercial preparations), reduced toxicity through reduction of individual dosage, and the ability to provide cover for mixed infections and to protect the seriously ill patient prior to diagnosis. These claims do not withstand closer examination. The position is that combinations of *bactericidal* antibiotics are probably never antagonistic but may perhaps be synergistic. Combinations of *bacteriostatic* antibiotics may have additive effects but are neither antagonistic nor synergistic. *Mixed* (bactericidal-bacteriostatic) combinations can be synergistic if the bacteria concerned show some resistance to the bacteriostatic component or antagonistic if they are very sensitive to this component. An example of antagonism is the effect of adding chlortetracycline to penicillin in the treatment of pneumococcal meningitis, when the mortality from the disease is very greatly increased[12]. The combination of penicillin with erythromycin also appears to be antagonistic in vivo[13]. In general it is rare in practice for a combination of two antibiotics to offer any advantage over the administration of either of them in adequate dosage. Furthermore, the literature contains many reports of cross resistance to an important antibiotic being induced by a little-used antibiotic which had been administered with it. An example is the introduction of erythromycin-resistant staphylococci through the use of the erythromycin-like antibiotic oleandomycin in a combination[14].

In view therefore of the doubtful advantages and undoubted disadvantages of antibiotic combinations, particularly fixed-ratio commercial preparations and those containing weakly-active or little-known antibiotics, their use should be avoided except in cases where there is ample well-controlled *clinical* evidence of their effectiveness *and where the infection cannot be adequately combatted by any single antibiotic*. The use of mixtures of antibiotics as "shotgun therapy" in substitution for accurate diagnosis is particularly to be deplored.

Combinations of antibiotics in which synergistic action has been clearly demonstrated in vivo are the following:

1. Penicillin + streptomycin in streptococcal endocarditis.
2. Streptomycin + a tetracycline or chloramphenicol in brucellosis.
3. Penicillin + chlortetracycline, or streptomycin + oxytetracycline, in staphylococcal endocarditis.

Local application of antibiotics

In view of the undesirability of risking both the development of drug resistance and sensitization in the treatment of a patient whose life is not in danger, local application should be restricted to antibiotics not used systemically. Mixed skin infections may be treated with bacitracin/neomycin or bacitracin/polymyxin B mixtures, both of which have a wide activity spectrum. In principle, however, measures other than antibiotics should first be tried.

Antibiotics in nonbacterial diseases

None of the antibiotics at present available is effective against the true viruses (see page 689) and any favorable effects exercised by antibiotics in virus diseases are probably connected with a disturbance of the symbiotic relationships between bacteria and viruses. In the light of the hazards of antibiotic therapy already mentioned, its use in the treatment of secondary bacterial infections should be severely restricted[15].

Antibiotics have been found to be effective in a number of rickettsial[16], protozoal and fungal infections, viz. chloramphenicol and oxytetracycline in rickettsiosis, tetracyclines in amebiasis *(Entamoeba histolytica)* and trichomoniasis, griseofulvin in dermatomycoses, nystatin in moniliasis, and amphotericin B in systemic mycoses (see also the table on pages 637–645).

Evidence has recently accumulated that certain antibiotics have marked antitumoral activity, for example actinomycin D in metastatic sarcomas in children[17].

It is not irrelevant to conclude with a mention of the increasing use of antibiotics as food preservatives and crop sprays and in animal nutrition and medication. These uses have greatly increased the chances of sensitization to antibiotics, especially penicillin, due to the persistence of antibiotic residues in foods[18].

***

The chemical constitution, properties and applications of the clinically useful antibiotics are summarized in the table on pages 637–645. The effectiveness of the principal antibiotics in relation to diseases caused by specific pathogenic organisms will be found in the tables on pages 646–688. Particulars of the international standards and reference preparations for antibiotics are given in the table on page 738.

1) Waksman, S. A., *Mycologia*, **39**, 565 (1947). *2)* Jawetz et al., *J. Amer. med. Ass.*, **150**, 693 (1952). *3)* Cf. Herrell, W. E., *J. Amer. med. Ass.*, **168**, 1875 (1958); Welch et al., *Antibiot. Med.*, **4**, 800 (1957); Welch et al., *Antibiot. Ann.*, **1957–1958**, 296; Editorial, *J. Amer. med. Ass.*, **166**, 927 (1958); Dunlop and Murdoch, *Brit. med. Bull.*, **16**, 67 (1960); Simon and Rantz, *Ann. Rev. Med.*, **12**, 111 (1960). *4)* Binns, T. B., in Daley and Miller (Eds.), *Progress in Clinical Medicine*, 4th ed., London, 1961, page 1. *5)* Cf. *Med. Letter*, **3**, No. 1 (1961); Rosenbach et al., *New Engl. J. Med.*, **263**, 724 (1960). *6)* Wier et al., *Dis. Chest*, **30**, 628 (1956). *7)* Editorial, *Practitioner*, **176**, 1 (1956); Clauberg, K. W., *Méd. et Hyg.* (*Genève*), **23**, 724 (1959). *8)* For reviews see Finland, M., *New Engl. J. Med.*, **252**, 570 (1955), and **253**, 909, 969, 1019 (1955); Bryson and Demerec, *Amer. J. Med.*, **18**, 723 (1955); Lowbury, E. J. L., *Brit. med. Bull.*, **16**, 73 (1960). *9)* Editorial, *Lancet*, **1**, 193 (1956). *10)* Cf. Editorial, *New Engl. J. Med.*, **255**, 1057 (1956); Dowling, H. F., *J. Amer. med. Ass.*, **164**, 44 (1957); Editorial, *Lancet*, **2**, 177 (1957); Wiesmann, E., *Schweiz. med. Wschr.*, **87**, 1045 (1957); Editorial, *New Engl. J. Med.*, **257**, 289 (1957); Lacey, B. W., *Brit. med. Bull.*, **16**, 42 (1960). *11)* Barber et al., *Brit. med. J.*, **1**, 11 (1960). *12)* Lepper and Bowling, *Arch. intern. Med.*, **88**, 489 (1951). *13)* Jones and Finland, *New Engl. J. Med.*, **255**, 1019 (1956). *14)* Garrod, L. P., *Brit. med. J.*, **2**, 56 (1957). *15)* Cf. Editorial, *J. Amer. med. Ass.*, **165**, 53 (1957). *16)* Ley and Smadel, *Antibiot. and Chemother.*, **4**, 792 (1954). *17)* Tan et al., *Pediatrics*, **24**, 544 (1959). *18)* Welch, H., *J. Amer. med. Ass.*, **170**, 2093 (1959).

Antibiotics of proven clinical efficacy

Name Synonyms	Source	Formula Mol. wt.	Constitution	Physical properties*	Stability	Toxicity[1]	Remarks (Clinical usefulness, resistance, etc.)
Actinomycin C (actinochrysin)	*Streptomyces antibioticus, S. chrysomallus*	$\sim C_{62}H_{89}O_{16}N_{11}$ ~ 1250 Actinomycin C_3: $C_{64}H_{90}O_{16}N_{12}$ 1283.52	Mixture of 4 weakly basic quinonoid chromopeptides (C_1, C_2, C_{2a}, C_3). With the exception of actinomycin C_3, their empirical constitution has not yet been fully elucidated	Actinomycin C_1: m.p. 241–243°C (decomposition) $[\alpha]_D^{20}$ −349° Actinomycin C_2: m.p. 237–239°C (decomposition) $[\alpha]_D^{19}$ −325° Actinomycin C_3: m.p. 232–235°C (decomposition) $[\alpha]_D^{19}$ −321°	Thermostable except in alkali and strong acid	LD_{100} mice: i.p. 5 mg/kg; oral 50 mg/kg In man, side effects are nausea, diarrhea, pharyngitis, alopecia, vaginitis, thrombocytopenia, stomatitis, skin pigmentation	By i.v. injection, in lymphogranulomatosis (HODGKIN'S disease), malignant conjunctival tumors
Amphotericin B	*Streptomyces* species	$C_{46}H_{73}O_{20}N$ > 1300 960.10 (calc.)	Conjugated heptaene of mainly unknown constitution	m.p. 170°C (decomposition) $[\alpha]_D^{23.5}$ − 33.6° (in 0.1-N HCl in methanol)	Unstable between pH 4 and 10	LD_{50} mice: i.v. 25 mg/kg In man, side effects are nausea, vomiting, anorexia, fever	Fungicide active against *Coccidioides, Cryptococcus, Blastomyces* and particularly *Histoplasma*. For International Reference Preparation see page 738
Bacitracin (bacitracin A = ayfivin)	*Bacillus subtilis, B. licheniformis*	Bacitracin A: $C_{66}H_{103}O_{16}N_{17}S$ 1470 (found)	Mixture of several weakly basic polypeptides (A, A', B, C, D, E, F, F_1, F_2, F_3, G). Constitution not yet fully elucidated	$[\alpha]_D^{23}$ + 5° ± 2.5° (in 0.02-N HCl) UV max.: 253 mμ (bacitracin A)	Thermostable at pH 4–5; unstable above pH 9; in aqueous solution unstable	LD_{50} mice: i.v. 360 mg/kg; s.c. 1300–2500 mg/kg In man, nephrotoxic and gastrointestinal symptoms; topically, skin effects rare	Bactericidal and bacteriostatic. Systemically, indicated only in infections resistant to penicillin, etc. Topically (or by infiltration) in abscesses, ulcers, surgical and other infections. See also page 636. Resistance not readily developed by sensitive bacteria. For International Standard see page 738
Carbomycin	*Streptomyces halstedii*	$C_{42}H_{67}O_{16}N$ 842.01	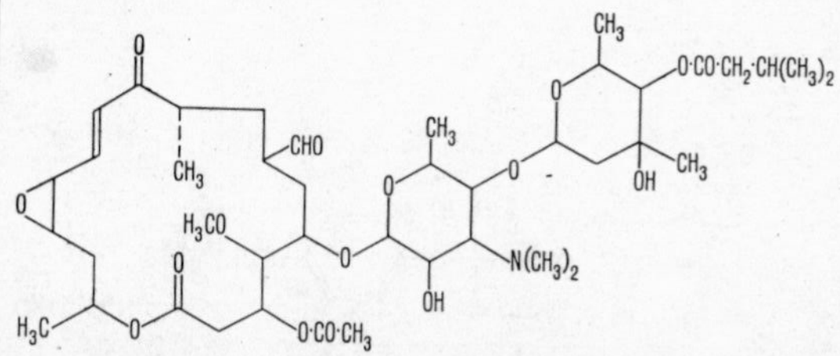	m.p. 212–214°C (decomposition) $[\alpha]_D^{25}$ −54° (in methanol) UV max.: 238, 327 mμ	Most stable at pH 5–7	LD_{50} mice: oral > 3500 mg/kg In man, oral doses of 2 g/day well tolerated; occasionally nausea, vomiting, diarrhea	Orally, in infections due to GRAM-positive organisms resistant to penicillin, particularly *Streptococcus pyogenes, Staphylococcus aureus, Diplococcus pneumoniae*; enterococcal urinary tract infections, gonorrhea, syphilis. Resistance pattern similar to penicillin. Cross resistance with erythromycin in streptococci and micrococci

* Melting point (m.p.); specific rotation [α], in water unless otherwise stated (for definition see footnote, page 336); ultraviolet absorption maxima (UV max.), in water unless otherwise stated.

1) Unless otherwise stated, toxicity data are from SPECTOR, W. S. (Ed.), *Handbook of Toxicology*, vol. II, Philadelphia and London, 1957.

Antibiotics of proven clinical efficacy (continued)

Name Synonyms	Source	Formula Mol. wt.	Constitution	Physical properties*	Stability	Toxicity[1]	Remarks (Clinical usefulness, resistance, etc.)
Chloramphenicol (D-[–]*threo*-1-*p*-nitrophenyl-2-[dichloro-acetylamino] propane-1,3-diol)	*Streptomyces venezuelae*; synthesis	$C_{11}H_{12}O_5N_2Cl_2$ 323.15	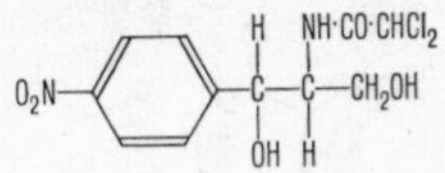 (The stereochemical configuration [D-*threo*-] is specific for the antimicrobial activity since the other 3 possible stereoisomers are inactive)	m.p. 149.7–150.7° C $[\alpha]_D^{25}$ + 19° (in ethanol) UV max.: 278 mμ	Thermostable; alkali labile; aqueous solutions sensitive to light and high temperature	LD_{50} mice: oral 2640 mg/kg In man, oral doses of 1–2 g daily well tolerated; side effects rare but include aplastic anemia[3] and agranulocytosis; topically, skin sensitization less than with sulfonamides, penicillin or streptomycin	Broad-spectrum antibiotic, especially effective against GRAM-negative infections and rickettsioses. Orally and parenterally, in typhoid fever, bacillary dysentery, cholera, gonorrhea, lymphogranuloma venereum, granuloma inguinale, urinary and intestinal tract infections, surgical infections, bacterial pneumonia, epidemic and scrub typhus, Rocky Mountain spotted fever, Q fever, tick fever, psittacosis, brucellosis (synergism with streptomycin), tularemia, primary atypical pneumonia, syphilis, relapsing fever, CARRION's disease (bartonellosis), nonspecific urethritis, smallpox, yaws, tropical ulcer, meningitis, anthrax. Topically, in ocular infections, especially trachoma. Resistance not readily developed
Chlortetracycline	*Streptomyces aureofaciens*	$C_{22}H_{23}O_8N_2Cl$ 478.90	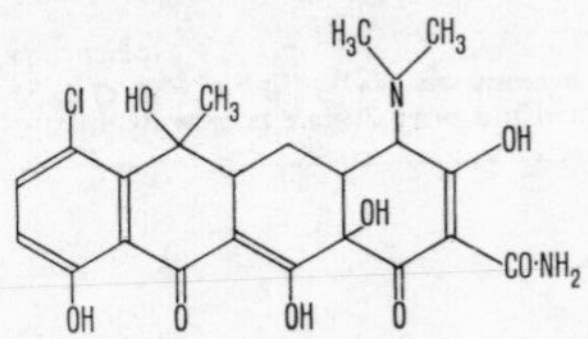	m.p. 168–169° C $[\alpha]_D^{23}$ – 227.9° UV max.: 229, 251, 265, 370 mμ (hydrochloride, pH 4.3)	Thermolabile in strong acids and alkalies; stable at pH 2.5, unstable at pH 7.0 and above at 25° C	LD_{50} mice: i.v. 134 mg/kg; s.c. ca. 3500 mg/kg In man, oral doses of 15–30 mg/kg/day usually well tolerated; side effects: nausea, vomiting, diarrhea, stomatitis; topically, skin sensitization less than with sulfonamides, penicillin or streptomycin	Broad-spectrum antibiotic, primarily bacteriostatic. Oral and parenteral use. For clinical use see the tables on pages 646–688. Resistance has been shown by *Staphylococcus aureus*, occasionally by *Streptococcus pyogenes*; resistant organisms often show cross resistance to other tetracyclines but not to other antibiotics. Synergistic with penicillin in staphylococcal endocarditis. For International Standard s. p. 738
Colimycin (colistin)	*Bacillus colistinus*	$C_{45}H_{85}O_{10}N_{13}$ 968.28	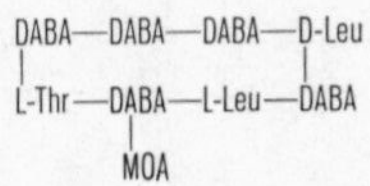 (DABA = αγ-diaminobutyric acid, MOA = 6-methyloctanoic acid)		Colimycin salts are relatively stable in solution at pH 2–6 but decrease in stability above pH 6. The salts are thermostable in solid form	LD_{50}[2]: mice: colimycin sulfate i.v. 5.46 mg base/kg, s.c. 48.6 mg base/kg colimycin methanesulfonate i.v. 222.33 mg base/kg, s.c. 138.00 mg base/kg In man only minor side effects, such as pruritus, vertigo, drug fever	Primarily bactericidal. Effective against a wide range of GRAM-negative bacteria, especially *Pseudomonas aeruginosa*, *Escherichia coli*, *Aerobacter aerogenes* and *Klebsiella pneumoniae*; not effective against *Proteus*. Particularly valuable in acute or resistant urinary infections. Resistant strains rare. Cross resistance to polymyxin B may occur
Cycloheximide	*Streptomyces griseus*, *S. noursei*	$C_{15}H_{23}O_4N$ 281.36	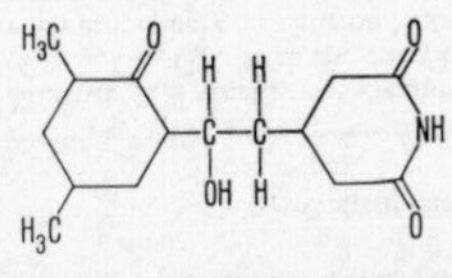	m.p. 115–116.5° C $[\alpha]_D^{25}$ – 6.8°	Thermostable	LD_{50} mice: i.v. 150 mg/kg Clinically toxic when administered intrathecally	Inactive against bacteria and dermatophytes. Effective against various fungi and yeasts, especially (in vitro) *Cryptococcus neoformans*. Used in laboratory culture media for isolation of microorganisms from mixed cultures in presence of saprophytic fungi

Cycloserine (D-4-amino-3-*iso*-oxazolidone; PA-94)	*Streptomyces garyphalus, S. orchidaceus, S. lavendulae*; synthesis	$C_{36}HO_2N_2$ 102.10	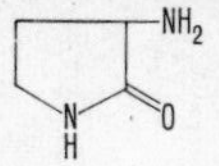	m. p. 154–155°C (decomposition) $[\alpha]_D^{20-25}$ + 115–116° (1.0–1.17 g/100 ml H_2O) UV max.: 226 mμ	Stable to alkali; thermostable	LD_{50} mice: oral > 5000 mg/kg In man, side effects appear at dosage > 1 g/day; headache, vertigo, drowsiness, anorexia, neurological symptoms	Orally, in advanced pulmonary tuberculosis, urinary tract infections, bacterial pneumonia, chronic upper respiratory tract infections
Demethylchlortetracycline	*Streptomyces aureofaciens*	$C_{21}H_{21}O_8N_2Cl$ 464.87	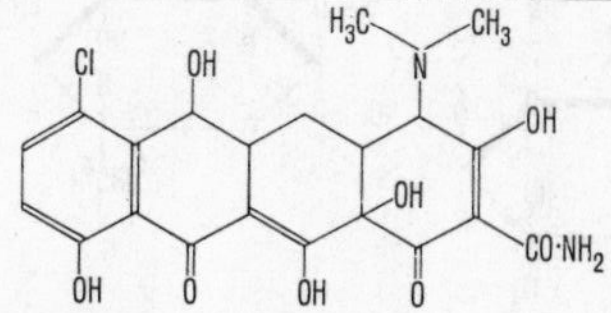	Sesquihydrate: $[\alpha]_D^{25}$ − 258° (0.5% in 0.1–N H_2SO_4) m.p. 174–178°C (decomposition)	Highly resistant to acids and alkalis	As for other tetracyclines. Phototoxicity: excessive reaction to unfiltered sunlight in 1.5% of patients	As for other tetracyclines, but levels of serum activity much higher and better sustained after single and repeated doses. Half-life in serum 44% longer than for tetracycline. Resistance as for other tetracyclines
Dihydrostreptomycin	Catalytic hydrogenation of streptomycin	$C_{21}H_{41}O_{12}N_7$ 583.62	As for streptomycin, with the –CHO group of the streptose component replaced by $-CH_2OH$	m. p. 255–256°C (sulfate) $[\alpha]_D^{25}$ − 82 to − 88.7° (hydrochloride)	More stable to alkali than streptomycin	As for streptomycin. Topically, dihydrostreptomycin is less likely to cause sensitization than streptomycin	See remarks under Streptomycin
Erythromycin	*Streptomyces erythraeus*	$C_{37}H_{67}O_{13}N$ 733.95	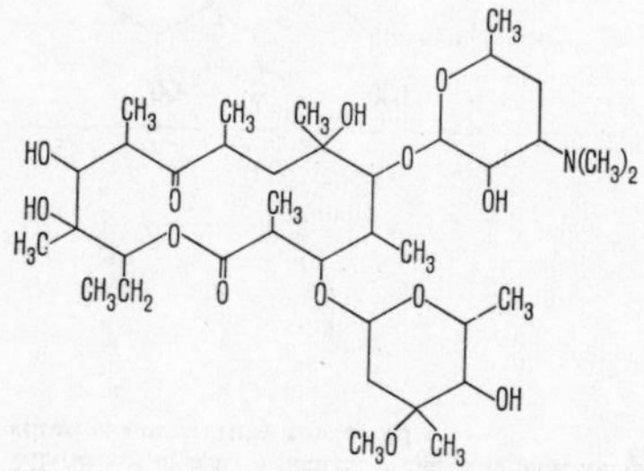	m. p. 136–140°C $[\alpha]_D^{20}$ − 73.5° (in methanol) UV max.: 278 mμ	Stable at − 25° to + 4°C; stable 4 days at 37°C; unstable at 60° to 100°C	LD_{50} mice: s.c. ca. 1800 mg/kg In man, generally no toxic symptoms up to doses of 300 to 500 mg; higher doses may cause gastric distress. Topically, skin sensitization less than with sulfonamides, penicillin or streptomycin	Highly active against GRAM-positive bacteria, including strains resistant to penicillin and tetracyclines. Orally, especially effective in pneumonia due to *Diplococcus pneumoniae*, and in micrococcal and streptococcal infections, including pharyngitis, tonsillitis, scarlet fever, cellulitis; also prophylactically in convalescence from rheumatic fever. *Staphylococcus aureus* and *Streptococcus pyogenes* may develop resistance. No significant cross resistance with other antibiotics except carbomycin. For International Standard see page 738
Framycetin (actiline)	*Streptomyces* spp. resembling *S. lavendulae*	— 1400–1500	Unknown	Picrate: m. p. 189°C (decomposition) $[\alpha]_D^{20}$ − 32°		LD_{50} mice: i.v. 65 mg/kg In man, oral doses up to 0.75–2.0 g/day well tolerated	Marked suppression of enteric bacteria; as aerosol in bronchopneumopathies; topically in staphylococcal infections

* Melting point (m.p.); specific rotation [α], in water unless otherwise stated (for definition see footnote, page 336); ultraviolet absorption maxima (UV max.), in water unless otherwise stated.

1) See reference *1*, page 637. *2)* SCHWARTZ et al., *Antibiotics Annual, 1959–1960*, New York, 1960, page 41. *3)* See reference *5*, page 636.

Antibiotics of proven clinical efficacy (continued)

Name Synonyms	Source	Formula Mol. wt.	Constitution	Physical properties*	Stability	Toxicity[1]	Remarks (Clinical usefulness, resistance, etc.)
Fumagillin (phagopedin sigma)	*Aspergillus fumigatus*	$C_{26-27}H_{34-36}O_7$ 436–488 (found)	Monoester of octa-1,3,5,7-tetraene-1,8-dicarboxylic acid with an alcohol of mainly unknown constitution	m.p. 189–194°C (decomposition) $[\alpha]_D^{25}$ − 26.6° (in methanol) UVmax.: 239, 304, 322, 336, 351 mμ	Thermolabile	LD_{50} mice: s.c. 800 mg/kg In man, oral doses of 5–10 mg/day for 10–12 days well tolerated; higher doses may cause abdominal pain and skin rash	Orally, in intestinal amebiasis, particularly from *Entamoeba histolytica*
Gramicidin	*Bacillus brevis*	$C_{148}H_{210}O_{26}N_{30}$ (?) 1000–3000 (found)	Mixture of at least 4 neutral cyclic polypeptides. Constitution not yet fully elucidated	m.p. 228–231°C $[\alpha]_D^{20}$ + 3° (in ethanol) UV max.: 271, 281.5, 290.5 mμ	Thermostable	LD_{100} mice: i.v. 2.5–5 mg/kg Oral doses of 1000 mg/kg nontoxic to mice and rats	Component of tyrothricin (page 645). Resistance readily developed by *Staphylococcus aureus*
Griseofulvin	*Penicillium griseofulvum*	$C_{17}H_{17}O_6Cl$ 352.78	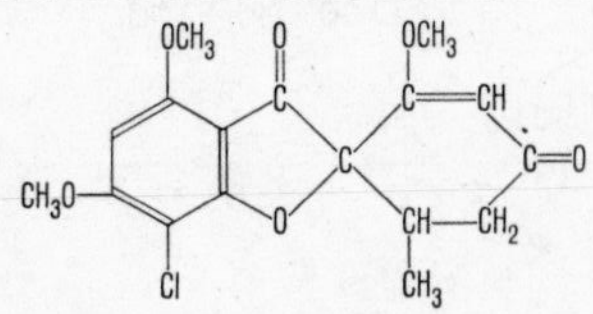	m.p. 218–221°C $[\alpha]_D^{17}$ + 370° (in chloroform) UV max.: 286, 325 mμ	Thermostable	In man, occasionally minor side effects such as malaise, headache, mild gastrointestinal disturbances, transient leukopenia, macular and papular eruptions	Fungistatic. Effective orally in dermatomycosis; see also page 699
Kanamycin	*Streptomyces kanamyceticus*	$C_{18}H_{36}O_{11}N_4$ 484.52	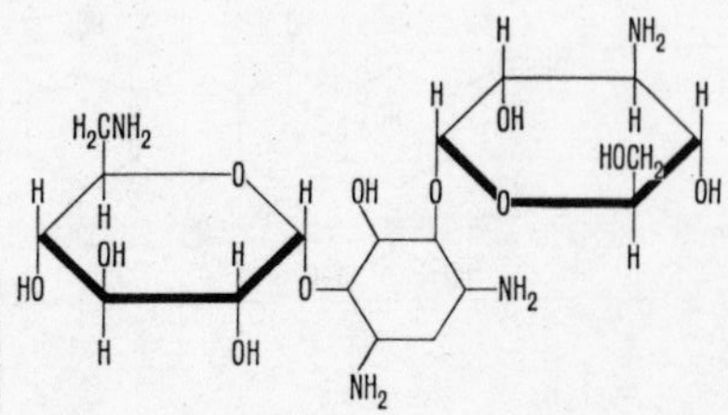	$[\alpha]_D^{24}$ + 146° (base)	Thermostable	LD_{50} mice[2]: i.v. 316 mg/kg; s.c. 1648 mg/kg; oral > 10 g/kg Side effects[3]: none in man in parenteral dosage up to 2 g. Prolonged administration results in toxic action on eighth nerve (hyaline and granular cylinders, tinnitus, deafness). Dosage should not exceed total of 40 g	Bactericidal for GRAM-positive and -negative bacteria, including strains of *Staphylococcus aureus*. Resistance developed by *Staphylococcus aureus* and *Escherichia coli* more slowly than to streptomycin. Complete cross resistance with neomycin, partial cross resistance with streptomycin. For International Reference Preparation see page 738

Neomycins (flavomycin) Neomycin A = Neamine; Neomycin B = Streptothricin B II; Neomycin C = Streptothricin B I	*Streptomyces fradiae* and other *Streptomyces* spp.	Neomycin A: $C_{12}H_{24-26}O_6N_4$ Neomycin B, C: $C_{23}H_{46}O_{12}N_6$ or $C_{23}H_{48}O_{13}N_6$ 507–669 (found)	Unknown (basic). Neomycin A is a methanolysis product of both neomycin B and C	Neomycin A: m.p. 250–256° C (decomposition) $[\alpha]_D^{25}$ + 123.5° Neomycin B: $[\alpha]_D^{25}$ + 71° (in 0.02-N NaOH) Neomycin C: $[\alpha]_D^{25}$ + 110° (in 0.02-N NaOH)	Thermo-, acid and alkali stable	LD_{50} mice: oral > 2880 mg/kg In man, oto- and nephrotoxicity preclude parenteral systemic use; oral doses of 6–10 g/day over 1–3 days tolerated. Topically, skin sensitization less than with sulfonamides, penicillin or streptomycin	Primarily bactericidal. Orally, as intestinal antiseptic prior to bowel surgery; also in bacillary dysentery, amebiasis, infantile diarrhea. Topically, in ocular and skin infections and combined with cortisol in external otitis. By instillation, in cervicitis, *Proteus* vaginitis, nongonococcal urethritis. Intraperitoneally, in peritonitis; intramuscularly, in urinary tract infections. Resistance pattern resembles penicillin. No appreciable cross resistance with other antibiotics. For International Reference Preparation see page 738
Novobiocin (PA-93; streptonivicin)	*Streptomyces niveus*, *S. spheroides*	$C_{31}H_{36}O_{11}N_2$ 612.65	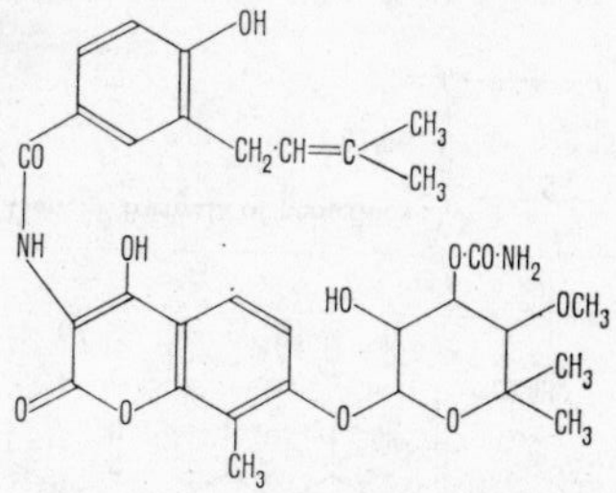	m.p. 152–154° C; 170–172° C (2 forms) $[\alpha]_D^{25}$ – 27° UV max.: 304 mμ (in pH 7 phosphate buffer)	Stable when dry at 24° C in absence of light; dilute aqueous solution stable at pH 2 at 24° C; half-life, 60 days at pH 7–10	LD_{50} mice: oral 962 to > 1000 mg/kg In man, doses of 1.5–2 g/day oral, 500 mg/12 hours i.v., or 250 mg i.m. well tolerated. Orally, allergic dermatitis is a frequent side effect, others are minimal	Bacteriostatic. Orally, in pneumococcal infections, FRIEDLÄNDER pneumonia, acute pharyngitis, sinusitis, otitis media, panophthalmitis, urinary tract infections, scarlet fever, cutaneous anthrax, breast abscesses, acute tracheobronchitis, bacteremia, osteomyelitis, wound infections (especially *Staphylococcus aureus* and *Streptococcus pyogenes*). Resistance developed fairly rapidly in vitro by *Staphylococcus aureus*. No cross resistance with other major antibiotics. For International Reference Preparation see page 738
Nystatin (fungicidin)	*Streptomyces noursei*	$C_{46}H_{77}O_{19}N$ 922, 956 (found)	Amphoteric mixture of polyenes of unknown constitution	Decomposition > 160° C $[\alpha]_D^{25}$ + 21° (in pyridine) UV max.: 280, 291, 304, 318 mμ	Unstable at pH 2 or 9	LD_{50} mice: i.p. 12–21 mg/kg In man, oral doses of 1.25 g daily well tolerated without significant side effects	Fungicidal and fungistatic. Orally and/or topically in all forms of moniliasis, including gastrointestinal due to tetracycline therapy. Possibly helpful in disinfestation in amebiasis due to *Entamoeba histolytica*. No significant resistance shown by *Candida albicans*. Cross resistance with other polyene-type antibiotics, e.g. trichomycin. Useful in control of fungi in samples of water, etc. being examined for enteric viruses. For International Reference Preparation see page 738

* Melting point (m.p.); specific rotation [α], in water unless otherwise stated (for definition see footnote, page 336); ultraviolet absorption maxima (UV max.), in water unless otherwise stated.
1) See reference *1*, page 637. *2)* TISCH et al., *Ann. N. Y. Acad. Sci.*, **76**, 44 (1958). *3)* BUNN et al., *Ann. N. Y. Acad. Sci.*, **76**, 109 (1958).

Antibiotics of proven clinical efficacy (continued)

Name Synonyms	Source	Formula Mol. wt.	Constitution	Physical properties*	Stability	Toxicity[1]	Remarks (Clinical usefulness, resistance, etc.)
Oleandomycin (PA-105; amimycin)	*Streptomyces antibioticus*	$C_{35}H_{61}O_{12}N$	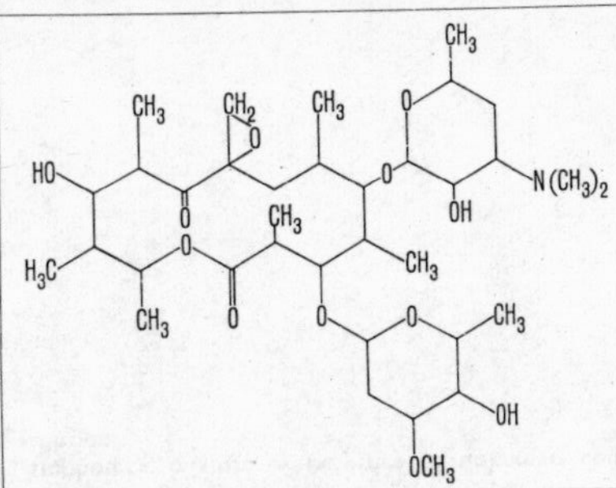	m.p. 125–128° C $[\alpha]_D^{25} - 54°$ (dihydrate in methanol) UV max: 286–289 mμ	Stable at room temperature at pH 2–9 in aqueous solution	LD_{50} mice: i.v. 550 mg/kg In children, oral doses of 40 mg/kg/day for 5–8 days well tolerated	Orally, in bacterial pneumonia and staphylococcal enteritis in children (dosage as under Toxicity). Cross resistance with carbomycin and erythromycin reported. For International Reference Preparation see page 738
Oxytetracycline	*Streptomyces rimosus*	$C_{22}H_{24}O_9N_2$ 460.45	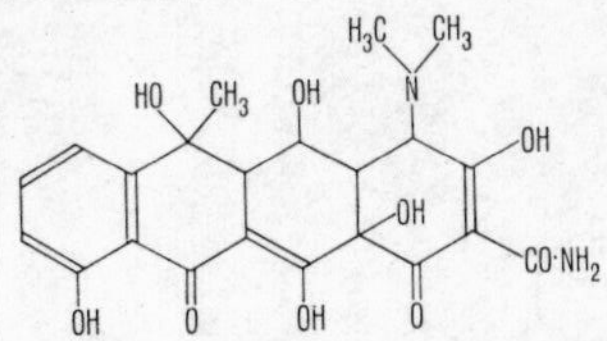	Dihydrate: m.p. 181–182° C (decomposition) $[\alpha]_D^{25} + 26.5°$ (in methanol) UV max.: 249, 276, 353 mμ (in pH 4.5 phosphate buffer)	Stable at acid pH; decreasing stability at pH 7 and above at 37° C	LD_{50} mice: oral 6696–7200 mg/kg In man, oral doses of 15–30 mg/kg/day usually well tolerated; side effects: nausea, vomiting, diarrhea, secondary infections with yeast-like organisms; topically, skin sensitization less than with sulfonamides, penicillin or streptomycin	Broad-spectrum antibiotic, primarily bacteriostatic. For clinical use see the tables on pages 646–688. Synergistic with streptomycin in staphylococcal endocarditis. Resistance shown by *Staphylococcus aureus*; resistant organisms show cross resistance to other tetracyclines but not to other antibiotics. For International Standard see page 738
Penicillins (F, dihydro-F, G, K, O, V, X) Penicillin I = Penicillin F; Penicillin II = Penicillin G; Penicillin III = Penicillin X *Semisynthetic penicillins:* Methicillin Phenethicillin For chemical names see under Constitution	*Penicillium notatum* (WESTLING); other *Penicillium* spp.; *Aspergillus* spp.	Penicillin F: $C_{14}H_{20}O_4N_2S$ 312.40 Dihydropenicillin F: $C_{14}H_{22}O_4N_2S$ 314.41 Penicillin G: $C_{16}H_{18}O_4N_2S$ 334.40 Penicillin K: $C_{16}H_{26}O_4N_2S$ 342.47 Penicillin O: $C_{13}H_{18}O_4N_2S_2$ 330.44 Penicillin V: $C_{16}H_{19}O_5N_2S$ 351.41 Penicillin X: $C_{16}H_{18}O_5N_2S$ 350.40	General formula of penicillins: 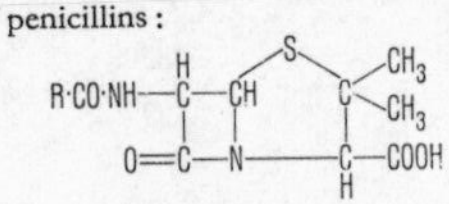 Penicillin F: $R = CH_3{\cdot}CH_2{\cdot}CH{=}CH{\cdot}CH_2{-}$ (2-pentenyl-) Dihydropenicillin F: $R = CH_3{\cdot}(CH_2)_4{-}$ (*n*-amyl-) Penicillin G: R = 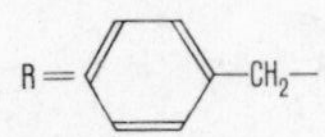 (benzyl-) Penicillin K: $R = CH_3{\cdot}(CH_2)_6{-}$ (*n*-heptyl-) Penicillin O: $R = CH_2{=}CH{\cdot}CH_2{\cdot}S{\cdot}CH_2{-}$ (allylmercaptomethyl-)	Penicillin F: m.p. 204–205° C (decomposition) (Na salt) $[\alpha]_D^{20} + 316°$ Penicillin G: m.p. 215° C (decomposition) (Na salt) $[\alpha]_D^{25} + 301–305°$ UV max.: 252, 257.5, 264 mμ Penicillin K: $[\alpha]_D^{25} + 258°$	All penicillins: Stable in aqueous solution when pure, unstable when impure; labile to acids, alkalies, heat, penicillinase	All penicillins: Penicillins are essentially non-toxic in animals, except guinea pigs. Sensitivity reactions in man vary from erythema and urticaria to severe serum sickness, exfoliative dermatitis and rarely fatal anaphylactic shock (see page 635), and may also occur following topical application. Penicillin O is clinically as effective as G and somewhat less likely to cause reactions. Persons sensitive to penicillin G can usually tolerate penicillin O	All penicillins: Bacteriostatic and slowly bactericidal. For clinical use see the tables on pages 646–688. Administration almost entirely by i.m. injection, very occasionally oral, when preferably as benzathine penicillin G. Penicillins are synergistic with chlortetracycline in staphylococcal endocarditis and with streptomycin in streptococcal endocarditis. Only organism showing clinically serious resistance is *Staphylococcus aureus*, resistant strains of which are penicillinase producers. On staphylococcal resistance see page 662. For International Standards and Reference Preparation see page 738

Penicillins *(continued)*			Penicillin V: 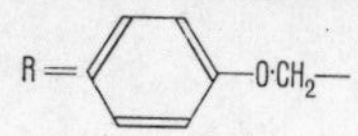 (phenoxymethyl-)	Penicillin V: UV max.: 268, 274 mμ	Penicillin V: More stable than other penicillins (both free and as salts) and also the only one stable in acid media such as gastric juice	Penicillin V: Clinically as effective as penicillin G and somewhat less likely to cause reactions	
			Penicillin X: 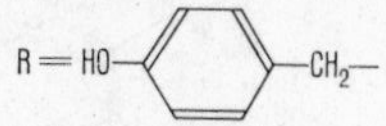 (*p*-hydroxybenzyl-)	Penicillin X: m.p. 228–235° C (decomposition) (Na salt) $[\alpha]_D^{20}$ + 267° UV max.: 278 mμ			
Semisynthetic penicillins		Methicillin: $C_{17}H_{20}O_6N_2S$ 380.43	Methicillin: 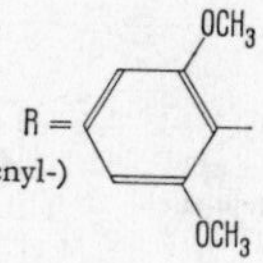 (dimethoxyphenyl-)		Methicillin: Resistant to penicillinase	Methicillin: Remarkably nontoxic but may induce sensitivity in patients sensitive to penicillin G	Methicillin: Range of antibacterial activity as for penicillin G, but also active against staphylococci resistant to penicillin G. Given by i.m. injection
		Phenethicillin: $C_{17}H_{20}O_5N_2S$ 364.43	Phenethicillin: 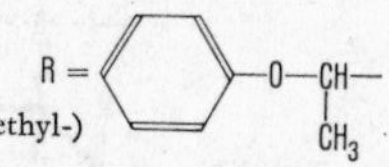 (α-phenoxyethyl-)	Phenethicillin: m.p. 230–231° C (decomposition) (racemate, K salt)	Phenethicillin: Resistant to acids	Phenethicillin: LD_{50} mice[2]: i.v. 312 mg/kg, oral > 2000 mg/kg	Phenethicillin: Range of activity as for other penicillins but produces higher serum concentrations orally than does penicillin V
Polymyxin B (bacillosporin B)	*Bacillus polymyxa*	Polymyxin B_1: $C_{56}H_{99}O_{14}N_{16}$ 1150 ± 50 (found)	Mixture of 2 basic cyclic polypeptides (B_1 and B_2) differing only in the nature of the fatty acid component. Constitution not yet fully elucidated	m.p. 228–235° C (decomposition) $[\alpha]_D^{25}$ − 85.1° (in ethanol)	Thermo- and acid stable; alkali unstable	LD_{50} mice: i.v. 6–9 mg/kg; s.c. 68–87 mg/kg In man, doses of 2.5 mg/kg/day i.m. fairly well tolerated, with minimal nephrotoxicity and other side effects; orally well tolerated; topically, skin sensitization less than with sulfonamides, penicillin or streptomycin. Less toxic than other polymyxins	Essentially bactericidal. Intramuscularly, in pertussis and infections with *Escherichia coli* and *Pseudomonas aeruginosa*. Topically, for corneal ulcers caused by *Pseudomonas aeruginosa*; also combined with oxytetracycline and other antibiotics in many skin infections. No significant resistance yet reported. For International Standard see page 738
Puromycin (6-dimethyl-amino-9[3'-(*p*-methoxy-L-phenylalanyl-amino)-β-D-ribofuranosyl] purine)	*Streptomyces alboniger*; synthesis	$C_{22}H_{29}O_5N_7$ 471.53	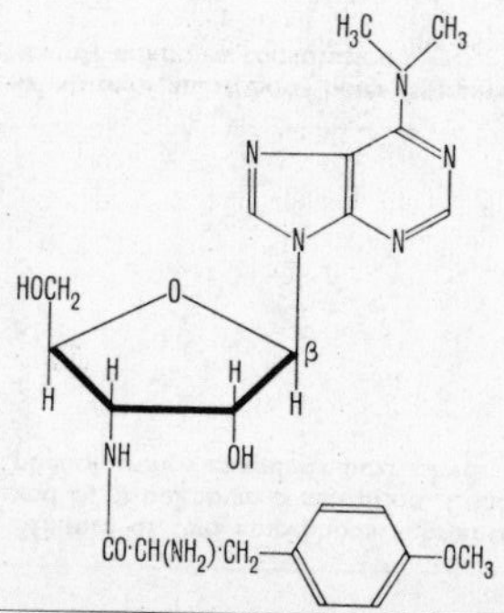	m.p. 175.5–177° C $[\alpha]_D^{25}$ − 11° (in ethanol) UV max.: 267.5 mμ (0.1-N HCl) 275 mμ (0.1-N NaOH)	Thermo- and pH stable	LD_{50} mice: oral 678–720 mg/kg In man, oral doses of 9.5–21 g/day for 8–10 days well tolerated; headache, nausea, asthenia, gastrointestinal distress are occasional side effects	Trypanostatic. Orally, in trypanosomiasis (*Trypanosoma gambiense*) and acute ulcerative and chronic amebiasis (*Entamoeba histolytica*)

* Melting point (m.p.); specific rotation [α], in water unless otherwise stated (for definition see footnote, page 336); ultraviolet absorption maxima (UV max.), in water unless otherwise stated.

1) See reference *1*, page 637. *2)* PINDELL et al., *Antibiotics Annual, 1959–1960*, New York, 1960, page 119.

Antibiotics of proven clinical efficacy (continued)

Name Synonyms	Source	Formula Mol. wt.	Constitution	Physical properties*	Stability	Toxicity[1]	Remarks (Clinical usefulness, resistance, etc.)
Ristocetin	*Nocardia lurida*	— ~ 5000	Mixture of two amorphous substances, ristocetin A and B, of unknown constitution. Contains amino and phenol groups as well as a carbohydrate residue	Ristocetin A: $[\alpha]_D^{25}$ − 120° to − 133° Ristocetin B: $[\alpha]_D^{25}$ − 144° to − 149° UV max.: ~ 280 mμ		LD_{50} mice[2]: i.v. Ristocetin A (sulfate): 1350–2000 mg/kg Ristocetin B (sulfate): 645–760 mg/kg Intramuscular administration causes severe tissue irritation so that intravenous route only should be used. Other side effects: skin eruptions, leukopenia, thrombophlebitis, fever, allergic reactions	Effective against GRAM-positive organisms (streptococci, enterococci, pneumococci, staphylococci, but tubercle bacilli only in vitro), but less active than penicillin, for which it is a possible substitute since no resistant strains of *Staphylococcus aureus* have yet been reported. No cross resistance with other antibiotics. For International Reference Preparation see page 738
Spiramycin	*Streptomyces ambofaciens*	I: $C_{45}H_{78}O_{15}N_2$ II: $C_{47}H_{80}O_{16}N_2$ III: $C_{48}H_{82}O_{16}N_2$	Mixture of amorphous bases (spiramycin I, II, III) of mainly unknown constitution	$[\alpha]_D^{20}$ − 80° (in methanol) UV max.: 231 mμ	Fairly stable in aqueous solution	LD_{50} mice: oral > 5000 mg/kg In man, oral doses up to 4 g daily induced no side effects	Orally, in *Staphylococcus aureus* infections, bacterial pneumonia. Cross resistance with carbomycin and erythromycin
Streptomycin	*Streptomyces griseus, S. bikiniensis, S. mashuensis*	$C_{21}H_{39}O_{12}N_7$ 581.60	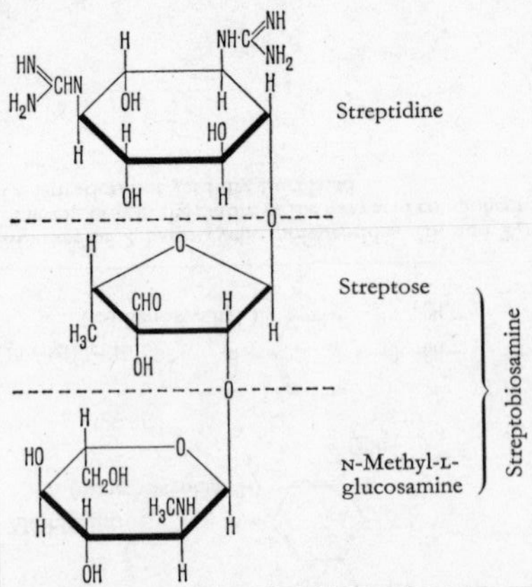	m.p. 164–165° C (reineckate) (decomposition) $[\alpha]_D^{25}$ − 79° (sulfate)	Stable at pH 3–7; less stable to heat, acid, alkali	LD_{50} mice: oral 9000 mg/kg In man, low toxicity; side effects are skin rash, malaise, fever, eosinophilia; in prolonged therapy, neurotoxic action on 8th cranial nerve, with vertigo, tinnitus, deafness, ataxia, from which recovery may be slow or incomplete	Bacteriostatic and bactericidal. Effective against GRAM-negative and -positive organisms. For clinical use see the tables on pages 646–688. For synergism in combination with other antibiotics see page 636. Resistance may be developed rapidly by tubercle bacilli and other organisms. For International Standard see page 738
Tetracycline	*Streptomyces* spp.; reduction of chlor-tetracycline	$C_{22}H_{24}O_8N_2$ 444.45	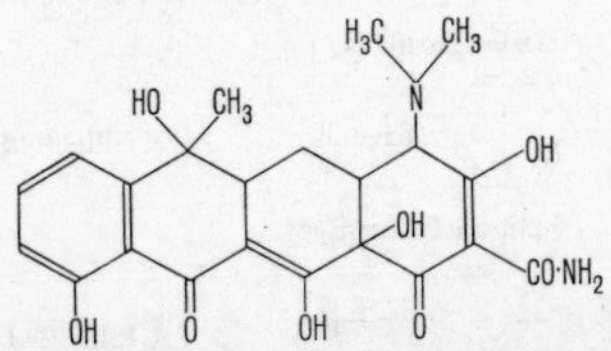	m.p. 170–175° C (decomposition); (hydrochloride 214° C) $[\alpha]_D^{25}$ − 239° (in methanol) UV max.: 220, 268, 355 mμ (in 0.1-N HCl)	Stable in solution at pH 7.0; less stable in acid or alkaline solution	LD_{50} mice: oral 2130 to > 3000 mg/kg In man, toxicity low; occasional side effects in oral therapy are nausea, vomiting, diarrhea, and are less frequent than with other tetracyclines; topically, skin sensitization less than with sulfonamides, penicillin or streptomycin	Broad-spectrum antibiotic, primarily bacteriostatic. Oral and parenteral use. For clinical use see the tables on pages 646–688. Resistance developed by *Staphylococcus aureus* and *Escherichia coli*. Resistant organisms show cross resistance to other tetracyclines but not to other antibiotics. For International Standard see page 738

Trichomycin	*Streptomyces hachijoensis*	Unknown	Unknown	m.p. 155° C (decomposition) UV max.: 286, 346, 364, 384, 405 mμ	Thermostable at pH 7–8.5; unstable at pH 2	LD_{50} mice: s.c. 160 mg/kg In man, oral doses of 50 mg tolerated	Orally or intravaginally in vaginitis caused by *Trichomonas vaginalis* or *Candida albicans*. Topically, in other *Candida albicans* infections. No significant resistance in vitro shown by *Candida albicans* or *Trichomonas vaginalis*
Tyrocidine	*Bacillus brevis*	Tyrocidine A: $C_{66}H_{86}O_{13}N_{13}$ 1270 (found) Tyrocidine B: $C_{68}H_{88}O_{13}N_{14}$ 1309.56	Basic cyclic polypeptides. Constitution not yet fully elucidated, but sequence and nature of amino acid residues has been established	Tyrocidine A: m.p. 240–242° C (decomposition) $[\alpha]_D^{25} - 111°$ (in 50% ethanol) UV max.: 290 mμ	Thermostable	LD_{50} mice: i.v. 15 mg/kg Oral doses of 1000 mg/kg nontoxic to mice	Component of tyrothricin (see below)
Tyrothricin	*Bacillus brevis*	See under the individual components	Mainly a mixture of gramicidin (10–20%) and tyrocidine (40–80%), the latter usually as hydrochloride	—	See under the individual components	LD_{50} mice: i.v. 3.7 mg/kg Oral doses of 1000 mg/kg are nontoxic to mice and rats. In man, high toxicity precludes parenteral use (orally ineffective); topically, skin sensitization less than with sulfonamides, penicillin or streptomycin	Bacteriostatic and bactericidal. Topically, in infections due to streptococci, *Diplococcus pneumoniae*, *Staphylococcus aureus*, particularly bronchitis, tonsillitis, otitis, dermatosis, mastoiditis, ulcers, empyema, wounds, burns, ocular infections; also combined with phenylmercuric acetate in *Trichomonas* vaginitis. Resistance developed by *Staphylococcus aureus*
Vancomycin	*Streptomyces orientalis*	— 3200–3500 ± 200	Amphoteric substance of unknown constitution but containing amino and phenol groups and a carbohydrate residue	UV max.: 282 mμ (hydrochloride)		LD_{50} mice: i.v. 400–500 mg/kg In man, doses of 50–100 mg i.v. 3–4 times daily well tolerated up to 7 days	Bactericidal. Intravenously, in pneumococcal pneumonia, streptococcal pharyngitis, erysipelas. Resistance very slowly developed by *Staphylococcus aureus*. For International Reference Preparation see page 738
Viomycin	*Streptomyces floridae*, *S. vinaceus*, *S. puniceus*	$C_{17-18}H_{31-35}O_8N_9$	Strongly basic polypeptide of unknown constitution	Sulfate: m.p. 252° C (decomposition) $[\alpha]_D^{20} - 39.8°$ (pH 6) UV max.: 268.5 mμ (pH 7)	Very stable in acid, less stable in alkaline solution	LD_{50} mice: i.v. 165–240 mg/kg; s.c. 1381 mg/kg In man, renal and neural toxicity: elevation of blood urea, serum electrolyte changes, vestibular and aural disturbances, eosinophilia, skin eruptions	Effective in tuberculosis, but less active and more toxic than streptomycin or isoniazid. Therapy should be intermittent (2 g i.m. twice weekly) in conjunction with isoniazid or PAS (not streptomycin). Resistance pattern of *Mycobacterium tuberculosis* similar to that to streptomycin. Resistant strains show no cross resistance to streptomycin or neomycin For International Reference Preparation see page 738

* Melting point (m.p.); specific rotation [α], in water unless otherwise stated (for definition see footnote, page 336); ultraviolet absorption maxima (UV max.), in water unless otherwise stated.

1) See reference *1*, page 637. *2)* Hwang et al., *Antibiotics Annual, 1957–1958*, New York, 1958, page 163.

For classification of organisms see pages 721–724; for index of synonyms see pages 725–734

Bacteria (Schizomycetes)

The table below and on pages 647–685 lists only those bacteria which as far as can be ascertained have been reported as pathogenic to man or closely associated with pathological processes in man. Organisms which are normally present in man but have not been reported as pathogenic have therefore been excluded. The data and arrangement are based on the 7th edition of *Bergey's Manual of Determinative Bacteriology*, supplemented by various standard works (see the bibliography below) and papers from the current literature.

The classification of the bacteria given in *Bergey's Manual* is reproduced on pages 721–724 with the genera numbered in **bold** figures. The corresponding **bold** figures in column 1 of the table thus enable the taxonomic position of each organism to be readily determined. In addition, the organisms are numbered consecutively (italic figures in column 2 of the table) so that information on any organism or disease can be quickly located by using the index of synonyms on pages 725–734.

The clinical effectiveness of antibiotics with respect to infections is indicated, where known, in column 7 of the table as follows: 1 = to be used in the first instance (drug of choice in **bold** type); 2 and 3 = to be used as second and third choice respectively; 0 = no clinically significant effect. See also the table on pages 637–645.

Bibliography (bacteria)

Breed et al. (Eds.), *Bergey's Manual of Determinative Bacteriology*, 7th ed., Baltimore, 1957; Dougherty and Lamberti, *Textbook of Bacteriology*, 3rd ed., St.Louis, 1954; Pullen, R. L. (Ed.), *Communicable Diseases*, Philadelphia, 1950; Manson-Bahr, P. H. (Ed.), *Manson's Tropical Diseases*, 14th ed., London, 1954; Mackie et al. (Eds.), *A Manual of Tropical Medicine*, 2nd ed., Philadelphia, 1954; Stitt et al., *Practical Bacteriology, Hematology and Animal Parasitology*, 10th ed., Philadelphia, 1948; Kauffmann, F., *Enterobacteriaceae*, 2nd ed., Copenhagen, 1954; Dubos, R. J. (Ed.), *Bacterial and Mycotic Infections of Man*, 3rd ed., Philadelphia and London, 1958; *Antibiotics Annual*, New York; *Antibiotics and Chemotherapy*, New York; and *Antibiotica et Chemotherapia*, Basle.

See pages 721–724	See pages 725–734	**Bacteria (Schizomycetes)** Classified name / *Synonyms* / Common names	Principal characteristics	Habitat, host, transmission, etc.	Associated diseases or source	Clinical application of antibiotics: Penicillin	Streptomycin	Tetracyclines	Remarks
37	*1*	**Pseudomonas aeruginosa** (Schroeter) Migula *Bacillus pyocyaneus, Bacterium aeruginosum, Pseudomonas pyocyanea* Blue pus organism (Bacille pyocyanique)	Gram-negative. Very motile, slender rods with 1–3 terminal flagella occurring singly, in pairs and in short chains. Gelatin colonies have sweetish smell and are surrounded by green fluorescent zone. Coagulates milk. β-Hemolysis on blood agar. Facultative aerobe	Ubiquitous saprophyte: water, sewage, soil, air, intestinal tract, skin	Suppuration of wounds (with other organisms; bluish green pus), purulent middle-ear infections, puerperal sepsis, inflammations of bile ducts and urinary tract; in children pyocyanic dysentery, purulent meningitis, hemorrhagic sepsis (pyocyanic sepsis of infants), cutaneous gangrene (ecthyma gangraenosum). May emerge as dominant organism following suppression of other bacterial flora during antibiotic therapy. For reviews see references[1,2]	**Polymyxin B**			Sensitivity of *Pseudomonas* species to antibiotics in vitro (concentrations in μg/ml to which at least half the strains are susceptible)[3] Colimycin 0.5 Polymyxin B 1.5 Neomycin 10 Streptomycins 50 Chloramphenicol 62.5 Kanamycin 125 Tetracycline > 125 Erythromycin > 200 Oxytetracycline 400 Chlortetracycline 400 Penicillin 3000
37	*2*	**Pseudomonas pseudomallei** (Whitmore) Haynes *Bacillus pseudomallei, Bacillus whitmori, Loefflerella pseudomallei, Malleomyces pseudomallei* Whitmore's bacillus	Gram-negative. Short rods occurring singly and in short chains. Motile with 1 to 4 polar flagella. Cream-colored, thick colonies on agar. Slow hemolysis. Facultative aerobe	Man and animals in Far East	Isolated from lesions and blood in man, and from water. Cause of a glanders-like disease (melioidosis) in man and animals				
63	*3*	**Vibrio comma** (Schroeter) Winslow et al. *Microspira comma, Spirillum cholerae asiaticae, Vibrio cholerae* Cholera vibrio, comma bacillus	Gram-negative. Curved rods occurring singly or in spiral chains. Motile with one polar flagellum. α-Hemolysis on blood agar. Rapid growth on peptone water. Aerobe, anaerobic growth slow	Intestines of cholera patients, contaminated water, foods, domestic articles	Pathogen of cholera. See the remarks below	0	2	1	

1) Jawetz, E., *Arch. intern. Med.*, **89**, 90 (1952). *2)* Forkner, C. E., *Pseudomonas Aeruginosa Infections*, New York and London, 1960. *3)* Welch, H., *A Guide to Antibiotic Therapy*, New York, 1959.

Cholera[1] *(No. 3)*

Cholera is endemic in some areas of India, Pakistan, Indochina and Burma. Epidemics in other localities have mostly been due to transmission of the disease from these countries on shipboard. Human infection occurs exclusively by the oral route, usually through contaminated water or food. The former was responsible for the last major European epidemic (Hamburg, 1892), while the 1947 epidemic in Egypt was caused by the consumption of cakes containing infected dates.

The incubation period is 3–5 days. The disease commences essentially in the small intestine, the primary symptoms being vomiting and diarrhea. The typical cholera stools resemble water in which rice has been boiled and contain masses of epithelial cells, mucus and cholera bacilli. The subsequent severe dehydration may be followed by hypochloremia, circulatory collapse, hypothermia and anuria. The injurious agent is not the cholera bacillus as such, but a toxin produced by it[2]. No therapeutically

See pages 721–724	See pages 725–734	**Bacteria (Schizomycetes)** Classified name / *Synonyms* / Common names	Principal characteristics	Habitat, host, transmission, etc.	Associated diseases or source	Clinical application of antibiotics: Penicillin	Streptomycin	Tetracyclines	Remarks
63	*4*	**Vibrio proteus** BUCHNER FINKLER-PRIOR bacillus	GRAM-negative. Motile curved rods with one flagellum. Facultative aerobe	Intestines of patients, contaminated water, foods, domestic articles	Pathogen of cholera infantum (cholera nostras)	0	2	1	
63	*5*	**Vibrio albensis** LEHMANN and NEUMANN *Microspira dunbari, Vibrio phosphorescens* (?)	GRAM-negative. Curved rods occurring singly or in pairs. Motile with one polar flagellum. β-Hemolysis on blood agar. Luminescent. Facultative aerobe	Fresh water, human feces and bile	Found in intestine of patients with cholera, gastroenteritis, typhoid *(V. phosphorescens)*. Pathogenicity doubtful				
63	*6*	**Vibrio fetus** SMITH and TAYLOR	GRAM-negative. Curved rods, possibly filamentous on transfer. Motile with one polar flagellum. No hemolysis. Aerobic to microaerophilic	Cattle and sheep	Cause of infectious abortion in cattle and sheep. Occasionally pathogenic to man[1]				
63	*7*	**Vibrio niger** (RIST) PRÉVOT *Spirillum nigrum*	GRAM-negative. Long, slender, comma or S-shaped cells with a black granule. Motile. Obligate anaerobe	In man in pathological conditions	Isolated in purulent otitis, mastoiditis, pulmonary gangrene, also meningitis and appendicitis				
63	*8*	**Vibrio sputorum** PRÉVOT	GRAM-negative. Straight or slightly curved rods occurring in pairs or short chains. Very motile with 1 to 3 polar flagella. Grows only on enriched media. Some α-hemolysis on blood agar. Anaerobe	Mouth	Isolated in fusospirochetal diseases of the mouth				
69	*9*	**Spirillum minus** CARTER *Spirochaeta muris*	GRAM-negative. Short, thick, motile cells with 2–3 windings. Not yet cultivated on artificial media. Facultative aerobe	Rats and mice. Widely distributed	Spirochetal rat-bite fever (sodoku). Cf. *Streptobacillus moniliformis (No. 93)*	2	2	1	Incubation period 1–3 weeks, after which inflammation and swelling at the site of the bite occur, with repeated bouts of fever of 1–2 days' duration at intervals of 3–10 days
88	*10*	**Chromobacterium janthinum** (ZOPF) HOLLAND *Bacterium janthinum*	GRAM-negative. Single rods, motile with peritrichous flagella. Cultures show violet coloration. Facultative aerobe	Water and soil	Causes fatal septicemia in man and animals				
89	*11*	**Alcaligenes bookeri** (FORD) BERGEY et al. *Bacillus bookeri*	GRAM-negative. Single nonmotile rods with peritrichous flagella, in some strains with single flagellum. No acid or gas formed in carbohydrate media. Gelatin and blood serum liquefied. Facultative aerobe	Intestinal canal	Isolated from stools of children with cholera infantum (cholera nostras)	0 Intestine: **neomycin**	2	1	

1) KAHLER and SHELDON, *New Engl. J. Med.*, **262**, 1218 (1960).

Cholera *(No. 3) (continued)*

effective antibiotic is yet known[3–5]. The tetracyclines eliminate the vibrio from the feces after the third day of treatment, but the mortality rate remains much the same. Antibiotics are therefore mainly of use in limiting epidemics. Chloramphenicol is less effective. The main aim of treatment is rehydration and correction of the electrolyte imbalance, combined with administration of antibiotics, sulfonamides[6] and possibly cortisone[7]. Short-lived immunity (3–6 months) is conferred by injection of cholera vaccine or antigen (for international reference preparations see page 735).

References

1) For a review of the literature see the *Bulletin of the World Health Organization*: (historical) POLLITZER, R., **10**, 421 (1954); (epidemiology) SWAROOP and POLLITZER, **12**, 311 (1955); POLLITZER, R., **16**, 783 (1957); (prevention and control) POLLITZER, R., **17**, 67 (1957); (bacteriology) POLLITZER, R., **12**, 777 (1955); (immunology and serology) POLLITZER and BURROWS, **12**, 945 (1955); (bacteriophages) POLLITZER, R., **13**, 1 (1955); (pathology) POLLITZER, R., **13**, 1075 (1955); (laboratory diagnosis) BURROWS and POLLITZER, **18**, 275 (1958). *2)* METCHNIKOFF, E., *Ann. Inst. Pasteur*, **7**, 403, 562 (1893). *3)* DAS et al., *Indian med. Gaz.*, **86**, 437 (1951). *4)* SEAL et al., *Brit. med. J.*, **1**, 740 (1954). *5)* DUTTA and HABBU, *Brit. J. Pharmacol.*, **10**, 153 (1955). *6)* LAKSANAPHUK et al., *Amer. J. trop. Med.*, **9**, 620 (1960). *7)* DE, S. N., *Cholera*, Edinburgh and London, 1961, page 124.

For classification of organisms see pages 721–724; for index of synonyms see pages 725–734

See pages 721–724	See pages 725–734	**Bacteria (Schizomycetes)** Classified name *Synonyms* Common names	Principal characteristics	Habitat, host, transmission, etc.	Associated diseases or source	Clinical application of antibiotics: Penicillin	Streptomycin	Tetracyclines	Remarks
94	*12*	**Escherichia coli** (MIGULA) CASTELLANI and CHALMERS *Bacillus coli, Bacillus escherichii, Bacterium coli, Bacterium coli commune* Colon bacillus, coli bacillus	GRAM-negative. Rods sometimes of coccoid form occurring singly, paired or in short chains. Motile or non-motile, in former case with peritrichous flagella. Some strains cause β-hemolysis on blood agar. Produces fecal odor. Aerobe and facultative anaerobe. For a review see KAUFFMANN[1]	Alimentary tract of man and animals, especially colon	Normal saprophyte of man and animals in colon and more rarely lower small intestine. Widely distributed in nature. Common cause of infections of urogenital system (up to 30% of cases, e.g. perinephritic abscesses, pyelonephritis, cystitis) and of cholecystitis and peritonitis	0	2 Intestine: **neomycin**	1	In the death agony *E. coli* often migrates into the tissues and blood stream. Some strains cause severe diarrhea in infants (neomycin). In order to avoid epidemics in infants' wards, all infants should be treated, whether ill or not. For further information see below[1–12]
94	*13*	**Escherichia aurescens** (PARR) MALLIGO et al. *Bacterium aurescens*	Similar to *E. coli* but produces golden brown to red pigment. Aerobe	Feces	Isolated from an infected eye, also from contaminated water				
95	*14*	**Aerobacter aerogenes** (KRUSE) BEIJERINCK *Bacillus aerogenes, Bacterium aerogenes, Bacterium lactis aerogenes*	GRAM-negative. Single rods, usually nonmotile and often capsulated. Aerobe and facultative anaerobe	On plants, in sour milk and to a varying degree in intestinal tract of man and animals. Widely distributed in nature	Normal intestinal saprophyte. Common cause of infections of the urogenital system (up to 40% of cases). Has also been isolated from blood	0	2 Intestine: **neomycin**	1	For a report of 20 cases of bacteremia due to *A. aerogenes* see MARTIN et al.[13]
95	*15*	**Aerobacter cloacae** (JORDAN) BERGEY et al. *Bacillus cloacae, Bacterium cloacae*	GRAM-negative. Single rods usually motile with peritrichous flagella. Not capsulated. Produces fecal odor. Aerobe and facultative anaerobe	Human and animal feces, sewage, soil, water	Normal intestinal saprophyte. Occasionally cause of purulent meningitis[14] and sepsis[15]	0	2 Intestine: **neomycin**	1	
96	*16*	**Klebsiella pneumoniae** (SCHROETER) TREVISAN *Bacillus pneumoniae, Bacterium pneumoniae crouposae, Hyalococcus pneumoniae, Klebsiella crouposa* FRIEDLÄNDER's bacillus, NEUMANN's bacillus, pneumobacillus	GRAM-negative. Nonmotile rods with rounded ends occurring singly and in pairs. Capsulated. No hemolysis on blood agar. Aerobe and facultative anaerobe	Upper respiratory tract	Normal saprophyte of the upper respiratory tract[16]. Cause of FRIEDLÄNDER's pneumonia, which constitutes ca. 5% of cases of lobar and bronchial pneumonia, with severer course than that due to *Diplococcus*. Also causes tonsillitis (especially in children), meningitis (mortality still ca. 50% in spite of antibiotics[17]) and inflammations of the maxillary sinuses and middle ear	0	2 3: chloramphenicol	1	Drugs of choice for all capsulated bacteria (*Nos. 14, 16–19*) are the **tetracyclines**[18–21]. In *Klebsiella* infections penicillin and streptomycin are both antagonistic to the tetracyclines and chloramphenicol[22]. FRIEDLÄNDER's pneumonia is always dangerous in alcoholics[23] and tetracyclines should be given immediately. In infants the organism is often found in the upper respiratory tract but is seldom pathogenic, in spite of a recent increase in the incidence of FRIEDLÄNDER's pneumonia in childhood[24]
96	*17*	**Klebsiella ozaenae** (ABEL) BERGEY et al. *Bacillus mucosus ozaenae, Bacillus ozaenae, Bacterium ozaenae* ABEL's bacillus	Similar to *K. pneumoniae* but occurring singly		Occurs in ozena and in nonstinking, pure atrophic rhinitis	0	2	1	
96	*18*	**Klebsiella rhinoscleromatis** TREVISAN Rhinoscleroma bacillus	Similar to *K. pneumoniae* but sometimes forms short chains		Isolated from nasal secretions in rhinoscleroma	0	2	1	

1) KAUFFMANN, F., *Enterobacteriaceae*, 2nd ed., Copenhagen, 1954. *2)* ADAM, A., *Jahrb. Kinderheilk.*, **101**, 295 (1923), and **116**, 8 (1927); *Acta paediat. (Uppsala)*, **11**, 145, 160 (1930); *Ärztl. Forsch.*, **6**, 59 (1952). *3)* KAUFFMANN and DUPONT, *Acta path. microbiol. scand.*, **27**, 552 (1950). *4)* OCKLITZ and SCHMIDT, *Arch. Kinderheilk.*, Suppl. No. 28 (1954). *5)* Editorial, *J. Amer. med. Ass.*, **154**, 837 (1954). *6)* GRABER and DUNLOP, *J. Lab. clin. Med.*, **44**, 417 (1954). *7)* ADAM, A., in BROCK, J. (Ed.), *Biologische Daten für den Kinderarzt*, 2nd ed., vol. I, Berlin, 1954, page 626. *8)* COOPER et al., *Pediatrics*, **16**, 215 (1955). *9)* NETER, E., *Amer. J. Dis. Child.*, **89**, 564 (1955). *10)* QUILLIGAN, J. J., *Amer. J. Dis. Child.*, **89**, 696 (1955); QUILLIGAN and SHADOMY, *ibid.*, **95**, 134 (1958). *11)* MARIE et al., *Sem. Hôp. Paris*, **31**, 2232 (1955). *12)* ØRSKOV, F., *Acta path. microbiol. Scand.*, **39**, 137 (1956. *13)* MARTIN et al., *Proc. Mayo Clin.*, **29**, 542 (1954). *14)* JESSEN, O., *Acta path. microbiol. scand.*, **43**, 219 (1958). *15)* FRITZSCHE, R., *Schweiz. med. Wschr.*, **88**, 951 (1958). *16)* BEESON, P. B., *Principles of Internal Medicine*, 2nd ed., London, 1954, page 847. *17)* BELL, A. L. L., *New Engl. J. Med.*, **252**, 1026 (1955). *18)* STULBERG et al., *Amer. J. Dis. Child.*, **90**, 125 (1955). *19)* LEGLER, F., *Zbl. Bakt.*, **159**, 101 (1952). *20)* NATARO et al., *J. Amer. med. Ass.*, **144**, 12 (1950). *21)* WYLIE and KIRSCHNER, *Amer. Rev. Tuberc.*, **61**, 465 (1950). *22)* DOWLING et al., *J. Amer. med. Ass.*, **151**, 813 (1953). *23)* LIMSON et al., *Antibiotics Annual, 1955–56*, New York, 1956, page 786; *Ann. intern. Med.*, **44**, 1070 (1956). *24)* STEINER and PUTNOKY, *Arch. Dis. Childh.*, **31**, 96 (1956).

For classification of organisms see pages 721–724; for index of synonyms see pages 725–734

See pages 721–724	See pages 725–734	**Bacteria (Schizomycetes)** Classified name *Synonyms* Common names	Principal characteristics	Habitat, host, transmission, etc.	Associated diseases or source	Penicillin	Streptomycin	Tetracyclines	Remarks
97	*19*	**Paracolobactrum aerogenoides** Borman et al. Para-aerogenes	Characters as for *Aerobacter aerogenes* and *A. cloacae* except for delayed fermentation of lactose	Surface water, soil, intestinal tract of man and animals	Saprophyte. Occasionally cause of enteritis and disturbances of urogenital system	0 Intestine: **neomycin**	2	1	
97	*20*	**Paracolobactrum intermedium** Borman et al. Para-freundii	Characters as for *Escherichia freundii* and *E. intermedia* except for delayed fermentation of lactose	As for *P. aerogenoides*	As for *P. aerogenoides*	0 Intestine: **neomycin**	2	1	
97	*21*	**Paracolobactrum coliforme** Borman et al. Para-coli	Characters as for *Escherichia coli* except for delayed fermentation of lactose	As for *P. aerogenoides*	As for *P. aerogenoides*	0 Intestine: **neomycin**	2	1	
101	*22*	**Proteus vulgaris** Hauser *Bacterium vulgare*	Gram-negative. Rods occurring singly, paired and often in long chains. Motile with peritrichous flagella. Produces putrefactive odor. Aerobe and facultative anaerobe. See also the table below	Found regularly on putrefying material, sewage, intestinal and urinary tracts	*Nos. 22–26: Proteus* organisms have become commoner in recent years in purulent lesions, probably as a result of their relative insensitivity to antibiotics. Of the species found in such lesions, 72% are *Pr. mirabilis*, 12% *Pr. morganii*, 11% *Pr. vulgaris*, 5% *Pr. rettgeri*. *Pr. mirabilis* is found mainly in the urogenital tract but also in superficial wounds, sputum and pharynx, sinuses of the nose, bile, cerebrospinal fluid, and in otitis and peritonitis. The other species are almost entirely confined to urine[1]	Intestine: **neomycin**			*Nos. 22–26: Intestine:* **neomycin**; *systemic:* (1) chloramphenicol, (2) streptomycin, (3) penicillin in high dosage. Sensitivity to antibiotics in vitro (concentrations in μg/ml to which at least half the strains are susceptible)[1]: Novobiocin 10 Chlortetracycline 15 Streptomycins 15 Kanamycin 15.6 Neomycin 15.6 Chloramphenicol 31.2 Polymyxin B > 60 Viomycin > 100 Tetracycline 125 Penicillin 150 Erythromycin > 250 Oxytetracycline 500 Colimycin > 500 Vancomycin > 500 Oleandomycins 900 Spiramycin > 1500
101	*23*	**Proteus mirabilis** Hauser *Bacterium mirabilis*	Resembles *Pr. vulgaris.* See also the table below	As for *Pr. vulgaris*		Intestine: **neomycin**			
101	*24*	**Proteus morganii** (Winslow et al.) Rauss *Bacillus morgani, Bacterium morgani, Salmonella morgani* Morgan's bacillus, type 1	Gram-negative. Motile single rods with peritrichous flagella. Aerobe and facultative anaerobe. See also the table below	As for *Pr. vulgaris*		Intestine: **neomycin**			
101	*25*	**Proteus rettgeri** (Hadley et al.) Rustigian and Stuart *Bacterium rettgeri, Proteus entericus, Shigella rettgeri*	Gram-negative. Rods occurring singly, paired and occasionally in long chains. Usually nonmotile. Aerobe and facultative anaerobe. See also the table below	As for *Pr. vulgaris*		Intestine: **neomycin**			
101	*26*	**Proteus inconstans** (Ornstein) Shaw and Clarke *Bacillus inconstans*	Gram-negative. Motile rods with peritrichous flagella. See also the table below	As for *Pr. vulgaris*		Intestine: **neomycin**			
102	*27*	**Salmonella choleraesuis** (Smith) Weldin *Bacterium cholerae suis, Pasteurella salmoni*	Gram-negative. Single motile rods with 4–5 peritrichous flagella. Aerobe and facultative anaerobe	In swine as secondary invader in (virus) hog cholera	Only a natural pathogen in swine. In man occasionally causes septicemia, pneumonia, abscesses, gastroenteritis. Also a cause of food poisoning	**Chloramphenicol** 0	3	2	See remarks on pages 651 and 652

Clinical application of antibiotics: Penicillin, Streptomycin, Tetracyclines.

1) Welch, H., *A Guide to Antibiotic Therapy*, New York, 1959.

Biochemical differentiation of Proteus species

A = acid formed; A, G = acid and gas formed; fast = within 48 hours; slow = in 3 days to 3 weeks. From Rustigian and Stuart, *J. Bact.*, **49**, 419 (1945), and Breed et al. (Eds.), *Bergey's Manual of Determinative Bacteriology*, 7th ed., Baltimore, 1957.

Test	*Pr. vulgaris*	*Pr. mirabilis*	*Pr. morganii*	*Pr. rettgeri*	*Pr. inconstans*
Sucrose fermentation	A, G	A, G, slow	–	A, slow	A, G, slow
Maltose fermentation	A, G	–	–	–	–
Mannitol fermentation	–	–	–	A, G	–
Indole production	+	–	+	+	+
Citrate as sole source of carbon	+ or –	usually +	–	+	usually +
Urea hydrolysis	+ fast	+ fast	+ slow	+ fast	–

For classification of organisms see pages 721–724; for index of synonyms see pages 725–734

See pages 721–724	See pages 725–734	**Bacteria (Schizomycetes)** Classified name *Synonyms* Common names	Principal characteristics	Habitat, host, transmission, etc.	Associated diseases or source	Clinical application of antibiotics				Remarks
							Penicillin	Streptomycin	Tetracyclines	
102	*28*	**Salmonella typhimurium** (LOEFFLER) CASTELLANI and CHALMERS *Bacillus typhi murium* NOCARD's bacillus	GRAM-negative. Single motile rods with peritrichous flagella. Aerobe and facultative anaerobe	Infected animals and man. Common sources of infection are poultry, especially ducks and duck eggs, swine, rodents, cattle, cats and dogs	Natural pathogen for all warm-blooded animals. In man infection takes the form of food poisoning	**Chloramphenicol**	0	3	2	See remarks on pages 651 and 652
102	*29*	**Salmonella enteritidis** (GÄRTNER) CASTELLANI and CHALMERS *Bacillus enteritidis* GÄRTNER's bacillus	GRAM-negative. Rods occurring singly, in pairs and sometimes in short chains. Motile with peritrichous flagella. Aerobe and facultative anaerobe	Widely distributed in man and animals, especially rodents	Gastroenteritis, commonly in meat poisoning. Human carriers are known	**Chloramphenicol**	0	3	2	See remarks on pages 651 and 652
102	*30*	**Salmonella typhosa** (ZOPF) WHITE *Bacillus typhi, Bacillus typhi abdominalis, Bacillus typhosus, Bacterium typhosum, Bacterium typhi, Eberthella typhi, Salmonella typhi* EBERTH's bacillus, typhoid bacillus (Typhus-Bazillus)	Similar to *S. enteritidis*	Infected persons, feces, contaminated water	Pathogen of typhoid fever in man. Only pathogenic for animals when injected parenterally	**Chloramphenicol**	0	3	2	See remarks on pages 651 and 652
102	*31*	**Salmonella hirschfeldii** (WELDIN) *Bacillus paratyphosus* β 5, *Bacillus paratyphosus C* Paratyphoid C bacillus, HIRSCHFELD's bacillus	Similar to *S. typhimurium*	Infected persons	Pathogen of paratyphoid fever in man	**Chloramphenicol**	0	3	2	See remarks on pages 651 and 652
102	*32*	**Salmonella paratyphi** (KAYSER) CASTELLANI and CHALMERS *Bacterium paratyphi, Bacterium paratyphi A* Paratyphoid A bacillus	Similar to *S. typhimurium*	Infected persons, contaminated water and food	Pathogen of paratyphoid fever in man	**Chloramphenicol**	0	3	2	See remarks on pages 651 and 652
102	*33*	**Salmonella schottmuelleri** (WINSLOW et al.) BERGEY et al. *Bacillus paratyphi alcaligenes, Bacillus schottmülleri, Bacterium paratyphi B* Paratyphoid B bacillus	GRAM-negative. Rods occurring singly and in pairs. Motile with peritrichous flagella. Aerobe and facultative anaerobe	As for *S. paratyphi*	Pathogen of paratyphoid fever in man, rarely in animals	**Chloramphenicol**	0	3	2	See remarks on pages 651 and 652
102	*34*	**Salmonella gallinarum** (KLEIN) BERGEY et al. *Bacillus gallinarum, Bacterium pullorum, Salmonella gallinarum-pullorum, Salmonella pullorum*	GRAM-negative. Rods occurring singly or, in blood, in short chains. Usually nonmotile. Aerobe and facultative anaerobe	Infected poultry and their excrement	Pathogen of fowl typhoid and white diarrhea in young chicks. Occasionally cause of food poisoning or gastroenteritis in man	**Chloramphenicol**	0	3	2	See remarks on pages 651 and 652
103	*35*	**Shigella dysenteriae** (SHIGA) CASTELLANI and CHALMERS *Bacillus dysenteriae, Bacillus shigae, Shigella shigae* OGATA's bacillus, SHIGA's bacillus, SHIGA-KRUSE bacillus	GRAM-negative. Nonmotile, nonencapsulated, nonsporing rods occurring singly. Ferments many carbohydrates with acid but not gas formation. Possesses distinctive antigenic structure. Aerobe, facultative anaerobe	Only in feces of affected persons	Cause of epidemic bacillary dysentery. Avirulent but toxic for man. Found mainly in tropical East Asia	**Chloramphenicol**	0	3	2	See remarks on page 653
103	*36*	**Shigella schmitzii** (WELDIN and LEVINE) HAUDUROY et al. *Bacillus ambiguus, Bacillus dysenteriae "SCHMITZ", Bacterium schmitzii, Shigella ambigua, Shigella parashigae* SCHMITZ's bacillus	Morphologically and culturally identical with *Sh. dysenteriae*	Feces of affected persons	Isolated in cases of dysentery. Relatively uncommon	**Chloramphenicol**	0	3	2	See remarks on page 653

For classification of organisms see pages 721–724; for index of synonyms see pages 725–734

Salmonella *(Nos. 27–34)*

The genus Salmonella, characterized by distinctive cultural and biochemical properties, is divided by serological reactions into various groups (A, B, C, etc.) with numerous serotypes. Up to 1956, 300 such serotypes had been described[6,7], distinguished by their somatic (O) and flagellar (F) antigens. A selection of the commoner serotypes is given in the adjoining table. On the classification and bacteriology of Salmonella see references[1–7].

It appears from the existence of many serotypes and the fact that new ones are constantly being discovered that Salmonella is still in a state of active evolution, with increasing specialization with regard to host and disease form giving rise to more and more serotypes[8]. In this development the ubiquitous *S. typhimurium*, the pathogen of various diseases in almost all warm-blooded animals, appears to represent a primitive type. *S. schottmuelleri* and *S. typhosa* seem to have become specialized for man, *S. abortivoequina (S. abortusequi)*, *S. typhisuis* and *S. abortusovis* for the horse, pig and sheep, *S. gallinarum* and *S. pullorum* for poultry, while at the same time they have lost most of their pathogenicity for other host species[9].

There are no saprophytic species of Salmonella in nature; all are pathogenic in one or more animal hosts. In every sporadic or epidemic outbreak due to Salmonella the chain of infection should be therefore traced back to the starting point, usually some person or animal showing signs of disease[22,23]. However, it is characteristic of Salmonella infections that the starting point is often a silent bacterial carrier who has recovered from the disease but continues to excrete the organisms in his feces for weeks and sometimes for months or years.

In man, infection with Salmonella[24] usually takes place by mouth, whence the bacteria reach the intestinal tract either directly (food poisoning) or by way of the lymph and blood streams (paratyphoid, typhoid). Symptoms of fever and of gastroenteritis are therefore typical of most infections with Salmonella. More rarely other symptoms predominate, as instanced by a review[10] of *S. choleraesuis* infections, where gastroenteritis occurred in only 20% of cases, septicemia in 55%, pneumonia in 10%, abscesses in 7%, ostomyelitis and osteoarthritis in 6%, meningitis in 1%. Human infections with Salmonella usually arise from food (in food poisoning and in paratyphoid) or from drinking-water (in typhoid). Whilst food-borne infection is actually on the increase even in countries with a high standard of living, typhoid is no longer of importance in temperate zones, especially in the towns. In rural, tropical and underdeveloped regions, however, it remains a problem of medical hygiene[11]. Malaria, relapsing fever, bartonellosis, viral hepatitis and sickle-cell anemia appear to cause specific predisposition to infection by Salmonella[24].

Food poisoning

Food poisoning by infection with Salmonella must be distinguished from the much rarer poisoning by bacterial toxins, such as staphylococcal poisoning and botulism. The most frequent cause of bacterial food poisoning is *S. typhimurium* (80% of cases), followed by *S. enteritidis*. As the adjoining table shows, however, many other serotypes may be concerned (cf. column 2, E = type causing enteritis). Extremely heavy infection with Salmonella is necessary before food poisoning occurs[12,13]. This degree of infection is rare in uncooked flesh or eggs from even heavily infected animals (the most dangerous in this respect are flesh from cows which have had to be slaughtered, and duck eggs). Food poisoning is thus rare in private households and on farms. On the

Commoner Salmonella serotypes

(selected from Kauffmann-White Schema, 1955[7])

Key to disease forms (column 2): C = associated with cystitis; E = enteric; M = often found in meninges; S = septicemic

Serotype	Form of disease	Group	Somatic antigens	Flagellar antigens	
				Phase 1	Phase 2
paratyphi	S	**A**	1, 2, 12	a	–
kisangani	E	**B**	1, 4, 5, 12	a	1, 2
arechavaleta	E	**B**	4, 5, 12	a	1, 7
bispebjerg	E	**B**	1, 4, 12	a	e, n, x
schottmuelleri	S	**B**	1, 4, 5, 12	b	1, 2
abony	S	**B**	1, 4, 5, 12	b	e, n, x
schleissheim	E	**B**	4, 12, 27	b, z_{12}	–
altendorf	E	**B**	4, 12	c	1, 7
stanley	E	**B**	4, 5, 12	d	1, 2
reading	E	**B**	4, 12	e, h	1, 5
kaposvar	E	**B**	4, 5, 12	e, (h)	1, 5
chester	E	**B**	4, 5, 12	e, h	e, n, x
derby	E, M	**B**	1, 4, 12	f, g	–
essen	E	**B**	4, 12	g, m	–
budapest	E	**B**	1, 4, 12	g, t	–
typhimurium	E, M	**B**	1, 4, 5, 12	i	1, 2
bredeney	E, M	**B**	1, 4, 12, 27	l, v	1, 7
brandenburg	E	**B**	4, 12	l, v	e, n, z_{15}
heidelberg	E	**B**	4, 5, 12	r	1, 2
coeln	E	**B**	4, 5, 12	y	1, 2
oslo	E	**C**	6, 7	a	e, n, x
hirschfeldii	S, M	**C**	6, 7, Vi	c	1, 5
choleraesuis	S, E, M	**C**	6, 7	c	1, 5
mission	E	**C**	6, 7	d	1, 5
braenderup	E	**C**	6, 7	e, h	e, n, z_{15}
montevideo	E	**C**	6, 7	g, m, s	–
thompson	E	**C**	6, 7	k	1, 5
irumu	E	**C**	6, 7	l, v	1, 5
oranienburg	E	**C**	6, 7	m, t	–
virchow	E	**C**	6, 7	r	1, 2
bareilly	E	**C**	6, 7	y	1, 5
narashino	S	**C**	6, 8	a	e, n, x
muenchen	E	**C**	6, 8	d	1, 2
newport	E	**C**	6, 8	e, h	1, 2
kottbus	E	**C**	6, 8	e, h	1, 5
manchester	E	**C**	6, 8	l, v	1, 7
fayed	E	**C**	6, 8	l, w	1, 2
bovismorbificans	E, S	**C**	6, 8	r	1, 5
duesseldorf	E	**C**	6, 8	z_4, z_{24}	–
glostrup	E	**C**	6, 8	z_{10}	e, n, z_{15}
sendai	S	**D**	1, 9, 12	a	1, 5
onarimon	S	**D**	1, 9, 12	b	1, 2
typhosa *(typhi)*	S, M	**D**	9, 12, Vi	d	–
eastbourne	S	**D**	1, 9, 12	e, h	1, 5
enteritidis	E, M	**D**	1, 9, 12	g, m	–
blegdam	E	**D**	9, 12	g, m, q	–
dublin	E	**D**	1, 9, 12	g, p	–
moscow	E	**D**	9, 12	g, q	–
panama	E	**D**	1, 9, 12	l, v	1, 5
goettingen	E	**D**	9, 12	l, v	e, n, z_{15}
daressalam	S	**D**	1, 9, 12	l, w	e, n
gallinarum	E	**D**	1, 9, 12	–	–
pullorum	E	**D**	9, 12	–	–
shangani	E	**E**	3, 10	d	1, 5
vejle	E	**E**	3, 10	e, h	1, 2
muenster	E	**E**	3, 10	e, h	1, 5
anatum	E	**E**	3, 10	e, h	1, 6
nyborg	E	**E**	3, 10	e, h	1, 7
meleagridis	E	**E**	3, 10	e, h	l, w
give	E	**E**	3, 10	l, v	1, 7
uganda	S	**E**	3, 10	l, z_{13}	1, 5
amager	E	**E**	3, 10	y	1, 2
newington	E	**E**	3, 15	e, h	1, 6
selandia	E	**E**	3, 15	e, h	1, 7
newbrunswick	E	**E**	3, 15	l, v	1, 7
niloese	E	**E**	1, 3, 19	d	z_6
senftenberg	E	**E**	1, 3, 19	g, s, t	–
aberdeen	E	**F**	11	i	1, 2
senegal	E	**F**	11	r	1, 5
rubislaw	E	**F**	11	r	e, n, x
wichita	E	**G**	1, 13, 23	d	z_{37}
habana	M	**G**	1, 13, 23	f, g	–
poona	E	**G**	13, 22	z	1, 6
onderstepoort	E	**H**	(1), 6, 14, 25	e, h	1, 5
carrau	E	**H**	6, 14, 24	y	1, 7
hvittingfoss	E	**I**	16	b	e, n, x
gaminara	E	**I**	16	d	1, 7
orientalis	E	**I**	16	k	e, n, z_{15}
kirkee	E	Further groups	17	b	1, 2
memphis	E	Further groups	18	k	1, 5
cerro	E	Further groups	18	z_4, z_{23}	–
waycross	C	Further groups	41	z_4, z_{23}	–

For classification of organisms see pages 721–724; for index of synonyms see pages 725–734

See pages 721–724	See pages 725–734	**Bacteria (Schizomycetes)** Classified name *Synonyms* Common names	Principal characteristics	Habitat, host, transmission, etc.	Associated diseases or source	Clinical application of antibiotics: Penicillin	Streptomycin	Tetracyclines	Remarks
103	*37*	**Shigella arabinotarda** Christensen and Gowen	Morphologically and culturally identical with *Sh. dysenteriae*	Only in feces of affected persons	Found occasionally in cases of dysentery due to *Sh. flexneri*	**Chloramphenicol** 0	3	2	See remarks on page 653
103	*38*	**Shigella boydii** Ewing	Similar to *Sh. dysenteriae* but some strains of type 2 may be encapsulated	Only in feces of affected persons	Isolated in cases of dysentery. Rare	**Chloramphenicol** 0	3	2	See remarks on page 653
103	*39*	**Shigella flexneri** Castellani and Chalmers *Bacillus dysenteriae* Flexner, *Bacillus dysenteriae* Shiga, *Bacillus paradysenteriae, Shigella paradysenteriae* Flexner's bacillus, pseudodysentery bacillus, Strong's bacillus	Similar to *Sh. dysenteriae* but cells are often filamentous and irregularly shaped in old cultures	Feces of affected persons	Commonest cause of epidemic dysentery. Also causes infantile gastroenteritis. Chiefly found in United States	**Chloramphenicol** 0	3	2	See remarks on page 653
103	*40*	**Shigella alkalescens** (Andrewes) Weldin *Bacillus alkalescens, Proshigella alkalescens*	Similar to *Sh. dysenteriae* except that cells also occur in pairs	Intestinal canal	Isolated from feces of dysentery convalescents, also from healthy persons, from blood cultures and from cases of bacilluria. May be a cause of diarrhea	**Chloramphenicol** 0	3	2	See remarks on page 653

Salmonella *(Nos. 27–34) (continued)*

other hand, much more favourable conditions for bacterial contamination and proliferation occur in large plants such as slaughter houses, jam and ice cream factories, bakeries and large kitchens, especially when the standards of hygiene are unsatisfactory, as is often the case in large impersonal undertakings in spite of stringent precautions. A bacterial carrier, a few infected mice or rats, the flesh of an infected cow, or a few infected eggs, are quite sufficient to contaminate large quantities of food. It is therefore understandable that food poisoning is caused mainly by food which has undergone much handling and processing, especially if flour or sugar, or both, has been added, and if the food has been kept a long time or warmed up again before use. About 50% of all food poisoning arises from meat products (1% only from fresh meat), 20% from duck eggs, 5% from hen eggs, 15% from sweet dishes such as cream, ice cream, etc., and 5% each from preserves and from milk products[14, 15].

The incubation period in food poisoning is 2–10 hours and the symptoms of gastroenteritis last 2–3 days or sometimes longer. The mortality is low. Antibiotic treatment is only indicated in long-standing cases or to reduce the period during which bacteria are excreted. Diagnosis is by bacteriological examination of the feces, and is usually obtained during the early stages of the diarrhea.

Paratyphoid, typhoid

The main organisms responsible for septicemic Salmonella infections are *S. schottmuelleri (S. paratyphi* B) and *S. typhosa*, followed by *S. paratyphi (S. paratyphi* A), *S. hirschfeldii (S. paratyphi* C), *S. sendai* (serotype) and *S. choleraesuis*. From the clinical standpoint, paratyphoid and typhoid usually resemble one another closely; in paratyphoid the temperature curve is steeper and higher, with fever of shorter duration than typhoid. The causative organism can be demonstrated in the blood before the onset of enteric symptoms. Paratyphoid is usually transmitted by food, typhoid usually by drinking water. Patients must be isolated and their feces disinfected; if they continue to excrete bacteria during convalescence they must be subjected to stringent hygienic precautions or better still detained until excretion of bacteria has ceased.

Attacks of paratyphoid and typhoid confer long-lasting immunity. Hence *prophylactic immunization* has proved practicable and is always to be recommended when there is danger of extensive infection, e.g. before journeys and expeditions into underdeveloped countries, in camps erected for large building projects, in floods which interfere with the piped water supply, and in wartime (for international reference antiserum see page 736).

Salmonella meningitis

This is rare: only about 3% of all suppurative meningitis is caused by Salmonella, in the main by *S. typhimurium, S. typhosa, S. bredeney* and *S. habana*. Newborn and infants are chiefly affected. The mortality is high, previously about 90%, now with antibiotics still about 50%. Previous diarrhea is observed only in about 60% of cases. Salmonella meningitis is rarely a mixed infection. For a review of Salmonella meningitis in children see Henderson[16] and Smith[17].

Antibiotic treatment

Chloramphenicol is the drug of choice in all Salmonella infections, followed by the tetracyclines. In typhoid, chloramphenicol treatment[18] should be on the following lines[19]: 50 mg/kg body weight peroral, followed for adults by 3 g per day peroral in 4 divided doses continued until the patient is afebrile, and subsequently by 2 g per day in 4 divided doses for 14 days. Children should receive half these doses. When oral administration is impossible, the antibiotic should be given intravenously or intramuscularly with an initial dose of 10–20 mg/kg followed by 25–50 mg/kg per day. In critical typhoid cases cortisol or cortisone may sometimes effect an improvement[10, 20, 21]. In severe cases, prognosis can relate only to the typhoid state itself since antibiotics have not significantly reduced the number of severe complications (hemorrhage, perforations). Relapses are rather more frequent after antibiotics, so that some authorities recommend a subsequent inoculation.

References

1) Kauffmann and Mitsui, *Z. Hyg. InfektKr.*, **111**, 749 (1930). *2*) Kauffmann and Burón, *Z. Hyg. InfektKr.*, **117**, 650 (1936). *3*) Kauffmann, F., *Die Bakteriologie der Salmonellagruppe*, Copenhagen, 1941. *4*) Edwards et al., *Acta path. microbiol. scand.*, **31**, 5 (1952), and **33**, 191 (1953). *5*) Kauffmann et al., *Acta path. microbiol. scand.*, **35**, 156 (1954). *6*) Edwards and Ewing, *Identification of Enterobacteriaceae*, Minneapolis, 1955. *7*) Kauffmann and Petersen, *Acta path. microbiol. scand.*, **38**, 481 (1956). *8*) Savage, W., *Proc. roy. Soc. Med.*, **33**, 357 (1940); Lovell, R., *ibid.*, **33**, 362 (1940). *9*) Savage, W., *Brit. med. J.*, **2**, 317 (1956). *10*) Saphra and Wassermann, *Amer. J. med. Sci.*, **228**, 525 (1954). *11*) Epidemiological and Morbidity Statistics Section, WHO, *Bull. Wld Hlth Org.*, **13**, 173 (1955). *12*) Hormaeche and Salsamendi, *Arch. urug. Med.*, **9**, 665 (1936), and **14**, 375 (1939). *13*) McCullough and Eisele, *J. infect. Dis.*, **88**, 278 (1951), and **89**, 209, 259 (1952). *14*) Savage, W., *J. prev. Med. (Baltimore)*, **6**, 425 (1932). *15*) *Monthly Bull. Minist. Hlth (Lond.)*, **13**, 12 (1954), and **14**, 34 (1955). *16*) Henderson, L. L., *Amer. J. Dis. Child.*, **75**, 351 (1948). *17*) Smith, E. S., *Amer. J. Dis. Child.*, **88**, 732 (1954). *18*) For a review see Höring and Steinbrecher, *Antibiot. et Chemother. (Basel)*, **4**, 158 (1957). *19*) Hornick, R. B., in Conn, H. F. (Ed.), *Current Therapy, 1961*, Philadelphia and London, 1961, page 62. *20*) Smadel et al., *Ann. intern. Med.*, **34**, 1 (1951). *21*) Durand and Renoux, *Sem. Hôp. Paris*, **29**, 2555 (1953). *22*) Buxton, A., *Proc. roy. Soc. Med.*, **48**, 636 (1955). *23*) Edwards, P. R., *Ann. N. Y. Acad. Sci.*, **70**, 598 (1958). *24*) For a review see Bennett and Hook, *Ann. Rev. Med.*, **10**, 1 (1959).

See pages 721–724	See pages 725–734	**Bacteria (Schizomycetes)** Classified name *Synonyms* Common names	Principal characteristics	Habitat, host, transmission, etc.	Associated diseases or source	Clinical application of antibiotics: Penicillin	Streptomycin	Tetracyclines	Remarks
103	*41*	**Shigella sonnei** (LEVINE) WELDIN *Bacillus dispar, Bacterium sonnei, Proshigella sonnei* DUVAL's bacillus, SONNE's bacillus	Similar to *Sh. dysenteriae* but agar colonies become characteristically pleomorphic	Feces of affected persons, also drinking water	Cause of mild dysentery. World-wide distribution	**Chloramphenicol** 0	3	2	See remarks below
103	*42*	**Shigella dispar** (ANDREWES) BERGEY et al. *Bacillus ceylanensis B, Bacillus dispar, Castellanus castellanii, Proshigella dispar*	Morphologically similar to *Sh. dysenteriae*, culturally similar to *Sh. sonnei*	Blood, feces, urine	Pathogenic for urinary tract. Rarely causes dysentery. Found in urine in cystitis, pyelitis and pyelonephritis, in blood in septicemia, and in dysenteric and healthy feces	**Chloramphenicol** 0	3	2	See remarks below
104	*43*	**Pasteurella multocida** LEHMANN and NEUMANN *Bacillus septicaemiae haemorrhagicae, Bacterium multocidum, Pasteurella septica*	GRAM-negative. Short ellipsoidal rods occurring singly, in pairs, rarely in chains. Nonmotile. Bipolar staining. Aerobe, facultative anaerobe	Warm-blooded animals	Cause of hemorrhagic septicemia in warm-blooded animals (chicken cholera in fowls). Occasionally pathogenic for man (chronic nasal sinusitis)				
104	*44*	**Pasteurella pestis** (LEHMANN and NEUMANN) HOLLAND *Bacterium pestis* KITASATO's bacillus, pest bacillus	GRAM-negative. Single, nonmotile rods showing characteristic bladder, safety-pin and ring forms. Polar staining. Aerobe, facultative anaerobe	Infected rodents, especially rats and their fleas, man. Transmitted by fleas	Cause of bubonic and pneumonic plague. Pathogenic for all rodents and man	0	1	2	See remarks on page 655

Shigella[1] *(Nos. 35–42)*

The epidemic or sporadic bacillary dysentery due to this genus is distinguishable from amebic dysentery *(No. 347)* by bacteriological examination of the feces. In infants, differential diagnosis must also take account of gastroenteritis due to *E. coli*. In bacillary dysentery the feces are usually streaked with blood, in contrast to the diffuse reddish coloration in amebic dysentery. In gastroenteritis due to *E. coli* the feces are generally free of blood. In England, over 95% of bacillary dysentery cases are due to *Sh. sonnei*[2].

The incubation time in bacillary dysentery is 2–3 days. *Sh. flexneri, boydii* and *sonnei* infections usually run a mild course and pass spontaneously[3]; blood is found in the feces in only 30% of cases, and medical treatment is often not demanded. Tropical dysentery, especially that due to *Sh. dysenteriae*, has a much more severe course, with a mortality of ca. 20%. After recovery there is some degree of short-lived immunity. Shigella bacilli multiply exclusively in the mucosa of the large intestine and are found only very rarely in the lymph glands and seldom in the blood. Dysentery in one member of a family usually results in the others becoming infected.

Sulfonamides are the drugs of choice, and although antibiotic treatment is not necessary in mild cases, it is advisable in order to curtail the time during which the bacilli continue to be discharged and thus reduce spread of the infection. Other members of the family should also be treated. The antibiotic of choice is chloramphenicol, then the tetracyclines. For dosage see under Salmonella, opposite. Increasing resistance of Shigella to sulfonamides has been observed[4] but resistance to antibiotics is less marked. For international standard antidysentery serum (SHIGA) see page 736.

References

1) For a review see BENSTED, H. J., *Canad. J. Microbiol.*, **2**, 163 (1956). *2) Report of the Medical Research Council, 1957–58*, London, 1959, page 20. *3)* MACLEOD, R. C., *Brit. med. J.*, **2**, 255 (1955). *4)* ROZANSKY et al., *J. lab. clin. Med.*, **52**, 728 (1958).

Biochemical differentiation of Shigella species

From BREED et al. (Eds.), *Bergey's Manual of Determinative Bacteriology*, 7th ed., Baltimore, 1957, page 384, and DOUGHERTY and LAMBERTI, *Textbook of Bacteriology*, 3rd ed., St.Louis, 1954, page 396

	Fermentation of: mannitol	dulcitol	sorbitol	rhamnose	lactose	sucrose	arabinose	xylose	Production of indole
Sh. dysenteriae	−	−	−	−	−	−	−		−
Sh. schmitzii	−	−	±	+	−	−	+ slow		+
Sh. arabinotarda	−			−			+ slow		−*
Sh. boydii	+			−	−			+	
Sh. flexneri	+	−	±	±	−	±		−	±
Sh. alkalescens	+	+	+	−	−	±			+
Sh. sonnei	+	−	−	+	+ slow	+			−
Sh. dispar	+	+	+	+	+ slow	+			+

* Except type 7.

For classification of organisms see pages 721–724; for index of synonyms see pages 725–734

Shigella *(Nos. 35–42) (continued)*

Nomenclature of serosubgroups and serotypes of Shigella species

(Enterobacteriaceae Subcommittee, Nomenclature Committee of the International Association of Microbiologists, 1953)

From EDWARDS and EWING, *Identification of Enterobacteriaceae*, Minneapolis, 1955

Subgroup A: *Shigella dysenteriae*		Subgroup B: *Shigella flexneri*				Subgroup C: *Shigella boydii*				Subgroup D: *Shigella sonnei*
Type	Earlier designations	Type	Earlier designations English	German	Other	Type	Earlier designations English	German	Other	Earlier designations
1	SHIGA-KRUSE bacillus, *Bacterium shigae*	1a	V	B, C	FLEXNER	1	170		IX	E (German)
		1b	VZ	A		2	P. 288		X	SONNE-DUVAL
2	*Shigella ambigua, S. schmitzii, Bacterium ambiguus*	2a	W	D	STRONG, HISS-RUSSEL	3	D. 1		XI	SONNE III
3	Q 771	2b	WX	DX		4	P. 274	R	XIV	*S. ceylonensis A*
4	Q 1167 LARGE-SACHS group (*S. arabinotarda*)	3	Z	H		5	P. 143		XIII	
5	Q 1030	4a	103	F	LENTZ Y2	6	D. 19		XII	
6	Q 454	4b	103 Z	J, F	*S. saigonensis, S. rio*	7		N	LAVINGTON type T, T, *S. etousae*	
7	Q 902	5	P. 119	G		8			Serotype 112	
8	Serotype 599–52	6	88	L	*S. newcastle*	9		P	Serotype 1296/7	
		X	X		VII	10			Serotype 430	
		Y	Y	Y	VIII, HISS-RUSSEL	11			Serotype 34	

See pages 721–724	See pages 725–734	**Bacteria (Schizomycetes)** Classified name *Synonyms* Common names	Principal characteristics	Habitat, host, transmission, etc.	Associated diseases or source	Clinical application of antibiotics: Penicillin	Streptomycin	Tetracyclines	Remarks
104	*45*	**Pasteurella pseudotuberculosis** (PFEIFFER) TOPLEY and WILSON *Bacillus pseudotuberculosis, Streptobacillus pseudotuberculosis rodentium*	GRAM-negative. Ellipsoidal, coccoidal and rod-shaped cells occurring singly, in groups or in short chains. Occasional filamentous forms. Nonmotile at 37° C, motile with peritrichous flagella at 22° C. Aerobe, facultative anaerobe	Mammals, especially rodents, birds; also soil, dust, water, milk. Widely distributed	Isolated from human blood, spleen, liver, gallbladder, appendix, cerebrospinal fluid. Can be pathogenic for man (mesenteric adenitis)[1–3]. Cause of pseudotuberculosis in animals				
104	*46*	**Pasteurella tularensis** (MCCOY and CHAPIN) BERGEY et al. *Bacterium tularense*	GRAM-negative. Cocci and rods in about equal numbers occurring singly. Very pleomorphic. Nonmotile. Staining may be bipolar. Strict aerobe	Mammals, especially rodents and their insect parasites, water. Transmitted by insects, contact or drinking water	Cause of tularemia in man and rodents. Penetrates unbroken skin to cause infection. Found especially in liver, blood, lymph nodes and spleen	0	1	2	
105	*47*	**Bordetella pertussis** (HOLLAND) MORENO-LÓPEZ *Hemophilus pertussis* BORDET-GENGOU bacillus (Microbe de la coqueluche)	GRAM-negative. Minute, nonmotile cocci occurring singly, in pairs and occasionally short chains. Staining may be bipolar. No growth on common media. Aerobe	Respiratory tract	Cause of whooping cough	3	3	1	2: chloramphenicol. See remarks on page 655
105	*48*	**Bordetella parapertussis** (ELDERING and KENDRICK) MORENO-LÓPEZ *Bacillus parapertussis, Haemophilus parapertussis*	Morphologically similar to *B. pertussis.* Aerobe	Respiratory tract	Causes a whooping-cough-like disease				
105	*49*	**Bordetella bronchiseptica** (FERRY) MORENO-LÓPEZ *Alcaligenes bronchisepticus, Bacillus bronchicanis, Bacillus bronchisepticus, Bacterium bronchisepticus, Brucella bronchiseptica, Haemophilus bronchisepticus*	Morphologically similar to *B. pertussis.* Aerobe	Respiratory tract	Mainly pathogenic for animals but occasionally causes a whooping-cough-like disease in man				

1) HECKER, W.C., *Arch. Kinderheilk.*, **156**, 151 (1957). *2)* GIRARD et al., *Presse méd.*, **67**, 249 (1959). *3)* KNAPP, W., *New Engl. J. Med.*, **259**, 776 (1958).

For classification of organisms see pages 721–724; for index of synonyms see pages 725–734

See pages 721–724	See pages 725–734	**Bacteria (Schizomycetes)** Classified name *Synonyms* Common names	Principal characteristics	Habitat, host, transmission, etc.	Associated diseases or source	Clinical application of antibiotics: Penicillin	Streptomycin	Tetracyclines	Remarks
106	*50*	**Brucella melitensis** (HUGHES) MEYER and SHAW *Micrococcus melitensis, Streptococcus melitensis*	GRAM-negative. Short ellipsoidal rods occurring singly, in pairs and rarely in short chains. Nonmotile. Best stained by the method of HANSEN and KOSTER[1]. Aerobe	Mainly the milch goat. World-wide distribution but especially Mediterranean area	Cause of undulant fever (brucellosis) in man and domestic animals	0	2	1	*Nos. 50–52:* Sensitivity of Brucella species to antibiotics in vitro (concentrations in µg/ml to which at least half the strains are susceptible)[2]: Chloramphenicol 0.5; Polymyxin B 1.3; Tetracycline 3.0; Chlortetracycline 3.0; Oxytetracycline 3.0; Kanamycin 3.1; Streptomycins 5.0; Erythromycin 5.0; Penicillin 6; Colimycin 25; Oleandomycins 25; Neomycin 31.2; Novobiocin 31.2; Spiramycin 50; Viomycin > 100. See also remarks on page 656
106	*51*	**Brucella abortus** (SCHMIDT and WEIS) MEYER and SHAW *Bacterium abortus* BANG's abortion bacillus	Morphologically and culturally similar to *B. melitensis* except that it requires 5% CO_2 for isolation and becomes aerobic after several transfers. Distinguishable from *Br. melitensis* but not from *Br. suis* by agglutinin absorption test	Mainly the milch cow. World-wide distribution but especially America and central and northern Europe	Cause of undulant fever (brucellosis) in man and domestic animals, also of infectious abortion in cattle and a wasting disease in chickens	0	2	1	
106	*52*	**Brucella suis** HUDDLESON *Bacillus abortus*	Morphologically and culturally similar to *Br. melitensis*	Mainly the hog	Cause of undulant fever (brucellosis) in man and domestic animals, also of abortion in swine and a wasting disease in chickens	0	2	1	

1) HANSEN and KOSTER, *Svensk. Vet. Tidskr.*, **46**, 69 (1941). *2)* WELCH, H., *A Guide to Antibiotic Therapy*, New York, 1959.

Plague *(No. 44)*

Streptomycin and the tetracyclines have proved to be the most effective antibiotics against bubonic and pneumonic plague. Sulfonamides are also effective if they can be given early enough, before the septicemic stage, and are thus particularly suitable for prophylaxis. They can be tried as the first drug in bubonic plague, but if they are ineffective or if pneumonic plague sets in they must be replaced immediately by the antibiotics mentioned. Penicillin is without effect.

References

POLLITZER, R., *Bull. Wld Hlth Org.*, **9**, 59, 131 (1953); SOKHEY et al., *Bull. Wld Hlth Org.*, **9**, 637 (1953); Expert Committee on Plague, *Bull. Wld Hlth Org.*, **9**, 707 (1953); MCCRUMB et al., *Amer. J. Med.*, **14**, 284 (1953); KARTMAN et al., *Ann. N. Y. Acad. Sci.*, **70**, 668 (1958).

Whooping cough (pertussis) *(No. 47)*

During the last ten years there has not only been a marked decline in the incidence of whooping cough as a result of vaccination but also a diminution in its severity. Thus in the United Kingdom deaths from the disease fell during this period from about 600 to 20[1,2].

The treatment of whooping cough with antibiotics remains disappointing and their main use is to prevent the appearance of secondary infections. No antibiotic is known which is specifically effective against *Bordetella pertussis*, and chloramphenicol and the tetracyclines are equally active in vitro. Early diagnosis of the disease in outbreaks is important, and a method of fluorescent-antibody staining of nasopharyngeal smears has recently been described[3].

Prophylactic immunization (from the age of 3–4 months upwards) is still to be recommended in spite of the decline in the disease. This should be preferably in the form of triple toxoid (diphtheria-whooping cough-tetanus) or the latter combined with poliomyelitis vaccine. Cf. also remarks on tetanus, page 676, and diphtheria, pages 671 and 672.

References

1) Editorial, *Brit. med. J.*, **2**, 1215 (1960). *2)* Annotations, *Lancet*, **2**, 139 (1960). *3)* DONALDSON and WHITAKER, *Amer. J. Dis. Child.*, **99**, 423 (1960).

Brucellosis (undulant fever) *(Nos. 50–52)*

Brucella abortus occurs mainly in cattle, *Br. melitensis* in goats and sheep, *Br. suis* in pigs. However, Brucella species are pathogenic in many domestic animals: the pig for instance can be infected also with *Br. melitensis*. The frequencies of the species causing human brucellosis are in direct relation to the distributions of the main hosts. In countries where cattle are raised extensively, *Br. abortus* causes about 75% of all human brucellosis[1,2,8], followed by *Br. melitensis* and *Br. suis* in that order. Human infection usually follows the consumption of fresh milk or lightly fermented cheese. Contact infection can occur in farmers, shepherds, goat- and swine-herds, workers in slaughter houses and veterinary surgeons.

The incubation period does not normally exceed 4 weeks but can sometimes amount to several months. The symptoms of brucellosis consist of fever, malaise, headache, and pain in the joints and muscles; it is characteristic of the disease that the leukocyte count usually remains normal or is somewhat reduced (occasionally with a relative lymphocytosis). The disease may take any of the following courses[3,4]:

1. An acute and violent bout of fever, followed by apparent recovery (frequent).

2. An illness of longer duration with episodes of acute fever (undulant fever, frequent).

3. A chronic course without obvious episodes of acute fever, and with a tendency to local complications, especially spondylitis (less frequent).

Brucellosis caused by *Br. abortus* and *Br. suis* usually clears up in a few months[3,5] and shows little tendency to local complications. Infections with *Br. melitensis* take a more chronic course, do not react so well to antibiotics, and are more prone to local complications and relapses[1].

The *diagnosis* can be confirmed only by a positive culture of Brucella (from blood, bone marrow, lymph nodes or any abscesses) or by a positive agglutination test with known antigens. Other tests are not conclusive[4,6,7].

For classification of organisms see pages 721–724; for index of synonyms see pages 725–734

See pages 721–724	See pages 725–734	**Bacteria (Schizomycetes)** Classified name *Synonyms* Common names	Principal characteristics	Habitat, host, transmission, etc.	Associated diseases or source	Clinical application of antibiotics: Penicillin	Streptomycin	Tetracyclines	Remarks
107	*53*	**Haemophilus influenzae** (LEHMANN and NEUMANN) WINSLOW et al. *Bacterium influenzae* Influenza bacillus, MORAX-AXENFELD bacillus, PFEIFFER's bacillus (Bacille de la grippe)	GRAM-negative. Very small nonmotile rods occurring singly, in pairs, occasionally in short chains or long threads. Some strains encapsulated. Staining may be bipolar. Aerobe, facultative anaerobe	Respiratory tract	Cause of acute respiratory infections, acute infectious conjunctivitis and, in children, purulent meningitis. See also the remarks below	0	3	1	2: chloramphenicol. Sensitivity of *H. influenzae* to antibiotics in vitro (concentrations in µg/ml to which at least half the strains are susceptible)[1]: Oleandomycins 0.078 Colimycin 0.1 Penicillin 0.3 Chloramphenicol 0.4 Polymyxin B 0.6 Novobiocin 0.8 Chlortetracycline 3.0 Oxytetracycline 3.0 Tetracycline 5.0 Streptomycins 5.0 Bacitracin 10.9 Erythromycin 12 Viomycin 12 Spiramycin 12.5 Ristocetin > 50 Neomycin 100 See also the remarks below
107	*54*	**Haemophilus aegyptius** (TREVISAN) PITTMAN AND DAVIS *Bacillus aegyptius, Bacterium aegyptiacum, Hemophilus conjunctivitidis* KOCH-WEEKS bacillus, WEEKS's bacillus	GRAM-negative. Small nonmotile rods occurring singly, in short chains and occasionally in threads. Bipolar staining. Aerobe, facultative anaerobe	Conjunctiva	Cause of acute and subacute infectious conjunctivitis in warm climates				
107	*55*	**Haemophilus haemolyticus** BERGEY et al. PRITCHETT-STILLMAN's bacillus X	Morphologically and culturally similar to *H. influenzae* but causes hemolysis on blood agar	Upper respiratory tract	Usually nonpathogenic but occasionally causes subacute endocarditis				
107	*56*	**Haemophilus parainfluenzae** RIVERS Para-influenza bacillus	Morphologically and culturally similar to *H. influenzae*	Upper respiratory tract	Usually nonpathogenic but occasionally causes subacute endocarditis				
107	*57*	**Haemophilus parahaemolyticus** PITTMAN *Hemophilus parainfluenzae*	Morphologically and culturally similar to *H. influenzae* but larger and staining more heavily	Upper respiratory tract	Occasionally causes subacute endocarditis				

1) WELCH, H., *A Guide to Antibiotic Therapy*, New York, 1959.

Brucellosis (undulant fever) *(Nos. 50–52) (continued)*

Treatment

Although the Brucella species do not develop resistance to specific antibiotics, relapses are frequent following antibiotic treatment (15–20% with *Br. abortus*, up to 50% with *Br. melitensis)* and the disease tends to become chronic. This is explained by the ability of Brucella to penetrate the cell and become fixed there, a property shared with the rickettsia and viruses. Treatment must therefore be continued for a long period, with brief intervals of rest. Of proven clinical effectiveness, especially for infections with *Brucella melitensis*, is the combination of streptomycin with one of the tetracyclines or with chloramphenicol. Sulfonamides should also be tried. *Brucella abortus* antiserum is available (for international standard preparation see page 736). Treatment with antibiotics may produce reactions of HERXHEIMER type.

References

1) SPINK, W. W., *Bull. Wld Hlth Org.*, **9**, 385 (1953). *8)* MCCULLOUGH, N. B., *Ann. N. Y. Acad. Sci.*, **70**, 541 (1958). *3)* Joint FAO/WHO Expert Panel on Brucellosis, *Wld Hlth Org. techn. Rep. Ser.*, **37** (1951). *4)* Joint FAO/WHO Expert Panel on Brucellosis, *Wld Hlth Org. techn. Rep. Ser.*, **67** (1953). *5)* SPINK, W. W., in *Symposium on Brucellosis, Bethesda, Md., 1949*, Washington, 1950. *6)* CASTAÑEDA, M. R., *Bull. Wld Hlth Org.*, **9**, 399 (1955). *7)* STEVENSON et al., *Amer. J. Hyg.*, **59**, 133 (1954). *8)* Annotations, *Lancet*, **2**, 694 (1960).

Haemophilus influenzae *(No. 53)*

Haemophilus influenzae is a saprophyte of the upper respiratory passages. When the resistance of the host is decreased it can propagate freely and often becomes pathogenic. Thus in influenza, a virus disease, *H. influenzae* is found in pure culture on the mucous membrane of the upper respiratory tract, whence its name. It is a frequent cause of diseases in this tract, as well as of conjunctivitis and purulent meningitis (the latter especially in children). It is also a rare cause of pneumonia (0.1% of all pneumonia cases[1]) but contrary to the usual statements, lobar and not bronchopneumonia is the type concerned[1]. The diagnosis is verified by blood cultures[2], a procedure seldom carried out in pneumonia. This may be the reason why pneumonia due to *H. influenzae* is so very rarely diagnosed.

H. influenzae shows high sensitivity *in vitro* to penicillin, but it is remarkable that penicillin is almost without effect *in vivo* (see the sensitivity data in the table above). On treatment of *H. influenzae* infections with antibiotics see DEL LOVE and FINLAND[3] and LEPPER et al.[4].

References

1) CROWELL and LOUBE, *Arch. intern. Med.*, **93**, 921 (1954). *2)* NYHAN et al., *Pediatrics*, **16**, 31 (1955). *3)* DEL LOVE and FINLAND, *J. Pediat.*, **45**, 531 (1954). *4)* LEPPER et al., *Amer. J. Dis. Child.*, **83**, 763 (1952).

Soft chancre (chancroid) *(No. 59)*

The incubation period of soft chancre is approximately 6–7 days. At one U.S. Army station it was reported that about 30% of all venereal infections were soft chancre, the remainder gonorrhea[1]. Simultaneous infection with syphilis is now rare. There is often difficulty in distinguishing soft chancre from infections of similar

See pages 721–724	See pages 725–734	**Bacteria (Schizomycetes)** Classified name *Synonyms* Common names	Principal characteristics	Habitat, host, transmission, etc.	Associated diseases or source	Clinical application of antibiotics: Penicillin	Streptomycin	Tetracyclines	Remarks
107	*58*	**Haemophilus aphrophilus** KHAIRAT	GRAM-negative. Nonmotile cocci occurring singly and in clumps. Filamentous after repeated culture. Microaerophile, facultative anaerobe		Isolated from blood and heart valve in a case of endocarditis				
107	*59*	**Haemophilus ducreyi** (NEVEU-LEMAIRE) BERGEY et al. *Bacillus ulceris cancrosi, Coccobacillus ducreyi* DUCREY's bacillus	GRAM-negative. Small nonmotile rods with rounded ends occurring singly and in short chains. Requires hemin and other enrichment for growth. Slowly hemolytic. Aerobe, facultative anaerobe	External genitals of affected persons	Cause of soft chancre (chancroid). See the remarks below				Sensitivity to antibiotics in vitro (concentrations in µg/ml to which at least half the strains are susceptible)[2]: Penicillin 0.09; Tetracycline 3.0; Chlortetracycline 7.5; Chloramphenicol 8.0; Streptomycins 10. See also the remarks below
108	*60*	**Actinobacillus lignieresii** BRUMPT	GRAM-negative. Nonmotile rods developing coccal and diplococcal forms on agar and streptobacillary forms on serum broth. Frequent bipolar staining. Aerobe, facultative anaerobe, primary cultures microaerophic	Affected animals	Cause of actinobacillosis of cattle and swine. Often confused with actinomycosis *(No. 196)*. Rare cases have been reported in man				
108	*61*	**Actinobacillus actinomycetemcomitans** TOPLEY and WILSON *Bacterium actinomycetem comitans, Bacterium comitans*	GRAM-negative. Nonmotile rods or cocci occurring in dense masses. Aerobe, facultative anaerobe. Possibly identical with *A. lignieresii*		Associated with human actinomycosis *(No. 196)*				
108	*62*	**Actinobacillus mallei** (ZOPF) THOMPSON *Bacillus mallei, Malleomyces mallei, Pfeifferella mallei* Glanders bacillus (Bacille de la morve, Rotz-Bazillus)	GRAM-negative. Slender rods with rounded ends occurring singly, in pairs or in groups, in cultures sometimes as filaments. Nonmotile. Irregular staining. Aerobe, facultative anaerobe	Solipeds (especially horses). Transmissible to other animals and man	Cause of glanders (equinia) in horses and occasionally in man	?	1	?	
109	*63*	**Calymmatobacterium granulomatis** ARAGÃO and VIANNA *Donovania granulomatis* DONOVAN bodies, epithelial cell parasites	GRAM-negative. Pleomorphic nonmotile rods with rounded ends occurring singly and in groups. Intracellular forms usually encapsulated. Grows readily in yolk sac of developing chick embryo	External genitals of affected persons	Cause of granuloma inguinale. Nonpathogenic for animals	0	2	1	On antibiotic treatment see KING[1]

1) KING, A. J., *Brit. med. J.*, **2**, 1396 (1959). *2)* WELCH, H., *A Guide to Antibiotic Therapy*, New York, 1959.

Soft chancre (chancroid) *(No. 59) (continued)*

type but nonvenereal in nature, especially since bacteriological examination of cultures of smears gives about 30% of negative results, while the *Haemophilus ducreyi* skin test with antigen gives about 60% of negatives[2]. A preliminary treatment with one of the common antiseptics is often of value, for instance with potassium permanganate, to which the nonvenereal infections, but not soft chancre, usually react.

H. ducreyi is sensitive to sulfonamides, streptomycins and tetracyclines[3] (see also sensitivity data in the table above). To avoid masking a simultaneous infection with syphilis, streptomycin plus a sulfonamide is recommended (1 g streptomycin plus 4 × 1 g sulfonamide per day for 4–7 days). Healing usually occurs within a week, although complete clearing up of the anatomical lesions may take somewhat longer. The tetracyclines are equally effective but the patient should then be kept under further observation for signs of syphilis.

References

1) PAPARELLA, J. A., *Amer. J. Syph.*, **38**, 345 (1954). *2)* MENDELL et al., *Amer. J. Syph.*, **38**, 483 (1954). *3)* KING, A. J., *Brit. med. J.*, **2**, 1396 (1959).

For classification of organisms see pages 721–724; for index of synonyms see pages 725–734

See pages 721–724	See pages 725–734	**Bacteria (Schizomycetes)** Classified name / *Synonyms* / Common names	Principal characteristics	Habitat, host, transmission, etc.	Associated diseases or source	Clinical application of antibiotics: Penicillin	Streptomycin	Tetracyclines	Remarks
110	*64*	**Moraxella lacunata** (Eyre) Lwoff *Bacillus duplex, Bacillus lacunatus, Bacterium conjunctivitidis, Bacterium conjunctivitis, Bacterium duplex, Diplobacillus moraxaxenfeld* (Diplobacille de la conjonctivite subaiguë)	Gram-negative. Short, nonmotile rods occurring singly, in pairs and in short chains. Requires blood serum for growth. Variably hemolytic. Aerobe, facultative anaerobe	Conjunctiva	Cause of subacute infectious conjunctivitis (angular conjunctivitis)	0	2	1	
110	*65*	**Moraxella liquefaciens** (McNab) Murray *Diplobacillus liquefaciens* (Diplobacille liquéfiant)	Gram-negative. Nonmotile rods occurring in pairs and occasionally singly. Does not require blood serum for growth. Aerobe	Conjunctiva	Isolated from cases of infectious conjunctivitis associated with corneal ulceration	0	2	1	
111	*66*	**Noguchia granulosis** (Noguchi) Olitsky et al. *Bacterium granulosis*	Gram-negative. Motile rods with one flagellum, usually polar. Involution forms in old cultures. Nonmotile in some cultures. Aerobe, facultative anaerobe		Has been regarded as a cause of trachoma[1]				
112	*67*	**Bacteroides fragilis** (Veillon and Zuber) Castellani and Chalmers *Bacillus fragilis, Ristella fragilis*	Gram-negative. Nonmotile rods occurring singly and in pairs. Staining deeper at the poles. Anaerobe	Intestinal tract	Isolated in acute appendicitis, pulmonary gangrene, abscesses of urinary tract and septicemia (bacteroidosis)	0	0	1 2: chloramphenicol	**Bacteroides:** The following table[2] gives for all species of *Bacteroides* the approximate *sensitivity* (µg/ml required to produce inhibition of cells in streaks) and *resistance* (percentage of resistant strains) to various antibiotics: µg/ml % Polymyxin B 500 16 Neomycin 100 Streptomycins 300 95 Bacitracin 90 Penicillin* 9 90 Sulfadiazine 16 Chloramphenicol 3 0 Erythromycin 1 13 Tetracyclines 0.3 0
112	*68*	**Bacteroides furcosus** (Veillon and Zuber) Hauduroy et al. *Bacillus furcosus, Ristella furcosa*	Gram-negative. Small nonmotile rods with forked ends. Anaerobe	Intestinal tract, lungs	Isolated from cases of appendicitis and lung abscesses	0	0	1 2: chloramphenicol	
112	*69*	**Bacteroides trichoides** (Potez and Compagnon) Hauduroy et al. *Bacillus trichoides, Ristella trichoides*	Gram-negative. Nonmotile rods. Pleomorphic with long filaments in cultures. Anaerobe	Presumably intestinal tract	Isolated in a case of cholecystitis	0	0	1 2: chloramphenicol	
112	*70*	**Bacteroides terebrans** (Brocard and Pham) Kelly *Bacillus terebrans, Ristella terebrans*	Gram-negative. Nonmotile rods. Pleomorphic with swollen bodies and chromatic granules. Anaerobe		Pathogenicity doubtful. Isolated from cases of gangrenous erysipelas	0	0	1 2: chloramphenicol	* A higher sensitivity to penicillin has also been reported[3]. See also remarks below

1) Noguchi, H., *J. exp. Med.*, **48**, Suppl. 2 (1928). *2)* Gillespie and Guy, *Lancet*, **1**, 1039 (1956). *3)* Garrod, J. P., *Brit. med. J.*, **2**, 1529 (1955).

Bacteroides *(Nos. 67–76)*

Bacteria of the genus Bacteroides, normally saprophytes of the upper respiratory passages, of the mouth, and especially of the intestinal and urogenital tracts, can also become pathogenic, in the same way as the coliform bacilli, when they penetrate susceptible or traumatized areas of the mucous membrane and reach the underlying tissue. The infections are usually mixed, and when localized within the abdomen they have the following approximate composition (as demonstrated by 111 investigations of pus[1]): 25% each of Bacteroides and coliform bacilli, 17% anaerobic and 15% aerobic streptococci, 8% staphylococci (of which half were *S. aureus)*, 8% other Gram-negative and aerobic bacteria not identified further, 2% Clostridia. Bacteroides species thus occur with approximately the same frequency as coliform organisms in suppurative infections arising from the lower bowel, in contrast to the usual view that the latter are the main cause of such infections. As the above table of sensitivity and resistance shows, the usual treatment of these infections with penicillin and streptomycin must frequently be ineffective. If this treatment is nevertheless preferred, the necessity of changing in good time to the tetracyclines or chloramphenicol, if there is no significant response, must be borne in mind.

References and bibliography

1) Gillespie and Guy, *Lancet*, **1**, 1039 (1956). – (Reviews) Gillespie and Guy, *loc. cit.*; Alston, J. M., *Brit. med. J.*, **2**, 1524 (1955); Beigelman and Rantz, *Arch. intern. Med.*, **84**, 605 (1949); Finegold and Hewitt, *Antibiotics Annual, 1955–56*, New York, 1956, page 794. (Gastroenterology) Rubin and Boyd, *Amer. J. Gastroent.*, **29**, 131 (1958). (Postoperative infections) Dixon and Deuterman, *J. Amer. med. Ass.*, **108**, 181 (1937). (Bacteremia) Thompson and Beaver, *Med. Clin. N. Amer.*, **15**, 1611 (1932); Lemierre, A., *Lancet*, **1**, 701 (1936); Alston, J. M., *loc. cit.* (Appendicitis) Lemierre, A., *loc. cit.*; Weinberg et al., *C. R. Soc. Biol. (Paris)*, **98**, 749 (1928). (Urogenital tract) Clark and Wiersma, *Amer. J. Obstet. Gynec.*, **63**, 371 (1952); Carter et al., *Obstet. and Gynec.*, **1**, 491 (1953). (Respiratory and urinary tracts, skin) McVay and Sprunt, *Ann. intern. Med.*, **36**, 56 (1952).

For classification of organisms see pages 721–724; for index of synonyms see pages 725–734

See pages 721–724	See pages 725–734	**Bacteria (Schizomycetes)** Classified name *Synonyms* Common names	Principal characteristics	Habitat, host, transmission, etc.	Associated diseases or source	Clinical application of antibiotics: Penicillin	Streptomycin	Tetracyclines	Remarks
112	*71*	**Bacteroides melaninogenicus** (Oliver and Wherry) Roy and Kelly *Bacterium melaninogenicum, Ristella melaninogenica*	Gram-negative. Nonmotile rods. Produces black pigment (hematin) in media containing hemoglobin. Growth poor in absence of body fluids. Anaerobe	Mucous membranes	Isolated from mouth, external genitalia, infected wounds, urine, feces	0	0 2: chloramphenicol	1	See remarks on page 658
112	*72*	**Bacteroides putredinis** (Weinberg et al.) Kelly *Bacillus putredinis, Ristella putredinis* Heyde's bacillus A	Gram-negative. Nonmotile rods, possibly with one swollen end. Cultures have foul odor. Anaerobe		Isolated from cases of acute appendicitis	0	0 2: chloramphenicol	1	See remarks on page 658
112	*73*	**Bacteroides glutinosus** (Guillemot and Hallé) Hauduroy et al. *Bacillus glutinosus, Ristella glutinosa*	Gram-negative. Long nonmotile rods occurring singly or in entangled clumps. Very long filamentous forms seen. Anaerobe	Respiratory tract, especially pleura	Isolated from cases of purulent pleurisy. Rare	0	0 2: chloramphenicol	1	See remarks on page 658
112	*74*	**Bacteroides destillationis** (Weinberg et al.) Kelly *Bacterium destillationis, Ristella destillationis*	Gram-negative. Nonmotile rods occurring singly or in clumps. Forms long filaments. Anaerobe	Respiratory tract	Isolated from a case of chronic bronchitis. Rare	0	0 2: chloramphenicol	1	See remarks on page 658
112	*75*	**Bacteroides viscosus** Hauduroy et al. *Bacterium mucosum, Capsularis mucosus, Coccobacterium mucosum anaerobicum*	Gram-negative. Short, nonmotile, ellipsoidal rods. Pleomorphic in culture media. Encapsulated. Bipolar staining. Anaerobe		Isolated from a brain abscess following bronchiectasis	0	0 2: chloramphenicol	1	See remarks on page 658
112	*76*	**Bacteroides serpens** (Veillon and Zuber) Hauduroy et al. *Bacillus serpens, Zuberella serpens*	Gram-negative. Thick motile rods occurring in pairs and short chains. Gas-former. Anaerobe		Isolated in acute appendicitis, mastoiditis, pulmonary gangrene, also from sea water	0	0 2: chloramphenicol	1	See remarks on page 658
113	*77*	**Fusobacterium polymorphum** Knorr	Gram-negative. Rods in pairs with pointed ends adjoining, often long threads. Pleomorphic. Nonmotile. Anaerobe	Mouth	Associated with gingivitis, pyorrhea and acute appendicitis				
113	*78*	**Fusobacterium nucleatum** Knorr	Gram-negative. Spindle-shaped rods occurring singly, often in pairs. Nonmotile. Granules present. Anaerobe	Mouth	Associated with gingivitis and pyorrhea				
113	*79*	**Fusobacterium biacutum** Weinberg and Prévot	Gram-negative. Rods occurring singly, in pairs or short chains. Nonmotile. Anaerobe	Unknown	Isolated from case of appendicitis				
113	*80*	**Fusobacterium fusiforme** (Veillon and Zuber) Hoffmann *Bacillus fusiformis, Bacillus hastilis, Corynebacterium fusiforme, Fusiformis dentium, Fusiformis fusiformis, Fusobacterium plauti-vincenti* Vincent's bacillus (Bacille de la pourriture d'hôpital)	Gram-negative. Straight or curved nonmotile rods occurring in pairs, in short curved chains or in long threads. Granules present. Anaerobe	Mouth	Associated with *Borrelia vincentii (No. 220)* in Vincent's angina	1	3	2	
114	*81*	**Dialister pneumosintes** (Olitsky and Gates) Bergey et al. *Bacterium pneumosintes*	Gram-negative. Very short rods occurring singly and occasionally in pairs, short chains or masses. Nonmotile. Anaerobe	Nasopharynx	Saprophyte of upper respiratory tract, present in 75% of healthy subjects. May become pathogenic in combination with other organisms. Associated with influenza				This organism is one of the smallest which is cultivable on synthetic media

For classification of organisms see pages 721–724; for index of synonyms see pages 725–734

See pages 721–724	See pages 725–734	**Bacteria (Schizomycetes)** Classified name *Synonyms* Common names	Principal characteristics	Habitat, host, transmission, etc.	Associated diseases or source	Clinical application of antibiotics: Penicillin	Streptomycin	Tetracyclines	Remarks
114	*82*	**Dialister granuliformans** (Pavlović) Bergey et al. *Bacterium granuliformans*	Generally similar to *D. pneumosintes*. Anaerobic to microaerophilic	Mucous membrane of respiratory tract	Isolated in cases of influenza. Pathogenicity doubtful				
115	*83*	**Sphaerophorus necrophorus** (Flügge) Prévot *Actinomyces necrophorus, Bacillus diphtheriae vitulorum, Bacillus funduliformis, Bacillus necrophorus, Bacillus thetoides, Bacterium funduliforme, Bacteroides funduliformis, Cohnistreptothrix cuniculi, Necrobacterium necrophorus, Spherophorus funduliformis, Streptothrix cuniculi* Bang's necrosis bacillus, Schmorl's bacillus (Bazillus der Kälberdiphtherie)	Gram-negative. Extremely pleomorphic rods showing filamentous and branching forms. Foul odor. Produces hemotoxin. Anaerobe	Mucous membranes	Isolated in urinary and puerperal infections, appendicitis, otitis, pulmonary gangrene, liver abscesses, septicemia, etc. Also associated with diphtheria in cattle and with other animal diseases[1]				Sensitivity to antibiotics in vitro (concentrations in µg/ml to which at least half the strains are susceptible)[2]: Polymyxin B > 4; Chloramphenicol > 5; Penicillin > 6; Streptomycins > 10; Bacitracin > 350. The tetracyclines are clinically effective[2]
115	*84*	**Sphaerophorus necroticus** (Nativelle) Prévot *Bacillus necroticus*	Gram-negative. Thin, nonmotile, irregular rods with bipolar staining in young cultures, breaking down to amorphous elements after 24 hours. Anaerobe	Necrotic tissue	Isolated from gangrenous appendicitis. Pathogenicity increased when mixed with *E. coli*				
115	*85*	**Sphaerophorus ridiculosus** Prévot	Gram-negative. Extremely pleomorphic rods. Often as round masses with rod-shaped appendices. Nonmotile. Anaerobe		Isolated from various lesions in man				
115	*86*	**Sphaerophorus mortiferus** (Harris) Prévot *Bacillus mortiferus*	Gram-negative. Nonmotile rods occurring singly, in pairs or in short chains. Filamentous and pleomorphic forms. Requires serum or ascitic fluid for growth. Anaerobe		Isolated from a liver abscess				
115	*87*	**Sphaerophorus freundii** (Hauduroy et al.) Prévot *Bacteroides freundii*	Gram-negative. Short, nonmotile, ellipsoidal rods occurring singly, in pairs and in chains. Pleomorphic with swollen and filamentous forms. Bipolar staining. Requires serum or ascitic fluid for growth. Anaerobe		Isolated from purulent meningitis following otitis				
115	*88*	**Sphaerophorus pyogenes** (Hauduroy et al.) Prévot *Bacillus pyogenes anaerobius, Bacteroides pyogenes*	Similar to *Sph. freundii*		Isolated from liver and lung abscesses and from blood after tonsillectomy				
115	*89*	**Sphaerophorus influenzaeformis** (Russ) Prévot *Bacillus influenzaeformis, Bacteroides russii*	Gram-negative. Short nonmotile rods. Some strains pleomorphic. Bipolar staining. Anaerobe		Isolated from a perianal abscess and in purulent meningitis				
115	*90*	**Sphaerophorus floccosus** (Weinberg et al.) Prévot *Bacillus floccosus, Bacteroides floccosus, Streptobacillus pyogenes floccosus*	Gram-negative. Small, nonmotile, ellipsoidal rods occurring singly, in pairs and in chains. Bipolar staining. Anaerobe		Isolated from blood in pyemia				

1) Alston, J.M., *Brit. med. J.*, **2**, 1524 (1955). 2) Welch, H., *A Guide to Antibiotic Therapy*, New York, 1959.

For classification of organisms see pages 721–724; for index of synonyms see pages 725–734

See pages 721–724	See pages 725–734	**Bacteria (Schizomycetes)** Classified name *Synonyms* Common names	Principal characteristics	Habitat, host, transmission, etc.	Associated diseases or source	Clinical application of antibiotics: Penicillin	Streptomycin	Tetracyclines	Remarks
115	*91*	**Sphaerophorus abscedens** TARDIEUX and MONTEVERDE	GRAM-negative. Pleomorphic rods. Nonmotile		Isolated from pus of a human abscess				
115	*92*	**Sphaerophorus glycolyticus** TARDIEUX and ERNST	GRAM-negative. Nonmotile, pleomorphic rods with bipolar staining. Requires serum or ascitic fluid for growth. Anaerobe		Isolated from genital infections and war wounds				
116	*93*	**Streptobacillus moniliformis** LEVADITI et al. *Actinomyces muris, Actinomyces muris ratti, Asterococcus muris, Haverhillia moniliformis, Haverhillia multiformis, Nocardia muris, Proactinomyces muris, Streptothrix muris ratti*	GRAM-negative. Highly pleomorphic rods forming long wavy filaments. Nonmotile. Aerobe, facultative anaerobe	Rats and mice. Transmitted by rat-bite and by ingestion of infected food, especially milk	Cause of one type of rat-bite fever and of Haverhill fever (erythema arthriticum epidemicum)	0	1	?	For rat-bite fever caused by *Spirillum minus* see *No. 9*
118	*94*	**Staphylococcus aureus** ROSENBACH *Micrococcus albus, Micrococcus aureus, Micrococcus citreus, Micrococcus pyogenes, Staphylococcus albus, Staphylococcus citreus, Staphylococcus pyogenes albus, Staphylococcus pyogenes aureus, Staphylococcus pyogenes citreus* Staphylococcus (Staphylocoque doré)	GRAM-positive. Nonmotile spheres 0.8–1 µm diameter, occurring singly, in pairs, in short chains or in irregular clumps. Many strains produce a yellow or orange pigment, especially on media containing much NaCl, otherwise colonies are dirty white. Forms α-, β- and γ-hemolysins. Aerobe and facultative anaerobe	Common saprophyte on human skin (hair follicles) and nasopharyngeal mucosa. Also found on food products	Suppuration of wounds, etc. See remarks below	1	?	?	See remarks below and on page 662

Staphylococci *(Nos. 94 and 95)*

The staphylococci are the most persistent and, sporadically, the most unpleasant of all the bacterial organisms which accompany man throughout his life. In infants, 90% are already nasal carriers of staphylococci one week after birth[1]. They are present in large numbers in the human environment, particularly on the skin and clothes. In the age group 15–44 years of patients in general medical practice, staphylococcal affections of the skin occupy fourth place in respect of frequency after bronchitis, colds and influenza[2], but are by far the commonest of all types of skin infections. Of all cases of staphylococcal skin infection, 90% occur in persons between the ages of 5 and 44 years[3]. Infection is preferentially in those areas of the skin either not protected by a horny outer layer or, like the head and neck (50%) and forearms (20%), especially subject to mechanical injuries such as scratches and abrasions[4].

Characteristic of the staphylococci are their facultative pathogenicity and the tendency of the infections to relapse. In the same or different individuals the same strain may bring about widely differing effects, either at different times or simultaneously: these vary from no reaction at all or a very small localized skin infection to extensive folliculitis, single or multiple furuncles, infection of internal organs, osteitis, and in severe cases fatal pyemia and toxemia. The initial reaction of the body is an attempt to localize the infection by proliferation of polymorphonuclear leukocytes and phagocytes at the point of attack. This is followed by thrombosis of the most prominent parts of the neighboring blood vessels, then ischemia, necrosis and abscess formation. From the thrombosed area the organisms may be carried by the blood stream to

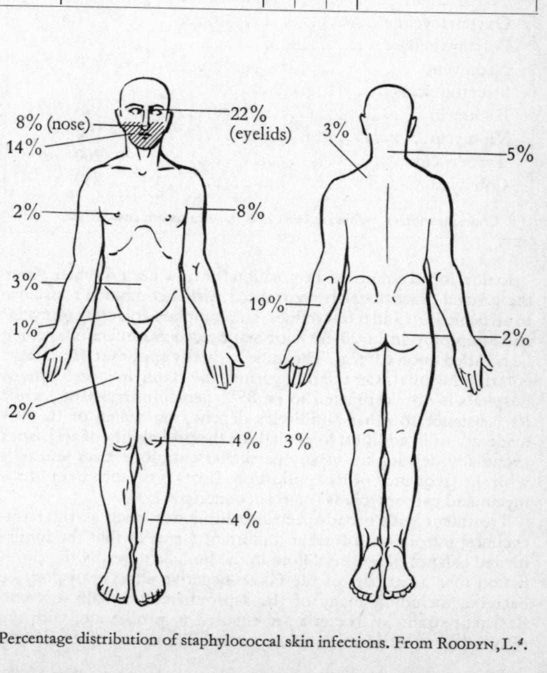

Percentage distribution of staphylococcal skin infections. From RODYN, L.[4].

Staphylococci *(Nos. 94 and 95) (continued)*

other parts of the body, with metastases occurring preferentially in those organs which are particularly susceptible to staphylococcal infection, such as the kidneys, endocardium, meninges, lungs, brain, liver and spleen. In the case of infection by toxin-forming strains there may be toxemia without pyemia, with exitus in a few days, even when the focal infection is hardly visible.

The reasons for the facultative pathogenicity of the organism, and for the varying degree of infection to which it gives rise, are not fully known. Apart from the varying resistance of the host (which has its origin in widely different causes), they are certainly due in part to differences in the virulence of different strains, or even of the same strain. Unfortunately there is no reliable means of recognizing the *in vivo* virulence of a strain from an *in vitro* culture. The deep orange strains are usually the most dangerous, but highly virulent strains may also give white cultures. Some strains give rise to hemolysis, in which case the latter generally runs parallel with the pathogenicity. For these reasons it is frequently a matter of the utmost difficulty for a bacteriologist examining a culture from a patient to determine whether the organism is the actual etiological agent, is merely secondary, is a harmless saprophyte, or is a simple contamination. In postmortem cases the problem is further complicated by the fact that staphylococci, even when not responsible for the fatal illness, may enter the blood stream in the death agony and thus be found in subsequent blood cultures. The ready ability of staphylococci to develop resistance to all antibiotics also presents the physician, and particularly the internist, with a serious problem. But for this, the high *in vitro* sensitivity of staphylococci to a variety of antibiotics, as exemplified by the data in the table below[10], would render the treatment of infections a simple matter.

	µg/ml*
Erythromycin	0.4
Penicillin	0.6
Novobiocin	0.8
Chlortetracycline	1.0
Oleandomycins	1.6
Vancomycin	1.87
Chloramphenicol	3.0
Spiramycin	3.5
Kanamycin	3.9
Ristocetin	5.0
Tetracycline	7.5
Oxytetracycline	7.5
Polymyxin B	16
Neomycin	20
Streptomycins	50
Bacitracin	90
Viomycin	> 100
Tyrothricin	200
Colimycin	250

* Concentrations to which at least half the strains are susceptible.

In developed countries the position has now been reached where the general practitioner is confronted with a combined resistance to all penicillins and tetracyclines, chloramphenicol, erythromycin[6] and streptomycin in 20–30% of staphylococcal infections which he is called upon to treat. The same naturally applies to fresh cases entering hospital. On the other hand, the staphylococcal flora of hospitals is now estimated to be 85% penicillin-resistant[7], while its resistance to other antibiotics depends on which of them is made use of in addition to penicillin; the probability of resistance eventually developing to any particular antibiotic rises and falls with the frequency of its application. Cross resistance to erythromycin and carbomycin is often encountered[8].

Treatment with broad-spectrum antibiotics, such as the tetracyclines, introduces a further important factor in that the fundamental balance of bacterial flora in the body is upset by the elimination of a great part of the GRAM-negative and GRAM-positive bacteria, including many of the saprophytes normally present. Resistant strains of bacteria are enabled to proliferate, with the result that superinfections may occur. These are often due to resistant staphylococci and represent a source of serious danger to patients in a weakened condition, especially after operations, as well as to infants and old people. The death rate from superinfections is high, and they often have a precipitate course[9]. On the whole, however, they are seldom encountered, and then mainly in patients whose illness would in any case have been fatal. The possibility of a superinfection should therefore certainly not be regarded as justifying the withholding of broad-spectrum antibiotics. Staphylococcal superinfections are a frequent and dangerous complication in gastrointestinal surgery, commencing 1–4 days after operation with symptoms of a severely toxic, choleriform dysentery which may be followed by death in 2–10 days. The antibiotics used for intestinal disinfection should therefore include one to which resistant staphylococci are sensitive.

Treatment

Apart from antibiotic treatment, the importance of surgical removal of all purulent and necrotic foci, as well as the drainage of infected serous cavities (joint cavities, pericardium, pleural cavity, etc.), cannot be too strongly emphasized.

In treating less severe staphylococcal infections which are following the normal course, the possibility of resistance should not deter the general practitioner from commencing with penicillin. It should be given in high dosage, up to 1 million units per day, and if it elicits no response should be replaced by other antibiotics (other penicillins, tetracyclines, chloramphenicol, erythromycin) which should be retained or discarded according to the degree of success achieved.

Fresh hospital cases should receive similar treatment. On the other hand, staphylococcal infections acquired in the hospital itself should be treated with appropriate antibiotics whose efficacy has been determined beforehand by a continuous check on the sensitivity of the staphylococcal flora carried by the hospital staff. Here again these should include penicillin. It is cheap, can be given in large doses owing to its low toxicity, and is never entirely without effect. In testing staphylococcal sensitivity, *in vitro* tests should not be wholly depended upon, since they do not always reflect the results *in vivo*. Where resistance to penicillin is encountered, the present antibiotic of choice in the U.K. is methicillin (see page 643), and in cases of severe infection (staphylococcal septicemia) it is recommended[11] that treatment should be started with this drug pending the results of sensitivity tests. In staphylococcal endocarditis the combinations of penicillin with chlortetracycline and of streptomycin with oxytetracycline show a synergistic action.

In hospital practice, the importance of taking all possible precautions to prevent or delay the development of staphylococcal resistance to antibiotics cannot be too strongly emphasized[11, 12], and the greatest care and economy in the use of these agents, particularly for prophylactic purposes, is essential.

The treatment of staphylococcal infections with staphylococcus antitoxin has proved disappointing[13] (for international standard staphylococcus antitoxin see page 736).

References

1) ROUNTREE and BARBOUR, *Med. J. Aust.*, **1**, 525 (1950). *2)* LOGAN, W. P. D., *Practitioner*, **173**, 188 (1954). *3)* ROODYN, L., *Brit. med. J.*, **2**, 1322 (1954). *4)* ROODYN, L., *Proc. roy. Soc. Med.*, **49**, 263 (1956). *5)* GARROD and WATERWORTH, *Brit. med. J.*, **2**, 61 (1956). *6)* BRODIE et al., *Lancet*, **1**, 19 (1956). *7)* DOWLING et al., *J. Amer. med. Ass.*, **157**, 327 (1955). *8)* WRIGHT et al., *J. Lab. clin. Med.*, **42**, 877 (1953). *9)* COOK et al., *Brit. med. J.*, **1**, 542 (1957). *10)* WELCH, H., *A Guide to Antibiotic Therapy*, New York, 1959. *11)* Editorial, *Lancet*, **1**, 866 (1961). *12)* WALLMARK and FINLAND, *J. Amer. med. Ass.*, **175**, 886 (1961). *13)* ELEK, S. D., *Staphylococcus pyogenes*, Edinburgh and London, 1959, page 350.

Bibliography

(General) Conference on staphylococcal infections, *Ann. N. Y. Acad. Sci.*, **65**, 57 (1956); MUDD, S., *J. Amer. med. Ass.*, **166**, 1177 (1958); FINLAND et al., *Antibiotics Annual, 1958–59*, New York, 1959, page 1051; WISE et al., *Antibiotics Annual, 1958–59*, New York, 1959, page 1073; ELEK, S. D., *Staphylococcus pyogenes*, Edinburgh and London, 1959. (Pathogenicity) BLAIR, J. E., *Ann. Rev. Microbiol.*, **12**, 491 (1958). (Resistance to antibiotics) FINLAND, M., *New Engl. J. Med.*, **253**, 909, 969, 1019 (1955); FAIRBROTHER, R. W., *Lancet*, **1**, 716 (1956); Editorial, *Brit. med. J.*, **2**, 720 (1960); LOWBURY, E. J. L., *Brit. med. Bull.*, **16**, 73 (1960). (Staphylococcal enteritis) DEARING and NEEDHAM, *J. Amer. med. Ass.*, **174**, 1597 (1960). (Staphylococcal endocarditis) FISHER et al., *Arch. intern. Med.*, **95**, 427 (1955); DORMER, A. E., *Brit. med. Bull.*, **16**, 61 (1960). (Postoperative enterocolitis) Editorial, *New Engl. J. Med.*, **253**, 201 (1955). (Staphylococcal pneumonia in infancy) WALLMAN et al., *Brit. med. J.*, **2**, 1423 (1955); HENDREN and HAGGERTY, *J. Amer. med. Ass.*, **168**, 6 (1958). (Staphylococcal infections of the newborn) FORFAR et al., *Lancet*, **1**, 584 (1955). (Staphylococcal food poisoning) DOLMAN, C. E., *Jap. J. med. Sci. Biol.*, **10**, 373 (1957).

See pages 721–724	See pages 725–734	**Bacteria (Schizomycetes)** Classified name *Synonyms* Common names	Principal characteristics	Habitat, host, transmission, etc.	Associated diseases or source	Clinical application of antibiotics: Penicillin	Streptomycin	Tetracyclines	Remarks
118	*95*	**Staphylococcus epidermidis** (WINSLOW and WINSLOW) EVANS *Albococcus epidermidis, Micrococcus epidermidis, Staphylococcus epidermidis albus*	GRAM-positive. Nonmotile spheres 0.5–0.6 μm diameter, occurring singly, in pairs and in irregular groups. Whitish colonies on common media. Aerobe and facultative anaerobe	Skin and mucous membranes	Isolated from small stitch abscesses and other skin wounds	1	?	?	See remarks on pages 661 and 662
119	*96*	**Gaffkya tetragena** (GAFFKY) TREVISAN *Micrococcus tetragenus* (Tétragène)	GRAM-positive. Spheres in groups of 4 surrounded by a pseudocapsule (in body fluids). Aerobe and facultative anaerobe	Mucous membrane of respiratory tract	Isolated from sputum, often together with *Haemophilus influenzae* and tubercle bacilli. Parasitic, but occasionally pathogenic	1	?	?	For a review see PEROU et al.[1]
122	*97*	**Peptococcus activus** (PRÉVOT and TAFFANEL) DOUGLAS *Staphylococcus activus*	GRAM-positive. Nonmotile spheres occurring singly, in pairs, tetrads or irregular groups. Produces gas from culture media. Anaerobe	Probably human body	Isolated from a case of puerperal septicemia				
122	*98*	**Peptococcus asaccharolyticus** (DISTASO) DOUGLAS *Micrococcus asaccharolyticus, Staphylococcus asaccharolyticus*	GRAM-positive. Large spheres occurring in massive clusters, also pairs and short chains. Foul odor. Anaerobe	Intestine	Isolated from a case of intestinal intoxication				
122	*99*	**Peptococcus aerogenes** (SCHOTTMÜLLER) DOUGLAS *Micrococcus aerogenes, Staphylococcus aerogenes*	Similar to *P. activus*	Body cavities, especially tonsils, female genital tract	Isolated from cases of puerperal fever and from infected tonsils	1	0	3	2: erythromycin
122	*100*	**Peptococcus grigoroffii** (PRÉVOT) DOUGLAS *Micrococcus grigoroffi*	GRAM-positive. Small spheres occurring singly or in irregular masses. Coagulates milk. Anaerobe	Digestive tract	Isolated in appendicitis				
122	*101*	**Peptococcus constellatus** (PRÉVOT) DOUGLAS *Diplococcus constellatus*	GRAM-positive. Spheres in pairs or tetrads, rarely in short chains. Agar colonies are thick, biconvex, opaque, yellowish, and surrounded by many small satellite colonies visible microscopically. No gas produced. Anaerobe	Digestive tract, especially lymphoid tissues such as tonsils and appendix	Isolated in chronic cryptic tonsillitis and from pus in acute appendicitis	1?	3?	2?	
122	*102*	**Peptococcus anaerobius** (HAMM) DOUGLAS *Micrococcus anaerobius, Staphylococcus anaerobius* Anaerobic staphylococcus	Similar to *P. activus* but smaller and not a gas-former	Probably human body	Isolated from case of cystitis, also from infected appendix and tonsils	1	0	3	2: erythromycin
123	*103*	**Neisseria gonorrhoeae** TREVISAN *Gonococcus neisseri, Micrococcus gonorrhoeae* Gonococcus (Micrococcus der Gonorrhöe)	GRAM-negative. Single or paired spheres. Grows best on media containing added body fluids. Colonies are grayish-white, small, transparent. Aerobe and facultative anaerobe	In venereal discharges, also blood, conjunctiva, etc. Transmission usually venereal but occasionally by contact with infected articles	Gonorrhea, gonorrheal ophthalmia of newborn. Metastases mainly in tendon sheaths, joints, bursae, eyes, endocardium	1	0	2	3: erythromycin. See remarks on page 664

1) PEROU et al., *J. Pediat.*, **53**, 484 (1958).

See pages 721–724	See pages 725–734	**Bacteria (Schizomycetes)** Classified name *Synonyms* Common names	Principal characteristics	Habitat, host, transmission, etc.	Associated diseases or source	Clinical application of antibiotics: Penicillin	Streptomycin	Tetracyclines	Remarks
123	*104*	**Neisseria meningitidis** (ALBRECHT and GHON) HOLLAND *Diplococcus intracellularis meningitidis* WEICHSELBAUM, *Micrococcus intracellularis, Micrococcus meningitidis, Neisseria weichselbaumii* Meningococcus, WEICHSELBAUM's bacillus	GRAM-negative. Spheres occurring singly in pairs and occasionally tetrads, markedly pleomorphic. On blood agar the colonies look like sprayed droplets of watery milk. Aerobe	Nasopharynx of man	Epidemic cerebrospinal meningitis (70% of acute cases); also sepsis without meningitic symptoms but marked by high fever, coma, purpura, adrenal hemorrhage, shock (WATERHOUSE-FRIEDRICHSEN syndrome). See remarks below	1	0	2	**Sulfonamides** are rather more effective than penicillin and should therefore be combined with this or any other antibiotic used
123	*105*	**Neisseria catarrhalis** (FROSCH and KOLLE) HOLLAND *Micrococcus catarrhalis*	Similar to *N. meningitidis*	Mucous membrane of respiratory tract	Often associated with other organisms in inflammations of the mucous membrane	1	0	2	
123	*106*	**Neisseria flavescens** BRANHAM	GRAM-negative. Biscuit-shaped cocci occurring in flattened pairs. Forms golden yellow pigment on blood agar. Aerobe and facultative anaerobe	Probably mucous membrane of respiratory tract	Isolated from cerebrospinal fluid in meningitis. Probably parasitic	1	0	2	
123	*107*	**Neisseria flava** BERGEY et al.	Similar to *N. subflava* but greenish yellow chromogenesis more marked	Mucous membrane of respiratory tract	Isolated from nasopharynx and cerebrospinal fluid in meningitis (very rare). Probably parasitic	1	0	2	
124	*108*	**Veillonella parvula** (VEILLON and ZUBER) PRÉVOT *Staphylococcus parvulus*	GRAM-negative. Very small spheres occurring in pairs, short chains or masses. Ferments polypeptides and sugars. Weakly hemolytic. Strict anaerobe	Body cavities, especially mouth and digestive tract	Normally harmless parasite but can become pathogenic. Isolated from pulmonary gangrene, abscesses, alveolar pyorrhea	1	?	2	

Gonorrhea *(No. 103)*

The incubation period of gonorrhea has lengthened somewhat since the introduction of sulfonamides and antibiotics and now averages 3–10 days. The lapse of time between the appearance of symptoms and the first consultation now averages 4 days compared to 2 days previously, indicating that the gonococcus may have become less virulent[1].

Treatment

The sensitivity of gonococci to antibiotics *in vitro* is as follows (concentrations in µg/ml to which at least half the strains are susceptible)[2]:

Penicillin	0.02
Bacitracin	0.13
Spiramycin	0.5
Chloramphenicol	1.0
Erythromycin	1.0
Chlortetracycline	1.0
Oxytetracycline	1.0
Kanamycin	2.5
Novobiocin	3.1
Streptomycins	5.0
Tetracycline	5.0
Oleandomycins	6.25
Polymyxin B	> 6.4
Tyrothricin	10
Neomycin	50

The antibiotic of choice in the treatment of gonorrhea is still penicillin[2,3] (minimum effective blood level: 0.35 IU/ml for 24 hours[6]), although gonococci are now showing a tendency to become resistant to this drug[4]. An apparent resistance may arise through too low a dosage, or through reinfection by the patient's wife (or husband), who should therefore be treated simultaneously whether showing symptoms or not. The single disadvantage of penicillin is that even in small doses it may suppress the early signs of incubating syphilis, which is not the case with streptomycin[5]. On treatment with these and other antibiotics see KING[5] and FIUMARA[6]. It is interesting to note that current strains of gonococci are once again sensitive to sulfonamides[2].

References

1) LODIN, A., *Acta derm.-venereol. (Stockh.)*, **35**, 457 (1955). *2)* WELCH, H., *A Guide to Antibiotic Therapy*, New York, 1959. *3)* DOWLING, H. F., in WELCH et al. (Eds.), *Principles and Practice of Antibiotic Therapy*, New York, 1954, page 349. *4)* Editorial, *Lancet*, **2**, 685 (1959). *5)* KING, A. J., *Brit. med. J.*, **2**, 1396 (1959). *6)* FIUMARA, N. J., in CONN, H. F. (Ed.), *Current Therapy 1961*, Philadelphia and London, 1961, page 401.

Meningococcus *(No. 104)*

Paradoxically, the pathogen of epidemic cerebrospinal meningitis affects mainly vigorous and healthy individuals rather than the sick or debilitated. Transmission is by droplet infection, presumably by way of the tonsils.

The disease is often difficult to distinguish either bacteriologically or clinically from other inflammatory affections of the meninges (pneumococcal, streptococcal, coli, etc.) since it favors the development of secondary purulent organisms. In such cases, the latter may predominate in the clinical picture and thus disguise the true cause of the meningitis.

For classification of organisms see pages 721–724; for index of synonyms see pages 725–734

See pages 721–724	See pages 725–734	**Bacteria (Schizomycetes)** Classified name *Synonyms* Common names	Principal characteristics	Habitat, host, transmission, etc.	Associated diseases or source	Clinical application of antibiotics: Penicillin	Streptomycin	Tetracyclines	Remarks
124	*109*	**Veillonella alcalescens** PRÉVOT *Micrococcus gazogenes, Micrococcus gazogenes alcalescens anaerobius, Veillonella gazogenes*	GRAM-negative. Spheres occurring singly, in pairs, short chains and masses. Does not ferment sugars and is non-hemolytic. Strict anaerobe	Saliva	Not normally pathogenic. Isolated from pulmonary gangrene and alveolar pyorrhea	1	?	2	
124	*110*	**Veillonella reniformis** (COTTET) PELCZAR *Diplococcus reniformis, Micrococcus reniformis, Neisseria reniformis*	GRAM-negative. Bean-shaped cells in pairs. No gas produced from culture media. Rancid odor. Strict anaerobe	Presumably in man	Pathogenic. Isolated in suppurations of urogenital system	1	0	2	
124	*111*	**Veillonella vulvovaginitidis** (REYNES) PELCZAR *Neisseria vulvovaginitis*	GRAM-negative. Spheres occurring in pairs or very short chains, rarely singly, often in masses. Liquefies gelatin. Strict anaerobe	Urogenital tract	Isolated from pus in vulvovaginitis in a child				
125	*112*	**Brevibacterium ammoniagenes** (COOKE and KEITH) BREED *Alcaligenes ammoniagenes, Bacterium ammoniagenes*	GRAM-positive. Single rods with rounded ends. Nonmotile. Aerobe, facultative anaerobe	Putrefying matter	Cause of diaper rash in infants				
127	*113*	**Diplococcus pneumoniae** WEICHSELBAUM FRÄNKEL's bacillus, micrococcus of rabbit septicemia, diplococcus, pneumococcus (Pneumoniemikrokokkus, coccus lancéolé, microbe septicémique de la salive)	GRAM-positive. Occurs typically in pairs, occasionally singly or in short chains, with distal ends tending to be lancet-shaped. Cultures in peritoneal sacs or blood serum media show encapsulation. Colonies on blood agar are glistening, watery to mucoid, elevated at the center, sharply delineated. Characterized by marked autolysis and bile solubility (differentiation from streptococci). Facultative aerobe	Respiratory tract	Many types are saprophytic. The pathogenic types cause various diseases: lobar pneumonia (90% of cases), bronchitis, bronchial pneumonia, conjunctivitis, otitis media, brain abscesses, meningitis, endocarditis, peritonitis, etc. See also remarks below	1	3	2	Sensitivity to antibiotics in vitro (concentrations in µg/ml to which at least half the strains are susceptible)[1]: Penicillin 0.02 Erythromycin 0.03 Oxytetracycline 0.5 Chloramphenicol 1.2 Chlortetracycline 3.0 Tetracycline 5.0 Neomycin 10 Kanamycin 11.2 Streptomycins 25 Bacitracin 55

1) WELCH, H., *A Guide to Antibiotic Therapy*, New York, 1959.

Pneumococcus *(No. 113)*

Agglutination reactions and capsular swelling tests by means of type-specific rabbit sera made possible the classification of all strains of pneumococci into the well-defined Types 1, 2 and 3 and a heterogeneous group known as Type X or Type 4, the latter consisting of a large number of subtypes[1]. A total of 80 serological types has since been distinguished[2]. Type 14 is closely related immunologically to blood group A substance.

The various types differ both in pathogenicity and in the forms of the disease with which they are associated[3]. A majority of all pneumococcal diseases is due to a relatively small number of the known types, a fact which explains the presence of pneumococci in many healthy persons: they are not immune carriers of the organism but carriers of nonpathogenic types.

Among some 17,000 lobar pneumonia cases in USA, 32.6% were due to Type 1, 19.6% to Type 2, 10.8% to Type 3 and 36.9% to the remaining types. Types 1, 2, 3, 5, 7 and 8 accounted for 75% of cases. In lobar pneumonia of Type 1 the sputum is reddish brown, and in 25–30% of cases there is bacteremia. Lobar pneumonia of Type 2 is more malignant, the sputum redder in color, and the temperature is septicemic with bacteremia in some 40% of cases. The Type 3 pneumococcus is also known as *Pn. mucosus* on account of the mucous nature of the colonies. It is less often the cause of pneumonia than Types 1 and 2 but more commonly found in inflammations of the middle ear. The prognosis in bacteremia of this type is poor.

Bronchopneumonia is almost exclusively due to the Type X (or 4) group of organisms. In children the commonest is Type 14, and the disease is often complicated by meningitis, pericarditis, and so on. With the advent of antibiotics the distinction between the pneumococcal types has become a matter of purely academic interest.

A number of antibiotics are clinically effective against the organism, all types of which are equally sensitive. No development of resistance has yet been observed. In all pneumococcal infections the antibiotic of choice is penicillin[4–8], but the tetracyclines are equally effective[6–12]. In pneumococcal meningitis[13], penicillin and the tetracyclines are antagonistic[14], but this antagonism has not been observed in pneumococcal pneumonia[7]. The parenteral dosage of penicillin is ca. 600,000 units per day (3,000,000 units per day peroral), the oral dosage of tetracyclines ca. 3–4 g per day. For international standard antipneumococcus sera see page 736.

References

1) DOCHEZ and GILLESPIE, *J. Amer. med. Ass.*, **61**, 727 (1913). *2)* LUND, E., *Acta path. microbiol. scand.*, **40**, 425 (1957). *3)* AVERY et al., *Acute Lobar Pneumonia*, Rockefeller Institute for Medical Research, Monograph No. 9, New York, 1919. *4)* AUSTRIAN et al., *Bull. Johns Hopk. Hosp.*, **88**, 264 (1951). *5)* AUSTRIAN et al., *Bull. Johns Hopk. Hosp.*, **91**, 323 (1952). *6)* FREI et al., *New Engl. J. Med.*, **252**, 173 (1955). *7)* AHERN and KIRBY, *Arch. intern. Med.*, **91**, 197 (1953). *8)* SCADDING et al., *Brit. Med. J.*, **2**, 1361 (1951). *9)* GOCKE et al., *Arch. intern. Med.*, **84**, 857 (1949). *10)* DOWLING et al., *J. Lab. clin. Med.*, **35**, 215 (1950). *11)* JACKSON et al., *Ann. intern. Med.*, **35**, 1175 (1951). *12)* AUSTRIAN et al., *Bull. Johns Hopk. Hosp.*, **89**, 407 (1951). *13)* SPINK and SU, *J. Amer. med. Ass.*, **173**, 1545 (1960). *14)* LEPPER and DOWLING, *Arch. intern. Med.*, **88**, 489 (1951).

For classification of organisms see pages 721–724; for index of synonyms see pages 725–734

See pages 721–724	See pages 725–734	**Bacteria (Schizomycetes)** Classified name *Synonyms* Common names	Principal characteristics	Habitat, host, transmission, etc.	Associated diseases or source	Clinical application of antibiotics: Penicillin	Streptomycin	Tetracyclines	Remarks
128	*114*	**Streptococcus pyogenes** ROSENBACH *Micrococcus scarlatinae, Streptococcus epidemicus, Streptococcus erysipelatos, Streptococcus hemolyticus, Streptococcus scarlatinae* Streptococcus (Erysipelokokkus)	GRAM-positive. Usually spherical in blood and exudates. Occurs in pairs or chains. Capsulation variable. Only grows well on media enriched with native proteins or modified with dextrose. β-Hemolytic. Constitutes LANCEFIELD group A. Facultative anaerobe	Mouth, throat, respiratory tract, blood stream. Also dust in hospitals and sick rooms; occasionally in milk and udders of cows infected by man	Pus-former. Associated with various diseases. May cause fatal septicemia	1	2	2	See remarks below and on pages 667 and 668
128	*115*	**Streptococcus equisimilis** FROST and ENGELBRECHT *Streptococcus pyogenes type B, Streptococcus pyogenes humanus C*	Similar to *Str. pyogenes* except that it is more tolerant of methylene blue and ferments glycerol. Constitutes LANCEFIELD group C. Facultative anaerobe	Upper respiratory tract, vagina, skin	Occasionally associated with erysipelas and puerperal fever	1	2	2	See remarks below and on pages 667 and 668
128	*116*	**Streptococcus sanguis** WHITE *Streptococcus* s.b.e.	GRAM-positive. Spherical or ovoid cells occurring in chains. Some strains nonhemolytic. Probably LANCEFIELD group H. Facultative anaerobe	Probably man	Isolated from heart valves in subacute bacterial endocarditis. Also found in infected sinuses and teeth and in house dust	1	2	2	
128	*117*	**Streptococcus anginosus** ANDREWES and HORDER Minute hemolytic streptococcus	GRAM-positive. Minute cocci occurring singly, in pairs, chains or masses. β-Hemolytic. LANCEFIELD group F and type 1 group G. Facultative anaerobe	Human respiratory tract	Found in throat, sinuses, abscesses, vagina, skin, feces. Associated with glomerular nephritis and mild respiratory diseases	1	2	2	
128	*118*	**Streptococcus agalactiae** LEHMANN and NEUMANN *Streptococcus mastitidis, Streptococcus nocardi*	GRAM-positive. Spherical or ovoid cocci in chains from 4 to many cells long. LANCEFIELD group B. Many strains hemolytic. Distinguished in pyogenic group by hydrolysis of sodium hippurate. Facultative anaerobe	Udders of cows with mastitis	Associated with various human infections, especially urogenital tract	1	2	2	See remarks below and on pages 667 and 668
128	*119*	**Streptococcus mitis** ANDREWES and HORDER *Streptococcus viridans*	GRAM-positive. Spherical or oval cells in short to very long chains. α-Hemolysis on blood agar. No LANCEFIELD group. Facultative anaerobe	Mouth, throat, nasopharynx	Isolated from saliva and sputum in pulmonary infections, pus from upper respiratory tract, blood and various organs in subacute endocarditis	1	2	2	See remarks below and on pages 667 and 668
128	*120*	**Streptococcus bovis** ORLA-JENSEN *emend.* SHERMAN	GRAM-positive. Spherical or ovoid cocci in pairs and chains. Serologically heterogeneous. α- and γ-hemolytic. Facultative anaerobe	Alimentary tract of cattle	Associated with subacute endocarditis in man	1	2	2	See remarks below and on pages 667 and 668

Streptococci *(Nos. 114–131)*

Streptococci are spherical bacteria which multiply in the form of chains the length and shape of which is extraordinarily varied. The systematic classification of the streptococci faces immense difficulties because of their great variability, and a definitive system which would meet all scientific requirements does not yet exist.

The first classification, undertaken by BROWN[1], was based on the hemolytic behavior of streptococci on blood agar and enabled four groups to be distinguished: 1. The α-group with a dark green and a light green zone surrounding the colonies; 2. The hemolytic β-group with a clear, transparent zone around the colonies; 3. The γ-group without hemolysis and without greening; 4. The α′-group, which shows a small hemolytic zone in addition to a green one and therefore lies between the α- and β-groups.

LANCEFIELD[2] grouped the streptococci according to their serological behavior in a precipitin reaction with group-specific rabbit sera. She distinguished 12 groups, designated by the letters A to N.

GRIFFITH[3] classified the *Strep. pyogenes* group into about 30 serological types on the basis of an agglutination reaction.

For classification of organisms see pages 721–724; for index of synonyms see pages 725–734

Streptococci *(Nos. 114–131) (continued)*

Sherman[4] attempted a classification which was based on the Lancefield groups, the hemolytic and temperature behavior and other properties. This classification is that best suited to clinical purposes and with a few abbreviations, amplifications and amendments is as follows.

Group	Lancefield group	Typical species	Human pathogenicity*	Hemolysis	Growth at 10°C	Growth at 45°C	Habitat*
		Streptococcus (or *Peptostreptococcus*)					
Pyogenic streptococci	A	*pyogenes*	+	β	—	—	Man
	B	*agalactiae (mastitidis)*	?	β/γ	—	—	Cattle
	C	*equi*	—	β	—	—	Horse
	C	*zooepidemicus (animalis C)*	—	β	—	—	Domestic animals
	C	*equisimilis (humanus C)*	+	β	—	—	Man, animals
	F	*anginosus*	+	β	—	—	Man
	G		**	β	—	—	Man, animals
	E		**	β	—	—	Man, animals
	H		**	β	—	—	Man, animals
Viridans streptococci	—	*mitis**	±	α	—	+	Man
	—	*equinus*	—	α	—	+	Horse
	—	*bovis*	?	α/γ	—	+	Man, cattle
	—	*thermophilus*	—	γ	—	+	Milk, cheese
Anaerobes*	—	*intermedius**	±	α	—	+	Man
	—	*evolutus**	±	α/γ	—	+	Man
	—	*micros**	±	γ	—	+	Man, animals
	—	*anaerobius**	±	Gas	—	+	Man, animals
	—	*foetidus**	±	Gas	—	+	Man, animals
	—	*putridus**	±	Gas	—	+	Man
Lacticus streptococci	L	*lactis*	—	γ	+	—	Milk products
	L	*cremoris*	—	γ	+	—	Milk products
Enterococci	D	*faecalis*	±	α/γ	+*	+	Man, Milk products
	D	*faecalis* var. *zymogenes*	—	β	+*	+	Man, animals
	D	*durans*	—	β	+*	+	Man, milk products

* Data amplified or amended from Breed et al.[5].
** In these groups there are both pathogenic and nonpathogenic streptococci.
± indicates facultative pathogen.

This summary shows that *all pyogenic streptococci are hemolytic* and relatively sensitive to temperature. All species can be classed in the various Lancefield groups except for the *viridans group* and the *anaerobes*, which are not amenable to the Lancefield technique (they do not possess the relevant polysaccharide, the so-called substance C), are *all nonhemolytic* (greening, unreactive or gas-forming) and sensitive to fairly low temperatures. The *lactic* group, which are of no medical but of great dairying importance, belong to Lancefield group L, and are also nonhemolytic and sensitive to fairly low temperatures. The *enterococci*, which all belong to Lancefield group D, show varying hemolytic behavior and are relatively insensitive to temperature.

The *pyogenic streptococci* are frequently the causative organisms of acute anginas, erysipelas, mouth infections, inflammation of the middle ear, puerperal sepsis, secondary infections in diphtheria and tuberculosis, and secondary bronchopneumonia in influenza and measles. They play an etiological role in rheumatic fever and are a co-factor, if not the causative factor, of scarlet fever. The cellulitis caused by them shows a phlegmonous, diffuse character and resembles more a tissue necrosis, in contrast to the circumscribed, purulent staphylococcal lesions. The course of pyogenic streptococcal infections is acute and differs in this respect from the subacute or chronic infections due to nonhemolytic streptococci and enterococci. In the absence of acquired immunity they are strictly pathogenic. Epidemic transmission is as a rule by droplet infection and often through contaminated milk.

The *nonhemolytic streptococci* (viridans group and anaerobes) and the enterococci are as a rule saprophytes, but only as long as they do not penetrate the skin or mucous membranes, for example via a mechanical lesion or one due to infection, into the tissues below. There, and *often as mixed infections*, they cause subacute or chronic inflammations which in contrast to those due to pyogenic streptococci are of a fetid, putrid, granulating or gangrenous character. They play a predominant role in "latent" foci and can often be found in chronic infections of tonsils, dental granulomas, sinuses, middle ear, endocardium, bile ducts, urinary tract, appendix and female genital organs, and also in gangrene of many different organs. They are the commonest cause of bacterial endocarditis (see Bibliography, page 668).

Treatment of streptococcal infections

The sensitivity of pyogenic streptococci to antibiotics in vitro is shown in the following table[6]:

	Sensitivity µg/ml*
Erythromycin	0.04
Oxytetracycline	0.5
Spiramycin	0.5
Penicillin	0.6
Oleandomycins	0.6
Ristocetin	0.8
Novobiocin	1.0
Chloramphenicol	1.2
Tyrothricin	2.0
Vancomycin	2.0
Chlortetracycline	3.0
Tetracycline	5.0
Bacitracin	18
Streptomycins	25
Kanamycin	25
Neomycin	30
Polymyxin B	64
Viomycin	> 100

* Concentrations to which at least half the strains are susceptible.

From the point of view of sensitivity, toxicity, price and medical "strategy" (reservation of erythromycin for resistant strains of streptococci and staphylococci), and despite the greater risk of developing resistance, penicillin is still the drug of choice in streptococcal infections. This is especially so since the resistance, in contrast to that of staphylococci, can almost always be overcome by increasing the dosage. High dosages of at least 600,000 units per day intramuscularly (adults) must be given. For prophylaxis in angina epidemics, penicillin has also proved to be the most effective antibiotic, either orally (200,000 units per day) or better as a single injection of benzathine penicillin G[7,8]. For the elimination and prevention of streptococcal infections in scarlet fever the following dosages of penicillin are employed[9]:

Age	Elimination* (intramuscular)	Maintenance** (oral)
0–12 months	120,000 IU	3 × 50,000 IU
1– 4 years	240,000 IU	3 × 100,000 IU
5– 9 years	360,000 IU	3 × 150,000 IU
10–14 years	480,000 IU	3 × 200,000 IU
15 years and over	600,000 IU	3 × 250,000 IU

* For 2–3 days at commencement of illness. ** Over 2–3 weeks.

Subacute and chronic streptococcal infections are mostly mixed infections whose foci are more or less cut off from the circulation by granulation, pus formation, necrosis, gangrene, etc. In such cases the highest penicillin doses (up to several million units per day; see under Staphylococci, page 662) should be given. In streptococcal endocarditis, penicillin and streptomycin act synergistically.

Streptococcal angina, rheumatic fever, scarlet fever

Streptococcal angina is a disease which occurs mainly in childhood. Medically, its frequency and serious aftermath make it by far the most important of the pyogenic streptococcal infections. Its course shows characteristic differences during the first years of life[10,11].

For classification of organisms see pages 721–724; for index of synonyms see pages 725–734

See pages 721–724	See pages 725–734	**Bacteria (Schizomycetes)** Classified name *Synonyms* Common names	Principal characteristics	Habitat, host, transmission, etc.	Associated diseases or source	Clinical application of antibiotics: Penicillin	Streptomycin	Tetracyclines	Remarks
128	*121*	**Streptococcus faecalis** ANDREWES and HORDER *Enterococcus proteiformis, Micrococcus ovalis, Streptococcus ovalis* Enterococcus	GRAM-positive. Ovoid cells occurring in pairs or short chains. Some strains motile. α- to γ-Hemolytic. LANCEFIELD group D. Facultative anaerobe	Intestine, milk, dairy products	Intestinal saprophyte, usually nonpathogenic. Isolated from blood in subacute endocarditis	1	2	2	See remarks on page 667. *Str. liquefaciens* is now regarded as a variety of this species
131	*122*	**Peptostreptococcus anaerobius** (KRÖNIG *emend.* NATVIG) KLUYVER and VAN NIEL *Streptococcus anaerobius*	GRAM-positive. Spherical cells in chains. Very peptolytic with gas formation, also in other media. Nonhemolytic. Anaerobe	Body cavities, especially vagina, and intestine of man and animals	Pathogenic (some strains). Can invade all tissues. Isolated from putrefactive gangrene, in pleurisy and appendicitis, from uterus, lochia and blood in puerperal infections	1	2	2	See remarks on page 667
131	*123*	**Peptostreptococcus foetidus** (VEILLON) SMITH *Micrococcus foetidus, Streptococcus foetidus*	GRAM-positive. Large spheres in short chains, also tetrads, double or zigzag chains. Nonhemolytic. Little gas from peptone broth. Anaerobe	Mouth, intestine and vagina of man and animals	Pathogenic (some strains). Isolated in pulmonary gangrene, LUDWIG's angina, perinephritic phlegmon, appendicitis, and from fetid pus from BARTHOLIN's gland	1	2	2	See remarks on page 667

Streptococci *(Nos. 114–131) (continued)*

In children under 3 years, the sudden onset with fever is usually lacking, the course of the disease is slow, and the patient's recovery hesitant. The most prominent symptom is rhinorrhea with many streptococci in the mucus. There is no significant involvement of the pharynx or tonsils, and no severe pain. It is never accompanied by skin erythema (scarlet fever) and rarely by rheumatic fever. On the other hand, purulent complications such as otitis media are very common. In older children the onset is more acute and pain and fever more marked, while nasal symptoms are rarer. As a rule there is exudative pharyngitis and tonsillitis, painful cervical adenitis, and commonly skin erythema. The course of the disease is shorter, recovery more spontaneous, and without purulent complications. There is a greater likelihood of rheumatic complications, especially in patients over 5 years. This change in the character of the disease is probably a reflection of the increase with age in the production of antibodies against pyogenic streptococci[12], an increase which is more likely to be due to increased immunity following repeated infection than to an increase in the body's capacity to produce antibodies[10]. This view is supported by the fact that in rheumatic fever, which only makes its appearance after repeated reinfection, the capacity to produce antibodies is always fully developed and independent of age[13].

As a result of extensive clinical and experimental work[14, 15] it has now been established with certainty that *rheumatic fever*, with or without involvement of the joints, follows from repeated infection with hemolytic streptococci of LANCEFIELD group A. However, it is not understood why an infection leaves some patients with rheumatic fever while others remain unaffected, and the mechanism of the process is still unknown. Diagnostically important is the titer of streptococcal antibodies during the first few days of the rheumatic affection, in particular that of antistreptolysin O: *a low titer (less than 50 units) rules out rheumatic fever, while higher titers (over 100 units) are a probable but not positive indication of the disease*[13]. A patient who has once contracted rheumatic fever should at all costs be protected from further streptococcal infections.

In the case of *scarlet fever* it is also now certain that hemolytic streptococci of LANCEFIELD group A play an important part, even if they are not the etiological agent of this disease. Evidence for this is provided by the (streptococcal) angina, the epidemiology, the SCHULTZ-CHARLTON reaction (blanching of the skin around an intracutaneous injection of scarlet fever convalescent serum or specific antitoxin[16–18]) and the DICK test (erythematous reaction in persons *not* suffering from scarlet fever after intracutaneous injection of a scarlet fever streptococcal culture filtrate[19]). The existence of other etiological factors, however, must be assumed from the fact that the disease follows its usual course, albeit with fewer complications, after the streptococci have been eradicated by antibiotics (as well as for other reasons). Supported in part by experimental data, some authorities[20–22] therefore consider that scarlet fever is due to the combined effects of streptococci and a virus. *The risk of complications in scarlet fever is reduced to a minimum by immediate elimination of streptococci from the patient and prevention of further infection* (for international standard antitoxin see page 736).

References

1) BROWN, J. H., *The Use of Blood Agar for the Study of Streptococci*, Rockefeller Institute for Medical Research, Monograph No. 9, New York, 1919. *2)* LANCEFIELD, R. C., *J. exp. Med.*, **57**, 571 (1933). *3)* GRIFFITH, F., *J. Hyg. (Lond.)*, **34**, 542 (1934). *4)* SHERMAN, J. M., *Bact. Rev.*, **1**, 3 (1937). *5)* BREED et al., *Bergey's Manual of Determinative Bacteriology*, 7th ed., Baltimore, 1957. *6)* WELCH, H., *A Guide to Antibiotic Therapy*, New York, 1959. *7)* BERNSTEIN et al., *Arch. intern. Med.*, **93**, 894 (1954). *8)* SEAL, C. J. R., *Antibiotics Annual, 1955–56*, New York, 1956, page 202. *9)* STRÖM and TUNEVALL, *Acta paediat. (Uppsala)*, **44**, 527 (1955). *10)* POWERS and BOISVERT, *J. Pediat.*, **25**, 481 (1944). *11)* RANTZ et al., *Pediatrics*, **12**, 498 (1953). *12)* RANTZ et al., *Arch. intern. Med.*, **87**, 360 (1951). *13)* RANTZ, L. A., *Med. Clin. N. Amer.*, **39**, 339 (1955). *14)* MURPHY and SWIFT, *J. exp. Med.*, **89**, 687 (1949). *15)* KIRSCHNER and HOWIE, *J. Path. Bact.*, **64**, 367 (1952). *16)* NEUMANN, J., *Dtsch. med. Wschr.*, **46**, 566 (1920). *17)* PASCHEN, E., *Derm. Wschr.*, **68**, 343 (1919). *18)* MAIR, W., *Lancet*, **2**, 1390 (1923). *19)* DICK and DICK, *J. Amer. med. Ass.*, **77**, 782 (1921), **81**, 1166 (1923), **82**, 265, 301 (1924). *20)* IMAMURA et al., *Jap. J. exp. Med.*, **12**, 601 (1934), and **13**, 341, 771 (1935). *21)* BINGEL, K. F., *Z. Hyg. InfektKr.*, **127**, 216, 280, 286, 434 (1947); *Dtsch. med. Wschr.*, **74**, 703 (1949). *22)* WILDFÜHR, G., *Z. Hyg. InfektKr.*, **133**, 248 (1951).

Bibliography

(General) MCCARTY, M. (Ed.), *Streptococcal Infections*, New York, 1954. (Rheumatic fever) RANTZ, L. A., *The Prevention of Rheumatic Fever*, Springfield, 1952; THOMAS, L. (Ed.), *Rheumatic Fever*, Minneapolis, 1952; American Council on Rheumatic Fever and Congenital Heart Disease and Medical Research Council, *Circulation*, **22**, 503 (1960), and *Brit. med. J.*, **2**, 1033 (1960); FINLAND, M., *J. Amer. med. Ass.*, **166**, 364 (1958).

For classification of organisms see pages 721–724; for index of synonyms see pages 725–734

See pages 721–724	See pages 725–734	**Bacteria (Schizomycetes)** Classified name *Synonyms* Common names	Principal characteristics	Habitat, host, transmission, etc.	Associated diseases or source	Clinical application of antibiotics: Penicillin	Streptomycin	Tetracyclines	Remarks
131	*124*	**Peptostreptococcus putridus** (SCHOTTMÜLLER *emend.* PRÉVOT) SMITH *Streptococcus putridus*	GRAM-positive. Spherical cells in chains. On blood agar blackish-brown colonies and zone. Nonhemolytic. No gas from peptone broth. Anaerobe	Mouth, intestinal tract, especially vagina	Isolated from normal and fetid lochia, blood in puerperal fever, in gangrenous appendicitis, gas gangrene, osteomyelitis	1	2	2	See remarks on page 667
131	*125*	**Peptostreptococcus productus** (PRÉVOT) SMITH *Streptococcus productus*	GRAM-positive. Large spheres occurring in chains. Coagulates milk. Nonhemolytic. No gas from peptone broth. Anaerobe	Body cavities, especially respiratory tract	Isolated from a case of pulmonary gangrene	1	2	2	
131	*126*	**Peptostreptococcus lanceolatus** (PRÉVOT) SMITH *Coccus lanceolatus anaerobius, Streptococcus lanceolatus*	GRAM-positive. Ovoid cells occurring in pairs or chains. Gas produced from peptone broth and especially from agar. Nonhemolytic. Anaerobe	Putrefying matter	Isolated from feces in diarrhea	1	2	2	
131	*127*	**Peptostreptococcus micros** (PRÉVOT) SMITH *Streptococcus anaerobius micros, Streptococcus micros*	GRAM-positive. Very small cells in pairs or long chains. No gas or fetid odor. Nonhemolytic. Anaerobe	Mouth and intestinal tract of man and animals	Isolated in pulmonary gangrene, from lochia and uterus in puerperal fever, in appendicitis	1	2	2	See remarks on page 667
131	*128*	**Peptostreptococcus intermedius** (PRÉVOT) SMITH *Streptococcus intermedius*	GRAM-positive. Very long chains. On blood agar no change or only slight α-hemolysis. Strongly acidifies media and coagulates milk. Anaerobe	Respiratory and digestive tracts, vagina	Isolated from lochia and uterus in puerperal fever, in pulmonary gangrene, pleurisy, bronchiectasis, appendicitis	1	2	2	See remarks on page 667
131	*129*	**Peptostreptococcus evolutus** (PRÉVOT) SMITH *Streptococcus evolutus, Streptococcus Sch., Streptococcus Schwarzenbeck*	GRAM-positive. Pairs and short or long chains. Pleomorphic. On agar grows in alternate zones with no change or slight α-hemolysis. Anaerobe becoming aerotolerant	Respiratory tract, mouth, vagina	Isolated from skin abscesses and in appendicitis, synergistic gangrene and endocarditis	1	2	2	See remarks on page 667
131	*130*	**Peptostreptococcus paleopneumoniae** (PRÉVOT) SMITH *Diplococcus paleopneumoniae*	GRAM-positive. Resembles *Diplococcus pneumoniae* but is a strict anaerobe	Buccal-pharyngeal cavity	Highly pathogenic. Isolated from lesions of pleuropneumonia, from a bone abscess, and from bronchitis and pneumonia	1?	3?	2?	
131	*131*	**Peptostreptococcus morbillorum** (PRÉVOT) SMITH *Diplococcus morbillorum, Diplococcus rubeolae*	GRAM-positive. Spheres occurring in short chains, rarely in small masses. Requires fresh serum or ascitic fluid in culture media. α-Hemolytic. Anaerobe usually becoming aerotolerant	Various organs, mucous secretions and blood	Found in throat and blood in cases of measles	1?	3?	2?	
133	*132*	**Eubacterium niosii** (HAUDUROY et al.) PRÉVOT *Bacteroides niosii*	GRAM-positive (in pus and young cultures). Short thick rods occurring singly, in pairs, chains and clumps. Nonmotile. Gas and fetid odor in cultures. Anaerobe	Respiratory tract	Isolated in purulent pleurisy				

For classification of organisms see pages 721–724; for index of synonyms see pages 725–734

See pages 721–724	See pages 725–734	**Bacteria (Schizomycetes)** Classified name *Synonyms* Common names	Principal characteristics	Habitat, host, transmission, etc.	Associated diseases or source	Clinical application of antibiotics: Penicillin	Streptomycin	Tetracyclines	Remarks
133	*133*	**Eubacterium rectale** (HAUDUROY et al.) PRÉVOT *Bacteroides rectalis*	GRAM-positive. Straight or curved rods, also long filaments. Nonmotile. Gas and fetid odor in cultures. Anaerobe	Rectum	Associated with rectal ulcer				
133	*134*	**Eubacterium quartum** PRÉVOT	GRAM-positive. Thick rods of varying length. Gas and fetid odor in cultures. Nonmotile. Anaerobe	Intestines of children, soil	Isolated from infantile diarrhea feces				
133	*135*	**Eubacterium pseudotortuosum** PRÉVOT	GRAM-positive. Straight or curved rods in twisted chains or filaments. Nonmotile. Gas but no odor in cultures. Anaerobe	Intestines	Isolated in acute purulent appendicitis				
133	*136*	**Eubacterium quintum** PRÉVOT	GRAM-positive. Thick rods of varying length. Nonmotile. Gas but no odor in cultures. Anaerobe	Intestines of children	Isolated from infantile diarrhea feces				
133	*137*	**Eubacterium ethylicum** PRÉVOT *Bacillus gracilis ethylicus*	GRAM-positive. Slender, straight or curved rods occurring singly, in pairs or short chains. Nonmotile. Granular. Gas but no odor in cultures. Anaerobe	Stomach	Isolated in gastritis				
133	*138*	**Eubacterium disciformans** (MASSINI) PRÉVOT *Bacillus disciformans*	GRAM-positive. Small, nonmotile, ovoid rods occurring singly, in pairs and in small masses. Anaerobe	Respiratory tract, liver, skin. Common	Pathogenic for man and various animals. Isolated from fetid suppurations in empyema, pulmonary gangrene, liver abscess and dermatosis				
134	*139*	**Catenabacterium filamentosum** PRÉVOT	GRAM-positive. Large, nonmotile rods occurring as short and swollen or long and curved forms. Bifurcation. Anaerobe	Body cavities. Common	Isolated in acute appendicitis, lung abscess, purulent pleurisy, uterine suppuration				
134	*140*	**Catenabacterium contortum** PRÉVOT	GRAM-positive. Rods occurring in twisted chains of 30–50 or more. Nonmotile. Gas but no odor in cultures. Anaerobe	Intestines	Isolated in putrid, gangrenous appendicitis				
134	*141*	**Catenabacterium lottii** PRÉVOT	GRAM-positive. Slender rods in chains of 3 or 4, also long filaments. Nonmotile. No gas in culture media. Anaerobe	Intestines and appendix	Isolated in appendicitis				
134	*142*	**Catenabacterium nigrum** PRÉVOT *Streptobacillus gangrenae pulmonaris*	GRAM-positive. Nonmotile, pleomorphic rods occurring in chains of varying length. Blackening on agar. Fetid odor. Anaerobe		Isolated from a gangrenous lung abscess				
135	*143*	**Ramibacterium ramosum** (VEILLON and ZUBER) PRÉVOT *Bacillus ramosus, Fusiformis ramosus*	GRAM-positive. Straight, slender, nonmotile rods, sometimes undulating or filamentous and forming acute angles (false branching). Spherical swellings. Gas and toxin formed. Anaerobe	Body cavities, sea water. Very common	Pathogenic. Associated with mastoiditis, otitis, pulmonary gangrene, purulent pleurisy, appendicitis, intestinal infections, balanitis, liver abscess, osteomyelitis, septicemia, etc.				

For classification of organisms see pages 721–724; for index of synonyms see pages 725–734

See pages 721–724	See pages 725–734	**Bacteria (Schizomycetes)** Classified name *Synonyms* Common names	Principal characteristics	Habitat, host, transmission, etc.	Associated diseases or source	Clinical application of antibiotics: Penicillin	Streptomycin	Tetracyclines	Remarks
135	*144*	**Ramibacterium pleuriticum** PRÉVOT	Similar to *R. ramosum*	Body cavities, especially respiratory tract	Isolated in fetid, purulent pleurisy				
135	*145*	**Ramibacterium ramosoides** (RUNEBERG) PRÉVOT *Bacillus ramosoides*	GRAM-positive. Nonmotile ovoid cells occurring in short chains or long filaments. False branching. Gas-former with fetid odor. Anaerobe	Appendix, lacrimal sac, lungs. Common	Isolated in appendicitis and various suppurations				
135	*146*	**Ramibacterium alactolyticum** PRÉVOT and TAFFANEL	GRAM-positive. Straight rods in sinuous short chains or zigzags. False branching. Nonmotile. Gas but no odor in cultures. Anaerobe	Mouth	Isolated from dental suppurations and in purulent pleurisy				
136	*147*	**Cillobacterium moniliforme** (REPACI) PRÉVOT *Bacillus moniliformis*	GRAM-positive. Motile straight rods, occurring singly or in pairs. Swellings and granules. Gas-former. Anaerobe	Respiratory system	Isolated in pulmonary gangrene				
136	*148*	**Cillobacterium endocarditidis** PRÉVOT *Cillobacterium endocarditis*	GRAM-positive. Motile pleomorphic rods. Gas and toxin formed. Anaerobe	Probably natural body cavities	Isolated in endocarditis				
136	*149*	**Cillobacterium meningitidis** PRÉVOT *Cillobacterium meningitis*	GRAM-positive. Actively motile pleomorphic rods, occasionally ovoid or filamentous. Bipolar staining. Gas-former. Anaerobe		Isolated from a fatal case of purulent meningitis of otic origin				
140	*150*	**Corynebacterium diphtheriae** (FLÜGGE) LEHMANN and NEUMANN *Bacillus diphtheriae, Corynebacterium ulcerans* Diphtheria bacillus, KLEBS-LÖFFLER bacillus, LÖFFLER's bacillus (KLEBSsche Stäbchen)	GRAM-positive but does not stain intensely in old cultures. Single rods often swollen at one or both ends. Stains in alternate bands with methylene blue. Metachromatic granules. Nonmotile. Facultative aerobe	Respiratory tract of diphtheria patients and healthy carriers; occasionally in conjunctiva and superficial wounds	The neurotropic exotoxin produced is the cause of diphtheria in man. See remarks below and on page 672	**Antitoxin plus penicillin or erythromycin**			See remarks below and on page 672

Diphtheria *(No. 150)*

The overall mortality from diphtheria has been very greatly reduced since the beginning of the century and now averages 5 deaths per million persons throughout the world, the rate in individual countries varying from 1 to 18 deaths per million[1]. Thanks to the extension of immunization and antitoxin treatment, the mortality among diphtheria cases, which at the end of the last century was as high as 46%[2], has fallen to 5%[3]. Where there is 100% immunization it has been brought down as low as 0.5%[4,5]. Mortality among males is about 1½ times higher than among females and it is also higher in patients under 5 and over 50 years. The highest mortality, 29%, is found among chronic alcoholics[6].

There are three distinct types of the diphtheria pathogen, *mitis, intermedius* and *gravis*, with frequencies in the ratio of 1:1:1.7 and mortalities among the cases they give rise to in the ratio of 1:2.7:3.1[7]. In earlier times a disease predominantly of infancy, diphtheria now occurs to an increasing extent also among children, adolescents and adults. In 60% of cases the site of the lesion is in the region of the tonsils and pharynx (mortality 1.8%); in some 8% the larynx is also affected (mortality 7.3%) and in another 8% also the nostrils (mortality 8.9%)[6]. If there is extensive spread of the infection, for example to the upper respiratory tract as far as the bronchial tubes or in the soft tissues toward the neck, the mortality rises as high as 90%[6].

The commonest complications of diphtheria[6] are myocarditis (10% of cases), with a mortality of 50%; bronchopneumonia (8%), mortality 68%; bulbar paralysis (4%), mortality 18%; peripheral paralysis (2%), mortality 13%; laryngeal paralysis (1%), mortality 7%; otitis media (2%), mortality 10%; and renal involvement (1%), with the highest mortality of 93%.

Treatment

Since the symptoms of diphtheria are caused solely by the toxin elaborated and disseminated by the diphtheria bacilli, a clinical diagnosis of the disease is always evidence that the toxin is being absorbed by the body. Immediate administration of antitoxin must therefore have a favorable effect and this has been amply confirmed by experience. It has been shown[6,8] that *during the first 10 days the mortality from the disease rises by 3% for every additional day of delay in administering antitoxin*. The risk of complications is correspondingly increased. The administration of antitoxin, as soon as possible and in adequate quantity, therefore remains the mainstay of diphtheria treatment. (For international standard antitoxin and toxoid preparations see pages 735 and 736.) Antitoxin is given preferably by means of a single intramuscular injection of 20,000–80,000 units, in severe cases intravenously. The dosage

See pages 721–724	See pages 725–734	**Bacteria (Schizomycetes)** Classified name *Synonyms* Common names	Principal characteristics	Habitat, host, transmission, etc.	Associated diseases or source	Clinical application of antibiotics: Penicillin	Streptomycin	Tetracyclines	Remarks
140	*151*	**Corynebacterium pyogenes** (GLAGE) EBERSON *Bacillus liquefaciens pyogenes bovis, Bacillus pyogenes*	GRAM-positive. Minute, nonmotile rods occurring singly and in chains. β-Hemolytic. Aerobe and anaerobe	Abscesses	Isolated from pus				
140	*152*	**Corynebacterium acnes** (GILCHRIST) EBERSON *Bacillus acnes, Bacillus parvus liquefaciens, Corynebacterium liquefaciens, Propionibacterium acnes*	GRAM-positive. Single, nonmotile rods staining in bands, occasionally club-shaped. Growth on culture media feeble. Anaerobic to aerotolerant	Sebaceous glands, hair follicles	Isolated from acne pustules	1	4	3	2: erythromycin
140	*153*	**Corynebacterium parvum** PRÉVOT *Corynebacterium parvum infectiosum*	GRAM-positive. Small, nonmotile, curved, club-shaped rods occurring in pairs. Strict anaerobe	Female urogenital organs	Associated with various female urogenital infections				
141	*154*	**Listeria monocytogenes** (MURRAY et al.) PIRIE *Bacterium monocytogenes*	GRAM-positive. Small rods occurring singly and in V-shaped or parallel pairs, motile with peritrichous flagella. β-Hemolysis on blood agar. Cultures have a rancid odor. Aerobe, facultative anaerobe	Organs, blood and cerebrospinal fluid of man and domestic animals	Listeriosis in animals (world-wide distribution). Sometimes causes meningitis and endocarditis in man[1]. Associated with infectious mononucleosis but connection is obscure	2	0	1	3: erythromycin. Sensitivity to antibiotics in vitro (concentrations in µg/ml causing complete bacteriostasis)[2]: Erythromycin 0.037–0.15; Carbomycin 0.18–0.75; Oleandomycin 0.25–6.0; Chlortetracycline 0.3–1.0; Oxytetracycline 0.6–1.25; Spiramycin 0.75–1.5; Chloramphenicol 1.0–3.0; Streptomycin 1.5–6.0; Novobiocin 1.5–12.0; Polymyxin B 12.0–25.0; Bacitracin 110–220

1) KREPLER and FLAMM, *Ergebn. inn. Med. Kinderheilk.*, 7, 64 (1956); Editorial, *Brit. med. J.*, 2, 209 (1957); WINN et al., *Ann. N. Y. Acad. Sci.*, **70**, 624 (1958); HOEPRICH, P. D., *Medicine (Baltimore)*, **37**, 143 (1958). 2) SEELIGER, H. P. R., *Listeriosis*, Basle and New York, 1961, page 185.

Diphtheria *(No. 150) (continued)*

should be ample: 20,000 units in pure nasal, cutaneous, tonsillar and laryngeal forms, 40,000 units in the pharyngeal form, and 80,000 units in complex nasopharyngeal-nasolaryngeal forms[9]. The patient should be tested beforehand for sensitivity to antitoxin by means of a skin test. Antibiotics (penicillin, erythromycin or a tetracycline) should be associated with antitoxin therapy in order to combat secondary (streptococcal and pneumococcal) infections and to hasten the disappearance of diphtheria bacilli. In general, nasal and pharyngeal swabs are rendered negative by 600,000 IU procaine penicillin G or 1–2 g erythromycin per day for 12 days[9].

The sensitivity of diphtheria bacilli to antibiotics in vitro is shown in the adjacent table[10].

	Sensitivity µg/ml*
Bacitracin	0.18
Penicillin	0.3
Tyrothricin	0.5
Novobiocin	0.78
Vancomycin	0.8
Neomycin	1.0
Oleandomycin	1.6
Chlortetracycline	1.6
Erythromycin	1.6
Chloramphenicol	2.0
Oxytetracycline	2.5
Tetracycline	5.0
Polymyxin B	6.4
Streptomycin	20
Dihydrostreptomycin	20
Viomycin	25

* Concentrations to which at least half the strains are susceptible.

Prophylaxis

Combined immunization with diphtheria-whooping cough or diphtheria-whooping cough-tetanus toxoid has been shown to be of great prophylactic value[12–18] and its use is strongly to be recommended (see also remarks on tetanus, page 676). It should not be started earlier than the third month of life since a fall in the blood level of maternal antibodies must first be awaited[12]. Satisfactory immunization is obtained by 3 injections, with an interval of 4–5 weeks between the 1st and 2nd injections and of 3–4 months between the 2nd and 3rd.

References

1) World Health Organization, *Chron. Wld Hlth Org.*, **10**, 83 (1956). 2) BOURDON, C. A., *Canad. J. publ. Hlth*, **36**, 305 (1945). 3) From a summary by NAIDITCH and BOWER, *Amer. J. Med.*, **17**, 229 (1954). 4) JOHNSTON, J., *Lancet*, **1**, 645 (1944). 5) RAMON, G., *J. Amer. med. Ass.*, **141**, 1028 (1949). 6) NAIDITCH and BOWER, *Amer. J. Med.*, **17**, 229 (1954). 7) MCLEOD, J. W., *Bact. Rev.*, **7**, 1 (1943). 8) BRAINERD and BRUYN, *California Med.*, **75**, 290 (1951). 9) TOP, F. H., in CONN, H. F. (Ed.), *Current Therapy 1961*, Philadelphia and London, 1961, page 10. 10) WELCH, H., *A Guide to Antibiotic Therapy*, New York, 1959. 11) BOUSFIELD, G., *Lancet*, **1**, 1028 (1951). 12) American Public Health Association, *Control of Communicable Diseases in Man*, 8th ed., New York, 1955. 13) BARR et al., *Brit. med. J.*, **2**, 635 (1955). 14) Editorial, *Brit. med. J.*, **2**, 663 (1955). 15) PARISH, H. J., *Brit. med. J.*, **2**, 631 (1955). 16) SPILLER et al., *Brit. med. J.*, **2**, 639 (1955). 17) BARR et al., *Lancet*, **1**, 6 (1950). 18) GREENBERG, L., *Bull. Wld Hlth Org.*, **12**, 751 (1955), and **13**, 367 (1955).

See pages 721–724	See pages 725–734	**Bacteria (Schizomycetes)** Classified name *Synonyms* Common names	Principal characteristics	Habitat, host, transmission, etc.	Associated diseases or source	Clinical application of antibiotics: Penicillin	Streptomycin	Tetracyclines	Remarks
142	*155*	**Erysipelothrix insidiosa** (TREVISAN) LANGFORD and HANSEN *Bacillus insidiosus, Erysipelothrix Erysipeloides, Erysipelothrix murisepticus, Erysipelothrix porci, Erysipelothrix rhusiopathiae* Swine erysipelas bacillus (Bacille du rouget, Bazillus des Schweinerotlaufs)	GRAM-positive, but some GRAM-negative cells may be found. Slender rods in smooth colonies. In rough cultures, short rods in tangled masses or filamentous. α-Hemolytic. Facultative anaerobe	Widely distributed in the animal kingdom, e.g. rodents, birds, dogs, horses, also surface slime of healthy fish[1]. Particularly virulent for swine, sheep and mice	Cause of swine erysipelas and of erysipeloid in man. Risk of infection specially high for persons coming into contact with infected meat (incubation time 2 days). Fish can also be infected, even postmortally	1	2	2	In contrast to swine erysipelas, human erysipeloid[4] is a localized infection, mainly on the hand (back, thumb, index finger). The swelling is very sensitive to touch, less so to pressure. The history is always characteristic (contact with meat or fish)[2]. Clinically, it may resemble paronychia and is often mistaken for it. Duration of infection (without antibiotics) 2–3 weeks. There may be intermittent fever, and associated septicemia with endocarditis has also been recorded[3]. For international standard vaccine and serum see pages 735 and 736
146	*156*	**Bacillus anthracis** COHN *emend.* KOCH Anthrax bacillus DAVAINE's bacillus (Bactéridie des charbons)	GRAM-positive. Nonmotile, encapsulated rods with square or concave ends, occurring in long chains with bamboo-rod appearance. Abundant growth on most media. Spores ellipsoidal or cylindrical. Variable hemolysis. Aerobe and facultative anaerobe	Infected animals and man. Transmitted by contact with hides and hair, also by biting flies	Cause of anthrax in man, cattle, swine, sheep, rabbits, guinea pigs, mice, etc.	1	0	1	
147	*157*	**Clostridium multifermentans** BERGEY et al. *Bacillus multifermentans tenalbus*	GRAM-positive in young cultures, becoming rapidly GRAM-negative. Motile slender rods occurring singly or in short chains. Ovoid spores. Anaerobe		Isolated from muscle with gas gangrene	1	0	1	On gas gangrene see remarks below
147	*158*	**Clostridium fallax** (WEINBERG and SÉGUIN) BERGEY et al. *Bacillus fallax, Clostridium pseudofallax*	GRAM-positive. Rods occurring singly or in pairs. Motile with peritrichous flagella. Spores rare and ovoid. Encapsulated in body fluids. Anaerobe	Presumably widely distributed	Isolated from war wounds with gas gangrene and in appendicitis	1	0	1	For a review of the genus *Clostridia* see McCLUNG[5]. On gas gangrene see remarks below

1) SNEATH et al., *Brit. med. J.*, **2**, 1063 (1951). 2) PRICE and BENNETT, *Brit. med. J.*, **2**, 1060 (1951). 3) LODENKÄMPER and NICKEL, *Ärztl. Wschr.*, **8**, 697 (1953). 4) For reviews see BINGOLD and TRUMMERT, *Ärztl. Wschr.*, **7**, 593 (1952); SIKES, D., *Ann. N. Y. Acad. Sci.*, **70**, 717 (1958). 5) McCLUNG, L. S., *Ann. Rev. Microbiol.*, **10**, 173 (1956).

Gas gangrene *(Nos. 157–178)*

All *gas gangrene* Clostridia, and also *Cl. tetani*, are putrefactive bacteria and thus typical inhabitants of soil, especially manured soils. In smaller numbers they also occur as saprophytes in the lower bowel and the vagina. The low incidence of infections due to Clostridia is in contrast to their wide distribution and is explained by their anaerobic metabolism. Optimal conditions for their growth occur in deep wounds contaminated by soil in which the lacerated or contused tissues are entirely or partly deprived of their normal circulation. Here progressive necrosis is accompanied by the development of edema and by the formation of toxin and gas, whence the designation gas gangrene.

Normally infection occurs from spores, the incubation period being 1–5 days, rarely longer. Complete development of symptoms and death within a few hours indicate that infection has been by vegetative cells (for instance on battlefields fought over for a long period, as at Verdun in the first World War[1]). As well as occurring in wounds contaminated by soil, gas gangrene may occur following abortions not performed under antiseptic conditions and occasionally after operations on the bowel.

Treatment

All contaminated injuries in which severe laceration, etc., give cause to anticipate development of gas gangrene must be carefully cleaned by extensive surgical debridement. Oxytetracycline (see remarks on tetanus, page 676) in normal dosage, or penicillin in high dosage, should be given immediately. In severely traumatized injuries, infiltration of the whole wound area with penicillin is recommended. If gas gangrene is already present, administration of antitoxin is essential. International standards for the antitoxins to the most important gas gangrene Clostridia have been set up by the World Health Organization (see page 736).

References

1) ZEISSLER, J., *Ärztl. Wschr.*, **9**, 769, 793 (1954).

For classification of organisms see pages 721–724; for index of synonyms see pages 725–734

See pages 721–724	See pages 725–734	**Bacteria (Schizomycetes)** Classified name *Synonyms* Common names	Principal characteristics	Habitat, host, transmission, etc.	Associated diseases or source	Clinical application of antibiotics: Penicillin	Streptomycin	Tetracyclines	Remarks
147	*159*	**Clostridium septicum** (MACÉ) FORD *Bacillus septicus, Vibrio pasteurii* GHON-SACHS bacillus (Vibrion septique, Pararauschbrandbazillus)	GRAM-positive. Rods occurring singly, in pairs and in short chains in cultures, in long chains and filaments in body exudates. Motile, peritrichous flagella. Spores ovoid. Anaerobe	Animal intestines, manured soils	Isolated from war wounds with gas gangrene and in appendicitis. Produces violent hemolytic exotoxin	1	0	1	On gas gangrene see remarks on page 673
147	*160*	**Clostridium novyi** Type A (MIGULA) BERGEY et al. *Bacillus novyi, Bacillus oedematis maligni No. II, Bacillus oedematis thermophilus* NOVY's bacillus (Bacille B de WEINBERG et SÉGUIN)	GRAM-positive. Rods occurring singly and in pairs. Motile with peritrichous flagella. Spores large, ovoid, subterminal. Anaerobe	Animal intestines, manured soils	Isolated from human gas gangrene and necrotic hepatitis. Produces violent exotoxin	1	0	1	On gas gangrene see remarks on page 673
147	*161*	**Clostridium botulinum** Type B (VAN ERMENGEM) HOLLAND *Bacillus botulinus*	GRAM-positive. Rods with rounded ends occurring singly, in pairs and occasionally long chains. Motile with peritrichous flagella. Ovoid spores. Strict anaerobe	Probably soils	No direct pathogenic action on man but produces an exotoxin which is an extraordinarily potent nerve poison (botulism). See remarks	**Antitoxin**			Most cases of botulism occur through eating preserves which have gone bad, particularly home-made preserves of beans, peas or meat served cold (ca. 80% of cases are due to bean salad). *Cooking destroys the toxin.* Administration of large doses of antitoxin or symptomatic detoxication is the sole effective treatment (gastric lavage is usually too late, as the toxin works slowly)
147	*162*	**Clostridium aerofoetidum** (WEINBERG and SÉGUIN) BERGEY et al. *Bacillus aerofoetidus* (Bacille D de WEINBERG et SÉGUIN)	GRAM-positive. Rods occurring singly, in pairs and in short chains. Motile with peritrichous flagella. Spores rare. Produces gas with fetid odor. Anaerobe	Probably soil and intestinal tract	Isolated from gas gangrene and feces	1	0	1	On gas gangrene see remarks on page 673
147	*163*	**Clostridium sporogenes** (METCHNIKOFF) BERGEY et al. *Bacillus sporogenes*	GRAM-positive. Rods occurring singly, in pairs and sometimes in chains or filaments. Motile with peritrichous flagella. Produces gas with putrid odor. Ovoid spores. Anaerobe	Soils and intestinal tract	Isolated from gas gangrene and intestine	1	0	1	On gas gangrene see remarks on page 673
147	*164*	**Clostridium tale** (PRÉVOT et al.) MCCLUNG and MCCOY *Inflabilis talis*	GRAM-positive. Nonmotile rods with subterminal spores. Anaerobe	Decomposing organic matter	Isolated in acute appendicitis	1	0	1	
147	*165*	**Clostridium bifermentans** (WEINBERG and SÉGUIN) BERGEY et al. *Bacillus bifermentans, Bacillus bifermentans sporogenes, Clostridium sordelli* (virulent strains) SORDELLI's bacillus	GRAM-positive. Rods occurring singly, in pairs and in short chains. Motile in young cultures only. Ovoid spores. Anaerobe	Feces, soils and sewage	Isolated from gas gangrene and putrid meat. Some strains produce a violent toxin	1	0	1	On gas gangrene see remarks on page 673
147	*166*	**Clostridium perfringens** (VEILLON and ZUBER) HOLLAND *Bacillus aerogenes capsulatus, Bacillus emphysematosus, Bacillus perfringens, Bacillus phlegmones emphysematosae, Bacillus welchii, Clostridium welchii* ACHALME's bacillus, gas bacillus, WELCH's bacillus	GRAM-positive. Short thick rods occurring singly and in pairs, sometimes in short chains. Nonmotile. Encapsulated. Ovoid spores. Stormy fermentation of milk. Anaerobe	Feces, soils and sewage	Isolated from gas gangrene. Produces a violent exotoxin. Cause of food poisoning (meat)[1]; incubation period 9–23 hours; and diarrhea	1	0	1	On gas gangrene see remarks on page 673

1) Editorial, *Brit. med. J.*, **1**, 711 (1960).

For classification of organisms see pages 721–724; for index of synonyms see pages 725–734

See pages 721–724	See pages 725–734	**Bacteria (Schizomycetes)** Classified name *Synonyms* Common names	Principal characteristics	Habitat, host, transmission, etc.	Associated diseases or source	Clinical application of antibiotics: Penicillin	Streptomycin	Tetracyclines	Remarks
147	*167*	**Clostridium sphenoides** (BULLOCH et al.) BERGEY et al. *Bacillus sphenoides*	GRAM-positive only in young cultures. Small fusiform rods occurring singly, in pairs and in short chains. Motile. Spherical spores. Anaerobe	Unknown	Isolated from gas gangrene	1	0	1	On gas gangrene see remarks on page 673
147	*168*	**Clostridium innominatum** PRÉVOT *Bacillus E* ADAMSON	GRAM-positive only in young cultures. Very small, thick rods tapering at one or both ends, occurring singly, in pairs, chains or filaments. Motile. Spherical spores. Anaerobe	Unknown	Isolated from septic and gangrenous wounds	1	0	1	On gas gangrene see remarks on page 673
147	*169*	**Clostridium microsporum** SPRAY	GRAM-positive. Single or paired rods, occasionally pleomorphic filaments. Actively motile. Tiny spherical spores. Anaerobe		Isolated from abdomen in peritonitis	1	0	1	
147	*170*	**Clostridium paraputrificum** (BIENSTOCK) SNYDER *Bacillus diaphthirus, Bacillus paraputrificus*	GRAM-positive. Straight or curved rods occurring singly, in pairs or in short chains. Motile with peritrichous flagella. Ovoid spores. Anaerobe	Presumably human intestine	Isolated from feces and gas gangrene	1	0	1	On gas gangrene see remarks on page 673
147	*171*	**Clostridium capitovale** (SNYDER and HALL) SNYDER *Bacillus capitovalis, Clostridium capitovalis*	GRAM-positive. Slender curved rods occurring singly, in pairs and rarely in short chains. Motile with peritrichous flagella. Ovoid spores. Anaerobe	Unknown	Isolated from feces, gas gangrene and septicemia	1	0	1	On gas gangrene see remarks on page 673
147	*172*	**Clostridium perenne** (PRÉVOT) MCCLUNG and MCCOY *Acuformis perennis*	GRAM-positive. Rods in pairs or chains. Nonmotile. Terminal ovoid spores. Anaerobe		Isolated in chronic appendicitis	1	0	1	
147	*173*	**Clostridium tetanoides** (ADAMSON) HAUDUROY et al. *Bacillus tetanoides (A)*	GRAM-positive only in young cultures. Rods occurring singly, in pairs and in chains of 3–5 cells. Motile in young cultures. Large spherical spores. Anaerobe	Unknown	Isolated from war wounds and garden soil	1	0	1	
147	*174*	**Clostridium tetani** (FLÜGGE) HOLLAND *Bacillus tetani* NICOLAIER's bacillus (Tetanusbazillus)	GRAM-positive. Rods occurring singly and in pairs, often in long chains and filaments. Motile with peritrichous flagella. Spherical spores. Hemolysis on blood agar. Strict anaerobe	Soil, intestines	Pathogen of tetanus. Produces potent exotoxin	**Antitoxin** 1	0	1	See remarks on page 676

For classification of organisms see pages 721–724; for index of synonyms see pages 725–734

See pages 721–724	See pages 725–734	**Bacteria (Schizomycetes)** Classified name *Synonyms* Common names	Principal characteristics	Habitat, host, transmission, etc.	Associated diseases or source	Clinical application of antibiotics: Penicillin	Streptomycin	Tetracyclines	Remarks
147	*175*	**Clostridium tetanomorphum** (BULLOCH et al.) BERGEY et al. *Bacillus pseudo-tetanus, Bacillus tetanomorphus*	GRAM-positive. Slender rods occurring singly and in pairs. Motile with peritrichous flagella. Spherical spores. Anaerobe	Soil	Isolated from wounds and soil	1	0	1	

Tetanus *(No. 174)*

Between 1939 and 1949 3–4 persons out of every million inhabitants of the USA died each year of tetanus[1]. The mortality is now probably somewhat lower, but it is still higher than it need be in view of the fact that tetanus could be practically eliminated by means of prophylactic immunization with toxoid[2], as was shown by the experience of the Allied Armies during World War II[3,4]. The use of the triple (whooping cough–diphtheria–tetanus) or quadruple (+ poliomyelitis)[5] toxoid is strongly recommended when parents wish to have a child immunized against any of these diseases (see also remarks on diphtheria, page 672). The immunity conferred against tetanus lasts 5–10 years and can be restored at any time within 4–5 days by means of a booster injection. This rapid restoration of immunity following earlier immunization for tetanus suffices to forestall onset of the disease in injuries in which there is a danger of it occurring[6]. The prophylactic administration of antitoxin, often harmful on account of anaphylactic reactions, is unnecessary in such cases[6]. If on the other hand the injured person has never previously received toxoid immunization, or if his last such immunization took place more than 10 years earlier, it would be too late if carried out in the ordinary way at the time of the injury since immunity is not established for 4–5 weeks after the injection. In such cases the injured person should be given 3000–5000 units or more of tetanus antitoxin, depending on the seriousness of the wound and the degree to which infection is suspected[8]. If the symptoms become evident within 1–10 days the mortality is at least twice as great as with longer incubation periods[1,7,9,10]. The prognosis is worse under 1 year of age and over 50 years than in the ages between. The average mortality for children and adults ranges from 20% to 50%[7,9,11–13]; for newborn infants it is 50% to 96%[14–16].

As a rule, the first symptoms consist of spastic rigidity in the muscles of the back and neck (the patient "carries his head high"), as also in the facial and jaw muscles (classical *risus sardonicus*). Finally all the muscles are affected, with opisthotonus, laryngospasm, etc., trismus and violent convulsions. The convulsions can be initiated or exaggerated by minimal stimuli of light, noise, etc. Usually death supervenes through respiratory failure.

The muscular symptoms result from the poisoning of the motor centers by the neurotoxin produced by *Cl. tetani*. This toxin possesses such a marked affinity for the nervous centers that once some has been absorbed and fixed there, it is no longer susceptible to treatment. Since patients with tetanus do not come for treatment until the symptoms have appeared, i.e. when toxin is already being produced freely and large amounts have been fixed, the most that can be attained by antitoxin and antibiotics is to render the freely circulating toxin harmless and to stop its further production. In established tetanus – and most of the fatal cases which reach hospital die there in the first few days after admission[9,17,18] – the patient's life thus depends not so much on antitoxic and antibiotic therapy as on the hospital equipment and the nursing care available to keep him alive by supportive measures.

The most urgent problem in such cases consists, when possible, of debridement of the infected tissue, injection in situ of 20,000 units of antitoxin followed by slow infusion of 50,000 units, and above all of treatment of the muscle cramps by sedation of the central nervous system, neuroleptic drugs[22], complete narcosis, peripheral sedation, curarization, or a combination of these methods[10,19,20]. All external stimuli must be eliminated (isolation, darkened room[21,29]). In severe cases the only possibility of keeping the patient alive lies in immediate tracheotomy or intubation, intravenous narcosis, complete curarization, and artificial respiration by machine, together with all the nursing care necessary in such circumstances. This treatment must be maintained for weeks until the muscular symptoms abate. Cases have been reported of complete cure following curare therapy for 26 days with a total of 7.64 g of D-tubocurarine and doses up to 0.64 g daily[19]. Such drastic therapy to the limit of modern possibilities is all the more justified in that the cure is complete and leaves no residue of mental or physical injury.

A prophylactic technique for injured persons suspected of tetanus infection which has proved reliable during the last decade consists of the single injection of 30,000–100,000 units of antitoxin[23–25], a dose sufficient to maintain an adequate level of antitoxin in the blood over the danger period (3–4 weeks). If the injection has to be repeated, an even larger dose should be given since the duration of protection conferred is progressively reduced[26]. Prior tests as a safeguard against anaphylactic reactions must of course be made. Intracutaneous tests often give false positive results and should be abandoned in favor of subcutaneous or intramuscular test doses[27].

Of even greater importance than prophylaxis with antitoxin is the immediate destruction of all the causative and other noxious organisms by adequate antibiotic treatment. This must be continued for at least 14 days, since antibiotics are only completely effective against the vegetative cells which gradually develop from the spores. On the basis of animal studies the most effective antibiotics against *Cl. tetani* appear to be oxytetracycline in normal dosage and penicillin in high dosage, as indicated in the following table.

50% protection against tetanus afforded in the mouse by various antibiotics in mg/kg body weight/day[28]

	Range	Mean
Tetracycline	11.8–16.6	14.1
Erythromycin	7 –19.2	11.6
Chlortetracycline	6 –18.5	10.6
Penicillin	4.7–13.9	8.1
Oxytetracycline	0.9– 2.3	1.4

References

1) FORBES and AULD, *Amer. J. Med.*, **18**, 947 (1955). *2)* RAMON, G., *Ann. Méd.*, **42**, 358 (1937). *3)* BARR and SACHS, *Army Pathology Advisory Committee Report*, London, War Office, 1955. *4)* SCHEIBEL, I., *Bull. Wld Hlth Org.*, **13**, 381 (1955). *5)* Annotations, *Lancet*, **2**, 1385 (1960). *6)* EDSALL, G., *J. Amer. med. Ass.*, **171**, 417 (1959). *7)* VINNARD, R. T., *Surgery*, **18**, 482 (1945). *8)* STAFFORD, E. S., in CONN, H. F. (Ed.), *Current Therapy 1961*, Philadelphia and London, 1961, page 58. *9)* NOËL and MCSWAIN, *South. med. J. (Bgham, Ala.)*, **43**, 53 (1950). *10)* BATTEN, R., *Lancet*, **1**, 231 (1956). *11)* CREECH et al., *Surgery*, **27**, 62 (1950). *12)* COOKE, J. V., *J. Pediat.*, **43**, 220 (1953). *13)* DIETRICH, H. F., in GRULEE and ELEY, *The Child in Health and Disease*, 2nd ed., Baltimore, 1952. *14)* SPIVEY et al., *J. Pediat.*, **42**, 345 (1953). *15)* FRIEDLÄNDER, J. C., *J. Pediat.*, **39**, 448 (1951). *16)* JELIFFE, D. B., *Arch. Dis. Childh.*, **25**, 190 (1950). *17)* CALVIN and GOLDBERG, *J. Amer. med. Ass.*, **94**, 1977 (1930). *18)* SPAETH, R., *Arch. intern. Med.*, **68**, 1133 (1941). *19)* SMITH et al., *Lancet*, **2**, 550 (1956). *20)* HONEY et al., *Brit. med. J.*, **2**, 442 (1954). *21)* LAWLER, H. J., *Amer. J. Dis. Childh.*, **90**, 701 (1955). *22)* KOCHHAR, K. S., *Brit. med. J.*, **2**, 789 (1961). *23)* SPAETH, R., *Amer. J. Dis. Child.*, **61**, 1146 (1941). *24)* COOKE and JONES, *J. Amer. med. Ass.*, **121**, 1201 (1943). *25)* SANDUSKY, W. H., in CONN, H. F. (Ed.), *Current Therapy 1960*, Philadelphia and London, 1960, page 62. *26)* LITTLEWOOD et al., *Brit. med. J.*, **2**, 444 (1954). *27)* MOYNIHAN, N. H., *Brit. med. J.*, **1**, 260 (1956). *28)* ANWAR and TURNER, *Bull. Johns Hopk. Hosp.*, **98**, 85 (1956). *29)* PERLSTEIN et al., *J. Amer. med. Ass.*, **173**, 1536 (1960).

For classification of organisms see pages 721–724; for index of synonyms see pages 725–734

See pages 721–724	See pages 725–734	**Bacteria (Schizomycetes)** Classified name *Synonyms* Common names	Principal characteristics	Habitat, host, transmission, etc.	Associated diseases or source	Clinical application of antibiotics: Penicillin	Streptomycin	Tetracyclines	Remarks
147	*176*	**Clostridium chromogenes** PRÉVOT *Bacillus anaerobius chromogenes*	GRAM-positive. Straight or curved rods, coccoid or elongated, occurring singly or in pairs, chains or filaments. Motile with peritrichous flagella. Many ovoid, central and subterminal spores. Encapsulated. Hemolysis on blood agar. Anaerobe		Isolated from a perinephritic abscess	1	0	1	
147	*177*	**Clostridium histolyticum** (WEINBERG and SÉGUIN) BERGEY et al. *Bacillus histolyticus*	GRAM-positive. Rods occurring singly and in pairs. Motile with peritrichous flagella. Ovoid spores. Hemolysis on blood agar. Anaerobe, but aerotolerant	Presumably soil	Isolated from wounds, where its cytolytic exotoxin induces active tissue necrosis	1	0	1	On gas gangrene see remarks on page 673
147	*178*	**Clostridium tertium** (HENRY) BERGEY et al. *Bacillus tertius*	GRAM-positive. Rods occurring singly and in pairs. Motile. Ovoid spores. Hemolysis on blood agar. Anaerobe but aerotolerant	Widely distributed in soil, feces, sewage	Isolated from gangrenous wounds and feces	1	0	1	On gas gangrene see remarks on page 673
154	*179*	**Mycobacterium fortuitum** CRUZ *Mycobacterium giae, Mycobacterium minetti*	GRAM-positive. Coccoid and short forms to long slender rods, occasionally with ovoid body at one end. In pus, long and filamentous forms. Nonmotile. Aerobe. Acid-fast	Soil, infections of animals including man	Isolated from human abscesses				
154	*180*	**Mycobacterium ulcerans** MACCALLUM	GRAM-positive. Single rods, frequently beaded. Acid-fast. Aerobe		Apparent cause of skin ulcers				
154	*181*	**Mycobacterium tuberculosis** (ZOPF) LEHMANN and NEUMANN *Bacillus tuberculosis, Bacterium tuberculosis, Mycobacterium tuberculosis* var. *hominis* Human tubercle bacillus, KOCH's bacillus, MUCH's bacillus	GRAM-positive. Straight or slightly curved rods occurring singly and occasionally in threads. Acid-fast. Slow growth in all media. Aerobe	Man. Transmission by airborne droplets	Pathogen of human tuberculosis (see remarks below and on pages 678 and 679). Possibly a cause of sarcoidosis[1]				See remarks below and on pages 678 and 679
154	*182*	**Mycobacterium bovis** BERGEY et al. *Mycobacterium tuberculosis* var. *bovis* Bovine tubercle bacillus	GRAM-positive. Rods shorter and plumper than human species. Occasional very short forms. Acid-fast. Aerobe	Cattle	Pathogen of tuberculosis in cattle. Transmissible to man and domestic animals (see remarks on page 678)				See remarks below and on pages 678 and 679

1) Editorial, *Brit. med. J.*, **2**, 1657 (1960).

Tuberculosis *(Nos. 181 and 182)*

Although the death rate from tuberculosis in countries with a high standard of living has fallen sharply, especially during the last two decades, and continues to fall (in USA per 100,000 from 194 in 1900 to 46 in 1940 to 8 in 1956), there is no evidence that the disease has been defeated[18] or that the tubercle bacillus has become any less virulent. Current statistics indicate that of the estimated 55 million persons in the USA, for example, who are infected with the bacillus, 2¾ million will break down with active tuberculosis some time during their lives[1]. The decline in mortality during the last few years is largely the outcome of the great advance made in chemotherapy, but better management of the disease in other ways, improved public health measures, and not least earlier detection of primary infection, have also played their part. The discovery of effective tuberculostatic drugs has not only rendered the disease a more chronic one but has also brought about a great change in surgical therapy. With their use, many sputum-positive patients are converted to sputum-negative over long periods, a circumstance which has greatly contributed to the reduction in the primary infection rate which has taken place. In developed countries the new drugs have also made it possible to replace hospital or sanatorium treatment to a large extent by ambulant treatment, so that there has been a great reduction in the occupancy of beds. These circumstances do not, of course, necessarily apply to under-developed countries, and in the tropics, now that malaria has been largely overcome, tuberculosis has replaced this disease as the major health problem.

For classification of organisms see pages 721–724; for index of synonyms see pages 725–734

See pages 721–724	See pages 725–734	**Bacteria (Schizomycetes)** Classified name *Synonyms* Common names	Principal characteristics	Habitat, host, transmission, etc.	Associated diseases or source	Clinical application of antibiotics: Penicillin	Streptomycin	Tetracyclines	Remarks
154	*182a*	**Mycobacterium kansasii** HAUDUROY *Mycobacterium luciflavum* Photochromogens	GRAM-positive. Cells larger than tubercle bacilli. Thread formation. Acid-fast. Photochromogenic (yellow to brick red pigmentation)		Isolated from patients with nontuberculous lung infections (mycobacterial pseudotuberculosis)				A similar disease is caused by some other nonphotochromogenic species of Mycobacteria (unnamed). For a review see *Lancet*[1]
154	*183*	**Mycobacterium leprae** (HANSEN) LEHMANN and NEUMANN *Bacillus leprae* HANSEN's bacillus, leprosy bacillus	GRAM-positive. Rods staining evenly or beaded. Generally in clumps or in groups of cells side by side. Acid-fast. Cannot be cultivated in bacteriological media or tissue cultures. Aerobe	Mainly human skin, testes, peripheral nerves	Obligate parasite in man and pathogen of leprosy[2]. Probably does not grow in internal organs. On relationship with tuberculosis see SHORT[3]				Drugs of choice: streptomycin plus sulfones. For a review of therapy see MANNWEILER[4]
156	*184*	**Nocardia asteroides** (EPPINGER) BLANCHARD *Cladothrix asteroides*	GRAM-positive. Straight, fine mycelium breaking up into small coccoid conidia. Acid-fast. Aerobe		A cause of mycetoma. Also found in conditions resembling pulmonary tuberculosis	0	?	1	Combined with sulfonamides[6] and followed by long-term oral treatment with dapsone[7]. For reviews of nocardiosis see references[5]

1) Editorial, *Lancet*, **2**, 1180 (1960). 2) For reviews see *Trop. Dis. Bull.*, **56**, 1094 (1959); Expert Committee on Leprosy, *Wld Hlth Org. techn. Rep. Ser.*, **189** (1959). 3) SHORT, G. M., *E. Afr. med. J.*, **36**, 298 (1959). 4) MANNWEILER, E., *Dtsch. med. Wschr.*, **84**, 686 (1959). 5) For reviews see MACKINNON and ARTAGAVEYTIA-ALLENDE, *Trans. roy. Soc. trop. Med. Hyg.*, **50**, 31 (1956); WICHELHAUSEN et al., *Amer. J. Med.*, **16**, 295 (1954); BALLENGER and GOLDRING, *J. Pediat.*, **50**, 145 (1957); PEABODY and SEABURY, *J. chron. Dis.*, **5**, 374 (1957). 6) SANFORD et al., *Antibiotics Annual, 1957–58*, New York, 1958, page 22. 7) COCKSHOTT and RANKIN, *Lancet*, **2**, 1112 (1960).

Tuberculosis *(Nos. 181 and 182) (continued)*

Tuberculosis in man due to the bovine type of bacillus has been very greatly reduced in many countries by means of energetic measures aimed at eliminating tubercle bacilli from milk[2].

Unless otherwise stated, the remarks which follow refer to pulmonary tuberculosis.

Chemotherapy

The successful chemotherapy of tuberculosis was for some years limited by the toxicity of the only highly tuberculostatic drug available, streptomycin (SM), and by the resistance which the bacillus rapidly developed to it. This usually limited treatment to 3–4 months at most. With the discovery of new drugs and the introduction of combined therapy, first with para-aminosalicylic acid (PAS) and later with isoniazid (INH), the situation changed radically. Toxic effects could be mitigated by reducing the dosage of SM, and the development of resistance hindered by suitable combinations.

As a result of the large-scale clinical trials carried out by the Veterans Administration–Armed Forces study group in USA[3] and by the Medical Research Council in England[4] there is now general agreement that any form of active tuberculosis should receive chemotherapy as primary treatment. The regimen of choice may be any pair of the three drugs named (dosages in combination: INH 200–300 mg per day; SM 1.0 g twice weekly to 1.0 g per day; PAS 12–20 g per day). It is also agreed that chemotherapy must be continued *uninterrupted* for at least 12 months if adequate assessment of the results and/or control of the disease is to be achieved. In particular it has been established that hematogenous dissemination of the bacilli may continue for several months after institution of chemotherapy[5].

The US trials have shown that judged by the criteria of incidence of sputum conversion, X-ray improvement, and closure of all visible cavities, the combination of INH+PAS is the most effective. However, these trials also indicate that there is a definite limit to the efficacy of all the above three regimens. If complete closure of cavities has not been achieved after 8 months the regimen should be changed, even in the presence of consistently negative sputum and gastric cultures. Only if cavities persist after 18 months' constant chemotherapy should resort to surgery be considered, and if for any reason the latter is impossible, chemotherapy should be prolonged indefinitely (see also remarks on surgical treatment opposite).

Chemotherapy with INH alone is justified in certain circumstances, for example in prophylaxis and in tuberculosis in pregnancy[6]. Not only is this drug clinically the most effective which has been tested extensively, but resistance developed to it is not accompanied by such deterioration in the patient's condition[7] as that which follows development of streptomycin resistance, for example. In fact, the appearance of INH-resistant bacilli in the sputum is not now considered a reason for discontinuance of INH therapy. Since INH is relatively cheap and is readily taken prophylactically by contacts who are not themselves sick, its use alone in field studies is recommended by the World Health Organization[8].

Of newer drugs which have been tested clinically on a large scale, cycloserine[9], either alone or in combination with INH, has been shown to be an effective tuberculostatic. Its use is limited,

Sensitivity of *Mycobacterium tuberculosis* to antibiotics in vitro[19]

	Sensitivity µg/ml*
Tyrothricin	0.03
Kanamycin	1.0
Ristocetin	2.0
Framycetin	4.0
Oxytetracycline	5.0
Streptomycin	5.0
Tetracycline	5.0
Viomycin	5.0
Polymyxin B	6.5
Neomycin	8.0
Cycloserine	10
Chloramphenicol	12.5
Erythromycin	40
Novobiocin	62
Chlortetracycline	100
Penicillin	140
Vancomycin	500

* Concentrations to which at least half the strains are susceptible.

See pages 721–724	See pages 725–734	**Bacteria (Schizomycetes)** Classified name *Synonyms* Common names	Principal characteristics	Habitat, host, transmission, etc.	Associated diseases or source	Clinical application of antibiotics: Penicillin	Streptomycin	Tetracyclines	Remarks
156	*185*	**Nocardia leishmanii** CHALMERS and CHRISTOPHERSON	GRAM-positive. Cells initially large and irregular, in short chains with branching filaments. Later entire colonies asteroid, with abundant mycelium. Slightly acid-fast. Aerobe		Isolated from a fatal case of lung disease and pericarditis	0	?	1	See remarks under *No. 184*

Tuberculosis *(Nos. 181 and 182) (concluded)*

however, by neurotoxicity. The tetracyclines and pyrizinamide are markedly less effective than INH or streptomycin and they are used only when required as alternatives to the latter drugs. Adrenal steroids as adjuncts to chemotherapy with the usual drugs have shown good results[10, 11], particularly in overwhelming infections, miliary tuberculosis and tuberculous meningitis. In view of the known hazards of corticosteroid therapy, however, its use should be limited to acute or resistant forms of tuberculosis or for the desensitization of persons allergic to the usual drugs.

Since the introduction of combined therapy with INH and intramuscular SM the long-term intraspinal administration of SM in tuberculous meningitis has become unnecessary[12]. Here INH is given in much higher dosage than in pulmonary tuberculosis, namely 10 mg/kg body weight[13].

The in vitro sensitivity of tubercle bacilli to various antibiotics is shown in the table on the opposite page.

Surgical treatment

The success of modern chemotherapy has brought fresh importance to the problem of the residual lesions. In the case of cavities, surgical resection has almost entirely superseded the various collapse methods (pneumothorax, pneumoperitoneum, etc.) earlier used for their closure. The circumstances under which resection should be resorted to for residual nodules, however, have been much debated. Earlier enthusiasm has been replaced by a more cautious attitude; large-scale studies have failed to show that resection of residual nodules has any significant effect on the relapse rate of the disease[14], and at least in the case of caseous nodules, it has been observed that viable bacilli can only be cultured from them with great difficulty, so that their importance as possible sources of relapse is uncertain[15].

Vaccination

Two vaccines have so far been employed, that of BCG ("bacille Calmette-Guérin"), which is an attenuated bovine strain, and that of the vole bacillus, a murine strain, but only the former has been put to extensive use (an estimated 100 million vaccinations up to 1955). The hotly debated question of the efficacy or usefulness of BCG vaccination has now to some extent been resolved as the result of large-scale trials, particularly that of the Medical Research Council in England (see bibliography). It is now accepted that:

1. Although BCG does not revert to the virulent state, it may cause occasional fatal disease in a very small proportion of persons lacking resistance to this particular strain[16];
2. BCG (and vole bacillus) vaccination confers substantial protection among children and adolescents with no previous natural infection, i.e. tuberculin-negative, and that the protection lasts for at least 4 years;
3. In under-developed countries where primary infections occur early in childhood, vaccination is definitely indicated at as early an age as possible. This is particularly important in view of the possibility of the development of miliary tuberculosis and tuberculous meningitis;
4. In view of the low and decreasing incidence of primary infections in countries with a high standard of living and well-organized public health services, it is questionable whether mass vaccination can play any great part in control of tuberculosis since the low rate of infection means that few will be able to benefit by it (most persons are now adult before acquiring primary infection);
5. Vaccination is justified for persons exposed to special risk of infection, e.g. hospital staffs.

It is also recognized, of course, that in highly developed countries vaccination destroys the usefulness of the tuberculin test and makes it impossible readily to identify naturally infected persons. With the decline in the infection rate, this test is becoming increasingly useful for epidemiological, case-finding and diagnostic purposes[17]. For international standard tuberculin preparations see page 735.

References

1) Medical News, *J. Amer. med. Ass.*, **166**, 1227 (1958). *2)* ANDERSON, R. J., *Ann. N.Y. Acad. Sci.*, **70**, 632 (1958). *3)* RALEIGH and STEELE, *J. Amer. med. Ass.*, **166**, 921 (1958). *4)* Medical Research Council, Tuberculosis Chemotherapy Trials Committee, *Brit. med. J.*, **1**, 435 (1955). *5)* HAEX and VAN BEEK, *Tuberculosis and Aspiration Liver Biopsy*, Haarlem, 1955. *6)* SELIKOFF et al., *J. Mt Sinai Hosp.*, **23**, 550 (1956). *7)* FOX and SUTHERLAND, *Thorax*, **10**, 85 (1955); DEUSCHLE et al., *Amer. Rev. Tuberc.*, **70**, 228 (1954). *8)* *The Work of WHO in 1956* (Official Records of the World Health Organization No. 75), Geneva, 1957, page 4. *9)* STOREY, P. B., in *Transactions of 16th Conference on Chemotherapy of Tuberculosis*, Veterans Administration, Washington, 1957, page 44. *10)* MILLER, A. B., *ibid.*, page 133; SHUBIN et al., *J. Amer. med. Ass.*, **170**, 1885 (1959); CLAYSON et al., *Brit. med. J.*, **2**, 1131 (1957). *11)* MLCZOCH, F., *Antibiot. et Chemotherap. (Basel)*, **7**, 302 (1960). *12)* ANDERSON, T., *Lancet*, **2**, 756 (1957). *13)* CROFTON, J., *Brit. med. Bull.*, **16**, 55 (1960). *14)* BELL, J. W., *New Engl. J. Med.*, **254**, 372 (1956). *15)* HOBBY et al., *Amer. Rev. Tuberc.*, **70**, 191 (1954); HOBBY, G. L., *Amer. J. Med.*, **18**, 753 (1955). *16)* FALKMER et al., *Acta paediat. (Uppsala)*, **44**, 219 (1955). *17)* PALMER et al., *Amer. Rev. Tuberc.*, **77**, 877 (1958). *18)* CROFTON, J., *Brit. med. J.*, **2**, 679 (1960). *19)* WELCH, H., *A Guide to Antibiotic Therapy*, New York, 1959.

Bibliography

(General) RALEIGH and STEELE, *J. Amer. med. Ass.*, **166**, 921 (1958); SELIKOFF and RABIN, *J. Mt Sinai Hosp.*, **23**, 401 (1956); KASS et al., *Ann. intern. Med.*, **47**, 744 (1957); CROFTON, J., *Brit. med. J.*, **2**, 679 (1960). (Chemotherapy) EBERT, R. H., *Amer. J. Med.*, **18**, 738 (1955); RALEIGH and STEELE, *loc. cit.*; Medical Research Council, Tuberculosis Chemotherapy Trials Committee, *Brit. med. J.*, **1**, 435 (1955); SELIKOFF and RABIN, *loc. cit.*; SELIKOFF, I. J., *J. Mt Sinai Hosp.*, **23**, 331 (1956); KASS et al., *loc. cit.*; RALEIGH, J. W., *Amer. Rev. Tuberc.*, **76**, 540 (1957); Therapeutic Trials Committee of Swedish National Association Against Tuberculosis, *Acta tuberc. scand.*, **30**, 165 (1955); Editorial, *Brit. med. J.*, **1**, 465 (1955); JOINER et al., *Lancet*, **2**, 165 (1956). (Surgery) SELIKOFF and RABIN, *loc. cit.*; AUFSES, A. H., *J. Mt Sinai Hosp.*, **23**, 475 (1956); RALEIGH and STEELE, *loc. cit.*; SCHAMAUN, M., *Schweiz. Z. Tuberk.*, **14**, 409 (1957) (579 resections); BARRETT et al., *J. thorac. Surg.*, **36**, 803 (1958) (1730 resections); EDGE and BOTTRILL, *Brit. med. J.*, **1**, 276 (1959) (170 resections); Editorial, *Lancet*, **2**, 25 (1956). (Collapse therapy) SELEY, G. P., *J. Mt Sinai Hosp.*, **23**, 493 (1956); SELIKOFF and RABIN, *loc. cit.* (Pediatric) GINANDES, G. J., *J. Mt Sinai Hosp.*, **23**, 464 (1956); WALKER, C. H. M., *Lancet*, **1**, 218 (1955). (Vaccination) Expert Committee on Tuberculosis, *Wld Hlth Org. techn. Rep. Ser.*, **88** (1954); *Report of the Medical Research Council, 1954–55*, London, 1956, page 12; WALLGREN, A., *Acta paediat. (Uppsala)*, **44**, 237 (1955); Medical Research Council, *Brit. med. J.*, **1**, 413 (1956), and **2**, 379 (1959); Editorial, *Brit. med. J.*, **2**, 414 (1959); PALMER et al., *Amer. Rev. Tuberc.*, **77**, 877 (1958); ARONSON et al., *Arch. intern. Med.*, **101**, 881 (1958); ANDERSON et al., *Brit. med. J.*, **1**, 1423 (1959). (Miliary tuberculosis) WILLIAMS, J. H., *Amer. Rev. Tuberc.*, **76**, 360 (1957); BIEHL, J. P., *Amer. Rev. Tuberc.*, **77**, 605 (1958). (Tuberculous meningitis) NATHANSON, M., *J. Mt Sinai Hosp.*, **23**, 512 (1956). (Tuberculous pleurisy) RABIN and WERTHER, *J. Mt Sinai Hosp.*, **23**, 455 (1956). (Tuberculous lymphadenitis) FRIEDMAN and SELIKOFF, *J. Mt Sinai Hosp.*, **23**, 529 (1956). (Renal tuberculosis) SPORER and OPPENHEIMER, *J. Mt Sinai Hosp.*, **23**, 521 (1956). (Cutaneous tuberculosis) GLICK, A. W., *J. Mt Sinai Hosp.*, **23**, 537 (1956). (Genito-urinary tuberculosis) ROSS et al., *Lancet*, **1**, 116 (1955). (Tuberculoma) KIRSCHNER, P. A., *J. Mt Sinai Hosp.*, **23**, 506 (1956). (Relation to leprosy) SHORT, G. M., *E. Afr. med. J.*, **36**, 298 (1959).

For classification of organisms see pages 721–724; for index of synonyms see pages 725–734

See pages 721–724	See pages 725–734	**Bacteria (Schizomycetes)** Classified name *Synonyms* Common names	Principal characteristics	Habitat, host, transmission, etc.	Associated diseases or source	Clinical application of antibiotics: Penicillin	Streptomycin	Tetracyclines	Remarks
156	*186*	**Nocardia pretoriana** PIJPER and PULLINGER	GRAM-positive. Small flat colonies made up of angular branched filaments and bearing short hyphae. Slightly acid-fast. Aerobe		Isolated from a case of mycetoma of the chest wall	0	?	1	See remarks under *No.184*
156	*187*	**Nocardia transvalensis** PIJPER and PULLINGER	GRAM-positive. Mycelium initially unicellular, later small colonies with hyphae in irregular spikes. Exudes colorless fluid and has pink coloration on glycerol agar. Acid-fast. Aerobe		Isolated from a case of mycetoma of the foot	0	?	1	See remarks under *No.184*
156	*188*	**Nocardia madurae** (VINCENT) BLANCHARD *Streptomyces madurae, Streptothrix madurae*	GRAM-positive. In tissues, radiating granules. In cultures, branched mycelium fragmenting into rods and coccoid bodies. No aerial hyphae. Not acid-fast. Aerobe		Associated with mycetoma of the foot but not always the cause of this disease[1]	0	?	1	See remarks under *No.184*
156	*189*	**Nocardia lutea** CHRISTOPHERSON and ARCHIBALD	GRAM-positive. Initially, swollen and segmented bodies giving rise to irregular colonies of variously-shaped cells with granular contents. Later more monomorphous. Not acid-fast. Aerobe		Isolated from actinomycosis of the lacrimal gland	0	?	1	See remarks under *No.184*
156	*190*	**Nocardia rangoonensis** (ERIKSON) WAKSMAN and HENRICI *Actinomyces rangoon*	GRAM-positive. Initial round cells give rise to branching hyphae and later to a profuse, waving aerial mycelium. Not acid-fast. Aerobe		Isolated from a case of pulmonary streptothricosis	0	?	1	See remarks under *No.184*
156	*191*	**Nocardia gibsonii** (ERIKSON) WAKSMAN *Actinomyces gibsonii, Streptomyces gibsonii*	GRAM-positive. Mycelium branching profusely at short intervals. Later long wavy filaments. No aerial mycelium. Hemolysis on blood agar. Not acid-fast. Aerobe		Isolated from spleen in a case of acholuric jaundice	0	?	1	See remarks under *No.184*
156	*192*	**Nocardia africana** PIJPER and PULLINGER *Streptomyces africanus*	GRAM-positive. Unicellular branching mycelium forming dense pink colonies with sparse aerial mycelium. Not acid-fast. Aerobe		Isolated from a case of mycetoma of the foot	0	?	1	See remarks under *No.184*
156	*193*	**Nocardia pelletieri** (LAVERAN) PINOY *Micrococcus pelletieri, Oospora pelletieri, Streptomyces pelletieri*	GRAM-positive. Mycelium of slender, straight filaments forming dense pink colonies with sparse aerial branches. Not acid-fast. Aerobe		Isolated from a case of crimson-grained mycetoma[2]	0	?	1	See remarks under *No.184*
156	*194*	**Nocardia fordii** (ERIKSON) WAKSMAN *Actinomyces fordii, Streptomyces fordii*	GRAM-positive. Straight filaments with sparse aerial mycelium. Not acid-fast. Aerobe		Isolated from spleen in a case of acholuric jaundice	0	?	1	See remarks under *No.184*

1) MACKINNON and ARTAGAVEYTIA-ALLENDE, *Trans. roy. Soc. trop. Med. Hyg.*, **50**, 31 (1956). *2)* ABBOTT, P., *Trans. roy. Soc. trop. Med. Hyg.*, **50**, 11 (1956); MACKINNON and ARTAGAVEYTIA-ALLENDE, *Trans. roy. Soc. trop. Med. Hyg.*, **50**, 31 (1956).

For classification of organisms see pages 721–724; for index of synonyms see pages 725–734

See pages 721–724	See pages 725–734	**Bacteria (Schizomycetes)** Classified name *Synonyms* Common names	Principal characteristics	Habitat, host, transmission, etc.	Associated diseases or source	Clinical application of antibiotics: Penicillin	Streptomycin	Tetracyclines	Remarks
157	*195*	**Actinomyces bovis** HARZ	GRAM-positive. Mycelium rapidly fragmenting, no aerial hyphae. In pus in actinomycosis as radiate, sulfur-colored granules. Not acid-fast. Anaerobic to microaerophilic	Cattle and other animals. World-wide distribution	Actinomycosis in cattle (lumpy jaw), sometimes also in man	1	?	2	
157	*196*	**Actinomyces israelii** (KRUSE) LACHNER-SANDOVAL *Actinomyces israeli, Streptothrix israeli*	GRAM-positive. Mycelium initially unicellular, fragmenting, with angular branching. Erect aerial hyphae under reduced oxygen tension. Not acid-fast. Anaerobic to microaerophilic	Human mouth and pharynx. World-wide distribution	Actinomycosis in man[1]	1	?	2	
158	*197*	**Streptomyces odorifer** (RULLMANN *emend.* LACHNER-SANDOVAL) WAKSMAN *Actinomyces odorifer, Cladothrix odorifera*	Mycelium. Vegetative growth colorless and folded. Aerial mycelium. Branching sporophores. Spherical spores. Strong odor of soil. Aerobe	Unknown	Isolated from sputum in a case of chronic bronchitis				
158	*198*	**Streptomyces gedanensis** (LÖHLEIN) MÜLLER *Streptothrix gedanensis*	Mycelium with aerial mycelium. Short, gnarled hyphae. Short spores. Aerobe	Unknown	Isolated from sputum in a case of chronic lung disease				
158	*199*	**Streptomyces upcottii** (ERIKSON) WAKSMAN and HENRICI *Actinomyces upcottii*	Long filaments interwoven into unicellular mycelium. Heavy cartilaginous colonies. No aerial mycelium. Slightly acid-fast. Aerobe	Unknown	Isolated from spleen in a case of acholuric jaundice				
158	*200*	**Streptomyces hortonensis** (ERIKSON) WAKSMAN and HENRICI *Actinomyces horton*	Very slow-growing unicellular mycelium. No aerial mycelium. Not acid-fast. Aerobe		Isolated from granules in pus from a parotid abscess				
158	*201*	**Streptomyces beddardii** (ERIKSON) WAKSMAN and HENRICI *Actinomyces beddardii*	Rapidly-growing mycelium of very long filaments. Aerial mycelium. Not acid-fast. Hemolysis on blood agar. Aerobe		Isolated from spleen in a case of splenic anemia				
158	*202*	**Streptomyces kimberi** (ERIKSON) WAKSMAN and HENRICI *Actinomyces kimberi*	Mycelium of profusely branching filaments forming circumscribed colonies. Abundant aerial mycelium. Not acid-fast. Aerobe		Isolated from blood in a case of acholuric jaundice				
158	*203*	**Streptomyces somaliensis** (BRUMPT) WAKSMAN and HENRICI *Indiella somaliensis, Nocardia somaliensis*	Simple branching unicellular mycelium forming circumscribed colonies. Short aerial mycelium. Hemolysis on blood agar. Aerobe		Isolated from cases of yellow-grained mycetoma and mycetoma of the foot[2]	?	?	1	See remarks under *No.184*
158	*204*	**Streptomyces panjae** (ERIKSON) WAKSMAN and HENRICI *Actinomyces panja*	Unicellular mycelium forming very small round colonies. No aerial mycelium. Not acid-fast. Aerobe		Isolated from an ulcer of the abdominal wall				

1) PEABODY and SEABURY, *J. chron. Dis.*, **5**, 374 (1957). *2*) For reviews see ABBOTT, P., *Trans. roy. Soc. trop. Med. Hyg.*, **50**, 11 (1956); MACKINNON and ARTAGAVEYTIA-ALLENDE, *Trans. roy. Soc. trop. Med. Hyg.*, **50**, 31 (1956).

For classification of organisms see pages 721–724; for index of synonyms see pages 725–734

See pages 721–724	See pages 725–734	**Bacteria (Schizomycetes)** Classified name *Synonyms* Common names	Principal characteristics	Habitat, host, transmission, etc.	Associated diseases or source	Clinical application of antibiotics: Penicillin	Streptomycin	Tetracyclines	Remarks
158	*205*	**Streptomyces willmorei** (Erikson) Waksman and Henrici *Actinomyces willmorei*	Unicellular mycelium branching at short intervals and presenting clubbed and budding forms and occasional round cells. Profuse aerial mycelium. Aerobe		Isolated from a case of streptothricosis of the liver				
187	*206*	**Borrelia recurrentis** (Lebert) Bergey et al. *Protomycetum recurrentis, Spiroschaudinnia recurrentis*	Gram-negative. Spiralling cylindrical or slightly flattened cells 8–16 μm long. Terminal filaments. Motile	Arthropod vector: body louse (*Pediculus humanus*). Transmission via conjunctival sac and skin abrasions. Also found in ticks but not transmitted	Cause of epidemic relapsing fever[1]	1	0	2	*Nos. 206–222:* Sensitivity of *Borrelia* species to antibiotics in vitro (concentrations in μg/ml to which at least half the strains are susceptible)[2]: Erythromycin (clinically effective)
187	*207*	**Borrelia berbera** (Sergent and Foley) Bergey et al. *Spirochaeta berbera*	Similar to and possibly identical with *B. recurrentis* but 12–24 μm long	Possibly body louse	Cause of relapsing fever in North Africa[1]	1	0	2	Oxytetracycline 1.0 Neomycin 2.5 Penicillin 6.0 Streptomycins 8.0 Chloramphenicol 8.0
187	*208*	**Borrelia carteri** (Mackie) Bergey et al. *Spirochaeta carteri*	As for *No. 207*	Arthropod vector: body louse	Cause of relapsing fever in India[1]	1	0	2	Tyrothricin 20
187	*209*	**Borrelia hispanica** (De Buen) Steinhaus *Spirochaeta hispanica*	Generally similar to other *Borrelia* species	Arthropod vector: large form of the tick *Ornithodoros erraticus*	Cause of relapsing fever in Spain, Portugal and northwest Africa[1]	1	0	2	
187	*210*	**Borrelia hermsii** (Davis) Steinhaus *Spirochaeta hermsi*	Generally similar to other *Borrelia* species	Arthropod vector: tick *Ornithodoros hermsi*. Not transmitted by other *Ornithodoros* species	Cause of relapsing fever in western North America[1]	1	0	2	
187	*211*	**Borrelia duttonii** (Novy and Knapp) Bergey et al. *Spirillum duttoni, Spirochaeta duttoni*	Similar to *B. recurrentis*	Arthropod vector: tick *Ornithodoros moubata*, in which there is hereditary transmission. Not transmitted by lice	Cause of relapsing fever in Central and South Africa and Madagascar[1]	1	0	2	
187	*212*	**Borrelia parkeri** (Davis) Steinhaus *Spirochaeta parkeri*	Generally similar to other *Borrelia* species	Arthropod vector: tick *Ornithodoros parkeri*. Not transmitted by other *Ornithodoros* species of Western Hemisphere	Cause of relapsing fever in western United States[1]	1	0	2	
187	*213*	**Borrelia venezuelensis** Brumpt *Borrelia neotropicalis, Spirochaeta neotropicalis, Treponema venezuelense*	Generally similar to other *Borrelia* species	Arthropod vector: tick *Ornithodoros rudis* (*O. venezuelensis*)	Cause of relapsing fever in Panama, Colombia, Venezuela and Ecuador[1]	1	0	2	
187	*214*	**Borrelia persica** (Dschunkowsky) Steinhaus *Spirochaeta persica*	Generally similar to other *Borrelia* species	Arthropod vector: tick *Ornithodoros tholozani*	Cause of relapsing fever in Iran[1]	1	0	2	
187	*215*	**Borrelia turicatae** (Brumpt) Steinhaus *Spirochaeta turicatae*	Generally similar to other *Borrelia* species	Arthropod vector: tick *Ornithodoros turicata*. Not transmitted by other *Ornithodoros* species of Western Hemisphere	Cause of relapsing fever in Mexico and southern United States[1]	1	0	2	
187	*216*	**Borrelia caucasica** (Maruashvili) Davis *comb. nov.* *Spirochaeta caucasica*	Generally similar to other *Borrelia* species	Arthropod vector: tick *Ornithodoros verrucosus*	Cause of relapsing fever in the Caucasus[1]	1	0	2	

1) For a review see Mooser, H., *Ergebn. Mikrobiol. Immunforsch.*, **31**, 184 (1958). *2)* Welch, H., *A Guide to Antibiotic Therapy*, New York, 1959.

For classification of organisms see pages 721–724; for index of synonyms see pages 725–734

See pages 721–724	See pages 725–734	**Bacteria (Schizomycetes)** Classified name *Synonyms* Common names	Principal characteristics	Habitat, host, transmission, etc.	Associated diseases or source	Clinical application of antibiotics: Penicillin	Streptomycin	Tetracyclines	Remarks
187	*217*	**Borrelia novyi** (SCHELLACK) BERGEY et al. *Spirochaeta novyi*	Similar to *B. recurrentis*	Arthropod vector unknown	Isolated from a relapsing fever patient in New York[1]	1	0	2	
187	*218*	**Borrelia kochii** (NOVY) BERGEY et al. *Spirochaeta kochi*	Similar to *B. recurrentis.* Possibly identical with *B. duttonii (No. 211)*	Arthropod vector unknown	Cause of African relapsing fever[1]	1	0	2	
187	*219*	**Borrelia buccalis** (STEINBERG) BRUMPT *Spirochaeta buccalis*	Spiralling cells 7–20 µm long (largest of mouth spirochetes). Sluggishly motile	Normal mouths	Invades lesions of respiratory mucous membrane	1	0	2	
187	*220*	**Borrelia vincentii** (BLANCHARD) BERGEY et al. *Spirochaeta vincenti*	GRAM-negative. Spiralling cells 8–12 µm long. Motile with rapid vibratory motion	Normal respiratory mucous membrane	Associated with *Fusobacterium fusiforme (No. 80)* in VINCENT's angina	1	0	2	
187	*221*	**Borrelia graingeri** (HEISCH) DAVIS, *comb. nov.* *Spirochaeta graingeri*	Generally similar to other *Borrelia* species	Arthropod vector: tick *Ornithodoros graingeri*	Present in blood in cases of general paralysis	1	0	2	
187	*222*	**Borrelia harveyi** (GARNHAM) DAVIS *Spirochaeta harveyi*	Generally similar to other *Borrelia* species	Arthropod vector unknown	Mild infection in man	1	0	2	
188	*223*	**Treponema pallidum** (SCHAUDINN and HOFFMANN) SCHAUDINN *Spirochaete pallida*	Fine, protoplasmic, spiral cells 6–14 µm long, with terminal spiral filament. Sluggishly motile. Not culturable on artificial media. Anaerobe	Man. Transmitted by contact	Pathogen of syphilis (lues)	1	0	2	See remarks below and on page 684

1) For a review see MOOSER, H., *Ergebn. Mikrobiol. Immunforsch.*, **31**, 184 (1958).

Treponematoses[1] *(Nos. 223–225)*

The pathogenic treponema *(pallidum, pertenue, carateum)* are morphologically identical in electron micrographs and a "unitarian concept" of the diseases they cause (syphilis, yaws, bejel, pinta) has been advanced[2,3]. According to this theory, these diseases are all variations of the same disease entity resulting from environmental factors such as different climatic and sociological conditions. Treponematosis is assumed to have originated in Central Africa, where it is now represented by yaws, and to have developed into various forms of endemic syphilis, such as bejel, as it advanced into more temperate climes. The venereal, neurotropic form now known as syphilis only developed as man adopted urban life.

Syphilis[1]

In highly civilized countries a precipitous fall in the incidence of primary and secondary syphilis followed the introduction of efficient chemotherapy and the concerted efforts to control the disease which this advance prompted. Since 1955, however, a resurgence of the disease has been reported, particularly in USA[4,5]. There is no doubt that this is due to complacency regarding the disease and the consequent relaxation of serological control and neglect of the disease in differential diagnosis.

Diagnosis[5]. The wide use of antibiotics with a suppressive effect on syphilis has rendered the clinical diagnosis of the disease more difficult. The resulting need for a reliable serologic test has been met by the development of treponemal antigen tests to supplement the classical WASSERMANN complement fixation reaction, which occasionally gives false positive reactions in persons with no clinical or anamnestic evidence of syphilis. These tests include the treponemal immobilization test (TPI), the treponemal agglutination test (TPA) and the treponemal immune adherence test (TPIA)[6–10]. Practical difficulties with these tests, however, have led to the development of a very specific treponemal WASSERMANN reaction (TWR) using mechanically disintegrated treponema suspensions[11]. This is likely to replace the original WASSERMANN reaction as the routine diagnostic test for syphilis.

Treatment[9, 12–16]. Penicillin has revolutionized the treatment of syphilis and there is now no reason to use the earlier arsenic and bismuth preparations except possibly in cardiovascular syphilis (see below). *Treponema pallidum* has proved remarkably sensitive to penicillin and development of resistance has not yet been observed. In particular, the drug has greatly reduced both the period of infectiousness and the incidence and intensity of HERXHEIMER reactions. In general, serological control should be continued for as long as possible after treatment so that a relapse or re-infection can be promptly dealt with. It should be noted that serological improvement may lag many months behind clinical improvement, especially in late syphilis, and the patient may even continue indefinitely to be seropositive (seroresistance). Seroresistance alone does not necessarily indicate persistence of infection and is no justification for re-treatment. The most effective forms of penicillin in syphilis are benzathine penicillin G (BPG), a single 2,400,000-unit treatment of which provides demonstrable blood levels of penicillin for at least 15 days[17], and procaine penicillin G with aluminum monostearate (PAM), both by intramuscular injection.

Early syphilis (primary and secondary) should be treated with a single injection of at least 1,200,000 units of BPG in each buttock. If PAM is used, four 1,200,000-unit doses should be given at intervals of 2–7 days. Patients seronegative before treatment may become seropositive after treatment, but should be seronegative again after one month. Seropositive patients should show a clear fall in reagin titer within 6 months. Re-treatment is only necessary when a rise in reagin titer is observed or when clinical signs of the disease appear, indicating either relapse or re-infection. Since a relapse is almost impossible to distinguish from a re-infection,

For classification of organisms see pages 721–724; for index of synonyms see pages 725–734

See pages 721–724	See pages 725–734	**Bacteria (Schizomycetes)** Classified name *Synonyms* Common names	Principal characteristics	Habitat, host, transmission, etc.	Associated diseases or source	Clinical application of antibiotics: Penicillin	Streptomycin	Tetracyclines	Remarks
188	*224*	**Treponema pertenue** CASTELLANI	Morphologically identical with *T. pallidum*. Not culturable on artificial media. Anaerobe	Man. Transmitted mainly by contact but also by *Hippelates pallipes* flies (West Indies) and by *Musca spectanda* flies (Africa)	Pathogen of yaws (frambesia). Other synonyms: aboukoué or ab-oukine (Gabun), boubas (Brazil), coko (Fiji), dube (West Africa), parangi (Ceylon), patek or purru (Malaya), pian (Guiana), tonga (New Caledonia). The Arabian bejel may be identical	1	0	2	Patients give positive WASSERMANN reaction. See remarks on page 683 and below
188	*225*	**Treponema carateum** BRUMPT *Treponema americanus*, *Treponema herrejoni*, *Treponema pictor*, *Treponema pintae*	Morphologically identical with *T. pallidum*. Not culturable on artificial media. Anaerobe	Man. Transmitted by contact, also possibly by insects	Pathogen of pinta (spotted sickness). Other synonyms: azul, boussarole, carate, mal del pinto, pinto	1	0	2	Patients give positive WASSERMANN, KAHN and MEINICKE reactions. See remarks on page 683 and below
188	*226*	**Treponema mucosum** NOGUCHI	Spiral cells 8–12 μm long with sharply pointed ends and a long curved projection. Cultures form mucin and have strong putrid odor. Anaerobe		Isolated from pus in a case of pyorrhea alveolaris. Has pyogenic properties	1	0	2	

Treponematoses[1] *(Nos. 223–225) (continued)*

re-treatment should be with PAM (in higher dosage) since this preparation gives higher blood levels of penicillin.

Latent syphilis[29] (diagnosed solely by serologic tests and history) should be distinguished from asymptomatic neurosyphilis by spinal fluid examination and from cardiovascular syphilis by fluoroscopy or teleroentgenography. In unequivocal cases, BPG or PAM should be given in the same dosage as for early syphilis, but if it is impossible to rule out neuro- or cardiovascular syphilis, PAM should be given in higher dosage. Indications for re-treatment are as for early syphilis.

Late symptomatic syphilis (e.g. neurosyphilis) should be treated with at least 3 doses of 2,400,000 units of BPG at not more than 7-day intervals, or with a total of 6–10 million units of PAM in divided doses. Re-treatment is indicated when there is a significant increase in reagin titer sustained over several months or when there is progression of syphilitic symptoms, although such progression may be due to causes other than syphilis. The prognosis of asymptomatic neurosyphilis treated with penicillin alone appears to be good[18].

Cardiovascular syphilis remains the only indication for therapy with arsenic or bismuth since it appears that patients treated with these agents in combination with penicillin have a better prognosis than those treated with penicillin alone[19–20].

Syphilis in pregnancy should be treated with BPG or PAM in the same dosage as for early syphilis. Treatment should be given even if syphilis is diagnosed very late in pregnancy since penicillin passes the placental barrier. Adequate treatment is usually effective in preventing infection of the fetus in utero.

Congenital syphilis in children should be treated in a similar manner to acquired syphilis, with PAM in a dosage of 150,000 to 300,000 units every 2–4 days up to a total of 75,000–100,000 units per kg of body weight. A seropositive reaction of the cord blood is not necessarily an indication for immediate treatment in the absence of clinical signs of syphilis since the WASSERMANN antibodies pass the placental barrier. Treatment should be given if the reagin titer is still high after several months or if it rises.

In patients allergic to penicillin, this drug is usually replaced by wide-spectrum antibiotics such as chloramphenicol, chlor- and oxy-tetracycline, and more recently erythromycin and triacetyloleandomycin[30]. In early syphilis the total dose is usually 20–40 g (at the rate of 3–4 g per day) except for erythromycin, of which a total of not more than 20 g is given, with correspondingly lower daily dosage. In late syphilis, WRIGHT[31] recommends erythromycin at the rate of 4 g per day for 2 weeks or 3 g per day for 3 weeks.

Syphiloid diseases

Yaws is endemic in many tropical countries and can be successfully combatted by mass treatment campaigns using penicillin[21–24]. Active cases over 15 years of age are given 1,200,000 units of PAM in a single intramuscular injection, children below this age 600,000 units. Latent cases and contacts are given half these amounts. Unlike syphilis, yaws is not transmitted congenitally.

Endemic syphilis, such as *bejel* (Iraq, Syria), has many similarities to yaws and its treatment is similar[3, 25–27].

Pinta (Central America)[28] is amenable to treatment as for yaws.

References

1) For reviews see BEERMAN et al., *Arch. intern. Med.*, **101**, 803, 952 (1958), and **103**, 460, 621 (1959); GUTHE and WILLCOX, *Chron. Wld Hlth Org.*, **8**, 37 (1954); WORTMANN, F., *Dermatologica*, **115**, 809 (1957). *2*) HUDSON, E. H., *Treponematosis*, New York, 1946; MOSCHELLA, S. L., *U.S. armed Forces med. J.*, **7**, 1101 (1956). *3*) GRIN, E. I., *Bull. Wld Hlth Org.*, **15**, 959 (1956). *4*) Editorial, *New Engl. J. Med.*, **255**, 357 (1956). *5*) FIUMARA et al., *New Engl. J. Med.*, **254**, 1127, 1173 (1956). *6*) *Report of the Medical Research Council for 1956–57*, London, 1958, page 23. *7*) REIN and KELCEC, *J. Amer. med. Ass.*, **163**, 1046 (1957). *8*) MOORE and MOHR, *J. Amer. med. Ass.*, **150**, 467 (1952). *9*) VANDOW and SOBEL, *N. Y. St. J. Med.*, **56**, 2796 (1956). 10) DOEPFMER, R., *Arch. klin. exp. Derm.*, **206**, 237 (1957). *11*) PRICE and WHELAN, *Brit. J. vener. Dis.*, **33**, 18 (1957). *12*) THOMAS, E. W., *N. Y. St. J. Med.*, **56**, 1918 (1956). *13*) THOMAS, E. W., *J. Amer. med. Ass.*, **162**, 1536 (1956). *14*) IDSOE et al., *Bull. Wld Hlth Org.*, **10**, 507 (1954). *15*) FISCHER, E., *Antibiot. et Chemotherap. (Basel)*, **2**, 233 (1955). *16*) CANNEFAX and JOHNWICK, *Amer. J. Syph.*, **38**, 18 (1954). *17*) SMITH et al., *Bull. Wld Hlth Org.*, **15**, 1087 (1956). *18*) HAHN et al., *Arch. Derm. Syph.*, **74**, 355, 367 (1956). *19*) LEONARD and SMITH, *Lancet*, **1**, 234 (1957). *20*) BEERMAN and EDEIKEN, *Antibiot. et Chemotherap. (Basel)*, **2**, 9 (1955). *21*) HACKETT and GUTHE, *Bull. Wld Hlth Org.*, **15**, 869 (1956). *22*) Report of Second International Conference on Control of Yaws, *J. trop. Med. Hyg.*, **60**, 27, 62 (1957). *23*) SAMAME, G.E., *Bull. Wld Hlth Org.*, **15**, 897 (1956). *24*) HUME and FACIO, *Bull. Wld Hlth Org.*, **15**, 1057 (1956). *25*) HUDSON, E. H., *Non-Venereal Syphilis: A Sociological and Medical Study of Bejel*, Edinburgh and London, 1958. *26*) KOCHS, A. G., *Hautarzt*, **9**, 125 (1958). *27*) GREMLIZA, F. G. L., *Z. Tropenmed. Parasit.*, **7**, 438 (1956). *28*) MARQUEZ et al., *Bull. Wld Hlth Org.*, **13**, 299 (1955). *29*) For a review see BARNETT, C. W., *Stanford med. Bull.*, **17**, 61 (1959). *30*) OLANSKY, S., in CONN, H. F. (Ed.), *Current Therapy 1961*, Philadelphia and London, 1961, page 403. *31*) WRIGHT, E.T., in CONN, H. F., *loc. cit.*, page 408.

For classification of organisms see pages 721–724; for index of synonyms see pages 725–734

See pages 721–724	See pages 725–734	**Bacteria (Schizomycetes)** Classified name *Synonyms* Common names	Principal characteristics	Habitat, host, transmission, etc.	Associated diseases or source	Clinical application of antibiotics: Penicillin	Streptomycin	Tetracyclines	Remarks
189	*227*	**Leptospira icterohaemorrhagiae** (INADA and IDO) NOGUCHI *Spirochaeta ictero-haemorrhagiae*, *Spirochaeta ictero-haemorrhagiae japonica*	Finely-coiled cells usually 6–9 µm long but occasionally up to 20–25 µm. One or both ends may be semicircularly hooked. Actively motile. Aerobe	Kidney and urine of rats and mice; other animals	Pathogen of leptospiral jaundice (WEIL's disease). Other synonyms: infectious jaundice, FIEDLER's disease. See remarks below	1	0	2	These data apply in general to the other parasitic serotypes of *Leptospira*. See remarks below
190	*228*	**Mycoplasma hominis** (FREUNDT) EDWARD *Micromyces hominis*, group I	GRAM-negative. Unstable, sparsely branched mycelioid structure with very short, almost bacillary filaments. Aerobe and facultative anaerobe	Genital and rectal mucosa	Associated with non-gonococcal urethritis and other inflammations of lower genital tract	0	2	1	*Nos. 228 and 229:* Known as pleuropneumonia-like organisms (PPLO)[1] from their resemblance to the organisms causing pleuropneumonia of cattle *(Mycoplasma mycoides)*. Distinct strains of PPLO found in the oral region of man *(M. salivarius)* are of doubtful pathogenicity
190	*229*	**Mycoplasma fermentans** EDWARD *Micromyces hominis*, group II	GRAM-negative. Generally similar to *M. hominis* but with longer bacillary filaments	Genital tract	Isolated from ulcerative genital lesions associated with fusiform bacilli and spirilla and also from normal genital mucosa	0	2	1	

1) For a review see MORTON, H. E., in DUBOS, R. J. (Ed.), *Bacterial and Mycotic Infections of Man*, 3rd ed., Philadelphia and London, 1958, page 563.

Leptospirosis[1] *(No. 227)*

Upwards of 40 distinct serotypes of *Leptospira* have been recognized[2], 15 of them in Europe. Some species are very widely distributed, notably *L. icterohaemorrhagiae*, *L. canicola*, *L. grippotyphosa* and *L. pomona*; others are confined to restricted areas, such as *L. naam* and *L. andaman A*. The principal serotypes are as follows:

Serotype	Principal host	Disease*	Distribution
L. ictero-haemorrhagiae	*Rattus norvegicus*	Leptospiral jaundice (WEIL's disease) (I)	Very wide
L. australis B	*Rattus culmorum*	Cane-sugar fever, field fever (II)	Very wide
L. autumnalis	*Apodemus speciosus*, *Microtus montebelloi*, *Rattus brevicaudatus*	Japanese autumn fever (aki-yami), Fort Bragg fever, tibial fever (II)	Very wide
L. bataviae	*Micromys minutus sorcinus*	Rice-field fever (II)	Very wide
L. pyrogenes	*Rattus brevicaudatus*	Field fever (II)	Southeast Asia, Italy
L. ballum	*Mus musculus musculus*	Rice-field fever (III)	Europe, N. America, Puerto Rico
L. canicola	Dog, jackal, pig	Canicola fever (III)	Very wide
L. grippo-typhosa	*Microtus arvalis*, *M. agrestis*, *Apodemus sylvaticus*, *Evotymis glareolus*	Swamp fever, mud fever, marsh fever, water fever, harvest fever, pea-pickers' disease, Charente fever (III)	Very wide
L. hebdomadis	*Microtus montebelloi*	Japanese seven-day fever (III)	Asia, Europe
L. hyos	Pig	Swineherd's disease (III)	Very wide
L. pomona	Pig	Swineherd's disease (III)	Very wide
L. sejroe	*Apodemus sylvaticus*, *Mus musculus musculus*	Harvest fever (III)	Europe

* GSELL[3] has classified the leptospires in accordance with the severity of the disease caused, viz., those usually causing jaundice (I), those sometimes causing jaundice (II), and benign species rarely causing jaundice (III).

All leptospires known to infect animals are potentially pathogenic for man[4]. Infection generally takes place via the skin following contact with material emanating from animal hosts. Transmission by the oral route or by bites is rare. The leptospires can exist outside their preferred hosts for a certain time; thus fresh water containing *L. icterohaemorrhagiae* remains infectious for 20 days[5, 6], while the organism is quickly killed in salt water. Survival in milk is of brief duration provided that the milk has not been diluted with water[7]. In urine, despite its important role in transmission, leptospires do not remain virulent longer than 24 hours[8]. In soils saturated with water, *L. pomona* has been known to remain infective for as long as 183 days[9]. The leptospires are very sensitive to heat[6] and to common antiseptic agents, particularly acids.

The severity of the disease varies with the serotype, the individual, and the mode of infection. In man, the leptospires tend to cause liver and kidney disease and nervous disorders. Thus *L. icterohaemorrhagiae* infections, which are almost always serious, are characterized mainly by hepatitis, those of *L. pomona*, *L. hyos* and *L. canicola* by meningitis. Kidney disease is common to all serotypes and is decisive for the prognosis[14], while in serious cases acute lower nephron nephrosis comparable with that associated with shock is responsible for the majority of deaths.

The incubation period for all serotypes is 3–20 days, with an average of 10 days. The diagnosis is confirmed by identification of the pathogen and by serological tests after the second week.

Treatment and prophylaxis

All the leptospires are sensitive to a variety of antibiotics[10-13, 15] but for treatment to be effective it must be commenced during the incubation period[11]. Although penicillin is active against *L. icterohaemorrhagiae*, it has not succeeded in reducing the mortality in leptospiral jaundice (22%) due to this organism in Great Britain[15]. More important are general measures designed to counteract oliguria and uremia.

Vaccination has proved effective in Italy among ricefield workers[16] subject to a limited risk but in general it is rendered impracticable owing to the large number of serotypes. More effective prophylactic measures are reduction of contact by means of protective clothing and elimination of the vector hosts.

References

1) For a review see ALSTON and BROOM, *Leptospirosis in Man and Animals*, Edinburgh and London, 1958. *2)* WHO Study Group on Leptospirosis, *Wld. Hlth Org. techn. Rep. Ser.*, **113** (1956). *3)* GSELL, O., *Leptospirosen*, Berne, 1952, page 24. *4)* GALTON et al., *Ann. N. Y. Acad. Sci.*, **70**, 427 (1958). *5)* VAN THIEL, P. H., *Ned. T. Geneesk.*, **81**, 6106 (1957). *6)* CHANG et al., *J. infect. Dis.*, **82**, 256 (1948). *7)* KIRSCHNER et al., *N. Z. med. J.*, **51**, 98 (1952). *8)* FÜHNER, F., *Städtehygiene*, **1**, 218 (1950). *9)* OKAZAKI and RINGEN, *Amer. J. vet. Res.*, **18**, 219 (1957). *10)* FAINE and KAIPAINEN, *J. infect. Dis.*, **97**, 146 (1955). *11)* ALSTON and BROOM, *Brit. med. J.*, **2**, 718 (1944). *12)* CHANG, S. L., *J. clin. Invest.*, **25**, 752 (1946). *13)* SCHLIPKÖTER and BECKERS, *Z. Immun.-Forsch.*, **108**, 301 (1951). *14)* Editorial, *Lancet*, **1**, 1333 (1960). *15)* MACKAY-DICK and ROBINSON, *Lancet*, **1**, 100 (1959). *16)* BABUDIERI, B., *Zbl. Bakt., I. Abt. Orig.*, **168**, 280 (1957).

For classification of organisms see pages 721–724; for index of synonyms see pages 725–734

Rickettsiales *(Nos. 230–247)*

The *Rickettsiales* (Rickettsiae and the psittacosis-lymphogranuloma venereum group of organisms) are often referred to as the "larger viruses" and share with the so-called "true" (filterable) viruses the property of multiplying within the cells of the host organism. Unlike the filterable viruses, however, the Rickettsiales do not behave exclusively in this fashion but may at one stage of the life cycle propagate in the intestinal tract of arthropod hosts. The Rickettsiales also differ from the filterable viruses in possessing characteristic morphology which can be demonstrated by staining techniques. Cf. also the general remarks on viruses on page 689.

The data on the Rickettsiales given in the table below and on pages 687 and 688 have been assembled from various standard works (see the bibliography below) and from numerous papers in the current literature.

The arrangement of the organisms listed is based on that in the 7th edition of *Bergey's Manual* (see Bibliography). For other relevant information see the introduction to the table of bacteria on page 646.

Bibliography (Rickettsiales)

BREED et al. (Eds.), *Bergey's Manual of Determinative Bacteriology*, 7th ed., Baltimore, 1957; BEDSON et al., *Virus and Rickettsial Diseases*, London, 1951; RIVERS and HORSFALL (Eds.), *Viral and Rickettsial Infections of Man*, 3rd ed., Philadelphia and London, 1959; HARTMAN et al. (Eds.), *The Dynamics of Virus and Rickettsial Infections*, New York, 1954.

See pages 721–724	See pages 725–734	**Rickettsiales** Classified name *Synonyms* Common names	Principal characteristics	Habitat, host, transmission, etc.	Associated diseases or source	Clinical application of antibiotics: Penicillin	Streptomycin	Tetracyclines	Remarks
191	*230*	**Rickettsia prowazekii** DA ROCHA-LIMA *Rickettsia exanthematotyphi, Rickettsia kairo*	GRAM-negative. Minute cocco-bacillary rods, occasionally filamentous, often occurring in pairs and sometimes in chains. Found in infected mammals in vascular endothelial and serosal cells. Nonmotile	Man. Transmitted by body louse *(Pediculus humanus* var. *corporis)*, head louse *(Pediculus humanus* var. *capitis)* and monkey louse *(Pedicinus longiceps)*	Pathogen of epidemic typhus (European typhus, classical typhus, typhus exanthematicus). "BRILL's disease" is a recrudescence of infection without intervention of lice	0	0	1	
191	*231*	**Rickettsia typhi** (WOLBACH and TODD) PHILIP *Dermacentroxenus typhi, Rickettsia exanthematofebri, Rickettsia fletcheri, Rickettsia manchuriae, Rickettsia mooseri, Rickettsia muricola, Rickettsia murina, Rickettsia murina mooseri, Rickettsia prowazeki* var. *mooseri, Rickettsia prowazeki* subsp. *typhi, Rickettsia typhi*	Similar to *R. prowazekii* but slightly smaller	Rats and mice. Transmitted by rat fleas *(Xenopsylla cheopsis, Xenopsylla astia, Nosopsylla fasciatua)*	Pathogen of endemic (murine) typhus (benign typhus) (in Latin America, tabardillo)	0	0	1	
191	*232*	**Rickettsia tsutsugamushi** (HAYASHI) OGATA *Dermacentroxenus orientalis, Rickettsia akamushi, Rickettsia megawai* var. *fletcheri, Rickettsia megawi, Rickettsia orientalis, Rickettsia pseudotyphi, Rickettsia sumatranus, Rickettsia tsutsugamushi-orientalis, Theileria tsutsugamushi, Trombidoxenus orientalis, Zinssera orientalis*	GRAM-negative. Ellipsoidal or rod-shaped organisms often occurring in pairs. Pleomorphic and less sharply defined than other Rickettsia species. Diffuse distribution in cell cytoplasm. Nonmotile	Probably rodents. Transmitted by trombiculid mites, especially *Trombicula akamushi* and *Trombicula deliensis*	Pathogen of tsutsugamushi disease (scrub typhus, Japanese river fever, flood fever, Kedani fever, Shimamushi mite-borne fever, Delhi pseudo-typhus)	0	0	1	
191	*233*	**Rickettsia rickettsii** (WOLBACH) BRUMPT *Dermacentroxenus rickettsi, Ixodoxenus rickettsi, Rickettsia brasiliensis, Rickettsia colombiensis, Rickettsia typhi*	GRAM-negative. Minute paired organisms surrounded by halo, often lanceolate and resembling pneumococci. Very pleomorphic. Nonmotile	Primarily wood tick *Dermacentor andersoni*. Also transmitted by dog tick, rabbit tick and others	Pathogen of Rocky Mountain spotted fever (São Paulo exanthematic typhus, Tobia fever, Minas Gerais typhus, Brazilian macular fever)	0	0	1	On treatment see PRICE[1] and CAWLEY[2]
191	*234*	**Rickettsia conorii** BRUMPT *Dermacentroxenus conori, Dermacentroxenus pijperi, Dermacentroxenus rickettsi* var. *conori, Ixodoxenus conori, Rickettsia blanci, Rickettsia megawi* var. *pijperi*	Similar to *R. rickettsii*	Probably dog, also rodents (South Africa). Transmitted by brown dog tick *(Rhipicephalus sanguineus)* and other ticks	Pathogen of boutonneuse fever (eruptive fever, Marseilles fever, Mediterranean fever, OLMER's disease, tick-bite fevers of India, South Africa and South America)	0	0	1	On treatment see LE GAC and ROUBY[3]

1) PRICE, W. H., *Amer. J. Hyg.*, **60**, 292 (1954). 2) CAWLEY et al., *J. Amer. med. Ass.*, **163**, 1003 (1957). 3) LE GAC and ROUBY, *Bull. Soc. Path. exot.*, **43**, 678 (1950).

For classification of organisms see pages 721–724; for index of synonyms see pages 725–734

See pages 721–724	See pages 725–734	**Rickettsiales** Classified name *Synonyms* Common names	Principal characteristics	Habitat, host, transmission, etc.	Associated diseases or source	Clinical application of antibiotics: Penicillin	Streptomycin	Tetracyclines	Remarks
191	*235*	**Rickettsia australis** PHILIP *Dermacentroxenus australis, Ixodoxenus australis*	Similar to *R. prowazekii (No. 230)*	Presumably ticks	Pathogen of rickettsial fever in Queensland, Australia	0	0	**1**	
191	*236*	**Rickettsia akari** HUEBNER et al. *Acaroxenus varioleidis, Dermacentroxenus akari, Gamasoxenus muris*	Similar to *R. rickettsii (No. 233)*	Transmitted by mite (rodents) *Allodermanyssus sanguineus*	Pathogen of rickettsialpox (vesicular rickettsiosis) of eastern United States and USSR	0	0	**1**	
191	*237*	**Rickettsia quintana** SCHMINCKE *Burnetia (Rocha-Limae) weigli, Burnetia (Rocha-Limae) wolhynica, Rickettsia pediculi, Rickettsia weigli, Rickettsia wolhynica, Wolhynia quintanae*	Similar to *R. prowazekii* but plumper and staining more deeply with GIEMSA's stain. Relatively resistant to heat and sunlight. Not filterable from plasma or serum. Exclusively extracellular in lice	Man. Transmitted by body louse *(Pediculus humanus* var. *corporis)* and by head louse *(Pediculus humanus* var. *capitis)*	Pathogen of trench fever (five-day fever, quintan fever, shin-bone fever, tibialgic fever, Volhynian fever)	0	0	**1**	
192	*238*	**Coxiella burnetii** (DERRICK) PHILIP *Burnetia (Dyera) burneti, Coxiella diaporica, Coxiella burneti, Rickettsia burneti, Rickettsia diaporica*	GRAM-negative. Small pleomorphic organisms showing both coccoid and rod forms. Nonmotile. Relatively resistant to heat, drying and chemical agents. Not filterable through bacterial filters	Various mammals. Distribution worldwide. Transmitted by many species of tick and by contact. Also airborne[1]	Pathogen of Q fever (query fever, Queensland fever, nine-mile fever, quadrilateral fever)[2]	0	0	**1**	For reviews see references[3]. For international standard antiserum see page 736
199	*239*	**Chlamydia trachomatis** (BUSACCA) RAKE *comb. nov. Chlamydozoon trachomatis, Rickettsia trachomae, Rickettsia trachomatis*	GRAM-negative. Coccoid cells with developmental cycle occurring intracytoplasmically in pairs or clusters. Larger forms encapsulated. Nonmotile	Man and animals	Pathogen of trachoma[5,6,9]. Sometimes included in the P-LV group[4]	2	?	**1**	
199	*240*	**Chlamydia oculogenitalis** (MOSHKOVSKIY) RAKE *comb. nov. Chlamydozoon oculogenitale*	Similar to *C. trachomatis*	Man and animals, water	Pathogen of swimming-pool conjunctivitis (neonatal or inclusion conjunctivitis)[6]. Sometimes included in the P-LV group[4]	0	0	**1**	
203	*241*	**Miyagawanella lymphogranulomatosis** BRUMPT *Chlamydozoon lymphophilus, Ehrlichia lymphogranulomatosis, Rickettsiaformis lymphogranulomatosis*	Similar to *Chlamydia trachomatis* and *C. oculogenitalis*. Cultivable in chick embryo. Nonfilterable	Man and animals. Transmitted by genital contact	Pathogen of lymphogranuloma venereum (lymphopathia venereum; lymphogranuloma inguinale; tropical, climatic, idiopathic, strumous or scrofulous bubo; esthiomene; NICOLAS-FAVRE disease; poradenitis)[4,5]	0	0	**1**	Sulfonamides coupled with tetracyclines or chloramphenicol are effective[8]
203	*242*	**Miyagawanella psittaci** (LILLIE) MOSHKOVSKIY *Chlamydozoon psittaci, Ehrlichia psittaci, Microbacterium multiforme psittacosis, Rickettsia psittaci, Rickettsiaformis psittacosis*	Similar to *M. lymphogranulamatosis* but partly filterable	Birds, especially parrots and finches	Pathogen of psittacosis (parrot fever)[2,4,5,7]	0	0	**1**	*Nos. 242 and 243:* After recovery from the disease, the pathogen can be identified in the blood several years later in the case of birds and up to 10 years later in the case of man. Similar persistence is known only for the pathogens of equine infectious anemia *(No. 287)* and of serum hepatitis *(No. 289)*

1) WELSH et al., *Ann. N. Y. Acad. Sci.*, **70**, 528 (1958). *2)* For reviews of viral pneumonias see REIMANN, H. A., *Arch. intern. Med.*, **89**, 115 (1952), and *J. Amer. med. Ass.*, **161**, 1078 (1956); LIPPELT, H., *Mschr. Kinderheilk.*, **104**, 84 (1956); GERMER, W. D., *ibid.*, **104**, 92 (1956). *3)* STOCKER, M. G. P., *Brit. med. Bull.*, **9**, 231 (1953); STOKER and MARMION, *Bull. Wld Hlth Org.*, **13**, 781 (1955). *4)* For reviews of the psittacosis-lymphogranuloma venereum (P-LV) group see BEDSON, S. P., *Brit. med. Bull.*, **9**, 226 (1953); WENNER, H. A., *Advanc. Virus Res.*, **5**, 39 (1958); MEYER, K. F., in HARTMAN et al. (Eds.), *The Dynamics of Virus and Rickettsial Infections*, New York, 1954, page 295. *5)* BEDSON, S. P., *Brit. med. Bull.*, **9**, 226 (1953). *6) Report of the Medical Research Council, 1957–58*, London, 1959, page 13; Expert Committee on Trachoma, *Wld Hlth Org. techn. Rep. Ser.*, **106** (1956); HASSOUNA, M. A. L., *Amer. J. Ophthal.*, **38**, 382 (1954). *7)* PERLMAN and MILZER, *Arch. intern. Med.*, **94**, 82 (1954); BEDSON, S. P., *Proc. roy. Soc. Med.*, **48**, 633 (1955). *8)* KING, A. J., *Brit. med. J.*, **2**, 1396 (1959). *9)* GRAYSTON et al., *J. Amer. med. Ass.*, **172**, 1577 (1960).

For classification of organisms see pages 721–724; for index of synonyms see pages 725–734

See pages 721–724	See pages 725–734	**Rickettsiales** Classified name *Synonyms* Common names	Principal characteristics	Habitat, host, transmission, etc.	Associated diseases or source	Clinical application of antibiotics: Penicillin	Streptomycin	Tetracyclines	Remarks
203	*243*	**Miyagawanella ornithosis** RAKE *Chlamydozoon columbi, Chlamydozoon meningophilus, Rickettsiaformis ornithosis*	Similar to *M. lymphogranulomatosis*	Birds, especially finches, pheasants, poultry, etc.	Pathogen of ornithosis and meningopneumonitis[1–3]	0	0	1	See remarks under *No. 242*
203	*244*	**Miyagawanella pneumoniae** RAKE *Chlamydozoon hominis, Ehrlichia pneumoniae, Rickettsiaformis pneumoniae*	Similar to *M. lymphogranulomatosis* but cells somewhat smaller	Presumably birds	Pathogen of a fatal pneumonitis[1–3]	0	0	1	
203	*245*	**Miyagawanella louisianae** RAKE *Ehrlichia louisianae*	Similar to *M. psittaci* but less filterable		Pathogen of Louisiana pneumonitis[1–3]	0	0	1	
203	*246*	**Miyagawanella illinii** RAKE *Ehrlichia illinii*	Similar to *M. lymphogranulomatosis*		Pathogen of Illinois pneumonitis[1–3]	0	0	1	
204	*247*	**Bartonella bacilliformis** (STRONG et al.) STRONG et al. *Bartonia bacilliformis*	GRAM-negative. Small, very pleomorphic organisms, typically bacilliform and often curved. With GIEMSA's stain appear as red-violet rods or coccoids in human erythrocytes. Motile in cultures with polar flagella. Not acid-fast. Obligate aerobe	Man. Probably also sand flies (*Phlebotomus verrucarum*)	Pathogen of bartonellosis, 3 forms of which occur in man: anemic (Oroya fever), eruptive (verruga peruana) and (rarely) a mixed form of these two (CARRIÓN's disease)	0	0	1	

1) For reviews of viral pneumonias see REIMANN, H. A., *Arch. intern. Med.*, **89**, 115 (1952), and *J. Amer. med. Ass.*, **161**, 1078 (1956); LIPPELT, H., *Mschr. Kinderheilk.*, **104**, 84 (1956); GERMER, W. D., *ibid.*, **104**, 92 (1956). *2)* For reviews of the psittacosis-lymphogranuloma venereum-(P-LV) group see WENNER, H. A., *Advanc. Virus Res.*, **5**, 39 (1958); MEYER, K. F., in HARTMANN et al. (Eds.), *The Dynamics of Virus and Rickettsial Infections*, New York, 1954, page 295. *3)* BEDSON, S. P., *Brit. med. Bull.*, **9**, 226 (1953).

For classification of organisms see pages 721–724; for index of synonyms see pages 725–734

Viruses *(Nos. 248–291)*

The term virus embraces very small pathogenic organisms ranging in size from 10 to ca. 300 mμ which are characterized by passing filters which retain bacteria and by the ability to multiply only in the presence of susceptible cells of the host organism. The growth of the smaller viruses is exclusively intracellular, while the Rickettsiales or larger viruses (see the remarks on page 686) can in some instances also multiply in the intestinal tract of their arthropod vectors. Unlike bacteria, viruses cannot be cultivated on cell-free nutrient media, however high the content of animal or plant protein.

The shape of the elementary bodies of the filterable viruses may be spherical (most animal viruses), brick-shaped or polyhedral (most plant viruses) or filamentous, while the bacteriophages (bacterial viruses) resemble spermatozoa in shape with a polyhedral head and a tail. The chemical constitution of some viruses has been elucidated. Tobacco mosaic virus, for example, has been found to be a nucleoprotein with 6% nucleic acid and 94% protein. Separately, these two components are inactive but can be recombined to form the active virus, which has also been isolated in crystalline form. The simplest viruses appear to consist only of nucleoproteins while the more complex may also contain lipids, carbohydrates and other substances. In the latter case a macrostructure has sometimes been recognized consisting of a nucleus of nucleic acid in a protein envelope with one or more outer membranes.

The infection of a cell by a virus is thought to take place in two phases. In the first, presumably under the influence of electrostatic forces, the virus particle attaches itself to the cell membrane (attraction between the positively charged amino groups of the virus nucleic acid and the negatively charged carboxyl groups of the membrane). Under certain conditions this phase is reversible. In the second phase, which is irreversible, the virus penetrates into the cell interior and multiplies by adapting the metabolism of the cell to its own needs.

In many virus diseases, including those due to the Rickettsiales, characteristic eosinophilic or basophilic "inclusion bodies" are seen in the nucleus or cytoplasm of the affected cells. These are of great value in diagnosis and almost certainly consist of aggregations of virus elementary bodies. However, inclusion bodies of similar appearance have also been observed in apparently healthy tissues such as the salivary glands of infants.

The genetic properties and infectivity of viruses appear to reside in the nucleic acid component, the antigenic properties in the protein component. Many viruses also contain a soluble antigen which is demonstrable in saline suspensions of the virus. This is known as the "S" antigen, while that situated in the elementary bodies is called the "V" (virus) antigen. The differing biological properties of viruses are usually reflected in differing antigenic structure, so that resistance acquired to one type of virus usually confers no protection against another type. There are exceptions, however, to this nonsharing of antigens, examples being the P-LV group of organisms (see *Nos. 239–246*) and some of the encephalitis viruses.

Antibiotics and viruses

The filterable viruses – as distinct from the "larger viruses" (Rickettsiales) whose reproductive process involves a stage of binary fission – are insensitive to the usual antibiotics, as to other known chemotherapeutic agents. The clinical use of these agents in the viral diseases concerned is therefore limited, at least at present, to combating secondary bacterial infections (cf. Editorial, *J. Amer. med. Ass.*, **165**, 53 [1957]). However, recent studies on interferon suggest that viral infections may eventually be amenable to chemotherapy (cf. Editorial, *Brit. med. J.*, **1**, 1745 [1961]).

* * *

The data on the pathogenic filterable viruses given in the table below and on pages 690–697 have been assembled from various standard works (see the bibliography below) and from numerous papers in the current literature.

Since there is as yet no internationally accepted system of classification of the viruses (see page 721) they have been arranged in accordance with the type of disease they produce: affections of the skin and mucous membranes, neurotropic diseases, arthropod-borne pyrexias, respiratory diseases, liver diseases. For explanation of the figures in columns 1 and 2 of the table see the introduction to the table of bacteria on page 646.

Bibliography (viruses)

Breed et al. (Eds.), *Bergey's Manual of Determinative Bacteriology*, 6th ed., Baltimore, 1948; Rhodes and van Rooyen, *Textbook of Virology*, 2nd ed., Baltimore, 1953; Pullen, R. L. (Ed.), *Communicable Diseases*, Philadelphia, 1950; Bedson et al., *Virus and Rickettsial Diseases*, London, 1951; Rivers and Horsfall (Eds.), *Viral and Rickettsial Infections of Man*, 3rd ed., Philadelphia and London, 1959; Hartman et al. (Eds.), *The Dynamics of Virus and Rickettsial Infections*, New York, 1954; Symposium on Viral and Rickettsial Diseases, *Med. Clin. N. Amer.*, **43**, No. 5 (1959); Viruses in Medicine, *Brit. med. Bull.*, **9**, No. 3 (1953); Current Virus Research, *Brit. med. Bull.*, **15**, No. 3 (1959).

See pages 721–724	See pages 725–734	**Viruses (Virales)** Name / Synonyms	Principal characteristics	Habitat, host, transmission, etc.	Associated diseases	Remarks (see also remarks above)
209	*248*	**Variola virus** *Borreliota variolae* (Lipschütz) Goodpasture *Strongyloplasma variolae* Lipschütz	All strains: Electron micrographs show rectangular bodies (280 × 220 × 220 mμ) with rounded corners usually containing 5 dense granules. About 6% consists of nucleic acid. Cultivation on chick-embryo chorio-allantois[1]	Transmitted usually by direct, occasionally by indirect contact. World-wide distribution		Cross immunization occurs between all strains of the variola group pathogenic for man, and they are practically indistinguishable serologically. See also remarks on page 690
		Strains: var. *hominis:* smallpox virus (typical strain), *Poxvirus variolae* (virus variolique, Pocken-Virus)		Man	Severe smallpox (variola major): mortality up to 80% among unvaccinated children. Also mild smallpox (variola minor, alastrim, parasmallpox, kaffirpox, milkpox, amaas) due to a less virulent strain, and varioloid (see remarks on page 690)	

1) Downie and Dumbell, *J. Path. Bact.*, **59**, 189 (1947).

See pages 721–724	See pages 725–734	**Viruses (Virales)** Name Synonyms	Principal characteristics	Habitat, host, transmission, etc.	Associated diseases	Remarks (see also page 689)
209	*248*	**Variola virus** ***(continued)*** *Strains (continued)*				
		var. *bovis*: cowpox virus, *Poxvirus bovis* (virus de la vacuna, Kuhpocken-Virus)		Cow	Cowpox: transmissible to man (in milkers usually on the hands: milker's nodes)	
		Vaccinia virus (probably identical with var. *bovis*), *Poxvirus officinale*		Vaccination strains	Vaccinia (lesion and mild systemic reaction following vaccination)	The origin of vaccination strains, some of which have been passed repeatedly in animals for over 60 years, is now obscure, but probably they were cowpox virus strains. See also remarks below
		Other animal strains		Rabbit, mouse, etc.	Rabbitpox, mousepox (ectromelia), etc. not transmissible to man	
209	*249*	**Varicella virus** *Briareus varicellae* spec. nov. Chickenpox virus (probably identical with herpes zoster virus)[1] (Spitzpocken-Virus, Windpocken-Virus)	Diameter 200–250 mμ. Cultivation in human tissues[1]	Man. Transmitted by contact and by droplets	Chickenpox (varicella), primary varicella pneumonia, occasionally encephalomyelitis	There is cross immunization between varicella and herpes zoster. The former probably represents primary invasion by the virus, the latter either localized re-invasion of an immune host or stimulation of latent infection by exposure to cold or other stresses[2]. An attack of varicella usually confers lifelong immunity to this disease. Incubation period 10–20 days. Infections in children receiving steroids may result in development of extremely virulent strains[7]. May be fatal in adults[8]. For reviews see references[3,4]
209	*250*	**Herpes zoster virus** (probably identical with varicella virus) (Virus du zona)	As for varicella virus (*No. 249*) above	Man. Possibly transmitted by contact and by droplets	Shingles (herpes zoster, zona)	See remarks under *No. 249* above. For reviews see references[5,6]
209	*251*	**Measles virus** *Briareus morbillorum* spec. nov. (virus rougeoleux, Masern-Virus) (closely related to pathogens of HECHT's giant-cell pneumonia, canine distemper and rinderpest[9])	Cultivation on chick-embryo chorio-allantois or in tissues. Diameter ca. 140 mμ	Man. Transmitted by contact and by droplets	Measles (morbilli, rubeola, sarampion), occasionally with encephalomyelitis[10–13]	Incubation period 12–19 days, usually 14. An attack normally confers lifelong immunity. For a review see YOSHIOKA[14]

1) Editorial, *Lancet*, **2**, 1019 (1960). *2)* STOKES, J., in RIVERS and HORSFALL (Eds.), *Viral and Rickettsial Infections of Man*, 3rd ed., Philadelphia and London, 1959, page 773. *3)* APPELBAUM et al., *Amer. J. Med.*, **15**, 223 (1953). *4)* JONES, A. T., *Brit. J. clin. Pract.*, **11**, 41 (1957). *5)* BURGOON et al., *J. Amer. med. Ass.*, **164**, 265 (1957). *6)* EPSTEIN and ALLINGTON, *Arch. Derm. Syph. (Chicago)*, **76**, 408 (1957). *7)* MEADE, R. H., *Med. Clin. N. Amer.*, **43**, 1355 (1959). *8)* Editorial, *J. Amer. med. Ass.*, **173**, 1030 (1960). *9)* MITUS et al., *New Engl. J. Med.*, **261**, 882 (1959); CARLSTRÖM, G., *Lancet*, **2**, 344 (1957); WARREN, J., *Advanc. Virus Res.*, **7**, 27 (1960). *10)* WEINSTEIN, L., *New Engl. J. Med.*, **253**, 679 (1955). *11)* WATSON, G. I., *Brit. med. J.*, **1**, 5 (1955). *12)* Review, *Brit. med. J.*, **2**, 90 (1956). *13)* APPENZELLER, K., *Helv. paediat. Acta*, **10**, 301 (1955). *14)* YOSHIOKA, H., *Dtsch. med. Wschr.*, **83**, 2100 (1958).

Smallpox[1] *(No. 248)*

Although no longer endemic in North America and Europe, smallpox remains a serious threat in these regions in view of the rapidity of modern communications with the main reservoirs of infection in the tropics. The disease has also lost nothing of its former virulence, and the relaxation in recent years of the vaccination of infants (in England now less than 20%) is therefore regarded by many authorities as potentially dangerous. When properly carried out, vaccination is with very rare exceptions a safe procedure and confers positive protection. The only serious complication now met with in vaccination, encephalomyelitis (< 1 case in 10,000 vaccinations[2]) has not been reported in children under 12 months, an argument in support of vaccination before this age. Prenatal infection with vaccinia virus is very rare[5].

The immunity to *variola major* conferred by vaccination is usually, but not invariably, lifelong, and infection with virulent strains of vaccinated persons whose immunity has decreased with time generally results in the mild form of the disease known as *varioloid*. The virus in varioloid, however, remains fully virulent and can thus cause variola major in unvaccinated contacts or in those who have lost their immunity. It is therefore important to distinguish between varioloid and the mild smallpox, known as *variola minor* or *alastrim*, caused by infection with a less virulent strain, which remains mild when transferred to vaccinated or unvaccinated contacts. In cases of smallpox contracted by persons known to have been vaccinated, the possibility of a virulent strain being present should therefore be assumed.

Smallpox cases are usually not infectious during the initial febrile stage but only on appearance of the skin eruption. An exception is the hemorrhagic form of the disease, *purpura variolosa*, which is nearly always fatal. In pregnant women, infection of the fetus may occur during the pre-eruptive febrile phase[3]. There is no specific medication for smallpox in any of its forms, and antibiotics and chemotherapeutic agents are only of use in controlling the secondary pyogenic infections. On the early diagnosis of the disease see MACCALLUM[4].

References

1) For a review see DOWNIE and MACDONALD, *Brit. med. Bull.*, **9**, 191 (1953). *2)* CLARK, W. G., *Bull. Hyg. (Lond.)*, **20**, 121 (1945); HURST, E. W., *Brit. med. Bull.*, **9**, 234 (1953). *3)* MARSDEN and GREENFIELD, *Arch. Dis. Childh.*, **9**, 309 (1934); DIXON, C. W., *J. Hyg. (Lond.)*, **46**, 351 (1948). *4)* MACCALLUM, F. O., in HARTMAN et al. (Eds.), *The Dynamics of Virus and Rickettsial Infections*, New York, 1954, page 324. *5)* WIELENGA et al., *Lancet*, **1**, 258 (1961).

For classification of organisms see pages 721–724; for index of synonyms see pages 725–734

See pages 721–724	See pages 725–734	**Viruses (Virales)** Name Synonyms	Principal characteristics	Habitat, host, transmission, etc.	Associated diseases	Remarks (see also page 689)
209	*252*	**Rubella virus**	Cultivation in kidney tissue and chick embryo	Man. Transmitted by droplets and contact	Rubella (German measles, rubeola, epidemic roseola, three-day measles)	Mainly a disease of childhood. Incubation period 14–23 days, usually 18. An attack normally confers lifelong immunity. Infection during pregnancy may result in congenital deformities in the child[7]
209	*253*	**Herpes virus** *Scelus recurrens* spec. nov., *Neurocystis herpetii* LEVADITI and SCHOEN, *Herpesvirus hominis* Virus of herpes simplex (febrilis)	Diameter 100–150 mμ. Cultivation on chick-embryo chorio-allantois or in tissues	Man. Transmitted by contact	Herpes simplex (h. labialis, h. facialis, h. febrilis, cold sore), eczema herpeticum, traumatic herpes, acute herpetic gingivostomatitis (aphthous, catarrhal, ulcerative or VINCENT's stomatitis), recurrent stomatitis, acute herpetic rhinitis, herpetic keratoconjunctivitis and keratitis, iridocyclitis, herpetic meningoencephalitis	The virus causes two types of disease due to primary infection, with local and systemic symptoms, and to recurrent infection, with local symptoms only. Primary infection from the mother occurs some months after birth, followed by lifelong latent infection with sporadic outbreaks often associated with severe bacterial infections. The commonest primary manifestation is gingivostomatitis, the commonest recurrent manifestation herpes simplex. For a review of the latter see VIVELL et al.[1]
209	*254*	**Herpesvirus simiae** B virus	Diameter 120–180 mμ. Cultivation on chick-embryo chorio-allantois or in tissues	Monkeys. Transmissible by contact to man	Encephalitis, encephalomyelitis, myelitis	Incubation period 10–20 days. Outcome usually fatal. For a review see PIERCE et al.[8]
209	*255*	**Foot-and-mouth disease virus** *Hostis pecoris* spec. nov. (virus de la fièvre aphteuse, Virus der Maul- und Klauenseuche)	Diameter 6.5–20 mμ	Cattle, swine, sheep, etc. Very occasionally transmitted to man. Distribution: world-wide except USA and Australasia	In man, symptoms similar to those in animals, viz. fever and typical vesicles in mouth and on skin of digits	For a review see GLEDHILL[2]
209	*256*	**Common-wart virus** *Molitor verrucae* spec. nov. Verrucae virus (virus papillomateux, Warzen-Virus)	Diameter ca. 55 mμ[3]	Man and possibly animals. Transmitted by contact	Common warts (verruca vulgaris), genital warts (condylomata acuminata), plane or juvenile warts (verruca plana)	Malignant changes may supervene on primary virus infection. Acquired immunity is unknown. Incubation period one to several months. For a review see COLES[4]
209	*257*	**Molluscum contagiosum virus** *Molitor hominis* comb. nov., *Strongyloplasma hominis* LIPSCHÜTZ (virus de l'acné varioliforme)	Mean dimensions 316×247 mμ[6]	Man. World-wide distribution. Transmitted by contact	Molluscum contagiosum. For reviews see references[5,6]	
209	*258*	**Louping-ill virus*** *Erro scoticus* spec. nov. Virus of sheep encephalitis (virus de l'encéphalite du mouton, Schaf-Encephalitis-Virus)	Diameter ca. 20 mμ. Cultivation in tissues and chick embryo	Sheep, man. Transmitted by ticks *Rhipicephalus appendiculitis* and *Ixodes ricinus*	In man, influenza-like illness possibly followed by mild or severe meningoencephalitis with benign course	It has been suggested[9] that this virus is one strain of a single virus responsible for a complex of diseases including spring-summer encephalitis *(No. 259)*. Member of arbor group B viruses*
209	*259*	**Spring-summer encephalitis virus*** *Erro silvestris* spec. nov. Forest spring encephalitis virus, tick-borne encephalitis virus (Virus de la méningo-encéphalite verno-estivale)	Diameter 20–25 mμ. Cultivation in tissues and chick embryo	Man, probably also cattle and horse. Distribution: USSR, Far East, Central Europe, India. Transmitted by ticks of the genera *Ixodes*, *Haemaphysalis* and *Dermacentor*	Russian spring-summer encephalitis (tick-borne encephalitis, undulant meningoencephalitis, diphasic milk fever). Three forms are known: polioencephalomyelitis (paralytic, mortality 5 to 30%), diphasic meningoencephalitis (benign) and hemorrhagic fever	Member of arbor group B viruses*. For reviews see references[10,11]

* Arbor virus = arthropod-borne animal virus, defined as a virus capable of infecting a vertebrate animal and of multiplying in an arthropod host (cf. CASALS and REEVES, in RIVERS and HORSFALL [Eds.], *Viral and Rickettsial Infections of Man*, 3rd ed., Philadelphia and London, 1959, page 269).

1) VIVELL et al., *Helv. paediat. Acta*, **12**, 127 (1957). *2)* GLEDHILL, A.W. *Brit. med. Bull.*, **9**, 237 (1953). *3)* WILLIAMS et al., *Nature*, **189**, 895 (1961). *4)* COLES, R. B., *Publ. Hlth (Lond.)*, **71**, 371 (1958). *5)* BEARE, J. M., *Med. ill. (Lond.)*, **9**, 683 (1955). *6)* NASEMANN, T., *Hautarzt*, **8**, 301, 352, 397, 443 (1957); **9**, 29, 113 (1958). *7)* GREENBERG et al., *J. Amer. med. Ass.*, **165**, 675 (1957); Editorial, *Lancet*, **2**, 800 (1960). *8)* PIERCE et al., *Amer. J. Hyg.*, **68**, 242 (1958). *9)* POND et al., *J. infect. Dis.*, **93**, 294 (1953). *10)* SMORODINTSEV, A. A., *Progr. med. Virol.*, **1**, 210 (1958). *11)* WORK, T.H., *Progr. med. Virol.*, **1**, 248 (1958).

For classification of organisms see pages 721–724; for index of synonyms see pages 725–734

See pages 721–724	See pages 725–734	**Viruses (Virales)** Name Synonyms	Principal characteristics	Habitat, host, transmission, etc.	Associated diseases	Remarks (see also page 689)
209	*260*	**Australian X-disease virus*** *Erro incognitus* spec. nov.	Diameter 20–50 mμ. Cultivation on chick-embryo chorio-allantois	Man. Distribution: Australia. Possibly transmitted by mosquitoes	Australian X-disease (Murray Valley encephalitis)	Member of arbor group B viruses*. Mortality is high (up to 70%) and children are specially prone. For a brief review see BURNET[8]
209	*261*	**Encephalitis lethargica virus** A Encephalitis virus (Virus de l'encéphalite épidémique)		Man (?)	Encephalitis lethargica (epidemic encephalitis Type A, VON ECONOMO'S disease, sleeping sickness, nona)	Incubation period probably 1–2 weeks. Symptomatic diagnosis only possible in epidemics[1–3]; in sporadic cases the diagnosis can only be confirmed anatomically[4]
209	*262*	**Japanese B encephalitis virus*** *Erro japonicus* spec. nov.	Diameter 15–30 mμ. Cultivation in chick embryos	Man. Possibly transmitted by *Culex* mosquitoes. Distribution: Japan, USSR	Japanese encephalitis (epidemic encephalitis Type B, Russian autumnal encephalitis)	Member of arbor group B viruses*. Mortality ca. 8.5%. For a review of 300 cases see LINCOLN and SIVERTSON[5]
209	*263*	**West Nile encephalitis virus*** *Erro nili* spec. nov.	Diameter 20–30 mμ.	Man. Distribution: Uganda	West Nile encephalitis (West Nile fever)	Member of arbor group B viruses*. Incubation period 3–6 days. For a review see GOLDBLUM et al.[6]
209	*264*	**St.Louis encephalitis virus*** *Erro scelestus* spec. nov. C Encephalitis virus	Diameter 20–30 mμ. Cultivation in tissues and chick embryo	Man, probably also animals. Distribution: USA. Transmitted by *Culex* mosquitoes	St.Louis encephalitis (American encephalitis, epidemic encephalitis Type C)	Member of arbor group B viruses*. Incubation period 4–21 days. Mortality ca. 20%. For a review see HESS and HOLDEN[7]
209	*265*	**Equine encephalitis viruses*** (Western, Eastern, Venezuelan) *Erro equinus* spec. nov. Equine encephalomyelitis virus (virus de l'encéphalite du cheval)	Diameter 30–50 mμ. Cultivation in tissues and chick embryo	Man and many animals. Distribution: N. and S. America. Transmitted to man, probably by mosquitoes, with mites or ticks as reservoirs	In man, acute encephalomyelitis, children especially prone	Member of arbor group A viruses*. Clinically indistinguishable from other viral encephalitides. For a review see HESS and HOLDEN[7]
209	*265a*	**Mayaro virus***		Man. Animal vectors unknown. Distribution: Trinidad, S. America	Cause of mild febrile illness	Member of arbor group A viruses*. For a review see CASALS and WHITMAN[9]
209	*266*	**Poliomyelitis virus**** *Legio debilitans* spec. nov. Virus of infantile paralysis (virus poliomyélitique, Virus der Kinderlähmung)	Diameter 27 mμ. For other physical properties see SCHAFFER and SCHWERDT[10]. Has been crystallized. Cultivation intracerebrally in monkeys and in human tissues	Man. Transmitted by contact, mainly via feces. Distribution almost world-wide	Poliomyelitis (infantile paralysis, HEINE-MEDIN disease, acute atrophic paralysis)	See the remarks opposite
209	*267*	**Coxsackie viruses****	Diameter 27 mμ. Have been crystallized. Cultivation in tissues	Man. Transmitted by contact, especially via feces, and by droplets. Distribution almost world-wide	Clinical picture varied: herpangina, epidemic pleurodynia (Bornholm disease), summer grippe, aseptic meningoencephalitis	Have been divided into two groups, A and B, on the basis of histologic signs in suckling mice. See the remarks opposite
209	*268*	**ECHO viruses****	Diameter 25–29 mμ, (type 10) 60–90 mμ	Man	Aseptic meningitic syndrome. Also associated (with Coxsackie viruses) in a paralytic poliomyelitis-like disease[12], with summer febrile illness and, in children, with summer diarrhea and a respiratory disease. For reviews see references[13–16]	28 immunological types have so far been differentiated. ECHO = enteric, cytopathogenic, human, orphan[11]. Type 10 almost certainly consists of a separate group of viruses (reoviruses)[17]

* Arbor virus. See footnote on page 691.

** In view of their overlapping characteristics, it has been suggested that the poliomyelitis, Coxsackie and ECHO viruses should be classified in one group as "enteroviruses".

1) VON ECONOMO, C., *Encephalitis lethargica*, Oxford, 1931. *2)* STERN, F., *Die epidemische Encephalitis*, 2nd ed., Berlin, 1928. *3)* PETTE, H., *Die akut entzündlichen Erkrankungen des Nervensystems*, Leipzig, 1942. *4)* DÖRING, G., *Münch. med. Wschr.*, **88**, 1053 (1941). *5)* LINCOLN and SIVERTSON, *J. Amer. med. Ass.*, **150**, 268 (1952). *6)* GOLDBLUM et al., *Amer. J. Hyg.*, **59**, 89 (1954). *7)* HESS and HOLDEN, *Ann. N. Y. Acad. Sci.*, **70**, 294 (1958). *8)* BURNET, F. M., *Amer. J. publ. Hlth*, **42**, 1519 (1952). *9)* CASALS and WHITMAN, *Amer. J. trop. Med.*, **6**, 1004 (1957). *10)* SCHAFFER and SCHWERDT, *Advanc. Virus Res.*, **6**, 159 (1959). *11)* Committee on ECHO Viruses, *Science*, **122**, 1187 (1956), and *Amer. J. publ. Hlth*, **47**, 1556 (1957); GELFAND, H. M., *Progr. med. Virol.*, **3**, 193 (1961). *12)* HAMMON et al., *J. Amer. med. Ass.*, **167**, 727 (1958). *13)* HSIUNG and MELNICK, *Ann. N. Y. Acad. Sci.*, **70**, 342 (1958). *14)* HORSTMANN, D. M., *Arch. intern. Med.*, **102**, 155 (1958). *15)* MELNICK, J. L., *Progr. med. Virol.*, **1**, 59 (1958). *16)* KIBRICK, S., *Med. Clin. N. Amer.*, **43**, 1291 (1959). *17)* SABIN, A. B., *Science*, **130**, 1387 (1959).

For classification of organisms see pages 721–724; for index of synonyms see pages 725–734

Poliomyelitis *(No. 266)*

The various strains of the poliomyelitis virus have been classified into three major immunologic groups: type 1 (Brunhilde), type 2 (Lansing) and type 3 (Leon). A study of 196 strains has revealed 82.1% of type 1, 10.2% of type 2, and 7.7% of type 3[1]. So far no relation has been observed between virus type and clinical form of the disease, but the three types vary in virulence and neurotropism.

Over 90% of poliomyelitis patients excrete virus in the stools, which constitute the main source of infection. The majority of infections remain subclinical or abortive, however, owing to the presence of circulating antibodies, and some precipitating factor is necessary for paralytic illness to occur. This may be a trauma such as tonsillectomy[4,5] or combined vaccination against diphtheria and whooping cough[6]. Physical exertion after onset of the disease[7], and pregnancy[5], also predispose to paralysis.

The probable pathogenic sequence is initial infection of the mucosa of the oropharynx and, if the dose is heavy enough, of the lower alimentary tract; this is followed by entry into the regional lymph nodes, whence the virus invades the central nervous system via the corresponding ganglia[2,3]. Viremia is also known to occur, but the extent to which this is involved in the invasion of the CNS is doubtful.

The clinical form of the disease which predominates, the paralytic or the more frequent nonparalytic, depends on the degree of involvement of the CNS. Age and sex affect both susceptibility to infection and the clinical course[9] and there is great diversity in the pattern of paralysis[10]. In children, a diphasic course is common[3], the initial gastrointestinal phase being uncharacteristic: constipation *or* diarrhea, fever, headache, sore throat, etc. After a short remission these symptoms reappear, together with pain and stiffness, and are usually followed by paralysis of some kind. On transmission of poliomyelitis to the fetus in utero see the remarks on page 605.

Diagnosis

Differential diagnosis must take account of meningitis of other viral origin, particularly Coxsackie and mumps meningitis and lymphocytic choriomeningitis[8]. Diagnosis is confirmed by tissue culture of the virus from the stools, and by the complement fixation test for increased antibody titer in the convalescent serum.

Vaccination[11]

Protection against paralytic poliomyelitis is provided by vaccines of two kinds: those containing killed virus (formalinized vaccines such as the SALK vaccine) and those containing live, attenuated virus. The former type are all based on the principle of inactivation of mixed cultures of the three types of virus by formalin and heat, and have been shown to confer a high degree of protection during extensive use on children in many countries[12] with minimal side effects[13]. The original SALK vaccine has been improved upon, particularly in England by replacement of the very virulent type 1 Mahoney strain of virus by the less virulent Brunenders strain[14], and at the Pasteur Institute in France (LÉPINE vaccine) by modifications of the inactivation process[15,16] designed to minimize chemical alteration in the antigens. Since these changes were made there have been no further cases of the disease being caused by vaccination. Killed vaccines suffer from the residual disadvantages, however, of complexity of manufacture, low potency and necessity for injection.

Live, attenuated vaccines, unlike killed vaccines, can be taken by mouth and thus simulate natural infection, so that the immunity they confer should be better and longer-lasting. Furthermore, the immunity can be transmitted to nonvaccinated persons, with the possibility of causing an "epidemic" of immunity which could result in eradicating or at least greatly reducing the virulent strains of the virus, something which the killed vaccines cannot do[12,18,24]. However, at present it appears that such transmission is limited to members of a family. Extensive trials with live vaccines in various countries have shown them to be not only safe but also effective in persons who have previously received killed vaccines[14,17,19–25], and the SABIN live vaccine has now been authorized for manufacture in the U.S. and U.K. Their manufacture is simpler than that of killed vaccines and this fact coupled with their ease of administration (a single oral dose as against 2–4 injections of killed vaccine) make their wide use feasible in underdeveloped countries. On the use of quadruple (diphtheria-whooping cough-tetanus-poliomyelitis) vaccine see the remarks on tetanus on page 676. For international reference antisera see page 737.

References

1) Committee on Typing of the National Foundation for Infantile Paralysis, *Amer. J. Hyg.*, **58**, 74 (1953). *2)* SABIN, A. B., *Science*, **123**, 1151 (1956). *3)* RHODES, A. J., *Brit. med. Bull.*, **9**, 196 (1953). *4)* Medical Research Council Committee on Inoculation Procedures and Neurological Lesions, *Lancet*, **2**, 5 (1955). *5)* PAFFENBARGER and WILSON, *Ann. N. Y. Acad. Sci.*, **61**, 856 (1955). *6)* RHODES, A. J., *Canad. med. Ass. J.*, **68**, 107 (1953). *7)* ALBRECHT and LOCKE, *J. Amer. med. Ass.*, **146**, 769 (1951); BRAHDY and KATZ, *ibid.*, **146**, 772 (1951). *8)* McMATH et al., *Lancet*, **2**, 275 (1956). *9)* WEINSTEIN, L., *New Engl. J. Med.*, **257**, 47 (1957). *10)* For a brief review see *Medical Research Council Report, 1956–57*, London, 1958, page 24. *11)* For reviews see MELNICK, J. L., *Progr. med. Virol.*, **1**, 59 (1958); Editorial, *Lancet*, **2**, 531 (1960); Expert Committee on Poliomyelitis, *Wld Hlth Org. techn. Rep. Ser.*, **203** (1960); Editorial, *J. Amer. med. Ass.*, **175**, 900 (1961). *12)* Expert Committee on Poliomyelitis, *Wld Hlth Org. techn. Rep. Ser.*, **101** (1956); **145** (1958). *13)* CHRISTENSEN, C. N., *J. Amer. med. Ass.*, **171**, 869 (1959). *14)* *Medical Research Council Report, 1955–56*, London, 1957, page 15. *15)* LÉPINE, P., *Presse méd.*, **67**, 941 (1959). *16)* LÉPINE and GRÉGOIRE, *La vaccination contre la poliomyélite dans la pratique médicale*, Paris, 1959. *17)* BARR et al., *J. Amer. med. Ass.*, **170**, 893 (1959). *18)* WILSON, G. S., *Ann. N. Y. Acad. Sci.*, **61**, 1059 (1955). *19)* ABAD-GOMÉZ et al., *J. Amer. med. Ass.*, **170**, 906 (1959). *20)* SABIN, A. B., *J. Amer. med. Ass.*, **171**, 863 (1959). *21)* SABIN, A. B., *Brit. med. J.*, **1**, 663 (1959). *22)* Editorial, *Lancet*, **2**, 531 (1960). *23)* KOPROWSKI, H., *J. Amer. med. Ass.*, **174**, 972 (1960). *24)* Editorial, *Brit. med. J.*, **2**, 293 (1961). *25)* Editorial, *Lancet*, **1**, 545 (1961); **2**, 586 (1961). *26)* BODIAN, D., *Science*, **134**, 819 (1961).

Coxsackie viruses[1] *(No. 267)*

The Coxsackie group consists of viruses of uniformly high pathogenicity and infectiveness for newborn mice. They are classified into two subgroups on the basis of the lesions caused: *Group A*, of which 24 immunologically different strains have been identified, cause generalized myositis of the skeletal muscles, but no other observable lesions, followed by death with flaccid paralysis; *Group B*, with 6 immunologically different strains, cause focal myositis, marked panniculitis and occasionally encephalitis, death occurring with spastic paralysis[2].

In man, the clinical picture of Coxsackie infection is varied, but the outcome is rarely fatal. Most of the serious infections occur in children[3,4], and family infections are common[5]. The most frequent manifestations are herpangina, Bornholm disease and aseptic meningo-encephalitis[6]. Patients excrete the virus in the feces, which are thus the main source of infection.

Herpangina[7,8]. This acute disease, due to various strains of Group A, is marked by fever, pharyngitis and ulcerative lesions on fauces and tonsils, together with anorexia, abdominal pain and convulsions. It is common during the summer in USA, especially in children.

Bornholm disease (pleurodynia)[9–12]. This disease is caused mainly by Group B strains but association of Group A has also been reported[11]. It is usually characterized by severe myalgia, fever, pharyngitis and sometimes a dry pleurisy, and is the commonest manifestation of adult Coxsackie infection.

Aseptic meningo-encephalitis[4,13–16]. Commonest in children, this condition is due mainly to Group B strains and resembles nonparalytic poliomyelitis. Strains A-9, B-3 and B-4 (and certain ECHO viruses [*No. 268*]) have also been identified as the cause of paralytic disease resembling poliomyelitis, and antigenic relationship to the virus of the latter has been demonstrated[17]. There is thus no clear dividing line between these groups of viruses.

Other diseases caused by Coxsackie viruses are myocarditis (or encephalomyocarditis) in the newborn and young children[3] (B types), and generalized febrile illness (A and B types).

References

1) For reviews see KIBRICK, S., *Med. Clin. N. Amer.*, **43**, 1291 (1959); TOBIN, J. O., *Brit. med. Bull.*, **9**, 201 (1953); DALLDORF, G., *Ann. Rev. Microbiol.*, **9**, 277 (1955), and *Ann. N. Y. Acad. Sci.*, **67**, 209 (1957); PARROTT, R. H., *Ann. N. Y. Acad. Sci.*, **67**, 230 (1957); MELNICK, J. L., *Progr. med. Virol.*, **1**, 59 (1958); GELFAND, H. M., *Progr. med. Virol.*, **3**, 193 (1961). *2)* TOBIN, J. O., *loc. cit.* *3)* GEAR, J. H. S., *Progr. med. Virol.*, **1**, 106 (1958). *4)* HOSIER and NEWTON, *Amer. J. Dis. Child.*, **96**, 251 (1958). *5)* JOHNSSON, T., *Arch. ges. Virusforsch.*, **5**, 384 (1954). *6)* KILBOURNE and GOLDFIELD, *Amer. J. Med.*, **21**, 175 (1956). *7)* HUEBNER et al., *New Engl. J. Med.*, **247**, 249, 285 (1952). *8)* ZISCHINSKY and MORITSCH, *Wien. klin. Wschr.*, **68**, 779 (1956). *9)* DISNEY et al., *Brit. med. J.*, **1**, 1351 (1953). *10)* WARIN et al., *Brit. med. J.*, **1**, 1345 (1953). *11)* WINDORFER and BORN, *Dtsch. med. Wschr.*, **77**, 1012 (1952). *12)* McLEAN et al., *Canad. med. Ass. J.*, **79**, 789 (1958). *13)* RHODES and BEALE, *Ann. N. Y. Acad. Sci.*, **67**, 212 (1957). *14)* HABEL et al., *Ann. N. Y. Acad. Sci.*, **67**, 223 (1957). *15)* SELTSER, R., *Milit. Med.*, **119**, 106 (1956). *16)* JOHNSSON et al., *Arch. ges. Virusforsch.*, **8**, 285 (1958). *17)* HAMMON et al., *J. Amer. med. Ass.*, **167**, 727 (1958).

For classification of organisms see pages 721–724; for index of synonyms see pages 725–734

See pages 721–724	See pages 725–734	**Viruses (Virales)** Name Synonyms	Principal characteristics	Habitat, host, transmission, etc.	Associated diseases	Remarks (see also page 689)
209	*269*	**Lymphocytic choriomeningitis virus** *Legio erebea* spec. nov.	Diameter 37–55 mμ (ultracentrifuge). Cultivation in tissues and chick embryo	Mice, man. Transmitted experimentally by contact and mosquitoes. Distribution: USA and Europe	Lymphocytic choriomeningitis (LCM), often subclinical	Incubation period 1–3 weeks. For a brief review see SCHEID et al.[1]
209	*270*	**Pseudolymphocytic choriomeningitis virus** *Legio simulans* spec. nov.	Diameter 150–225 mμ (filtration)	Man	Pseudolymphocytic choriomeningitis (benign aseptic). Clinically indistinguishable from lymphocytic choriomeningitis, with which there is no cross immunity	
209	*271*	**Rabies virus** *Formido inexorabilis* spec. nov. Street virus (virus rabique, Tollwut-Virus)	Diameter 100–150 mμ. Infected cells show typical dark inclusions (NEGRI bodies). Cultivation on chick-embryo chorio-allantois or in tissues	Dogs and other animals, man (main reservoir, dogs). Usually transmitted by bite. Distribution almost world-wide	Rabies (hydrophobia, lyssa). In man, always fatal once symptoms have appeared	Incubation period 27–64 days. Rabies vaccine (see page 735) should be given following bites or scratches from animals in which the presence of rabies cannot be positively excluded. For bibliography see below. For international standard antirabies serum see page 736
209	*272*	**Yellow-fever virus*** *Charon evegatus* spec. nov. (virus de la fièvre jaune, Gelbfieber-Virus)	Diameter 18–27 mμ. Cultivation in tissues and chick embryo	Man and primates. Transmitted by mosquitoes: man to man cycle mainly by *Aedes aegypti* (Africa and South America); monkeys to man cycle in Africa by *A. africanus*, *A. luteocephalus*, *A. simpsoni*, in South America by *A. leucocelaenus* and *Haemagogus* group	Yellow fever, Bwamba fever (Uganda)	Member of arbor group B viruses*. Incubation period 3 to 10 days. Various strains are known, with atypical, benign or severe course of the disease. Cross immunization between all strains (also between African and South American strains)[3]. An attack confers practically lifelong immunity. Subcutaneous vaccination of adults confers ca. 9 years immunity[2]. For reviews see references[3–5]
209	*273*	**Chikungunya disease virus***		Man. Transmitted by mosquitoes of genera *Culex* and *Aedes*. Distribution: South and East Africa	Chikungunya disease. For a review see ROBINSON[6]	Member of arbor group A viruses*. Incubation period 3 to 12 days
209	*274*	**Colorado tick fever virus***		Man. Transmitted by tick *Dermacentor andersoni*. Distribution: Rocky Mountains area, N. America	Colorado tick fever (mountain fever, nonexanthematous tick fever). For a review see LLOYD[8]	Ungrouped arbor virus*. Incubation period 4–5 days
209	*275*	**Dengue virus***	Diameter 17–25 mμ	Man. Transmitted by mosquitoes, especially *Aedes aegypti*	Dengue fever (break-bone fever, dandy fever, bouquet fever, giraffe fever, polka fever, five-day fever, seven-day fever)	At least 2 immunologically distinct types are known. Closely related to yellow-fever virus. Member of arbor group B viruses*. Incubation period 5–8 days. For a review see SABIN[7]
209	*276*	**Rift Valley fever virus** *Charon vallis* spec. nov.	Diameter ca. 50 mμ. Cultivation in tissues (suspended cells)	Man, sheep. Transmitted probably by mosquitoes. Distribution: East and South Africa	Rift Valley fever (enzootic hepatitis)	Incubation period ca. 6 days. For a review see GLEDHILL[9]
209	*277*	**Mumps virus**** *Rabula inflans* spec. nov. Virus of epidemic parotitis (virus ourlien)	Diameter 140 ± 30 mμ (from electron micrographs). Agglutinates erythrocytes. Cultivation in chick embryo	Man. Transmitted by droplets. Distribution world-wide	Mumps (epidemic parotitis). About one-third of infections are subclinical	Incubation period 18–21 days. An attack confers almost lifelong immunity. Mumps orchitis may be a cause of infertility[10]. For a review see BALLEW and MASTERS[10]

* Arbor virus. See footnote on page 691.

** Member of the so-called myxovirus group, all of which possess an enzyme capable of splitting off neuraminic acid derivatives from mucoproteins. Cf. ANDREWES et al., *Virology*, **1**, 176 (1955).

1) SCHEID et al., *Dtsch. med. Wschr.*, **84**, 1293 (1959). *2)* DICK and GEE, *Trans. roy. Soc. trop. Med.*, **46**, 449 (1952). *3)* DICK, G. W. A., *Brit. med. Bull.*, **9**, 215 (1953). *4)* GEAR and DEUTSCHMAN, *Chron. Wld Hlth Org.*, **10**, 301 (1956). *5)* SOPER, F. L., *Mosquito News*, **18**, 203 (1958). *6)* ROBINSON, M. C., *Trans. roy. Soc. trop. Med. Hyg.*, **49**, 28 (1955). *7)* SABIN, A. B., *Amer. J. trop. Med.*, **4**, 198 (1955). *8)* LLOYD, L. W., *Med. Clin. N. Amer.*, **35**, 587 (1951). *9)* GLEDHILL, A. W., *Brit. med. Bull.*, **9**, 237 (1953). *10)* BALLEW and MASTERS, *Fertil. and Steril.*, **5**, 536 (1954). *11)* SPOONER, E. T. C., *Brit. med. Bull.*, **9**, 212 (1953).

Bibliography on rabies *(No. 271)*

(General) Expert Committee on Rabies, *Wld Hlth Org. techn. Rep. Ser.*, **121** (1957); RODEWALD and WIDOW, *Med. Mschr.*, **11**, 74 (1957). (Transmission) CARNEIRO, V., *Bull. Wld Hlth Org.*, **10**, 775 (1954); CLOUGH, P. H., *Ann. intern. Med.*, **42**, 1330 (1955); MEYER, K. F., *J. Amer. med. Ass.*, **165**, 158 (1957). (Prophylaxis) FOX, J. P., *Ann. N. Y. Acad. Sci.*, **70**, 480 (1958). (Treatment) VEERARAGHAVAN et al., *Bull. Wld Hlth Org.*, **17**, 943 (1957).

See pages 721–724	See pages 725–734	**Viruses (Virales)** Name Synonyms	Principal characteristics	Habitat, host, transmission, etc.	Associated diseases	Remarks (see also page 689)
209	*278*	**Influenza A virus*** *Tarpeia alpha* spec. nov. (virus de la grippe type A)	PR 8 strain: Spherical particles of diameter 80 mμ containing protein, lipid, nucleic acids (RNA 0.8–4.5%, DNA 0–0.9%) and some polysaccharide. Filamentous forms sometimes seen. Cultivation in tissues and chick embryo. Agglutinates erythrocytes. For further details see BUZZELL and HANIG[1]	Man. Transmitted by contact and droplets. Distribution world-wide	Influenza (grippe, catarrhal fever, acute nasopharyngitis, febrile or epidemic catarrh), atypical pneumonia[2]	See remarks below. May be identical with virus of swine-filtrate disease (swine influenza)
209	*278a*	**Influenza B virus*** *Tarpeia beta* spec. nov. (virus de la grippe type B)	Similar to influenza A virus	Similar to influenza A virus but may be less widely distributed	As for influenza A virus, above	See remarks below. Immunologically distinct from influenza A virus. Types C and D have also been described
209	*279*	**"Para-influenza" viruses***		Man	Disease of upper respiratory tract, pneumonitis; in children, croup (acute laryngotracheobronchitis)	A group of viruses not yet intensively studied and embracing the Sendai, croup associated, and hemadsorption viruses[3]
209	*280*	**Respiratory syncytial virus**	Diameter 90–130 mμ	Man	Associated with lower respiratory tract disease in children and with afebrile upper respiratory tract affections in adults	For reviews see references[6,7]
209	*281*	**Salivary gland virus (SGV)** Cytomegalic inclusion disease virus	Cultivation in tissues	Man	Cytomegalic inclusion disease, mainly in children (cytomegalia infantum)[4]	For a review see SMITH[5]

* Myxovirus. See footnote on the opposite page.

1) BUZZELL and HANIG, *Advanc. Virus Res.*, **5**, 289 (1958). *2)* For reviews of viral pneumonias see REIMANN, H. A., *Arch. intern. Med.*, **89**, 115 (1952); REIMANN, H. A., *J. Amer. med. Ass.*, **161**, 1078 (1956); LIPPELT, H., *Mschr. Kinderheilk.*, **104**, 84 (1956); GERMER, W. D., *ibid.*, **104**, 92 (1956). *3)* KNEELAND, Y., *Med. Clin. N. Amer.*, **43**, 1327 (1959); Editorial, *Lancet*, **1**, 98 (1961). *4)* BIRDSONG et al., *J. Amer. med. Ass.*, **162**, 1305 (1956). *5)* SMITH, M. G., *Progr. med. Virol.*, **2**, 171 (1959). *6)* CHANOCK and JOHNSON, *Ann. Rev. Med.*, **12**, 1 (1961). *7)* Editorial, *Lancet*, **2**, 473 (1961).

Influenza[1] *(Nos. 278 and 278a)*

No other disease affects such a high proportion of persons in such a short space of time as influenza. The case incidence in epidemics reaches 5–10% of the population in a few weeks, and many other infections probably remain subclinical[2]. In crowded groups such as schools the attack rate may be as high as 70%[3]. Although influenza is itself a disease of low mortality, epidemics are marked by a sharp rise in the general death rate, especially among older persons, mainly as a consequence of secondary bacterial pneumonia.

The epidemiology of influenza is still largely obscure. Apart from natural spread of the virus, it is possible that it remains latent in a population since instances are known of a winter outbreak following a summer outbreak in the same locality, the virus strains responsible being antigenically identical[4,5]. The 1957 epidemic became world-wide in 6 months, a shorter space of time than earlier epidemics[3,15].

The antigenic character of influenza virus strains shows extreme variations, and four main serological groups have been distinguished, designated A, B, C and D[2,6]. Of these, only influenza A and B strains appear to be of epidemiological importance. Nearly all major influenza epidemics, which occur every 2–3 years, are due to A strains, while B strains are responsible for the annual localized winter outbreaks. The pandemic of 1917–19 was probably due to A strains antigenically related to those of swine influenza, while that of 1957 (Asian influenza) was the result of the emergence of new A strains departing distinctly from the previous antigenic A pattern[6,14]. The mortality of the 1917–19 influenza was 2% (most of the estimated 20–30 million deaths were caused by secondary pneumonia), that of the 1957 disease negligible.

Influenza is difficult to diagnose on clinical evidence, especially in sporadic cases. On diagnosis and differential diagnosis from other viral and rickettsial respiratory tract infections see GERMER[13].

Treatment

The high incidence of attack in epidemic influenza has made this disease the classic case of the misuse of antibiotics (and other chemotherapeutic drugs), and the 1957 pandemic prompted the issue of a special warning on the subject by the American Medical Association[7,8]. It cannot be too strongly emphasized that antibiotics have no place in the primary treatment of influenza, nor in that of any virus disease*, but should be reserved for use in patients in whom secondary bacterial infection has been demonstrated. Not only do antibiotics have side effects which may be disastrous in the critically ill, but they seriously disturb the physiological flora of the body. This may result in replacement of the normal bacterial inhabitants by resistant and often pathogenic organisms and thus the actual encouragement of superinfections[8,9] (see also page 635). The effect of antibiotics is here in contrast to that of antisera, which in the main do no harm even when they do no good.

Before administering antibiotics, the sensitivity to them of the bacterial strains concerned should be tested, and the choice of drugs guided by the result. In severe cases requiring immediate treatment, massive doses of penicillin plus 1 g streptomycin per day should be given until the result of the sensitivity tests is known[7]. In view of the known prevalence of resistant staphylococcal strains in hospitals (see remarks on staphylococci, page 662), hospitalization of influenza patients should be avoided as far as possible[7].

Vaccination

Only parenteral injection of a polyvalent influenza virus vaccine offers any protection against the disease[5]. However, vaccines are only effective when they are antigenically related to the strains in circulation. The extremely wide strain variation in influenza virus therefore renders early identification of the strains responsible for an outbreak of paramount importance. This is the main function of the World Influenza Centre set up in London by the Medical Research Council with the support of the World Health Organization[10].

* This does not apply to the rickettsia and P-LV group of organisms (the "larger viruses"). Cf. remarks on page 689.

For classification of organisms see pages 721–724; for index of synonyms see pages 725–734

See pages 721–724	See pages 725–734	**Viruses (Virales)** **Name** Synonyms	Principal characteristics	Habitat, host, transmission, etc.	Associated diseases	Remarks (see also page 689)
209	*282*	**Common-cold virus** *Tarpeia premens* spec. nov. (virus du refroidissement, Virus der Erkältung)	Diameter probably between 30 and 70 $m\mu$. Propagation in human embryonic lung cultures	Man, chimpanzee. Transmission probably by contact or droplets	Common cold[10] (acute coryza, acute rhinitis)	For reviews see ANDREWES[2]
209	*283*	**Newcastle disease virus (NDV)*** *Tortor furens* spec. nov. (Virus der atypischen Hühnerpest)	Diameter 150 ± 50 $m\mu$ (from electron micrographs). Agglutinates erythrocytes	Domestic fowl, transmissible to man. Distribution: England, East Asia, America, Australia	In man, Newcastle disease (conjunctivitis)	For a review see HANSON and BRANDLY[1]
209	*284*	**Adenoviruses** APC, RI, ARD viruses	Diameter 80–120 $m\mu$. Cultivation in tissues. For further properties see GINSBERG[9]	Man	Isolated from cultures of tonsillar and adenoid tissue. Associated with acute respiratory disease (ARD, "febrile catarrh"; RI = respiratory illness)[10] and acute inflammatory eye disease (e.g. pharyngoconjunctival fever, keratoconjunctivitis, follicular conjunctivitis). (APC = adenoidal, pharyngeal, conjunctival)	At least 23 distinct serotypes have been differentiated. For reviews see references [3–8]
209	*285*	**Virus of primary atypical pneumonia** EATON agent	Diameter 180–250 $m\mu$. Cultivation in chick embryo[11,12]	Man	Primary atypical pneumonia (PAP)[10]	Incubation period 1–3 weeks (average 12–14 days). Reported to be sensitive to tetracyclines and streptomycin[18]. No cross reaction with influenza or adenovirus antigens. For reviews see references[6,13,14,18]
209	*286*	**Pappataci fever virus** Sandfly fever virus (Stechmückenfieber-Virus)	Diameter probably ca. 50 $m\mu$. Cultivation in chick embryo	Man. Transmitted by sandflies (*Phlebotomus papatasii*)	Pappataci fever (sandfly fever, phlebotomus fever, three-day fever, mosquito fever)	Incubation period 3–4 days. For a review see SABIN[15]
209	*287*	**Equine infectious anemia virus** *Trifur equorum* spec. nov.		Horse, transmissible to man. Distribution: world-wide except Australia	Anemia milder in man than in horses but may persist 2–4 years	Virus can be identified in human blood 15 years after recovery, a persistence only approached by the pathogens of psittacosis *(No. 242)*, ornithosis *(No. 243)* and serum hepatitis *(No. 289)*. For a review see DREGUSS and LOMBARD[16]
209	*288*	**Hepatitis virus A** Virus of infectious hepatitis	Cultivation in tissues and chick embryo	Man. Excreted in feces. Transmission probably by droplets or via feces	Infectious hepatitis (epidemic jaundice), also occasionally serum hepatitis. May be transmitted to the fetus in late pregnancy	See remarks opposite
209	*289*	**Hepatitis virus B** Virus of serum hepatitis	Diameter probably < 26 $m\mu$. Cultivation in tissues and chick embryo	Man. Transmission by parenteral injection, possibly also during blood transfusion	Serum (inoculation) hepatitis	See remarks opposite
209	*290*	**Catscratch-fever virus** (virus de la maladie des griffes de chat)		Cat (?). Transmitted by bites and scratches from cats, possibly also by contact	Catscratch fever	See remarks opposite. It has been suggested that this organism belongs to the P-LV group *(Nos. 239–246)*[17]

* Myxovirus. See footnote on page 694.

1) HANSON and BRANDLY, *Ann. N. Y. Acad. Sci.*, **70**, 585 (1958). *2)* ANDREWES, C. H., *Brit. med. Bull.*, **9**, 206 (1953); *Bull. Johns Hopk. Hosp.*, **103**, 1 (1958). *3)* ROWE and HUEBNER, *Amer. J. trop. Med. Hyg.*, **5**, 453 (1956). *4)* ROWE et al., *Ann. N. Y. Acad. Sci.*, **67**, 255 (1957). *5)* HILLEMAN et al., *Proc. Soc. exp. Biol. (N. Y.)*, **92**, 377 (1956). *6)* LIPPELT, H., *Mschr. Kinderheilk.*, **104**, 84 (1956). *7)* Discussion on adenovirus infections, *Proc. roy. Soc. Med.*, **50**, 753 (1957). *8)* WARD, T. G., *Progr. med. Virol.*, **2**, 203 (1959). *9)* GINSBERG, H. S., *Ann. N. Y. Acad. Sci.*, **67**, 383 (1957). *10)* For reviews of viral pneumonias see REIMANN, H. A., *Arch. intern. Med.*, **89**, 115 (1952), and *J. Amer. med. Ass.*, **161**, 1078 (1956); LIPPELT, H., *Mschr. Kinderheilk.*, **104**, 84 (1956); GERMER, W. D., *ibid.*, **104**, 92 (1956). *11)* EATON et al., *J. exp. Med.*, **79**, 649 (1944), and **82**, 329 (1945). *12)* LIU, C., *J. exp. Med.*, **106**, 455 (1957). *13)* Editorial, *Lancet*, **2**, 180 (1956). *14)* REIMANN, H. A., *J. Amer. med. Ass.*, **161**, 1078 (1956). *15)* SABIN, A. B., *Amer. J. trop. Med.*, **4**, 198 (1955). *16)* DREGUSS and LOMBARD, *Experimental Studies in Equine Infectious Anemia*, Philadelphia, 1954. *17)* MOLLARET et al., *Presse méd.*, **64**, 1177 (1956). *18)* CHANOCK and JOHNSON, *Ann. Rev. Med.*, **12**, 1 (1961).

Influenza[1] *(Nos. 278 and 278a) (continued)*

A vaccine containing 400 CCA (chick-cell-egg-agglutination) test units per milliliter has been recommended[11] (not to be given to persons who are sensitive to eggs). Dosages[12]: *adults:* 1 ml s.c. or 0.1 ml intracut.; *children:* 3 months to 5 years: 0.1 ml intracut. or s.c., repeated after 1–2 weeks; 5–12 years: 0.5 ml s.c., repeated after 1–2 weeks; over 12 years: as for adults.

References

1) For reviews see FRANCIS, T., *Med. Clin. N. Amer.*, **43**, 1309 (1959); FLORMAN, A. L., *J. Mt Sinai Hosp.*, **25**, 29 (1958); HAAS, R., *Mschr. Kinderheilk.*, **104**, 76 (1956). *2)* ISAACS, A., *Brit. med. Bull.*, **9**, 208 (1953). *3)* DUNN, F. L., *J. Amer. med. Ass.*, **166**, 1140 (1958). *4)* ISAACS and ANDREWES, *Brit. med. J.*, **2**, 921 (1951). *5)* U.S. Army Commission on Influenza, *J. Amer. med. Ass.*, **124**, 982 (1944). *6)* JENSEN, K. E., *J. Amer. med. Ass.*, **164**, 2025 (1957); *Advanc. Virus Res.*, **4**, 279 (1957). *7)* Special Committee on Influenza, *J. Amer. med. Ass.*, **165**, 58 (1957). *8)* Editorial, *J. Amer. med. Ass.*, **165**, 53 (1957). *9)* HENNESSEN, W., *Dtsch. med. Wschr.*, **82**, 1206 (1957). *10)* *Report of the Medical Research Council, 1956–57*, London, 1958, page 15. *11)* Commission on Influenza of the Armed Forces Epidemiological Board, *J. Amer. med. Ass.*, **165**, 2055 (1957). *12)* Special Committee on Influenza, *J. Amer. med. Ass.*, **165**, 356 (1957). *13)* GERMER, W. D., *Mschr. Kinderheilk.*, **104**, 92 (1956). *14)* LÖFFLER, H., *Praxis*, **47**, 621 (1958). *15)* VENSEN et al., *Progr. med. Virol.*, **1**, 165 (1958).

For classification of organisms see pages 721–724; for index of synonyms see pages 725–734

See pages 721–724	See pages 725–734	Viruses (Virales) Name Synonyms	Principal characteristics	Habitat, host, transmission, etc.	Associated diseases	Remarks (see also page 689)
209	*291*	Virus of epidemic hemorrhagic fever		Mice (?). Transmitted probably by mites and ticks	Epidemic hemorrhagic fever (EHF, "Manchurian" fever, hemorrhagic nephrosonephritis, Far Eastern or Yaroslavl hemorrhagic fever)	Incubation period ca. 2 weeks. For reviews see references[1–4]

1) SHEEDY et al., *Amer. J. Med.*, **16**, 619 (1954). *2)* LUKES, R. J., *Amer. J. Med.*, **16**, 639 (1954). *3)* BROWN, K. P., *Trans. roy. Soc. trop. Med. Hyg.*, **48**, 105 (1954). *4)* KNUDSEN, A., *Trans. roy. Soc. trop. Med. Hyg.*, **48**, 112 (1954).

Viral hepatitis[1–7] *(Nos. 288 and 289)*

Viral hepatitis seems well on the way to becoming the most widespread of diseases in the United States and Europe (50,000 new cases in USA in 1960), while the permanent after effects seen in about 10% of cases render it economically important. Two varieties of the disease are known, *infectious hepatitis* (virus A or IH) and *serum hepatitis* (virus B or SH), the latter being much less common after the age of 15 years. These two viruses are probably antigenically different strains of a single virus. Clinically and pathologically, the two diseases are very similar (the main differences are summarized in the table below) and acute jaundice is common to both. In infectious hepatitis, the anicteric form often remains undiagnosed, although it can be detected by serum transaminase and other enzyme tests[8]. It is particularly common in children and the only symptom may be mild diarrhea; the feces remain infective for several months and probably constitute the reservoir of the virus[9].

Blood and feces are the only known sources of the viruses (see the table below). Virus A is transmitted mainly by the natural intestinal-oral route (children), virus B by inadequately sterilized transfusion fluids or instruments. Persons with no history of hepatitis may be carriers of either virus, and the fetus can be infected in this way.

Prophylaxis against viral hepatitis is made difficult by the lack of serological tests to detect carriers and by the fact that there are practical difficulties in the way of adequate sterilization of instruments used in transfusions. However, storage of plasma for 6 months at room temperature appears to eliminate the virus of serum hepatitis[11]. Infectious hepatitis can be prevented by intramuscular injection of γ-globulin at a dosage of 0.02 ml per kg of body weight *prior* to onset of the disease. Since it is usually impossible to distinguish infectious from serum hepatitis in sporadic cases, γ-globulin should be given routinely.

Treatment of viral hepatitis consists basically of reduction of physical activity (but *not* prolonged bed rest[12]) and dietary control. In view of the difficulty in distinguishing between the two infections in sporadic cases, both feces and blood should be assumed to be infectious from the point of view of management. Cortisone and ACTH have given good results in severe complicated cases.

Characteristics of viral hepatitis A and B[1, 2, 10]

Observation	Virus A or IH	Virus B or SH
Experimental		
Usual type of onset	Abrupt; febrile, often high fever; often one chill	Insidious; afebrile or temperature usually not over 38° C; rarely a chill
Abnormal hepatic tests	Follow first symptoms	Precede symptoms by several to many days
Usual incubation period (virus entry to clinical onset)	2–6 weeks	6–25 weeks
Route of inoculation	Oral or parenteral	Parenteral only
Virus demonstrated in:	Blood and feces	Blood only
Form of disease after		
(*a*) Oral ingestion of known infectious serum	Clinical hepatitis	No hepatitis
(*b*) Parenteral injection of infectious serum	Clinical hepatitis	Clinical hepatitis
(*c*) Oral ingestion of feces suspensions	Clinical hepatitis	No hepatitis
Resistance to infection after		
(*a*) virus A infection	Present (probably lifelong)	Absent
(*b*) virus B infection	Absent	Present (up to 1 year)
Epidemiologic		
Seasonal incidence	Autumn-winter	All year
Age of predilection	Before 30 years (65% between 5 and 15 years[13])	None
Carrier states		
in blood	Up to 8 months	Up to 5 years
in feces	Up to 16 months	Unknown
Prophylactic value of γ-globulin	Good	Doubtful

References

1) MACCALLUM, F. O., *Brit. med. Bull.*, **9**, 221 (1953). *2)* NEEFE, J. R., *Amer. J. Med.*, **16**, 710 (1954). *3)* Expert Committee on Hepatitis, *Wld Hlth Org. techn. Rep. Ser.*, **62** (1953). *4)* CULLINAN, E. R., *Dtsch. med. Wschr.*, **82**, 237 (1957). *5)* HAVENS, W. P., *J. Amer. med. Ass.*, **165**, 1091 (1957). *6)* HANGER, F. M., *J. Amer. med. Ass.*, **165**, 1696 (1957). *7)* VONKILCH, E., *Wien. med. Wschr.*, **108**, 1034 (1958). *8)* SCHÖN et al., *Dtsch. med. Wschr.*, **85**, 265 (1960). *9)* CAPPS et al., *J. clin. Invest.*, **29**, 802 (1950). *10)* HAVENS and PAUL, in RIVERS and HORSFALL (Eds.), *Viral and Rickettsial Infections of Man*, 3rd ed., Philadelphia and London, 1959, page 574. *11)* HOXWORTH et al., *Surg. Gynec. Obst.*, **109**, 38 (1959). *12)* CHALMERS et al., *J. Amer. med. Ass.*, **159**, 1431 (1955). *13)* BOHRMANN, F., *Ergebn. inn. Med. Kinderheilk.*, **58**, 201 (1940).

Catscratch fever[1] *(No. 290)*

This disease (nonbacterial regional lymphadenitis, benign inoculation lymphoreticulosis) is now an established clinical entity of world-wide distribution. The etiological association with cats is also established, but since the animals involved are usually healthy they are possibly only intermediate hosts of the virus.

Infection occurs predominantly in younger persons and may be subclinical. In overt cases the bite or scratch is followed by an incubation period of 3–14 days before appearance of the primary lesion (papule) and 7–21 days before lymphadenopathy develops. This is the principal feature and is characterized histologically by tuberculoid, necrotic granulomatosis. It is usually regional but occasionally generalized. Nodes are enlarged up to several centimeters in diameter and suppuration is common. There is usually spontaneous regression in 2 weeks to 2 months but in obstinate cases surgical removal may be desirable[2].

General symptoms are fever, headache and malaise. The disease is often associated with neurological manifestations 1–5 weeks after onset. Depending on the localization of the inoculation with virus, it may assume a pseudo-venereal, buccopharyngeal (anginal), ocular, mesenteric, thoracic or meningo-encephalitic form. The protean nature of the disease causes difficulties in diagnosis, and the only reliable diagnostic aid is the skin test with antigen prepared from lymph nodes of patients[3].

References

1) For reviews see GSELL and GSELL-BUSSE, *Ergebn. inn. Med. Kinderheilk.*, **8**, 76 (1957); WENTWORTH, F. H., *Pediatrics*, **22**, 376 (1958); BRAND and FINKEL, *Brit. med. J.*, **1**, 88 (1956); PRIER, J. E., *Ann. N. Y. Acad. Sci.*, **70**, 650 (1958); Editorial, *J. Amer. med. Ass.*, **173**, 1665 (1960); Editorial, *Lancet*, **2**, 532 (1960); Editorial, *Brit. med. J.*, **1**, 189 (1961). *2)* SMALL and SNIFFEN, *New Engl. J. Med.*, **255**, 1029 (1956). *3)* KALTER et al., *Ann. intern. Med.*, **42**, 562 (1955).

For classification of organisms see pages 721–724; for index of synonyms see pages 725–734

Eumycetes (Fungi) *(Nos. 292–331)*

In the last few years fungal infections appear to have become commoner and more virulent, partly no doubt as a result of the widespread use of antibiotics in bacterial infections. In general, the fungi are saprophytic for the human organism, a property which was recognized long before their facultatively pathogenic nature. Overt infections are predominantly endemic and sporadic, and epidemics rare. Subclinical infections, however, are much commoner than is usually thought, and may exceed the numbers of known subclinical cases of tuberculosis and viral infections.

Like the bacteria and unlike the algae, fungi have no chlorophyll. They differ from bacteria, however, in possessing a distinct cell membrane, protoplasm, and usually several nuclei. The mycobacteria *(Nos. 179–183)*, in which branching is observed, as well as the Actinomycetes *(Nos. 184–196)* and Streptomycetes *(Nos. 197–205)*, whose fungi-like structure is unmistakable, may be regarded as intermediate between bacteria and fungi.

The high mortality of some mycotic tissue diseases has stimulated the search for effective chemotherapeutic substances and antibiotics. Those so far found look promising but their effectiveness still awaits confirmation. The aromatic diamidines have given good results in systemic mycoses (for example, hydroxystilbamidine in North American blastomycosis), and the antibiotic nystatin has been found effective in moniliasis. An antibiotic effective against dermatomycoses (see opposite) appears to have been found in the shape of griseofulvin, which can be given orally. Amphotericin B has been reported to give good results in systemic mycoses which have hitherto been resistant to chemotherapy.

The most important fungi pathogenic to man are listed below and on pages 699–703. The data have been assembled from various standard works (see the bibliography below) and from numerous papers in the current literature. For explanation of the figures in columns 1 and 2 of the table see the introduction to the table of bacteria on page 646.

Bibliography (Eumycetes)

CONANT et al., *Manual of Clinical Mycology*, 2nd ed., Philadelphia and London, 1954; SIMONS, R. D. G. P. (Ed.), *Medical Mycology*, Amsterdam, 1954; COUDERT, J., *Guide pratique de mycologie médicale*, Paris, 1955; HALLMANN, L., *Bakteriologie und Serologie*, 2nd ed., Stuttgart, 1955; WEGMANN, T., *Ergebn. inn. Med. Kinderheilk.*, **8**, 457 (1957); STERNBERG and NEWCOMER (Eds.), *Therapy of Fungus Diseases*, London, 1955; DUBOS, R. J. (Ed.), *Bacterial and Mycotic Infections of Man*, 3rd ed., Philadelphia and London, 1958; MOSS and MCQUOWN, *Atlas of Medical Mycology*, 2nd ed., Baltimore, 1960; SMITH, D. T., *J. chron. Dis.*, **5**, 371 (1957); SUTLIFF, W. D., *Ann. Rev. Med.*, **9**, 15 (1958).

See pages 721–724	See pages 725–734	**Eumycetes (Fungi)** Classified name *Synonyms*	Principal characteristics	Habitat, host, transmission, etc.	Associated diseases	Remarks (see also remarks above)
210	*292*	**Absidia corymbifera** COHN *Mucor corymbifer*	Rapidly growing cultures. Branched, nonseptate mycelium. Abundant, woolly aerial mycelium, at first white, later gray. Branching sporangiophores with terminal spherical sporangia containing numerous endospores	Common in human sputum and on the skin of horses and other animals	Pathogenicity uncertain; may cause mucormycosis[1,2], an infection of the lungs and outer ear (otomycosis), also of the nose, skin, nails and occasionally the central nervous system; often associated with uncontrolled diabetes[6]. Similar diseases are caused by the genera *Rhizopus* and *Mucor*	Local treatment with iodides. Amphotericin B is effective in vitro[7]
211	*293*	**Rhinosporidium seeberi** (WERNICKE) SEEBER *emend.* ASHWORTH	Not yet cultivated. In tissues as spherical sporangia of various sizes (up to 250 µm) containing endospores	Man and animals. Widely distributed, endemic in India and Ceylon. Method of transmission uncertain	Rhinosporidiosis, chiefly of the nasal mucosa, with formation of polypoid tumors	No reliable chemotherapy; surgical treatment
212	*294*	**Coccidioides immitis** RIXFORD and GILCHRIST	In the tissues as large spheres of 20–80 µm. Multiplies by endosporulation. Whitish cultures, resembling cotton wool, with branched septate hyphae and chlamydospores	Man and animals, chiefly in California and Argentina. Infection by inhalation of chlamydospores	Coccidioidomycosis (San Joaquin fever); manifested as (a) *acute bronchitis* self-terminating in 14 days, (b) *a chronic form* with features resembling those of pulmonary tuberculosis. Also often causes skin eruptions similar to those of erythema nodosum or erythema multiforme, and rarely endocarditis[4] and meningitis[8]	Treatment with amphotericin B[3,8,9]. For a review see references[5]
213	*295*	**Ctenomyces interdigitalis** PRIESTLEY *Epidermophyton interdigitale, Trichophyton interdigitale*	Three kinds of colonies: a downy-white form, a granular form (without aerial hyphae) and a rare form with cerebriform growth	World-wide distribution. Transmission direct (infection in baths, schools, etc.)	Dermatomycosis: tinea corporis, tinea pedis, tinea manuum, tinea unguium, tinea capitis. See remarks opposite	On treatment see remarks opposite
213	*296*	**Ctenomyces mentagrophytes** ROBIN *Ctenomyces asteroides, Trichophyton asteroides, Trichophyton gypseum, Trichophyton mentagrophytes*	Cultures grayish-white with a granular surface, growing rapidly at first and later slowly. Not to be confused with the granular form of *C. interdigitalis (No. 295)*, with which it is regarded by some authorities as identical	Man and domestic animals	Dermatomycosis: tinea capitis, tinea corporis, tinea barbae, tinea cruris, tinea pedis, tinea manuum, tinea unguium. See remarks opposite	On treatment see remarks opposite

1) BAKER, R. D., *J. Amer. med. Ass.*, **163**, 805 (1957). *2)* SMITH and YANAGISAWA, *New Engl. J. Med.*, **260**, 1007 (1959). *3)* SUTLIFF et al., *Med. Clin. N. Amer.*, **43**, 219 (1959); REES, R. B., in CONN, H. F. (Ed.), *Current Therapy 1961*, Philadelphia and London, 1961, page 440; SMITH, J. G., *ibid.*, page 458. *4)* MERCHANT et al., *Ann. intern. Med.*, **48**, 242 (1958). *5)* O'LEARY and CURRY, *Amer. Rev. Tuberc.*, **73**, 501 (1956); WINN, W. A., *J. chron. Dis.*, **5**, 430 (1957). *6)* BAKER, R. D., *Diabetes*, **9**, 143 (1960). *7)* WATSON and NEAME, *J. Lab. clin. Med.*, **56**, 251 (1960). *8)* WINN, W. A., *Amer. J. Med.*, **27**, 617 (1959). *9)* NEWCOMER et al., *Ann. N. Y. Acad. Sci.*, **89**, 221 (1960).

For classification of organisms see pages 721–724; for index of synonyms see pages 725–734

See pages 721–724	See pages 725–734	**Eumycetes (Fungi)** Classified name *Synonyms*	Principal characteristics	Habitat, host, transmission, etc.	Associated diseases	Remarks (see also remarks on page 698)
213	*297*	**Ctenomyces persicolor** SABOURAUD *Trichophyton persicolor*	Similar to *C. mentagrophytes*	Domestic animals, man. Found throughout Europe	Dermatomycosis: tinea corporis. See remarks below	On treatment see remarks below
214	*298*	**Epidermophyton floccosum** HARZ *Epidermophyton cruris, Epidermophyton clypeiforme, Epidermophyton inguinale, Trichophyton intertriginis, Trichophyton cruris*	Colonies resembling cotton wool, at first greenish-yellow, later white. Typical spindle-shaped spores, numerous chlamydospores and occasionally spirally twisted hyphae	World-wide distribution, especially in humid, warm climates. Infection in baths etc., also by sexual intercourse	Dermatomycosis: tinea cruris, tinea pedis, tinea manuum, tinea unguium. See remarks below	On treatment see remarks below
215	*299*	**Sabouraudites audouini** GRUBY *Microsporum audouini, Trichophyton decalvans*	White, downy, slow-growing cultures with little mycelium. Small round closely packed spores easily recognized on the outside of the hair	World-wide distribution, chiefly in children. Transmission mostly indirect (by hairdressers)	Dermatomycosis: tinea capitis, tinea corporis. See remarks below	On treatment see remarks below
215	*300*	**Sabouraudites canis** BODIN *Microsporum canis, Microsporum felineum, Microsporum lanosum*	White to yellowish, rapidly-growing colonies. Woolly aerial mycelium, with abundant spindle-shaped spores with protruberances	Infection from dogs (more rarely cats)	Dermatomycosis: tinea capitis, tinea corporis, tinea barbae. See remarks below	On treatment see remarks below
215	*301*	**Sabouraudites gypseus** BODIN *Microsporum fulvum, Microsporum gypseum, Achorion gypseum*	Rapidly-growing cultures with a granular yellowish-brown surface. Many spindle-shaped macrospores	Man, horses, dogs, cats. Found in Europe, Africa and America	Dermatomycosis: tinea capitis, favus, tinea corporis. See remarks below	On treatment see remarks below

Dermatomycosis[1] *(Nos. 295–309)*

Dermatomycoses (tinea, ringworm) are infections of the keratinous tissues (skin, hair and nails) by dermatophytes*, viz., species of *Ctenomyces*, *Epidermophyton*, *Sabouraudites (Microsporum)* and *Trichophyton* (epidermophytosis, microsporosis, trichophytosis). In general, the infections respond well to oral griseofulvin. The activity spectrum of this antibiotic is strictly limited to the above species, so that careful prior identification of the causative organism is necessary. Griseofulvin concentrates specifically in the keratinous cells of the skin, hair and nails; the growth and spread of fungi in these structures are inhibited and infected tissues are eliminated by desquamation and/or replacement.

Tinea capitis (scalp, including hair shafts and follicles). Synonyms: tinea tonsurans, herpes tonsurans. All types are equally susceptible to griseofulvin and clinical resistance has not yet been encountered. Adequate doses result in improvement within 2–4 weeks, and in cure in general after 3–10 weeks of treatment, although occasionally up to 10 months may be necessary. Adjuvant therapy (shampooing and shaving the infected areas and application of conventional topical fungicides) is important since the emerging infected hairs still contain viable organisms. Therapy should be continued until three successive weekly negative cultures are obtained. X-ray epilation of the scalp is contraindicated.

The **favosa** type of tinea capitis (favus, eczema capitis, tinea ficosa, tinea lupinosa, tinea maligna, tinea vera, porrigo favosa, porrigo larvalis, porrigo lupinosa, porrigo sentulata, porrigophyta, dermatomycosis favosa, trichomycosis favosa, honeycomb ringworm, crusted ringworm) involves the deeper layers of the skin and is characterized by golden-yellow crusts (scutula) over the hair follicles. It may be resistant to treatment.

Tinea corporis (glabrous skin). Synonyms: tinea circinata, tinea glabrosa, ringworm of the body. Infections respond readily to griseofulvin and are usually cured within 2–4 weeks.

* Also often included under this heading are *Piedraia hortai (No. 316)*, *Geotrichum beigeli (No. 318)*, *Malassezia furfur (No. 319)*, *Candida albicans (No. 322)* and others.

Tinea imbricata (glabrous skin). Synonyms: Burmese, Chinese, Indian or Tokelau ringworm, Malabar itch. Very resistant to treatment.

Tinea barbae (bearded area of face and neck). Synonyms: tinea sycosis, parasitic sycosis, sycosis barbae, trichophytosis barbae, barber's itch. Treatment as for tinea capitis.

Tinea cruris (inguinal and perianal regions, axillae). Synonyms: tinea axillaris, tinea inguinalis, eczema marginatum, epidermophytosis cruris, trichophytosis cruris, jockey-strap itch, dhobie itch, red flap. Treatment as for tinea capitis.

Tinea pedis (feet), **tinea manuum** (hands). Synonyms: tinea interdigitalis, athlete's foot, Hong-Kong foot, dermatophytosis. Griseofulvin has not been so successful with infections of the soles of the feet due to *T. rubrum (No. 306)* and recurrences are very common, although appropriate adjuvant measures, such as topical antifungal powders, lotions and tinctures, increase the proportion of cures. Infections of the palms due to *T. rubrum* usually improve in 1–2 weeks with griseofulvin and cures may be expected in 2–8 weeks but may take as long as 4 months. Griseofulvin has little clinical effect on acute infections due to *C. mentagrophytes (No. 296)* but bed rest and symptomatic treatment are helpful; corticosteroids are of value in severe cases.

Tinea unguium (toenails and fingernails). Synonyms: onychomycosis, onychosis trichophytina. Infected fingernails are usually cured in 3–4 months by griseofulvin. If no significant improvement has occurred after this time, evulsion of the remaining affected nails may have to be considered. Griseofulvin alone has proved disappointing for treatment of infected toenails, and relapses often occur in spite of continuing therapy. When the large toenails are extensively involved treatment must often be continued for 9 months or more. All infected parts of the nails must be removed before treatment is stopped.

References

1) For reviews of therapy see ROTH, F. J., *Ann. N. Y. Acad. Sci.*, **89**, 247 (1960); Editorial, *Lancet*, **1**, 1175 (1960); SMITH, J. G., in CONN, H. F. (Ed.), *Current Therapy 1961*, Philadelphia and London, 1961, page 458; STERNBERG et al., *Med. Clin. N. Amer.*, **45**, 781 (1961).

For classification of organisms see pages 721–724; for index of synonyms see pages 725–734

See pages 721–724	See pages 725–734	**Eumycetes (Fungi)** Classified name *Synonyms*	Principal characteristics	Habitat, host, transmission, etc.	Associated diseases	Remarks (see also remarks on page 698)
216	*302*	**Trichophyton concentricum** BLANCHARD *Endodermophyton indicum, Endodermophyton tropicale*	Yellow to reddish cerebriform, slow-growing colonies with short, white hyphae. Numerous chlamydospores	Transmission direct, but also by contact with infected objects	Dermatomycosis: tinea imbricata in Oceania, Indochina, Formosa, Indonesia. See remarks on *Nos. 295–309* on page 699	On treatment see remarks on *Nos. 295–309* on page 699
216	*303*	**Trichophyton flavum** BODIN *Trichophyton cerebriforme, Trichophyton epilans*	Similar to *T. concentricum*, but faster growing	Animals (cats), man. Fairly common in Europe	Dermatomycosis: tinea capitis. See remarks on *Nos. 295–309* on page 699	On treatment see remarks on *Nos. 295–309* on page 699
216	*304*	**Trichophyton tonsurans** MALMSTEN *Trichophyton crateriforme*	Slow-growing, cream-colored colonies, some with a central crater. Club-shaped microconidia; macroconidia usually absent	Chiefly in school children. Transmission direct. World-wide distribution	Dermatomycosis: tinea capitis, tinea corporis. See remarks on *Nos. 295–309* on page 699	On treatment see remarks on *Nos. 295–309* on page 699
216	*305*	**Trichophyton sulfureum**	Cultures similar to *T. tonsurans* except that at first primrose-colored, later yellow. Microscopically identical to *T. tonsurans*	Transmission direct. World-wide distribution	Dermatomycosis: tinea capitis, especially in Northern Ireland, rarely tinea corporis. See remarks on *Nos. 295–309* on page 699	On treatment see remarks on *Nos. 295–309* on page 699
217	*306*	**Trichophyton rubrum** CASTELLANI *Epidermophyton rubrum, Trichophyton purpureum*	Colonies at first white, later reddish. Numerous microconidia; macroconidia occasionally seen	Transmission probably direct. World-wide distribution	Dermatomycosis: tinea corporis, tinea capitis, tinea cruris, tinea barbae, tinea pedis, tinea manuum, tinea unguium. See remarks on *Nos. 295–309* on page 699	On treatment see remarks on *Nos. 295–309* on page 699
217	*307*	**Trichophyton violaceum** BODIN *Achorion violaceum*	Slow-growing colonies, at first cream-colored, later violet and forming an aerial mycelium. No macroconidia; chlamydospores	Transmission direct. World-wide distribution	Dermatomycosis: tinea capitis, tinea corporis, favus, tinea barbae, tinea unguium. See remarks on *Nos. 295–309* on page 699	On treatment see remarks on *Nos. 295–309* on page 699
218	*308*	**Trichophyton quinckeanum** ZOPF *Achorion quinckeanum*	Downy-white cultures with radial fissures. Microconidia	Mouse, rabbit, hen, guinea pig, horse. Directly or indirectly transmitted by mice. World-wide distribution	Dermatomycosis: favus, tinea corporis, rarely tinea capitis. See remarks on *Nos. 295–309* on page 699	On treatment see remarks on *Nos. 295–309* on page 699
218	*309*	**Trichophyton schönleini** LEBERT *Achorion schönleini, Oidium schönleini*	Snow-white, stellate colonies on gelatin. Chlamydospores; microconidia rare	Man and animals. Transmission chiefly under bad hygienic conditions, especially among children. World-wide distribution	Dermatomycosis: main cause of favus. Also tinea corporis, tinea capitis, tinea pedis, tinea manuum, tinea unguium. See remarks on *Nos. 295–309* on page 699	On treatment see remarks on *Nos. 295–309* on page 699
219	*310*	**Allescheria boydii** SHEAR *Glenospora boydii, Indiella americana, Monosporium apiospermum*	In the tissues as white, macroscopic granules made up of branched hyphae. Fast-growing white colonies. Broad, hyaline, septate, branched mycelium. Numerous unicellular, elliptic conidia	Man and animals. Infection by trauma. In tropical and subtropical regions (especially India)	Normally a saprophyte but also causes mycetoma and occasional systemic infections	Treatment with penicillin or broad-spectrum antibiotics followed by long-term oral dapsone[1]

1) COCKSHOTT and RANKIN, *Lancet*, 2, 1112 (1960).

For classification of organisms see pages 721–724; for index of synonyms see pages 725–734

See pages 721–724	See pages 725–734	**Eumycetes (Fungi)** Classified name *Synonyms*	Principal characteristics	Habitat, host, transmission, etc.	Associated diseases	Remarks (see also remarks on page 698)
220	311	**Aspergillus fumigatus** FRESENIUS *Aspergillus bronchialis*	Predominantly GRAM-negative. Fruiting heads with a club-shaped terminal vesicle carrying radially-arranged sterigmata with chains of spherical conidia separate from one another. Fast-growing colonies	Widely-distributed on foodstuffs (cereals), etc. Infection apparently only after long exposure (for example during harvest work)	Commonest cause of aspergillosis; pneumonomycosis (recognizable by fungal threads growing from spores in the sputum), otomycosis, fungal eczema	Iodides or amphotericin B may be effective in systemic aspergillosis. Pulmonary aspergillosis has been successfully treated with nystatin[1]. External treatment of eczema with thymol. For reviews see references[2–4]
220	312	**Aspergillus niger** VAN TIEGHEM	Cultures darker than those of *A. fumigatus*	Found chiefly on decomposing organic matter	Otomycosis, occasionally pneumonomycosis	Treatment with penicillin. See also *No. 311*
221	313	**Penicillium bertai** TALICE and MACKINNON	Fast-growing colonies, at first white, later gray. Conidia arranged in the form of a brush	Widely-distributed saprophyte	Pneumonomycosis	Treatment with iodides
221	314	**Penicillium crustaceum** FRIES	Similar to *P. bertai*	Found chiefly on decomposing organic matter	Otomycosis, lung abscesses	Treatment with iodides
221	315	**Penicillium mycetomagenum** MANTELLI and NEGRI	Similar to *P. bertai*		Mycetoma	Resistant to iodides
222	316	**Piedraia hortai** BRUMPT *Trichosporum hortai*	Small, brownish-black, slow-growing colonies with septate mycelium; does not liquefy gelatin	Found chiefly in humid, warm climates (South America, Indochina, Japan)	Dermatomycosis: piedra nigra (black hair-nodule disease)	Treatment with iodine combined with salicylic acid and resorcinol
223	317	**Geotrichum candidum** LINK	Gray colonies with hyaline, branched mycelium. Distinguished from *Candida* by its rectangular arthrospores, although spherical ones are also occasionally seen. Does not liquefy gelatin	Very common saprophyte (cheese, eggs and other foodstuffs)	Chronic bronchitis; also infections of the skin and gastrointestinal tract	Treatment of pulmonary infections with iodides, of cutaneous and gastrointestinal infections with gentian violet. For a review see SMITH[3]
223	318	**Geotrichum beigeli** RABENHORST *Trichosporum beigeli*	Grayish-white colonies, similar to *G. candidum*	Widely distributed	Dermatomycosis: piedra alba (white hair-nodule disease)	Treatment with iodine combined with salicylic acid and resorcinol
224	319	**Malassezia furfur** ROBIN *Microsporon furfur*	Small yellow scales showing many hyphae and clusters of spherical spores. Culture rarely succeeds	Widely distributed; in Samoa infects 50% of the population	Dermatomycosis: pityriasis versicolor (chromophytosis, dermatophytosis furfuracea, tinea versicolor)	Treatment with iodine or ointments containing sulfur, benzoic acid and salicylic acid
225	320	**Cryptococcus neoformans** SAN FELICE *Cryptococcus meningitidis, Torula histolytica, Torulopsis neoformans*	In tissues, sputum, etc. as round, GRAM-positive cells enclosed in a GRAM-negative capsule of diameter 6–20 μm. Simple budding only; no mycelium. Cultures yeast-like, white to brownish, slimy	Widely-distributed saprophyte. Infection via the respiratory tract and possibly the skin	Cryptococcosis[6,8] (torulosis, European blastomycosis, BUSCHKE's disease, BUSSE-BUSCHKE disease). Organs affected are the skin (tumors with gelatinous content) and especially the central nervous system (torula meningitis), rarely other organs or joints	Drug of choice: amphotericin B[5,7–9]
226	321	**Pityrosporum ovale** BIZZOZERO *Pityrosporum malassezii*	Coccus-like forms becoming flask-shaped by budding. Cultivation difficult	Widely distributed	Pityriasis capitis. Clinically of little importance	

1) MANNING and ROBERTSON, *Brit. med. J.*, **1**, 345 (1959). *2)* SUTLIFF et al., *Med. Clin. N. Amer.*, **43**, 219 (1959). *3)* SMITH, D. T., *J. chron. Dis.*, **5**, 528 (1957). *4)* FINEGOLD et al., *Amer. J. Med.*, **27**, 463 (1959). *5)* CROUNSE and LERNER, *Arch. Derm. Syph. (Chicago)*, **77**, 210 (1958). *6)* LITTMAN and ZIMMERMANN, *Cryptococcosis, Torulosis or European Blastomycosis*, New York, 1956; BEER, K., *Schweiz. Z. allg. Path. Bakt.*, **19**, 534 (1956); WILSON, J. W., *J. chron. Dis.*, **5**, 445 (1957). *7)* SMITH, J. G., in CONN, H. F. (Ed.), *Current Therapy 1961*, Philadelphia, 1961, page 458. *8)* LITTMAN, M. L., *Amer. J. Med.*, **27**, 976 (1959). *9)* SEABURY and DASCOMB, *Ann. N. Y. Acad. Sci.*, **89**, 202 (1960); NEWCOMER et al., *ibid.*, **89**, 221 (1960).

For classification of organisms see pages 721–724; for index of synonyms see pages 725–734

See pages 721–724	See pages 725–734	**Eumycetes (Fungi)** **Classified name** *Synonyms*	Principal characteristics	Habitat, host, transmission, etc.	Associated diseases	Remarks (see also remarks on page 698)
227	*322*	**Candida albicans** ROBIN *Monilia albicans, Oidium albicans*	Occurs in sputum and on the skin as oval budding cells (4–6 µm) and occasionally as hypha-like fragments. On glucose-agar cream-colored colonies with oval budding cells on the surface over a pseudomycelium. On corn-meal agar numerous thick-walled chlamydospores	World-wide distribution; common saprophyte of the mucosa of the mouth and throat, vagina, digestive tract and skin in man and animals	Usually harmless but a facultative pathogen in specific pathological conditions of the tissues (nutritional disturbances, alteration of the balance of the microflora by antibiotics, etc.): Causes 1. Moniliasis of the mucosa (thrush, mycotic stomatitis, white mouth, oidiomycosis, muguet): extensive fungal proliferation with a grayish-white membranous covering, especially common in infants; 2. Moniliasis of the outer skin (moniliids, erosio interdigitalis, nonspecific forms); 3. Systemic moniliasis: infection of the air passages (bronchomoniliasis), gastrointestinal tract, urinary tract, occasionally endocarditis[2]. Dissemination through the bloodstream is possible	Nystatin has given good results in local infections[1] and amphotericin B in systemic infections[5,13,14]. Apart from *Candida albicans* 7 other species of *Candida* are often found in man[3]. On moniliasis in children see DOBIAS[4], in adults see references[6]
228	*323*	**Torula mansoni** CASTELLANI *Cladosporium mansoni*	Occurs on skin as unbranched mycelium with round spores. Blackish-green cultures with short hyphae	Mainly in eastern Asia	Tinea nigra (dermatomycosis with characteristic dark pigmentation). See also *No. 328*	Local treatment with salicylic acid, benzoic acid, sulfur, etc. For a review see CASTELLANI and DE SILVA[7]
229	*324*	**Blastomyces dermatitidis** GILCHRIST and STOKES *Zymonema dermatitidis*	Spherical or oval yeast-like cells, diameter 5–20 µm, which also show budding (simple budding only), with a thick, double-contoured membrane. In cultures also forms a mycelium	Found chiefly on damp, decaying wood; infects animals and man. Human infection chiefly by contact with plants and animals. Restricted to North America	North American blastomycosis (GILCHRIST's disease), chiefly affecting the skin (granuloma, ulcerations) and lungs; other internal organs rarely affected	Drug of choice: 2-hydroxystilbamidine[1] or amphotericin B[5,8,12,14,15]. For a review of North American blastomycosis see references[9,12]
229	*325*	**Blastomyces brasiliensis** SPLENDORE *Paracoccidioides brasiliensis*	Similar to *B. dermatitidis* but with multiple budding, up to 60 µm in size	Chiefly on plants. Limited to South America	South American blastomycosis (paracoccidioidosis, ALMEIDA's disease). In exogenous infections found particularly in the mouth and nose. Also a lymphangitic type with enlargement of the lymphatic glands, and visceral forms with infection of the lung, liver, spleen and abdominal organs (ulceration of the gastrointestinal tract)	Sulfonamides or amphotericin B[14]
230	*326*	**Histoplasma capsulatum** DARLING *Cryptococcus capsulatus*	Very small, oval cells, diameter 1–3 µm. Multiplication by budding. In cultures a septate mycelium and chlamydospores	In soils, dogs, cats, man. Infection by inhalation of dust containing spores. Widely distributed in North and South America and Africa	Histoplasmosis; in children often accompanied by hepatosplenomegaly and anemia. In adults infection of the lungs (calcareous deposits) with ulceration in the regions of the nose and ears; also infection of the bone marrow, spleen and central nervous system, rarely with endocarditis[2]	Drug of choice: amphotericin B[5,8,14,15]. On histoplasmosis see references[10]; on epidemiology see LEHAN and FURCOLOW[11]

1) SUTLIFF, W. D., *Ann. Rev. Med.*, **9**, 15 (1958). *2)* MERCHANT et al., *Ann. intern. Med.*, **48**, 242 (1958). *3)* BENHAM, R.W., *J. chron. Dis.*, **5**, 460 (1957). *4)* DOBIAS, B., *Amer. J. Dis. Child.*, **94**, 234 (1957). *5)* SMITH, J.G., in CONN, H. F. (Ed.), *Current Therapy 1961*, Philadelphia, 1961, page 458. *6)* BRAUDE and ROCK, *Arch. intern. Med.*, **104**, 91 (1959); Editorial, *J. Amer. med. Ass.*, **174**, 405 (1960). *7)* CASTELLANI and DE SILVA, *J. trop. Med. Hyg.*, **60**, 193 (1957). *8)* SUTLIFF et al., *Med. Clin. N. Amer.*, **43**, 219 (1959); UTZ et al., *Antibiotics Annual, 1958–59*, New York, 1959, page 628. *9)* CURTIS and BOCOBO, *J. chron. Dis.*, **5**, 404 (1957). *10)* LOOSLI, C.G., *Med. Clin. N. Amer.*, **39**, 171 (1955), and *J. chron. Dis.*, **5**, 473 (1957); SILVERMAN et al., *Amer. J. Med.*, **19**, 410 (1955); VANBREUSEGHEM, R., *Ann. Soc. Sci. méd. nat. Brux.*, **11**, 282 (1958); RUBIN et al., *Amer. J. Med.*, **27**, 278 (1959). *11)* LEHAN and FURCOLOW, *J. chron. Dis.*, **5**, 489 (1957). *12)* HARRELL and CURTIS, *Amer. J. Med.*, **27**, 750 (1959). *13)* LOURIA and DINEEN, *J. Amer. med. Ass.*, **174**, 273 (1960). *14)* NEWCOMER et al., *Ann. N. Y. Acad. Sci.*, **89**, 221 (1960). *15)* SEABURY and DASCOMB, *Ann. N. Y. Acad. Sci.*, **89**, 202 (1960).

See pages 721–724	See pages 725–734	**Eumycetes (Fungi)** Classified name *Synonyms*	Principal characteristics	Habitat, host, transmission, etc.	Associated diseases	Remarks (see also remarks on page 698)
231	*327*	**Rhinocladium schenkibeurmanni** HEKTOEN and PERKINS *Sporotrichum beurmanni, Sporotrichum schenki*	In the tissues spindle-shaped spores resembling bacteria, 2–4 µm long, but demonstrable only with difficulty. Cultures at first bacteria-like, later with branched aerial mycelium with small oval spores on short stalks	On plants and wood. Infection by laceration with thorns, etc. Widely distributed, common in Mexico	Sporotrichosis: skin abscesses, rarely pulmonary forms[1]	Treatment with iodides or amphotericin B[4–6]. Griseofulvin may be effective[7]. For a review see SMITH[2]
232	*328*	**Cladosporium wernecki** HORTA	On the skin a simple or branched mycelium with round spores. Grayish-black, polymorphic cultures	South America	Tinea nigra (dermatomycosis with characteristic dark pigmentation). See also *No. 323*	Local treatment with salicylic acid, benzoic acid, sulfur, etc.
233	*329*	**Phialophora pedrosoi** BRUMPT *Fonsecacea pedrosoi, Hormodendron pedrosoi*	In the tissues thick-walled cells (diameter 6–12 µm), single or in clusters, which are often divided; no budding. Cultures resemble molds, with slow formation of an olive-black pigment	Man, in America and Africa. Infection by dust and dirt after injury, etc.	Commonest cause of chromomycosis (chromoblastomycosis, dermatitis verrucosa), a chronic fungal infection chiefly on the extremities: at first in the form of pustules, later as warty nodules or papillomata	Iodides or amphotericin B may be effective[3, 4, 6]. For a review see SMITH[2]
233	*330*	**Phialophora verrucosa** MEDLAR *Cadophora americana*	Similar to *P. pedrosoi*	Man (rare) in America and North Africa	As for *No. 329*	As for *No. 329*
234	*331*	**Madurella mycetomi** LAVERAN	Polymorphic. Colonies with brown pigmentation and white aerial mycelium and chlamydospores. Forms black granules in the tissues	In soils and dust. Infection often by laceration with thorns. Widely distributed, especially in Africa	Cause of black-grained mycetoma	Treatment with penicillin or broad-spectrum antibiotics followed by long-term oral dapsone[8]

1) POST et al., *Dis. Chest*, **34**, 455 (1958). *2*) SMITH, D. T., *J. chron. Dis.*, **5**, 528 (1957). *3*) DEFEO and HARBER, *J. Amer. med. Ass.*, **171**, 1961 (1959). *4*) SMITH, J. G., in CONN, H. F. (Ed.), *Current Therapy 1961*, Philadelphia, 1961, page 458. *5*) SEABURY and DASCOMB, *Ann. N. Y. Acad. Sci.*, **89**, 202 (1960). *6*) NEWCOMER et al., *Ann. N. Y. Acad. Sci.*, **89**, 221 (1960). *7*) GONZÁLES-OCHOA, A., *Ann. N. Y. Acad. Sci.*, **89**, 254 (1960). *8*) COCKSHOTT and RANKIN, *Lancet*, **2**, 1112 (1960).

For classification of organisms see pages 721–724; for index of synonyms see pages 725–734

Protozoa *(Nos. 332–363)*

The table below and on pages 706–709 lists the most important protozoa pathogenic to man. On account of their very high incidence of human infestation, a few species not so far reported as being pathogenic have also been included. The data have been assembled from various standard works (see the bibliography) and from papers in the current literature. For explanation of the numbers in columns 1 and 2 of the table see the introduction to the table of bacteria on page 646.

The figures on pages 705, 708 and 710 are mainly from PIEKARSKI, G., *Lehrbuch der Parasitologie unter besonderer Berücksichtigung der Parasiten des Menschen,* Springer, Berlin, 1954.

Bibliography (Protozoa)

BRUMPT, E., *Précis de Parasitologie,* 6th ed., Paris, 1949; CHANDLER, A. C., *Introduction to Parasitology,* 9th ed., New York, 1955; MACKIE et al., *A Manual of Tropical Medicine,* 2nd ed., Philadelphia, 1954; PIEKARSKI, G., *Lehrbuch der Parasitologie unter besonderer Berücksichtigung der Parasiten des Menschen,* Berlin, 1954; CAMERON, T. W. M., *Parasites and Parasitism,* London, 1956; MANSON-BAHR, P. H. (Ed.), *Manson's Tropical Diseases,* 15th ed., London, 1960; FAUST, E. C., *Ann. Rev. Microbiol.,* **12**, 103 (1958).

See pages 721–724	See pages 725–734	**Protozoa** Classified name *Synonyms*	Principal characteristics	Habitat, host, transmission, etc.	Occurrence and associated diseases	Remarks
235	*332*	**Trypanosoma gambiense** DUTTON	Length 15–30 μm, polymorphic (see the figure opposite)	Vectors: tsetse flies *(Glossina palpalis, G. tachinoides)*	Trypanosomiasis: African (Gambian) sleeping sickness in Gambia, Liberia, Ghana, Sierra Leone, the Congo, southern Sudan. A chronic infection lasting for years. Infection of central nervous system only after some months	Preferred drug at all stages of the disease and for relapses is Mel B (for International Reference Preparation see page 739), the toxicity of which demands hospitalization. Otherwise ambulant treatment with tryparsamide combined with either pentamidine or suramin sodium[1]. Prophylaxis with pentamidine injections every 6 months[1]
235	*333*	**Trypanosoma rhodesiense** STEPHENS and FANTHAM	Morphologically and culturally similar to *T. gambiense*	Vectors: tsetse flies *(Glossina morsitans, G. pallidipes, G. swynnertoni)*	Trypanosomiasis: African (Rhodesian) sleeping sickness in south-eastern tropical Africa, Rhodesia, Tanganyika. Infection usually lasts a few weeks. Acute, turbulent course, and early death with toxic symptoms	Preferred drug is Mel B but only in advanced cases, otherwise suramin sodium; pentamidine is less effective[1]. Prophylaxis as for *T. gambiense*[1]
235	*334*	**Trypanosoma brucei** PLIMMER and BRADFORD	Length 15–30 μm, polymorphic, similar to *T. gambiense*	Vectors: tsetse flies	Cause of nagana disease of cattle and other domesticated animals. Infection in man is asymptomatic	
235	*335*	**Trypanosoma cruzi** CHAGAS *Schizotrypanum cruzi*	Length 20 μm. Morphologically similar to other trypanosomes	Vectors: bugs *(Triatoma megista, T. festans, Rhodnius prolixus)*	CHAGAS' disease (thyroiditis parasitaria, careotrypanosis) in Central and South America (especially Minas Gerais in Brazil). Symptoms: myxedema-like swellings, fever, fatal outcome possible. Children are especially prone	No reliable chemotherapy. The parasites are temporarily suppressed by primaquine and puromycin. For a review of CHAGAS' disease see references[2]
236	*336*	**Leishmania donovani** (LAVERAN and MESNIL) ROSS *Leishmania canis, Leishmania chagasi, Leishmania infantum*	Size 2–4 μm (see the figure opposite)	Transmitted by sandflies *(Phlebotomus)*. Reservoir hosts: dogs, cats	Visceral leishmaniasis (kala-azar, black fever, febrile tropical splenomegaly, Dumdum fever, cachectic fever, ponos) in India, northern China, Sudan. Particularly injurious to the spleen, liver and lymphatic glands. Leishmaniasis infantum in children (especially in the Mediterranean region). For distribution see the map opposite	Antimonials (e.g. sodium stibogluconate) and aromatic diamidines (e.g. diamidinostilbene isethionate). For complications penicillin and sulfonamides. Artificial immunization is partially effective. For reviews see references[3]
236	*337*	**Leishmania tropica** (WRIGHT) LÜHE	Similar to *L. donovani*	Transmitted by sandflies and by contact	Cutaneous leishmaniasis in the Near East and India (Aleppo boil, Bouton d'Orient, Delhi sore, Jericho boil, oriental sore, tropical ulcer). For distribution see the map opposite	Local treatment with quinacrine or berberine. In advanced cases antimonials (see *No. 336*). Amphotericin B may be effective[4]

1) NASH, T. A. M., *Trop. Dis. Bull.,* **57**, 973 (1960). *2)* LARANJA et al., *Circulation (N. Y.),* **14**, 1035 (1956); KÖBERLE, F., *Ztschr. f. Tropenmed. u. Parasit.,* **10**, 236 (1959). *3)* RODRIGUES DA SILVA, J., *Leishmaniose visceral (Calazar),* Thesis, Rio de Janeiro, 1957. *4)* SAMPAIO et al., *Arch. Dermat.,* **82**, 627 (1960).

For classification of organisms see pages 721–724; for index of synonyms see pages 725–734

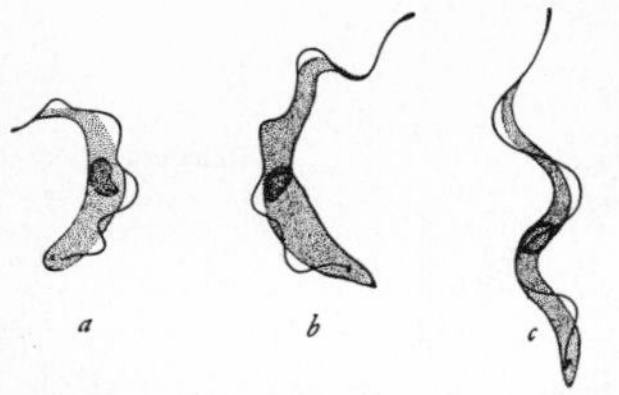

No. 332. Trypanosoma gambiense. The three main types: *a* short stumpy form with short flagellum; *b* intermediate form; *c* long slender form with long flagellum. Types *a* and *b* are from the blood of infected monkeys. (After MINCHIN.)

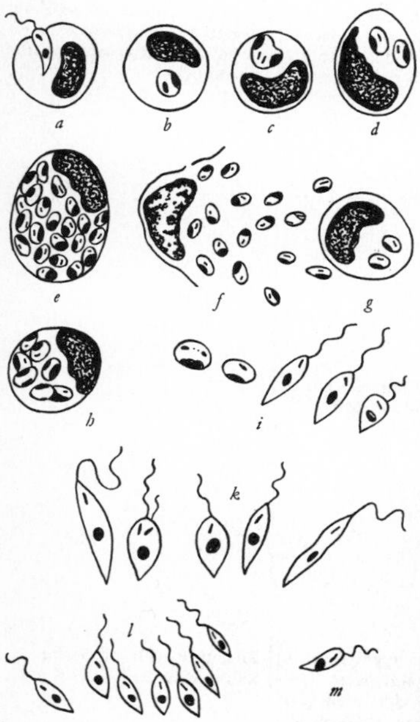

No. 336. Leishmania donovani. Cycle of development: *a* leptomonad flagellate entering endothelial cell; *b* to *g* multiplication by binary fission and infection of further endothelial cells and monocytes; *h* transformation of leishmania in the stomach of the infected Phlebotomi into the flagellate form (*k, l, m*), which moves forward into the pharynx and renews the cycle of infection as the metacyclic form (*m*). (After PIEKARSKI, 1954.)

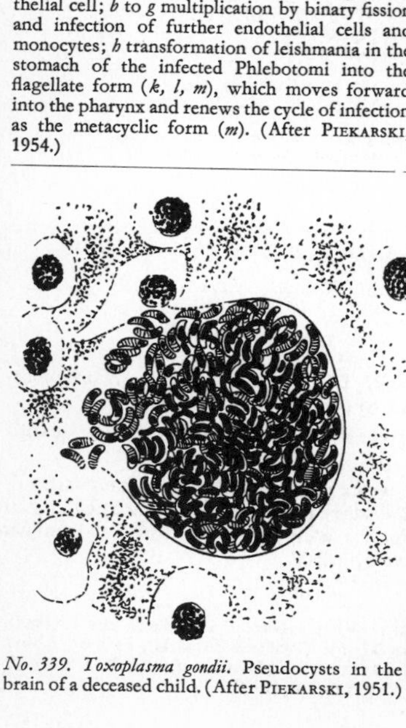

No. 339. Toxoplasma gondii. Pseudocysts in the brain of a deceased child. (After PIEKARSKI, 1951.)

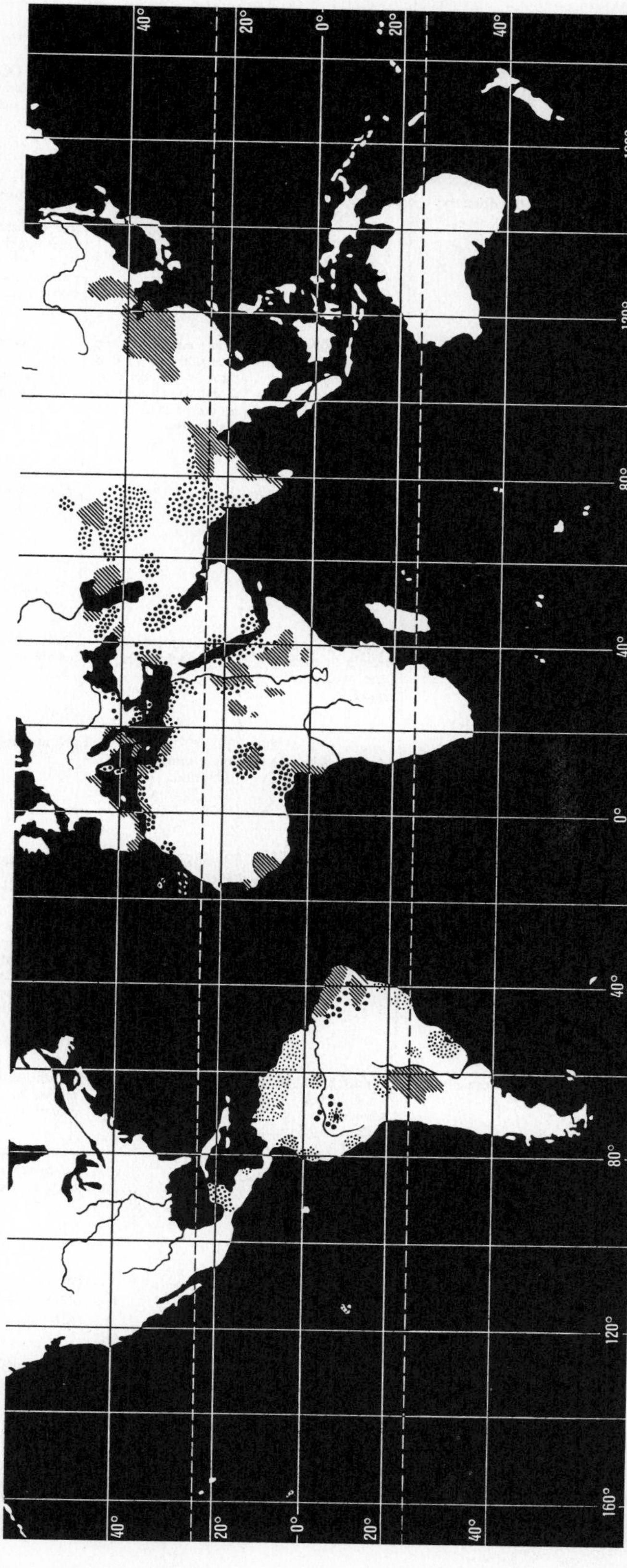

Nos. 336–338. Geographical distribution of Leishmania: *Leishmania donovani* (visceral leishmaniasis) *Leishmania tropica* (cutaneous leishmaniasis) *Leishmania brasiliensis* (mucocutaneous leishmaniasis)
(After CRAIG and FAUST, 1951.)

See pages 721–724	See pages 725–734	**Protozoa** Classified name *Synonyms*	Principal characteristics	Habitat, host, transmission, etc.	Occurrence and associated diseases	Remarks
236	*338*	**Leishmania brasiliensis** VIANNA	Similar to *L. donovani*	Transmitted by sandflies and by contact	Mucocutaneous leishmaniasis of tropical America, affecting the mucosa of the mouth, nose and throat (forest yaws, Bahia boil, bouba braziliana, espundia, uta). For distribution see the map on page 705	Treatment as for *No. 337*
237	*339*	**Toxoplasma gondii** NICOLLE and MANCEAUX *Toxoplasma hominis*	Size 3–6 μm, crescent-shaped (see the figure on page 705)	Host: man, dogs, etc. Transmission by contact or by milk or feces; also to the fetus in utero. World-wide distribution	Toxoplasmosis. Children are especially prone. May cause abortion and/or fetal death[1]. See the remarks below	Up to the present 24 probably identical varieties have been reported. For treatment see the remarks below
238	*340*	**Sarcocystis lindemanni** RIVOLTA	The individual parasites, 8–9 μm long, occur in thin capsules, lying lengthwise inside the muscle fibers and containing many individuals in various stages of development	Animals, man	12 cases of *Sarcocystis* infection of man have been reported	
239	*341*	**Encephalitozoon cuniculi** (LEVADITI, NICOLAU and SCHOEN)	Length 1–2 μm, straight or slightly bent, occasionally round	Host: rodents. Probably widely distributed	Pathogenicity for man not established with certainty	
240	*342*	**Chilomastix mesnili** WENYON	Length (6)10–15(20) μm, 3 flagella (see the figure on page 708)	Large intestine of man, world-wide distribution. Found in 3–10% of all individuals	Nonpathogenic	
241	*343*	**Lamblia intestinalis** BLANCHARD *Giardia intestinalis*	Size 10–18 μm, 2 nuclei, 8 flagella (see the figure on page 708)	Small intestine and occasionally the bile of man. World-wide distribution, commoner in children than in adults	Occasionally asymptomatic, but usually pathogenic (lambliasis[2]). The thin coating of lamblias along the mucosa interferes particularly with fat absorption, so that symptoms similar to those of celiac disease (GEE-HERTER disease) appear, viz., sprue or chronic infections of the gallbladder	Treatment with quinacrine or chloroquine, both orally[2]
242	*344*	**Trichomonas hominis** DAVAINE	Length 8–12 μm, with 3 *(T. faecalis)*, 4 *(T. hominis)* or 5 *(T. ardindelteili)* flagella	Large intestine of man	Pathogenicity uncertain, occasionally associated with diarrhea	Treatment with oral tetracyclines

1) WEINMAN, D., *Fertil. and Steril.*, **11**, 525 (1960); ROBERTSON, J. S., *Brit. med. J.*, **2**, 91 (1960).
2) WEBSTER, B. H., *Amer. J. dig. Dis.*, **3**, 64 (1958); SCHWARZ and LIENHARD, *Praxis*, **46**, 50 (1957).

Toxoplasmosis[1] *(No. 339)*

Congenital form: Chorioretinitis, cerebral calcifications, hydrocephalus, microcephaly, psychomotor disturbances.

Acquired form: Similar to the congenital form but usually without cerebral calcifications.

1. *T. acquisita exanthematica:* eruptive fever (resembling typhus), an acute generalized form of toxoplasmosis; in addition to fever and exanthemata there are symptoms of pneumonia and myocarditis and disturbances of the central nervous system. A fatal outcome is possible.
2. *T. acquisita cerebrospinalis:* Febrile or afebrile meningoencephalitis.
3. *T. acquisita ophthalmica:* Chiefly chorioretinitis[3].
4. *T. acquisita lymphonodosa:* The commonest form of toxoplasmosis[2]: febrile, afebrile or subclinical lymphadenitis.

Diagnosis: By demonstration of the causative organism or antibodies.

Treatment: Sulfonamides or pyrimethamine combined with sulfonamides (chiefly sulfadiazine) have some effect, particularly in acute infections. Antibiotics and the drugs usually given for protozoal infections have no effect.

References

1) For reviews see WRIGHT, W. H., *Amer. J. clin. Path.*, **28**, 1 (1957); FELDMAN, H. A., *Pediatrics*, **22**, 559 (1958); WAHLE, H., *Fortschr. Neurol. Psychiat.*, **26**, 6 (1958). *2)* BEVERLEY and BEATTIE, *Lancet*, **2**, 379 (1958). *3)* Editorial, *J. Amer. med. Ass.*, **173**, 915 (1960).

For classification of organisms see pages 721–724; for index of synonyms see pages 725–734

See pages 721–724	See pages 725–734	**Protozoa** Classified name *Synonyms*	Principal characteristics	Habitat, host, transmission, etc.	Occurrence and associated diseases	Remarks
242	*345*	**Trichomonas vaginalis** DONNÉ	Length (10)15–20(30) µm, 4 flagella directed forward, 1 backward (see the figure on page 708)	Vagina, urethra, occasionally the cervix and prostate. Transmitted by sexual contact. Widely distributed (in 20–70% of women, 4–15% of men)	Cause of, or associated with, vaginitis and urethritis: trichomoniasis urogenitalis (vaginalis). May be epidemic[3]	Treatments with arsenicals, nitrofurans, iodine preparations and antibiotics (tetracyclines, trichomycin, etc.) have all been recommended. Metronidazole has given encouraging results[1]. Sexual partners must be treated concurrently to avoid reinfection. On trichomoniasis see references[2,3]
242	*346*	**Trichomonas tenax** MÜLLER *Trichomonas elongata*	Length 6–10 µm. Structure similar to that of other trichomonads	Buccal cavity, widely distributed	Associated with diseases of the mouth and teeth, but itself only slightly pathogenic	
243	*347*	**Entamoeba histolytica** SCHAUDINN *Entamoeba dispar, Entamoeba dysenteriae* (Ruhramöbe)	Size: magna-form (trophozoite) 20–30 µm, minuta-form (intestinal lumen form) 12–18 µm, quadrinucleate cysts, 14–16 µm (see the figure on page 708)	Host: man. Transmission by ingestion of cysts (contaminated water and contaminated food, especially salads). World-wide distribution, also in temperate climates	Amebiasis (see the remarks below)	See the remarks below
243	*348*	**Entamoeba coli** SCHAUDINN	Size (10–)30 µm. Mature cysts have 8 nuclei (see the figure on page 708)	As for *No. 347*	Usually nonpathogenic. Found in about 50% of the population	
243	*349*	**Entamoeba gingivalis** (GROS)	Size 12–20 µm. Similar to *E. histolytica*. Cysts are not known	Host: man (dental fur), widely distributed. Transmission by close contact	Nonpathogenic, except that it may increase alveolar suppuration. Not a normal mouth saprophyte	No effective treatment known
244	*350*	**Endolimax nana** (WENYON and O'CONNOR)	Size 6–12 µm. Cysts usually have 4 nuclei	As for *No. 347*	Nonpathogenic; found in about 15–30% of all individuals	Treatment with chloroquine is variably effective
245	*351*	**Iodamoeba bütschlii** (VON PROWAZEK) *Endolimax williamsi, Iodamoeba williamsi*	Size 12–20 µm. 1 nucleus	As for *No. 347*	Very probably nonpathogenic. Found in about 2–6% of humans and about 20–50% of swine	See remarks under *Nos. 347* and *350*
246	*352*	**Dientamoeba fragilis** (JEPPS and DOBELL)	Size 5–12 µm. 1 or 2 nuclei	As for *No. 347*	Almost certainly pathogenic[4]; causes fibrosis and appendicitis	See remarks under *Nos. 347* and *350*

1) Editorial, *Brit. med. J.*, **2**, 922 (1960). *2)* BERNSTINE and RAKOFF, *Vaginal Infections, Infestations, and Discharges*, New York, 1953, page 211; SCHOOG-LÜTZENKIRCHEN, A., *Med. Klin.*, **53**, 1521 (1958). *3)* WHITTINGTON, M. J., *Brit. J. vener. Dis.*, **33**, 80 (1957). *4)* SWERDLOW and BURROWS, *J. Amer. med. Ass.*, **158**, 176 (1955).

Amebiasis[1] *(No. 347)*

The *magna* form of *Entamoeba histolytica* is pathogenic, whilst the cyst-forming *minuta* form is pathogenic only in so far as it can pass into the *magna* form. The conditions under which this transformation takes place are not fully understood.

A. **Intestinal amebiasis.** 1. Asymptomatic in about 90% of carriers in temperate climates. 2. *Non-dysenteric amebiasis* with vague abdominal pains, flatulence, nausea, mild fatigue, headache, nervousness. 3. *Amebic dysentery*, acute as well as chronic, mainly as a result of previous intestinal lesions due to bacterial infections. The amebae cause ulceration of the intestinal mucosa, shown by the presence of blood and mucus in the feces.

B. **Extraintestinal amebiasis**[4]. Almost all organs may be infected: liver[2] (hepatitis, liver abscess), lungs[3], pleura, urogenital system (amebic vaginitis), skin (amebiasis of the skin, ameboma) and brain, rarely the spleen and gallbladder.

Treatment

Of the many treatments which have been recommended, none is completely satisfactory. The following have been utilized: Quinacrine plus carbamidophenylarsonic acid for 10 days, repeated for the same period if the liver is infected[5]. If quinacrine is not tolerated, it can be replaced by paromomycin. In the case of liver involvement, chloroquine should be given additionally[5]. Emetine or emetine bismuth iodide[7], in cases of liver abscess combined with chloroquine[6,7], which is stored preferentially in this organ. In intestinal amebiasis, tetracyclines alone[7] or combined with emetine, an arsonic acid derivative and diiodohydroxyquinoline[6] or with chloroquine and diiodohydroxyquinoline[8]. The last-named drug has been used alone, and is the preferred drug for infants[5]. Newer amebicides include phenanthrolines, dichloroacetamide derivatives and diethylaminocresols; these have the advantage of being less toxic than some of the older drugs[7]. The action of the tetracyclines is apparently not direct but due to the fact that certain bacterial species necessary for the growth of the amebae are destroyed.

E. histolytica readily penetrates the intestinal tissues and mesenteric veins so that differentiation in the treatment of the intestinal and metastatic (extraintestinal) forms of the disease is pointless[5].

References

1) For reviews see ANDERSON et al., *Amebiasis*, Springfield, 1953; REES, C.W., *Problems in Amebiasis*, Springfield, 1955; KEAN et al., *Ann. intern. Med.*, **44**, 831 (1956). *2)* LAMONT and POOLER, *Quart. J. Med.*, **27**, 389 (1958); Editorial, *Lancet*, **2**, 300 (1960). *3)* ABDEL-HAKIM and HIGAZI, *Dis. Chest.*, **34**, 607 (1958). *4)* TAKARO and BOND, *Int. Abstr. Surg.*, **107**, 209 (1958). *5)* RADKE, R., in CONN, H. F. (Ed.), *Current Therapy 1961*, Philadelphia and London, 1961, page 3. *6)* KEAN and CHOWDHURY, in MODELL, W. (Ed.), *Drugs of Choice, 1958–59*, St. Louis, 1958, page 412. *7)* ADAMS, A. R. D., *Brit. med. J.*, **1**, 956 (1960). *8)* POWELL et al., *Lancet*, **1**, 76 (1960).

For classification of organisms see pages 721–724; for index of synonyms see pages 725–734

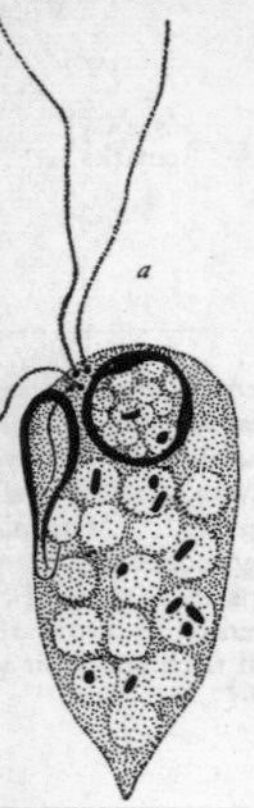

No. 342. Chilomastix mesnili. a vegetative form; *b* cysts. (Preparation from feces, iron-hematoxylin staining.) (After PIEKARSKI, 1954.)

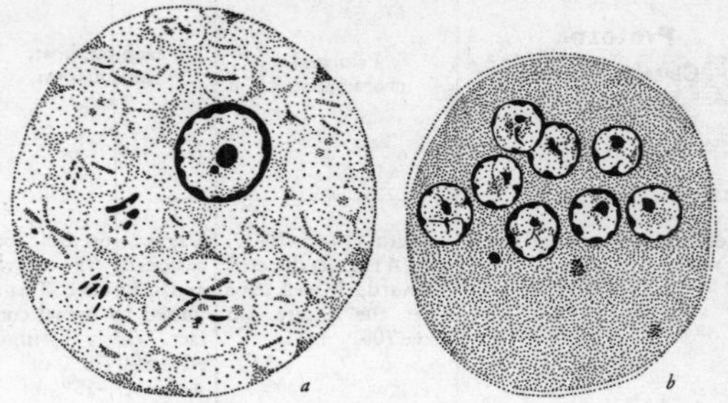

No. 348. Entamoeba coli. a vegetative form; *b* mature eight-celled cyst. (After PIEKARSKI, 1954.)

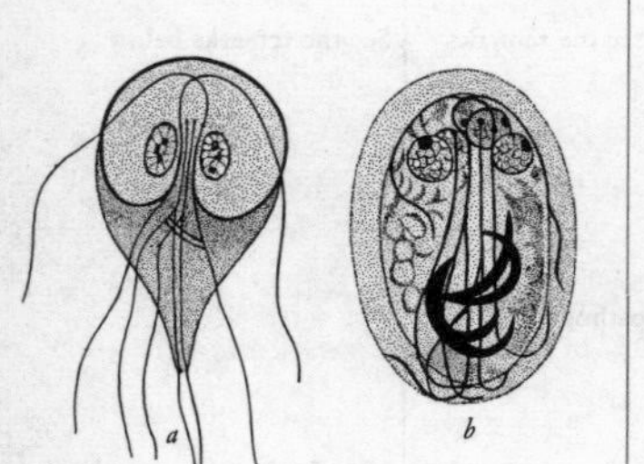

No. 343. Lamblia intestinalis. a vegetative form; *b* cysts. (After REICHENOW.)

No. 354. Isospora hominis. Mature oocyst containing two spores each with four sporozoites. (After HERRLICH and LIEBMANN, 1944.)

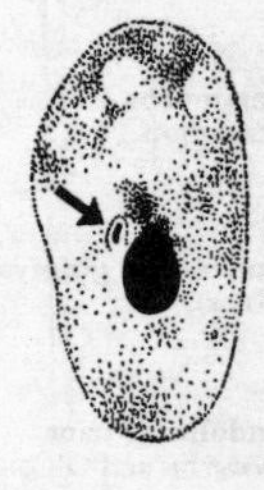

No. 359. Balantidium coli. In the center is the macronucleus with the micronucleus (arrowed) beside it. (After VON WASIELEWSKI, 1913.)

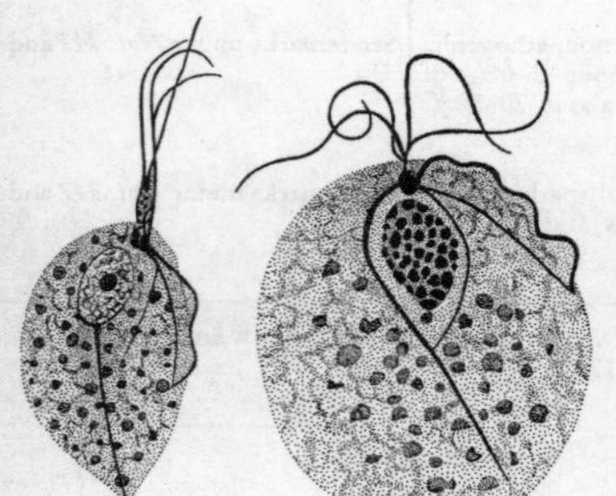

No. 345. Trichomonas vaginalis. Preserved moist, HEIDENHAIN staining. (After FISCHER-REICHENOW, 1952.)

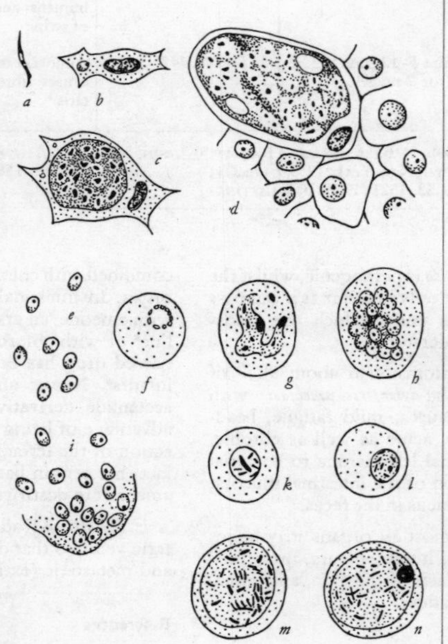

No. 355. Plasmodium vivax. Above: Life cycle in man. *a* sporozoite; *b* to *e* pre-erythrocytic schizogony (endothelial); *e* to *i* erythrocytic schizogony; *k, m* micro- and *l, n* macro-gametocytes. (After PIEKARSKI, 1954.)

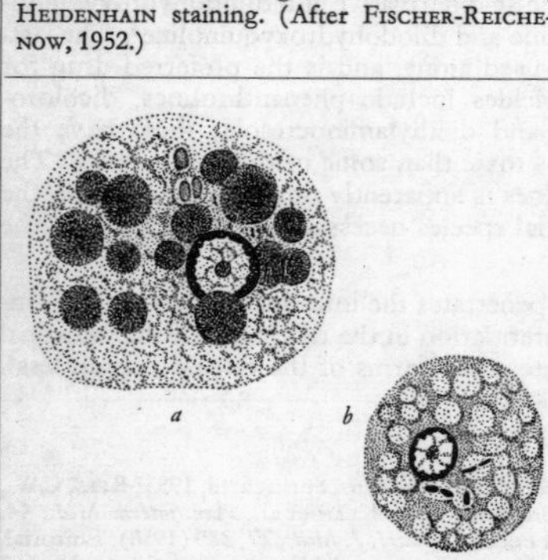

No. 347. Entamoeba histolytica (HEIDENHAIN staining). *a* histolytica form with erythrocytes; *b* minuta form. (After PIEKARSKI, 1954.)

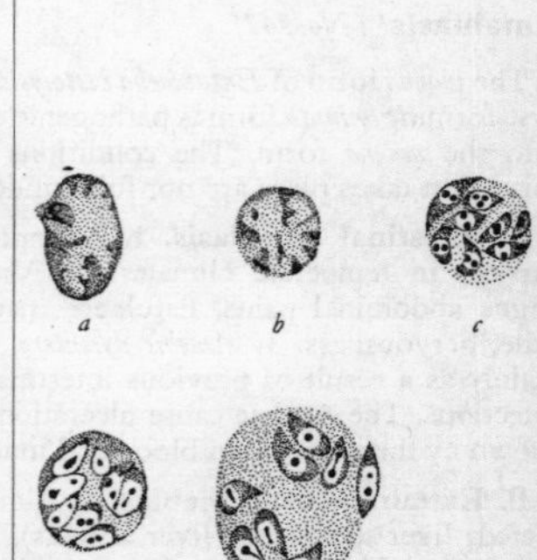

No. 360. Pneumocystis carinii. Stages in development (erroneously regarded as schizogony of *Trypanosoma cruzi* [No. 335]). The magnification of *e* is twice that of *a* to *d*. (After CHAGAS.)

For classification of organisms see pages 721–724; for index of synonyms see pages 725–734

See pages 721–724	See pages 725–734	**Protozoa** Classified name *Synonyms*	Principal characteristics	Habitat, host, transmission, etc.	Occurrence and associated diseases	Remarks
247	*353*	**Isospora belli** (WENYON)	Size 25–30 μm	Host: man. Widely distributed, especially in the south-west Pacific region, South America, Africa and the Mediterranean coast	Mildly pathogenic (isosporiasis) with mild enteritis	Self-terminating in a few weeks, treatment unnecessary
247	*354*	**Isospora hominis** RAILLIET and LUCET	Similar to *I. belli* (see the figure opposite)	As for *No. 353*	As for *No. 353*	See remarks under *No. 353*
248	*355*	**Plasmodium vivax** GRASSI and FELETTI *Haemamoeba vivax, Plasmodium tertianae*	See the figures on pages 708 and 710. Interval between sporulations: 48 hours	Intermediate host and vector: mosquitoes (*Anopheles claviger [maculipennis], A. bifurcatus, A. superpictus, A. pseudopictus, A. gambiae*)	Cause of tertian malaria (benign tertian malaria, tertian)	See remarks below and on page 710
248	*356*	**Plasmodium malariae** (LAVERAN) GRASSI and FELETTI *Haemamoeba malariae, Plasmodium quartanae*	See the figures on page 710. Interval between sporulations: 72 hours	As for *No. 355*	Cause of quartan malaria (quartan). Constitutes only 2% of all cases of malaria	See remarks below and on page 710
248	*357*	**Plasmodium ovale** STEPHENS	Morphologically similar to *P. malariae*. The erythrocyte changes are similar to those caused by *P. vivax*	As for *No. 355*	Causes a milder form of the disease similar to tertian malaria	See remarks below and on page 710
248	*358*	**Plasmodium falciparum** (WELCH) *Haemamoeba praecox, Laverania malariae, Plasmodium immaculatum, Plasmodium perniciosum*	See the figure on page 710. Interval between sporulations: 48 hours	As for *No. 355*	Cause of subtertian malaria (malignant tertian malaria, tropical paludism, estivo-autumnal fever)	See remarks below and on page 710
249	*359*	**Balantidium coli** (MALMSTEN) STEIN *Paramaecium coli*	Length 30–150 μm, width 20–100 μm. See the figure opposite	Intestine of swine. Transmission by ingestion of cysts	Pathogenic for man (balantidiasis)[1]: (1) asymptomatic (carriers), (2) chronic with diarrhea, or (3) dysenteric, possibly with fatal outcome	Treatment with tetracyclines, up to 28 g in 10–15 days; also with diiodohydroxyquinoline and carbamidophenylarsonic acid
250	*360*	**Pneumocystis carinii** DELANOË	Diameter 2–3 μm, roundish, enclosed in a mucous cyst 7–10 μm in diameter. See the figure opposite	Hosts: rodents, dogs, man. Transmission by droplets	Cause of an interstitial pneumonia, especially in infants[2]. Common in Europe, rare in North America	No effective remedy known. Treatment remains pragmatic

1) For a review see AREÁN and KOPPISCH, *Amer. J. Path.*, **32**, 1089 (1956).

2) For reviews see JÍROVEC, O., *Mschr. Kinderheilk.*, **102**, 476 (1954); RUBIN and ZAK, *New Engl. J. Med.*, **262**, 1315 (1960).

Malaria[1] *(Nos. 355–358)*

Although malaria can now be effectively combated by means of specific chemotherapeutic agents (measures for control of malaria parasites will not be discussed here) it nevertheless remains one of the most important infectious diseases and affects the population over wide areas of the world. A knowledge of the **life cycle of the Plasmodia** is important to an understanding of the proper use of antimalarial agents:

Host I: Man.

1st Phase: *Tissue phase.* As a result of the bite of an infected mosquito, the sporozoites enter the blood stream and after a short interval disappear into the tissues. In the tissue phase there are no clinical symptoms.

2nd Phase: *Blood phase.*

(*a*) Asexual blood phase. After a short latent period (several days to a week) the trophozoites produced in the tissues pass into the blood stream and invade the erythrocytes. Here they undergo multiplication (schizogony) at certain definite intervals (depending on the species). This schizogonic phase is responsible for the principal clinical symptoms (febrile attacks, etc.).

(*b*) Sexual blood phase. In addition to undergoing schizogony the trophozoites develop finally into the sexual gametocytes. These circulate for a long time in the blood stream, without, however, causing clinical symptoms.

Host II: Mosquitoes.

When the gametocytes enter a mosquito they copulate and develop finally into sporozoites, whereby the cycle is completed when the latter are again transmitted to man.

In **falciparum malaria** the tissue phase produces only *one* batch of trophozoites, after which it dies out or becomes unproductive: this infection is short-lived and there is no recidivism (except by reinfection). Chemotherapeutic destruction of the schizogonic phase (asexual blood phase), the only active phase, thus terminates a *falciparum* infection immediately even when the agent is absolutely ineffective with regard to the tissue phase.

In contrast to this, the tissue stage of **vivax malaria** establishes itself as a chronic condition which if untreated can last for years. It is only gradually attenuated by immunobiological processes. At intervals of several weeks or more this persistent tissue stage continues to produce fresh batches of trophozoites which are the

For classification of organisms see pages 721–724; for index of synonyms see pages 725–734

Malaria[1] *(Nos. 355–358) (continued)*

cause of the many relapses. The development of *vivax* malaria takes two distinct courses: the *tropical form* (India, south-west Pacific, tropical America, equatorial Africa, Mediterranean, Rome) has a short latent period of about one week between the first attack and the subsequent first relapse, after which further relapses follow fairly regularly at the above-mentioned intervals.

The *temperate-zone form* (Macedonia, northern Italy, Holland, central Russia, temperate zones of America, Madagascar, Korea) is characterized by a long latent period of 6–10 months between the first attack and the first relapse, the subsequent relapses then following, as in the tropical form, regularly at shorter intervals. Here it appears to be a case of adaptation of the Plasmodia life-cycle to a season unfavorable to transmission by mosquitoes.

In contrast to *falciparum* malaria, the *vivax* infection is therefore not amenable to treatment by drugs which destroy only the schizogonic phase of Plasmodia, and only the clinical symptoms of the attacks can be eliminated by this means. The avoidance of further relapses and the final eradication of the infection require either an agent which can be relied upon to destroy simultaneously both the tissue and schizogonic phases (such an agent has not yet been discovered) or the use of specific drugs for each of these two phases:

1. *Effective on tissue phase* (curative agents):	Primaquine Chlorguanide Pyrimethamine
2. *Effective on schizonts* (asexual blood phase; suppressive agents):	Chloroquine Amodiaquine Chlorguanide Pyrimethamine Quinacrine (Mepacrine) Quinine
3. *Effective on gametocytes* (sexual blood phase):	Primaquine Pamaquine Pentaquine Isopentaquine

Of the curative agents, primaquine is the drug of choice with respect to effectiveness, toxicity and also ease of administration. Of the suppressive agents, chloroquine and amodiaquine are about equally effective, about three times more so than quinacrine. Pyrimethamine is the only one of the above antimalarials which is tasteless. Cross resistance can develop between pyrimethamine and chlorguanide, a possibility which must be taken into account when pyrimethamine is used in areas where chlorguanide has already been given.

Treatment

Falciparum infections. Oral chloroquine: 1.0 g initially, 0.5 g 6–8 hours later, followed by 0.5 g on each of the two following days. In the event of complications developing, chloroquine should also be given parenterally.

Vivax infections. Combined treatment with chloroquine (dosage as above) plus primaquine (26.5 mg – for Negroes 15 mg – daily for 14 days). Treatment with primaquine should be stopped if signs of hemolytic anemia appear.

Prophylaxis. For suppression of febrile attacks in malarial districts: 0.5 g chloroquine once weekly; addition of chloroquine[2] or pyrimethamine[3] to table and cooking salt is also recommended.

Blackwater fever. When malaria parasites are present, chloroquine should be given without fail, either intramuscularly or intravenously. *Quinine and quinacrine are contraindicated.*

References

1) For reviews see Covell et al., *Chemotherapy of Malaria*, Geneva, 1955; Crowther, A. F., *J. Pharm. (Lond.)*, **10**, 337 (1958); Report, *Nature*, **190**, 971 (1961). *2)* Pinotti, M., *Triangle*, **4**, 110 (1959). *3)* Coatney et al., *Bull. Wld Hlth Org.*, **19**, 53 (1958).

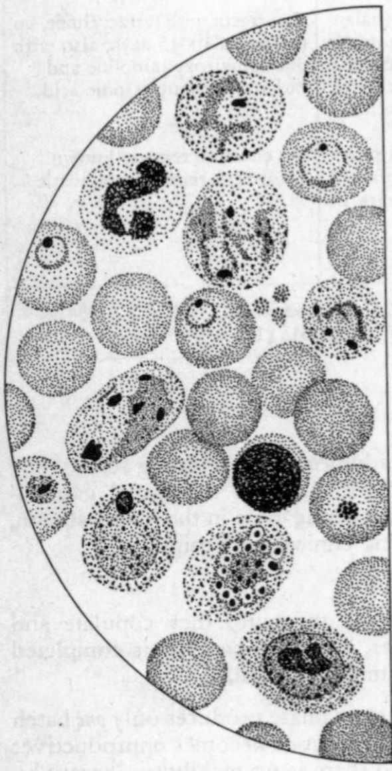

No. 355. Plasmodium vivax. Blood smear. Various stages of development are shown from top to bottom: ring forms, multinuclear stage, segmenters (16–24 nuclei); to the left and right of the segmenter are female and male gametocytes respectively. On the extreme left of the smear are two erythrocytes containing immature gametocytes. (After Piekarski, 1954.)

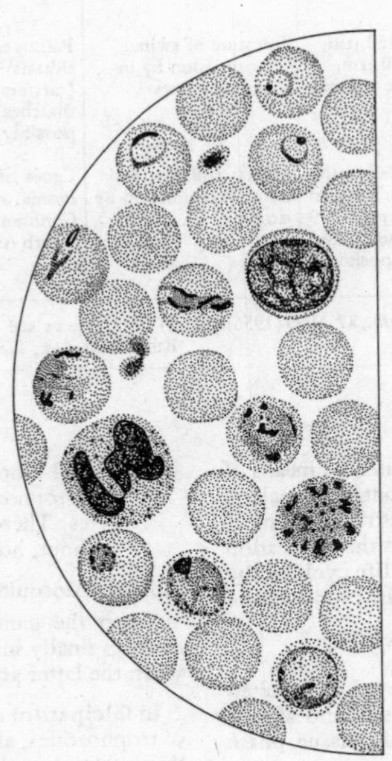

No. 356. Plasmodium malariae. Blood smear. Various stages of development are shown from top to bottom: ring forms, multinuclear band forms, segmenters ("daisy heads"); at the bottom from left to right are an immature, a male and a female gametocyte. (After Piekarski, 1954.)

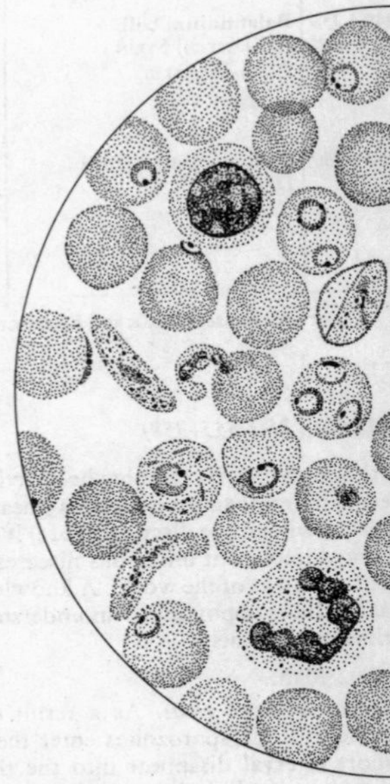

No. 358. Plasmodium falciparum. Blood smear showing only ring forms and sickle-shaped gametocytes. (After Piekarski, 1954.)

Helminths (worms) *(Nos. 361–395)*

The organisms listed in the table below and on pages 712–720 are those helminths which are important internal parasites of man and which belong to the phylla Platyhelminthes (flatworms) and Nemathelminthes (nematodes or roundworms). The Acanthocephala (spiny-headed worms) and Annelida (segmented worms including the leeches) are not included. See also the classification on page 724.

The importance of helminth infections in medicine is indicated by STOLL's 1947 estimate[1] of just over 2200 million individual major flatworm or roundworm infections among a world population of just under 2200 million. In this connection it should be noted that the term "infestation" is here used to denote infections in which the parasites do not multiply in the body of the host. As a rule therefore, infestations in man are only dangerous when the organisms succeed in entering the body in large numbers.

The data given in this table have been assembled from various standard works (see bibliography) and from papers in the current literature. For explanation of the numbers in columns 1 and 2 of the table see the introduction to the table of bacteria on page 646. The figures on pages 713 and 717 are mainly from PIEKARSKI[2].

References

1) STOLL, N. R., *J. Parasitol.*, **33**, 1 (1947). *2)* PIEKARSKI, G., *Lehrbuch der Parasitologie unter besonderer Berücksichtigung der Parasiten des Menschen*, Springer, Berlin 1954.

Bibliography (helminths)

BRUMPT, E., *Précis de Parasitologie*, 6th ed., Paris, 1949; CHANDLER, A. C., *Introduction to Parasitology*, 9th ed., New York, 1955; MACKIE et al., *Manual of Tropical Medicine*, 2nd ed., Philadelphia, 1954; PIEKARSKI, G., *loc. cit.*; CAMERON, T. W. M., *Parasites and Parasitism*, London, 1956; MACKETT et al., *Manual of Medical Helminthology*, London, 1954; MANSON-BAHR, P. H. (Ed.), *Manson's Tropical Diseases*, 15th ed., London, 1960; WATSON, J. M., *Medical Helminthology*, London, 1960; FAUST, E. C., *Ann. Rev. Microbiol.*, **12**, 103 (1958); WIGAND and MATTES, *Helminthen und Helminthiosen des Menschen*, Jena, 1958.

Platyhelminthes

See pages 721–724	See pages 725–734	Classified name / *Synonyms* / Common names	Principal characteristics	Habitat, host, transmission, etc.	Occurrence and associated diseases	Treatment and other remarks
251	*361*	**Fasciolopsis buski** (LANKESTER) ODHNER *Distomum buski, Distomum crassum, Fasciolopsis fülleborni* BUSK's fluke (großer Darmegel)	Length 2–7.5 cm. See the figure on page 713	**Intermediate host:** aquatic snails of the genus *Segmentina*. **Host:** man, pigs, dogs, goats. **Infestation:** by ingestion of red caltrop (*Trapa natans* in China, *T. bicornis* in eastern Bengal) and water chestnut *(Eleocharis tuberosa)* infected with the cysts	Fasciolopsiasis is endemic in China and some parts of India in all places where the nuts mentioned are often eaten. The fluke lives in the small intestine, causes local inflammation and excretes toxins; symptoms are hemorrhagic diarrhea, severe anemia, finally ascites and edema of the limbs and face. May be fatal	Immediately expelled by hexylresorcinol, thymol, chenopodium oil, carbon tetrachloride, tetrachloroethylene[1]. For a review of fasciolopsiasis see SADUN and MAIPHOOM[2]
251	*362*	**Fasciola hepatica** LINNÆUS *Distomum hepaticum, Fasciola humana, Fasciola californica, Fasciola halli* Common liver fluke, sheep liver fluke (grosser Leberegel)	Length 20–40 mm, width 8–13 mm. Similar to *Fasciolopsis buski* (above)	**Intermediate host:** snails of the genus *Galba*. **Host:** herbivora (sheep, oxen, goats, etc., rarely man). **Infestation:** by ingestion of plants infected with the cysts. Occurs mainly in Europe and western and northern Asia	Initially infection of the liver parenchyma (loss of blood, often secondary infections). The mature worms inhabit the bile ducts (chronic fascioliasis, with not very characteristic symptoms)	Readily expelled by emetine if treated early; also carbon tetrachloride or gentian violet. Chloroquine relieves symptoms but does not kill the flukes[3]. For a review of fascioliasis see FACEY and MARSDEN[3]
252	*363*	**Dicrocoelium dendriticum** (RUDOLPHI) LOOSS *Dicrocoelium lanceolatum, Distomum lanceatum, Distomum lanceolatum, Fasciola dendritica, Fasciola lanceolata* Lanceolate fluke (kleiner Leberegel)	Length 5–12 mm	**1st intermediate host:** snails of the genus *Helicella* and others. **2nd intermediate host:** plants (cercariae in slime-balls), ants (metacercariae). **Final host:** herbivora, especially sheep, rarely man	Occurrence associated with calcareous soils (snails). The ingested metacercariae bore through the intestinal wall and wander in the veins to the bile duct system of the liver. Symptoms of dicroceliasis are not characteristic (enlargement of the liver, anemia, loss of appetite, etc.)	No drug particularly effective. Stibophen, emetine, thymol may be tried
253	*364*	**Echinostoma ilocanum** (GARRISON) ODHNER *Euparyphium ilocanum, Fascioletta ilocana*	Length 2.5–6.5 mm, width 0.5–1.5 mm	**1st intermediate host:** snails *(Gyraulus prasbadi)*. **2nd intermediate host:** snails (*Pila luzonica*). **Final host:** rats; also man where the snails are eaten raw	Intestinal parasite, common in the Philippines, India, Java (echinostomiasis)	After thorough intestinal lavage, chenopodium oil, thymol, santonin, carbon tetrachloride, hexylresorcinol
254	*365*	**Heterophyes heterophyes** (VON SIEBOLD) STILES and HASSALL *Distoma heterophyes* GARRISON's fluke (Zwergdarmegel)	Length 1–1.7 mm, width 0.3–0.6 mm. See the figure on page 713	**1st intermediate host:** aquatic snails (in Egypt *Pirenella conica*). **2nd intermediate host:** marine mullet *(Mugil cephalus*, syn. *Mugil japonicus)*. **Final host:** cats, dogs, also man where the fish concerned are eaten raw	Heterophyiasis is common in Egypt, Palestine and the Far East. The worm inhabits the duodenum but causes no symptoms and may be considered a "normal" parasite. Severe infestations can cause mild digestive troubles and diarrhea	See remarks under *No. 364*. Piperazine appears effective[4]

1) KANT and RAMA, *Indian med. Gaz.*, **89**, 89 (1954). *2)* SADUN and MAIPHOOM, *Amer. J. trop. Med. Hyg.*, **2**, 1070 (1953). *3)* FACEY and MARSDEN, *Brit. med. J.*, **2**, 619 (1960). *4)* NAGATY and KHALIL, *Lancet*, **1**, 978 (1960).

For classification of organisms see pages 721–724; for index of synonyms see pages 725–734

See pages 721–724	See pages 725–734	**Platyhelminthes** Classified name *Synonyms* Common names	Principal characteristics	Habitat, host, transmission, etc.	Occurrence and associated diseases	Treatment and other remarks
254	*366*	**Metagonimus yokogawai** KATSURADA *Heterophyes yokogawai, Loossia dobrogiensis, Loossia parva, Loossia romanica, Loxotrema ovatum, Metagonimus ovatus* YOKOGAWA's fluke	Length 1–2.5 mm, width 0.4–0.7 mm	**1st intermediate host:** snails of the genus *Melania*. **2nd intermediate host:** freshwater fish (of the trout variety, especially *Plecoglossus altivelis*). **Final host:** cats, dogs and other fish-eating animals, also man where the fish concerned are eaten raw	Metagonimiasis is widespread in Japan, eastern Siberia and the Philippines. Also in Spain and the Balkan countries. Otherwise as for *No. 365*	See remarks under *No. 364*
255	*367*	**Opisthorchis tenuicollis** (RUDOLPHI) EJSMONT *Distoma felineum, Distoma tenuicollis, Opisthorchis felineus* Cat liver fluke, Siberian liver fluke (Katzenleberegel)	Length 5–8(12) mm, width 0.5–2.5 mm	**1st intermediate host:** snails of the species *Bithynia leachi*. **2nd intermediate host:** freshwater fish. **Final host:** cats, also man and dogs. **Infestation:** by ingestion of inadequately cooked fish	Opisthorchiasis is widespread in eastern Europe, Russia, Danube basin, Holland, lower courses of the Seine, etc. Disorders in the region of the bile ducts, gallbladder and liver, in severe cases cirrhosis of the liver. See also *No. 368*	No reliable remedy. Gentian violet and related dyes or stibophen may be tried
255	*368*	**Clonorchis sinensis** (COBBOLD) LOOSS *Distoma sinense, Opisthorchis sinensis* Chinese liver fluke, oriental liver fluke (chinesischer Leberegel)	Length 10–20 mm, width 3–5 mm. See the figure opposite	**1st intermediate host:** snails, especially *Parafossarulus striatulus*. **2nd intermediate host:** fish of the carp family *(Cyprinidae)*. **Final host:** dogs, cats, also man where the fish concerned are eaten raw	Clonorchiasis is widespread throughout the Orient, especially Japan, Canton, Indochina (bile ducts, sporadically also pancreatic ducts). Mild infestations are asymptomatic, more severe ones cause diarrhea (often hemorrhagic), edema, enlargement of the liver, anemia	See remarks under *No. 367*. Successful results have been obtained with chloroquine. For a review see references[1]
256	*369*	**Paragonimus westermani** (KERBERT) BRAUN *Distoma ringeri, Distoma westermani, Paragonimus compactus, Paragonimus kellicotti, Paragonimus ringeri* Oriental lung fluke (Lungenegel)	Length 8–16 mm, width about 6 mm. See the figure opposite	**1st intermediate host:** snails (*Melania libertina* in the Orient, *Pomatiopsis lapidaria* in North America and elsewhere). **2nd intermediate host:** crabs and crayfish. **Final host** (normal): cats, dogs, swine. **Infestation:** by ingestion of infected crabs and crayfish	Paragonimiasis is endemic in the Orient and Japan, sporadic in North America. Infestation of almost all organs possible, especially the lungs; parasitic or oriental hemoptysis, with symptoms suggestive of tuberculosis (bloody sputum) but not serious. In the brain causes symptoms of epilepsy and cerebral tumor and is fatal. Lung infestations heal after 5–6 years provided that fresh infestation does not occur. See also references[3]	*P. kellicotti* (North America) is probably identical with *P. westermani*. No reliable remedy known. Antimonials (parenteral) and combinations of sulfonamides and emetine have been successful, as also chloroquine[2]
257	*370*	**Schistosoma haematobium** (BILHARZ) WEINLAND *Bilharzia capensis, Bilharzia haematobia, Distoma haematobium, Gynaecophorus haematobius, Thecosoma haematobia* Blood fluke (Pärchenegel)	Males: length 8–16 mm, thickness 0.5 mm, with ventral groove *(gynecophoric canal)* in which the female is carried. Eggs 115–170 × 45–65 µm	**Intermediate host:** snails *(Physopsis africana, P. globosa*, in Egypt especially *Bulinus truncatus)*. **Host:** man	Bilharziasis (schistosomiasis) in Africa (especially Egypt, in about 60–85% of the population), Madagascar and southwest Asia. See remarks on page 714	See remarks on page 714
257	*371*	**Schistosoma japonicum** KATSURADA *Schistosoma cattoi* Asiatic blood fluke	Males 12–20 mm, females up to 26 mm. Eggs 70–100 × 50–65 µm	**Intermediate host:** snails: Amnicolidae *(Katayama, Oncomelania, Schistosomophora)*. **Host:** man	Bilharziasis (schistosomiasis) in the Orient including Japan, Philippines, Formosa and parts of China. See remarks on page 714	See remarks on page 714
257	*372*	**Schistosoma mansoni** SAMBON *Bilharzia mansoni, Schistosoma americanum*	Similar to *S. haematobium (No. 371)*. See the figure opposite	**Intermediate host:** Planorbis snails (in North Africa *Planorbis boissyi*, South Africa *Planorbis pfeifferi*, tropical America *Australorbis glabratus = Planorbis guadelupensis*). **Host:** man	Bilharziasis (schistosomiasis) in Africa and tropical America (in Venezuela up to 90% of the male population over 10 years of age). See remarks on page 714	See remarks on page 714
258	*373*	**Gastrodiscoides hominis** (LEWIS and MACCONNELL) LEIPER *Amphistomum hominis, Gastrodiscus hominis*	Length 4–8 mm, width 3–4 mm	Life cycle unknown. Normal host apparently the pig	Gastrodisciasis is widespread in India, especially Assam (up to 40% of the population), Indochina. Inhabits the cecum and large intestine and causes diarrhea	Chenopodium oil, santonin, carbon tetrachloride, etc. Enemas of soap and water

1) GERMER et al., *Z. Hyg. InfektKr.*, **141**, 132 (1955); EHRENWORTH and DANIELS, *Ann. intern. Med.*, **49**, 419 (1958). 2) CHUNG and HOU, *Chin. med. J.*, **72**, 407 (1954); BUCK et al., *Z. Tropenmed. Parasit.*, **9**, 310 (1958). 3) CHANG et al., *Chin. med. J.*, **77**, 3 (1958); THIELE, H.-G., *Dtsch. med. Wschr.*, **84**, 752 (1959).

For classification of organisms see pages 721–724; for index of synonyms see pages 725–734

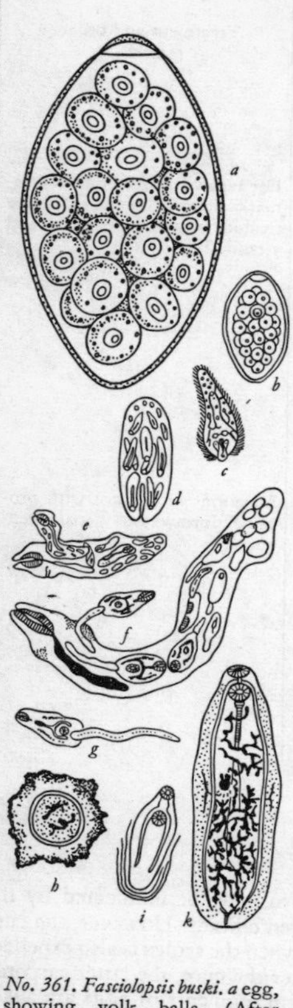

No. 361. Fasciolopsis buski. a egg, showing yolk balls. (After Looss, 1905.) *b* to *k* life cycle from snail (1st intermediate host, *b* to *f*), through red caltrop (*Trapa natans*, 2nd intermediate host, *h*) to man (final host, *h* to *k*). *b* unripe egg as laid; *c* free-swimming miracidium; *d* sporocyst with rediae; *e* mother redia containing daughter rediae; *f* daughter redia with cercariae; *g* free-swimming cercaria; *h* metacercaria; *i* metacercaria escaping from cyst in intestine; *k* adult fluke. (Different magnifications; after Piekarski, 1954.)

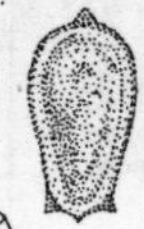

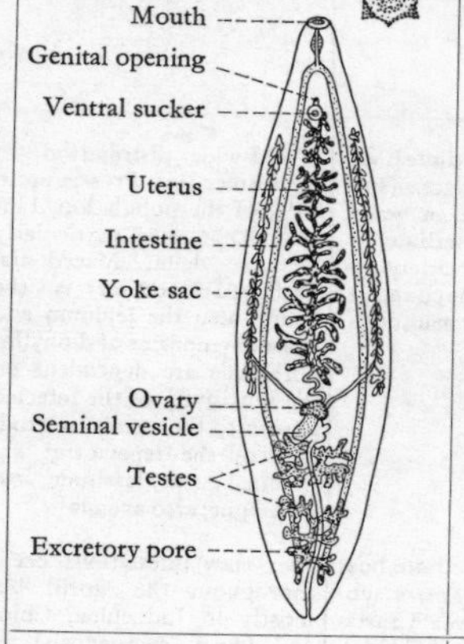

No. 368. Clonorchis sinensis. Right: egg; below: schematic arrangement of organs. (After Piekarski, 1954.)

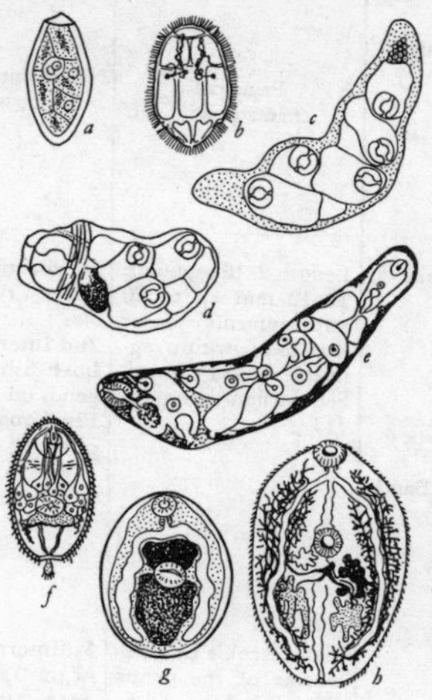

No. 369. Paragonimus westermani. Life cycle from snail (1st intermediate host, *b* to *e*), through crab or crayfish (2nd intermediate host, *f* and *g*) to man (final host for adult worm, *h*). *a* unripe egg as laid; *b* miracidium (only excretory system and ciliated flame cells shown); *c* mature sporocyst with mother rediae; *d* mature mother redia with daughter rediae; *e* mature daughter redia with cercariae; *f* free-swimming cercaria after leaving snail; *g* metacercaria from crab; *h* adult fluke. (Different magnifications; after Piekarski, 1954.)

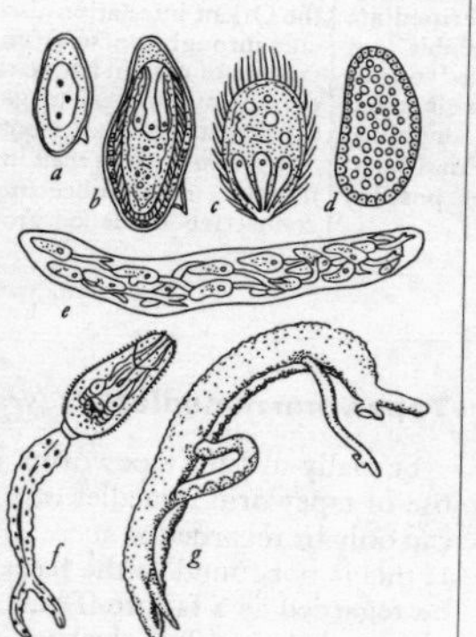

No. 372. Schistosoma mansoni. Life cycle from snail (intermediate host, *c* to *e*) to man (final host, which the cercariae [*f*] enter via the skin). *a* freshly laid egg from a vein; *b* excreted egg with miracidium; *c* miracidium; *d* young mother sporocyst with germ masses; *e* older daughter sporocyst with cercariae; *f* cercaria; *g* adult fluke. (Different magnifications; after Piekarski, 1954.)

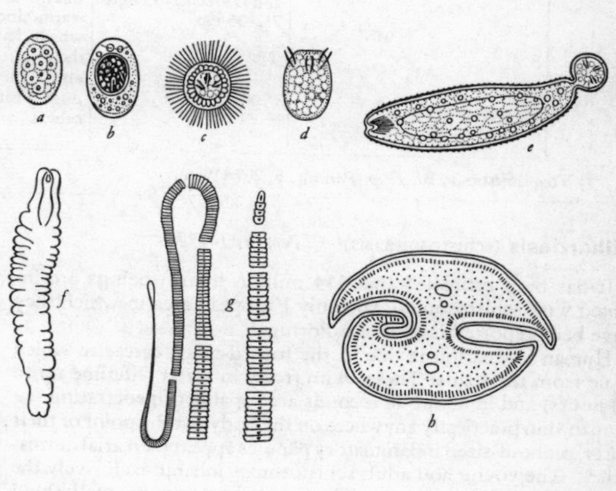

No. 374. Diphyllobothrium latum. Diagrammatic scheme of life cycle from *Cyclops* (1st intermediate host, *c* to *e*) through fish (2nd intermediate host with plerocercoid, *f*) to man (final host). *a* freshly laid egg; *b* egg with 6-hooked embryo (oncosphere); *c* coracidium; *d* free oncosphere from *Cyclops*; *e* mature procercoid; *f* plerocercoid; *g* adult tapeworm; *h* section through head. (Different magnifications; *a* to *g* after Piekarski, 1954, *h* after Braun.)

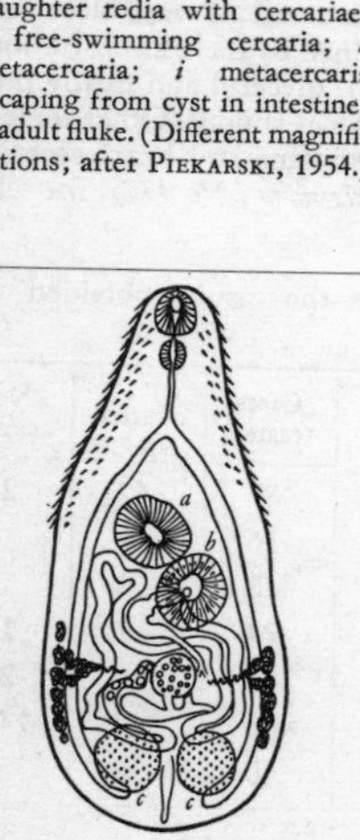

No. 365. Heterophyes heterophyes. a ventral sucker; *b* genital "sucker"; *c* two testes. (After Piekarski, 1954.)

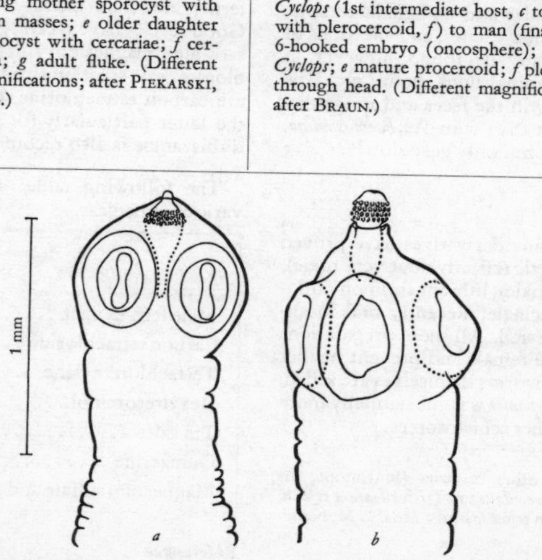

No. 376. Dipylidium caninum. Scolex of worm. *a* with retracted, *b* with protruded rostellum. (After Witenberg, 1932.)

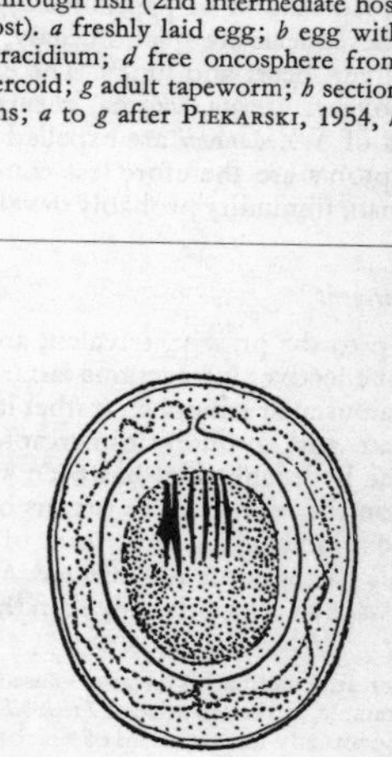

No. 377. Hymenolepis nana. Egg. (After Piekarski, 1954.)

For classification of organisms see pages 721–724; for index of synonyms see pages 725–734

See pages 721–724	See pages 725–734	**Platyhelminthes** Classified name *Synonyms* Common names	Principal characteristics	Habitat, host, transmission, etc.	Occurrence and associated diseases	Treatment and other remarks
259	*374*	**Diphyllobothrium latum** (LINNÆUS) LÜHE *Bothriocephalus latus, Dibothriocephalus latus, Diphyllobothrium parvum, Taenia lata* Broad tapeworm, fish tapeworm (ténia à épine, breiter Bandwurm, Fischbandwurm)	Length 2–10 m, width 10–12 mm up to 20 mm, segments broader than long, mature segments almost square. See the figure on page 713	**1st intermediate host:** lower Crustacea (species of *Diaptomus*). **2nd intermediate host:** fish (variety depends on the country). **Final host:** man, dogs, cats, etc.	World-wide distribution; in the former East Prussia up to 44% of the population, Finland 20%, also particularly Danube delta, Macedonia. Preferred location is the ileum, also the jejunum and colon. Symptoms of diphyllobothriasis are dependent on the sensitivity of the infected person to the metabolic products of the tapeworm: abdominal pains, lassitude, loss of weight; also anemia[1]	For tapeworm remedies see remarks below. Anemia should be treated with liver extracts and vitamin B_{12}
259	*375*	**Sparganum mansoni**	Plerocercoids of tapeworms of the genus *Diphyllobothrium* (subgenus *Spirometra*, very probably *D. mansoni* and *D. erinacei*). Length 7½–35 cm	**1st intermediate host** of the *Spirometra* subgenus: lower Crustacea (species of *Cyclops*). **2nd intermediate host:** amphibia or warm-blooded animals which have ingested the infested amphibia, also man. **Final host:** dogs, cats, possibly others	*Sparganum* infestations occur throughout the world but mostly in Indochina, China and Japan (sparganosis). In the Orient infestation also occurs through contact from the custom of certain native races of putting skinned frogs on inflammations and wounds. *Sparganum* lives in man in the muscles, in the subcutaneous connective tissue or around the eyes	Injections of ethanol with procaine. Intravenous neoarsphenamine

1) VON BONSDORF, B., *Exp. Parasit.*, **5**, 207 (1956).

Bilharziasis (schistosomiasis)[1,2] *(Nos. 370–372)*

It has been estimated that 114 million human beings are infected with schistosomes. The only European area in which they have been reported is southern Portugal.

Human infestation is due to the forked-tailed cercariae which issue from the snails. These swim freely in water (lifetime up to 60 hours) and in about 10 seconds are capable of penetrating the human skin practically anywhere on the body. At the point of their entry, pinhead-sized inflammatory papules appear (cercarial dermatitis*). The young and adult schistosomes inhabit exclusively the mesenteric and pelvic veins. The female lays eggs in small blood vessels, whence they gradually work their way into the intestine and urinary bladder and pass out in the feces and urine. *Sch. haematobium* causes mainly inflammation of the urogenital system, hematuria (formation of papillomata), fistulas and malignant tumors. Other sequelae are splenomegaly, anemia, ascites, and affections of the liver, heart and lungs. The eggs are also found, however, in the ovary, uterus, vagina, cervix, seminal fluid, brain, etc. The eggs of *Sch. mansoni* are expelled only in the feces and urogenital symptoms are therefore less common than with *Sch. haematobium*. In man, immunity probably develops, but only very slowly.

Treatment

Up to the present, trivalent antimony derivatives have proved most effective: intravenous tartar emetic (effective but very toxic), intramuscular stibophen (rather less toxic), lithium antimony thiomalate and antimony dimercaptosuccinate. Recently oral lucanthone hydrochloride[3] has been suggested. All these preparations act on the reproductive organs of the female and prevent further deposition of eggs. Only some of the worms themselves are killed, while the eggs are not affected. *Sch. japonicum* is substantially more resistant to chemotherapy than the other schistosomes.

* Cercarial dermatitis is also caused by other cercariae (in Europe, for example, by the cercariae of *Trichobilharzia ocellata* and *Trichobilharzia szidati*, the sexually-mature forms of which live in aquatic birds. See also MCNEIL[1].

References

1) MCNIEL, J. R., *Medicinal Times*, **85**, 159 (1957). *2)* DIAZ-RIVERA, R. S., *Amer. J. Med.*, **21**, 918 (1956). *3)* KING, B. A., *Brit. med. J.*, **1**, 185 (1955); ALVES, W., *Bull. Wld Hlth Org.*, **18**, 1109 (1958).

Tapeworm remedies[1–4] *(Nos. 374–380)*

Sexually-mature tapeworms can usually be eliminated by the use of tapeworm remedies of proven efficacy. However, the cure can only be regarded as successful when the scolex is also expelled. If this is not found in the feces after the cure, the latter can only be regarded as a failure if tapeworm segments or eggs are again observed about 12 weeks later. It is important that the remedy be taken after 12 hours' fasting and that it be followed by a strong purgative to empty the intestine.

Pumpkin seeds are a harmless remedy for children or may be taken by adults as a preliminary treatment. Also harmless and effective are tin salts (SnO, $SnCl_2$), and quinacrine has also proved successful[3,4]. Side effects (nausea, vomiting) can be lessened by giving sodium bicarbonate. The commonly used extract of male fern (Extractum filicis) is rather toxic and of variable efficacy. Good results have recently been obtained by the administration of saturated magnesium sulfate solution, glycerol and finally physiological salt solution through a duodenal sound[1]. Other remedies are carbon tetrachloride, tetrachlorethylene and hexylresorcinol, the latter particularly for *Hymenolepsis nana (No. 377)*, for which dithiazanine is also recommended[4].

The following table[1] summarizes the results obtained with various remedies:

	Cases treated	Cured	Not cured
Male fern extract	87	62	25
Carbon tetrachloride	16	12	4
Tetrachlorethylene	8	3	5
Hexylresorcinol	24	7	17
Tin salts	202	180	22
Quinacrine	488	347	141
Magnesium sulfate and glycerol	40	36	4

References

1) ROSEN and KIEFER, *J. Amer. med. Ass.*, **167**, 2065 (1958). *2)* HENNEMANN and D'HEUREUSE, *Ther. Gegenwart*, **97**, 1 (1958). *3)* SODEMAN and JUNG, *J. Amer. med. Ass.*, **148**, 285 (1952). *4)* CHOWDHURY, A. B., in CONN, H. F. (Ed.), *Current Therapy 1961*, Philadelphia and London, 1961, page 18.

For classification of organisms see pages 721–724; for index of synonyms see pages 725–734

Platyhelminthes

See pages 721–724	See pages 725–734	Classified name *Synonyms* Common names	Principal characteristics	Habitat, host, transmission, etc.	Occurrence and associated diseases	Treatment and other remarks
260	*376*	**Dipylidium caninum** (LINNÆUS) RAILLIET *Dipylidium cucumerinum,* *Taenia canina,* *Taenia cucumerina* Common dog tapeworm (Gurkenkernbandwurm)	Length 15–40 cm, width up to 3 mm, mature segments reddish colored. See the figure on page 713	**Intermediate host:** dog louse *(Trichodectes canis)*, dog flea *(Ctenocephalides canis)*, also human flea. **Final host:** dogs, cats, foxes, man. **Infestation:** by ingestion of infested dog fleas or dog lice	In man, dipylidiasis is rare and mainly in children. Inhabits the small intestine, usually without causing symptoms	For tapeworm remedies see remarks opposite
261	*377*	**Hymenolepis nana** (VON SIEBOLD) BLANCHARD *Hymenolepis fraterna,* *Taenia aegyptica,* *Taenia murina,* *Taenia nana* Dwarf tapeworm (Zwergbandwurm)	Length up to 40 mm, width up to 1 mm, characteristic elliptical eggs of maximum size 50×40 µm. See the figure on page 713	**Host:** man *(H. nana)*, rodents *(H. fraterna)*. Development proceeds without an intermediate host. **Infestation:** oral ingestion of eggs voided with the feces	Hymenolepiasis is world-wide but less common in areas with moderate and cold climates. In children occasionally causes severe toxic symptoms	For tapeworm remedies see remarks opposite
262	*378*	**Taenia solium** LINNÆUS *Taenia dentata* Armed tapeworm, measly tapeworm, pork tapeworm (ténia armé, ver solitaire, Einsiedlerbandwurm, Schweinebandwurm)	Length 2–3 m, proglottids 1 m behind the head; square, mature proglottids 10–12 mm long, 5–6 mm wide. See the figure on page 717	**Host:** man (tapeworm). **Intermediate host:** swine and man (cysticercus: *Cysticercus cellulosae*). The oncosphere developing from the ingested egg in the intermediate host (swine, but also man) penetrates into the muscles and there develops into a cysticercus. **Infestation:** by ingestion of meat containing cysticerci, which develop in the human intestine into tapeworms. In man, infestation can also take place by ingestion of the eggs, which then develop into cysticerci in the muscles. It is also possible that these cysticerci may originate from proglottids regurgitated into the stomach	Abdominal pains, abnormal appetite, weakness and loss of weight are the commonest symptoms of taeniasis. The pathogenicity has been rather exaggerated, and the majority of infestations with *T. solium* and *T. saginata* are asymptomatic. Infestations occur chiefly where pork is eaten, especially in Europe. It is remarkable that *T. solium* is very rare in North America, the Philippines and India in spite of the widespread consumption of pork. Cysticerci are often found in human carriers of the tapeworm and may be found in all organs, especially at the base of the brain (cysticercosis). Here they often show a branched structure *(Cysticercus racemosus)*	For tapeworm remedies see remarks opposite
262	*379*	**Taenia saginata** GOEZE *Taenia bremneri, Taenia confusa, Taenia hominis, Taenia mediocanellata, Taeniorhynchus saginatus* Beef tapeworm, fat tapeworm, unarmed tapeworm (ténia inerme, Rinderbandwurm, unbewaffneter Bandwurm)	Length 4–10 m, mature segments in the form of pumpkin seeds, 16–20 mm long, 4–7 mm wide. See the figure on page 717	**Host:** man (tapeworm). **Intermediate host:** cattle (cysticercus: *Cysticercus bovis, Cysticercus inermis*). Development as for *T. solium*	Pathogenicity as for *T. solium*. It is the commonest tapeworm and has a world-wide distribution. In Africa, Tibet and Syria infests 25–75% of the population. In India very rare (Hindu religion forbids consumption of beef). Cysticerci of *T. saginata* are very rare in man	For tapeworm remedies see remarks opposite. *T. saginata* is more difficult to expel than *T. solium*
262	*380*	**Multiceps multiceps** (LESKE) HALL *Coenurus cerebralis,* *Multiceps gaigeri,* *Polycephalus ovinus,* *Taenia coenurus,* *Taenia multiceps* (Quesenbandwurm)	Length ½–1 m. Develops multiple heads in the cysticercal stage *(Coenurus)*	**Host:** dogs and other carnivores. **Intermediate host:** sheep, man. Infestation by ingestion of the mature eggs. The coenurus develops in the brain, more rarely in the spinal cord	Cause of staggers (gid) in sheep. World-wide distribution, very rare in man (central Europe, South Africa, U.S.A.). Symptoms are epileptic attacks, severe headache, coma	For tapeworm remedies see remarks opposite
262	*381*	**Echinococcus granulosus** (BATSCH) RUDOLPHI *Echinococcus alveolaris,* *Echinococcus cysticus,* *Echinococcus multilocularis,* *Hydatigena granulosa,* *Taenia echinococcus* Case worm, dwarf dog tapeworm, hydatid tapeworm (ténia échinocoque, Hunde[band]wurm)	Length 3–6 mm, only 3–4 segments. See the figure on page 717	**Host** (tapeworm): dogs, wolves, coyotes and related species, with often up to thousands in the intestine. **Intermediate host** (cysticercus): practically all warm-blooded animals, especially herbivores. Infestation by ingestion of the eggs	Echinococciasis is world-wide, especially in countries with intensive rearing of sheep and cattle. Cysticercosis occurs in almost all organs, especially in the liver, and has two forms: (*a*) *Echinococcus cysticus:* typical bladders (hydatids) with endogenous daughter bladders; symptoms mostly uncharacteristic, with enlargement of liver and spleen, etc., but dangerous complications may arise when a liver cyst breaks into the abdominal cavity; world-wide distribution. (*b*) *Echinococcus alveolaris:* sponge-like mass without hydatid fluid; infiltrative growth with extensive destruction of the liver parenchyma and jaundice; distribution relatively restricted (southern Germany, the Alps, Russia, Siberia)	Surgical removal when possible. Probably there are two species[1]: *E. granulosus (= E. cysticus)* and *E. multilocularis (= E. alveolaris)*. For reviews see references[1,2]

1) KATZ and PAN, *Amer. J. Med.*, **25**, 759 (1958). *2)* WEGMANN and FÜRST, *Schweiz. med. Wschr.*, **89**, 32 (1959).

For classification of organisms see pages 721–724; for index of synonyms see pages 725–734

See pages 721–724	See pages 725–734	**Nemathelminthes** Classified name *Synonyms* Common names	Principal characteristics	Habitat, host, transmission, etc.	Occurrence and associated diseases	Treatment and other remarks
263	*382*	**Trichuris trichiura** (LINNÆUS) STILES *Ascaris trichiura, Trichocephalus dispar, Trichocephalus hominis, Trichocephalus suis, Trichocephalus trichiuris* Whipworm (Haarschopf, Peitschenwurm)	Length 30–50 mm. The tail end of the body of the male is curled. Eggs 50 × 22 μm. See the figure opposite	Very widely distributed in man and swine. Inhabits large and small intestine. Infestation by ingestion of eggs in contaminated water, and from soil, particularly via the hands. Often occurs together with *Ascaris lumbricoides (No. 388)*	Trichuriasis symptoms are mostly not severe: abdominal pains as in appendicitis, digestive disturbances, loss of appetite, loss of weight, etc. Heavy infestations cause severe diarrhea and anemia	Trichurids are very difficult to remove since they are too deep in the intestine to be reached by anthelmintics in sufficient concentration and too high up for the worms to be reached by enemas. Drug of choice *in patients with overt symptoms:* dithiazanine[1–3]. The following have been used with limited success: tetrachlorethylene, chenopodium oil, hexylresorcinol, emetine hydrochloride, piperazine derivatives. Enzyme preparations (from the milky sap of various fig trees) have also proved efficacious. See also references[4]
264	*383*	**Trichinella spiralis** (OWEN) RAILLIET *Trichina spiralis* Pork worm, trichina worm (Trichine)	Males 1.5 mm long, 0.04 mm thick; females 3–4 mm long, 0.06 mm thick	The embryos born from the trichinas living in the intestine of the host wander, partly actively, partly passively, into the blood and lymph streams all over the body and finally settle in the striated muscles, where they coil themselves up. The tissue around them reacts by the formation of a connective tissue capsule, which ultimately becomes calcified. Infestation by consumption of infected meat raw or insufficiently-cooked. **Host:** in addition to man, rats (normal host), swine, bears, dogs, etc. World-wide distribution; in about 20% of the U.S. population[5]	The intestinal trichinas developing from ingested muscle trichinas cause intestinal inflammation with diarrhea and fever (typhoid type). The migration of the trichinas into the muscles is followed by muscle and joint pains and a rise of temperature (rheumatic form), later by loss of tendon reflexes, difficulty in breathing, capillary hemorrhages in the eyes, edema of eyelids and knuckles. Eosinophilia and leukocytosis occur about 1–3 weeks after infection. Trichinosis results in the formation of specific antibodies, and true immunity in man is very probable	Treatment is only likely to be successful in the intestinal stage of trichina infection: diethylcarbamazine, piperazine citrate. Symptomatic therapy with ACTH and corticosteroids[11]
265	*384*	**Ancylostoma duodenale** (DUBINI) CREPLIN *Dochmius duodenalis, Sclerostoma duodenale, Uncinaria duodenalis* Assassin worm, hookworm (anquilostoma, Grubenwurm, Hakenwurm)	Males 10 mm long, 0.5 mm thick; females 12–15 mm long. See the figure opposite	The filariform juveniles from soil and water penetrate the skin and by way of the blood stream reach the heart and lungs and thence the trachea, pharynx, stomach and small intestine, where they develop into the adult worm. World-wide distribution	Ancylostomiasis: The worm inhabits the small intestine of man where, buried deep in the mucosa, it feeds by sucking blood. The loss of blood caused by the constant blood-sucking causes severe anemia. Symptoms: *Preintestinal phase:* penetration of the larvae into the skin (cutaneous *larva migrans*[8]) causes pruritus or inflammation ("ground itch", "water sore"), also secondary bacterial invasion. Migration in the body may cause pneumonia, eosinophilia and occasionally leukocytosis. *Intestinal phase:* infestation is followed after several weeks by anemia, the symptoms being lassitude, muscular weakness, breathlessness on exertion, edema, enlargement of the heart and palpitation, flatulence, abdominal disturbances. In children growth is retarded and mental alertness impaired. Hookworm infestation during pregnancy is the cause of many stillbirths	Treatment with tetrachlorethylene[3] (contraindicated in hepatitis) alone or combined with dithiazanine[2] has given the best results. Recently bephenium salts[2,6] have proved equally effective. Other remedies for hookworm are carbon tetrachloride and hexylresorcinol, the latter also in combination with chenopodium oil. Iron should be given for anemia (parenterally when diarrhea is present), also vitamins and a protein-rich diet. For a review see DESENNE[7]

For bibliographical references see page 718.

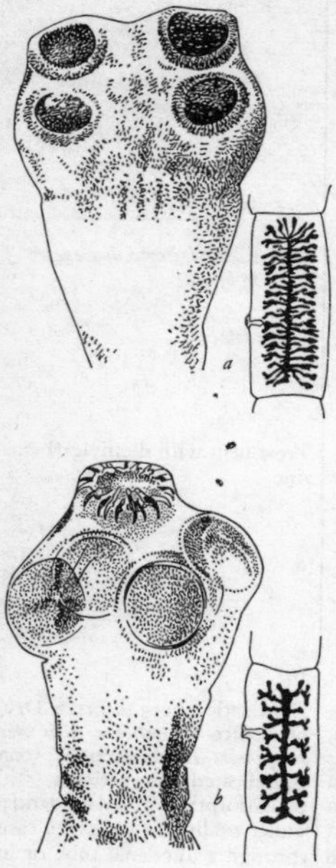

No. 379. Taenia saginata (*a*).
No. 378. Taenia solium (*b*).
Left: Head. (After Szidat and Wigand, 1934.) Right: Tapeworm segments with branching uterus filled with eggs. (After Ribbert-Hamperl, 1944.)

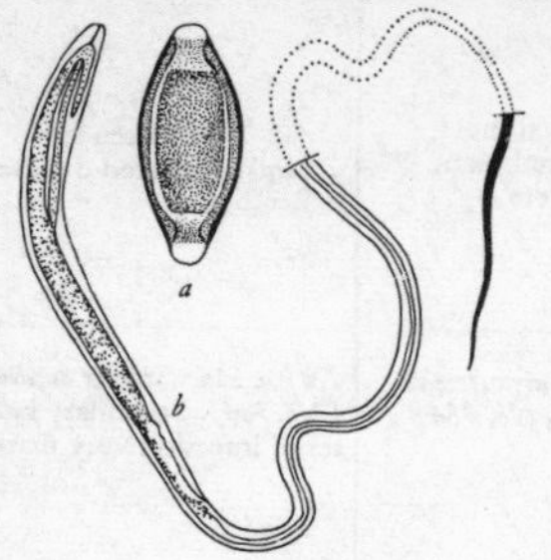

No. 382. Trichuris trichiura.
a egg; *b* complete worm. The head is at the slender end; the dotted section lies in the intestinal mucosa. (After Faust, 1930.)

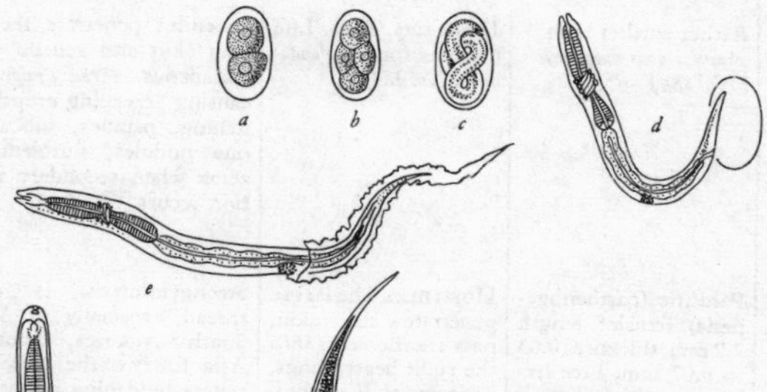

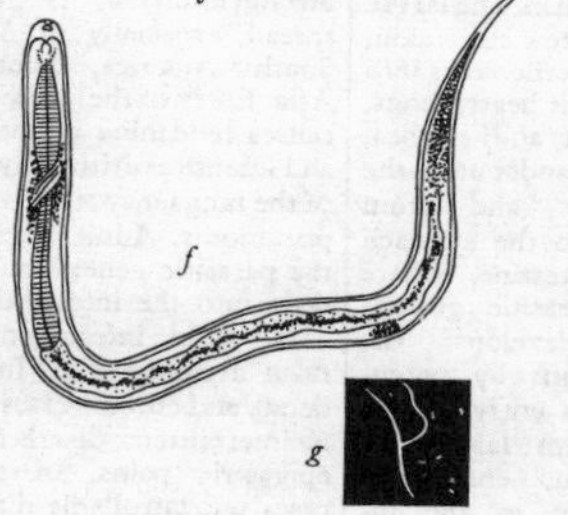

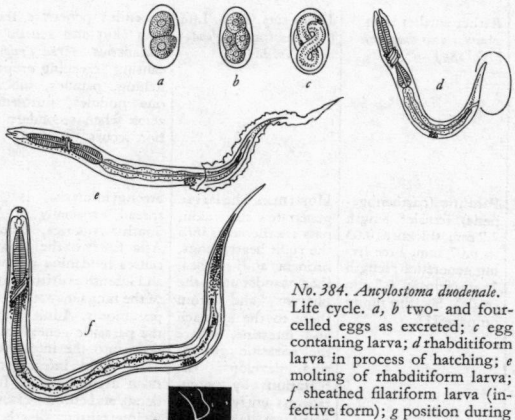

No. 384. Ancylostoma duodenale.
Life cycle. *a, b* two- and four-celled eggs as excreted; *c* egg containing larva; *d* rhabditiform larva in process of hatching; *e* molting of rhabditiform larva; *f* sheathed filariform larva (infective form); *g* position during copulation. (Different magnifications; after Piekarski, 1954.)

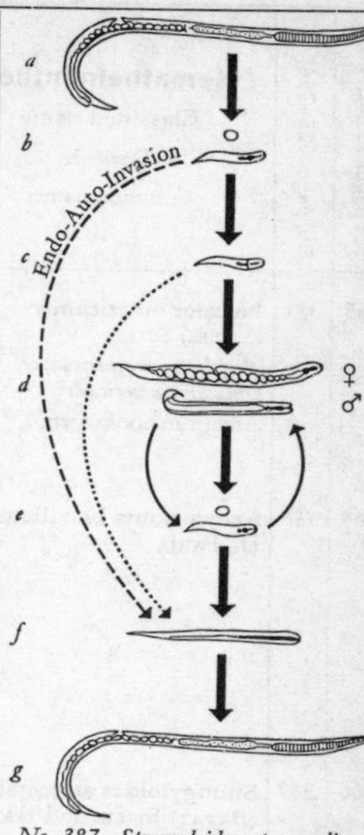

No. 387. Strongyloides stercoralis.
Life cycle. *a, b, c, d, e, f, g* indirect development; *a, b, c, f, g* direct development (exo-auto-invasion in the anal region). *a* parthenogenetic female (in intestine); *b* egg and rhabditiform larva (in intestine); *c* rhabditiform larva (free-living); *d* bisexual generation (free-living); *e* egg and rhabditiform larva (free-living); *f* filariform larva; *g* parthenogenetic female (in intestine). (After Piekarski, 1954.)

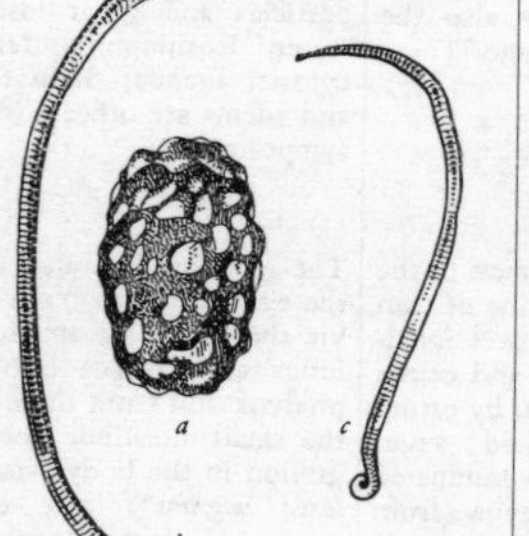

No. 388. Ascaris lumbricoides.
a egg (external appearance); *b* female worm; *c* male worm. (After Szidat and Wigand.)

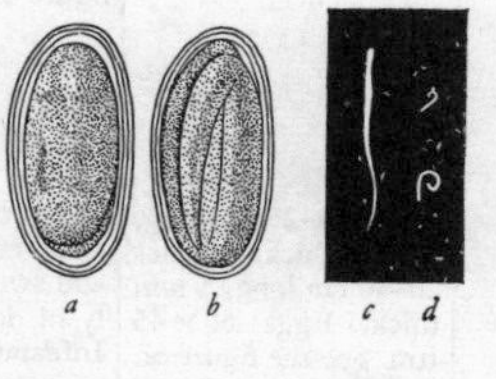

No. 389. Enterobius vermicularis.
a freshly laid egg, so-called tadpole stage; *b* infective larva in egg capsule; *c, d* mature worms, natural size: *c* female, *d* two males. (*a* and *b* after Piekarski, 1954; *c* and *d* after Ribbert-Hamperl, 1944.)

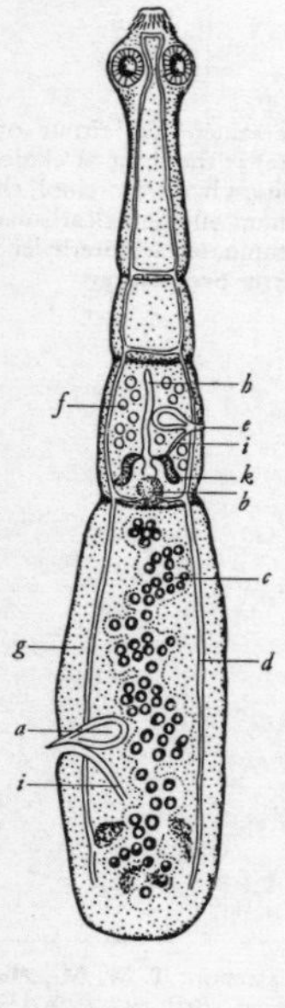

No. 381. Echinococcus granulosus.
Adult worm. *a* cirrus sac; *b* yolk sac; *c* eggs; *d* excretory canal; *e* genital orifice; *f* testes; *g* mature segment; *h* uterus; *i* vagina; *k* ovary. (After Piekarski, 1954.)

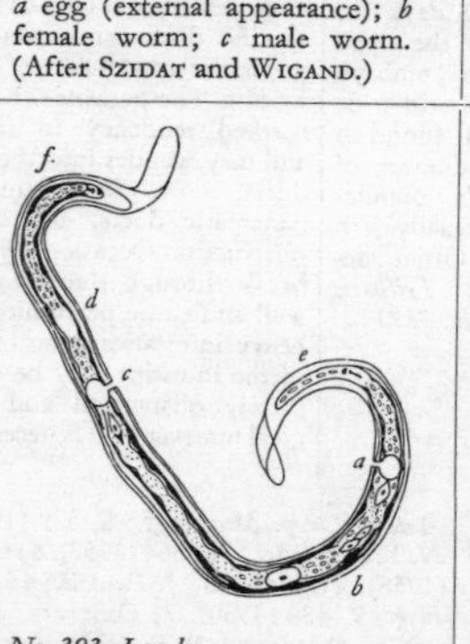

No. 393. Loa loa.
Sheathed microfilaria. *a* anus; *b* intestine; *c* excretory pore; *d* nerve ring; *e* tail end; *f* head end. (After Piekarski, 1954.)

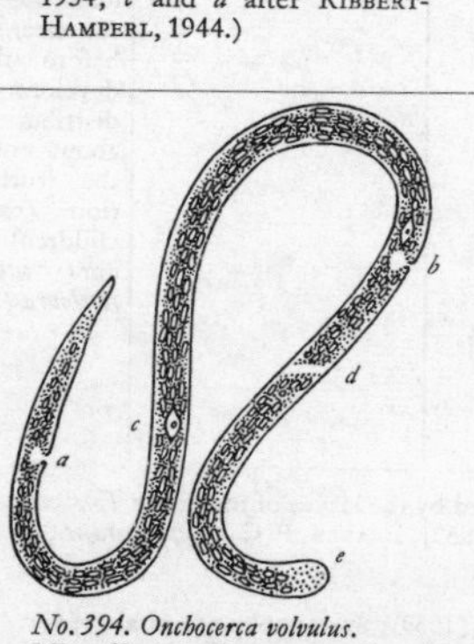

No. 394. Onchocerca volvulus.
Microfilaria without sheath. *a* anal pore; *b* excretory pore; *c* genital cell; *d* nerve ring; *e* head end. (After Faust.)

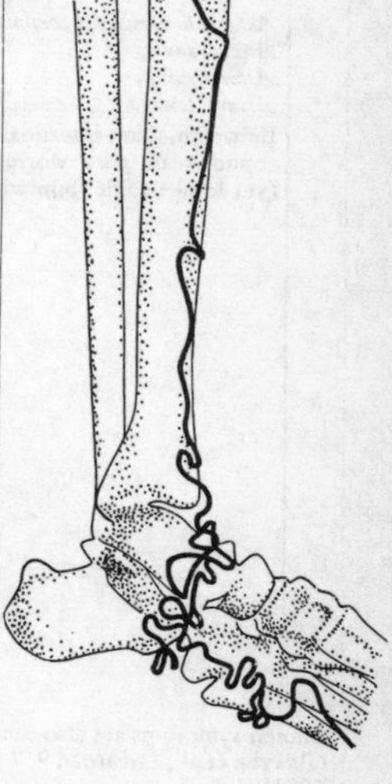

No. 395. Dracunculus medinensis.
X-Ray photograph of worm injected with contrast medium in an infested joint. (After Botreau-Roussel.)

For classification of organisms see pages 721–724; for index of synonyms see pages 725–734

See pages 721–724	See pages 725–734	**Nemathelminthes** Classified name *Synonyms* Common names	Principal characteristics	Habitat, host, transmission, etc.	Occurrence and associated diseases	Treatment and other remarks
265	*385*	**Necator americanus** (Stiles) Stiles *Ancylostoma americanum,* *Uncinaria americana* American hookworm	Rather smaller than *Ancylostoma duodenale (No. 384)*, but otherwise morphologically very similar	As for *Ancylostoma duodenale (No. 384)*	As for *Ancylostoma duodenale (No. 384)*. Secondary bacterial infection very marked	As for *Ancylostoma duodenale (No. 384)*
265	*386*	**Ancylostoma braziliense** De Faria	Rather smaller than *Ancylostoma duodenale (No. 384)*	**Host:** cats, dogs. Life cycle as for *A. duodenale (No. 384)*	Juveniles penetrate the human skin and remain there (cutaneous *larva migrans*[8]), causing "creeping eruption": itching, papules, subcutaneous nodules, purulent eczema when secondary infection occurs	Treatment with diethylcarbamazine
266	*387*	**Strongyloides stercoralis** (Bavay) Stiles and Hassall *Anguillula intestinalis,* *Anguillula stercoralis,* *Strongyloides intestinalis* (Zwergfadenwurm)	Parasitic (parthenogenetic) female: length 2.2 mm, thickness 0.03 to 0.07 mm. Free-living generation: length 1 mm (female), 0.7 mm (male). See the figure on page 717	**Host:** man. The larvae penetrate the skin, pass via the veins into the right heart, lungs, bronchi and trachea, then wander into the pharynx and from there to the stomach and intestine, where the parasitic generation develops. **Infestation:** by percutaneous entry of the filariform larvae. In addition, endo-autoinvasion in the intestine and exo-autoinvasion in the anal region. See also the figure on page 717	Strongyloidiasis is widespread, especially in Africa, South America, southeast Asia. Entry of the larvae often causes reddening of the skin and intense pruritus. Invasion of the lungs may lead to acute pneumonia. Adult worms of the parasitic generation bore deep into the intestinal mucosa. Mild infestations remain asymptomatic. In moderate and chronic cases there is intermittent diarrhea and epigastric pains, in severe cases uncontrollable diarrhea (often hemorrhagic) with voiding of undigested food particles and great loss of water. Eosinophilia, leukocytosis, anemia, slight fever and edema are other possible symptoms	Elimination very difficult. Drug of choice *in patients with overt symptoms:* dithiazanine[2,3] (contraindicated in patients with malabsorption[10]). Also gentian violet orally, or in severe cases through a duodenal tube or intravenously
267	*388*	**Ascaris lumbricoides** Linnæus *Ascaris lumbricoides hominis,* *Ascaris suum,* *Ascaris suilla,* *Ascaris texana* Eelworm, giant intestinal roundworm, maw worm (ver lombricoïde, Spulwurm)	Males 14–25 cm long, 3 mm thick, females 20–40 cm long, 5 mm thick. Eggs 60 × 45 µm. See the figure on page 717	**Host:** common in the small intestine of man and swine, occasionally in dogs and cattle. **Infestation:** by eating of uncooked vegetables contaminated with the eggs (from liquid manure). Autoinfection is impossible since the eggs passed in the feces must lie at least 30–40 days (in summer) in the open before the embryo develops. World-wide distribution; found in about one-quarter of the world's population (especially in children). Often occurs with *Trichuris trichiura (No. 382)*	The embryos liberated from the eggs in the stomach pass via the blood stream, heart, lungs and trachea into the pharynx and from there into the small intestine. The migration in the body (visceral *larva migrans**) may cause pneumonia but certainly always eosinophilia. Symptoms of ascariasis depend on severity of infestation and on allergic sensitivity; also on nonspecific disturbances due to metabolic products of the worms. The parasites show a marked tendency to travel and may wander into the bile ducts, more rarely into the pancreatic ducts, and cause obstruction. Occasionally they break through the intestinal wall and cause peritonitis. In heavy infestations the lumen of the intestine may be completely obstructed and surgical intervention is necessary	Piperazine[3,9] (as citrate or hydrate) is the drug of choice. In addition hexylresorcinol, chenopodium oil, diethylcarbamazine, santonin, tetrachlorethylene and enzyme preparations

* Similar symptoms are also caused by the larvae of the genus *Toxocara* (Beaver et al., *Pediatrics*, **9**, 7 [1952]; Beaver, P. C., *Exp. Parasit.*, **5**, 587 [1956]).

1) Paine et al., *Brit. med. J.*, **1**, 93 (1959); Swartzwelder et al., *Amer. J. trop. Med. Hyg.*, **7**, 329 (1958). *2)* Swartzwelder et al., *J. Amer. med. Ass.*, **165**, 2063 (1957). *3)* Chowdhury, A. B., in Conn, H. F. (Ed.), *Current Therapy 1961*, Philadelphia and London, 1961, page 18. *4)* Culbertson, J. T., *Med. Clin. N. Amer.*, **40**, 527 (1956); Hoekenga, M. T., *Amer. J. trop. Med. Hyg.*, **5**, 529 (1956). *5)* Cameron, T. W. M., *Ann. N. Y. Acad. Sci.*, **70**, 564 (1958). *6)* Goodwin et al., *Brit. med. J.*, **2**, 1572 (1958); Young et al., *J. Parasit.*, **44**, 611 (1958), and *Amer. J. trop. Med. Hyg.*, **9**, 488 (1960). *7)* Desenne, J. J., *Med. Tms (Lond.)*, **85**, 1027. (1957). *8)* Beaver, P. C., *Exp. Parasit.*, **5**, 587 (1956). *9)* Culbertson, J. T., *Med. Clin. N. Amer.*, **40**, 527 (1956); Goodwin and Standen, *Brit. med. J.*, **1**, 131 (1958). *10)* Stemmermann and Nakasone, *J. Amer. med. Ass.*, **174**, 1250 (1960). *11)* Sadusk, J. F., in Conn, H. F. (Ed.), *Current Therapy 1961*, Philadelphia and London, 1961, page 60.

See pages 721–724	See pages 725–734	**Nemathelminthes** Classified name / *Synonyms* / Common names	Principal characteristics	Habitat, host, transmission, etc.	Occurrence and associated diseases	Treatment and other remarks
268	*389*	**Enterobius vermicularis** (LINNÆUS) LEACH *Ascaris vermicularis, Oxyuris vermicularis* Pinworm, seatworm, threadworm (Madenwurm, Pfriemenschwanz)	Males 2–5 mm, females 8–13 mm long. Eggs 55 × 30 μm. See the figure on page 717	**Host:** man. The eggs are deposited in the perianal region, pass by auto-infection into the mouth (via fingernails, etc.). World-wide distribution; in many places (Holland, Germany, etc.) up to 100% of the population are infected. Especially common in school children	Enterobiasis: The nocturnal movements of the worms, which leave the rectum to lay eggs, cause severe pruritus. The itching thus caused leads repeatedly to fresh infections. The adult worm lives in the colon, cecum and neighboring regions. The males remain there and die soon after fertilization, whilst the females wander into the rectum to lay eggs. Exceptionally the worms pass into the vagina. Infestation may be asymptomatic	Treatment with piperazine citrate[2], dithiazanine[1–3] or pyrvinium salts[2,4,5]. Good results also obtained with tetracyclines, gentian violet; also sulfonamides, phenothiazines, tetrachlorethylene. Treatment should always include the whole family. Strict personal and family hygiene are important in prophylaxis
269	*390*	**Gnathostoma spinigerum** OWEN *Cheiracanthus robustus, Cheiracanthus siamensis*	Females 30–54 mm, males 11–24 mm long. About 1–3 mm wide	**1st intermediate host:** crustacea *(Cyclops)*. **2nd intermediate host:** fish. **Final host:** dogs, cats. In man only immature worms are found. Occurs in Thailand and southern Japan	Gnathostomiasis: the worm passes the intestinal wall and wanders throughout the body. Symptoms: swellings in the skin and mucous membranes, prickling pain, moderate eosinophilia; hematuria if the worms pass into the bladder	Operative removal from the skin. Diethylcarbamazine
270	*391*	**Wuchereria bancrofti** (COBBOLD) SEURAT *Filaria bancrofti, Filaria nocturna, Filaria sanguinis hominis, Filaria philippinensis, Filaria wuchereri* BANCROFT's filaria (filaire de BANCROFT)	Females about 83 mm long, 0.25 mm thick. Males about half as long. Microfilariae ca. 260 μm long	**Host:** man. **Transmission:** by mosquitoes; in most regions *Culex quinquefasciatus*, in Java *Anopheles ludlovi* and *A. subpictus*, in Africa *A. gambiae*, in China and Egypt *Culex pipiens*, in Oceania *Aedes scutellaris*	Bancroftian filariasis: in tropical and subtropical areas of Africa, the Far East, north-eastern South America. See remarks below	See remarks below
270	*392*	**Wuchereria malayi** (BRUG) RAO and MAPLESTONE *Filaria malayi*	Females about 55 mm long, 0.16 mm thick; males about 23 mm long, microfilariae about 220 μm long	**Host:** man. **Transmission:** by mosquitoes of genus *Mansonia*, chiefly *M. annulifera* (India) and *M. longipalpis* (Malaya)	Malayan filariasis: in East India, southern Asia. See remarks below	See remarks below

1) SWARTZWELDER et al., *J. Amer. med. Ass.*, **165**, 2063 (1957). *2)* CHOWDHURY, A. B., in CONN, H. F. (Ed.), *Current Therapy 1961*, Philadelphia and London, 1961, page 18. *3)* SWARTZWELDER et al., *Amer. J. trop. Med. Hyg.*, **7**, 329 (1958). *4)* BUMBALO et al., *Amer. J. trop. Med. Hyg.*, **7**, 212 (1958). *5)* WAGNER, W. H., *Antibiot. et Chemotherap. (Basel)*, **3**, 343 (1956).

Filariasis (Bancroftian and Malayan)[1] *(Nos. 391* and *392)*

The adult worms resemble long white hairs. They are found, usually tangled together, in the lymphatic vessels of the pelvis, extremities and genital organs. The female worms give birth to numerous microfilariae which appear during the night in the peripheral blood (so-called nocturnal cycle, *Microfilaria nocturna*). The mosquitoes act only as intermediate hosts and passive vectors in which the infective larvae develop. Following the bite of the mosquito, the larvae gain access into the blood stream.

Symptoms

In Bancroftian filariasis[2], infection is followed by an incubation period of about 12 months which is essentially asymptomatic for natives of hyper-endemic areas. In immigrants there may be severe local inflammation around immature worms, particularly in the legs and scrotum, with lymphadenopathy, pain, fatigue, nausea, etc. This period is followed by an acute stage characterized by numerous microfilariae in the blood and inflammatory phenomena, with recurrent attacks of lymphangitis, lymphadenitis, orchitis, funiculitis and swelling and pain in the affected parts. The acute stage is succeeded by a chronic one marked by absence or near absence of microfilariae in the peripheral blood and obstructive phenomena: lymph varices, lymph scrotum, hydrocele, chyluria, recurrent lymphangitis. This stage culminates in elephantiasis in 1–20% of persons affected.

The pathogenesis of Malayan filariasis[2] is essentially similar but the resulting elephantiasis is mainly restricted to the upper extremities.

Treatment[3]

Diethylcarbamazine is the drug of choice. Dosage: 2 mg/kg peroral three times daily, continued in acute cases for 3–4 weeks. After two days most of the microfilariae will have disappeared from the blood, although the adult worms are hardly affected.

References

1) For reviews see WATSON, J. M., *Medical Helminthology*, London, 1960, page 175; HAWKING, F., *Sci. American*, **199**, 94 (1958); Onchocerciasis and filariasis, *Bull. Wld Hlth Org.*, **16**, 480 (1957). *2)* WATSON, J. M., *loc. cit.* *3)* WAGNER, W. H., *Antibiot. et Chemotherap. (Basel)*, **3**, 343 (1956); A.M.A. Council on Drugs, *New and Nonofficial Drugs 1961*, Philadelphia and Montreal, 1961, page 201.

For classification of organisms see pages 721–724; for index of synonyms see pages 725–734

Nemathelminthes

See pages 721–724	See pages 725–734	Classified name *Synonyms* Common names	Principal characteristics	Habitat, host, transmission, etc.	Occurrence and associated diseases	Treatment and other remarks
270	*393*	**Loa loa** (COBBOLD) (CASTELLANI and CHALMERS) *Dracunculus loa,* *Filaria loa,* *Filaria oculi humani,* *Filaria sanguinis hominis major,* *Microfilaria diurna,* *Strongylus loa* Eye worm (Wanderfilarie)	Females about 60 mm, males about 32 mm, microfilariae about 275 µm long. See the figure on page 717	**Host:** man. **Transmission:** by tabanid flies of genus *Chrysops.* Development similar to that of *W. bancrofti (No. 391)*, but the microfilariae appear in the peripheral blood during the day *(Microfilaria diurna)*. Occurs in Congo and West Africa	Lives chiefly in and around the eye, also in the subcutaneous connective tissue. The worms are very active and wander under the skin from place to place (up to an inch in 2 minutes), causing severe pruritus and unpleasant creeping sensations. *Loa loa* causes relatively little damage; as a rule loaiasis is accompanied by painless edematous swellings the size of a pigeon's egg (Calabar swellings), which disappear after a few days but appear again at some other place. Worms in the eye can easily be removed surgically	Diethylcarbamazine[1], effective against both microfilariae and adult worms
270	*394*	**Onchocerca volvulus** (LEUCKART) RAILLIET and HENRY *Filaria volvulus,* *Microfilaria nuda,* *Onchocerca caecutiens* Blinding filaria	Males up to 40 mm long and 0.2 mm thick. Females up to 500 mm long, in tangled masses. Microfilariae about 300 µm long. See the figure on page 717	**Host:** man. **Transmission:** by blackflies of the genus *Simulium* (*S. damnosum* and *S. neavei* in Africa, *S. metallicum*, *S. ochraceum*, *S. callidum* and others in Guatemala and Mexico). Development is similar to that of *W. bancrofti (No. 391)*. Occurs in Central Africa, Mexico, Guatemala	In contrast to *W. bancrofti* the adult worms and the microfilariae live in the subcutaneous connective tissue and cause nodules ranging from the size of a pigeon's to that of a hen's egg (often multiple up to the number of 200). Onchocerciasis causes severe pruritus. When the iris and cornea are infested blindness often results. For reviews of onchocerciasis see references[3–5]	Surgical removal of the nodules. Treatment with suramin plus diethylcarbamazine[2], which kills the microfilariae but not the adult worms
271	*395*	**Dracunculus medinensis** (LINNÆUS) REICHARD *Dracunculus graecorum,* *Filaria medinensis,* *Füllebornius medinensis,* *Furia vena medinensis,* *Gordius medinensis,* *Vena medinensis* Dragon worm, Guinea worm, Medina worm, serpent worm (filaire de Médine, ver de Guinée, Medinawurm)	Females 50–120 cm long, 0.5–1.5 mm thick. Males 2–4 cm long. See the figure on page 717	**Host:** man. **Intermediate host and vector:** lower Crustacea (species of *Cyclops*). **Infestation:** by drinking contaminated water. Occurs in the zone from Central India to Arabia, sporadically in the East Indies, Egypt and Central Africa (in some 50 million carriers)	The worm inhabits the subcutaneous connective tissues of man, causing swellings the size of a pigeon's egg which ulcerate so that the end of the sexually-mature female projects. The worm is stimulated by cold water to discharge the embryos, with the result that each contact of the swellings with water leads to a massive discharge of embryos. The symptoms of dracunculiasis begin with the swelling and appear to be of an anaphylactic kind: urticaria, nausea, vomiting, diarrhea, asthma, fainting attacks. Later symptoms are caused by bacterial infection of the swelling. Marked eosinophilia	An old method which is today still the most widely used consists in the slow extraction of the living worm by winding it gradually on to a small stick. Injection around the worm of phenothiazine (total 2–4 g), mercuric chloride or chloroform has proved effective, the worm then being easily extracted after 5–7 days

1) WAGNER, W. H., *Antibiot. et Chemotherap. (Basel)*, **3**, 343 (1956). *2)* RODGER, F. C., *Trans. roy. Soc. trop. Med. Hyg.*, **52**, 462 (1958); WOODRUFF et al., *ibid.*, **52**, 97 (1958); CHERRY, J. K. T., *E. Afr. med. J.*, **8**, 550 (1960), quoted in *Trop. Dis. Bull.*, **58**, 725 (1961). *3)* ADAMS, A. R., *Trans. roy. Soc. trop. Med. Hyg.*, **52**, 95 (1958). *4)* BRANLY, M. A., *Klin. Mbl. Augenheilk.*, **128**, 1 (1956). *5)* Onchocerciasis and filariasis, *Bull. Wld Hlth Org.*, **16**, 480 (1957).

The classification of these organisms is the subject of considerable controversy, and it is understandable that the ever-widening scope of observational data should preclude the setting up of any system of classification which can lay claim to finality.

The classification of the **bacteria** (Schizomycetes) and **Rickettsiales** reproduced here is that given in *Bergey's Manual*[1]. It is the complete classification, and only a minority of the genera listed contain pathogenic species. For earlier classifications see LEHMANN and NEUMANN[2], WEINBERG et al.[3], and PRIBRAM[4].

No satisfactory systematic classification of the **viruses** (Virales) has yet been achieved, and that given in the 6th edition of *Bergey's Manual* (1948) was omitted from the 7th edition on the grounds that it was premature. The viruses listed in the table on pages 689 to 697 have therefore been arranged simply by the type of disease they give rise to. For a discussion of virus classification see COOPER[9].

The classification of the **fungi** (Eumycetes) has been taken from COUDERT[5]. Only sufficient of the classification is reproduced here to show the systematic arrangement of the species listed in the table on pages 698–703. For a detailed discussion of this subject see WOLF and WOLF[6].

The classifications given here for the **protozoa** and for the **helminths** are taken from those given by PIEKARSKI[7]. Here again, only the relevant part of the classification is reproduced. For a more detailed classification of these invertebrate parasites see FIEBIGER[8].

* * *

The **bold** figures against the genera, read in conjunction with those in column 1 of the tables of pathogenic organisms on pages 646–720, provide a key to the position of each organism in the classification.

References

1) BREED et al. (Eds.), *Bergey's Manual of Determinative Bacteriology*, 7th ed., Baltimore, 1957. *2)* LEHMANN and NEUMANN, *Bakteriologische Diagnostik*, 7th ed., Munich, 1927. *3)* WEINBERG et al., *Les microbes anaérobies*, Paris, 1937. *4)* PRIBRAM, E., *Klassifikation der Schizomyceten*, Leipzig and Vienna, 1933; *J. Bact.*, **18**, 361 (1929). *5)* COUDERT, J., *Guide pratique de mycologie médicale*, Paris, 1955. *6)* WOLF and WOLF, *The Fungi*, vol. I, New York, 1947, page 29. *7)* PIEKARSKI, G., *Lehrbuch der Parasitologie*, Berlin, 1954. *8)* FIEBIGER, J., *Die tierischen Parasiten der Haus- und Nutztiere sowie des Menschen*, 4th ed., Vienna, 1947. *9)* COOPER, P. D., *Nature*, **190**, 302 (1961).

Schizomycetes, Rickettsiales, Virales

Class: *Schizomycetes* VON NÄGELI

Order I. *Pseudomonadales* ORLA-JENSEN

Suborder I. *Rhodobacteriineae* BREED, MURRAY and HITCHENS

Family I. *Thiorhodaceae* MOLISCH

Genus I. *Thiosarcina* WINOGRADSKY **1**
Genus II. *Thiopedia* WINOGRADSKY **2**
Genus III. *Thiocapsa* WINOGRADSKY **3**
Genus IV. *Thiodictyon* WINOGRADSKY **4**
Genus V. *Thiothece* WINOGRADSKY **5**
Genus VI. *Thiocystis* WINOGRADSKY **6**
Genus VII. *Lamprocystis* SCHROETER **7**
Genus VIII. *Amoebobacter* WINOGRADSKY **8**
Genus IX. *Thiopolycoccus* WINOGRADSKY **9**
Genus X. *Thiospirillum* WINOGRADSKY **10**
Genus XI. *Rhabdomonas* COHN **11**
Genus XII. *Rhodothece* MOLISCH **12**
Genus XIII. *Chromatium* PERTY **13**

Family II. *Athiorhodaceae* MOLISCH

Genus I. *Rhodopseudomonas* KLUYVER and VAN NIEL *emend.* VAN NIEL **14**
Genus II. *Rhodospirillum* MOLISCH *emend.* VAN NIEL ... **15**

Family III. *Chlorobacteriaceae* LAUTERBORN

Genus I. *Chlorobium* NADSON **16**
Genus II. *Pelodictyon* LAUTERBORN **17**
Genus III. *Clathrochloris* GEITLER **18**
Genus IV. *Chlorobacterium* LAUTERBORN **19**
Genus V. *Chlorochromatium* LAUTERBORN **20**
Genus VI. *Cylindrogloea* PERFILIEV **21**

Suborder II. *Pseudomonadineae* BREED, MURRAY and SMITH, *sub-ordo nov.*

Family I. *Nitrobacteriaceae* BUCHANAN

Genus I. *Nitrosomonas* WINOGRADSKY **22**
Genus II. *Nitrosococcus* WINOGRADSKY **23**
Genus III. *Nitrosospira* WINOGRADSKY **24**
Genus IV. *Nitrosocystis* WINOGRADSKY **25**
Genus V. *Nitrosogloea* H. WINOGRADSKY **26**
Genus VI. *Nitrobacter* WINOGRADSKY **27**
Genus VII. *Nitrocystis* H. WINOGRADSKY **28**

Family II. *Methanomonadaceae* BREED, *fam. nov.*

Genus I. *Methanomonas* ORLA-JENSEN **29**
Genus II. *Hydrogenomonas* ORLA-JENSEN **30**
Genus III. *Carboxydomonas* ORLA-JENSEN **31**

Family III. *Thiobacteriaceae* JANKE

Genus I. *Thiobacterium* JANKE **32**
Genus II. *Macromonas* UTERMÖHL and KOPPE **33**
Genus III. *Thiovulum* HINZE **34**
Genus IV. *Thiospira* VISLOUCH **35**
Genus V. *Thiobacillus* BEIJERINCK **36**

Family IV. *Pseudomonadaceae* WINSLOW et al.

Genus I. *Pseudomonas* MIGULA **37**
Genus II. *Xanthomonas* DOWSON **38**
Genus III. *Acetobacter* BEIJERINCK **39**
Genus IV. *Aeromonas* KLUYVER and VAN NIEL **40**
Genus V. *Photobacterium* BEIJERINCK *emend.* BREED and LESSEL **41**
Genus VI. *Azotomonas* STAPP **42**
Genus VII. *Zymomonas* KLUYVER and VAN NIEL **43**
Genus VIII. *Protaminobacter* DEN DOOREN DE JONG **44**
Genus IX. *Alginomonas* THJØTTA and KASS **45**
Genus X. *Mycoplana* GRAY and THORNTON **46**
Genus XI. *Zoogloea* COHN **47**
Genus XII. *Halobacterium* ELAZARI-VOLCANI **48**

Family V. *Caulobacteriaceae* HENRICI and JOHNSON *emend.* BREED

Genus I. *Caulobacter* HENRICI and JOHNSON **49**
Genus II. *Gallionella* EHRENBERG **50**
Genus III. *Siderophacus* BEGER **51**
Genus IV. *Nevskia* FAMINTZIN **52**

Family VI. *Siderocapsaceae* PRIBRAM

Genus I. *Siderocapsa* MOLISCH **53**
Genus II. *Sidersphaera* BEGER **54**
Genus III. *Sideronema* BEGER **55**
Genus IV. *Ferribacterium* BRUSSOFF **56**
Genus V. *Sideromonas* CHOLODNY **57**
Genus VI. *Naumanniella* DORFF **58**
Genus VII. *Ochrobium* PERFILIEV **59**
Genus VIII. *Siderococcus* DORFF **60**
Genus IX. *Siderobacter* NAUMANN **61**
Genus X. *Ferrobacillus* LEATHEN and BRALEY **62**

Family VII. *Spirillaceae* MIGULA

Genus I. *Vibrio* MÜLLER **63**
Genus II. *Desulfovibrio* KLUYVER and VAN NIEL **64**
Genus III. *Methanobacterium* KLUYVER and VAN NIEL ... **65**
Genus IV. *Cellvibrio* WINOGRADSKY **66**
Genus V. *Cellfalcicula* WINOGRADSKY **67**
Genus VI. *Microcyclus* ØRSKOV **68**
Genus VII. *Spirillum* EHRENBERG **69**
Genus VIII. *Paraspirillum* DOBELL **70**
Genus IX. *Selenomonas* VON PROWAZEK **71**
Genus X. *Myconostoc* COHN **72**

Order II. *Chlamydobacteriales* BUCHANAN

Family I. *Chlamydobacteriaceae* MIGULA

Genus I. *Sphaerotilus* KÜTZING **73**
Genus II. *Leptothrix* KÜTZING **74**
Genus III. *Toxothrix* MOLISCH **75**

Family II. *Peloplocaceae* BEGER, *fam. nov.*

Genus I. *Peloploca* LAUTERBORN **76**
Genus II. *Pelonema* LAUTERBORN **77**

Family III. *Crenotrichaceae* HANSGIRG

Genus I. *Crenothrix* COHN **78**
Genus II. *Phragmidiothrix* ENGLER **79**
Genus III. *Clonothrix* ROZE **80**

Order III. *Hyphomicrobiales* DOUGLAS, *ordo nov.*

Family I. *Hyphomicrobiaceae* BABUDIERI

Genus I. *Hyphomicrobium* STUTZER and HARTLEB **81**
Genus II. *Rhodomicrobium* DUCHOW and DOUGLAS **82**

Family II. *Pasteuriaceae* LAURENT *emend.* HENRICI and JOHNSON

Genus I. *Pasteuria* METCHNIKOFF **83**
Genus II. *Blastocaulis* HENRICI and JOHNSON **84**

Schizomycetes, Rickettsiales, Virales (continued)

Order IV. *Eubacteriales* Buchanan

Family I. *Azotobacteraceae* Bergey, Breed and Murray

Genus I. *Azotobacter* Beijerinck ... 85

Family II. *Rhizobiaceae* Conn

Genus I. *Rhizobium* Frank ... 86
Genus II. *Agrobacterium* Conn ... 87
Genus III. *Chromobacterium* Bergonzini ... 88

Family III. *Achromobacteraceae* Breed

Genus I. *Alcaligenes* Castellani and Chalmers ... 89
Genus II. *Achromobacter* Bergey et al. ... 90
Genus III. *Flavobacterium* Bergey et al. ... 91
Genus IV. *Agarbacterium* Angst ... 92
Genus V. *Beneckea* Campbell, *gen. nov.* ... 93

Family IV. *Enterobacteriaceae* Rahn

Tribe I. *Escherichieae* Bergey, Breed and Murray
Genus I. *Escherichia* Castellani and Chalmers ... 94
Genus II. *Aerobacter* Beijerinck ... 95
Genus III. *Klebsiella* Trevisan ... 96
Genus IV. *Paracolobactrum* Borman, Stuart and Wheeler ... 97
Genus V. *Alginobacter* Thjøtta and Kass ... 98

Tribe II. *Erwinieae* Winslow et al.
Genus VI. *Erwinia* Winslow et al. ... 99

Tribe III. *Serratieae* Bergey, Breed and Murray
Genus VII. *Serratia* Bizio *emend.* Breed and Breed ... 100

Tribe IV. *Proteeae* Castellani and Chalmers
Genus VIII. *Proteus* Hauser ... 101

Tribe V. *Salmonelleae* Bergey, Breed and Murray
Genus IX. *Salmonella* Lignières ... 102
Genus X. *Shigella* Castellani and Chalmers ... 103

Family V. *Brucellaceae, nom. nov.*

Genus I. *Pasteurella* Trevisan ... 104
Genus II. *Bordetella* Moreno-López ... 105
Genus III. *Brucella* Meyer and Shaw ... 106
Genus IV. *Haemophilus* Winslow et al. ... 107
Genus V. *Actinobacillus* Brumpt ... 108
Genus VI. *Calymmatobacterium* Aragão and Vianna ... 109
Genus VII. *Moraxella* Lwoff ... 110
Genus VIII. *Noguchia* Olitsky, Syverton and Tyler ... 111

Family VI. *Bacteroidaceae* Breed, Murray and Smith, *fam. nov.*

Genus I. *Bacteroides* Castellani and Chalmers ... 112
Genus II. *Fusobacterium* Knorr ... 113
Genus III. *Dialister* Bergey et al. ... 114
Genus IV. *Sphaerophorus* Prévot ... 115
Genus V. *Streptobacillus* Levaditi, Nicolau and Poincloux ... 116

Family VII. *Micrococcaceae* Pribram

Genus I. *Micrococcus* Cohn ... 117
Genus II. *Staphylococcus* Rosenbach ... 118
Genus III. *Gaffkya* Trevisan ... 119
Genus IV. *Sarcina* Goodsir ... 120
Subgenus I. *Zymosarcina* Smit
Subgenus II. *Methanosarcina* Kluyver and van Niel
Subgenus III. *Sarcinococcus* Breed
Subgenus IV. *Urosarcina* Miquel
Genus V. *Methanococcus* Kluyver and van Niel *emend.* Barker ... 121
Genus VI. *Peptococcus* Kluyver and van Niel ... 122

Family VIII. *Neisseriaceae* Prévot

Genus I. *Neisseria* Trevisan ... 123
Genus II. *Veillonella* Prévot ... 124

Family IX. *Brevibacteriaceae* Breed

Genus I. *Brevibacterium* Breed ... 125
Genus II. *Kurthia* Trevisan ... 126

Family X. *Lactobacillaceae* Winslow et al.

Tribe I. *Streptococceae* Trevisan
Genus I. *Diplococcus* Weichselbaum ... 127
Genus II. *Streptococcus* Rosenbach ... 128
Genus III. *Pediococcus* Balcke *emend.* Mees ... 129
Genus IV. *Leuconostoc* van Tieghem *emend.* Hucker and Pederson ... 130
Genus V. *Peptostreptococcus* Kluyver and van Niel ... 131

Tribe II. *Lactobacilleae* Winslow et al.
Genus I. *Lactobacillus* Beijerinck ... 132
Subgenus I. *Lactobacillus* Beijerinck
Subgenus II. *Saccharobacillus* van Laer
Genus II. *Eubacterium* Prévot ... 133
Genus III. *Catenabacterium* Prévot ... 134
Genus IV. *Ramibacterium* Prévot ... 135
Genus V. *Cillobacterium* Prévot ... 136

Family XI. *Propionibacteriaceae* Delwiche, *fam. nov.*

Genus I. *Propionibacterium* Orla-Jensen ... 137
Genus II. *Butyribacterium* Barker and Haas ... 138
Genus III. *Zymobacterium* Wachsman and Barker ... 139

Family XII. *Corynebacteriaceae* Lehmann and Neumann

Genus I. *Corynebacterium* Lehmann and Neumann ... 140
Genus II. *Listeria* Pirie ... 141
Genus III. *Erysipelothrix* Rosenbach ... 142
Genus IV. *Microbacterium* Orla-Jensen ... 143
Genus V. *Cellulomonas* Bergey et al. *emend.* Clark ... 144
Genus VI. *Arthrobacter* Fischer *emend.* Conn and Dimmick ... 145

Family XIII. *Bacillaceae* Fischer

Genus I. *Bacillus* Cohn ... 146
Genus II. *Clostridium* Prazmowski ... 147

Order V. *Caryophanales* Peshkoff

Family I. *Caryophanaceae* Peshkoff

Genus I. *Caryophanon* Peshkoff ... 148
Genus II. *Lineola* Pringsheim ... 149
Genus III. *Simonsiella* Schmid ... 150

Family II. *Oscillospiraceae* Peshkoff

Genus I. *Oscillospira* Chatton and Pérard ... 151

Family III. *Arthromitaceae* Peshkoff

Genus I. *Arthromitus* Leidy ... 152
Genus II. *Coleomitus* Duboscq and Grassé ... 153

Order VI. *Actinomycetales* Buchanan

Family I. *Mycobacteriaceae* Chester

Genus I. *Mycobacterium* Lehmann and Neumann ... 154
Genus II. *Mycococcus* Krassilnikov ... 155

Family II. *Actinomycetaceae* Buchanan

Genus I. *Nocardia* Trevisan ... 156
Genus II. *Actinomyces* Harz ... 157

Family III. *Streptomycetaceae* Waksman and Henrici

Genus I. *Streptomyces* Waksman and Henrici ... 158
Genus II. *Micromonospora* Ørskov ... 159
Genus III. *Thermoactinomyces* Tsiklinsky ... 160

Family IV. *Actinoplanaceae* Couch

Genus I. *Actinoplanes* Couch ... 161
Genus II. *Streptosporangium* Couch ... 162

Order VII. *Beggiatoales* Buchanan, *ordo nov.*

Family I. *Beggiatoaceae* Migula

Genus I. *Beggiatoa* Trevisan ... 163
Genus II. *Thiospirillopsis* Uphof ... 164
Genus III. *Thioploca* Lauterborn ... 165
Genus IV. *Thiothrix* Winogradsky ... 166

Family II. *Vitreoscillaceae* Pringsheim

Genus I. *Vitreoscilla* Pringsheim ... 167
Genus II. *Bactoscilla* Pringsheim ... 168
Genus III. *Microscilla* Pringsheim ... 169

Family III. *Leucotrichaceae* Buchanan, *fam. nov.*

Genus I. *Leucothrix* Oersted *emend.* Harold and Stanier ... 170

Family IV. *Achromatiaceae* Massart

Genus I. *Achromatium* Schewiakoff ... 171

Order VIII. *Myxobacterales* Jahn

Family I. *Cytophagaceae* Stanier

Genus I. *Cytophaga* Winogradsky ... 172

Family II. *Archangiaceae* Jahn

Genus I. *Archangium* Jahn ... 173
Genus II. *Stelangium* Jahn ... 174

Classification of Bacteria, Rickettsiales, Viruses, Fungi, Protozoa and Helminths (continued)

Schizomycetes, Rickettsiales, Virales (concluded)

Eumycetes

Classification of Bacteria, Rickettsiales, Viruses, Fungi, Protozoa and Helminths (concluded)

Protozoa

Class: *Mastigophora* Diesing

Order: *Protomonadina* Blochmann

Family: *Trypanosomidae* Doflein

- Genus: *Trypanosoma* 235
- Genus: *Leishmania* 236
- Genus: *Toxoplasma* 237
- Genus: *Sarcocystis* 238
- Genus: *Encephalitozoon* 239

Family: *Embadomonadidae* Alexeieff

- Genus: *Chilomastix* 240

Family: *Distomatidae* Klebs

- Genus: *Lamblia* 241

Order: *Polymastigina* Blochmann

Family: *Trichomonadidae* Wenyon

- Genus: *Trichomonas* 242

Class: *Rhizopoda* von Siebold

Order: *Amoebina* Ehrenberg

Family: *Amoebidae* Bronn

- Genus: *Entamoeba* 243
- Genus: *Endolimax* 244
- Genus: *Iodamoeba* 245
- Genus: *Dientamoeba* 246

Class: *Sporozoa* Leuckart (*Telosporidia* Schaudinn)

Order: *Coccidia* Leuckart

Family: *Eimeriidae* Lühe

- Genus: *Isospora* 247

Order: *Haemosporidia* Danilewsky

Family: *Plasmodiidae* Mesnil

- Genus: *Plasmodium* 248

Class: *Ciliata* Bütschli

Order: *Spirotricha* Bütschli

- Genus: *Balantidium* 249

Classification uncertain

- Genus: *Pneumocystis* 250

Helminthes

Phylum: *Platyhelminthes* (Flatworms)

Class: *Trematoda*

Order: *Digenea*

Superfamily: *Fascioloidea*
- Family: *Fasciolidae* Railliet 251

Superfamily: *Plagiorchoidea*
- Family: *Dicrocoeliidea* Looss 252

Superfamily: *Echonostomatoidea*
- Family: *Echinostomadidae* Looss 253

Superfamily: *Opisthorchoidea*
- Family: *Heterophyidae* Odhner 254
- Family: *Opisthorchidae* Lühe 255

Superfamily: *Troglotrematoidea*
- Family: *Troglotremadidae* Odhner 256

Superfamily: *Schistosomatoidea*
- Family: *Schistosomatidae* Looss 257
- Family: *Paramphistomidae* 258

Class: *Cestoda* (Tapeworms)

Order: *Pseudophyllidea*
- Family: *Diphyllobothriidae* Lühe 259

Order: *Cyclophyllidea*
- Family: *Dilepididae* Fuhrmann 260
- Family: *Hymenolepididae* Fuhrmann 261
- Family: *Taeniidae* Ludwig 262

Phylum: *Nemathelminthes* (Roundworms)

Order: *Nematoda* (Threadworms)

Superfamily: *Trichuroidea*
- Family: *Trichuridae* Railliet 263

Superfamily: *Strongyloidea*
- Family: *Trichinellidae* Ward 264
- Family: *Ancylostomatidae* Looss 265

Superfamily: *Rhabditoidea*
- Family: *Strongyloididae* Chitwood and McIntosh 266

Superfamily: *Ascaroidea*
- Family: *Ascarididae* Baird 267
- Family: *Oxyuridae* Cobbold 268

Superfamily: *Spiruroidea*
- Family: *Gnathostomatidae* Blanchard 269

Superfamily: *Filariodea*
- Family: *Filariidae* Cobbold 270
- Family: *Dracunculidae* Leiper 271

This index of the names and synonyms of pathogenic organisms and their associated diseases provides a key to their position in the descriptive tables (and accompanying texts) on pages 646–720 (*italic serial numbers* in column 2 of the tables)

This index of the names and synonyms of pathogenic organisms and their associated diseases provides a key to their position in the descriptive tables (and accompanying texts) on pages 646–720 (*italic serial numbers* in column 2 of the tables)

This index of the names and synonyms of pathogenic organisms and their associated diseases provides a key to their position in the descriptive tables (and accompanying texts) on pages 646–720 (*italic serial numbers* in column 2 of the tables)

This index of the names and synonyms of pathogenic organisms and their associated diseases provides a key to their position in the descriptive tables (and accompanying texts) on pages 646–720 (*italic serial numbers* in column 2 of the tables)

This index of the names and synonyms of pathogenic organisms and their associated diseases provides a key to their position in the descriptive tables (and accompanying texts) on pages 646–720 (*italic serial numbers* in column 2 of the tables)

I, J, K *No.*

I

J

K

L *No.*

L

M *No.*

M

This index of the names and synonyms of pathogenic organisms and their associated diseases provides a key to their position in the descriptive tables (and accompanying texts) on pages 646–720 (*italic serial numbers* in column 2 of the tables)

M

N, O

N

O

P

P

This index of the names and synonyms of pathogenic organisms and their associated diseases provides a key to their position in the descriptive tables (and accompanying texts) on pages 646–720 (*italic serial numbers* in column 2 of the tables)

This index of the names and synonyms of pathogenic organisms and their associated diseases provides a key to their position in the descriptive tables (and accompanying texts) on pages 646–720 (*italic serial numbers* in column 2 of the tables)

S

This index of the names and synonyms of pathogenic organisms and their associated diseases provides a key to their position in the descriptive tables (and accompanying texts) on pages 646–720 (*italic serial numbers* in column 2 of the tables)

This index of the names and synonyms of pathogenic organisms and their associated diseases provides a key to their position in the descriptive tables (and accompanying texts) on pages 646–720 (*italic serial numbers* in column 2 of the tables)

Reproduced from *Wld Hlth Org. techn. Rep. Ser.*, **222**, 24–47 (1961) by permission of the World Health Organization, Section of Biological Standardization, Geneva
(For bibliographical references concerning the substances listed see the above report)

Description	International Unit (IU) mg	Form in which dispensed	Year of establishment
		I. Immunological substances	
		Held by the International Laboratory for Biological Standards, Statens Seruminstitut, Copenhagen	
		1. Antigens	
Old tuberculin[1]	0.0100	Ampoules containing 2 ml (100,000 IU per ml)	1935 (2nd Standard)
Mammalian tuberculin (purified protein derivative)	–	Ampoules containing 10 mg plus 4 mg of salts (500,000 IU per ampoule)	1951 (1st Standard)
Avian tuberculin (purified protein derivative)	0.000 0726	Ampoules containing 10 mg plus 26.3 mg of salts (500,000 IU per ampoule)	1954 (1st Standard)
Tetanus toxoid (alcohol purified)	0.03	Ampoules containing 25 mg (420 Lf*) plus glycine (833 IU per ampoule)	1951 (1st Standard)
Diphtheria toxoid (plain, alcohol purified)	0.50	Ampoules containing 50 mg (1730 Lf*) plus glycine (100 IU per ampoule)	1951 (1st Standard)
Diphtheria toxoid (adsorbed to aluminum hydroxide, dried)	0.75	Ampoules containing 80 mg (50 Lf*) plus an equal part of guinea-pig serum (107 IU per ampoule)	1955 (1st Standard)
Schick test toxin (diphtheria) (purified)	0.0042	Ampoules containing 0.005 mg (0.9 Lf*) plus 1 mg of bovine albumin and 2.74 mg of phosphate buffer salts (900 IU per ampoule)	1954 (1st Standard)
Pertussis vaccine (dried)	1.5	Ampoules containing 52 mg (34.7 IU per ampoule)	1957 (1st Standard)
Cholera antigen (Inaba) (dried)	–	Ampoules containing approximately 100 mg	1953 (1st Reference Preparation)
Cholera antigen (Ogawa) (dried)	–	Ampoules containing approximately 100 mg	1953 (1st Reference Preparation)
Cholera vaccine (Inaba) (dried)	–	Ampoules containing 20 mg (1.6×10^{10} organisms per ampoule)	1953 (1st Reference Preparation)
Cholera vaccine (Ogawa) (dried)	–	Ampoules containing 20 mg (1.6×10^{10} organisms per ampoule)	1953 (1st Reference Preparation)
Cardiolipin (purified)	–	Ampoules containing 4, 8 or 16 ml of a solution in ethanol (6.4 mg cardiolipin per ml, as calculated from the phosphorus content)	1958 (3rd Reference Preparation)
Lecithin (beef heart, purified)	–	Bottles containing 30 ml of a solution in ethanol (30.3 mg lecithin per ml)	1953 (2nd Reference Preparation)
Lecithin (egg, purified)	–	Ampoules containing 4, 8 or 16 ml of a solution in ethanol (26.7 mg of lecithin per ml, as calculated from the phosphorus content)	1959 (3rd Reference Preparation)
Rabies vaccine	–	Ampoules containing 38 mg of a UV-inactivated, freeze-dried suspension of rabbit brain infected with fixed rabies virus	1960 (1st Reference Preparation)
Swine erysipelas vaccine (adsorbed to aluminum hydroxide, dried)	0.50	Ampoules containing 499 mg, derived from formalin-treated *Erysipelothrix rhusiopathiae (E. insidiosa)* type B	1959 (1st Standard)
		2. Antibodies	
Tetanus antitoxin (hyperimmune horse serum, dried)[1]	0.3094	Bottles containing dried material from 10 ml of a solution in saline, containing 66 vol% glycerol (5 IU per ml)	1928 (1st Standard)
Diphtheria antitoxin (hyperimmune horse serum, dried)[1]	0.0628	Bottles containing dried material from 10 ml of a solution in saline, containing 66 vol% glycerol (10 IU per ml)	1922 (1st Standard)

* 1 Lf dose = the amount of a toxin which produces optimal flocculation with one unit of antitoxin.

1) See also *Pharmacopoea Internationalis*, 1st English edition, vol. I, Geneva, 1951.

Description	International Unit (IU) mg	Form in which dispensed	Year of establishment
Diphtheria antitoxin for flocculation test (hyperimmune horse serum)	–	Bottles containing 10 ml of a dilution in phosphate-buffered saline, containing 0.01 g thiomersal per 100 ml (500 IU per ml)	1956 (4th Reference Preparation)
Antidysentery serum (SHIGA) (hyperimmune horse serum, dried)	0.05	Bottles containing dried material from 10 ml of a solution in saline, containing 66 vol% glycerol (200 IU per ml)	1928 (1st Standard)
Gas-gangrene antitoxin *(perfringens)* (*Clostridium welchii* type A antitoxin; hyperimmune horse serum, dried)[1]	0.1132	Bottles containing dried material from 10 ml of a solution in saline, containing 66 vol% glycerol (20 IU per ml)	1953 (4th Standard)
Clostridium welchii (perfringens) type B antitoxin (hyperimmune horse serum, dried)	0.0137	Ampoules containing 68.5 mg (5000 IU per ampoule)	1954 (1st Standard)
Clostridium welchii (perfringens) type D antitoxin (hyperimmune horse serum, dried)	0.0657	Ampoules containing 65.7 mg (1000 IU per ampoule)	1954 (1st Standard)
Gas-gangrene antitoxin *(vibrion septique)* (hyperimmune horse serum, dried)[1]	0.118	Ampoules containing 59 mg of a 1:3 dilution in phosphate-buffered saline (500 IU per ampoule)	1957 (3rd Standard)
Gas-gangrene antitoxin *(oedematiens)* (hyperimmune horse serum, dried)	0.1135	Bottles containing dried material from 10 ml of a solution in saline, containing 66 vol% glycerol (20 IU per ml)	1952 (2nd Standard)
Gas-gangrene antitoxin *(histolyticus)* (hyperimmune horse serum, dried)	0.2	Bottles containing dried material from 10 ml of a solution in saline, containing 66 vol% glycerol (20 IU per ml)	1951 (2nd Standard)
Gas-gangrene antitoxin *(Sordelli)* (hyperimmune horse serum, dried)	0.1334	Bottles containing dried material from 10 ml of a solution in saline, containing 66 vol% glycerol (20 IU per ml)	1938 (1st Standard)
Staphylococcus α antitoxin (hyperimmune horse serum, dried)	0.2376	Bottles containing dried material from 10 ml of a solution in phosphate-buffered saline, containing 0.01 g thiomersal per 100 ml (20 IU per ml)	1938 (2nd Standard)
Scarlet fever streptococcus antitoxin (hyperimmune horse serum, dried)	0.049	Ampoules containing 490 mg (10,000 IU per ampoule)	1952 (1st Standard)
Anti-streptolysin O (human, dried)	0.0213	Ampoules containing 46 mg	1959 (1st Standard)
Swine erysipelas serum (anti-N) (hyperimmune horse serum, dried)	0.14	Ampoules containing 87.9 mg (628 IU per ampoule)	1954 (1st Standard)
Antipneumococcus serum (type 1) (hyperimmune horse serum, dried)	0.0886	Bottles containing dried material from 10 ml of a solution in saline, containing 66 vol% glycerol (200 IU per ml)	1934 (1st Standard)
Antipneumococcus serum (type 2) (hyperimmune horse serum, dried)	0.0894	Bottles containing dried material from 10 ml of a solution in saline, containing 66 vol% glycerol (200 IU per ml)	1934 (1st Standard)
Anti-*Brucella abortus* serum (bovine, dried)	0.091	Ampoules containing 91 mg (1000 IU per ampoule)	1952 (1st Standard)
Anti-Q-fever serum (bovine, dried)	0.1017	Ampoules containing 101.7 mg (1000 IU per ampoule)	1953 (1st Standard)
Antirabies serum (hyperimmune horse serum, dried)	1.0	Ampoules containing 86.6 mg (86.6 IU per ampoule)	1955 (1st Standard)
Anti-A blood-typing serum (human, dried)	0.3465	Ampoules containing 88.7 mg (256 IU per ampoule)	1950 (1st Standard)
Anti-B blood-typing serum (human, dried)	0.3520	Ampoules containing 90.1 mg (256 IU per ampoule)	1950 (1st Standard)
Syphilitic human serum (dried)	3.617	Ampoules containing 177.4 mg (49 IU per ampoule)	1958 (1st Standard)
Antityphoid serum (provisional) (hyperimmune horse serum, dried)	–	Ampoules containing dried material from 5 ml serum	1952 (1st Reference Preparation)
Cholera agglutinating serum (INABA, monospecific)	–	Ampoules containing 0.6 ml	1953 (1st Reference Preparation)
Cholera agglutinating serum (OGAWA, monospecific)	–	Ampoules containing 0.6 ml	1953 (1st Reference Preparation)

1) See also *Pharmacopoea Internationalis*, 1st English edition, vol. I, Geneva, 1951.

Description	International Unit (IU) mg	Form in which dispensed	Year of establishment
Antipoliomyelitis serum (type 1) (hyperimmune monkey serum, dried)	–		
Antipoliomyelitis serum (type 2) (hyperimmune monkey serum, dried)	–	Ampoules containing dried material from 1 ml of a 1% solution in 6% dextran in distilled water	1958 (1st Reference Preparation)
Antipoliomyelitis serum (type 3) (hyperimmune monkey serum, dried)	–		
Anti-*Leptospira saxkoebing* serum (hyperimmune rabbit serum, dried)	–		
Anti-*Leptospira ballum* AB serum (hyperimmune rabbit serum, dried)	–		
Anti-*Leptospira canicola* serum (hyperimmune rabbit serum, dried)	–		
Anti-*Leptospira sejroe* serum (hyperimmune rabbit serum, dried)	–		
Anti-*Leptospira mini* AB serum (hyperimmune rabbit serum, dried)	–		
Anti-*Leptospira grippotyphosa* serum (hyperimmune rabbit serum, dried)	–		
Anti-*Leptospira australis* A serum (hyperimmune rabbit serum, dried)	–		
Anti-*Leptospira icterohaemorrhagiae* AB serum (hyperimmune rabbit serum, dried)	–		
Anti-*Leptospira icterohaemorrhagiae* A serum (hyperimmune rabbit serum, dried)	–		
Anti-*Leptospira hyos* serum (hyperimmune rabbit serum, dried)	–	Ampoules containing dried material from 0.5 or 1.0 ml serum	1958 (1st Reference Preparation)
Anti-*Leptospira autumnalis* AB serum (hyperimmune rabbit serum, dried)	–		
Anti-*Leptospira autumnalis* A serum (hyperimmune rabbit serum, dried)	–		
Anti-*Leptospira pomona* serum (hyperimmune rabbit serum, dried)	–		
Anti-*Leptospira bataviae* serum (hyperimmune rabbit serum, dried)	–		
Anti-*Leptospira semarang* serum (hyperimmune rabbit serum, dried)	–		
Anti-*Leptospira hebdomadis* serum (hyperimmune rabbit serum, dried)	–		
Anti-*Leptospira andamana* serum (hyperimmune rabbit serum, dried)	–		
Anti-*Leptospira javanica* serum (hyperimmune rabbit serum, dried)	–		
Anti-*Leptospira pyrogenes* serum (hyperimmune rabbit serum, dried)	–		
		3. Miscellaneous	
Opacity reference preparation (aqueous suspension of pyrex-glass particles)	–	Ampoules containing 20 ml (10 IU of opacity per ml)	1953 (1st Reference Preparation)

II. Pharmacological substances

Held by the International Laboratory for Biological Standards, National Institute for Medical Research, London

1. Antibiotics

Description	International Unit (IU) mg	Form in which dispensed	Year of establishment
Penicillin (sodium benzylpenicillin)[1]	0.000 5988	Ampoules containing 30 mg (1670 IU per mg)	1952 (2nd Standard)
Penicillin K (89.9% pure sodium *n*-heptylpenicillin, with 9.6% penicillin dihydro F and 0.5% penicillin F)	–	Ampoules containing 20 mg	1951 (1st Reference Preparation)
Phenoxymethylpenicillin	0.000 59	Ampoules containing 75 mg (1695 IU per mg)	1957 (1st Standard)
Streptomycin (sulfate)[1]	0.001 282	Ampoules containing 175 mg (780 IU per mg)	1958 (2nd Standard)
Dihydrostreptomycin (sulfate)[1]	0.001 316	Ampoules containing 70 mg (760 IU per mg)	1953 (1st Standard)
Bacitracin	0.0182	Ampoules containing 50 mg (55 IU per mg)	1953 (1st Standard)
Tetracycline (hydrochloride)	0.001 01	Ampoules containing 200 mg (990 IU per mg)	1957 (1st Standard)
Chlortetracycline (hydrochloride)[1]	0.001	Ampoules containing 60 mg (1000 IU per mg)	1953 (1st Standard)
Oxytetracycline (dihydrate)[1]	0.001 11	Ampoules containing 100 mg (900 IU per mg)	1955 (1st Standard)
Erythromycin (dihydrate)	0.001 053	Ampoules containing 200 mg (950 IU per mg)	1957 (1st Standard)
Polymyxin B (sulfate, purified)	0.000 127	Ampoules containing 19 mg (7874 IU per mg)	1955 (1st Standard)
Amphotericin B	–	Ampoules in preparation	1959 (1st Reference Preparation)
Kanamycin (sulfate)	–	Ampoules containing 50 mg	1959 (1st Reference Preparation)
Vancomycin (sulfate)	–	Ampoules containing 50 mg	1959 (1st Reference Preparation)
Viomycin (sulfate)	–	Ampoules containing 35 mg	1959 (1st Reference Preparation)
Neomycin (sulfate)	–	Ampoules containing 100 mg	1958 (1st Reference Preparation)
Nystatin	–	Ampoules containing 75 mg	1958 (1st Reference Preparation)
Novobiocin (sodium novobiocin)	–	Ampoules containing 150 mg	1958 (1st Reference Preparation)
Oleandomycin (chloroform adduct)	–	Ampoules containing 75 mg	1958 (1st Reference Preparation)
Ristocetin	–	Ampoules containing 45 mg	1960 (1st Reference Preparation)

1) See also *Pharmacopoea Internationalis*, 1st English edition, vol. II, Geneva, 1955.

Description	International Unit (IU) mg	Form in which dispensed	Year of establishment
		2. Hormones	
Oxytocic, vasopressor and antidiuretic substances (posterior ox pituitary, acetone-dried, powdered)[1]	0.5	Ampoules containing 30 mg (2 oxytocic, 2 vasopressor and 2 antidiuretic IU per mg)	1957 (3rd Standard)
Prolactin (active principle from anterior ox pituitary, dried)	0.1	Ampoules containing ten 10-mg tablets (ca. 100 IU per tablet)	1939 (1st Standard)
Corticotropin (ACTH) (from anterior pig pituitary, crude)	0.88	Ampoules containing 28 mg (1.14 IU per mg)	1955 (2nd Standard)
Thyrotropin (from anterior ox pituitary, purified)	13.5	Ampoules containing ten 20-mg tablets of a blend of 1 part thyrotropin and 19 parts lactose (ca. 1.48 IU per tablet)	1954 (1st Standard)
Growth hormone (active principle from anterior pituitary, dried)	1.0	Ampoules containing 30 mg (1 IU per mg)	1955 (1st Standard)
Human menopausal gonadotropin (from post-menopausal urine, dried)	–	Ampoules containing 22 mg	1959 (1st Reference Preparation)
Serum gonadotropin (active principle from serum of pregnant mares, dried)[2]	0.25	Ampoules containing ten 25-mg tablets diluted with lactose (ca. 100 IU per tablet)	1939 (1st Standard)
Chorionic gonadotropin (active principle from human urine of pregnancy, dried)[2]	0.1	Ampoules containing twenty-five 10-mg tablets diluted with lactose (ca. 100 IU per tablet)	1939 (1st Standard)
Insulin (52 % bovine and 48 % porcine pancreas, purified)[2]	0.041 67	Ampoules containing 110–125 mg (24 IU per mg)	1958 (4th Standard)
Heparin (sodium salt of purified active principle from bovine tissue)[1]	0.0077	Ampoules containing 20 mg (130 IU per mg)	1958 (2nd Standard)
		3. Miscellaneous	
Vitamin D_3[1]	0.000 025	Bottles containing 10 g of a solution in vegetable oil (1000 IU per g)	1949 (2nd Standard)
Vitamin B_{12} (cyanocobalamin)	–	Ampoules containing ten 20-mg tablets	1959 (1st Reference Preparation)
Hyaluronidase (from bovine testes, dried)	0.1	Ampoules containing ten 20-mg tablets diluted with lactose (ca. 200 IU per tablet)	1955 (1st Standard)
Digitalis (dry powdered leaf of *Digitalis purpurea*)[1]	76.0	Ampoules containing 2500 mg (0.01316 IU per mg)	1949 (3rd Standard)
Neoarsphenamine[1]	–	Ampoules containing 300 mg	1940 (3rd Reference Preparation)
Sulfarsphenamine[1]	–	Ampoules containing 300 mg	1951 (3rd Reference Preparation)
Oxophenarsine (hydrochloride)[2]	–	Sets of 3 ampoules containing (*a*) 120 mg oxophenarsine hydrochloride, (*b*) 100 mg anhydrous sodium carbonate, and (*c*) 500 mg anhydrous sucrose	1951 (1st Reference Preparation)
Mel B (melaminyl-4-phenyl-arsenodithioglycerol)	–	Ampoules containing 100 mg	1954 (1st Reference Preparation)
MSb (sodium *p*-melaminyl-phenylstibonate polymer)	–	Ampoules containing 500 mg	1954 (1st Reference Preparation)
Dimercaprol (BAL; 2,3-dimercaptopropanol)[2]	–	Ampoules containing 2 ml	1952 (1st Reference Preparation)
Protamine	–	Ampoules containing 60 mg	1954 (1st Reference Preparation)
Pyrogen (purified "O" antigen of *Shigella dysenteriae*, dried)	–	Ampoules containing 2 mg	1958 (1st Reference Preparation)

1) See also *Pharmacopoea Internationalis*, 1st English edition, vol. I, Geneva, 1951. *2*) See also *Pharmacopoea Internationalis*, 1st English edition, vol. II, Geneva, 1955.

Following a similar decision by the International Union of Pure and Applied Physics in 1960, the International Union of Pure and Applied Chemistry gave approval at its 1961 Meeting for the replacement of the existing scale of atomic weights by one based on the relative nuclidic mass of the isotope carbon-12 taken as the exact number **12**, thus finally eliminating the discrepancy between the chemical scale, based on the atomic weight of natural oxygen = **16**, and the physical scale, based on the atomic weight of the isotope oxygen-16 = **16** (cf. also page 246).

The table gives the new values resulting from this change as well as from the normal re-evaluation of experimental data.

Name	Symbol	Atomic number	Atomic weight	Name	Symbol	Atomic number	Atomic weight
Actinium	Ac	89		Mercury	Hg	80	200.59
Aluminum	Al	13	26.9815	Molybdenum	Mo	42	95.94
Americium	Am	95		Neodymium	Nd	60	144.24
Antimony	Sb	51	121.75	Neon	Ne	10	20.183
Argon	Ar	18	39.948	Neptunium	Np	93	
Arsenic	As	33	74.9216	Nickel	Ni	28	58.71
Astatine	At	85		Niobium	Nb	41	92.906
Barium	Ba	56	137.34	Nitrogen	N	7	14.0067
Berkelium	Bk	97		Nobelium	No	102	
Beryllium	Be	4	9.0133	Osmium	Os	76	190.2
Bismuth	Bi	83	208.980	Oxygen	O	8	15.9994
Boron	B	5	10.811	Palladium	Pd	46	106.4
Bromine	Br	35	79.909	Phosphorus	P	15	30.9738
Cadmium	Cd	48	112.40	Platinum	Pt	78	195.09
Calcium	Ca	20	40.08	Plutonium	Pu	94	
Californium	Cf	98		Polonium	Po	84	
Carbon	C	6	12.01115	Potassium	K	19	39.102
Cerium	Ce	58	140.12	Praseodymium	Pr	59	140.907
Cesium	Cs	55	132.905	Promethium	Pm	61	
Chlorine	Cl	17	35.453	Protactinium	Pa	91	
Chromium	Cr	24	51.996	Radium	Ra	88	
Cobalt	Co	27	58.9332	Radon	Rn	86	
Copper	Cu	29	63.54	Rhenium	Re	75	186.2
Curium	Cm	96		Rhodium	Rh	45	102.905
Dysprosium	Dy	66	162.50	Rubidium	Rb	37	85.47
Einsteinium	Es	99		Ruthenium	Ru	44	101.07
Erbium	Er	68	167.26	Samarium	Sm	62	150.35
Europium	Eu	63	151.96	Scandium	Sc	21	44.956
Fermium	Fm	100		Selenium	Se	34	78.96
Fluorine	F	9	18.9984	Silicon	Si	14	28.086
Francium	Fr	87		Silver	Ag	47	107.870
Gadolinium	Gd	64	157.25	Sodium	Na	11	22.9898
Gallium	Ga	31	69.72	Strontium	Sr	38	87.62
Germanium	Ge	32	72.59	Sulfur	S	16	32.064
Gold	Au	79	196.967	Tantalum	Ta	73	180.948
Hafnium	Hf	72	178.49	Technetium	Tc	43	
Helium	He	2	4.0026	Tellurium	Te	52	127.60
Holmium	Ho	67	164.930	Terbium	Tb	65	158.924
Hydrogen	H	1	1.00797	Thallium	Tl	81	204.37
Indium	In	49	114.82	Thorium	Th	90	232.038
Iodine	I	53	126.9044	Thulium	Tm	69	168.934
Iridium	Ir	77	192.2	Tin	Sn	50	118.69
Iron	Fe	26	55.847	Titanium	Ti	22	47.90
Krypton	Kr	36	83.80	Tungsten	W	74	183.85
Lanthanum	La	57	138.91	Uranium	U	92	238.03
Lead	Pb	82	207.19	Vanadium	V	23	50.942
Lithium	Li	3	6.939	Xenon	Xe	54	131.30
Lutetium	Lu	71	174.97	Ytterbium	Yb	70	173.04
Magnesium	Mg	12	24.312	Yttrium	Y	39	88.905
Manganese	Mn	25	54.9380	Zinc	Zn	30	65.37
Mendelevium	Md	101		Zirconium	Zr	40	91.22

The following special indexes can also be referred to: Statistical Methods, pages 197 and 198; Symbols and Abbreviations of Units, page 200; Pathogenic Organisms and Infectious Diseases, pages 725–734

A

General Index

The following special indexes can also be referred to: Statistical Methods, pages 197 and 198; Symbols and Abbreviations of Units, page 200; Pathogenic Organisms and Infectious Diseases, pages 725–734

The following special indexes can also be referred to: Statistical Methods, pages 197 and 198; Symbols and Abbreviations of Units, page 200; Pathogenic Organisms and Infectious Diseases, pages 725–734

The following special indexes can also be referred to: Statistical Methods, pages 197 and 198; Symbols and Abbreviations of Units, page 200; Pathogenic Organisms and Infectious Diseases, pages 725–734

The following special indexes can also be referred to: Statistical Methods, pages 197 and 198; Symbols and Abbreviations of Units, page 200; Pathogenic Organisms and Infectious Diseases, pages 725–734

The following special indexes can also be referred to: Statistical Methods, pages 197 and 198; Symbols and Abbreviations of Units, page 200; Pathogenic Organisms and Infectious Diseases, pages 725–734

The following special indexes can also be referred to: Statistical Methods, pages 197 and 198; Symbols and Abbreviations of Units, page 200; Pathogenic Organisms and Infectious Diseases, pages 725–734

The following special indexes can also be referred to: Statistical Methods, pages 197 and 198; Symbols and Abbreviations of Units, page 200; Pathogenic Organisms and Infectious Diseases, pages 725–734

The following special indexes can also be referred to: Statistical Methods, pages 197 and 198; Symbols and Abbreviations of Units, page 200; Pathogenic Organisms and Infectious Diseases, pages 725–734

The following special indexes can also be referred to: Statistical Methods, pages 197 and 198; Symbols and Abbreviations of Units, page 200; Pathogenic Organisms and Infectious Diseases, pages 725–734

The following special indexes can also be referred to: Statistical Methods, pages 197 and 198; Symbols and Abbreviations of Units, page 200; Pathogenic Organisms and Infectious Diseases, pages 725–734

The following special indexes can also be referred to: Statistical Methods, pages 197 and 198; Symbols and Abbreviations of Units, page 200; Pathogenic Organisms and Infectious Diseases, pages 725–734

The following special indexes can also be referred to: Statistical Methods, pages 197 and 198; Symbols and Abbreviations of Units, page 200; Pathogenic Organisms and Infectious Diseases, pages 725–734

The following special indexes can also be referred to: Statistical Methods, pages 197 and 198; Symbols and Abbreviations of Units, page 200; Pathogenic Organisms and Infectious Diseases, pages 725–734

The following special indexes can also be referred to: Statistical Methods, pages 197 and 198; Symbols and Abbreviations of Units, page 200; Pathogenic Organisms and Infectious Diseases, pages 725–734

The following special indexes can also be referred to: Statistical Methods, pages 197 and 198; Symbols and Abbreviations of Units, page 200; Pathogenic Organisms and Infectious Diseases, pages 725–734

The following special indexes can also be referred to: Statistical Methods, pages 197 and 198; Symbols and Abbreviations of Units, page 200; Pathogenic Organisms and Infectious Diseases, pages 725–734

The following special indexes can also be referred to: Statistical Methods, pages 197 and 198; Symbols and Abbreviations of Units, page 200; Pathogenic Organisms and Infectious Diseases, pages 725–734

The following special indexes can also be referred to: Statistical Methods, pages 197 and 198; Symbols and Abbreviations of Units, page 200; Pathogenic Organisms and Infectious Diseases, pages 725–734

The following special indexes can also be referred to: Statistical Methods, pages 197 and 198; Symbols and Abbreviations of Units, page 200; Pathogenic Organisms and Infectious Diseases, pages 725–734

I

The following special indexes can also be referred to: Statistical Methods, pages 197 and 198; Symbols and Abbreviations of Units, page 200; Pathogenic Organisms and Infectious Diseases, pages 725–734

The following special indexes can also be referred to: Statistical Methods, pages 197 and 198; Symbols and Abbreviations of Units, page 200; Pathogenic Organisms and Infectious Diseases, pages 725–734

The following special indexes can also be referred to: Statistical Methods, pages 197 and 198; Symbols and Abbreviations of Units, page 200; Pathogenic Organisms and Infectious Diseases, pages 725–734

The following special indexes can also be referred to: Statistical Methods, pages 197 and 198; Symbols and Abbreviations of Units, page 200; Pathogenic Organisms and Infectious Diseases, pages 725–734

The following special indexes can also be referred to: Statistical Methods, pages 197 and 198; Symbols and Abbreviations of Units, page 200; Pathogenic Organisms and Infectious Diseases, pages 725–734

The following special indexes can also be referred to: Statistical Methods, pages 197 and 198; Symbols and Abbreviations of Units, page 200; Pathogenic Organisms and Infectious Diseases, pages 725–734

The following special indexes can also be referred to: Statistical Methods, pages 197 and 198; Symbols and Abbreviations of Units, page 200; Pathogenic Organisms and Infectious Diseases, pages 725–734

The following special indexes can also be referred to: Statistical Methods, pages 197 and 198; Symbols and Abbreviations of Units, page 200; Pathogenic Organisms and Infectious Diseases, pages 725–734

The following special indexes can also be referred to: Statistical Methods, pages 197 and 198; Symbols and Abbreviations of Units, page 200; Pathogenic Organisms and Infectious Diseases, pages 725–734

The following special indexes can also be referred to: Statistical Methods, pages 197 and 198; Symbols and Abbreviations of Units, page 200; Pathogenic Organisms and Infectious Diseases, pages 725–734

The following special indexes can also be referred to: Statistical Methods, pages 197 and 198; Symbols and Abbreviations of Units, page 200; Pathogenic Organisms and Infectious Diseases, pages 725–734

Q, R

Q

R

R

R

The following special indexes can also be referred to: Statistical Methods, pages 197 and 198; Symbols and Abbreviations of Units, page 200; Pathogenic Organisms and Infectious Diseases, pages 725–734

The following special indexes can also be referred to: Statistical Methods, pages 197 and 198; Symbols and Abbreviations of Units, page 200; Pathogenic Organisms and Infectious Diseases, pages 725–734

S Page

S Page

S Page

The following special indexes can also be referred to: Statistical Methods, pages 197 and 198; Symbols and Abbreviations of Units, page 200; Pathogenic Organisms and Infectious Diseases, pages 725–734

The following special indexes can also be referred to: Statistical Methods, pages 197 and 198; Symbols and Abbreviations of Units, page 200; Pathogenic Organisms and Infectious Diseases, pages 725–734

T Page

T Page

T Page

The following special indexes can also be referred to: Statistical Methods, pages 197 and 198; Symbols and Abbreviations of Units, page 200; Pathogenic Organisms and Infectious Diseases, pages 725–734

The following special indexes can also be referred to: Statistical Methods, pages 197 and 198; Symbols and Abbreviations of Units, page 200; Pathogenic Organisms and Infectious Diseases, pages 725–734

The following special indexes can also be referred to: Statistical Methods, pages 197 and 198; Symbols and Abbreviations of Units, page 200; Pathogenic Organisms and Infectious Diseases, pages 725–734

Notes

Notes

Notes

Notes

Notes

Notes

Notes

Notes

Notes

Notes